MITCHELL

1981 IMPORTED CARS & TRUCKS TUNE-UP MECHANICAL SERVICE & REPAIR

National Service Data
Manuals For The Automotive Professional

Published By:
MITCHELL MANUALS, INC.
A Cordura Company
P.O. BOX 26260
SAN DIEGO, CA 92126

ISBN 0-8470-5781-X

ACKNOWLEDGEMENT

Mitchell Manuals thanks the automotive and equipment manufacturers, distributors, dealers and the entire automotive industry for their fine cooperation and assistance which makes the publication of this manual possible.

MITCHELL MANUALS, INC.

A Cordura Company

PUBLISHER

Barry A. Norton, Vice President

EDITORIAL

Editor in Chief
Laurence E. Laumann

Managing Editor
Kenneth A. Young

Ass't. Managing Editor
Daniel M. Kelley

Art Director
Eloise S. Stiverson

Detroit Editor
Lynn D. Meeker

Technical Editors
Daryl F. Visser
Michael Roeder
Terry L Blomquist
Thomas L. Landis
Daniel D. Fleming
Philip G. Wallen
Cliff Herrin
Eric M. Hamm
Jeffrey C. Wedeking
Thomas J. Kelley
Barbara A. Siesel

PUBLISHED BY

MITCHELL MANUALS, INC.
9889 Willow Creek Road
P.O. Box 26260
San Diego, California 92126

a subsidiary of
CORDURA PUBLICATIONS, INC.
C.L. Kobrin, President
John Opelt, Vice President of Finance & Administration
Malcolm Ferrier, Vice President of Operations

For Subscription Information:
CALL TOLL FREE 800 - 854-7030. In California CALL COLLECT 714-578-8770. Or WRITE: P.O. Box 26260, San Diego, CA 92126

ISBN 0-8470-5781-X

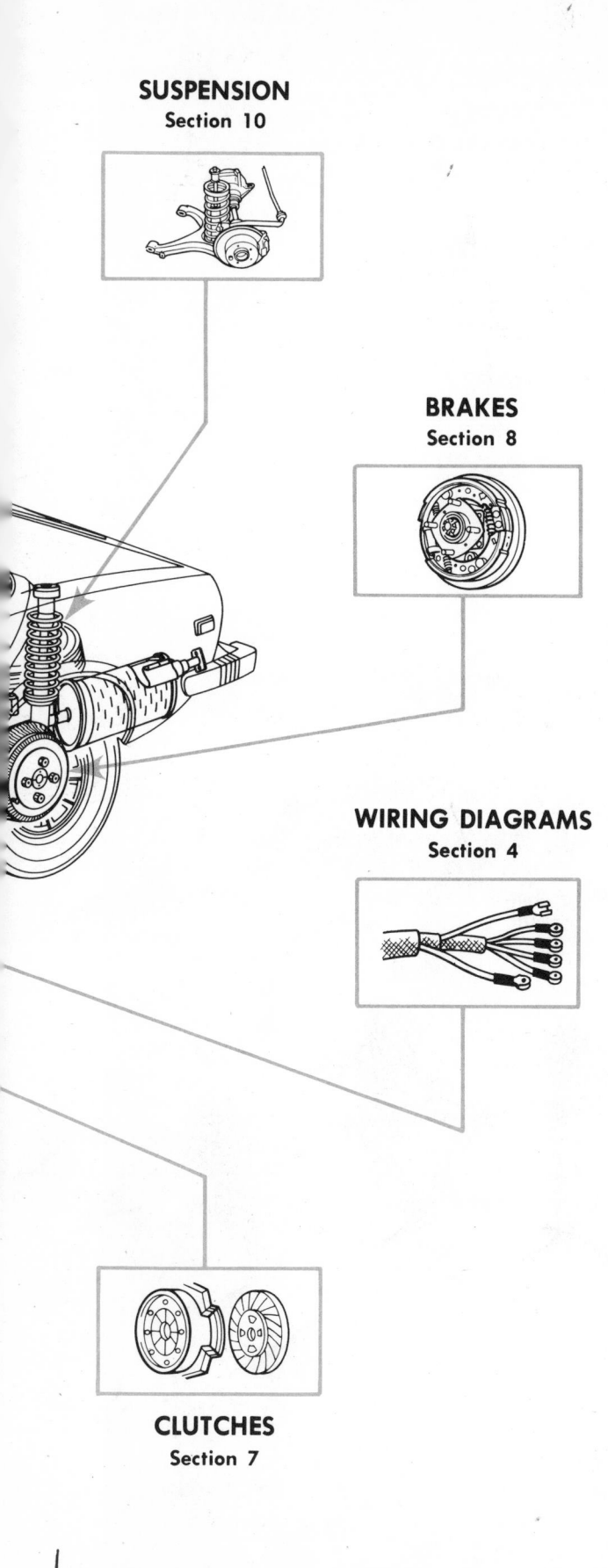

SUSPENSION
Section 10

BRAKES
Section 8

WIRING DIAGRAMS
Section 4

CLUTCHES
Section 7

PREFACE

This is the 1981 edition of Mitchell Manuals'
Imported Car Tune-Up/Mechanical Service and Repair Manual.
This book, like the many Mitchell publications which have preceded it,
represents our commitment to professionalism
in the automotive service market.

The automotive industry advances every year,
and Mitchell Manuals pledges to advance and improve its products
as we maintain the quality and usefulness of all Mitchell Manuals' publications.

We cordially acknowledge the good will
and mutual goals that exist in the automotive business,
and it is in this spirit that we thank the automotive manufacturers,
distributors, dealers and the entire automotive industry
for their fine cooperation and assistance
which have made this publication possible.

310-A

GENERAL INDEX

General Index

General Index

General Index

E

General Index

General Index

General Index

General Index

General Index

General Index

General Index

QUICK-CHECK
TUNE-UP SPECIFICATIONS
1981 Models

1981 Tune-Up Specifications

CAR MODEL	SPARK PLUGS		FUEL SYSTEM	VALVE CLEARANCE		DISTRIBUTOR	
	Type	Gap	Make & Model	Int.	Exh.	Make	No.
AUDI	Bosch						
4000							
4-Cyl.	W7D①	.028″	Bosch CIS Fuel Inj.	.010″H	.018″H	Bosch	1
5-Cyl.	W7D①	.028″	Bosch CIS Fuel Inj.	.010″H	.018″H	Bosch	2
5000	W7D①	.028″	Bosch CIS Fuel Inj.	.010″H	.018″H	Bosch	3
5000 Turbo	WR7DS	.028″	Bosch CIS Fuel Inj.	.010″H	.018″H	Bosch	4
BMW	Bosch						
320i	WR9DS	.024″	Bosch CIS Fuel Inj.	.006″C	.006″C	Bosch	5
528i	WR9DS	.024″	Bosch AFC Fuel Inj.	.010″C	.010″C	Bosch	6
633CSi & 733i	WR9DS	.024″	Bosch AFC Fuel Inj.	.010″C	.010″C	Bosch	7
CHRYSLER CORP.							
IMPORTS	NGK						
1400 cc	BPR-6ES-11	.041″	Solex 28-32 DIDTA	.006″H①	.010″H	Mitsubishi	8
1600 cc	BPR-6ES-11	.041″	Solex 28-32 DIDTA	.006″H①	.010″H	Mitsubishi	9
2000 cc	BPR-6ES-11	.041″	Solex 30-32 DIDTA	.006″H①	.010″H	Mitsubishi	10
2600 cc	BPR-5ES-11	.041″	Solex 30-32 DIDTA	.006″H①	.010″H	Mitsubishi	11
COURIER	NGK						
2000 cc	BPR-5ES	.031″	Nikki 2-Bbl.	.012″H	.012″H	Mitsubishi	12
2600 cc	BPR-5EFS	.034″	Hitachi DCS 328 2-Bbl.	Hyd.	Hyd.	Mitsubishi	13
DATSUN	NGK						
200SX	BP-6ES	.033″	Bosch AFC Fuel Inj.	.012″H	.012″H	Hitachi	14
210	BP-5ES-11	.041″	Hitachi DCR 306	.014″H	.014″H	Hitachi	15
280ZX	BP-6ES-11	.041″	Bosch AFC Fuel Inj.	.010″H	.012″H	Hitachi	16
280ZX Turbo	BPR-6ES-11	.041″	Bosch AFC Fuel Inj.	.010″H	.012″H	Hitachi	17
310	BP-5ES-11	.041″	Hitachi DCR 306	.014″H	.014″H	Hitachi	18
510	BP-6ES	.033″	Hitachi DCR 342	.012″H	.012″H	Hitachi	19
810	BP-6ES-11	.041″	Bosch AFC Fuel Inj.	.010″H	.012″H	Hitachi	20
Pickup	BP-6ES	.033″	Hitachi DCR 342	.012″H	.012″H	Hitachi	21
FIAT	Champion						
Brava & Spider	RN9Y	.029″	Bosch AFC Fuel Inj.	.019″C	.021″C	Marelli	22
Strada & X1/9	RN9Y	.029″	Bosch AFC Fuel Inj.	.014″C	.018″C	Bosch	23
HONDA	NGK						
Accord & Prelude	B6EB-L11	.041″	Keihin 2-Bbl.	.006″C①	.011″C	Hitachi	24
Civic							
1300 cc	B6EB-11	.041″	Keihin 2-Bbl.	.006″C①	.008″C	Hitachi	25
1500 cc	B6EB-11	.041″	Keihin 2-Bbl.	.006″C①	.008″C	Hitachi	26
ISUZU	NGK						
1800 cc	BPR-6ES-11	.040″	Hitachi DCH 340	.006″C	.010″C	Nippondenso	27
JAGUAR	Champion						
XJ6L	N12Y	.035″	Bosch AFC Fuel Inj.	.013″C	.013″C	Lucas	28
LUV	NGK						
Pickup	BPR-6ES-11	.040″	Hitachi DCH 340	.006″C	.010″C	Nippondenso	29
MAZDA	NGK						
GLC	BPR-5ES①	.031″	Hitachi 2-Bbl.	.010″H	.012″H	Mitsubishi	30
626	BPR-5ES①	.031″	Nikki 2-Bbl.	.012″H	.012″H	Mitsubishi	31
RX7	BR-8EQ-14	.055″	Hitachi 4-Bbl.	.....	.....	Mitsubishi	32
B2000 Pickup	BPR-5ES①	.031″	Nikki 2-Bbl.	.012″H	.012″H	Mitsubishi	33

1981 Tune-Up Specifications

QUICK CHECK TUNE UP SPECS

No.	IGNITION TIMING	HOT IDLE SPEED		FAST IDLE RPM	EXHAUST CO READING At Idle Speed	Remarks
		Man. Trans.	Auto. Trans.			
1	3°ATDC	850-1000	850-1000	.....	0.3-1.2%	① — WR7DS on Calif. models.
2	3°ATDC	850-1000②	850-1000②	.....	0.4-1.2%	② — 880-1000 on Calif. models.
3	3°ATDC	800-1000②	800-1000②	.....	0.4-1.2%	③ — Set @ 3000 RPM.
4	21°ATDC③	.....	880-1000	.....	0.4-1.2%	
5	25°BTDC①	800-900	900-1000	.....	0.2-1.2%②	① — Set @ 2200 RPM.
6	22°BTDC①	850-950	850-950	.....	0.2-0.8%②	② — With oxygen sensor disconnected.
7	22°BTDC③	850-950	850-950	.....	0.2-0.8%②	③ — Set @ 1650 RPM.
8	5°BTDC	700	.....	.....	0.5%②	① — Set Jet valves to .006"H.
9	5°BTDC	700	750	.....	0.5%②	② — Air injection disconnected.
10	5°BTDC	750	750	.....	0.5%②	
11	7°BTDC	800	800	.....	0.5%②	
12	8°BTDC	650	650	.....	1.0%②	① — With transmission in "D".
13	6°BTDC	850	700①	.....	3.5%②	② — Air injection disconnected.
14	6°BTDC	750	700	.....	6.0%④	① — 7°BTDC on 1200 cc Eng.
15	5°BTDC①	700⑤	650	2300-3200③	4.0%④	② — 800 RPM on 4-WD models.
16	8 BTDC	700	700	.....	5.0%④	③ — 2600-3500 RPM on A/T.
17	20° BTDC⑥	.....	650⑥	.....	5.0%④⑥	④ — Less than.
18	5 BTDC	750	750	2300-3200	4.0%④	⑤ — 650 RPM on 1400 cc Engine.
19	6°BTDC	600	600	.....	5.0%④	⑥ — No Adjustment Necessary
20	10°BTDC	700	650	.....	5.0%④	Controlled by ECCS,
21	5°BTDC	650②	650	.....	5.0%④	
22	10°BTDC	850	750①	.....	0.5-0.9%	① — Transmission in "D".
23	10°BTDC	850	750①	.....	0.5-0.9%	
24	TDC	800	800③	2600-2700	.....	① — Set Aux. valves to .006"C.
						② — 10°BTDC on Fed. M/T Hatchback. 4°BTDC on Fed. M/T Sedan & Wagon.
25	2°BTDC	800	800	2800-3000	.....	③ — Transmission in "D".
26	2°ATDC②	750	750③	2800-3000④	.....	④ — 3200 RPM on Calif. M/T. 2700 RPM on Calif A/T.
27	6°BTDC	800①	900	3200	.....	① — 900 RPM Calif. Pickup M/T.
28	4°BTDC	.....	800	.....	0.5-1.5%①	① — With oxygen sensor disconnected.
29	6°BTDC	800①	900	3200	.....	① — 900 RPM on Calif. M/T.
30	8°BTDC	850②	750	.....	.....	① — Or BPR-6ES.
31	5°BTDC	650	650	.....	.....	② — 800 RPM on Wagon.
32	TDC③	750	750④	.....	.....	③ — Trailing Timing is 20° ATDC.
33	8°BTDC	650	.....	.....	.....	④ — Transmission in "D".

1981 Tune-Up Specifications

CAR MODEL	SPARK PLUGS		FUEL SYSTEM	VALVE CLEARANCE		DISTRIBUTOR	No.
	Type	Gap	Make & Model	Int.	Exh.	Make	
MERCEDES BENZ	Bosch						
280 Series	W9D	.032"	Bosch CIS Fuel Inj.	.004"C	.010"C	Bosch	34
380 Series	W9D	.032"	Bosch CIS Fuel Inj.	Hyd.	Hyd.	Bosch	35
PEUGEOT	Bosch						
505	WR7DS	.024"	Bosch CIS Fuel Inj.	.004"C	.010"C	Ducellier	36
PORSCHE	Bosch						
911SC	W225T30	.028"	Bosch CIS Fuel Inj.	.004"C	.004"C	Bosch	37
924	WR6DS	.028"	Bosch CIS Fuel Inj.	.008"H	.018"H	Bosch	38
924 Turbo	WR6DS	.028"	Bosch CIS Fuel Inj.	.008"H	.018"H	Bosch	39
928	WR8DS	.030"	Bosch AFC Fuel Inj.	Hyd.	Hyd.	Bosch	40
RENAULT	Bosch						
Le Car	WD9DS①	.024"	Weber 32 DIR	.006"C	.008"C	Ducellier	41
18i	WR7DS	.026"	Bosch AFC Fuel Inj.	.008"C	.010"C	Ducellier	42
SAAB	NGK						
900	BP-6ES	.026"	Bosch CIS Fuel Inj.	.009"H	.017"H	Bosch	43
900 Turbo	BP-7ES	.026"	Bosch CIS Fuel Inj.	.009"H	.019"H	Bosch	44
SUBARU	NGK						
1600 cc	BP-6ES-11	.040"	Hitachi DCP 2-Bbl.	.010"C	.014"C	Nippondenso①	45
1800 cc	BP-6ES-11	.040"	Hitachi DCP 2-Bbl.	.010"C	.014"C	Nippondenso①	46
TOYOTA	NGK						
Celica	BPR-5EA-L	.031"	Aisan 2-Bbl.	.008"H	.012"H	Nippondenso	47
Corolla	BPR-5EA-L11	.043"	Aisan 2-Bbl.	.008"H	.013"H	Nippondenso	48
Corona	BPR-5EA-L	.031"	Aisan 2-Bbl.	.008"H	.012"H	Nippondenso	49
Cressida	BPR-5EY	.031"	Bosch AFC Fuel Inj.	.011"H	.014"H	Nippondenso	50
Land Cruiser	BPR-4EY	.031"	Aisan 2-Bbl.	.008"H	.014"H	Nippondenso	51
Pickup	BPR-5EA-L	.031"	Aisan 2-Bbl.	.008"H	.012"H	Nippondenso	52
Starlet	BPR-5EA-L11①	.043"②	Aisan 2-Bbl.	.008"H	.012"H	Nippondenso	53
Supra	BPR-5EY	.031"	Bosch AFC Fuel Inj.	.011"H	.014"H	Nippondenso	54
Tercel	BPR-5EA-L11	.043"	Aisan 2-Bbl.	.008"H	.012"H	Nippondenso	55
TRIUMPH	Champion						
TR7	N12Y	.025"	Bosch AFC Fuel Inj.	.008"C	.018"C	Lucas	56
TR8	N12Y	.030"	Bosch AFC Fuel Inj.	Hyd.	Hyd.	Lucas	57
VOLKSWAGEN	Bosch						
Jetta	W7D①	.028"	Bosch CIS Fuel Inj.	.010"H	.018"H	Bosch	58
Rabbit	W7D①	.028"	Bosch CIS Fuel Inj.	.010"H	.018"H	Bosch	59
Rabbit Pickup	W7D①	.028"	Bosch CIS Fuel Inj.	.010"H	.018"H	Bosch	60
Scirocco	W7D①	.028"	Bosch CIS Fuel Inj.	.010"H	.018"H	Bosch	61
Vanagon	W8CO	.026"	Bosch AFC Fuel Inj.	Hyd.	Hyd.	Bosch	62
VOLVO	Bosch						
4-Cyl.	WR7DS	.030"	Bosch CIS Fuel Inj.	.015"C	.015"C	Bosch③	63
6-Cyl.	HR6DS	.030"	Bosch CIS Fuel Inj.	.006"C	.012"C	Bosch③	64

No.	IGNITION TIMING	HOT IDLE SPEED		FAST IDLE RPM	EXHAUST CO READING At Idle Speed	Remarks
		Man. Trans.	Auto. Trans.			
34	10°BTDC	.....	700	.....	.....	
35	5°BTDC	.....	500	.....	.....	
36	8°BTDC	900	900	1500	0.5-1.5%	
37	5°BTDC[1]	850-950	.....	.....	0.4-0.8%[4]	[1] — Vacuum hoses disconnected.
38	TDC[2]	750-800	750-800		0.6-1.0%[4]	[2] — Vacuum hoses connected.
39	8°BTDC[2]	900	.....		0.5-1.0%[4]	[3] — At 3000 RPM.
40	23°BTDC[1][3]	700-800	700-800		0.4-0.8%[4]	[4] — With oxygen sensor disconnected.
41	3°BTDC	750	.....		0.5-2.0%[2][3]	[1] — Champion RN12Y on Fed. models.
42	10°BTDC	800	800		1.0-2.5%[2]	[2] — Air injection disconnected. [3] — Not measured for Calif.
43	20°BTDC[1]	875	875	.....	.....	[1] — At 2000 RPM.
44	20°BTDC[1]	875	875	.....	.....	
45	8°BTDC	700	800	.....	.....	[1] — Hitachi on 4-WD.
46	8°BTDC	700	800	.....	.....	
47	8°BTDC	700	750	2600	.....	[1] — BPR-5EA-L for Calif.
48	7°BTDC	650[3]	750[3]	3400[4][5]	.....	[2] — .031" for Calif.
49	8°BTDC	700	750	2600	.....	[3] — 850 RPM with power steering.
50	8°BTDC	800	800	.....	.....	[4] — 3200 RPM for Auto. Trans.
51	7°BTDC	650	.....	1800	.....	[5] — 200 RPM less with power steering.
52	8°BTDC	700	750[6]	2600	.....	[6] — 700 RPM for Fed. 4 Spd.
53	8°BTDC	650[7]	.....	3500	.....	[7] — 700 RPM for Calif.
54	8°BTDC	800	800	.....	.....	
55	5°BTDC	650	800	3600	.....	
56	2°ATDC	800	800	.....	.....	
57	TDC	800	800	.....	.....	
58	3°ATDC	880-1000[5]	880-1000[5]	.....	0.3-1.2%	[1] — WR7DS on Calif.
59	3°ATDC	880-1000[5]	880-1000[5]	.....	0.3-1.2%	[2] — 5°ATDC on Calif.
60	3°ATDC	880-1000[5]	.....	.....	0.5-0.9%[3]	[3] — 0.3-1.2% on Calif.
61	3°ATDC	880-1000[5]	880-1000[5]	.....	0.3-1.2%	[4] — 850-950 RPM on Calif.
62	7.5°BTDC[2]	800-950[4]	850-1000[4]	.....	0.5-1.5%[3]	[5] — 850-1000 RPM w/o Idle Stabilizer.
63	8°BTDC[1]	900	900	.....	0.7-1.3%[2]	[1] — 12° BTDC on Turbo and MPG.
64	10°BTDC	900	900	.....	0.7-1.3%[2]	[2] — With oxygen sensor disconnected. [3] — MPG uses Volvo H.E. Dist.

Section 1
TUNE-UP

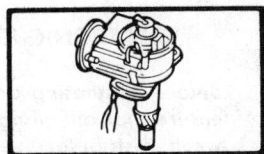

Contents

NOTE — ALSO SEE GENERAL INDEX

Tune-Up

TUNE-UP TROUBLE SHOOTING

| CONDITION & POSSIBLE CAUSE | CONDITION & POSSIBLE CAUSE |

SPARK PLUG DIAGNOSIS

Normal Spark Plug Condition

- Light tan or gray deposits on insulator.
- Electrode not burned or fouled.
- Gap tolerance not significantly changed.

Cold Fouling or Carbon Deposits

- Over rich air-fuel mixture, possibly from a faulty choke, clogged air cleaner, improper idle adjustment or dirty carburetor.
- Faulty ignition wires.
- Prolonged operation at idle.
- Sticking valves or worn valve guide seals.

Wet Fouling or Oil Deposits

- Worn rings and pistons.
- Excessive cylinder wear.
- Excessive valve guide clearance.
- Worn or loose bearings.

Gap Bridged

- Deposits in combustion chamber becoming fused to electrode under high heat.

Blistered Electrode or Overheating

- Engine overheating.
- Wrong type of fuel.
- Loose spark plugs.
- Over-advanced ignition timing.

Pre-ignition or Melted Electrodes

- Incorrect type of gasoline.
- Incorrect ignition timing.
- Burned valves.
- Engine overheating.
- Wrong type of spark plug, too hot.

Chipped Insulators

- Severe detonation.
- Improper gapping procedure.

Rust Colored Deposits

- Additives in unleaded fuel may create this condition. It may be misdiagnosed as water in the combustion chamber. These deposits do not affect plug performance.

ELECTRONIC IGNITION DIAGNOSIS

Before diagnosing an electronic ignition system, ensure that all wiring is connected properly between distributor, wiring connector and spark plugs. Ignition problems will show up either as: engine will not start or engine runs rough.

Engine Will Not Start

- Open circuit between distributor and bulkhead connector.
- Open circuit between bulkhead connector and ignition switch.
- Open circuit between ignition switch and starter solenoid.

Engine Runs Rough

- Fuel lines leaking or clogged.
- Initial timing incorrect.
- Centrifugal advance malfunction.
- Worn or defective spark plugs.
- Worn or defective secondary wiring.

If the above checks do not locate the problem, check the components listed below.

Component Failure

- Spark arc-over on distributor cap, rotor or coil.
- Defective pick-up coil.
- Defective ignition coil.
- Defective vacuum unit.
- Defective control module.

ELECTRONIC IGNITION DIAGNOSIS BY OSCILLOSCOPE PATTERN

Firing Voltage Lines are the Same, but Abnormally High

- Retarded ignition timing.
- Too lean of a fuel mixture.
- High resistance in coil wire.
- Corrosion in coil tower terminal.
- Corrosion in distributor coil terminal.

Firing Voltage Lines are the Same, but Abnormally Low

- Too rich of a fuel mixture.
- Breaks in coil wire causing arcing.
- Cracked coil tower causing arcing.
- Low coil output.
- Low engine compression.

TUNE-UP TROUBLE SHOOTING (Cont.)

CONDITION & POSSIBLE CAUSE	CONDITION & POSSIBLE CAUSE

One or More, but Not All Firing Voltage Lines are Higher Than the Others

- Carburetor idle mixture not balanced.
- EGR valve stuck open.
- High resistance in spark plug wire.
- Cracked or broken spark plug insulator.
- Intake vacuum leak.
- Defective spark plugs.
- Corroded spark plug terminals.

One or More, but Not All Firing Voltage Lines are Lower Than the Others

- Curb idle mixture not balanced.
- Breaks in spark plug wires causing arcing.
- Cracked coil tower causing arcing.
- Low compression.
- Defective spark plugs, or spark plugs fouled.

One or More Cylinders Not Firing

- Cracked distributor cap terminals.
- Shorted spark plug wire.
- Mechanical problem in engine.
- Defective spark plugs.
- Spark plugs fouled.

GENERAL DIAGNOSIS

Hard Starting

- Binding carburetor linkage, choke linkage or choke piston.
- Restricted choke vacuum.
- Worn or dirty needle valve and seat.
- Float sticking.
- Incorrect choke adjustment.
- Defective coil.
- Improper spark plug gap.
- Incorrect ignition timing.

Detonation

- Over-advanced ignition timing.
- Defective spark plugs.
- Fuel lines clogged.
- EGR system malfunction.
- PCV system malfunction.
- Vacuum leaks.
- Loose fan belts.
- Restricted air flow.
- Vacuum advance malfunction.

Dieseling

- Binding carburetor linkage, throttle linkage, choke linkage or fast idle cam.
- Defective idle solenoid.
- Improper base idle speed.
- Incorrect ignition timing.
- Incorrect idle mixture setting.

Faulty Acceleration

- Incorrect ignition timing.
- Engine cold and choke too lean.
- Defective spark plugs.
- Defective coil.

Faulty Low Speed Operation

- Clogged idle transfer slots.
- Restricted idle air bleeds and passages.
- Clogged air cleaner.
- Defective spark plugs.
- Defective ignition cables.
- Defective distributor cap.

Faulty High Speed Operation

- Incorrect ignition timing.
- Defective distributor centrifugal advance.
- Defective distributor vacuum advance.
- Incorrect spark plugs or plug gap.
- Faulty choke operation.
- Clogged vacuum passages.
- Improper size or clogged main jet.
- Restricted air cleaner.
- Defective distributor cap, rotor or coil.
- Worn distributor shaft.

Misfire at All Speeds

- Defective spark plugs.
- Defective spark plug wires.
- Defective distributor cap, rotor or coil.
- Cracked or broken vacuum hoses.
- Vacuum leaks.
- Fuel lines clogged.

Hesitation

- Cracked or broken vacuum hoses.
- Vacuum leaks.
- Binding carburetor linkage, throttle linkage, choke linkage or fast idle cam.
- Improper float setting.
- Cracked or broken ignition wires.

Tune-Up

TUNE-UP TROUBLE SHOOTING (Cont.)

CONDITION & POSSIBLE CAUSE	CONDITION & POSSIBLE CAUSE
Rough Idle, Missing or Stalling • Incorrect curb idle or fast idle speed. • Incorrect basic timing. • Improper idle mixture adjustment. • Improper feedback system operation. • Incorrect spark plug gap. • Moisture in ignition components. • Loose or broken ignition wires. • Damaged distributor cap or rotor. • Faulty ignition coil. • Fuel filter clogged or worn. • Damaged idle mixture screw. • Improper fast idle cam adjustment. • Improper EGR valve operation. • Faulty PCV valve air flow. • Choke binding, or improper choke setting. • Vacuum leak. • Improper float bowl fuel level. • Clogged air bleed or idle passages. • Clogged or worn air cleaner. • Faulty choke vacuum diaphragm. • Exhaust manifold heat valve inoperative. • Improper distributor spark advance. • Leaking valves or valve components. • Improper carburetor mounting. • Excessive play in distributor shaft. • Loose or corroded wiring connections. **Engine Surges** • Improper PCV valve air flow. • Vacuum leaks. • Clogged main jets. • Clogged air bleeds. • EGR valve malfunction. • Restricted air cleaner. • Cracked or broken vacuum hoses. • Cracked or broken ignition wires. • Vacuum advance malfunction. • Defective or fouled spark plugs.	**Ping or Spark Knock** • Incorrect ignition timing. • Distributor centrifugal or vacuum advance malfunction. • Carburetor setting too lean. • Vacuum leak. • EGR valve malfunction. **Poor Gasoline Mileage** • Cracked or broken vacuum hoses. • Vacuum leaks. • Defective ignition wires. • Incorrect choke setting. • Defective vacuum advance. • Defective spark plugs. • Binding carburetor power piston. • Dirt in carburetor jets. • Incorrect float adjustment. • Defective power valves. **Power Not Up to Normal** • Incorrect ignition timing. • Defective distributor cap, rotor, coil or ignition wires. • Incorrect spark plug gap. • Incorrect idle speeds. • Improper float level. • Leaking needle valve and seat. • Choke sticking. **Engine Stalls** • Incorrect idle speed. • Improper float level. • Leaking needle valve and seat. • Sticking choke. • Carburetor mounting gasket air leaks. • Vacuum leaks. • Defective ignition wires, distributor cap or rotor. • Loose condensor. • Shorted distributor wires. • Defective spark plugs. • Clogged fuel filter.

TUNE-UP

4000

ENGINE IDENTIFICATION

Engine number is stamped on left side of engine block near distributor.

Engine Code

Application	Code
All Models	WT

COMPRESSION PRESSURE

Check compression with engine warm, all spark plugs removed and throttle wide open. Crank engine at least 6 "puffs" per cylinder to determine engine compression.

NOTE — *Connect coil high tension wire to ground before cranking engine for compression test.*

Compression Pressure Specifications

Application	Pressure psi (kg/cm^2)
Normal (New Engine)	131-174 (9-12)
Minimum	102 (7)
Maximum Variation	44 (3)

VALVE CLEARANCE

1) Adjust valves with engine at normal operating temperature. Clearance adjustments are to be checked and made according to firing order sequence (1-3-4-2). Rotate crankshaft until cam lobes for No. 1 cylinder valves point upward, then measure valve clearances of No. 1 cylinder.

NOTE — *When adjusting valves, rotate engine CLOCKWISE only, otherwise timing belt may slip.*

2) If adjustment is necessary, use special tools 10-208 (disc removal tool) and VW546 (tappet depressing tool) to remove and install adjusting discs. Rotate camshaft until cam lobes no longer rest on adjusting discs of cylinder to be adjusted. Turn tappet until notches are at 90° to camshaft. Insert tool VW546 and depress tappet. Using tool 10-208, grasp tappet disc and rotate it out from under camshaft.

3) Thickness is stamped on bottom side of disc. Using clearance measurement, determine thickness of adjusting disc necessary to bring valve clearances within specifications. Discs are available in .0019" (.05 mm) increments from .1181" (3.0 mm) to .1673" (4.25 mm). Reverse removal procedure to install proper disc. Repeat procedure as required for remaining valves.

Valve Clearance Specifications①

Application	Intake In. (mm)	Exhaust In. (mm)
All Models	.010 (.3)	.018 (.5)

① — Adjust with engine warm.

VALVE ARRANGEMENT

E-I-E-I-I-E-I-E (front to rear).

SPARK PLUGS

Application	Gap In. (mm)	Torque Ft. Lbs. (N·m)
All Models	.028 (.7)	22 (29)

Spark Plug Type

Application	Bosch	Champion
Federal	W7D	N8Y
Calif.	WR7DS	N8GY

HIGH TENSION WIRE RESISTANCE

Carefully remove ends of wire from spark plug and distributor. Using an ohmmeter, check resistance of wire while gently twisting wire. If resistance is not to specification, or fluctuates from infinity to any value, replace wire.

Resistance (Ohms) Per Wire

Application	Resistance
Ignition Wire Only	800-1400
Ignition Wire With Connector	4800-7400
Coil Wire	1600-2400

DISTRIBUTOR

All models are equipped with breakerless electronic ignition systems that use a Hall generator and an idle stabilizer unit.

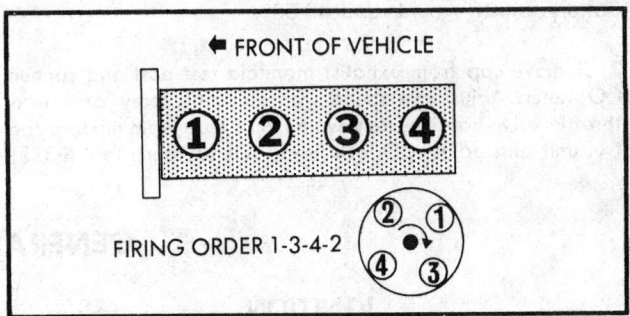

Fig. 1 Firing Order and Distributor Rotation

IGNITION TIMING

CAUTION — *Do not connect any test instruments to terminal 15 (+) of ignition coil. Use fuse 10 for connection.*

1) Warm engine to normal operating temperature. Stop engine and disconnect oxygen sensor, then disconnect both plugs from idle stabilizer and connect them together.

2) Pull PCV hose from valve cover, adjust idle speed, then check ignition timing. Adjust by turning distributor. All vacuum hoses must remain connected.

TUNE-UP (Cont.)

NOTE — *Electric cooling fan must not run while adjustments are made.*

Ignition Timing Specifications

Application	RPM	Timing
All Models	850-1000	①3°ATDC

① — With vacuum hoses connected.

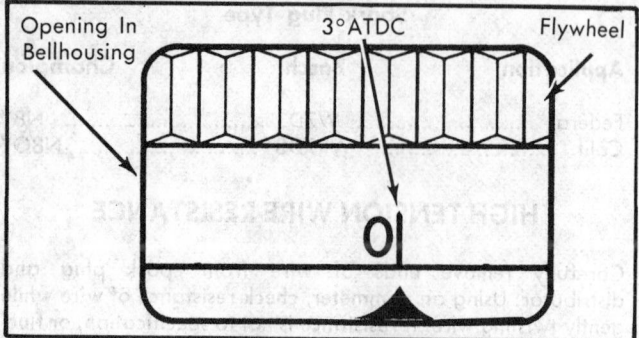

Fig. 2   Ignition Timing Mark Location

IDLE SPEED & MIXTURE

1) With engine at normal operating temperature, check and adjust ignition timing and valve clearances. Engine fan must come on at least once before adjustment, but must not be on during adjustment.

2) Pull PCV hose from valve cover and plug it. Disconnect Green oxygen sensor wire, then disconnect both plugs from idle stabilizer and connect plugs together. Connect a dwell meter (set to 4-Cyl. scale) to frequency valve connector near battery. Meter should read 40-50°.

3) Remove cap from exhaust manifold test port and connect CO meter. Adjust idle speed with adjusting screw on side of throttle valve housing. Remove mixture plug from mixture control unit and adjust CO level using Allen wrench tool (P377).

CAUTION — *Do not press down on tool while adjusting CO, and do not accelerate engine with tool in place. Remove tool after each adjustment and accelerate engine briefly before checking CO reading. Always adjust CO level from lean to rich.*

4) Reconnect oxygen sensor wire. Dwell meter reading should begin to vary and CO level should be within 0.3-1.2%. Stop engine and remove test equipment. Reconnect all wiring and hoses.

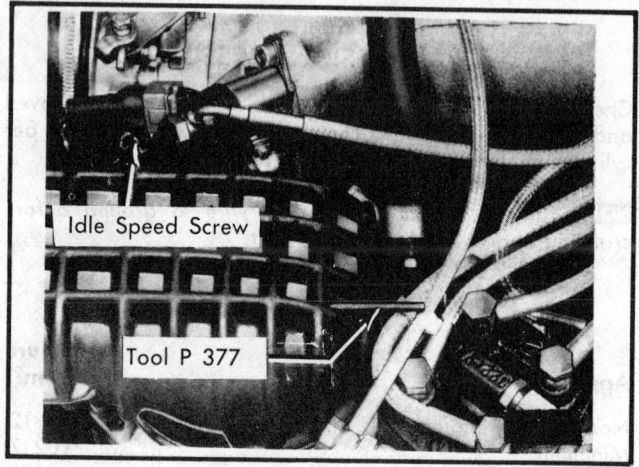

Fig. 3   Adjusting Idle Speed and Mixture

Idle Speed & CO Level

Application	Idle RPM	CO%
All Models	850-1000	0.3-1.2

FUEL PUMP PRESSURE & VOLUME

Pressure .... 64-74 psi (4.5-5.2 kg/cm²)
Volume .... 1qt. in 40 sec.

EMISSION CONTROL SYSTEMS

See Mitchell Manuals' Emission Control Manual.

GENERAL SERVICING

IGNITION

DISTRIBUTOR

All models are equipped with Bosch breakerless electronic ignition with idle stabilizer unit.

IGNITION COIL

Resistance Specifications

Application	Primary	Secondary
All Models	.52-.76	2400-3500

FUEL SYSTEMS

FUEL INJECTION

All models are equipped with Bosch Continuous Injection System (CIS). California models use an oxygen sensor system.

ELECTRICAL

BATTERY

Application	Amp. Hr. Capacity
Without A/C	55
With A/C	90

Battery Location — Right side of engine compartment.

GENERAL SERVICING (Cont.)

STARTER

All models are equipped with Bosch starters. Minimum cranking voltage is 8 volts.

ALTERNATOR

Application	Rated Amp. Output
Without A/C	55
With A/C	75

ALTERNATOR REGULATOR

Motorola and Bosch — Non-adjustable, integral with alternator.

Operating Voltage .... 12.5-14.5 Volts

BELT ADJUSTMENT

When depressed with firm thumb pressure, deflection should be 3/8 -9/16" (10-15 mm) for all belts.

FILTERS

Filter	Service Interval (Miles)
Oil Filter	Replace every 15,000
Air Filter	Replace every 30,000
Fuel Filter	Replace every 15,000

CAPACITIES

Application	Quantity
Crankcase (Includes Filter)	3.2 qts.
Cooling System	7.4 qts.
Man. Transaxle (SAE 80W-90)	1.8 qts.
Fuel Tank	15.9 gals.

1981 Audi 5 Tune-Up

TUNE-UP

4000
5000
5000 Turbo

ENGINE IDENTIFICATION

Engine number is stamped on left side of block near No. 3 cylinder.

Engine Code

Application	Code
4000 & 5000	WE
5000 Turbo	WK

COMPRESSION PRESSURE

Check compression with engine warm, all spark plugs removed and throttle wide open. Crank engine at least 6 "puffs" per cylinder to determine engine compression.

Compression Pressure Specifications

Application	Pressure psi (kg/cm²)
All Except Turbo	
Normal (New Engine)	131-174 (9-12)
Minimum	102 (7)
Maximum Variation	44 (3)
Turbo	
Normal (New Engine)	100-128 (7-9)
Minimum	71 (5)
Maximum Variation	28 (2)

VALVE CLEARANCE

1) Adjust valves with engine at normal operating temperature. Remove accelerator linkage and cylinder head cover. Clearance adjustments are to be checked and made according to firing order sequence (1-2-4-5-3). Rotate crankshaft until cam lobes for No. 1 cylinder valves point upward; then measure valve clearances of No. 1 cylinder.

NOTE — When adjusting valves, turn engine CLOCKWISE only, or timing belt may slip.

2) If adjustment is necessary, use special tools US 4476 (disc removal tool) and 2078 (tappet depressing tool) to remove and install adjusting discs. Turn tappet until notches are at 90° to camshaft. Insert tool 2078 and depress tappet. Using tool US 4476, grasp tappet disc and rotate it out from under camshaft.

3) Thickness is stamped on bottom side of disc. Using clearance measurement, determine thickness of adjusting disc necessary to bring valve clearance within specifications. Discs are available in .0019" (.05 mm) increments from .1181-.1673" (3.0-4.25 mm). Repeat procedure as required for remaining valves.

Valve Clearance Specifications①

Application	Intake In. (mm)	Exhaust In. (mm)
All Models	.010 (.3)	.018 (.5)

① — Set with engine warm.

VALVE ARRANGEMENT

E-I-E-I-I-E-I-E (front to rear)

SPARK PLUGS

Application	Gap In. (mm)	Torque Ft. Lbs. (N·m)
All Models	.028 (.7)	22 (30)

① — Turbo models are equipped with 2 oil filters. Both should be changed at 15,000 mile intervals.

Spark Plug Type

Application	Bosch	Champion
4000 & 5000		
Federal	W7D	N8Y
Calif.	WR7DS	N8GY
5000 Turbo	WR7DS	N8GY

HIGH TENSION WIRE RESISTANCE

Carefully remove ends of wire from spark plug and distributor. Using an ohmmeter, check resistance of wire while gently twisting wire. If resistance is not to specification, or fluctuates from infinity to any value, replace wire.

NOTE — Wire resistance cannot be measured if the wires are marked with this symbol: ◄▷|

Resistance (Ohms) Per Wire

Application	Resistance
Ignition Wire Only	800-1400
Ignition Wire With Connector	4800-7400
Coil Wire	1600-2400

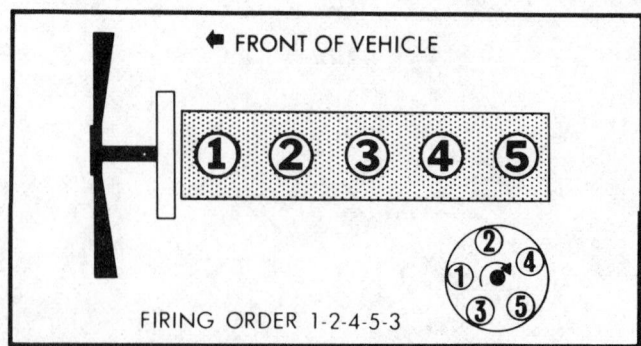

Fig. 1 *Firing Order and Distributor Rotation*

DISTRIBUTOR

All models are equipped with electronic, breakerless ignition systems. All California models and Federal Turbo models have an idle stabilizer unit, which adjusts ignition timing to maintain a constant idle speed. Some models without idle stabilizers may be equipped with an impedance transformer, which is gray in color.

TUNE-UP (Cont.)

IGNITION TIMING

Turbo — Disconnect and plug both hoses at distributor. With engine at 3000 RPM, adjust timing by turning distributor.

All Except Turbo — Disconnect 2 plugs at idle stabilizer unit (if equipped) and connect them together. Leave vacuum hoses connected at distributor. With engine idling, adjust ignition timing by turning distributor. Reconnect idle stabilizer unit.

NOTE — *If equipped with an impedance transformer in place of an idle stabilizer, do not disconnect it when checking ignition timing.*

Ignition Timing Specifications

Application	RPM	Timing
4000 & 5000		
Federal	①800-1000	3° ATDC
Calif.	880-1000	3° ATDC
5000 Turbo	3000	21° BTDC

① — 5000 reading should be 850-1000 RPM.

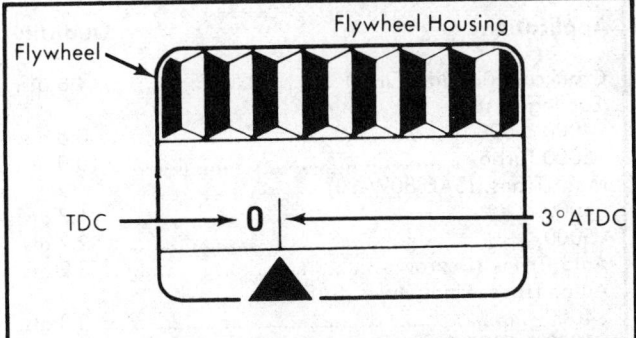

Fig. 2 Ignition Timing Mark Location

IDLE SPEED & MIXTURE

1) With engine at normal operating temperature, turn all electrical accessories off. With engine stopped, disconnect both plugs from idle stabilizer unit and connect them together. Disconnect and plug PCV valve hose.

2) Check and adjust ignition timing as necessary. Adjust idle speed to specified RPM using adjusting screw on side of throttle valve housing.

NOTE — *Engine cooling fan must not run while adjustments are being made.*

3) Remove cap from CO test receptacle on exhaust manifold and connect CO tester hose directly to test receptacle. Connect a dwell meter to frequency valve electrical connector. Zero dwell meter and set it to the 4-cylinder scale.

NOTE — *When taking CO reading on California models, turn all electrical sources off; on Federal models turn lights on high beam.*

4) Disconnect oxygen sensor wire at connector and check dwell meter reading. Meter reading must be constant between 40-50°.

5) Adjust CO level to specifications using adjusting tool (P377). Turn adjusting tool clockwise to increase CO and counterclockwise to decrease CO.

CAUTION — *Do not press down on adjusting tool when adjusting CO level. Also, do not accelerate engine with tool in place. Remove tool after each adjustment and accelerate engine briefly before reading CO level. Always adjust CO level from lean to rich.*

6) Reconnect oxygen sensor wire and check dwell meter reading. Meter reading should now pulsate. Reconnect all hoses and wiring at idle stabilizer, then recheck idle speed.

Idle Speed & CO Level

Application	Idle RPM	CO%
4000 & 5000		
Federal	①800-1000	0.4-1.2%
Calif.	880-1000	0.4-1.2%
5000 Turbo	880-1000	0.4-1.2%

① — 5000 reading should be 850-1000 RPM.

FUEL PUMP PRESSURE & VOLUME

System Pressure
4000 & 5000 .... 65-75 psi (4.5-5.2 kg/cm²)
5000 Turbo .... 72-82 psi (4.9-5.6 kg/cm²)
Volume .... Approx. 1 quart in 40 sec.

EMISSION CONTROL SYSTEMS

See Mitchell Manuals' Emission Control Manual.

GENERAL SERVICING

IGNITION

DISTRIBUTOR

All models are equipped with electronic ignition. California 4000 and 5000 models and all Turbo models use an idle stabilizer in addition to the Hall generator ignition system. Some models without the idle stabilizer may have an impedance transformer in its place.

IGNITION COIL

Resistance Specifications
(Ohms@68°F)

Application	Primary	Secondary
All Models	.52-.76	2400-3500

1981 Audi 5 Tune-Up

GENERAL SERVICING (Cont.)

FUEL SYSTEMS

FUEL INJECTION

All models are equipped with Bosch CIS Continuous Injection System.

ELECTRICAL

BATTERY

Application	Amp. Hr. Capacity
All Models	63

Battery Location — On models with factory-installed air conditioning, the battery is located under the left side of the rear seat. On all other models, the battery is located in the engine compartment.

STARTER

All models are equipped with Bosch Starters.

ALTERNATOR

Application	Rated Amp. Output
4000	
Without A/C	55
With A/C	75
5000	75
5000 Turbo	90

ALTERNATOR REGULATOR

Bosch — Non-adjustable, integral with alternator.

Operating Voltage	12.5-14.5 Volts

BELT ADJUSTMENT

All Models — With a 20 lbs. (9.1 kg) pressure, belt should be able to be depressed 3/8 -9/16" (10-15 mm).

FILTERS

Filter	Service Interval (Miles)
Oil Filter①	15,000
Air Filter	30,000
Fuel Filter	15,000

① — Turbo models are equipped with 2 oil filters. Both should be changed at 15,000 mile intervals.

CAPACITIES

Application	Quantity
Crankcase (Includes Filter)	4.8 qts.
Cooling System	
4000 & 5000	8.6 qts.
5000 Turbo	10.0 qts.
Man. Trans. (SAE 80W-90)	
4000	1.7 qts.
5000	2.7 qts.
Auto. Trans. (Dexron)	3.2 qts.
Auto. Trans. Final Drive (SAE 90)	
4000	0.8 qts.
5000 & 5000 Turbo	1.1 qts.
Fuel Tank	
4000	15.9 gals.
5000 & 5000 Turbo	19.8 gals.

TUNE-UP

4000 Diesel
5000 Diesel

ENGINE IDENTIFICATION

Engine number is stamped into left side of block near number 3 cylinder.

Engine Code

Application	Code
4000 (4-Cylinder)	CR
5000 (5-Cylinder)	CN

COMPRESSION PRESSURE

Remove electrical wire from fuel shut-off solenoid on injection pump. Remove injector pipes, injectors and heat shields. Insert old heat shield into head, then adapter (VW 1323/2) and compression tester. Check compression after cranking engine through at least 6 strokes.

Compression Pressure Specifications

Application	Pressure psi (kg/cm^2)
Normal (New Engine)	406-493 (28-34)
Minimum	400 (28)
Maximum Variation	73 (5)

VALVE CLEARANCE

1) Turn engine clockwise until camshaft lobes for valves to be checked point upwards. Check valve clearance. If not within tolerance, adjusting disc must be changed.

2) Turn crankshaft ¼ turn after TDC (so valves will not hit piston top). Depress cam followers with tool (VW 2078), then remove disc with pliers (VW 4476). Calculate thickness of disc needed, coat with oil and install with marks down.

NOTE — *Discs are available in thicknesses from .120" (3.00 mm) to .167" (4.25 mm) in increments of .002" (0.05 mm).*

3) Check valve clearance on remaining cylinders, proceeding in firing order. Be sure to check valve clearance at TDC, then turn ¼ turn after TDC before depressing valves.

Valve Clearance Specifications

Application	Clearance In. (mm)
Checking	
Cold	
Intake	.006-.010 (.15-.25)
Exhaust	.014-.018 (.35-.45)
Warm	
Intake	.008-.012 (.20-.30)
Exhaust	.016-.020 (.40-.50)
Adjustment	
Cold	
Intake	.008 (.20)
Exhaust	.016 (.40)
Warm	
Intake	.010 (.25)
Exhaust	.018 (.45)

VALVE ARRANGEMENT

4000 Diesel — E-I-E-I-I-E-I-E (Front-to-rear)
5000 Diesel — E-I-E-I-I-E-I-E-I-E (Front-to-rear)

Fig. 1   *4000 Diesel Firing Order Illustration*

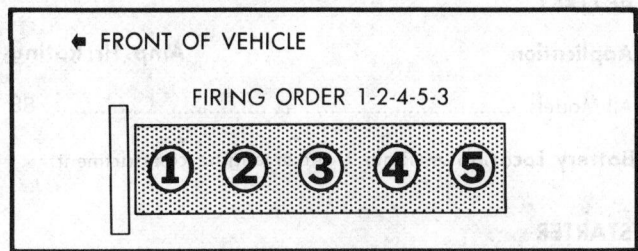

Fig. 2   *5000 Diesel Firing Order Illustration*

GLOW PLUGS

Glow Plug Type

Application	Bosch
All Models	N 019 100 6

IDLE SPEED ADJUSTMENT

1) With engine at normal operating temperature, turn idle speed control knob on dash panel counterclockwise to stop.

2) Connect diesel tachometer (VW 1367) according to instructions from manufacturer. Adjust speed to specifications with idle adjusting screw. Tighten lock nut. *See Fig. 3.*

3) Open throttle fully and quickly adjust maximum speed to specifications using maximum RPM screw. Tighten lock nut.

Fig. 3   *Adjusting Idle Speed and Maximum Speed*

Idle Speed Specifications

Application	Idle RPM	Maximum RPM
4000 Diesel	770-870	5300-5400
5000 Diesel	720-880	5350-5450

GENERAL SERVICING

FUEL SYSTEMS

FUEL INJECTION

All models use Bosch mechanical diesel fuel injection.

ELECTRICAL

BATTERY

Application	Amp. Hr. Rating
All Models	88

Battery Location — Right front of engine compartment.

STARTER

All models are equipped with Bosch Starters.

ALTERNATOR

All models are equipped with Bosch alternators.

Application	Rated Amp. Output
All Models	75

ALTERNATOR REGULATOR

All models are equipped with Bosch non-adjustable voltage regulators with operating voltage of 13.9-14.8 volts.

BELT ADJUSTMENT

Adjust belts for deflection of ⅜-⁹⁄₁₆" (10-15 mm) when depressed firmly, halfway between pulleys.

FILTERS

Filter	Service Interval (Miles)
Oil Filter	Replace every 15,000
Fuel Filter	Drain every 7500
Air Filter	Replace every 30,000

CAPACITIES

Application	Quantity
Crankcase (Includes Filter)	4.8 qts.
Cooling System	9.9 qts.
Man. Transaxle (SAE 80)	2.0 qts.
Auto. Trans.	3.2 qts.
Fuel Tank	19.8 gals.

TUNE-UP

320i

ENGINE IDENTIFICATION

Engine number is stamped into engine block on left side above starter. Engine can also be identified by first 4 numbers in chassis code, located on sill above right front wheel.

Engine Code

Application	Code
Man. Trans.	1739
Auto. Trans.	1749

COMPRESSION PRESSURE

With battery fully charged, engine at normal operating temperature, throttle fully open and engine at cranking speed, compression pressure should be as follows:

Compression Pressure Specifications

Condition	Pressure
Good	Above 149 psi (10.5 kg/cm²)
Normal	135-149 psi (9.5-10.5 kg/cm²)
Poor	Below 128 psi (9.0 kg/cm²)

VALVE CLEARANCE

Adjust valves with engine cold. Remove valve cover, loosen nut on rocker arm, and use a piece of wire to adjust eccentric cam. Adjust valves in firing order sequence at TDC of compression stroke.

Adjust Cylinder at Top Dead Center	When Valves Of Cylinder Overlap
No. 1	No. 4
No. 3	No. 2
No. 4	No. 1
No. 2	No. 3

Valve Clearance Specifications

Application	Clearance In. (mm)
Intake & Exhaust (Cold)	.006-.008 (.15-.20)

VALVE ARRANGEMENT
Left Side — All Intake.
Right Side — All Exhaust.

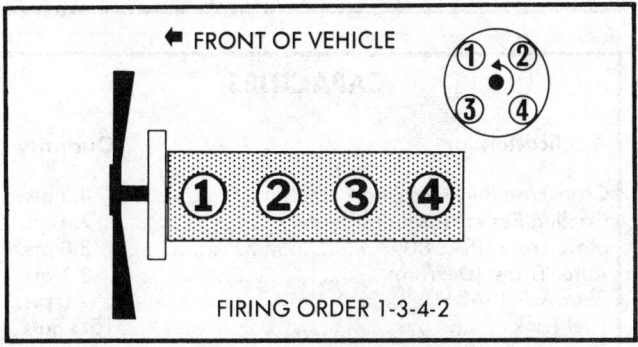

FRONT OF VEHICLE

FIRING ORDER 1-3-4-2

Fig. 1   Firing Order and Distributor Rotation

SPARK PLUGS

Application	Gap In. (mm)	Torque Ft. Lbs. (N·m)
All Models	.024 (.6)	18 (24)

Spark Plug Type

Application	Bosch No.
All Models	WR9DS

HIGH TENSION WIRE RESISTANCE

Carefully remove ends of wire from spark plug and distributor. Using an ohmmeter, check resistance of wire while gently twisting wire. If resistance is not to specification, or fluctuates from infinity to any value, replace wire.

Resistance (Ohms) Per Wire

Application	Resistance
All Models	25,000-30,000

DISTRIBUTOR

All models are equipped with Bosch transistorized electronic ignition. No adjustments are necessary.

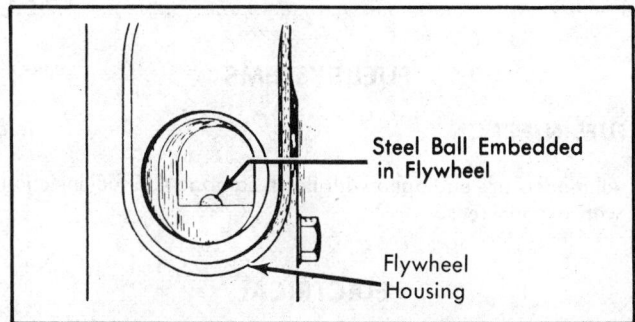

Steel Ball Embedded in Flywheel

Flywheel Housing

Fig. 2   Ignition Timing Mark Location

IGNITION TIMING

With engine at normal operating temperature, connect a timing light and tachometer to vehicle. Disconnect and plug distributor vacuum line. Start engine and adjust speed to specifications shown in following table. To adjust ignition timing, rotate distributor until center of ball embedded in flywheel is visible at edge of inspection hole.

Ignition Timing Specifications

Application	RPM	Dynamic Timing
All Models	2200	25° BTDC

1981 BMW 4 Tune-Up

TUNE-UP (Cont.)

IDLE SPEED & MIXTURE

1) Connect tachometer to engine. Remove caps at exhaust manifold test points and connect CO meter. Warm engine to normal operating temperature and check ignition timing and idle speed. Adjust idle by turning idle air screw on throttle housing.

2) Measure CO level. Disconnect oxygen sensor (plug below distributor on fender panel) and note CO reading. If level changes, adjustment is necessary.

NOTE — *Do not accelerate engine while adjusting CO%.*

3) Adjust mixture with Allen wrench through opening in fuel distributor (remove plug). After adjustment, reconnect oxygen sensor and ensure CO level does not change. Repeat procedure until both mixture and idle speed are correct.

Idle Speed & CO Level

Application	Idle RPM	CO%
Man. Trans.	800-900	① 0.2-1.2
Auto. Trans.	900-1000	① 0.2-1.2

① — Oxygen sensor disconnected.

FUEL PUMP PRESSURE

Application	psi (kg/cm²)
All Models	64-74 (4.5-5.2)

EMISSION CONTROL SYSTEMS

See Mitchell Manuals' Emission Control Manual.

GENERAL SERVICING

IGNITION

DISTRIBUTOR

All models are equipped with Bosch electronic ignition systems.

IGNITION COIL

Resistance	Ohms at 68°F (20°C)
Primary	1.7-2.1

FUEL SYSTEMS

FUEL INJECTION

All models are equipped with Bosch Lambda CIS fuel injection with oxygen sensor.

ELECTRICAL

BATTERY

Application	Amp. Hr. Rating
All Models	55

Battery Location — In engine compartment.

STARTER

All models are equipped with Bosch Starters.

ALTERNATOR

Application	Rated Amp. Output
All Models	65

ALTERNATOR REGULATOR

All models are equipped with Bosch Alternator Regulators with an operating voltage of 13.9-14.2 volts at 68°F (20°C).

BELT ADJUSTMENT

Application	①Deflection
Alternator Belt	.2-.4" (5-10 mm)
Air Conditioning Belt	.5" (12 mm)

① — Measured with moderate hand pressure applied midway between pulleys on longest belt run.

FILTERS

Filter	Service Interval (Miles)
Oil Filter	Replace every 7500
Air Filter	Replace every 30,000
Fuel Filter	Replace every 30,000

CAPACITIES

Application	Quantity
Crankcase (Includes Filter)	4.3 qts.
Cooling System (Includes Heater)	7.4 qts.
Man. Trans. (SAE 80)	3.0 pts.
Auto. Trans. (Dexron)	2.1 qts.
Rear Axle (SAE 90)	2.0 pts.
Fuel Tank	15.3 gals.

TUNE-UP

528i
633CSi
733i

ENGINE IDENTIFICATION

All engines have a serial number stamped on block on left side above starter motor. Engines can also be identified by first 4 numbers in chassis code, stamped on sill above right front wheel on 528i, and on firewall on 633CSi and 733i.

Engine Code

Application	Code
528i	
Man. Trans.	3995
Auto. Trans.	3997
633CSi	
Man. Trans.	5235
Auto. Trans.	5245
733i	
Man. Trans.	6633
Auto. Trans.	6643

COMPRESSION PRESSURE

NOTE — *Deactivate fuel injection system by pulling off connection "1" at the coil prior to compression test.*

With battery fully charged, engine at normal operating temperature, throttle fully open and engine at cranking speed, compression pressure should be as follows:

Compression Pressure Specifications

Application	Pressure
528i	
Good	Above 156 psi (11 kg/cm²)
Normal	142-156 psi (10-11 kgcm²)
Poor	Below 142 psi (10 kg/cm²)
633CSi & 733i	
Good	Above 142 psi (10 kg/cm²)
Normal	121-142 psi (8.5-10 kg/cm²)
Poor	Below 121 (8 kg/cm²)

VALVE CLEARANCE

With engine cold, loosen nut on rocker arm and adjust position of eccentric cam to obtain proper clearance. Adjust valves in firing order sequence at TDC of compression stroke. Use feeler gauge to measure clearance between rocker arm eccentric and valve stem.

Adjust Cylinder at Top Dead Center	When Valves Of Cylinder Overlap
No. 1	No. 6
No. 5	No. 2
No. 3	No. 4
No. 6	No. 1
No. 2	No. 5
No. 4	No. 3

Valve Clearance Specifications

Application	Clearance In. (mm)
All Models	.012-.014 (.30-.35)

VALVE ARRANGEMENT

Left Side — All Intake.
Right Side — All Exhaust.

SPARK PLUGS

Application	Gap In. (mm)	Torque Ft. Lbs. (N·m)
All Models	.024 (.6)	18 (24)

Spark Plug Type

Application	Bosch No.
All Models	WR9DS

HIGH TENSION WIRE RESISTANCE

Carefully remove ends of wire from spark plug and distributor. Using an ohmmeter, check resistance of wire while gently twisting wire. If resistance is not to specification, or fluctuates from infinity to any value, replace wire.

Resistance (Ohms) Per Wire

Application	Resistance
All Models	25,000-30,000

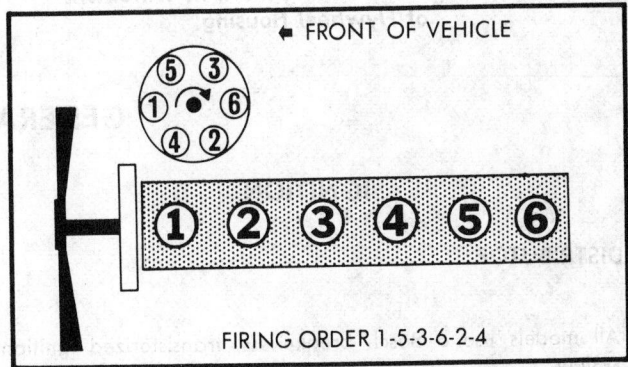

Fig. 1 Firing Order and Distributor Rotation (BMW 528i, 633CSi & 733i)

DISTRIBUTOR

All models use a Bosch breakerless, transistorized ignition system.

1981 BMW 6 Tune-Up

TUNE-UP (Cont.)

IGNITION TIMING

1) Check and adjust timing with engine at normal operating temperature and distributor vacuum hoses disconnected. Connect timing light, start engine and increase engine speed to specified timing RPM. Steel ball embedded in flywheel (long pin on Auto. Trans. models) should line up with pointer attached to hole in flywheel housing.

2) Loosen distributor clamp, turn distributor until proper timing is achieved and tighten clamp. Connect distributor vacuum hoses and set idle speed to specified RPM.

Ignition Timing Specifications

Application	RPM	Dynamic Timing
528i	2100	22° BTDC
633CSi & 733i	1650	22° BTDC

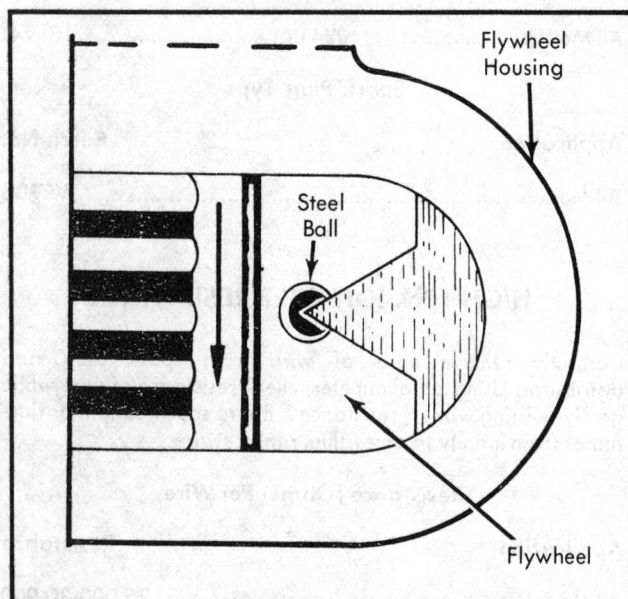

Fig. 2   Ignition Timing Mark In Window of Flywheel Housing

IDLE SPEED & MIXTURE

NOTE — *The following adjustments must be performed with the air filter in good condition, ignition timing and valve clearance adjusted to specifications and engine at normal operating temperature.*

1) Disconnect charcoal canister-to-throttle housing hose at throttle housing, but do not plug port. Connect a tachometer to engine.

2) Connect a CO meter to test points in exhaust manifold. Set idle speed by turning idle adjusting screw (below throttle switch). Read and record CO level. Disconnect oxygen sensor wire in right rear corner of engine compartment. CO reading should not change.

3) If CO reading changes with sensor disconnected, level must be adjusted. Remove plug under left rear corner of air flow meter and adjust with short screwdriver.

4) Check CO readings and adjust until values are within specifications and do not change when sensor is disconnected or connected. Remove test equipment, replace manifold plugs, and connect hose to throttle housing.

Idle Speed & CO Level

Application	Idle RPM	CO%
All Models	850-950	①0.2-0.8

① — With oxygen sensor disconnected.

FUEL PUMP PRESSURE & VOLUME

Pressure	33.4-39.2 psi (2.3-2.7 kg/cm²)
Volume	1.9 pints in 30 seconds

EMISSION CONTROL SYSTEMS

See Mitchell Manuals' Emission Control Manual.

GENERAL SERVICING

IGNITION

DISTRIBUTOR

All models use a Bosch breakerless, transistorized ignition system.

IGNITION COIL

Resistance Specifications
(Ohms@68°F)

Application	Primary	Secondary
All Models	0.4	.....

FUEL SYSTEMS

FUEL INJECTION

All models are equipped with Bosch AFC electronic fuel injection with oxygen sensor.

ELECTRICAL

BATTERY

Application	Amp. Hr. Rating
All Models	66

GENERAL SERVICING (Cont.)

Battery Location — All models have battery in front left area of engine compartment.

STARTER

All models are equipped with Bosch Starters.

ALTERNATOR

Application	Rated Amp. Output
All Models	65

ALTERNATOR REGULATOR

All models are equipped with Bosch Alternator Regulators with an operating voltage of 13.5-14.2 volts at 68°F (20°C).

BELT ADJUSTMENT	
Application	①Deflection
Air Conditioning Belt	.5" (12 mm)
All Others	.2-.4" (5-10 mm)

① — When depressed with firm hand pressure midway between pulleys.

FILTERS	
Filter	Service Interval (Miles)
Oil Filter	Replace every 7500
Air Filter	Replace every 30,000
Fuel Filter	Replace every 30,000

CAPACITIES	
Application	Quantity
Crankcase (Includes Filter)	6.1 qts.
Cooling System (Includes Heater)	12.7 qts.
Man. Trans. (SAE 90)	
528i	3.4 pts.
633CSi & 733i	2.4 pts.
Auto. Trans. (Dexron)	
528i & 633CSi	2.1 qts.
733i	2.4 qts.
Rear Axle (SAE 90)	
528i & 633CSi	3.4 pts.
733i	4.0 pts.
Fuel Tank	
528i & 633CSi	16.4 gals.
733i	22.5 gals.

TUNE-UP

Arrow Pickup	Colt
Challenger	Ram-50 Pickup
Champ	Sapporo

ENGINE IDENTIFICATION

Engine code numbers are stamped on top edge of right front side of cylinder block.

Engine Code

Application	Code
1400 cc	G12B
1600 cc	G32B
2000 cc	G52B
2600 cc	G54B

COMPRESSION PRESSURE

Check compression pressure with engine at normal operating temperature, choke and throttle valves wide open and engine at cranking speed (250 RPM). Crank engine at least 6 "puffs" per cylinder to determine engine compression.

Compression Pressure Specifications

Application	Pressure psi (kg/cm²)
Normal (New Engine)	149 (10.5)
Maximum Variation	15 (1.1)

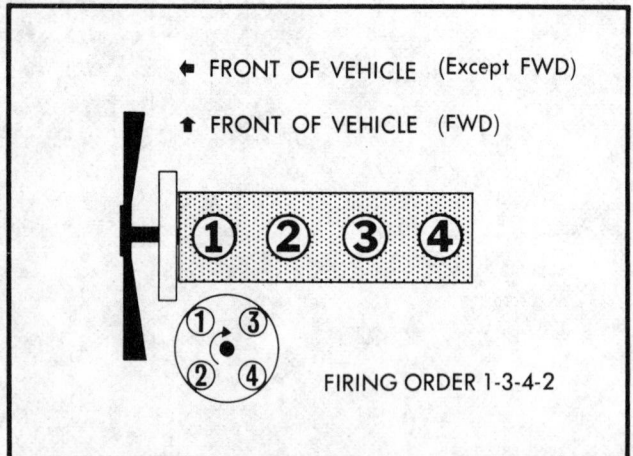

Fig. 1 *Firing Order and Distributor Rotation*

VALVE CLEARANCE

CAUTION — *Jet valve clearance must be adjusted before adjusting intake valve clearance. Loosen intake valve adjusting screw at least 2 full turns before adjusting jet valve.*

Check or adjust valve clearance with engine off and at normal operating temperature. To adjust valves, loosen lock nut and turn adjusting screw until specified clearance is obtained.

Valve Clearance Specifications

Application	Clearance
Jet	.006" (.15 mm)
Intake	.006" (.15 mm)
Exhaust	.010" (.25 mm)

VALVE ARRANGEMENT

Right Side — All Exhaust.
Left Side — All Intake.

SPARK PLUGS

Application	Gap In. (mm)	Torque Ft. Lbs. (N·m)
All Models	.041 (1.0)	20 (27)

Spark Plug Type

Application	NGK	Champion
2600 cc	BPR-5ES-11	RN-12Y
All Others	BPR-6ES-11	RN-9Y

HIGH TENSION WIRE RESISTANCE

Carefully remove high tension wires from spark plugs and distributor cap. Using an ohmmeter, check resistance of wire while gently twisting wire. If resistance is not to specification, or fluctuates from infinity to any value, replace wire.

Resistance (Ohms) Per Wire

Application	Resistance
All Models	Less Than 22,000

DISTRIBUTOR

All models use Mitsubishi electronic, breakerless ignition systems with an electronic control unit.

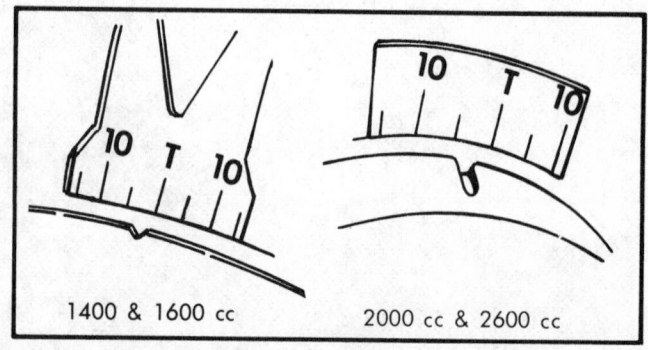

1400 & 1600 cc   2000 cc & 2600 cc

Fig. 2 *Ignition Timing Mark Location*

TUNE-UP (Cont.)

IGNITION TIMING

1) With engine at normal operating temperature, turn A/C controls and headlights off. Connect tachometer and timing light.

2) Loosen distributor nut and rotate distributor as necessary to adjust timing. Tighten mounting nut when timing is set to basic timing specification.

Ignition Timing Specifications
(Degrees BTDC@RPM)

Application	Timing
1400 cc	5@700
1600 cc	①5@700
2000 cc	5@750
2600 cc	7@800

① — Auto. Trans. — 750 RPM.

IDLE SPEED & MIXTURE

NOTE — *Mixture adjustment is NOT a part of normal tune-up procedure and should not be performed unless carburetor is disassembled or vehicle fails emission testing.*

1) Remove carburetor from engine and place on bench in suitable holder. Drill out concealment plug and remove from carburetor. See Fig. 3. Drive out roll pin. With concealment plug and roll pin removed, reinstall carburetor on engine.

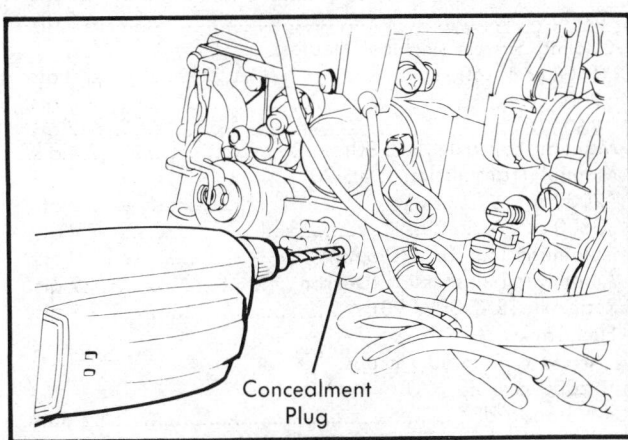

Fig. 3   Drilling Out Concealment Plug

2) Warm engine to normal operating temperature. Adjust idle speed with speed adjusting screw on throttle lever. If equipped with air conditioning, turn system on with blower at low speed. Adjust screw on side of throttle opener to obtain "A/C RPM".

3) Remove air cleaner-to-reed valve hose and plug inlet side of reed valve. Accelerate engine to 3000 RPM for 10 seconds, then allow to idle for 2 minutes. Adjust CO level to 0.5% using idle mixture screw. Unplug reed valve air inlet and reconnect air hose.

4) If necessary, reset idle speed with idle speed adjusting screw. Install roll pin and concealment plug into their respective holes to seal idle mixture adjusting screw. See Fig. 4.

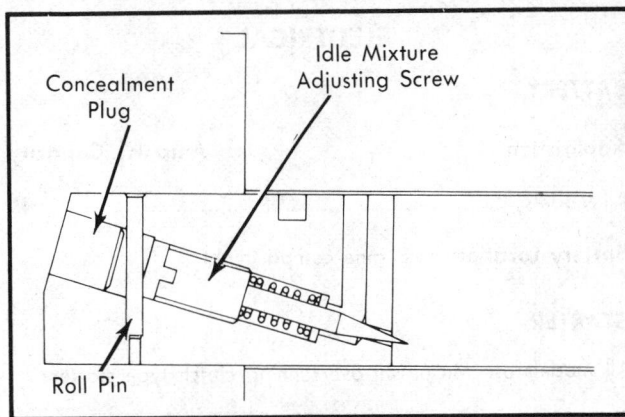

Fig. 4   Exploded View of Tamper-Proof Idle Mixture System

Idle Speed & CO Level

Application	Idle RPM	A/C RPM	①CO%
1400 cc	700	③850	0.5
1600 cc	②700	③850	0.5
2000 cc	750	900	0.5
2600 cc	800	900	0.5

① — With air injection disconnected.
② — Set Auto. Trans. to 750 RPM.
③ — Set Auto. Trans. to 900 RPM.

FUEL PUMP PRESSURE & VOLUME

Pressure (At Idle)
1400 cc & 1600 cc .... 3.7-5.1 psi (.26-.36 kg/cm²)
2000 cc & 2600 cc .... 4.6-6.0 psi (.32-.42 kg/cm²)
Volume (At Cranking Speed)
1400 cc .... 1.4 pts. in 30 sec.
1600 cc .... 1.7 pts. in 30 sec.
2000 cc & 2600 cc .... 2.1 pts. in 30 sec.

EMISSION CONTROL SYSTEMS

See Mitchell Manuals' Emission Control Manual.

GENERAL SERVICING

IGNITION

DISTRIBUTOR

All models use Mitsubishi electronic, breakerless ignition systems with an electronic control unit.

IGNITION COIL

Resistance Specifications
(Ohms@68°F)

Application	Primary	Secondary
All Models	.70-.85	9000-11,000

GENERAL SERVICING (Cont.)

FUEL SYSTEMS

CARBURETORS

Application	Model
1400 cc & 1600 cc	Solex 30-32 DIDTA 2-Bbl.
2000 cc & 2600 cc	Solex 28-32 DIDTA 2-Bbl.

ELECTRICAL

BATTERY

Application	Amp. Hr. Capacity
All Models	45

Battery Location — Engine compartment.

STARTER

All models use Mitsubishi overrunning clutch type starters.

Starter Specifications

Application	Volts	Amps	Test RPM
1400 cc & 1600 cc			
Man. Trans.	11.5	60	6500
Auto. Trans.	11.5	60	6600
2000 cc & 2600 cc			
Man. Trans.	11.5	60	6600
Auto. Trans.	11.5	90	3300

ALTERNATOR

All models are equipped with Mitsubishi alternators.

Application	Rated Amp. Output
1400 cc, 1600 cc & 2000 cc	45
2600 cc	
Arrow & Ram-50 Pickups	45
Challenger & Sapporo	50

ALTERNATOR REGULATOR

All models use Mitsubishi alternator regulators with the regulator mounted internally to the brush holder.

Operating Voltage .... 14.1-14.7 @ 68°F (20°C)

BELT ADJUSTMENT

Pull belt between alternator and water pump pulley, using 22 lbs. force. Belt should deflect ¼-⅜" (7-10 mm).

FILTERS

Filter	Service Interval (Miles)
Oil Filter	①Replace every 15,000
Air Filter	Replace every 30,000
Fuel Filter	Replace every 50,000
Canister Filter	Replace every 50,000

① — At first 7,500 miles, then every other oil change.

CAPACITIES

Application	Quantity
Crankcase (Includes Filter)	
1400 cc	3.7 qts.
1600 cc	4.2 qts.
2000 cc	4.5 qts.
2600 cc	4.5 qts.
Cooling System (Includes Heater)	
1400 cc & 1600 cc	5.0 qts.
2000 cc	9.5 qts.
2600 cc	9.7 qts.
Manual Transaxle (SAE 80)	2.4 qts.
Manual Transmission (SAE 90)	
2000 cc	2.2 qts.
2600 cc	2.4 qts.
Automatic Transaxle (Dexron)	6.0 qts.
Automatic Transmission (Dexron)	7.2 qts.
Rear Axle (SAE 80W-90)	2.7 qts.
Fuel Tank	
Arrow & Ram-50 Pickups	
2000 cc	
Standard	15.1 gals.
Optional	18.0 gals.
2600 cc	18.0 gals.
Challenger & Sapporo	15.8 gals.
Champ & Colt	
Luxury & Rally Sports	13.2 gals.
All Others	10.6 gals.

TUNE-UP

Pickup

ENGINE IDENTIFICATION

The engine identification number is stamped on right side of engine block below distributor and on model identification plate attached to body at right rear corner of engine compartment. Engine model code is the 8th digit of identification number.

Engine Code Numbers

Application	Code
2000 cc	1
2300 cc	2

COMPRESSION PRESSURE

Check compression pressure with engine at normal operating temperature, all spark plugs removed, throttle valve wide open and engine at cranking speed. Compression pressure is within specifications if lowest reading cylinder is more than 75% of highest.

VALVE TAPPET CLEARANCE

NOTE — *2300 cc engines are equipped with hydraulic valve lifters which require no adjustment during engine tune-up.*

Valve Clearance Specifications

Application	Clearance
2000 cc Intake & Exhaust	①.012″ (.3 mm)

① — Adjust with engine off and at normal operating temperature.

VALVE ARRANGEMENT

2000 cc
 Right Side — All Exhaust
 Left Side — All Intake
2300 cc — E-I-E-I-E-I-E-I

SPARK PLUGS

Application	Gap In. (mm)	Torque Ft. Lbs. (N·m)
2000 cc	.031 (.8)	11-15 (15-20)
2300 cc	.034 (.9)	5-10 (7-13)

Spark Plug Type

Application	NGK No.
2000 cc	BPR5ES
2300 cc	BPR5EFS

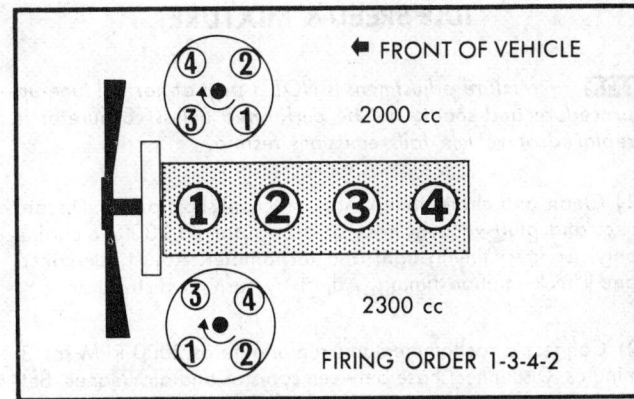

Fig. 1   Distributor Rotation and Firing Order

HIGH TENSION WIRE RESISTANCE

Carefully remove ends of wire from spark plug and distributor. Using an ohmmeter, check resistance of wire while gently twisting wire. If resistance exceeds 570 ohms per inch of wire or fluctuates from infinity to any value, replace wire.

DISTRIBUTOR

All models are equipped with breakerless, electronic ignition systems.

Armature Tooth-to-Magnetic
 Pickup Gap .... .008-.024″ (.2-.6 mm)

IGNITION TIMING

Check or adjust ignition timing with engine at normal operating temperature, at correct idle speed, and with distributor vacuum advance line disconnected and plugged.

Ignition Timing Specifications
(Degrees BTDC@RPM)

Application	Timing
2000 cc	8@650
2300 cc Man. Trans.	6@850
Auto. Trans.①	6@850

① — Transmission in "D".

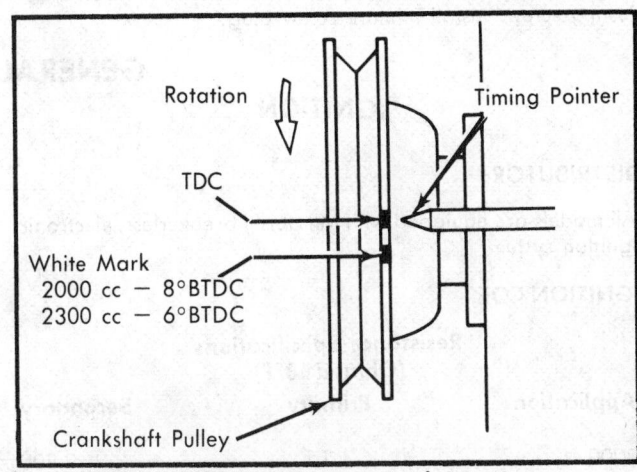

Fig. 2   Ignition Timing Mark Locations

TUNE-UP (Cont.)

IDLE SPEED & MIXTURE

NOTE — *Mixture adjustment is NOT a part of normal tune-up procedure and should not be performed unless carburetor is replaced or vehicle fails emissions testing.*

1) Clean and chalk timing mark on crankshaft pulley. Disconnect and plug vacuum hose at distributor on 2300 cc engine only. Connect timing light and tachometer. Adjust idle speed and check ignition timing. Adjust by turning distributor.

2) Connect a tachometer and run engine at 2000 RPM for 3 minutes. Disconnect hose between canister and air cleaner. Set idle speed to specification by turning throttle adjusting screw. Reconnect hose.

3) Remove mixture adjusting screw shell by pulling outward on shell while turning it counterclockwise or cut shell off at points shown in *Fig. 3.* Connect exhaust gas analyzer to vehicle.

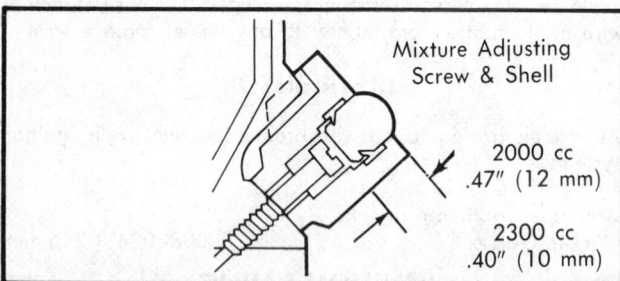

Mixture Adjusting Screw & Shell

2000 cc .47" (12 mm)

2300 cc .40" (10 mm)

Fig. 3   Mixture Adjust Screw and Shell Removal

4) On Calif. models, disconnect air by-pass valve hose at check valve and plug valve port. On Federal models, disconnect air cleaner hose at reed valve and plug valve port.

5) On 2000 cc models only, adjust speed to 20 RPM higher than mixture RPM by turning throttle adjusting screw. Adjust mixture screw to obtain highest possible RPM, then reset engine speed to 20 RPM higher than mixture RPM by turning throttle adjusting screw.

6) Turn mixture screw clockwise to obtain mixture RPM. If CO level is now less than 1.0%, turn mixture screw out ¼ turn. Reconnect air hose and adjust idle speed with throttle adjusting screw. Install mixture screw plug.

7) On 2300 cc models only, adjust idle speed to mixture RPM by turning throttle adjusting screw. Check CO level and adjust by turning mixture screw. If idle speed changes, adjust back to mixture RPM with throttle adjusting screw.

8) Reconnect air hose. Check and, if necessary, adjust idle speed to curb idle RPM. Install and plug new mixture adjusting screw shell.

Idle Speed & CO Level

Application	Mixture RPM	Curb Idle RPM	①CO%
2000 cc			
Federal	650	650	1.0
Calif.	600	650	1.0
2300 cc			
Man. Trans.	750	850	3.5
Auto. Trans.	②625	②700	3.5

① — Air injection disconnected.
② — Transmission in "D".

COLD (FAST) IDLE RPM

With choke valve fully closed, position fast idle screw on highest step of fast idle cam. Measure clearance between lower edge of throttle valve and wall of throttle bore. If clearance is not within specifications, adjust by turning screw clockwise to increase clearance, counterclockwise to decrease clearance.

Fast Idle Specifications

Application	Clearance
2000 cc	.055" (1.4 mm)
2300 cc	
Federal	.062" (1.6 mm)
Calif.	.066" (1.7 mm)

FUEL PUMP PRESSURE & VOLUME

Pressure	2.8-3.6 psi (.20-.25 kg/cm²)
Volume	1 pt. in 30 sec.

EMISSION CONTROL SYSTEMS

See Mitchell Manuals' Emission Control Manual.

GENERAL SERVICING

IGNITION

DISTRIBUTOR

All models are equipped with Mitsubishi breakerless, electronic ignition system.

IGNITION COIL

Resistance Specifications
(Ohms@68°F)

Application	Primary	Secondary
2000 cc	1.15	9,800
2300 cc	.81-.99	6,800-9,200

FUEL SYSTEMS

CARBURETORS

Application	Model
2000 cc	Nikki 2-Bbl.
2300 cc	Hitachi DCS 328 2-Bbl.

ELECTRICAL

BATTERY

Application	Amp. Hr. Rating
All Models	
Standard	45
Optional	70

GENERAL SERVICING (Cont.)

Battery Location — The battery is located in the engine compartment.

STARTER

Nippondenso solenoid-actuated with overrunning clutch.

Application	Volts	Amps.	Test RPM
All Models	11	50	5000

ALTERNATOR

All models are equipped with Mitsubishi alternators.

Application	Rated Amp. Output
All Models	35

ALTERNATOR REGULATOR

All models are equipped with externally mounted Mitsubishi regulators having an operating voltage of 14.5-15.8 volts.

FILTERS

Filter	Service Interval (Miles)
Oil Filter	Replace every 7500
Air Filter	①Replace every 30,000
Fuel Filter	Replace every 15,000

① — Inspect and clean every 15,000 miles.

BELT ADJUSTMENT

Application	①Deflection New Belt	①Deflection Used Belt
2000 cc		
Alternator	0.3-0.4" (8-10 mm)	0.5-0.6" (13-15 mm)
Air Pump	0.4-0.6" (10-15 mm)	0.6-0.7" (15-18 mm)
2300 cc		
Alternator	0.4-0.45" (10-11 mm)	0.45-0.5" (11-13 mm)
Air Pump	0.6-0.7" (15-18 mm)	0.8-0.9" (20-23 mm)

① — Deflection is with 22 lbs. (10 kg) pressure applied midway on longest belt run.

CAPACITIES

Application	Quantity
Crankcase (Includes Filter)	
2000 cc	4.7 qts.
2300 cc	5.0 qts.
Cooling System	
2000 cc	7.6 qts.
2300 cc	8.8 qts.
Man. Trans.(SAE 90 with EP)	
4-Speed	1.5 qts.
5-Speed	1.8 qts.
Auto. Trans. (Type F Trans. Fluid)	6.6 qts.
Rear Axle (Hypoid Gear Lubricant)	2.8 pts.
Fuel Tank	
Standard	14.8 gals.
Optional	17.5 gals.

1981 Datsun 4 Tune-Up

TUNE-UP

**200SX
210
310
510
Pickup**

ENGINE IDENTIFICATION

Engine code number followed by engine serial number is stamped on left side of cylinder block for 200SX and Pickup models and on right side of cylinder block for all other models, just below cylinder head mating surface.

Engine Code

Application	Code
200SX	Z20E
210	
1237 cc	A12A
1397 cc	A14
1488 cc	A15

COMPRESSION PRESSURE

Check compression pressure with engine at normal operating temperature, all spark plugs removed, electrical lead to anti-dieseling solenoid disconnected, choke and throttle valves wide open and engine at cranking speed. Crank engine at least 6 "puffs" per cylinder to determine engine compression. Lowest cylinder pressure should be at least 80% that of the highest cylinder pressure.

Compression Pressure Specifications
Reading@350 RPM

Application	Pressure psi (kg/cm²)
200SX, 510 & Pickup	128-171 (9.0-12.0)
210 & 310	178-192 (12.5-13.5)

VALVE CLEARANCE

NOTE — *On all models, start and run engine to normal operating temperature. Turn engine off, remove valve cover and adjust clearances immediately. Do not allow engine to cool before or during adjustment, or incorrect valve clearances may be obtained.*

200SX, 510 & Pickup — 1) Rotate crankshaft to bring the first cam lobe to a straight down position. Adjust intake valves on cylinders No. 1 and No. 2, and exhaust valves on cylinders No. 3 and No. 4.

2) Rotate crankshaft 360° to bring the first cam lobe to a straight up position. Adjust intake valves on cylinders No. 2 and No. 4, and exhaust valves on cylinders No. 1 and No. 3.

210 & 310 — 1) Rotate crankshaft to bring No. 1 piston to TDC on compression stroke. Adjust intake valves on cylinders No. 1 and No. 2, and adjust exhaust valves on cylinders No. 1 and No. 3.

2) Rotate crankshaft 360° to bring No. 4 piston to TDC on compression stroke. Adjust intake valves on cylinders No. 3 and No. 4, and adjust exhaust valves on cylinders No. 2 and No. 4.

Valve Clearance Specifications①

Application	Intake In. (mm)	Exhaust In. (mm)
200SX, 510 & Pickup	.012 (.30)	.012 (.30)
210 & 310	.014 (.35)	.014 (.35)

① — Set with engine warm.

VALVE ARRANGEMENT

200SX, 510 & Pickup
Right Side — All Intake.
Left Side — All Exhaust.
210 & 310 — E-I-I-E-E-I-I-E (front-to-rear).

SPARK PLUGS

Application	Gap In. (mm)	Torque Ft. Lbs. (N·m)
200SX, 510 & Pickup	.033 (0.8)	14 (19)
210 & 310	.041 (1.0)	14 (19)

Spark Plug Type

Application	NGK No.
200SX, 510 & Pickup	BP6ES
210 & 310	BP5ES-11

HIGH TENSION WIRE RESISTANCE

Remove distributor cap from distributor but do not disconnect high tension wires from cap. Disconnect high tension wires from spark plugs. Using an ohmmeter, check resistance from contact at spark plug end of wires to contact inside of distributor cap. Resistance should be less than 30,000 ohms. If resistance is more, disconnect wire from cap and recheck resistance. Replace wire if resistance still exceeds specification.

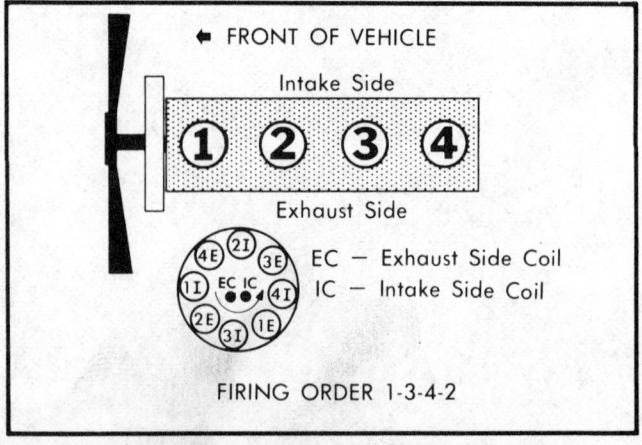

Fig. 1 Firing Order and Distributor Rotation (200SX, 510 and Pickup Models)

TUNE-UP (Cont.)

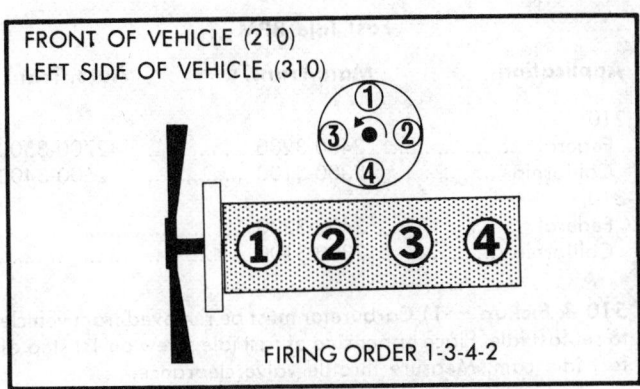

Fig. 2   Firing Order and Distributor Rotation
(210 and 310 Models)

DISTRIBUTOR

All models are equipped with breakerless, transistorized ignition systems. 200SX, 510 and Pickup models have 2 spark plugs per cylinder and the distributor is equipped with 8 secondary wires and a dual level rotor which fires both spark plugs at the same time.

Air Gap .... .012-.020" (.3-.5 mm)

IGNITION TIMING

Check and adjust ignition timing with engine at normal operating temperature, air gap set within specifications and engine idle speed correct. Disconnect and plug distributor vacuum hose. To adjust, loosen distributor set screw and rotate distributor until correct timing is achieved. Tighten set screw, recheck timing and reconnect distributor vacuum hose.

Ignition Timing Specifications
(Degrees BTDC@RPM)

Application	Man. Trans.	Auto. Trans.
200SX	6@650-850	6@600-800
210		
1200 cc Eng.	7@650-750	
1400 cc Eng.	5@600-700	
1500 cc Eng.	5@650-750	5@600-700
310	5@700-800	
510	6@500-700	6@500-700
Pickup	① 5@550-750	5@550-750

① — 4-WD — 5@700-900.

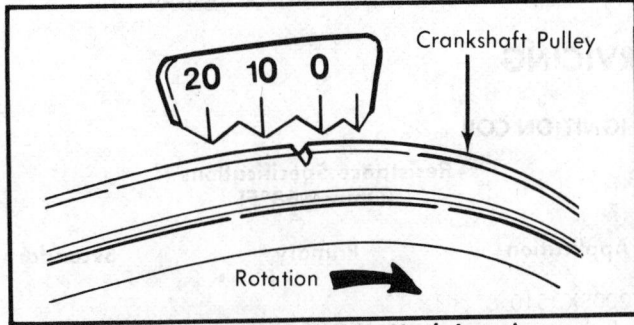

Fig. 3   Ignition Timing Mark Location
(200SX, 510 and Pickup Models)

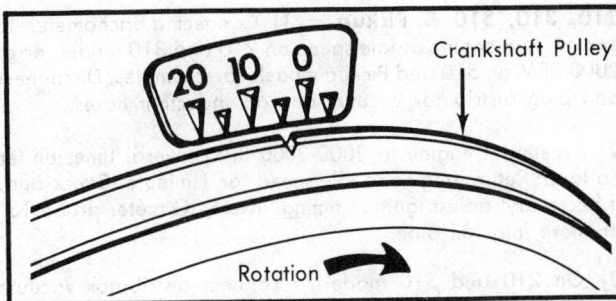

Fig. 4   Ignition Timing Mark Location
(210 and 310 Models)

IDLE SPEED & MIXTURE

NOTE — Mixture adjustment is NOT a part of normal tune-up procedure and should not be performed unless mixture control unit is replaced, carburetor overhauled or vehicle fails emissions testing.

NOTE — The following adjustment procedures should be performed with engine at normal operating temperature, air conditioning "OFF" (if equipped), ignition timing set to specifications and air cleaner installed. Set parking brake, block drive wheels and on models with automatic transmission, place gear selector in "D" position.

200SX — 1) Connect a tachometer to engine and run at 2000 RPM for 5 minutes to stabilize operating condition. Accelerate engine 2-3 times and return to idle. Turn idle speed adjusting screw to obtain specified idle RPM.

2) Turn ignition switch off and disconnect throttle valve switch harness connector. Position harness connector at least 4" away from any secondary ignition wires. Disconnect and plug distributor vacuum hose.

3) Check and, if necessary, adjust ignition timing. Connect a jumper wire between throttle valve switch harness connector terminals No. 24 and No. 30. Insert CO meter probe into tail pipe at least 16".

NOTE — Connecting jumper wire between connector terminals signals the control unit of a full throttle condition which allows the idle mixture to run at full load enrichment. This step is necessary to enrich the CO% level at idle enough to be read by the CO meter.

4) With engine idling, check CO level. If necessary to adjust CO, remove air flow meter and drill a small hole in plug covering air by-pass screw. DO NOT allow drill to contact screw. Clean up metal shavings. Install self-tapping screw into hole and pull plug from bore. Install air flow meter.

5) Adjust CO level by turning air by-pass screw clockwise to richen mixture and counterclockwise to lean mixture. Remove air flow meter. Tap new seal plug, with convex side up, into air by-pass screw bore. Install air flow meter.

6) Stop engine and remove jumper wire from throttle valve switch harness connector. Reconnect harness and all hoses. Reset idle speed to specified RPM.

1981 Datsun 4 Tune-Up

TUNE-UP (Cont.)

210, 310, 510 & Pickup — 1) Connect a tachometer to engine. Run engine at idle speed on 210 and 310 models or at 2000 RPM on 510 and Pickup models for 2 minutes. Disconnect and plug distributor vacuum and air induction hoses.

2) Accelerate engine to 2000-3000 RPM several times under no load. Return engine to idle speed for 1 minute. Check and, if necessary, adjust ignition timing. Insert CO meter probe 16" or more into tail pipe.

3) On 210 and 310 models, reconnect distributor vacuum hoses. Accelerate engine to 2000-3000 RPM several times under no load and return to idle speed. On all models, check and, if necessary, adjust idle speed. Again accelerate engine several times and return to idle. Check CO level.

4) If necessary to adjust CO, remove carburetor and drill a small hole in plug covering mixture adjusting screw. DO NOT allow drill to contact screw or metal shavings to enter carburetor. Reinstall carburetor.

5) Adjust CO level by turning mixture adjusting screw clockwise to richen mixture and counter-clockwise to lean mixture. Reconnect all hoses and install new plug in mixture adjusting screw bore.

Idle Speed & CO Level

Application	Idle RPM	CO%
200SX		
Man. Trans.	750	Less than 6.0
Auto. Trans.	700	Less than 6.0
210		
1200 cc Eng.	700	Less than 4.0
1400 cc Eng.	650	Less than 4.0
1500 cc Eng.		
Man. Trans.	700	Less than 4.0
Auto. Trans.	650	Less than 4.0
310	750	Less than 4.0
510	600	Less than 5.0
Pickup		
Man. Trans.		
2-WD	650	Less than 5.0
4-WD	800	Less than 5.0
Auto. Trans.	650	Less than 5.0

COLD (FAST) IDLE RPM

210 & 310 — Adjust fast idle speed with engine at normal operating temperature, transmission in neutral and fast idle speed screw on 2nd higest step of fast idle cam. Adjust Man. Trans. models to 2300-3200 RPM or Auto. Trans. models to 2600-3500 RPM.

Fast Idle RPM

Application	Man. Trans.	Auto. Trans.
210		
Federal	2400-3200	2700-3500
California	2300-3100	2600-3400
310		
Federal	2400-3200	
California	2300-3100	

510 & Pickup — 1) Carburetor must be removed from vehicle to set fast idle. Place upper side of fast idle screw on 1st step of fast idle cam. Measure throttle valve clearance.

2) Clearance should be .030-.035" (.76-.90 mm) on 510 Man. Trans. models and .038-.043" (.96-1.1 mm) on 510 Auto. Trans. models. Clearance should be .032-.038" (.81-.95 mm) on Pickup Man. Trans. models and .039-.044" (.98-1.12 mm) on Pickup Auto. Trans. models. If not, adjust clearance by turning fast idle screw.

DASHPOT ADJUSTMENT

With engine at normal operating temperature and idle speed and mixture correctly set, turn throttle valve by hand and read engine speed when dashpot just contacts adjusting screw on stop lever. Turn adjusting screw on stop lever to obtain specified engine speed. Accelerate engine and release. When dashpot plunger contacts stop lever, engine should decelerate smoothly from 2000 RPM to 1000 RPM in about 3 seconds.

Dashpot Adusting Specifications

Application①	RPM
210	1900-2100
510 & Pickup	1400-1600

① — Auto. Trans. models only.

FUEL PUMP PRESSURE & VOLUME

Pressure	3.0-3.8 psi (.21.27 kg/cm²)
Volume (at 1000 RPM)	
210 & 310	1 pt. per minute
510 & Pickup	3.7 pts. per minute

EMISSION CONTROL SYSTEMS

See Mitchell Manuals' Emission Control Manual.

GENERAL SERVICING

IGNITION

DISTRIBUTOR

All models are equipped with Hitachi breakerless, transistorized ignition systems.

IGNITION COIL

Resistance Specifications
(Ohms@68°F)

Application	Primary	Secondary
200SX, 510 &		
Pickup	1.04-1.27	7300-11,000
210 & 310	0.84-1.02	8200-12,400

GENERAL SERVICING (Cont.)

FUEL SYSTEMS

CARBURETORS

Application	Model
210 & 310	Hitachi DCR 306
510 & Pickup	Hitachi DCR 342

FUEL INJECTION

200SX models are equipped with Bosch AFC electronic fuel injection.

ELECTRICAL

BATTERY

Application	Amp. Hr. Rating
All Models	60

Battery Location — Engine Compartment.

STARTER

Hitachi solenoid actuated with overrunning clutch.

Application	Volts	Amps	Test RPM
All Models	11.5	60	①7000

① — 510 & Pickup Auto. Trans. models, 6000 RPM.

ALTERNATOR

Application	Rated Amp. Output
200SX	60
210, 310 & 510	50
Pickup	
Standard	50
Heavy Duty	60

ALTERNATOR REGULATOR

All Models use a Hitachi alternator regulator with an operating voltage of 14.4-15.0 volts at 68°F (20°C).

BELT ADJUSTMENT

Application	①Deflection
All Models	
All Belts	5/16-1/4" (8-12 mm)

① — Deflection is with 22 lbs. (10 kg) pressure applied midway on longest belt run.

FILTERS

Filter	Service Interval (Miles)
Oil Filter	Replace every 7500
Air Filter	Replace every 30,000
Fuel Filter	Replace every 30,000
PCV Filter	Replace every 30,000
Canister Filter	Replace every 30,000

CAPACITIES

Application	Quantity
Crankcase (Includes Filter)	
200SX & 510	4.6 qts.
210 & 310	3.4 qts.
Pickup	
2-WD	4.6 qts.
4-WD	4.5 qts.
Cooling System (Includes Heater)	
200SX	10.0 qts.
510	9.3 qts.
210	
Man. Trans.	6.3 qts.
Auto. Trans.	6.0 qts.
Pickup	
Man. Trans.	10.7 qts.
Auto. Trans.	10.6 qts.
Man. Trans (SAE 80W-90/API GL-4)	
200X	4.3 pts.
210	
4-Speed	
1200 cc	2.5 pts.
1400 cc	2.8 pts.
5-Speed	2.5 pts.
310	4.9 pts.
510	
4-Speed	3.1 pts.
5-Speed	3.7 pts.
Pickup	
4-Speed	3.7 pts.
5-Speed	4.3 pts.
Auto. Trans. (Dexron)	
All Models	5.9 qts.
Front Axle (SAE 80W-90/API GL-5)	2.1 pts.
Transfer Case	3.0 pts.
Rear Axle (SAE 80W-90/API GL-5)	
200SX & 510	2.4 pts.
210	1.9 pts.
Pickup	2.6 pts.
Fuel Tank	
200SX	
Hardtop	14.0 gals.
Hatchback	15.9 gals.
210, 310 & 510	13.3 gals.
Pickup	
Shortbed①	
2-WD	13.3 gals.
4-WD	15.9 gals.
Longbed	
2-WD	16.9 gals.
4-WD	19.9 gals.

① — Includes King Cab model.

TUNE-UP

Diesel Pickup

ENGINE IDENTIFICATION

Engine number is stamped into right side of block.

Engine Code

Application	Code
All Models	SD22

COMPRESSION PRESSURE

1) Check compression pressure with engine at normal operating temperature. Remove injection tube on nozzle side, spill tube assembly and nozzle assemblies with washers.

2) Fit compression gauge adapter (ED19600000) to No. 1 cylinder. Hand tighten bleeder screw on gauge. Crank engine at least 6 "puffs" and check compression.

3) Remove compression gauge adapter and repeat step 2) for remaining cylinders. Install nozzle assemblies with washers, spill tube assembly, and injection tube. Bleed fuel system. See *BLEED FUEL SYSTEM*.

Compression Pressure Specifications

Application	Pressure psi (kg/cm²)
Normal (New Engine)	427 (30)
Minimum	356 (25)
Maximum Variation	43 (3)

VALVE CLEARANCE

1) Warm up engine to normal operating temperature. Turn engine off. Remove valve cover. Rotate crankshaft to bring No. 1 piston to TDC on compression stroke. Adjust intake valves on cylinder No. 1 and 2, and exhaust valves on cylinder No. 1 and 3.

2) Rotate crankshaft to bring No. 4 piston to TDC on compression stroke. Adjust intake valves on cylinder No. 3 and 4, and exhaust valves on cylinder No. 2 and 4.

Valve Clearance Specifications①

Application	Clearance In. (mm)
All Models (Intake & Exhaust)	.014 (35)

① — Adjust with engine warm.

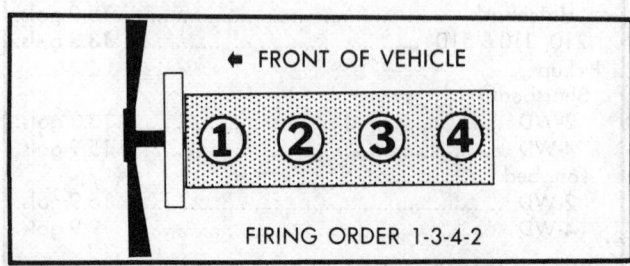

← FRONT OF VEHICLE

① ② ③ ④

FIRING ORDER 1-3-4-2

Fig. 1   Firing Order Illustration

VALVE ARRANGEMENT

E-I-I-E-E-I-I-E (Front-to-rear)

IDLE SPEED ADJUSTMENT

1) With transmission in neutral, parking brake applied and all wheels blocked, warm up engine to normal operating temperature. Connect tachometer to No. 1 injection tube. Remove clamp from No. 1 injection tube.

2) Push in throttle control knob under dash panel. Loosen idle adjusting screw lock nut. Start engine and adjust idle by turning idle adjusting screw. See *Fig. 2*. Tighten idle adjusting screw lock nut.

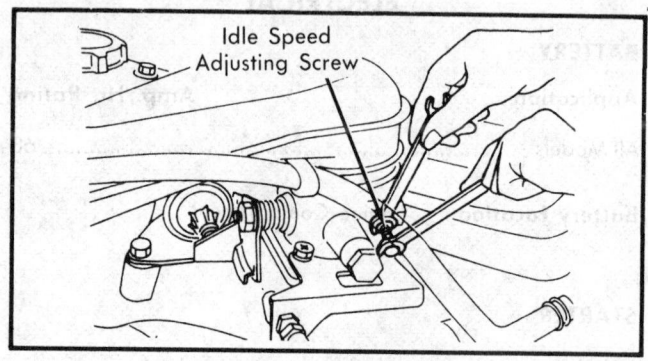

Idle Speed Adjusting Screw

Fig. 2   Idle Speed Adjustment

Idle Speed Specifications

Application	Idle RPM
All Models	550-700

DASHPOT ADJUSTMENT

1) Warm up engine to normal operating temperature. Connect tachometer to No. 1 injection tube. Remove clamp from No. 1 injection tube. Loosen dashpot lock nut.

2) Hold throttle lever to maintain engine speed at 1280-1350 RPM. Adjust dashpot so that control lever tip contacts dashpot tip. See *Fig. 3*. Tighten dashpot lock nut.

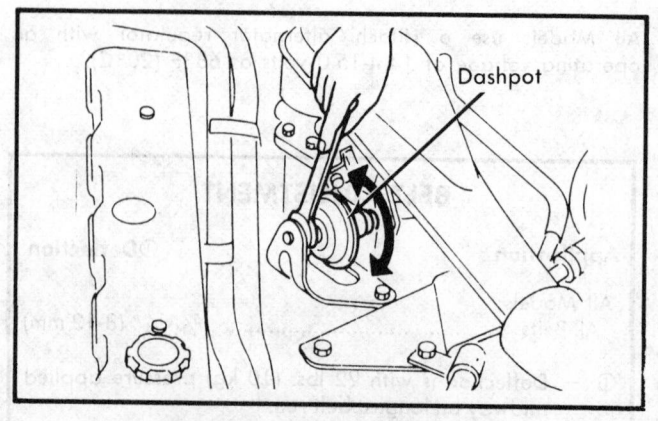

Dashpot

Fig. 3   Dashpot Adjustment

TUNE-UP (Cont.)

Dashpot Adjustment Specifications

Application	RPM
All Models	1280-1350

BLEED FUEL SYSTEM

Bleed fuel system by removing primary pump cap and loosening air vent screw. Turn priming pump counterclockwise and move up and down until no air comes out air vent screw. Tighten screw. Push and turn priming pump clockwise. Install cap. Wipe off excess fuel.

GENERAL SERVICING

FUEL SYSTEMS

FUEL INJECTION

All models use Bosch mechanical diesel fuel injection.

ELECTRICAL

BATTERY

Application	Amp. Hr. Rating
All Models	70

Battery Location — Engine Compartment.

STARTER

Hitachi solenoid actuated with overrunning clutch.

Starter Specifications

Application	Volts	Amps	Test RPM
All Models	12	90	4000

ALTERNATOR

All models are equipped with Hitachi alternators.

Application	Rated Amp. Output
All Models	50

ALTERNATOR REGULATOR

All models use a Hitachi alternator regulator with an operating voltage of 14.4-15.0 volts at 68°F (20°C).

BELT ADJUSTMENT

Application	①Deflection
All Models	
All Belts	5⁄16"-1⁄4" (8-12 mm)

① — Deflection is with 22 lbs. (10 kg) pressure applied midway on longest belt run.

FILTERS

Filter	Service Interval (Miles)
Oil Filter	Replace every 6,000
Fuel Filter	Replace every 15,000
Air Filter	Replace every 30,000

CAPACITIES

Application	Quantity
Crankcase (Includes Filter)	6.4 qts.
Cooling System (Includes Heater)	10.5 qts.
Man. Trans. (SAE 80W-90/API GL-4)	4.3 pts.
Rear Axle (SAE 80W-90/API GL-5)	2.6 pts.
Fuel Tank	
Shortbed①	13.3 gals.
Longbed	16.9 gals.

① — Includes King Cab model.

1981 Datsun 6 Tune-Up

TUNE-UP

280ZX
280ZX Turbo
810

ENGINE IDENTIFICATION

Engine serial number is stamped on right rear side of cylinder block at cylinder head contact surface. Serial number is preceded by engine model number.

Engine Code

Application	Code
280ZX	L28E
280ZX Turbo	L28ET
810	L24E

COMPRESSION PRESSURE

Test compression with engine at normal operating temperature, spark plugs removed, all injector connectors and cold start valve disconnected, throttle valve fully open and engine at cranking speed (350 RPM). Lowest reading cylinder must be at least 80% of highest reading cylinder.

Compression Pressure Specifications

Application	Pressure psi (kg/cm²)
280ZX & 810	
Normal (New Engine)	171 (12)
Minimum	128 (9)
280ZX Turbo	
Normal (New Engine)	142 (10)
Minimum	100 (7)

VALVE CLEARANCE

1) Adjust valves with engine off and at normal operating temperature. Remove rocker cover. Rotate crankshaft until No. 1 cam lobe points up. Adjust intake valves on cylinder No. 2, 4 and 6, and exhaust valves on cylinder No. 1, 4 and 5.

2) Rotate crankshaft so that No. 1 cam lobe points down. Adjust intake valves on cylinder No. 1, 3 and 5, and exhaust valves on cylinder No. 2, 3 and 6.

Valve Clearance Specifications①

Application	Intake In. (mm)	Exhaust In. (mm)
All Models	.010 (.25)	.012 (.30)

① — Set with engine warm.

VALVE ARRANGEMENT

E-I-I-E-I-E-E-I-E-I-I-E (front to rear).

SPARK PLUGS

Application	Gap In. (mm)	Torque Ft. Lbs. (N·m)
All Models	.039-.043 (1.0-1.1)	11-14 (15-19)

Spark Plug Type

Application	NGK No.
280ZX & 810	BP6ES-11
280ZX Turbo	BPR6ES-11

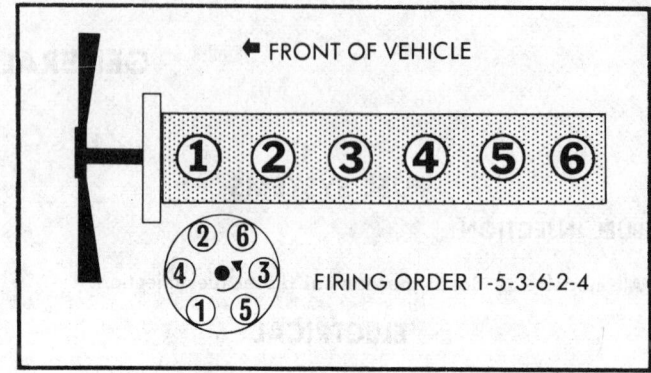

Fig. 1 Firing Order and Distributor Rotation

HIGH TENSION WIRE RESISTANCE

Remove distributor cap from distributor but do not disconnect high tension wires from cap. Disconnect high tension wires from spark plugs. Using an ohmmeter, check resistance from contact at spark plug end of wires to contact inside of distributor cap. Resistance should be less than 30,000 ohms. If resistance is more, disconnect wire from cap and recheck resistance. Replace wire if resistance still exceeds specifications.

DISTRIBUTOR

All models use a single pick-up transistor ignition system with no point set. The only adjustment needed is for air gap between the reluctor and pick-up coil.

Measure air gap using a non-magnetic feeler gauge. If gap is not to specifications, loosen pickup coil screws and adjust gap.

Air Gap .... .012-.020" (.3-.5 mm)

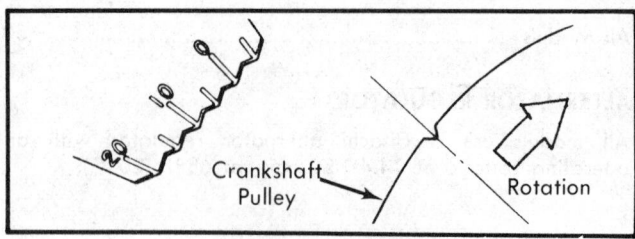

Fig. 2 Ignition Timing Mark Location

IGNITION TIMING

NOTE — *Regular ignition timing adjustment is not necessary on 280ZX Turbo models. Timing cannot be changed by turning distributor. For adjustment procedures, see Electronic Concentrated Engine Control System (ECCS) article in ELECTRICAL Section.*

1) With engine at normal operating temperature, connect a timing light and tachometer to engine. With Man. Trans. in

TUNE-UP (Cont.)

neutral or Auto. Trans. in "D", check and, if necessary, adjust air gap and idle speed.

2) On all models except 280ZX Turbo, disconnect and plug distributor vacuum hose. Adjust timing by loosening set screw and rotating distributor until timing is set. Tighten set screw and recheck timing.

Ignition Timing Specifications
(Degrees BTDC @ RPM)

Application	Man. Trans.	① Auto. Trans.
280ZX	8@600-800	8@600-800
280ZX Turbo	.....	20@600-700
810	10@600-800	10@550-750

① — Transmission in "D".

IDLE SPEED & MIXTURE

NOTE — Regular idle speed and mixture adjustments are not necessary on 280ZX Turbo models. For testing procedures, see Electronic Concentrated Engine Control System (ECCS) article in ELECTRICAL Section.

NOTE — Mixture adjustment is NOT a part of normal tune-up procedure and should not be performed unless mixture control unit is replaced or vehicle fails emissions testing.

NOTE — The following adjustment procedures should be performed with engine at normal operating temperature, air conditioning "OFF" (if equipped), ignition timing set to specifications and air cleaner installed. Set parking brake, block drive wheels and, on models with automatic transmission, place gear selector in "D" position.

1) Connect a tachometer to engine and run at 2000 RPM for 5 minutes to stabilize operating condition. Accelerate engine 2-3 times and return to idle. Turn idle speed adjusting screw to obtain specified idle RPM.

2) Turn ignition switch off and disconnect throttle valve switch harness connector. Position harness connector at least 4" away from any secondary ignition wires.

3) Disconnect and plug distributor vacuum hose. Disconnect air induction hose and canister purge hose at intake manifold. Plug air induction pipe and purge hose fitting on intake manifold. Start engine, accelerate 2-3 times and allow to idle for 1 minute.

4) Check and, if necessary, adjust ignition timing. Connect a jumper wire between throttle valve switch harness connector terminals No. 24 and No. 30. See Fig. 3. Insert CO meter probe into tail pipe at least 16".

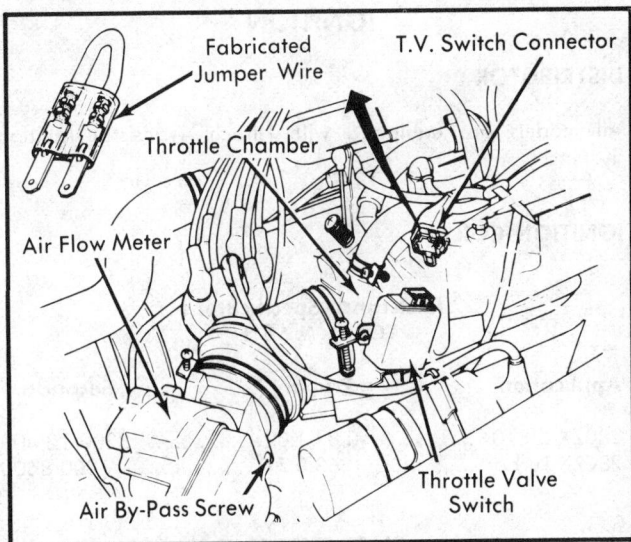

Fig. 3 Idle Mixture Adjustment (CO%)
(280ZX Shown — 810 Similar)

NOTE — Connecting jumper wire between connector terminals signals the control unit of a full throttle condition which allows the idle mixture to run at full load enrichment. This step is necessary to enrichen the CO% level at idle enough to be read by the CO meter.

5) With engine idling, check Co level. If necessary to adjust CO, remove air flow meter and drill a small hole in plug covering air by-pass screw. DO NOT allow drill to contact screw. Clean up metal shavings. Install self-tapping screw into hole and pull plug from bore. Install air flow meter.

6) Adjust CO level by turning air by-pass screw clockwise to richen mixture and counter-clockwise to lean mixture. Remove air flow meter. Tap new seal plug, with convex side up, into air by-pass screw bore. Install air flow meter.

7) Stop engine and remove jumper wire from throttle valve switch harness connector. Reconnect harness and all hoses. Reset idle speed to specified RPM.

Idle Speed & CO Level

Application	Idle RPM①	CO%
280ZX	700	Less than 5.0
810		
Man. Trans.	700	Less than 5.0
Auto. Trans.	650	Less than 5.0

① — Auto. Trans. in "D".

FUEL PUMP PRESSURE

Pressure .... 36.3 psi (2.6 kg/cm²)

EMISSION CONTROL SYSTEMS

See Mitchell Manuals' Emission Control Manual.

1981 Datsun 6 Tune-Up

GENERAL SERVICING

IGNITION

DISTRIBUTOR

All models are equipped with Hitachi Transistor Ignition System.

IGNITION COIL

Resistance Specificatons
(Ohms @ 68°F)

Application	Primary	Secondary
280ZX & 810	0.84-1.02	8200-12,400
280ZX Turbo	0.63-0.77	7000-8600

FUEL SYSTEMS

FUEL INJECTION

All models are equipped with Bosch AFC Fuel Injection System.

ELECTRICAL

BATTERY

Application	Amp. Hr. Rating
All Models	60

Battery Location — Right side of engine compartment.

STARTER

All models use Hitachi reduction gear type starters.

Application	Volts	Amps	Test RPM
All Models	11	100	3900

ALTERNATOR

Application	Rated Amp. Output
All Models	60

ALTERNATOR REGULATOR

All models use a Hitachi alternator regulator with an operating voltage of 14.5 -15.0 volts at 68°F (20°C).

BELT ADJUSTMENT

Application	①Deflection
All Belts	5/16-1/2" (8-12 mm)

① — Deflection is with 22 lbs. (10 kg) pressure applied midway on belt run.

FILTERS

Filter	Service Interval (Miles)
Oil Filter	Replace every 7500
Air Filter	Replace every 30,000
Fuel Filter	Replace every 30,000
Canister Filter	Replace every 30,000

CAPACITIES

Application	Quantity
Crankcase (Includes Filter)	
280ZX & 280ZX Turbo	4.8 qts.
810	5.3 qts.
Cooling System (Includes Heater)	
280ZX & 280ZX Turbo	
With Reservoir	11.1 qts.
Without Reservoir	10.3 qts.
810	11.6 qts.
Man. Trans. (API GL-5/SAE 80)	4.3 pts.
Auto. Trans. (Dexron)	5.9 qts.
Rear Axle (API GL-5/SAE 80-90)	
280ZX	
Model R-180	2.1 pts.
Model R-200	2.8 pts.
280ZX Turbo	2.8 pts.
810	2.1 pts.
Fuel Tank	
280ZX & 280ZX Turbo	21.1 gals.
810	
Sedan	16.4 gals.
Station Wagon	15.9 gals.

TUNE-UP

810 Diesel

ENGINE IDENTIFICATION

Engine number is stamped into right side of cylinder block near the dipstick. First 4 digits indicate engine code.

Engine Code

Application	Code
All Models	LD28

COMPRESSION PRESSURE

Warm engine to normal operating temperature. Stop engine. Remove spill tube assembly, injection tubes on nozzle side and nozzle assemblies taking care to remove nozzle washer with tweezers. Install compression gauge adapter on cylinder head. Close bleeder screw on compression gauge. Crank engine and note compression reading as quickly as possible.

Compression Pressure Specifications

Application	Pressure psi (kg/cm^2)
Normal (New Engine)	455 (32)
Minimum	356 (25)
Maximum Variation	71 (5)

VALVE CLEARANCE

1) Adjust valves with engine off and at normal operating temperature. Remove rocker cover. Rotate crankshaft until No. 1 cam lobe points up. Adjust intake valves on cylinder No. 2, 4 and 6, and exhaust valves on cylinder No. 1, 4 and 5.

2) Rotate crankshaft so that No. 1 cam lobe points down. Adjust intake valves on cylinder No. 1, 3 and 5, and exhaust valves on cylinder No. 2, 3 and 6. Install rocker cover.

Valve Clearance Specifications

Application	Intake In. (mm)	Exhaust In. (mm)
All Models	.010 (.25)	.012 (.30)

VALVE ARRANGEMENT

E-I-I-E-I-E-E-I-E-I-I-E

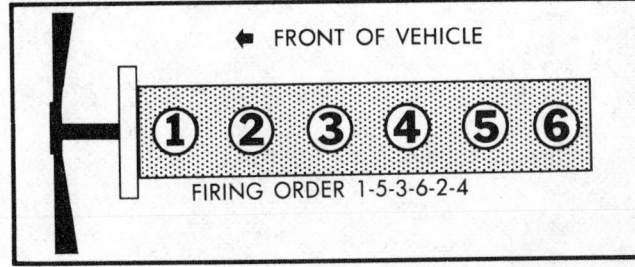

Fig. 1   Diesel Firing Order Illustration

GLOW PLUGS

Glow Plug Torque Specifications

Application	
All Models	20-25 ft. lbs. (27-33 N·m)

IDLE SPEED ADJUSTMENT

1) With engine at normal operating temperature and all electrical accessories off, attach tachometer. Start engine and run at 2000 RPM for 2 minutes. Return engine to idle for 1 minute. Check that idle speed is to specification (Auto. Trans. in "D").

2) If adjustment is required, loosen idle adjusting screw lock nut on idle adjusting screw. Turn screw until proper idle RPM is obtained. Tighten lock nut. See *Fig. 2*.

3) With engine idling and air conditioning turned on (if so equipped), set high idle speed. Locate Fast Idle Control Device (F.I.C.D.) diaphragm. Turn adjusting screw on accelerator drum until fast idle speed is to specification. See *Fig. 3*.

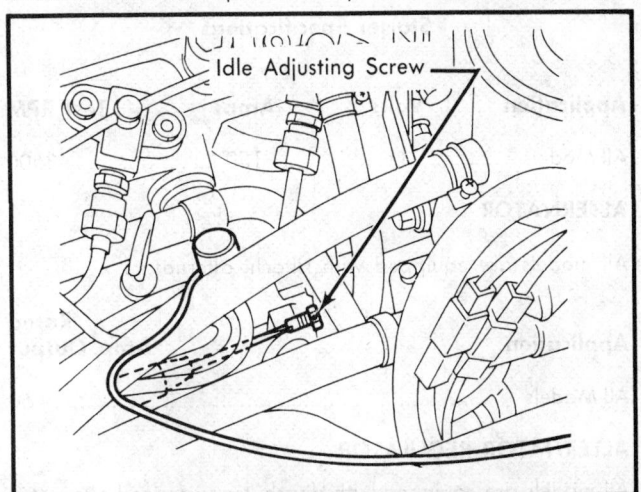

Fig. 2   Idle Adjusting Screw Location

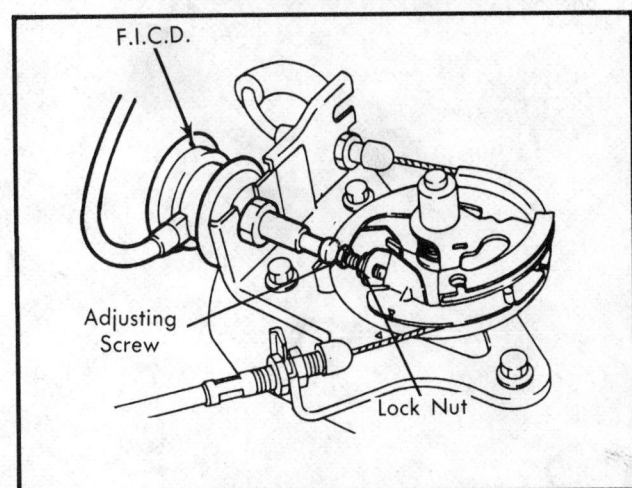

Fig. 3   Fast Idle Control Device

Idle Speed Specifications

Application	Idle RPM	Fast Idle RPM
All Models	600-750	800

GENERAL SERVICING

FUEL SYSTEMS

FUEL INJECTION

All models use Bosch mechanical diesel fuel injection.

ELECTRICAL

BATTERY

Battery Location – Battery is located in right front engine compartment.

Application	Amp. Hr. Rating
All Models	70

STARTER

All models are equipped with Hitachi starters.

Starter Specifications

Application	Volts	Amps	Test RPM
All Models	11	150	3500

ALTERNATOR

All models are equipped with Hitachi alternators.

Application	Rated Amp. Output
All Models	60

ALTERNATOR REGULATOR

All models are equipped with Hitachi transistorized alternator regulators with an operating voltage of 14.5-15.0 volts at 68° F (20° C).

BELT ADJUSTMENT

Application	①Deflection
Alternator	$\frac{5}{16}$-$\frac{1}{2}$" (8-12 mm)
Power Steering	$\frac{9}{32}$-$\frac{3}{8}$" (7-9 mm)

① – Deflection is with 22 lbs. (10 kg) pressure applied midway on belt run.

FILTERS

Filter	Service Interval (Miles)
Air Filter	Replace every 30,000
Fuel Filter	Replace every 30,000
Oil Filter	Replace every 6000

CAPACITIES

Application	Quantity
Crankcase (Includes Filter)	6.3 qts
Cooling System	11.6 qts.
Auto. Trans. (Dexron)	5.9 qts.
Differential (API GL-5/SAE 80-90)	2.1 pts.
Fuel Tank	
Sedan	16.4 gals.
Station Wagon	15.9 gals.

TUNE-UP

Brava
Spider 2000
Spider 2000 Turbo
Strada
X1/9

ENGINE IDENTIFICATION

Brava & Spider Models — Engine code and identification numbers are stamped on crankcase near oil filter mount.

Strada & X1/9 Models — Engine code and identification numbers are stamped on crankcase (flywheel end).

Engine Code

Application	Code
Brava & Spider	132C3.031
Strada	138B2.031
X1/9	138BS.031

VALVE CLEARANCE

Application	①Intake In. (mm)	①Exhaust In. (mm)
Brava & Spider	.019 (.48)	.021 (.53)
Strada & X1/9	.014 (.35)	.018 (.45)

① — Set valves with engine cold.

VALVE ARRANGEMENT

Brava & Spider Models
Right Side - All Exhaust
Left Side - All Intake
Strada & X1/9 — E-I-I-E-E-I-I-E

SPARK PLUGS

Application	Gap In. (mm)	Torque Ft. Lbs. (mkg)
All Models	.029 (.73)	25 (3.5)

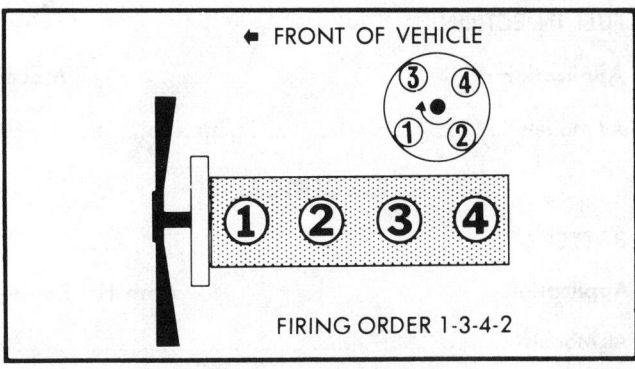

Fig. 1   Firing Order and Distributor Rotation (Brava & Spider — 2000 cc)

Spark Plug Type

Application	Champion No.	Torque Ft. Lbs. (N·m)
All Models	RN9Y	25 (33)

HIGH TENSION WIRE RESISTANCE
Resistance (Ohms) Per Wire

Application	Resistance
All Models	25,000-30,000

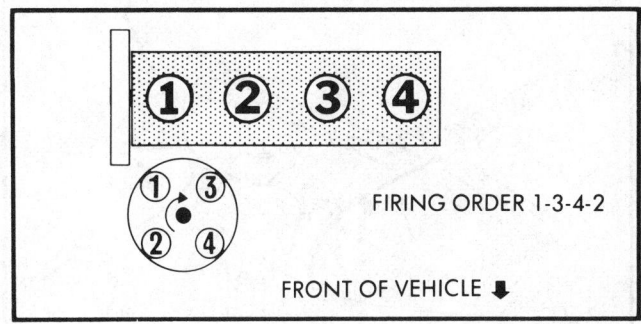

Fig. 2   Firing Order and Distributor Rotation (Strada & X1/9 — 1500 cc)

DISTRIBUTOR

All models are equipped with breakerless, electronic ignition systems. Brava and Spider use a Marelli system, and Strada and X1/9 use a Bosch unit.

IGNITION TIMING

Check or adjust ignition timing with engine at normal operating temperature, Man. Trans. in neutral or Auto. Trans. in "D" and idle speed set to specifications. To adjust timing, align mark on drive pulley or flywheel with specified pointer by turning distributor.

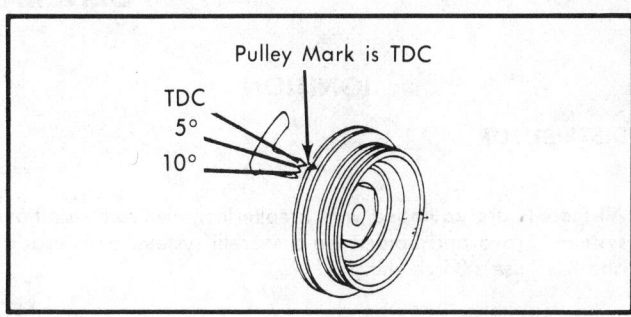

Fig. 3   Ignition Timing Mark Location

Ignition Timing Specifications (Degrees BTDC@RPM)

Application	Man. Trans.	①Auto. Trans.
All Models	10@825	10@725

① — Transmission in "D".

TUNE-UP (Cont.)

IDLE SPEED & MIXTURE

NOTE — *Mixture adjustment is NOT a part of normal tune-up procedure and should not be performed unless injection system components are being replaced or vehicle fails emissions testing.*

1) Warm engine to operating temperature (electric fan has cycled twice). Place manual transmission in neutral or automatic in "D". Wait until electric fan is off to adjust idle.

Fig. 4   Fuel Injection Idle Speed Adjustment

2) Turn air bypass screw on top of intake manifold to adjust idle speed to specifications. See *Fig. 4.*

3) Connect CO meter to pipe tap in front of catalytic converter. Disconnect plug from oxygen sensor and ensure that neither side is grounded. Remove plug from airflow meter and adjust CO to 0.5-0.9%. See *Fig. 5.*

4) Ground control unit side of oxygen sensor connector. CO level should rise to at least 1.5%. Reconnect oxygen snesor and check for CO level of 0.3-0.6%. Remove test equipment and plug air flow meter screw. See *Fig. 5.*

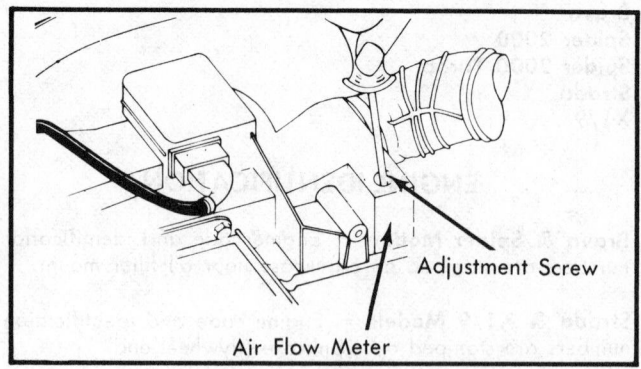

Fig. 5   Fuel Injection Mixture Adjustment

Idle Speed & CO Level

Application	Idle RPM	CO%
All Models		
Man. Trans.	800-900	.... 0.5-0.9
Auto. Trans.①	700-800	.... 0.5-0.9

① — With transmission in "D".

FUEL PUMP PRESSURE

All Models① .... 39-45 psi (2.8-3.2 kg/cm²)

① — Disconnect hose to pressure regulator.

EMISSION CONTROL SYSTEMS

See *Mitchell Manuals' Emission Control Manual.*

GENERAL SERVICING

IGNITION

DISTRIBUTOR

All models are equipped with breakerless, electronic ignition systems. Brava and Spider use a Marelli system, and Strada and X1/9 use a Bosch unit.

IGNITION COIL

Resistance Specifications
(Ohms@68°F)

Application	Primary	Secondary
Bosch Coil	1.1-1.7	6,000-10,000
Marelli Coil	.75-.81	10,000-11,000

FUEL SYSTEMS

FUEL INJECTION

Application	Model
All Models	Bosch AFC

ELECTRICAL

BATTERY

Application	Amp Hr. Rating
All Models	60

Battery Location — Battery is located in engine compartment on all except Spider 2000 models. On these models, battery is located in trunk.

GENERAL SERVICING (Cont.)

STARTER

Brava and Spider 2000 models are equipped with Fiat starters. Strada and X1/9 models use Bosch starters on Man. Trans. models and Marelli starters on Auto. Trans. models.

Starter Specifications

Application	Volts	Amps	Test RPM
Brava & Spider	12	12	4700-5700
Strada & X1/9			
Man. Trans.	11.5	35-55	6000-8000
Auto. Trans.	11.5	30-40	5500-6500

ALTERNATOR

All models are equipped with Bosch alternators.

Application	Rated Amp. Output
All models	65

ALTERNATOR REGULATOR

All models have alternators with internal regulators. With headlights on and heater fan on high speed, operating voltage should be 12.5-14.5 volts at 2500 RPM.

BELT ADJUSTMENT

Application	①Deflection
All Drive Belts	.4-.6" (10-15 mm)

① — Deflection is with 22 lbs. (10 kg) pressure applied midway on longest belt run.

FILTERS

Filter	Service Interval (Miles)
Oil Filter	Replace every 7,500
Air Cleaner	Replace every 15,000
Fuel Filter	Replace every 15,000

CAPACITIES

Application	Quantity
Crankcase (Includes Filter)	
Brava, Spider & X1/9	4.3 qts.
Strada	4.6 qts.
Cooling System	
Brava & Spider	8.5 qts.
Strada	7.5 qts.
X1/9	12.2 qts.
Man. Trans. (SAE 90)	
All Models	3.5 pts.
Auto. Trans. (Dexron)	
Brava, Spider & Strada	6.0 pts.
Rear Axle (SAE 90)	
Brava & Spider	1.4 qts.
Man. Transaxle (SAE 90)	
X1/9	3.2 qts.
Strada	3.5 qts.
Auto. Transaxle	
Transmission (Dexron)	3.2 qts.
Differential (SAE 90)	1.5 pts.
Fuel Tank	
Brava	12.2 gals.
Spider	11.4 gals.
Strada & X1/9	12.1 gals.

1981 Honda 4 Tune-Up

TUNE-UP

Accord
Civic
Prelude

ENGINE IDENTIFICATION

Engine serial number is stamped on a machined surface at the right rear of the engine, near the starter. Engine serial number is preceded by the engine code.

Engine Code

Application	Code
Accord & Prelude	EK1
Civic	
1300	EJ1
1500	EM1

COMPRESSION PRESSURE

Check compression with engine at normal operating temperature, air cleaner and spark plugs removed, throttle and choke valve wide open and engine at normal cranking speed (300 RPM). Crank engine at least 6 "puffs" per cylinder to determine engine compression.

Compression Pressure Specifications

Application	Pressure psi (kg/cm²)
All Models	
Normal (New Engine)	185 (13)
Minimum	156 (11)
Maximum Variation	28 (2)

VALVE CLEARANCE

1) Adjust valves with engine cold. Remove valve cover and set No. 1 piston at TDC. Cutaway notch in camshaft belt pulley should be at top (Civic) or word "UP" should be at top (Accord and Prelude). Adjust valves for No. 1 cylinder.

2) Repeat procedure for remaining valves in firing order sequence, rotating crankshaft 180° counterclockwise after each adjustment to position piston of next cylinder in sequence at TDC of compression stroke.

Valve Clearance Specifications

Application	Clearance
Accord & Prelude	
Intake & Auxiliary	.005-.007" (.12-.17 mm)
Exhaust	.010-.012" (.25-.30 mm)
Civic	
Intake & Auxiliary	.005-.007" (.12-.17 mm)
Exhaust	.007-.009" (.17-.22 mm)

VALVE ARRANGEMENT

All Models
  Left Side — I-E-E-I-I-E-E-I
  Right Side — All Auxiliary.

SPARK PLUGS

Application	Gap In. (mm)	Torque Ft. Lbs. (N·m)
Accord & Prelude	.041 (1.0)	17 (23)
Civic	.041 (1.0)	13 (18)

Spark Plug Type

Application	Nippondenso	NGK
Accord & Prelude	W21ES-L11	B6EB-L11
Civic	W20ES-L11	B6EB-11

HIGH TENSION WIRE RESISTANCE

Carefully remove ends of wire from spark plug and distributor. Using an ohmmeter, check resistance of wire while gently twisting wire. If resistance is not to specification, or fluctuates from infinity to any value, replace wire.

Resistance (Ohms) Per Wire

Application	Resistance
All Models (2 ft. length)	25,000 Max.

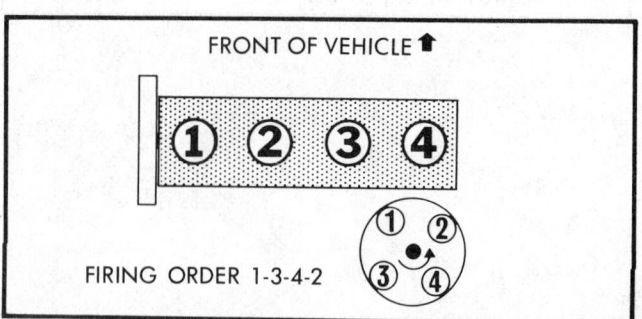

Fig. 1 Firing Order and Distributor Rotation

DISTRIBUTOR

All models are equipped with electronic breakerless ignition systems and no adjustments are necessary.

TUNE-UP (Cont.)

IGNITION TIMING

1) Remove rubber inspection cap from window on cylinder block. Attach timing light. Engine should be idling at normal operating temperature.

2) Timing is correct if specified mark on flywheel is aligned with index pointer on crankcase.

3) To adjust, loosen distributor bolt and turn body counterclockwise to retard timing and clockwise to advance timing.

Ignition Timing Specifications

Application	Man. Trans.	① Auto. Trans.
Accord & Prelude	TDC	TDC
Civic		
1300	2°BTDC	2°BTDC
1500		
Federal		
Hatchback	10°BTDC	2°ATDC
Sedan & Wagon	4°BTDC	2°ATDC
Calif.	2°ATDC	2°ATDC

① — Transmission in Drive.

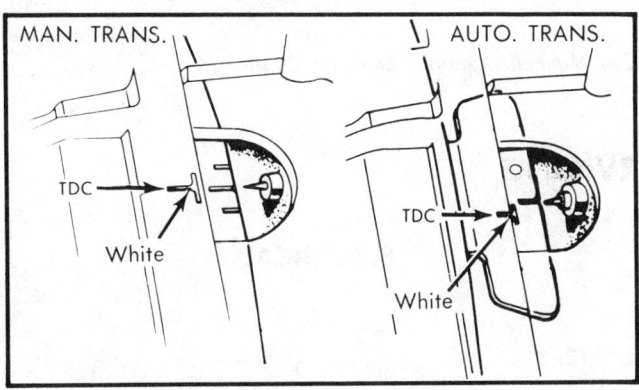

Fig. 2   Ignition Timing Mark Location (Accord & Prelude)

IDLE SPEED & MIXTURE

PROPANE ENRICHMENT PROCEDURE

NOTE — *Mixture adjustment is NOT a part of normal tune-up procedure and should not be performed unless carburetor is overhauled or vehicle fails emissions testing.*

1) Start engine and warm up to normal operating temperature. Remove vacuum tube from hot air door on air cleaner and plug tube. Connect tachometer and check idle speed with all electrical accessories off.

2) If necessary, adjust idle speed with throttle screw. If equipped with air conditioning, turn system on. Idle speed should not change. If necessary, turn adjusting screw on idle boost diaphragm to return idle to specification.

3) Pull air cleaner intake tube from air duct near radiator. Insert propane hose 4" into air intake tube and slowly open valve. Engine should be idling (in Drive on automatics).

4) Engine speed should increase to enriched RPM. If not, remove carburetor from engine, disconnect throttle opener linkage and remove throttle opener bracket. Remove mixture adjusting screw hole cap. Replace bracket and linkage. Reinstall carburetor.

5) Repeat steps 1) through 3). If peak RPM is below enriched RPM, turn mixture adjusting screw clockwise to lean out mixture and increase RPM. If above enriched RPM, turn mixture adjusting screw counterclockwise to enrichen mixture and lower RPM.

6) Run engine at 2500 RPM for 10 seconds to stabilize mixture, then test again. Repeat procedure until idle speed and increase are correct.

7) Remove propane equipment and reconnect vacuum hose to air cleaner hot air door. Recheck idle speed with air conditioning on, if so equipped, and adjust idle boost diaphragm screw. See Fig. 4. Replace idle mixture adjusting screw hole cap.

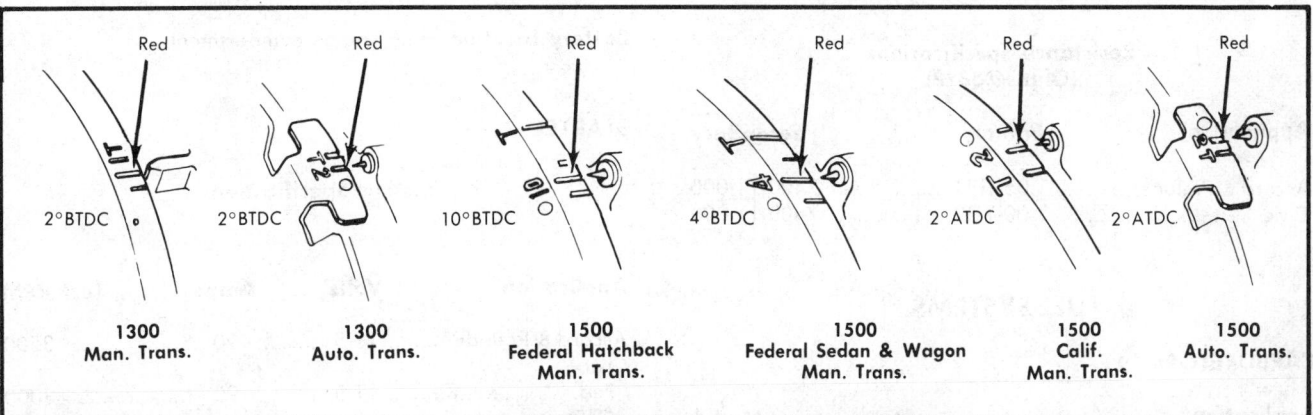

Fig. 3   Ignition Timing Mark Location (Civic 1300 & 1500)

TUNE-UP (Cont.)

Idle Speed & Enriched Speed

Application	Idle RPM	Enriched RPM
Accord & Prelude		
Man. Trans.	800	900
Auto. Trans.①	800	850
Civic		
Man. Trans.		
1300	800	925
1500	750	850
Auto. Trans.①	750	800

① — Transmission in Drive.

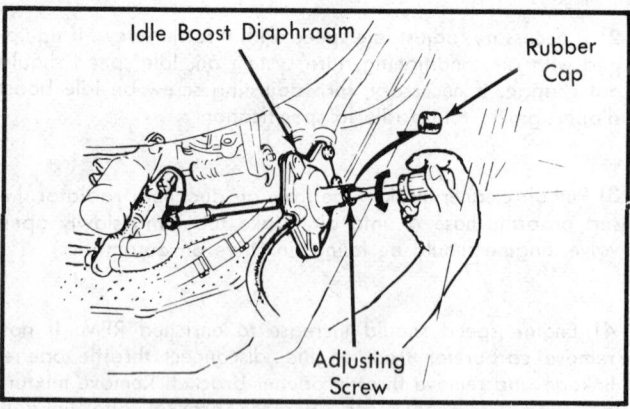

Fig. 4 Adjusting Idle Boost Diaphragm

COLD (FAST) IDLE RPM

All Models — 1) Connect tachometer to engine. Disconnect and plug vacuum hose to fast idle unloader. With the engine off, hold choke valve closed, then open and close throttle to engage fast idle cam.

2) Start engine, run one minute, and check idle. If not within specifications, adjust by turning fast idle screw.

Application	Fast Idle RPM Man. Trans.	Auto. Trans.
Accord & Prelude	2600	2700
Civic		
1300	3000	2850
1500		
Federal	3000	2800
Calif.	3200	2700

FUEL PUMP PRESSURE & VOLUME

Pressure	2.1-2.8 psi (.15-.20 kg/cm²)
Volume	
Accord & Prelude	.7 pts. in 30 sec.
Civic	.5 pts. in 30 sec.

EMISSION CONTROL SYSTEMS

See Mitchell Manuals' Emission Control Manual.

GENERAL SERVICING

IGNITION

DISTRIBUTOR

All models are equipped with Hitachi electronic ignition.

IGNITION COIL

Resistance Specifications (Ohms@68°F)

Application	Primary	Secondary
Accord & Prelude	1.06-1.24	7400-11,000
Civic	1.00-1.30	7400-11,000

FUEL SYSTEMS

CARBURETORS

Application	Model
All Models	Keihin 2-Bbl.

ELECTRICAL

BATTERY

Application	Amp. Hr. Rating
All	47

Battery Location — In engine compartment.

STARTER

Testing Specifications

Application	Volts	Amps	Test RPM
Accord & Prelude	11.5	90	3500
Civic			
Fed.	11.5	90	3000
Calif.			
Nippon.	11.0	50	5000
Hitachi	11.0	70	6000

GENERAL SERVICING (Cont.)

ALTERNATOR

All models are equipped with Nippondenso alternators.

Application	Rated Amp. Output
Accord & Prelude	50
Civic	45

ALTERNATOR REGULATOR

All models are equipped with Nippondenso alternator regulators with an operating voltage of 13.5-14.5 volts.

BELT ADJUSTMENT

All Models — Deflection of belt should be .5-.7" (12-17 mm) when 22 lbs. (10 kg) pressure is applied to belt midway between alternator and fan pulleys.

FILTERS

Filter	Service Interval (Miles)
Oil Filter	Replace every 7500
Air Filter	Replace every 30,000
Fuel Filter	Replace every 60,000

CAPACITIES

Application	Quantity
Crankcase (Including Filter)	
Accord & Prelude	4.2 qts.
Civic	3.6 qts.
Cooling System	
Civic 1300	5.6 qts.
All Others	6.4 qts.
Man. Transaxle (SAE 10W-40)	2.6 qts.
Auto. Transaxle (Dexron)	
Drain & Refill	2.6 qts.
Overhaul	5.2 qts.
Fuel Tank	
Accord & Prelude	13.2 gals.
Civic	
Hatchback & Wagon	10.8 gals.
Sedan	12.2 gals.

TUNE-UP

I-Mark
Pickup

ENGINE IDENTIFICATION

Engine serial number is stamped on pad between distributor and cylinder head.

Engine Code

Application	Code
1817 cc	G180Z

COMPRESSION PRESSURE

Test compression with engine at normal operating temperature, spark plugs removed, throttle valve wide open and engine at cranking speed (300 RPM).

Compression Pressure Specifications

Application	Pressure psi (kg/cm²)
Normal (New Engine)	170 (12)
Minimum	120 (8.4)
Maximum Variation	9 (0.6)

VALVE CLEARANCE

NOTE — *Before adjusting valve clearance, check torque of cylinder head and camshaft bolts. Valves should be adjusted every 15,000 miles with engine cold.*

1) Measure valve clearance between rocker arm and valve stem. Position No. 1 piston on TDC of compression stroke. Adjust intake valves on cylinder No. 1 and 2, and exhaust valves on cylinder No. 1 and 3.

2) Turn crankshaft 1 full revolution until No. 4 piston is at TDC of compression stroke. Adjust intake valves on cylinder No. 3 and 4, and exhaust valves on cylinder No. 2 and 4.

Valve Clearance Specifications①

Application	Intake In. (mm)	Exhaust In. (mm)
All Models		
Cold	.006 (.15)	.010 (.25)
Hot	.008 (.20)	.012 (.30)

① — Set with engine cold.

VALVE ARRANGEMENT

All Models
  Right Side — Intake
  Left Side — Exhaust

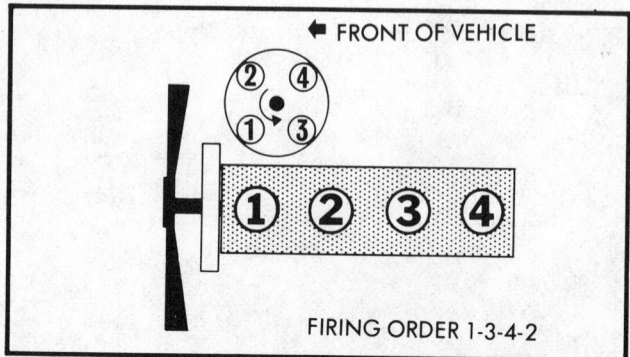

← FRONT OF VEHICLE

FIRING ORDER 1-3-4-2

Fig. 1 *Firing Order and Distributor Rotation*

SPARK PLUGS

Application	Gap In. (mm)	Torque Ft. Lbs. (N·m)
All Models	.040 (1.0)	18-25 (24-34)

Spark Plug Type

Application	NGK
All Models	BPR6ES11

HIGH TENSION WIRE RESISTANCE

Carefully remove high tension wire from spark plugs and from distributor cap. Using an ohmmeter, check resistance of wire while gently twisting wire. If resistance is not to specifications, or fluctuates from infinity to any value, replace wire.

Resistance (Ohms)

Application	Resistance
All Models	31,500-73,500 per foot

DISTRIBUTOR

All models are equipped with Nippondenso electronic ignition system. No adjustments are required.

Air Gap .... .008-.016" (.2-.4 mm)

IGNITION TIMING

1) Ensure engine is warmed to normal operating temperature, and that air gap in distributor is correct.

2) Connect timing light to either No. 1 or No. 4 cylinder. Disconnect and plug distributor vacuum advance line.

3) Loosen distributor clamping bolts and turn distributor until timing is within specifications.

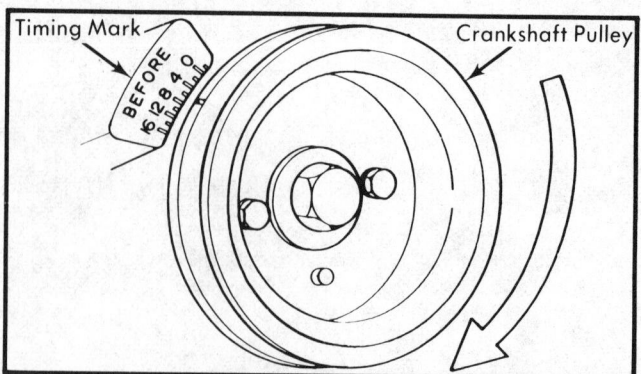

Timing Mark   Crankshaft Pulley

BEFORE 6 2 8 4 0

Fig. 2 *Ignition Timing Mark Location*

Ignition Timing Specifications
(Degrees BTDC @ RPM)

Application	①Timing
I-Mark Man. Trans.	6@800
Federal Pickup Man. Trans.	6@800
All Other Models	6@900

① — Distributor vacuum hose disconnected and plugged.

TUNE-UP (Cont.)

IDLE SPEED & MIXTURE

NOTE — *Mixture adjustment is NOT a part of normal tune-up procedure and should not be performed unless carburetor is replaced or vehicle fails emissions testing.*

1) Warm engine to normal operating temperature. Check valve clearance and ignition timing. Choke should be open, air conditioning off and air cleaner installed.

2) Disconnect and plug vacuum lines for distributor, hot idle compensator and EGR valve.

3) Turn idle mixture adjusting screw fully in, then back out 2 turns (Federal pickup) or 1 turn (all others). Set throttle adjusting screw to obtain specified mixture RPM.

4) Adjust idle mixture screw to obtain maximum RPM, then reset throttle adjusting screw to achieve specified mixture RPM. Turn idle mixture screw clockwise until speed drops to specified curb idle.

5) If equipped with air conditioner, turn on to maximum cooling and high blower. Open throttle slightly to allow solenoid to extend, then close throttle. Adjust solenoid screw to give 850-950 RPM idle.

Idle Speed & Mixture Adjustment

Application	Idle RPM	Mixture RPM
I-Mark		
Man. Trans.	800	850
Auto. Trans.	900	950
Pickup		
Fed. Man. Trans.	800	850
All Other Models	900	950

COLD (FAST) IDLE RPM

Automatic choke fast idle is adjusted by opening angle of throttle valve on carburetor, rather than by engine speed. Adjust valve opening at 1st step of fast idle cam to 15-17° on Man. Trans. models or 16-18° on Auto. Trans. models.

Disconnect and plug distributor, hot idle compensator and EGR valve vacuum hoses after engine warm-up. Fast idle speed should be as follows:

Fast Idle Specifications

Application	Engine RPM
All Models	3200

AUTOMATIC CHOKE

Automatic choke is set from factory and is non-adjustable.

FUEL PUMP PRESSURE

Pressure .... 2.4-3.3 psi (.17-.23 kg/cm²)

EMISSION CONTROL SYSTEMS

See *Mitchell Manuals' Emission Control Manual.*

GENERAL SERVICING

IGNITION

DISTRIBUTOR

All models are equipped with a Nippondenso electronic distributor.

IGNITION COIL

Coil Resistance (Ohms @ 68°F)

Application	Primary	Secondary
All Models	1.13-1.53	10,200-13,800

FUEL SYSTEMS

CARBURETORS

Application	Model
All Models	Hitachi DCH 340 2 Bbl.

ELECTRICAL

BATTERY

Application	Amp. Hr. Rating
All Models	50

Battery Location — Engine compartment, left side of engine.

STARTER

Hitachi .... Overrunning Clutch

Starter Specifications

Application	Volts	Amps	Test RPM
All Models	12	70	6000

ALTERNATOR

Application	Rated Amp. Output
All Models	40 or 50

ALTERNATOR REGULATOR

All models utilize a Hitachi adjustable alternator regulator with an operating voltage of 13.8-14.8 volts.

1981 Isuzu 4 Tune-Up

GENERAL SERVICING (Cont.)

BELT ADJUSTMENT

Application	①Deflection
All Belts	.4" (10 mm)

① — Measured between longest span and depressed with firm thumb pressure.

FILTERS

Filter	Service Interval (Miles)
Oil Filter	①Replace every 15,000
Air Filter	Replace every 30,000
Fuel Filter	Replace every 30,000
PCV Valve	Replace every 15,000

① — First change after 7500 miles.

CAPACITIES

Application	Quantity
Crankcase	①3.8 qts.
Cooling System	
Man. Trans.	6.8 qts.
Auto. Trans.	6.4 qts.
Auto. Trans. (Dexron II)	7.0 qts.
Man. Trans. (SAE 30)	
4-Spd.	2.7 pts.
5-Spd.	
I-Mark	3.3 pts.
Pickup	2.7 pts.
Front Axle (SAE 90)	1.7 pts.
Rear Axle (SAE 90)	2.7 pts.
Transfer Case (SAE 30)	5.2 pts.
Fuel Tank	
Pickup (Long Bed)	19.1 gals.
All Other Models	13.2 gals.

① — 3.4 quarts without filter.

TUNE-UP

I-Mark
Pickup

ENGINE IDENTIFICATION

First 4 digits of engine identification code are used to identify engine models. Code is stamped on right side of cylinder block.

Engine Code

Application	Code
I-Mark (1800 cc)	4FB1
Pickup (2300 cc)	C223

COMPRESSION PRESSURE

Start and run engine until normal operating temperature is obtained. Remove sensing resistor, glow plug connectors, glow plugs and fuel cut solenoid connector. Disconnect fusible link wire of "Quick Start" system at harness connector. Install compression gauge adapter (J-29762) and compression gauge. Operate starter and read compression.

Compression Pressure Specifications
(Reading @ 200 RPM)

Application	Pressure psi (kg/cm²)
Normal (New Engine)	441 (31)
Minimum	
I-Mark	370 (26)
Pickup	398 (28)

VALVE CLEARANCE

CAUTION — *Before adjusting valves, check rocker arm shaft bracket bolts for looseness and tighten as necessary.*

1) Rotate crankshaft until No. 1 piston is at TDC of compression stroke. Measure between adjusting screw and valve stem end cap. With No. 1 piston at TDC, adjust intake valves on cylinder No. 1 and 2, and exhaust valves on cylinder No. 1 and 3.

2) Rotate crankshaft 1 complete revolution until No. 4 piston is at TDC of compression stroke. Adjust intake valves on cylinder No. 3 and 4, and exhaust valves on cylinder No. 2 and 4.

Valve Clearance Specifications

Application	Intake In. (mm)	Exhaust In. (mm)
I-Mark (Hot & Cold)	.010 (.25)	.014 (.35)
Pickup		
Hot	.015 (.38)	.015 (.38)
Cold	.016 (.40)	.016 (.40)

VALVE ARRANGEMENT

I-Mark — I-E-I-E-I-E-I-E
Pickup — E-I-I-E-E-I-I-E

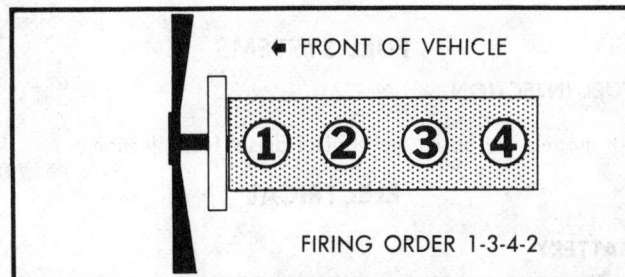

Fig. 1   Diesel Firing Order Illustration

IDLE SPEED ADJUSTMENT

Set parking brake and block drive wheels. Connect tachometer to warm engine and start engine. Check that idle speed is correct with accelerator lever touching idle adjusting screw. To adjust idle speed, loosen lock nut and turn adjusting screw until idle speed is set to specifications. Tighten lock nut.

Idle Speed Specifications

Application	Idle RPM
I-Mark	
Man. Trans.	575-675
Auto.Trans.	675-775
Pickup	700-800

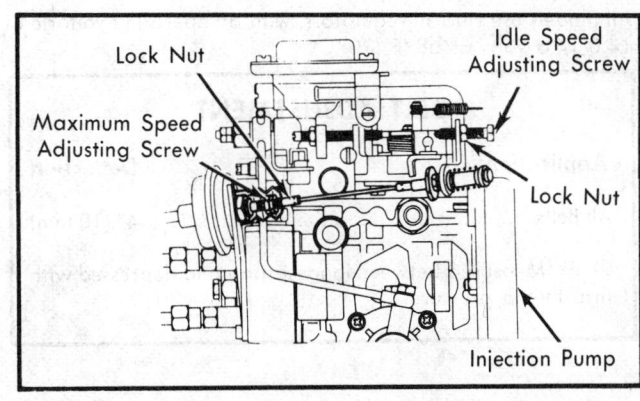

Fig. 2   Idle and Maximum Speed Adjustment

MAXIMUM SPEED ADJUSTMENT

Connect tachometer to warm engine. Start engine and check idle speed. Disconnect hoses from vacuum switch valve and connect together with piping. Accelerate engine briefly to full throttle. If maximum speed does not conform to specifications, loosen lock nut and adjust speed by turning maximum speed adjusting screw. Tighten lock nut. On I-Mark models with automatic transmission, hold injection pump control lever in contact with maximum speed stop and set clearance between end of inner cable stopper and rubber tube to .04" (1 mm) maximum. On all models, reconnect hoses to vacuum switch valve.

Maximum Speed Specifications

Application	Maximum RPM
All Models	900-950

GENERAL SERVICING

FUEL SYSTEMS

FUEL INJECTION

All models use Bosch mechanical diesel fuel injection.

ELECTRICAL

BATTERY

Battery Location — Battery is located in engine compartment.

Application	Amp. Hr. Rating
All Models	80

STARTER

All models use Hitachi starters.

ALTERNATOR

Application	Rated Amp. Output
2-WD Pickup	40
All Other Models	50

All models use Hitachi alternators.

ALTERNATOR REGULATOR

All models use Hitachi regulators, with an operating voltage of 14.0-14.6 volts at 68°F (20°C).

BELT ADJUSTMENT

Application	①Deflection
All Belts	.4" (10 mm)

① — Measured between longest span and depressed with firm thumb pressure.

FILTERS

Filter	Service Interval (Miles)
Oil Filter	①Replace every 7500
Air Filter	Replace every 30,000
Fuel Filter	Replace every 30,000

① — First change after 3750 miles.

CAPACITIES

Application	Quantity
Crankcase (Includes Filter)	
I-Mark	①5.5 qts.
Pickup	②5.1 qts.
Cooling System	
I-Mark	7.5 qts.
Pickup	8.5 qts.
Man. Trans. (SAE 30)	
I-Mark	
4 Spd.	2.7 pts.
5 Spd.	3.3 pts.
Pickup (4 & 5 Spd.)	2.7 pts.
Auto. Trans. (Dexron II)	
I-Mark	6.7 qts.
Pickup	7.0 qts.
Transfer Case (SAE 30)	5.2 pts.
Rear Differential (SAE 90)	2.5 pts.
Front Differential (SAE 90)	1.7 pts.
Fuel Tank	
I-Mark	13.7 gals.
Pickup	
Short Bed	13.2 gals.
Long Bed	19.1 gals.

① — 5.0 quarts without filter.
② — 4.2 quarts without filter.

TUNE-UP

XJ6L

ENGINE IDENTIFICATION

Engine number is stamped on top of cylinder block at rear of engine. Number is also stamped on Commission Plate, which is located in the engine compartment. Suffix following engine number indicates compression ratio, "L" — Low.

COMPRESSION PRESSURE

Check compression pressure with engine at normal operating temperature, throttle valve wide open, all spark plugs removed and coil wire disconnected. Compression pressure is normal if all cylinders are within 5 psi (.35 kg/cm^2) of each other.

VALVE CLEARANCE

1) With camshaft covers removed, rotate camshafts and record clearance between heel of each cam lobe and its respective tappet. If adjustment is necessary, rotate camshaft and install valve timing gauge (C.3993) before removing final camshaft retaining nut. If required, disconnect sprockets from camshafts.

NOTE — *DO NOT rotate engine while camshaft sprockets are disconnected.*

2) Remove camshaft bearing caps and lift off camshaft. Remove each tappet that requires adjustment and note its location for reassembly in its original position. Remove adjusting pad and measure thickness.

3) Use measured pad thickness and difference between measured valve clearance and specified clearance to calculate required thickness of new adjusting pad. Adjusting pads are available in increments of .001" (.03 mm) from .085" (2.16 mm) to .110" (2.79 mm) and are marked with letters from "A" to "Z" respectively.

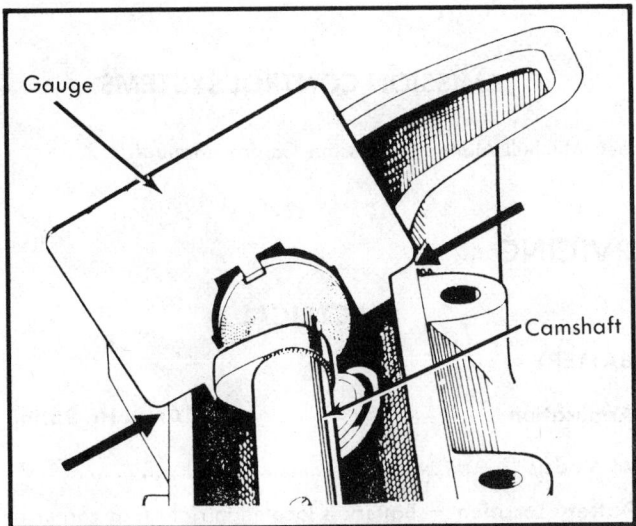

Fig. 1   Position of Valve Timing Gauge

4) Insert correct adjusting pads and install tappets. Attach camshafts (using timing gauge). Torque camshaft bearing cap nuts to 9 ft. lbs. (1.2 mkg), connect camshaft sprockets, and install camshaft covers.

Valve Clearance Specifications

Application	Clearance In. (mm)
All Models (Intake & Exhaust)	.012-.014 (.30-35)

VALVE ARRANGEMENT

Left Side — All Exhaust

Right Side — All Intake

SPARK PLUGS

Application	Gap In. (mm)	Torque Ft. Lbs. (N·m)
All Models	.035 (.9)	27 (36)

Spark Plug Type

Application	Champion No.
All Models	N12Y

HIGH TENSION WIRE RESISTANCE

Carefully remove high tension wires from spark plugs and distributor cap. Using an ohmmeter, check resistance of each wire while gently twisting wire. If resistance is not to specifications, or fluctuates from infinity to any value, replace wire.

Resistance (Ohms) Per Wire

Application	Resistance
All Models	25,000-30,000

DISTRIBUTOR

All models are equipped with a breakerless, electronic ignition system.

Air Gap .... ①.006-.008" (.15-.20)

① — Measured between timing rotor and pick-up module.

IGNITION TIMING

Check or adjust ignition timing with engine at normal operating temperature, idle speed set to specification and distributor vacuum line connected. If timing is not correct, loosen distributor clamp bolt and rotate distributor to achieve specified timing. Then tighten clamp bolt.

Ignition Timing Specifications
(Degrees BTDC@RPM)

Application	Timing
All Models	4@800

1981 Jaguar 6 Tune-Up

TUNE-UP (Cont.)

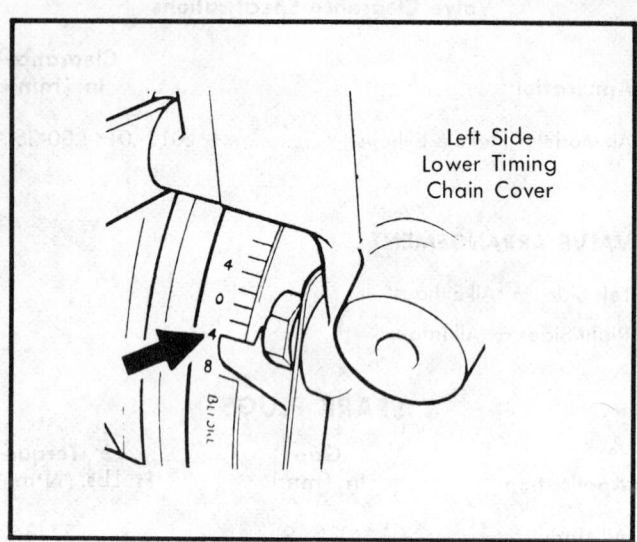

Left Side
Lower Timing
Chain Cover

Fig. 2   Ignition Timing Mark Location

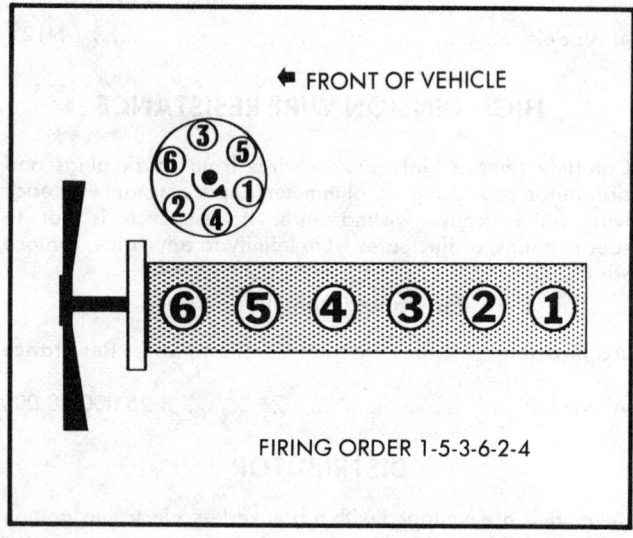

← FRONT OF VEHICLE

FIRING ORDER 1-5-3-6-2-4

Fig. 3   Firing Order and Distributor Rotation

IDLE SPEED & MIXTURE

NOTE — *Mixture adjustment is NOT a part of normal tune-up procedure and should not be performed unless fuel injection parts are replaced or vehicle fails emissions testing.*

1) Connect a tachometer and CO% meter to engine (at exhaust manifold test points). Run engine until normal operating temperature is reached.

2) Adjust idle with air volume screw at overrun valve housing. Use $7/32$" Allen wrench and turn clockwise to lower idle; counterclockwise to raise engine idle.

3) Remove plug on airflow meter to locate mixture adjustment screw. Disconnect oxygen sensor and allow engine to idle for 1 minute to stabilize mixture.

4) Turn mixture screw clockwise to richen mixture and counterclockwise to lean mixture. If correct setting cannot be attained, check all electrical connections and all hoses for proper location.

5) Replace oxygen sensor lead and disconnect test instruments.

Idle Speed & CO Level

Application	Idle RPM	CO %
All Models	750-850	.5-1.5

FUEL PUMP PRESSURE

Pressure	36 psi (2.5 kg/cm²)

EMISSION CONTROL SYSTEMS

See Mitchell Manuals' Emission Control Manual.

GENERAL SERVICING

IGNITION

DISTRIBUTOR

All models are equipped with Lucas Opus Electronic Ignition System.

FUEL SYSTEMS

FUEL INJECTION

All models are equipped with Lucas-Bosch fuel injection.

ELECTRICAL

BATTERY

Application	Amp. Hr. Rating
All Models	75

Battery Location — Battery is located in right rear corner of engine compartment.

STARTER

All models are equipped with Lucas pre-engaged Starters.

Free Speed Amperage
All Models .... 100 at 5000-6000 RPM

GENERAL SERVICING (Cont.)

ALTERNATOR

Application	Rated Amp. Output
All Models	60

ALTERNATOR REGULATOR

Lucas — Non-Adjustable; Integral with Alternator.

BELT ADJUSTMENT

Belt	① Deflection
Fan/Steering Pump	Self-Adjusting
Alternator	.15″ (3.8 mm)
A/C Compressor	.17″ (4.3 mm)

① — Deflection is with pressure applied midway on longest belt run.

FILTERS

Filter	Service Intervals (Miles)
Oil Filter	Replace every 6000
Air Filter	Replace every 12,000
Engine Breather Filter	Replace every 12,000
Fuel Filter	Replace every 12,000

CAPACITIES

Application	Quantity
Crankcase (Includes Filter)	8.7 qts.
Cooling System	19.5 qts.
Auto. Trans. (ATF Type F)	7.5 qts.
Rear Axle (SAE 90 EP)	3.3 pts.
Fuel Tank	
Right Side	11.8 gals.
Left Side	11.8 gals.

1981 LUV 4 Tune-Up

TUNE-UP

Pickup

ENGINE IDENTIFICATION

Engine serial number is stamped on pad between distributor and cylinder head.

Engine Code

Application	Code
1817 cc	G1802

COMPRESSION PRESSURE

Test compression with engine at normal operating temperature, spark plugs removed, throttle valve wide open and engine at cranking speed (300 RPM).

Compression Pressure Specifications

Application	Pressure psi (kg/cm²)
Normal (New Engine)	170 (12)
Minimum	120 (8.4)
Maximum Variation	10.0 (.6)

VALVE CLEARANCE

NOTE — *Before adjusting valve clearance, check torque of cylinder head and camshaft bolts. Valves should be adjusted every 15,000 miles with engine cold.*

1) Measure valve clearance between rocker arm and valve stem. Position No. 1 piston on TDC of compression stroke. Adjust intake valves on cylinder No. 1 and 2, and exhaust valves on cylinder No. 1 and 3.

2) Turn crankshaft 1 full revolution until No. 4 piston is at TDC of compression stroke. Adjust intake valves on cylinder No. 3 and 4, and exhaust valves on cylinder No. 2 and 4.

Valve Clearance Specifications①

Application	Intake In. (mm)	Exhaust In. (mm)
All Models	.006 (.15)	.010 (.25)

① — Set with engine cold.

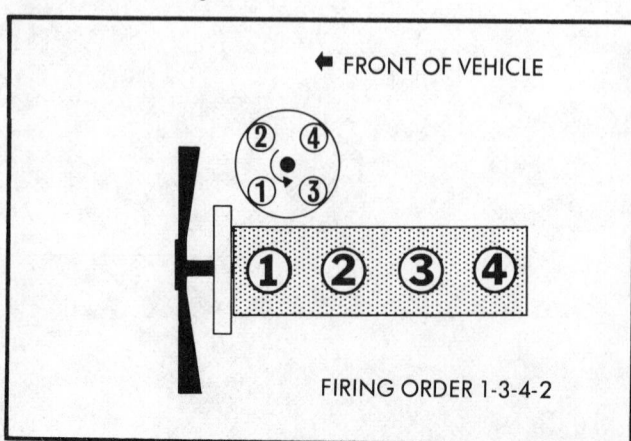

◀ FRONT OF VEHICLE

FIRING ORDER 1-3-4-2

Fig. 1 Firing Order and Distributor Rotation

VALVE ARRANGEMENT

All Models
  Right Side — All Intake
  Left Side — All Exhaust

SPARK PLUGS

Application	Gap In. (mm)	Torque Ft. Lbs. (N·m)
All Models	.040 (1.05)	18-25 (24-33)

Spark Plug Type

Application	NGK
All Models	BPR6ES11

HIGH TENSION WIRE RESISTANCE

Carefully remove high tension wires from spark plugs and from distributor cap. Using an ohmmeter, check resistance of wire while gently twisting wire. If resistance is not to specification, or fluctuates from infinity to any value, replace wire.

Resistance (Ohms)

Application	Resistance
All Models	31,500-73,500 per foot

DISTRIBUTOR

All models equipped with Nippondenso electronic ignition system. No adjustments are required.

Air Gap .... .008-.016" (.2-.4mm)

IGNITION TIMING

1) Ensure engine is warmed up to normal operating temperature, and that air gap in distributor is correct.

2) Connect timing light to either No. 1 or No. 4 cylinder. Remove distributor vacuum advance line and plug.

3) Loosen distributor clamping bolts and turn distributor until timing is within specifications.

Ignition Timing Specifications (Degrees BTDC @ RPM)

Application	①Timing
Federal Man. Trans.	6@800
All Other Models	6@900

① — With distributor vacuum hose disconnected and plugged.

TUNE-UP (Cont.)

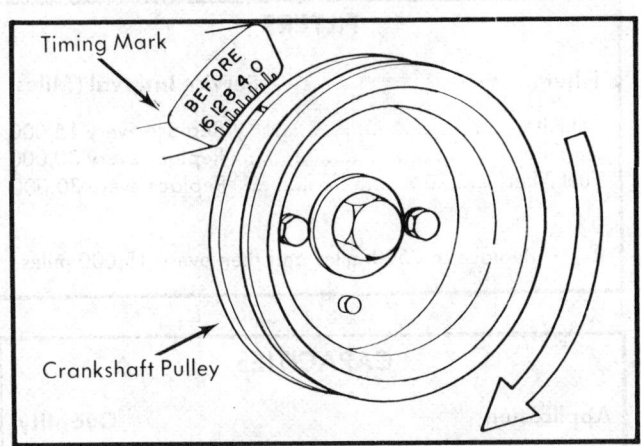

Fig. 2 Ignition Timing Mark Location

IDLE SPEED & MIXTURE

NOTE — *Mixture adjustment is NOT a part of normal tune-up procedure and should not be performed unless carburetor is replaced or vehicle fails emissions testing.*

1) Warm engine to normal operating temperature. Check valve clearance and ignition timing. Choke should be open, air conditioning off and air cleaner installed.

2) Disconnect and plug vacuum lines for distributor, hot idle compensator, and EGR valve.

3) Turn idle mixture adjusting screw fully in, then back out 2 turns (Federal) or 1 turn (Calif.). Set throttle adjusting screw to obtain specified mixture RPM.

4) Adjust idle mixture screw to obtain maximum RPM, then reset throttle adjusting screw to achieve specified mixture RPM. Turn idle mixture screw clockwise until speed drops to specified curb idle.

5) If equipped with air conditioner, turn on to maximum cooling and high blower. Open throttle slightly to allow solenoid to extend, then close throttle. Adjust solenoid screw to give 900 RPM idle.

Idle Speed & Mixture Adjustment

Application	Idle RPM	Mixture RPM
Federal		
Man. Trans.	800	850
Auto. Trans.	900	950
Calif.	900	950

COLD (FAST) IDLE ADJUSTMENT

Automatic choke fast idle is adjusted by opening angle of throttle valve on carburetor, rather than by engine speed. Adjust valve opening at 1st step of fast idle cam to 16-18°.

Disconnect and plug distributor, hot idle compensator and EGR valve vacuum hoses after engine warm-up. Fast idle speed should be as follows:

Fast Idle Specifications

Application	Engine RPM
All Models	3200

AUTOMATIC CHOKE

Automatic choke is set from factory and is non-adjustable.

FUEL PUMP PRESSURE

Pressure	3.6 psi (.25 kg/cm^2)

EMISSION CONTROL SYSTEMS

See Mitchell Manuals' Emission Control Manual.

GENERAL SERVICING

IGNITION

DISTRIBUTOR

All models are equipped with a Nippondenso electronic distributor.

IGNITION COIL

Coil Resistance (Ohms@68° F)

Application	Primary	Secondary
All Models	0.83-1.02	12,150-14,850

FUEL SYSTEMS

CARBURETORS

Application	Model
All Models	Hitachi 2-Bbl.

ELECTRICAL

BATTERY

Application	Amp. Hr. Rating
All Models	50

Battery Location — Engine compartment, left side of engine.

GENERAL SERVICING (Cont.)

STARTER

Hitachi.............................. Overrunning Clutch

Starter Specifications

Application	Volts	Amps	Test RPM
All Models	12	70	6000

ALTERNATOR

Application	Rated Amp. Output
All Models	40 or 50

ALTERNATOR REGULATOR

All models utilize a Hitachi adjustable alternator regulator with an operating voltage of 13.8-14.8 volts.

BELT ADJUSTMENT

Belt deflection for all drive belts should be .4" (10 mm) with pressure applied midway on belt run.

FILTERS

Filter	Service Interval (Miles)
Oil Filter	①Replace every 15,000
Air Filter	Replace every 30,000
Fuel Filter	Replace every 30,000

① — Replace at 7500 miles and then every 15,000 miles.

CAPACITIES

Application	Quantity
Crankcase (Includes Filter)	4.2 qts.
Cooling System	
Auto. Trans.	6.4 qts.
Man. Trans.	6.8 qts.
Man. Trans. (SAE 30)	
2-WD	2.7 pts.
4-WD (Includes Trans. Case)	5.3 pts.
Auto. Trans. (Dexron II)	
Refill	3.5 qts.
Overhaul (Includes Converter)	7.0 qts.
Front Axle (SAE 90)	1.7 pts.
Rear Axle (SAE 90)	2.7 pts.
Fuel Tank	
Short Wheelbase	13.2 gals.
Long Wheelbase	18.5 gals.

TUNE-UP

Pickup

ENGINE IDENTIFICATION

First 4 digits of engine identification are used to identify engine models. Code is stamped on right side of cylinder block.

Engine Code

Application	Code
Pickup (2238 cc)	C223

COMPRESSION PRESSURE

Start and run engine until normal operating temperature is obtained. Remove sensing resistor, glow plug connectors, glow plugs and fuel cut solenoid connector. Disconnect fusible link wire of "Quick Start" system at harness connector. Install compression gauge adapter (J-29762) and compression gauge. Operate starter and read compression.

Compression Pressure Specifications (Reading @ 200 RPM)

Application	Pressure psi (kg/cm²)
Normal (New Engine)	441 (31)
Minimum	398 (28)

VALVE CLEARANCE

CAUTION — *Before adjusting valves, check rocker arm shaft bracket bolts for looseness and tighten as necessary.*

1) Rotate crankshaft until No. 1 piston is at TDC of compression stroke. Measure between adjusting screw and valve stem end cap. With No. 1 piston at TDC, adjust intake valves on cylinder No. 1 and 2, and exhaust valves on cylinder No. 1 and 3.

2) Rotate crankshaft 1 complete revolution until No. 4 piston is at TDC of compression stroke. Adjust intake valves on cylinder No. 3 and 4, and exhaust valves on cylinder No. 2 and 4.

Valve Clearance Specifications

Application	Intake In. (mm)	Exhaust In. (mm)
Pickup		
Hot	.015 (.38)	.015 (.38)
Cold	.016 (.40)	.016 (.40)

VALVE ARRANGEMENT

Pickup — E-I-I-E-E-I-I-E

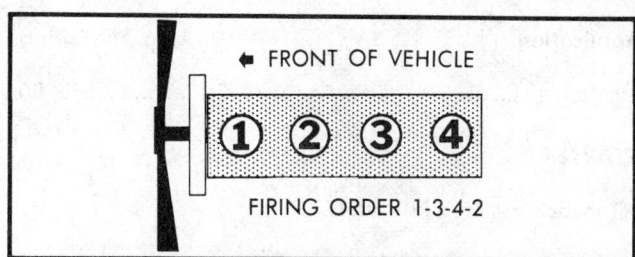

Fig. 1 *Diesel Firing Order Illustration*

IDLE SPEED ADJUSTMENT

Set parking brake and block drive wheels. Connect tachometer to warm engine and start engine. Check that idle speed is correct with accelerator lever touching idle adjusting screw. To adjust idle speed, loosen lock nut and turn adjusting screw until idle speed is set to specifications. Tighten lock nut.

Idle Speed Specifications

Application	Idle RPM
Pickup	700-800

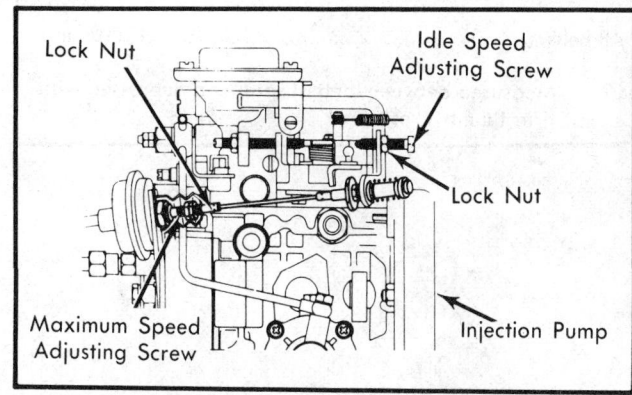

Fig. 2 *Idle and Maximum Speed Adjustment*

MAXIMUM SPEED ADJUSTMENT

Connect tachometer to warm engine. Start engine and check idle speed. Disconnect hoses from vacuum switch valve and connect together with piping. Accelerate engine briefly to full throttle. If maximum speed does not conform to specifications, loosen lock nut and adjust speed by turning maximum speed adjusting screw. Tighten lock nut.

Maximum Speed Specifications

Application	Maximum RPM
Pickup	900-950

GENERAL SERVICING

FUEL SYSTEMS

FUEL INJECTION

All models use Bosch mechanical diesel fuel injection.

ELECTRICAL

BATTERY

Battery Location — Battery is located in engine compartment.

GENERAL SERVICING (Cont.)

Application	Amp. Hr. Rating
All Models	80

STARTER

All models use Hitachi starters.

ALTERNATOR

All models use Hitachi alternators.

Application	Rated Amp. Output
All Models	50

ALTERNATOR REGULATOR

All models use Hitachi regulators, with an operating voltage of 14.0-14.6 volts at 68°F (20°C).

BELT ADJUSTMENT

Application	①Deflection
All Belts	.4" (10 mm)

① — Measured between longest span and depressed with firm thumb pressure.

FILTERS

Filter	Service Interval (Miles)
Oil Filter	①Replace every 7500
Air Filter	Replace every 30,000
Fuel Filter	Replace every 30,000

① — First change after 3750 miles.

CAPACITIES

Application	Quantity
Crankcase (Includes Filter)	①5.1 qts.
Cooling System	8.5 qts.
Man. Trans. (SAE 30)	
4 Spd	2.7 pts.
5 Spd	3.3 pts.
Auto. Trans. (Dexron II)	5.0 qts.
Transfer Case (SAE 30)	5.2 pts.
Rear Differential (SAE 90)	2.7 pts.
Front Differential (SAE 90)	1.7 pts.
Fuel Tank	
Short Wheelbase	13.2 gals.
Long Wheelbase	18.5 gals.

① — 4.2 quarts without filter.

TUNE-UP

GLC
626
B2000 Pickup

ENGINE IDENTIFICATION

Engine serial number and model code are stamped on right front upper wall of cylinder block.

COMPRESSION PRESSURE

Check compression pressure with engine at normal operating temperature, spark plugs removed, throttle valve wide open and engine at cranking speed. Crank engine until maximum pressure is reached at each cylinder. Compression is normal if lowest cylinder reading is at least 75% of highest reading.

Compression Pressure Specifications
(Reading @ 250 RPM)

Application	Pressure psi (kg/cm²)
Normal (New Engine)	171 (12)
Minimum	128 (9)
Maximum Variation	28 (2)

VALVE CLEARANCE

Adjust valves with engine at normal operating temperature.

Valve Clearance Specifications

Application	Intake In. (mm)	Exhaust In. (mm)
GLC	.010 (.25)	.012 (.30)
626 & B2000	.012 (.30)	.012 (.30)

VALVE ARRANGEMENT

All Models
  Right Side — All Exhaust.
  Left Side — All Intake.

SPARK PLUGS

Application	Gap In. (mm)	Torque Ft. Lbs. (N·m)
All Models	.031 (0.8)	13 (18)

Spark Plug Type

Application	Nippondenso	NGK
All Models		BPR-5ES or BPR-6ES

HIGH TENSION WIRE RESISTANCE

Carefully remove high tension wires from spark plugs and distributor cap. Using an ohmeter, check resistance of wires while gently twisting wire. If resistance is not to specification, or fluctuates from infinity to any value, replace wire.

Resistance (Ohms) of Wire

Application	Resistance
All Models	3300-7000 Ohms per Foot

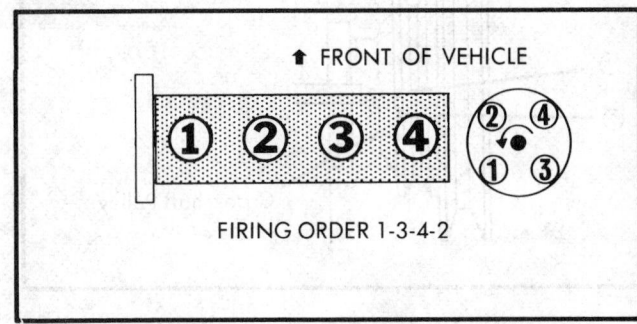

Fig. 1   Firing Order and Distributor Rotation (GLC Exc. Wagon)

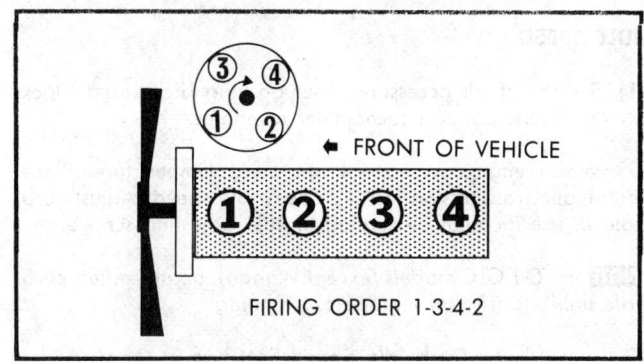

Fig. 2   Firing Order and Distributor Rotation (GLC Wagon, 626 & B2000)

DISTRIBUTOR

All models are equipped with a Mitsubishi breakerless electronic ignition system and no adjustments are needed.

IGNITION TIMING

With engine at normal operating temperature, idle speed set to specification and Man. Trans. in neutral or Auto. Trans. in "D", connect timing light, start engine and rotate distributor until specified mark on crankshaft pulley aligns with indicator pin.

Ignition Timing Specifications
(Degrees BTDC @ RPM)

Application	Man. Trans.	①Auto. Trans.
GLC	8@850	8@750
GLC Wagon	8@800	8@750
626	5@650	5@650
B2000	8@650	

① — Auto. Trans. in "D".

TUNE-UP (Cont.)

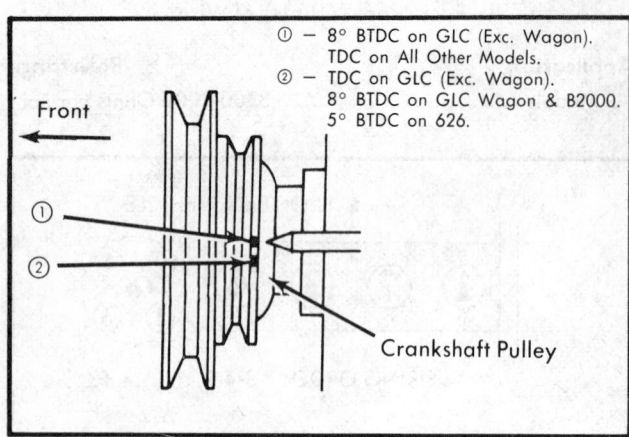

Front ←

① — 8° BTDC on GLC (Exc. Wagon).
   TDC on All Other Models.
② — TDC on GLC (Exc. Wagon).
   8° BTDC on GLC Wagon & B2000.
   5° BTDC on 626.

① ②

Crankshaft Pulley

Fig. 3   Ignition Timing Mark Location

IDLE SPEED AND MIXTURE

IDLE SPEED

1) Switch off all accessories. Set parking brake and block drive wheels. Connect tachometer to engine.

2) Warm engine to normal operating temperature. Place automatic transmission in "D". Check idle speed. Adjust curb idle to specification by turning throttle adjusting screw.

NOTE — *On GLC models (except Wagon), do not adjust curb idle until electric fan motor stops running.*

Curb Idle Speed Settings

Application	Man. Trans.	① Auto. Trans.
GLC	850	750
GLC Wagon	800	750
626	650	650
B2000	650	

① — Auto. Trans. in "D".

IDLE MIXTURE

NOTE — *Idle mixture adjustment is generally not required. Idle mixture adjustment should be performed during carburetor overhaul. All models require removal and disassembly of carburetor to remove idle mixture screw limiter shell and blind cap.*

1) Remove carburetor from engine. Separate carburetor main body and throttle body. Using a hacksaw, cut through limiter shell (from cap end) .27" (7 mm) on GLC models (except Wagon) or .47" (12 mm) on all other models. See *Fig. 5*. Remove and discard limiter shell, mixture spring and mixture screw.

2) Install new limiter shell with flat portion facing up. To install new mixture screw, tighten screw lightly and ensure it is fully seated. Back screw out 3 turns on B2000 models and 4 turns on all other models for preliminary adjustment.

3) Reinstall carburetor with new gaskets and warm engine to normal operating temperature. Connect exhaust gas analyzer. Switch off all accessories.

4) On Federal B2000 models, disconnect air cleaner-to-reed valve hose at reed valve port. On Calif. B2000 models, disconnect air by-pass valve-to-check valve hose at check valve and plug check valve port. On all other models, disconnect air control valve-to-check valve hoses at check valves and plug check valve ports.

5) On all models, adjust idle speed to idle set specification using throttle adjusting screw. See *Mixture Adjustment chart*. Using mixture screw, set idle speed to highest obtainable RPM.

6) Using throttle screw, set idle speed to idle set specification. Turn mixture screw clockwise until lean drop specification is obtained. See *Mixture Adjustment chart*.

7) Check CO concentration. If less than 1%, turn mixture screw counterclockwise ½ turn (¼ turn on 626 and B2000 models). Reconnect air hoses and check curb idle speed. After adjusting idle mixture, install blind plug in limiter shell.

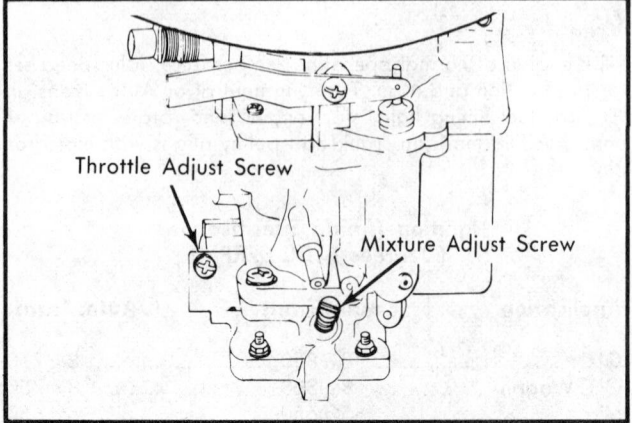

Throttle Adjust Screw

Mixture Adjust Screw

Fig. 4   Carburetor Adjustment Screw Location

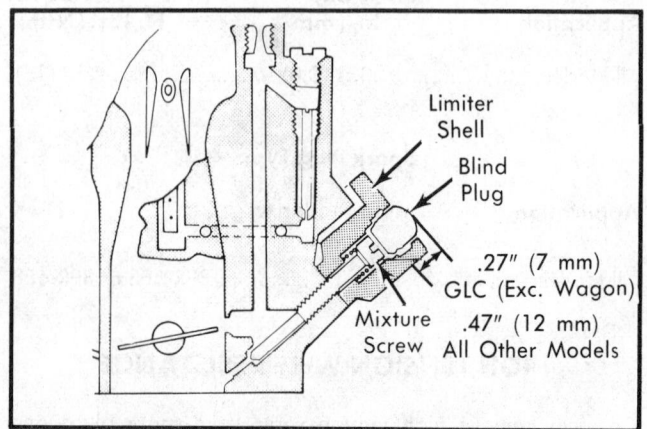

Limiter Shell

Blind Plug

.27" (7 mm) GLC (Exc. Wagon)

.47" (12 mm) All Other Models

Mixture Screw

Fig. 5   Idle Mixture Limiter Shell and Blind Plug on Carburetor

TUNE-UP (Cont.)

Mixture Adjustment①

Application	Idle Set RPM	Lean Drop RPM
GLC		
Man. Trans.	880	850
Auto. Trans.	1030	1000
GLC Wagon		
Man. Trans.	830	800
Auto. Trans.	1030	1000
626		
Man. Trans.	670	650
Auto. Trans.	850	820
B2000		
Federal	670	650
Calif.	620	600

① — Auto. Trans. in "N".

COLD (FAST) IDLE RPM

1) Adjust fast idle by setting angle of primary throttle valve with choke fully closed. Position fast idle cam on first step (second step on GLC Wagon and 626 models).

2) Clearance between primary throttle valve and throttle bore should be .031-.035" (.78-.92 mm) on GLC models; .033" (.85 mm) on GLC Wagon models; .019-.026" (.50-.65 mm) on 626 models; and .05-.06" (1.3-1.5 mm) on B2000 models. Adjust angle to specifications by turning adjusting screw.

FUEL PUMP PRESSURE & VOLUME

Pressure (At Idle)
GLC .... 2.8-3.8 psi (.20-.27 kg/cm²)
626 & B2000 .... 2.8-3.6 psi (.20-.25 kg/cm²)
Volume (At Idle)
GLC .... .7 pts. in 30 seconds
626 & B2000 .... .8 pts. in 30 seconds

EMISSION CONTROL SYSTEMS

See Mitchell Manuals' Emission Control Manual.

GENERAL SERVICING

IGNITION

DISTRIBUTOR

All models are equipped with a Mitsubishi breakerless electronic ignition system.

IGNITION COIL

Resistance Specifications
(Ohms @ 68°F)

Application	Primary	Secondary
GLC, GLC Wagon & 626	1.15	.....
B2000	.90	7000

FUEL SYSTEMS

CARBURETORS

Application	Model
GLC	Hitachi 2-Bbl.
626	Nikki 2-Bbl.
B2000	Nikki 2-Bbl.

ELECTRICAL

BATTERY

Application	Amp. Hr. Rating
GLC	
Federal	45
Calif.	33
GLC Wagon, 626 & B2000	①45

① — 70 Amp. battery also available on B2000.

STARTER

Mitsubishi .... Overrunning Clutch

Starter Specifications

Application	Volts	Amps	Test RPM
626 Auto Trans.	11.5	60	6600
All Other Models	11.5	53	6800

ALTERNATOR

All models are equipped with Mitsubishi alternators.

Application	Load Test Amp. Output
GLC & B2000	30@2500 RPM or less
626	42@2500 RPM or less

ALTERNATOR REGULATOR

All models are equipped with a Mitsubishi adjustable alternator regulator with an operating voltage of 14-15 volts.

GENERAL SERVICING (Cont.)

BELT ADJUSTMENT

Application	①Deflection
Alternator Belt	②.3-.4" (8-10 mm)
Air Conditioner Belt	.6-.7" (15-18 mm)
Air Pump Belt	
GLC Wagon	③.3-.4" (8-10 mm)
626 & B2000	.4-.6" (10-15 mm)

① — Deflection is with 22 lbs. (10 kg) pressure applied midway on longest belt run.

② — GLC (except Wagon) is .47-.50" (12-13 mm).

③ — GLC (except Wagon is .63-.70" (16-18 mm); with A/C, .43-.50" (11-13 mm).

FILTERS

Filter	Service Interval (Miles)
Oil Filter	Replace every 7500
Air Filter	Replace every 30,000
Fuel Filter (B2000)	Replace every 15,000

CAPACITIES

Application	Quantity
Crankcase (Includes Filter)	
GLC	3.2 qts.
626 & B2000	4.1 qts.
Cooling System (Includes Heater)	
GLC	5.8 qts.
626	7.9 qts.
B2000	7.6 qts.
Manual Transaxle (ATF Type "F")	3.4 qts.
Manual Transmission (SAE 80W-90)	
4-Speed	
GLC Wagon	1.4 qts.
B2000	1.6 qts.
5-Speed	1.8 qts.
Automatic Transaxle (ATF Type "F")	6.0 qts.
Automatic Transmission (ATF Type "F")	
GLC Wagon	6.0 qts.
626	6.6 qts.
Rear Axle (SAE 80W-90)	
GLC Wagon	1.6 pts.
626	2.6 pts.
B2000	2.8 pts.
Fuel Tank	
GLC	11.1 gals.
GLC Wagon	11.9 gals.
626	14.5 gals.
B2000	
Standard Bed	14.8 gals.
Long Bed	17.4 gals.

TUNE-UP

RX7

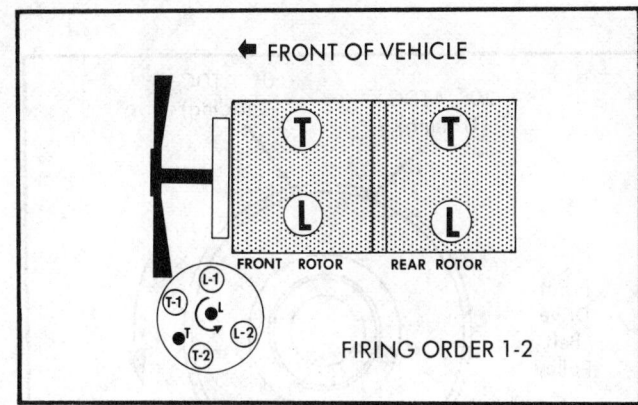

Fig. 1   Firing Order and Distributor Rotation

ENGINE IDENTIFICATION

Engine type code is stamped on rear rotor housing, to the rear of oil filter. Engine serial number is stamped on front rotor housing behind distributor.

COMPRESSION PRESSURE

Start and run engine until it reaches normal operating temperature. Disconnect all spark plug wires and remove 1 spark plug from each chamber. Check compression of each chamber with engine at cranking speed (250 RPM).

Compression Pressure Specifications

Application	Pressure psi (kg/cm²)
Minimum	85 (6.0)
Maximum Variation	21 (1.5)

SPARK PLUGS

Application	Gap In. (mm)	Torque Ft. Lbs. (N·m)
All Models	.055 (1.4)	11 (15)

Spark Plug Type

Application	Nippondenso	NGK
All Models	W25EDR14	BR8EQ14

HIGH TENSION WIRE RESISTANCE

Carefully remove high tension wires from spark plugs and distributor cap. Using an ohmmeter, measure resistance of wires while gently twisting wires. If resistance is not to specifications, or fluctuates from infinity to any value, replace high tension wire(s).

Resistance (Ohms) Per Wire

Application	Resistance
All Models	3300-7000 Ohms per foot

DISTRIBUTOR

All models are equipped with electronic ignition with 2 pick-up coils. Air gap is non-adjustable, but should measure .020-.035" (.5-.9 mm).

IGNITION TIMING

NOTE — *On vehicles equipped with automatic transmission, place selector lever in "D" position and block the wheels.*

1) Warm engine to normal operating temperature. Connect a tachometer, then connect timing light to leading (lower) spark plug of front rotor. Start engine and run at idle speed.

2) Check ignition timing and rotate distributor to correct if necessary. Tighten distributor lock nut and recheck timing.

3) Connect timing light to trailing (upper) plug of front rotor. Start engine and check timing. If not correct, loosen vacuum unit attaching screws and move vacuum unit in or out to adjust trailing timing. Remove test equipment.

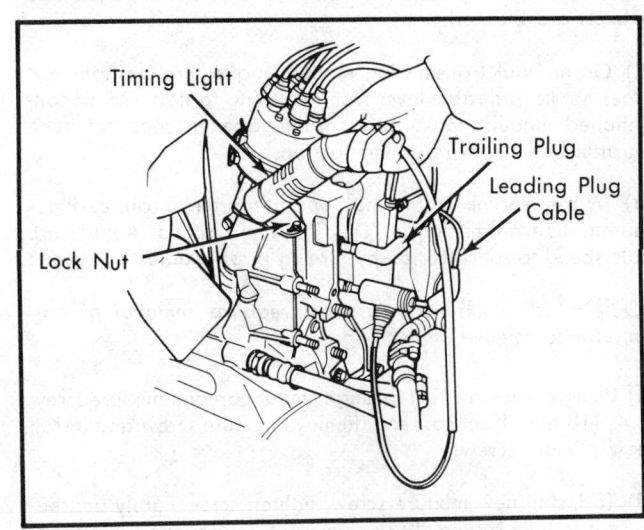

Fig. 2   Connecting Timing Light (Shown Connected to Leading Plug Wire)

TUNE-UP (Cont.)

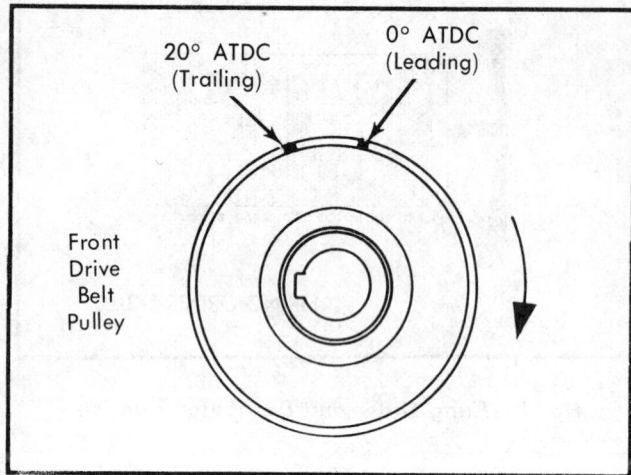

Fig. 3 Ignition Timing Mark Location

Ignition Timing Specifications

Application	Timing
Leading	TDC
Trailing	20°ATDC

IDLE SPEED & MIXTURE

NOTE — *Mixture adjustment is NOT part of normal tune-up procedure and should not be performed unless carburetor is overhauled or vehicle fails emissions testing.*

1) Switch off all accessories. Remove fuel filler cap. Disconnect and plug idle compensator tube at air cleaner. Connect tachometer to engine. Ensure parking brake is engaged and wheels are blocked.

2) On manual transmission models, make sure dashpot rod does not keep throttle lever from returning to stop. On air conditioned models, make sure throttle opener does not keep throttle lever from returning to stop.

3) Warm engine to normal operating temperature. Place automatic transmission in "D". Check idle speed. Adjust curb idle speed to specification by turning throttle adjusting screw.

NOTE — *Idle mixture adjustment requires removal of carburetor to remove limiter cap.*

4) Using a hacksaw, cut through limiter cap and mixture screw 0.4" (10 mm) from cap end. Remove mixture screw and install new mixture screw.

5) To install new mixture screw, tighten screw lightly and ensure it is fully seated. Back screw out 3 turns for preliminary adjustment. Reinstall carburetor with new gaskets and warm engine to normal operating temperature.

6) To adjust idle mixture, set idle speed to idle set specification by turning throttle set screw (automatic transmission in "N"). Set idle speed to highest RPM obtainable by turning mixture screw. Reset idle speed to idle set specification by turning throttle screw. See *Fig. 4.*

7) Turn mixture screw until lean drop specification is obtained (automatic transmission in "N"). On automatic transmission, shift transmission to "D" and set idle speed to curb idle specification by turning throttle screw.

Idle Speed & Mixture Adjustment

Application	Curb Idle RPM	Idle Set RPM	Lean Drop RPM
Man. Trans.	750	770	750
Auto. Trans	①750	②850	②840

① — Transmission in "D".
② — Transmission in "N".

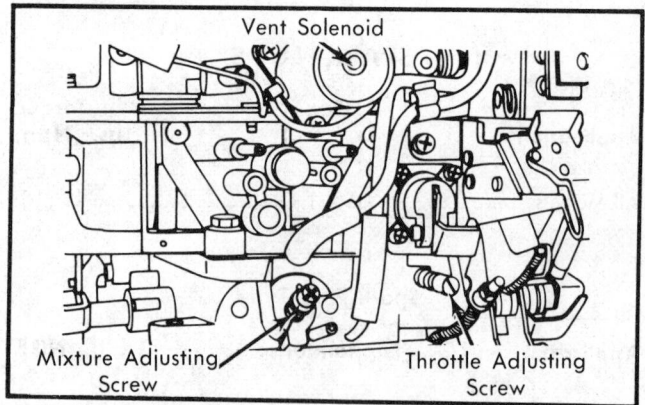

Fig. 4 Carburetor Adjusting Screw Locations

COLD (FAST) IDLE RPM

NOTE — *Carburetor must be removed to check and/or adjust fast idle.*

Adjust fast idle by setting angle of primary throttle valve with choke valve fully closed. Clearance between primary throttle valve and throttle bore should be .032-.040" (0.8-1.0 mm). If not to specification, bend fast idle rod until correct clearance is obtained.

FUEL PUMP PRESSURE & VOLUME

Pressure	3.7-4.7 psi (.26-.33 kg/cm²)
Volume	1.16 qts. per min.

EMISSION CONTROL SYSTEMS

See Mitchell Manuals' Emission Control Manual.

GENERAL SERVICING

IGNITION

DISTRIBUTOR

All models are equipped with Mitsubishi electronic ignition systems.

IGNITION COIL

**Resistance Specifications
(Ohms@68°F)**

Application	Primary	Secondary
All Models	0.81-0.99	....

FUEL SYSTEMS

CARBURETOR

Application	Model
All Models	Hitachi 4-Bbl.

ELECTRICAL

BATTERY

Application	Amp. Hr. Capacity
G60-5 & Y60-5	45
NS70S	55

Battery Location — In engine compartment.

STARTER

Mitsubishi	Overrunning Clutch

Starter Specifications

Application	Volts	Amps	Test RPM
Man. Trans.	11.5	50	5600
Auto. Trans.	11.5	100	3500

ALTERNATOR

Application	Rated Amp. Output
All Models	50

BELT ADJUSTMENT

Application	①Deflection
Alternator Belt	.5-.7" (13-17 mm)
Air Pump Belt	.43-.51" (11-13 mm)
A/C Belt	.39-.47 (10-12 mm)

① — Deflection is with 22 lbs. (10 kg) pressure applied midway on longest belt run.

FILTERS

Filter	Service Interval (Miles)
Oil Filter	Replace every 15,000
Air Filter	Replace every 30,000

CAPACITIES

Crankcase (Includes Filter)	5.5 qts.
Cooling System (Includes Heater)	10.0 qts.
Man. Trans. (SAE 90)	3.6 pts.
Auto. Trans. (ATF Type F)	6.6 qts.
Rear Axle (SAE 90)	2.6 pts.
Fuel Tank	16.6 gals.

TUNE-UP

240D
300 Diesel Series

ENGINE IDENTIFICATION

First six digits of engine identification number, located on a tag at the rear, left side of engine crankcase, identify engines as follows:

Engine Code

Application	Code
240D	616.912
300D & 300CD	617.912
300SD (Turbocharged)	617.951
300TD (Turbocharged)	617.952

COMPRESSION PRESSURE

Check compression pressure with engine at normal operating temperature and throttle valve fully open. Crank engine through at least 8 revolutions.

Compression Pressure Specifications

Application	Pressure psi (kg/cm²)
Normal	319-348 (22.5-24.5)
Minimum	218 (15.0)
Maximum Variation Between Cylinders	44 (3.0)

VALVE CLEARANCE

Valves must be adjusted at ignition TDC and in firing order of individual cylinders. With engine cold, measure clearance between rocker arm and base circle of cam. Adjust valves to following specifications:

Valve Clearance Specifications

Application	Intake In. (mm)	Exhaust In. (mm)
240D, 300D & 300CD		
Cold	.004 (10)	.012 (30)
Warm	.006 (15)	.014 (35)
300SD & 300TD		
Cold	.004 (10)	.014 (35)
Warm	.006 (15)	.016 (40)

VALVE ARRANGEMENT

4-Cylinder
E-I-I-E-E-I-I-E (front-to-rear)
5-Cylinder
E-I-I-E-E-I-I-E-E-I (front-to-rear)

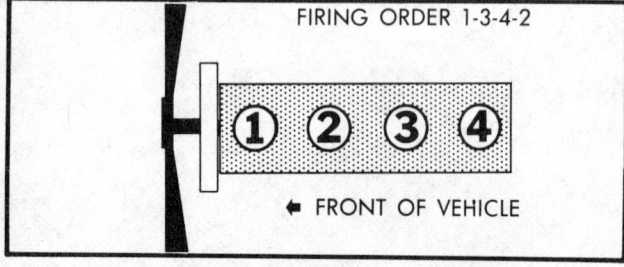

Fig. 1   240D Firing Order Illustration

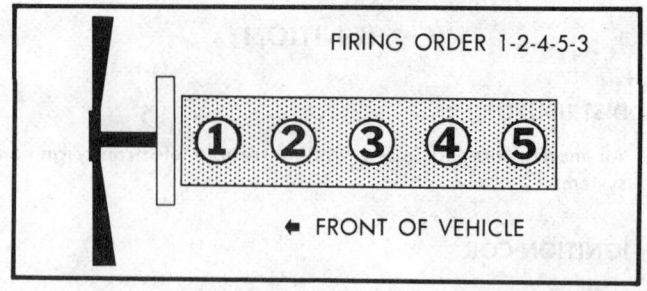

Fig. 2   300 Series Firing Order Illustration

GLOW PLUGS

Type	Bosch 0 100 221 107
Torque	15-22 ft. lbs. (20-30 N·m)

IDLE SPEED ADJUSTMENT

1) Start engine and run until normal operating temperature is reached, at least 176° F (80° C) oil temperature. If equipped, turn idle adjusting knob on dashboard clockwise to stop.

2) Disconnect throttle linkage push rod at angle lever. Check idle speed. If necessary, loosen lock nut and adjust with idle adjusting screw.

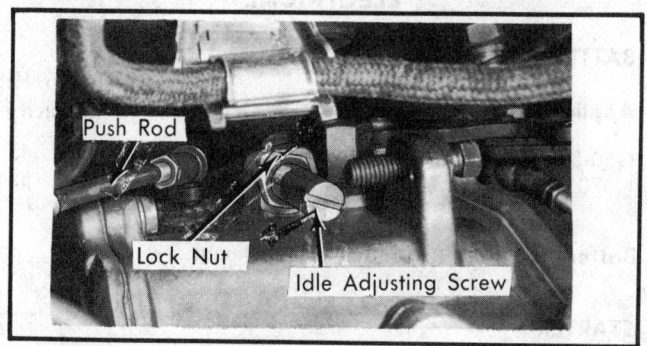

Fig. 3   Idle Adjusting Screw Location

3) On non-Turbo models, adjust push rod so guide lever cam is just resting against switch-over valve lever (free of tension). Injection pump lever should be resting against idle speed stop. Push shutoff lever ("STOP") and ensure cruise control cable is not too tight. Adjust by turning cable nut. When lever is released, a slight amount of clearance should be present. See Fig. 4.

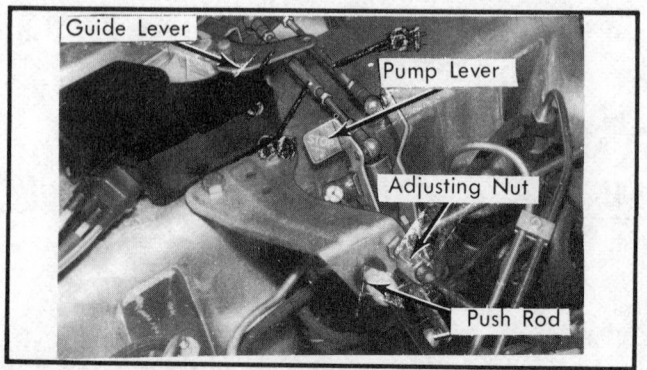

Fig. 4   Injection Linkage Adjustment
(Non-Turbo Models)

TUNE-UP (Cont.)

4) On Turbo models, adjust push rod so roller in guide lever rests free of tension against end stop. Disconnect cruise control connecting rod and push lever against idle speed stop. Reattach connecting rod so lever has .039" (1 mm) clearance from stop. *See Fig. 5.*

5) On all models, place transmission in "D", turn on air conditioning and turn wheels to full lock. Engine must run smoothly. If not, readjust idle speed slightly higher.

CAUTION — *If engine speed is adjusted too high, it will be above governor control range and could increase to maximum RPM when engine is not loaded.*

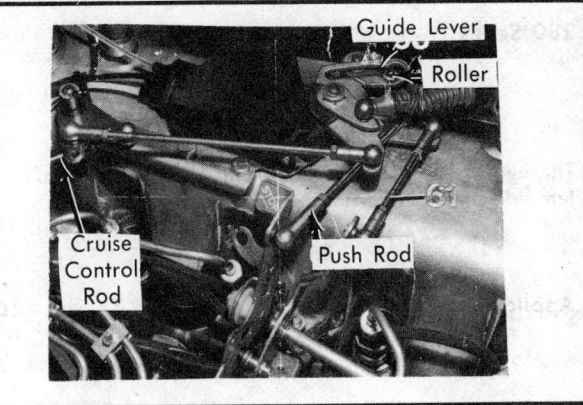

Fig. 5   Injection Linkage Adjustment (Turbo Models)

Idle Speed Specifications

Application	Idle RPM
240D, 300D & 300CD	700-800
300SD & 300TD	650-850

GENERAL SERVICING

FUEL SYSTEMS

FUEL INJECTION

All Models use Bosch Diesel Fuel Injection.

ELECTRICAL

BATTERY

Application	Amp. Hr. Rating
All Models	88

STARTER

All models are equipped with Bosch Starters.

Starter Specifications

Application	Volts	Amps	Test RPM
All Models	11.5	65-95	6500

ALTERNATOR

Application	Rated Amp. Output
All Models	55

ALTERNATOR REGULATOR

Bosch — Non-Adjustable; integral with alternator.

BELT ADJUSTMENT

Application	①Deflection
Power Steering Belt	.40" (10 mm)
All Other Belts	.20" (5 mm)

① — Deflection is with a pressure of 13 lbs. (6 kg) applied midway on longest belt run.

FILTERS

Filter	Service Interval (Miles)
Oil Filter	Replace every 5000
Air Filter	Replace every 30,000
Fuel Filter	Replace every 30,000

CAPACITIES

Application	Quantity
Crankcase (Includes Filter)	
240D, 300D & 300CD	7.0 qts.
300SD & 300TD	7.5 qts.
Cooling System (Includes Heater)	
240D	10.6 qts.
300D & 300CD	11.6 qts.
300SD & 300TD	12.5 qts.
Man. Trans. (SAE 10W-20)	3.4 pts.
Auto. Trans. (Dexron)	
240D, 300D & 300CD	5.0 qts.
300SD & 300TD	7.3 qts.
Rear Axle (SAE 90)	
240D, 300D & 300CD	2.1 pts.
300SD	2.6 pts.
300TD	2.0 pts.
Fuel Tank	
240D	17.2 gals.
300D & 300CD	21.1 gals.
300SD	22.4 gals.
300TD	20.2 gals.

TUNE-UP

280 Series

ENGINE IDENTIFICATION

The engine identification number is located on front left side of engine crankcase.

Engine Code

Application	Code
All Models	110.984

COMPRESSION PRESSURE

Check compression pressure with engine at normal operating temperature, throttle valve fully open and all spark plugs removed. Crank engine at least 8 "puffs" per cylinder.

Compression Pressure Specifications

Application	Pressure psi (kg/cm²)
Normal	130-144 (9-10)
Minimum	180 (7.5)
Maximum Variation	21 (1.5)

VALVE CLEARANCE

Adjust valves by rotating engine to TDC in the correct firing order.

Valve Clearance Specifications

Application	Intake In. (mm)	Exhaust In. (mm)
Cold	.004 (.10)	.010 (.25)
Warm	.006 (.15)	.012 (.30)

VALVE ARRANGEMENT

All Models
Right Side — All Exhaust.
Left Side — All Intake.

SPARK PLUGS

Application	Gap In. (mm)	Torque Ft. Lbs. (N·m)
All Models	.031 (0.8)	22 (30)

Spark Plug Type

Application	Bosch No.	Champion No.
All Models	W9D	N12Y

HIGH TENSION WIRE RESISTANCE

Carefully remove high tension wires from spark plugs and distributor cap. Using an ohmmeter, measure resistance while gently twisting wire. If resistance is not to specifications or fluctuates from infinity to any value, replace wire(s).

Resistance (Ohms) Per Wire

Application	Ohms
All Models	25,000-30,000

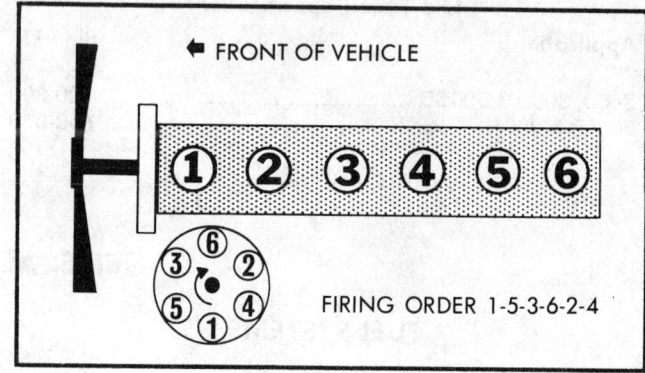

Fig. 1   Firing Order and Distributor Rotation

DISTRIBUTOR

All models are equipped with Bosch breakerless electronic ignition systems.

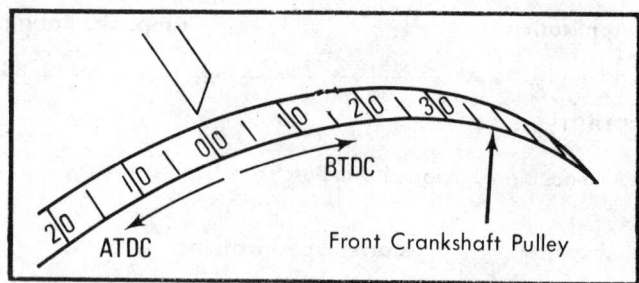

Fig. 2   Ignition Timing Mark Location

IGNITION TIMING

Check or adjust ignition timing with engine at normal operating temperature, idle speed set to specifications and distributor vacuum lines connected.

Ignition Timing Specifications

Application	RPM	Timing
All Models	750	10° BTDC

IDLE SPEED & MIXTURE

IDLE SPEED

1) Connect tachometer and warm engine to normal operating temperature. Turn air conditioning and all electrical accessories off. Place transmission selector in "P" position.

TUNE-UP (Cont.)

2) Ensure throttle valve lever is against idle speed stop. Disconnect rod from cruise control actuator and ensure speed control lever is against idle speed stop, then adjust rod so lever is .039" (1 mm) away from stop.

3) Adjust idle speed using idle speed screw. *See Fig. 3.*

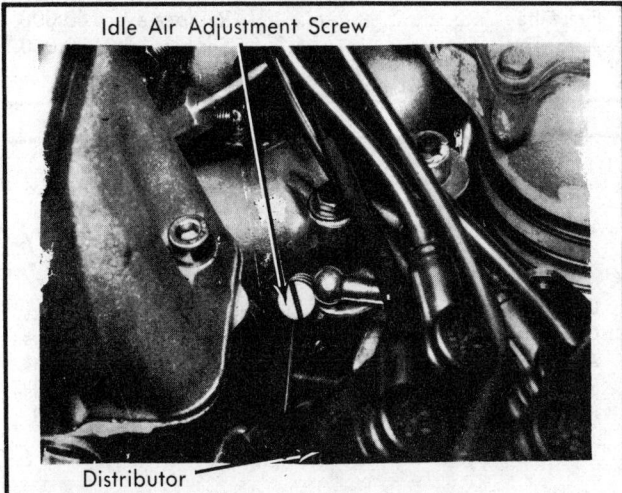

Fig. 3 Idle Air Adjustment Screw

IDLE MIXTURE

NOTE — *Mixture control unit adjustment screw opening is plugged to prevent tampering. Adjustment is not a normal maintenance procedure and should not be performed unless mixture control unit is replaced or vehicle fails emissions testing.*

1) Warm engine to normal operating temperature and adjust timing and idle speed. Remove cover from diagnostic plug (on fender panel near hood hinge). Connect voltmeter negative lead to pin 3 of plug, and positive lead to battery voltage.

2) Disconnect oxygen sensor plug (near sensor under vehicle). Observe voltmeter reading and place a piece of tape on voltmeter dial to indicate needle position. Needle should not be moving.

NOTE — *Oxygen sensor plug is inside a holder. Unscrew holder bolt (if necessary), push plug out of holder, and disconnect.*

3) Reconnect oxygen sensor. Needle should vibrate and vibrations should be centered around mark on voltmeter. If not, adjustment is necessary.

4) Remove plug from mixture control unit. Insert hex wrench and adjust mixture screw carefully until needle is centered around mark on voltmeter dial. Remove test equipment and plug adjustment opening.

Idle Speed

Application	RPM
All Models	700-800

FUEL PUMP PRESSURE & VOLUME

Pressure	72-81 psi (5.0-5.6 kg/cm²)
Volume	1 qt. in 30 sec.

EMISSION CONTROL SYSTEMS

See Mitchell Manuals' Emission Control Manual.

GENERAL SERVICING

IGNITION

DISTRIBUTOR

All models are equipped with Bosch breakerless, transistorized distributors.

IGNITION COIL

Resistance Specifications
(Ohms@68°F)

Application	Primary	Secondary
All Models	.7	.....

FUEL SYSTEMS

FUEL INJECTION

All models are equipped with Bosch Lambda CIS fuel injection systems with oxygen sensor.

ELECTRICAL

BATTERY

Application	Amp. Hour Rating
All Models	55

Battery Location — In engine compartment.

STARTER

All models are equipped with Bosch starters.

Starter Specifications

Application	Volts	Amps	Test RPM
All Models	11.5	50-80	8300

GENERAL SERVICING (Cont.)

ALTERNATOR

All models are equipped with Bosch alternators.

Application	Rated Amp. Output
All Models	65

ALTERNATOR REGULATOR

All models are equipped with Bosch electronic voltage regulators with an operating voltage of 13.0-14.5 volts.

BELT ADJUSTMENT

Application	①Deflection
Power Steering Belt	.40″ (10 mm)
All Other Belts	.20″ (5 mm)

① — Deflection with 12 lbs. pressure applied midway on belt run.

FILTERS

Filter	Service Interval (Miles)
Oil Filter	Replace every 7500
Air Filter	Replace every 30,000
Fuel Filter	Replace every 60,000
Auto. Trans. Filter	Replace every 30,000

CAPACITIES

Application	Quantity
Crankcase (Includes Filter)	6.3 qts.
Cooling System (Includes Heater)	10.6 qts.
Auto. Trans. (Dexron)	5.6 qts.
Rear Axle (SAE 90)	2.1 pts.
Fuel Tank	21.1 gals.

TUNE-UP

380 Series

ENGINE IDENTIFICATION

The engine identification number is located on rear left side of engine crankcase.

Engine Code

Application	Code
380SEL	116.961
380SL & 380SLC	116.960

COMPRESSION PRESSURE

Check compression pressure with engine at normal operating temperature, throttle valve fully open and all spark plugs remove. Crank engine at least 8 "puffs" per cylinder.

Compression Pressure Specifications

Application	Pressure psi (kg/cm²)
Normal	130-144 (9-10)
Minimum	108 (7.5)
Maximum Variation	21 (1.5)

VALVE CLEARANCE

Mercedes-Benz V8 engines use hydraulic valve lifters and no adjustment is necessary.

VALVE ARRANGEMENT

450 Series
  Right Bank — E-I-E-I-E-I-I-E (front to rear).
  Left Bank — E-I-I-E-I-E-I-E (front to rear).

SPARK PLUGS

Application	Gap In. (mm)	Torque Ft. Lbs. (N·m)
All Models	.031 (0.8)	22 (30)

Spark Plug Type

Application	Bosch No.	Champion No.
All Models	W9D	N12Y

HIGH TENSION WIRE RESISTANCE

Carefully remove high tension wires from spark plugs and distributor cap. Using an Ohmmeter, check resistance of wires while gently twisting wire. If resistance is not to specifications, or fluctuates from infinity to any value, replace wire(s).

Resistance (Ohms) Per Wire

Application	Ohms
All Models	25,000-30,000

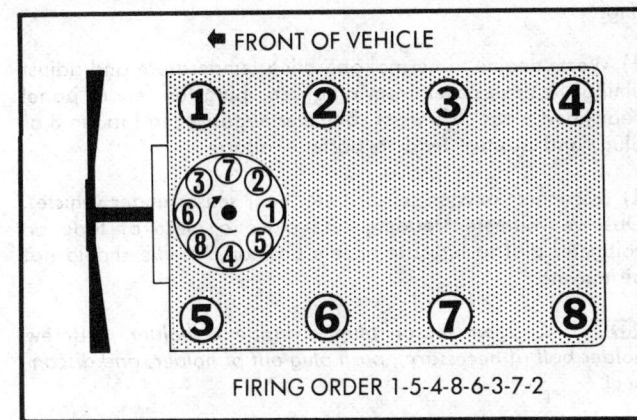

Fig. 1 Firing Order and Distributor Rotation

DISTRIBUTOR

All models feature a breakerless, transistorized ignition system.

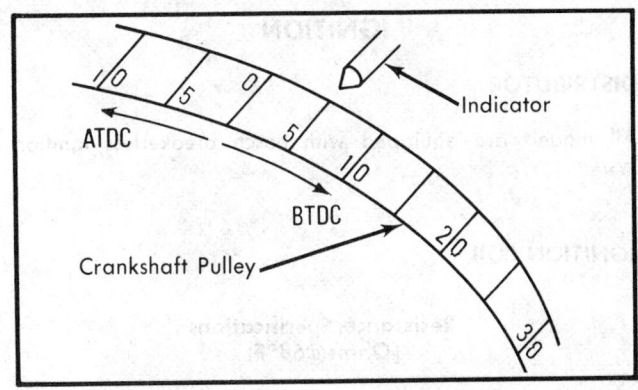

Fig. 2 Ignition Timing Mark Location

IGNITION TIMING

Check or adjust ignition timing with engine at normal operating temperature, idle speed set to specifications and distributor vacuum lines connected.

Ignition Timing Specifications (Degrees BTDC@RPM)

Application	Timing
All Models	5@500

IDLE SPEED & MIXTURE

IDLE SPEED

All models are equipped with electronic idle speed control and no adjustments are necessary.

TUNE-UP (Cont.)

IDLE MIXTURE

NOTE — *Mixture control unit adjustment screw opening is plugged to prevent tampering. Adjustment is not a normal maintenance procedure and should not be performed unless mixture control unit is replaced or vehicle fails emissions testing.*

1) Warm engine to normal operating temperature and adjust timing. Remove cover from diagnostic plug (on fender panel near hood hinge). Connect voltmeter negative lead to pin 3 of plug, and positive lead to battery voltage.

2) Disconnect oxygen sensor plug (near sensor under vehicle). Observe voltmeter reading and place a piece of tape on voltmeter dial to indicate needle position. Needle should not be moving.

NOTE — *Oxygen sensor plug is inside a holder. Unscrew holder bolt (if necessary), push plug out of holder, and disconnect.*

3) Reconnect oxygen sensor. Needle should vibrate and vibrations should be centered around mark on voltmeter. If not, adjustment is necessary.

4) Remove plug from mixture control unit. Insert hex wrench and adjust mixture screw carefully until needle is centered around mark on voltmeter dial. Remove test equipment and plug adjustment opening.

Idle Speed

Application	RPM
All Models①	
Engine Cold	750
Engine Warm	500

① — Non-adjustable.

FUEL PUMP PRESSURE & VOLUME

Pressure	72-81 psi (5.0-5.6 kg/cm^2)
Volume	1 qt. in 30 sec.

EMISSION CONTROL SYSTEMS

See Mitchell Manuals' Emission Control Manual.

GENERAL SERVICING

IGNITION

DISTRIBUTOR

All models are equipped with Bosch breakerless ignition system.

IGNITION COIL

Resistance Specifications
(Ohms@68°F)

Application	Primary	Secondary
All Models	.38-.42	8000-11,000

FUEL SYSTEMS

FUEL INJECTION

All models use Bosch Lambda Continuous Injection System fuel injection.

ELECTRICAL

BATTERY

Application	Amp. Hr. Rating
380SEL	55
380SL & 380SLC	88

Battery Location — Battery is located in engine compartment on 380SEL models, and in right side of trunk on 380SL and 380SLC models.

STARTER

All models are equipped with Bosch starters.

Starter Specifications

Application	Volts	Amps	Test RPM
All Models	11.5	50-80	8300

ALTERNATOR

All models are equipped with Bosch alternators.

Application	Rated Amp. Output
All Models	70

ALTERNATOR REGULATOR

All models use Bosch integral alternator regulators with an operating voltage of 13.0-14.5 volts.

GENERAL SERVICING (Cont.)

BELT ADJUSTMENT

Application	① Deflection
Power Steering Belt	.40" (10 mm)
All Other Belts	.20" (5 mm)

① — Deflection with 12 lbs. pressure applied midway on belt run.

FILTERS

Filter	Service Interval (Miles)
Oil Filter	Replace every 7500
Air Filter	Replace every 30,000
Fuel Filter	Replace every 60,000
Auto. Trans. Filter	Replace every 30,000

CAPACITIES

Application	Quantity
Crankcase (Includes Filter)	8.0 qts.
Cooling System (Includes Heater)	13.0 qts.
Auto. Trans. (Dexron)	7.3 qts.
Rear Axle (SAE 90)	2.6 pts.
Fuel Tank	
380SEL	25.6 gals.
380SL & 380SLC	24.7 gals.

TUNE-UP

505

ENGINE IDENTIFICATION

Engine in all 505 models is referred to as XN6 version. Engine codes are stamped on camshaft tunnel on left side of block.

Engine Code

Application	Code
505	
Man. Trans.	M5 BVM
Auto. Trans.	A3 BVA

VALVE CLEARANCE

Valves must be set with engine cold. To adjust valves, remove valve cover and rotate crankshaft until valve listed in first column of table is fully open, then adjust valves listed in second column of table. Replace valve cover.

NOTE — *Valves and cylinders are numbered from REAR to FRONT.*

Valve Open	Valves to Adjust
No. 1 Exh.	No. 3 Int. & No. 4 Exh.
No. 3 Exh.	No. 4 Int. & No. 2 Exh.
No. 4 Exh.	No. 2 Int. & No. 1 Exh.
No. 2 Exh.	No. 1 Int. & No. 3 Exh.

Valve Clearance Specifications①

Application	Intake In. (mm)	Exhaust In. (mm)
All Models	.004 (10)	.010 (25)

① — Engine cold.

VALVE ARRANGEMENT

All Models
 Right Side — All Exhaust.
 Left Side — All Intake.

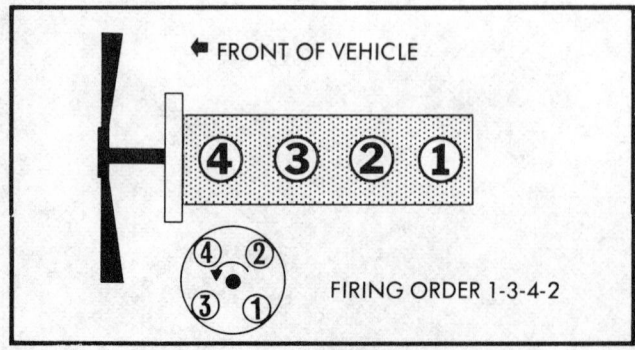

← FRONT OF VEHICLE

④ ③ ② ①

④ ② / ③ ①

FIRING ORDER 1-3-4-2

SPARK PLUGS

Gap .... .024" (.6 mm)

Spark Plug Type

Application	Bosch No.
All Models	WR7DS

HIGH TENSION WIRE RESISTANCE

Carefully remove high tension wires from spark plugs and distributor cap. Using an ohmmeter, check high tension wire resistance while gently twisting wire. If resistance is not to specification, or fluctuates from infinity to any value, replace wire(s).

Resistance (Ohms) Per Wire

Application	Ohms
All Models	6000

DISTRIBUTOR

All models use a Ducellier single pickup breakerless distributor in conjunction with an AC Delco coil and transistorized amplifier module. The only adjustment provided is for air gap between the reluctor and pickup coil in the distributor. Measure gap using a non-magnetic feeler gauge. If gap is not to specifications, loosen pickup coil screws and adjust gap.

Air Gap .... .012-.020" (.30-.50 mm)

IGNITION TIMING

1) Disconnect and plug distributor vacuum line. Connect a timing light to No. 1 cylinder. Start engine and warm to normal operating temperature.

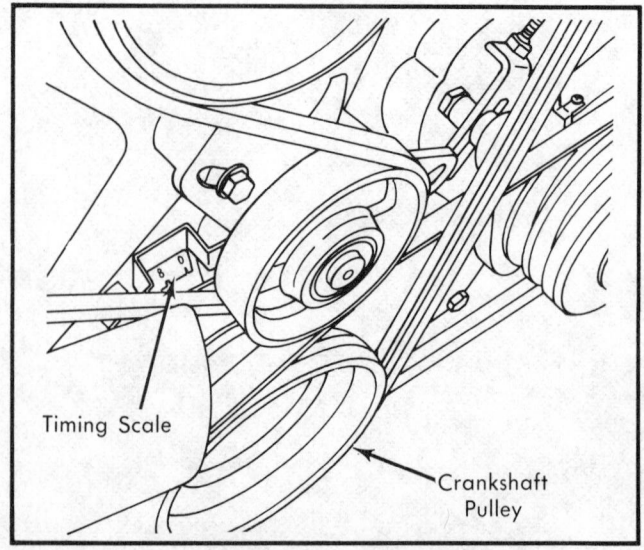

Timing Scale

Crankshaft Pulley

Fig. 1 Firing Order and Distributor Rotation

Fig. 2 Ignition Timing Marks

TUNE-UP (Cont.)

2) With engine idling at 900 RPM, check ignition timing. If timing is not correct, loosen distributor flange and rotate distributor to adjust timing to correct specification. When timing is correct, tighten distributor flange and reconnect distributor vacuum hose.

Ignition Timing Specifications
(Degrees BTDC @ RPM)

Application	Timing
505	①8@900

① — Transmission in neutral

IDLE SPEED & MIXTURE

NOTE — *Mixture adjustment is not a part of normal tune-up procedure and should not be performed unless mixture control unit is replaced or vehicle fails emissions testing. To adjust, first remove tamper-proof plug.*

1) Connect CO meter to front tap in catalytic converter. Disconnect wire 47C from thermovalve and ground it. Disconnect and plug vacuum supply hose to canister purge valve and air injection hose at diverter valve.

2) With air conditioning and all accessories off, connect tachometer. Insure that transmission is in neutral and air cleaner is in place. Start engine and warm to normal operating temperature. Using special screwdriver (Peugeot Part No. 8.0141 BA), adjust idle at air bleed screw to 900-950 RPM. Check CO reading. If reading is not to specification given in table, proceed with mixture adjustment.

3) Stop engine and disconnect battery. Remove mixture control unit and set it upside down. Pull out plug at mixture adjustment opening. Push anti-stall stop into control unit. Reinstall mixture control unit and reconnect battery.

4) Start engine and warm to normal operating temperature. If necessary, readjust idle at air bleed screw. Using special tool (Peugeot Part No. 8.014 LZ), adjust fuel mixture to obtain correct CO specification. Accelerate engine and recheck CO reading. If not correct, repeat adjustment procedure.

5) Remove testing equipment and reconnect thermovalve wire 47C, canister purge and air injection hoses. Install new plug in mixture adjustment opening.

Idle Speed & CO Level

Application	Idle RPM	CO%
505	900-950	①0.5-1.5

①—With air injection disconnected.

COLD (FAST) IDLE RPM

1) With engine at operating temperature and idle correctly adjusted, place transmission in neutral and turn off all accessories. Stop engine.

2) Disconnect hose with green ring from vacuum "T" near Solex valve (right fender panel). Disconnect hose with red ring from Solex valve and connect it to "T". This applies vacuum to idle speed diaphragm.

3) Remove domed nut "1" in *Fig. 3*. Loosen lock nut "2" and start engine. Engine speed should be 1500-1550 RPM.

4) If engine speed is not correct, adjust screw "3" to specification, using a 3 mm Allen wrench. Tighten lock nut "2" and install domed nut "1", making sure gasket is in place.

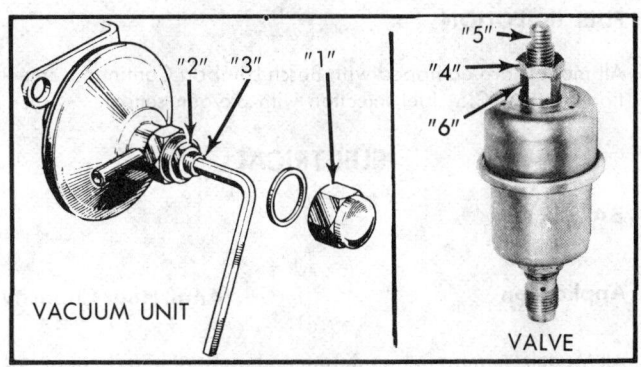

Fig. 3   Adjusting Fast Idle at Deceleration Vacuum Unit

5) Return vacuum hoses to original locations. Loosen lock nut "4" on Solex valve (not vacuum unit). Screw in threaded rod "5" to obtain 1500 RPM idle.

NOTE — *Always hold part "6" with wrench when loosening or tightening lock nut on deceleration valve, so as not to exert force on diaphragm.*

6) Increase engine speed to 3000 RPM without load, and allow engine speed to decrease. Unscrew threaded rod "5" one-half a turn at a time until normal idle (900 RPM) is obtained.

7) Then unscrew threaded rod one additional half turn and tighten lock nut.

Fast Idle RPM

Application	RPM
All Models	1500-1550

EMISSION CONTROL SYSTEMS

See Mitchell Manuals' Emission Control Manual.

1981 Peugeot 4 Tune-Up

GENERAL SERVICING

IGNITION

DISTRIBUTOR

All models are equipped with Ducellier breakerless electronic ignition systems.

IGNITION COIL

Coil Resistance (Ohms@68°F)

Application	Primary	Secondary
All Models	.48-.61	9000-11,000

FUEL SYSTEMS

FUEL INJECTION

All models are equipped with Bosch Lambda Continuous Injection System (CIS) fuel injection with oxygen sensor.

ELECTRICAL

BATTERY

Application	Amp. Hour Capacity
All Models	60

Battery Location — Left side of engine compartment.

STARTER

All models use Paris Rhone starters.

ALTERNATOR

All models are equipped with Paris Rhone Alternators.

Application	Rated Amp. Output
All Models	75

ALTERNATOR REGULATOR

A solid state, integral alternator regulator is used on all models.

BELT ADJUSTMENT

Loosen idler pulley mounting bolts and apply 36 ft. lbs. (48 N·m) to pivot nut above idler pulley. Tighten bolts, then turn engine one revolution. Loosen bolts and apply 58 ft. lbs. (77 N·m) to pivot nut. Tighten idler pulley mounting bolts.

Air conditioning belt is tightened by pivoting compressor. The belt from crankshaft pulley to water pump is a force-fit and no adjustment is possible.

FILTERS

Filter	Service Interval (Miles)
Oil Filter	①Replace every 10,000
Fuel Filter	Replace every 30,000
Air Filter	Replace every 30,000

① — First replacement at 5000 miles.

CAPACITIES

Application	Quantity
Crankcase (Includes Filter)	4.2 qts.
Cooling System	
Man. Trans.	7.5 qts.
Auto. Trans.	7.7 qts.
Man. Trans. (SAE10W-40)	3.4 pts.
Auto. Trans. (Dexron)	5.5 qts.
Rear Axle (SAE80)	3.3 pts.
Fuel Tank	18.0 gals.

TUNE-UP

504 Diesel
505 Diesel
505 Turbo Diesel
604 Turbo Diesel

ENGINE IDENTIFICATION

Engine number is stamped on left side of block just below cylinder head and is followed by VIN number.

Engine Code

Application	Code
Exc. Turbo	XD2C
Turbo	XD2S

COMPRESSION PRESSURE

With engine at normal operating temperature, disconnect injection lines, then remove return lines and nozzle holders. Lock pump stop control in off position. Connect pressure gauge and crank for 4 seconds at 300 RPM. Compression pressure should be as follows:

Compression Pressure Specifications

Application	Pressure psi (kg/cm²)
Minimum	261 (18.3)
Maximum Variation	72 (5.1)

VALVE CLEARANCE

Valves must be set with engine cold. To adjust valves, rotate crankshaft until valve listed in first column of table is fully open, then adjust valves listed in second column of table. Note that valves (and cylinders) are numbered from REAR to FRONT.

Valve Adjustment Sequence

Valve Open	Valves to Adjust
No. 1 Exh.	No. 3 Int. & No. 4 Exh.
No. 3 Exh.	No. 4 Int. & No. 2 Exh.
No. 4 Exh.	No. 2 Int. & No. 1 Exh.
No. 2 Exh.	No. 1 Int. & No. 3 Exh.

Valve Clearance Specifications①

Application	Intake In. (mm)	Exhaust In. (mm)
Exc. Turbo	.010 (25)	.010 (25)
Turbo	.006 (15)	.010 (25)

① — Engine Cold

VALVE ARRANGEMENT

All Models — I-E-E-I-I-E-E-I (rear to front)

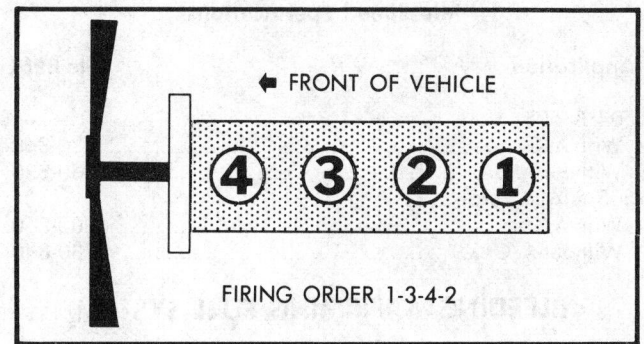

Fig. 1   Diesel Firing Order Illustration

GLOW PLUGS

Torque .... 33 Ft. Lbs. (44 N·m)

IDLE SPEED ADJUSTMENT

1) With engine warm, attach tachometer. Check to see that accelerated idle stop is not in contact with throttle lever and that accelerator cable is released. Adjust set screw to obtain idle speed as listed in table. See *Fig. 2*.

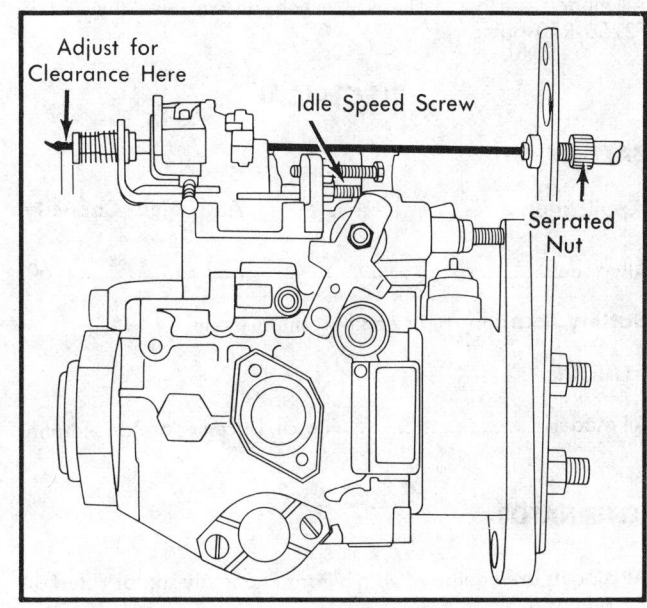

Fig. 2   Diesel Idle Adjustment Locations

2) Turn fast idle cable sleeve nut to obtain a clearance of .04" (1 mm) between fast idle cable end and fast idle stop. Start engine and warm to operating temperature. Compress the fast idle stop and check idle speed. Engine speed should be 1200-1400 RPM. Adjust if necessary. Adjust cable and clearance.

TUNE-UP (Cont.)

Idle Speed Specifications

Application	Idle RPM
504 & 505	
With A/C	830-860
Without A/C	730-830
505 & 604 Turbo	
With A/C	800-860
Without A/C	780-840

BLEEDING & PRIMING FUEL SYSTEM

1) Loosen bleed screw at bottom of filter bowl. Pump lever or button on top of filter to force out water. Retighten bleed screw and loosen air bleed screw. Pump button until resistance is felt, then tighten air bleed screw.

NOTE — *Bleed filter every 3000 miles, or more often if necessary.*

2) If vehicle ran out of fuel and injector pump is dry, continue to pump fuel filter button approximately 40 times. Turn key on and activate starter for 15 seconds, then press accelerator until engine starts.

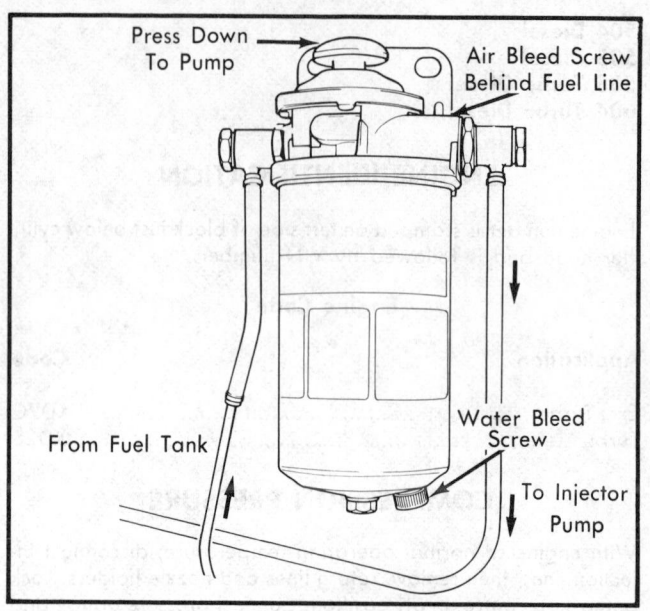

Fig. 3 Fuel System Bleeding Locations

GENERAL SERVICING

FUEL SYSTEMS

FUEL INJECTION

All models use Bosch Diesel Injection Systems with the VE4/9 F2250 R50 pump.

ELECTRICAL

BATTERY

Application	Amp. Hour Capacity
All Models	60

Battery Location — In engine compartment.

STARTER

All Models	Bosch, Ducellier or Paris-Rhone

ALTERNATOR

All models are equipped with a Paris Rhone alternator rated at 75 amperes.

ALTERNATOR REGULATOR

All models are equipped with a Paris Rhone integral alternator regulator.

BELT ADJUSTMENT

Using a "Krikit" gauge (Part No. 9797.09) check belt tension for the following values:

Belt	New	Used
Vacuum Pump	44-66 lbs.	33 lbs. max.
All Other Belts	88-110 lbs.	44 lbs. max.

FILTERS

Filter	Service Interval (Miles)
Air Filter	
Exc. Turbo	Replace every 15,000
Turbo	Service every 30,000
Oil Filter	Replace every 3000
Fuel Filter	Replace every 12,500

CAPACITIES

Application	Quantity
Crankcase (Includes Filter)	5.3 qts.
Cooling System	10.5 qts.
Man. Trans. (SAE 10W-40)	2.4 pts.
Auto. Trans. (Dexron)	5.4 qts.
Rear Axle (SAE 80)	3.3 pts.
Fuel Tank	18.0 gals.

TUNE-UP

924
924 Turbo

ENGINE IDENTIFICATION

Engine identification number is located on the left side of the engine crankcase next to the clutch housing.

Engine Code

Application	Code
924	VC
924 Turbo	M 31/04

COMPRESSION PRESSURE

Check compression with engine at normal operating temperature, fully open throttle, all spark plugs removed and at normal cranking speed. Crank engine at least 12 "puffs" per cylinder.

Compression Pressure Specifications

Application	Pressure psi (kg/cm²)
Normal (New Engine)	114-156 (8-11)
Minimum	85 (6)
Maximum Variation	42 (3)

VALVE CLEARANCE

1) Warm engine to normal operating temperature. Remove cylinder head cover. Rotate crankshaft until cam lobe of cylinder to be adjusted points upward. Check valve clearance.

2) Correct adjustment (if necessary) by using US 8005 adjusting tool and making complete turns of adjusting screw. See Fig. 1. Each turn changes clearance by .002" (.05 mm).

NOTE — *Various adjusting screws are available. Camshaft must be removed to replace screws.*

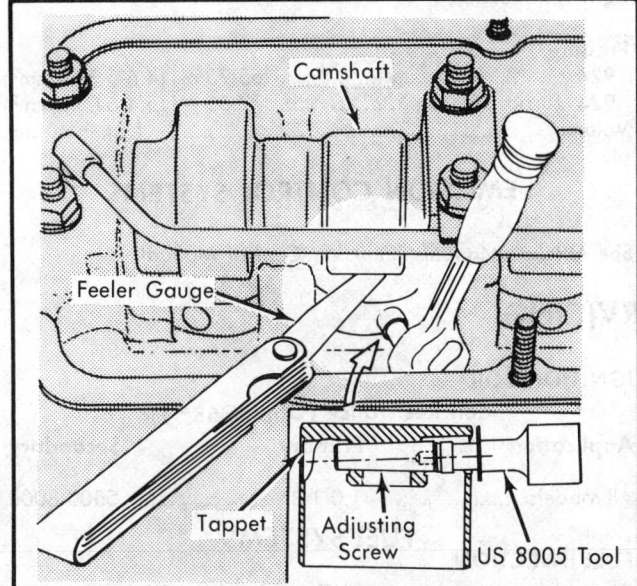

Fig. 1 Adjusting Valve Clearance

Valve Clearance Specifications

Application	Intake In. (mm)	Exhaust In. (mm)
All Models		
Warm	.008 (.20)	.018 (.45)
Cold	.004 (.10)	.016 (.40)

VALVE ARRANGEMENT

I-E-I-E-I-E-I-E (front to rear).

SPARK PLUGS

Application	Gap In. (mm)	Torque Ft. Lbs. (N·m)
All Models	.028 (0.7)	22 (30)

Spark Plug Type

Application	Bosch
All Models	①WR6DS

① — 924 Turbo also uses Champion N7GY.

HIGH TENSION WIRE RESISTANCE

Carefully remove high tension wires from spark plugs and distributor cap. Using an ohmmeter, check resistance of high tension wires while gently twisting wire. If resistance is not to specification, or fluctuates from infinity to any value, replace high tension wire(s).

Resistance (Ohms) Per Wire

Application	Ohms
All Models	6,000

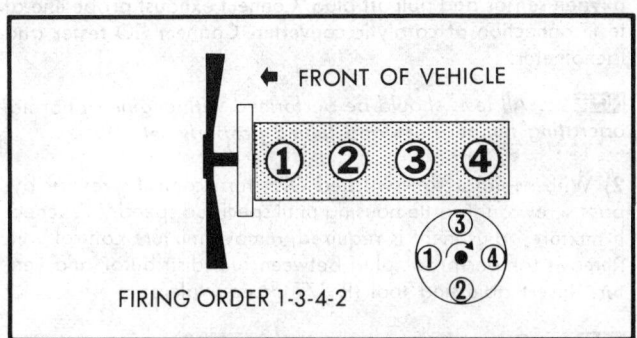

Fig. 2 Firing Order and Distributor Rotation

DISTRIBUTOR

All models are equipped with a breakerless, electronic ignition system. On 924 models, a Bosch Hall Effect distributor is used with an electronic idle stabilizer. 924 Turbo models have an electronic digital ignition timing control (DITC) system, using a flywheel sensor and a timing control unit. Distributors on 924 Turbo models are used only to distribute the spark to the proper spark plug.

Air Gap (Rotor-to-Stator) .... .010" (.25 mm)

1981 Porsche 4 Tune-Up

TUNE-UP (Cont.)

IGNITION TIMING

924 — Check or adjust ignition timing with engine at normal operating temperature and RPM, as specified in the following table. When timing engine, idle stabilizer connectors should be disconnected and plugged together, by-passing the idle stabilizer.

924 Turbo — The 924 Turbo uses a DITC (digital ignition timing control) system. With this system ignition timing is controlled electronically and no timing adjustment is necessary.

Ignition Timing Specifications

Application	Timing RPM	Setting
924	750-800	①TDC
924 Turbo	Less than 900	②6-10° BTDC

① — With distributor vacuum hoses connected.
② — No adjustment necessary.

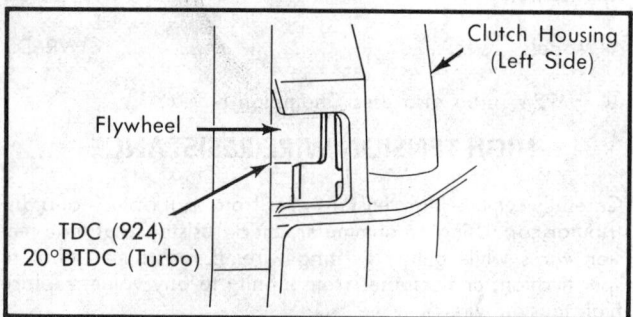

Clutch Housing (Left Side)

Flywheel

TDC (924)
20°BTDC (Turbo)

Fig. 3   924 Flywheel Ignition Timing Marks

IDLE SPEED & MIXTURE

924 Models — **1)** Remove rubber cap from plug terminal for oxygen sensor and pull off plug. Connect exhaust probe line at test connection of catalytic converter. Connect CO tester and tachometer.

NOTE — *All tests should be performed with engine at normal operating temperature and timing properly set.*

2) With radiator fan switched OFF, turn control screw or by-pass screw on throttle housing until specified speed is reached. If mixture adjustment is required, remove mixture control unit. Remove tamper-proof plug between fuel distributor and venturi. Insert adjusting tool (P 377 or equivalent).

NOTE — *Do not force or press down on adjusting tool during adjustments or engine will stall. Turn adjusting screw in very*

small increments as the slightest adjustment will change the CO level considerably.

3) Remove adjusting tool and install plug each time CO level is checked or adjustment is made or a false CO level will be indicated. Accelerate engine briefly and allow engine to return to stabilized idle. Recheck both CO level and idle speed. Adjust if necessary. Install plug terminal for oxygen sensor and install cap on probe connection at catalytic converter.

924 Turbo Models — **1)** Remove temperature sensor from intake manifold and plug hole with suitable plug (M 14 x 1.5). With wiring still connected to temperature sensor, place it in fresh air tray behind firewall. Sensor temperature must be below 120°F (50°C).

2) Start engine and warm to normal operating temperature. Connect CO tester and timing light.

3) Adjust idle control screw (by-pass air screw) until timing mark on flywheel is completely visible and jumps partially below reference mark.

4) Idle speed should now be below 900 RPM. Timing will vary slightly because it is being regulated.

5) If mixture adjustment is necessary, remove plug from mixture control unit. Insert adjusting tool (P 377) and turn carefully to adjust mixture. Replace plug after each adjustment and remove test equipment.

Idle Speed (RPM) & CO Level (%)

Application	Idle RPM	CO%
924	750-800	①.5-1.0
924 Turbo	900	①.5-1.0

① — Measured ahead of catalytic converter with oxygen sensor wire off.

FUEL PUMP PRESSURE & VOLUME

Two electric fuel pumps are used, one in fuel tank and one in right rear fender.

Pressure
924 .... 65-75 psi (4.6-5.3 kg/cm²)
924 Turbo .... 77-85 psi (5.4-6.0 kg/cm²)
Volume .... 1 qt. in 40 sec.

EMISSION CONTROL SYSTEMS

See Mitchell Manuals' Emission Control Manual.

GENERAL SERVICING

IGNITION

DISTRIBUTOR

All models are equipped with breakerless, electronic ignition systems. The 924 models have a Bosch Hall Effect distributor and electronic idle stabilizer. Turbo models are equipped with digital ignition timing control (DITC) system. The distributor only distributes spark to the appropriate spark plug.

IGNITION COIL

Coil Resistance (Ohms@68° F)

Application	Primary	Secondary
All Models	1.0-1.35	5500-8000

FUEL SYSTEMS

FUEL INJECTION

All models are equipped with Bosch Lambda CIS fuel injection with oxygen sensor.

GENERAL SERVICING (Cont.)

ELECTRICAL

BATTERY

Application	Amp. Hr. Rating
All Models	45 or 63

Battery Location — Battery is located at right rear corner of engine compartment.

ALTERNATOR

Application	Rated Amp. Output
All Models	75

ALTERNATOR REGULATOR

All models are equipped with Bosch alternator regulators. With rear window defogger and headlights turned on, operating voltage should be 13.5-14.5 volts at 2000 RPM.

BELT ADJUSTMENT

Tension is correct when center portion of belt can be depressed approximately $3/16$ to $3/8"$ (5-10 mm) by firm thumb pressure. Adjustment is made by shifting position of alternator. Remove small plate from alternator cover for access to adjustment lock screw.

REPLACEMENT INTERVALS

Component	Interval (Miles)
Oil Filter	
924	15,000
924 Turbo	7,500
Air Filter	30,000
Fuel Filter	30,000
Spark Plugs	30,000
Oxygen Sensor	30,000

CAPACITIES

Application	Quantity
Crankcase (Includes Filter)	5.3 qts.
Cooling System	8.5 qts.
Man. Trans. (Hypoid Gear Lube)	2.6 qts.
Auto. Trans. (Dexron II)	
Drain & Refill	3.0 qts.
Overhaul	6.4 qts.
Differential (Hypoid Gear Lube)	1.1 qts.
Fuel Tank	17.4 gals.

1981 Porsche 6 Tune-Up

TUNE-UP

911SC

ENGINE IDENTIFICATION

Engine identification number is stamped on engine crankcase near oil temperature sensor. The first three digits in engine number identify engine type and year.

Application	Engine Type	Code
911SC	930/16	641

COMPRESSION PRESSURE

Perform compression test with wide open throttle and oil temperature not less than 140°F (60°C). Remove all spark plugs and allow about 12 piston strokes per cylinder test. Pressure difference between cylinders should not exceed 22 psi (1.5 kg/cm²).

Compression Pressure Specifications

Application	Pressure psi (kg/cm²)
Normal	142-184 (10-13)
Minimum	107 (7.5)
Maximum Variation	22 (1.5)

VALVE CLEARANCE

Adjust valve clearance to specifications with engine cold.

Valve Clearance Specifications

Application	Clearance
All Models (Intake & Exhaust)	.004" (.1 mm)

VALVE ARRANGEMENT

Engine cylinders have individual heads and contain one intake and one exhaust valve per head. Upper valves are intake and lower valves are exhaust.

SPARK PLUGS

Application	Gap In. (mm)	Torque Ft. Lbs. (N·m)
911SC	.028 (0.7)	22 (30)

Spark Plug Type

Application	Bosch No.
911SC	W225T30 (WD5)

HIGH TENSION WIRE RESISTANCE

Carefully remove high tension wires from spark plugs and distributor cap. Using an ohmmeter, check high tension wire resistance while gently twisting wires. If resistance is not to specifications, or fluctuates from infinity to any value, replace high tension wire(s).

Resistance (Ohms) Per Wire

Application	Ohms
All Models	25,000-30,000

DISTRIBUTOR

All models use Bosch breakerless electronic distributors. No adjustments are necessary.

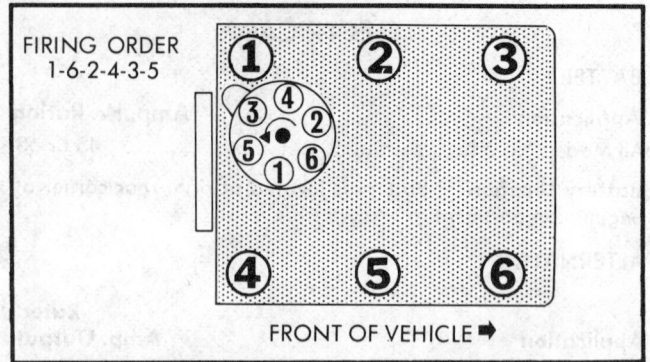

Fig. 1   Firing Order and Distributor Rotation

IGNITION TIMING

Warm engine to normal operating temperature and disconnect both distributor vacuum lines. Connect tachometer and timing light. With engine idling, rotate distributor until mark on pulley is lined up with reference mark on blower housing.

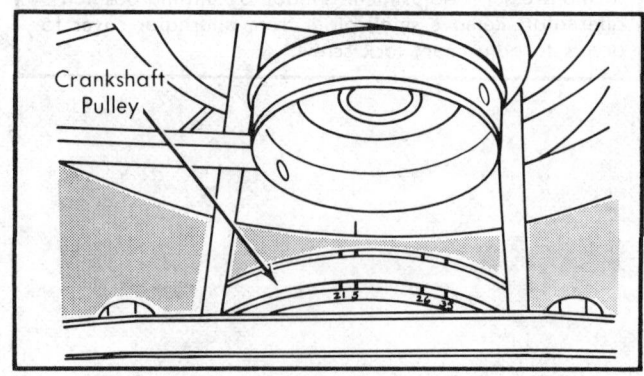

Fig. 2   911 Ignition Timing Marks

Ignition Timing Specifications
(Degrees BTDC @ RPM)

Application	Timing
911SC	5 @ 850-950

IDLE SPEED & MIXTURE

1) Engine should be at normal operating temperature and oil filler cap must be tightly sealed. Connect CO level meter to pickup point on catalytic converter and connect tachometer to ignition control box black/purple wire.

2) Disconnect plug from oxygen sensor (left side of engine compartment). Turn idle by-pass screw on throttle housing to obtain correct idle RPM. If mixture must be adjusted, remove plug from mixture control unit.

3) Insert adjusting tool and rotate clockwise to richen mixture; counterclockwise to lean mixture. Turn tool in small amounts without pressing down. Be sure to remove tool and plug opening before accelerating engine or testing mixture.

TUNE-UP (Cont.)

4) Accelerate engine briefly, then allow idle to stabilize before taking readings. When CO level is correct, check idle speed and readjust if necessary. Remove test equipment, coat threads of test point cap (on converter) with anti-seize compound, and reconnect oxygen sensor.

Idle Speed & CO Level

Application	Idle RPM	CO%
All Models	850-950	0.4-0.8

GENERAL SERVICING

IGNITION

DISTRIBUTOR

All models are equipped with Capacitive Discharge Ignition systems with Bosch breakerless distributors.

IGNITION COIL

Coil Resistance (Ohms@68°F)

Application	Primary	Secondary
All Models	0.4-0.6	600-790

FUEL SYSTEMS

FUEL INJECTION

All models are equipped with Bosch Lambda Continuous Injection System (CIS) with oxygen sensor.

ELECTRICAL

BATTERY

Application	Amp. Hr. Rating
All Models	66

Battery Location — Battery is located on left in front luggage compartment, under the floor mat.

STARTER

Bosch .... Overrunning Clutch

Starter Specifications

Application	Volts	Amps	Test RPM
911SC	11.5	50-80	7300-9300

FUEL PUMP PRESSURE & VOLUME

Pressure .... 65-75 psi (4.5-5.2 kg/cm²)
Volume .... 1.5 pts. in 30 sec.

EMISSION CONTROL SYSTEMS

See *Mitchell Manuals' Emission Control Manual.*

ALTERNATOR

Application	Rated Amp. Output
All Models	70

ALTERNATOR REGULATOR

All models are equipped with Bosch or Motorola alternator regulators with an operating voltage of 13.5-14.5 volts at 2500 RPM.

BELT ADJUSTMENT

Belt should deflect from ¼-½" (5-10 mm) when light thumb pressure is applied halfway between pulleys. Adjustment is made by removing or adding spacers between pulley halves. Rotate belt several times and recheck adjustment after changing spacers.

FILTERS

Filter	Service Interval (Miles)
Oil Filter	Replace every 15,000
Air Filter	Replace every 30,000
Fuel Filter	Replace every 30,000

CAPACITIES

Application	Quantity
Crankcase	
Total Capacity	13.7 qts.
Oil Change	10.6 qts.
Transaxle (SAE 90)	
911SC	3.2 qts.
Fuel Tank	①21 gals.

① — Includes 2.1 gals. in reserve.

1981 Porsche V8 Tune-Up

TUNE-UP

928

ENGINE IDENTIFICATION

The engine identification number is stamped on the front reinforcing rib in the top half of the crankcase, directly behind the fan. The first 3 digits in engine number identify type and model year.

Application	Engine Type	Code
928		
Man. Trans.	M28/15	811
Auto. Trans.	M28/16	811

COMPRESSION PRESSURE

With engine at normal operating temperature, remove all plugs and allow 12 compression strokes per cylinder. Pressure should not vary more than 21 psi (1.5 kg/cm²) between cylinders.

Compression Pressure Specifications

Application	Pressure psi (kg/cm²)
Normal	142-199 (10-14)
Minimum	114 (8)

VALVE CLEARANCE

Porsche 928 models are equipped with hydraulic valve lifters and no adjustments are necessary.

VALVE ARRANGEMENT

Both Banks — I-E-I-E-I-E-I-E (front to rear)

SPARK PLUGS

Application	Gap In. (mm)	Torque Ft. Lbs. (N·m)
All Models	.028 (0.7)	18 (24)

Spark Plug Type

Application	Bosch
All Models	WR8DS

HIGH TENSION WIRE RESISTANCE

Carefully remove high tension wires from spark plugs and distributor cap. Using an ohmmeter, check resistance of high tension wires while gently twisting wires. If resistance is not to specification, or fluctuates from infinity to any value, replace wires.

Resistance (Ohms) Per Wire

Application	Ohms
All Wires	2,500

DISTRIBUTOR

All models use Bosch breakerless electronic ignition and no adjustment in distributor is necessary.

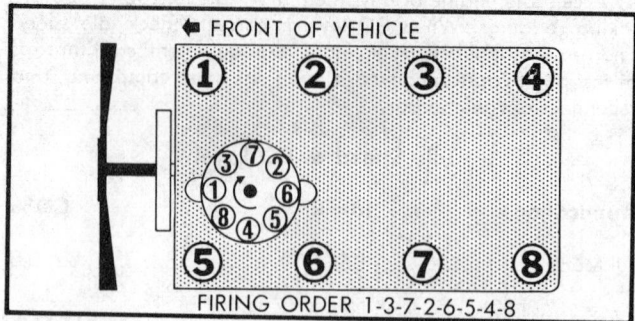

Fig. 1   Firing Order and Distributor Rotation

IGNITION TIMING

1) With engine at normal operating temperature, disconnect and plug hoses at distributor advance unit. Stop engine and connect timing light to No. 1 cylinder and tachometer to connection stud above ignition control unit in engine compartment.

CAUTION — *Dangerous voltage exists on primary and secondary side of entire ignition system as well as wiring from ignition control unit to tachometer, plug connections and any testing equipment connected. Ignition must be off when attaching or removing testing equipment, or severe shock may occur.*

2) Start engine and increase speed to 3000 RPM. Timing should be as specified. Adjust if necessary by turning distributor. Return engine to idle and connect vacuum hoses. Timing should now read TDC to 7° BTDC. If not, distributor should be removed and tested.

Ignition Timing Specifications

Application	RPM	Timing
All Models	3000	①23° BTDC

① — With distributor vacuum advance hoses disconnected and plugged.

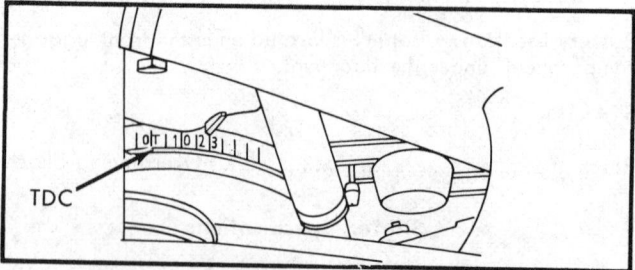

Fig. 2   Timing Marks on Crankshaft Pulley

IDLE SPEED & MIXTURE

1) Fold up foot support on passenger side under dashboard. Disconnect plug for oxygen sensor (left side of footwell). Connect CO meter to test point on catalytic converter and connect tachometer.

2) Adjust idle speed using screw in front of throttle housing. If mixture must be adjusted, insert tool through opening in air flow sensor. Turn clockwise to richen mixture and counterclockwise to lean mixture.

TUNE-UP (Cont.)

3) When idle mixture and speed are correct, remove test equipment. Connect oxygen sensor plug and coat threads of catalytic converter test cap with anti-seize compound.

Idle Speed & CO Level

Application	Idle RPM	CO%
All Models	700-800	①0.4-0.8

① — With oxgen sensor disconnected.

FUEL PUMP PRESSURE & VOLUME

Pressure (At Idle) .... 26-32 psi (1.8-2.2 kg/cm²)
Volume .... 1.2 qts. in 30 sec.

EMISSION CONTROL SYSTEMS

See Mitchell Manuals' Emission Control Manual.

GENERAL SERVICING

IGNITION

DISTRIBUTOR

All models are equipped with Bosch transistorized ignition systems.

IGNITION COIL

Coil Resistance (Ohms@68°F)

Application	Primary	Secondary
All Models	0.4-0.6	650-790

FUEL SYSTEMS

FUEL INJECTION

All models are equipped with Bosch AFC Lambda fuel injection system with oxygen sensor.

ELECTRICAL

BATTERY

Application	Amp. Hr. Rating
All Models	66 or 88

Battery Location — Battery is located under spare tire in rear of passenger compartment.

STARTER

Bosch .... Overrunning Clutch

Starter Test Specifications

Application	Volts	Amps	Test RPM
All Models	11.5	55-85	8500-10,500

ALTERNATOR

Application	Rated Amp. Output
All Models	90

ALTERNATOR REGULATOR

All Models use Bosch or Motorola solid state alternator regulators.

BELT ADJUSTMENT

Tension is correct when belts can be depressed .4" (10 mm) by thumb pressure on center portion of belt.

FILTERS

Filter	Service Interval (Miles)
Oil Filter	Replace every 15,000
Air Filter	Replace every 30,000
Fuel Filter	Replace every 30,000

CAPACITIES

Application	Quantity
Crankcase (Includes Filter)	8.5 qts.
Cooling System	16.8 qts.
Man. Trans. (SAE 75W-90)	①4.0 qts.
Auto. Trans. (Dexron II)	①5.8 qts.
Differential (SAE 90)	2.1 qts.
Fuel Tank	23.0 gals.

① — Includes Limited Slip Differential.
② — Including Torque Converter, 6.4 qts.

TUNE-UP

Le Car
18i

ENGINE IDENTIFICATION

Type of vehicle and engine number are marked on a number plate riveted to the left rear side of the engine block. Plate is located just below cylinder head mating surface. First 5 digits on Le Car or 6 digits on 18i indicate engine type.

Engine Code

Application	Code
Le Car	847-25
18i	
Man. Trans.	843-7-18
Auto. Trans.	843-7-19

VALVE CLEARANCE

Valves must be set with engine cold. To adjust valves, rotate crankshaft until valve listed in first column of table is fully open, then adjust valves listed in second column of table. On 18i models, note that valves (and cylinders) are numbered from REAR to FRONT.

Valve Open	Valves to Adjust
No. 1 Exh.	No. 3 Int. & No. 4 Exh.
No. 3 Exh.	No. 4 Int. & No. 2 Exh.
No. 4 Exh.	No. 2 Int. & No. 1 Exh.
No. 2 Exh.	No. 1 Int. & No. 3 Exh.

Valve Clearance Specifications ①

Application	Intake In. (mm)	Exhaust In. (mm)
Le Car	.006 (.15)	.008 (.20)
18i	.008 (.20)	.010 (.25)

① — Set valves with engine cold.

VALVE ARRANGEMENT

E-I-I-E-E-I-I-E (Front to Rear)

SPARK PLUGS

Application	Gap In. (mm)	Torque Ft. Lbs. (N·m)
Le Car	.024 (.6)	20 (27)
18i	.026 (.65)	20 (27)

Spark Plug Type

Application	Bosch	Champion
Le Car		
Federal		RN12Y
Calif.	WD9DS	
18i	WR7DS	

HIGH TENSION WIRE RESISTANCE

Carefully remove high tension wires from spark plugs and distributor cap. Using an ohmmeter, check resistance of high tension wires while gently twisting wires. If resistance is not to specification, or fluctuates from infinity to any value, replace high tension wire(s).

Resistance (Ohms) Per Wire

Application	Ohms
All Models	25,000-30,000

DISTRIBUTOR

All models are equipped with dual pick-up electronic ignition distributors. Trigger plate gap is adjustable and should be set to .012-.024" (.3-.6 mm).

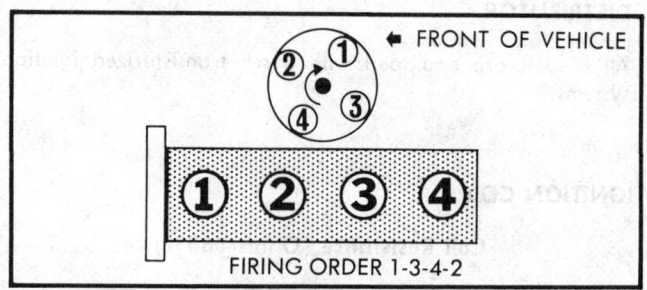

Fig. 1   Le Car Firing Order and Distributor Rotation

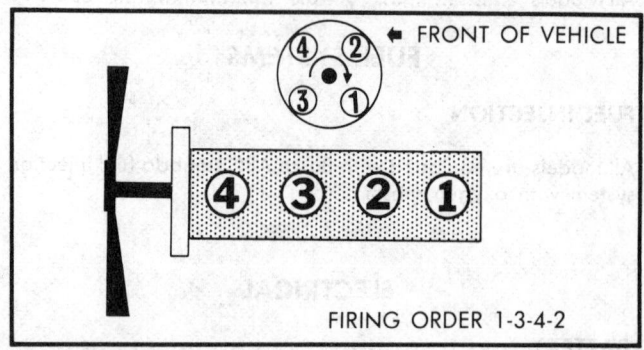

Fig. 2   18i Firing Order and Distributor Rotation

IGNITION TIMING

Check or adjust ignition timing with vacuum line disconnected and plugged and engine running at idle speed. To adjust, turn distributor until specified mark on flywheel is aligned with specified graduation mark on clutch housing. Reconnect distributor vacuum hose.

Ignition Timing Specifications
(Degrees BTDC @ RPM)

Application	Timing
Le Car	3@750
18i	10@800

TUNE-UP (Cont.)

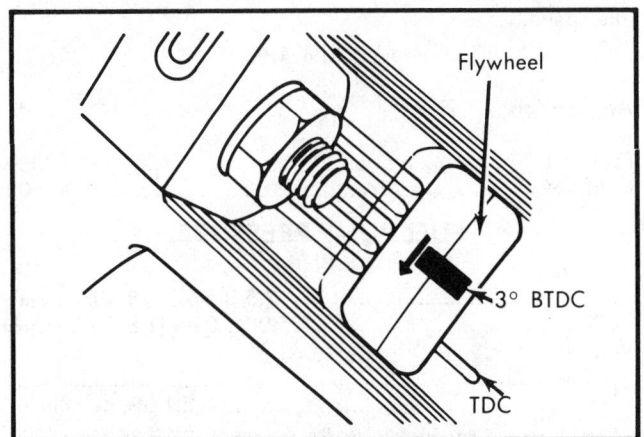

Fig. 3   Le Car Timing Mark Location

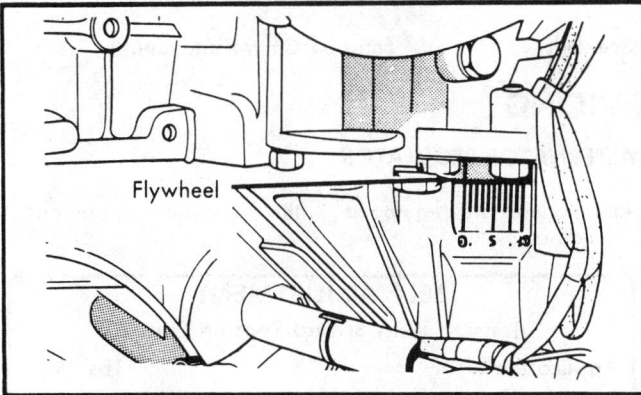

Fig. 4   18i Timing Mark Location (Man. Trans. Models)

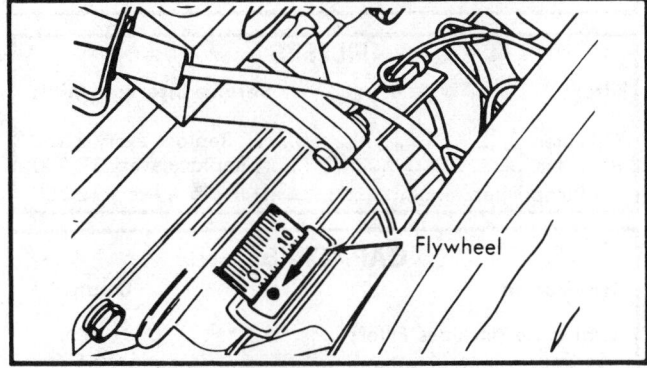

Fig. 5   18i Timing Mark Location (Auto. Trans. Models)

IDLE SPEED & MIXTURE

CARBURETED MODELS (LeCar)

Federal — 1) Clamp, or disconnect and plug air pump hose to injection manifold. Connect tachometer.

2) Adjust idle speed screw to obtain 675-725 RPM idle. Remove cap and adjust fuel metering screw to obtain 0.5-2.0% CO level. Repeat procedure if necessary to have both speed and mixture correct.

3) Reconnect air injection. Idle speed must be 700-800 RPM. If not, adjust with idle speed screw. Remove test equipment.

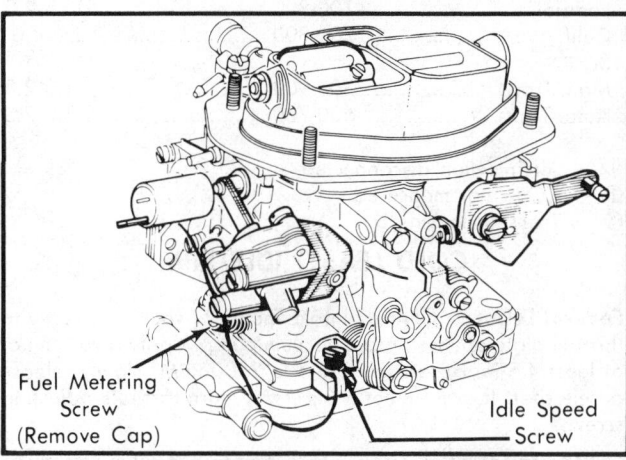

Fig. 6   Carburetor Adjustment Locations (Federal Models)

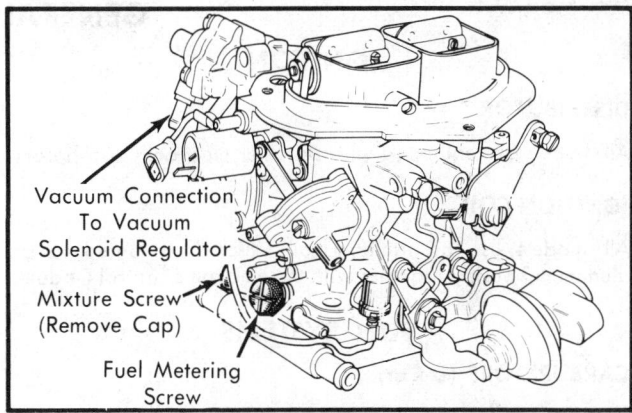

Fig. 7   Carburetor Adjustment Locations (Calif. Models)-

California — 1) Start engine and bring to normal operating temperature. Using a "T" connector, connect accurate vacuum gauge to line between carburetor and vacuum solenoid regulator.

2) Start engine and adjust idle speed with fuel metering screw to 700-800 RPM. Vacuum gauge should indicate 1.5±1.2 in. Hg.

3) If vacuum reading is not correct, remove brass cap from mixture screw. Adjust carefully until vacuum reading is within specifications. Remove test equipment.

FUEL INJECTED MODELS (18i)

NOTE — *Idle mixture screw is sealed and idle mixture is normally adjusted only when air flow meter is replaced or vehicle fails emissions testing.*

With engine at normal operating temperature, attach tachometer and adjust throttle plate bypass screw to obtain specified idle speed.

TUNE-UP (Cont.)

Idle Speed & CO Level

Application	Idle RPM	CO%
Le Car		
Federal	700-800	①0.5-2.0
Calif.	700-800	②
18i		
Man. Trans.	800-900	①1.0-2.5
Auto. Trans.③	600-700	①1.0-2.5

① — Air injection disconnected.
② — CO% not measured.
③ — Transmission in "D".

COLD (FAST) IDLE RPM

Federal LeCar — Connect intake manifold vacuum directly to throttle plate opener or to a vacuum pump. Apply a vacuum of at least 4.5 in. Hg or accelerate to 2500 RPM. Slowly release accelerator. If adjustment is necessary, turn fast idle adjusting screw.

California LeCar — Apply intake manifold vacuum directly to vacuum regulator (or apply 6 in. Hg vacuum on throttle plate opener diaphragm). Set throttle plate opener to achieve fast idle speed.

Fast Idle RPM

Application	RPM
Federal LeCar	1800-2000
Calif. LeCar	1400-1600

FUEL PUMP PRESSURE

Pressure	
LeCar	2.5-3.5 psi (.18-.24 kg/cm²)
18i	①25.0-31.0 psi (1.8-2.2 kg/cm²)
Volume	
Le Car	
18i	2.1 pts. per minute

① — Vacuum connected. If disconnected, 33.0-39.0 psi (2.3-2.7 kg/cm²).

EMISSION CONTROL SYSTEMS

See Mitchell Manuals' Emission Control Manual.

GENERAL SERVICING

IGNITION

DISTRIBUTOR

All models are equipped with Ducellier electronic distributors.

IGNITION COIL

All models use an ignition coil which is mounted in an aluminum housing together with the electronic control module.

FUEL SYSTEMS

CARBURETORS (LeCar)

Application	Model
Federal	Weber 32 DIR 87
Calif.	Weber 32 DIR 80

FUEL INJECTION (18i)

All 18i models use Bosch L-Jetronic fuel injection systems.

ELECTRICAL

BATTERY

Application	Amp. Hr. Rating
Le Car	50
18i	①45

① — 60 with air conditioning.

Battery Location — Battery is located in right front corner of engine compartment.

STARTER

All models are equipped with a Paris Rhone starter.

ALTERNATOR

LeCar models are equipped with Paris Rhone alternators; 18i models may be equipped with Motorola, SEV Marchal, or Ducellier alternators.

ALTERNATOR REGULATOR

All models are equipped with Paris Rhone alternator regulators.

BELT ADJUSTMENT
Tension With Strand Tension Gauge

Application	Lbs. (kg)
Alternator Belt	80-90 (36-41)
Air Pump Belt	75-80 (34-36)
A/C Compressor Belt	80 (36)

FILTERS

Filter	Service Interval (Miles)
Oil Filter	Replace every 6,250
Air Filter	Replace every 12,500
Air Pump Filter	Replace every 12,500

CAPACITIES

Application	Quantity
Crankcase (Includes Filter)	
Le Car	3.5 qts.
18i	4.5 qts.
Cooling System (Includes Heater)	
LeCar	6.5 qts.
18i	6.6 qts.
Manual Transaxle (SAE 80)	2.0 qts.
Automatic Transaxle①	3.0 qts.
Fuel Tank	
Le Car	10 gals
18i	
Sedan	14 gals.
Station Wagon	15 gals.

① — Only acceptable fluid is part number R8980022. Do not use AMC fluid, part number 8992447 or 8992449.

TUNE-UP

900

ENGINE IDENTIFICATION

Engine number is stamped on a machined pad on engine block below CIS throttle housing.

Engine Code

Application	Code
Non-Turbocharged	
Man. Trans.	BI 20 P11
Auto. Trans.	BI 20 P12
Turbocharged	BSI 20 P02

VALVE CLEARANCE

Bring camshaft into correct position for checking valves. Using a suitable go and no-go feeler gauge, check that clearance between valve tappet and heel of cam is to specifications given under "Preliminary Check." If within specifications, no further adjustment is necessary. If not, proceed as follows:

NOTE — *Turbo valve clearances are critical. Use only specifications listed for Turbo.*

1) Using special tool (8391450) and a dial indicator, measure clearance of each valve. With measuring point of dial indicator resting on tip of cam, zero dial indicator.

2) Lift valve depressor with special tool and note movement of dial indicator, indicating present valve clearance. Any valve not within "Adjustment Limit" specifications should be adjusted as follows:

3) Remove camshaft, valve depressors and adjusting pads of valves needing adjustment. Measure thickness of adjusting pad with micrometer (8391633) and calculate thickness of new pad required to bring valve clearance within "Adjustment Limit" specifications.

4) Measured valve clearance plus adjusting pad thickness equals total distance between valve and cam. This total distance less the specified valve clearance, determines thickness of new adjusting pad to be installed.

5) Install new adjusting pad, valve depressors, and camshaft and recheck that clearances are correct.

Valve Clearance Specifications

Application	Clearance In. (mm)
Preliminary Check	
Intake	.006-.012 (.15-.30)
Exhaust	
All Except Turbo	.014-.020 (.35-.50)
Turbo	.016-.020 (.40-.50)
Adjustment Limit	
Intake	.008-.010 (.20-.25)
Exhaust	
All Except Turbo	.016-.018 (.40-.45)
Turbo	.018-.020 (.45-.50)

VALVE ARRANGEMENT

E-I-I-E-E-I-I-E (front to rear).

SPARK PLUGS

Application	Gap In. (mm)	Torque Ft. Lbs. (N·m)
All Models	.024-.028 (.6-.7)	18-22 (24-30)

Spark Plug Type

Application	Bosch No.	NGK No.
Non-Turbo	W-175-T30	BP-6ES
Turbo	....	BP-7ES

HIGH TENSION WIRE RESISTANCE

Carefully remove high tension wires from spark plugs and distributor cap. Using an ohmmeter, check high tension wire resistance while gently twisting wires. If resistance is not to specifications, or fluctuates from infinity to any value, replace high tension wire(s).

Resistance (Ohms) Per Wire

Application	Ohms
All Models	
Wires to Cylinder 1 & 2	2600-3900
Wires to Cylinder 3 & 4	2400-3600
Wire from Coil to Distributor	800-1200

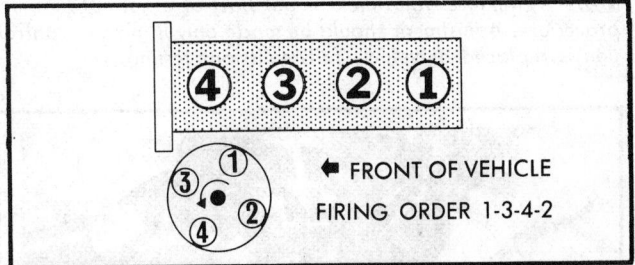

Fig. 1   Firing Order and Distributor Rotation

DISTRIBUTOR

All models are equipped with Bosch breakerless electronic ignition systems. No adjustments are required for distributor.

IGNITION TIMING

1) Connect tachometer and timing light. Disconnect vacuum hose and place transmission in neutral position. Check timing at 2000 RPM.

2) If not within specifications, loosen distributor retaining screw and rotate distributor housing. Turn clockwise for earlier ignition; counterclockwise for later.

3) Reconnect vacuum hose and adjust engine idle speed.

TUNE-UP (Cont.)

Ignition Timing Specifications
(Degrees BTDC @ RPM)

Application	Timing
All Models	20@2000

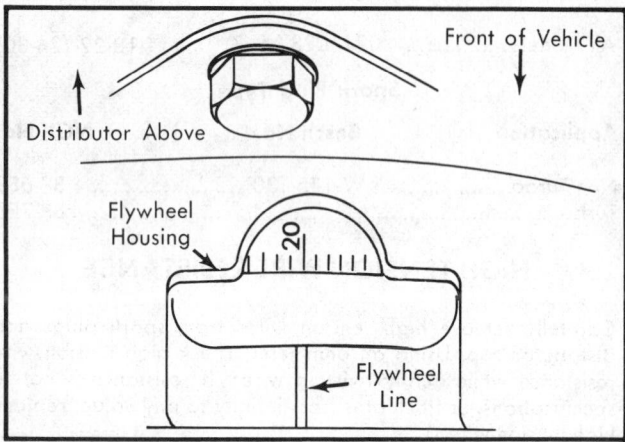

Fig. 2   Saab Timing Mark Location

IDLE SPEED & MIXTURE

1) Warm engine to operating temperature and set ignition timing. Check and adjust engine idling speed, using idle adjusting screw on throttle valve housing.

NOTE — *Mixture adjustment is not part of a normal tune-up procedure. Adjustment should be made only if mixture control unit is replaced or vehicle fails emissions testing.*

Fig. 3   Adjusting Idle Speed

2) Connect Bosch tester (KDJE 7453) or dwell meter to test connector in front of fuse box. See *Fig. 4.* Start engine and observe scale on tester. If needle fluctuates between 10-90% on Bosch tester or 10-80° on dwell meter (4 cyl. scale), no adjustment is needed.

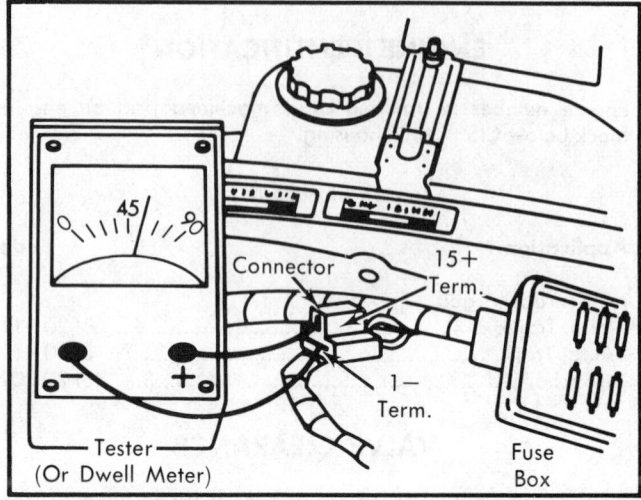

Fig. 4   Mixture Adjustment Tester Connections

3) If adjustment is necessary, remove mixture control unit from vehicle. Disassemble sensor plate and lever, then drive out mixture adjustment opening plug with punch. Reassemble mixture control unit and install on vehicle.

4) With engine idling, adjust mixture with hex head wrench until tester indicates 55-65% operation. Dwell meter will show 50-60° on 4 cyl. scale. Accelerate engine and recheck adjustment, then reinstall plug. Remove test equipment.

Idle Speed

Application	Idle RPM
All Models	875

DASHPOT ADJUSTMENT

1) Bring engine to normal operating temperature. On Turbo models, disconnect and plug EGR hose. On all other models, disconnect and plug vacuum advance. Connect tachometer and check idle speed. Adjust if necessary.

2) Rotate throttle lever and check that dashpot rod strikes the stop at 2100-2300 RPM on Turbo models, or 2400-2600 RPM on all others. If not, adjust by turning dashpot.

3) Accelerate engine to 3000 RPM and measure time from release of throttle until engine reaches idle speed. Deceleration time should be 3-6 seconds. If not, turn dashpot in towards stop to lengthen delay, or away from stop to shorten delay time.

FUEL PUMP PRESSURE & VOLUME

Pressure	64-72 psi (4.5-5.1 kg/cm²)
Volume	①1.9 pts. in 30 sec.

① — Measured in return fuel line

EMISSION CONTROL SYSTEMS

See Mitchell Manuals' Emission Control Manual.

GENERAL SERVICING

IGNITION

DISTRIBUTOR

All models are equipped with Bosch electronic breakerless distributors.

IGNITION COIL

Coil Resistance Specifications
(Ohms @ 75°F)

Application	Primary	Secondary
All Models	1.05-1.35	5500-8500

FUEL SYSTEMS

FUEL INJECTION

All models are equipped with Bosch Lambda Continuous Injection System (CIS) with oxygen sensor and catalytic converter.

ELECTRICAL

BATTERY

Application	Amp. Hr. Rating
All Models	60

Battery Location — In engine compartment on right side.

STARTER

Bosch .... Overrunning Clutch

Starter Specifications

Application	Volts	Amps	Test RPM
All Models	11.5	35-55	6500-8500

ALTERNATOR

All models are equipped with Motorola or Bosch alternators.

Application	Rated Amp. Output
All Models	72

ALTERNATOR REGULATOR

All alternators have built-in regulators which require no adjustment.

BELT ADJUSTMENT

Application	①Deflection
Alternator Belt	.2" (5 mm)

① — Deflection is with 3.3 lbs. (1.5 kg) pressure applied midway on longest belt run.

FILTERS

Filter	Service Interval (Miles)
Oil Filter	
Turbo	Replace every 5000
All Other Models	Replace every 7500
Air Filter	Replace every 30,000
Fuel Filter	Replace every 30,000

CAPACITIES

Application	Quantity
Crankcase (Includes Filter)	
Turbo	4.5 qts.
All Other Models	4.0 qts.
Cooling System	
All Models	10.5 qts.
Man. Trans. (SAE 10W-30)①	3.0 qts.
Auto. Trans. (ATF Type F)	8.5 qts.
Auto. Trans. Final Drive (SAE 80)	1.3 qts.
Fuel Tank	14.5 gals.

① — Including Final Drive.

1981 Subaru 4 Tune-Up

TUNE-UP

DL
GL
GLF

ENGINE IDENTIFICATION

Engine can be identified by a combination letter-number code stamped on machined pad on front right side of engine, near distributor.

Engine Code

Application	Code
1600	
4-Spd.	EA71A
5-Spd.	EA71G
1800	
2-WD	
Man. Trans.	
4-Spd.	EA81A
5-Spd.	EA81G
Auto. Trans.	
Hardtop & Sedan	EA81T
Station Wagon	EA81M
4-WD	
Brat	
DL	EA81J
GL	EA81K
All Other Models	
DL & Standard	EA81W
GL	EA81P

COMPRESSION PRESSURE

Check pressure with engine warm, plugs removed, throttle valve wide open and engine at cranking speed.

Compression Pressure @350 RPM

Application	Pressure psi (kg/cm²)
Normal (New Engine)	
1600	175 (12.3)
1800	171 (12.0)
Minimum	128 (9)
Maximum Variation	7 (0.5)

VALVE CLEARANCE

With engine cold, bring piston to be checked to top dead center of compression stroke. Loosen lock nuts and turn adjusting screws to proper clearance. Adjust valves in firing order sequence using valve clearance adjusting tool 498767000 (or equivalent).

Valve Clearance Specifications①

Application	Intake In. (mm)	Exhaust In. (mm)
All Models	.010 (.25)	.014 (.35)

① — Set with engine cold.

VALVE ARRANGEMENT

I-E-E-I (both banks, front to rear).

SPARK PLUGS

Application	Gap In. (mm)	Torque Ft. Lbs. (N·m)
All Models	.040 (1.0)	15 (20)

Spark Plug Type

Application	NGK	Nippondenso
All Models	BP6ES-11	W20EP-11

HIGH TENSION WIRE RESISTANCE

Carefully remove high tension wires from spark plugs and ignition coil. Remove distributor cap with wires still in place. Using an ohmmeter, check high tension wire resistance between free end of wire and distributor cap electrode. If resistance is not to specifications, or fluctuates from infinity to any value, replace high tension wire(s).

Resistance (Ohms) Per Wire

Application	Ohms
All Models	25,000

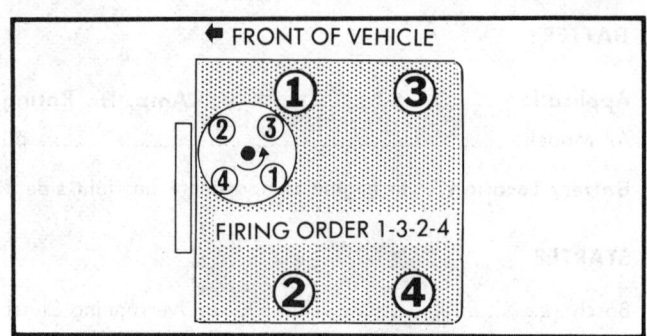

Fig. 1   Firing Order and Distributor Rotation

DISTRIBUTOR

All models are equipped with breakerless, electronic ignition systems. Nippondenso distributors are used in 2-WD models and Hitachi distributors are used in 4-WD models.

Air Gap Specifications

Application	Gap In. (mm)
Hitachi	.012-.020 (.3-.5)
Nippondenso	.008-.016 (.2-.4)

IGNITION TIMING

Adjust timing with engine at normal operating temperature and transmission in neutral. Disconnect and plug vacuum hoses at distributor. With engine at idle, check timing and turn distributor to adjust.

Ignition Timing Specifications (Degrees BTDC @ RPM)

Application	Man. Trans.	Auto. Trans.
All Models	8@700	8@800

TUNE-UP (Cont.)

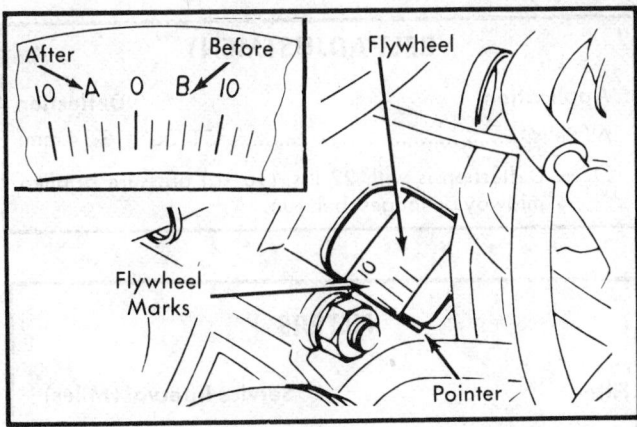

Fig. 2   Subaru Timing Mark Location

IDLE SPEED & MIXTURE

NOTE — *Ignition timing and valve clearances must be correct and engine must be at normal operating temperature prior to adjusting idle speed and mixture.*

1) Disconnect canister purge hose at check valve near intake manifold. Plug hose, then start engine and warm up for at least 5 minutes. Adjust idle speed with transmission in neutral.

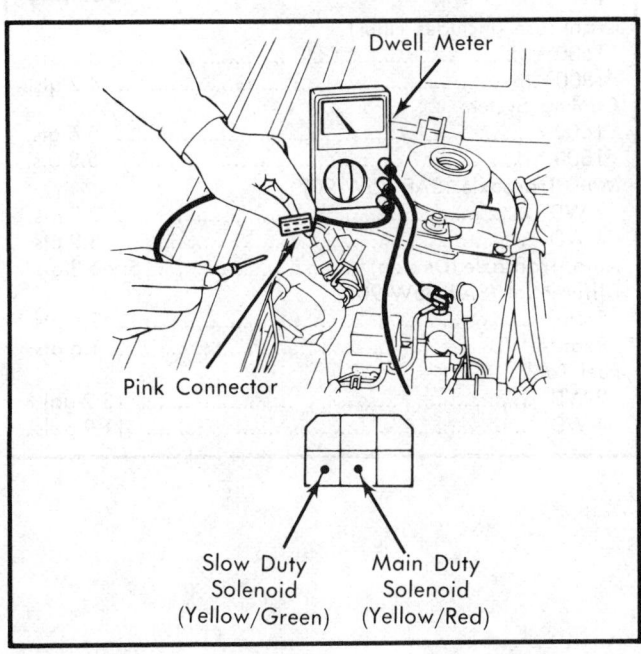

Fig. 3   Idle Mixture Test Connections

NOTE — *Idle mixture should not need adjustment unless carburetor has been removed and disassembled. Roll pin must be removed from in front of idle mixture screw before adjustments can be made.*

2) Connect a dwell meter to Yellow/Red wire in Pink connector near right front shock tower. Set meter on 4 cylinder scale and observe needle movement with engine idling. See Fig. 3.

3) Dwell meter needle should move up and down within a 30-40° range. If not moving, run engine at 2000-3000 RPM for at least 2 minutes, then recheck. After noting movement, move dwell meter lead to Yellow/Green wire in Pink connector and repeat check.

4) If dwell meter needle movement is not within specified range, adjust idle mixture screw until needle movement is between 27-36°. Repeat adjustment and check with both solenoid wires in Pink test connector. Recheck idle speed, then remove test equipment, reconnect purge hose and install roll pin.

Idle Speed Specifications

Application	Man. Trans.	Auto. Trans.
All Models	600-800	①700-900

① — In neutral.

FAST IDLE ADJUSTMENT

With cam adjusting lever on first step of fast idle cam, primary throttle valve opening angle and clearance should be as follows. If not, adjust fast idle screw.

Fast Idle Specifications

Application	Throttle Valve Opening Angle	Clearance Valve-to-Body
1600	17°	.046" (1.17mm)
1800	19°	.054" (1.38mm)

FUEL PUMP PRESSURE & VOLUME

Pressure	1.3-2.1 psi (.095-.145 kg/cm²)
Volume	1.0 pts./min.

EMISSION CONTROL SYSTEMS

See Mitchell Manuals' Emission Control Manual.

GENERAL SERVICING

IGNITION

DISTRIBUTORS

Breakerless, electronic ignition systems are used on all models. Hitachi systems are used on four-wheel-drive models, and Nippondenso systems are used on all other models.

IGNITION COIL

Coil Resistance (Ohms@68°F)

Application	Primary	Secondary
Hitachi	1.04-1.27	7,360-11,040
Nippondenso	1.06-1.30	12,150-14,850

1981 Subaru 4 Tune-Up

GENERAL SERVICING (Cont.)

FUEL SYSTEMS

CARBURETORS

Hitachi DCP 2-Bbl. Zenith-Stromberg type carburetors are used on all models.

ELECTRICAL

BATTERY

Application	Amp. Hr. Capacity
Man. Trans. w/o Power Steering	60
All Other Models	65

Battery Location — Engine compartment; front.

STARTER

All vehicles use Nippondenso starters.

Application	Type
Man. Trans.	Magnetic Switch
Auto. Trans.	Gear Reduction

Starter Specifications

Application	Volts	Amps	Test RPM
Man. Trans.	11.0	50	5000
Auto. Trans.	11.5	90	4100

ALTERNATOR

Application	Rated Amp. Output
All Models	55

ALTERNATOR REGULATOR

All models are equipped with Hitachi alternator regulators with an operating voltage of 14.0-14.5 volts.

BELT ADJUSTMENT

Application	①Deflection
All Belts	.51-.55" (13-14 mm)

① — Deflection is with 22 lbs. (10 kg) pressure applied midway on longest belt run.

FILTERS

Filter	Service Interval (Miles)
Oil Filter	Replace every 7500
Air Filter	Replace every 30,000
Fuel Filter	Replace every 15,000

CAPACITIES

Application	Quantity
Crankcase (Includes Filter)	
1600	3.7 qts.
1800	4.2 qts.
Cooling System	
1600	5.6 qts.
1800	5.8 qts.
Man. Transaxle (SAE 85W-90)	
2-WD	2.9 pts.
4-WD	3.2 pts.
Auto. Transaxle (Dexron)	5.9-6.3 qts.
Differential (SAE 85W-90)	
Front	2.6 pts.
Rear (4-WD)	1.6 pts.
Fuel Tank	
2-WD	13.2 gals.
4-WD	11.9 gals.

TUNE-UP

Celica   Pickup
Corolla   Starlet
Corona   Tercel

ENGINE IDENTIFICATION

Each engine serial number contains an identifying code for engine identification. All numbers are stamped on the left side of engine block. Engine codes are also provided on decal at front edge of valve cover.

Engine Code

Application	Code
Celica, Corona & Pickup	22R
Corolla	3T-C
Starlet	4K-C
Tercel	3A-C

COMPRESSION PRESSURE

With engine at normal operating temperature, spark plugs removed, throttle valve wide open and engine at cranking speed, compression pressures should be as follows with a maximum variation between cylinders of 14 psi (1 kg/cm²):

Compression Pressure Specifications

Application	Standard psi (kg/cm²)	Minimum psi (kg/cm²)
Celica, Corona & Pickup	171 (12.0)	142 (10.0)
Corolla	163 (11.5)	128 (9.0)
Starlet	156 (11.0)	128 (9.0)
Tercel	177 (12.5)	128 (9.0)

VALVE CLEARANCE

NOTE — *Before starting the engine, plug hose end for following systems: Starlet and Corolla, HIC system. Tercel, Air Suction (AS) system for Federal models and HIC system, all models. Celica, Corona and Pickup, HAI system & MC system.*

Check or adjust valve clearance with engine at normal operating temperature. Remove valve cover and set No. 1 cylinder at TDC. Turn crankshaft with a wrench to align timing marks. Check that rocker arms for No. 1 cylinder are loose and for No. 4 cylinder are tight. Adjust intake valve on cylinders No. 1 and No. 2 and exhaust valve on cylinders No. 1 and No. 3. Turn crankshaft 360°. Adjust intake valve on cylinders No. 3 and No. 4 and exhaust valve on cylinders No. 2 and No. 4.

Valve Clearance Specifications①

Application	Intake In. (mm)	Exhaust In. (mm)
Corolla	.008 (.20)	.013 (.33)
All Other Models	.008 (.20)	.012 (.30)

① — Set with engine warm.

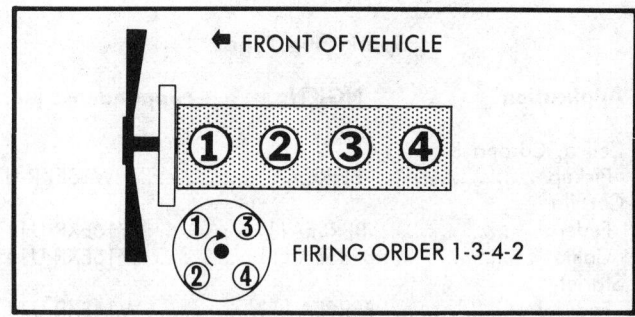

Fig. 1   Firing Order and Distributor Rotation (Celica, Corona and Pickup)

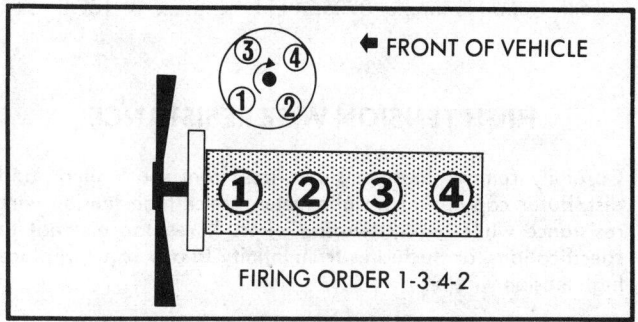

Fig. 2   Firing Order and Distributor Rotation (Corolla and Starlet)

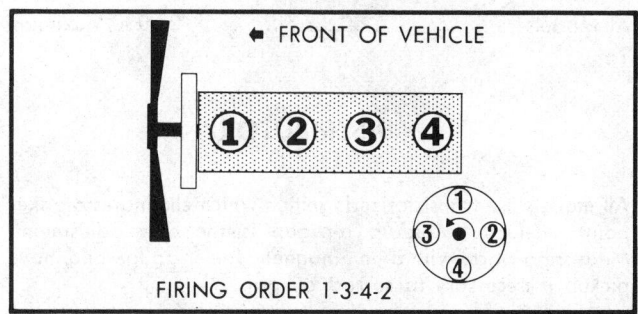

Fig. 3   Firing Order and Distributor Rotation (Tercel)

VALVE ARRANGEMENTS

Starlet — E-I-I-E-E-I-I-E
Tercel — I-E-E-I-I-E-E-I
All Other Models
  Right Side — All Intake
  Left Side — All Exhaust

SPARK PLUGS

Application	Gap In. (mm)	Torque Ft. Lbs. (N·m)
Celica, Corona & Pickup	.031 (0.8)	11-15 (15-20)
Corolla	.043 (1.1)	11-15 (15-20)
Starlet		
Federal	.043 (1.1)	11-15 (15-20)
Calif.	.031 (0.8)	11-15 (15-20)
Tercel	.043 (1.1)	11-15 (15-20)

TUNE-UP (Cont.)

Spark Plug Type

Application	NGK No.	Nippondenso No.
Celica, Corona &		
Pickup	BPR5EA-L	W16EXR-U
Corolla		
Federal	BPR5EA11	W16EXR-U11
Calif.	BPR5EA-L11	W16EXR-U11
Starlet		
Federal	BPR5EA-L11	W14EXR-U11
Calif.	BPR5EA-L	W14EXR-U
Tercel		
Federal	BPR5EA11	W16EXR-U11
Calif.	BPR5EA-L11	W16EXR-U11

HIGH TENSION WIRE RESISTANCE

Carefully remove high tension wires from spark plugs and distributor cap. Using an ohmmeter, check high tension wire resistance while gently twisting wires. If resistance is not to specifications, or fluctuates from infinity to any value, replace high tension wire(s).

Resistance (Ohms) Per Wire

Application	Ohms
All Models	25,000 Maximum

DISTRIBUTOR

All models use transistorized ignition which eliminates breaker points. Reluctor-to-pickup air gap is the only adjustment. Measure air gap with a non-magnetic feeler gauge and move pickup if necessary to correct air gap.

Air Gap .... .008-.016" (.2-.4 mm)

IGNITION TIMING

1) Connect a tachometer and timing light to engine. The positive lead of tachometer is connected to the (−) terminal of coil on all models except Celica, Corona and Pickup. On these models, connect tachometer positive lead to service connector from igniter, located at coil (covered with rubber cap).

2) With engine at normal operating temperature, be sure all hoses are connected, choke valve is fully open, transmission in "N" position, and all accessories are turned off. Adjust idle speed to timing specifications.

3) On models with dual diaphragm distributors, disconnect and plug hoses at sub-diaphragm and main diaphragm. On all models, check timing and adjust by turning distributor. When timing is set, reconnect sub-diaphragm hose. Timing marks should move. Reconnect main diaphragm hose.

Ignition Timing Specifications
(Degrees BTDC @ RPM)

Application	①Setting
Celica, Corona &	
Pickup	8 @ 950
Corolla	7 @ 950
Starlet	8 @ 950
Tercel	5 @ 950

① — With distributor sub-diaphragm hose disconnected.

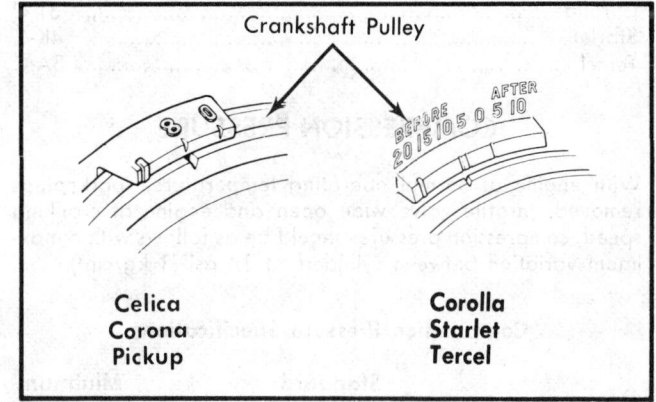

Fig. 4   Ignition Timing Marks

IDLE SPEED & MIXTURE

NOTE — *Mixture adjustment is NOT a part of normal tune-up procedure and should not be performed unless carburetor is overhauled or vehicle fails emissions testing.*

1) With air cleaner installed, engine at normal operating temperature, choke fully open, all accessories off and vacuum lines connected, be sure timing is set.

2) Place transmission in neutral and check that fuel level in carburetor sight glass is about mid-way. Remove idle mixture screw protective cover and idle limiter caps, if installed, and adjust idle speed to specifications.

3) Turn idle mixture adjusting screw to obtain maximum RPM. Now, turn idle speed screw until IDLE MIXTURE SPEED is obtained. Repeat adjustments again, turning idle mixture screw to obtain maximum RPM, then idle speed screw to obtain idle mixture speed. Repeat until highest RPM is obtained before setting final idle mixture speed.

4) Once idle mixture speed is set after the highest possible RPM is obtained using the previous procedures, turn in idle mixture adjusting screw until normal IDLE SPEED is obtained. Install replacement mixture screw caps and protective cover, if so equipped.

TUNE-UP (Cont.)

Fig. 5 Carburetor Adjusting Screws (All Models)

Idle Speed & Mixture Specifications

Application	Idle Mixture RPM	Idle Speed RPM
Celica & Corona		
Man. Trans.	740	700
Auto. Trans.	790	750
Corolla		
Man. Trans.①	820	650
Auto. Trans.①	880	750
Pickup		
Man. Trans.	740	700
Auto. Trans.②	790	750
Starlet		
Federal	680	650
Calif.	730	700
Tercel		
Man. Trans.		
4-Spd.	600	550
5-Spd.	700	650
Auto. Trans.	850	800

① — With power steering, set to 940/850 RPM.
② — With Federal 4-Spd. Auto. Trans., set to 740/700 RPM.

COLD (FAST) IDLE RPM

Celica, Corona & Pickup — 1) After setting idle speed and mixture, stop engine. Remove air cleaner. Disconnect and plug hoses at distributor vacuum advance, choke opener diaphragm and EGR valve. On manual transmission models, disconnect and plug hoses for hot air intake and mixture control system.

2) On all models, hold throttle valve slightly open. Push choke valve closed and release throttle valve. Without touching accelerator, start engine. Set fast idle to specifications by turning fast idle adjusting screw.

Corolla — 1) After setting idle speed and mixture, stop engine. Remove air cleaner. Disconnect hoses at hot idle compensation system, choke opener diaphragm to BVSV at diaphragm, and 2nd stage choke breaker diaphragm to jet restrictor at diaphragm.

2) Hold throttle valve slightly open. Push choke valve closed and release throttle valve. Without touching accelerator, start engine. Set fast idle to specifications by turning fast idle adjusting screw.

Starlet — 1) After setting idle speed and mixture, stop engine. Remove air cleaner. Disconnect and plug hoses for hot idle compensation system, EGR valve and choke opener diaphragm.

2) Start engine. Pull choke knob out about half way and depress accelerator pedal once. Check that fast idle cam is at 2nd stage and that engine speed has increased to about 3500 RPM.

3) Fully open choke valve. With engine cooling fan off, adjust fast idle speed to specifications by turning fast idle adjusting screw.

Tercel — 1) After setting idle speed and mixture, stop engine. Remove air cleaner. Disconnect and plug air suction (AS) hose on Federal models. Disconnect hose from EGR valve and from choke opener diaphragm. Hold throttle valve slightly open. Push choke valve closed and release throttle valve.

2) Without touching accelerator, start engine. With engine cooling fan off, adjust fast idle speed to specifications by turning fast idle adjusting screw.

Fast Idle Speed Specifications

Application	Fast Idle RPM
Celica, Corona & Pickup	2600
Corolla	
Man. Trans.①	3400
Auto. Trans.①	3200
Starlet	3500
Tercel	3600

① — If equipped with power steering set speed 200 RPM lower.

FUEL PUMP PRESSURE & VOLUME

Pressure	2.1-4.3 psi (.15-.3 kg/cm²)
Volume	1 pint in 30 seconds

EMISSION CONTROL SYSTEM

See Mitchell Manuals' Emission Control Manual.

1981 Toyota 4 Tune-Up

GENERAL SERVICING

IGNITION

DISTRIBUTOR

All models are equipped with transistorized ignition systems.

IGNITION COIL

Resistance Specifications
(Ohms @ 68°F)

Application	Primary	Secondary
Celica, Corona, Corolla & Tercel	0.8-1.0	11,500-15,500
Pickup	0.4-0.5	8500-11,500
Starlet	1.3-1.7	11,900-16,100

FUEL SYSTEMS

CARBURETORS

All models use Aisan 2-Bbl. carburetors.

ELECTRICAL

BATTERY

Application	Amp. Hr. Rating
Standard	50
Optional	60

Battery Location — In engine compartment.

STARTER

All models are equipped with Nippondenso starters.

Starter Specifications

Application	Volts	Amps	Test RPM
Celica, Corolla, Corona & Pickup	11.5	90	3000
Starlet & Tercel			
Conventional	11.0	50	5000
Reduction	11.5	90	3000

ALTERNATOR

Application	Rated Amp. Output
Celica, Corona & Pickup	40, 55 & 60
Corolla, Starlet & Tercel	50 & 55

ALTERNATOR REGULATOR

All models are equipped with Nippondenso alternator regulators. Operating voltage range is 13.8-14.8 volts.

BELT ADJUSTMENT
Tension Using Tension Gauge

Application	New Belt Lbs. (kg)	Used Belt Lbs. (kg)
All Models	100-150 (45-68)	60-100 (27-45)

FILTERS

Filter	Service Interval (Miles)
Oil Filter	Replace every 10,000
Air Filter	Replace every 30,000
Fuel Filter	Replace every 60,000

CAPACITIES

Application	Quantity
Crankcase (Includes Filter)	
Celica, Corona & Pickup	4.9 qts.
Corolla	4.0 qts.
Starlet & Tercel	3.7 qts.
Cooling System (Includes Heater)	
Celica, Corona & Pickup	8.9 qts.
Corolla	7.8 qts.
Starlet	6.0 qts.
Tercel	5.5 qts.
Man. Trans. (SAE 80W-90)	
Celica	2.5 qts.
Corolla	1.8 qts.
Corona	2.7 qts.
Pickup	
4-Spd.	2.1 qts.
5-Spd.	2.7 qts.
Starlet	2.6 qts.
Man. Transaxle (SAE 80W-90)	3.5 qts.
Auto. Trans. (ATF Type F)	2.5 qts.
Auto. Transaxle (ATF Type F)	2.3 qts.
Transfer Case (SAE 80W-90)	3.4 pts.
Differential (SAE 80W-90)	
Celica & Corona	
Banjo-Type	2.8 pts.
Unitized-Type	2.6 pts.
Corolla & Starlet	2.2 pts.
Pickup	
2-WD	
7.5"	3.6 pts.
8.0"	3.8 pts.
4-WD (Front and Rear)	4.6 pts.
Tercel (Front with Auto. Transaxle)	2.0 pts.
Fuel Tank	
Celica	16.1 gals.
Corolla	
Exc. Station Wagon	13.2 gals.
Station Wagon	12.4 gals.
Corona	
Exc. Station Wagon	16.1 gals.
Station Wagon	15.5 gals.
Pickup	
Short Bed	13.5 gals.
Long Bed	16.0 gals.
Starlet	10.6 gals.
Tercel	11.9 gals.

TUNE-UP

Diesel Pickup

ENGINE IDENTIFICATION

Engine code is located on decal at front edge of valve cover.

Engine Code

Application	Code
All Models	LN40

COMPRESSION PRESSURE

With engine at normal operating temperature, remove all glow plugs. Install special tool (Toyota 09992-00021) in glow plug mounting hole and attach a compression gauge. Disconnect wire at fuel cut solenoid. Crank engine at 250 RPM and measure compression.

CAUTION — *Make sure glow plug wiring does not ground.*

NOTE — *Count number of revolutions it took for No. 1 cylinder to reach maximum compression reading and use same number of revolutions to determine compression on remaining cylinders.*

Compression Pressure Specifications①

Application	Pressure psi (kg/cm²)
Normal (New Engine)	427 (30)
Minimum	284 (20)
Maximum Variation	71 (5)

① — With engine warm.

VALVE CLEARANCE

1) With engine at normal operating temperature, remove valve cover and rotate crankshaft until No. 1 cylinder is at TDC on compression stroke.

NOTE — *If No. 1 cylinder is at TDC on compression stroke, rocker arms will be loose on No. 1 cylinder and tight on No. 4 cylinder.*

2) Adjust intake valves on cylinder No. 1 and 2, and exhaust valves on cylinder No. 1 and 3. Rotate crankshaft 360°. Adjust intake valves on cylinder No. 3 and 4, and exhaust valves on cylinder No. 2 and 4.

3) Recheck clearance. There should be a slight drag on feeler gauge as it is pulled between rocker arm and valve stem. Replace valve cover.

Valve Clearance Specifications①

Application	Intake In. (mm)	Exhaust In. (mm)
All Models	.010 (25)	.014 (36)

① — With engine warm.

VALVE ARRANGEMENT

All Models — E-I-E-I-E-I-E-I

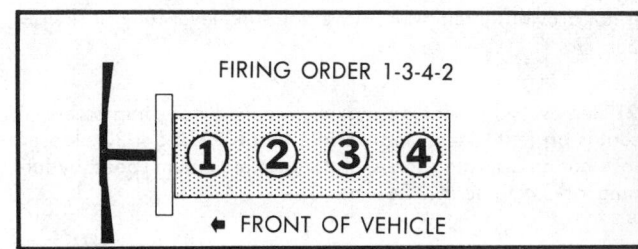

FIRING ORDER 1-3-4-2

① ② ③ ④

← FRONT OF VEHICLE

Fig. 1   Diesel Firing Order Illustration

IDLE SPEED ADJUSTMENT

1) With engine at normal operating temperature, air cleaner installed, all accessories off, and transmission in neutral, turn idle adjusting knob counterclockwise. Be sure that it fully returns to the unlocked position.

2) Remove the accelerator connection rod. See *Fig. 2.* Connect a tachometer to engine. Start engine and check idle speed. If necessary, adjust by turning idle speed adjusting screw on injection pump. See *Fig. 3.* Then check maximum speed adjustment.

Idle Speed Specifications

Application	Idle RPM
All Models	700

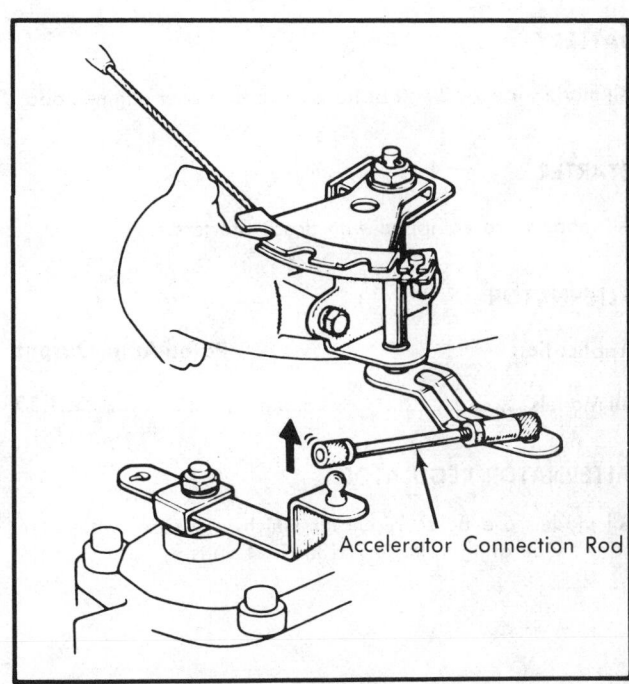

Accelerator Connection Rod

Fig. 2   Accelerator Connection Rod Removal

1981 Toyota Diesel 4 Tune-Up

TUNE-UP (Cont.)

MAXIMUM SPEED ADJUSTMENT

1) Install tachometer and run engine until normal operating temperature is obtained. Remove accelerator connection rod, if not previously removed. Move adjusting lever fully clockwise. See *Fig. 3*.

2) Remove wire seal on maximum speed adjusting screw, if seal is present. Using appropriate tool (09275-54020), loosen lock nut on adjusting screw and adjust maximum speed by turning adjusting screw. See *Fig. 3*.

3) Install accelerator connection rod and adjust so there is no slack in accelerator cable. Fully depress accelerator pedal, checking to see that adjusting lever is stopped by maximum speed adjusting screw. Adjust accelerator pedal with the stop bolt.

NOTE — *Be sure engine speed increases when idle adjusting knob is pulled out and turned clockwise and returns to idle when turned fully counterclockwise.*

4) Tighten lock nut at adjusting screw, and remove tachometer.

Maximum Speed Specifications

Application	Maximum RPM
All Models	4900

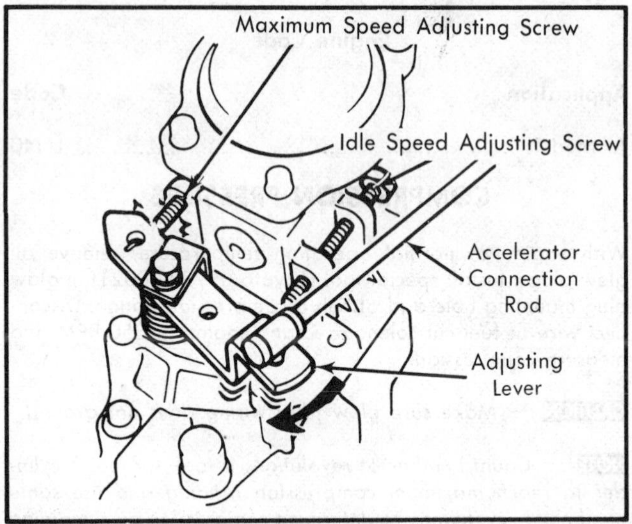

Fig. 3 Idle Speed and Maximum Speed Adjusting Screws

GENERAL SERVICING

FUEL SYSTEM

FUEL INJECTION

All Models use KIKI-Bosch mechanical fuel injection.

ELECTRICAL

BATTERY

All models use 2-12 volt batteries located under engine hood.

STARTER

All models are equipped with Bosch Starters.

ALTERNATOR

Application	Rated Amp. Output
All Models	55

ALTERNATOR REGULATOR

All models use Bosch regulator which is integral with alternator. Operating voltage is 13.8-14.4 volts.

BELT ADJUSTMENT

Tension (Lbs.) Using Strand Tension Gauge

Application	New Belt	Used Belt
Drive Belt	100-150	60-100

FILTERS

Filter	Service Interval (Miles)
Oil Filter	Replace every 3750
Air Filter	Replace every 30,000
Fuel Filter	Replace every 30,000

CAPACITIES

Application	Quantity
Crankcase (Includes Filter)	6.1 qts.
Cooling System	11.1 qts.
Man. Trans. (SAE 80W-90)	4.0 pts.
Differential (SAE 90W)	4.0 pts.
Fuel Tank	16.1 gals.

TUNE-UP

Cressida
Land Cruiser
Supra

ENGINE IDENTIFICATION

Engines can be identified by prefix of engine serial number, stamped on right side of engine block. Engine code can also be found on front of valve cover.

Engine Code

Application	Code
Cressida & Supra	5M-E
Land Cruiser	2F

COMPRESSION PRESSURE

Check compression pressure with engine at normal operating temperature, all spark plugs removed, throttle valve wide open and engine at cranking speed.

Compression Pressure Specifications

Application	Pressure psi (kg/cm²)
Normal (New Engine)	
Cressida & Supra	156 (11.0)
Land Cruiser	149 (10.5)
Minimum	
Cressida & Supra	128 (9.0)
Land Cruiser	114 (8.0)
Maximum Variation	14 (1.0)

VALVE CLEARANCE

NOTE — *Check or adjust valve clearance with engine at normal operating temperature.*

Cressida & Supra — 1) Set No. 1 cylinder at TDC on compression stroke. Remove valve cover. No. 1 rocker arms should be loose, No. 6 rocker arms should be tight. Adjust No. 1, 2, & 4 intake valves and 1, 3, and 5 exhaust valves. Turn crankshaft 360°. Adjust No. 3, 5, & 6 intake valves and 2, 4, & 6 exhaust valves.

2) Recheck clearance. Feeler gauge should have slight drag when pulled between valve stem and rocker arm. Install valve cover.

Land Cruiser — Remove valve cover. Adjust valves from front to rear. Recheck clearance. Feeler gauge should have slight drag when pulled between valve stem and rocker arm. Install valve cover.

Valve Clearance Specifications①

Application	Intake In. (mm)	Exhaust In. (mm)
Cressida & Supra	.011 (.28)	.014 (.36)
Land Cruiser	.008 (.21)	.014 (.36)

① — Valve clearance set with engine at normal operating temperature.

VALVE ARRANGEMENT

Cressida & Supra
Left Side — All Intake
Right Side — All Exhaust

Land Cruiser — E-I-I-E-E-I-I-E-E-I-I-E

SPARK PLUGS

Application	Gap In. (mm)	Torque Ft. Lbs. (N·m)
All Models	.031 (0.8)	11-15 (15-20)

Spark Plug Type

Application	NGK	Nippondenso
Cressida & Supra	BPR5EA-L or BPR5EY	W14EXR-U
Land Cruiser	BPR4EY	W14EXR-U

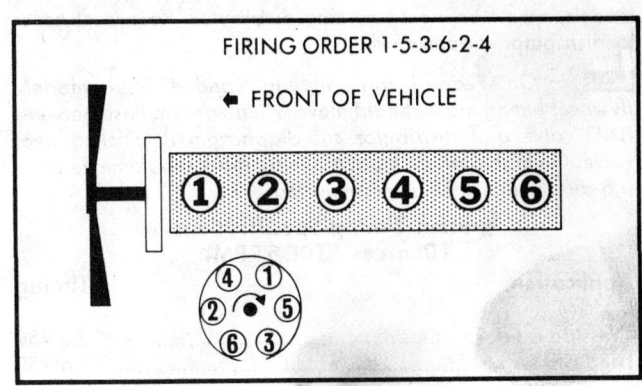

Fig. 1   Firing Order and Distributor Rotation (Cressida & Supra)

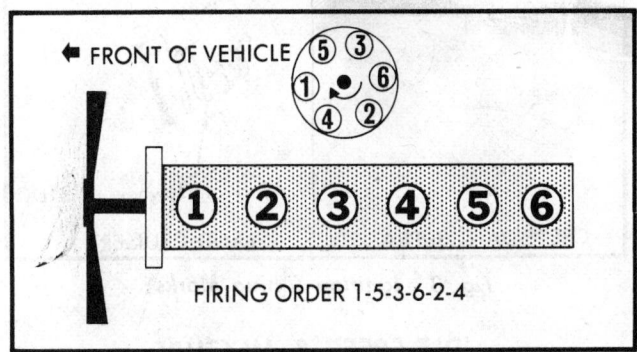

Fig. 2   Firing Order and Distributor Rotation (Land Cruiser)

HIGH TENSION WIRE RESISTANCE

Carefully remove high tension wires from spark plugs and distributor cap. Using an ohmmeter, check high tension wire resistance while gently twisting wires. If resistance is not to specifications, or fluctuates from infinity to any value, replace high tension wire(s).

Resistance (Ohms) Per Wire

Application	Ohms
All Models	16,000-25,000

DISTRIBUTOR

All models with 6-cylinder engines are fitted with Nippondenso Transistorized Electronic Ignition Systems. The only in-service adjustment possible is to set the air gap.

Air Gap .008-.016" (.2-.4 mm)

TUNE-UP (Cont.)

IGNITION TIMING

1) Connect tachometer and timing light to engine. The positive (+) lead of tachometer is connected to negative (−) terminal of ignition coil. With engine at normal operating temperature, choke valve fully opened, and transmission in "N" position, be sure all hoses are connected and accessories turned off. Adjust idle speed to correct specification.

CAUTION — *Do not allow tachometer connector to touch ground, or damage may occur to the system.*

2) On models with dual diaphragm distributors, disconnect and plug hoses at both main and sub-diaphragms. On all models, adjust timing by turning distributor. Reconnect hoses to distributor diaphragms.

NOTE — *On Federal low altitude Land Cruiser models, flywheel timing mark should move when vacuum hose between HAC valve and distributor sub-diaphragm is pinched near valve. On high altitude models, timing mark should move when sub-diaphragm hose is reconnected.*

Ignition Timing Specifications①
(Degrees BTDC@RPM)

Application	Timing
Cressida & Supra	8@950
Land Cruiser	7@950

① — With distributor sub-diaphragm hose disconnected and plugged.

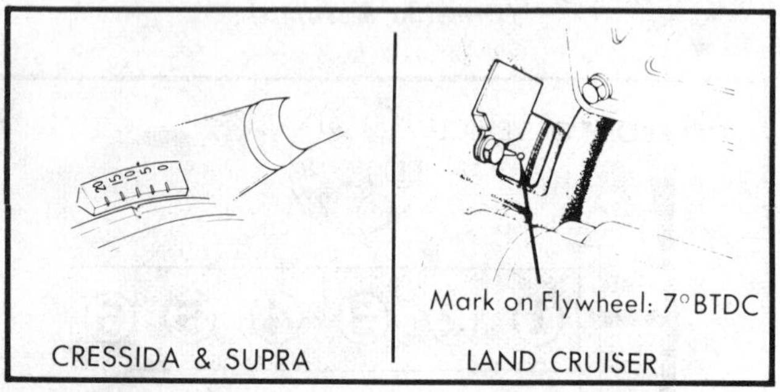

Mark on Flywheel: 7°BTDC

CRESSIDA & SUPRA | LAND CRUISER

Fig. 3 Ignition Timing Marks

IDLE SPEED & MIXTURE

NOTE — *Mixture adjustment is NOT a part of normal tune-up procedure and should not be performed unless carburetor is overhauled, mixture control unit is replaced or vehicle fails emissions testing.*

CARBURETED MODELS

NOTE — *Attach tachometer positive terminal to coil negative terminal. Do not allow tachometer connector to touch ground, or damage may occur to system.*

1) With air cleaner installed, engine at normal operating temperature, choke fully open, all accessories off and vacuum lines connected, be sure timing is set.

2) Set transmission in neutral and check to see that fuel level in carburetor sight glass is midway between marks. Remove idle mixture screw protective cover and idle limiter caps, if installed, and adjust idle speed to 650 RPM.

3) Turn idle mixture adjusting screw to obtain maximum RPM. Now, turn idle speed screw until 690 RPM is obtained. Repeat adjustments again, turning idle mixture screw to maximum

RPM, then turn idle speed screw to idle mixture speed. Repeat until highest RPM is obtained before setting final idle mixture speed.

4) Once idle mixture speed is set after the highest possible RPM is obtained using the above procedure, turn in idle mixture adjusting screw until 650 RPM is obtained. Install replacement mixture screw caps and protective cover, if so equipped.

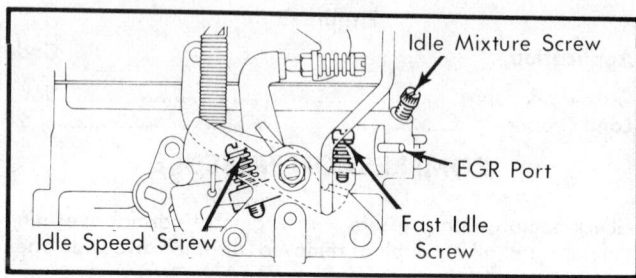

Fig. 4 Carburetor Adjustment Screw Locations

FUEL INJECTED MODELS

NOTE — *Attach tachometer positive terminal to coil negative terminal. Do not allow tachometer connector to touch ground, or damage may occur to system.*

1) With air cleaner installed, engine at normal operating temperature, all wiring connectors, vacuum lines, pipes and hoses connected and all accessories off, be sure timing is at correct specification.

2) Set transmission in neutral. Start engine and run at idle. Pinch air valve hose checking to see that engine RPM does not drop more than 150 RPM.

3) Remove rubber cap from service connector at left front fender and connect voltmeter positive probe to "VF" and negative probe to "E1". See Fig. 5.

CAUTION — *Do not connect the voltmeter probes directly to the service connector.*

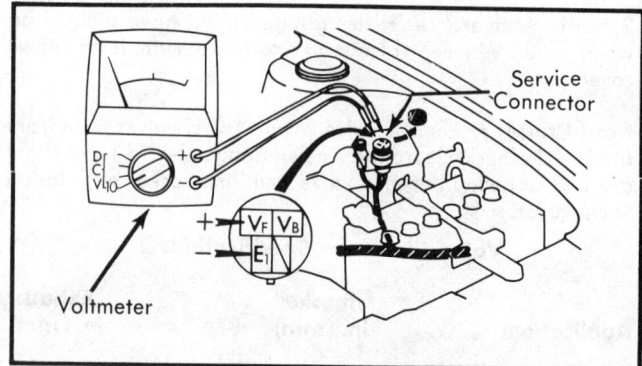

Fig. 5 Idle Speed Service Connections

4) Warm up engine at 2500 RPM for about 2 minutes. Voltmeter needle should fluctuate 8 times or more in 10 seconds. If it does not, check fuel injection system and replace oxygen sensor, if necessary.

5) Set idle speed to 800 RPM with idle speed adjusting screw. Voltmeter reading should now be 3-9 volts. If more than 9 volts, check air intake system for leaks. If less than 3 volts, check fuel injection system.

TUNE-UP (Cont.)

COLD (FAST) IDLE RPM

NOTE — *There is no fast idle speed adjustment for Electronic Fuel Injection equipped vehicles.*

Land Cruiser — 1) After setting idle speed and mixture, stop engine. Pull choke knob fully out. Disconnect and plug hoses from distributor vacuum advance and from evaporation ports of the VCV and EGR valves.

2) Start engine and adjust idle speed to specification with fast idle adjusting screw. Engine should return to normal idle when choke knob is pushed in fully.

Fast Idle Specifications

Application	RPM
Land Cruiser	①1800

① — EGR, EVAP, and distributor diaphragm disconnected.

FUEL PUMP PRESSURE & VOLUME

Pressure
Cressida & Supra .... ①33-38 psi (2.3-2.7 kg/cm²)
Land Cruiser .... 3.4-4.8 psi (.24-.34 kg/cm²)

Volume
Land Cruiser .... 2.5 pints in 30 sec.

① — Measured with vacuum hose at pressure regulator disconnected. With hose connected, 28 psi (2.0 kg/cm²)

EMISSION CONTROL SYSTEMS

See Mitchell Manuals' Emission Control Manual.

GENERAL SERVICING

IGNITION

DISTRIBUTOR

All models are equipped with Nippondenso Transistorized Electronic Ignition Systems.

IGNITION COIL

Coil Resistance (Ohms @ 68°F)

Application	Primary	Secondary
All Models	.5-.6	11,500-15,500

FUEL SYSTEMS

CARBURETORS

Land Cruiser models are equipped with Aisan 2-Bbl. carburetors.

FUEL INJECTION

Cressida and Supra Models are equipped with Bosch AFC fuel injection with oxygen sensor.

ELECTRICAL

BATTERY

Application	Amp. Hr. Rating
All Models	70

Battery Location — In engine compartment.

STARTER

All models are equipped with Nippondenso Starters.

Starter Specifications

Application	Volts	Amps	Test RPM
Cressida & Supra			
Conventional	11.0	50	5000
Reduction	11.5	90	3500
Land Cruiser	11.0	50	5000

ALTERNATOR

Application	Rated Amp. Output
Cressida & Supra	
With Integral Regulator	65
With External Regulator	60
Land Cruiser	55

ALTERNATOR REGULATOR

All models are equipped with Nippondenso alternators and regulators. Some alternators are equipped with integrated circuit regulators (mounted integrally with alternator). Operating voltage for these regulators is 13.8-14.4 volts. Operating voltage for externally mounted regulators is 14.0-14.9 volts.

CAPACITIES

Application	Quantity
Crankcase (Includes Filter)	
Cressida & Supra	4.9 qts.
Land Cruiser	8.2 qts.
Cooling System	
Cressida	11.6 qts.
Supra	9.5 qts.
Land Cruiser	
Station Wagon	17.4 qts.
All Others	16.9 qts.
Man. Trans. (SAE 80W-90)	
Land Cruiser	7.6 pts.
Supra	5.4 pts.
Auto. Trans. (ATF Type F)	2.5 qts.
Differential (SAE 90)	
Cressida & Supra	3.2 pts.
Land Cruiser	5.2 pts.
Transfer Case (SAE 90)	5.2 pts.
Fuel Tank	
Cressida	
Sedan	17.2 gals.
Station Wagon	16.2 gals.
Land Cruiser	
Station Wagon	23.8 gals.
All Others	22.4 gals.
Supra	16.1 gals.

1981 Toyota 6 Tune-Up

GENERAL SERVICING (Cont.)

BELT ADJUSTMENT

Tension (Lbs.) Using Strand Tension Gauge

Application	New Belt	Used Belt
Cressida & Supra	100-150	60-100
Land Cruiser		
A/C Belt	100-150	60-100
All Others	120-170	80-120

FILTERS

Filter	Service Interval (Miles)
Oil Filter	
Cressida & Supra	Replace every 10,000
Land Cruiser	Replace every 10,000
Air Filter	Replace every 30,000
Fuel Filter	Replace every 60,000

TUNE-UP

TR7

ENGINE IDENTIFICATION

Engine number is stamped on the cylinder head.

Engine Code

Application	Code
All Models	CK

COMPRESSION PRESSURE

Check compression with engine at normal operating temperature, spark plugs removed and throttle wide open. Crank engine at least 4 "puffs" per cylinder. Lowest pressure should be at least 85% that of highest cylinder.

VALVE CLEARANCE

1) Disconnect battery and remove camshaft cover. Loosen camshaft bearing cap nuts and retighten to 10-14 ft. lbs. (1.4-1.9 mkg). Rotate engine. Check and record clearance between cam heel and tappet. Maximum clearance is present when cam is in verticle position.

2) If clearance is not within specifications, remove camshaft and individually lift out each tappet and adjusting shim.

3) Using a micrometer, measure thickness of adjusting shim removed. Add to this the measured valve clearance and subtract the specified clearance from the total. This will offer you the thickness of adjusting shim necessary to bring the clearance within specifications.

4) Install tappets and add shims as needed. Install camshaft and tighten bearing caps. Recheck valve clearance, and, when correct, replace camshaft cover.

Valve Clearance Specifications ①

Application	Intake In. (mm)	Exhaust In. (mm)
All Models	.008 (.20)	.018 (.50)

① — Engine cold.

VALVE ARRANGEMENT

E-I-I-E-E-I-I-E (front to rear).

SPARK PLUGS

Application	Gap In. (mm)	Torque Ft. Lbs. (N·m)
All Models	.025 (.64)	20 (27)

Spark Plug Type

Application	Champion No.
All Models	N12Y

HIGH TENSION WIRE RESISTANCE

Carefully remove high tension wires from spark plugs and distributor cap. Using an ohmmeter, check high tension wire resistance while gently twisting wires. If resistance is not to specifications, or fluctuates from infinity to any value, replace high tension wire(s).

Resistance (Ohms) Per Wire

Application	Ohms
All Models	25,000-30,000

DISTRIBUTOR

All models are equipped with Opus Electronic Ignition System and the only adjustment required is adjusting the Pick-Up Module air gap.

CAUTION — *DO NOT insert feeler gauge into pick-up air gap when the ignition circuit is energized.*

Air Gap .... ①.010-.017" (.25-.43 mm)

① — Measured between timing rotor and pick-up module.

IGNITION TIMING

Check or adjust engine timing with engine idling at normal operating temperature. If correction is needed, rotate distributor.

Ignition Timing Specifications

Application	RPM	Timing
All Models	800	2° ATDC

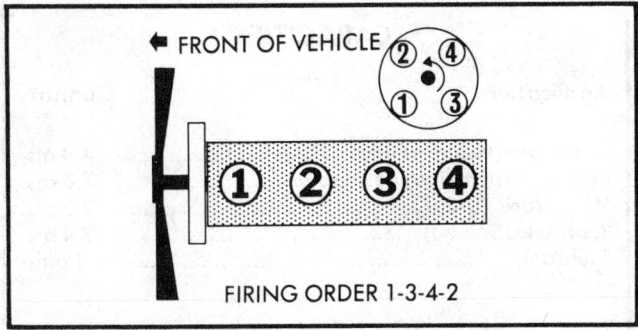

Fig. 1 Firing Order and Distributor Rotation

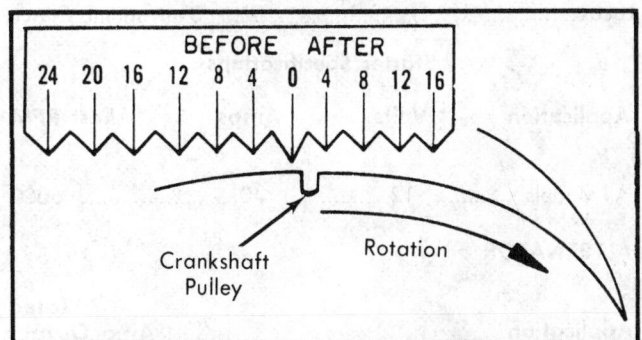

Fig. 2 Ignition Timing Mark Location

1981 Triumph 4 TuneUp

TUNE-UP (Cont.)

IDLE SPEED & MIXTURE

NOTE — *The following adjustments must be performed with air filter in good condition, ignition timing and valve clearance adjusted to specifications and engine at normal operating temperature.*

Use a 7/32" Allen wrench to turn air screw clockwise to lower idle speed or counterclockwise to increase idle speed. Screw is located on air plenum chamber.

NOTE — *Mixture adjustment is not a normal tune-up procedure. Mixture should not be adjusted unless vehicle fails emission testing or air flow meter is replaced. If adjustment is necessary, use Feedback Monitor Tool (60973066).*

Idle Speed & CO Level

Application	Idle RPM	CO%
All Models	700-900	①

① — Use special tester (No. 60973066).

FUEL PUMP PRESSURE

Pressure .... 36 psi (2.5 kg/cm²)

EMISSION CONTROL SYSTEMS

See Mitchell Manuals' Emission Control Manual.

GENERAL SERVICING

IGNITION

DISTRIBUTOR

All models are equipped with Lucas Opus Electronic Ignition System.

IGNITION COIL

Resistance Specifications
(Ohms @ 68°F)

Application	Primary	Secondary
All Models	1.3-1.5	

FUEL SYSTEMS

FUEL INJECTION

Fuel injected models are equipped with Bosch Air Flow Controlled (AFC) electronic fuel injection with oxygen sensor.

ELECTRICAL

BATTERY

Application	Amp. Hr. Capacity
All Models	50

Battery Location — In engine compartment, on firewall.

STARTER

Lucas .... Overrunning Clutch

Starter Specifications

Application	Volts	Amps	Test RPM
All Models	12	40	6000

ALTERNATOR

Application	Rated Amp. Output
All Models	65

ALTERNATOR REGULATOR

Lucas — Non-Adjustable, integral with alternator, with an operating voltage of 13.6-14.4 volts.

BELT ADJUSTMENT

Application	①Deflection
Fan Belt	.75-1.0" (19-25 mm)
Air Pump Belt	.25-.50" (6-13 mm)

① — Deflection is with pressure applied midway on longest belt run.

FILTERS

Filter	Service Interval (Miles)
Oil Filter	Replace every 7500
Air Filter	Replace every 36,000
Fuel Filter	Replace ever 36,000

CAPACITIES

Application	Quantity
Crankcase (Includes Filter)	4.8 qts.
Cooling System (Includes Heater)	7.8 qts.
Man. Trans. (SAE 75)	3.3 pts.
Rear Axle (SAE 75)	2.4 pts.
Fuel Tank	14.4 gals.

TUNE-UP

TR8

ENGINE IDENTIFICATION

Engine number is stamped on left side of block near No. 3 spark plug.

Engine Code

Application	Code
Man. Trans.	14E
Auto. Trans.	15E

COMPRESSION PRESSURE

Check compression with engine warm, spark plugs removed, and throttle wide open. Crank engine through at least 4 compression strokes before taking reading. Minimum pressure should not be less than 135 psi (9.5 kg/cm²).

VALVE CLEARANCE

TR8 engines are equipped with hydraulic valve lifters and no adjustment is necessary.

VALVE ARRANGEMENT

E-I-E-I-I-E-I-E

SPARK PLUGS

Application	Gap In. (mm)	Torque Ft. Lbs. (N·m)
All Models	.030 (.8)	12 (16)

Spark Plug Type

Application	Champion No.
All Models	N12Y

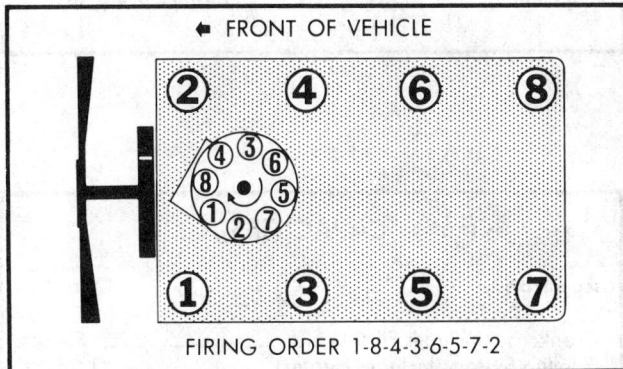

Fig. 1   Firing Order and Distributor Rotation

← FRONT OF VEHICLE

FIRING ORDER 1-8-4-3-6-5-7-2

HIGH TENSION WIRE RESISTANCE

Carefully remove high tension wires from spark plugs and distributor cap. Using an ohmmeter, check high tension wire resistance while gently twisting wires. If resistance is not to specifications, or fluctuates from infinity to any value, replace high tension wire(s).

Resistance (Ohms) Per Wire

Application	Ohms
All Models	25,000-30,000

DISTRIBUTOR

All models are equipped with Lucas electronic breakerless ignition systems. The only maintenance is adjusting air gap between timing rotor and pick-up module.

CAUTION — *DO NOT insert feeler gauge into pick-up air gap when the ignition circuit is energized.*

Air Gap .... .012-.017" (.3-.4 mm)

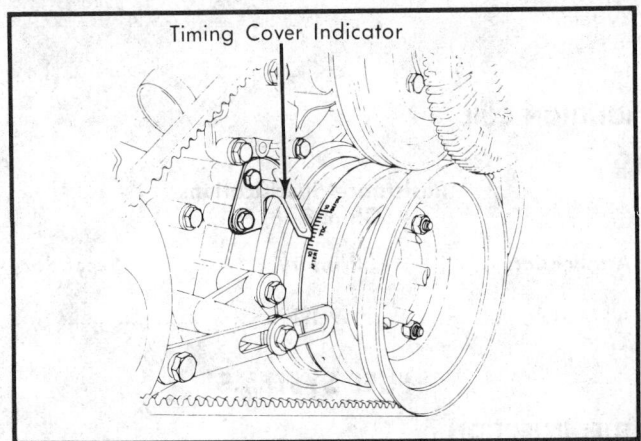

Timing Cover Indicator

Fig. 2   Ignition Timing Mark Location

IGNITION TIMING

Check or adjust ignition timing with engine at normal operating temperature, idle speed set to specification, and distributor hoses disconnected. If adjustment is necessary, rotate distributor.

Ignition Timing Specifications

Application	RPM	Timing
All Models	750-900	TDC

IDLE SPEED & MIXTURE

NOTE — *The following adjustments must be performed with air filter in good condition, ignition timing and valve clearance adjusted to specifications and engine at normal operating temperature.*

Use a 7/32" Allen wrench to turn air screw clockwise to lower idle speed or counterclockwise to increase idle speed. Screw is located on plenum chamber.

NOTE — *Mixture adjustment is not a normal tune-up procedure. Mixture should not be adjusted unless vehicle fails emission testing or air flow meter is replaced. If adjustment is necessary, use Feedback Monitor Tool (60973066).*

TUNE-UP (Cont.)

Idle Speed & CO Level

Application	RPM	CO%
All Models	800	①

① — Use special tester (No. 60973066).

FUEL PUMP PRESSURE

Pressure .... 36 psi (2.5 kg/cm²)

EMISSION CONTROL SYSTEMS

See Mitchell Manuals' Emission Control Manual.

GENERAL SERVICING

IGNITION

DISTRIBUTOR

All models are equipped with Lucas Opus Electronic Ignition System.

IGNITION COIL

Resistance Specifications (Ohms@68°F)

Application	Primary	Secondary
All Models	.9-1.1	

FUEL SYSTEMS

FUEL INJECTION

All models are equipped with Bosch Air Flow Controlled fuel injection systems with oxygen sensor.

ELECTRICAL

Battery Location — Battery is located in trunk.

Application	Amp. Hr. Capacity
All Models	68

STARTER

Lucas .... Overrunning clutch

Starter Specifications

Application	Volts	Amps	Test RPM
All Models	12	65	6000

ALTERNATOR

Application	Rated Amp. Output
All Models	65

ALTERNATOR REGULATOR

All models are equipped with Lucas integral alternator regulators.

BELT ADJUSTMENT

Application	①Deflection
Alternator	.5-.75" (13-19 mm)
A/C & Power Steering	.75-1.0" (19-25 mm)

① — Deflection is with moderate pressure applied midway on longest belt run.

FILTERS

Application	Service Interval (Miles)
Oil Filter	Replace every 7500
Air Filter	Replace every 36,000
Crankcase Breather Filter	Replace every 36,000
Fuel Filter	Replace every 36,000

CAPACITIES

Application	Quantity
Crankcase (Includes Filter)	5.4 qts.
Cooling System (Includes Heater)	11.5 qts.
Man. Trans. (SAE 75)	3.3 pts.
Rear Axle (SAE 75)	3.3 pts.
Fuel Tank	14.4 gals.

TUNE-UP

Jetta
Rabbit
Rabbit Pickup
Scirocco
Vanagon

ENGINE IDENTIFICATION

Engine code prefixes are placed in the following locations:

Vanagon — Engine serial number is stamped on crankcase below breather.

All Other Models — Engine serial number is stamped on left side of engine near ignition distributor.

Engine Code

Application	Code
Jetta, Rabbit, Rabbit Pickup & Scirocco	EN
Vanagon	CV

COMPRESSION PRESSURE

Check compression with engine warm, all spark plugs removed and throttle wide open. Maximum variation permitted between cylinders is 44 psi (3.0 kg/cm²).

CAUTION — *On models with electronic ignition, connect coil high tension wire to ground before cranking engine.*

Compression Pressure Specifications

Application	Standard Pressure psi (kg/cm²)	Minimum Pressure psi (kg/cm²)
Vanagon	87-131 (6.0-9.0)	73 (5.0)
All Others	131-174 (9.0-12.0)	102 (7.0)

VALVE CLEARANCE

Vanagon — No adjustment is needed as engine is equipped with hydraulic valve lifters.

All Other Models — 1) The clearance between cam lobe and cam follower is adjusted by means of replaceable discs. Discs are avaiable in 26 thicknesses from .119-.166″ (3.0-4.25 mm). Discs most frequently used are .140-.150″ (3.55-3.80 mm).

2) Warm up engine to normal operating temperature. Using wrench on center bolt of crankshaft pulley, hand turn crankshaft clockwise until cam lobes for cylinder being tested are pointing upward. Use feeler gauge to check valve clearance.

3) Use special tool VW546 to press down cam follower, so that adjusting disc can be readily removed with tool US4476. When depressing cam followers, turn so that openings are at 90° angle to cam.

Valve Clearance Specifications①

Application	Intake In. (mm)	Exhaust In. (mm)
All Models (Exc. Vanagon)	.010 (.25)	.018 (.45)

① — Set with engine warm.

VALVE ARRANGEMENT

Vanagon — E-I-I-E (Both banks)
All Others — E-I-E-I-I-E-I-E (front-to-rear).

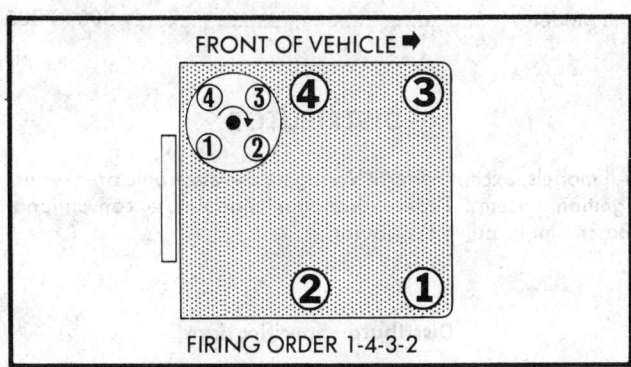

FRONT OF VEHICLE ➡

FIRING ORDER 1-4-3-2

Fig. 1 Firing Order & Distributor Rotation (Vanagon)

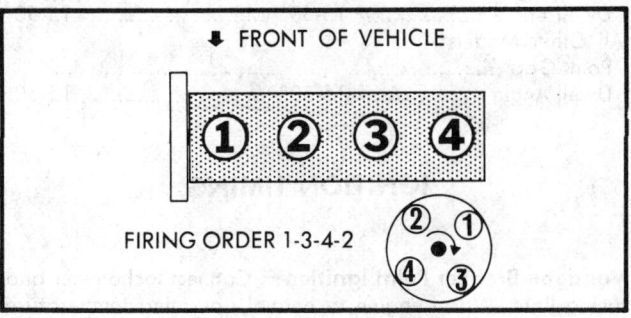

⬇ FRONT OF VEHICLE

FIRING ORDER 1-3-4-2

Fig. 2 Firing Order & Distributor Rotation (All Except Vanagon)

SPARK PLUGS

Application	Gap In. (mm)	Torque Ft. Lbs. (N·m)
Vanagon	.026 (.65)	22 (29)
All Other Models	.028 (.7)	22 (29)

Spark Plug Type

Application	Bosch	Champion
Vanagon	W8CO	N288
All Other Models		
Federal	W7D	N8Y
Calif.	WR7DS	N8GY

HIGH TENSION WIRE RESISTANCE

Remove distributor cap and disconnect high tension wires from spark plugs (not distributor cap). Using an ohmmeter, measure resistance from cap terminal to other end of wire. If resistance is not to specifications, or fluctuates when wire is twisted gently, replace wire(s).

NOTE — *High tension wire resistance cannot be measured if wire ends are marked with the following symbol:* ▬◄►▬

TUNE-UP (Cont.)

Resistance (Ohms) Per Wire

Application	Ohms
All Models	5000-7000

DISTRIBUTOR

All models, except Federal Vanagon, use electronic breakerless ignition systems. Federal Vanagon models use conventional Bosch single point distributor.

Distributor Specifications

Application	Federal	California
Vanagon		
Point Gap	Elec. Ign.	Elec. Ign.
Dwell Angle	15-50°	15-50°
All Other Models		
Point Gap	.....	.....
Dwell Angle	15-50°	15-50°

IGNITION TIMING

Vanagon Breaker Point Ignition — Connect tachometer and timing light. Warm engine to normal operating temperature and check idle speed. Adjust timing with vacuum disconnected and plugged. Connect test equipment at fuse 10, not from coil terminal 15(+).

All Other Models Electronic Ignition — **1)** Warm engine to normal operating temperature. Turn engine off. Connect tachometer and timing light, following manufacturer's instructions.

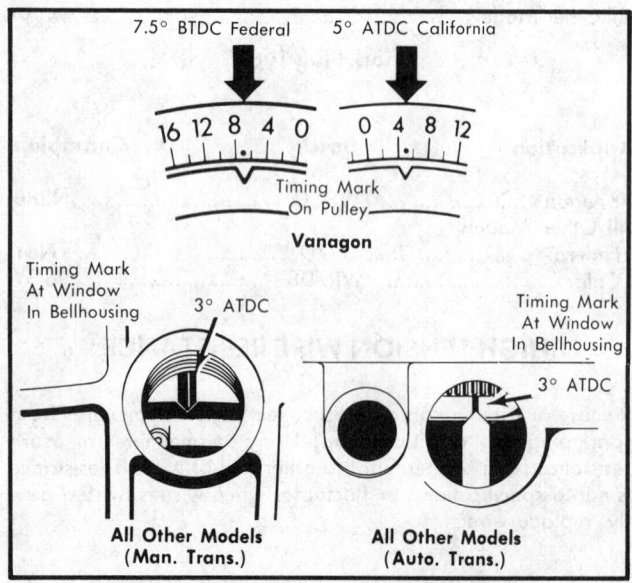

7.5° BTDC Federal   5° ATDC California

16 12 8 4 0   0 4 8 12

Timing Mark
On Pulley

Vanagon

Timing Mark
At Window
In Bellhousing

3° ATDC

Timing Mark
At Window
In Bellhousing

3° ATDC

All Other Models
(Man. Trans.)

All Other Models
(Auto. Trans.)

*Fig. 3   Ignition Timing Mark Locations
(All Models)*

2) Disconnect both plugs at idle stabilizer unit (squeeze connector to loosen). Connect plugs together. Check idle speed, then adjust timing by turning distributor.

Ignition Timing Specifications

Application	RPM	Timing
Vanagon①		
Federal	800-950	7.5° BTDC
Calif.	850-950	5° ATDC
All Other Models	850-1000	3° ATDC

① — All electrical equipment off.

IDLE SPEED & MIXTURE

NOTE — *Mixture adjustment is NOT a part of normal tune-up procedure and should not be performed unless mixture control unit is replaced or vehicle fails emissions testing.*

Vanagon — 1) With engine at normal operating temperature, connect CO tester at probe receptacle on exhaust pipe in front of catalytic converter. Connect a tachometer to engine.

2) Adjust idle screw until idle speed is to specifications. Check CO reading. If not to specifications, turn engine off and disconnect oxygen sensor plug. Disconnect idle stabilizer plugs and connect together.

3) Remove intake air sensor. Center punch plug in CO adjusting hole. Using a 3/32" (2.5 mm) drill bit, drill hole in center of plug 9/64-5/32" (3.5-4.0 mm) deep. Clean up any metal shavings.

4) Screw in 1/8" (3.0 mm) sheet metal screw into plug and remove plug with screw, using pliers. Reinstall intake air sensor. Start engine and adjust CO to specifications. Turn engine off and drive in new adjusting hole plug flush with air intake sensor. Reconnect all other plugs and remove test equipment.

All Other Models — 1) With engine at normal operating temperature, disconnect and plug PCV hose. Turn air conditioner and all accessories off.

2) Connect a tachometer, timing light and CO meter (to test receptacle) to engine. Check timing and, if necessary, adjust to specifications by turning distributor. Check idle speed and, if necessary, adjust to specifications by turning idle speed screw on CIS throttle plate housing.

3) Check CO reading. If not to specifications, remove boot on mixture control unit. Center punch plug in CO adjusting hole. Using a 3/32" (2.5 mm) drill bit, drill hole in center plug 9/64-5/32" (3-4 mm) deep. Clean up any metal shavings.

4) Screw in 1/8" (3 mm) sheet metal screw and remove plug with screw, using pliers. Reinstall boot on mixture control unit. Start engine and adjust CO to specifications by using 3 mm allen wrench inserted into CIS housing by fuel distributor.

TUNE-UP (Cont.)

Idle Speed & CO Level

Application	Idle Speed	CO%
Vanagon		
Federal		
Man. Trans.	800-950	0.5-1.5
Auto. Trans.	850-1000	0.5-1.5
Calif.	850-950	0.3-1.1
All Others		
With Idle Stab.	①880-1000	②0.3-1.2
Without Idle Stab.	850-1000	②0.3-1.2

① — By-pass idler stabilizer by connecting plugs together.
② — Federal Pickup CO reading is 0.5-0.9%.

GENERAL SERVICING

IGNITION

DISTRIBUTOR

All models, except Federal Vanagon, use electronic breakerless ignition systems. Federal Vanagon models use conventional Bosch single point distributor.

FUEL SYSTEMS

FUEL INJECTION

Vanagon — All models use Bosch AFC Electronic Fuel Injection.

Jetta, Rabbit, Rabbit Pickup & Scirocco — All models use Bosch Continuous Injecton System (CIS).

ELECTRICAL

BATTERY

Application	Standard Amp. Hr.	Optional Amp. Hr.
Vanagon	54	
Rabbit Pickup	54	
All Other Models	45	54

Battery Location — Battery is located under right front seat on Vanagon models, and in engine compartment on all other models.

STARTER

All models are equipped with Bosch starters.

ALTERNATOR

Application	Rated Amp. Output
Rabbit & Rabbit Pickup	55 & 65
Rabbit Convertible, Jetta & Scirocco	45 & 65
Vanagon	65

ALTERNATOR REGULATOR

Bosch & Motorola — Non-Adjustable; integral with alternator.

5) Turn engine off and drive in new adjusting hole plug flush with mixture control unit. Reconnect other plugs and remove test equipment.

EMISSION CONTROL SYSTEMS

See *Mitchell Manuals' Emission Control Manual.*

BELT ADJUSTMENT

Application	① Deflections
All Models	.4-.6" (10-15 mm)

① — Deflection is with thumb pressure, about 16.5 lbs. (7.5 kg), applied midway on longest belt run.

FILTERS

Filter	Service Interval (Miles)
Oil Filter	Replace every 15,000
Air Filter	Replace every 30,000
Fuel Filter	Replace every 15,000

CAPACITIES

Application	Quantity
Crankcase (Including Filter)	
Vanagon	3.7 qts.
All Other Models	4.7 qts.
Cooling System	
Vanagon	AIR
All Other Models	4.9 qts.
Man. Transaxle (SAE 80W-90)	
Vanagon	3.7 qts.
All Other Models	
4-Speed	1.6 qts.
5-Speed	2.1 qts.
Auto. Transaxle (Dexron)	3.2 qts.
Auto. Transaxle Differential (SAE 90)	
Vanagon	3.0 pts.
All Other Models	1.6 pts.
Fuel Tank	
Rabbit Pickup	15.0 gals.
Vanagon	15.9 gals.
All Other Models	10.0 gals.

TUNE-UP

Dasher
Rabbit
Rabbit Pickup
Vanagon

ENGINE IDENTIFICATION

First 2 letters of engine identification code are used to identify engine models. Code is stamped on cylinder block below No. 3 glow plug and is as follows:

Engine Code

Application	Code
Vanagon	CS
Dasher, Rabbit & Rabbit Pickup	CR

COMPRESSION PRESSURE

Remove electrical wire from fuel shut-off solenoid on injection pump. Insulate wire end and remove injection pipes. Disconnect fuel return hoses. Remove injectors with tool US 2775 (or equivalent). Remove heat shields from injectors and place in cylinder as it is being tested. Install test gauge adapter (VW 1323/2) and test gauge (VW 1323) to glow plug hole, operate starter and read compression. Install new injector heat shields when reinstalling injectors.

Compression Pressure Specifications

Application	Pressure psi (kg/cm)
Normal (New Engine)	500 (34.5)
Minimum	400 (28)
Maximum Variation	70 (5)

VALVE CLEARANCE

CAUTION — *When adjusting valves, pistons MUST NOT be at TDC. Turn crankshaft ¼ turn past TDC so valves do not hit pistons when tappets are depressed.*

CAUTION — *When adjusting valves, do not rotate crankshaft by turning camshaft pulley. This will stretch the drive belt. Place vehicle in 4th gear and push to turn crankshaft.*

1) Valves must be checked with engine warm, coolant above 95° F (35° C). Check valve clearance in firing order, 1-3-4-2.

2) Measure between cam lobes and adjusting disc, when both lobes to be checked point upward. Adjust clearance to specifications by changing disc thickness. Twenty six discs are available in thicknesses from .118-.167" (3.00-4.25 mm).

3) To remove adjusting discs, use a 10-208 removal tool, while holding cam follower down with special tool VW 546 (10-209).

Valve Clearance Specifications①

Application	Intake In. (mm)	Exhaust In. (mm)
All Models	.008-.012 (20-30)	.016-.020 (40-50)

① — Engine warm.

VALVE ARRANGEMENT

All Models — E-I-E-I-I-E-I-E

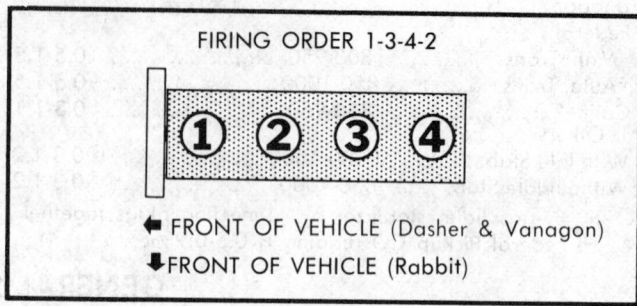

FIRING ORDER 1-3-4-2

← FRONT OF VEHICLE (Dasher & Vanagon)
↓ FRONT OF VEHICLE (Rabbit)

Fig. 1   Diesel Firing Order Illustration

IDLE SPEED ADJUSTMENT

Run engine until warm. Mount tachometer sensor (US 1324) on valve cover and connect to battery. Attach tachometer to sensor and check idle speed. If adjustment is needed, loosen locknut on idle screw. Turn in to increase idle, out to decrease. Apply thread sealer and tighten locknut.

Idle Speed Specifications

Application	Idle RPM
All Models	925-975

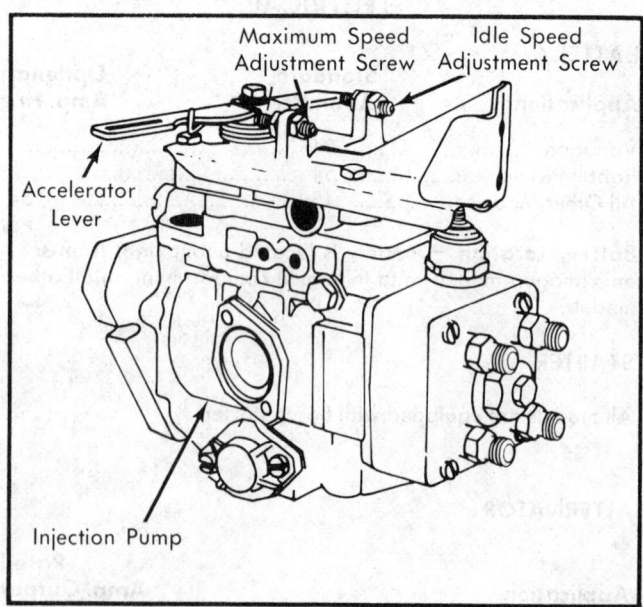

Maximum Speed Adjustment Screw
Idle Speed Adjustment Screw
Accelerator Lever
Injection Pump

Fig. 2   Idle and Maximum Speed Adjustment

MAXIMUM SPEED ADJUSTMENT

Run engine until warm and install tachometer sensor (US 1324). Connect tachometer and set idle speed. Accelerate

TUNE-UP (Cont.)

engine briefly to full throttle. If maximum speed does not match specifications, loosen speed locknut and adjust. Turning screw out raises speed, turning screw in lowers speed. Apply thread sealer and tighten locknut.

Maximum Speed Specifications

Application	Maximum RPM
Vanagon	4750-4850
All Other Models	5300-5400

GENERAL SERVICING

FUEL SYSTEMS

FUEL INJECTION

All models use Bosch Diesel Fuel Injection.

ELECTRICAL

BATTERY

Application	Amp. Hr. Rating
All Models	63

Battery Location — Battery is located in engine compartment.

STARTER

All models are equipped with Bosch Starters.

ALTERNATOR

Application	Rated Amp. Output
Vanagon	65
All Other Models	55

ALTERNATOR REGULATOR

Bosch & Motorola — Non-Adjustable; integral with alternator.

BELT ADJUSTMENT

Application	①Deflection In. (mm)
All Belts	⅜-⁹⁄₁₆ (10-15)

① — Measured between longest span and depressed with firm thumb pressure.

FILTERS

Filter	Service Interval (Miles)
Oil Filter	Replace every 7500
Air Filter	Replace every 15,000
Fuel Filter	Replace every 15,000

CAPACITIES

Application	Quantity
Crankcase (Includes Filter)	
Dasher	①3.7 qts.
Rabbit & Rabbit Pickup	4.7 qts.
Vanagon	4.2 qts.
Cooling System	
Dasher	5.9 qts.
Rabbit & Rabbit Pickup	7.3 qts.
Vanagon	16.9 qts.
Manual Transmission (SAE80W-90)	
4-Speed	3.1 pts.
5-Speed	4.2 pts.
Fuel Tank	
Dasher	11.9 gals.
Rabbit	10.0 gals.
Rabbit Pickup	15.0 gals.
Vanagon	16.0 gals.

① — 3.2 quarts without filter.

TUNE-UP

DL
  Standard Engine
   MPG Engine
GL
  GLT Turbo

ENGINE IDENTIFICATION

B21F type engine identification number is stamped on left side of engine block near the distributor.

Engine Code

Application	Code
Standard Engine	
Federal	
Man. Trans.	498-920
Auto. Trans.	498-921
Calif.	
Man. Trans.	498-892
Auto. Trans.	498-893
MPG Engine	
Man. Trans.	498-896
Auto. Trans.	498-897
Turbo Engine	498-898

COMPRESSION PRESSURE

Check compression with engine at normal operating temperature, all spark plugs removed, throttle valve wide open and at normal cranking speed (250-300 RPM). Crank engine at least 6 "puffs" per cylinder.

Compression Pressure Specifications

Application	Pressure psi (kg/cm²)
All Models	128-156 (9-11)

VALVE CLEARANCE

1) Valve clearance is adjusted with engine shut off and either warm or cold. Remove valve cover. Turn crankshaft center bolt until camshaft is in position for firing No. 1 cylinder. Both cam lobes should point up at equally large angles. Pulley timing mark should be at 0°.

2) Check valve clearance of No. 1 cylinder, using a feeler gauge between camshaft lobe and adjusting discs. Intake and exhaust valves have same clearances.

3) If clearances are incorrect adjust by changing thickness of discs, which are available in .05 mm increments from 3.30 to 4.50 mm. Use tools 5022 and 5026 to depress and remove discs.

4) After valves for No. 1 cylinder are properly adjusted, rotate crankshaft to firing position for No. 3, No. 4, and No. 2 cylinders in sequence and complete adjustment.

Valve Clearance Specifications

Application	Cold In. (mm)	Hot In. (mm)
Intake and Exhaust		
Checking	.010-.018	.012-.020
	(.30-.45)	(.35-.50)
Setting	.014-.016	.016-.018
	(.35-.40)	(.40-.45)

VALVE ARRANGEMENT

E-I-E-I-E-I-E-I (front to rear).

SPARK PLUGS

Application	Gap In. (mm)	Torque Ft. Lbs. (N·m)
All Models	.030 (.75)	19 (26)

Spark Plug Type

Application	Bosch No.
All Models	WR7DS

DISTRIBUTOR

All models except the GL with the MPG engine are equipped with Bosch Electronic Ignition Systems and no adjustments are required. The MPG engine is equipped with a Volvo Breakerless Ignition System, featuring computer-controlled spark advance and a Hall Effect distributor.

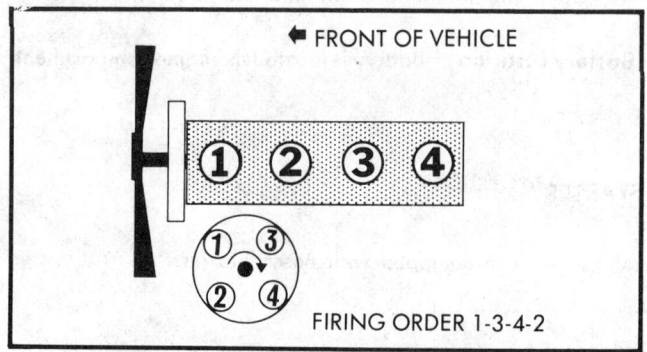

Fig. 1 *Firing Order and Distributor Rotation*

IGNITION TIMING

Connect timing light and tachometer. Disconnect and plug vacuum hose at distributor. Use idle air adjusting screw to set idle speed to specified timing RPM. Rotate distributor to set timing, then reconnect vacuum hose and reset idle.

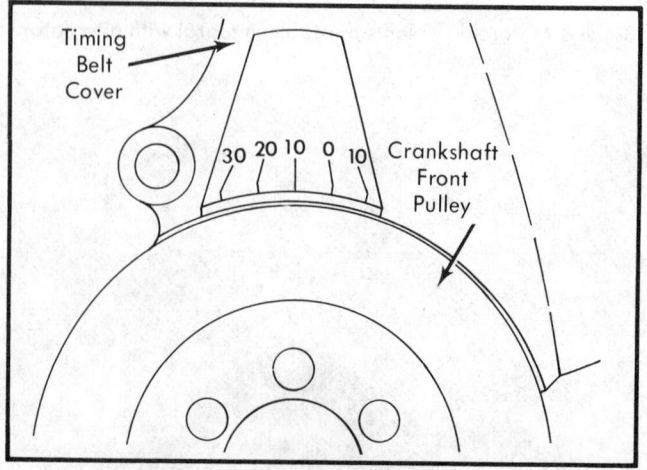

Fig. 2 *Timing Mark Location*

TUNE-UP (Cont.)

Ignition Timing Specifications
(Degrees BTDC @ RPM)

Application	① Timing
Standard Engine	
Federal	8 @ 750
Calif.	8 @ 900
MPG Engine	12 @ 750
Turbo Engine	12 @ 900

① — With distributor vacuum hose connected and plugged.

IDLE SPEED & MIXTURE

NOTE — *Mixture control adjustment screw opening is plugged to prevent tampering. Adjustment is not a normal maintenance procedure and should not be performed unless mixture control unit is replaced or vehicle fails emissions testing.*

1) Remove mixture control unit, separate control unit and drive out mixture plug (steel ball) with a punch. Reassemble control unit and reinstall.

2) Disconnect oxygen sensor electrical connector. Remove plug in exhaust pipe in front of catalytic converter and insert CO probe. Connect tachometer. Start engine and run to normal operating temperature. Adjust idle speed to specification.

NOTE — *Idle speed cannot be adjusted on vehicles with constant idle speed system (all except DL and GL models with standard engine). Idle adjustment is factory-sealed and no adjustment is required.*

3) If CO reading is not within specifications, insert adjusting wrench (5015) into adjustment hole and adjust CO reading to specifications. Reconnect oxygen sensor electrical connector and check CO reading. Repeat adjustment procedure if necessary. See Fig. 3.

NOTE — *After each adjustment, the adjusting wrench must be removed and the hole covered to prevent a lean mixture while taking a CO reading.*

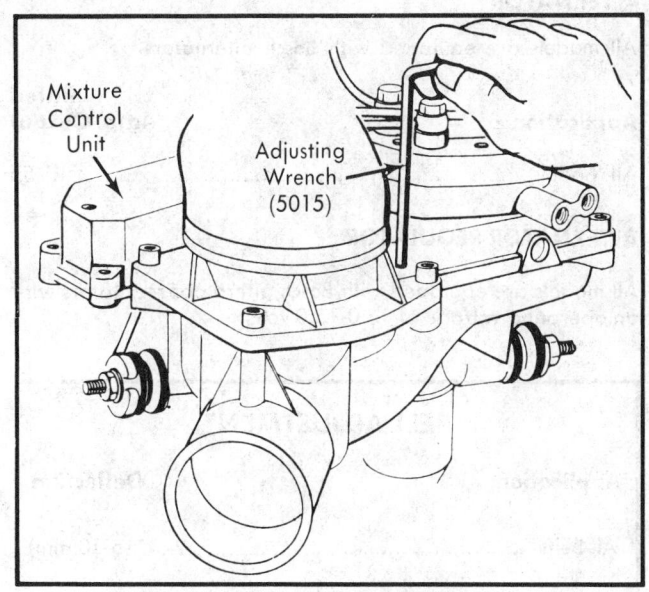

Fig. 3   Idle Mixture Adjustment

4) After CO adjustment, adjust idle speed as necessary on vehicles without constant idle speed system. Remove test equipment, insert exhaust pipe plug and seal mixture adjustment hole.

Idle Speed & CO Level

Application	Idle RPM	CO%
MPG Engine	750	① 0.7-1.3
All Other Models	900	① 0.7-1.3

① — With sensor disconnected. With sensor connected, level should be below 1%.

FUEL PUMP PRESSURE

Pressure .... 64-74 psi (4.5-5.2 kg/cm²)

EMISSION CONTROL SYSTEMS

See *Mitchell Manuals' Emission Control Manual.*

GENERAL SERVICING

DISTRIBUTOR
All models except those with the MPG engine are equipped with Bosch Electronic Ignition Systems. The MPG engine has a Volvo Breakerless Ignition System with computer-controlled spark advance and a Hall Effect distributor.

FUEL SYSTEM

FUEL INJECTION
All models are equipped with Bosch Lambda CIS fuel injection with oxygen sensor.

ELECTRICAL

BATTERY
Battery Location — Battery is located in left front of engine compartment.

Application	Amp. Hour Rating
All Models	60

STARTER

Bosch...	Overrunning Clutch

Starter Specifications

Application	Volts	Amps	Test RPM
All Models	11.5	30-50	5500-7500

TUNE-UP (Cont.)

ALTERNATOR

All models are equipped with Bosch alternators.

Application	Rated Amp. Output
All Models	55

ALTERNATOR REGULATOR

All models are equipped with Bosch alternator regulators with an operating voltage of 13.0-15.0 volts.

BELT ADJUSTMENT

Application	①Deflection
All Belts	.2-.4" (5-10 mm)

① — Deflection is with thumb pressure applied midway on longest belt run.

FILTERS

Filter	Service Interval (Miles)
Oil Filter	
Exc. Turbo	Replace every 7500
Turbo	Replace every 3750
Air Filter	Replace every 30,000
Fuel Filter	Replace every 45,000
Fuel Tank Filter	Replace every 60,000

CAPACITIES

Application	Quantity
Crankcase (Including Filter)	
Exc. Turbo	4.0 qts.
Turbo	4.7 qts.
Cooling System (Includes Heater)	10.0 qts.
Man. Trans. (ATF Type F)	
With Overdrive	2.4 qts.
Without Overdrive	1.6 pts.
Auto. Trans. (ATF Type F)	7.3 qts.
Rear Axle (SAE 90)	3.4 pts.
Fuel Tank	15.8 gals.

TUNE-UP

Coupe
GLE

ENGINE IDENTIFICATION

B28F engine identification number is stamped in lower left front corner of block above oil pan.

Engine Code

Application	Code
Federal	
Man. Trans.	498-640
Auto. Trans.	498-641
Calif.	
Man. Trans.	498-638
Auto. Trans.	498-639

COMPRESSION PRESSURE

Check compression with engine at normal operating temperature, all spark plugs removed, throttle valve wide open and at normal cranking speed (250-300 RPM). Crank engine at least 6 "puffs" per cylinder.

Compression Pressure Specifications

Application	Pressure psi (kg/cm²)
All Models	114-156 (8-11)

VALVE CLEARANCE

1) Adjust valves with engine cold. Rotate crankshaft so No. 1 cylinder is at TDC of ignition stroke (both rocker arms for No. 1 cylinder have clearance).

NOTE — *Crank pulley has 2 notches. When No. 1 cylinder is at TDC, upper notch will align with "0" notch on timing marker and lower crank pulley notch will be 150° counterclockwise from upper notch. (Second notch is TDC for No. 6 cylinder when aligned with "0" on timing marker).*

2) Adjust valves in sequence as follows:

Intake	Exhaust
Cyl. 1	Cyl. 1
Cyl. 2	Cyl. 3
Cyl. 4	Cyl. 6

3) Rotate crankshaft 360°. This will set No. 1 cylinder at TDC of exhaust stroke (rocker arms for No. 1 cylinder indicating no clearance). Adjust valves in following sequence:

Intake	Exhaust
Cyl. 3	Cyl. 2
Cyl. 5	Cyl. 4
Cyl. 6	Cyl. 5

Valve Clearance Specifications

Application	Intake In. (mm)	Exhaust In. (mm)
All Models	.004-.006 (.10-.15)	.010-.012 (.25-.30)

VALVE ARRANGEMENT①

Right Bank: E-I-E-I-E-I (front to rear).
Left Bank: I-E-I-E-I-E (front to rear).

① — Intake valves are inside the engine's "V"; exhaust valves are on outer sides of heads.

SPARK PLUGS

Application	Gap In. (mm)	Torque Ft. Lbs. (N·m)
All Models	.030 (.75)	9 (12)

Spark Plug Type

Application	Bosch No.
All Models	HR6DS

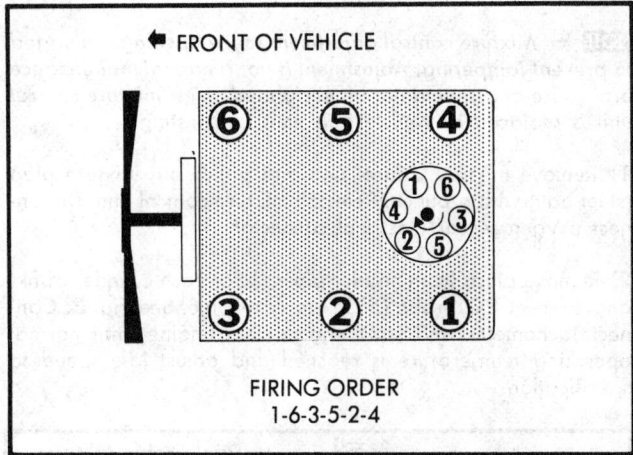

Fig. 1 *Firing Order and Distributor Rotation*

DISTRIBUTOR

All models are equipped with the Bosch Electronic Ignition System and no adjustments are required.

IGNITION TIMING

Connect a timing light and tachometer. Disconnect and plug distributor vacuum hose. Use idle air adjusting screw to set idle speed to specified timing RPM. Rotate distributor to set timing to specifications. Reconnect distributor vacuum hose.

TUNE-UP (Cont.)

Ignition Timing Specifications
(Degrees BTDC @ RPM)

Application	① Timing
Federal	10@750
Calif.	10@900

① — With distributor vacuum hose disconnected and plugged.

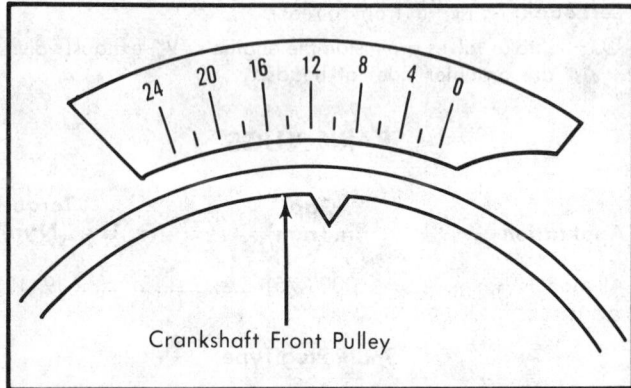

Fig. 2   Ignition Timing Mark Location

IDLE SPEED & MIXTURE

NOTE — *Mixture control adjustment screw opening is plugged to prevent tampering. Adjustment is not a normal maintenance procedure and should not be performed unless mixture control unit is replaced or vehicle fails emissions testing.*

1) Remove mixture control unit and punch out mixture plug (steel ball) with a punch. Reinstall mixture control unit. Disconnect oxygen sensor electrical connector.

2) Remove plugs from header pipes (1 for each cylinder bank) and connect CO probe (5151) to each pipe. See *Fig. 3.* Connect tachometer and start engine. Run engine until normal operating temperature is reached and adjust idle speed to specification.

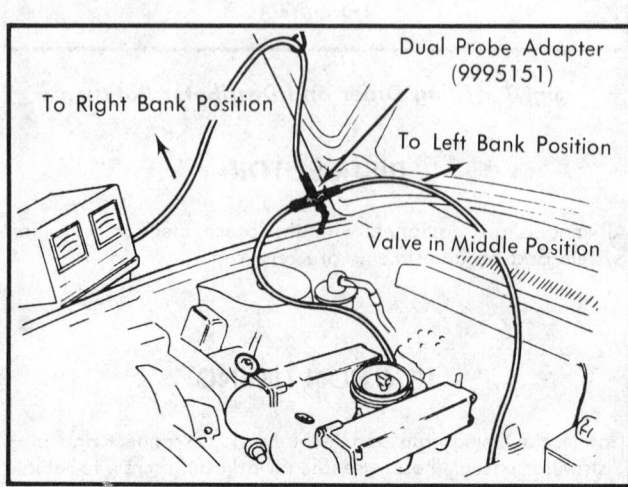

Fig. 3   CO Meter Installation

NOTE — *Idle speed cannot be adjusted on California vehicles with costant idle speed system. Idle adjustment is factory-sealed and no adjustment is required.*

3) Turn dual probe adapter to center position. In this position exhaust gases are admitted from both cylinder banks for total CO level reading. Read CO level.

NOTE — *When checking CO level, mixture adjustment hole must be covered to prevent a lean mixture.*

4) With CO meter and tachometer still installed, install air cleaner and connect hoses. To adjust CO level, insert adjusting wrench (5102) into adjustment hole and adjust CO to specifications. See *Fig. 4.*

NOTE — *After each adjustment, adjusting wrench must be removed and adjustment hole covered to prevent a lean mixture while checking CO level.*

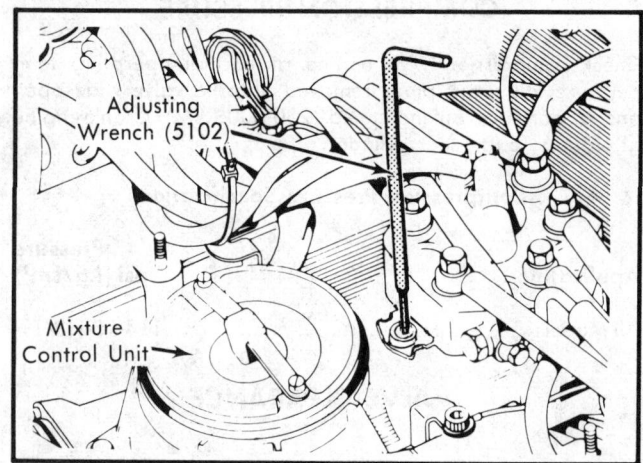

Fig. 4   Idle Mixture Adjustment

5) To check CO balance between left and right cylinder banks, proceed as follows: Turn dual probe adapter toward left cylinder bank and check CO reading. If left bank CO level is not within specifications, correct by removing balance screw plug and adjusting balance screw "2". See *Fig. 5.*

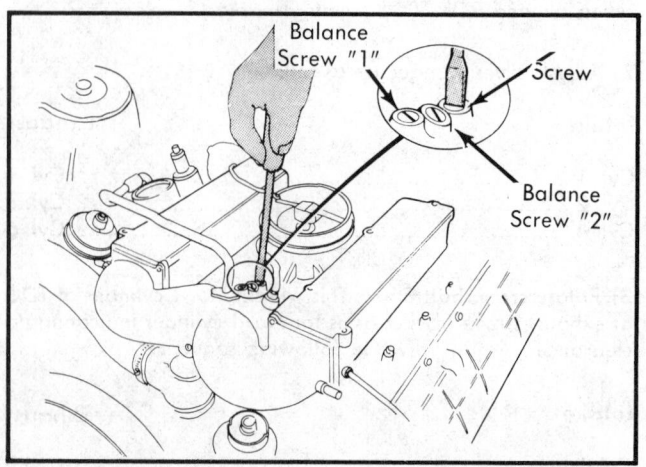

Fig. 5   Idle and Mixture Adjusting Screws

1981 Volvo V6 Tune-Up

TUNE-UP (Cont.)

NOTE — *Left balance screw goes to right side manifold and right balance screw goes to left side manifold.*

6) Turn dual probe adapter toward right cylinder bank and check CO reading. If right bank CO level is not within specifications, correct by removing balance screw plug and adjusting balance screw "1". See *Fig. 5.*

NOTE — *CO reading should be equal for both banks and correct for the total system.*

7) Recheck CO level with dual probe adapter in center position. If necessary, repeat adjustment procedure. Reconnect oxygen sensor electrical connector.

8) Recheck idle speed and adjust as necessary on vehicles without constant idle speed system. Remove test equipment, insert exhaust pipe plugs and seal mixture adjustment hole.

Idle Speed & CO Level

Application	Idle RPM	CO%
All Models	900	①0.7-1.3

① — With oxygen sensor connected, CO level should drop below 1.0%.

FUEL PUMP PRESSURE

Pressure .... 64-74 psi (4.5-5.2 kg/cm²)

EMISSION CONTROL SYSTEMS

See *Mitchell Manuals' Emission Control Manual.*

GENERAL SERVICING

IGNITION

DISTRIBUTOR

All models are equipped with the Bosch Electronic Ignition System.

FUEL SYSTEM

FUEL INJECTION

All models are equipped with Bosch Lambda/CIS fuel injection systems.

ELECTRICAL

BATTERY

12 Volt — Negative Ground.

Application	Amp. Hr. Rating
All Models	70

Battery Location — In engine compartment on right side.

STARTER

Bosch .... Overrunning Clutch

Starter Specifications

Application	Volts	Amps	Test RPM
All Models	11.5	30-50	5500-7500

ALTERNATOR

All models are equipped with SEV Marchal alternators.

Application	Rated Amp. Output
All Models	70

ALTERNATOR REGULATOR

All models are equipped with Bosch regulators with an operating voltage of 13.0-15.0 volts at 4000 RPM.

BELT ADJUSTMENT

Application	①Deflection
All Belts	.2-.4" (5-10 mm)

① — Deflection is measured with thumb pressure applied at midpoint of longest belt run.

FILTERS

Filter	Service Interval (Miles)
Oil Filter	Replace every 7500
Air Filter	Replace every 30,000
Fuel Filter	Replace every 45,000
Fuel Tank Filter	Replace every 60,000

CAPACITIES

Application	Quantity
Crankcase (Includes Filter)	6.9 qts.
Cooling System (Includes Heater)	11.5 qts.
Man. Trans. with Overdrive (ATF Type F)	2.4 qts.
Auto. Trans. (ATF Type F)	7.3 qts.
Rear Axle (SAE 90)	1.7 qts.
Fuel Tank	15.8 gals.

TUNE-UP

GL Diesel

ENGINE IDENTIFICATION

D24 diesel engine identification numbers are stamped on left side of block under vacuum pump.

Engine Code

Application	Code
Man. Trans.	498-704
Auto. Trans.	498-705

COMPRESSION PRESSURE

Disconnect wire at stop valve on injection pump. Remove vacuum pump and pump plunger. Clean fuel delivery pipes, remove pipes, and plug all openings. Remove injectors and heat shields. Place heat shield back in injector opening, followed by adapter 5191. Connect compression gauge and test compression.

Compression Pressure Specifications

Application	Pressure psi (kg/cm²)
Normal (New Engine)	485 (34.0)
Minimum	400 (28.0)
Maximum Variation	70 (5.0)

VALVE CLEARANCE

1) Turn engine using wrench on crankshaft pulley until No. 1 cylinder is at TDC on compression stroke. Remove valve cover. Both cam lobes should point upwards at equal angles.

2) Check valve clearance for No. 1 cylinder. If not correct, turn crankshaft ¼ turn ATDC (so valves will not hit piston top). Depress cam followers with tool 5196. Using pliers (tool 5195), remove disc. Calculate thickness of disc needed, coat with oil, and install.

NOTE — *New discs are available in thicknesses from .130" (3.30 mm) to .167" (4.25 mm) in increments of .002" (.05 mm). New discs should be positioned with marks down.*

3) Check valve clearance on remaining cylinders, proceeding in firing order. Be sure to check valve clearance at TDC and turn ¼ turn after TDC before depressing valves.

Valve Clearance Specifications

Application	Clearance In. (mm)
Checking	
Cold	
Intake	.006-.010 (.15-.25)
Exhaust	.014-.018 (.35-.45)
Warm	
Intake	.008-.012 (.20-.30)
Exhaust	.016-.020 (.40-.50)
Adjustment	
Cold	
Intake	.008 (.20)
Exhaust	.016 (.40)
Warm	
Intake	.010 (.25)
Exhaust	.018 (.45)

VALVE ARRANGEMENT

E-I-E-I-E-I-I-E-I-E-I-E

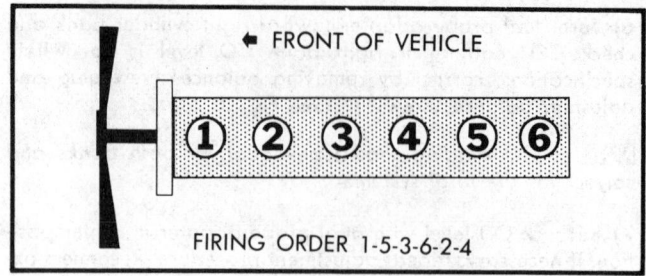

Fig. 1 Firing Order Illustration

GLOW PLUGS

Glow Plug Type

Application	Volvo Part No.
All Models	1257141-0

IDLE SPEED ADJUSTMENT

1) Connect photo-electric tachometer. Warm engine to normal operating temperature. Adjust low idle speed to 750-850 RPM. Check maximum engine speed and adjust if necessary to 5100-5300 RPM. *See Fig. 2.*

2) Stop engine and disconnect link rod at lever on injection pump. Adjust throttle cable by turning cable sheath nut. Cable should be tight but not move pulley. Depress accelerator pedal and ensure that pulley touches full speed stop.

3) On automatic transmission models, depress accelerator to floor. Kickdown cable should move 2.05" (52 mm) between end positions. In idle position, cable should be stretched and clearance between clip and cable sheath should be .01-.04" (.25-1.0 mm)

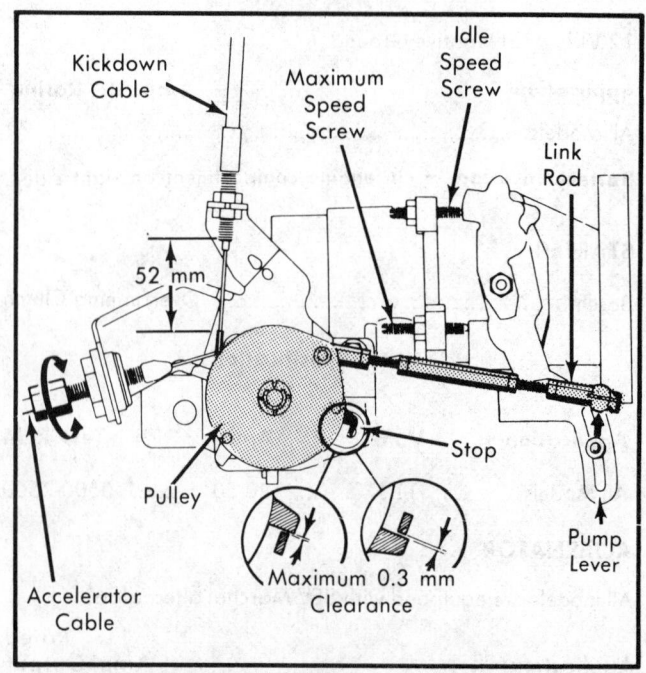

Fig. 2 Adjusting Idle Speed and Throttle Linkage

TUNE-UP (Cont.)

4) Connect link rod to injection pump lever. Turn pulley to maximum throttle position and adjust length of link (by rotating) until lever touches maximum speed screw.

5) Return pulley to idle position and move link rod ball joint in lever slot until lever touches idle adjusting screw. Recheck adjustments and repeat if necessary until idle speed and throttle positions are correct.

NOTE — *A clearance of .012" (.3 mm) is permissible between pulley and stop.*

Idle Speed Specification

Application	Idle RPM	Maximum RPM
All Models	750-850	5100-5300

GENERAL SERVICING

FUEL SYSTEM

FUEL INJECTION

All models use Bosch diesel fuel injection.

ELECTRICAL

BATTERY

Application	Amp. Hr. Rating
All Models	88

Battery Location — Left front of engine compartment.

STARTER

All models are equipped with Bosch starters.

ALTERNATOR

All models are equipped with Bosch alternators.

Application	Rated Amp. Output
All Models	55

ALTERNATOR REGULATOR

All models are equipped with Bosch non-adjustable voltage regulators with operating voltage of 13.9-14.8 volts.

BELT ADJUSTMENT

Adjust belts for deflection of ³⁄₁₆-³⁄₈" (5-10 mm) when depressed firmly halfway between pulleys.

FILTERS

Filter	Service Interval (Miles)
Oil Filter	①Replace every 15,000
Fuel Filter	Drain every 7500
	Replace every 15,000
Air Filter	Replace every 30,000

① — First change at 7500 miles.

CAPACITIES

Application	Quantity
Crankcase (Includes Filter)	7.4 qts.
Cooling System (Includes Heater)	
Man. Trans.	10.0 qts.
Auto. Trans.	9.8 qts.
Man. Trans. (ATF Type F)	2.4 qts.
Auto. Trans. (ATF Type F)	7.3 qts.
Rear Axle (SAE 90)	1.7 qts.
Fuel Tank	15.8 gals.

Section 2
FUEL SYSTEMS

Contents

NOTE — ALSO SEE GENERAL INDEX

CARBURETION TROUBLE SHOOTING

CONDITION & POSSIBLE CAUSE	CONDITION & POSSIBLE CAUSE

COLD STARTING SYMPTOM

Engine Cranks, Will Not Start

- Choke not closing (frozen).
- Choke cable or linkage binding or out of adjustment.
- Pinched or blocked fuel line or filter.
- Faulty fuel pump (pressure too high).
- Faulty cold start or thermo start valve.
- Poor contact or damaged needle valve and valve seat.

Flooding

- Faulty fuel inlet needle and/or seat.
- Dirty needle valve and seat.
- Excessive fuel pump pressure.
- Improper fuel/float level (too high).
- Ruptured, split internal carburetor seals or gaskets.
- Choke plate setting (vacuum kick) too narrow.
- Wrong fast idle cam index.
- Fast idle RPM too low.

Engine Stalls After Starting

- Choke plate setting (vacuum kick) too wide.
- Fast idle RPM too low.
- Wrong fast idle cam index.
- Vacuum leak.
- Low fuel pump output.
- Fuel/float level too low.
- Faulty intake manifold gasket.
- Incorrect air/fuel mixture setting.
- Faulty idle fuel shut-off valve.
- Blocked idler jet.

Engine Starts; Idles Rough and Erratic

- Vacuum leak.
- Incorrect idle RPM.
- Damaged idle adjust screw.
- Clogged slow jet.
- Incorrect fast idle cam index setting.
- Leaking carburetor seals.
- Incorrect fuel/float level.
- Blocked idling air and/or by-pass holes.
- Faulty anti-dieseling solenoid valve.
- Worn throttle shafts.
- Stuck anti-stall dashpot.

HOT STARTING SYMPTOM

Engine Cranks, Will Not Start

- Engine flooded (fuel/float level too high).
- Fuel vapors in carburetor bowl.
- Fuel line hot (touching engine block or exhaust).

COLD ENGINE DRIVEABILITY SYMPTOM

Engine Stalls When Put in Gear

- Incorrect choke vacuum kick setting.
- Fast idle RPM too low.
- Incorrect fast idle cam setting.
- Improper choke adjustment.
- Improper accelerator pump operation.
- Incorrect fuel/float level (too low).

Hesitation, Stalling During Acceleration (Backfire, Stumble)

- Defective choke control switch.
- Incorrect choke vacuum kick setting.
- Incorrect fuel/float level (too low).
- Faulty accelerator pump or blocked pump discharge.
- Secondary throttle not closed, wrong lockout adjustment.
- Blocked by-pass holes and ducts.
- Incorrect intake air preheater setting.
- Blocked main and/or air corrector jets.
- Faulty power valve.
- Plugged heat crossover system.

WARM ENGINE DRIVEABILITY SYMPTOM

Low Power, Surging High Speed Operation

- Clogged main jets.
- Dirty (restricted) fuel filter.
- Blocked (pinched) fuel line.
- Faulty power valve.
- Improperly adjusted throttle linkage (not opening fully).
- Incorrect fuel pump output (too low).
- Improper fuel/float level.
- Leaking carburetor seals.
- Incorrect air/fuel mixture setting.
- Constant operation of choke valve.

Excessive Fuel Consumption

- Fuel system leak.
- Wrong size jets.
- Faulty fuel inlet needle and/or seat.
- Incorrect fuel mixture setting.
- Dirty (restircted) air cleaner.
- Excessive accelerator pump discharge.
- Intake air preheater not ON or OFF according to season.
- Faulty enrichment system (constant operation).
- Choke valve not opening completely.
- Secondary throttle opens too early.

GASOLINE FUEL INJECTION TROUBLE SHOOTING

CONDITION & POSSIBLE CAUSE	CONDITION & POSSIBLE CAUSE

COLD START SYMPTOM

Engine Cranks, Will Not Start

- Inoperative fuel pump (blown fuse or relay).
- Incorrect "cold" control pressure (CIS).
- Auxiliary air valve does not operate.
- Cold start injector does not operate.
- Incorrectly adjusted sensor plate stop (CIS).
- Incorrectly adjusted throttle switch (AFC).
- Sensor plate and/or plunger sticking.
- Vacuum leak(s).
- Fuel system leak(s).
- Faulty thermo time switch.
- Distributor triggering contacts (AFC).
- Faulty temperature sensors (AFC).
- Faulty air flow meter potentiometer (AFC).
- Faulty air flow meter (AFC).

Engine Hard Starting

- Incorrect "cold" control pressure (CIS).
- Auxiliary air valve does not open.
- Cold start injector does not open.
- Cold start injector leaking.
- Incorrectly adjusted sensor plate stop (CIS).
- Incorrectly adjusted throttle switch (AFC).
- Vacuum leak(s).
- Fuel leak(s).
- Thermo time switch does not close.
- Faulty air flow meter potentiometer (AFC).

HOT STARTING SYMPTOM

Engine Cranks, Will Not Start

- Inoperative fuel pump (blown fuse or relay).
- Incorrect "warm" control pressure (CIS).
- Incorrectly adjusted sensor plate (CIS).
- Incorrectly adjusted throttle switch (AFC).
- Sensor plate and/or plunger stuck (CIS).
- Vacuum leak(s).
- Fuel system leak(s).
- Injectors leaking.
- Improper idle mixture setting.

Engine Hard Starting
(Long Cranking Time)

- Incorrect "warm" control pressure (CIS).
- Auxiliary air valve does not close.
- Incorrectly adjusted sensor plate stop (CIS).
- Incorrectly adjusted throttle switch (AFC).
- Vacuum leak(s).
- Fuel system leak(s).
- Injectors leaking.
- Improper Idle mixture setting.

Rough Idle During Warm-Up

- Incorrect "cold" control pressure.
- Auxiliary air valve does not close.
- Auxiliary air valve does not open.
- Cold start injector leaking.
- Vacuum leak(s).
- Fuel system leak(s).
- Injectors leaking.
- Thermo time switch inoperative.

HOT ENGINE DRIVEABILITY SYMPTOM

Rough Idle With Warm Engine

- Incorrect "warm" control pressure (CIS).
- Auxiliary air valve does not close.
- Faulty cold start injector.
- Sensor plate and/or plunger stuck (CIS).
- Throttle valve stuck (AFC).
- Incorrectly adjusted throttle switch (AFC).
- Vacuum leak(s).
- Fuel system leak(s).
- Injectors leaking.
- Improper idle mixture setting.
- Defective air temperature sensor (AFC).

CO Level Too High at Idle

- Incorrect "warm" control pressure (CIS).
- Cold start injector leaking.
- Sensor plate and/or plunger stuck (CIS).
- Incorrectly adjusted throttle switch (AFC).
- Fuel system leaking.
- Improper idle mixture setting.
- Improper fuel pressure.
- Faulty oxygen sensor.
- Faulty air flow meter potentiometer (AFC).
- Faulty temperature sensors (AFC).
- Dirty (restricted) air cleaner.

CO Level Too Low at Idle

- Incorrect "warm" control pressure (CIS).
- Vacuum leak(s).
- Improper idle mixture setting.

Poor Engine Performance

- Incorrect "warm" control pressure (CIS).
- Cold start injector leaking.
- Sensor plate and/or plunger stuck (CIS).
- Incorrectly adjusted throttle switch (AFC).
- Improper idle mixture setting.
- Throttle valve not opening completely.

GASOLINE FUEL INJECTION TROUBLE SHOOTING (Cont.)

CONDITION & POSSIBLE CAUSE

Excessive Fuel Consumption

- Incorrect "warm" control pressure (CIS).
- Cold start injector leaking.
- Fuel system leak(s).
- Improper idle mixture setting.
- Improper fuel pressure.
- Defective air flow meter potentiometer (AFC).
- Defective sensors (AFC).

Engine Misfire at High Speed

- Loose electrical contact at fuel pump.
- Primary pressure too low or too high (CIS).
- Fuel system leak(s).
- Defective air flow meter (AFC).
- Defective fuel pump circuit (AFC).

Engine Backfires into Intake Manifold

- Incorrect "warm" control pressure (CIS).
- Vacuum leak(s).
- Improper idle mixture setting.
- Defective air flow meter (AFC).

CONDITION & POSSIBLE CAUSE

Engine "Diesels"

- Sensor plate and/or plunger stuck (CIS).
- Incorrectly adjusted throttle switch (AFC).
- Injectors leaking.
- Faulty cold start injector.
- Defective air flow meter potentiometer (AFC).
- Defective sensors (AFC).

Idle Speed Too High; Cannot Be Lowered

- Auxiliary air valve does not close.
- Faulty throttle valve (AFC).

Engine Backfires into Exhaust Manifold

- Incorrect "warm" control pressure (CIS).
- Cold start injector leaks.
- Fuel system leaking.
- Improper idle mixture setting.
- Defective control unit.
- Improper fuel pressure.

DIESEL FUEL INJECTION TROUBLE SHOOTING

CONDITION & POSSIBLE CAUSE

HARD STARTING SYMPTOMS

Engine Cranks, Will Not Start

- Incorrect fuel or no fuel.
- Faulty glow plug.
- Air in fuel system.
- Faulty injector(s).
- Faulty injection pump.
- Improper injection pump timing.

Engine Starts, Will Not Run

- Air in fuel system.
- Modulator valve out of adjustment.
- Fuel lines, filter or tank plugged.
- Incorrect idle speed setting.

LOW SPEED DRIVEABILITY SYMPTOM

Engine Runs Rough

- Air or dirt in fuel system.
- Fuel system leak(s).
- Clogged or sticking injectors.
- Incorrect fuel.
- Governor or timing incorrect.
- Incorrect injection pump timing.

CONDITION & POSSIBLE CAUSE

Engine Idle Speed Too High

- Incorrect idle speed setting.
- Jammed modulator valve.
- Improperly adjusted governor.
- Vacuum leak(s) in manifold.

Poor Acceleration

- Incorrect fuel.
- Timing device stuck in idle position.
- Faulty fuel pump.
- Air or dirt in fuel system.
- Improper injection pump timing.
- Dirty or faulty injectors.

Engine Knocks

- Incorrect fuel.
- Air in fuel system.
- Incorrect injection pump timing.
- Dirt in injection pump or injectors.
- Incorrect idle speed setting.

DIESEL FUEL INJECTION TROUBLE SHOOTING (Cont.)

CONDITION & POSSIBLE CAUSE	CONDITION & POSSIBLE CAUSE
HIGH SPEED DRIVEABILITY SYMPTOM **Engine Smokes** ● Incorrect fuel. ● Air in fuel system. ● Incorrect injection pump adjustment. ● Incorrect injection pump timing. **Engine Exceeds Maximum Permissible Speed** ● Maximum speed stop misadjusted. ● Faulty governor. ● Control rod sticks open. ● Vacuum leak(s).	**Engine Has Loss of Power** ● Throttle valve not fully open. ● Clogged air filter. ● Badly worn pump plungers. ● Low fuel pressure. ● Timing device stuck in idle position. ● Control rod stuck. ● Incorrect fuel. **Engine Will Not Stop** ● Stop cable broken or misadjusted. ● Incorrect idle speed setting. ● Faulty governor. ● Defective solenoid.

ELECTRIC FUEL PUMP TROUBLE SHOOTING

NOTE — *This is a general trouble shooting guide. Not all steps will apply to all fuel pumps. Most electrical fuel pumps are sealed units and must be replaced if defective.*

CAUTION — *Be sure to relieve fuel pressure before opening a pressurized fuel injection system. Do not allow smoking, open flame or sparks in area while working on fuel system components. Fuel vapors may be present and danger of fire or explosion exists. Disconnect battery while working on fuel system.*

CONDITION & POSSIBLE CAUSE	CONDITION & POSSIBLE CAUSE
Pump Motor Not Operating; No Fuel Output ● Faulty wiring. ● Blown fuse. ● Defective fuel pump circuit. ● Defective inertia switch. ● Damaged pump body. ● Defective fuel pump relay. **Pump Operating; No Fuel Output** ● No fuel supply. ● Pinched or blocked fuel line. ● Blocked fuel filter. ● Faulty fuel cut-off valve. ● Faulty fuel pump contact points.	**Pump Operating; Low Fuel Output** ● Restricted fuel line, filter or damper. ● Poor fuel tank venting (may cause vacuum in tank if blocked). ● Air leak on inlet side of fuel pump. **Pump Noisy** ● Air leak on inlet side of fuel pump. ● Insecure fuel pump mounting. ● Metal fuel lines not secured. ● Defective insulation at pump mounting. **Excessive Pump Pressure** ● Defective pressure relief valve.

TURBOCHARGER TROUBLE SHOOTING

CONDITION & POSSIBLE CAUSE	CONDITION & POSSIBLE CAUSE
Excessive Charge Pressure • Leak at exhaust pressure line connection. • Clogged exhaust pressure line. • Damaged diaphragm in charge pressure regulator. • Charge pressure regulator valve stuck closed. • Ice formation in exhaust line. • Charge pressure regulator set wrong. **Engine Knocking** • Excessive charge pressure. • Fuel octane too low. • Ignition setting too far advanced. **Oil Leakage At Turbo Shaft** **(Oil Fumes in Exhaust)** • Poor oil return flow from turbocharger. • Turbocharger seals damaged. **Lack of Power** • Low cylinder compression. • Incorrect valve timing and/or clearance. • Incorrect ignition timing. • Restricted air cleaner element. • Insufficient fuel supply. • Fuel enrichment system not operating. **Detonation** **With No Boost** • Low grade fuel. • Ignition timing too far advanced. • Rough edge or foreign object in cylinder.	**Detonation** **With Normal Boost** • Low grade fuel. • Ignition timing too far advanced. • Insufficient fuel supply. • Fuel enrichment system not working. **Detonation** **With Excessive Boost** • Wastegate signal actuator line leaking. • Actuator tampered with. • Wastegate or actuator tampered with. **Excessive Fuel Consumption** **(Black Exhaust Smoke)** • Engine out of tune. • Intake air flow restricted. • Air delivery hoses kinked or collapsed. • Cold start valve or injectors leaking. • Fuel enrichment system will not shut off. **Excessive Oil Consumption** **(Blue, Gray or White Exhaust Smoke)** • Incorrect type of oil. • Extended oil change interval. • Clogged air cleaner element. • Excessive engine wear. • Internal leakage at seals in turbocharger. • Crankcase emission check valve stuck open or installed wrong.

AISAN 2-BARREL — TOYOTA 2F ENGINE

Land Cruiser

DESCRIPTION

Carburetor is a 2-barrel, downdraft type with vacuum operated choke breaker to improve cold engine operation. A secondary slow port helps fuel mixing at start of secondary valve opening. Improvement of operation is noticed during low speed load. A piston type accelerator pump is incorporated into the primary barrel and an auxiliary accelerator pump system aids in cold engine operation. Other equipment includes a diaphragm to open secondary valve at high speed and full throttle operation and a throttle positioner to prevent complete closing of throttle during deceleration. A throttle stop solenoid is also used to prevent dieseling during engine shut down.

CARBURETOR IDENTIFICATION

Application	Part No.
All Models	21100-61140

ADJUSTMENTS

HOT (SLOW) IDLE RPM

See appropriate TUNE-UP SERVICE PROCEDURES article.

IDLE MIXTURE

See appropriate TUNE-UP SERVICE PROCEDURES article.

COLD (FAST) IDLE RPM

See appropriate TUNE-UP SERVICE PROCEDURES article.

NOTE — It is recommended that Toyota carburetor adjusting kits 09240-00014 and 9240-00020 be used to make the following adjustments.

FLOAT LEVEL ADJUSTMENT

Turn air horn assembly upside-down. Measure clearance between upper surface of float and gasket surface of air horn. Bend center float tab until float level is correct. See Fig. 1

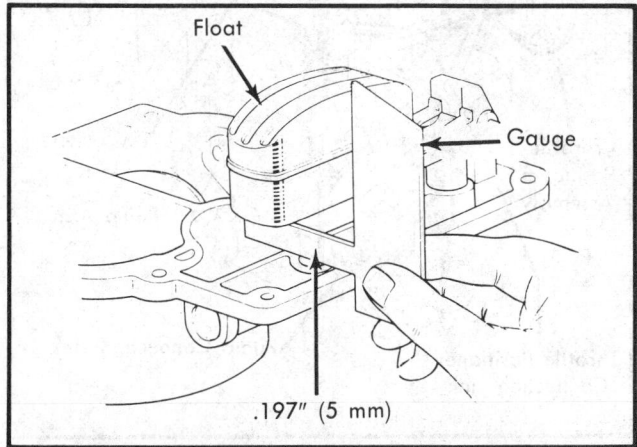

Fig. 1   Float Level Measurement Points

FLOAT DROP ADJUSTMENT

Lift up float assembly and measure clearance between needle valve plunger and float lip. Adjust clearance to specification by bending both outside float tabs. See Fig. 2.

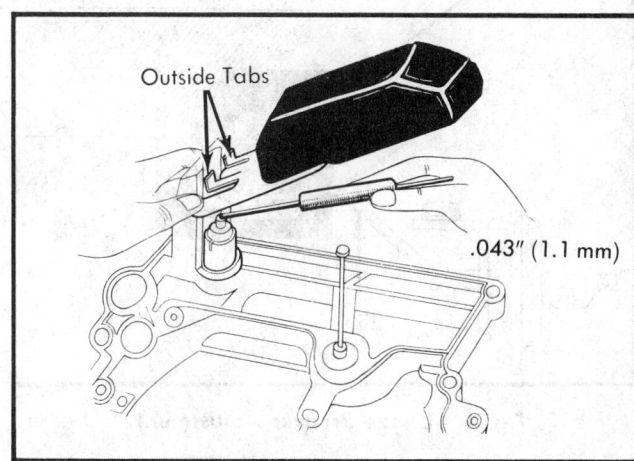

Fig. 2   Measuring Carburetor Float Drop with Gauge

PRIMARY & SECONDARY THROTTLE VALVE ADJUSTMENT

1) Open primary throttle valve. Then, open secondary throttle valve. Make sure valves are perpendicular to flange surface when fully opened.

2) Bend throttle lever stopper(s) until proper opening is obtained.

FAST IDLE (BENCH ADJUSTMENT)

Fully close choke valve. Check clearance between throttle bore and primary throttle valve. Adjust clearance to .051" (1.3 mm) by turning fast idle adjusting screw. See Fig. 3.

Fig. 3   Making Fast Idle Measurement and Adjustment

CHOKE BREAKER ADJUSTMENT

Push choke vacuum breaker diaphragm rod to open choke valve. Insert angle gauge. Set choke valve angle to 45° by bending choke-to-vacuum breaker diaphragm rod at existing bend. After adjustment, ensure smooth operation of choke valve. See Fig. 4.

1981 Aisan Carburetors

AISAN 2-BARREL — TOYOTA 2F ENGINE (Cont.)

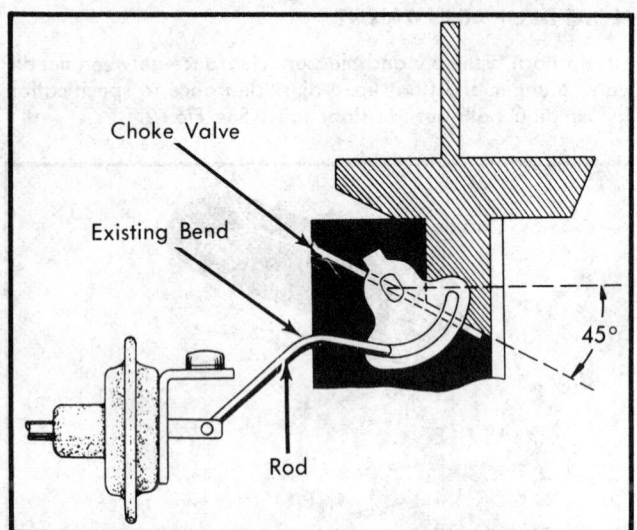

Fig. 4   Choke Breaker Adjustment

THROTTLE POSITIONER ADJUSTMENT

Turn carburetor upside-down and place throttle positioner adjusting screw against tab on throttle lever. Check clearance between throttle bore and primary valve. Adjust clearance to .031" (.8 mm) by turning throttle positioner adjusting screw. See Fig. 5.

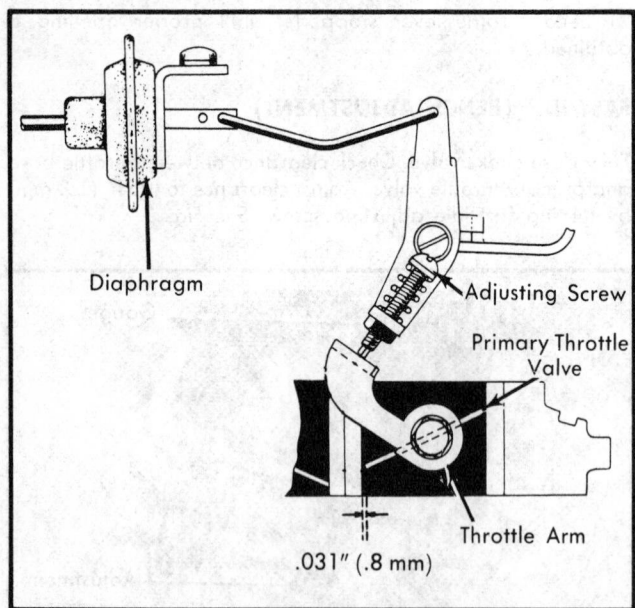

Fig. 5   Making Throttle Positioner Adjustment

SECONDARY THROTTLE OPENING ANGLE (KICK-UP)

Bend secondary throttle lever to obtain 25° angle between secondary throttle valve and bore when primary valve is fully open. See Fig. 6.

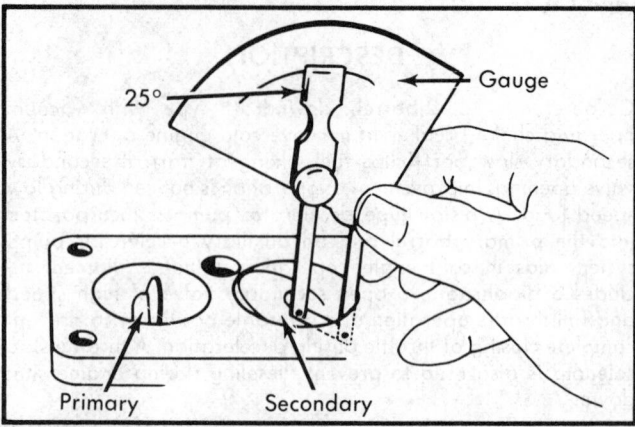

Fig. 6   Adjusting Secondary Throttle Opening Angle (Kick-Up)

OVERHAUL

NOTE — It is recommended that Toyota carburetor driver kit 09860-11010 be used during carburetor overhaul.

DISASSEMBLY

Body and Air Horn — Remove pump arm, pump connecting link, choke breaker connecting link, fast idle connecting link and throttle positioner assembly. See Fig. 7. Remove screws securing air horn to carburetor body and carefully lift off air horn assembly.

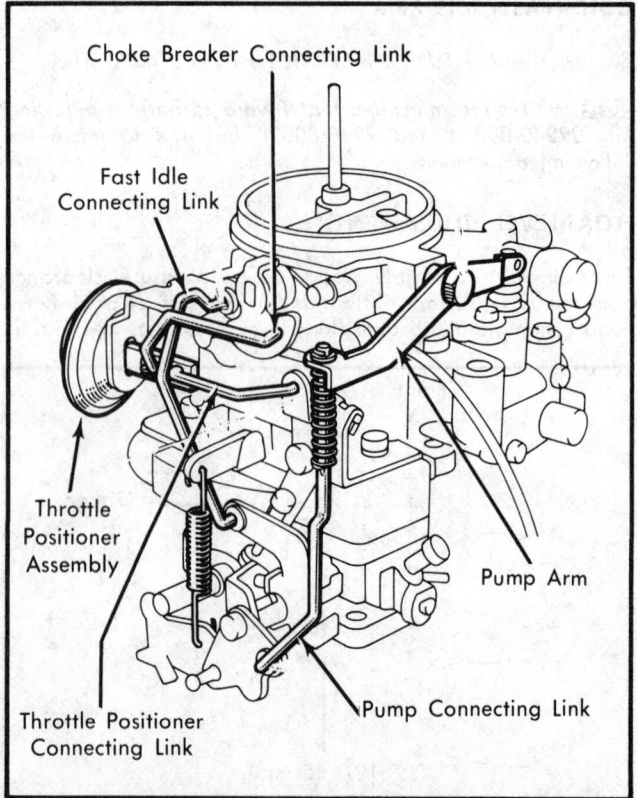

Fig. 7   Air Horn and Carburetor Body

AISAN 2-BARREL — TOYOTA 2F ENGINE (Cont.)

Air Horn — 1) Remove float assembly, needle valve and seat and pump plunger. Remove power piston retaining screw and retaining clip, then remove power piston and spring. Remove fuel shut-off solenoid. See Fig. 8.

NOTE — *Perform step 2 only if required.*

2) File off peened part of valve set screw and remove choke valve. Disconnect choke shaft return spring and pull out choke shaft.

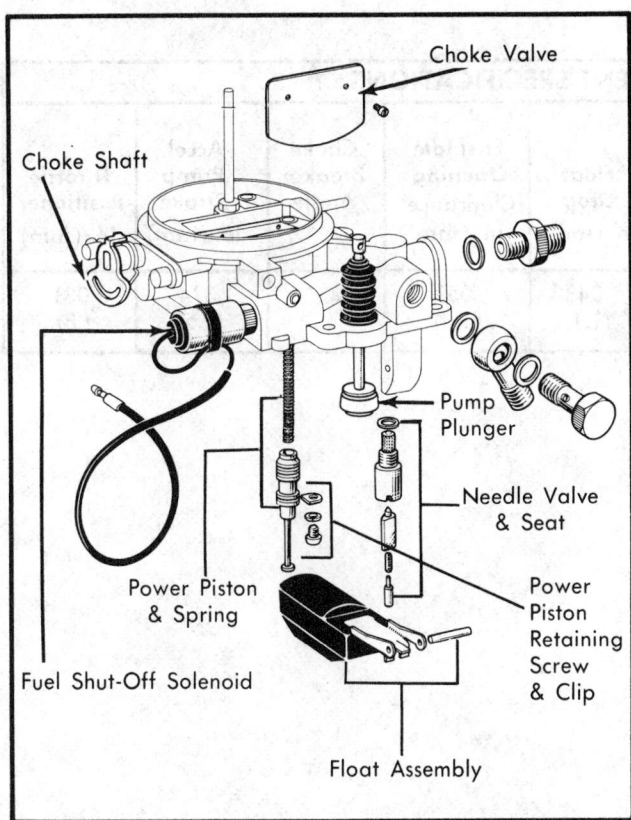

Fig. 8   Exploded View of Air Horn Assembly

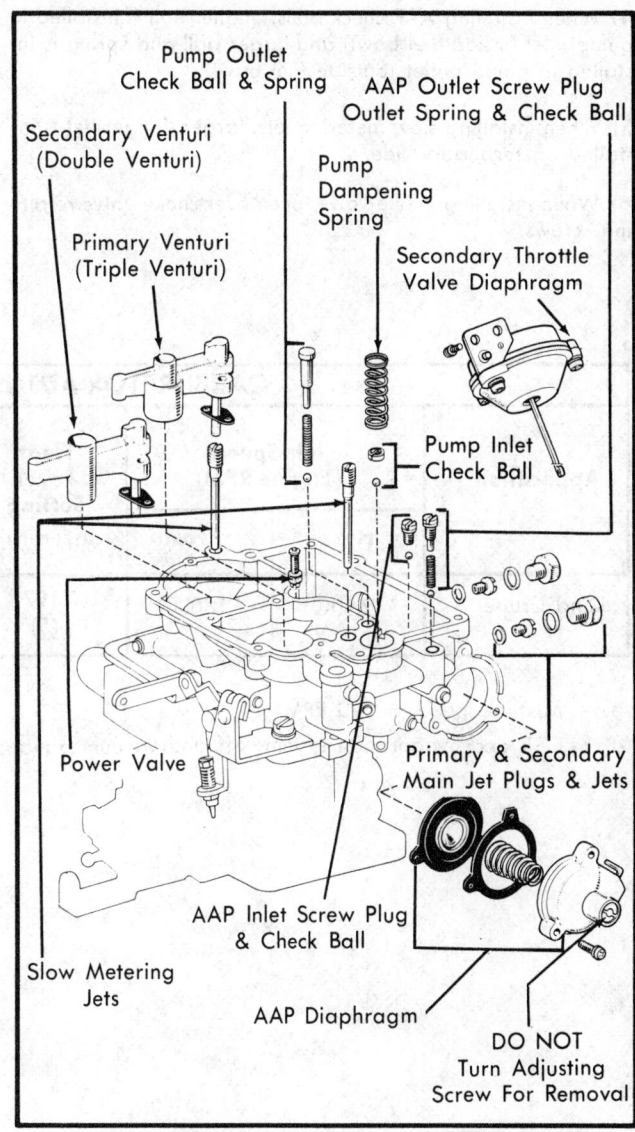

Fig. 9   Exploded View of Carburetor Main Body

Main Body — 1) Remove pump outlet check ball and spring, pump dampening spring and inlet check ball, and slow metering jets. See Fig. 9.

2) Loosen auxiliary accelerator pump (AAP) outlet screw plug, then remove outlet spring and check ball. Loosen AAP inlet screw plug, then remove check ball. Note size of check balls for reassembly reference.

3) Remove power valve. Remove primary and secondary main jet plugs and jets. Remove primary (triple venturi) and secondary (double venturi) venturi. Remove AAP diaphragm without turning adjusting screw. Remove secondary throttle valve diaphragm. Remove flange from carburetor body.

Flange Parts — Remove only those parts which are necessary for proper cleaning and inspection.

CLEANING & INSPECTION

Clean all parts in suitable solvent (carburetor cleaner) and blow dry. Do not attempt to clean jets or other passages with wire or other metal objects. Inspect all parts for wear or damage and replace necessary parts.

REASSEMBLY

1) When assembling AAP diaphragm, spring should be installed with small end away from diaphragm or toward cover.

2) When installing venturi, primary venturi is triple venturi and secondary is double venturi.

3) When installing primary and secondary main jets, primary jet is "brass" colored and secondary jet is "chrome" colored.

1981 Aisan Carburetors

AISAN 2-BARREL – TOYOTA 2F ENGINE (Cont.)

4) When installing AAP check balls, smaller ball is installed in pump inlet (inside fuel bowl) and larger ball and spring is installed in pump outlet (outside fuel bowl).

5) When installing slow metering jets, larger (longer) jet is installed on secondary side.

6) When installing choke valve, peen over choke valve retaining screws.

7) Make sure power piston operates smoothly after installing retaining clip and screw.

8) Make sure that needle valve, spring and plunger are properly installed in correct order. Float must be correctly adjusted.

9) When installing air horn to main body, take care not to damage pump plunger leather.

Application	Idle Speed (Engine RPM)		Float Level Setting In. (mm)	Float Drop In. (mm)	Fast Idle Opening Clearance In. (mm)	Choke Breaker Angle	Accel. Pump Stroke In. (mm)	Throttle Positioner In. (mm)
	Hot	Fast						
Land Cruiser	650①	1800②	.197 (5)	.043 (1.1)	.051 (1.3)	45°	.374 (9.5)	.031 (.8)

CARBURETOR ADJUSTMENT SPECIFICATIONS

① — Mixture speed — 690 RPM.
② — EGR and evaporation systems off and vacuum advance cut.

AISAN 2-BARREL — TOYOTA 3 A-C ENGINE

Tercel

DESCRIPTION

Carburetor is of 2-barrel, downdraft design and is equipped with automatic choke which is heated by an electrically operated bimetal heating coil. A piston type accelerator pump is incorporated into the primary barrel and an auxiliary accelerator pump system aids in cold engine acceleration. Other equipment includes diaphragms which open secondaries at high speed and full throttle operation. Other features include dash pot, mixture control, choke breaker, choke opener, deceleration fuel cut, hot idle compensation and high altitude compensation (Federal) devices.

CARBURETOR IDENTIFICATION

Application	Part No.
Federal	21100-15160
California	21100-15200

ADJUSTMENTS

HOT (SLOW) IDLE RPM

See appropriate TUNE-UP SERVICE PROCEDURES article.

IDLE MIXTURE

See appropriate TUNE-UP SERVICE PROCEDURES article.

COLD (FAST) IDLE RPM

See appropriate TUNE-UP SERVICE PROCEDURES article.

NOTE — It is recommended that Toyota carburetor adjusting kits 09240-00014 and 09240-00020 be used to make the following adjustments.

FLOAT LEVEL ADJUSTMENT

NOTE — When top and bottom lever positions are properly adjusted, float will maintain specified fuel level (glass level mark) when engine is running.

Hold air horn upside-down. Allow float to hang by its own weight. Measure gap between float lip and air horn gasket

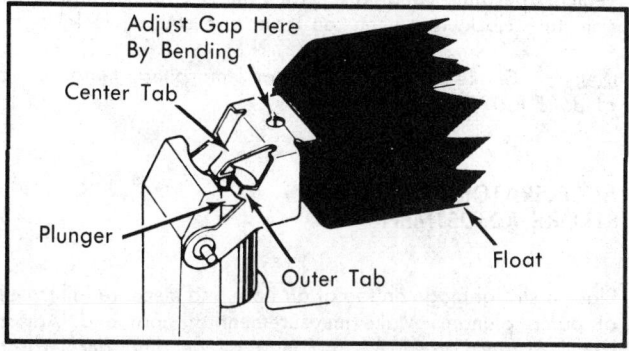

Fig. 1   Adjusting Carburetor Float Level

surface (gasket removed). Bend float by inserting suitable tool in hole until gap is correct. See Fig. 1 and 2.

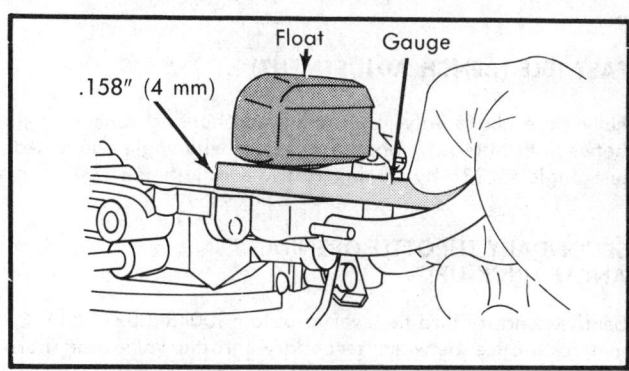

Fig. 2   Float Level Measurement Points and Gauge

FLOAT DROP ADJUSTMENT

Lift up float. Measure gap between needle valve and float lip. Bend float outer tab until gap is correct. See Fig. 3 and 4. After adjustment ensure plunger moves smoothly.

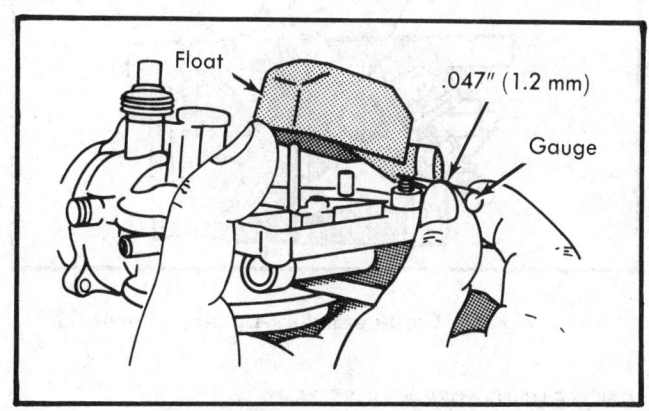

Fig. 3   Float Drop Measurement Points and Gauge

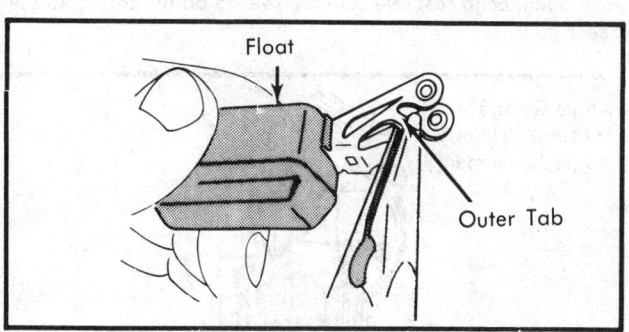

Fig. 4   Position for Adjusting Float Drop

PRIMARY & SECONDARY THROTTLE VALVES

1) Open primary throttle valve. Insert angle gauge. Adjust primary throttle valve angle to 90° (fully open) by bending throttle lever stopper.

AISAN 2-BARREL — TOYOTA 3 A-C ENGINE (Cont.)

2) With primary throttle valve fully open, open secondary throttle valve. Insert angle gauge. Adjust secondary throttle valve angle to 75° (fully open) by bending throttle lever stopper.

FAST IDLE (BENCH ADJUSTMENT)

Fully close choke valve by turning coil housing. Check angle between throttle valve and throttle bore with angle gauge. Adjust angle to 22° by turning fast idle adjusting screw.

SECONDARY THROTTLE OPENING ANGLE (KICK-UP)

Bend secondary throttle lever to obtain .0043-.0087" (.11-.22 mm) clearance between secondary throttle valve and bore when primary valve is fully open. See Fig. 5.

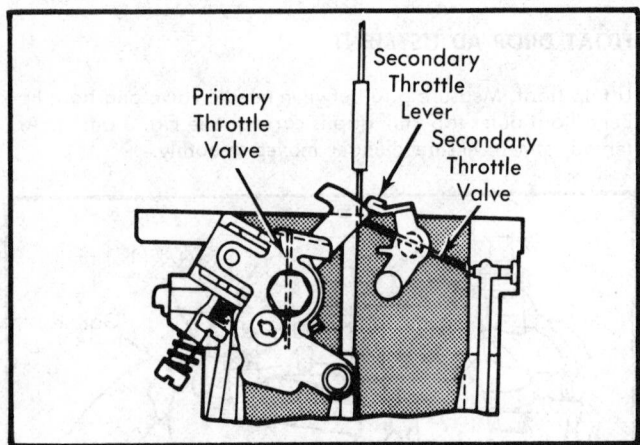

Fig. 5   Carburetor Kick-Up Adjustment

CHOKE UNLOADER ADJUSTMENT

Insert angle gauge. Adjust angle of choke valve so it will be 47° from fully closed position when primary throttle valve is fully open. Bend fast idle cam follower to obtain correct angle. See Fig. 6.

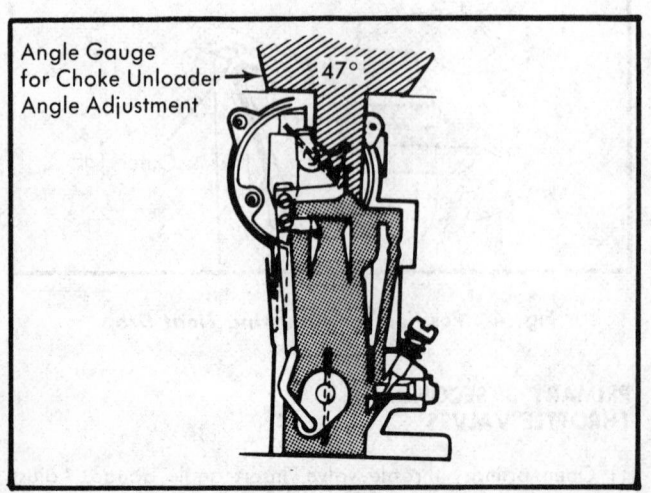

Fig. 6   Adjusting Choke Unloader Angle with Gauge

CHOKE BREAKER ADJUSTMENT

Fully close choke valve by turning coil housing. Connect hoses to breaker vacuum diaphragm and apply vacuum. With vacuum applied, adjust 1st choke angle to 37° and 2nd choke angle to 55° by bending release tang.

CHOKE OPENER ADJUSTMENT

Fully close choke valve by turning coil housing. Connect hose to opener diaphragm and apply vacuum. With vacuum applied, adjust choke angle 77° (between choke valve and bore) by bending relief lever tang.

THROTTLE POSITIONER ADJUSTMENT

1) Warm engine to normal operating temperature. Check and adjust idle speed if required. Disconnect and plug vacuum hoses from EGR valve and throttle positioner diaphragms. Throttle positioner should now be set.

2) With throttle positioner activated, engine speed should be 1400 RPM. If not, correct by turning throttle positioner adjusting screw making sure cooling fan is off.

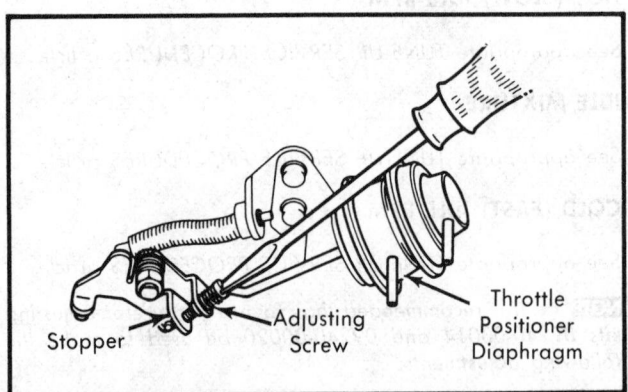

Fig. 7   Adjusting Throttle Positioner Setting Speed

AUTOMATIC CHOKE ADJUSTMENT

Set coil housing scale to center line of thermostat case. Turn coil housing and adjust engine starting mixture to conform with vehicle operating conditions. When mixture for starting is too rich, turn clockwise; when too lean, turn counterclockwise.

NOTE — Choke valve fully closes at atmospheric temperature of 86°F (30°C).

ACCELERATOR PUMP STROKE ADJUSTMENT

Place a straightedge on top of air horn and measure full travel of pump plunger. Make measurement at boot end. Adjust travel distance to .118" (3.0 mm) by bending accelerator pump actuating rod at existing bend. See Fig. 8.

AISAN 2-BARREL — TOYOTA 3 A-C ENGINE (Cont.)

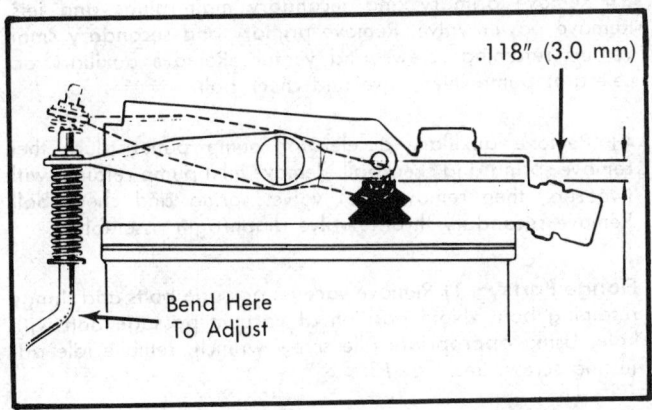

Fig. 8   Carburetor Accelerator Pump Stroke Adjustment

OVERHAUL

NOTE — *It is recommended that Toyota carburetor driver kit 09860-11011 be used during carburetor overhaul.*

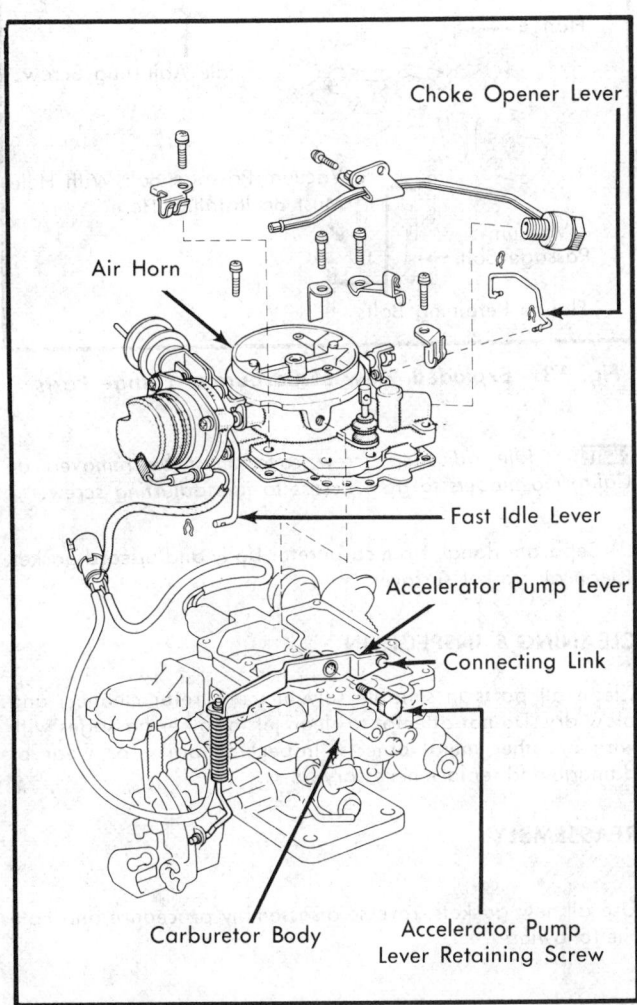

Fig. 9   Exploded View of Carburetor Air Horn

DISASSEMBLY

Air Horn — 1) Remove accelerator pump retaining screw and connecting link. Remove pump lever and connecting rod. Remove circlip from fast idle lever and disconnect lever. Remove choke opener lever circlips and lever. *See Fig. 9.*

2) Remove fuel inlet fitting and line. Remove 8 air horn retaining screws and auxiliary mounting clips. Remove air horn from carburetor body.

Float Assembly — 1) Remove pump plunger and float retaining pin and float. Remove needle valve pin, spring and valve. Remove power piston retaining screw and clip. Remove power piston and spring assembly. *See Fig. 10.*

2) Using appropriate driver from carburetor kit, remove needle valve seat and filter. Remove and discard gasket. Clean gasket mounting surface.

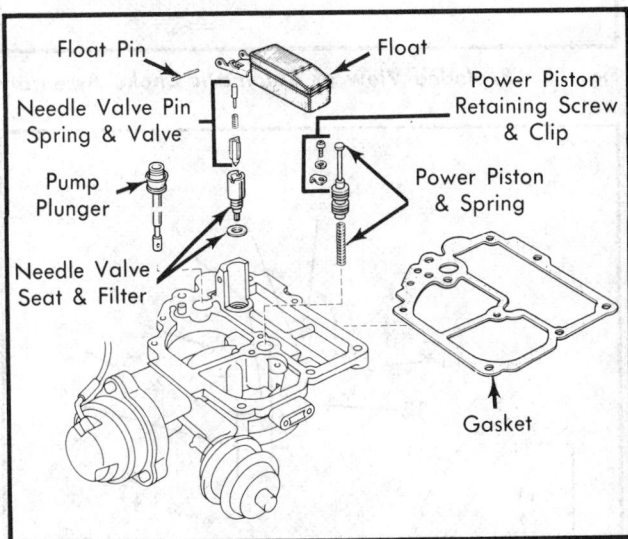

Fig. 10   Exploded View of Carburetor Float Assembly

Automatic Choke — 1) Remove coil housing. Remove choke lever retaining screw and lever. Remove thermostat case and gasket. Remove choke breaker cam, lever and choke breaker diaphragm assembly. *See Fig. 11.*

2) Remove relief lever and cam. Remove choke valve retaining screws and choke valve. Remove choke valve shaft.

Main Body — 1) Remove throttle positioner and operating lever. Remove choke opener assembly and auxiliary acceleration pump diaphragm. Remove deceleration solenoid valves. *See Fig. 12.*

2) Remove acceleration pump discharge weight, valve, spring and check ball and arrange properly for reassembly reference. Remove slow jet. Loosen throttle lever set nut about 4 turns.

1981 Aisan Carburetors

AISAN 2-BARREL — TOYOTA 3 A-C ENGINE (Cont.)

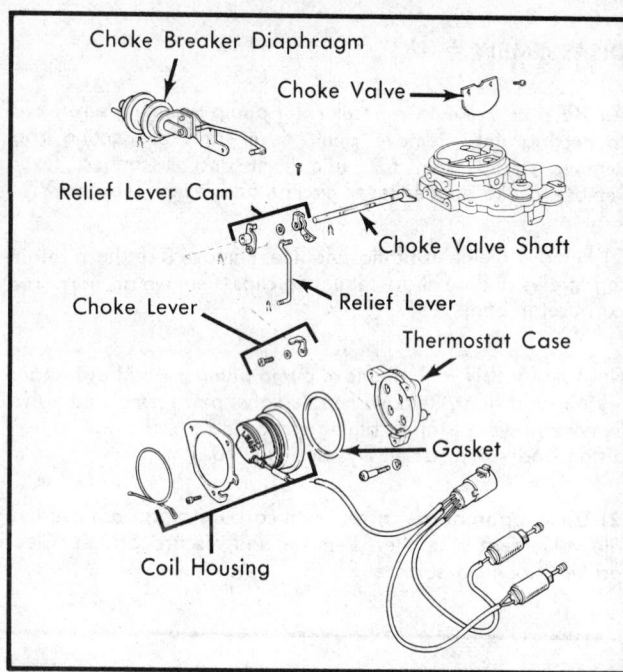

Fig. 11 Exploded View of Automatic Choke Assembly

Choke Breaker Diaphragm
Choke Valve
Relief Lever Cam
Choke Valve Shaft
Choke Lever
Relief Lever
Thermostat Case
Gasket
Coil Housing

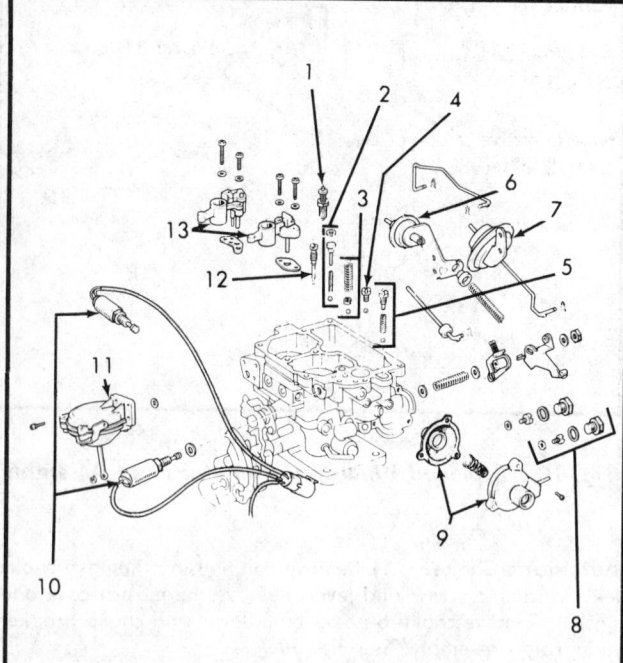

Fig. 12 Exploded View of Carburetor Main Body

1. Power Valve
2. Pump Discharge Weight, Valve & Check Ball
3. Pump Inlet Valve Assy.
4. AAP Inlet Valve
5. AAP Outlet Valve Assy.
6. Choke Opener
7. Throttle Positioner
8. Primary & Secondary Main Jet Plugs & Jets
9. Auxiliary Accelerator Pump Diaphragm
10. Deceleration Solenoid Valves
11. Secondary Throttle Valve Diaphragm
12. Slow Jet
13. Primary & Secondary Small Venturi

3) Remove primary and secondary main plugs and jets. Remove power valve. Remove primary and secondary small venturi retaining screws and venturi. Remove auxiliary accelerator pump inlet valve and check ball.

4) Remove auxiliary accelerator pump outlet plug, then remove spring and checkball. Remove inlet pump retainer with tweezers, then remove inlet valve, spring and check ball. Remove secondary throttle valve diaphragm assembly.

Flange Parts — 1) Remove vacuum passage bolts and flange retaining bolts. Note position of vacuum passage bolt with hole. Using appropriate idle screw wrench, remove idle adjusting screw. See Fig. 13.

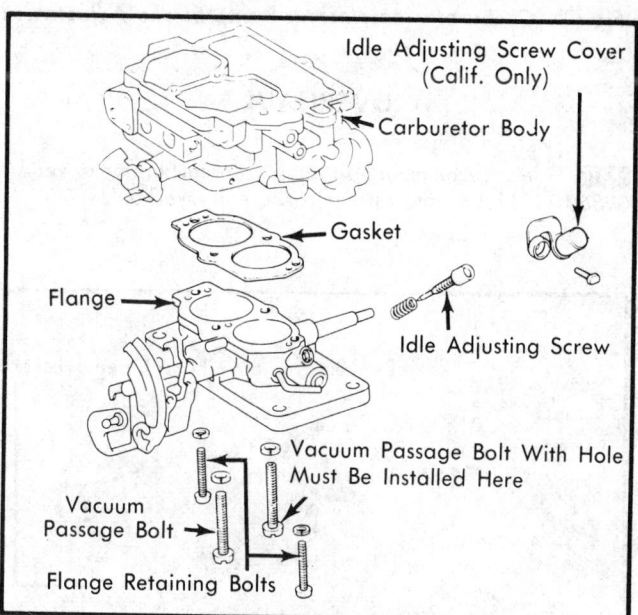

Idle Adjusting Screw Cover (Calif. Only)
Carburetor Body
Gasket
Idle Adjusting Screw
Flange
Vacuum Passage Bolt With Hole Must Be Installed Here
Vacuum Passage Bolt
Flange Retaining Bolts

Fig. 13 Exploded View of Carburetor Flange Parts

NOTE — Idle adjusting screw cover must be removed on California models to gain access to idle adjusting screw.

2) Separate flange from carburetor body and discard gasket. Clean all gasket surfaces.

CLEANING & INSPECTION

Clean all parts in suitable solvent (carburetor cleaner) and blow dry. Do not attempt to clean jets or other passages with wire or other metal objects. Inspect all parts for wear or damage and replace necessary parts.

REASSEMBLY

Use all new gaskets, reverse disassembly procedure and note the following:

1) When assembling flange assembly, install vacuum passage bolt with hole in correct position. See Fig. 13. California models must have idle adjusting screw cover installed.

AISAN 2-BARREL — TOYOTA 3 A-C ENGINE (Cont.)

2) When installing main jets, primary jet is "brass" colored and secondary jet is "chrome" colored. When assembling accelerator pump components, ensure check balls are positioned correctly.

3) When assembling air horn, tighten 8 retaining screws in criss-cross pattern. Tighten each screw a little at a time to prevent damage.

	CARBURETOR ADJUSTMENT SPECIFICATIONS							
Application	Idle Speed (Engine RPM)		Float Level Setting In. (mm)	Float Drop In. (mm)	Fast Idle Opening Angle	Choke Unloader Angle	Accel. Pump Stroke In. (mm)	Throttle Positioner Speed (Eng. RPM)
	Hot	Fast						
Tercel	650①②	3600①③	.158 (4)	.047 (1.2)	22°	47°	.118 (3)	1400①③

① — Cooling fan "OFF".
② — Auto. Trans. (Neutral) 800 RPM.
③ — EGR Off.

1981 Aisan Carburetors

AISAN 2-BARREL – TOYOTA 3T-C ENGINE

Corolla

DESCRIPTION

Carburetor is of 2-barrel, downdraft design and is equipped with automatic choke which is heated by an electrically operated bimetal heating coil. A piston type accelerator pump is incorporated into the primary barrel and an auxiliary accelerator pump system aids in cold engine acceleration. Other features include diaphragms which open secondaries at high speed and full throttle operation, mixture control (Man. Trans. only), throttle positioner, choke opener, choke breaker, deceleration fuel cut, hot idle compensation, and high altitude compensation (Federal) devices.

CARBURETOR IDENTIFICATION

Application	Part No.
Man. Trans.	
W/O High Alt. Comp.	21100-28170
W/High Alt. Comp.	21100-28180
Auto. Trans.	
W/O High Alt. Comp.	21100-28150
W/High Alt. Comp.	21100-28160

ADJUSTMENTS

HOT (SLOW) IDLE RPM

See appropriate TUNE-UP SERVICE PROCEDURES article.

IDLE MIXTURE

See appropriate TUNE-UP SERVICE PROCEDURES article.

COLD (FAST) IDLE RPM

See appropriate TUNE-UP SERVICE PROCEDURES article.

NOTE – It is recommended that Toyota carburetor adjusting kits 09240-00014 and 09240-00020 be used to make the following adjustments.

ACCELERATOR PUMP STROKE ADJUSTMENT

Place a straight edge on top of air horn and measure full travel of pump plunger. Make measurement at boot end. Adjust travel distance to .197" (5.0 mm) by bending accelerator pump actuating rod at existing bend.

FLOAT LEVEL ADJUSTMENT

Hold air horn upside-down. Allow float to hang by its own weight. Measure gap between float tip and air horn gasket surface (gasket removed). Bend float by inserting suitable tool in hole until gap is correct. See Fig. 1 and 2.

Fig. 1   Point for Adjusting Carburetor Float Level

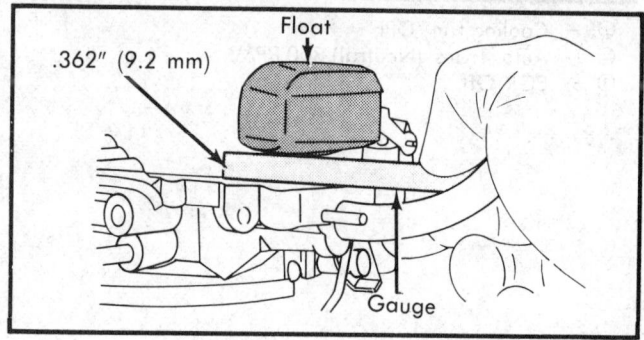

Fig. 2   Float Level Measurement Points and Gauge

FLOAT DROP ADJUSTMENT

Lift up float. Measure gap between needle valve and float lip. Bend float outer tab until gap is correct. See Fig. 3 and 4. After adjustment, ensure plunger moves smoothly.

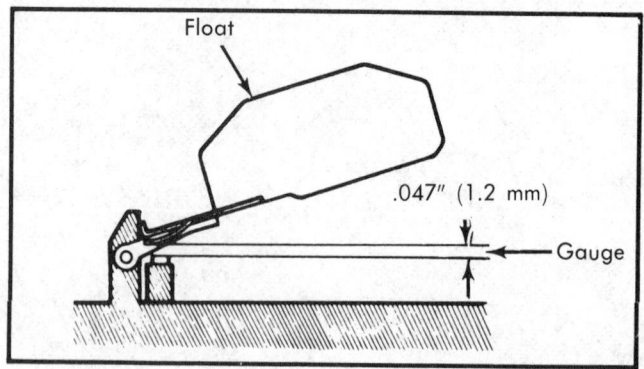

Fig. 3   Float Drop Measurement Points and Gauge

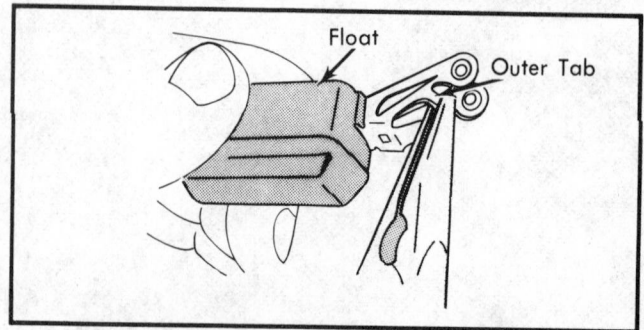

Fig. 4   Position for Adjusting Float Drop

AISAN 2-BARREL – TOYOTA 3T-C ENGINE (Cont.)

PRIMARY & SECONDARY THROTTLE VALVE ADJUSTMENT

When primary throttle valve is fully opened (90°), secondary throttle valve should also be completely open (80°). If adjustment is necessary, bend throttle shaft link.

NOTE — *The secondary throttle valve should begin to open when primary throttle valve is open 57° from bore surface.*

FAST IDLE (BENCH ADJUSTMENT)

Fully close choke valve by turning coil housing. Check angle between throttle valve and throttle bore with angle gauge. Adjust angle to 25° by turning fast idle adjusting screw.

SECONDARY THROTTLE OPENING ANGLE (KICK-UP)

Bend secondary throttle lever to obtain .0059" (.15 mm) clearance between secondary throttle valve and bore when primary throttle valve is fully open. See *Fig. 5*.

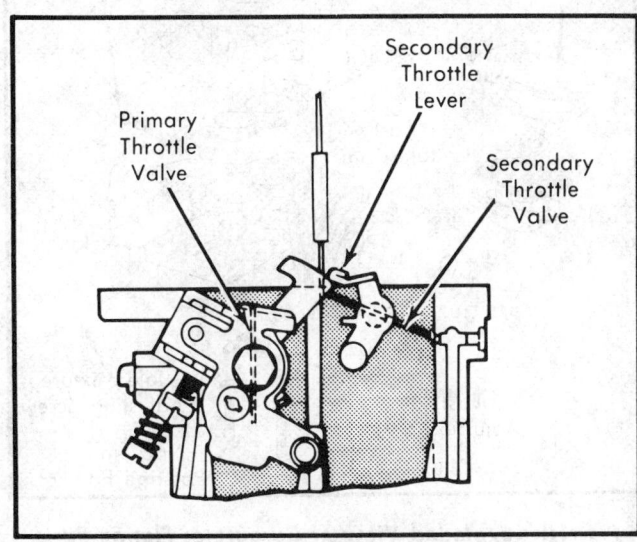

Fig. 5 Carburetor Kick-Up Adjustment

CHOKE UNLOADER ADJUSTMENT

Insert angle gauge. With primary throttle valve fully open, adjust angle of choke valve to 47° from fully closed position. Bend fast idle lever to obtain correct angle. See *Fig. 6*.

CHOKE OPENER ADJUSTMENT

Fully close choke valve by turning coil housing. Connect hose to opener diaphragm and apply vacuum. With vacuum applied, adjust choke angle to 85° (between choke valve and bore) by bending relief tang.

CHOKE BREAKER ADJUSTMENT

Connect hoses to both breaker vacuum diaphragms and apply vacuum. With vacuum applied, check that first choke angle is 38° and second choke angle is 55°. If not, replace air horn assembly.

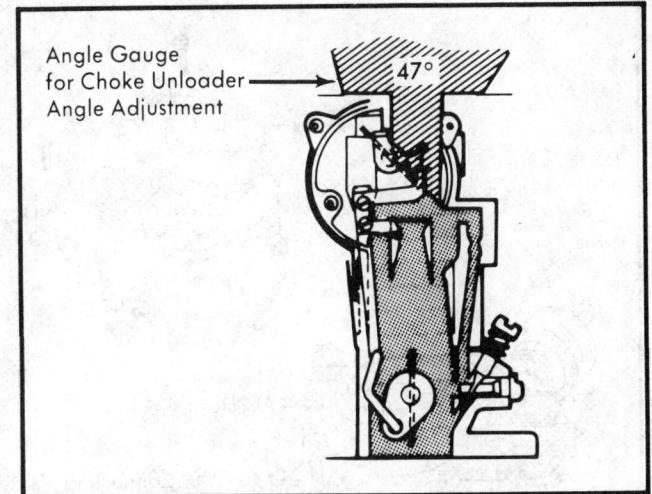

Fig. 6 Adjusting Choke Unloader Angle with Gauge

THROTTLE POSITIONER ADJUSTMENT

Turn carburetor upside-down and place throttle positioner adjusting screw against tab on throttle lever. Check angle between throttle valve and bore. Adjust angle to 16° by turning throttle positioner adjusting screw. See *Fig. 7*.

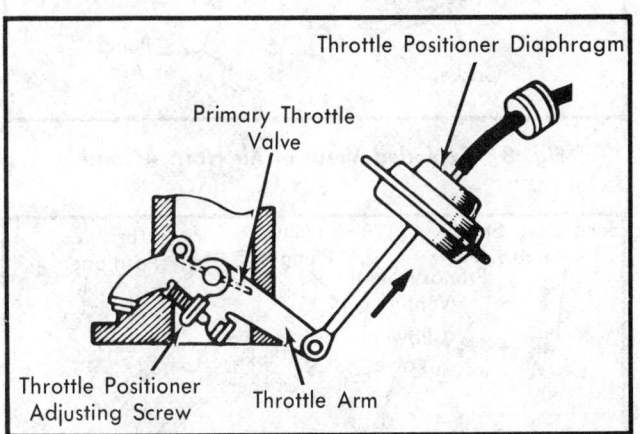

Fig. 7 Making Throttle Positioner Adjustment

OVERHAUL

NOTE — *It is recommended that Toyota carburetor driver kit 09860-11011 be used during carburetor overhaul.*

DISASSEMBLY

Air Horn – 1) Remove pump arm pivot screw and pump arm with connecting rod. Disconnect and remove both choke breaker vacuum hoses. Remove upper connecting link and 8 air horn connecting screws. Lift air horn and gasket from carburetor body. See *Fig. 8*.

2) Remove float pivot pin and float. Remove air horn gasket. Remove needle valve, spring and plunger with gasket and seat. Pull out pump plunger. Remove boot, power piston retainer, piston and spring.

1981 Aisan Carburetors

AISAN 2-BARREL – TOYOTA 3T-C ENGINE (Cont.)

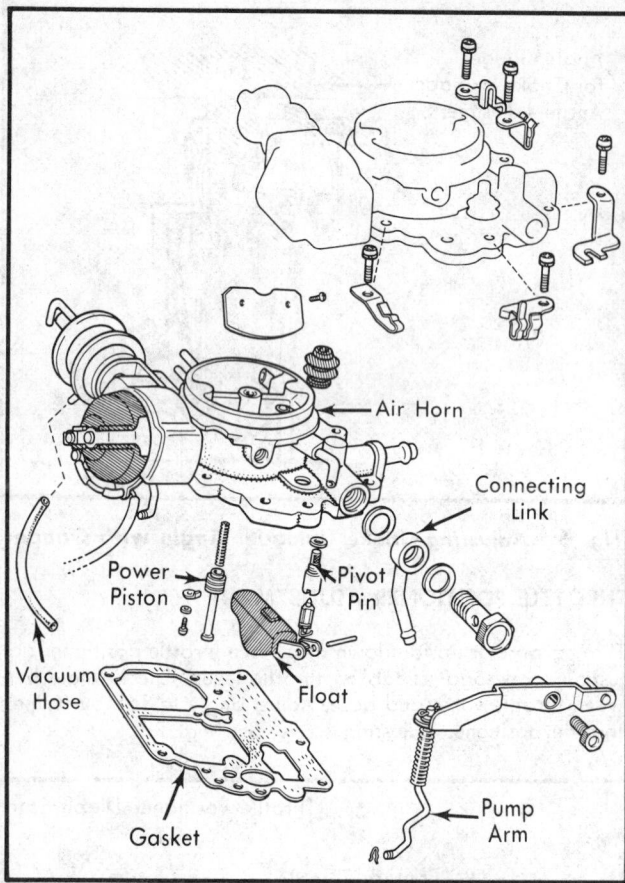

Fig. 8 Exploded View of Air Horn Assembly

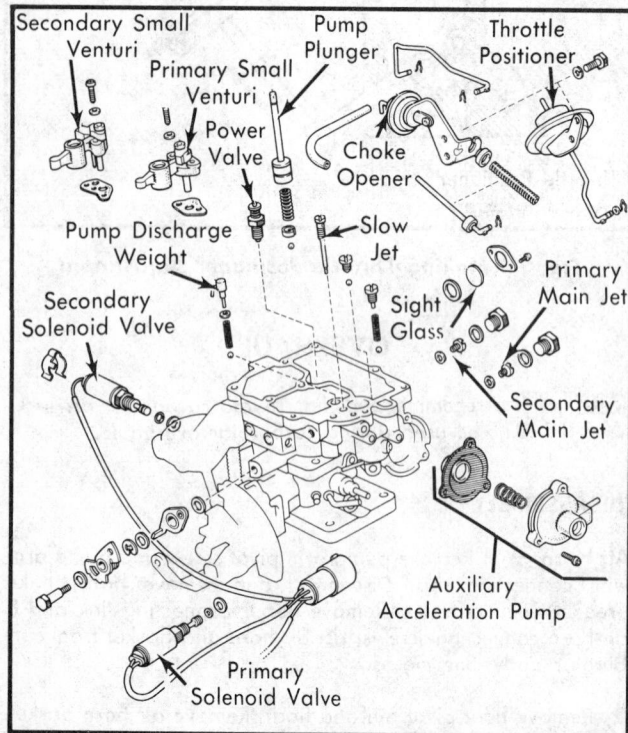

Fig. 9 Exploded View of Carburetor Main Body

Main Body — 1) Remove venturis and gaskets. Lift out pump discharge weight, O-ring and ball. Lift out pump damping spring. Using tweezers, take out retainer and ball. Remove slow jet and power valve. See Fig. 9.

2) Remove auxiliary acceleration pump inlet and outlet plugs, spring and balls. Remove pump housing, diaphragm, spring and gasket. Disconnect throttle positioner and choke opener links. Remove throttle positioner and choke opener.

3) Remove main jet plugs and main jets. Remove sight glass retainer, sight glass and O-ring. Remove primary and secondary solenoid valves.

Flange Parts — Remove rear spring. Disconnect secondary throttle diaphragm link and remove diaphragm. Remove fast idle cam. Loosen 2 flange bolts and 2 vacuum passage bolts. Remove flange from carburetor body. See Fig. 10.

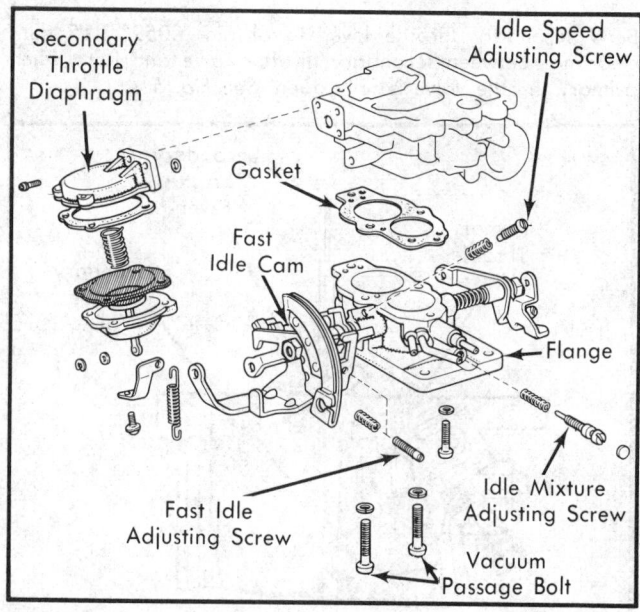

Fig. 10 Exploded View of Carburetor Flange Parts

CLEANING & INSPECTION

Clean all parts in suitable solvent (carburetor cleaner) and blow dry. Do not attempt to clean jets or other passages with wire or other metal objects. Inspect all parts for wear or damage and replace necessary parts.

REASSEMBLY

Use all new gaskets, reverse disassembly procedure and note the following:

1) When assembling flange parts, ensure vacuum passage bolts are installed in correct position.

2) When assembling secondary throttle valve diaphragm, ensure gasket is properly installed and seated.

AISAN 2-BARREL — TOYOTA 3T-C ENGINE (Cont.)

3) Ensure AAP and pump valves, springs and check balls are properly installed in appropriate orifices.

4) When installing main jets, primary jet is "brass" colored and secondary jet is "chrome" colored.

5) When installing pump discharge weight and outlet valve assembly, ensure all components are installed in correct order.

6) After installing power piston retaining clip and screw, check power piston for smooth operation.

Application	Idle Speed (Engine RPM)		Float Level Setting In. (mm)	Float Drop In. (mm)	Fast Idle Angle	Choke Breaker Opening Angle	Accel. Pump Stroke In. (mm)	Throttle Positioner Angle
	Hot	Fast						
Corolla	650①②	3400③④	.362 (9.2)	.047 (1.2)	25°	38°⑤	.197 (5.0)	16°

CARBURETOR ADJUSTMENT SPECIFICATIONS

① — Auto. Trans. — 750 RPM.
② — Power Steering — 850 RPM.
③ — Auto. Trans. — 3200 RPM.
④ — 200 RPM less with power steering.
⑤ — Second angle — 55°.

AISAN 2-BARREL – TOYOTA 4K-C ENGINE

Starlet

DESCRIPTION

Carburetor is a 2-barrel, downdraft design and is equipped with a manual choke and a thermostatically operated choke opener system. A piston type accelerator pump is used and a throttle positioner system which aids in cold engine acceleration. Other features include a solenoid valve which controls air-/fuel mixture and high altitude compensation (Federal) devices.

CARBURETOR IDENTIFICATION

Application	Part No.
Federal	21100-13210
Calif.	21100-13230

ADJUSTMENTS

HOT (SLOW) IDLE RPM

See appropriate TUNE-UP SERVICE PROCEDURES article.

IDLE MIXTURE

See appropriate TUNE-UP SERVICE PROCEDURES article.

COLD (FAST) IDLE RPM

See appropriate TUNE-UP SERVICE PROCEDURES article.

NOTE – It is recommended that Toyota carburetor adjusting kits 09240-00014 and 09240-00020 be used to make the following adjustments.

ACCELERATOR PUMP STROKE ADJUSTMENT

Place a straightedge on top of air horn and measure full travel of pump plunger. Make measurement at boot end. Adjust travel distance to .128" (3.25 mm) by bending accelerator pump actuating rod at existing bend. See Fig. 1.

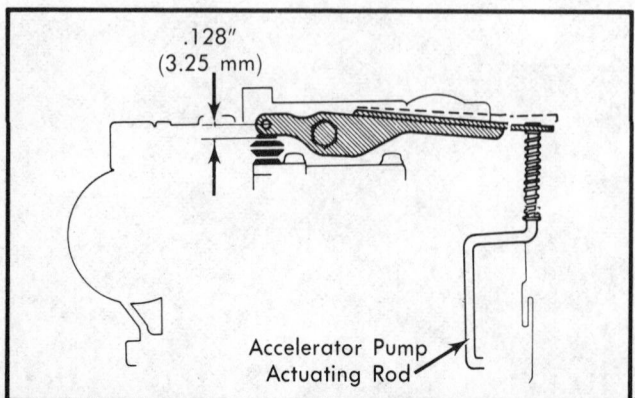

Fig. 1   Accelerator Pump Adjustment and Measurement

FLOAT LEVEL ADJUSTMENT

Allow float to hang down by its own weight. Adjust clearance between float top and air horn to .295" (7.5 mm) by bending float tab at "A". See Fig. 2.

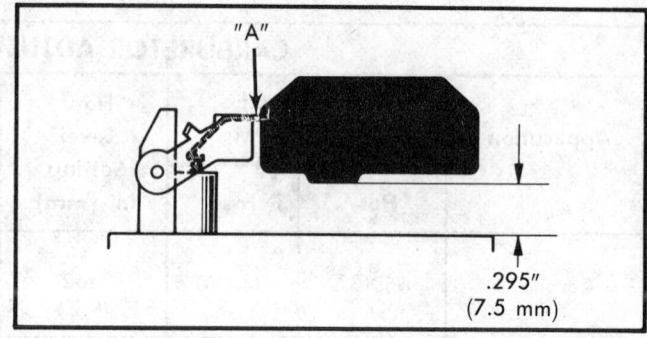

Fig. 2   Float Level Adjustment and Measurement

FLOAT DROP ADJUSTMENT

Lift up float and adjust clearance between needle valve plunger and float lip to .035" (.9 mm) by bending float tab at "B". See Fig. 3.

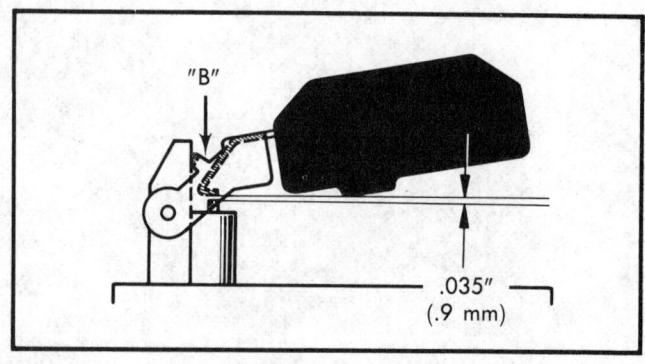

Fig. 3   Float Drop Adjustment and Measurement

PRIMARY & SECONDARY THROTTLE VALVE ADJUSTMENT

1) Fully open primary throttle valve. Insert angle gauge. Adjust primary throttle valve angle to 90° (fully open) by bending throttle lever stopper.

2) With primary throttle valve fully open, open secondary throttle valve. Insert angle gauge. Adjust secondary throttle valve angle to 75° (fully open) by bending throttle shaft link.

FAST IDLE (BENCH ADJUSTMENT)

Fully close choke valve by turning choke shaft lever. Set throttle shaft lever to fast idle cam. Using an angle gauge, check that primary throttle valve opening angle is 26°. If necessary, adjust by turning fast idle adjustment screw.

AISAN 2-BARREL — TOYOTA 4K-C ENGINE (Cont.)

SECONDARY THROTTLE KICK-UP ADJUSTMENT

Fully open secondary throttle valve. Insert wire gauge between high speed valve and bore. Adjust clearance to .0087" (.22 mm) by bending valve set screws and shifting high speed valve. See Fig. 4.

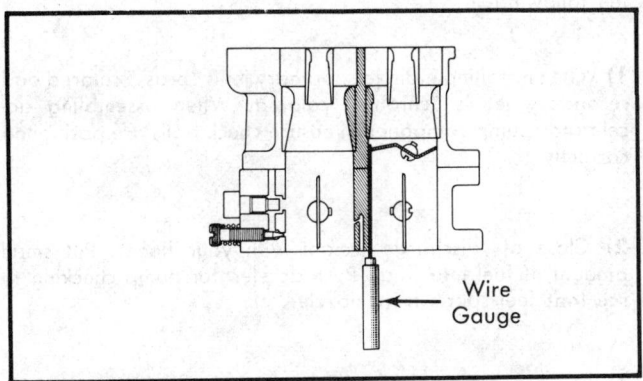

Fig. 4   Carburetor Kick-Up Adjustment

CHOKE OPENER ADJUSTMENT

Fully close choke valve. Connect hose to opener diaphragm and apply vacuum. With vacuum applied, adjust choke angle to 72° by bending relief lever tang.

OVERHAUL

NOTE — *It is recommended that Toyota carburetor driver kit 09860-11011 be used during carburetor overhaul.*

DISASSEMBLY

Air Horn — Remove pump arm set screw, pump lever and connecting link. Remove throttle positioner, back spring and fast idle cam connecting link. Remove air horn screws and air horn. See Fig. 5.

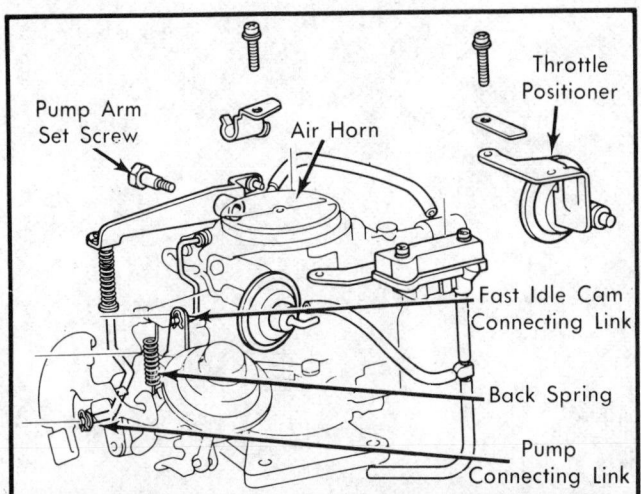

Fig. 5   View of Carburetor Air Horn

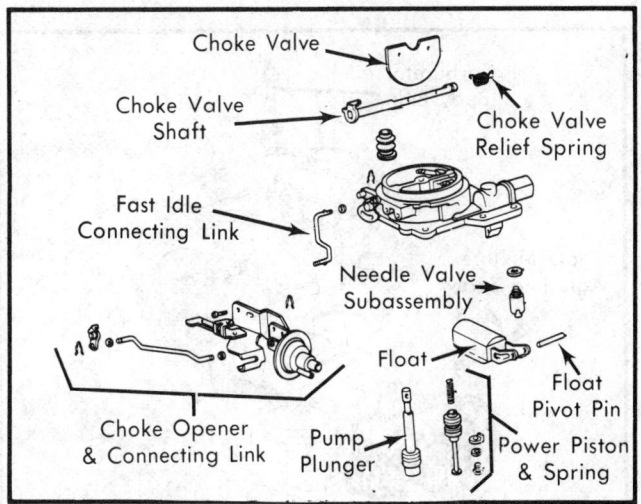

Fig. 6   Exploded View of Carburetor Float Assembly

Float Assembly — Remove float pivot pin, float and needle valve subassembly. Remove pump plunger, power piston and spring. Remove choke opener and connecting link. If necessary to replace choke valve or shaft, file off ends of choke valve set screws. Remove choke valve, shaft and relief spring. See Fig. 6.

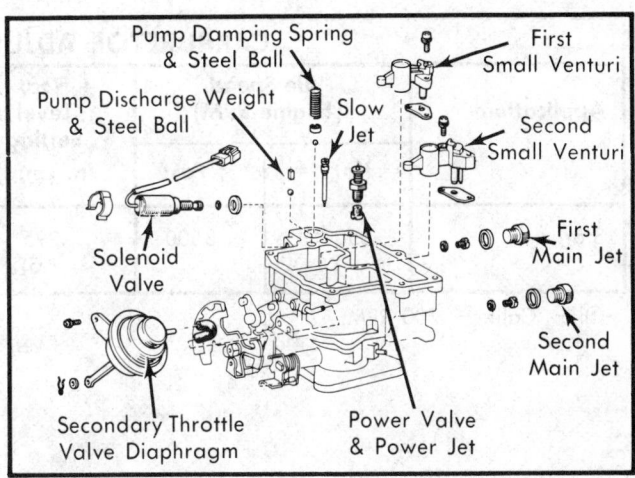

Fig. 7   Exploded View of Carburetor Main Body

Main Body — Removal pump discharge weight, damping spring and steel balls. Remove slow jet, power valve and power jet. Remove first and second main jets. Remove first and second small ventures, secondary throttle valve diaphragm and solenoid valve. See Fig. 7.

Flange Parts — Remove idle mixture adjusting screw. Remove bolts from body and flange. Remove flange from body. See Fig. 8.

CLEANING & INSPECTION

Clean all parts in suitable solvent (carburetor cleaner) and blow dry. Do not attempt to clean jets or other passages with

1981 Aisan Carburetors

AISAN 2-BARREL — TOYOTA 4K-C ENGINE (Cont.)

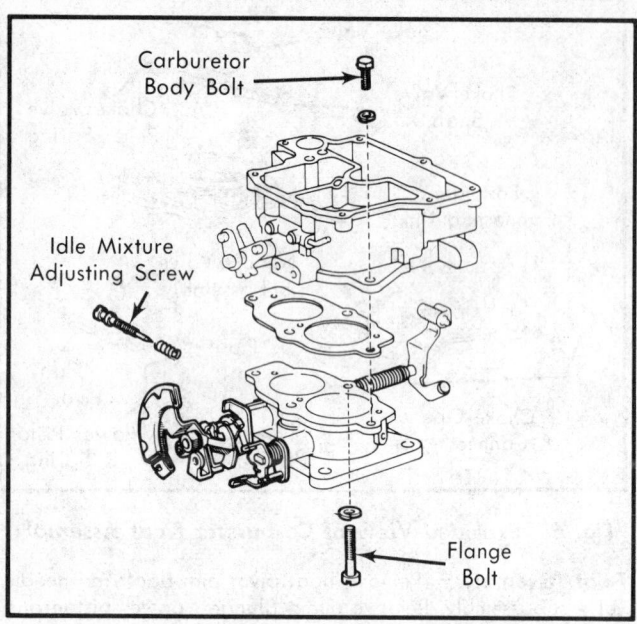

Fig. 8 Exploded View of Carburetor Flange Parts

Carburetor Body Bolt

Idle Mixture Adjusting Screw

Flange Bolt

wire or other metal objects. Inspect all parts for wear or damage and replace necessary parts.

REASSEMBLY

Use all new gaskets, reverse disassembly procedure and note the following:

1) When installing main jets, primary jet is "brass" colored and secondary jet is "chrome" colored. When assembling accelerator pump components, ensure check balls are positioned correctly.

2) Close off discharge weight with your finger. Put small amount of fuel into float. Push accelerator pump checking to see that fuel spurts from nozzle.

3) If necessary to replace choke valve, peen ends of screws. Install valve seat, needle valve, spring and push pin in that order.

CARBURETOR ADJUSTMENT SPECIFICATIONS

Application	Idle Speed (Engine RPM)		Float Level Setting In. (mm)	Float Drop In. (mm)	Fast Idle Opening Angle	Choke Opener Angle	Accel. Pump Stroke In. (mm)	Throttle Positioner Angle
	Hot	Fast						
Starlet	650①	3500	.295 (7.5)	.035 (.9)	26°	72°	.128" (3.25 mm)	8.5°

① — Calif. — 700 RPM.

AISAN 2-BARREL – TOYOTA 22R ENGINE

Celica
Corona
Pickup

DESCRIPTION

Carburetor is a 2 barrel downdraft design with primary and secondary venturi. An automatic choke containing a bimetal spring heated by coolant provides proper air/fuel mixture control during engine warm-up. Secondary throttle valve is actuated by a vacuum diaphragm unit with a kick-up (open) lever. Secondary valve begins to open when primary throttle valve opening exceeds 50°. A thermostatic valve provides air flow under secondary throttle valve when ambient air temperature is high to maintain proper combustion. Other features include choke opener, auxiliary accelerator pump, secondary slow circuit fuel cut system, fast idle cam breaker, deceleration fuel cut system and a solenoid valve.

CARBUARETOR IDENTIFICATION

Application	Part No.
Celica & Corona	
Man. Trans.	
W/O High Alt. Comp.	21100-35180
W/High Alt. Comp.	21100-35031
Auto. Trans.	
W/O High Alt. Comp.	21100-35021
W/High Alt. Comp.	21100-35041
Pickup	
2-WD①	
Federal	21100-35050
Calif.	21100-35010
High Alt. Comp.	21100-35080
4-WD	
Federal	21100-35090
Calif.	21100-35060
High Alt. Comp.	21100-35100

① – 4-Speed Auto. Trans. – 21100-35110.

ADJUSTMENTS

HOT (SLOW) IDLE RPM

See appropriate TUNE-UP SERVICE PROCEDURES article.

IDLE MIXTURE

See appropriate TUNE-UP SERVICE PROCEDURES article.

COLD (FAST) IDLE RPM

See appropriate TUNE-UP SERVICE PROCEDURES article.

NOTE – Manufacturer recommends that Toyota carburetor adjustment kit (Part No. 09240-00014) be used to make carburetor adjustments.

ACCELERATOR PUMP STROKE ADJUSTMENT

Place a straightedge on top of air horn and measure full travel of pump plunger. Make measurement at boot end. Adjust travel distance to .161" (4.1 mm) by bending accelerator pump actuating rod at existing bend. See Fig. 1.

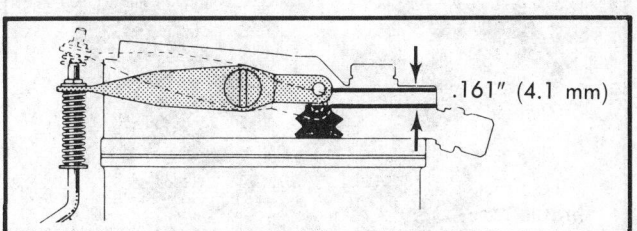

Fig. 1   Accelerator Pump Adjustment and Measurement

FLOAT LEVEL ADJUSTMENT

Allow float to hang down by its own weight. Adjust clearance between float top and air horn to .386" (9.8 mm) by bending float tab at "A". See Fig. 2

NOTE – Measurement must be made without gasket on air horn.

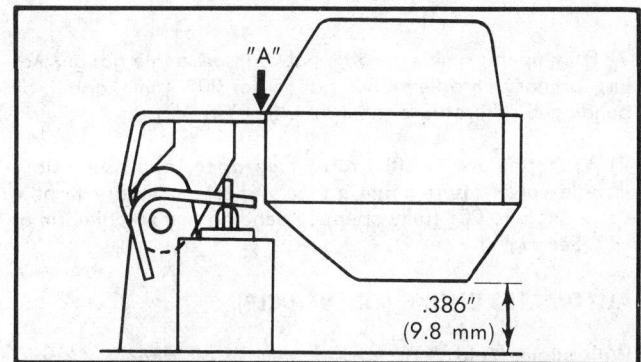

Fig. 2   Adjustment Points for Float Level

FLOAT DROP ADJUSTMENT

Lift up float and adjust clearance between needle valve plunger and float lip to 1.89" (48 mm) by bending float tab at "B". See Fig. 3.

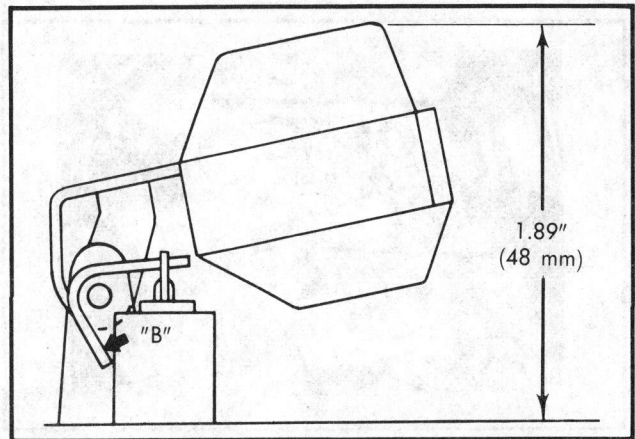

Fig. 3   Float Drop Adjustment Using Angle Gauge

UNLOADER ADJUSTMENT

Fully open primary throttle valve. Insert angle gauge. Adjust choke valve angle to 45° by bending first throttle arm at "A". See Fig. 4.

AISAN 2-BARREL — TOYOTA 22R ENGINE (Cont.)

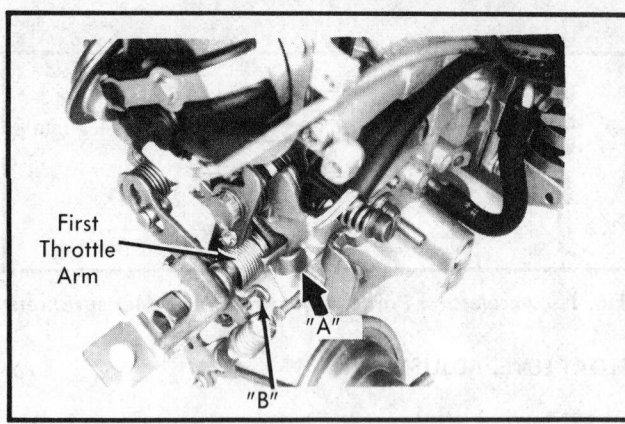

Fig. 4   Choke Unloader and Throttle Valve Adjustment Points

PRIMARY & SECONDARY THROTTLE VALVE ADJUSTMENT

1) Fully open primary throttle valve. Insert angle gauge. Adjust primary throttle valve gauge to 90° (fully open) by bending first throttle arm at "A". See Fig. 4.

2) With primary throttle valve fully open, open secondary throttle valve. Insert angle gauge. Adjust secondary throttle valve angle to 90° (fully open) by bending first throttle arm at "B". See Fig. 4.

AUTOMATIC CHOKE (ON VEHICLE)

With engine cold and stopped, remove air cleaner. Depress and release accelerator. Choke valve should be almost closed. Start engine and after warm-up, choke valve should be open.

FAST IDLE (BENCH ADJUSTMENT)

Set throttle shaft lever to first step of fast idle cam. See Fig. 5. Fully close choke valve. Insert angle gauge. Adjust primary throttle valve angle to 24° by turning fast idle adjusting screw.

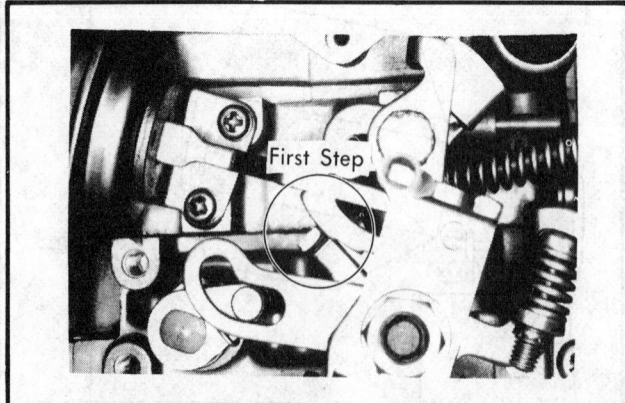

Fig. 5   Fast Idle Cam First Step

CHOKE BREAKER ADJUSTMENT

Apply vacuum to choke breaker diaphragm. Close choke valve by hand. Insert angle gauge. Adjust choke valve opening angle to 38° by bending relief lever. See Fig. 6.

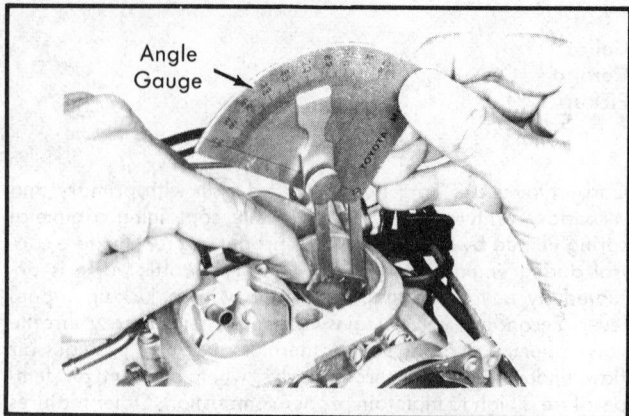

Fig. 6   Choke Breaker Adjustment

CHOKE OPENER ADJUSTMENT

Apply vacuum to choke opener diaphragm. Check that fast idle cam is released to fourth step. If not, adjust by bending choke opener lever at "A". See Fig. 7. Close choke valve. Set fast idle lever to first step. See Fig. 5. Check for clearance between choke opener lever and fast idle cam.

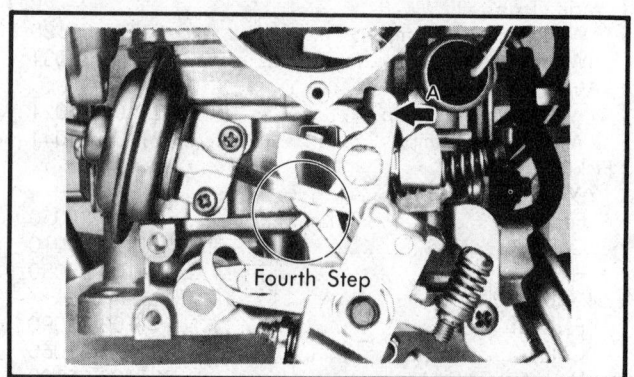

Fig. 7   Choke Opener Adjustment

THROTTLE POSITIONER (CALIF. 4-WD PICKUP)

Apply vacuum to diaphragm. Insert angle gauge. Adjust throttle valve opening angle to 16° by turning throttle positioner adjusting screw.

OVERHAUL

NOTE — *It is recommended that Toyota carburetor driver kit 09860-11011 be used during carburetor overhaul.*

DISASSEMBLY

Air Horn — 1) Remove metering needle, fast idle link, air horn screws, mixture control valve support and outer vent control valve. See Fig. 8.

2) Remove air horn from carburetor body. Loosen solenoid valve and remove by rotating carburetor body counterclockwise. Take care not to bend or distort solenoid valve lead wires.

Float Assembly — Remove pivot pin and float. Remove needle valve and seat. Remove power piston retainer, piston and spring. See Fig. 9.

AISAN 2-BARREL — TOYOTA 22R ENGINE (Cont.)

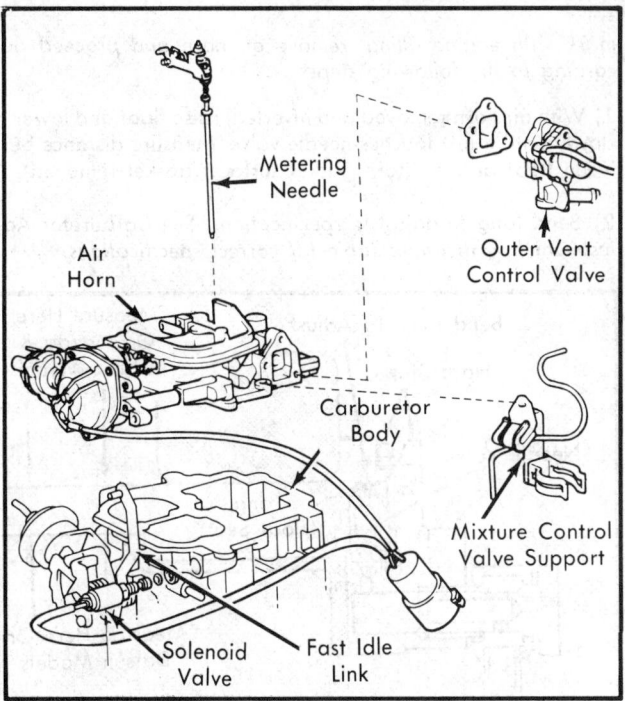

Fig. 8 *Exploded View of Carburetor Air Horn*

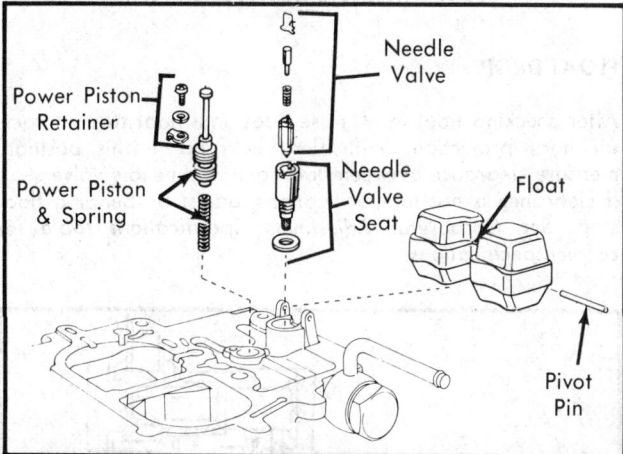

Fig. 9 *Exploded View of Carburetor Float Assembly*

Main Body — 1) Remove slow jet, power valve, metering needle guide and secondary main jet. Remove plug and primary main jet. Remove main and auxiliary acceleration pumps. See Fig. 10.

2) Remove thermostatic valve. On Calif. 4-WD Pickup models, remove throttle positioner. On all models, remove fast idle cam, choke opener, idle speed adjusting screw and, on Celica and Corona models with automatic transmission, remove dash pot.

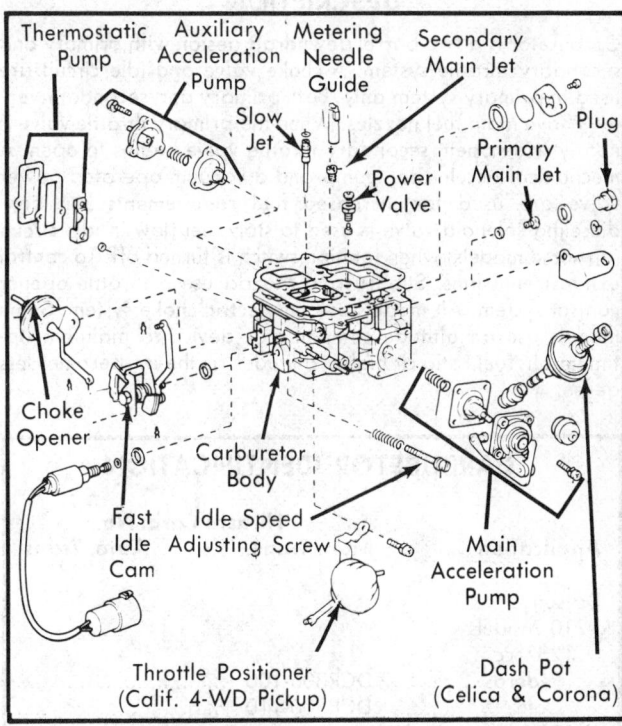

Fig. 10 *Exploded View of Carburetor Main Body*

CLEANING & INSPECTION

CAUTION — *Do not immerse synthetic components (gaskets, plastics, rubber) or thermostat and diaphragm valves in carburetor cleaner.*

Clean all parts in suitable solvent (carburetor cleaner) and blow dry. Do not attempt to clean jets or other passages with wire or other metal objects. Inspect all parts for wear or damage and replace necessary parts.

REASSEMBLY

Reassembly of carburetor components is performed by following reverse order of disassembly. Make sure to install new gaskets where required and check for smooth operation of all valves and linkage.

CARBURETOR ADJUSTMENT SPECIFICATIONS

Application	Idle Speed (Engine RPM)		Float Level Setting In. (mm)	Float Drop In. (mm)	Choke Opener Clearance	Choke Breaker Angle	Accel. Pump Stroke In. (mm)	Throttle Positioner Angle
	Hot	Fast						
22R Engine	700①②	2600③	.386 (9.8)	1.89 (48)	.047 (1.2)	38°	.161 (4.1)	16°

① — 3-Speed Auto. Trans. should be 750 RPM.
② — Mixture Speeds: 3-Speed Auto. Trans., 790 RPM; All Others, 740 RPM.
③ — With EGR, vacuum advance and fast idle cam breaker disconnected.

1981 Hitachi Carburetors

HITACHI DCG 306, DCH 306, DCP 306 & DCR 306 2-BARREL

Datsun 210 & 310
Mazda GLC
Subaru

DESCRIPTION

Carburetor is a two barrel downdraft design with primary and secondary throttle system. A choke valve and idle circuit are used in primary system only. Both primary and secondary venturis have main fuel nozzles. When the primary throttle valve is nearly wide open, secondary throttle valve begins to open. A mechanical accelerator pump and a vacuum operated power valve are used for increased fuel requirements. An anti-dieseling solenoid valve is used to stop fuel flow in idle circuit (on some models) when ignition switch is turned off. To control exhaust emissions, Subaru and Mazda use a throttle opener control system. All models use an electric choke system. Some models use an altitude compensator device to maintain optimum air/fuel ratio at higher altitudes as the air becomes less dense.

CARBURETOR IDENTIFICATION

Application	Hitachi Carb. No.	
	Man. Trans.	Auto. Trans.
Datsun		
210 Models		
1237 cc		
Federal	DCR306-100	
Calif.	DCR306-110	
1397 cc		
Federal	DCR306-104	
1488 cc		
Federal	DCR306-101	DCR306-102
Calif.	DCR306-111	DCR306-112
310 Models		
1397 cc		
Federal	DCR306-103	
Calif.	DCR306-113	
Mazda		
GLC	E508-13-600①	E508-13-600①
Subaru		
1600 cc Eng.	DCP306-11	
1800 cc Eng.	DCP360-12	DCP306-12

① — Number listed is Mazda part number.

ADJUSTMENTS

HOT (SLOW) IDLE RPM

See appropriate *TUNE-UP SERVICE PROCEDURES* article.

IDLE MIXTURE

See appropriate *TUNE-UP SERVICE PROCEDURES* article.

COLD (FAST) IDLE RPM

See appropriate *TUNE-UP SERVICE PROCEDURES* article.

FLOAT LEVEL

NOTE — *Float level may be checked through the sight glass of the float chamber. If fuel is not within .06" (1.5 mm) of the*

mark with engine idling, remove air horn and proceed according to the following steps.

1) With air horn removed and inverted, raise float and lower it slowly until it just touches needle valve. Measure distance between float and air horn gasket surface (gasket removed).

2) Bend tang to adjust to specifications. *See Carburetor Adjustment Specifications table for correct specifications.*

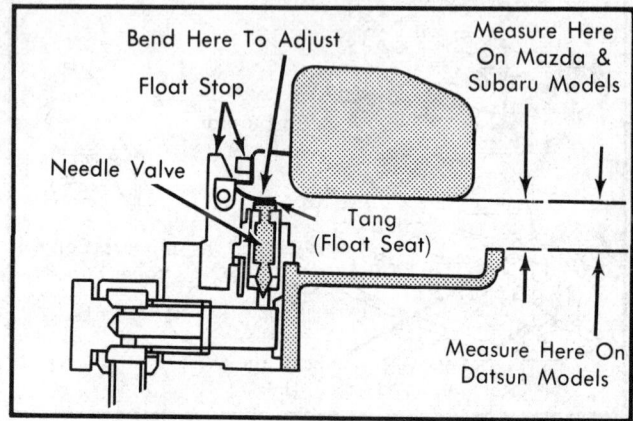

Fig. 1 Float Level Measurement and Adjustment Points

FLOAT DROP

After checking float level, raise float until float stop contacts air horn projection. With float held up in this position, measure clearance between float tang and needle valve seat. If clearance is not to specifications, adjust by bending float stop. *See Carburetor Adjustment Specifications table for correct specifications.*

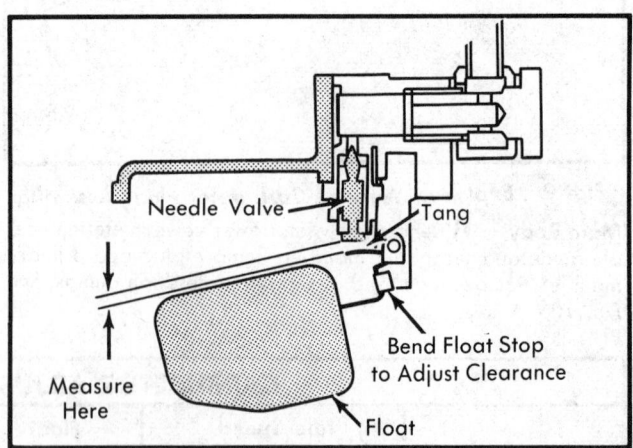

Fig. 2 Float Drop Measurement and Adjustment Points

FAST IDLE (OFF CAR)

Datsun — With choke cover removed, place fast idle screw on second step of fast idle cam and measure clearance between primary throttle valve and throttle bore. To adjust, turn fast idle screw.

HITACHI DCG 306, DCH 306, DCP 306 & DCR 306 2-BARREL (Cont.)

Mazda — Ensure that long arm of cam lever is on first step of fast idle cam and hold choke in fully closed position. Measure clearance between throttle plate and throttle bore wall. Adjust to specifications by turning fast idle screw clockwise to increase or counterclockwise to decrease clearance.

Subaru — With choke in closed position, place fast idle lever on second step of fast idle cam. Adjust clearance between primary throttle valve and throttle bore, by turning fast idle screw, to specifications.

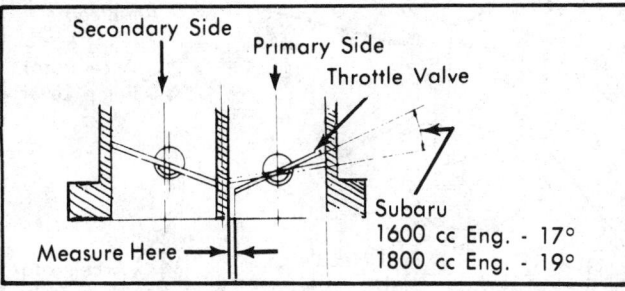

Fig. 3   Fast Idle Bench Adjustment

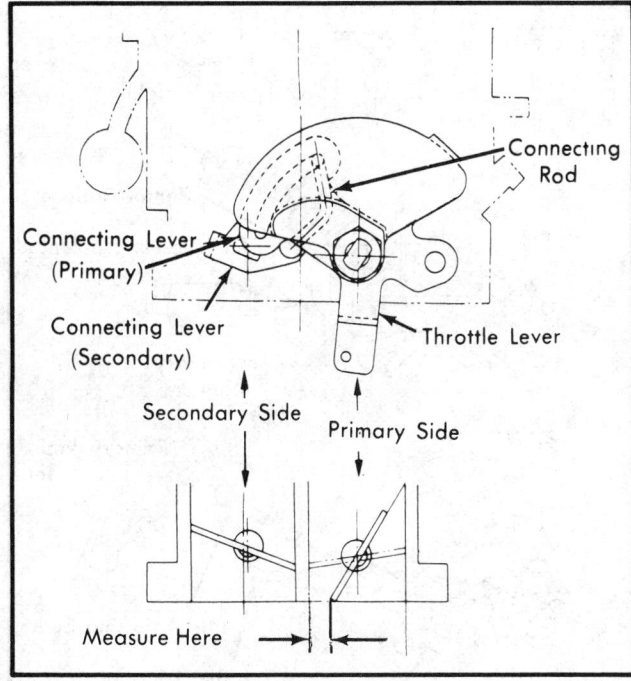

Fig. 4   Secondary Throttle Initial Opening Adjustment

SECONDARY THROTTLE INITIAL OPENING

All Models — With primary-to-secondary throttle connecting rod contacting end of slot in primary throttle lever, measure clearance between primary throttle plate and bore. If adjustment is necessary, bend connecting rod to obtain specified clearance. See Carburetor Adjustment Specifications table for correct specifications. See Fig. 4.

VACUUM BREAK

Datsun & Mazda — Open throttle and close choke. Release throttle lever first, to hold choke closed. Remove choke cover, and using rubber band, hold choke valve closed. Manually pull vacuum break diaphragm stem out fully (keep straight) in order to compress diaphragm. Measure clearance between choke valve and air horn wall. If adjustment is necessary, bend vacuum break connecting rod. See Fig. 5.

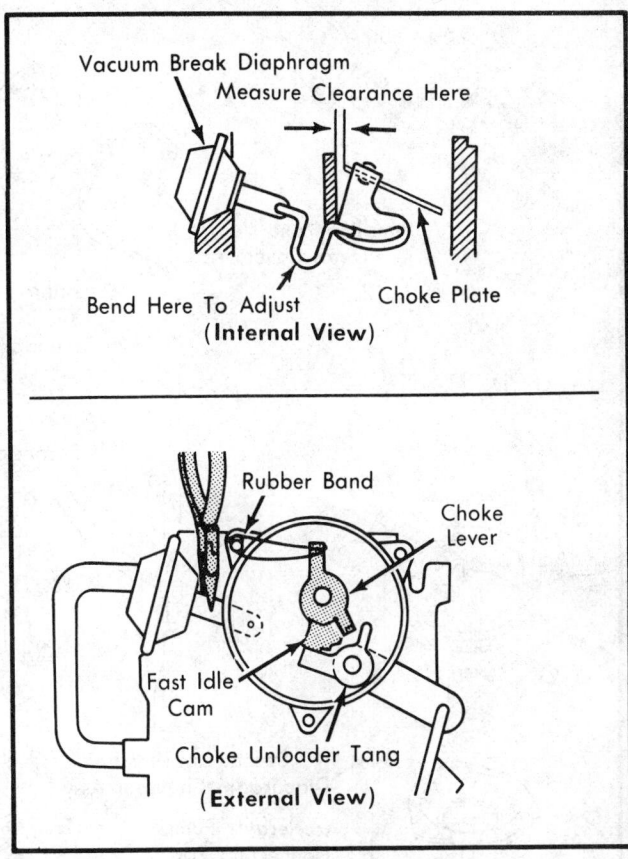

Fig. 5   Vacuum Break Adjustment

CHOKE UNLOADER

All Models — Open throttle valve to wide open position. Hold choke valve closed with rubber band (see Fig. 9). With throttle wide open and choke closed with rubber band, measure clearance between choke valve and air horn wall. If adjustment is necessary, bend choke unloader tang. See Carburetor Adjustment Specifications Table for correct specifications.

OVERHAUL

DISASSEMBLY

1) Main jets and needle valves on both primary and secondary sides are accessible from outside carburetor. Remove for service as necessary.

2) Remove throttle return spring, accelerator pump lever and connecting rod. Remove spring hanger and choke linkage (if equipped) and remove choke housing. Remove carburetor main body cover using care not to damage float.

1981 Hitachi Carburetors

HITACHI DCG 306, DCH 306, DCP 306 & DCR 306 2-BARREL (Cont.)

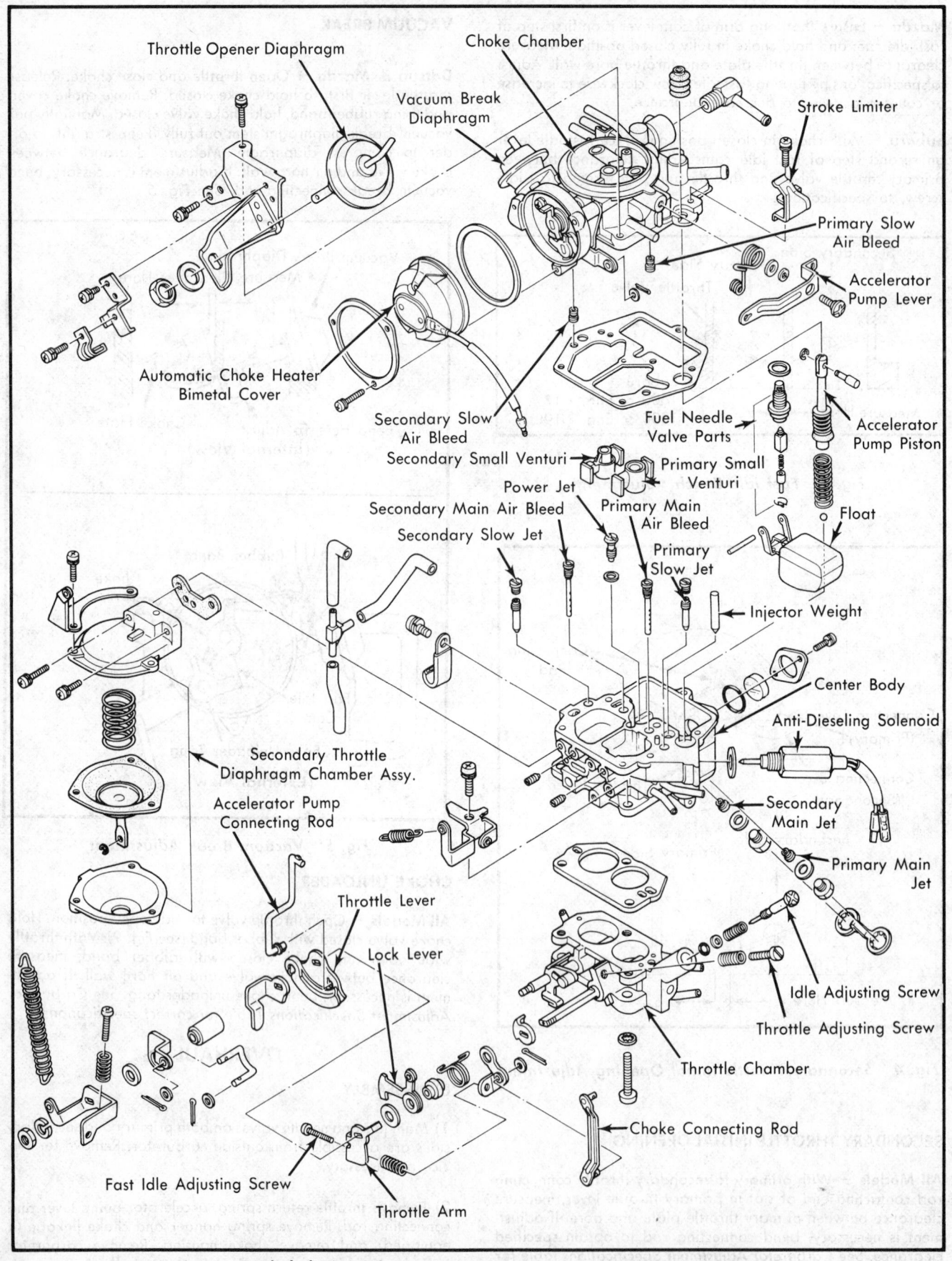

Throttle Opener Diaphragm

Choke Chamber

Vacuum Break Diaphragm

Stroke Limiter

Primary Slow Air Bleed

Accelerator Pump Lever

Automatic Choke Heater Bimetal Cover

Secondary Slow Air Bleed

Secondary Small Venturi

Power Jet

Secondary Main Air Bleed

Secondary Slow Jet

Fuel Needle Valve Parts

Primary Small Venturi

Primary Main Air Bleed

Primary Slow Jet

Accelerator Pump Piston

Float

Injector Weight

Center Body

Anti-Dieseling Solenoid

Secondary Main Jet

Primary Main Jet

Secondary Throttle Diaphragm Chamber Assy.

Accelerator Pump Connecting Rod

Throttle Lever

Lock Lever

Idle Adjusting Screw

Throttle Adjusting Screw

Throttle Chamber

Choke Connecting Rod

Fast Idle Adjusting Screw

Throttle Arm

Fig. 6   Exploded View of Datsun 210 & 310 Hitachi DCR 306 Carburetor

HITACHI DCG 306, DCH 306, DCP 306 & DCR 306 2-BARREL (Cont.)

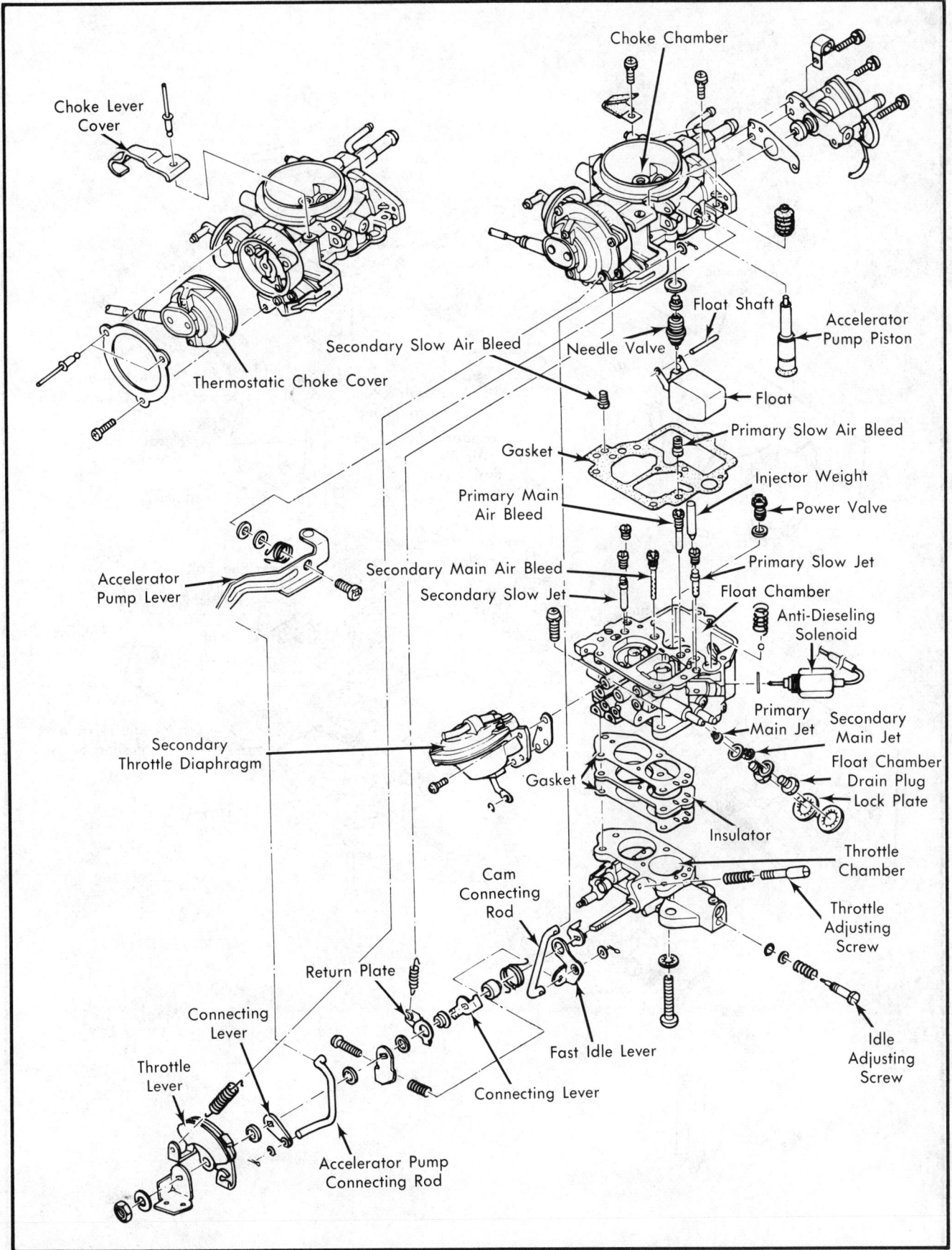

Choke Lever Cover

Choke Chamber

Thermostatic Choke Cover

Secondary Slow Air Bleed

Needle Valve

Float Shaft

Accelerator Pump Piston

Float

Primary Slow Air Bleed

Gasket

Primary Main Air Bleed

Injector Weight

Power Valve

Accelerator Pump Lever

Secondary Main Air Bleed

Secondary Slow Jet

Primary Slow Jet

Float Chamber

Anti-Dieseling Solenoid

Secondary Throttle Diaphragm

Primary Main Jet

Secondary Main Jet

Float Chamber Drain Plug

Lock Plate

Gasket

Insulator

Throttle Chamber

Cam Connecting Rod

Throttle Adjusting Screw

Return Plate

Connecting Lever

Fast Idle Lever

Idle Adjusting Screw

Throttle Lever

Connecting Lever

Accelerator Pump Connecting Rod

Fig. 7 *Exploded View of Subaru Hitachi DCP 306 Carburetor*

1981 Hitachi Carburetors

HITACHI DCG 306, DCH 306, DCP 306 & DCR 306 2-BARREL (Cont.)

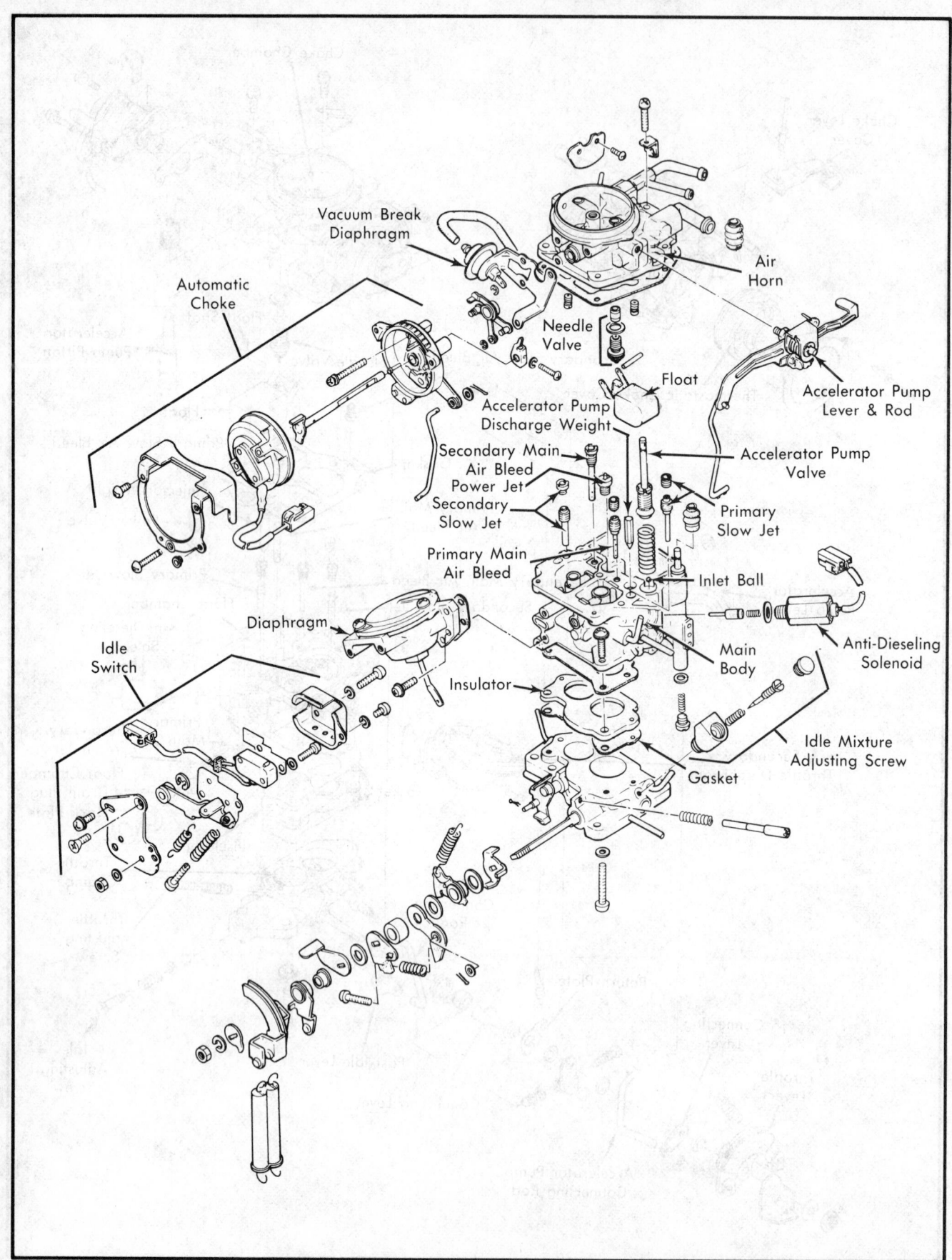

Fig. 8 *Exploded View of Mazda GLC Hitachi Carburetor*

HITACHI DCG 306, DCH 306, DCP 306 & DCR 306 2-BARREL (Cont.)

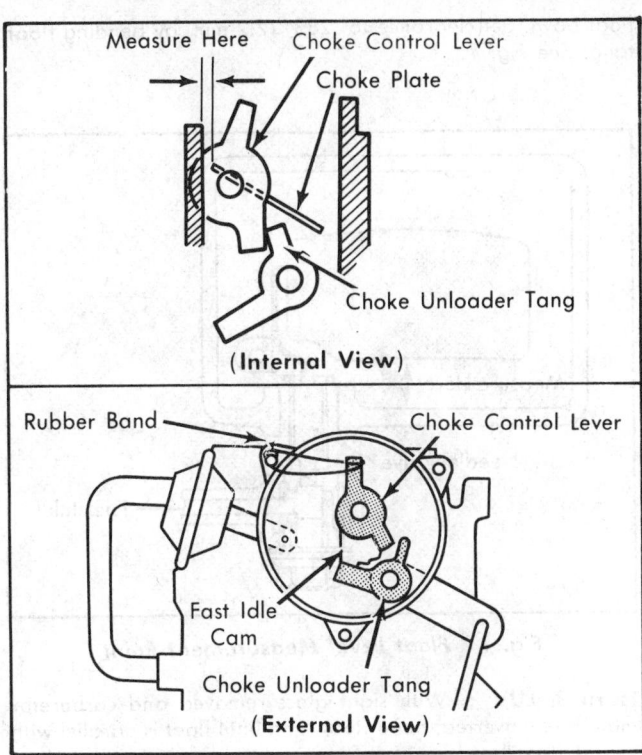

Fig. 9 Choke Unloader Adjustment

3) Remove accelerator piston, return spring and check ball. Remove float, needle valve and filter. Remove air bleeds and emulsion tubes. Remove slow jets and power valve. Remove drain plugs and main jets. Remove servo diaphragm by-pass jet and air bleed.

4) Remove throttle body from main body with (3) set screws. Do not remove anti-dieseling solenoid except to replace. Throttle body should not be disassembled unless a throttle valve or rod is being replaced.

CLEANING & INSPECTION

Replace all parts contained in service overhaul kits. Soak metal parts (except anti-dieseling solenoid) in a suitable cleaner. Blow air through passages to clean and dry. Inspect all parts for wear and replace as necessary.

REASSEMBLY

Reverse disassembly procedure and note the following: Check each link system for smooth operation. Adjust float and linkage as required.

CARBURETOR ADJUSTMENT SPECIFICATIONS

Application	Idle Speed (Engine RPM)		Float Level	Float Drop Setting	Fast Idle Throttle Valve Setting	Secondary Throttle Clearance	Unloader Setting	Vacuum Break
	Hot	Fast	In. (mm)	In. (mm)	In. (mm)	In. (mm)	In. (mm)	In. (mm)
Datsun 210	700①	②	.75 (19)	.051-.067 (1.30-1.70)	.026-.031③ (.650-.790)	.209-.249 (5.33-6.33)	.093 (2.36)	.063-.070 (1.61-1.79)
310	750	2400-3200④	.75 (19)	.051-.067 (1.30-1.70)	.029-.034 (.730-.870)	.209-.249 (5.33-6.33)	.093 (2.36)	.063-.070 (1.61-1.79)
Mazda GLC	850 ⑤		.43 (11)	.051-.067 (1.30-1.70)	.031-.035 (.790-.920)	.236 (6.0)	.073-.094 (1.86-2.40)	.060-.080 (1.53-2.03)
Subaru	600-800⑥	.....	.41 (10.5)	.051-.067 (1.30-1.70)	.054⑦ (1.38)	.236 (6.0)	17 & 19°	.....

① — Set Auto. Trans. to 650 RPM.
② — Set fast idle on 2nd step of cam: 1237 &1397 cc Engine — 2400-3200 RPM; 1488 cc Engine — 2700-3500 RPM.
③ — Table lists 1237 cc Engine specification. Set 1397 & 1488 Engines (Man. Trans.) to .029-.034" (.730-.870 mm); set 1488 cc Engine (Auto. Trans.) to .039-045" (1.00-1.14 mm).
④ — Set Calif. models to 2300-3500 RPM.
⑤ — Set Auto. Trans. to 750 RPM.
⑥ — Set Auto. Trans. to 700-900 RPM.
⑦ — Table lists 1800 cc Engine specification. Set 1600 cc Engine to .046" (1.17 mm).

1981 Hitachi Carburetors

HITACHI DCH 340 & DCR 342 2-BARREL

Datsun 510   Isuzu I-Mark
Datsun Pickup   Isuzu P'UP
LUV Pickup

DESCRIPTION

Carburetor is a 2-barrel downdraft type with piston type accelerator pump. Carburetor consists of low speed (primary) barrel and high speed (secondary) barrel integrated into a single unit with a common fuel bowl. Secondary throttle is actuated by a vacuum diaphragm when primary throttle is open a predetermined amount. Additional equipment includes an anti-dieseling solenoid, electric choke, coasting riching solenoid (Isuzu and LUV), idle compensator (Datsun), a dashpot (Datsun with Auto. Trans.), and an altitude compensator (Calif. Datsun).

CARBURETOR IDENTIFICATION
Carburetor No.

Application	Man. Trans.	Auto. Trans.
Datsun 510		
Federal	DCR342-4	DCR342-6
	DCR342-5①	
Calif.	DCR342-1	DCR342-3
	DCR342-2①	
Datsun Pickup		
Federal		
Standard	DCR342-14	DCR342-16
	DCR342-15①	
Heavy Duty	DCR342-23	
	DCR342-24①	
Calif.		
Standard	DCR342-11	DCR342-13
	DCR342-12①	
Heavy Duty	DCR342-21	
	DCR342-22①	
4WD	DCR342-17	
	DCR342-18①	
Isuzu & LUV		
I-Mark	DCH340-251	DCH340-252
P'PUP & LUV		
Federal	DCH340-211	DCH340-212
Calif.	DCH340-213	DCH340-214

① — With air conditioning.

ADJUSTMENTS

HOT (SLOW) IDLE RPM

See appropriate TUNE-UP SERVICE PROCEDURES article.

IDLE MIXTURE

See appropriate TUNE-UP SERVICE PROCEDURES article.

COLD (FAST) IDLE RPM

See appropriate TUNE-UP SERVICE PROCEDURES article.

FLOAT LEVEL

NOTE — Fuel bowl is equipped with a sight glass. Line on sight glass indicates proper fuel level. If adjustment must be made to correct improper level, use following procedure.

Datsun — With sight glass removed and carburetor main body inverted, measure distance from top of float to top of

float bowl. Set clearance to .283" (7.2 mm) by bending float tang. See Fig. 1.

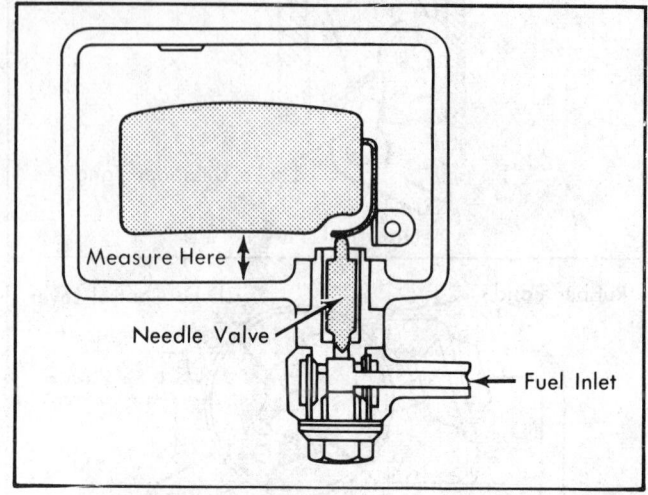

Fig. 1   Float Level Measurement Point

Isuzu & LUV — With sight glass removed and carburetor main body inverted, bend float tang until float is parallel with top of float bowl.

FLOAT DROP

With float bowl removed and held upright, measure clearance between needle valve and float tang. If clearance is not .059" (1.5 mm), adjustment will be necessary. Adjust by bending float tang which contacts needle valve. See Fig. 2.

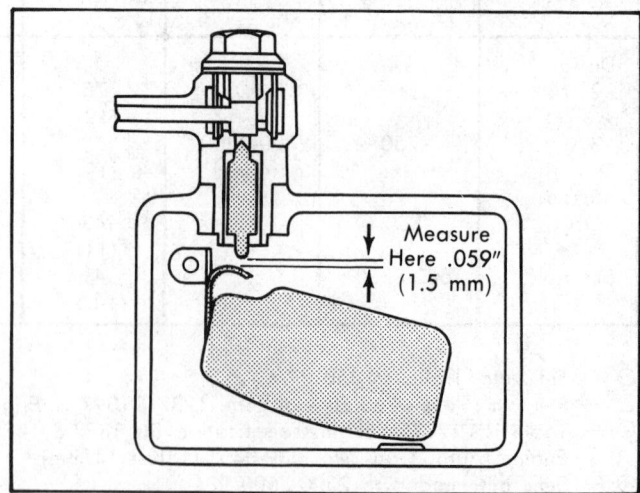

Fig. 2   Float Drop Measurement Point

VACUUM BREAK

Datsun — Close choke and hold closed with rubber band stretched between choke piston and stationary part of carburetor. Grip stem of vacuum break diaphragm and pull straight outward (stem extended). Adjust gap between choke plate and air horn wall to .123-.147" (3.12-3.72 mm) on California models or .103-.127" (2.62-3.22 mm) on Federal models by bending vacuum break rod. See Fig. 3.

HITACHI DCH 340 & DCR 342 2-BARREL (Cont.)

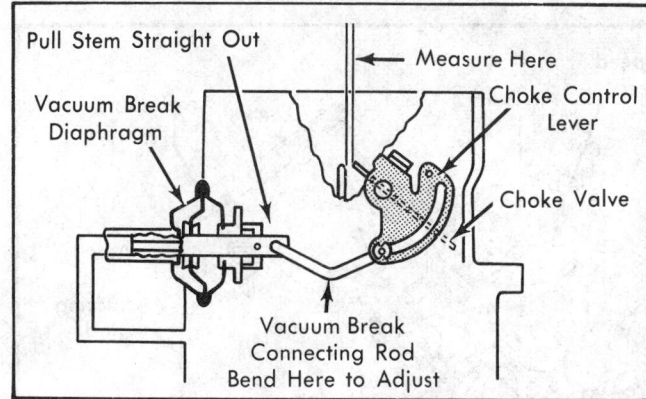

Fig. 3   Vacuum Break Adjustment for Datsun Models

Isuzu & LUV — Fully depress vacuum break diaphragm stem and measure clearance between choke plate and air horn wall. Adjust gap to .050-.059" (1.28-1.75 mm) on manual transmission models and to .055-.064" (1.40-1.63 mm) on automatic transmission models by bending vacuum break rod. See *Fig. 4.*

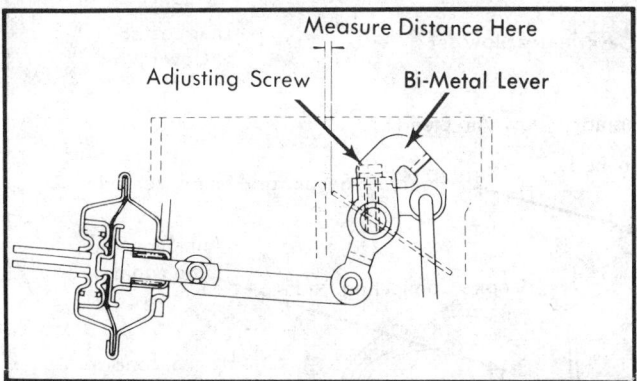

Fig. 4   Vacuum Break Adjustment (Isuzu and LUV)

CHOKE UNLOADER

Datsun — 1) Close choke plate. Hold in position with a rubber band. Place throttle in wide open position.

2) Measure clearance between choke plate and air horn wall. Clearance should be as specified in table. Bend unloader tang to adjust. See *Fig. 5.*

NOTE — *It is important to check that throttle valve opens fully when carburetor is mounted on vehicle. If throttle does fail to open, unloader becomes inoperative.*

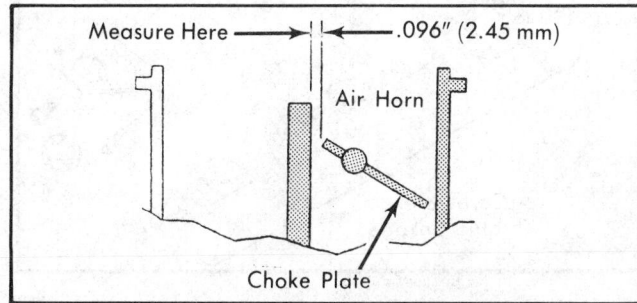

Fig. 5   Datsun Choke Unloader Adjustment

SECONDARY THROTTLE INITIAL OPENING

When primary throttle valve opens 50° (47° on Isuzu and LUV), primary throttle lever tang contacts secondary throttle lockout. Any further opening of throttle valve will force secondary throttle lock-out lever to actuate secondary throttle lever and secondary throttle valve will begin to open. Check and adjust as follows:

Open primary throttle valve until it is observed that secondary is just begining to open. Hold throttle in this position and measure clearance between primary throttle valve and throttle bore. If clearance is not to specifications, adjust by bending primary throttle tang. See *Fig. 6.*

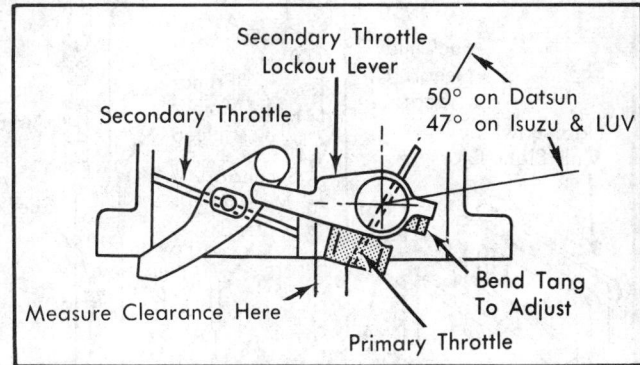

Fig. 6   Secondary Throttle Initial Opening Adjustment

CHOKE LINKAGE (FAST IDLE BENCH)

With fast idle screw on first step of fast idle cam, invert carburetor and close choke valve. Measure clearance (angle on Isuzu and LUV) between throttle plate and throttle bore. If adjustment is necessary, turn fast idle speed screw. Set clearance to .030-.035" (.76-.90 mm) on Datsun Man. Trans. or to .040-.043" (.96-1.1 mm) on Datsun Auto Trans. Set angle to 16-18° on Isuzu and LUV models. See *Fig. 7.*

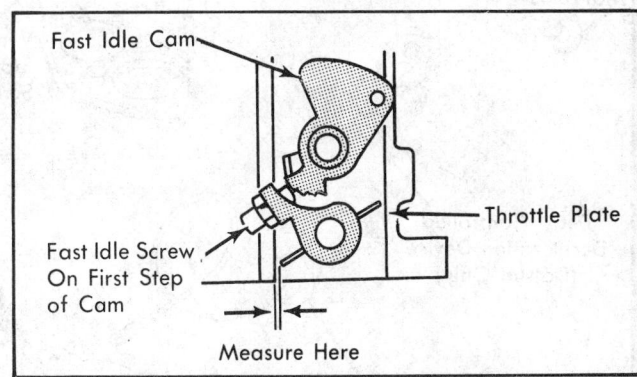

Fig. 7   Choke Linkage Adjustment

OVERHAUL

NOTE — *Procedure given is for LUV DCH340 Hitachi carburetor but can be applied to Datsun DCR342 Hitachi carburetor.*

DISASSEMBLY

1) With carburetor removed, perform the following steps:

- Disconnect accelerator pump lever.
- Remove throttle return spring.
- Remove choke thermostat housing and wire.

HITACHI DCH 340 & DCR 342 2-BARREL (Cont.)

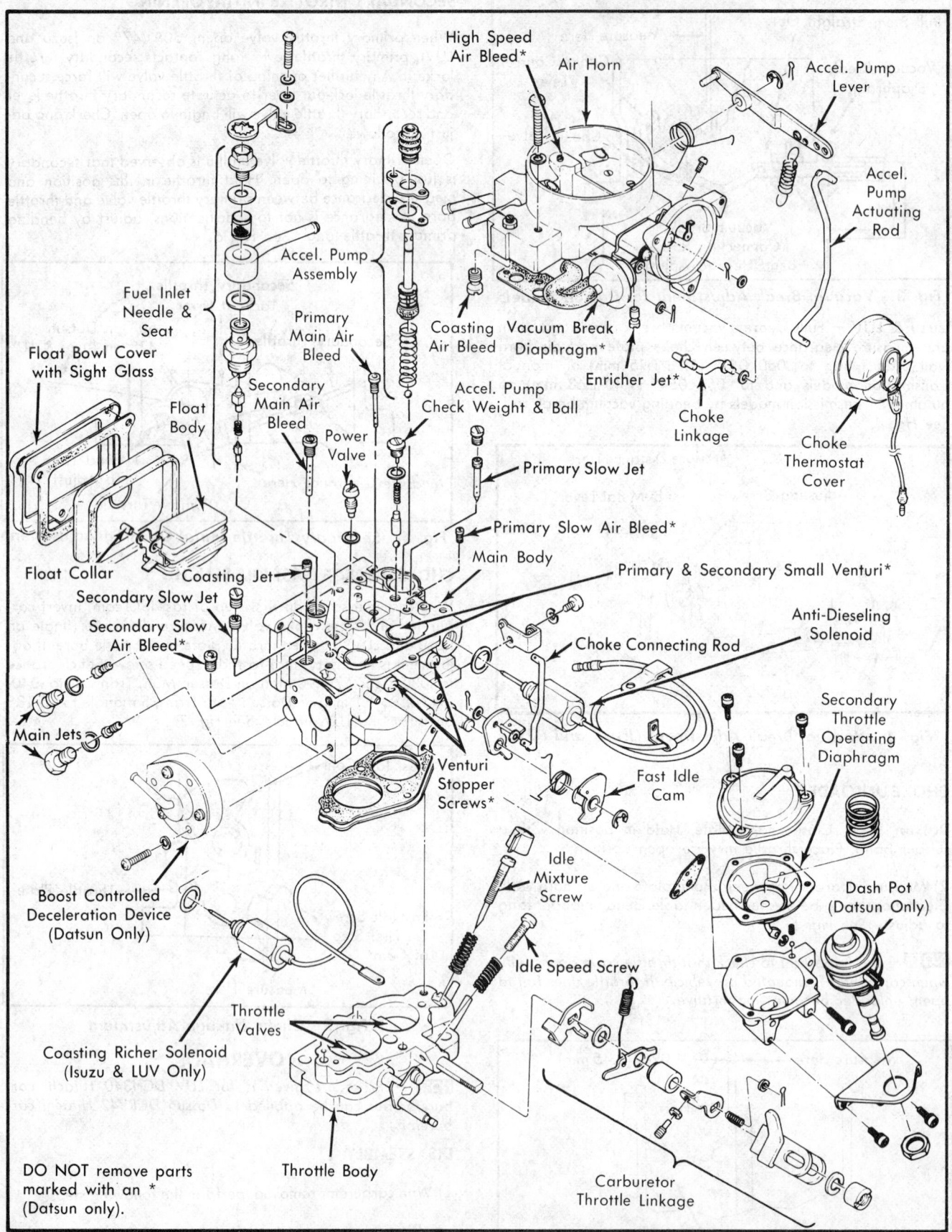

Fig. 8 *Exploded View of Hitachi DCH & DCR Carburetor Assembly*

HITACHI DCH 340 & DCR 342 2-BARREL (Cont.)

- Remove fuel pipe nipple and strainer.
- Remove screw attaching choke lever to choke shaft.
- Move choke lever toward choke chamber.
- Remove choke connecting rod from counter lever.
- Disconnect vacuum hose from float chamber.

2) Remove bolts attaching choke chamber from float chamber. Remove choke chamber from float chamber, then perform the following steps:

- Remove cotter pin between diaphragm rod and secondary throttle lever.
- Separate lever and diaphragm.
- Remove the two solenoid valve harness clips.
- Remove diaphragm attaching screws.
- Remove diaphragm assembly.

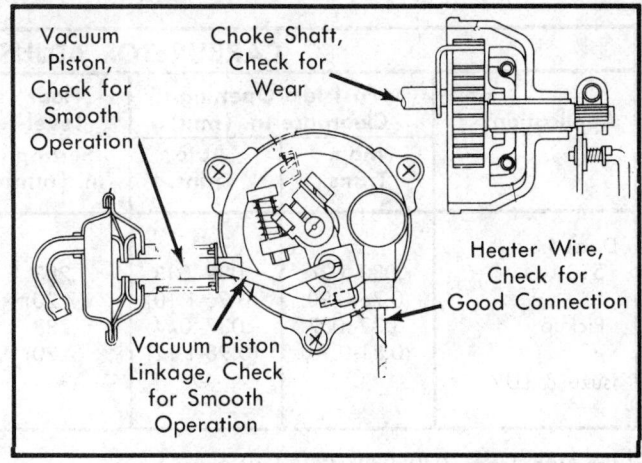

Fig. 10   Inspection of Automatic Choke

INSPECTION

Choke Chamber — Inspect chamber for cracks and damage particularly on joining face of chamber. Inspect choke shaft holes for wear, vacuum piston and choke valve for smoothness of operation. See *Fig. 10.*

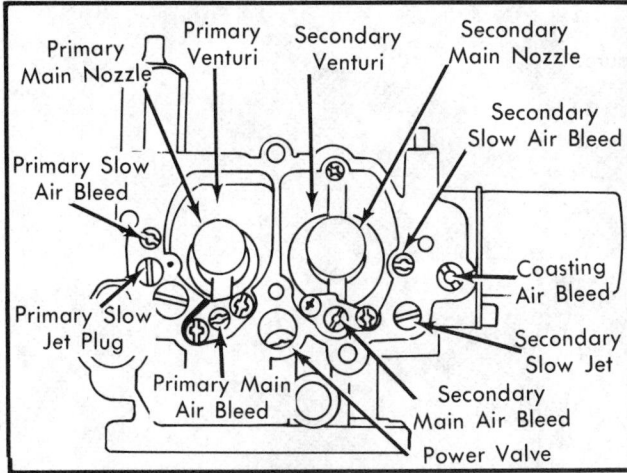

Fig. 9   Location of Jets and Small Venturi in Float Chamber

3) Separate float chamber from throttle valve body. These parts are attached by one screw on the upper part and three screws on the lower part. One of the three lower screws is used to remove the negative pressure developed in the venturi. Remove this screw carefully.

4) Remove accelerator pump plunger attaching screws. Invert float chamber and remove plunger assembly. Then perform the following:

- Remove float needle valve assembly.
- Remove float level gauge cover. Do not lose the float collar.

5) To disassemble rest of carburetor, proceed as follows:
- Remove screws attaching diaphragm cover.
- Remove diaphragm cover, spring and diaphragm. Do not lose ball and small spring.
- Remove all jets from upper part of float chamber.
- Remove small venturi from both primary and secondary venturi on Federal Datsun models only.
- Invert float chamber.
- Remove small venturi from both primary and secondary venturi on all except Federal Datsun models.
- Remove injector weight plug.
- Invert float chamber and remove injector weight and ball.
- Remove power jet, main jet plugs and main jets.
- Remove primary vacuum jet.

NOTE — *Do not remove throttle valves or choke valve unless components are damaged.*

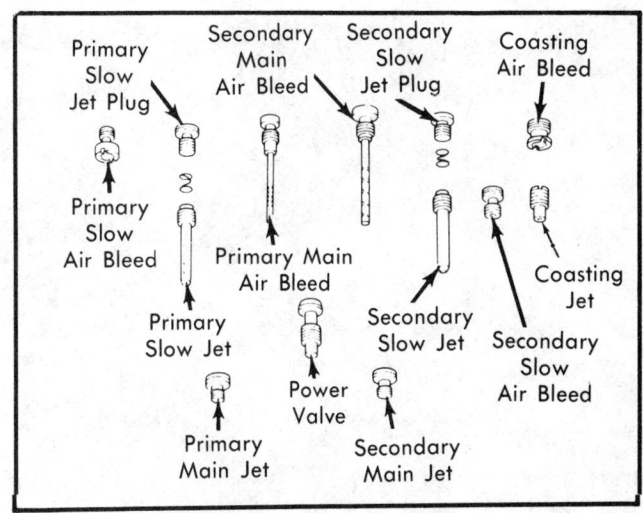

Fig. 11   Metering Component Identification

Float Chamber — Inspect body for cracks, jointing surfaces and threaded holes for damage. Check power valve for leaks and smoothness of operation. Inspect float needle valve and float pin hole for wear. Check accelerator pump plunger for damage, wear and smoothness of operation.

Throttle Chamber — Check throttle valves and shafts for wear; slow and idle ports for clogging. Inspect mixture screw seating and mixture screw for step wear.

REASSEMBLY

Reverse disassembly procedures and note following: Ensure jets are installed in correct positions. If choke and throttle valve have been removed, install valves making necessary adjustments and seal screws with a suitable wear. Check accelerator pump operation by filling cylinder with gasoline and operating plunger by hand.

1981 Hitachi Carburetors

HITACHI DCH 340 & DCR 342 2-BARREL (Cont.)

	CARBURETOR ADJUSTMENT SPECIFICATIONS							
Application	Fast Idle Opening Clearance In. (mm)		Float Level Setting In. (mm)	Float Drop Setting In. (mm)	Choke Linkage Setting In. (mm)	Secondary Throttle In. (mm)	Unloader Setting In. (mm)	Vacuum Break In. (mm)
	Man. Trans.	Auto Trans.						
Datsun 510	.030-.034 (0.76-0.90)	.039-.043 (0.96-1.10)	.283 (7.20)	.051-.067 (1.30-1.70)	.030-.035① (0.76-0.90)	.291-.330 (7.40-8.40)	.081-.112 (2.10-2.90)	.103-.127⑤ (2.62-3.22)
Pickup	.032-.037 (0.81-0.95) ②	.037-.044 (0.98-1.12) ②	.283 (7.20) ③	.051-.067 (1.30-1.70)	.030-.035① (0.76-0.90)	.291-.330 (7.40-8.40)	.081-.112 (2.10-2.90)	.103-.127⑤ (2.62-3.22)
Isuzu & LUV				.059 (1.50)	16-18°	.240-.300 (6.10-7.60)	....	.050-.059④ (1.28-1.75)

① — Auto. Trans. .040-.043" (0.96-1.10 mm).
② — 3200 RPM.
③ — Float parallel with top of float bowl. See adjustment procedure.
④ — Auto. Trans. .055-.064" (1.40-1.63 mm).
⑤ — California models .123-.147" (3.12-3.72 mm).

HITACHI DCS 328 2-BARREL

Courier (2000 cc & 2300 cc)

DESCRIPTION

Carburetor is a 2-stage, 2-barrel downdraft type. The primary stage includes a curb idle system, a piston-type accelerator pump system, idle transfer system, main metering system and power enrichment system. The secondary stage includes an idle transfer system and main metering system. An electric heater warms a bi-metal connected to the choke valve, controlling choke valve and throttle valve position automatically. Carburetor also features a coasting richer (deceleration) valve, slow fuel cut valve, secondary throttle diaphragm and dash pot (Calif. Man. Trans.).

CARBURETOR IDENTIFICATION

Application	Carburetor No.
2000 cc	
Federal	215282-B21
Calif.	215282-B31
2300 cc	
Federal	DCS328-8
Calif.	DCS328-7

ADJUSTMENTS

HOT (SLOW) IDLE RPM

See appropriate TUNE-UP SERVICE PROCEDURES article.

IDLE MIXTURE

See appropriate TUNE-UP SERVICE PROCEDURES article.

COLD (FAST) IDLE RPM

See appropriate TUNE-UP SERVICE PROCEDURES article.

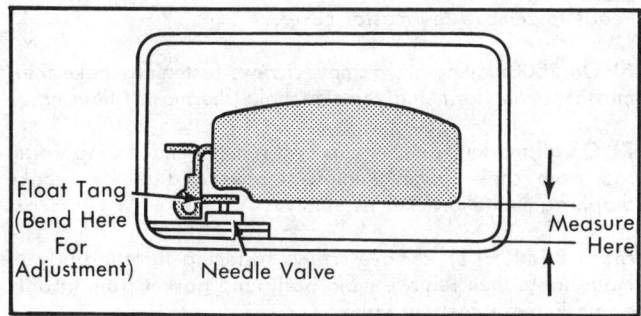

Fig. 1   Measurement for Float Level Adjustment (Carburetor Upside-Down)

FLOAT LEVEL

With engine running, check fuel level in bowl sight glass. If fuel level is not within specified range, remove carburetor from engine. Remove fuel bowl cover and invert carburetor. Allow float to lower by its own weight. Measure clearance between float and edge of bowl. If clearance is not to specifications, bend float tang to achieve proper clearance.   See Fig. 1.

FAST IDLE CAM ADJUSTMENT

Close choke valve fully. Place fast idle screw on the high (1st) step of fast idle cam. Adjust throttle valve opening clearance by turning fast idle adjusting screw clockwise to increase or counterclockwise to decrease the opening clearance. See Fig. 2.

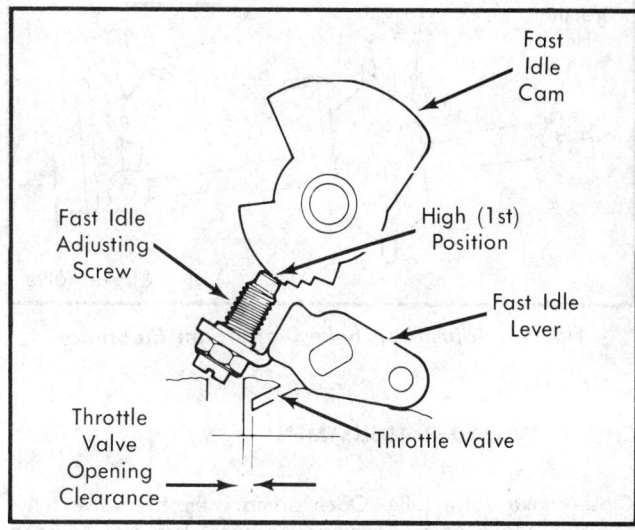

Fig. 2   Adjusting Fast Idle Cam

CHOKE VALVE OPENING ANGLE ADJUSTMENT

Adjust fast idle cam. Position fast idle adjusting screw on 2nd step of fast idle cam. See Fig. 3. Adjust choke valve opening clearance to specification by bending starting arm. If a large adjustment is needed, bend choke rod.

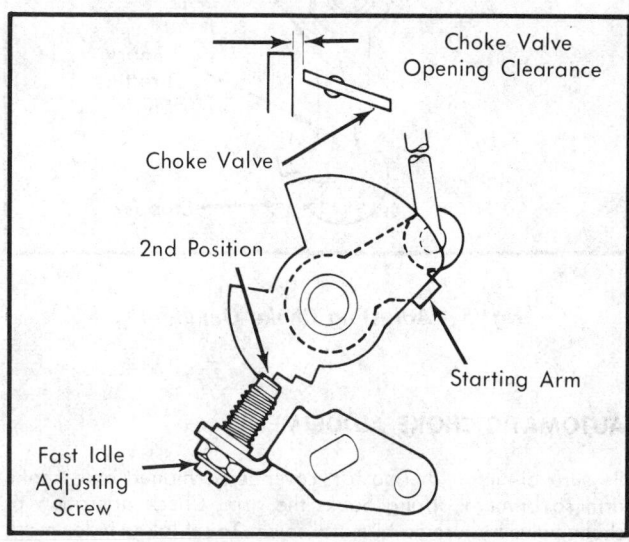

Fig. 3   Adjusting Choke Valve Opening Clearance

HITACHI DCS 328 2-BARREL (Cont.)

CHOKE DIAPHRAGM ADJUSTMENT

Apply approximately 15.6 in.Hg vacuum to choke diaphragm vacuum tube. See Fig. 4. Check that fast idle cam is on high (1st) position. Press choke valve slightly, then adjust choke valve opening to specifications by bending choke lever.

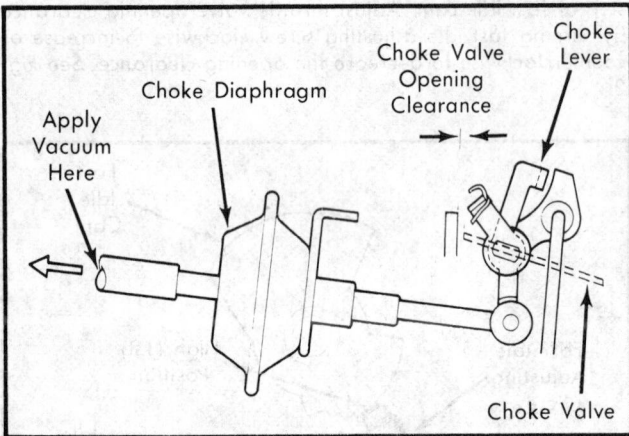

Fig. 4   Adjusting Choke Diaphragm Clearance

CHOKE UNLOADER ADJUSTMENT

Close choke valve fully. Open primary throttle valve fully. Measure choke valve opening clearance. See Fig. 5. Bend unloader adjusting nail to obtain specified clearance.

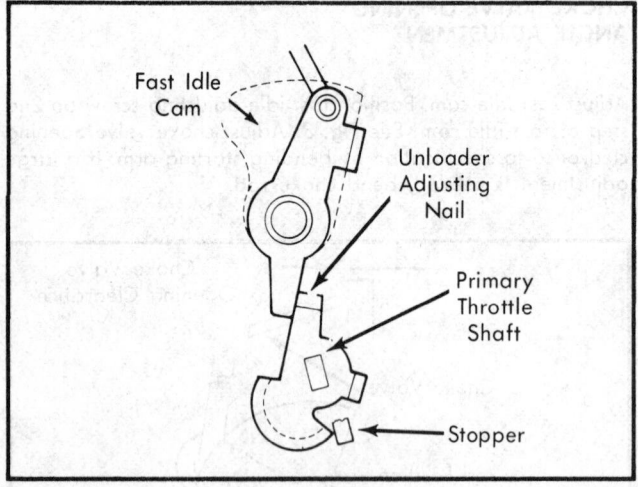

Fig. 5   Adjusting Choke Unloader

AUTOMATIC CHOKE ADJUSTMENT

Be sure bi-metal (thermostat) cover is positioned over choke arm so bi-metal spring hooks the arm. Check operation of choke valve by turning bi-metal cover. To set, align index mark on bi-metal cover with center mark on choke housing. Tighten attaching screws. See Fig. 6.

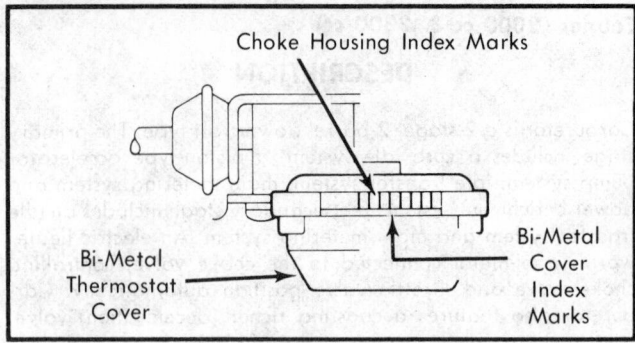

Fig. 6   Adjusting Automatic Choke

OVERHAUL

DISASSEMBLY

Air Horn — 1) Unhook and remove throttle return spring and remove vacuum sensing tube from choke diaphragm. Remove clip fastening choke thermostat lead to diaphragm cover and remove lead.

2) Remove accelerator pump rod from lever. Remove clip fastening pump lever to pump shaft and remove lever.

NOTE — On 2300 cc engines, it is also necessary to loosen screw in pump lever.

3) Remove clip and remove choke rod from starting arm.

NOTE — On 2300 cc engines, it is also necessary to unhook unloader return spring.

4) Mark position of choke thermostat cover index mark on choke housing.

5) Remove screws fastening air horn to main body and remove air horn and choke thermostat assembly. Remove choke thermostat cover by removing screws.

NOTE — On 2300 cc engines, it is necessary to grind off rivet heads to remove thermostat cover.

6) On 2000 cc engines, remove screws fastening choke thermostat to air horn and remove choke thermostat housing.

7) On all models, remove clip and remove choke diaphragm rod from choke lever. Remove screws and remove choke diaphragm and bracket assembly.

Main Body — 1) Remove screws fastening throttle body to main body, then remove main body and gasket from throttle body. Remove fuel cut valve.

2) On 2300 cc engines, remove screws fastening coasting richer valve to main body and remove coasting richer solenoid valve.

3) On all models, remove bolt fastening fuel inlet fitting to main body and remove fitting. Remove fuel strainer and then remove fuel inlet bolt and needle valve assembly.

4) Remove screws fastening fuel bowl sight glass cover and remove cover gasket, glass and rubber gasket from main body. Remove float lever pin, then remove float.

HITACHI DCS 328 2-BARREL (Cont.)

5) Remove accelerator pump plunger boot and plunger assembly. Remove plunger spring, then invert carburetor and remove inlet check ball.

NOTE — *On 2300 cc engines, remove screws fastening accelerator pump plunger to main body and remove cover plunger and gasket.*

6) Remove screw and washer that retain pump discharge weight and ball, invert carburetor, and remove weight, spring and check ball.

7) Remove jets, emulsion tubes, power valve and all air bleeds from main body.

8) On 2300 cc engines, remove screws fastening diaphragm chamber to main body and remove diaphragm chamber assembly.

Throttle Body (2000 cc Engines Only) — **1)** Remove cotter pin and washer, then disconnect throttle. Remove the screws fastening throttle lever bracket to diaphragm chamber and remove throttle lever bracket. Remove diaphragm cover and diaphragm return spring.

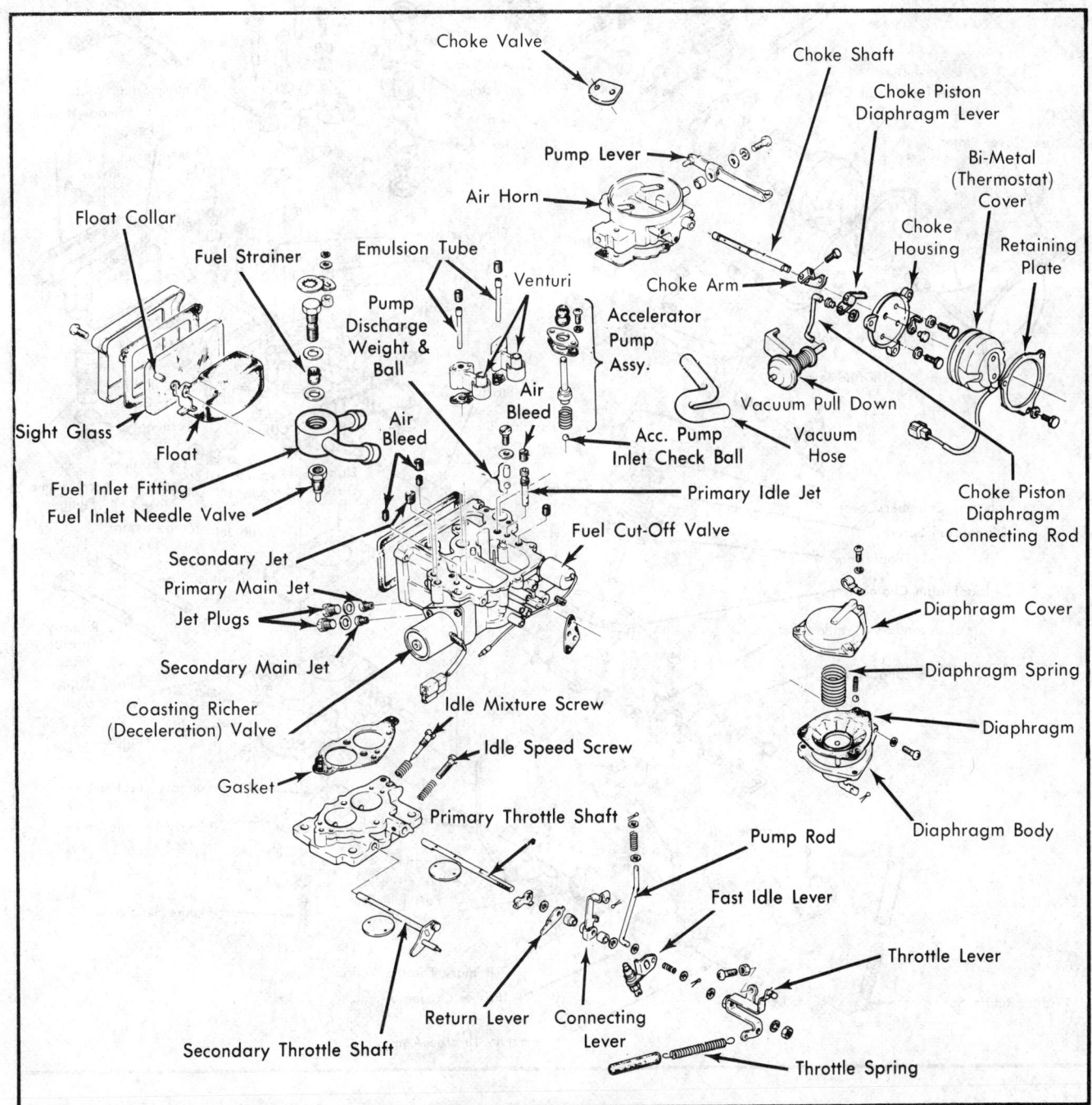

Fig. 7 Exploded View of Hitachi DCS 328 2-Barrel Carburetor (Ford Courier 2300)

1981 Hitachi Carburetors

HITACHI DCS 328 2-BARREL (Cont.)

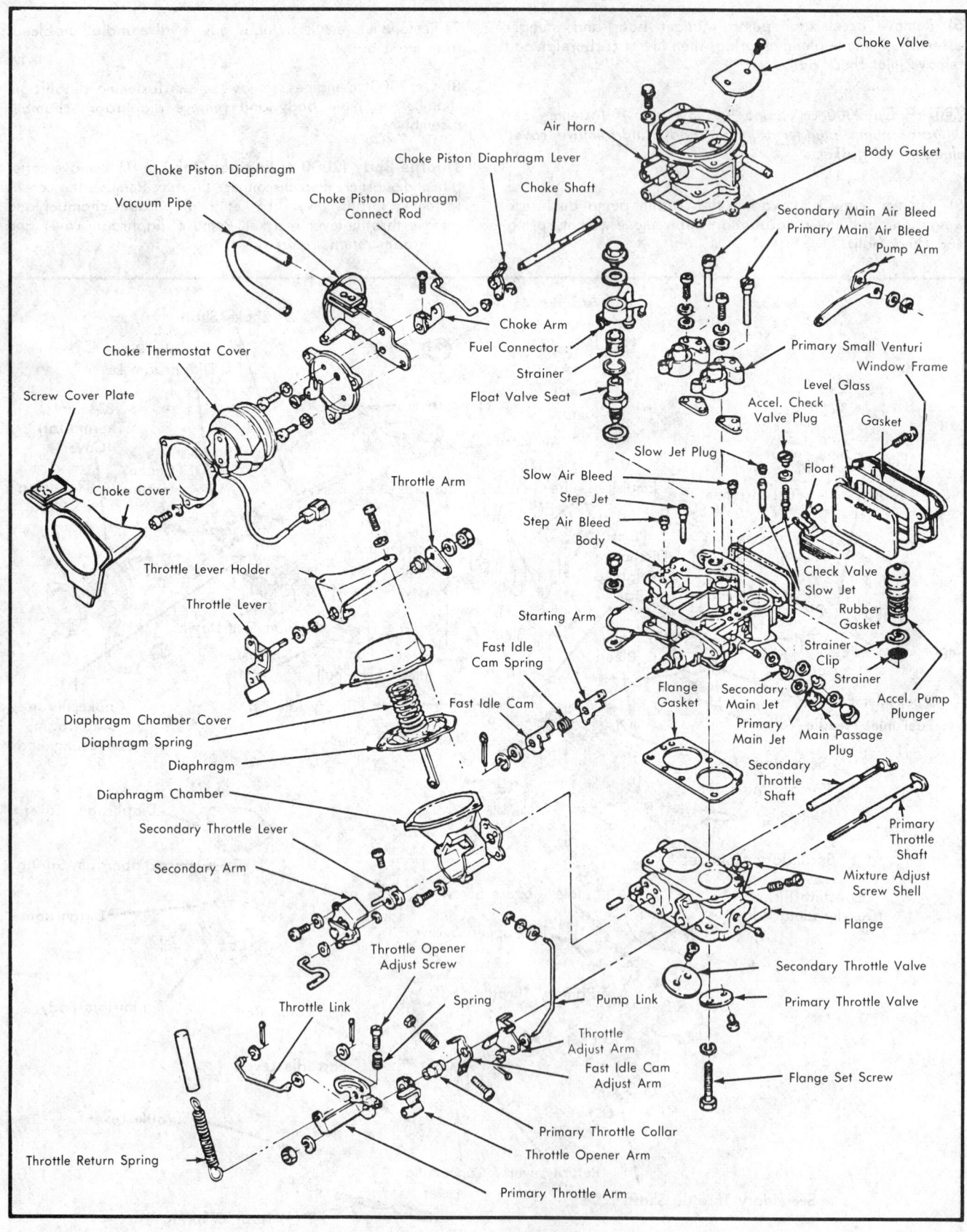

*Fig. 8 Exploded View of Hitachi DCS 328 2-Barrel Carburetor
(Ford Courier 2000)*

HITACHI DCS 328 2-BARREL (Cont.)

2) Remove clip and disconnect secondary throttle rod. Unhook secondary arm spring from bolt and loosen bolt and screw. Remove secondary arm and spring assembly from diaphragm chamber.

3) Remove clip from diaphragm rod and remove diaphragm. Loosen screw and remove secondary throttle lever from secondary throttle shaft.

4) Remove three screws fastening diaphragm chamber to throttle body and remove diaphragm chamber.

5) Remove mixture adjust screw cap by pulling entire shell outward while turning it counterclockwise, or shell can be cut off. Remove mixture adjusting screw from throttle body.

INSPECTION & CLEANING

Clean all parts thoroughly in solvent and check all passages and parts for wear or damage. Make sure that all jets are clear and clean. Do not attempt to clean jets by using wire or other objects which might damage calibrated orifices. Discard old gaskets and use new gaskets for assembly.

REASSEMBLY

Reassemble carburetor in reverse order of disassembly. Make sure that primary and secondary components are installed in their correct locations. When installing throttle valve or choke valve, make sure to eliminate gap between valve and wall of carburetor. When assembling float, ensure float collar is installed.

CARBURETOR ADJUSTMENT SPECIFICATIONS					
Application	Fast Idle Adjustment In. (mm)	Choke Valve Adjustment In. (mm)	Choke Diaphragm Adjustment In. (mm)	Choke Unloader Adjustment In. (mm)	Float Level Adjustment In. (mm)
Courier 2000cc Eng.					
Federal	.051-.059 (1.3-1.5)	.016-.028 (0.4-0.7)	.047-.067 (1.2-1.7)	.079-.099 (2.0-2.5)	.335 (8.5)
Calif.	.051-.059 (1.3-1.5)	.024-.036 (0.6-0.9)	.065-.085 (1.7-2.2)	.079-.099 (2.0-2.5)	.335 (8.5)
2300cc Eng.					
Federal	.058-.066 (1.5-1.7)	.039-.051 (1.0-1.3)	.051-.071 (1.3-1.8)	.090-.110 (2.3-2.8)	.236 (6.0)
Calif.	.061-.071 (1.6-1.8)	.041-.067 (1.1-1.7)	.063-.079 (1.6-2.0)	.094-.126 (2.4-3.2)	.236 (6.0)

HITACHI 4-BARREL

Mazda RX7

DESCRIPTION

Carburetor is of 4-barrel, 2-stage design. Primary stage includes idle system, slow speed circuit, accelerator pump system and main metering system. In addition, Federal models are equipped with a sub-zero starting device which admits fluid into the primary stage. Secondary stage contains secondary vacuum diaphragm operating system, stepping circuit and main metering system. Choking is accomplished through a semi-automatic choke. Other features include a deceleration control system, automatic choke return, hot start assist, idle compensation and dashpot (manual transmission).

ADJUSTMENTS

HOT (SLOW) IDLE RPM

See appropriate *TUNE-UP SERVICE PROCEDURES* article.

IDLE MIXTURE

See appropriate *TUNE-UP SERVICE PROCEDURES* article.

COLD (FAST) IDLE RPM

See appropriate *TUNE-UP SERVICE PROCEDURES* article.

FLOAT LEVEL ADJUSTMENT

Before assembling air horn to main body, adjust float level. Invert air horn on stand and allow float to drop by its own weight. Measure clearance between float and air horn gasket. *See Fig. 1.* Clearance should be .61-.65" (15.5-16.5 mm). If not within specifications, bend float seat lip as necessary.

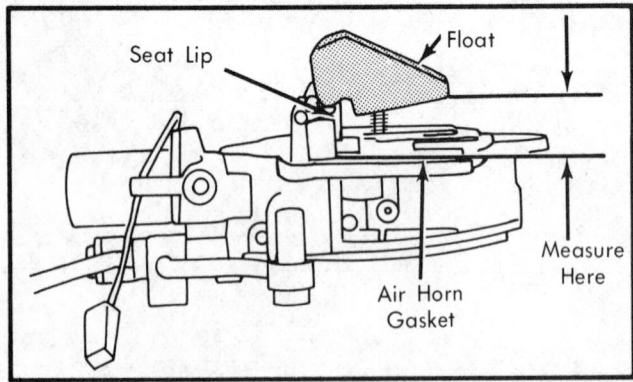

Fig. 1   Adjusting Float Level

FLOAT DROP ADJUSTMENT

Turn air horn over to its normal position and allow float to lower by its own weight. Measure distance between bottom of float and air horn gasket. *See Fig. 2.* Distance should be 1.98-2.03" (50.5-51.5 mm). If not, bend float stopper to obtain proper distance.

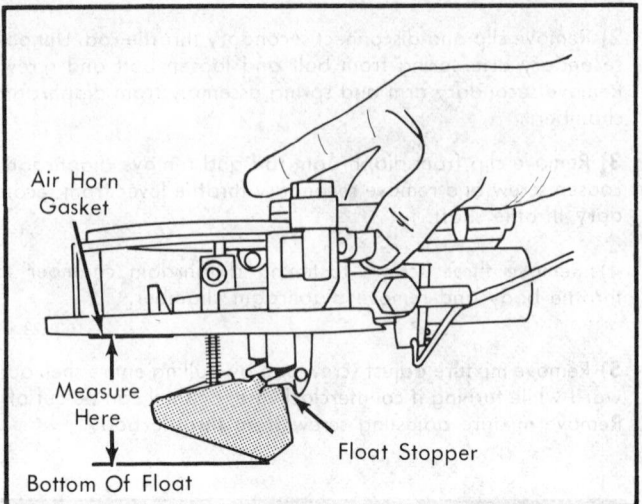

Fig. 2   Adjusting Float Drop

CHOKE LINKAGE ADJUSTMENT (FAST IDLE OPENING ANGLE)

Close choke valve fully and measure clearance between primary throttle valve and wall of throttle bore. Set clearance to .03-.04" (0.8-1.0 mm) by bending fast idle rod. *See Fig. 3.*

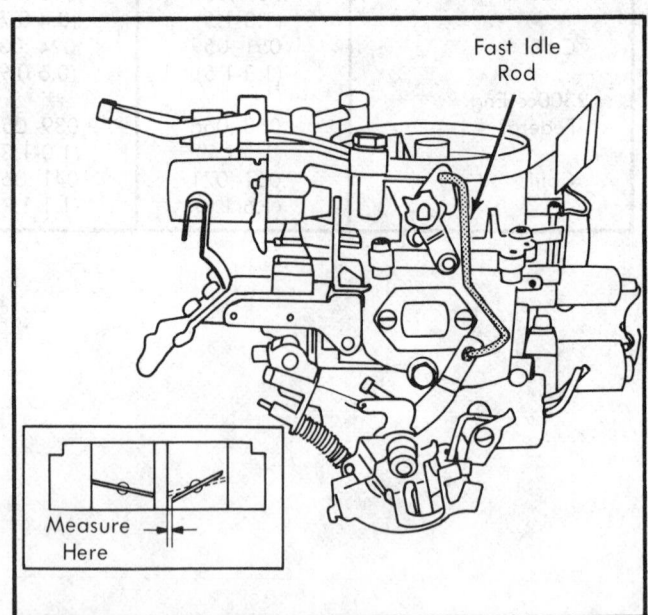

Fig. 3   Adjusting Choke Linkage Fast Idle Opening Angle

CHOKE VALVE OPENING ANGLE ADJUSTMENT

Disconnect vacuum sensing tubes from No. 1 vacuum diaphragm. Pull choke lever link out fully and hold in place. Apply more than 19.7 in. Hg to upper vacuum sensing tube. *See Fig. 4.* With vacuum applied, clearance "A" shown in *Fig. 4* should be .22-.24" (5.5-6.2 mm). Apply more than 19.7 in Hg to both vacuum hoses and measure clearance again. With vacuum applied to both hoses, clearance "A" should be .45-.51" (11.5-13.0 mm).

HITACHI 4-BARREL (Cont.)

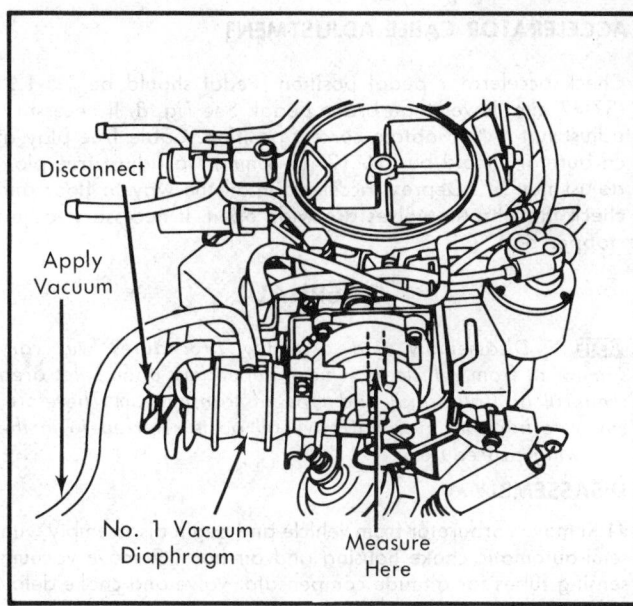

Fig. 4 Adjusting Choke Valve Opening Angle

NO. 2 CHOKE DIAPHRAGM

Disconnect vacuum sensing tubes from No. 2 vacuum diaphragm. Pull choke lever link out fully and hold in place. Choke valve should close fully. (Cool bi-metal coil if necessary). Apply more than 19.7 in. Hg to vacuum diaphragm and measure clearance between choke plate and bore. Clearance should be .057-.070" (1.46-1.80 mm).

CHECKING CHOKE DIAPHRAGM OPERATION (NO. 1 & NO. 2 DIAPHRAGMS)

Remove air cleaner. Start engine and run at idle. Disconnect vacuum sensing tubes from both diaphragms. Each diaphragm shaft should move outward from diaphragm.

CHECKING CHOKE DELAY VALVE OPERATION

Warm engine to normal operating temperature. Stop engine and remove assembly. Disconnect vacuum sensing tube from No. 1 choke diaphragm. Start engine and run at idle speed. Diaphragm shaft should move fully inward within 10-20 seconds after reconnecting vacuum sensing tube to choke diaphragm.

NOTE — *Automatic transmission must be in Neutral.*

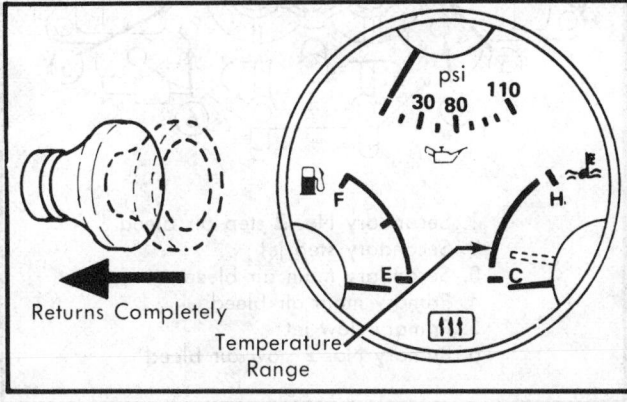

Fig. 5 Checking Automatic Choke Release

CHECKING AUTOMATIC CHOKE RELEASE

With engine cold and ignition off, pull choke knob out fully and release. Knob should return automatically and freely. Connect tachometer to engine. Start engine and set engine speed at 2000 RPM with choke knob. As engine temperature reaches range indicated in *Fig. 5*, choke knob should return automatically and freely.

CHECKING CARBURETOR HEATER

1) Disconnect electrical connector from No. 1 water temperature switch and connect jumper wire to both terminals of connector. Connect tachometer to engine. Disconnect carburetor heater electrical connector and connect voltmeter to connector. Start engine and set engine speed at 2000 RPM with choke knob.

2) With choke knob pulled out, current should flow to carburetor heater lead. Current should not flow to heater lead with choke knob pushed in.

3) Connect ohmmeter between carburetor heater lead and carburetor body. If ohmmeter shows no movement, carburetor heater is defective and must be replaced.

HOT START ASSIST CABLE ADJUSTMENT

Remove lock spring of hot start assist cable from cable bracket. Slowly pull outer cable until hot start lever just touches stopper lever. Check clearance between cable bracket and lock nut on cable. See *Fig. 6*. Clearance should be .02-.08" (0.5-2.0 mm). If not within specifications, adjust by turning lock nut. Then install lock spring securely on cable.

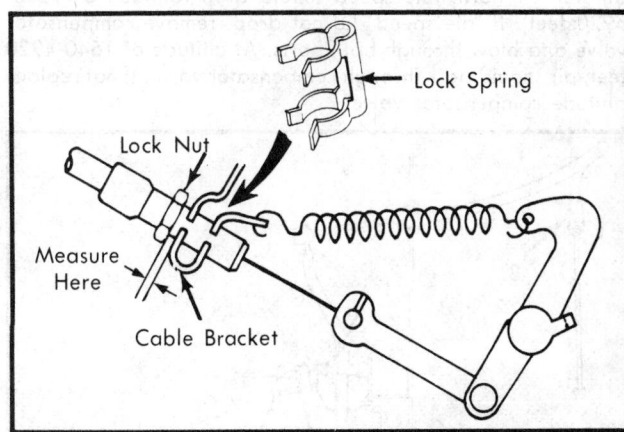

Fig. 6 Adjusting Hot Start Assist Cable

THROTTLE OPENER ADJUSTMENT (A/C MODELS ONLY)

1) Turn off all accessories. Remove fuel filler cap. Disconnect and plug idle compensator tube at air cleaner. Connect tachometer to engine and warm engine to normal operating temperature. Disconnect electrical connector from air switching solenoid valve (Gray color dot). Disconnect and plug vacuum sensing tubes at distributor vacuum control units.

HITACHI 4-BARREL (Cont.)

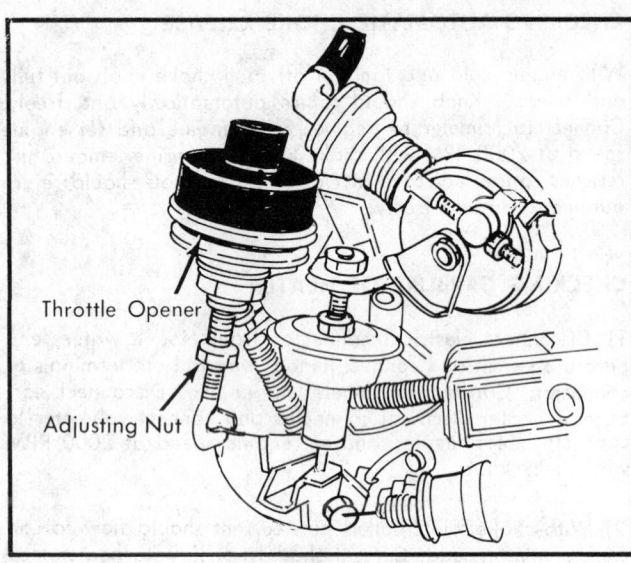

Fig. 7 Adjusting Throttle Opener (A/C Models Only)

2) Turn off air conditioner switch. Disconnect electrical connector from air conditioner solenoid (except Calif. Man. Trans.). Connect battery power to one terminal in connector and ground the other terminal. Throttle opener should operate and engine speed should increase to 1150-1250 RPM in neutral. If engine speed is not to specification, turn adjusting nut shown in Fig. 7.

CHECKING ALTITUDE COMPENSATOR

NOTE – Altitude compensator must be checked at altitudes of 1640-4920 feet.

Remove air cleaner and start engine. Engine should run smoothly at specified idle. Place finger over slow port on carburetor air horn; idle speed should drop (altitude of 1640-4920 feet). If idle speed did not drop, remove compensator valve and blow through both ports. At altitude of 1640-4920 feet, air should pass through compensator valve. If not replace altitude compensator valve.

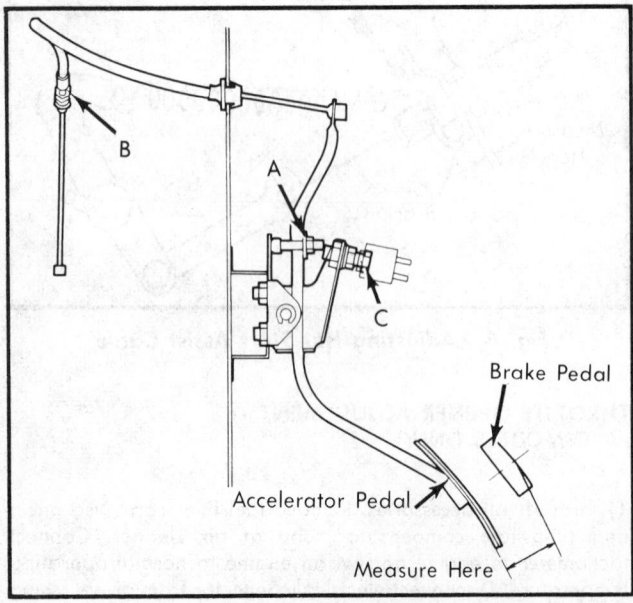

Fig. 8 Adjusting Accelerator Cable and Pedal Height

ACCELERATOR CABLE ADJUSTMENT

Check accelerator pedal position. Pedal should be 1.5-1.9" (37-47 mm) lower than brake pedal. See Fig. 8. If necessary, adjust nut "A" to obtain correct position. Cable free play at carburetor should be .04-.12" (1-3 mm). To adjust free play, adjust nut "B". Depress accelerator all the way to floor and check that throttle valves are wide open. If necessary, adjust stopper bolt "C".

OVERHAUL

NOTE – Disassembly and assembly procedures will vary somewhat from vehicle to vehicle, depending upon sales area (Federal or California) and type of transmission. Therefore, some carburetors may not have all parts referred to in the following procedures.

DISASSEMBLY

1) Remove carburetor from vehicle and begin disassembly with semi-automatic choke housing and air horn. Remove vacuum sensing tubes for altitude compensator valve and choke delay valve. Remove choke heater lead. Remove choke diaphragm No. 2 vacuum sensing tube. Remove altitude compensator valve.

2) Remove throttle opener and bracket assembly. Remove No. 1 choke diaphragm vacuum sensing tube. Remove dashpot diaphragm and bracket assembly (Man. Trans. only). Remove throttle return spring, sub-return spring, return spring bracket, bi-metal spring housing and bracket assembly and No. 1 choke diaphragm.

3) Remove split pin and fast idle rod, hot start assist lever spring and bracket assembly, choke lever, choke return diaphragm and bracket. Remove No. 2 choke diaphragm. Remove air horn attaching screws and remove air horn assembly from main body. Disconnect float pin and remove float, needle valve, spring, valve stem and retainer.

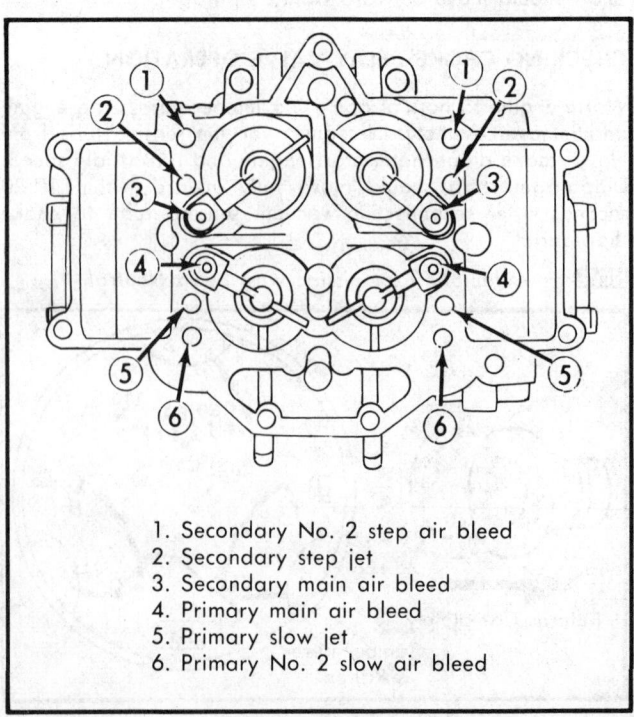

1. Secondary No. 2 step air bleed
2. Secondary step jet
3. Secondary main air bleed
4. Primary main air bleed
5. Primary slow jet
6. Primary No. 2 slow air bleed

Fig. 9 Removing Jets and Air Bleeds

HITACHI 4-BARREL (Cont.)

4) From main body, remove accelerator pump rod, secondary throttle valve rod, throttle sensor and main body attaching bolts. Remove main body from throttle body. Remove secondary throttle attaching screws, cover, return spring, pin and clip, diaphragm, housing and gasket.

5) Remove "E" clip, washer and shaft, accelerator pump lever, attaching screws, cover, diaphragm and return spring. From main body, remove accelerator pump injection screw, nozzle, gasket, weight, outlet check valve, check valve seat, weight and inlet check valve. Remove retainer, blind plug and washer, primary main jet and secondary main jet.

6) Remove air bleeds and jets. *See Fig. 9.* Using a hacksaw, remove idle limiter cap by cutting through limiter cap and mixture adjusting screw 0.4" (10 mm) from cap end. Remove and discard mixture adjusting screw and spring.

INSPECTION

Wash all parts in clean solvent, blow fuel passages with compressed air and remove dirt. Never use wire for cleaning jets. Inspect air horn, main body and throttle body for cracks or breakage. Inspect choke shaft and throttle shaft for wear, linkage and connecting rods for bends, and return springs for damage. Inspect float, needle valve and seat and strainer for damage. Check air vent solenoid valve for proper operation.

REASSEMBLY

To assemble, reverse disassembly procedure. Discard all old gaskets, using new ones. Clean and inspect all parts. Prevent primary and secondary system parts from becoming mixed. When installing bi-metal spring housing, fit choke shaft lever to bi-metal spring by closing choke valve and pulling vacuum diaphragm shaft.

CARBURETOR ADJUSTMENT SPECIFICATIONS

Application	Idle Speed (Engine RPM)		Float Level Setting In. (mm)	Float Drop Setting In. (mm)	Choke Linkage (Off Car) In. (mm)	Accelerator Cable Free Play	Choke Valve Opening In. (mm)
	Hot	Fast					
RX7	750	①	.61-.65 (15.5-16.5)	1.8-2.2 (46-56)	.22-.24 (5.5-6.2)	.04-.12 (1-3)	.03-.04 (0.8-1.0)

① — Manufacturer does not supply fast idle speed. See Choke Linkage (Fast Idle Opening Angle).

1981 Keihin Carburetors

KEIHIN 2-BARREL — HONDA

Accord
Civic
Prelude

DESCRIPTION

Carburetor is a two barrel, three venturi downdraft design. Carburetor contains two systems, primary and auxiliary. Primary system utilizes primary and secondary venturi, float system, accelerator pump system, and an idle system. Auxiliary system utilizes an auxiliary venturi with a float and idle system. Auxiliary system provides fuel to the pre-combustion chamber.

Carburetor components include electrically heated, automatic choke, choke opener diaphragm, secondary throttle opener diaphragm, fuel shut-off solenoid, primary/secondary main fuel cut-off solenoid, primary slow mixture cut-off solenoid, fast idle unloader and air jet controller (Calif. and high altitude models).

NOTE — *Air jet controller (AJC) is an atmospheric pressure sensing device, controlling the amount of air flow into slow and main air jets of auxiliary carburetor and secondary slow air jet of main carburetor.*

CARBURETOR IDENTIFICATION

Application	Carburetor No.	
	Man. Trans.	Auto. Trans.
Civic		
Federal	CB31E	CB31D
Calif.	CB32C	CB32E
High Alt.	CB32K	CB32J
Accord LX		
Federal	CB38A	CB38B
Calif.	CB40A	CB40B
High Alt.	CB40C	CB40D
Accord & Prelude		
Federal	CB37A	CB37B
Calif.	CB39A	CB39B
High Alt.	CB39C	CB39D

ADJUSTMENTS

HOT (SLOW) IDLE RPM

See appropriate *TUNE-UP SERVICE PROCEDURES* article.

IDLE MIXTURE

See appropriate *TUNE-UP SERVICE PROCEDURES* article.

COLD (FAST) IDLE RPM

See appropriate *TUNE-UP SERVICE PROCEDURES* article.

AUTOMATIC CHOKE

Both the choke valve setting and fast idle position are controlled during engine warmup by the automatic choke. It consists of a 5 ohm resistor on the firewall, an air intake sensor in the air cleaner assembly, thermovalve in thermostat housing, voltage regulator, choke opener and fast idle unloader.

Choke Coil Tension and Linkage — Remove air cleaner and open and close throttle fully to engage fast idle cam. If choke valve does not fully close, remove choke cover and inspect linkage. Reinstall cover, aligning index marks. Recheck clearance. If choke still does not close properly, replace cover.

Choke Opener and Linkage — 1) Open and close throttle fully to engage fast idle cam. Start engine. Choke valve should partially open. If choke opens partially, go on to step **3)**. If choke does not partially open, check linkage for free movement and retest.

2) If choke still does not partially open, check position of choke opener lever. Clearance should exist between choke opener lever and stop when engine coolant temperature is below 52° F (11°C). If engine stalls or runs rough when lever is pulled against stop, go to step **3)**. Clearance should not exist between choke lever and stop when engine coolant temperature exceeds 66°F (19°C). If clearance exists, go on to step **4)**.

3) With coolant temperature below 52°F (11°C), disconnect choke opener-to-thermovalve tube at choke opener. If choke opener lever moves away from stop, replace thermovalve and retest. If lever touches stop, clean choke opener joint orifice and retest. If lever is still against stop, replace choke opener diaphragm and retest.

4) With coolant temperature above 66°F (19°C), disconnect and plug choke opener hose. Lever should touch stop. If lever does not touch stop, replace thermovalve.

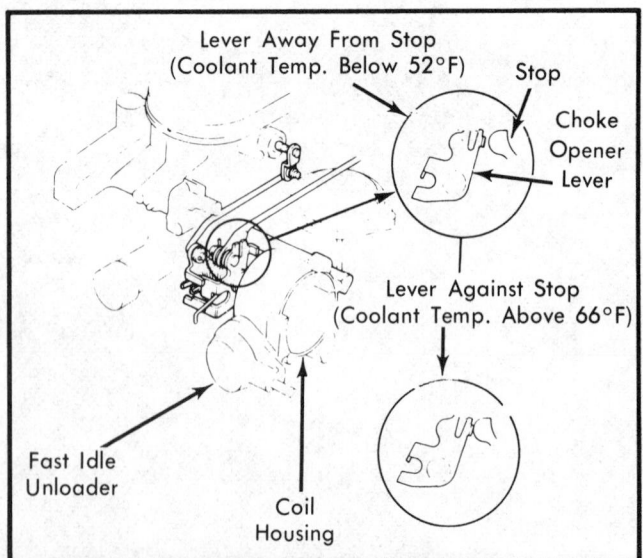

Fig. 1 Checking Choke Opener Lever Position

Choke Valve Opening Adjustment — 1) Remove choke cover. Fully close choke valve. Fully open, then close throttle valve. Disconnect choke opener tube and apply 85 psi (6 kg/cm²) air to choke opener.

KEIHIN 2-BARREL – HONDA (Cont.)

2) Reconnect choke opener tube. Push choke opener rod towards the opener diaphragm until it stops, then pull choke drive lever down against choke opener lever and measure clearance between choke blade and carburetor body. Adjust to 1st stage clearance specification by bending Tab D.

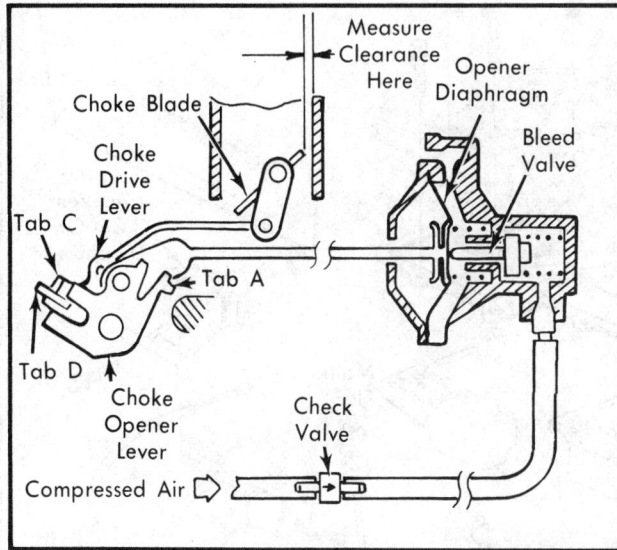

Fig. 2 Measuring Choke Valve Clearance

3) Hold choke opener lever and choke drive lever together and push them toward opener diaphragm until they stop. Measure choke blade clearance and adjust to 2nd stage clearance by bending Tab A.

4) While still holding choke opener lever, release choke drive lever and measure choke blade clearance. Adjust to 3rd stage clearance specification by bending Tab C.

Choke Coil Tension – 1) With engine cold, remove air cleaner. Then open and close throttle fully. Choke blade should close completely; above 82°F (28°C) choke will only partially close.

2) If choke does not close properly, remove choke cover and check for free movement of linkage and repair as necessary. If choke still does not close properly, replace choke cover.

Choke Coil Heater – 1) As engine reaches normal operating temperature, choke blade should fully open. If it does not, inspect choke linkage and repair as necessary.

2) If choke still does not open fully, disconnect air temperature sensor connector and check for voltage at Blue/White wire to choke cover, (leave choke wires connected).

3) If there is no voltage, check for an open circuit between choke heater and battery. Repair as necessary.

4) If there is voltage, check for voltage at Red wire to choke cover. If there is no voltage, replace choke cover. If there is voltage, check for open circuit in external resistor or short in choke heater. Repair as necessary.

Fast Idle Unloader – 1) Connect tachometer to cold engine. Start engine and allow to reach operating temperature. Do not manually open throttle. As engine warms up, speed should drop below 1400 RPM.

2) If engine speed does not drop below 1400 RPM, disconnect fast idle unloader hose and check for vacuum. If vacuum is present, check diaphragm for leaks and free movement of unloader rod and retest.

3) If no vacuum is present, test voltage at unloader solenoid valve-to-emission control box connector. If no voltage is present, replace unloader solenoid and retest.

4) On all, except California models, if voltage is present, replace thermosensor and retest. On California models, disconnnect thermosensor connector. If voltage at connector disappears, replace thermosensor. If voltage remains, replace diode in emission control box and retest.

Air Temperature Sensor – Disconnect and remove sensor from air cleaner. Check for voltage across sensor lead wires. Voltage should be present at 40-73° (4.5-23°C), but absent below this temperature range. Replace air temperature sensor if not to specifications.

Thermovalve – Drain engine coolant until level is below distributor holder. Remove distributor holder and thermovalve. Suspend thermovalve in cold water with vacuum pump attached to thermovalve. Slowly heat water and note temperature and vacuum readings. Valve should open below 60°F (15°C) and not hold vacuum. Valve should close above 77°F (25°C) and hold vacuum.

THROTTLE CABLE

1) Check that throttle cable operates smoothly with no binding or sticking. Check cable free play at linkage. Adjust cable deflection to .16-.40" (4-10 mm) by turning adjusting nut. Tighten lock nut.

2) Throttle valve should open fully when accelerator pedal is depressed and return to idle position when pedal is released.

FLOAT LEVEL

NOTE – Be sure to use correct float gauge and catch tray when checking float level. Use Float Level Gauge 07501-6950100 for all models. Use Catch Tray 07501-6950202 for Civic and 07501-6950201 for Accord and Prelude models. Gauge includes a see through adapter, with a red line as a fuel level indicator. Gauge is installed where primary main cut-off solenoid, auxiliary main jet plug and air vent cut-off diaphragm mount to carburetor body.

1) With air cleaner removed and carburetor installed on vehicle, remove primary main cut-off solenoid, auxiliary main jet plug and air vent cut-off diaphragm. Attach special float level gauge, catch tray and drain bottle to carburetor.

2) Start engine and allow to stabilize. Float level should remain at red line on gauge. If not, adjustment is made by turning external float level adjusting screws. See Fig. 4.

1981 Keihin Carburetors

KEIHIN 2-BARREL — HONDA (Cont.)

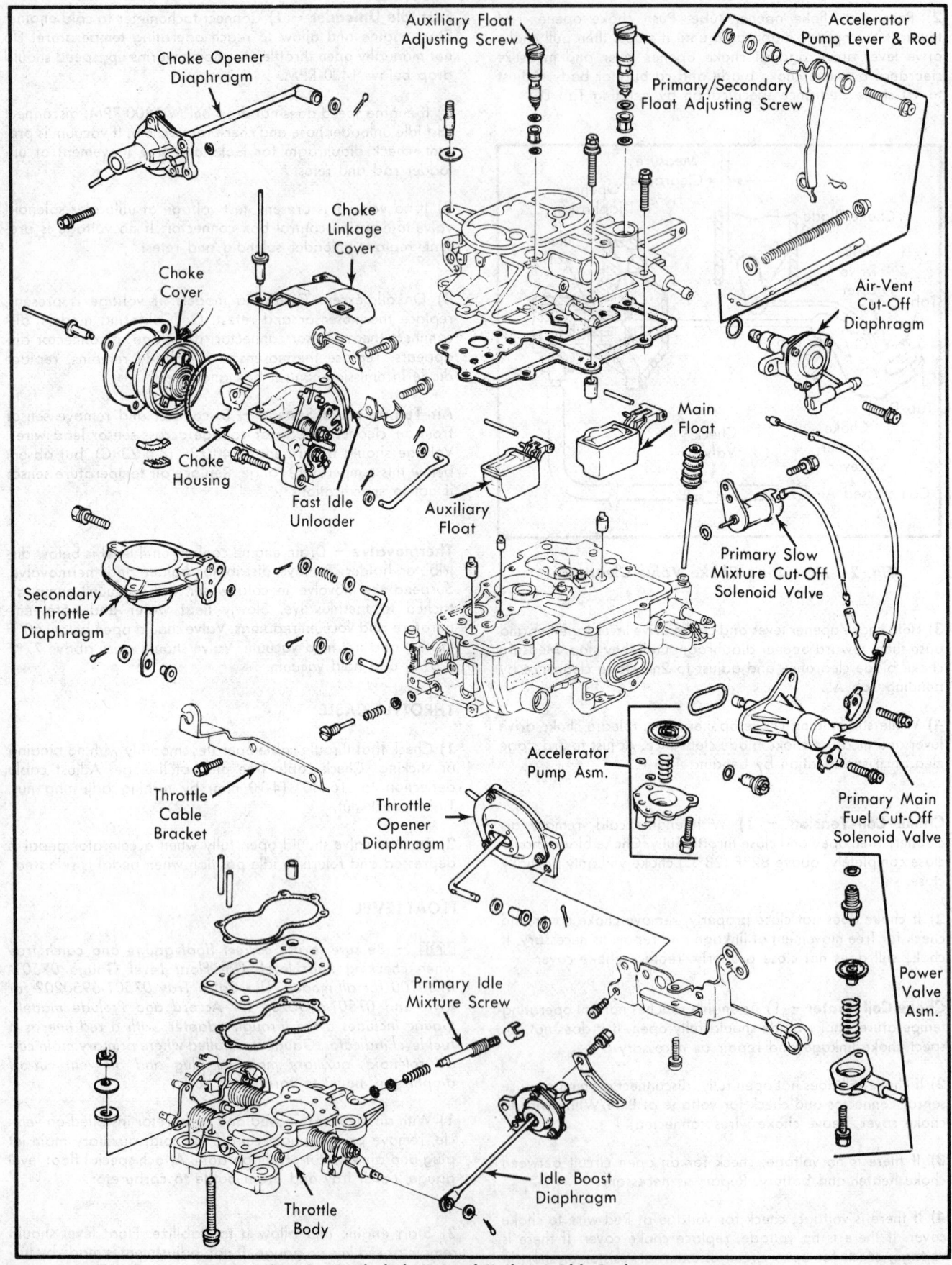

Choke Opener Diaphragm

Auxiliary Float Adjusting Screw

Primary/Secondary Float Adjusting Screw

Accelerator Pump Lever & Rod

Choke Linkage Cover

Choke Cover

Choke Housing

Air-Vent Cut-Off Diaphragm

Fast Idle Unloader

Auxiliary Float

Main Float

Primary Slow Mixture Cut-Off Solenoid Valve

Secondary Throttle Diaphragm

Accelerator Pump Asm.

Primary Main Fuel Cut-Off Solenoid Valve

Throttle Cable Bracket

Throttle Opener Diaphragm

Power Valve Asm.

Primary Idle Mixture Screw

Throttle Body

Idle Boost Diaphragm

Fig. 3 *Exploded View of Keihin 2-Bbl. Carburetor*

KEIHIN 2-BARREL — HONDA (Cont.)

3) Allow time for fuel level to stabilize and check again. When correct float level is achieved, paint adjusting screws to keep adjustment from changing.

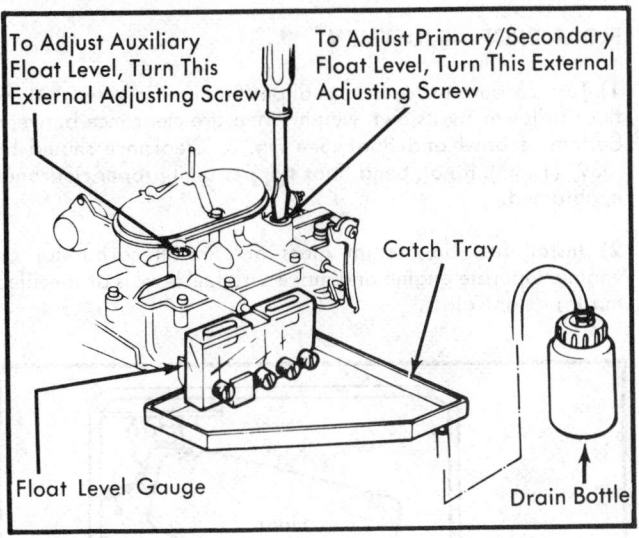

Fig. 4 Keihin Float Level Adjustment (External)

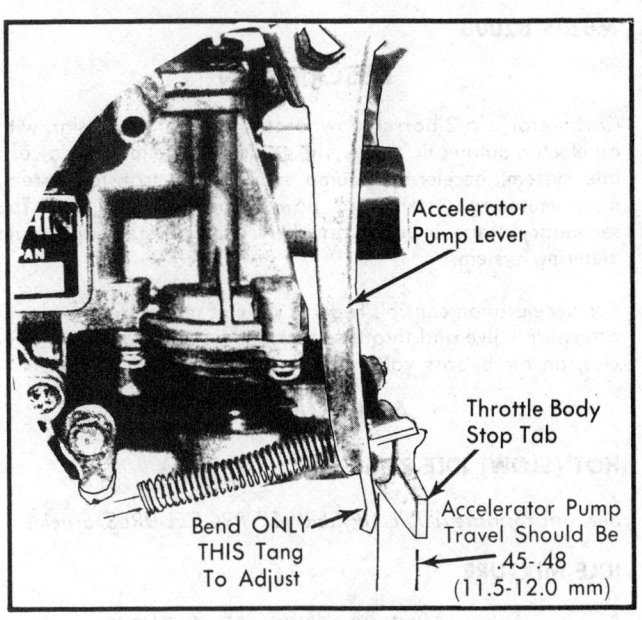

Fig. 5 Keihin Accelerator Pump Adjustment

ACCELERATOR PUMP

Accelerator pump stroke is adjusted by bending accelerator pump lever tang to obtain a clearance of .45-.48" (11.5-12.0 mm) between tang and throttle body stop tab. See *Fig. 5*.

AUXILIARY IDLE MIXTURE

Auxiliary idle mixture screw position should be marked before removal. If screw is removed and not marked, lightly seat screw then back out 1¾ turns.

CHOKE VALVE CLEARANCES						
Application	**1st Stage Clearance In. (mm)**		**2nd Stage Clearance In. (mm)**		**3rd Stage Clearance In. (mm)**	
	Man. Trans.	Auto. Trans.	Man. Trans.	Auto. Trans.	Man. Trans.	Auto. Trans.
Accord Federal	.040-.046 (1.02-1.16)	.034-.040 (.863-1.02)	.072-.080 (1.83-2.03)	.072-.080 (1.83-2.03)	.151-.169 (3.84-4.29)	.151-.169 (3.84-4.29)
Calif.	.040-.046 (1.02-1.16)	.040-.046 (1.02-1.16)	.072-.080 (1.83-2.03)	.072-.080 (1.83-2.03)	.151-.169 (3.84-4.29)	.151-.169 (3.84-4.29)
High Alt.	.046-.052 (1.16-1.32)	.040-.046 (1.02-1.16)	.072-.080 (1.83-2.03)	.072-.080 (1.83-2.03)	.161-.179 (4.08-4.55)	.151-.169 (3.84-4.29)
Civic 1300 All Models	.034-.040 (.863-1.02)	.034-.040 (.863-1.02)	.065-.073 (1.65-1.85)	.065-.073 (1.65-1.85)	.142-.160 (3.61-4.06)	.142-.160 (3.61-4.06)
1500 Exc. High Alt.	.034-.040 (.863-1.02)	.034-.040 (.863-1.02)	.065-.073 (1.65-1.85)	.065-.073 (1.65-1.85)	.142-.160 (3.61-4.06)	.142-.160 (3.61-4.06)
1500 High Alt.	.040-.046 (1.02-1.16)	.034-.040 (.863-1.02)	.065-.073 (1.65-1.85)	.065-.073 (1.65-1.85)	.142-.160 (3.61-4.06)	.142-.160 (3.61-4.06)
Prelude Federal	.040-.046 (1.02-1.16)	.034-.040 (.863-1.02)	.072-.080 (1.83-2.03)	.072-.080 (1.83-2.03)	.151-.169 (3.84-4.29)	.151-.169 (3.84-4.29)
Calif.	.040-.046 (1.02-1.16)	.040-.046 (1.02-1.16)	.072-.080 (1.83-2.03)	.072-.080 (1.83-2.03)	.151-.169 (3.84-.4.29)	.151-.169 (3.84-4.29)
High Alt.	.046-.052 (1.16-1.32)	.040-.046 (1.02-1.16)	.072-.080 (1.83-2.03)	.072-.080 (1.83-2.03)	.161-.179 (4.08-4.55)	.151-.169 (3.84-4.29)

NIKKI 2-BARREL – MAZDA B2000

Mazda B2000

DESCRIPTION

Carburetor is a 2-barrel, downdraft type, 2-stage design with an electric automatic choke. The primary stage includes a curb idle system, accelerator pump system, idle transfer system, main metering system and power enrichment system. The secondary stage includes an idle transfer system and main metering system.

For deceleration control, Federal vehicles make use of an anti-afterburn valve and throttle positioner system; California vehicles, an air bypass valve and throttle positioner system.

ADJUSTMENTS

HOT (SLOW) IDLE RPM

See appropriate TUNE-UP SERVICE PROCEDURES article.

IDLE MIXTURE

See appropriate TUNE-UP SERVICE PROCEDURES article.

COLD (FAST) IDLE RPM

See appropriate TUNE-UP SERVICE PROCEDURES article.

AUTOMATIC CHOKE SETTING

Align index mark on thermostat cover with center of choke housing index mark. See Fig. 1. Tighten attaching screws.

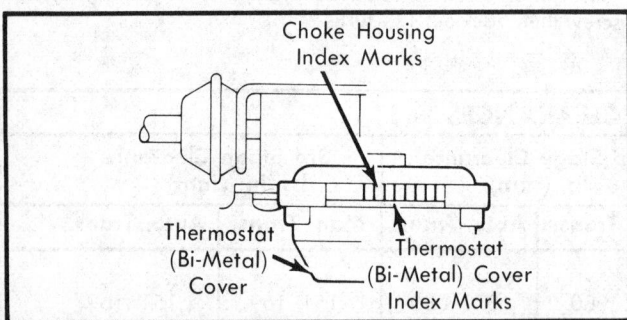

Fig. 1   Choke Thermostat Cover Index Marks

FLOAT LEVEL ADJUSTMENT

1) With engine running, check fuel level in fuel bowl sight glass. If fuel level is not to specified mark on sight glass, remove carburetor from vehicle. Remove fuel bowl cover and sight glass.

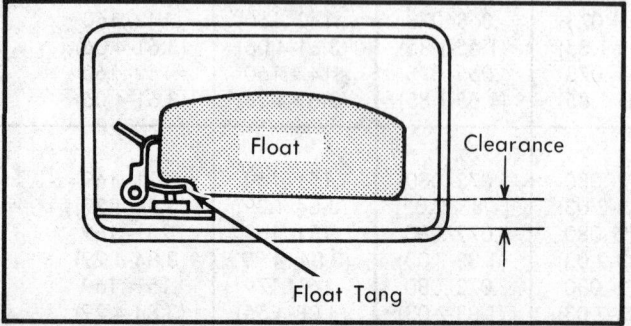

Fig. 2   Checking Float Level Ajustment

2) Invert carburetor on stand and allow float to lower by its own weight. Measure clearance as shown in Fig. 2. Clearance should be .335" (8.5 mm). To adjust clearance, bend float tang until proper clearance is obtained.

FLOAT DROP ADJUSTMENT

1) Turn carburetor to its normal position (not inverted). Allow float to lower by its own weight. Measure clearance between bottom of bowl and float. See Fig. 3. Clearance should be .039" (1 mm). If not, bend float stopper until proper clearance is obtained.

2) Install fuel bowl sight glass and install carburetor on engine. Operate engine and make sure fuel level is at specified mark in sight glass.

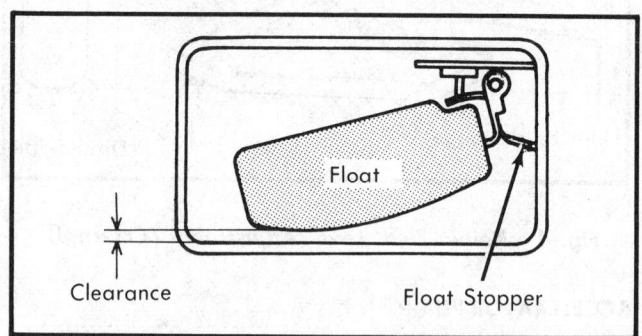

Fig. 3   Checking Float Drop Adjustment

CHOKE LINKAGE ADJUSTMENT (FAST IDLE OPENING ANGLE)

Fully close choke valve. Place fast idle screw on high (1st) step of fast idle cam. Measure throttle valve opening clearance between throttle bore wall and lower edge of throttle plate. Clearance should be .051-.059" (1.2-1.5 mm). Adjust clearance by turning adjusting screw. See Fig. 4.

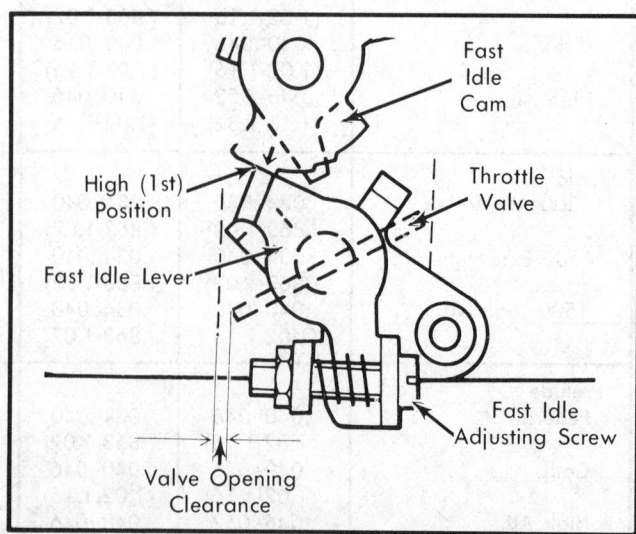

Fig. 4   Adjusting Choke Linkage (Fast Idle Opening Angle)

CHOKE VALVE OPENING ANGLE

Place fast idle screw on 2nd step of fast idle cam. Measure clearance between choke valve bore and upper edge of valve. Clearance should be .016-.028" (.40-.70 mm) on Federal models and .024-.035" (.60-.90 mm) on California models. Adjust clearance by bending starting arm. See Fig. 5.

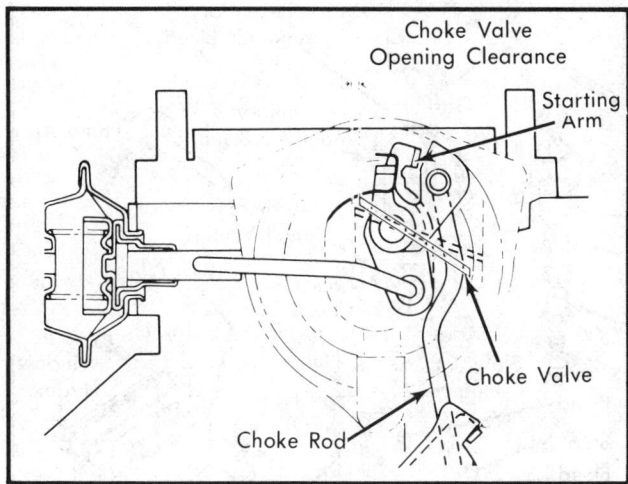

Fig. 5   Adjusting Choke Valve Opening Angle

CHOKE UNLOADER ADJUSTMENT

Close choke valve fully and then open primary valve fully. Measure choke valve clearance between air horn and choke valve. See Fig. 6. Clearance should be .079-.099" (2.0-2.5 mm). To adjust clearance, bend throttle adjusting arm.

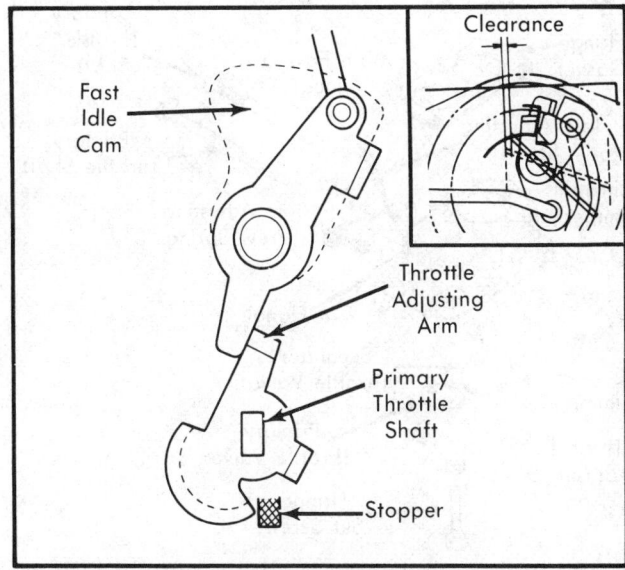

Fig. 6   Adjusting Choke Unloader

CHOKE DIAPHRAGM ADJUSTMENT

Apply approximately 15.7 in. Hg vacuum to choke diaphragm. Press choke valve slightly to closed position and measure clearance between choke valve and air horn. Adjust clearance to .047-.067" (1.2-1.7 mm) on Federal models and .065-.085" (1.65-2.15 mm) on California models.

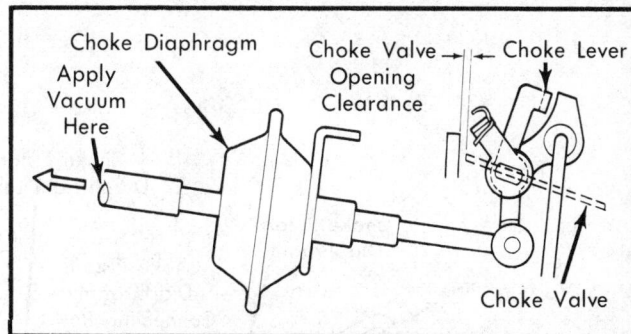

Fig. 7   Adjusting Choke Diaphragm

ACCELERATOR PEDAL HEIGHT ADJUSTMENT

Check accelerator pedal position. Pedal should be 1.57-1.97" (40-50 mm) lower than brake pedal. Throttle valves should be wide open when accelerator pedal is against the floor. To adjust pedal height, loosen lock nuts on longer linkage rod ("A" in Fig. 8). Rotate rods in sockets until proper height is obtained and tighten lock nuts.

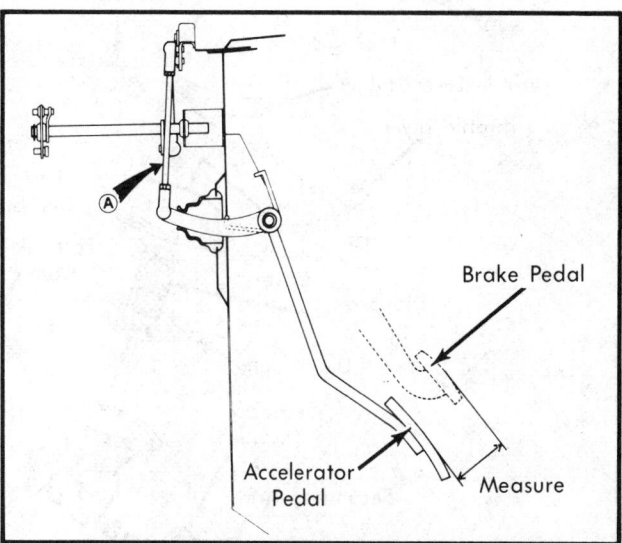

Fig. 8   Accelerator Pedal Height Adjustment

OVERHAUL

DISASSEMBLY

1) Remove carburetor and cover intake manifold port with clean shop towel to prevent dust and dirt from entering. Disconnect accelerator pump rod from lever and remove lever from main body.

2) Remove throttle return spring. Disconnect choke diaphragm-to-main body vacuum hose at main body. Spread clips and remove solenoid valve and choke heater leads. Remove choke rod retaining clip and remove choke rod. Remove air horn retaining screws. Separate air horn from main body and discard gasket.

1981 Nikki Carburetors

NIKKI 2-BARREL — MAZDA B2000 (Cont.)

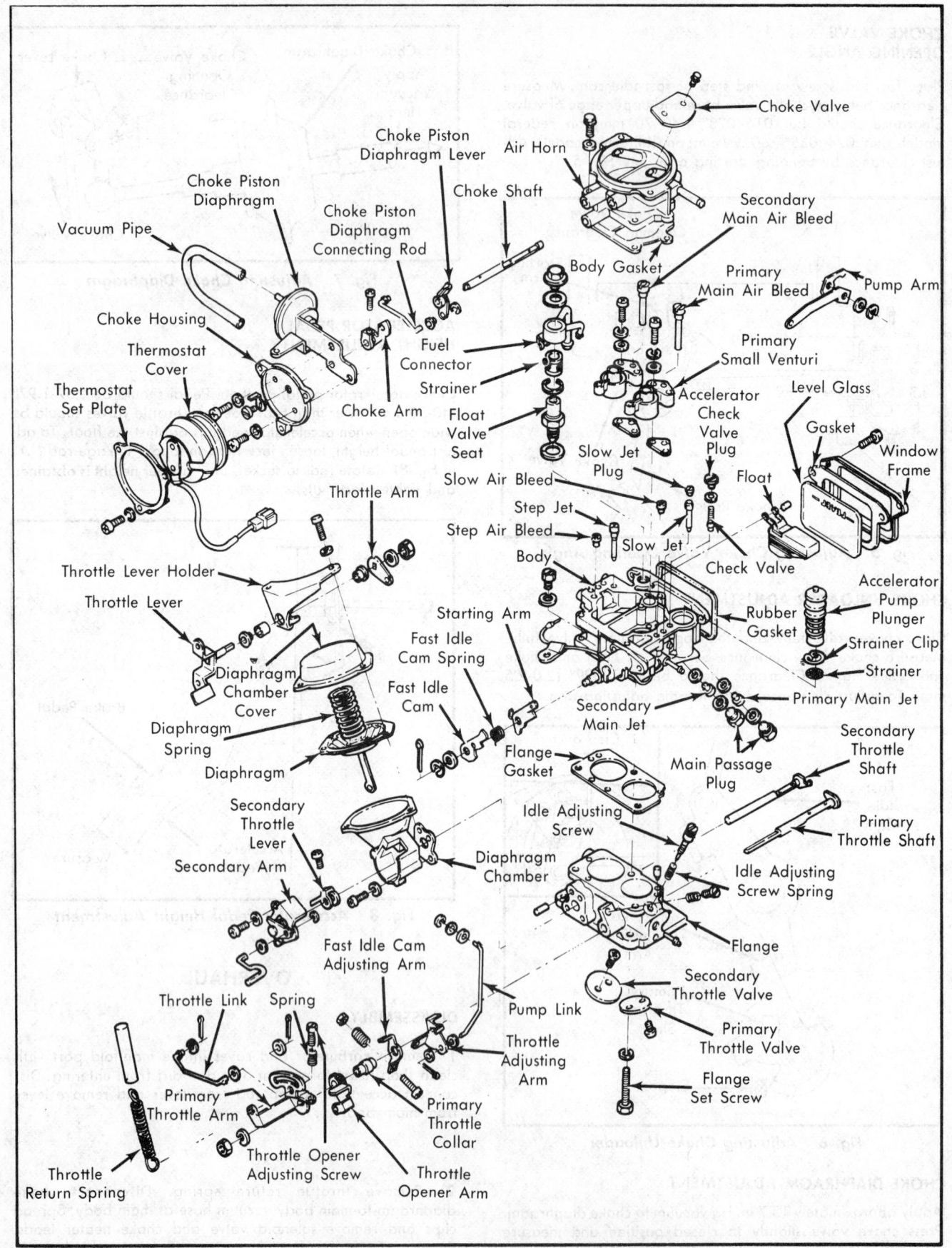

Fig. 9 Exploded View of Nikki 2-Bbl. Carburetor

NIKKI 2-BARREL – MAZDA B2000 (Cont.)

3) Remove choke cover retaining screws and remove choke cover. Mark position of choke thermostat cover index mark on choke housing and remove thermostat cover. Remove fuel inlet fitting from main body. Remove fuel inlet fitting, filter and packing. Remove accelerator pump piston assembly from main body.

4) Remove inlet check ball retainer clip. Invert carburetor and remove strainer and inlet check ball. Remove pump check valve retainer. Invert carburetor and remove check valve. Remove main body attaching bolts (1 bolt on bottom of throttle body). Separate throttle body from main body.

5) Remove fuel inlet bolt and washers from main body. Remove needle valve, spring and valve stem. Remove fuel bowl sight glass cover screws, cover, gasket, glass and rubber gasket. Remove float pin and float. Remove diaphragm cover retaining screws, diaphragm cover and spring.

6) Remove screw and bolt attaching secondary arm to main body, then remove throttle lever assembly. Remove clip securing diaphragm rod to secondary throttle shaft. Remove secondary throttle shaft retaining screw and throttle lever. Remove diaphragm body. Using power valve remover (490118870A), remove power valve.

7) Remove primary jet plugs, gaskets and main jets. Remove idle jets and all air bleeds from main body. See Fig. 10. Using a hacksaw, cut through mixture limiter shell .47" (12 mm) from shell end. Remove and discard mixture screw, spring and shell.

CLEANING & INSPECTION

1) Thoroughly clean all parts in clean solvent and dry with compressed air. Use care when blowing out passages in carburetor. Inspect air horn, main body and throttle body for cracks and breakage.

2) Inspect choke and throttle shafts for wear. Examine all jets and air bleeds. Never use wire to eliminate clogged condition. Inspect pump piston cup and replace if worn. Check accelerating pump valves for proper operation.

3) Examine power valve operation and check float needle and float. Inspect mixture adjusting screw for burrs or ridges. Check diaphragm and solenoid operation. Check for clogs at fuel return orifice. Discard and use all new gaskets when assembling carburetor.

REASSEMBLY

To assemble, reverse disassembly procedure. Be careful not to mistake primary and secondary parts. When installing thermostat cover on automatic choke housing, hook choke arm to bi-metal spring. Check correct operation of choke valve by turning thermostat cover. Then align index mark on cover with center mark on choke housing and tighten screws. Install new mixture screw and limiter shell.

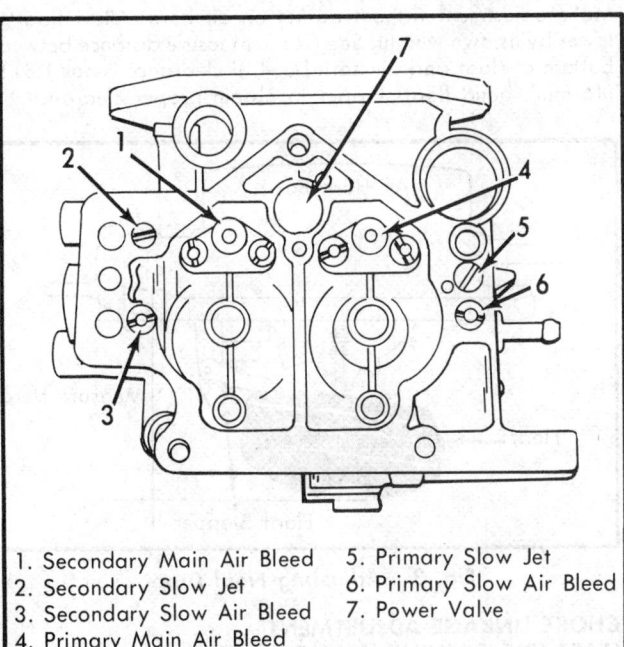

1. Secondary Main Air Bleed
2. Secondary Slow Jet
3. Secondary Slow Air Bleed
4. Primary Main Air Bleed
5. Primary Slow Jet
6. Primary Slow Air Bleed
7. Power Valve

Fig. 10 Removing and Installing Jets and Air Bleeds

	CARBURETOR ADJUSTMENT SPECIFICATIONS						
Application	Idle Speed (Engine RPM)		Float Level Setting In. (mm)	Float Drop Setting In. (mm)	Choke Linkage (Off Car) In. (mm)	Accelerator Cable Free Play	Choke Valve Opening In. (mm)
	Hot	Fast					
B2000	650	①	.335 (8.5)	.039 (1.0)	.051-.059 (1.2-1.5)	.....	②.016-.028 (.40-.70)

① — Manufacturer does not supply fast idle speed. See Choke Linkage (Fast Idle Opening Angle).
② — Calif. models — .024-.035" (.60-.90 mm).

1981 Nikki Carburetors

NIKKI 2-BARREL — MAZDA 626

Mazda 626

DESCRIPTION

Carburetor is a 2-barrel downdraft type. It is equipped with an electric automatic choke, an air by-pass valve for deceleration control, an idle compensator, high altitude compensator, air vent solenoid, slow fuel cut solenoid and throttle positioner system for air conditioned models. A double venturi provides for high air flow velocity at the venturi under all operating conditions, resulting in more efficient atomization of fuel for smooth combustion.

ADJUSTMENTS

HOT (SLOW) IDLE RPM

See *appropriate TUNE-UP SERVICE PROCEDURES article.*

IDLE MIXTURE

See *appropriate TUNE-UP SERVICE PROCEDURES article.*

COLD (FAST) IDLE RPM

See *appropriate TUNE-UP SERVICE PROCEDURES article.*

AUTOMATIC CHOKE SETTING

Before starting engine, fully depress accelerator pedal to ensure choke valve closes properly. Push choke valve with finger to check for binding. Be sure thermostat cover index mark is set at second choke housing index mark. *See Fig. 1.* Warm engine and check that choke valve is fully open. Tighten all attaching screws after aligning index mark.

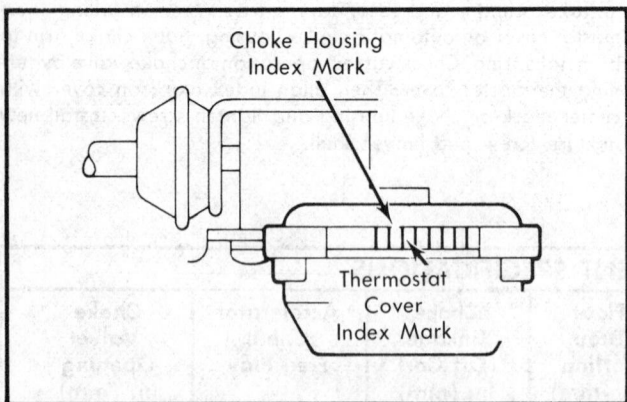

Fig. 1   Adjusting Automatic Choke

FLOAT LEVEL ADJUSTMENT

Remove air horn from carburetor. Remove air horn gasket. Invert air horn on stand and allow float to lower by its own weight. Bend float seat lip until clearance between float and air horn bowl is .452" (11.5 mm). See *Fig. 2.*

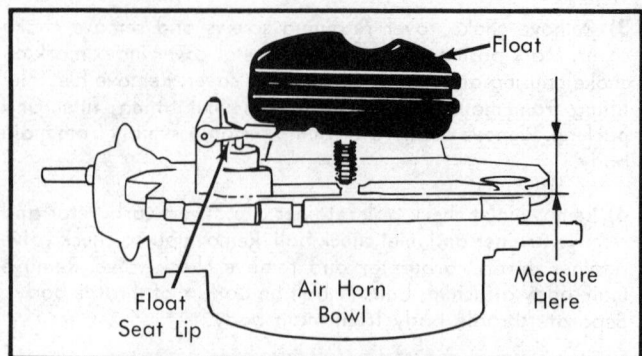

Fig. 2   Adjusting Float Level

FLOAT DROP ADJUSTMENT

Adjust float level and turn air horn over to its normal position. Make adjustment without gasket on air horn. Allow float to lower by its own weight. *See Fig. 3.* Measure distance between bottom of float and air horn bowl. If clearance is not 1.811" (46 mm), bend float stopper to obtain proper clearance.

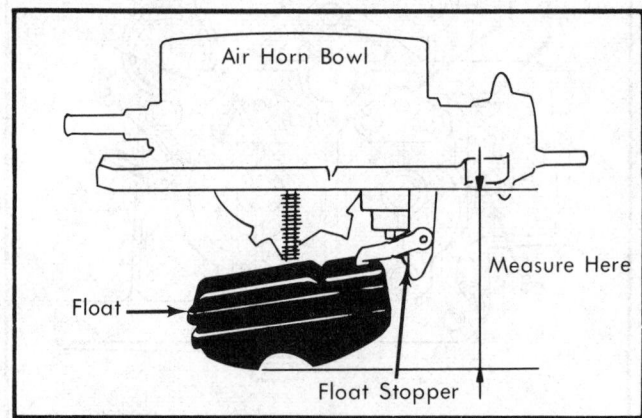

Fig. 3   Adjusting Float Drop

**CHOKE LINKAGE ADJUSTMENT
(FAST IDLE OPENING ANGLE)**

Fully close choke valve. Position fast idle lever on second step of fast idle cam. Set clearance between throttle valve and throttle bore to .018-.030" (.45-.75 mm) by turning fast idle adjusting screw. Turning screw clockwise increases angle size. See *Fig. 4.*

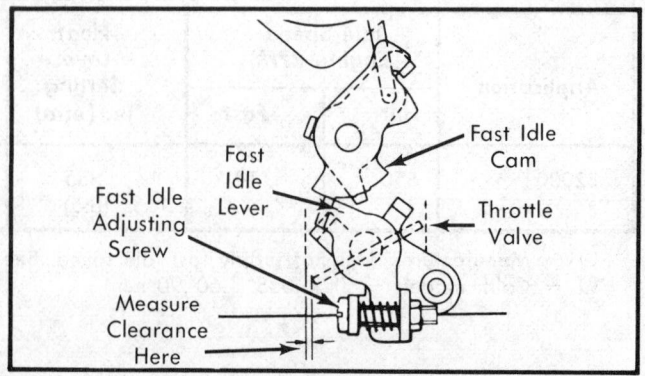

**Fig. 4   Choke Linkage Adjustment
(Fast Idle Opening Angle)**

NIKKI 2-BARREL — MAZDA 626 (Cont.)

CHOKE VALVE OPENING ANGLE

Check choke linkage adjustment, then place fast idle lever on second step of fast idle cam. Measure clearance between choke valve and carburetor bore. Choke valve clearance should be .026-.041" (.65-1.05 mm). Adjust clearance by bending starting arm. If large adjustment is necessary, bend choke rod. See *Fig. 5.*

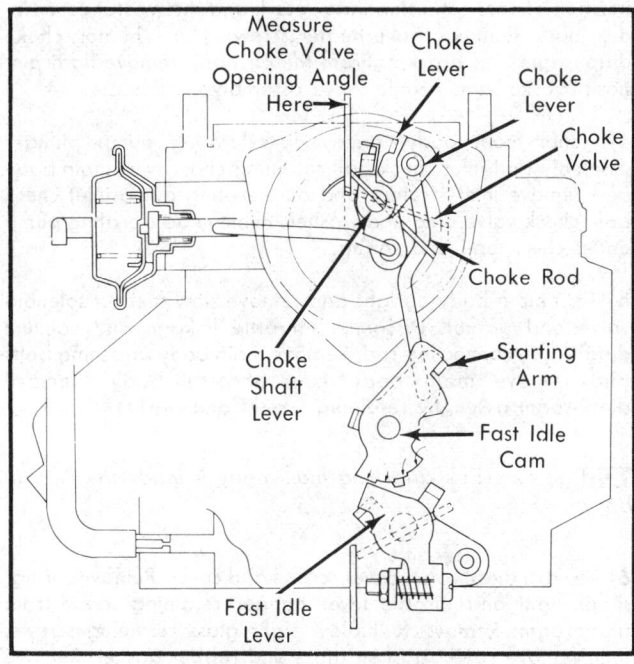

Fig. 5   Adjusting Choke Valve Opening Angle

CHOKE DIAPHRAGM ADJUSTMENT

Apply approximately 15.7 in. Hg vacuum to choke diaphragm vacuum tube. Fast idle lever should be on high step of cam. Press choke valve slightly and check choke valve opening clearance. Bend choke lever until clearance is .057-.077" (1.45-1.95 mm). See *Fig. 6.*

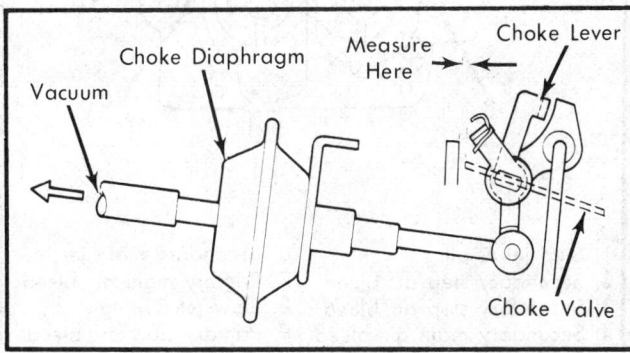

Fig. 6   Adjusting Choke Diaphragm

CHOKE UNLOADER ADJUSTMENT

Fully close choke valve and then open primary throttle valve. Measure choke valve clearance. Adjust clearance to .104-.136" (2.65-3.45 mm) by bending tab. See *Fig. 7.*

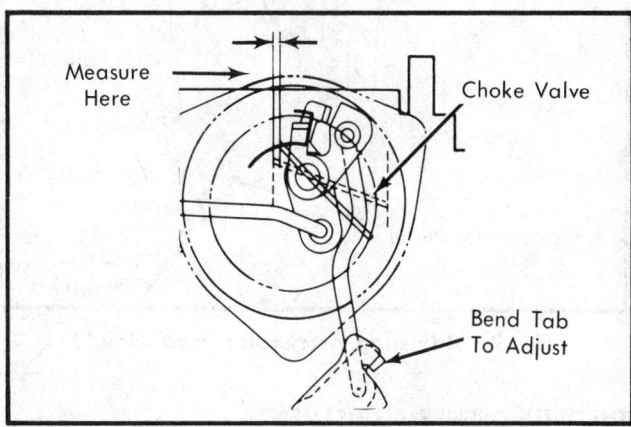

Fig. 7   Adjusting Choke Unloader

SECONDARY THROTTLE VALVE OPENING ANGLE

The secondary valve should begin to open when primary throttle valve opens 50° and should be fully open when primary valve is fully open. Check clearance of primary throttle valve and wall of throttle bore as secondary throttle valve begins to open. Bend throttle arm until clearance is .244-.283" (6.2-7.2 mm). See *Fig. 8.*

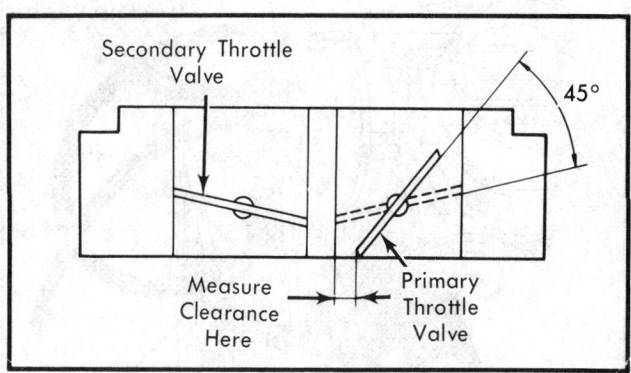

Fig. 8   Adjusting Secondary Throttle Valve Opening Clearance

ACCELERATOR PEDAL HEIGHT ADJUSTMENT

Accelerator pedal should be 1.5-1.9" (40-50 mm) lower than brake pedal. Cable free play at carburetor should be .04-.12" (1-3 mm). If free play is not to specifications, adjust nut "A" on cylinder head cover. As final check, depress pedal to the floor and check that throttle valves are wide open. If necessary, adjust stopper bolt. See *Fig. 9.*

NIKKI 2-BARREL — MAZDA 626 (Cont.)

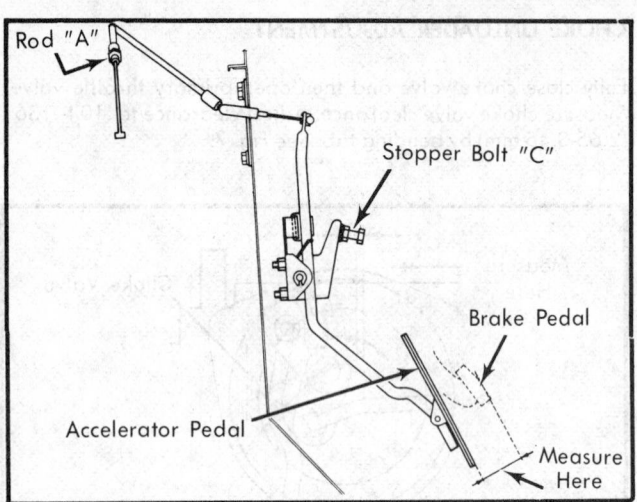

Fig. 9 Adjusting Accelerator Pedal Height

THROTTLE OPENER ADJUSTMENT

1) Connect tachometer to engine. Warm engine to normal operating temperature and set idle at specified idle RPM. Stop engine and remove air cleaner. Disconnect 3-way solenoid valve-to-servo diaphragm vacuum sensing tube from servo diaphragm.

2) Connect inlet manifold vacuum directly to servo diaphragm. Start engine and increase engine speed to 2000 RPM. Turn air conditioner on. Decrease engine speed and make sure speed remains at 1100-1300 RPM by turning adjusting screw.

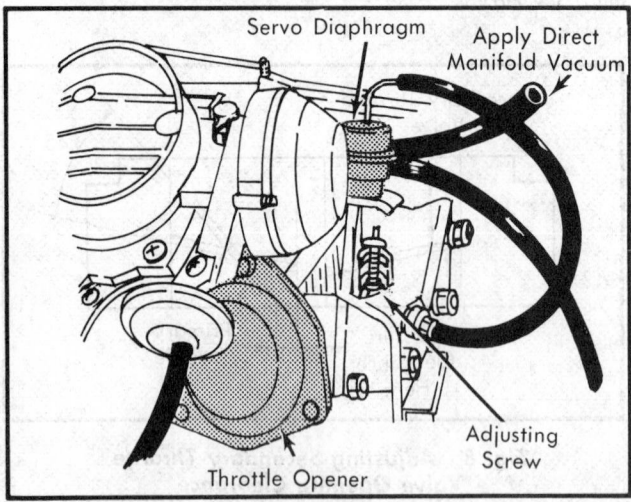

**Fig. 10 Adjusting Throttle Opener
(A/C Models Only)**

OVERHAUL

DISASSEMBLY

1) Remove carburetor and cover intake manifold with clean shop towel. Begin disassembly with air horn and automatic choke. Remove vacuum tube, accelerating pump connecting rod and lever. Remove connecting spring. Spread clip that retains choke heater lead and slow fuel cut solenoid valve lead and remove leads.

2) Disconnect choke rod. Remove fuel inlet fitting, filter and packing. Remove air vent solenoid valve. Separate air horn and automatic choke assembly from main body. Remove choke cover attaching screws and choke cover.

3) Disconnect choke diaphragm rod from choke lever. Mark position of choke housing index mark and thermostat cover index mark. Remove choke heater screws, choke heater, choke diaphragm and bracket. From the air horn, remove float pin, float, gasket and needle valve assembly.

4) From main body, remove accelerating pump plunger assembly and inlet check ball retaining clip. Invert main body and remove inlet strainer and accelerating pump inlet check ball, check valve plug and washer. Remove accelerating pump outlet check ball and spring.

5) Turn main body upright and remove slow fuel cut solenoid valve and gasket. Disconnect throttle linkage and vacuum diaphragm connecting rod. Remove main body attaching bolts and remove main body from throttle body. Remove diaphragm assembly retaining screws and gasket.

NOTE — *One bolt attaching main body is inside the throttle body.*

6) Remove diaphragm cover screws and cover. Remove spring, diaphragm and throttle lever hanger retaining screw from diaphragm. Remove fuel blow sight glass retaining screws, then remove cover, gasket, glass and rubber gasket. Remove all air bleeds and jets from main body. Note size of all jets and bleeds for reinstallation in original position. See *Fig. 11.*

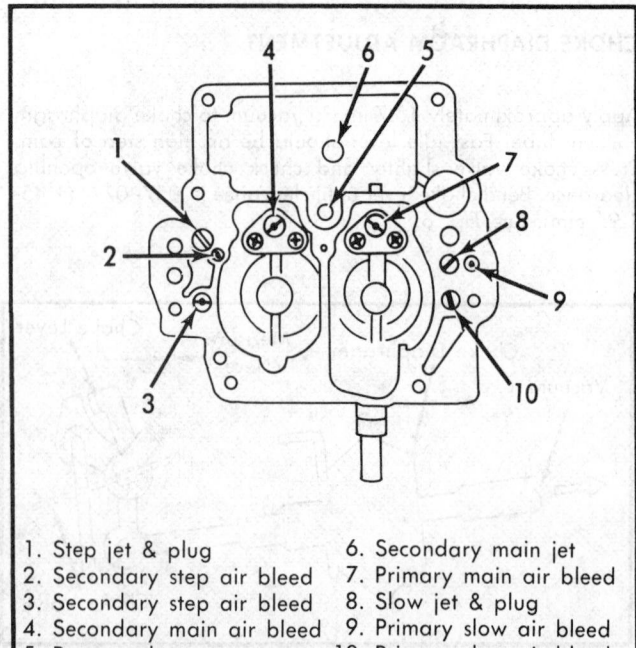

1. Step jet & plug
2. Secondary step air bleed
3. Secondary step air bleed
4. Secondary main air bleed
5. Power valve
6. Secondary main jet
7. Primary main air bleed
8. Slow jet & plug
9. Primary slow air bleed
10. Primary slow air bleed

Fig. 11 Removing Air Bleeds and Jets

NIKKI 2-BARREL — MAZDA 626 (Cont.)

7) Remove throttle hanger and other levers, but do not remove throttle valve and shaft, venturi or choke valve and shaft from throttle body. *See Fig. 12.* Using a hacksaw, cut through mixture screw shell ½" (12 mm) from shell end. Remove and discard mixture screw, spring and shell.

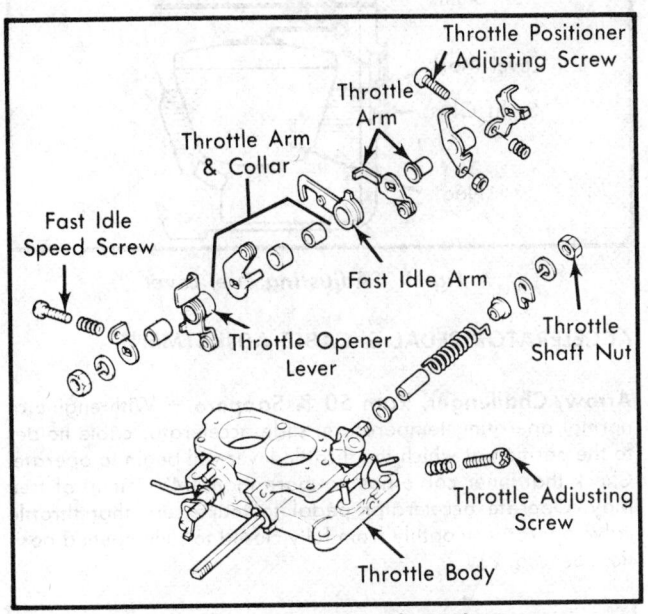

Fig. 12 Removing Throttle Body Parts

INSPECTION

1) Wash all parts in clean gasoline and blow out fuel passages with compressed air. Never use wire for cleaning jets. Inspect air horn, main body and throttle body for cracks and breakage.

2) Check float needle and seat for wear and float for damage. Inspect choke shaft and throttle shaft for wear. Examine all jets and air bleeds for clogs. Inspect accelerator pump plunger for wear or damage. Check diaphragms and inspect mixture adjusting screws.

3) Test solenoid valve operation by grounding body while terminal is touched to battery positive post. Valve stem should pull into solenoid body.

REASSEMBLY

To assemble, reverse disassembly procedure. Be careful not to mistake primary and secondary parts. When installing thermostat cover on automatic choke housing, hook choke arm to bi-metal spring. Check correct operating of choke valve by turning thermostat cover. Then align index marks. Install new mixture screw and limiter shell.

Application	Idle Speed (Engine RPM)		Float Level Setting In. (mm)	Float Drop Setting In. (mm)	Choke Linkage (Off Car) In. (mm)	Accelerator Cable Free Play In. (mm)	Choke Valve Opening In. (mm)
	Hot	Fast					
626	①650	3000-4000	.452 (11.5)	1.811 (46)	.018-.030 (.45-.75)	.04-.12 (1-3)	.026-.041 (.65-1.05)

CARBURETOR ADJUSTMENT SPECIFICATIONS

① — Auto. Trans. in "D" range.

1981 Solex Carburetors

SOLEX (MIKUNI) DIDTA 2-BARREL

Arrow Pickup   Colt
Challenger   Ram-50 Pickup
Champ   Sapporo

DESCRIPTION

The Solex (Mikuni) 28-32 DIDTA Carburetor is used on all 1400 cc and 1600 cc models and the 30-32 DIDTA on all 2000 cc and 2600 cc models. These 2-barrel, 2-stage carburetors utilize primary and secondary circuits. Components include a conventional accelerator pump, a vacuum-actuated secondary throttle diaphragm, a sub-EGR valve system, a fully automatic choke, a vacuum kick (choke breaker), an air switching valve, a jet air control valve, a fuel cut-off solenoid, a dashpot, and an anti-overfill device.

CARBURETOR IDENTIFICATION

Application	Carburetor No.	
	Man. Trans.	Auto. Trans.
Champ & Colt (28-32DIDTA)		
Federal		
1400 cc	30797	
1600 cc	34082	34083
Calif.		
1400 cc	30796	
1600 cc	34080	34081
All Others (30-32DIDTA)		
2000 cc	①	①
2600 cc	①	①

① — Carburetor identified by 30-32DIDTA only.

ADJUSTMENTS

HOT (SLOW) IDLE RPM

See appropriate TUNE-UP SERVICE PROCEDURES article.

IDLE MIXTURE

See appropriate TUNE-UP SERVICE PROCEDURES article.

COLD (FAST) IDLE RPM

See appropriate TUNE-UP SERVICE PROCEDURES article.

FACTORY ADJUSTMENTS ONLY

The automatic choke, choke breaker (vacuum kick), fast idle, secondary throttle opener, accelerator pump and sub-EGR valve have all been factory-calibrated and should not be changed for any reason, according to manufacturer.

FUEL LEVEL ADJUSTMENT

The float chamber is fitted with a sight glass. Check that fuel level is nearly in the middle of dot on sight glass. If fuel level is either .16" (4 mm) above or below dot on sight glass window, fuel level is okay. If float level is not within this specified range, adjust as necessary. Adjustment is accomplished by increasing or decreasing number of needle valve gaskets. See Fig. 1.

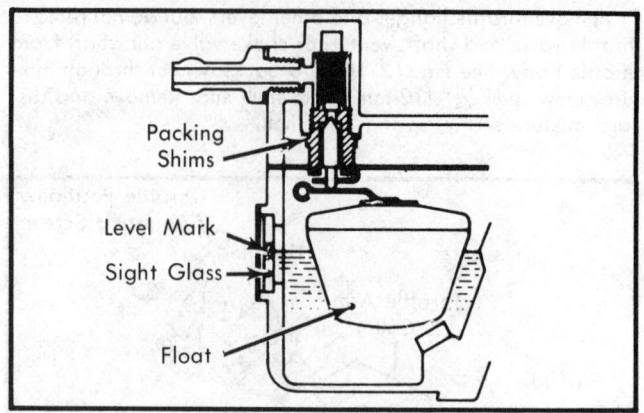

Fig. 1   Adjusting Fuel Level

ACCELERATOR PEDAL & CABLE ADJUSTMENT

Arrow, Challenger, Ram 50 & Sapporo — With engine at normal operating temperature, slide accelerator cable holder to the position at which the throttle lever will begin to operate. Check that inner cable has no more than .04" (1 mm) of free play. Operate accelerator pedal to make sure that throttle valve operates smoothly from fully closed to fully opened position. See Fig. 2.

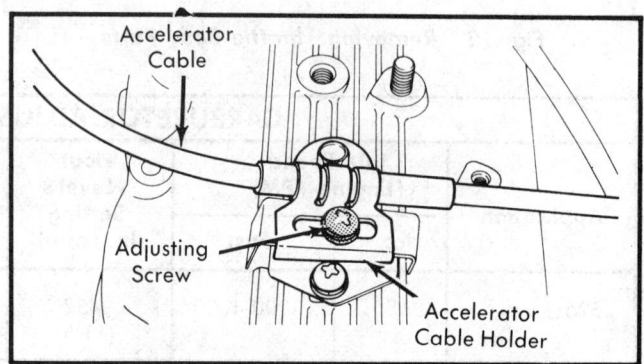

Fig. 2   Adjusting Accelerator Cable
(Arrow, Challenger, Ram 50 & Sapporo)

Champ & Colt — With engine at normal operating temperature, adjust accelerator cable so that there is no more than .04" (1 mm) of free play. Adjust cable free play adjusting nut and tighten lock nut after adjustment is made. See Fig. 3. After adjustment is made, check that accelerator pedal operates throttle valve from fully closed to fully opened position smoothly.

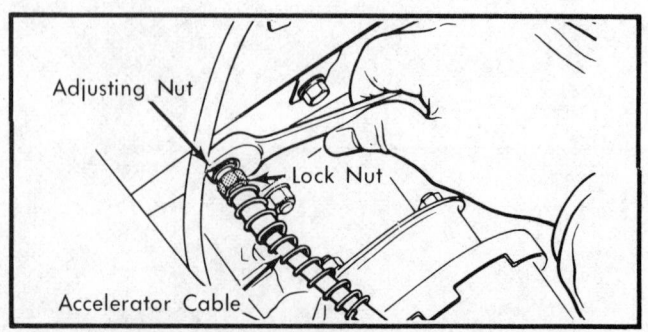

Fig. 3   Adjusting Accelerator Cable Free Play
(Champ & Colt)

SOLEX (MIKUNI) DIDTA 2-BARREL (Cont.)

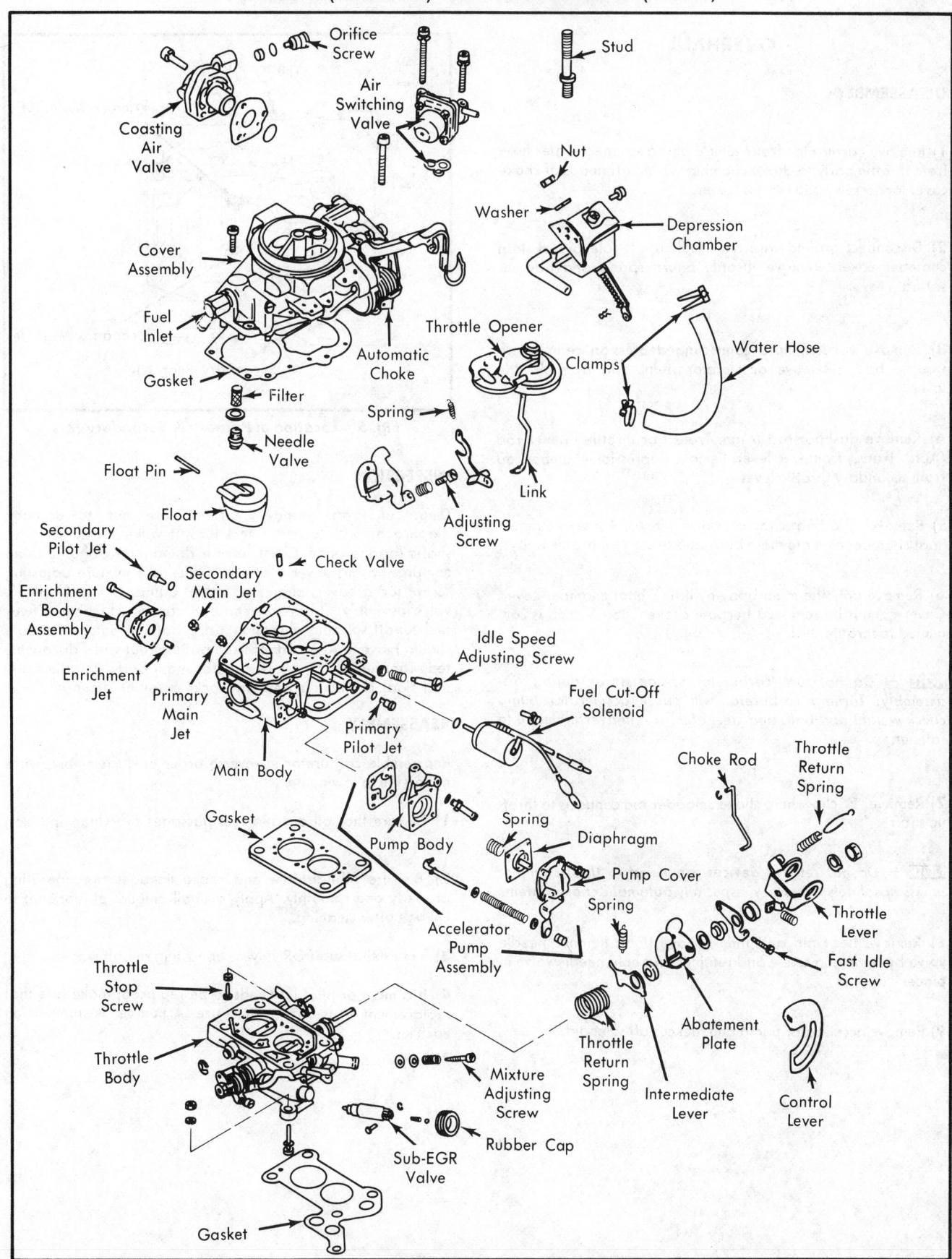

*Fig. 4   Exploded View of Solex (Mikuni) DIDTA
2-Barrel Carburetor*

SOLEX (MIKUNI) DIDTA 2-BARREL (Cont.)

OVERHAUL

DISASSEMBLY

1) Remove carburetor from vehicle and disconnect water hose from throttle body to choke chamber. Grind off heads of choke cover lock screws and remove cover.

2) Disconnect ground wire from fuel cut-off solenoid at float chamber cover. Remove throttle return spring and damper spring.

3) Remove vacuum hose connecting depression chamber to throttle body. Remove accelerator pump rod from throttle lever.

4) Remove dashpot rod (Man. Trans.) or throttle opener rod (Auto. Trans.) from free lever. Remove depression chamber rod from secondary throttle lever.

5) Remove all 6 float chamber cover screws; 4 screws connect float chamber cover to main body and two go to throttle body.

6) Remove only the main body by lifting float chamber cover. Cover cannot be removed because choke unloader rod is connected to throttle shaft.

NOTE — *Do not turn carburetor upside down during disassembly. Turning carburetor will cause accelerator pump check weight and ball, and steel ball for anti-overfill device to fall out.*

7) Remove "E" clip where choke unloader rod connects to throttle shaft.

NOTE — *Do not remove devices connected to float chamber unless absolutely necessary, especially automatic choke system.*

8) Remove float pin and then remove float. Remove needle valve by removing screw and retainer that hold needle valve in place.

9) Remove accelerator pump and fuel cut-off solenoid.

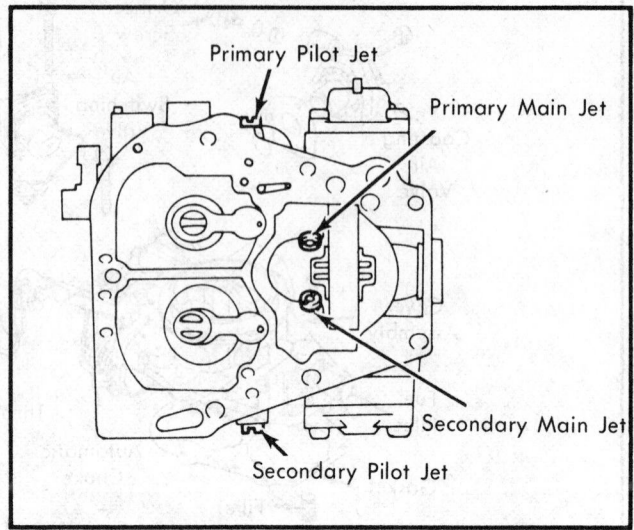

Fig. 5   Location of Primary & Secondary Jets

INSPECTION

Clean all parts removed, using care not to damage diaphragms with solvent. Check throttle valve and choke valve shafts for operation. Check jets for damage or clogging using compressed air, never use wire. Check idle mixture adjusting screw for grooves, ridges or other damage. Check needle valve assembly, strainer screen and vacuum chamber. Check fuel cut-off solenoid operation, using battery. Solenoid needle should move in when attached to battery, out when disconnected. Thoroughly inspect carburetor main body, throttle body and float chamber cover for cracks or other damage.

REASSEMBLY

Reassemble carburetor in reverse order of disassembly, while noting the following items:

1) Be sure that all air and fuel passages are clear and clog free.

2) Be sure that throttle and choke linkages are operating properly and smoothly. Apply a small amount of lubricant to linkage after cleaning.

3) Be sure that sub-EGR valve is operating smoothly.

4) If a main or pilot jet needs to be replaced, make sure that replacement jet is of the same size. A number is stamped on each jet.

WEBER 32 DIR 2-BARREL

Renault
Le Car

DESCRIPTION

The Weber 32 DIR carburetor is a 2-barrel downdraft type. The carburetor base is heated by engine coolant flowing through it.

The California model has a fuel feedback system, a fast idle (throttle opener) system, a dashpot, idle cut-off, an electromagnetic vent cut-off valve and a cold start system (manual choke).

The Federal model has a throttle plate opener, an electromagnetic vent valve, idle cut-off and manual choke, but has no dashpot or fuel feedback system.

CARBURETOR IDENTIFICATION

Application	Carb. No.
LeCar	
Federal	32 DIR 87
Calif.	32 DIR 80

ADJUSTMENTS

HOT (SLOW) IDLE RPM

See appropriate TUNE-UP SERVICE PROCEDURES article.

IDLE MIXTURE

See appropriate TUNE-UP SERVICE PROCEDURES article.

COLD (FAST) IDLE RPM

See appropriate TUNE-UP SERVICE PROCEDURES article.

FLOAT LEVEL & FLOAT DROP (TRAVEL)

California Models — 1) Hold the fuel bowl top vertically with its gasket in place, so that the float weight closes the needle without pushing the ball inward.

2) Check dimension between bowl gasket and float, float level dimension "A" in *Fig. 1*, against specifications. To adjust bend float arm "1" until inner tab "2" resting against needle, is perpendicular to needle. Tab "3" should permit float travel, dimension "B", as noted in specifications.

Federal Models — 1) Remove float bowl and hold top in vertical position. *See Fig. 2.* Allow weight of float to close needle without allowing ball to enter valve.

2) Measure dimension "A" in *Fig. 2* to check float level. If necessary, adjust by bending float arm. Measure dimension "B" for float drop or travel. If necessary, adjust by bending float tab.

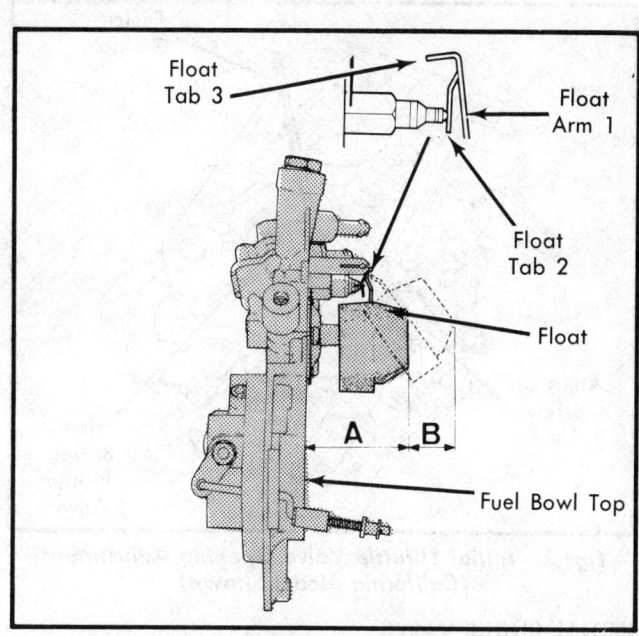

Fig. 1 Float Level and Drop (Travel) Adjustment (California Models)

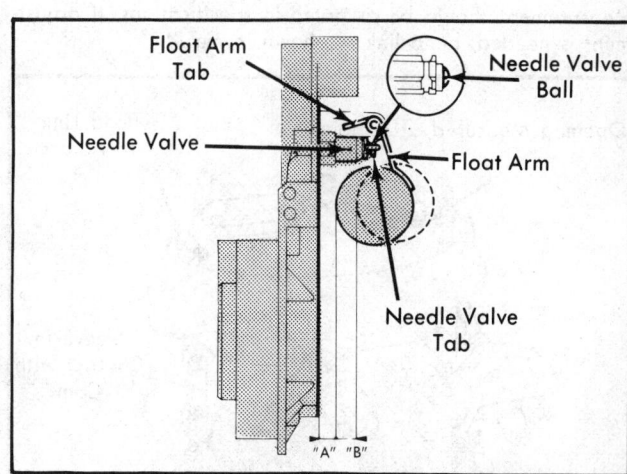

Fig. 2 Float Level and Drop (Travel) Adjustment (Federal Models)

INITIAL THROTTLE VALVE OPENING ADJUSTMENT

1) Put choke lever in cold start position. Measure initial opening of first barrel throttle, using feeler gauges (MS 787).

2) To adjust, remove plastic cap and turn adjusting screw until specification is reached. *See Fig. 3.* After adjustment, tighten lock nut (if equipped) and install new plastic cap over adjusting screw.

NOTE — *To remove brass cap, drill a .118" (3 mn. insert screw in hole and lift off.*

WEBER 32 DIR 2-BARREL (Cont.)

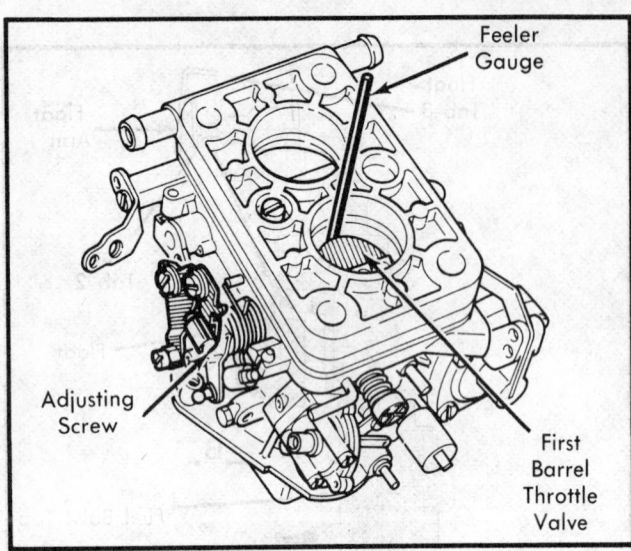

Fig. 3 Initial Throttle Valve Opening Adjustment (California Model Shown)

INITIAL CHOKE VALVE MECHANICAL OPENING ADJUSTMENT

With choke valve fully closed, push on sleeve until it contacts cam lever. Measure opening at bottom of choke valve. Measurement should be as noted in specifications. If adjustment is needed, bend link as shown in *Fig. 4*.

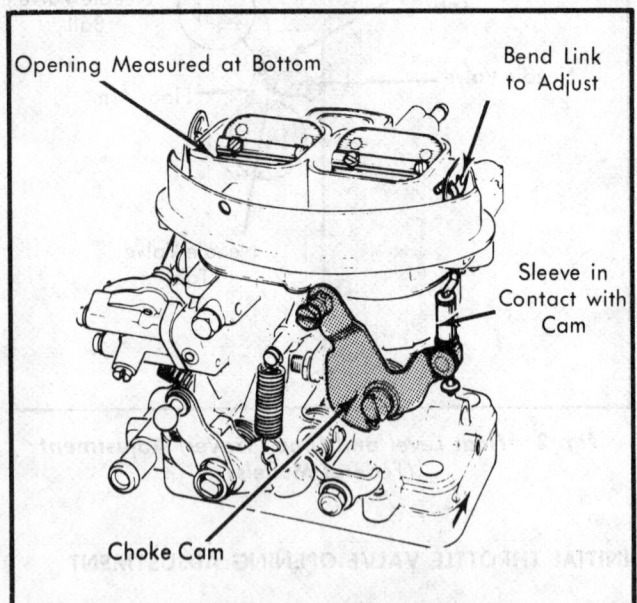

Fig. 4 Initial Choke Valve Mechanical Adjustment (Federal Model Shown)

INITIAL CHOKE VALVE VACUUM OPENING ADJUSTMENT

California Models — 1) Place choke lever in cold start position. Push in diaphragm link until it is against stop. Measure initial opening of choke valve on the large section side. *See Fig. 5*. Measure at bottom of valve.

2) Remove brass cap from adjusting screw. Turn screw, as necessary, to obtain specified valve vacuum opening.

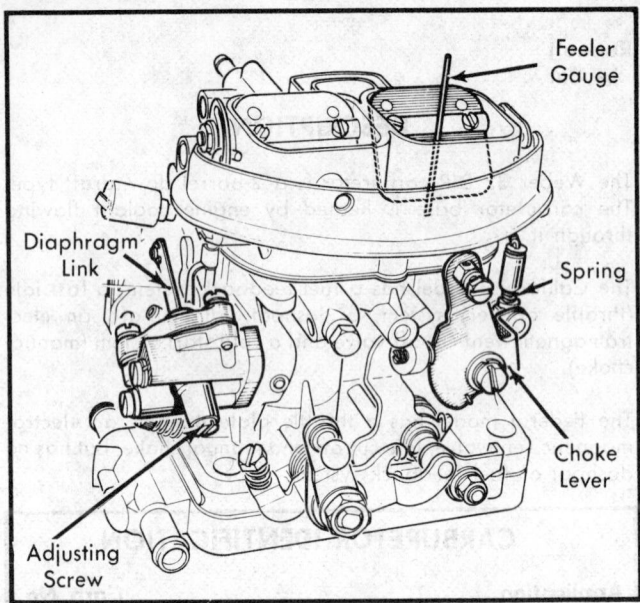

Fig. 5 Initial Choke Valve Vacuum Adjustment (California Model Shown)

NOTE — *To remove brass cap, drill a .118" (3 mm) hole and then insert a screw in cap hole and lift off.*

Federal Models — 1) Push diaphragm link in as far as possible. Now close choke valves with choke lever until spring on link is slightly compressed. Measure opening at bottom of choke valve.

2) Measurement should be as specified. If adjustment is needed, remove screw from end of diaphragm and turn set rew until choke valve vacuum opening is correct.

DASHPOT ADJUSTMENT (CALIFORNIA MODELS ONLY)

1) Install .059" (1.5 mm) feeler gauge as shown in *Fig. 3* to maintain the initial opening of the first barrel throttle plate.

2) Cut plastic cover off dashpot assembly to gain access to adjustment screw. *See Fig. 6*. Position dashpot so that it just contacts the throttle lever. Install new cover, and lock it in place by driving pin in dashpot bracket hole provided for locking purposes.

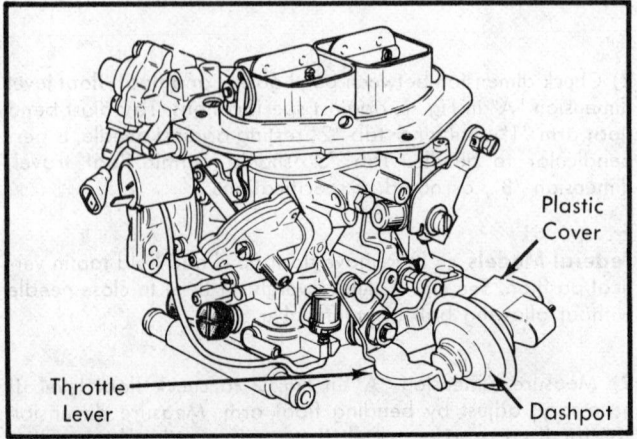

Fig. 6 Dashpot Adjustment (California Only)

WEBER 32 DIR 2-BARREL (Cont.)

CARBURETOR ADJUSTMENT SPECIFICATIONS

Carb. No.	Idle Speed (Engine RPM)		Float Level Setting In. (mm)	Float Drop Setting In. (mm)	Choke Plate (Vacuum) In. (mm)	Choke Plate (Mech.) In. (mm)	Unloader Setting In. (mm)	Vacuum Break In. (mm)
	Hot	Fast						
Federal (DIR 87)	675-725①	.....	.276 (7.0)	.315 (8.0)	.354 (9.0)	.236 (6.0)	.....	.....
Calif. (DIR 80)	700-800	.....	1.50 (38.0)	.315 (8.0)	.393 (10.0)	.250 (6.5)	.....	.....

① — 700-800 RPM with air injection.

1981 Bosch Fuel Injection

BOSCH AFC FUEL INJECTION — EUROPEAN MODELS

BMW
 528i
 633CSi
 733i
Fiat
 Brava
 Spider 2000
 Spider 2000 Turbo
 Strada
 X1/9

Porsche
 928
Renault
 18i
Volkswagen
 Vanagon

NOTE — *The Bosch AFC Fuel Injection system is used on all models. Variations may exist between model applications with the addition of auxiliary control systems. This article covers the Bosch AFC system in general, with manufacturer's differences noted. Federal Vanagon models do not use an oxygen sensor, so disregard oxygen sensor information for these vehicles.*

DESCRIPTION

The Bosch Air Flow Controlled (AFC) fuel injection system is an electronically controlled system operated by incoming air flow. The AFC fuel injection system also contains a feedback system which measures oxygen content of exhaust gases and maintains the air/fuel ratio at about 14.7:1. The fuel injection system consists of an electric fuel pump, fuel pressure regulator, fuel injectors, Electronic Control Unit (ECU), air flow meter, air temperature sensor, throttle switch, coolant temperature switch (temperature switch on Vanagon), oxygen sensor, catalytic converter and electrical relays.

In addition, all models are equipped with a cold start system to aid in cold engine starts. The cold start system consists of an auxiliary air valve, cold start injector and thermo time switch.

An air conditioning solenoid valve is installed on Renault models equipped with air conditioning to provide additional air when compressor is activated. Fiat Spider 2000 Turbo models are equipped with a boost enrichment circuit, load enrichment circuit and an overboost protection circuit which provide necessary information to ECU on turbo operation. California Vanagon models are equipped with a speed limit switch between throttle switch and ECU which deactivates the oxygen sensor at engine speeds in excess of 3000 RPM.

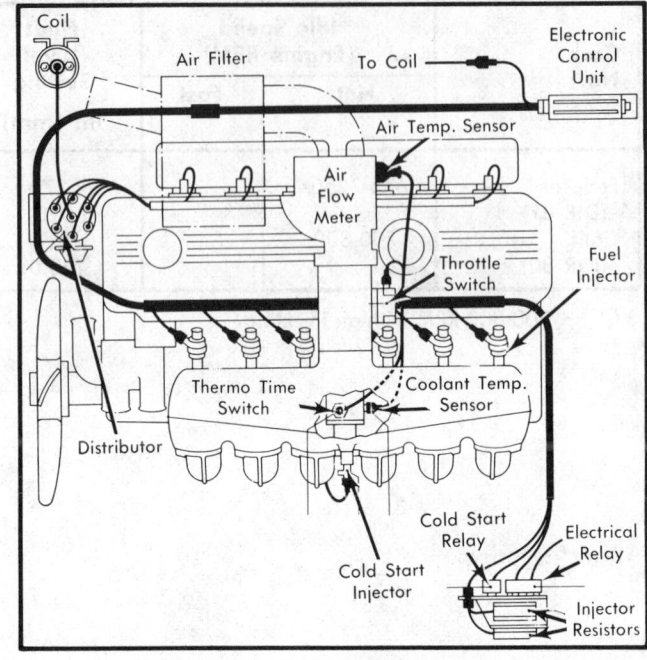

Fig. 2   BMW AFC Fuel Injection System

ELECTRIC FUEL PUMP

The fuel pump provides fuel under pressure to the fuel pressure regulator. Power for operation during cranking mode is provided from starter relay via the electrical relay. After the engine has started, control of the fuel pump is by a fuel pump circuit in the air flow meter. The first movement of the air flow meter air measuring flap (about 5°) closes the fuel pump contacts and provides power to fuel pump after engine has started. With engine stopped, no air flow is present, measuring flap closes and fuel pump contacts are opened to cut power to fuel pump. This circuit reduces the risk of fire in a collision. The fuel pump is a sealed unit; no service is required.

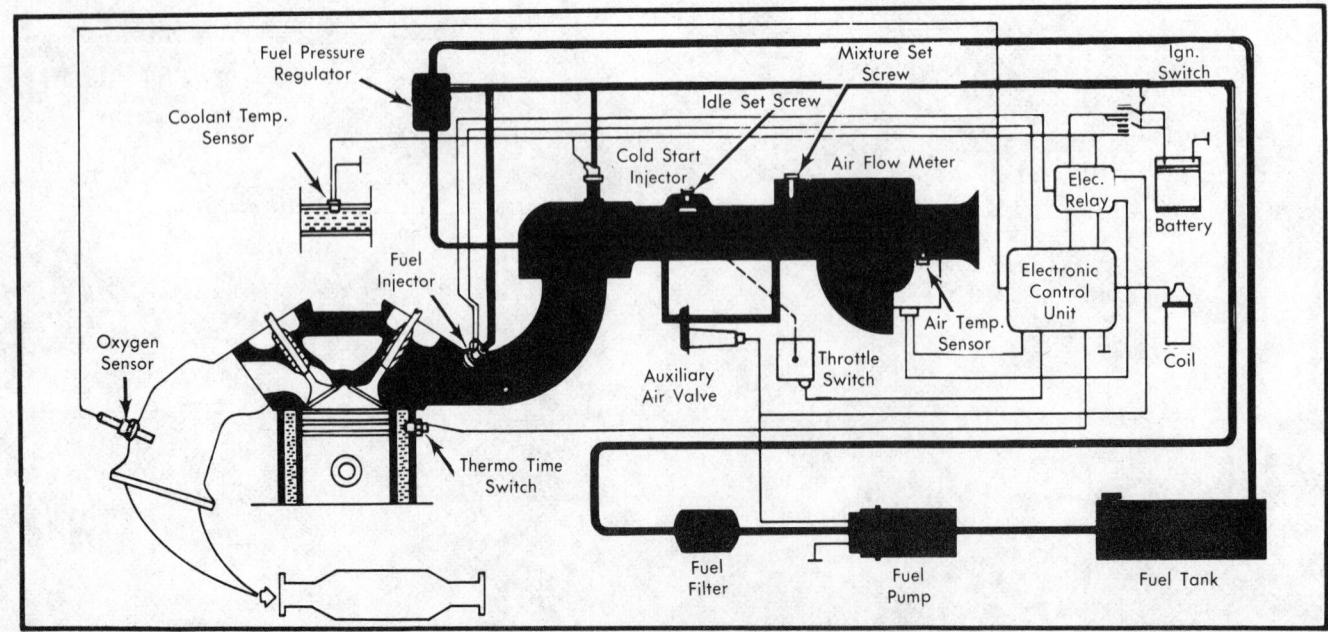

Fig. 1   Fiat AFC Fuel Injection System

BOSCH AFC FUEL INJECTION — EUROPEAN MODELS (Cont.)

FUEL PRESSURE REGULATOR

The pressure regulator (2 on Porsche) consists of a sealed, spring loaded diaphragm with a connection for intake manifold vacuum. Fuel is provided to fuel injectors under approximately 36 psi (2.5 kg/cm²) pressure. A connection for intake manifold vacuum provides a constant pressure differential which ensures that the amount of fuel injected is solely dependent upon injector "open" time. Excess fuel is returned to fuel tank. No service of pressure regulator is required.

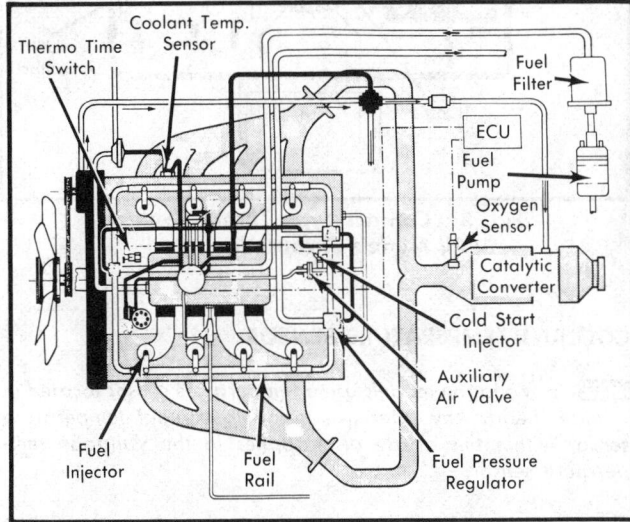

Fig. 3   Porsche 928 AFC Fuel Injection System

FUEL INJECTORS

A fuel rail links the fuel pressure regulator with the fuel injectors. Each cylinder is provided with a solenoid-operated injector which sprays fuel towards back of each inlet valve. Each injector is energized through the ignition coil and grounded through the ECU to complete the circuit. Each injector is linked to a resistor (resistor may be external or integral with injector or ECU) to reduce operating voltage to 3 volts and to protect injectors from power surges. The ECU controls the length of time each injector is open. The "open" time of the injector governs the amount of fuel delivered. The injectors deliver ½ the amount of fuel required for an operating cycle each time they open (twice per cycle).

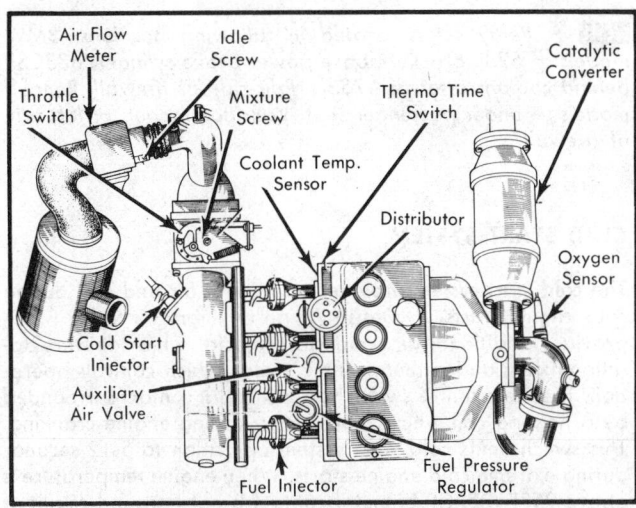

Fig. 4   Renault 18i AFC Fuel Injection System

ELECTRONIC CONTROL UNIT (ECU)

All components of the control system are electrically connected to the ECU. See Fig 5. The ECU is a preprogrammed computer which receives and interprets data from various sensors. It calculates the amount of fuel required by the engine to maintain efficiency with minimum exhaust emissions. Impulses from the oxygen sensor inform the ECU of oxygen content of exhaust gases and the ECU constantly adjusts the air/fuel ratio by controlling the injector "open" time.

The ECU provides fuel enrichment whenever engine is cranked, regardless of engine temperature. This is activated by a direct electrical connection from the starter circuit to the ECU. The ECU is a sealed unit; no service is required.

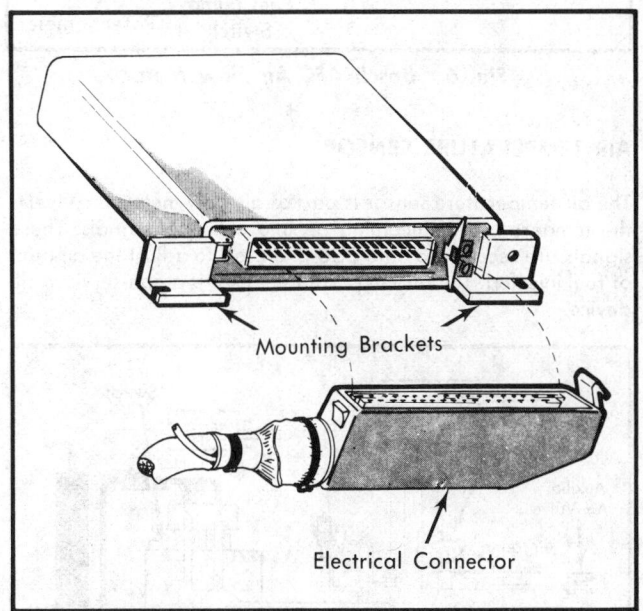

Fig. 5   Electronic Control Unit (ECU)

AIR FLOW METER

All engine air is drawn through the air flow meter. The meter contains a tunnel with measuring flap and dampening flap (offset 90° on same casting). The measuring flap swings in air stream against pressure of a spiral spring and is connected to a potentiometer. The potentiometer transmits an electrical signal proportionate to the measuring flap position to inform the ECU of engine load. See Fig. 6.

In addition to monitoring the air flow, the meter also controls fuel pump operation and idling. At idle, the measuring flap is almost closed due to spiral spring pressure. An idle air by-pass receives air from main air flow through a small hole, the size of which is controlled by the idle mixture screw. This adjustable air by-pass influences CO levels at low engine speeds.

BOSCH AFC FUEL INJECTION — EUROPEAN MODELS (Cont.)

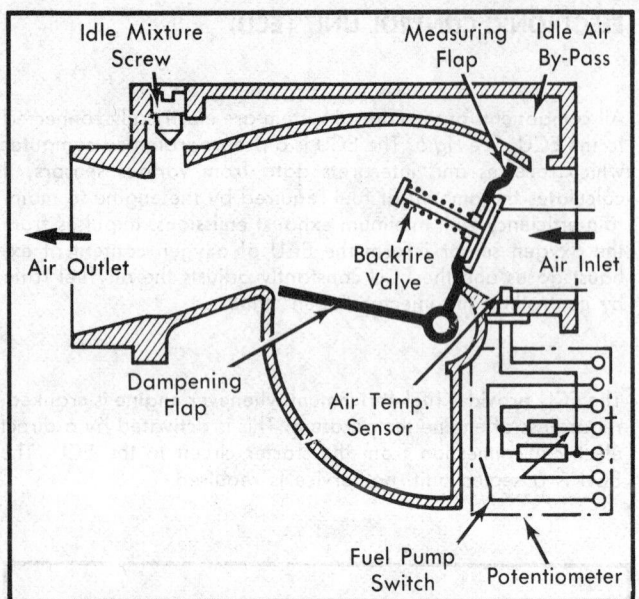

Fig. 6   Bosch AFC Air Flow Meter

AIR TEMPERATURE SENSOR

The air temperature sensor is part of air flow meter. It converts the temperature of incoming air into electrical signals. These signals are received by the ECU and used to adjust the amount of fuel injected. The air temperature sensor is a non-serviceable device.

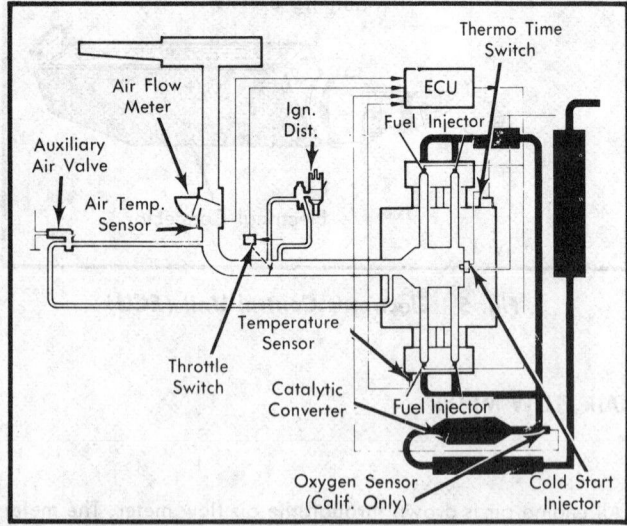

Fig. 7   Vanagon AFC Fuel Injection System

THROTTLE SWITCH

NOTE — *Vanagon models use a contact type throttle switch with 2-wire connector.*

A contact-type throttle switch is installed on the throttle chamber of all models. It converts throttle position into electrical signals to inform ECU of throttle position. Signals are sent to ECU when throttle is fully open or at idle. See *Fig. 8*. The potentiometer within the air flow meter prevents loss of engine power during sudden acceleration/deceleration by signaling the ECU of necessary fuel enrichment requirements.

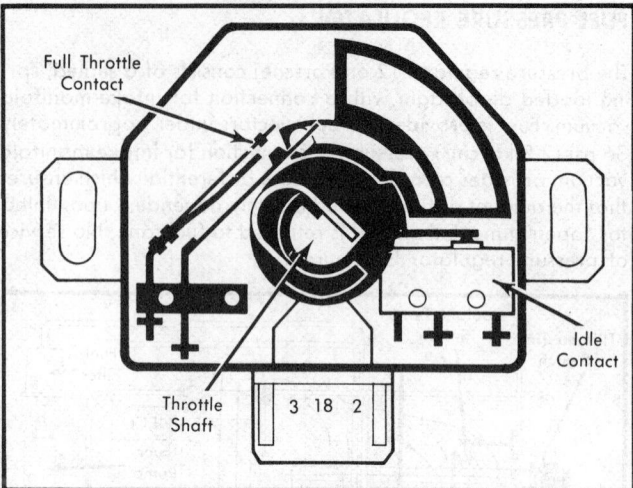

Fig. 8   Contact Type Throttle Switch (All Models Except Vanagon)

COOLANT TEMPERATURE SENSOR

NOTE — *Vanagon models use a temperature sensor located in cylinder head. Any reference made to coolant temperature sensor within this article also applies to the Vanagon temperature sensor.*

This sensor provides ECU with engine temperature information relating to warm-up enrichment operation. During warm-up period after a cold engine start, additional fuel is required to maintain engine performance. As engine temperature increases, the ECU decreases fuel enrichment until engine reaches normal operating temperature.

ELECTRICAL RELAYS

The main relay activates the ECU, injector circuit and starting circuit when ignition is switched to start mode. The fuel pump relay activates the fuel pump during the start mode and is then controlled by air flow during operating mode. Some models incorporate all relays within a single relay set or dual relay. The cold start system is also activated through the relay set.

NOTE — *Relay set is located in following positions: BMW models — 528i, bracket above power brake cylinder; 633CSi, behind coolant reservoir; 733i, right side of firewall. Renault models — under passenger seat. Vanagon models — left side of firewall.*

COLD START SYSTEM

The cold start system provides additional air and fuel during cold engine starts. It consists of an auxiliary air valve which provides additional air, cold start injector which delivers additional fuel and a thermo time switch which controls operation. The thermo time switch has a bi-metal contact surrounded by a heating coil which is energized during engine cranking. This switch limits cold start system operation to 5-12 seconds during extreme cold engine starts. When engine temperature is above 95°F (35°C), bi-metal contact breaks ground circuit of cold start injector and cold start enrichment is by-passed.

BOSCH AFC FUEL INJECTION — EUROPEAN MODELS (Cont.)

The auxiliary air valve provides additional air during cold engine starts and warm-up. The valve consists of an electrically heated bi-metal strip, movable disc and air by-pass channel. The heater coil on the bi-metal strip is energized by the fuel pump relay. Control of the valve is based upon engine temperature; the air by-pass channel is open when engine is cold and gradually closes as temperature rises. At predetermined temperatures, air by-pass channel is blocked and additional air flow stops. See Fig. 9.

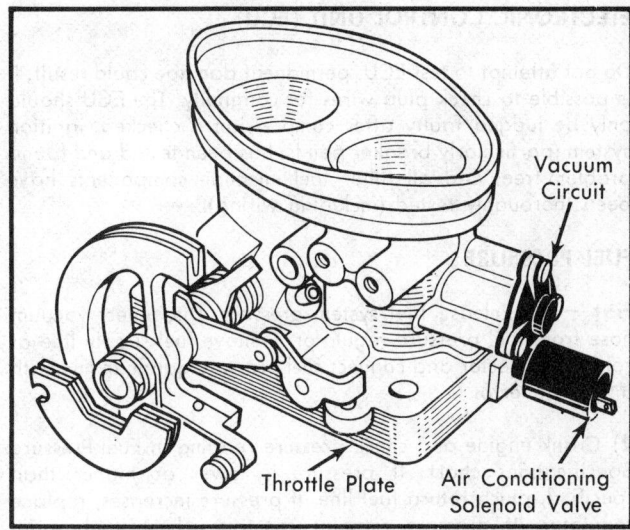

Fig. 10   Renault Air Conditioning Solenoid Valve

Load Enrichment Circuit — This circuit consists of 1 boost pressure switch wired into the throttle switch of the fuel injection electrical system. This switch provides a wide open throttle signal to the ECU whenever boost pressure is present, which in turn signals the ECU to provide power enrichment. See Fig. 11.

Overboost Protection Circuit — This circuit consists of 1 boost pressure switch wired into the fuel injection electrical system. If boost pressure exceeds 9 psi (.66 kg/cm^2), the overboost switch opens, to signal the ECU that boost pressure is excessive. The ECU cuts electrical signal to the fuel injectors. When boost pressure drops within safe limits, the overboost switch closes and ECU provides power to fuel injectors. See Fig. 11.

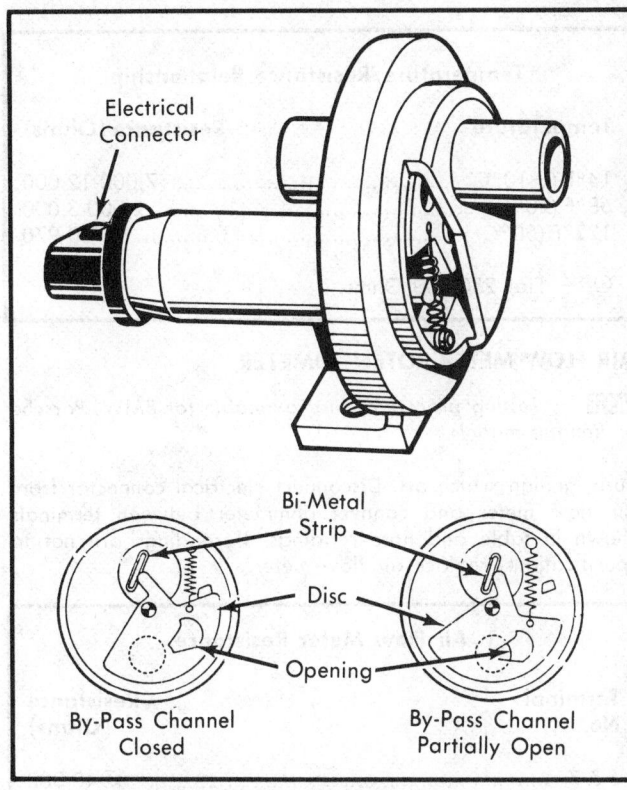

Fig. 9   Auxiliary Air Valve

AIR CONDITIONING SOLENOID VALVE (RENAULT ONLY)

On vehicles equipped with air conditioning, a solenoid valve delivers additional air to compensate for drop in idle speed when air conditioner is activated. The solenoid is electrically actuated through the compressor clutch circuit to open a circuit behind throttle plate. The diameter of the air circuit on manual transmission models is .118″ (3 mm) and .138″ (3.5 mm) on automatic transmission models. See Fig. 10.

FIAT TURBO ACCESSORIES (FIAT SPIDER 2000 TURBO ONLY)

The addition of a turbocharger to the Fiat Spider 2000 requires additional devices. These devices and their operation is as follows:

Boost Enrichment Circuit — This circuit consists of 2 boost pressure switches wired into the fuel injection electrical system. These switches provide an electrical signal to the ECU to provide additional fuel while engine is operating with boost from the turbocharger. See Fig. 11.

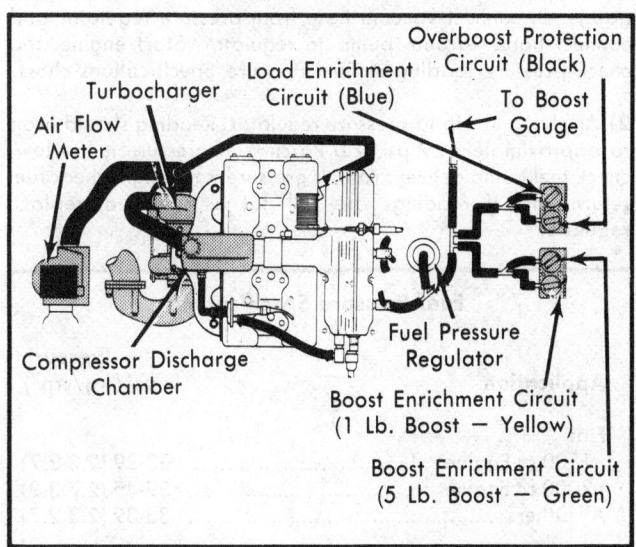

Fig. 11   Fiat Spider 2000 Turbo Accessories

TESTING

NOTE — The Bosch AFC fuel injection system maintains constant fuel pressure in fuel lines and component parts at all times. Be sure to relieve pressure before attempting to open system at any point for testing. Do not allow fuel to flow onto engine or electrical parts or allow an open flame in area while testing fuel system components.

1981 Bosch Fuel Injection

BOSCH AFC FUEL INJECTION – EUROPEAN MODELS (Cont.)

ELECTRONIC CONTROL UNIT (ECU)

Do not attempt to test ECU, permanent damage could result. It is possible to check plug wires for continuity. The ECU should only be judged faulty after compression is checked, ignition system (particularly breaker points) has been tested and found problem-free, and all other fuel injection components have been thoroughly tested (including wiring).

FUEL PRESSURE

Fiat – 1) Release fuel system pressure. Disconnect vacuum hose from fuel pressure regulator. Remove fuel supply line at cold start injector and connect fuel pressure gauge in line with a "Y" connector.

2) Crank engine and check pressure reading in Fuel Pressure Specifications chart. If pressure is lower or higher than specified, pinch return fuel line. If pressure increases, replace regulator. If pressure remains constant, check fuel pump operation. If no reading is measured, replace fuel pump and repeat test.

Porsche – 1) Remove capped nut from test connection on fuel rail without damaging seal. Connect fuel pressure gauge to test connection.

2) Working inside passenger compartment, fold up passenger foot support and unplug fuel pump relay from central electric board (2nd box from right side on bottom row). Using jumper wire, connect terminals 30 and 87 together. Fuel pump should run. Fuel pressure should be as specified in chart. If not, replace fuel pump.

All Other Models – 1) Release fuel system pressure. Remove fuel supply line at cold start injector and connect fuel pressure gauge. Disconnect vacuum hose from pressure regulator and connect hand vacuum pump to regulator. Start engine and check pressure reading in Fuel Pressure Specifications chart.

2) Apply 16 in. Hg to pressure regulator. Reading should drop to approximately 29 psi (2.0 kg/cm²). If pressure is too low, check fuel pump delivery rate. If pressure is too high, check fuel return line. If readings are still not as specified, replace regulator.

Fuel Pressure Specifications

Application	Pressure psi (kg/cm²)
Fiat	
1500 cc Engine	33-39 (2.3-2.7)
2000 cc Engine	39-45 (2.7-3.2)
All Others	33-39 (2.3-2.7)

FUEL PUMP CIRCUIT

Remove electrical connector from air flow meter. Connect terminals 36 and 39 with jumper wire. Disconnect fuel input line at fuel pressure regulator and place in container. Turn ignition on and push air measuring flap open. Fuel should flow into container. If fuel does not flow but clicking sound is heard, replace fuel pump. Fuel circuit is good. If no clicking sound is heard, replace air flow meter assembly and repeat test.

AIR TEMPERATURE SENSOR

NOTE – *Testing procedure not available for Porsche or Renault.*

Turn ignition switch off. Disconnect electrical connector at air flow meter and connect ohmmeter between terminals 6 and 27. Readings should be as follows. If not, replace temperature sensor and air flow meter as an assembly.

Temperature/Resistance Relationship

Temperature	Resistance (Ohms)
14°F (−10°C)	7,000-12,000
68°F (20°C)	2,000-3,000
122°F (50°C)	①760-970

① – Fiat 250-400 Ohms.

AIR FLOW METER POTENTIOMETER

NOTE – *Testing procedures not available for BMW, Porsche or Renault models.*

Turn ignition switch off. Disconnect electrical connector from air flow meter and connect ohmmeter between terminals shown in table and note readings. If readings are not to specifications, replace air flow meter.

Air Flow Meter Resistance

Terminal No.	Resistance (Ohms)
6 & 7	①40-300
6 & 8	①30-260
6 & 9	①200-400
7 & 8	100-500
8 & 9	70-140

① – Vanagon only.

AUXILIARY AIR VALVE

NOTE – *Testing procedures not available for Porsche.*

BMW – With engine at normal operating temperature and idle speed set to specifications, turn air conditioner on. Connect ohmmeter to Black wire of valve connector. Voltage should be registered and air should flow through valve. Turn air conditioner off. No voltage or air should flow through valve. If valve does not respond as outlined, replace auxiliary air valve.

Fiat – 1) With engine warm and at idle speed, pinch off hose between throttle chamber and air valve. Engine speed should drop. If not, proceed to next step.

2) Remove hoses from each end of regulator. Visually check opening in valve. Valve should be open when cold and close as temperature increases.

BOSCH AFC FUEL INJECTION — EUROPEAN MODELS (Cont.)

3) Check continuity of valve at electrical connector. If continuity does not exist, air valve is defective and should be replaced. Check operation ot valve by carefully prying valve open with a flat bladed screwdriver and then closing valve. Replace valve if operation is not smooth.

Renault — Warm engine to temperature of about 68°F (20°C) and stop engine. Disconnect air hoses and electrical connector from valve. Visually check that diaphragm is partially open. Connect battery power to valve terminals. After 8 minutes, diaphragm should be completely closed. If not, check internal resistance of valve with an ohmmeter connected to both terminals. Resistance should be 49 ohms. If valve does not respond as outlined, replace auxiliary air valve.

Volkswagen — Disconnect electrical connector and connect ohmmeter leads to valve terminals. Resistance should measure approximately 30 ohms. Pull off hoses and disconnect ohmmeter. Valve should be open on cold engine and closed on warm engine. Reconnect electrical connector and turn ignition switch on. Valve should be completely closed after 5 minutes. If valve does not respond as outlined, replace auxiliary air valve.

THERMO TIME SWITCH

NOTE — *Testing procedures not available for Porsche.*

BMW — 1) Disconnect electrical connector at thermo time switch. Connect ohmmeter to terminal "G" and ground. Reading should be 40-70 ohms.

2) Connect ohmmeter between terminal 85 ("W" on switch) and ground. Connect terminal 86 with terminal 30 ("G" on switch). For temperatures above 59°F (15°C), infinity reading should be obtained. Below 59°F (115°C), zero reading should be obtained for 0-8 seconds.

NOTE — *Terminal "W" on 528i thermo time switch is connector terminal number 86c.*

Fiat — 1) Disconnect electrical connector from cold start injector. Connect test light between terminals, operate starter and note time test light glows. Light should not glow if coolant temperature is above 95°F (35°C) and should glow for 1-8 seconds at temperatures below 95°F (35°C).

2) If light does not glow as outlined, check relay and wiring. If good, replace thermo time switch.

Renault — 1) Remove thermo time switch and install plug to prevent loss of coolant. Cool thermo time switch by immersing in cold water. Connect Black wire to a test lamp and battery positive terminal. Connect battery negative terminal to switch body. Test lamp should glow. See Fig. 12.

2) Insert thermometer in water and gradually heat water. Test lamp should glow until temperature reaches 88-102°F (31-39°C). If switch does not respond as outlined, continue testing as follows:

3) Cool switch to temperature below that stamped on side of switch. Connect ohmmeter between terminal "G" and switch housing (ground); reading should be 25-40 ohms. Connect ohmmeter between terminal "W" and ground; reading should be 0 ohms. Connect ohmmeter between both terminals; reading should be 25-40 ohms.

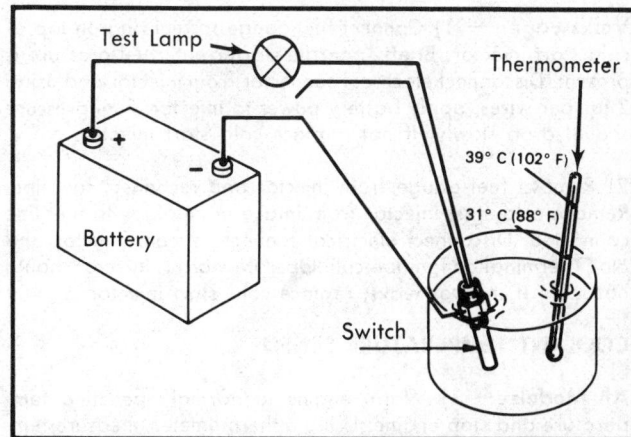

Fig. 12   Testing Renault Thermo Time Switch

4) Heat switch to temperature above 104°F (40°C). Connect ohmmeter between terminal "G" and switch housing (ground); reading should be 50-80 ohms. Connect ohmmeter between terminal "W" and ground; reading should be 100-160 ohms. Connect ohmmeter between both terminals; reading should be 50-80 ohms. If switch does not respond as outlined in steps **3)** and **4)**, replace thermo time switch.

Volkswagen — 1) With engine cold and air temperature below 68°F (20°C), disconnect electrical connector from cold start injector and connect test lamp to connector terminals. Disconnect electrical connector from No. 1 ignition coil terminal.

2) Operate starter. Test lamp should glow brightly. After 11 seconds (maximum), test lamp should dim or go out. If not replace thermo time switch.

COLD START INJECTOR

NOTE — *Testing procedures not available for Porsche or Renault models.*

BMW — 1) With ignition off, disconnect electrical connector from cold start injector. Release pressure from fuel system and remove cold start injector with fuel lines connected.

2) Place container under injector. Disconnect air flow meter electrical connector and connect jumper wire between terminals 36 and 39. Connect another jumper wire between cold start relay terminals 87 and 30. Turn ignition on. Cold start injector should spray fuel. If not, replace cold start injector.

NOTE — *On 528i models, connect lead 61 1 440 to cold start injector, then connect terminal "B+" to ground after jumping air flow meter connector.*

Fiat — 1) Release fuel system pressure and remove cold start injector from intake manifold without removing fuel lines or electrical connector. Place injector in container.

2) Turn ignition on and crank engine. With engine coolant temperature below 95°F (35°C), fuel should be sprayed for 1-8 seconds; above that temperature, no fuel should be sprayed.

3) If injector sprays continuously, drips or does not spray fuel as outlined, replace cold start injector.

BOSCH AFC FUEL INJECTION – EUROPEAN MODELS (Cont.)

Volkswagen – 1) Connect fuel gauge to fuel ring on top of cold start injector. Briefly operate starter until fuel pressure is present. Disconnect electrical connector from injector and using 2 jumper wires, apply battery power to injector. Fuel pressure should drop slowly. If not, replace cold start injector.

2) Remove fuel gauge from injector and reconnect fuel line. Remove cold start injector from intake manifold with fuel line connected. Disconnect electrical connectors from injector and No. 1 terminal on ignition coil. Operate starter. Injector should not leak. If injector leaks, replace cold start injector.

COOLANT TEMPERATURE SENSOR

All Models – 1) Warm engine to normal operating temperature and stop engine. Using a thermometer, measure temperature of coolant (oil on Volkswagen models). Disconnect electrical connector from temperature sensor and connect 1 lead of ohmmeter to terminal in sensor and other lead to ground. Ohmmeter readings should be as specified in table. If not, replace temperature sensor.

2) On Volkswagen models, if resistance reading is too high, touch ground lead of ohmmeter to sensor body. If resistance is as specified in table, corrosion is present between sensor and cylinder head. If resistance is still not as specified, replace temperature sensor.

Temperature/Resistance Relationship

Temperature	Resistance (Ohms)
14°F (−10°C)	7,000-12,000
68°F (20°C)	2,000-3,000
176°F (80°C)	200-400

FIAT TURBO ACCESSORIES (FIAT SPIDER 2000 TURBO ONLY)

CAUTION – *Do not exceed 12 psi (.84 kg/cm²) air pressure during any test.*

Boost Enrichment Switches – 1) Disconnect vacuum hoses from "Y" fittings and connect an air pressure regulator with pressure gauge attached to "Y" fitting. Disconnect boost enrichment electrical connectors. *See Fig. 13.*

2) Connect an ohmmeter to boost enrichment electrical connector terminals 1 and 2. Slowly apply air pressure to regulator and check that switch makes an audible click at 0.5-1.5 psi (0.04-0.11 kg/cm²). Ohmmeter should read 1500-2000 ohms.

3) Slowly increase pressure and check that other switch makes an audible click at 4.5-5.5 psi (0.32-0.39 kg/cm²). Ohmmeter should read 1750-2750 ohms. If not replace boost enrichment switches.

NOTE – *The 1 lb. enrichment switch is color coded Yellow and the 5 lb. enrichment switch is color coded Green.*

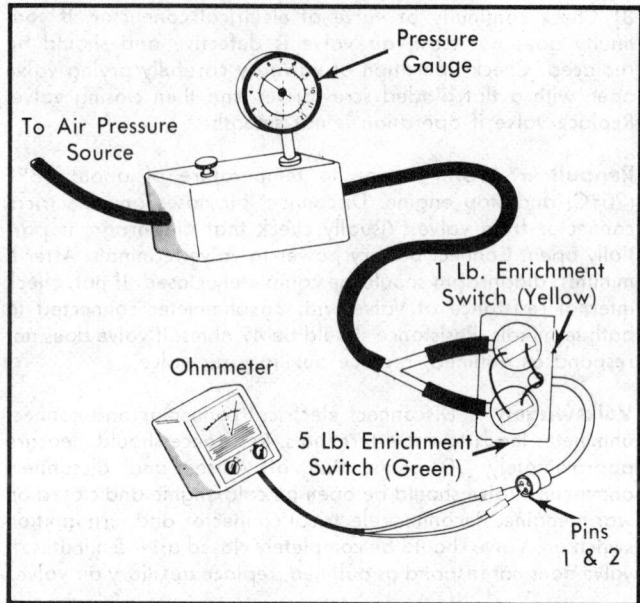

Fig. 13 Testing Fiat Spider 2000 Turbo Boost Enrichment Switches

Load Enrichment Switch – 1) Disconnect vacuum hoses from "Y" fittings and connect an air pressure regulator with pressure gauge attached to "Y" fitting. Disconnect load enrichment switch electrical connector. *See Fig. 14.*

2) Connect an ohmmeter to load enrichment electrical connector terminals 1 and 3. Zero ohmmeter. Ohmmeter should give infinity reading. Slowly apply air pressure to regulator and check that switch makes an audible click at about 1 psi (.07 kg/cm²) and ohmmeter reads 0 ohms. If not, replace load enrichment switch (color coded Blue).

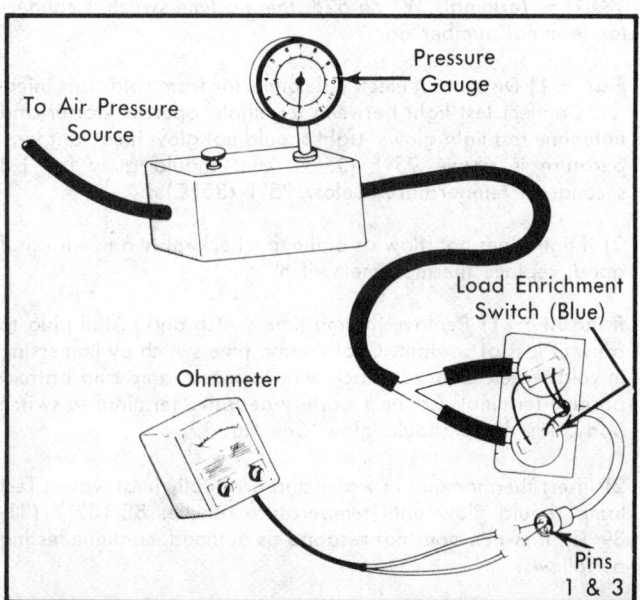

Fig. 14 Testing Fiat Spider 2000 Turbo Load Enrichment Switch

Overboost Protection Switch – 1) With air pressure regulator still connected to "Y" connector, move ohmmeter leads to electrical connector terminals 1 and 2. Ohmmeter should give an infinity reading. *See Fig. 15.*

BOSCH AFC FUEL INJECTION — EUROPEAN MODELS (Cont.)

2) Slowly apply air pressure to regulator and check that switch makes an audible click at about 9 psi (.63 kg/cm^2) and ohmmeter reads 0 ohms. If not, replace overboost protection switch (color coded Black).

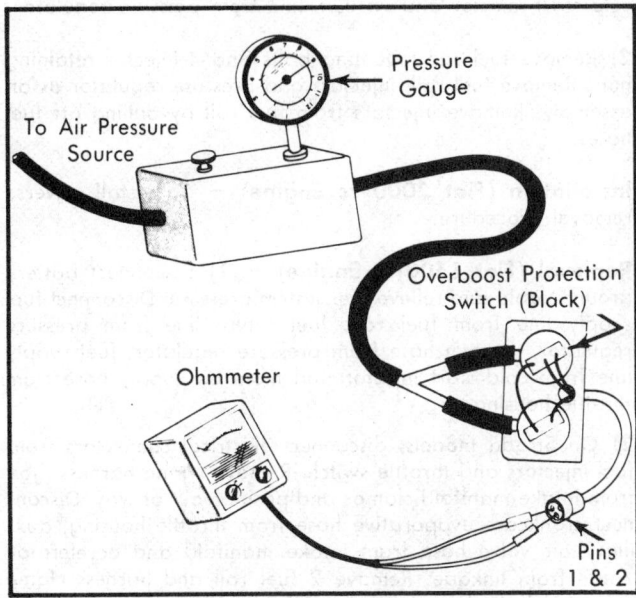

Fig. 15 Testing Fiat Spider 2000 Turbo Overboost Protection Switch

SPEED LIMIT SWITCH (CALIF. VOLKSWAGEN ONLY)

Remove speed limit switch from firewall and connect positive voltmeter lead to terminal 8 and negative voltmeter lead to terminal 6. Start engine and accelerate to 3000 RPM. Voltmeter should indicate battery voltage. If not replace speed limit switch.

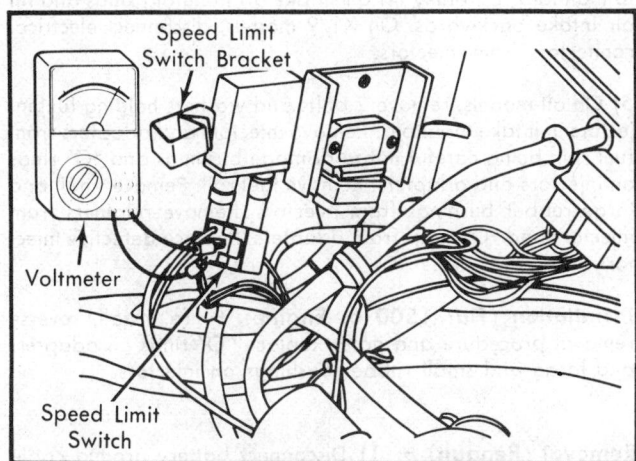

Fig. 16 Testing Speed Limit Switch (Calif. Volkswagen Only)

REMOVAL & INSTALLATION

NOTE — *The Bosch AFC fuel injection system maintains constant fuel pressure in fuel lines and component parts at all times. Be sure to relieve pressure before attempting to open system at any point for removal or installation of components. Do not allow fuel to flow onto engine or electrical parts and do not allow open flame or sparks in area while servicing fuel system components.*

ELECTRONIC CONTROL UNIT (ECU)

Removal & Installation (All Models) — Disconnect battery ground cable. On Renault models, remove passenger seat and fold back carpet. On all models, disconnect electrical connector retaining clamps or press back on clip located on wire end of connector. Disconnect electrical connector, swinging to right if necessary to remove. Remove ECU retaining screws and remove ECU. To install, reverse removal procedure. ECU is located as follows:

- BMW 528i & 633Csi — Glove compartment.
- BMW 733i — Right kick panel, behind speaker.
- Fiat — Under dash on right side.
- Porsche — Right kick panel.
- Renault — Under carpet under passenger seat.
- Volkswagen — Right side of engine compartment.

AIR FLOW METER

NOTE — *Removal and installation procedures not available for Porsche or Volkswagen models.*

Removal & Installation (BMW) — Disconnect battery ground cable. Disconnect electrical connector from air flow meter and loosen clamps on both sides of meter. Remove air cleaner and lift air flow meter out of its holder. To install, reverse removal procedure.

Removal (Fiat) — Disconnect battery ground cable and air flow meter electrical connector. Remove air hoses from both sides of air flow meter. Remove mounting clamp bolt and washer from top of meter, then remove clamp. From under meter, remove spacer and bushing. Remove 2 bolts, lock washers, plain washers and bushings securing meter to bracket. Remove air flow meter.

Installation (Fiat) — To install, reverse removal procedure and note the following: Make sure rubber bushing is installed under air flow meter and air hose connections are tight.

Removal & Installation (Renault) — Disconnect battery ground cable. Disconnect electrical connector from air flow meter. Separate air hoses from air flow meter. Unclip retaining hook and remove air flow meter. To install, reverse removal procedure and ensure retaining hook is secured.

THROTTLE SWITCH

Removal & Installation (All Models) — Disconnect battery ground cable. Disconnect throttle switch electrical connector. Remove 2 screws securing throttle switch to housing. Remove switch by slowly pulling switch off throttle shaft. To install, reverse removal procedure and note the following: Make sure switch is aligned on throttle shaft and after replacement perform throttle switch adjustment. *See Adjustments in this article.*

COLD START INJECTOR

Removal & Installation (All Models) — Disconnect battery ground cable and remove electrical connector from cold start injector. Release fuel system pressure and remove fuel supply line from injector. Remove injector retaining bolts and remove injector. To install, reverse removal procedures.

BOSCH AFC FUEL INJECTION – EUROPEAN MODELS (Cont.)

AUXILIARY AIR VALVE

NOTE – *Replacement of auxiliary air valve requires that immediate replacement be available or draining cooling system (oil on Volkswagen models) below level of valve.*

Removal & Installation (All Models) – Disconnect battery ground cable and remove electrical connector from air valve. Remove air hoses from valve. Remove 2 bolts securing valve to cylinder head and remove valve. To install, reverse removal procedure.

COOLANT TEMPERATURE SENSOR

NOTE – *Replacement of temperature sensor should be done only when engine is cold. Removal of sensor requires having replacement sensor ready for immediate installation or draining cooling system below level of sensor (oil on Volkswagen models).*

Removal (All Models) – Disconnect battery ground cable. Drain coolant as required and disconnect electrical connector from sensor. Loosen and remove sensor.

Installation (All Models) – To install, reverse removal procedure using suitable sealer on threads of sensor. Replace sealing washers, if equipped.

THERMO TIME SWITCH

NOTE – *Thermo time switch removal should be done only when engine is cold. Removal of switch requires having replacement switch ready for immediate installation or draining cooling system (oil on Volkswagen models) below level of switch.*

Removal (All Models) – Disconnect battery ground cable and drain cooling system as required. Disconnect electrical connector from switch. Loosen and remove switch.

Installation (All Models) – To install, reverse removal procedure, using suitable sealer on switch threads.

FUEL PRESSURE REGULATOR

Removal & Installation (All Models) – Disconnect battery ground cable and relieve fuel system pressure. Disconnect fuel lines and vacuum line at regulator. Remove pressure regulator, separating from bracket, if installed. To install, reverse removal procedure.

FUEL INJECTORS

NOTE – *Removal and installation procedures not available for Porsche or Volkswagen models.*

Removal (BMW) – **1)** Disconnect battery ground cable and relieve fuel system pressure. Remove electrical connectors from injectors, fuel line at pressure regulator and fuel return line. Remove injector mounting bolts. Remove fuel rail with injectors attached.

2) Remove injector-to-fuel rail sleeve by cutting sleeve. Remove injector from fuel rail by melting hose with a soldering gun until injector can be removed from fuel rail.

Installation (BMW) – To install, reverse removal procedure and install new hoses between injectors and fuel rail. Ensure new hose is sealed at fuel rail with new sleeve.

Removal (Fiat 2000 cc Engine) – **1)** Disconnect battery ground cable and relieve fuel system pressure. Disconnect electrical connectors at all injectors. Remove fuel supply hose from fuel rail, fuel return line from pressure regulator, fuel line from cold start injector and vacuum line from pressure regulator.

2) Remove fuel rail mounting bolts and 4 injector retaining nuts. Remove fuel rail, injectors and pressure regulator as an assembly. Remove injectors from fuel rail by pulling off fuel hoses.

Installation (Fiat 2000 cc Engine) – To install, reverse removal procedure.

Removal (Fiat 1500 cc Engine) – **1)** Disconnect battery ground cable and relieve fuel system pressure. Disconnect fuel supply line from fuel rail, fuel return line from pressure regulator, vacuum hose from pressure regulator, fuel supply line from cold start injector and main air supply hose from throttle housing.

2) On Strada models, disconnect electrical connectors from fuel injectors and throttle switch. Remove wiring harness tube from intake manifold clamps and position out of way. Disconnect crankcase evaporative hose from throttle housing, auxiliary air valve hose from intake manifold and accelerator cable from linkage. Remove 2 fuel rail and harness clamp retaining bolts from intake manifold and remove clamps.

3) On X1/9 models, disconnect accelerator cable from linkage, electrical connectors for throttle switch and cold start injector, auxiliary air valve hose from intake manifold and crankcase evaporative by-pass hose from intake manifold. Remove 2 intake manifold cooling air duct retaining nuts and washers. Disconnect cooling air hose from duct and remove duct.

4) On all models, remove nuts and washers holding air intake to manifold. Carefully lift air intake off manifold studs and tilt air intake backwards. On X1/9 models, disconnect electrical connectors from injectors.

5) On all models, remove 2 bolts and washers holding fuel injectors in intake manifold. Remove injectors and adapters from fuel rail, being careful not to damage bushings and "O" rings on injectors and adapters. Remove fuel rail. Remove small and large rubber bushings from injectors. Remove retainers from injectors and "O" rings from adapters. Replace defective injectors with new hose.

Installation (Fiat 1500 cc Engine) – To install, reverse removal procedure and note: Replace "O" rings on adapters and large and small rubber bushings on injectors.

Removal (Renault) – **1)** Disconnect battery ground cable and relieve fuel system pressure. Remove injector retaining bolts. Disconnect fuel lines and electrical connectors. Remove fuel rail with injectors attached. Remove injector seals.

2) Remove injectors from fuel rail by melting hose lengthwise with a soldering gun until injector can be removed from fuel rail. Thoroughly clean fuel rail assembly of rubber.

Installation (Renault) – To install, reverse removal procedure and note: Install injector on fuel rail with new hose and ensure hose is fully seated on injector and fuel rail. Connect hose with a clamp. Ensure injector seals are installed.

BOSCH AFC FUEL INJECTION – EUROPEAN MODELS (Cont.)

ADJUSTMENTS

HOT (SLOW) IDLE RPM

See appropriate TUNE-UP SERVICE PROCEDURES article.

IDLE MIXTURE

See appropriate TUNE-UP SERVICE PROCEDURES article.

THROTTLE SWITCH

NOTE – No adjustment procedures available for Porsche models.

BMW – 1) Connect Bosch tester (0684 100 202) to ECU connector. Set cylinder selector switch to "6" and program selector switch to "5". Turn ignition on. Tester gauge should read 0 ohms with throttle valve at idle position; infinite for partial throttle valve position and 0 ohms for full throttle valve position.

2) If throttle switch does not respond as described, loosen throttle switch screws and place throttle valve in idle position. At idle, tester reading should be 0 ohms. When throttle valve is moved .118-.157" (3-4 mm), tester reading should read infinity. If relocating throttle switch does not produce above results, replace throttle switch.

NOTE – Throttle switch contacts can be tested for continuity on 633CSi and 733i models with an ohmmeter. With ohmmeter connected between terminal 18 (center) and 2 (top), 0 ohms should be measured with throttle at idle position. With ohmmeter connected between terminal 18 and 3 (bottom), 0 ohms should be measured with throttle at full throttle position.

Fiat – 1) Before adjusting throttle switch, ensure engine speed is set to specifications. With engine off, remove electrical connector from throttle switch, loosen 2 screws and connect an ohmmeter between terminls 18 (center) and 2 (right of center).

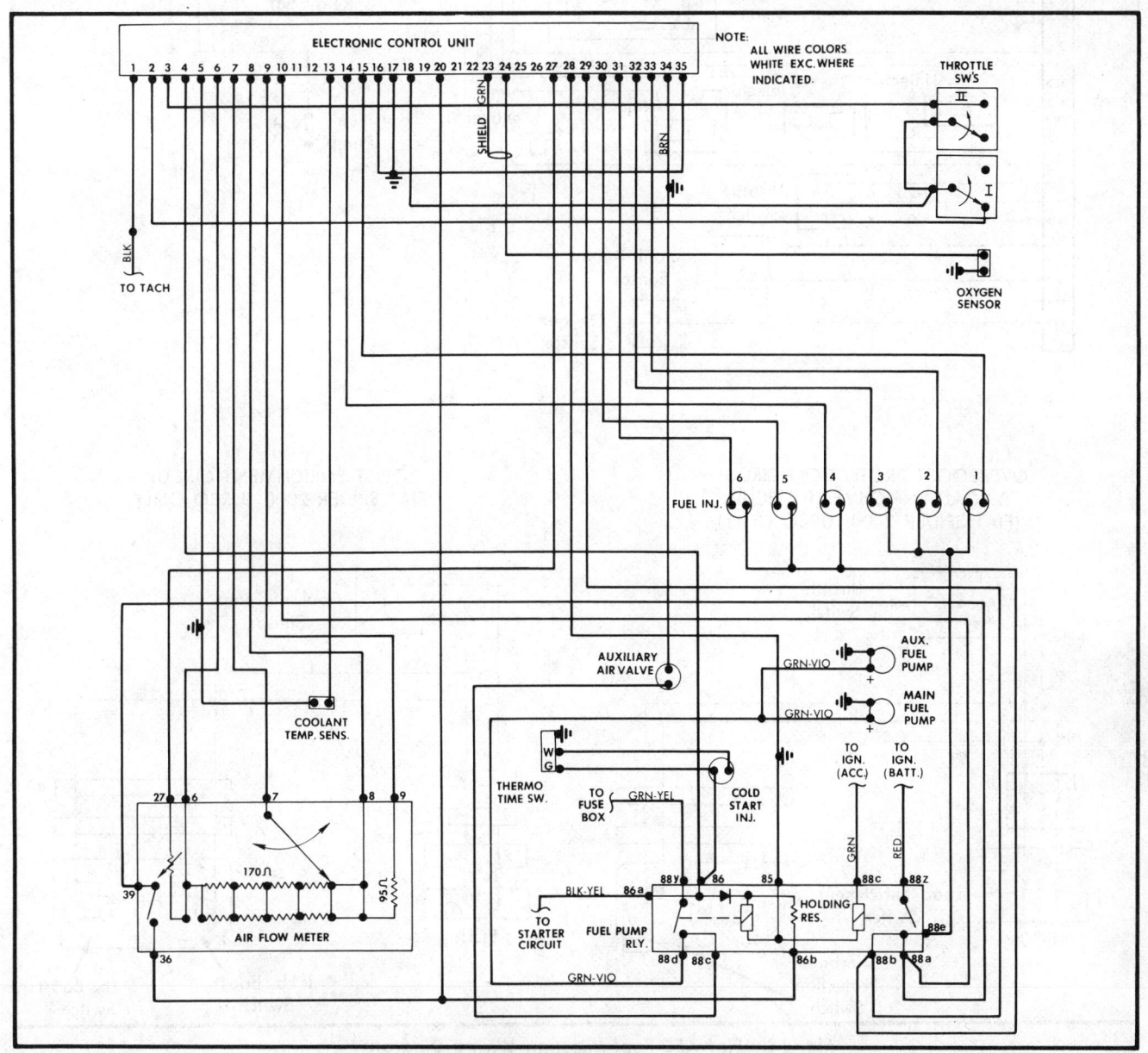

Fig. 17 BMW AFC Fuel Injection Wiring Diagram

BOSCH AFC FUEL INJECTION — EUROPEAN MODELS (Cont.)

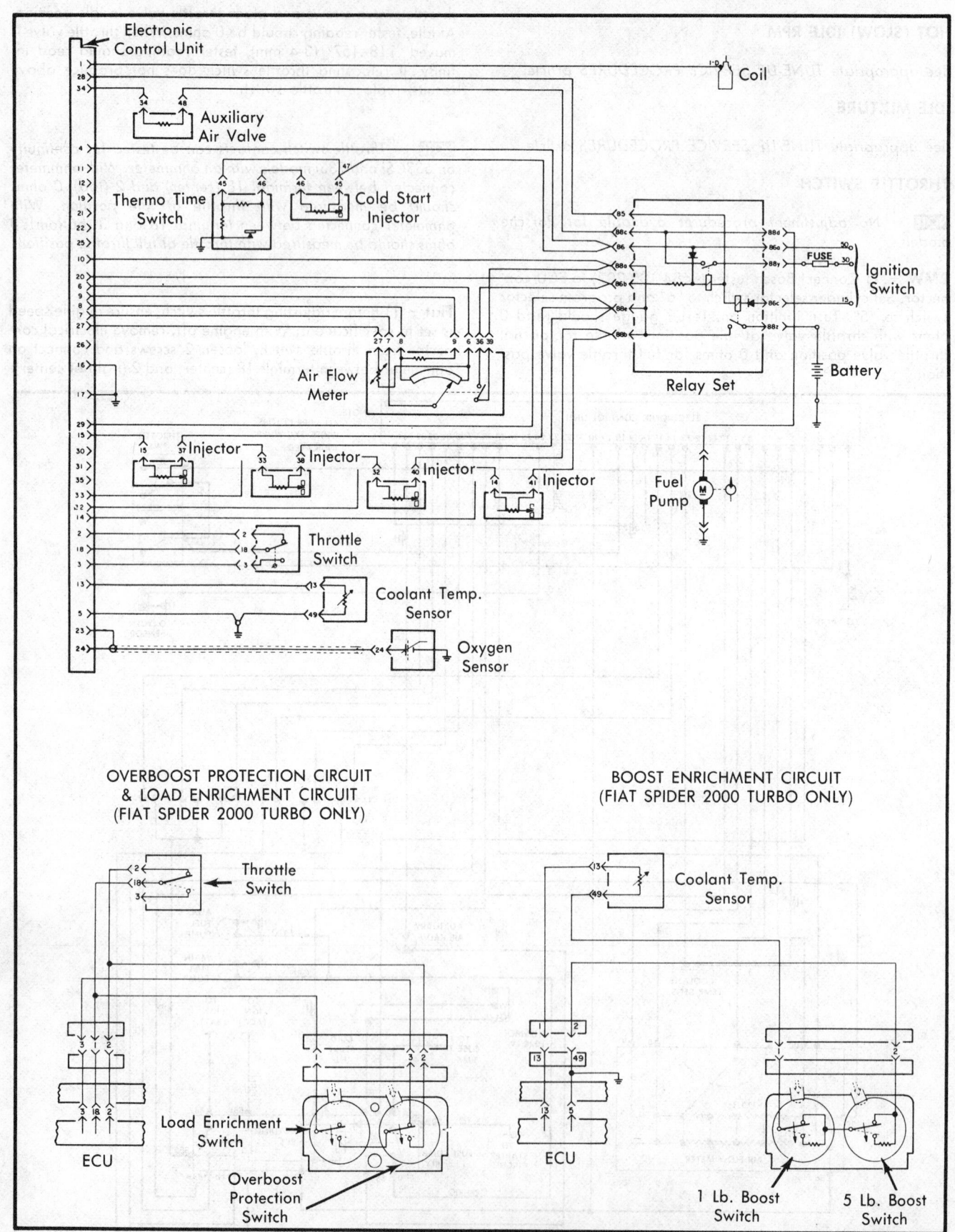

Fig. 18   Fiat AFC Fuel Injection Wiring Diagram

BOSCH AFC FUEL INJECTION — EUROPEAN MODELS (Cont.)

2) Rotate switch clockwise until ohmmeter reading is 0 ohms. Tighten mounting screws at point ohmmeter reading registers 0 ohms. If throttle switch cannot be adjusted as described, replace switch.

Volkswagen — 1) Disconnect electrical connector at throttle switch. Zero ohmmeter and connect ohmmeter leads to both terminals on switch. With throttle valve closed, ohmmeter reading should register infinity reading. Slowly open throttle valve, just before reaching stop, ohmmeter reading should register 0 ohms.

2) If switch does not respond as outlined in step **1)**, fully depress accelerator pedal and hold in position. Loosen throttle switch and move switch until ohmmeter reading changes from infinity reading to 0 ohms and tighten switch. Roller of switch should be centered on curved arm of throttle lever. If switch cannot be adjusted as described, replace throttle switch.

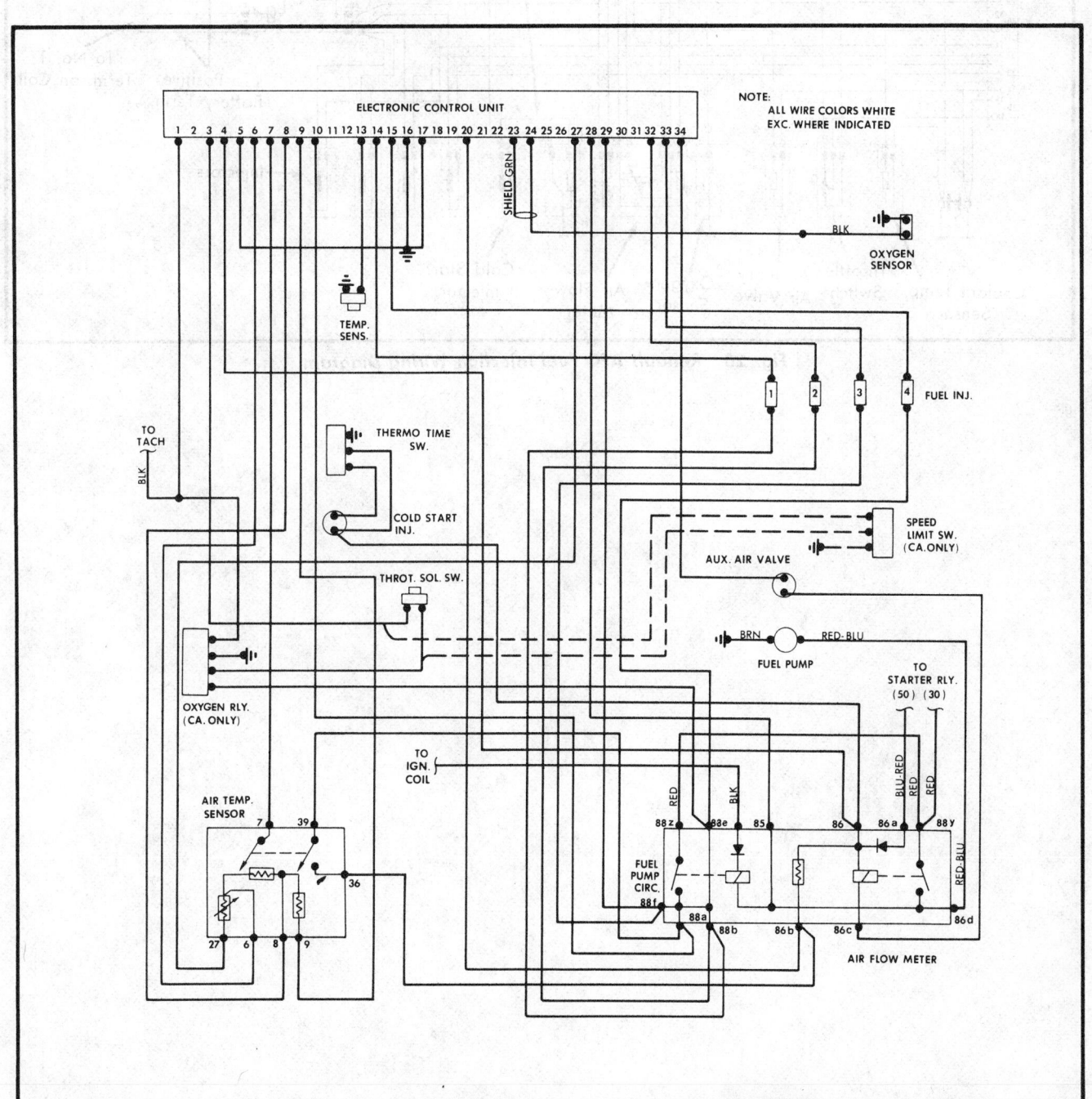

Fig. 19 Volkswagen AFC Fuel Injection Wiring Diagram

BOSCH AFC FUEL INJECTION — EUROPEAN MODELS (Cont.)

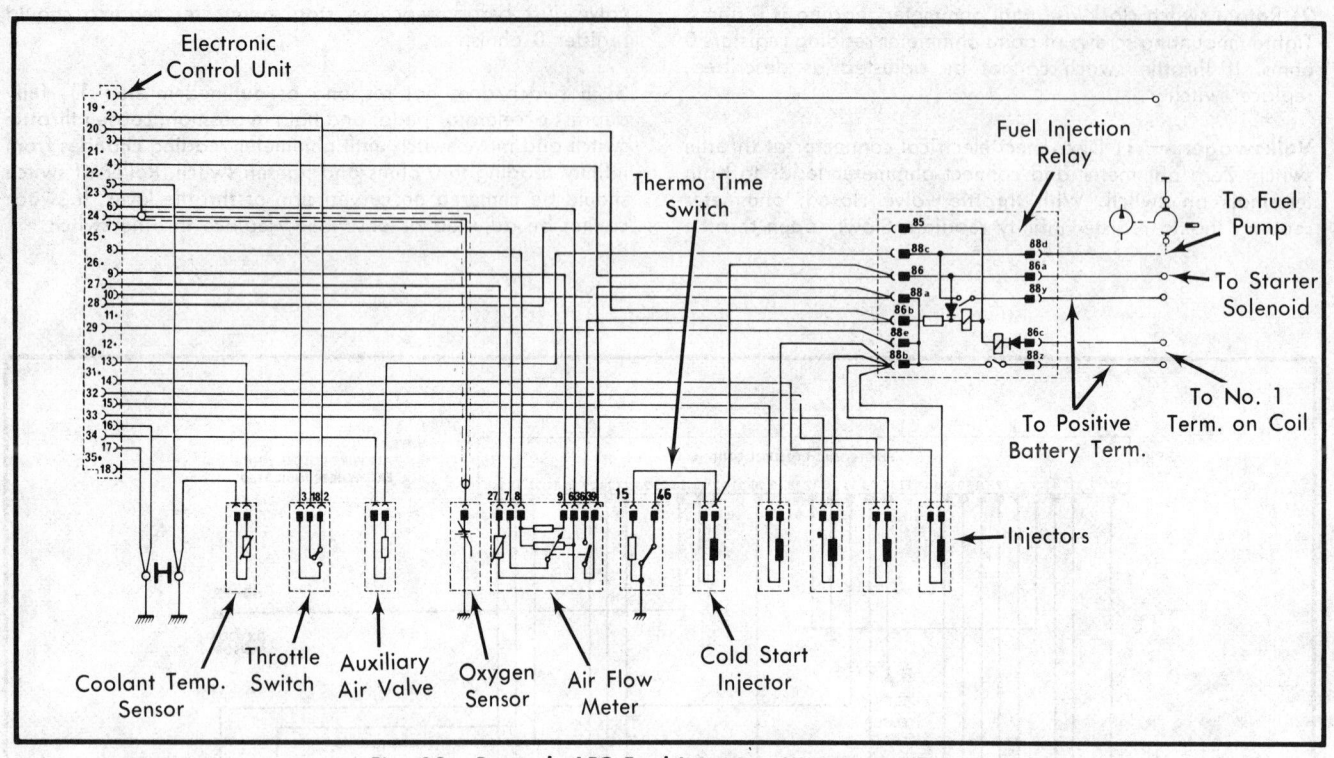

Fig. 20 Renault AFC Fuel Injection Wiring Diagram

BOSCH AFC FUEL INJECTION — JAPANESE MODELS

Datsun
  200SX
  280ZX
  280ZX Turbo
  810
Toyota
  Cressida
  Supra

NOTE — *The Bosch AFC Fuel Injection system is used on all models and variations may exist between model applications with the addition of auxiliary control systems. This article covers the Bosch AFC system in general, with manufacturer's differences noted.*

DESCRIPTION

The Bosch Air Flow Controlled (AFC) fuel injection system is an electronically controlled system operated by incoming air flow. The AFC fuel injection system also contains a feedback system which measures oxygen content of exhaust gases and maintains the air/fuel ratio at about 14.7:1. The fuel injection system consists of an electric fuel pump, fuel pressure regulator, fuel damper (except Toyota models), fuel injectors, Electronic Control Unit (ECU), air flow meter, air temperature sensor, throttle switch, coolant temperature sensor (cylinder head temperature sensor on Datsun models), oxygen sensor, catalytic converter, auxiliary air valve and electrical relays.

In addition, all models except 200SX and 280ZX Turbo are equipped with a cold start system which consists of an auxiliary air valve, cold start injector and thermo time switch. A dash pot is installed on the throttle chamber of 200SX models with automatic transmission to prevent engine stalls due to abrupt closing of throttle valve.

The electronic control system of 280ZX Turbo models controls emission control system, idle speed control system, fuel injection system, spark timing and fuel pump operation. Under normal service procedures, it is not necessary to adjust idle mixture, idle speed or ignition timing.

ELECTRIC FUEL PUMP

Fuel under pressure from electric fuel pump flows through a fuel damper (some models) and fuel filter to the fuel pressure regulator. Power for operation during cranking mode is provided from starter relay via the fuel pump relay and ECU. After the engine has started, control of the fuel pump is by a fuel pump circuit in the air flow meter (Toyota models only). The first movement of the air flow meter measuring flap (about 5°) closes the fuel pump contacts and provides power to fuel pump after engine has started. With engine stopped, no air flow is present, measuring flap closes and fuel pump contacts are opened to cut power to fuel pump. This method reduces the risk of fire in a collision.

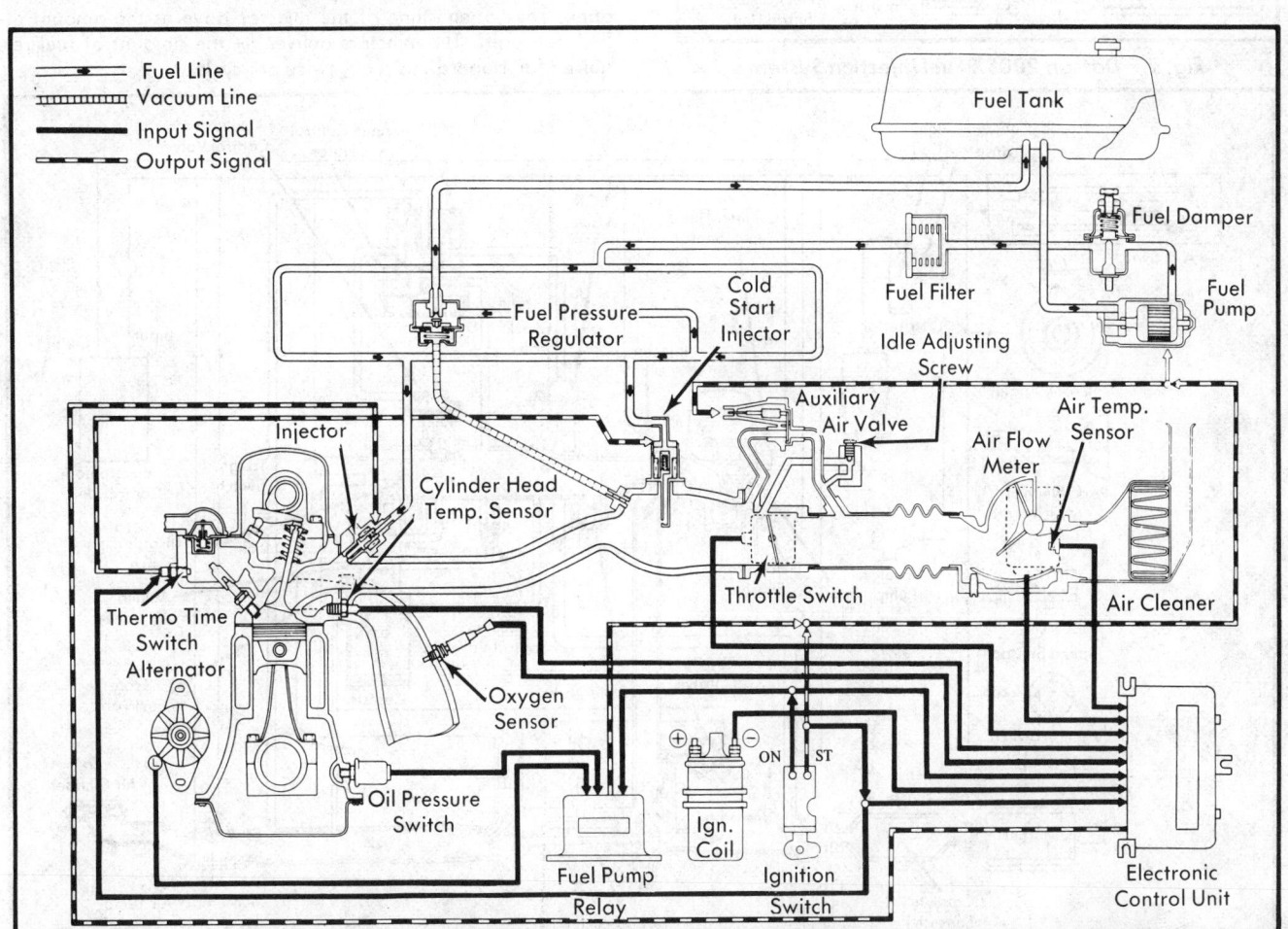

Fig. 1 Datsun 280ZX and 810 Fuel Injection System

1981 Bosch Fuel Injection

BOSCH AFC FUEL INJECTION – JAPANESE MODELS (Cont.)

On Datsun models, power for operation during cranking mode is provided by the ECU through the fuel pump relay. After the engine has started, control of the fuel pump is by the charging system and oil pressure switch. Power to fuel pump is stopped if alternator does not generate a charge and oil pressure decreases. This method reduces risk of fire in a collision.

FUEL PRESSURE REGULATOR

The pressure regulator consists of a sealed, spring loaded diaphragm with a connection for intake manifold vacuum. Fuel is provided to fuel injectors under approximately 36 psi (2.5 kg/cm^2) pressure. A connection for intake manifold vacuum provides a constant pressure differential which ensures that the amount of fuel injected is solely dependent upon injector "open" time. Excess fuel is returned to fuel tank. No service of pressure regulator is required.

FUEL INJECTORS

A fuel rail links the fuel pressure regulator with the fuel injectors. Each cylinder is provided with a solenoid-operated injector which sprays fuel towards back of each inlet valve. Each injector is energized through the ignition coil and grounded through the ECU. The injectors are linked to resistors to reduce operating voltage to 3 volts and to protect injectors from power surges.

The ECU controls the injectors and the length of time they are open. The "open" time of the injector governs the amount of fuel delivered. The injectors deliver $\frac{1}{2}$ the amount of fuel required for 1 operating cycle, twice per cycle.

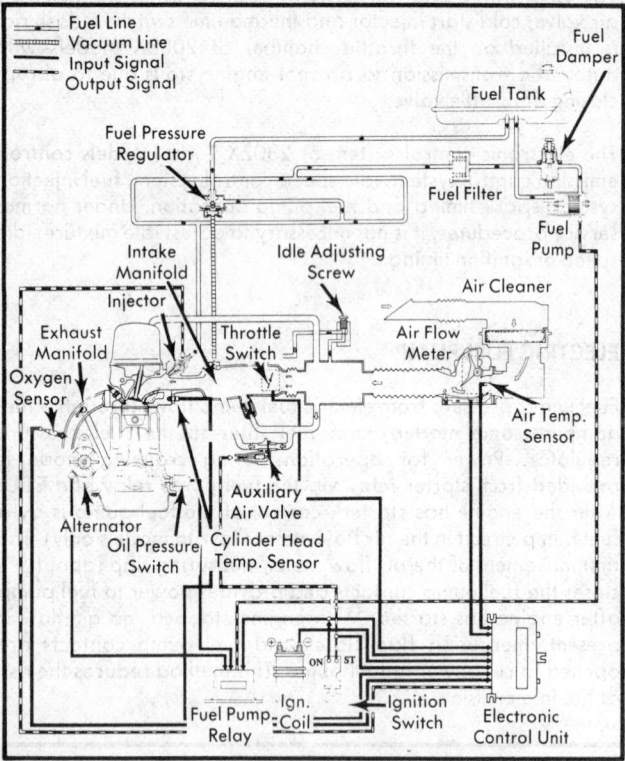

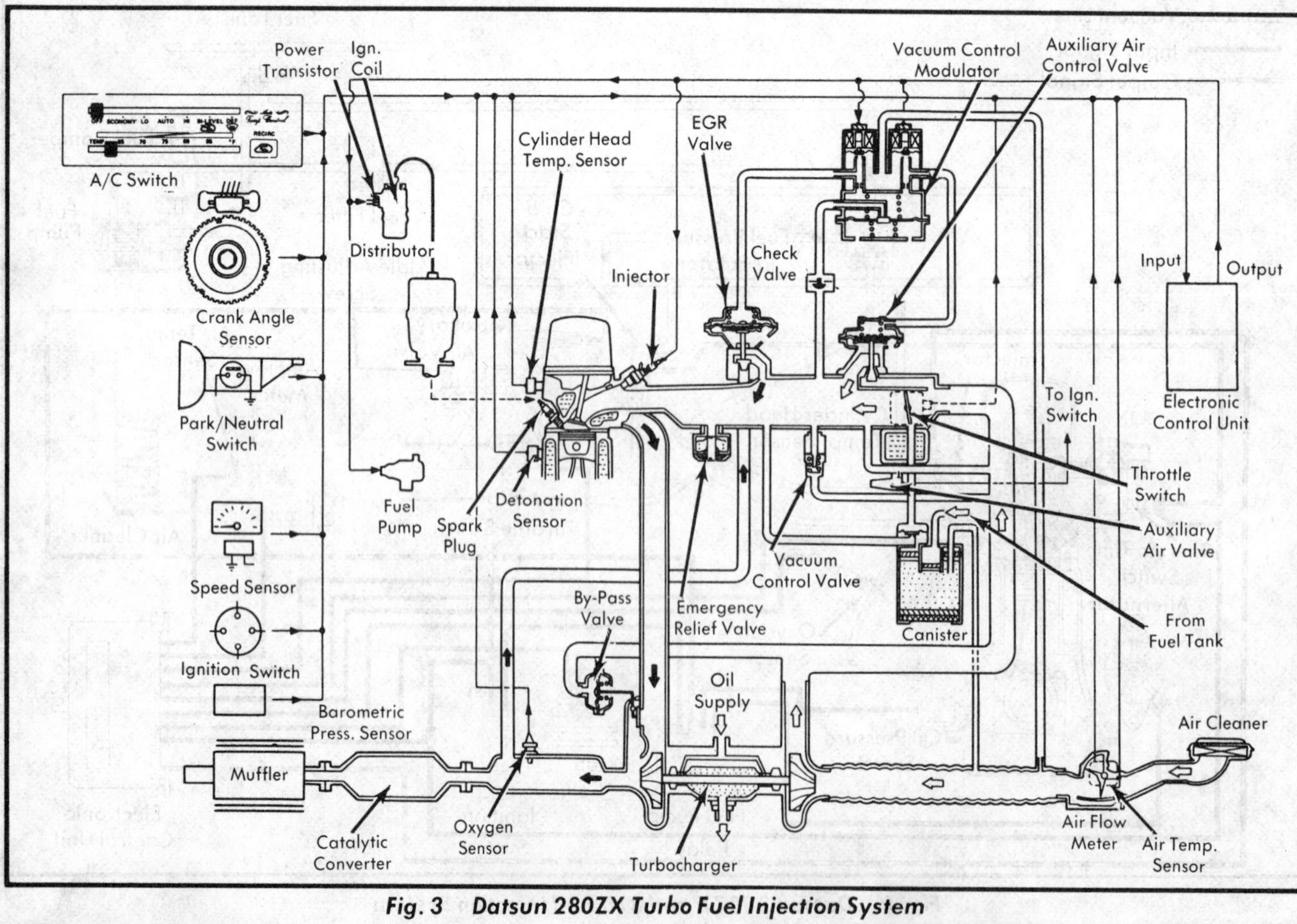

Fig. 2   Datsun 200SX Fuel Injection System

Fig. 3   Datsun 280ZX Turbo Fuel Injection System

BOSCH AFC FUEL INJECTION – JAPANESE MODELS (Cont.)

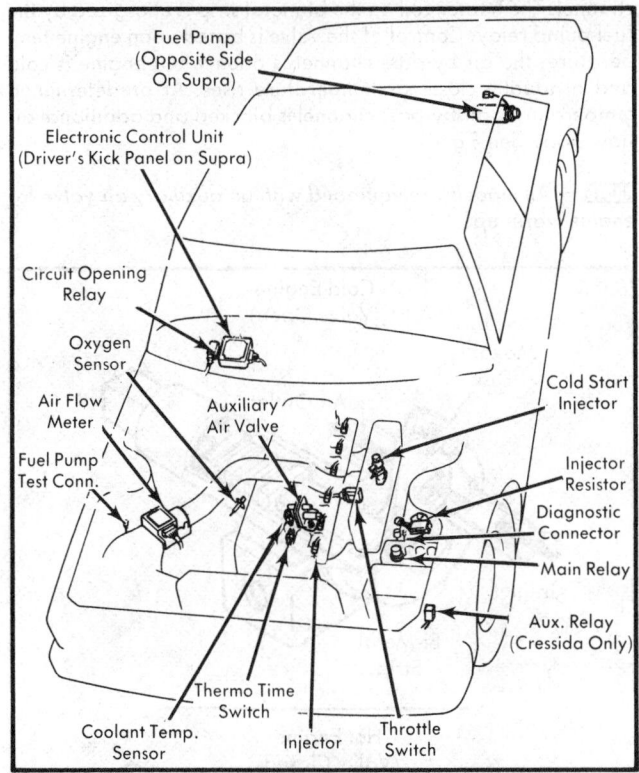

Fig. 4   Toyota Fuel Injection System

ELECTRONIC CONTROL UNIT (ECU)

All components of the control system are electrically connected to the ECU. See Fig. 5. The ECU is a preprogrammed computer which receives and interprets data from various sensors to calculate the amount of fuel required by the engine to maintain efficiency with minimum exhaust emissions. The oxygen sensor informs the ECU of oxygen content of exhaust gases and the ECU constantly adjusts the air/fuel ratio by controlling the injector "open" time.

An automatic function of the ECU is to provide fuel enrichment whenever engine is cranked, regardless of engine temperature. This is activated by a direct electrical connection from the starter circuit to the ECU (most models). The ECU is a sealed unit; no service required.

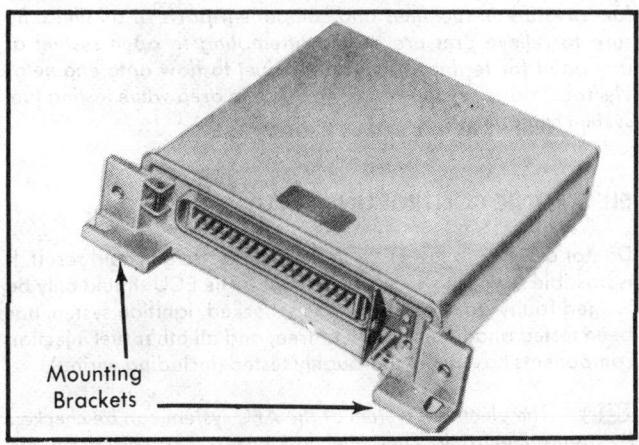

Fig. 5   Electronic Control Unit (ECU)

NOTE – *The ECU of Datsun 280ZX Turbo models controls all operations of the engine electronically (ignition timing, idle speed, etc.). The ECU on this model is referred to as the Electronic Concentrated Engine Control System (ECCS).*

AIR FLOW METER

All engine air is drawn through the air flow meter. The meter is basically a tunnel with similarly shaped measuring flap and dampening flap (offset 90° on same casting). The measuring flap swings on an axis in air stream against pressure of a spiral spring and is connected to a potentiometer. The potentiometer transmits an electrical signal to inform the ECU of engine load. See Fig. 6.

In addition to monitoring the air flow, the meter also controls fuel pump operation (Toyota models) and idling. At idle, the measuring flap is almost closed due to spring pressure. An idle air by-pass receives air from main air flow through a small hole, the size of which is controlled by the idle mixture screw. This adjustable air by-pass influences CO levels at low engine speeds.

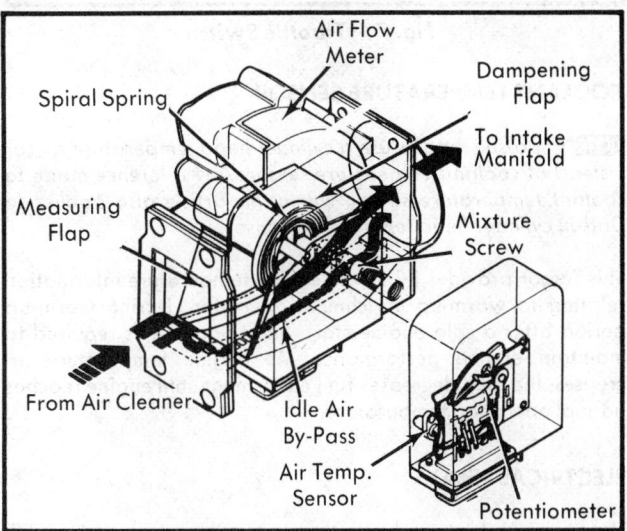

Fig. 6   Bosch AFC Air Flow Meter

AIR TEMPERATURE SENSOR

The air temperature sensor is an integral component of the air flow meter which converts temperature of incoming air into electrical signals. These signals are received by the ECU and processed to adjust the amount of fuel delivered by the injectors. The air temperature sensor is non-serviceable.

THROTTLE SWITCH

A contact type throttle switch is installed on the throttle chamber of all models which converts throttle position into electrical signals to inform ECU of throttle position. Signals are sent to ECU when throttle is fully open or at idle. See Fig. 7. The potentiometer prevents loss of power during sudden acceleration/deceleration by signaling the ECU of necessary fuel enrichment requirements.

NOTE – *Datsun 200SX models with automatic transmissions are also equipped with a dash pot to prevent abrupt closing of throttle valve.*

BOSCH AFC FUEL INJECTION – JAPANESE MODELS (Cont.)

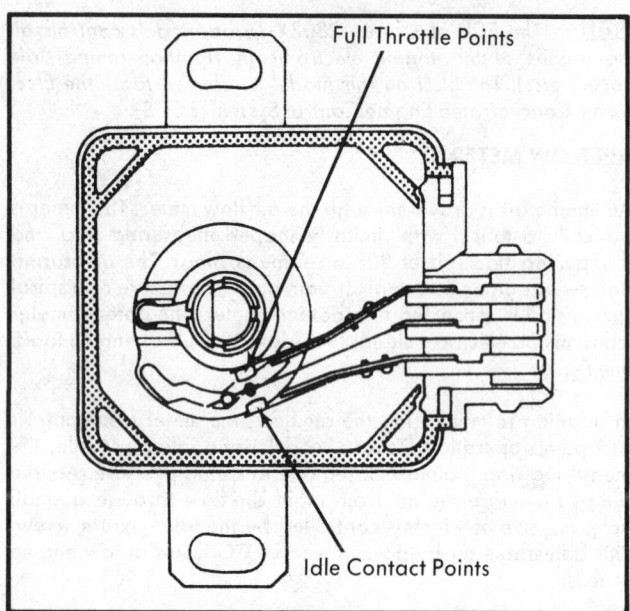

Full Throttle Points

Idle Contact Points

Fig. 7   Throttle Switch

COOLANT TEMPERATURE SENSOR

NOTE – *Datsun models use a cylinder head temperature sensor instead of coolant temperature sensor. Any reference made to coolant temperature sensor within this article also applies to Datsun cylinder head temperature sensor.*

This sensor provides ECU with engine temperature information relating to warm-up enrichment operation. During warm-up period after a cold engine start, additional fuel is required to maintain engine performance. As engine temperature increases, the ECU decreases fuel enrichment until engine reaches normal operating temperature.

ELECTRICAL RELAYS

The various relays used with the electronic controls of the AFC injection system control power to injectors, fuel pump, ECU and cold start system. The electrical relays may consist of 1 component for all relays or a combination of individual relays.

COLD START SYSTEM (EXC. 200SX & 280ZX TURBO)

The cold start system provides additional air and fuel during cold engine starts. The cold start system consists of an auxiliary air valve which provides additional air, cold start injector which delivers additional fuel and a thermo time switch which controls operation of the cold start system.

The thermo time switch has a bi-metal contact surrounded by a heating coil which is energized during engine cranking. This switch limits cold start system to 1-12 seconds under extreme cold engine starts in relation to engine temperature. When engine temperature is above 95°F (35°C), bi-metal contact breaks ground circuit of cold start injector and cold start enrichment is by-passed.

The auxiliary air valve provides additional air during cold engine starts and warm-up periods. The valve consists of an electrically heated bi-metal strip, movable disc and air by-pass

channel. The heater coil on the bi-metal strip is energized by the fuel pump relay. Control of the valve is based upon engine temperature; the air by-pass channel is open when engine is cold and gradually closes as temperature rises. At predetermined temperatures, air by-pass channel is blocked and additional air flow stops. See Fig. 8.

NOTE – *All models are equipped with an auxiliary air valve for engine warm-up.*

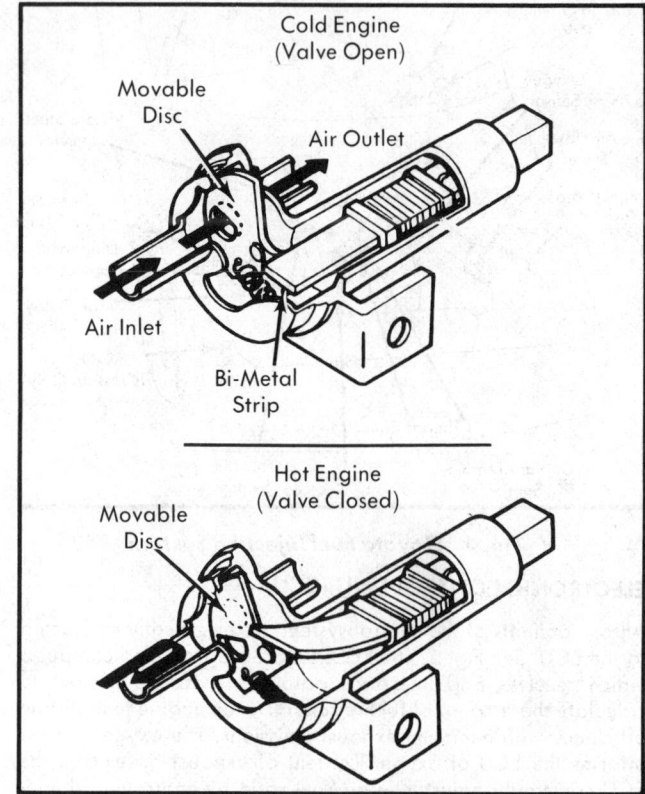

Cold Engine
(Valve Open)

Movable Disc

Air Outlet

Air Inlet

Bi-Metal Strip

Hot Engine
(Valve Closed)

Movable Disc

Fig. 8   Auxiliary Air Valve

TESTING

NOTE – *The Bosch AFC fuel injection system maintains constant fuel pressure in fuel lines and component parts at all times. Be sure to relieve pressure before attempting to open system at any point for testing. Do not allow fuel to flow onto engine or electrical parts or allow an open flame in area while testing fuel system components.*

ELECTRONIC CONTROL UNIT (ECU)

Do not attempt to test ECU, permanent damage could result. It is possible to check wires for continuity. The ECU should only be judged faulty after compression is checked, ignition system has been tested and found problem-free, and all other fuel injection components have been thoroughly tested (including wiring).

NOTE – *The electrical system of the AFC system can be checked by using Electronic Fuel Injection testers prescribed by the manufacturer. Instructions for use of testers must be followed carefully to prevent damage to system.*

BOSCH AFC FUEL INJECTION – JAPANESE MODELS (Cont.)

FUEL PRESSURE

Datsun – 1) To release fuel system pressure on 280ZX Turbo models, start engine, disconnect fuel pump electrical connector in luggage compartment; after engine stalls, crank engine 2 or 3 times, turn ignition off and reconnect fuel pump. On all other models, start engine, disconnect No. 2 fuel pump relay; after engine stalls, crank engine 2 or 3 times, turn ignition off and reconnect No. 2 fuel pump relay.

2) Remove fuel filter-to-fuel rail hose and connect a pressure gauge using a "T" fitting. Start engine and read fuel pressure at idle. If pressure is not as specified, replace pressure regulator.

3) Disconnect vacuum line from fuel pressure regulator and connect a hand vacuum pump. On 280ZX Turbo models, disconnect fuel pump connector and apply battery power. On all other models, disconnect alternator field plug and oil pressure sending unit lead wire.

4) On 280ZX models, leave ignition and engine off. On all other models, turn ignition on. As vacuum is applied to pressure regulator, pressure reading should decrease. If pressure and vacuum readings do not conform as shown in chart, replace fuel pressure regulator.

Datsun Fuel Pressure Specifications	
Condition In. Hg	Pressure psi (kg/cm^2)
Idle①	30 (2.1)
0	36-37 (2.5-2.6)
5	33-35 (2.3-2.5)
10	31-32 (2.2-2.3)
15	29-30 (2.0-2.1)
20	26-28 (1.8-2.0)
① – Vacuum hose connected at pressure regulator.	

Toyota – 1) Disconnect battery ground cable and cold start injector electrical connector. Place container or shop rag under fuel rail at union bolt of cold start injector hose. Remove union bolt and drain fuel rail. Remove cold start injector hose from union bolt and install fuel pressure gauge with hose to union bolt. Install gauge and bolt to fuel rail with a gasket on each side of gauge fitting.

2) Reconnect battery cable and start engine. Disconnect vacuum line from fuel pressure regulator and pinch line closed. Gauge reading should be 33-38 psi (2.3-2.7 kg/cm^2). If pressure is too high, replace fuel pressure regulator; if too low check fuel system for leaks.

3) Reconnect vacuum line to pressure regulator. Pressure reading should decrease to 28 psi (2.0 kg/cm^2) with engine at idle speed. If not, replace fuel pressure regulator. Stop engine. If pressure drops quickly, check fuel pump, pressure regulator and/or injectors.

FUEL PUMP CIRCUIT

Datsun – On 280ZX Turbo models, turn ignition on and listen for fuel pump operation (pump operates for 5 seconds after ignition switch is turned on). On all other models, turn ignition on, disconnect oil pressure switch electrical harness or alternator terminal "L"; fuel pump operation should be heard. On all models, if fuel pump does not operate, check relays, fuel pump, alternator terminal "L" (if used) and oil pressure switch (if used).

Toyota – Turn ignition on. Remove cap from fuel pump test connector and, using a jumper wire, jump both terminals of connector. Fuel pressure should be felt at cold start injector hose and noise of fuel returning to tank should be heard at fuel pressure regulator. Remove jumper wire, install connector cap and turn ignition off. If none of the above conditions were met, check fusible link, engine fuse, fuel injection fuse, circuit opening relay, fuel pump and all electrical connectors.

AIR TEMPERATURE SENSOR

1) With ignition off, disconnect electrical connector at air flow meter. Connect an ohmmeter between terminals 30 and 33 (280ZX Turbo), terminals E_2 and THA (Toyota) or terminals 25 and 34 (all other models). Measure and record air temperature.

2) Ohmmeter readings should be as shown in chart. If not, check insulation resistance with ohmmeter between terminal 30 (280ZX Turbo), terminal THA (Toyota) or terminal 25 (all other models) and ground (use air flow meter as ground). Infinity ohmmeter reading should be obtained. If values are not as specified, replace electrical harness or air flow meter assembly, as required.

Temperature/Resistance Relationship	
Temperature °F (°C)	Resistance (Ohms)
Below 68 (20)	Above 2900
68 (20)	2100-2900
Above 68 (20)	Below 2100

AIR FLOW METER POTENTIOMETER

Turn ignition switch off. Disconnect electrical connector from air flow meter and connect ohmmeter between terminals shown in table and note readings. If readings are not to specifications, replace air flow meter.

Air Flow Meter Resistance			
Terminal No.			Resistance (Ohms)
280ZX Turbo	Toyota	All Others	
33 & 26	E_2 & Vb	34 & 35	200-500
31 & 33①	E_1 & Fc	32 & 34①	0-Infinity
.....	E_2 & Vc	33 & 34	100-400
.....	E_2 & Vs	.....	20-100
②	.....	②	Continuity

① – Moving air flow measuring flap.
② – Between any terminal and air flow case (ground).

1981 Bosch Fuel Injection

BOSCH AFC FUEL INJECTION – JAPANESE MODELS (Cont.)

AUXILIARY AIR VALVE

Start cold engine. Pinch rubber hose between air valve and throttle chamber; engine speed should decrease. After engine reaches operating temperature, pinch hose again; engine speed should not decrease (not more than 150 RPM on Toyota). If valve does not operate as outlined, replace auxiliary air valve.

THERMO TIME SWITCH (EXC. 200SX & 280ZX TURBO)

Datsun – Disconnect negative battery cable and switch connector. Connect ohmmeter between terminal 45 and switch body (ground). Reading should be 40-70 ohms. Connect ohmmeter between terminal 46 and ground. At coolant temperature below 57°F (14°C), reading should be 0 ohms; above 77°F (25°C), reading should be infinity; between 57-77°F (14-25°C), reading should be 0 or infinity. If readings are not as specified, replace thermo time switch.

Toyota – Disconnect negative battery cable and switch connector. Connect ohmmeter between both terminals; reading should be 20-40 ohms at coolant temperature below 95°F (35°C) and 40-60 ohms at temperature above 95°F (35°C). Measure resistance between terminal STA and switch body (ground); reading should be 20-80 ohms. If readings are not as specified, replace thermo time switch.

COLD START INJECTOR (EXC. 200SX & 280ZX TURBO)

Disconnect negative battery cable and cold start injector connector. Remove cold start injector (with fuel supply connected) and place over glass container. Connect battery power to injector terminals (use injector harness connector on Toyota). Fuel should spray from injector. If not, replace cold start injector.

COOLANT TEMPERATURE SENSOR

Warm engine to normal operating temperature and stop engine. Using a thermometer, measure temperature of coolant. Disconnect negative battery cable and sensor electrical connector. Connect ohmmeter leads to both terminals of sensor. Readings should be as shown in chart for corresponding temperature. If not, replace coolant temperature sensor.

Coolant Temperature Sensor Resistance	
Temperature °F (°C)	Resistance (Ohms)
14 (10)	7,000-11,500
68 (20)	2,100-2,900
122 (50)	700-1,000

REMOVAL & INSTALLATION

NOTE – *The Bosch AFC fuel injection system maintains constant fuel pressure in fuel lines and component parts at all times. Be sure to relieve pressure before attempting to open system at any point for removal or installation of components. Do not allow fuel to flow onto engine or electrical parts and do not*

allow open flame or sparks in area while servicing fuel system components. Always disconnect negative battery cable before disconnecting any electrical component.

ELECTRONIC CONTROL UNIT (ECU)

Removal & Installation – Disconnect negative battery cable. On Cressida models, ECU is located behind glove compartment; on all other models, ECU is located behind kick panel on driver's side. Clear area for access to ECU. Disconnect electrical connector lock lever (if used) and carefully remove connector. Remove ECU retaining screws and remove ECU. To install, reverse removal procedure.

AIR FLOW METER

Removal & Installation – Disconnect negative battery cable. Disconnect air ducts and hoses connecting air cleaner and air flow meter. Remove air cleaner cover, if required. Remove air flow meter retaining bolts. Disconnect air flow meter electrical connector and remove air flow meter. To install, reverse removal procedure.

THROTTLE SWITCH

Removal & Installation – Disconnect negative battery cable. Disconnect throttle switch electrical connector. Remove 2 screws securing throttle switch to housing. Remove switch by slowly pulling switch off throttle shaft. To install, reverse removal procedure and note the following: Make sure switch is aligned on throttle shaft and after replacement, perform throttle switch adjustment. See *Adjustments in this article.*

COLD START INJECTOR (EXC. 200SX & 280ZX TURBO)

Removal & Installation – Disconnect negative battery cable and remove electrical connector from cold start injector. Release fuel system pressure and remove fuel supply line from injector. Remove injector retaining bolts and remove injector. To install, reverse removal procedure.

AUXILIARY AIR VALVE

NOTE – *Replacement of auxiliary air valve on Toyota models requires that immediate replacement be available or cooling system be drained below level of valve.*

Removal & Installation – Disconnect negative battery cable and remove electrical connector from air valve. Drain engine coolant, if required. Remove air hoses and coolant hoses (if equipped). Remove retaining bolts and remove air valve. To install, reverse removal procedure.

COOLANT TEMPERATURE SENSOR

NOTE – *Replacement of temperature sensor on Toyota models requires that immediate replacement be available or cooling system be drained below level of sensor.*

Removal & Installation – Disconnect negative battery cable and remove electrical connector from coolant sensor (cylinder head sensor on Datsun models). Drain engine coolant, if required. Remove sensor. To install, reverse removal procedure, using suitable sealer on Toyota sensor.

BOSCH AFC FUEL INJECTION – JAPANESE MODELS (Cont.)

THERMO TIME SWITCH
(EXC. 200SX & 280ZX TURBO)

NOTE – *Thermo time switch removal should be done only when engine is cold. Removal of switch requires having replacement switch ready for immediate installation or cooling system be drained below level of switch.*

Removal & Installation – Disconnect negative battery cable and electrical connector from switch. Drain cooling system as required. Remove switch. To install, reverse removal procedure, using suitable sealer on switch threads.

FUEL PRESSURE REGULATOR

NOTE – *Fuel pressure regulator removal for Toyota models requires removal of fuel rail. See Fuel Injector removal in this article.*

Removal & Installation – Disconnect negative battery cable and relieve fuel system pressure. Disconnect fuel lines and vacuum line at regulator. Remove pressure regulator mounting bolts and separate regulator from bracket, if installed. Remove pressure regulator. To install, reverse removal procedure.

FUEL INJECTORS

Removal (Datsun) – **1)** Release fuel system pressure and disconnect negative battery cable. Disconnect electrical connectors from cold start injector and fuel injectors. Disconnect fuel injection wiring harness from clip on fuel rail. Clear fuel rail and injectors by disconnecting all air, vacuum, fuel supply and fuel return lines.

2) Remove cold start injector fuel rail and fuel injector retaining bolts. Remove fuel rail, cold start injector and fuel injectors as an assembly. Remove fuel supply hose retaining clip from cold start injector and each fuel injector and remove injectors.

3) To replace injector fuel supply hose, cut hose with soldering iron just enough to remove hose. Do not touch any part of injector with soldering iron, or mount injector in a vise.

Installation (Datsun) – To install, reverse removal procedure and note the following: Coat inside of new fuel hose with gasoline and slide hose onto injector.

Removal (Toyota) – **1)** Release fuel system pressure and disconnect negative battery cable. Drain cooling system. Clear fuel rail and intake air chamber by disconnecting air hoses, coolant hoses, vacuum hoses and fuel hoses. Remove EGR valve and pipe, and intake air duct.

2) Remove intake air chamber and support bracket. Disconnect fuel injection wiring harness from all connectors near fuel rail and place harness on top of engine. Remove fuel rail retaining bolts. Remove fuel rail, injectors and fuel pressure regulator as an assembly.

3) Separate fuel injectors from fuel rail by pulling injectors; discard sealing grommet and "O" ring. Remove insulators from injector holes in intake manifold.

Installation (Toyota) – To install reverse removal procedure and note the following: Install new insulators in injector holes in intake manifold. Install new grommets and "O" rings on fuel injectors. Coat grommets and "O" rings with gasoline and push injectors onto fuel rail. Coat insulators and injector tips with gasoline prior to installation of injectors. Ensure injectors rotate freely.

ADJUSTMENTS

HOT (SLOW) IDLE RPM

See appropriate *TUNE-UP SERVICE PROCEDURES* article.

IDLE MIXTURE

See appropriate *TUNE-UP SERVICE PROCEDURES* article.

THROTTLE SWITCH

Datsun – **1)** With engine running at specified idle RPM, disconnect throttle switch electrical connector. Connect ohmmeter leads to terminals 18 and 25 (280ZX Turbo) or 29 and 30 (all others) of throttle switch.

NOTE – *Do not connect ohmmeter leads to electrical connector of harness or damage to ohmmeter may result.*

2) With engine operating at idle, 0 ohms should register on ohmmeter. Loosen throttle switch retaining screws and increase engine speed to 900 RPM (750 RPM on 200SX and 280ZX Turbo). Adjust position of throttle switch so that ohmmeter reading changes from 0 ohms to infinity reading. If ohmmeter registers correctly, proceed to step **4)**. If readings are not correct, proceed with next step.

3) Turn engine off and set clearance between throttle valve shaft lever and stopper screw to .012" (0.3 mm). Adjust throttle switch position until ohmmeter reading goes from 0 ohms to infinity. If switch does not perform as described, replace throttle valve switch.

4) To check full throttle contact, stop engine and disconnect negative battery cable. Connect ohmmeter between terminals 24 and 30 (except 280ZX Turbo). Continuity should not exist when throttle valve is in idle position. Depress accelerator to full throttle position; continuity should exist. If not, replace throttle switch.

Toyota – **1)** Construct an angle gauge as shown in *Fig. 9*. Insert angle gauge in throttle body to obtain a 61° or 71° throttle valve angle. Check continuity between each terminal of switch (IDL-TL, IDL-PSW and PSW-TL).

2) At 61° throttle opening, ohmmeter reading should show no continuity between any terminals. At 71° throttle opening, continuity should exist between terminals PSW and TL only. If not, proceed to step **3)**. If readings are correct, throttle switch is properly adjusted.

1981 Bosch Fuel Injection

BOSCH AFC FUEL INJECTION — JAPANESE MODELS (Cont.)

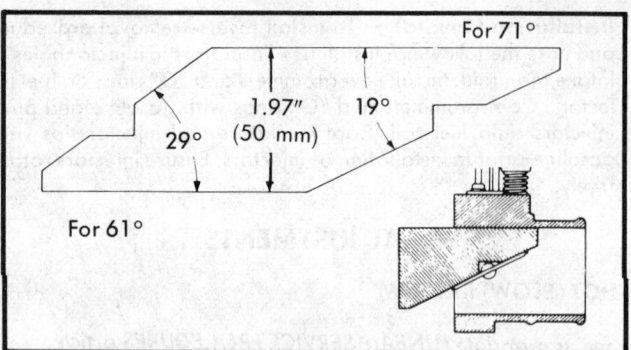

Fig. 9   Adjusting Toyota Throttle Switch

3) To adjust throttle switch, loosen retaining screws and insert a .020" (.52 mm) feeler gauge between throttle stop screw and lever. Connect ohmmeter to terminals IDL and TL. Continuity should be registered. Gradually turn throttle switch counter-clockwise until ohmmeter deflects and tighten screws. Remove feeler gauge.

4) To recheck, insert a .017" (.44 mm) feeler gauge between throttle stop and lever. Ohmmeter should register continuity. Remove feeler gauge and insert a .026" (.66 mm) feeler gauge. Ohmmeter should not register continuity.

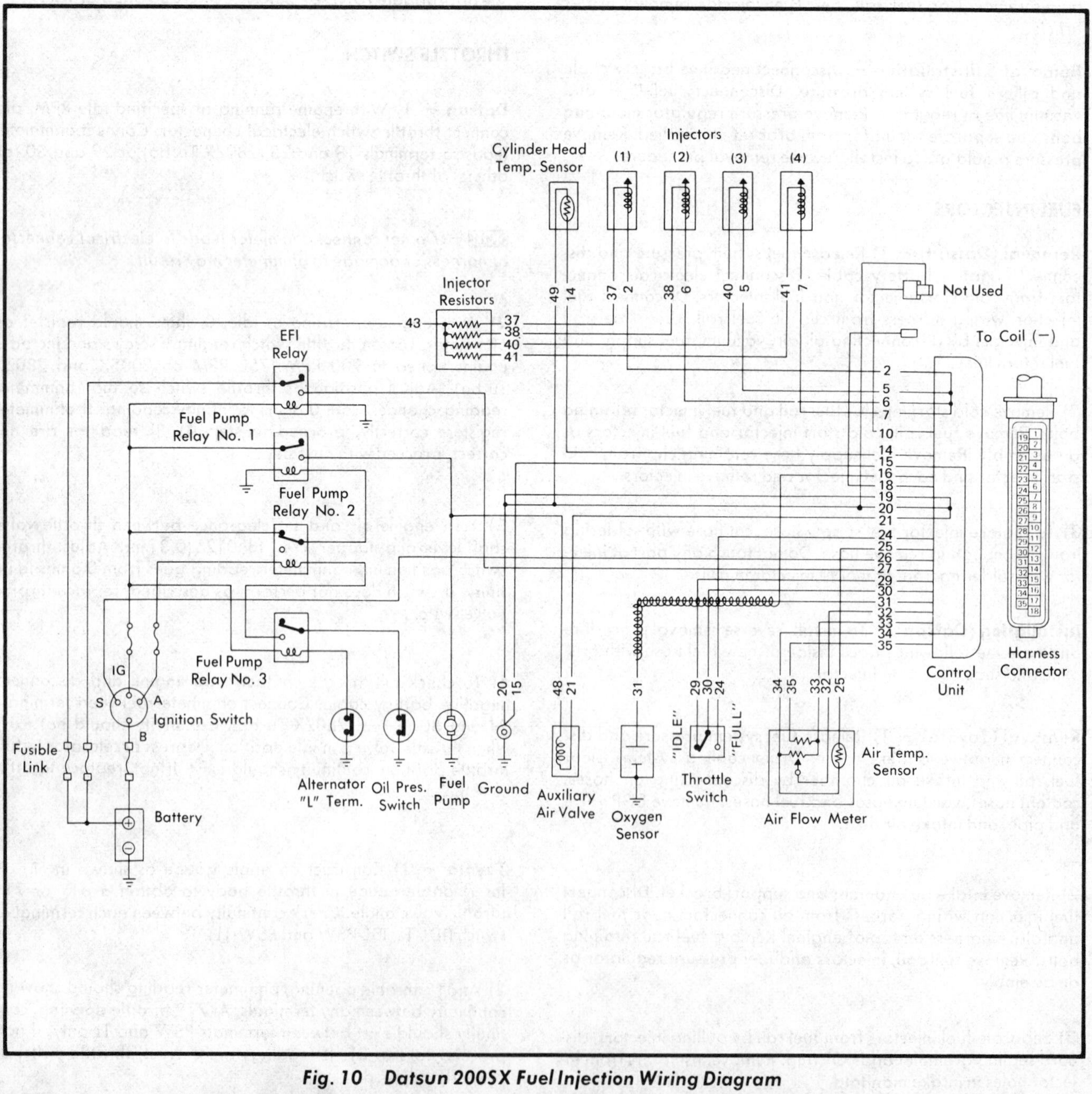

Fig. 10   Datsun 200SX Fuel Injection Wiring Diagram

BOSCH AFC FUEL INJECTION – JAPANESE MODELS (Cont.)

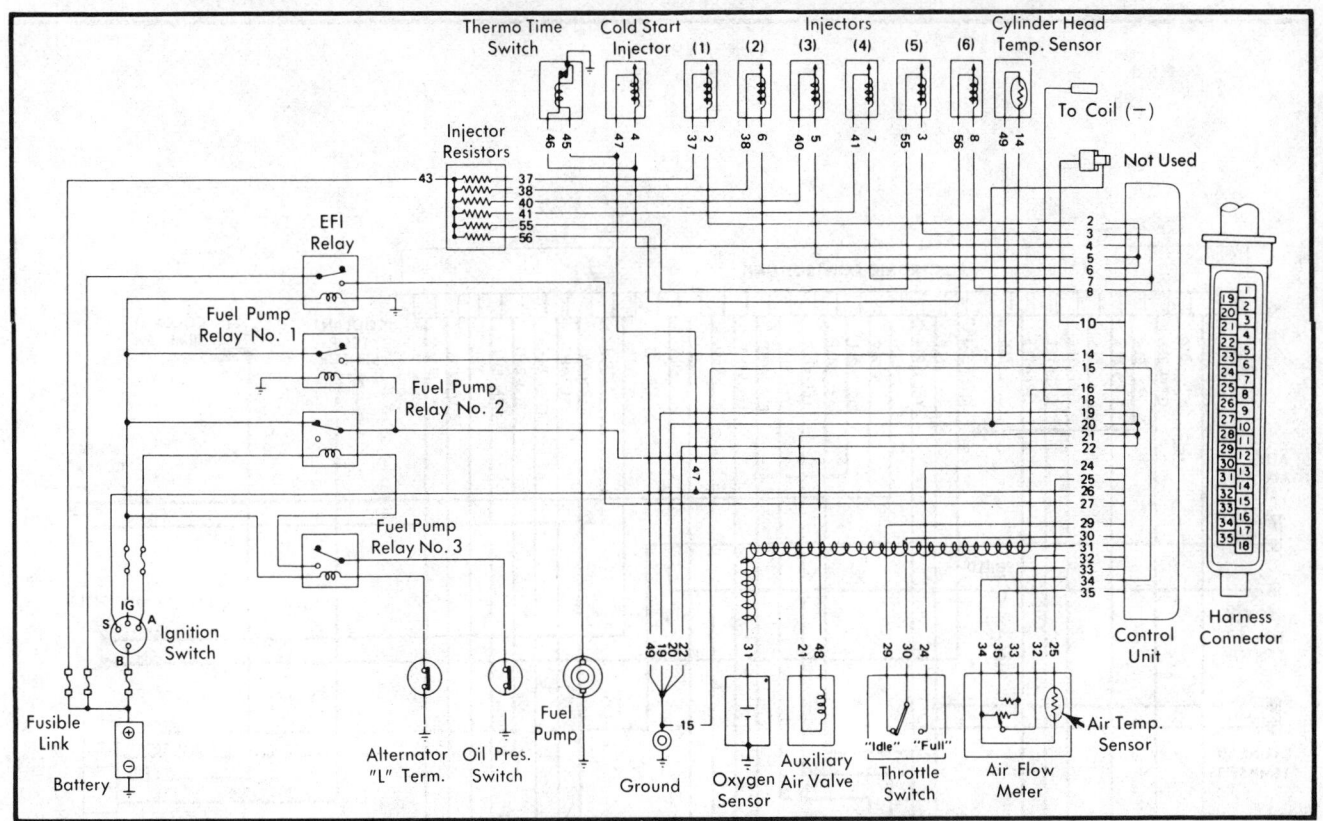

Fig. 11 Datsun 810 Fuel Injection Wiring Diagram

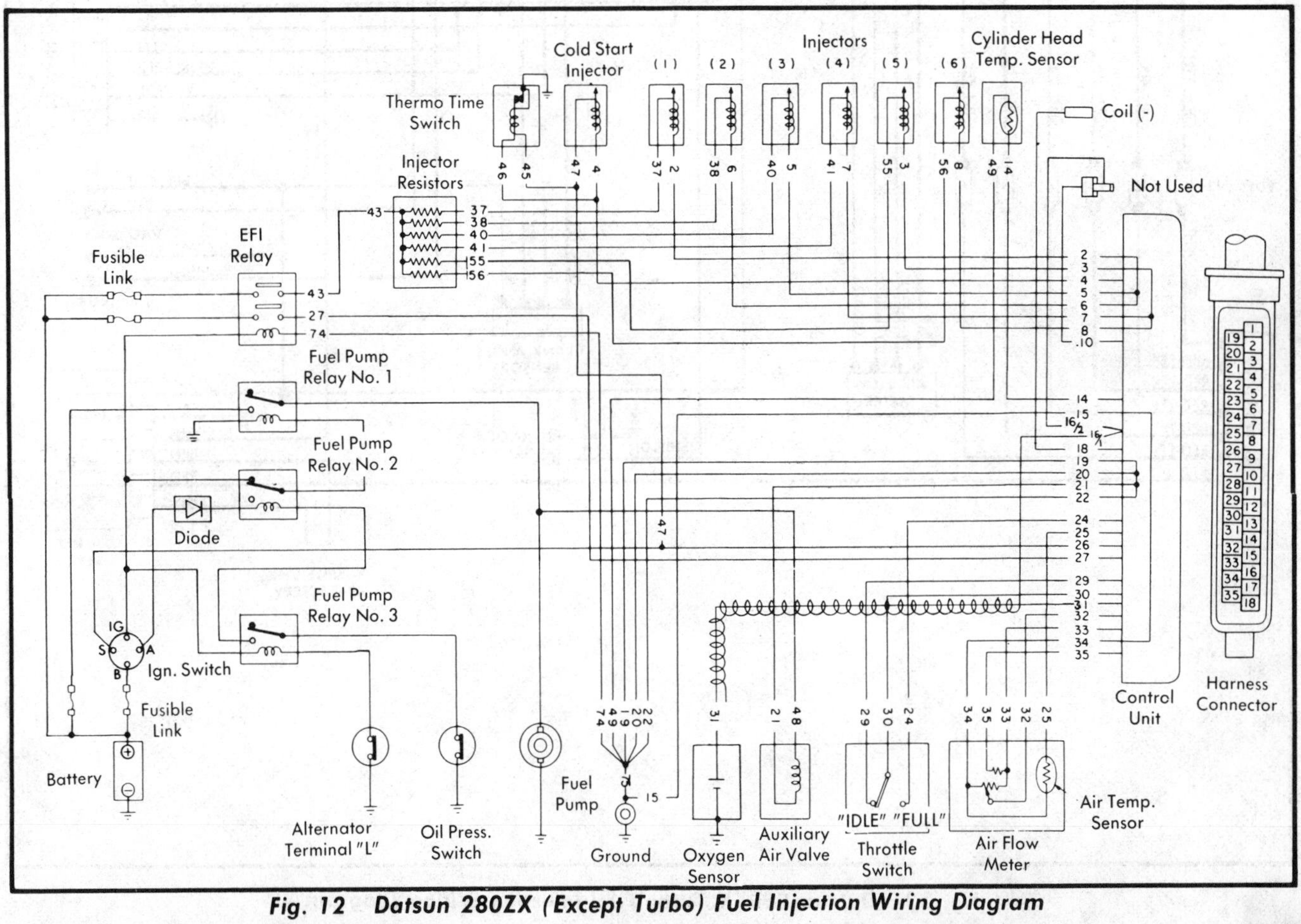

Fig. 12 Datsun 280ZX (Except Turbo) Fuel Injection Wiring Diagram

BOSCH AFC FUEL INJECTION – JAPANESE MODELS (Cont.)

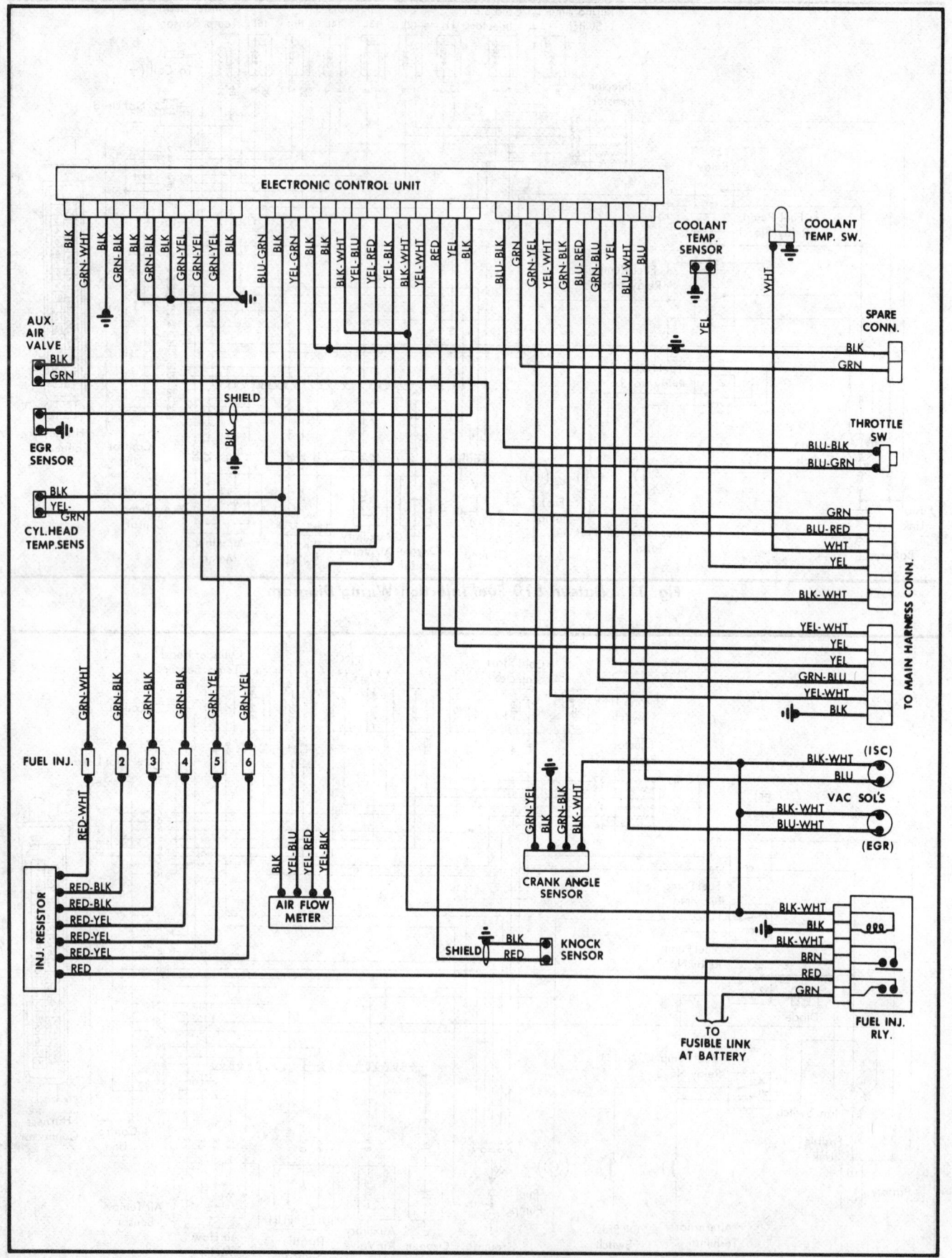

Fig. 13   Datsun 280ZX Turbo Fuel Injection Wiring Diagram

BOSCH AFC FUEL INJECTION – JAPANESE MODELS (Cont.)

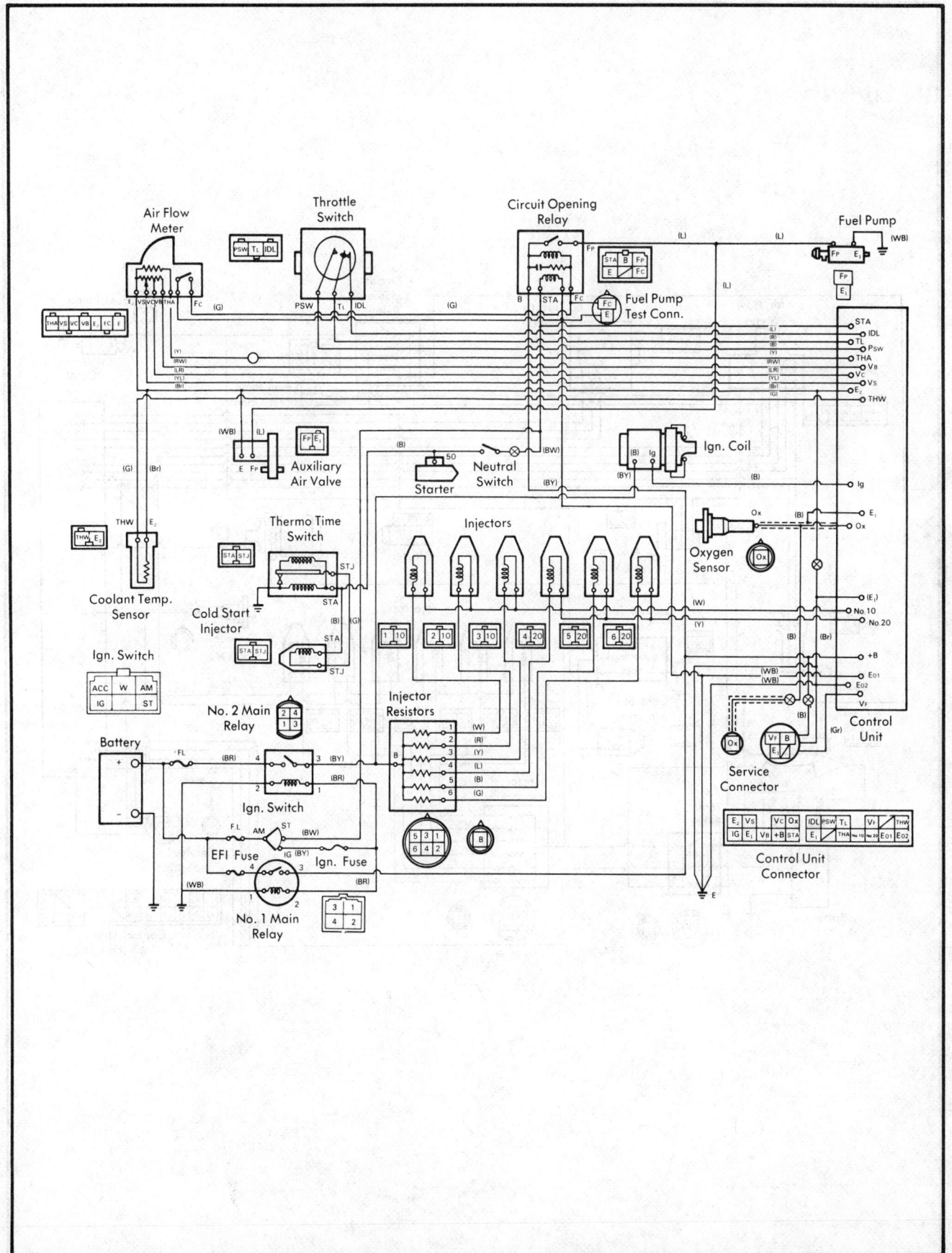

Fig. 14 Toyota Cressida Fuel Injection Wiring Diagram

BOSCH AFC FUEL INJECTION – JAPANESE MODELS (Cont.)

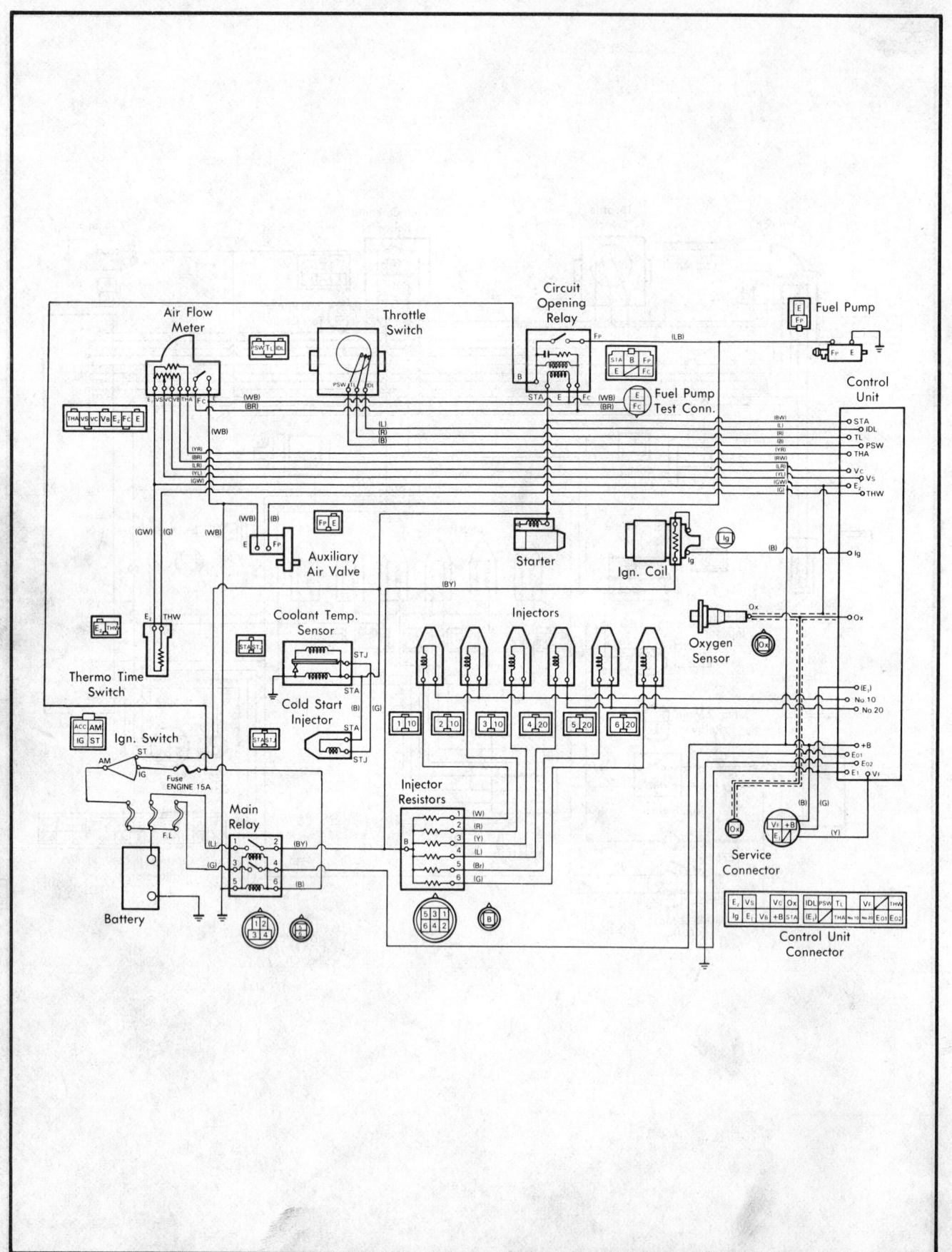

Fig. 15   *Toyota Supra Fuel Injection Wiring Diagram*

BOSCH CIS (LAMBDA) FUEL INJECTION

Audi
  4000
  5000
  5000 Turbo
BMW 320i
Mercedes-Benz
  280 Series
  380 Series
Peugeot 505
Porsche
  911SC
  924
  924 Turbo

Saab
  900
  900 Turbo
Volkswagen
  Jetta
  Rabbit
  Scirocco
  Rabbit Pickup
Volvo
  All Models

DESCRIPTION

The Bosch Continuous Injection System is a mechanical fuel injection system operated by incoming air flow. The Lambda system is a feedback control capable of measuring air/fuel ratios and correcting them constantly. The combination of the 2 systems makes it possible to obtain good economy and performance while minimizing exhaust emissions.

The system consists of the mixture control unit (air flow sensor and fuel distributor), control pressure regulator, auxiliary air valve, cold start valve, thermo-time switch, injector nozzles, fuel pump, filter, oxygen sensor, electronic control unit, frequency valve, and catalytic converter. Some models use additional components, such as a thermo-vacuum valve, hot start pulse relay, or a constant idle speed control system.

NOTE — *Rabbit Pickup Federal models use the CIS injection system without oxygen sensor, so disregard oxygen sensor information for these vehicles.*

OPERATION

MIXTURE CONTROL UNIT

The air flow sensor contains a plate mounted on a hinged lever which moves in a cone shaped venturi. All engine air is drawn through this sensor. The plate moves as air passes through, pulling the hinged lever up or down. This raises or lowers a fuel control plunger in the fuel distributor, determining the amount

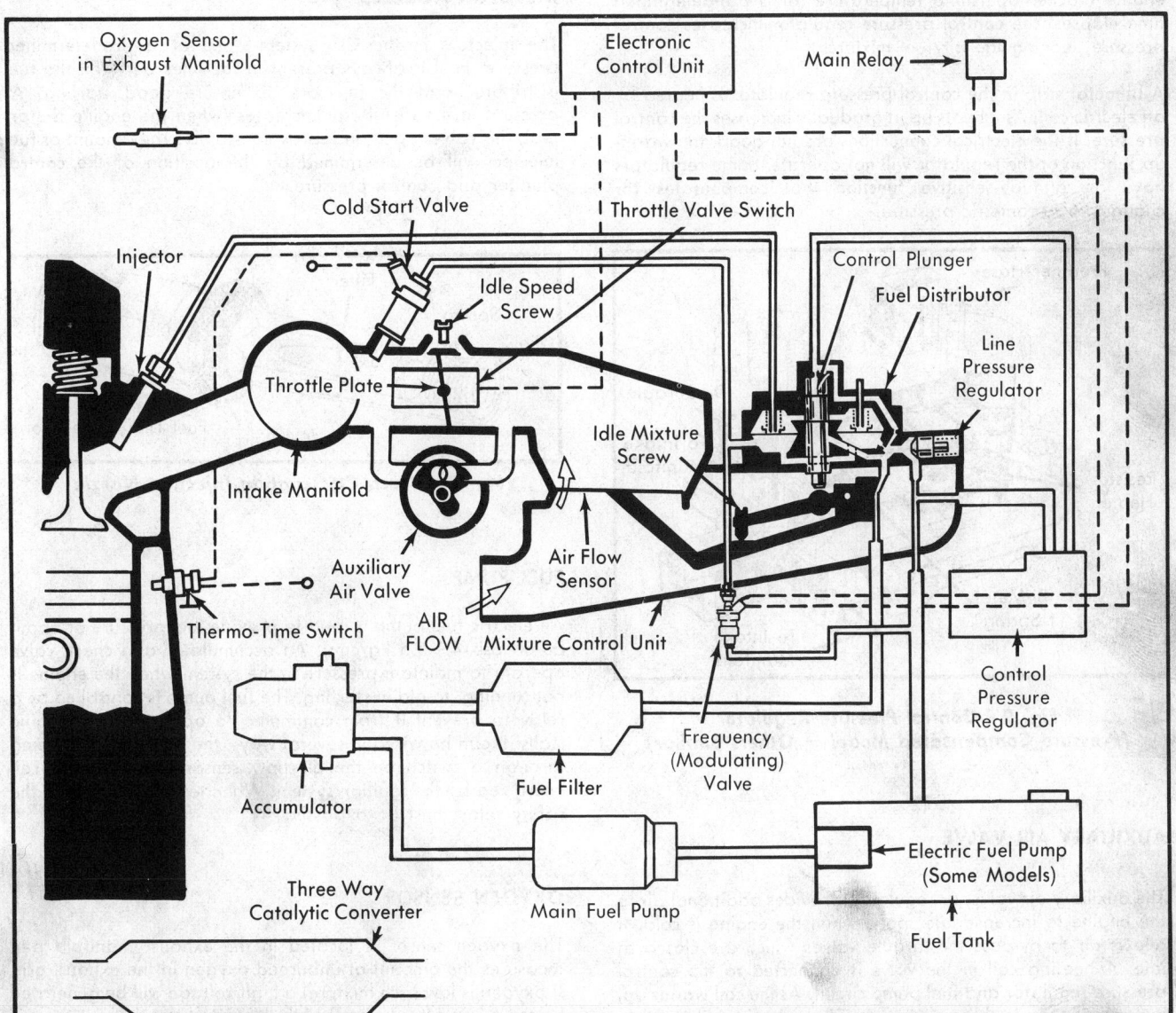

Fig. 1 Bosch CIS Lambda Fuel Injection System Diagram
(Typical of All Models — Details May Vary)

BOSCH CIS (LAMBDA) FUEL INJECTION (Cont.)

of fuel to be injected into each cylinder. The movement of the plate is controlled by air flow, cone shape of venturi, a balance weight, and fuel pressure.

NOTE — *Air flows UP through the sensor on most inline engines, and DOWN through the sensor on V6, V8, and turbocharged engines. The direction of air flow does not affect system operation, it is changed for convenience of routing air flow.*

Fuel distribution can be equal only if the pressure to each injector is equal. Pressure regulating valves in the fuel distributor equalize system pressure. These valves are adjusted during assembly of distributor and cannot be adjusted in service.

CONTROL PRESSURE REGULATOR

The control pressure regulator provides fuel pressure to the top of the plunger in the fuel distributor. Reduced pressure allows the plate to move farther with the same air flow. This supplies more fuel to the cylinders to improve warming up. As the engine reaches operating temperature (or a pre-determined time elapses) the control pressure regulator increases control pressure, leaning the air/fuel mixture.

A bi-metal strip in the control pressure regulator is heated by an electric coil. As it heats up, it gradually increases the control pressure. If the electrical connections are not good, the warm-up function of the regulator will not operate. Some regulators have an altitude-sensitive function that compensates for changes in barometric pressure.

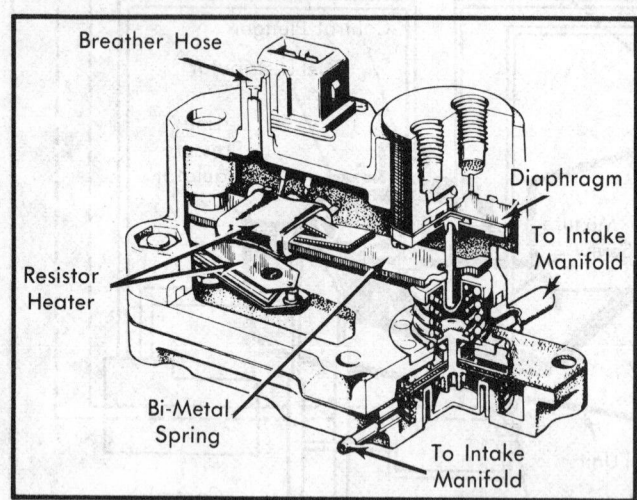

**Fig. 2   Control Pressure Regulator
(Pressure Compensated Model — Others Similar)**

AUXILIARY AIR VALVE

The auxiliary air valve, or regulator, provides additional air to the engine to increase idle speed when the engine is cold. It allows air to by-pass the throttle valves which are closed at idle. A heating coil in the valve is connected to the control pressure regulator and fuel pump circuit. As the coil warms up, it gradually closes the air passage. The valve is calibrated to keep idle smooth without a large speed change as the engine is warming up.

COLD START VALVE

The cold start valve is located in the intake manifold and sprays fuel during starting. It enrichens the mixture so the engine will start easily. The valve is powered through the starter circuit and grounded through the thermo-time switch so it operates for only a short time while the engine is being cranked.

THERMO-TIME SWITCH & HOT START RELAY

The thermo-time switch is affected by coolant or block temperature and starter current. Depending on engine temperature, the switch will take from 3-10 seconds to open. Injection through the cold start valve will then stop. Some models use a hot start pulse relay to improve hot starting. The relay will operate the cold start valve in short pulses after it would normally have been turned off by the thermo-time switch.

INJECTOR NOZZLES

The injectors in the CIS system open at a predetermined pressure. Fuel is always present in the lines between the fuel distributor and the injectors, to ensure good starting. As pressure in the distributor increases (when the engine is started), the valves open and spray constantly. The amount of fuel injected will be determined by the position of the control plunger and control pressure.

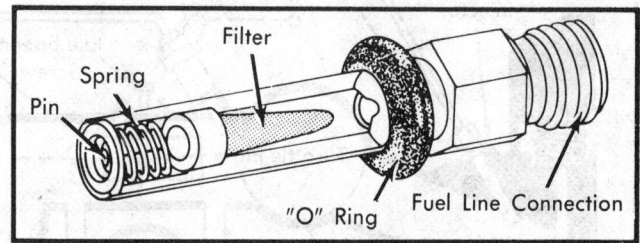

Fig. 3   Bosch CIS Lambda Injection Nozzle

FUEL PUMP

An electric fuel pump is used to provide fuel pressure of about 60-80 psi (4.1-5.5 kg/cm^2). An accumulator and check valve operate to maintain pressure in the system when the engine is not running, to aid in starting. The fuel pump is controlled by a relay to prevent it from continuing to operate if the engine stalls. It can be wired in several ways, the most common being through a switch on the air flow sensor or through a coil energized by the ignition system. When testing the system, the safety relay must be bypassed.

OXYGEN SENSOR

The oxygen sensor is located in the exhaust manifold and measures the amount of unburned oxygen in the exhaust gas. If oxygen is low (rich mixture) a high voltage will be generated by the sensor. If oxygen is high (lean mixture) the voltage will be low. The signal from the oxygen sensor goes to an electronic control unit which determines engine mixture.

BOSCH CIS (LAMBDA) FUEL INJECTION (Cont.)

ELECTRONIC CONTROL UNIT & FREQUENCY VALVE

The electronic control unit is designed to continually correct the air/fuel mixture, based on signals from the oxygen sensor. It sends a series of pulses to a frequency valve. The frequency valve is located in a fuel line that connects the upper and lower halves of the fuel distributor.

When the frequency valve is closed, fuel pressure to the injectors is determined by a spring in each pressure regulating valve. When the frequency valve is open, fuel pressure decreases in the lower half of the fuel distributor, the tension on the spring is relieved, and more fuel goes to the cylinders.

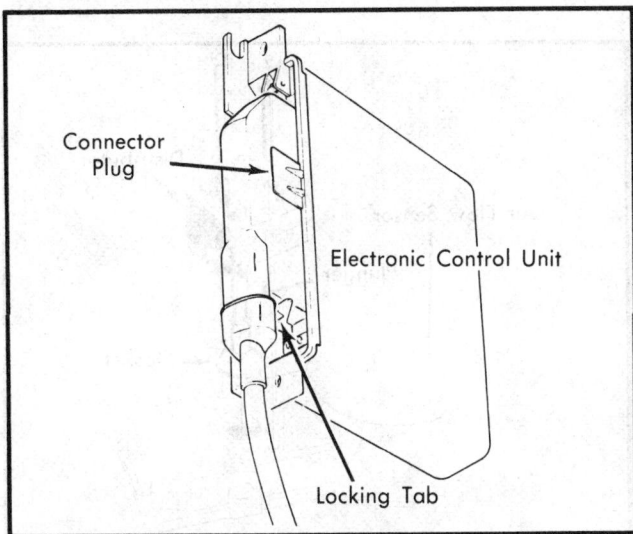

Fig. 4   Bosch CIS Lambda Electronic Control Unit

The electronic control unit opens and closes the frequency valve many times a second to ensure a smooth regulation of fuel pressure and mixture. When the engine is cold, the ratio of valve open to valve closed is about 50%. After the engine warms up, the voltage produced by the oxygen sensor determines the amount of time the frequency valve must be open or closed. This ratio can be read with a special tester or with a dwell meter (on most models). A dwell reading of 45° indicates a ratio of 50% open, 50% closed.

CATALYTIC CONVERTER

CIS Lambda systems can control air/fuel ratios within .02%. This close regulation allows the use of a 3-way catalyst that can decrease NOx, HC, and CO emissions. The converter can be damaged by improper adjustment of the system or by the use of leaded fuels.

IDLE SPEED CONTROL SYSTEMS

Mercedes-Benz Electronic Idle Speed Control — The system controls a variable air bleed into the intake system. Idle speed is held constant by increasing or decreasing the amount of extra air injected through an insulating sleeve around each fuel injector. A high idle speed is maintained when engine temperature is below 107°F (40°C), then idle speed drops to a constant low idle RPM when engine temperature is above 107°F (40°C). The idle speed control system consists of an idle speed adjuster, intake air distributor and a electronic control unit.

Volvo Electronic Idle Speed Control — System maintains a constant idle speed by varying the amount of air by-passing throttle valve. This air is controlled by the air control valve. The air control valve is operated by the electronic idle speed control unit which receives engine information from the throttle switch, coolant temperature sensor and the ignition coil.

TESTING

NOTE — *Testing procedures described below will apply to all models using the CIS Lambda system unless otherwise noted. Not all models will use all components.*

PREPARATION FOR TESTING

1) All CIS systems are very sensitive to air leaks. Check condition of rubber boots, hoses, and gaskets. Other areas of leakage are injectors, cold start valve, and PCV system (filler cap and dipstick).

2) A pressure gauge must be installed to perform fuel pressure tests. On all models, pressure gauge is installed between the control pressure regulator and the center fitting on fuel distributor.

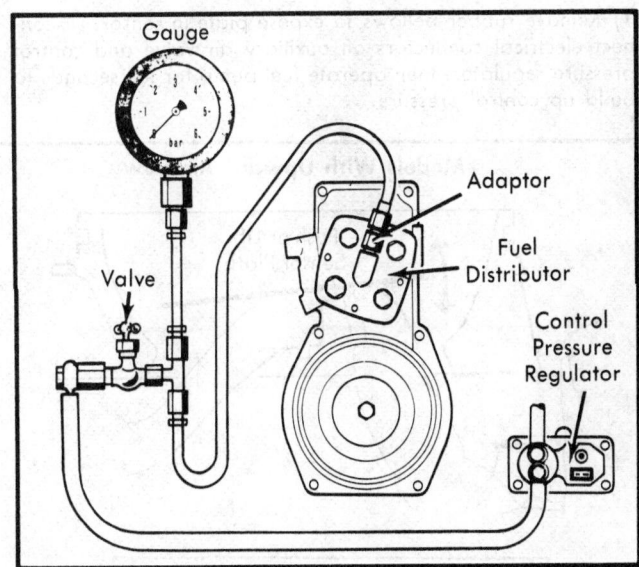

Fig. 5   Pressure Gauge Installation

3) To operate fuel pump with engine off, disconnect fuel pump relay from relay panel (VW, Porsche, Audi, Saab, Mercedes Benz). Insert a jumper wire into sockets that correspond to terminals 30 and 87 on relay. On Peugeot, remove steering wheel and lower left dash panel. Install switch and harness (8.0141 P) to tachymetric relay connector, or jumper across 30 and 87B. On Volvo, Mercedes-Benz, and other models so equipped, disconnect safety switch connector on air flow sensor.

BOSCH CIS (LAMBDA) FUEL INJECTION (Cont.)

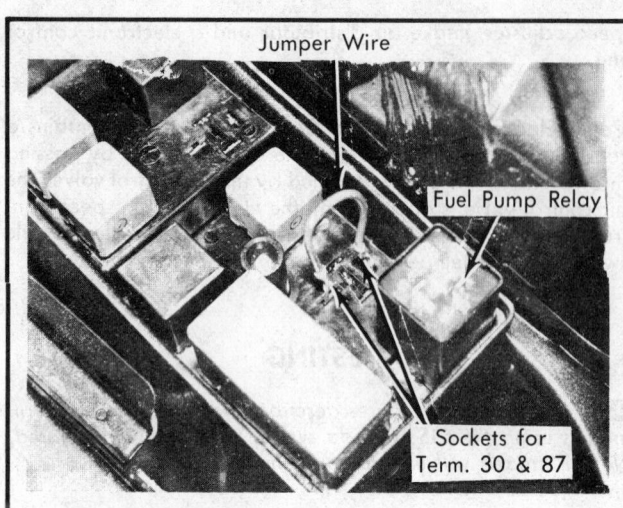

Fig. 6   Fuel Pump Jumper Wire For Testing (Saab Shown, Others Similar)

4) Operate fuel pump on Peugeot by depressing switch on harness. On all other models, turn ignition on. Place pressure gauge as low as possible in engine compartment, then open and close valve 5 times to bleed gauge. Place valve in open position and hang in convenient location. Turn pump off.

AIR/FUEL MIXTURE CONTROL (AIR FLOW SENSOR)

1) Remove rubber bellows to expose plate in sensor. Disconnect electrical connectors on auxiliary air valve and control pressure regulator, then operate fuel pump for ten seconds to build up control pressure.

NOTE — Directions given for moving sensor plate apply to engines where sensor plate moves UP with air flow. Reverse directions if servicing an engine where air flow moves DOWN.

2) Lift sensor plate slowly with magnet or pliers. Resistance due to control pressure should be constant throughout range of plate. Release plate slowly, lever and control piston should follow.

3) Lift plate, then return it rapidly to lower position. The piston moves more slowly and should be heard hitting the lever. If not, control piston is sticking. Remove 3 screws from fuel distributor and lift off of air flow sensor housing. Be careful not to drop control piston.

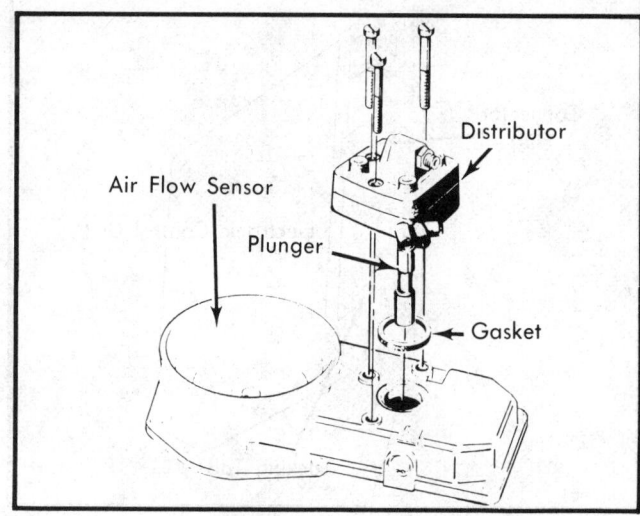

Fig. 8   Checking Fuel Distributor Plunger

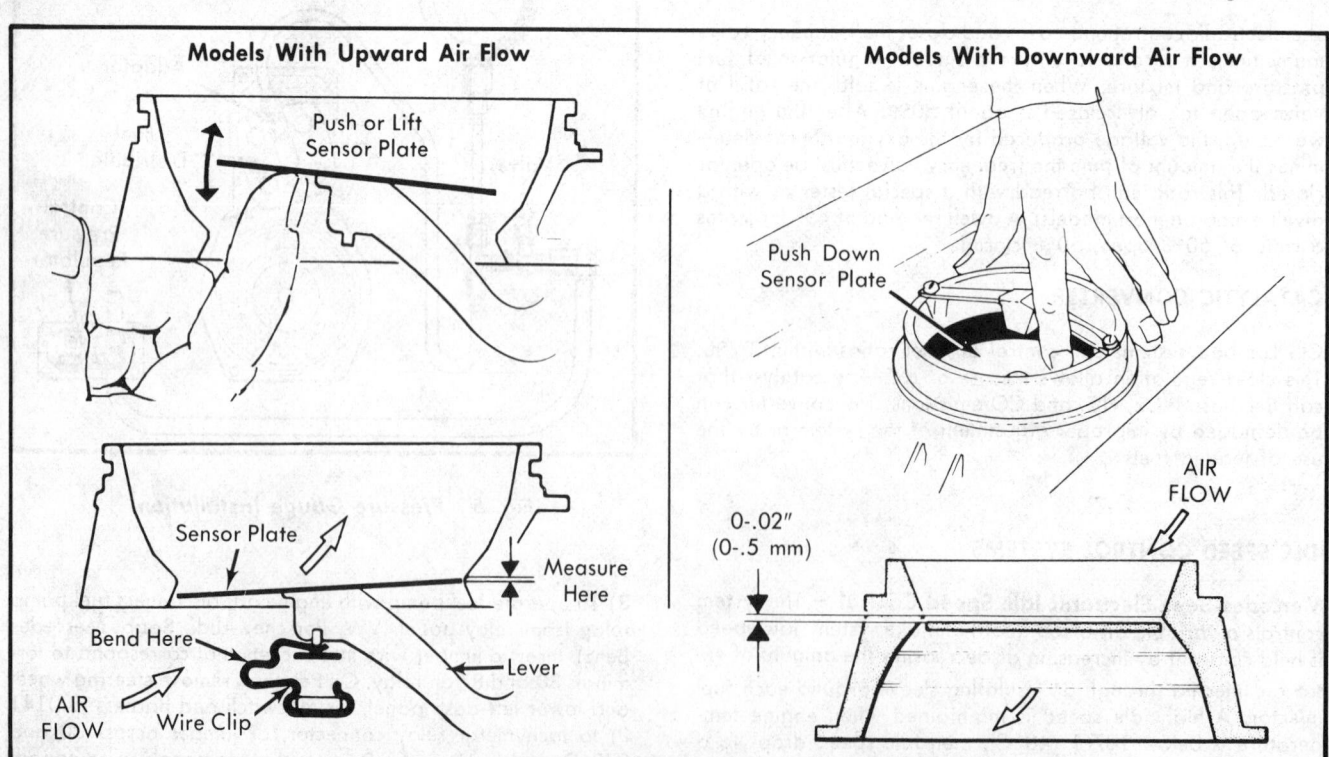

Fig. 7   Checking Air Flow Sensor Operation and Alignment

BOSCH CIS (LAMBDA) FUEL INJECTION (Cont.)

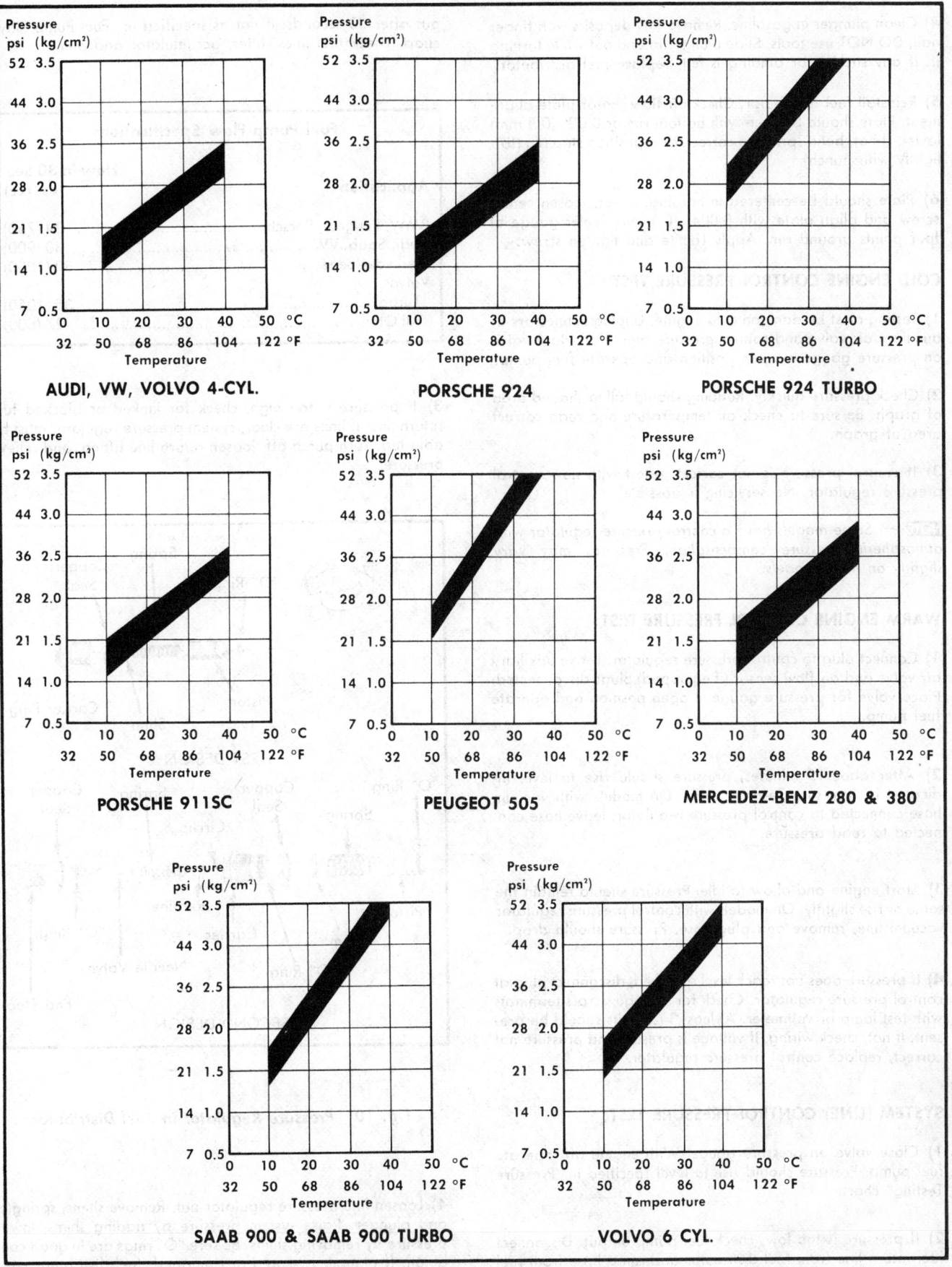

Fig. 9   Cold Engine Control Pressure Test Graphs

BOSCH CIS (LAMBDA) FUEL INJECTION (Cont.)

4) Clean plunger in gasoline. Remove any deposits with finger nail; DO NOT use tools. Slide plunger in and out while turning it. If any sticking or binding is felt, replace fuel distributor.

5) Reinstall fuel distributor. Check air flow sensor plate alignment. Plate should be even with bottom rim or 0.02" (0.5 mm) lower. If not, bend spring to correct, or reposition stop pin (tap lightly with punch).

6) Plate should be centered in housing. If not, loosen center screw and align plate with 0.004" (0.1 mm) feeler gauge at four points around rim. Apply Loctite and tighten screw.

COLD ENGINE CONTROL PRESSURE TEST

1) Testing must be done on cold engine. Unplug connectors at auxiliary air valve and control pressure regulator. Place valve on pressure gauge in open position and operate fuel pump.

2) Check pressure quickly. Reading should fall in shaded area of graph. Be sure to check air temperature and read correct area of graph.

3) If control pressure is not correct, retest with new control pressure regulator. No servicing is possible.

NOTE — *Some models have a control pressure regulator with atmospheric pressure compensation. Pressures may vary slightly on these models.*

WARM ENGINE CONTROL PRESSURE TEST

1) Connect plug to control pressure regulator. Leave auxiliary air valve and air flow sensor (if equipped) plugs disconnected. Place valve for pressure gauge in open position and operate fuel pump.

2) After about 5 minutes, pressure should rise to level indicated in "Pressure Testing" chart. On models with vacuum hose connected to control pressure regulator, leave hose connected to read pressure.

3) Start engine and allow to idle. Pressure should remain the same or rise slightly. On models with control pressure regulator vacuum line, remove and plug hose. Pressure should drop.

4) If pressure does not reach level specified, disconnect plug at control pressure regulator. Check for voltage across terminals with test lamp or voltmeter. At least 11.5 volts should be present. If not, check wiring. If voltage is present and pressure not correct, replace control pressure regulator.

SYSTEM (LINE) CONTROL PRESSURE TEST

1) Close valve on pressure gauge. With engine off, operate fuel pump. Pressure should rise to level specified in "Pressure Testing" chart.

2) If pressure is too low, check fuel pump output. Disconnect fuel return line from fuel distributor and run a hose from fuel distributor to container. Operate fuel pump and measure out-

put after 30 seconds. If not as specified in "Fuel Pump Flow" chart, check fuel lines, filter, accumulator and pump.

Fuel Pump Flow Specifications	
Application	**Flow in 30 Sec. oz. (cc)**
BMW, Peugeot, Porsche	24 (750)
Audi, Saab, VW	30 (900)
Mercedes-Benz	32 (1000)
Volvo	
Turbo	35 (1050)
All Others	27 (800)

3) If pressure is too high, check for kinked or blocked fuel return line. If lines are clear, system pressure regulator must be adjusted. Turn pump off, loosen return line fitting, and relieve pressure.

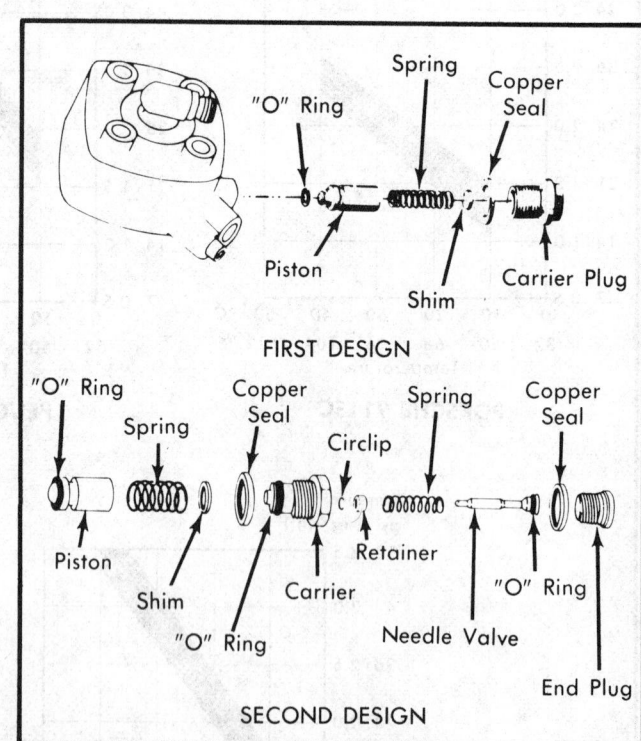

Fig. 10   Pressure Regulator in Fuel Distributor

4) Loosen line pressure regulator nut. Remove shims, spring(s) and plunger. Raise system pressure by adding shims; lower pressure by removing shims. Be sure "O" rings are in good condition. If plunger is scored or damaged, fuel distributor must be replaced.

BOSCH CIS (LAMBDA) FUEL INJECTION (Cont.)

REST PRESSURE & LEAK TEST

1) After correct warm engine control pressure has been obtained, stop fuel pump and note pressure drop. Valve should be in open position. Minimum pressure after 20 minutes must be as specified in "Pressure Testing" chart.

2) If pressure drops too rapidly, run pump again and close valve. Stop pump and observe pressure. If values are now correct, control pressure regulator is faulty and must be replaced.

3) If pressure still drops, check all connections, fuel pump check valve, cold start valve, and fuel injectors.

COLD START VALVE, THERMO-TIME SWITCH & HOT START PULSE RELAY

1) If engine coolant is below 85°F (30°C), disconnect plug on cold start valve and connect test lamp across terminals. Remove coil high tension wire to prevent starting. Operate starter.

2) On models without hot start pulse relay, test lamp will light for several seconds, then go out. On models with relay, lamp will continue to flash off and on.

3) If lamp does not light, test thermo-time switch for continuity below opening temperature. If good, check wiring to starter terminal.

4) Remove cold start valve from manifold but leave fuel line connected. Place valve in a container. Connect a jumper wire from one terminal to ground, and from other terminal of cold start valve to a switch. The other side of switch should be connected to battery voltage.

CAUTION — *Do not connect wire directly to battery. Extreme fire danger is present due to atomized fuel. Sparks may result if wire is touched to battery.*

5) Operate fuel pump. Turn switch to "ON" position. Cold start injector should spray. Turn switch "OFF", but leave fuel

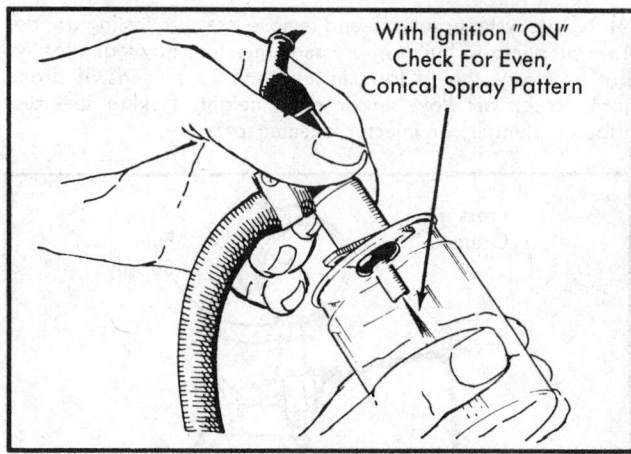

With Ignition "ON"
Check For Even,
Conical Spray Pattern

Fig. 11   Testing Cold Start Injector Valve

pump running. Injector should not spray. Wipe off nozzle and check for leakage. With pump running, no drops should form within one minute.

6) Replace cold start valve if faulty. Reinstall original valve if good, making sure that "O" ring is properly positioned.

FUEL INJECTORS

1) Remove injectors but leave hoses connected. Place injectors in individual measuring containers. Operate fuel pump to build up pressure, then turn pump off.

2) Lift air flow sensor plate half-way to operate injectors until one container has filled to 3.4 oz. (100 cc). Other container volume should not vary more than 10-20°.

3) If one injector is outside specifications, swap hoses from it and one good injector at fuel distributor and retest. If same container is low, injector is faulty. If other container is low, fuel distributor must be replaced.

FUEL INJECTION PRESSURE TESTING

Application	Line Pressure psi (kg/cm²)	Warm Control Pressure psi (kg/cm²)	Rest Pressure psi (kg/cm²)	Nozzle Opening Pressure psi (kg/cm²)
Audi 5000 Turbo	72-81 (5.0-5.6)	49-55 (3.4-3.8)①	23-37 (1.6-2.6)	38-53 (2.7-3.7)
Audi 4000, 5000	64-74 (4.5-5.2)	49-55 (3.4-3.8)	23-37 (1.6-2.6)	41-59 (2.9-4.1)
BMW 320i	64-75 (4.5-5.2)	49-55 (3.4-3.8)	24 (1.7)	44 (3.1)
Mercedes-Benz	72-81 (5.0-5.6)	49-55 (3.4-3.8)①	36-41 (2.5-2.8)	43 (3.0)
Peugeot 505	64-75 (4.5-5.2)	49-55 (3.4-3.8)	38-39 (2.6-2.7)	43-59 (3.0-4.1)
Porsche 911SC	64-75 (4.5-5.2)	49-55 (3.4-3.8)	②	36-52 (2.5-3.6)
Porsche 924	64-75 (4.5-5.2)	49-55 (3.4-3.8)	21-24 (1.5-1.7)	36-52 (2.5-3.6)
Porsche 924 Turbo	78-87 (5.4-6.0)	49-55 (3.4-3.8)③	14 (1.0)	38-55 (2.7-3.8)
Saab	64-75 (4.5-5.2)	49-55 (3.4-3.8)	24-34 (1.7-2.4)	43-55 (3.0-3.8)
Volkswagen	68-78 (4.8-5.5)	49-55 (3.4-3.8)	35-38 (2.4-2.6)	46-55 (3.2-3.8)
Volvo 4 Cyl.	64-75 (4.5-5.2)	50-56 (3.5-3.9)	24-34 (1.7-2.4)	37-51 (2.6-3.6)
Volvo 6 Cyl.	64-75 (4.5-5.2)	45-49 (3.1-3.4)	24 (1.7)	37-51 (2.6-3.6)

① — Vacuum lines connected.
② — Information not available from manufacturer.
③ — No Vacuum applied.

BOSCH CIS (LAMBDA) FUEL INJECTION (Cont.)

4) Relieve system pressure and remove pressure testing gauge. Turn on pump to build up pressure. Injectors may leak slightly, but no drops should form in less than 15 seconds. If drops form, check air flow sensor plate height, sticking fuel distributor plunger, or injector opening pressure.

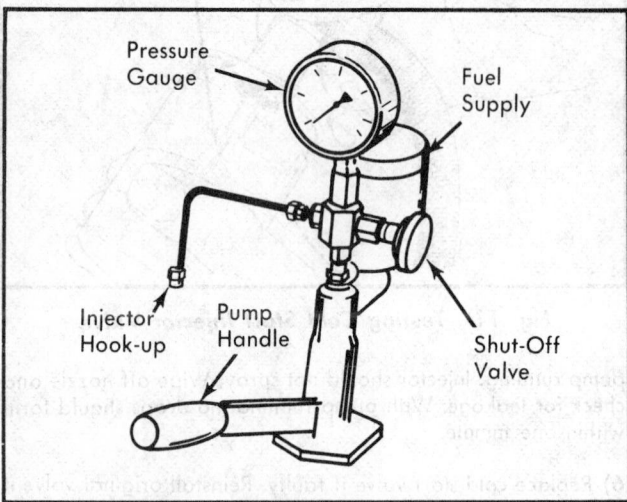

Fig. 12   Fuel Injector Tester

5) Remove injectors from vehicle and use injector tester to determine opening pressure. Check specifications in "Pressure Testing" chart and replace injectors if faulty.

AUXILIARY AIR VALVE

1) Disconnect hoses from auxiliary air valve. Shine a light through valve. At room temperature, valve should be slightly open. Turn ignition "ON" (disconnect wires from air flow sensor, if equipped) and see that opening is closed in less than 5 minutes. Tap valve slightly to assist in closing.

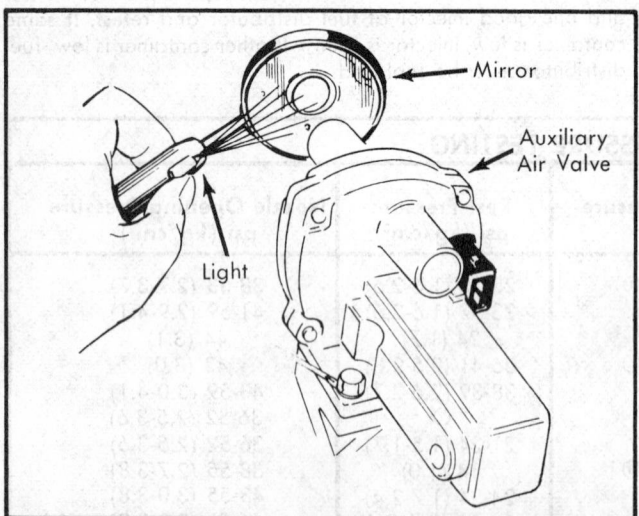

Fig. 13   Checking Auxiliary Air Valve Operation

2) If valve does not operate properly, check for power at connector with engine running. Connect a test lamp across connector terminals. If lamp does not light, check fuse and wiring. If

lamp lights, check resistance of auxiliary air valve. If no resistance is measured, valve is bad. If resistance is measured, clean terminals and make sure connection is good.

LAMBDA CONTROL SYSTEM CHECKS

PREPARATION FOR CHECKS

NOTE — *The frequency valve is operated by a pulsating voltage from the electronic control unit. By measuring this signal, certain functions of the system can be tested. A special tester (Bosch KDJE 7453) is recommended, but a high quality dwell meter may be used instead. A voltmeter is used for Mercedes-Benz.*

1) Connect dwell meter to testing connector. Connector is located on left side near windshield washer container on Peugeot, beside brake booster on Volvo, and to left of fuse and relay panel on Saab. Connector is behind throttle valve housing on Volkswagen and Audi. Set meter on 4-cyl. scale.

2) On Mercedes-Benz, remove cap from diagnostic plug connector (rear of left fender panel). Connect positive lead of voltmeter to battery and negative lead to pin 3 of diagnostic plug. Start engine and run until warm. Disconnect oxygen sensor and observe needle (should not fluctuate). Place a piece of tape on meter face to indicate 50% position.

OPERATION CHECK

1) Remove fuel pump relay and connect jumper wire across sockets corresponding to terminals 30 and 87. If equipped, remove plug at air flow sensor. Turn ignition "ON".

2) Frequency valve should operate, making a buzzing noise. Dwell meter should indicate 45-65°. Disconnect wire from oxygen sensor and touch wire end to ground. Readings on dwell meter should rise. Ground one end of a 1.5 volt flashlight battery, and touch positive end to sensor wire. Readings should drop to less than 15°.

3) On models with throttle enrichment switch, operate throttle. Readings should be higher at idle or wide open throttle. *See wiring diagram for enrichment switches used.*

4) If engine is cold, enrichment switches will be closed. Disconnect lead at temperature sender. Readings should drop slightly. If engine is hot, connect temperature sender lead to ground. Reading should rise. *See wiring diagram for enrichment switches used.*

5) If starter enrichment relay is used, disconnect high tension lead at coil and crank engine. Readings should rise above normal level. If vacuum switches are used, apply vacuum to switch and note readings. Level should be higher with switch closed, and lower with switch open.

6) Connect oxygen sensor and start engine. With cold engine, dwell reading should be stable. When engine warms up, meter needle should fluctuate 10-20°. It may be necessary to run engine faster than idle to heat oxygen sensor and cause needle fluctuation.

BOSCH CIS (LAMBDA) FUEL INJECTION (Cont.)

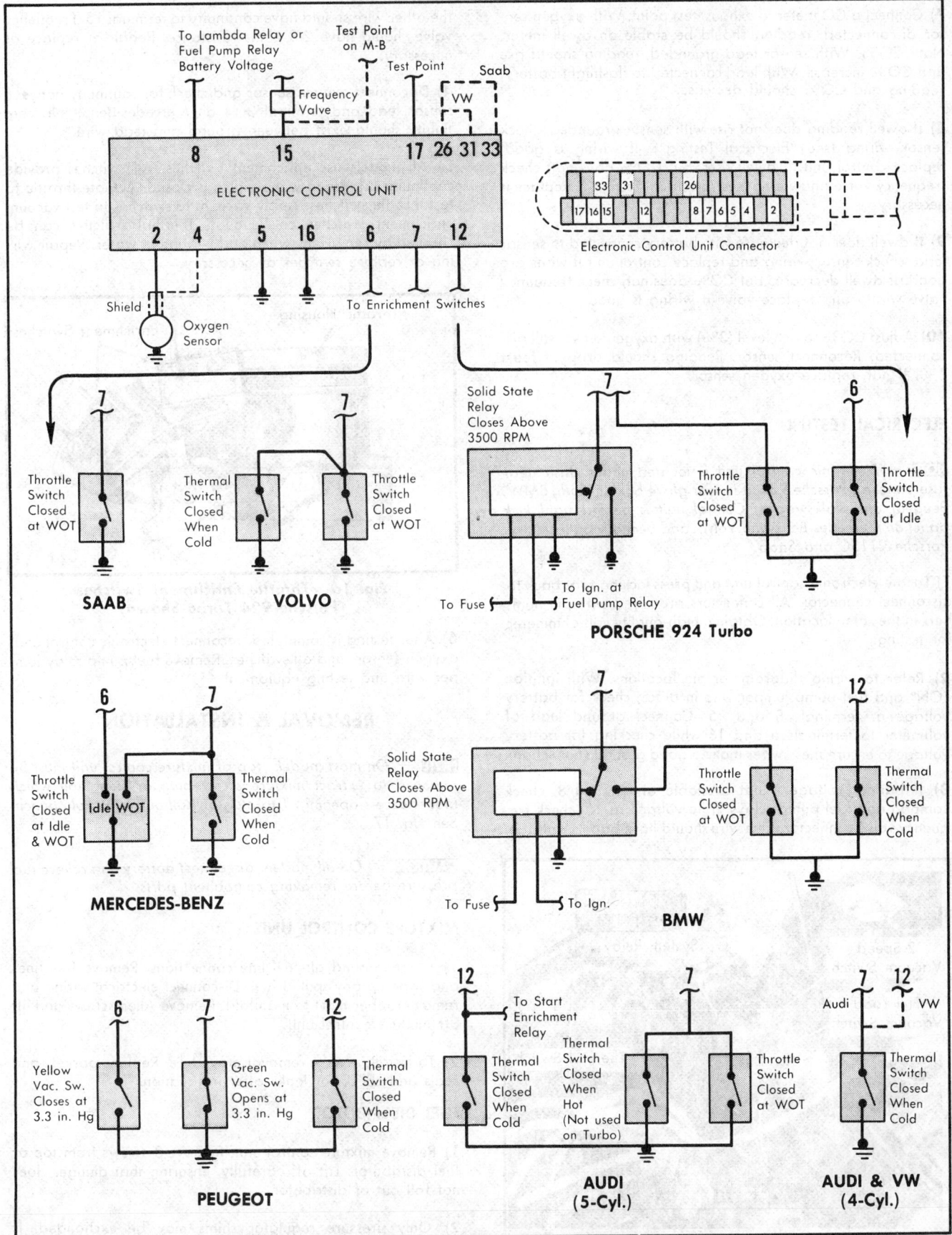

Fig. 14   Bosch CIS Lambda Electronic Control Unit Wiring Diagram

BOSCH CIS (LAMBDA) FUEL INJECTION (Cont.)

7) Connect a CO meter to exhaust test point. With oxygen sensor disconnected, reading should be stable on dwell meter. Note CO%. With sensor lead grounded, reading should rise and CO% increase. With lead connected to flashlight battery, reading and CO% should decrease.

8) If dwell reading does not rise with sensor grounded, check sensor wiring (see "Electrical Testing"). If wiring is good, replace control unit. If dwell rises, but CO% does not, check frequency valve and wiring (see "Electrical Testing"). Replace if necessary.

9) If dwell does not decrease with battery connected to sensor lead, check sensor wiring and replace control unit if wires are good. If dwell decreases but CO% does not, check frequency valve wiring and replace valve if wiring is good.

10) Adjust CO% to rich level (3%) with oxygen sensor still disconnected. Reconnect sensor. Reading should drop at least 1%. If not, replace oxygen sensor.

ELECTRICAL TESTING

NOTE — *Electronic control unit is located under dash near fuse panel on Porsche 924. It is near glove box on Audi, BMW, Peugeot and Volkswagen. Control unit is behind right kick panel on Mercedes-Benz and Volvo, and beneath right seat on Porsche 911SC and Saab.*

1) Locate electronic control unit and press locking tabs back to disconnect connector. All connectors are wired with pin numbers in the same location. Obtain a high-quality volt-ohmmeter for testing.

2) Refer to wiring diagram for pin locations. With ignition "ON" and fuel pump jumper wire in place, check for battery voltage at terminals 8 and 15. Connect ground lead of voltmeter to terminals 5 and 16 while checking for battery voltage to ensure these wires make a good ground connection.

3) If battery voltage is not available at terminal 8, check Lambda and fuel pump relays. If no voltage at 15, check frequency valve connector. One wire should have battery voltage;

the other wire should have continuity to terminal 15. Frequency valve should have 2-3 ohms resistance. Repair or replace as necessary.

4) Disconnect oxygen sensor and check for continuity between sensor lead and terminal 2 (4 on Mercedes-Benz). No continuity should exist between ground and lead wire.

5) All models use enrichment switches. All switches provide continuity to ground when switch is closed. Actuate throttle to test throttle switches. Apply vacuum to switches to test vacuum enrichment switches on Peugeot. Thermal switches can be checked by removing switch and heating in water. Repair wiring or replace switches as necessary.

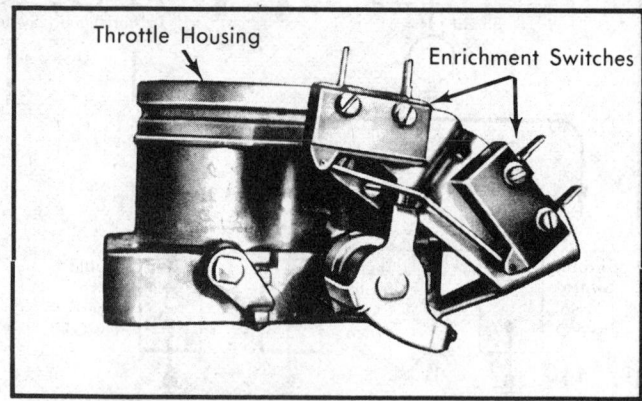

**Fig. 16   Throttle Enrichment Switches
(Porsche 924 Turbo Shown)**

6) After testing is completed, reconnect electronic control unit, oxygen sensor, and all switches. Remove fuel pump relay jumper wire and testing equipment.

REMOVAL & INSTALLATION

NOTE — *On most models, top of mixture control unit must be removed to extract mixture screw plug or steel ball which blocks access opening. Tap plug or ball out with a pin punch. See Fig. 17.*

CAUTION — *On all models, disconnect battery and relieve fuel pressure before removing component parts.*

MIXTURE CONTROL UNIT

1) Clean around all fuel line connections. Remove fuel lines and wipe up any spilled fuel. Disconnect electrical wiring and remove rubber boot to manifold. Remove Allen screws and lift off mixture control unit.

2) To install, reverse removal procedure. Replace gaskets and seals and check for leaks after installation.

FUEL DISTRIBUTOR

1) Remove mixture control unit. Remove 3 screws from top of fuel distributor. Lift off carefully, ensuring that plunger does not fall out of distributor.

2) Only pressure regulator shims may be exchanged. If plunger or piston is scored, replace fuel distributor. Be sure "O" ring is in place and in good condition when replacing unit.

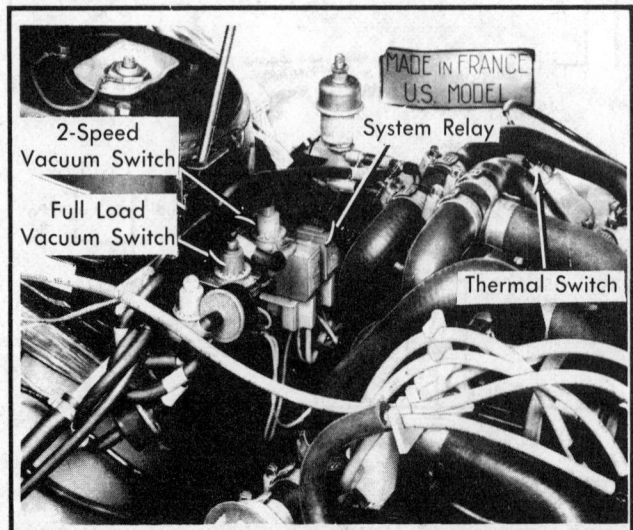

Fig. 15   Peugeot Enrichment Vacuum Switches

BOSCH CIS (LAMBDA) FUEL INJECTION (Cont.)

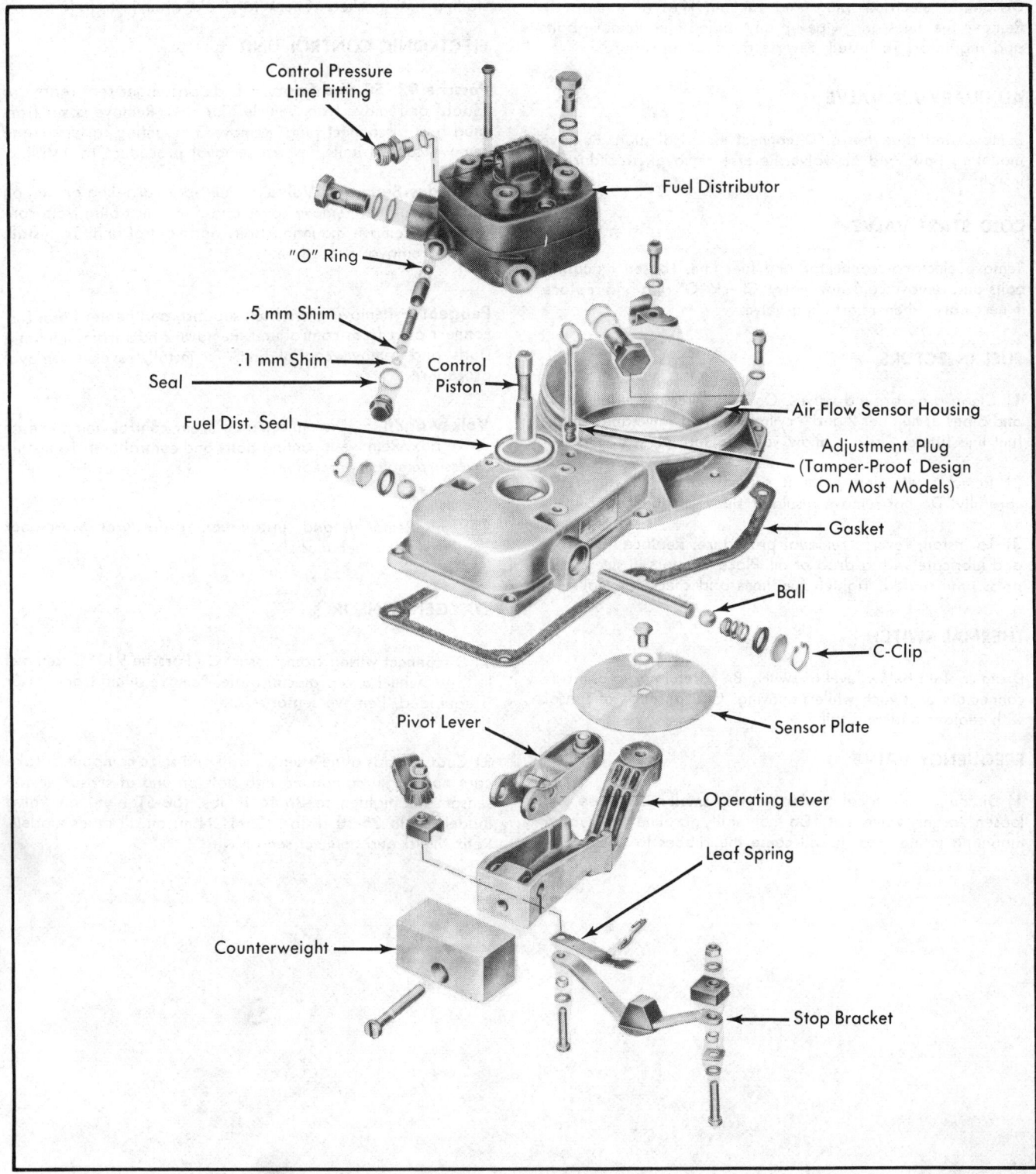

Control Pressure
Line Fitting

Fuel Distributor

"O" Ring

.5 mm Shim

.1 mm Shim

Seal

Control
Piston

Fuel Dist. Seal

Air Flow Sensor Housing

Adjustment Plug
(Tamper-Proof Design
On Most Models)

Gasket

Ball

C-Clip

Sensor Plate

Pivot Lever

Operating Lever

Leaf Spring

Counterweight

Stop Bracket

Fig. 17   Exploded View of Mixture Control Unit for Porsche 924 Model

BOSCH CIS (LAMBDA) FUEL INJECTION (Cont.)

CONTROL PRESSURE REGULATOR

Disconnect electrical plug and vacuum lines (if equipped). Remove fuel lines and wipe up any spilled fuel. Remove bolts and regulator. To install, reverse removal procedure.

AUXILIARY AIR VALVE

Remove and plug hoses. Disconnect electrical plug. Remove mounting bolts and air valve. Reverse removal procedure to install.

COLD START VALVE

Remove electrical connector and fuel line. Loosen mounting bolts and remove cold start valve. Check "O" ring and replace if necessary when reinstalling valve.

FUEL INJECTORS

1) Clean area around valves. On BMW, remove intake cowl and pipes at number 2 and 3 cylinders. Hold valve and remove fuel line fitting. Do not allow valve to turn.

2) Remove retaining plate if present, and pull valves out carefully. Do not remove insulator sleeve if possible.

3) To install, reverse removal procedure. Replace "O" rings and lubricate with a drop of oil. Place injectors in sleeve and press until seated. Tighten fuel lines and check for leaks.

THERMAL SWITCH

Drain coolant below level of switch. Be careful not to damage connectors on switch while removing. Coat threads of sensor with sealant and reinstall.

FREQUENCY VALVE

1) Disconnect electrical connector. Hold small nut at hose and loosen larger valve nut. Do not spill gasoline on rubber mounting insulator as it will cause the rubber to swell.

2) Remove return lines at fuel distributor and/or control pressure regulator. To install, reverse removal procedure, installing new gaskets. Check for leaks after installation.

ELECTRONIC CONTROL UNIT

Porsche 911SC and Saab — Slide passenger seat rearward (Saab) or remove from vehicle (Porsche). Remove cover from plug and disconnect plug. Remove 3 mounting fasteners and remove control unit. Reverse removal procedure to install.

Mercedes-Benz and Volvo — Pull back carpeting or trim on right kick panel. Remove cover and disconnect plug from control unit. Remove mounting bolts and control unit. To install, reverse removal procedure.

Peugeot — Remove glove box, support, and heater hose. Disconnect plug from control unit. Remove 2 nuts from mounting studs and remove control unit. To install, reverse removal procedure.

Volkswagen — Disconnect plug from control unit beneath glove box. Remove mounting bolts and control unit. To install, reverse removal procedure.

NOTE — *Removal and installation procedures were not available for other models.*

OXYGEN SENSOR

1) Disconnect wiring from sensor. On Porsche 911SC, remove left rear wheel and protector plate. Remove shield from sensor if equipped. Remove sensor.

2) Coat threads of new sensor with anti-seize compound. Take care not to get compound into slots on end of sensor. Install sensor and tighten to 36-44 ft. lbs. (50-61 N·m) on Volvo models or to 25-30 ft. lbs. (35-41 N·m) on all other models. Refit shield and connect sensor wire.

LUCAS-BOSCH AFC FUEL INJECTION SYSTEM

Jaguar
XJ6L
Triumph
TR7
TR8

NOTE — *The Lucas-Bosch AFC Fuel Injection system is used on all models. Variations may exist between model applications with the addition of auxiliary control systems. This article covers the Lucas-Bosch AFC system in general, with manufacturer's differences noted.*

DESCRIPTION

The Lucas-Bosch Air Flow Controlled (AFC) fuel injection system is an electronically controlled system operated by incoming air flow. The AFC fuel injection system also contains a feedback system which measures oxygen content of exhaust gases and maintains the air/fuel ratio at about 14.7:1. The system consists of an electric fuel pump, fuel pressure regulator, fuel injectors, Electronic Control Unit (ECU), air flow meter, air temperature sensor, throttle switch, coolant temperature sensor, oxygen sensor (2 on TR8), 3-way catalytic converter and electrical relays. In addition, all models are equipped with a cold start system to aid in cold engine starts. The cold start system consists of an auxiliary air valve, cold start injector and thermo time switch.

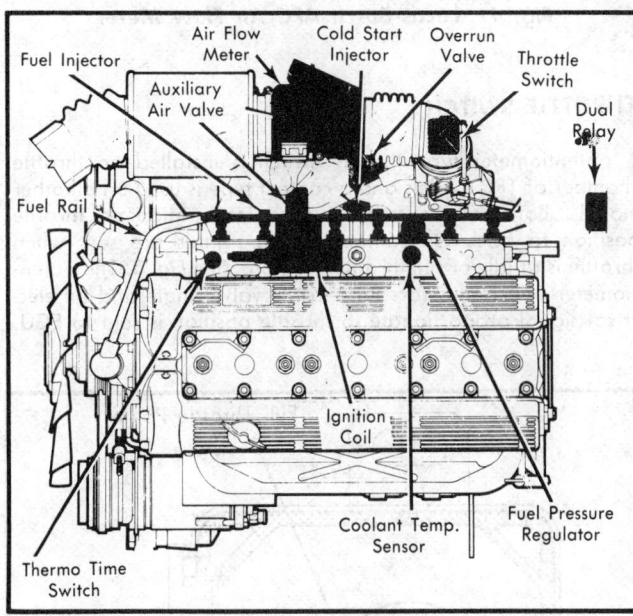

Fig. 1   Jaguar AFC Fuel Injection System

OPERATION

ELECTRIC FUEL PUMP

The fuel pump provides fuel under pressure to the fuel pressure regulator. Power for operation during cranking mode is provided from starter relay via the electrical relay. After the engine has started, control of the fuel pump is by a fuel pump circuit in the air flow meter. The first movement of air flow meter air measuring flap (about 5°) closes the fuel pump contacts and provides power to fuel pump after engine has started. With engine stopped, no air flow is present, measuring

flap closes and fuel pump contacts are opened to cut power to fuel pump. This method of circuitry reduces the risk of fire in a collision. The fuel pump is a sealed unit; no service required.

FUEL PRESSURE REGULATOR

The pressure regulator consists of a sealed, spring loaded diaphragm with a connection for intake manifold vacuum. Fuel is provided to fuel injectors under 36 psi ($2.5 kg/cm^2$) pressure. A connection for intake manifold vacuum provides a constant pressure differential which ensures that the amount of fuel injected is solely dependent upon injector "open" time. Fuel in excess of fuel pressure or pressure differential is returned to fuel tank. No service of pressure regulator is required.

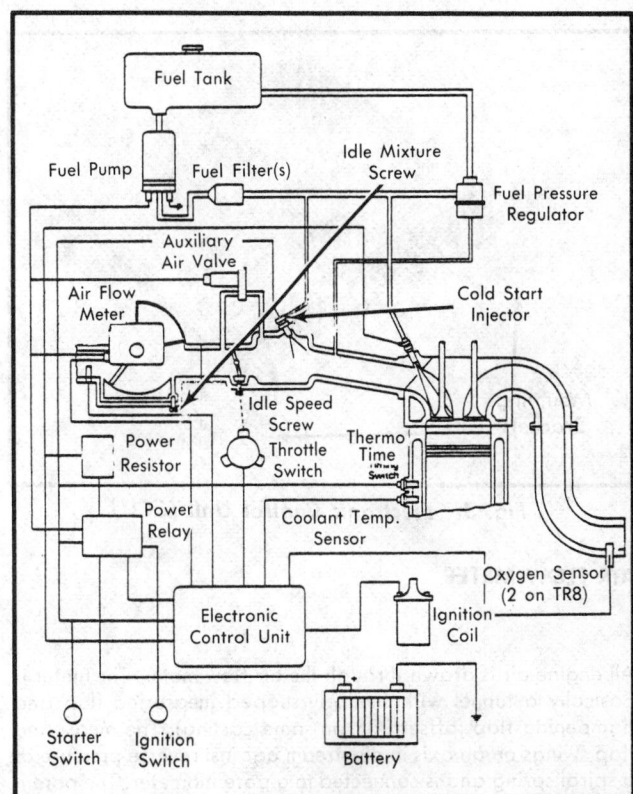

Fig. 2   Triumph AFC Fuel Injection System

FUEL INJECTORS

A fuel rail links the fuel pressure regulator with the fuel injectors. Each cylinder is provided with a solenoid-operated injector which sprays fuel towards back of each inlet valve. Each injector is energized through the ignition coil and grounded through the ECU to complete the circuit.

Each injector is linked to a resistor to reduce operating voltage to 3 volts and to protect injectors from power surges (except TR7 models). Resistors for Jaguar models are located in a single unit mounted on right side of firewall; TR8 resistors are located between ECU and injectors.

The ECU controls the length of time each injector is open. The "open" time of the injector governs the amount of fuel delivered. The injectors deliver ½ the amount of fuel required for 1 operating cycle each time they spray (twice per cycle).

1981 Bosch Fuel Injection

LUCAS-BOSCH AFC FUEL INJECTION SYSTEM (Cont.)

ELECTRONIC CONTROL UNIT (ECU)

All components of the control system are electrically connected to the ECU. *See Fig. 3.* The ECU is a pre-programmed computer which receives and interprets data from various sensors to calculate the amount of fuel required by the engine to maintain efficiency with minimum exhaust emissions. Impulses from the oxygen sensor(s) informs the ECU of oxygen content of exhaust gases and the ECU constantly adjusts the air/fuel ratio by controlling the injector "open" time.

The ECU provides fuel enrichment whenever engine is cranked, regardless of engine temperature. This is activated by a direct electrical connection from the starter circuit to the ECU. The ECU is a sealed unit; no service is required.

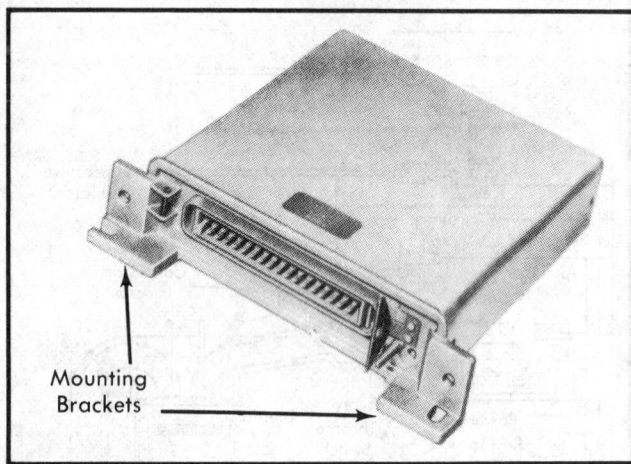

Fig. 3   Electronic Control Unit (ECU)

AIR FLOW METER

All engine air is drawn through the air flow meter. The meter is basically a tunnel with similarly shaped measuring flap and dampening flap (offset 90° on same casting). The measuring flap swings on an axis in air stream against reverse pressure of a spiral spring and is connected to a potentiometer. The potentiometer transmits an electrical signal proportionate to the angular displacement of the measuring flap to inform the ECU of engine load. See Fig. 4.

In addition to monitoring air flow, the meter also controls fuel pump operation and idling. At idle, the measuring flap is almost closed due to spiral spring pressure. An idle air by-pass receives air from main air flow through a small hole, the size of which is controlled by the idle mixture screw. This adjustable air by-pass influences CO levels at low engine speeds.

AIR TEMPERATURE SENSOR

The air temperature sensor is an integral component of the air flow meter which converts the temperature of incoming air into electrical signals. These electrical signals are received by the ECU and processed to adjust the amount of fuel injected by the injectors. The air temperature sensor is a non-serviceable device.

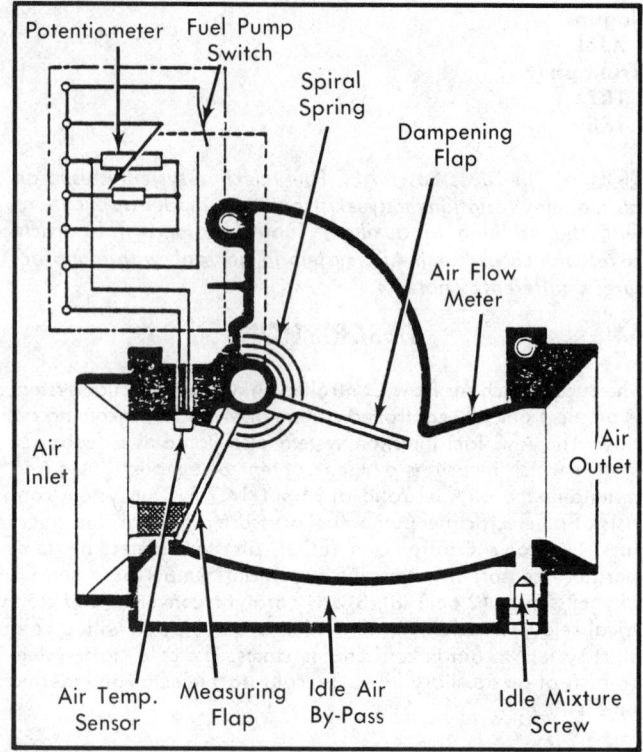

Fig. 4   Lucas-Bosch AFC Air Flow Meter

THROTTLE SWITCH

A potentiometer type throttle switch is installed on throttle chamber of TR8 models and a contact type is used on all other models. Both throttle switches send information on throttle position to ECU. On contact switch, signals are sent when throttle is at idle or full throttle positions. See Fig. 5. The potentiometer switch monitors the throttle valve angle and an electrical signal proportionate to throttle position is sent to ECU.

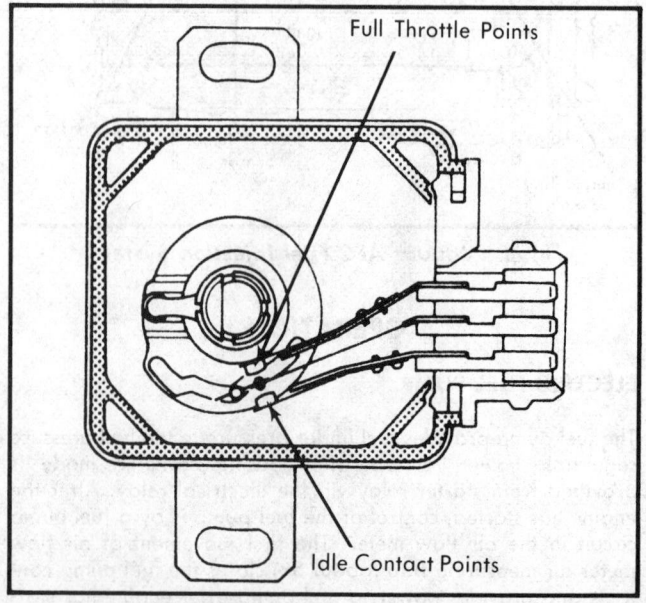

Fig. 5   Contact Type Throttle Switch

LUCAS-BOSCH AFC FUEL INJECTION SYSTEM (Cont.)

COOLANT TEMPERATURE SENSOR

This sensor provides ECU with engine temperature information relating to warm-up enrichment operation. During warm-up period after a cold engine start, additional fuel is required to maintain engine performance. As coolant temperature increases, the ECU decreases fuel enrichment until engine reaches normal operating temperature.

ELECTRICAL RELAYS

The main (double) relay activates the ECU, injector circuit and starting circuit when ignition is switched to start mode. The fuel pump relay activates the fuel pump during start mode. It is then controlled by air flow during operating mode. Relay for Jaguar models is located in engine compartment, near battery. On all other models, it is located in passenger compartment, behind the glove compartment.

COLD START SYSTEM

The cold start system provides additional air and fuel during cold engine starts. The cold start system consists of an auxiliary air valve which provides additional air, cold start injector which delivers additional fuel and a thermo time switch which controls operation of the cold start system. The thermo time switch has a bi-metal contact surrounded by a heating coil which is energized during engine cranking. This switch limits cold start system to 5-12 seconds under extreme cold engine starts in relation to engine coolant temperature. When coolant temperature is above 95°F (35°C), bi-metal contact breaks ground circuit of cold start injector and cold start enrichment is by-passed.

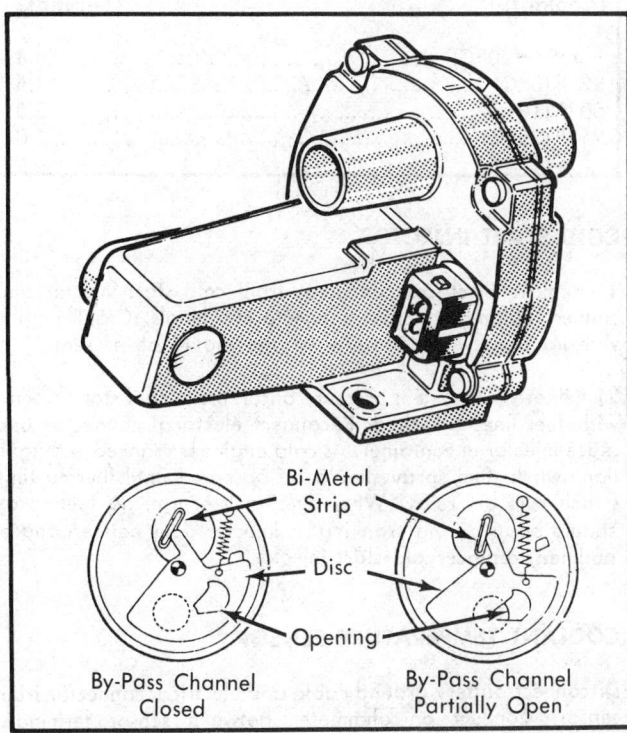

Bi-Metal Strip

Disc

Opening

By-Pass Channel Closed

By-Pass Channel Partially Open

Fig. 6   Auxiliary Air Valve

The auxiliary air valve provides additional air during cold engine starts and warm-up period. The valve consists of an

electrically heated bi-metal strip, movable disc and air by-pass channel. The heater coil on the bi-metal strip is energized by the fuel pump relay. Control of the valve is based upon engine temperature; the air by-pass channel is open when engine is cold and gradually closes as temperature rises. At predetermined temperatures, air by-pass channel is blocked and additional air flow stops. *See Fig. 6.*

TESTING

NOTE — *The Lucas-Bosch AFC fuel injection system maintains constant fuel pressure in fuel lines and components at all times. Be sure to relieve pressure before attempting to open system at any point for testing. Do not allow fuel to flow onto engine or electrical parts, or allow an open flame in area while testing fuel system or components.*

ELECTRONIC CONTROL UNIT (ECU)

Do not attempt to test ECU, permanent damage could result. It is possible to check plug wires for continuity. The ECU should only be judged faulty after compression is checked, ignition system (particularly breaker points) has been tested and found problem-free, and all other fuel injection components have been thoroughly tested (including wiring).

FUEL PRESSURE

1) Depressurize fuel system by disconnecting fuel pump ground lead and cranking engine for a few seconds. Turn ignition switch off and reconnect fuel pump ground lead. Disconnect fuel rail at cold start injector and connect fuel pressure gauge.

2) Disconnect negative lead from ignition coil and turn ignition switch on. Pressure reading should be 35.5-37 psi (2.5-2.6 kg/cm²). Slow pressure drop is permissible; sudden pressure drop requires check of entire fuel system for leaks. After testing fuel pressure, depressurize fuel system, remove test equipment and reconnect fuel lines and ignition coil negative lead.

3) On Jaguar only, operate fuel change-over switch on dash and recheck reading. Reading from both fuel tanks should agree. On all models, if pressure reading is not to specifications, replace fuel pressure regulator.

FEEDBACK MONITORING SYSTEM (TRIUMPH MODELS ONLY)

1) Start and run engine until normal operating temperature is obtained. If engine is already hot, run engine for 2 minutes before testing. Connect feedback monitor (60973066) to diagnostic connector in harness near ECU. Place feedback monitor switch in "LOW" position. *See Fig. 7.*

2) Mixture is correct when either No. 2 or No. 3 lights in either row glows. Any other light combination, except No. 1 or No. 4 lights in either row, is acceptable.

3) If both No. 3 lights glow, remove mixture screw plug and adjust mixture until No. 2 and No. 3 lights in either row glow. Turning mixture screw clockwise richens mixture, counterclockwise leans mixture.

LUCAS-BOSCH AFC FUEL INJECTION SYSTEM (Cont.)

4) After setting mixture, remove vacuum pipe from fuel pressure regulator with feedback monitor still connected. Lights should move to left, indicating richer mixture (for example, from No. 2 to No. 1). If lights do not shift, check wiring circuit and/or replace oxygen sensor.

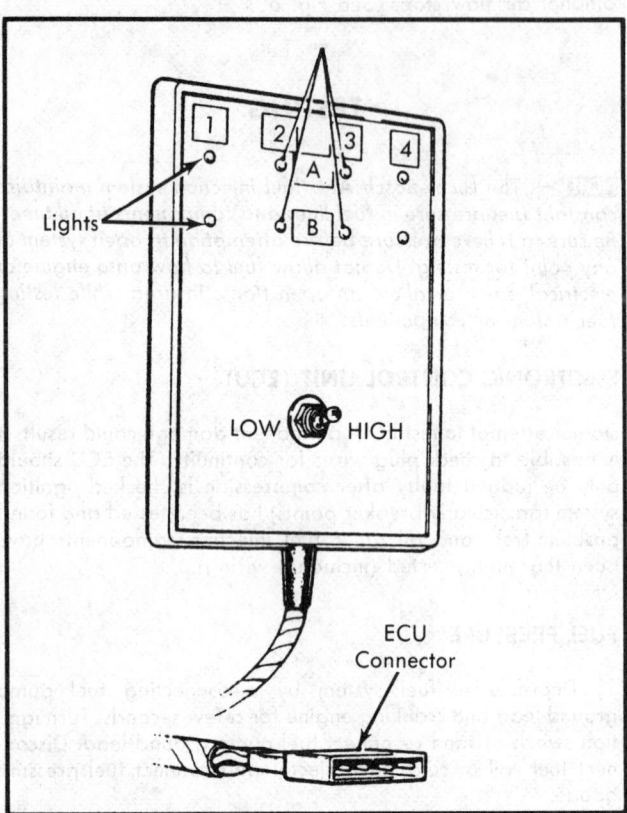

Fig. 7 Triumph Feedback Monitor

AIR TEMPERATURE SENSOR

Disconnect negative battery strap and air flow meter connector. Connect ohmmeter leads to terminals 6 and 27 on potentiometer connector. Readings should be as shown in Temperature/Resistance Relationship chart. If not, replace temperature sensor and air flow meter as an assembly.

Temperature/Resistance Relationship	
Temperature	**Resistance (Ohms)**
14°F (−10°C)	9200
32°F (0°C)	5900
68°F (20°C)	2500
104°F (40°C)	1180
140°F (60°C)	600

AUXILIARY AIR VALVE

1) Remove auxiliary air valve connector and connect an ohmmeter to both terminals. Resistance should read approximately 33 ohms. If not, continue testing as follows:

2) Remove auxiliary air valve from inlet manifold and immerse mounting plate in cold water, avoiding contact of terminals and by-pass channel with water. The movable plate should fully expose by-pass channel. Gradually heat water; as temperature increases, channel should become blocked. If valve does not respond as outlined, replace auxiliary air valve.

THERMO TIME SWITCH

1) Using a thermometer, check engine coolant temperature. Compare coolant temperature with value stamped on thermo time switch body. Connect an ohmmeter between terminal "W" on switch and ground.

2) If coolant temperature is higher than switch value, a very high resistance denoting an open circuit should be obtained. If coolant temperature is lower than switch value, a very low resistance denoting a closed circuit should be obtained. If switch does not respond as outlined, replace thermo time switch.

3) If switch passes resistance test, allow coolant temperature to cool below stamped value on switch. With ohmmeter connected, connect battery power via an isolating switch to terminal "G". Using a stop watch, check delay time as ohmmeter changes between high and low resistance. Delay period should be as shown in Coolant/Delay Time Relationship chart. If not, replace thermo time switch.

Coolant/Delay Time Relationship	
Temperature (Coolant)	**Delay (Seconds)**
−4°F (−20°C)	8
32°F (0°C)	4.5
50°F (10°C)	3.5
95°F (35°C)	0

COLD START INJECTOR

1) Remove electrical connector from cold start injector and connect voltmeter across connector terminals. Crank engine with ignition switch. Battery voltage should be present.

2) Release fuel system pressure and remove cold start injector with fuel lines attached. Reconnect electrical connector and place injector in container. As cold engine is cranked with ignition switch, fuel spray should be observed until thermo time switch cuts off relay. When engine is warm, no fuel spray should occur during cranking. If injector does not respond as outlined, replace cold start injector.

COOLANT TEMPERATURE SENSOR

Disconnect battery ground cable and electrical connector from sensor. Connect an ohmmeter between sensor terminals. Reading should be as shown in Temperature/Resistance Relationship chart. Disconnect ohmmeter and check resistance between each terminal and sensor body. A very high resistance denoting an open circuit should be obtained. If sensor does not respond as outlined, replace coolant temperature sensor.

LUCAS-BOSCH AFC FUEL INJECTION SYSTEM (Cont.)

Temperature/Resistance Relationship	
Temperature (Coolant)	Resistance (Ohms)
14°F (−10°C)	9200
32°F (0°C)	5900
68°F (20°C)	2500
104°F (40°C)	1180
140°F (60°C)	600
176°F (80°C)	325

THROTTLE SWITCH (JAGUAR & TR7 MODELS ONLY)

Disconnect battery ground cable and throttle switch electrical connector. Connect a powered test lamp between terminals 3 and 18 of throttle switch. Open throttle; test lamp should glow when throttle nears wide open position. If not, replace throttle switch.

REMOVAL & INSTALLATION

AIR FLOW METER

Removal & Installation — Disconnect battery ground cable. Disconnect rubber hose from both sides of air flow meter. Disconnect air flow meter ground cable and remove bolts securing meter to bracket. Move air flow meter upward, disconnect electrical connector and remove air flow meter. To install, reverse removal procedure.

ELECTRONIC CONTROL UNIT (ECU)

Removal — Disconnect battery ground cable. ECU is located in glove compartment on TR7; below glove compartment on TR8 and at forward end of luggage compartment on Jaguar. Remove ECU cover, retaining band and cable clamp clip. Unclip end cover and lift out ECU. Disconnect pin connector and remove ECU.

Installation — To install, reverse removal procedure, making sure pin connector is installed squarely and securely.

COLD START INJECTOR

Removal & Installation — Disconnect battery ground cable and remove electrical connector from injector. Release fuel line pressure. Remove injector retaining screws and remove injector. To install, reverse removal procedure.

AUXILIARY AIR VALVE

CAUTION — *Auxiliary air valve removal should be done only when engine is cold. Removal of valve requires having replacement valve ready for immediate installation or draining cooling system below level of valve.*

Removal & Installation — Disconnect battery ground cable. Disconnect air hoses and electrical connector from auxiliary air valve. Remove coolant system cap. Remove valve retaining bolts and air valve. Clean all gasket material from mating surfaces without damaging seating area. To install, coat new gasket with non-hardening sealing compound and reverse removal procedure.

COOLANT TEMPERATURE SENSOR

CAUTION — *Coolant temperature sensor removal should be done only when engine is cold. Removal of sensor requires having replacement sensor ready for immediate installation or draining cooling system below level of sensor.*

Removal & Installation — Disconnect battery ground cable. Drain coolant and disconnect sensor electrical connector. Loosen and remove sensor. To install, reverse removal procedure using suitable sealing compound on sensor threads. Replace sealing washers, if equipped.

THERMO TIME SWITCH

CAUTION — *Thermo time switch removal should be done only when engine is cold. Removal of switch requires having replacement switch ready for immediate installation or draining cooling system below level of switch.*

Removal & Installation — Disconnect battery ground cable. Drain coolant and disconnect switch electrical connector. Loosen and remove switch. To install, reverse removal procedure using suitable sealing compound on switch threads.

FUEL PRESSURE REGULATOR

CAUTION — *Fuel system pressure must be relieved before removing fuel pressure regulator.*

Removal & Installation — Disconnect battery ground cable. Disconnect fuel lines and vacuum line at regulator. Remove pressure regulator (separating from bracket, if installed). To install, reverse removal procedure.

FUEL INJECTORS

CAUTION — *Fuel system pressure must be relieved before removing fuel injectors.*

Removal — 1) Disconnect battery ground cable. Disconnect electrical connectors at injectors. Remove screws attaching fuel rail to intake manifold. Release clips holding fuel supply and return rails.

2) Remove manifold pressure pipe. Remove nuts and washers from injector clamps. On Jaguar models, lift off fuel rail with injectors, loosen injector clamps and remove injectors from fuel rail. Remove and discard "O" rings if equipped. On Triumph models, remove fuel rail and unscrew injectors.

Installation — To install, reverse removal procedure, making sure electrical connectors are properly installed on injectors before installing fuel rail assembly to manifold and new "O" rings are installed on injectors, if equipped.

ADJUSTMENTS

HOT (SLOW) IDLE RPM

See appropriate TUNE-UP SERVICE PROCEDURES article.

IDLE MIXTURE

See appropriane TUNE-UP SERVICE PROCEDURES article.

LUCAS-BOSCH AFC FUEL INJECTION SYSTEM (Cont.)

THROTTLE SWITCH (TR8 ONLY)

Disconnect electrical connector at throttle switch and connect throttle tester (60973067) to switch. With engine at normal operating temperature and idle speed set to specifications, adjust throttle switch until green light on tester glows. Remove tester and reconnect electrical connector.

THROTTLE VALVE (JAGUAR ONLY)

1) Remove air intake hose and elbow to expose throttle valve. Loosen throttle valve lock nut on stop screw and loosen stop screw. Ensure throttle valve closes fully.

2) Insert a .002" (.05 mm) feeler gauge between throttle valve and throttle housing bore. See Fig. 8. With feeler gauge in position, adjust stop screw so it just touches stop arm. Tighten lock nut. Press stop arm against stop screw and remove feeler gauge.

3) Seal threads of adjusting screws and lock nuts with paint spots. Install hose and elbow. Check operation of throttle

linkage and adjust if required by ensuring outer cable is secured in bracket so inner cable is under light tension, but not enough to move operating lever. Tighten lock nuts.

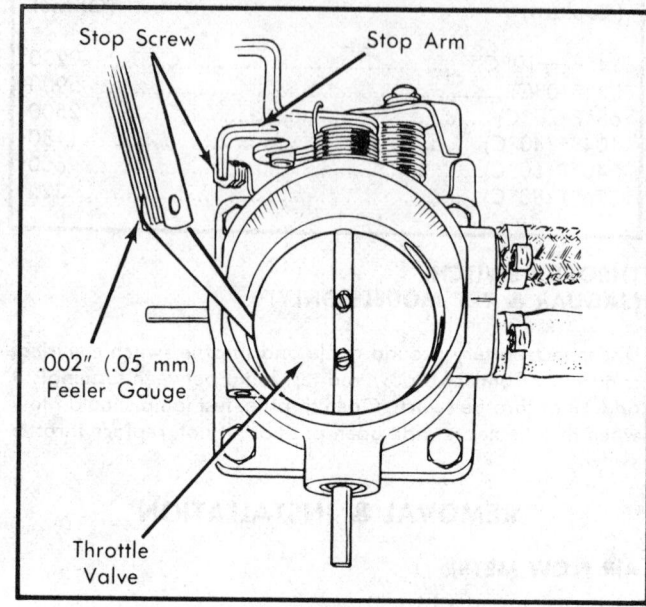

Fig. 8   Adjusting Jaguar Throttle Valve Clearance

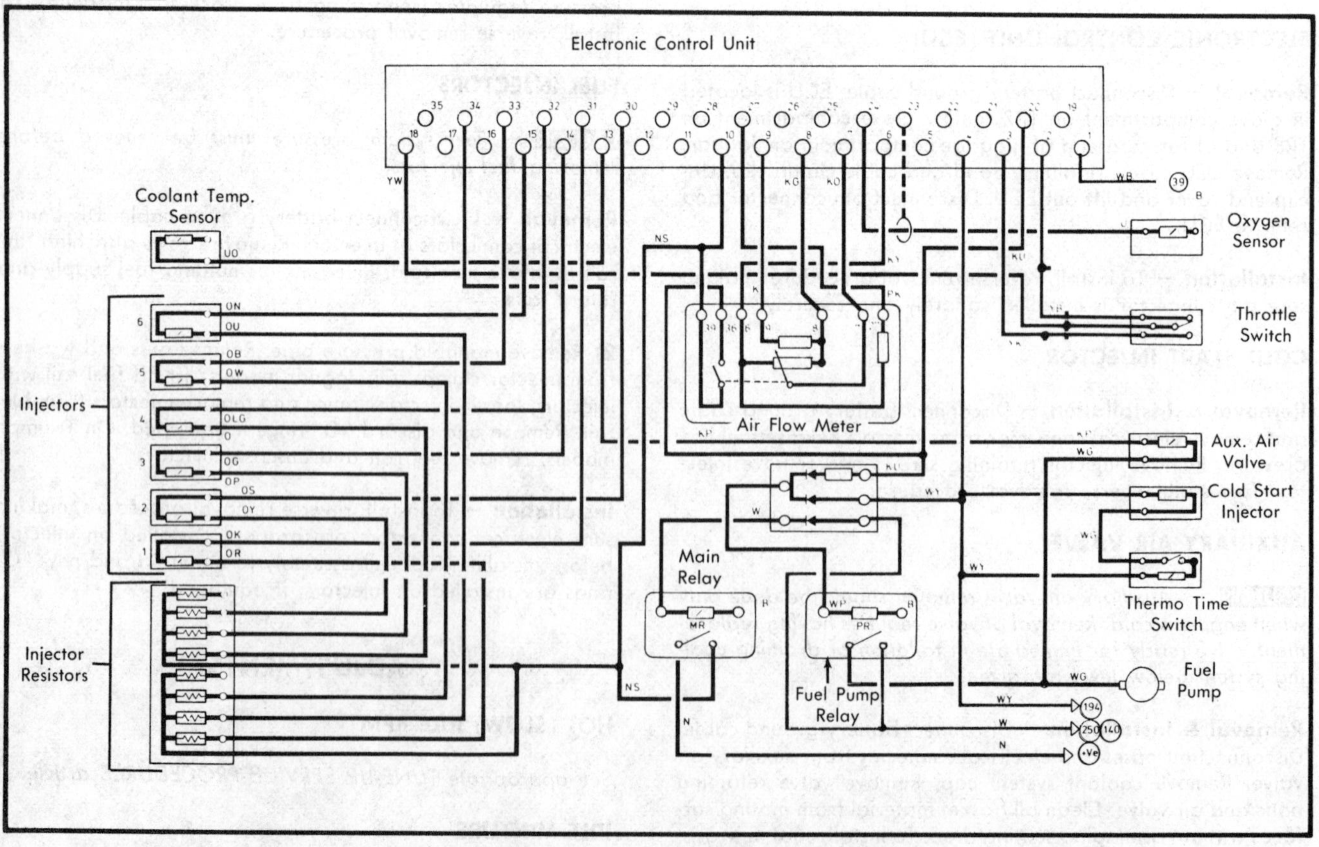

Fig. 9   Jaguar XJ6L Fuel Injection Wiring Diagram

LUCAS-BOSCH AFC FUEL INJECTION SYSTEM (Cont.)

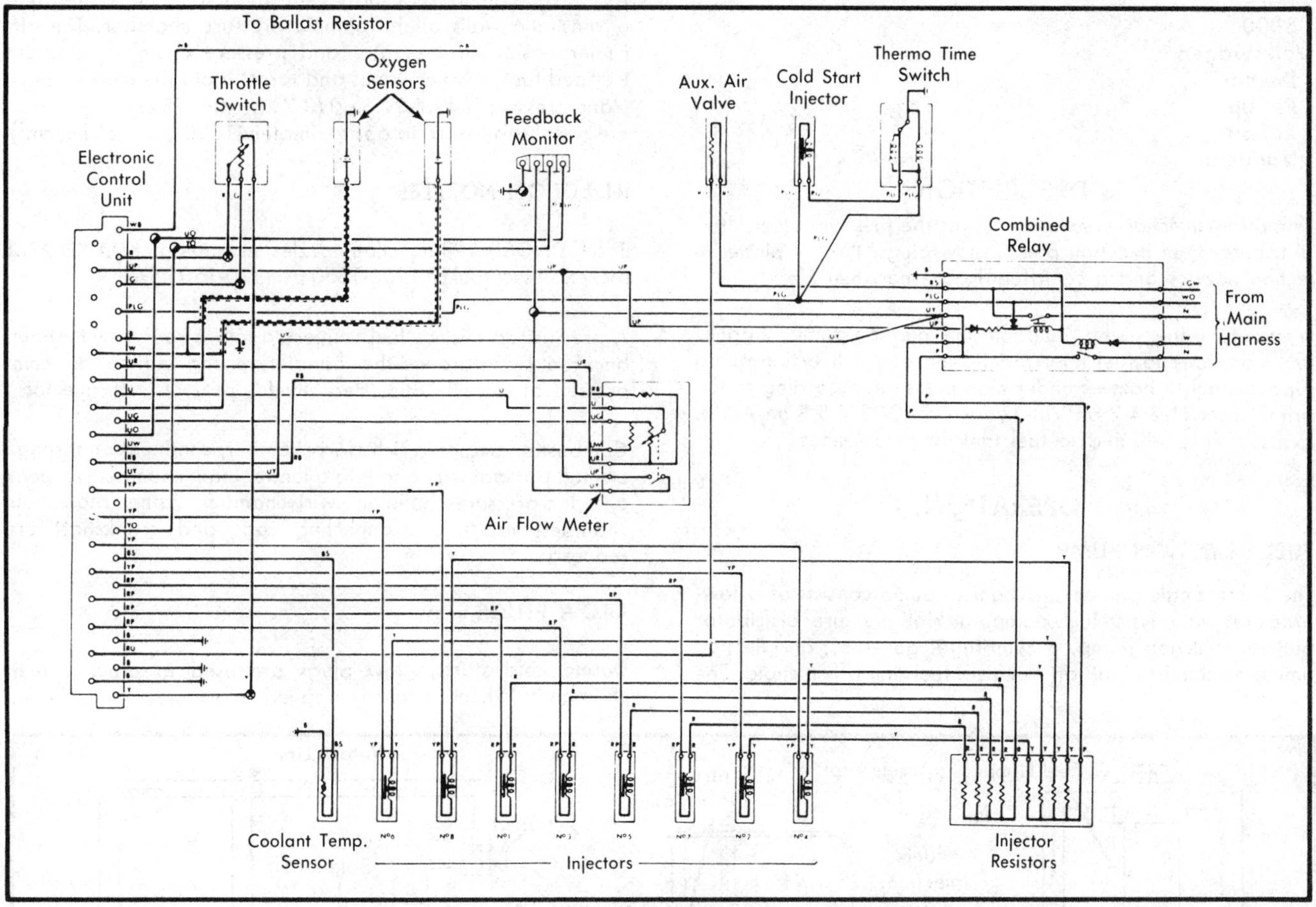

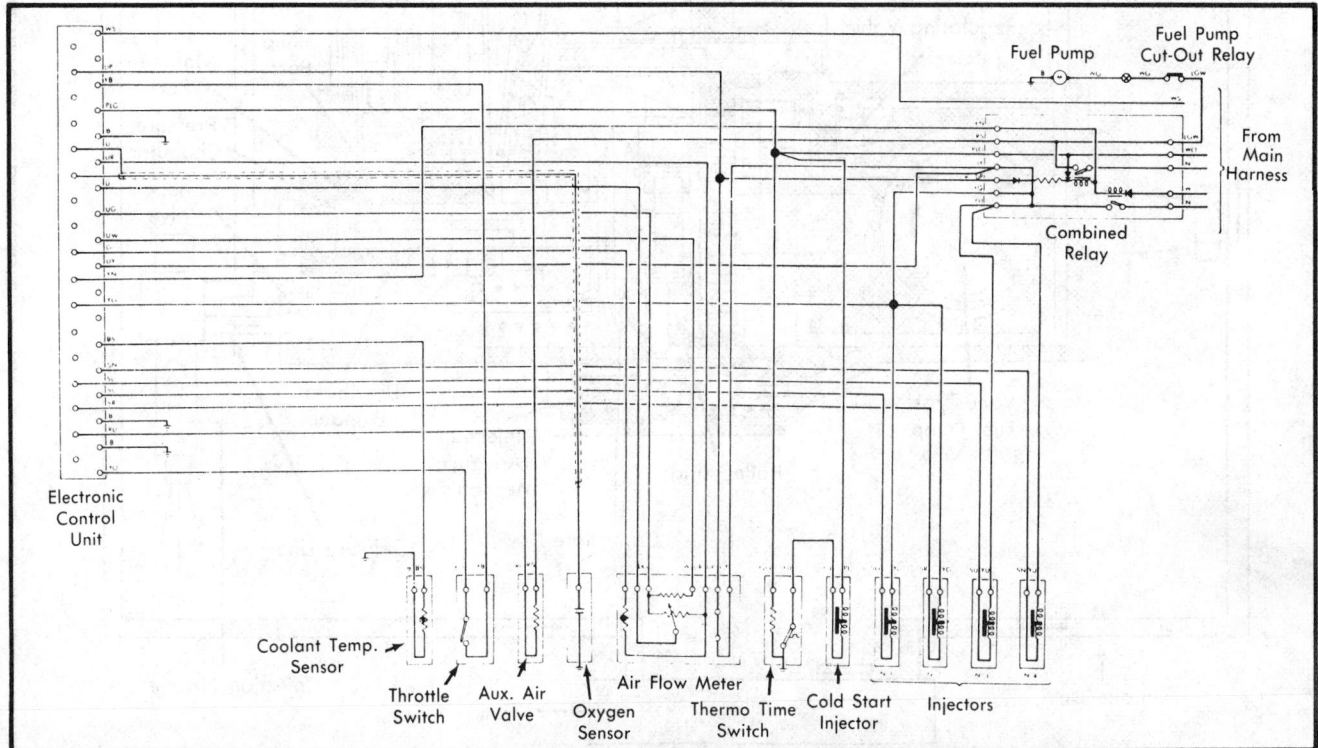

Fig. 10   Triumph TR8 Fuel Injection Wiring Diagram

Fig. 11   Triumph TR7 Fuel Injection Wiring Diagram

1981 Bosch Diesel Fuel Injection

BOSCH DIESEL FUEL INJECTION – AUDI & VOLKSWAGEN

Audi
  5000
Volkswagen
  Dasher
  Pickup
  Rabbit
  Vanagon

DESCRIPTION

Diesel fuel injection systems consist of the fuel tank, fuel filter, distributor-type injection pump, glow plugs, throttle pintle injection nozzles and a centrifugal governor. See *Fig. 1.*

A vane-type fuel pump, built into the injection pump, supplies fuel from tank to fuel filter to injection pump. Injection pump supplies fuel to nozzles under high pressure, according to the firing order (1-3-4-2 on Volkswagen and 1-2-4-5-3 on Audi). Excess fuel is returned to fuel tank by return lines.

OPERATION

FUEL INJECTION PUMP

The Bosch single plunger mechanical pump consists of a low-pressure, vane-type fuel pump, a high-pressure distributor plunger injection pump, a centrifugal governor, an injection timing mechanism, and an electrical fuel shut-off solenoid. See *Fig. 1.*

As the vane pump rotor turns, centrifugal force holds the vanes against the walls of the pump's pressure chamber. The off-center design of the rotor and pressure chamber squeezes trapped fuel between vanes and forces it out the delivery port. Vane pressure is 42.7-99.6 psi (3-7 kg/cm^2). The main pump increases this pressure to approximately 1800 psi (126 kg/cm^2).

INJECTION NOZZLES

Bosch DNOSD 193 injection nozzles, mounted in KDA SD 27/4 sockets, inject fuel at 1706-1850 psi (120-130 kg/cm^2).

A pressurized mist of fuel is injected into a round swirl chamber. Fuel swirls around the chamber, mixing with hot air, compressed at a 23:1 ratio. Heat shields protect each injector.

Combustion begins in rich swirl chamber, continues on through a small passageway and into a leaner main chamber. As peak cylinder pressures build in swirl chamber, rather than main chamber, loads on connecting rods and crankshaft are reduced.

GLOW PLUGS

During cold starts, glow plugs are used to preheat swirl chambers. When current is applied, glow plugs become red

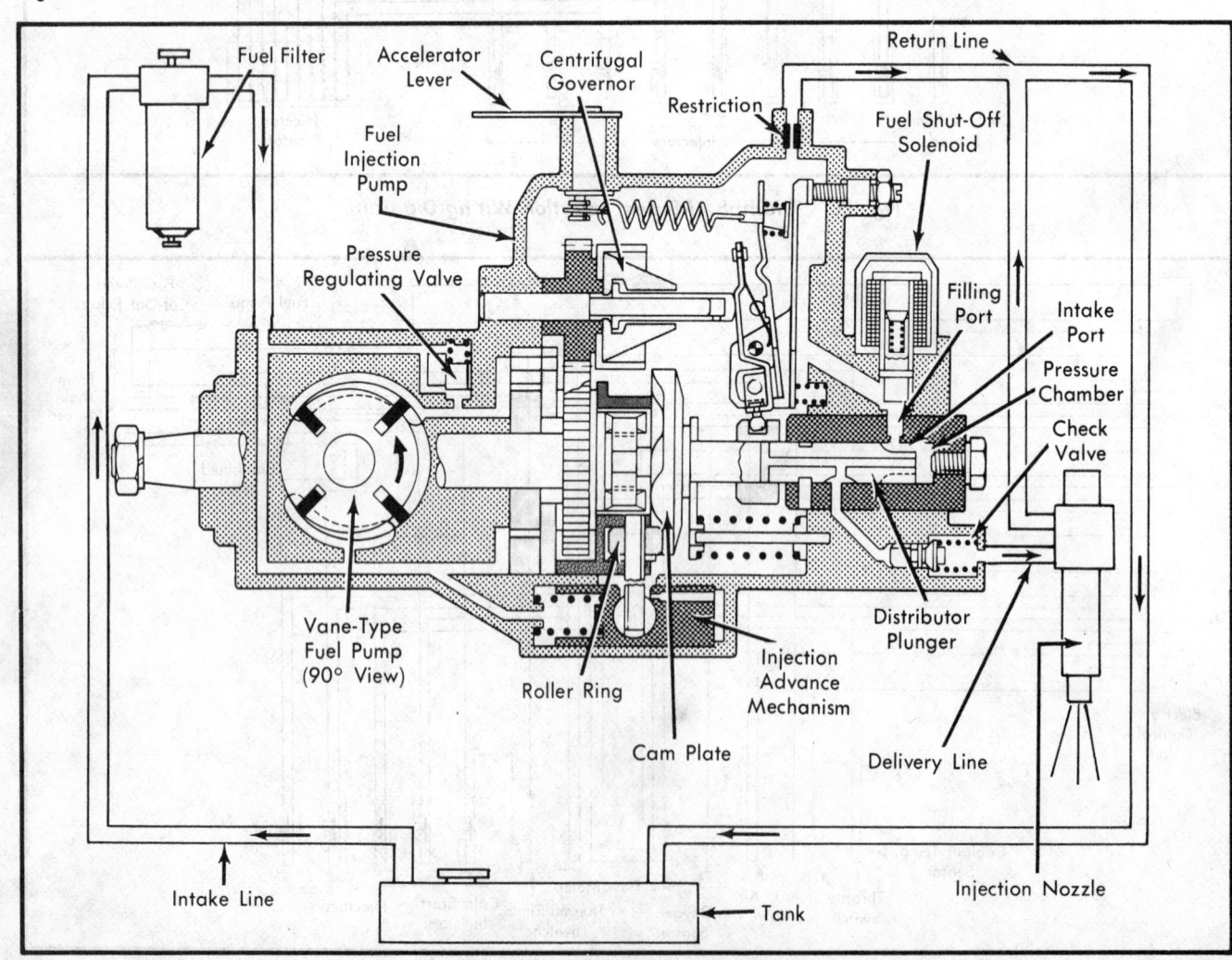

Fig. 1 Diesel Fuel Supply System

BOSCH DIESEL FUEL INJECTION — AUDI & VOLKSWAGEN (Cont.)

hot. A temperature sensor connected to a time circuit in relay controls pre-heating time.

To start a cold engine, pull out cold start knob to left of steering column (Volkswagen only). Turn ignition switch to glow plug position (No. 2). When light goes out, crank the engine. At below freezing temperatures, depress accelerator pedal while cranking. About 2 minutes after engine starts, push cold start knob in fully.

NOTE — Cold starting device of Audi 5000 is automatically controlled by engine coolant passing over a thermostat. When engine is cold, thermostat pulls on advance lever advancing injection timing.

FUEL FILTER

The fuel filter allows unrestricted flow of fuel from the tank to the injection pump, but stops any dirt or water. A replaceable element, similar to an oil filter cartridge, threads onto a removable flange. See Fig. 2.

To drain water from filter, open vent screw on top of filter flange. If there is no vent screw, remove fuel return line at injection pump. Remove flange mounting nuts and lift filter. Open water drain on bottom of filter. Drain until clean fuel runs out. Close water drain and vent screw (or reattach return line).

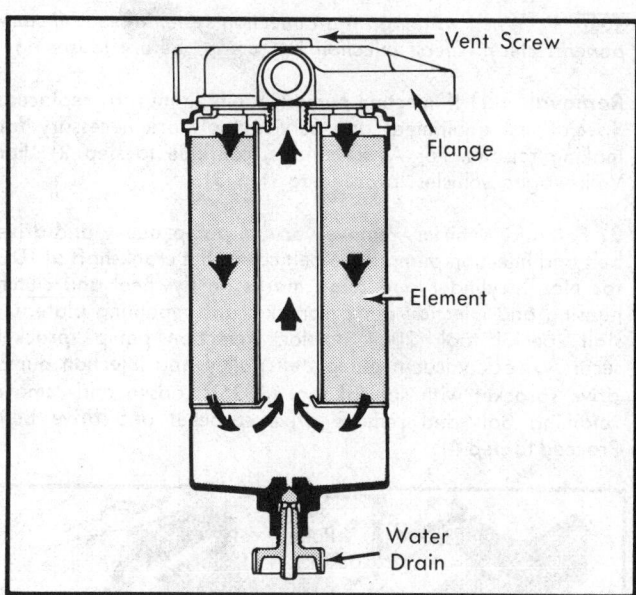

Fig. 2 Components of Fuel Filter

CENTRIFUGAL GOVERNOR

The amount of fuel injected is controlled by changing the injection cut-off point according to engine speed and load conditions. The cut-off point is controlled by the position of the metering sleeve around the distributor plunger. The sleeve normally covers a relief port in the plunger. Uncovering the port stops injection. The sleeve position is determined by a

centrifugal governor, and accelerator linkage. A large quantity of fuel is supplied during starting, and less at idle. No fuel is allowed to pass when the engine exceeds a predetermined maximum RPM.

TESTING

INJECTION NOZZLES

Injection nozzle problems usually are accompanied by knocking in one or more cylinders, engine overheating, loss of power or performance, black exhaust smoke and increased fuel consumption. To locate and correct faulty injectors, proceed as follows:

1) Loosen line unions on each injection nozzle, one at a time with engine running at fast idle. If engine speed remains constant with line removed, that nozzle is defective.

2) To remove nozzle, detach injector line. Use special tool (US 2775) to remove injection nozzles. To disassemble, place upper part in vise and loosen lower part. Then reverse position and carefully remove parts from lower part. Do not interchange parts from one injector to another.

3) To install, insert new heat shield with recess pointing upward. Tighten nozzles to 51 ft. lbs. (69 N.m) and lines to 18 ft. lbs. (24 N.m). Bleeding is not necessary.

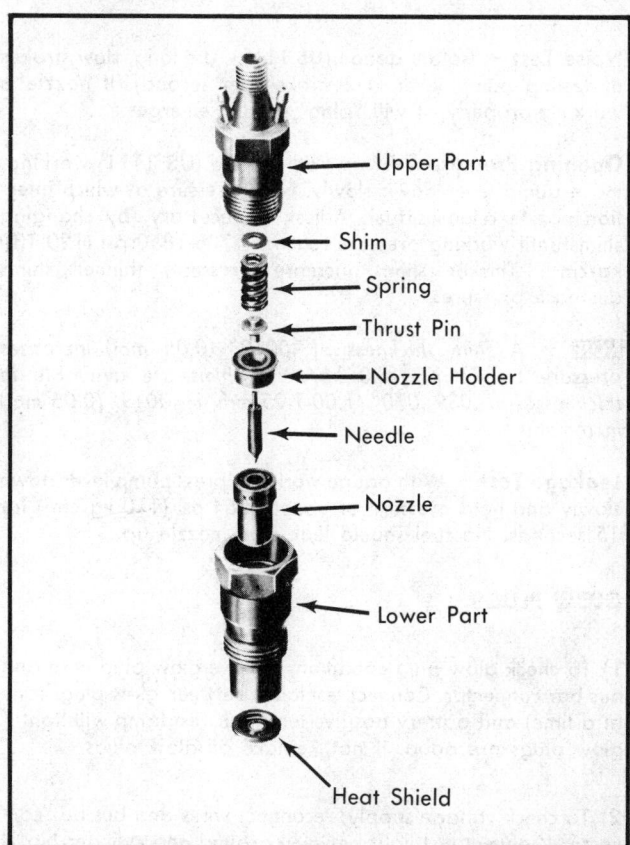

Fig. 3 Exploded View of Injection Nozzle

1981 Bosch Diesel Fuel Injection

BOSCH DIESEL FUEL INJECTION – AUDI & VOLKSWAGEN (Cont.)

Spray Formation Test – Isolate special testing gauge (US1111). Use short rapid strokes of testing pump lever (4-6 strokes per second). Spray should be even and stop cleanly. Nozzles should not drip.

CAUTION – *Do not expose hands to injector spray during testing, as working pressure will cause fuel oil to penetrate the skin.*

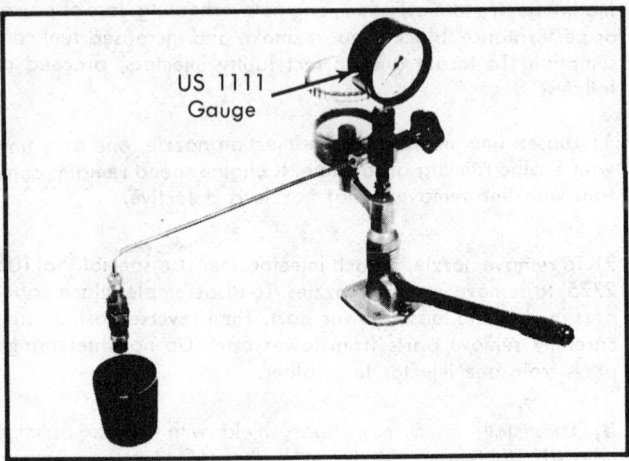

Fig. 4.   Injection Nozzle Test Gauge

Noise Test – Isolate gauge (US 1111). Use long, slow strokes of testing pump lever (1-2 strokes per second). If nozzle is working properly, it will "ping" as fuel emerges.

Opening Pressure Test – With gauge (US 1111) working, move pump lever down slowly. Note pressure at which injection nozzle releases fuel. Adjust, if necessary, by changing shims until working pressure reaches 1706-1850 psi (120-130 kg/cm²). Thicker shims increase pressure, thinner shims decrease pressure.

NOTE – *A shim thickness of .0019" (0.05 mm) increases pressure by 71 psi (5.0 kg/cm²). Shims are available in thicknesses of .039-.070" (1.00-1.95 mm) in .0019" (0.05 mm) increments.*

Leakage Test – With gauge working, press pump lever down slowly and hold pressure at about 1564 psi (110 kg/cm²) for 15 seconds. No fuel should leak from nozzle tip.

GLOW PLUGS

1) To check glow plug condition, remove glow plug wire and bus bar connector. Connect test lamp between glow plugs (one at a time) and battery positive terminal. Test lamp will light if glow plugs are good. If not, replace all glow plugs.

2) To check voltage supply, reconnect wires and bus bar connector. Connect test light between ground and cylinder No. 4 glow plug. Turn ignition switch to glow plug position and lamp should light. If not, check for a defective glow plug fuse located to the left of the steering column behind instrument panel.

3) If fuse is OK, check terminal No. 30 of glow plug relay for voltage. If voltage is not present, check for defective relay plate or break in wiring from relay plate terminal No. 30 to relay terminal No. 30.

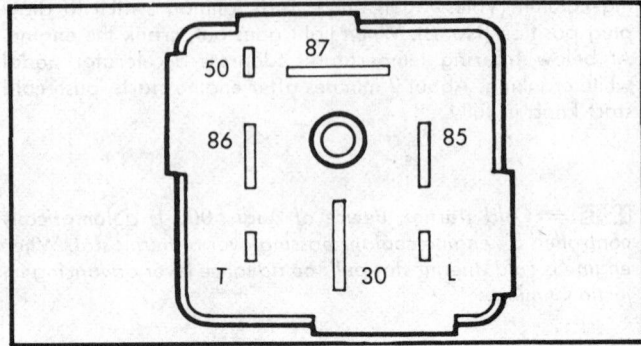

Fig. 5   Glow Plug Relay Terminals

4) If voltage is present, relay is not working. Connect test lamp to terminal No. 86 on relay and turn ignition switch to glow plug position. If lamp lights up, repair connection from terminal No. 85 to ground, or from terminal No. 87 to glow plugs, or replace relay. If lamp does not light, repair connection from relay plate to relay terminal No. 86, or replace relay plate.

REMOVAL & INSTALLATION

FUEL INJECTION PUMP

NOTE – *When working on an injection system, keep all components clean. Clean injection line unions before loosening.*

Removal – 1) If injection pump is faulty, it must be replaced. Special test equipment and service tools are necessary for making repairs. For Audi vehicles, continue to step **2)**. For Volkswagen vehicles, proceed to step **3)**.

2) For Audi vehicles, remove vacuum pump pulley and drive belt and injection pump drive belt cover. Set crankshaft at TDC for No. 1 cylinder and align marks on flywheel and clutch housing and injection pump sprocket and mounting plate. Install special tool (2064) to lock injection pump sprocket securely. Lock vacuum pump belt pulley and injection pump drive sprocket with special tool (3036). Loosen and remove retaining bolt and remove drive sprocket and drive belt. Proceed to step **4)**.

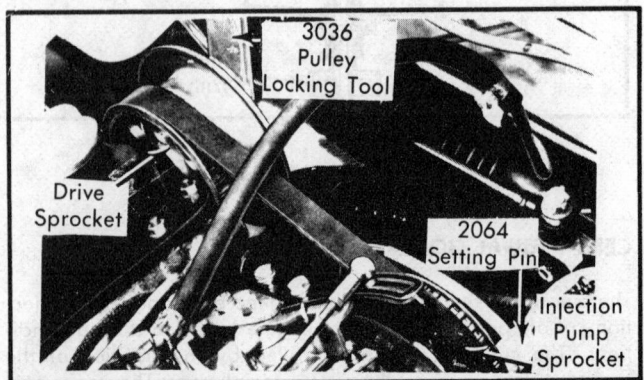

Fig. 6   Locking Injection and Vacuum Pump Pulleys (Audi)

BOSCH DIESEL FUEL INJECTION — AUDI & VOLKSWAGEN (Cont.)

3) For Volkswagen vehicles, turn engine to TDC on No. 1 cylinder. Lock camshaft with special setting bar (2065). Remove drive belt. Proceed to step 4).

**Fig. 7   Camshaft Locking Tool Installation
(Volkswagen Shown)**

4) Loosen injection pump sprocket retaining nut approximately one turn. On Audi vehicles, remove special tool (2064) from sprocket.

5) Attach puller (VW203B for Volkswagen; 3032 for Audi) to injection pump sprocket and apply light tension to puller. Tap lightly on puller spindle head until sprocket loosens from pump shaft.

**Fig. 8   Fuel Injection Pump Gear Removal
(Audi Shown)**

6) Remove puller and nut and remove sprocket by hand. Disconnect all fuel pipes from pump. Cover unions with clean cloth. Disconnect wire from fuel shut-off solenoid and detach accelerator cable. Remove pump mounting bolts. Support and remove pump.

Installation — 1) Install pump, aligning marks on pump and mounting plate. For Volkswagen vehicles, install injection pump sprocket. Tighten pump mounting bolts and fuel pipes to 18 ft. lbs. (24 N.m) and pump sprocket to 33 ft. lbs. (45 N.m). Adjust injection pump/valve timing and injection timing.

2) On Audi vehicles, align rear support so it contacts cylinder block and injection pump free of tension. Tighten support mounting bolts. Install injection pump sprocket and turn it until marks on sprocket and mounting plate are in line.

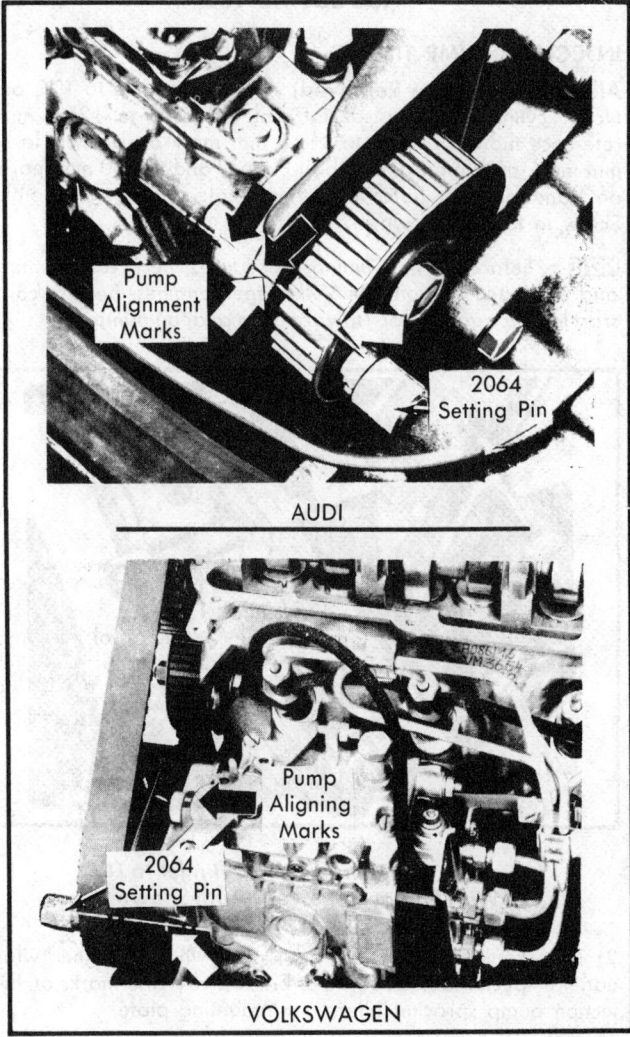

Fig. 9   Aligning Injection Pump Reference Marks

3) Lock pump with special tool (2064) and tighten retaining nut to 33 ft. lbs. (45 N.m). Install drive belt and injection pump drive sprocket. Tighten drive sprocket retaining bolt so that sprocket can still be turned by hand. Check drive belt tension with VW 210 scale. Value should register 12-13 on scale.

4) If not, adjust drive belt tension by loosening bolts and moving mounting plate with pump. Check if TDC mark on flywheel is still aligned with reference mark. Tighten injection pump drive sprocket using special tool (3036), tightening bolt to 72 ft. lbs. (98 N.m). Remove special tool (2064). Check injection pump/valve timing and injection timing.

5) Reinstall fuel pipes, drive belt cover, and vacuum pump pulley and drive belt. Reattach accelerator cable and wire to fuel shut-off solenoid.

FUEL FILTER

Service is limited to replacing filter at proper interval and draining water, when present. Bleeding is not required.

BOSCH DIESEL FUEL INJECTION – AUDI & VOLKSWAGEN (Cont.)

ADJUSTMENTS

INJECTION PUMP TIMING

All Models (Engine Removed) – 1) Set engine to TDC on No. 1 cylinder. Adjust special tool (2068/A) to 125.5 mm reference mark on Audi, to 112.8 mm mark on Dasher, to 5 mm mark on Rabbit and Rabbit Pickup, and to 100 mm mark on Vanagon. Left notch of vernier scale is reference point. Screw in tool as shown in *Fig. 10*.

NOTE – *Before starting timing procedure, check valve timing and drive belt tension. On Volkswagen engines, be sure cold start lever is against stop (toward drive gear on pump).*

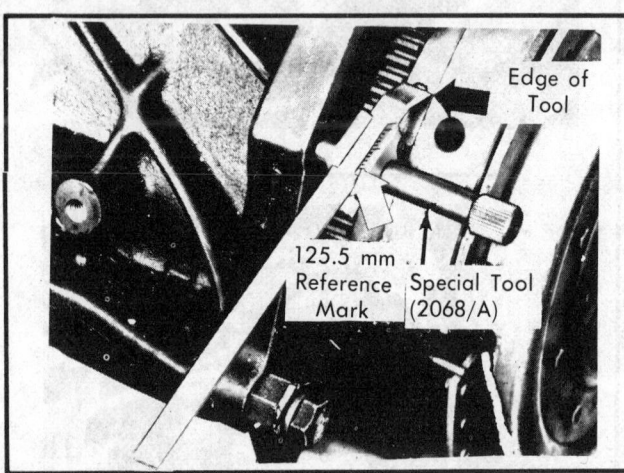

Fig. 10   Adjusting No. 1 Cylinder to TDC With Engine Removed (Audi Shown)

2) Turn crankshaft until TDC mark on flywheel is aligned with edge of special tool (2068/A) at black arrow and marks on injection pump sprocket align with mounting plate.

All Models (Engine Installed) – 1) Set crankshaft to TDC on No. 1 cylinder and align marks on flywheel and clutch housing. Check marks on injection pump sprocket and mounting plate.

2) If timing adjustment is necessary, remove plug from injection pump cover and install adapter and dial indicator in place of plug. On Audi models only, loosen cold start device cable by loosening screw No. 1 and turning clamp 90°. See *Fig. 11*.

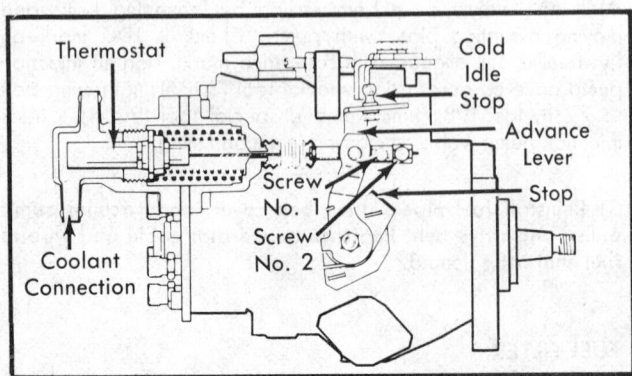

Fig. 11   Loosening Cold Start Device Screw No. 1.

CAUTION – *Do not loosen screw No. 2 or pump recalibration will be necessary.*

3) Preload dial indicator to .097" (2.5 mm). Turn engine slowly counterclockwise until dial indicator needle stops moving. Zero indicator.

4) Turn engine clockwise until TDC mark on flywheel is lined up with reference mark. Check dial indicator reading against specifications.

Fig. 12   Preloading Injection Pump With Dial Indicator (2066)

5) If necessary, loosen bolts on mounting plate and support. Turn pump to adjust timing and tighten bolts. Recheck dial indicator readings. On Audi vehicles, turn clamp on cold start device back 90° to original position and tighten screw No. 1.

Injection Pump Timing Specifications

Application	Dial Indicator Reading
Audi	.033" (.85 mm)
Volkswagen	
Dasher & Vanagon	.034" (.86 mm)
Rabbit & Rabbit Pickup①	.045" (1.15 mm)

① – Only those models with yellow paint mark on pump advance cover. Models without paint dot, .034" (.86 mm).

ACCELERATOR CABLE

Place accelerator pedal in full throttle position. Adjust cable with nuts until pump lever contacts stop free of strain. Be sure ball pin on pump lever is pointing upward and touching end of elongated hole. Accelerator cable should be attached at upper hole in bracket.

BOSCH DIESEL FUEL INJECTION — AUDI & VOLKSWAGEN (Cont.)

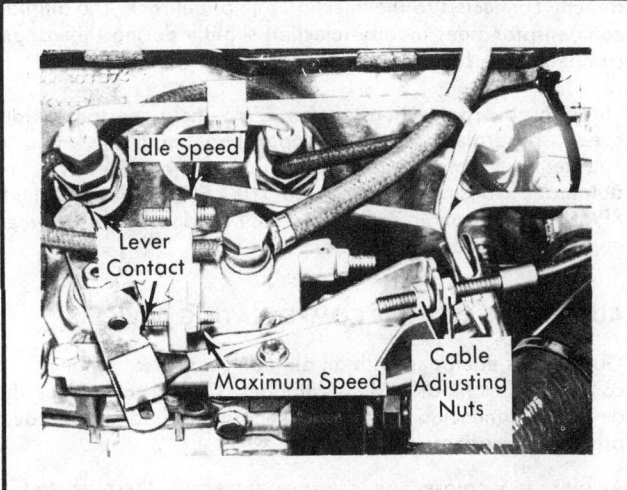

Fig. 13   Accelerator Cable Adjusting Points

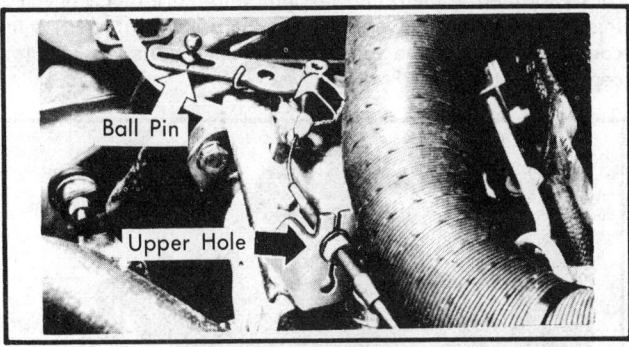

Fig. 14   Accelerator Cable Attaching Points

COLD STARTING CABLE

On Volkswagen vehicles, insert washer onto cable and install cable into bracket with rubber bushing. Insert cable into pin. Install lock washer and move lever as far as possible in direction of arrow. Pull cable tight and secure pin with clamping screw.

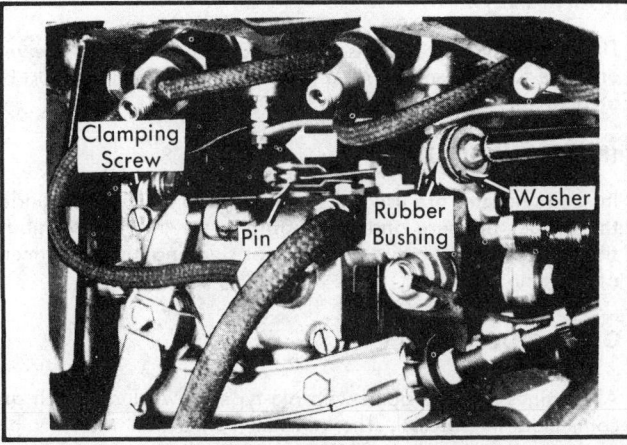

Fig. 15   Cold Starting Cable Adjustment

IDLE SPEED

Audi — 1) Warm engine to normal operating temperature (oil temperature of 122-158°F or 50-70°C). Turn idle speed control knob on instrument panel counterclockwise to stop.

2) Connect tachometer (VW 1367 or Siemans 451) according to instructions. Adjust speed to 700-800 RPM by loosening lock nut, and turning screw in to raise idle speed, or out to lower idle speed. Retighten lock nut.

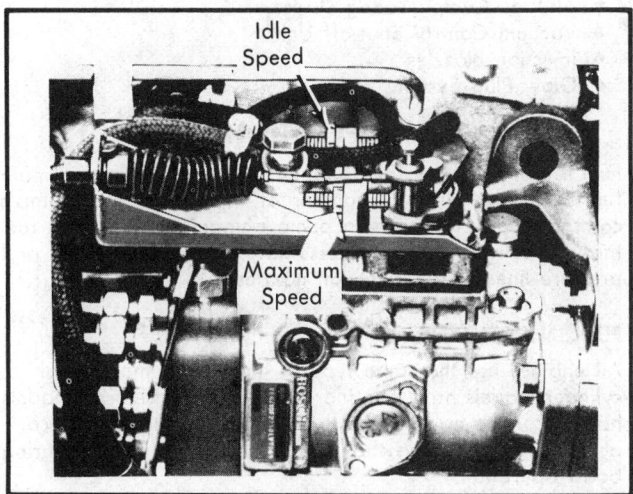

**Fig. 16   Idle and Maximum Speed Adjustments
(Audi)**

Volkswagen — 1) Warm engine to normal operating temperature (oil temperature of 122-158°F or 50-70°C). Adjust idle speed to 925-975 RPM on Dasher, 800-850 RPM for all other models.
2) To adjust, loosen locknut and turn screw in to raise idle speed, or out to lower idle speed. Retighten lock nut and seal with paint.

MAXIMUM SPEED

Adjust idle speed to proper setting and then open throttle fully. Maximum speed for Audi should be 5350-5450 RPM, for Volkswagen except Vanagon, 5300-5400 RPM and for Vanagon, 4750-4850 RPM. To adjust, loosen locknut and turn screw out to raise maximum speed, or in to lower it. Tighten locknut when adjustment is complete. Seal locknut and screw with paint.

TIGHTENING SPECIFICATIONS

Application	Ft. Lbs. (N.m)
Injection Pump Mounting Bolts	18 (24)
Fuel Injection Line Unions	18 (24)
Fuel Injection Pump Gear Nut	33 (45)
Camshaft Gear Bolt	33 (45)
Injection Nozzle-to-Socket	51 (69)
Nozzle (Upper-to-Lower Part)	51 (69)
Injection Pump Drive Gear	72 (98)

1981 Bosch Diesel Fuel Injection

BOSCH DIESEL INJECTION — MERCEDES-BENZ

240D
300D
300CD
300SD
300TD

DESCRIPTION

The fuel injection system used on Mercedes diesel models includes the following components:

- Pre-Filter and Main Filter
- Fuel Injection Pump with mechanical governor
- Altitude Compensating Device
- Vacuum Control Shut-off Unit
- Injection Nozzles
- Glow Plug System

OPERATION

Fuel is pumped from fuel tank, through a pre-filter and main fuel filter into suction chamber of injection pump. Pump's camshaft operates injection pump plungers, which force fuel through delivery valves, reverse-flow dampening valves, and pressure lines to fuel injection nozzles.

FUEL INJECTION PUMP

All engines use the same type of injection pump, though 5-cylinder models have one more pump element. Turbo models have a connection from the turbocharger to the altitude compensator which allows that unit to enrich the mixture during boost operation.

The vacuum shut-off unit stops fuel delivery when the key is turned off. If it fails, a manual "STOP" lever is provided on the side of the pump. A mechanical fuel pump draws fuel from the tank and supplies it to the high pressure section of the injection pump. The pump is lubricated by engine oil.

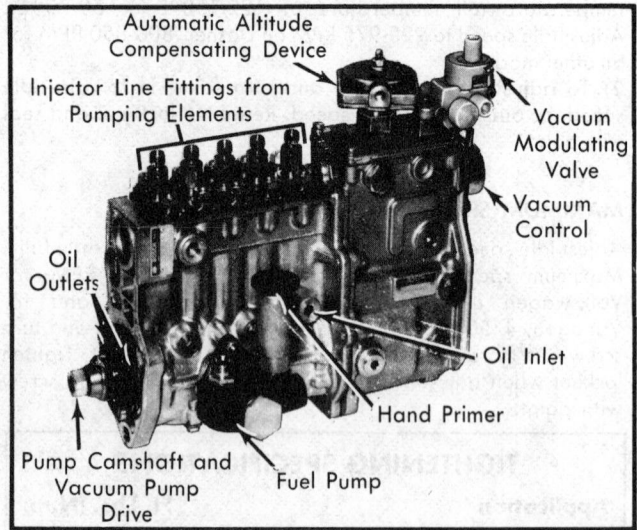

Automatic Altitude
Compensating Device

Injector Line Fittings from
Pumping Elements

Vacuum
Modulating
Valve

Vacuum
Control

Oil
Outlets

Oil Inlet

Hand Primer

Pump Camshaft and
Vacuum Pump
Drive

Fuel Pump

Fig. 1 Fuel Injection Pump Components

GOVERNOR

The governor controls idle and maximum RPM. Internal design enables the governor to have no effect on pump operation during normal operating speed range, when the accelerator is

directly connected to the injection pump fuel rack. The altitude compensator does modify injection slightly during this range, compensating for air pressure variations with altitude.

Through governor action, engine RPM is held constant at idle speed, regardless of engine operating conditions — cold engine, air conditioner operation, power steering, or automatic transmission. At 5000-5100 RPM, governor limits RPM by pulling main rack back, until balance exists between engine RPM and fuel delivery.

AUTOMATIC ALTITUDE COMPENSATING DEVICE

Governor is equipped with an altitude compensating device to control emissions at various altitudes. On Turbo engines the device is connected to the intake manifold to sense boost pressure variations as well.

As altitude increases, air pressure decreases, the push rod in the compensator moves downward and pushes the main rack, slightly decreasing the amount of fuel injected (leans out the mixture). When Turbo models are operating under boost, the rack is pushed in the other direction and more fuel is injected. Injection pump and governor operation are not affected by the compensator when the vehicle is operating near sea level (except Turbo) or idle RPM.

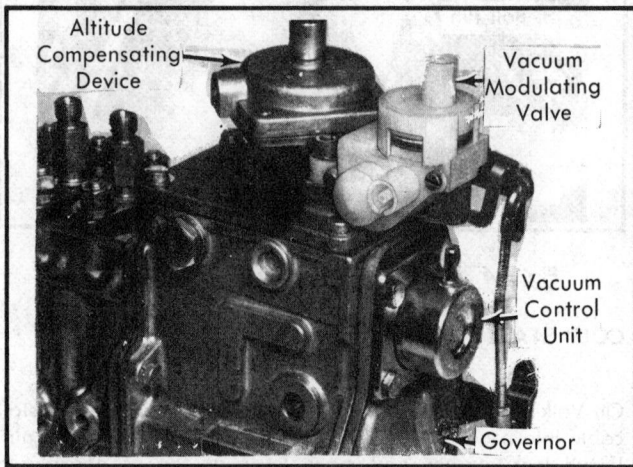

Altitude
Compensating
Device

Vacuum
Modulating
Valve

Vacuum
Control
Unit

Governor

Fig. 2 Altitude Compensation & Vacuum Units

MAIN FUEL FILTER

The main fuel filter is a disposable cartridge which is screwed onto the filter assembly. After filter is replaced, system must be bled of air.

INJECTION NOZZLES

Injection nozzles are used to spray fuel into the cyinders under the proper pressure and spray pattern for optimum combustion. Nozzles can be disassembled for cleaning and adjustment of opening pressure.

GLOW PLUG SYSTEM

All engines are equipped with pin-type glow plugs which are connected in parallel. The parallel connection allows glow plugs to operate independently of each other and provides 11 volts to each plug during the preglow process. A dual material

BOSCH DIESEL INJECTION — MERCEDES-BENZ (Cont.)

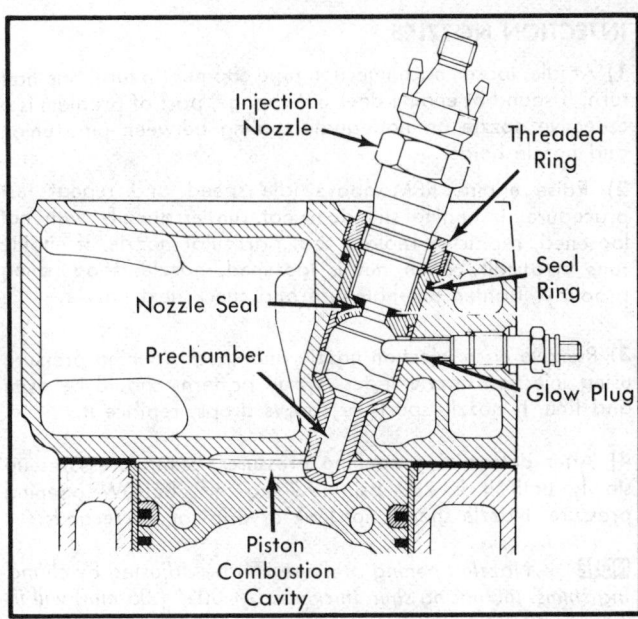

Fig. 3   Cross Section of Cylinder Head

heating element which consists of a heating coil and a control coil has allowed the heating process to be shortened to 5-7 seconds at 32°F (0°C).

NOTE — *This type plug is called the "Quick-Preglow" plug and is identified by a brass hexagon. It must not be interchanged with glow plugs used in previous models.*

The glow plugs are grounded directly to the cylinder head through plug body. Each receives separate power directly from preglow time relay (total initial current draw is approximately 200 amperes).

The preglow time relay is located on the left inner fenderwell. The relay is protected by an 80A fusible link, mounted outside on the cover of the relay. The relay contains a temperature sensitive resistor which replaces the coolant temperature sensor used with previous relays.

A safety cutout in the relay turns off glow plug power 20-35 seconds after the glow plug light goes off when no attempt has been made to start the engine. This keeps battery drain to a minimum and protects the glow plugs.

A switch in the relay is triggered if one or more glow plugs fail. This turns off the indicator lamp and signals a need for repair. The indicator will normally come on for at least one second even if engine is warm.

OVER-BOOST PROTECTION (TURBO MODELS ONLY)

Turbo models are equipped with an over-boost protection circuit, consisting of a pressure switch, switch-over valve and wiring. When boost pressure exceeds 16 psi (1.12 kg/cm^2), the pressure switch closes, grounding the switch-over valve. The valve vents manifold pressure which would otherwise affect the aneroid compensator on the injection pump. This reduces the quantity of fuel injected and engine speed.

TROUBLE SHOOTING

INTERMITTENT BLACK SMOKE

Uneven nozzle operation. Opening pressures, nozzle seals and poor injection pipe sealing.

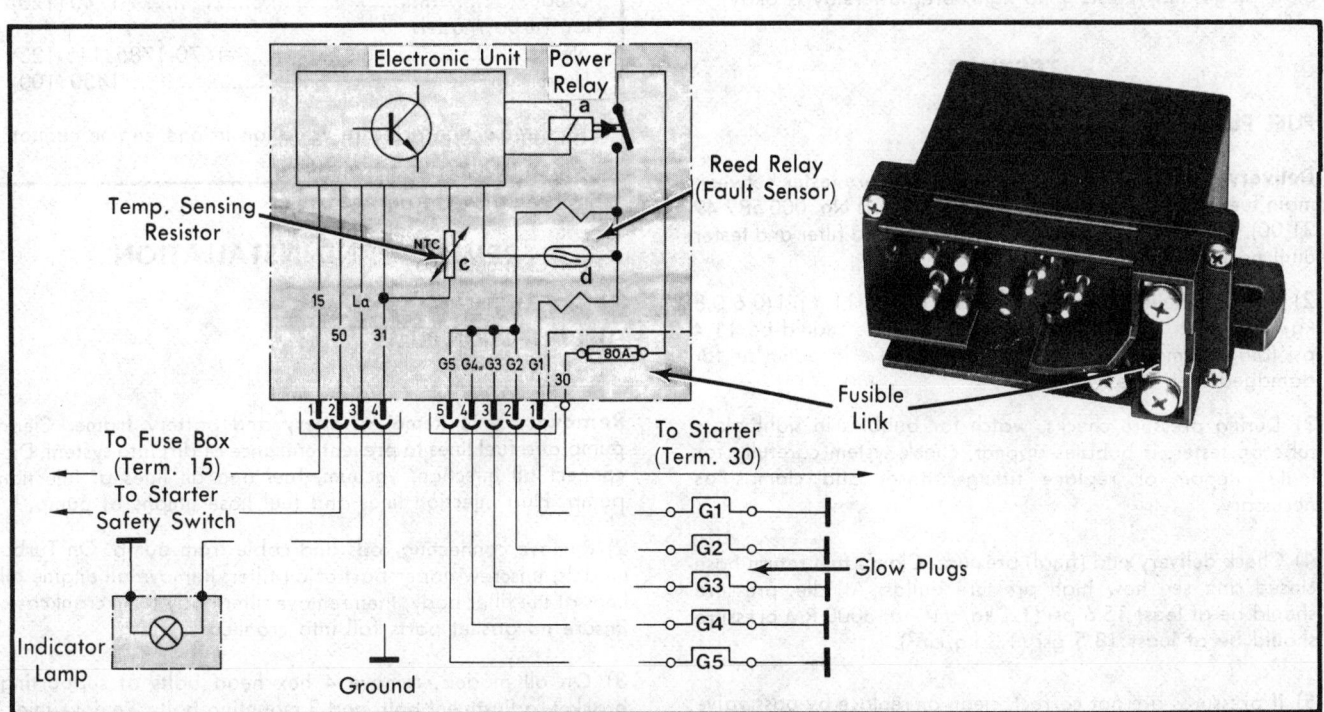

Fig. 4   Glow Plug Relay & Wiring Diagram

BOSCH DIESEL INJECTION — MERCEDES-BENZ (Cont.)

KNOCKING SOUND

Incorrect fuel. Injection pump delivery timing. Valve adjustment. Nozzle spray pattern and opening pressures. Reverse flow dampening valves. Poor compression.

ENGINE DOES NOT STOP

Defective vacuum control unit. Vacuum valve in ignition lock. Poor connections or vacuum leaks.

GLOW PLUG INDICATOR DOES NOT LIGHT
ENGINE STARTS

Burned out bulb. Broken wire to indicator.

GLOW PLUG INDICATOR DOES NOT LIGHT
ENGINE WILL NOT START

Fusible link burned out. Defective preglow relay.

GLOW PLUG INDICATOR DOES NOT LIGHT
ENGINE STARTS WITH DIFFICULTY & MISSES

Glow plug in cylinder No. 1 defective or broken wire. One or more of glow plugs in cylinders 2 through 4 or 5 defective.

GLOW PLUG INDICATOR LIGHTS
ENGINE STARTS WITH DIFFICULTY & MISSES

One or more of glow plugs in cylinders 2 through 4 or 5. (Indicator may light if just 1 glow plug is defective. Disconnect 2 glow plugs and retest. If no light, preglow relay is okay).

TESTING

FUEL PUMP

Delivery Pressure Check — 1) Install pressure tester between main fuel filter and injection pump (Bosch Part No. 000 589 49 21 00). Check for air bubbles in fuel and bleed filter and tester until no bubbles are present.

2) With engine idling, pressure should be 8.5-11.4 psi (0.6-0.8 kg/cm²). With engine at 3000 RPM, pressure should be 11.4 psi (0.8 kg/cm²). If not, check by-pass valve in pump or for damaged fuel lines.

3) During pressure checks, watch for bubbles in sight glass tube on tester. If bubbles appear, check system carefully for leaks. Repair or replace fittings, hoses and clamps as necessary.

4) Check delivery end (final) pressure. Clamp fuel return hose closed and see how high pressure builds. At idle, pressure should be at least 15.6 psi (1.1 kg/cm²); at 3000 RM pressure should be at least 18.5 psi (1.3 kg/cm²).

5) If pressures are not correct, clean or replace by-pass valve or fuel pump.

INJECTION NOZZLES

1) At idle, loosen each injection pipe cap nut (in turn) one-half turn. If sound of engine does not change, part of problem is a defective nozzle or inadequate sealing between pipe union and nozzle holder.

2) Raise engine RPM above idle speed and repeat test procedure. If engine still does not run erratically with nut loosened, repair or replace that particular nozzle. If engine runs erratically when nut is loosened, nozzle is operating properly. Tighten one-half turn and check next nozzle.

3) Remove each injection nozzle and check opening pressure using injection nozzle tester. Spray patterns should be even and fine. If nozzle spurts or sprays drops, replace it.

4) After determining opening pressures, pump pressures up slowly until it is 280 psi (19.7 kg/cm²) BELOW opening pressure. Nozzle should not leak or drip for 10 seconds.

NOTE — *Nozzle opening pressure can be adjusted by changing shims. Increasing shim thickness by .002" (.05 mm) will increase injection pressure by about 45 psi (3 kg/cm²). Shims are available in thicknesses from .039-.070" (1.0-1.8 kg/cm²) in increments of .002" (.05 mm).*

5) When replacing nozzles, always install new seal between nozzle and prechamber. Tighten nozzles carefully to specified torque.

Injection Nozzle Opening Pressures①	
Application	**psi (kg/cm²)**
Turbo Models	
New	1960-2075 (135-143)
Used	1740 (120)
Non-Turbo Models	
New	1670-1785 (115-123)
Used	1450 (100)
① — Maximum pressure variation in one engine cannot exceed 71 psi (5 kg/cm²).	

REMOVAL AND INSTALLATION

FUEL INJECTION PUMP

Removal — 1) Remove battery and battery frame. Clean pump and fuel lines to prevent entrance of dirt into system. Disconnect all injection, vacuum, fuel and oil lines at injection pump. Plug injection lines and fuel hose unions at pump.

2) Remove connecting rods and cable from pump. On Turbo models, unscrew upper part of oil filter. Remove all engine oil lines at the filter body, then remove filter body from crankcase. Ensure no gasket parts fall into crankcase.

3) On all models, remove 4 hex head bolts at supporting bracket, adjustment bolt, and 3 mounting bolts. Remove injection pump rearward.

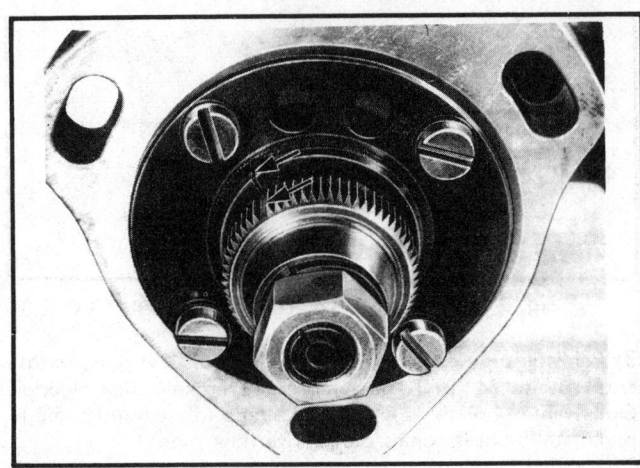

Fig. 5   Injection Pump Mark Alignment

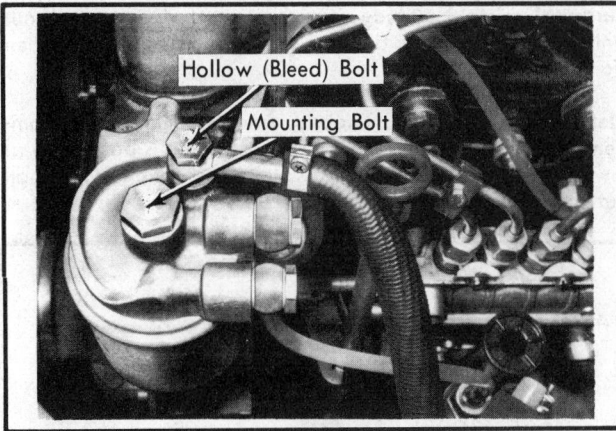

Fig. 6   Fuel Filter Replacement

Installation – **1)** Remove plug on side of pump and add ½ pint engine oil for initial lubrication. Move throttle lever to full throttle stop. Vacuum valve rod should be adjusted so operating lever has .020" (.5 mm) clearance from lever stop. See *Fig. 11*.

2) Attach supporting holder to new pump and turn crankshaft to 24° BTDC. Using new gasket, install pump with shaft and flange marks aligned. See *Fig. 5*.

3) Adjust injection pump timing, then tighten mounting bolts. Install oil and fuel lines, then reinstall oil filter base and filter. Bleed fuel system.

FUEL LINE FITTINGS

Removal & Installation – **1)** If leakage occurs between pipe connection fitting (union) and injection pump adjusting plate, install new seals with "grooved" fittings. DO NOT loosen adjusting plate, or pump recalibration will be necessary.

2) Install new copper gasket whenever fittings are removed. Grooved end of valve carrier should be installed downward. Install other components, then oil fittings and install, tightening smoothly.

3) Install injection lines and operate primer pump until by-pass valve is heard to open. Operate engine and check for leaks.

FUEL FILTER

Removal & Installation – **1)** Replace filter every 30,000 miles. Loosen mounting bolt and pull downward on element and lower housing. See *Fig. 6*.

2) Install new lower housing and element. Tighten mounting bolt. Loosen hollow bolt and operate hand pump (on side of injection pump) until fuel emerges free of bubbles.

3) Retighten hollow bolt and pump until by-pass valve in injection pump opens, signalled by buzzing sound. Start engine and check for leaks.

VACUUM CONTROL UNIT

Removal – **1)** Unscrew lower right-hand mounting screw from vacuum control unit. See *Fig. 7*.

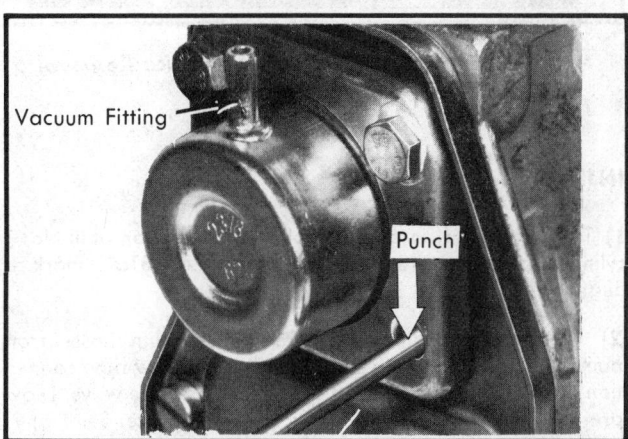

Fig. 7   Vacuum Control Unit Removal & Installation

2) Depress "stop" lever on cylinder head cover. Measure position of main rack by inserting punch into screw bore until it touches main rack. Mark this position on punch.

3) Unscrew remaining three mounting screws and remove control unit.

Installation – **1)** Install new gasket and steel ring. Make sure tang on vacuum control unit engages in main rack. Install last three mounting screws removed.

2) Insert punch in lower right-hand screw bore. Check main rack position with mark on punch. When punch touches main rack, press lightly on punch and move control lever on injection pump from "stop" position to "full load" stop. Punch must follow the main rack smoothly. If correct, install remaining screw.

AUTOMATIC ALTITUDE COMPENSATING DEVICE

NOTE – *Do not attempt to remove upper cover of governor housing. Governor linkage is assembled to altitude compensating device.*

BOSCH DIESEL INJECTION — MERCEDES-BENZ (Cont.)

Removal — Hold altitude compensating device by small nut while turning large nut. Unscrew device and remove shims. See Fig. 8.

Installation — Using previously removed shims, screw compensating device into place. Be sure vent tube is positioned at lowest point to drain off any possible condensation. Hold small nut and tighten large nut.

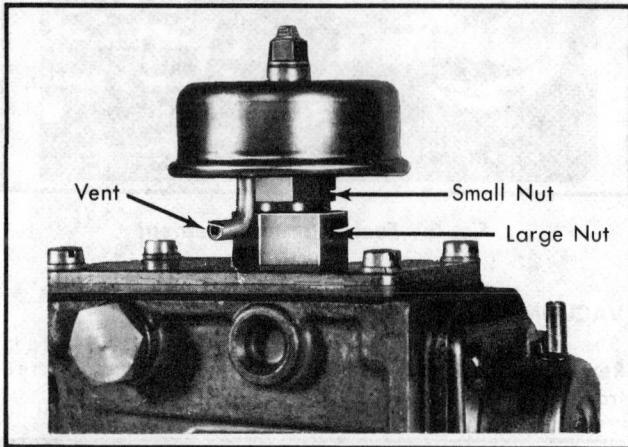

Fig. 8 Altitude Compensating Device Removal

ADJUSTMENTS

INJECTION PUMP TIMING

1) Turn crankshaft in direction of normal rotation until No. 1 cylinder is in compression stroke and 24° BTDC mark is aligned with pointer.

2) Clean pump connections. Remove vacuum hoses from pump. Remove No. 1 injection line, then unscrew pipe connection and remove compression spring and pressure valve. Leave pressure valve carrier and copper gasket in place. See Fig. 9.

CAUTION — Do not unscrew element connection below pipe connection or pump recalibration will be necessary.

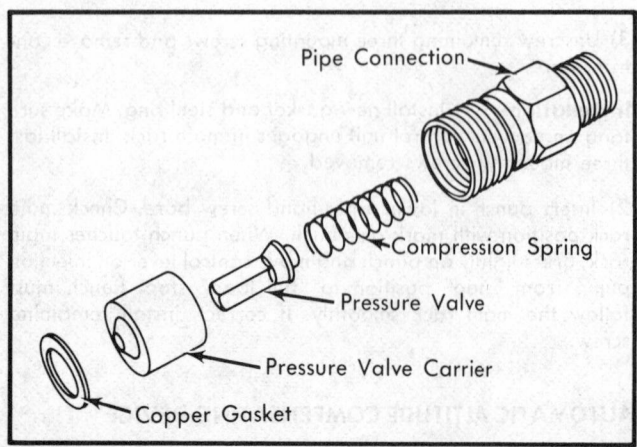

Fig. 9 Injection Pump Pipe Connection Fittings

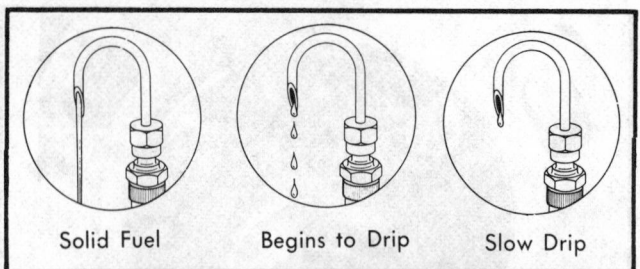

Fig. 10 Checking Overflow Pipe Fuel Flow

3) Reinstall pipe connection and install overflow pipe. Rotate crankcase to 24° BTDC on compression stroke of first cylinder. Open vent or hollow screw on fuel filter and use hand pump to pump fuel until it comes out of overflow pipe.

NOTE — Place throttle lever at full-throttle position while adjusting pump timing and checking overflow.

4) Rotate crankshaft until fuel just stops dripping. One drop should fall about 3 seconds later. Note position on crankshaft pulley and adjust pump position so injection stops at 24° BTDC.

5) Turn crankshaft 2 full turns and check that fuel dripping stops with pump and crankshaft marks in correct position. Tighten pump bolts. Remove overflow pipe and install pressure valve, spring and pipe connection. Tighten fitting to 29-36 ft. lbs. (39-49 N.m) in one smooth motion.

6) Install injection line and bleed fuel system. Run engine and check for leaks. If fitting leaks, replace pipe connection and copper gasket under pressure valve carrier.

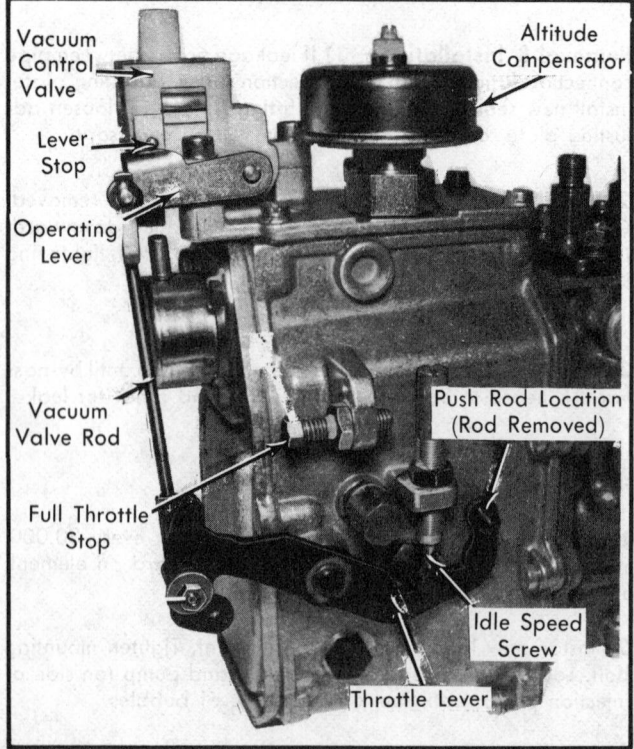

Fig. 11 Injection Pump Adjustment Locations

BOSCH DIESEL INJECTION — MERCEDES-BENZ (Cont.)

IDLE SPEED

1) Warm engine to normal operating temperature. Turn idle speed knob in dashboard clockwise to stop (if equipped). Disconnect push rod on throttle lever. See *Fig. 11.*

2) Adjust idle speed to 700-800 RPM using idle speed screw. Adjust push rod so no pressure is exerted against "Stop" lever and throttle lever is against idle speed screw. Reconnect push rod.

MAXIMUM SPEED

Adjust full throttle stop screw so maximum engine speed does not exceed 4900-5200 RPM.

TIGHTENING SPECIFICATIONS	
Application	**Ft. Lbs. (N.m)**
Rocker Arm Cover	3.6 (5)
Glow Plugs	36.0 (49)
Nozzle-to-Holder	54.0 (73)
Nozzle Holder-to-Head	54.0 (73)
Nozzle Holder Connector	54.0 (73)
Injection Pump Shaft Nut	50.6 (69)
Connecting Fitting (Union)	29.0-39.0 (39-49)
Injection Pipe Cap Nuts	18.0 (24)

BOSCH DIESEL FUEL INJECTION — PEUGEOT & VOLVO

Peugeot
504
505
505 Turbo
604 Turbo
Volvo
Diesel

DESCRIPTION

The diesel fuel injection systems consist of the fuel tank, fuel filter, distributor-type injection pump, glow plugs, throttle pintle injection nozzles and a centrifugal governor. *See Fig. 1.*

A vane type fuel pump, built into the injection pump, supplies fuel from the fuel filter to the injection pump. Injection pump supplies fuel to injection nozzles under high pressure, according to firing sequence (1-3-4-2 on Peugeot and 1-5-3-6-2-4 on Volvo). Excess fuel is returned to fuel tank by return lines.

SYSTEM COMPONENTS

FUEL INJECTION PUMP

The Bosch single plunger mechanical pump consists of a low-pressure, vane-type fuel pump, a high-pressure distributor-type plunger injection pump, a centrifugal governor, and an injection timing advance mechanism. Both pumps are equipped with an electrical fuel shut-off solenoid. *See Fig. 1.*

As the vane type pump rotor turns, centrifugal force holds the vanes against the walls of the pump's pressure chamber. The offset design of the rotor and pressure chamber, squeezes trapped fuel between vanes and forces it out the delivery port.

Vane pressure of the Peugeot pump is 65-73 psi (4.6-5.1 kg/cm^2) at 1600 RPM or 87-94 psi (6.1-6.6 kg/cm) at 2200 RPM. The main pump increases this pressure to approximately 1800 psi (126 kg/cm^2).

NOTE — *Vane pressures are given at pump speed, not engine speed and were not available for Volvo models.*

INJECTION NOZZLES

The Peugeot engines use DNO SD 1510 nozzles with KCA 17S38/4 holders. Opening pressure is 1775-1917 psi (124.8-134.8 kg/cm^2). Volvo engines use DNO SD 193 nozzles with KCA 30 SD 27/4 holders. Opening pressure is 1706-1849 (120-130 kg/cm^2).

A pressurized mist of fuel is injected into a round swirl chamber. Fuel swirls around the chamber mixing with hot air, compressed at 23:1 for Peugeot and 23.5:1 for Volvo.

Combustion actually begins in the rich swirl chamber and continues on through a small passageway and into the leaner main chamber. As peak cylinder pressures build in swirl chamber, rather than main chamber, loads on connecting rods and crankshaft are reduced.

GLOW PLUGS

Glow plugs are used during cold starts to preheat swirl chambers. The system is switched "ON" when the key switch is turned to position 2. Preheating time depends on a coolant temperature switch connected to time circuit in the glow plug relay. Glow plugs remain on approximately 10-25 seconds after the dashboard indicator light has gone out.

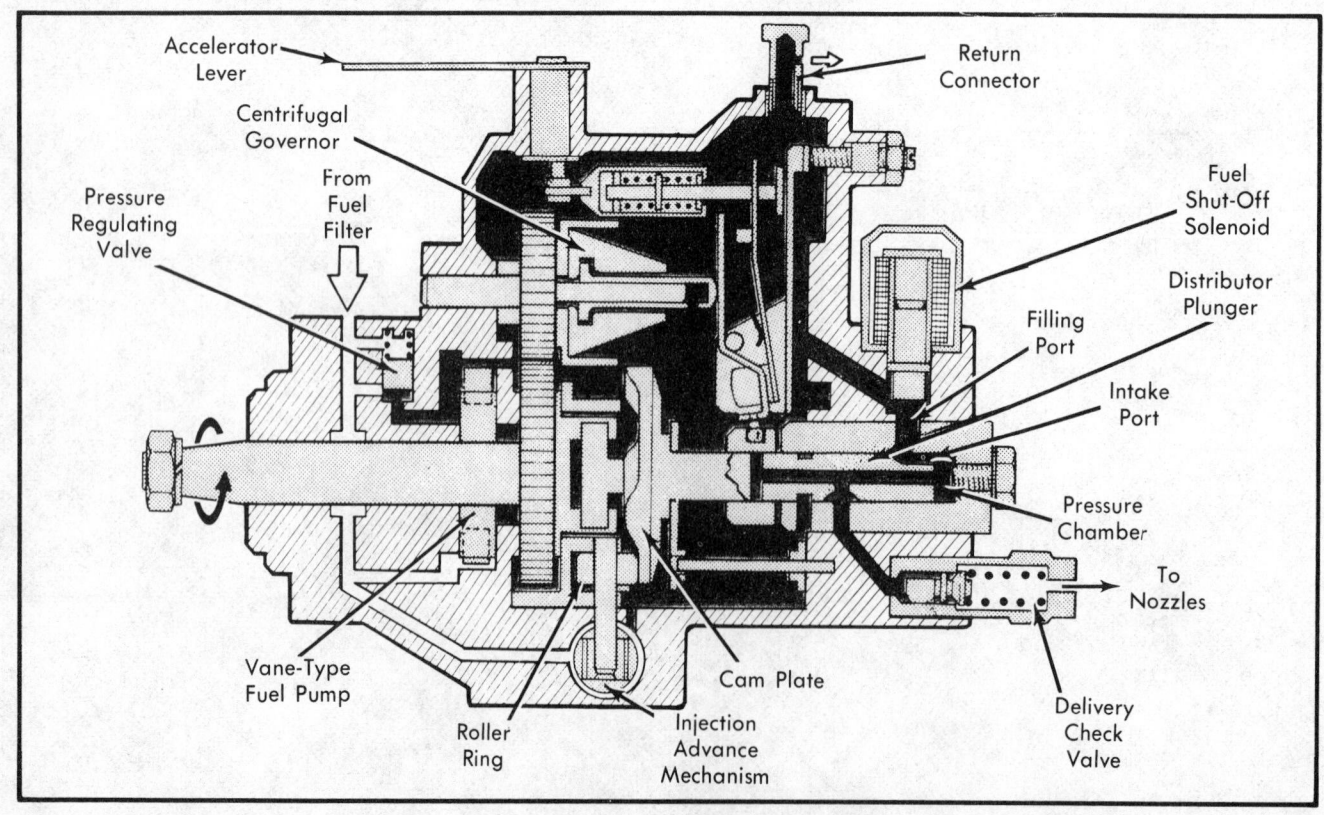

Fig. 1 Cutaway View of Volvo Fuel Injection Pump

BOSCH DIESEL FUEL INJECTION – PEUGEOT & VOLVO (Cont.)

Glow plugs operate when starter motor is rotating (key position 3) and cut out when engine starts and start key is released back to position 2. To repeat starting attempt, key switch must first be returned to position 1. A blocking relay is incorporated in the system to interrupt electrical circuit between the control unit and glow plug relay when alternator starts charging.

NOTE – *Automatic cold starting devices are also incorporated into the injection pump to assist starting by advancing injection timing.*

FUEL FILTER

The fuel filter is a cartridge type filter, with the housing and filter being replaced as a unit. A water separator is built into the filter, as diesel systems are highly susceptible to water damage. For example, diesel fuel is used to lubricate the injection pump, and water would cause contamination and corrosion.

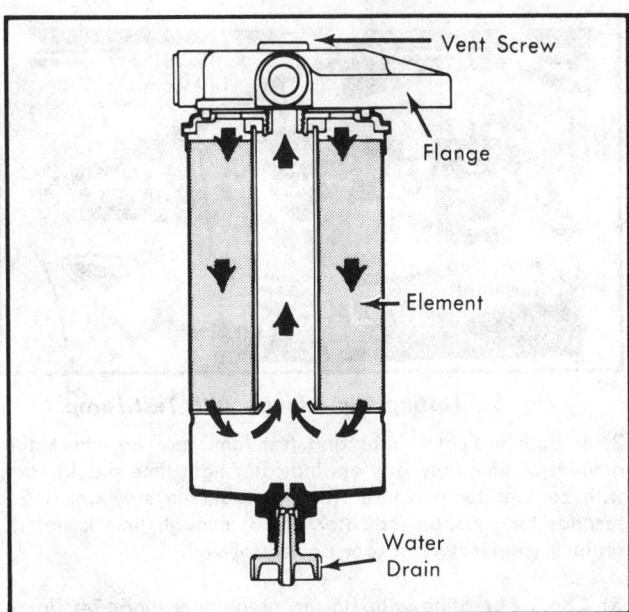

Fig. 2 Components of Fuel Filter

CENTRIFUGAL GOVERNOR

The amount of fuel injected is controlled by changing the injection cut-off point according to engine speed and load conditions. The cut-off point is controlled by the position of the metering sleeve around the distributor plunger. The sleeve normally covers a relief port in the plunger. Uncovering the port stops injection. The sleeve position is determined by a centrifugal governor, and accelerator linkage. A large quantity of fuel is supplied during starting, and less at idle. No fuel is allowed to pass when the engine exceeds a predetermined maximum RPM.

TESTING

INJECTION NOZZLES

Problems with injection nozzles usually are accompanied by knocking in one or more cylinders, engine overheating, loss of power or performance, black exhaust smoke and increased fuel consumption. To locate and correct faulty injectors, proceed as follows:

1) Remove vacuum pump and vacuum pump plunger. Loosen line unions on each injection nozzle, one at a time with engine running at fast idle. If engine speed remains constant with line removed, that nozzle is defective.

2) To remove nozzle, detach injector line after cleaning connection. Plug all openings to keep dirt out of fuel system. To disassemble, place upper section in vise and loosen lower section, then reverse position and carefully remove parts from lower section. Do not interchange parts from one injector to another.

3) Clean all parts in diesel oil. Install new heat shields with recess in shield pointing upward. On Peugeot, use new copper gaskets. Tighten nozzles to secified torque.

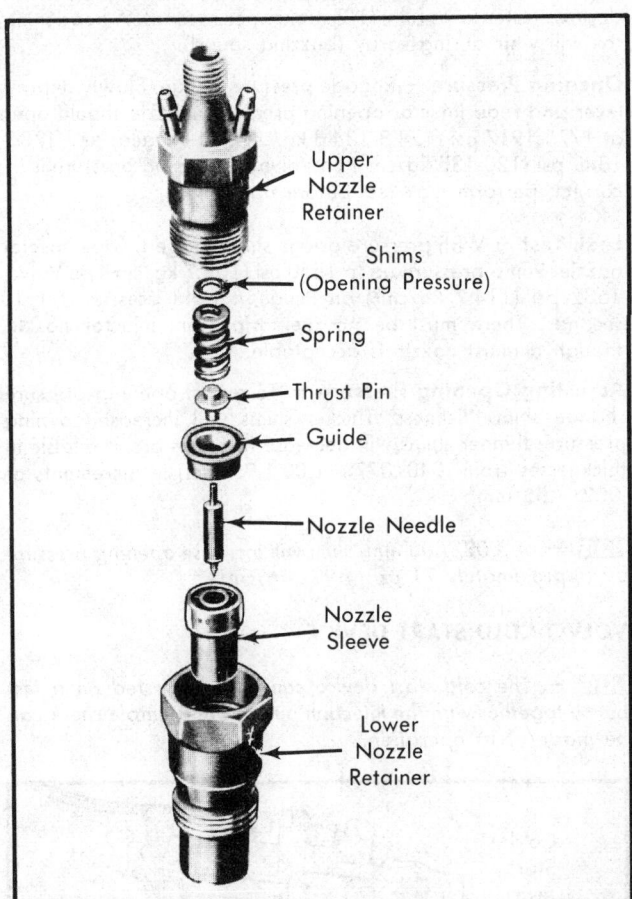

Fig. 3 Disassembled View of Injector Nozzle

Spray Pattern – Install injector in tester. Seal fuel return lines with rubber plugs and hose clamps. Disengage pressure gauge. Pump lever with short, quick strokes (4-6 per second). Spray jet should be compact and stop abruptly. Injector must not drip.

CAUTION – *Do not expose hands to injector spray during testing, as working pressure will cause fuel oil to penetrate the skin.*

BOSCH DIESEL FUEL INJECTION — PEUGEOT & VOLVO (Cont.)

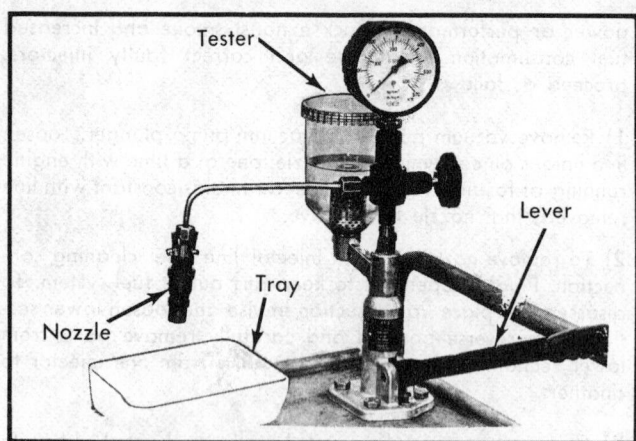

Fig. 4   Injection Nozzle Test Gauge

Injection Sound — With gauge still disengaged, slowly depress tester lever fully (1-2 strokes per second). A good injector will whir during spray (buzzing sound).

Opening Pressure — Engage pressure gauge. Slowly depress lever and read injector opening pressure. Nozzle should open at 1775-1917 psi (124.8-134.8 kg/cm²) on Peugeot and 1706-1849 psi (120-130 kg/cm²) on Volvo. If opening pressure is incorrect, perform leak test before adjusting.

Leak Test — With pressure gauge still engaged, wipe injector nozzle. Pump pressure up to 1560 psi (109.7 kg/cm²) on Volvo, 1632 psi (114.7 kg/cm²) on Peugeot. Hold pressure for 10 seconds. There must be no fuel drip from injector nozzle, though a moist nozzle is acceptable.

Adjusting Opening Pressure — To adjust opening pressure change shim thickness. Thicker shims will increase opening pressure; thinner shims will decrease it. Shims are available in thicknesses from .040-.077" (1.00-1.95 mm) in increments of .002" (.05 mm).

NOTE — *A .002" (.05 mm) shim will increase opening pressure by approximately 71 psi (4.992 kg/cm²).*

VOLVO COLD START DEVICE

NOTE — *The cold start device can only be tested on a test bench together with the injection pump, but a simple check can be made of its operation.*

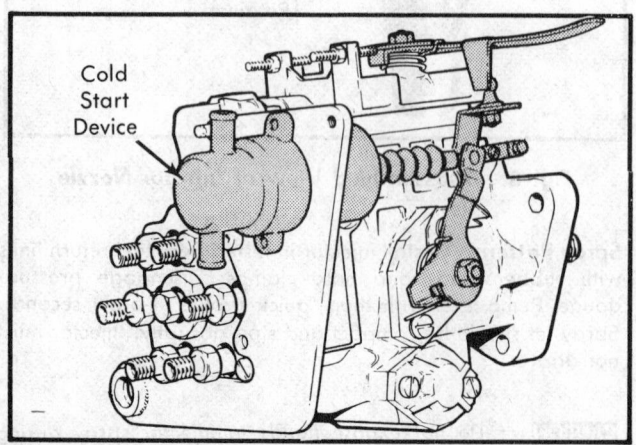

Fig. 5   Volvo Cold Start Device Check

1) Cold start malfunction usually is indicated by hard starting of a cold engine, failure of engine to start below 14°F (−10°C), or blue-white exhaust smoke. Check idle speed with engine cold and at normal operating temperature.

2) With cold engine, below 70°F (20°C), engine should idle at approximately 950 RPM. With engine at normal operating temperature, idle speed should be lower, approximately 750-800 RPM. The cold start lever should clear lever on injection pump. If idle speeds do not vary as specified, cold start device is defective.

VOLVO GLOW PLUG SYSTEM

1) Connect 12-volt test lamp across glow plug terminal and ground. Check test lamp and indicator light on instrument panel. If both are out, control unit is defective. If indicator light is on, but test lamp is not, glow plug relay is defective. If indicator light is out, but test lamp is on, check coolant temperature sender or control unit.

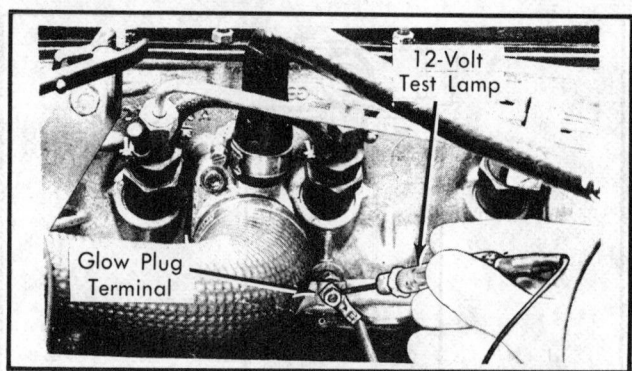

Fig. 6   Testing Glow Plugs with Test Lamp

2) If both indicator light and test lamp are on, check the amount of time they stay on. Indicator light time should vary with coolant temperature. Test lamp should stay on 10-25 seconds longer than indicator. If not enough time is noted, replace temperature sender or control unit.

3) Check operation with starter motor operating. Test lamp should light, indicating voltage at glow plugs. If not, check voltage with test lamp at terminal 50 (blue-yellow wire) of control unit. If there is voltage, control unit is defective. If no voltage, check for open circuit between connector and control unit.

4) If test light was on during starter operation, check glow plugs one at a time. Place key switch in position "0". Remove bar between glow plug terminals. Connect test lamp across battery positive terminal and one glow plug. If light is out at one or more glow plugs, glow plugs are faulty. If test lamp and indicator fail to light, replace control unit.

5) If indicator light and test lamp are both out, make progressive voltage checks as indicated:

- Terminal 15 (blue-red wire) of control unit. If no voltage, check for open circuit between fuse box and control unit.
- Terminal 31 (black wire) of control unit (test lamp connected to battery positive terminal and terminal 31). If no voltage, check for faulty ground. If voltage, check for defective control unit.

6) If indicator light is on, but test lamp is out, make the following progressive voltage checks:

BOSCH DIESEL FUEL INJECTION — PEUGEOT & VOLVO (Cont.)

- Terminal 86 (red wire) of glow plug relay (test lamp connected to battery positive terminal and terminal 86). Voltage indicates faulty glow plug relay. No voltage indicates incorrect ground connection.
- Terminal G (blue wire) of control unit. No voltage indicates faulty control unit.
- Terminal 30 (blue wire) of blocking relay. No voltage indicates open circuit in wire between control unit and blocking relay.
- Terminal 87 (red wire) of blocking relay. Voltage indicates open circuit in wire between blocking relay and glow plug relay.
- Terminal 86 (blue-red wire) of blocking relay. No voltage indicates open circuit in wire between fuse box and blocking relay.
- Terminal 85 (red wire) of blocking relay (connect test lamp between fuse box positive and terminal 85). No voltage indicates faulty blocking relay. Voltage indicates open circuit in wire between blocking relay and instrument panel or defect in instrument panel printed circuit.

7) If indicator light is out, but test lamp is on, this usually indicates a failure of either the temperature sender or control unit. Disconnect wire at temperature sender. Indicator light should now be on. If so, this indicates circuit from sender to indicator light is OK, but sender is defective.

8) Check ground connection at terminal K (yellow wire) of control unit. Connect test lamp from battery positive terminal to terminal K. If voltage is indicated, indicator light on instrument panel is defective, there is a defective wire between control unit and indicator light or printed circuit is faulty. If no voltage exists, either the control unit is defective or wire between temperature sender and control unit is grounded.

9) If indicator light comes on when engine is warm, disconnect wire at temperature sender and ground it. Turn key switch to driving position "2" and check indicator light. If light is on, there is an open circuit in wire between temperature sender and control unit or control unit is defective. If indicator light is out, temperature sender is faulty.

PEUGEOT GLOW PLUG SYSTEM

Current to glow plugs flows through starter relay to Pre-Heat Control Box (located at center of firewall). A timer in control box provides power to glow plugs for 10-90 seconds, depending on ambient temperature. The following checks can be made on this system:

1) Check system ground between terminal 2 on control box and frame. Check condition of glow plug bulb and ground connection in instrument panel.

2) To locate shorted glow plugs, remove connecting straps between plugs. Connect a heavy jumper wire between terminal 5 of control box and each plug, one at a time. Leave jumper wire connected for about 2 seconds.

3) If glow plugs are bad, glow plug relay will cycle rapidly on and off. Replace shorted glow plugs.

REMOVAL & INSTALLATION

VOLVO FUEL INJECTION PUMP

NOTE — *As injectors are manufactured to extremely small tolerances (pump cylinder and bore clearance is .00004-.00008" or .001-.002 mm), extreme cleanliness is a necessity. Clean all injection pump and nozzle unions before removal.*

Removal — 1) Use clamping pliers to pinch off coolant hoses for cold start device. Disconnect hoses at cold start device. Disconnect accelerator cable and kickdown cable (automatic transmission) from cable pulley. Disconnect wire at fuel shut-off solenoid.

2) Remove rear timing gear cover. Clean fuel line connections at injection pump. Disconnect fuel supply and return lines at pump. Plug open connections to prevent dirt from entering fuel system.

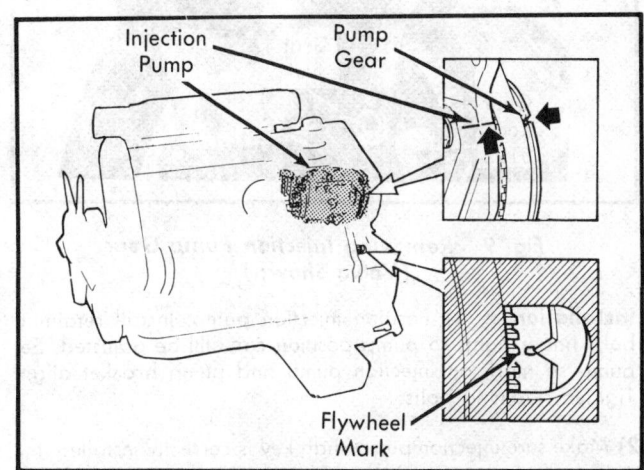

Fig. 8   Volvo Injection Pump Timing Mark Alignment (Check Before Removing Pump)

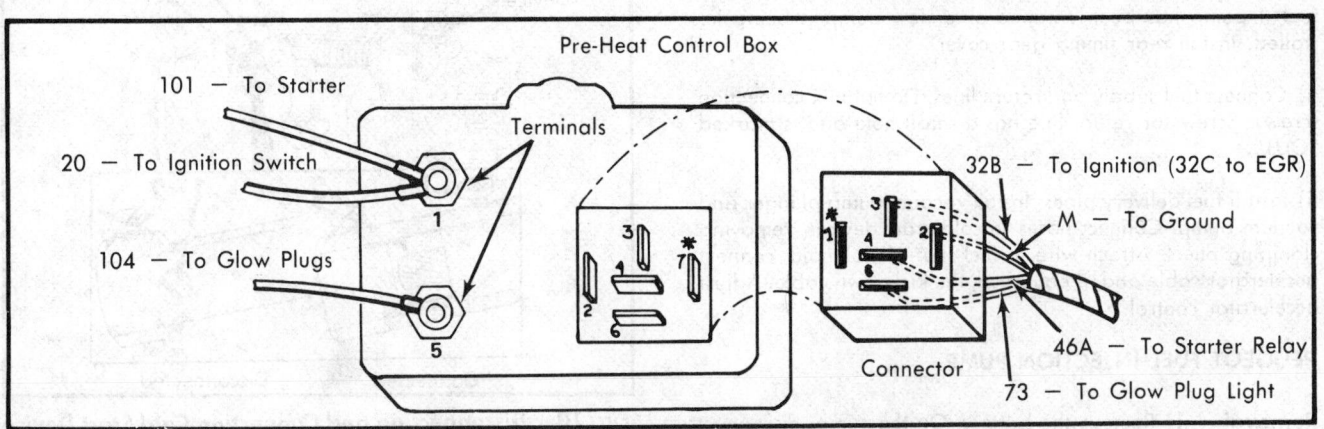

Fig. 7   Peugeot Pre-Heat Control Box Connections

BOSCH DIESEL FUEL INJECTION – PEUGEOT & VOLVO (Cont.)

3) Remove vacuum pump and pump plunger. Remove injection pump delivery pipes. Plug all openings. Set cylinder No. 1 at TDC on compression stroke. Timing marks should align.

4) Remove injection pump drive belt, after relieving tension by loosening injection pump bracket bolts. Tighten one bolt to retain injection pump in upper position.

5) Loosen camshaft rear gear, using special tool (5199) to hold gear while loosening with special tool (5201). Camshaft must not rotate. Loosen bolts only enough to let gear rotate on camshaft.

6) Lock injection pump gear with stop (5193). Remove gear nut with special tool (5201). Remove pump gear with puller (5204). Remove injection pump front bracket bolts and rear retaining bolts. Lift off pump and front bracket.

Fig. 9   Removing Injection Pump Gear (Volvo Shown)

Installation – 1) Position injection pump. Install retaining bolts finger tight, so pump position can still be adjusted. Set pump so mark on injection pump and pump bracket align. Tighten retaining bolts.

2) Make sure injection pump shaft key is correctly installed. Install gear, washer and nut. Lock gear with special tool (5193) and tighten nut with special tool (5201).

3) Set injection pump timing. Fill injection pump with diesel fuel if pump has been emptied or a new pump is being installed. Install rear timing gear cover.

4) Connect fuel supply and return lines. Do not mix connection screws. Screw for return line has a small hole and is marked "OUT".

5) Install fuel delivery pipes. Install vacuum pump plunger and vacuum pump. Connect hoses to cold start devices, removing clamping pliers. Attach wire to fuel shut-off solenoid, connect accelerator cable and, if equipped, the kickdown cable. Adjust accelerator control.

PEUGEOT FUEL INJECTION PUMP

Removal – 1) Remove the battery. On the pump, disconnect fuel supply and return lines. Disconnect control cables, fuel shut-off electrovalve wire, and load sensor harness (if equipped).

2) Remove injector pipes. Remove 2 front mounting bolts and pump rear support. Remove the pump and cap all fuel openings.

Installation – 1) Remove engine valve cover. Bring valves of No. 1 cylinder to a rocking position, then turn engine back approximately 90°. Using a valve spring compresssor, compress No. 4 exhaust valve spring and move rocker arm to one side.

2) Rotate the engine back to rocking position of No. 1 cylinder. Remove half cones, washers and springs from No. 4 exhaust valve. Install a dial indicator onto No. 4 exhaust valve stem, using suitable supports (8.0177 ZZ).

3) Bring the engine to TDC at No. 4 cylinder. Zero the dial indicator. Rotate the engine backwards to 7 mm BTDC. Clean the hydraulic head on the injection pump and remove the inspection plug. Turn the pump shaft to bring the double tooth of the injection pump in line with the double groove of the engine pump hub pinion.

4) Coat a new gasket with grease and install on pump flange. Install pump on engine and install mounting bolts without tightening. Adjust timing as outlined in *Adjustments*.

FUEL FILTER

Service is limited to draining water periodically and normal filter replacement. To drain water, loosen bleed screw on top several turns with screw driver. Loosen drain screw by hand and drain fluid until only clean fuel runs out. On Volvo, close both screws. On Peugeot, close drain screw and actuate manual primer pump until fuel flows without bubbles at bleed screw. Retighten bleed screw.

ADJUSTMENTS

FUEL INJECTION PUMP TIMING

Volvo – 1) Remove rear timing gear cover. Disconnect cold start device by loosening screw "1", pushing lever forward and rotating it 90°. DO NOT touch screw "2". If it is loosened, cold start device must be reset on a test bench.

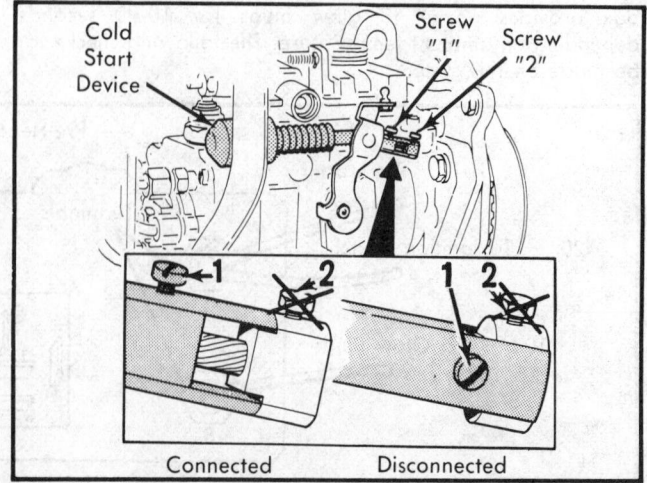

Fig. 10   Disconnecting and Connecting Cold Start Device (Volvo Shown)

BOSCH DIESEL FUEL INJECTION – PEUGEOT & VOLVO (Cont.)

2) Set cylinder No. 1 at TDC and injection. Both cam lobes should point up at equally large angles. Flywheel timing mark should be at "0". *See Fig. 3.*

3) Remove the plug from the injection pump cover. Install dial indicator holder (5194) and a 0-.12" (0-3 mm) dial indicator gauge. Preset indicator to approximately .08" (2 mm). Turn engine counterclockwise until indicator gauge is at minimum. Set gauge to zero.

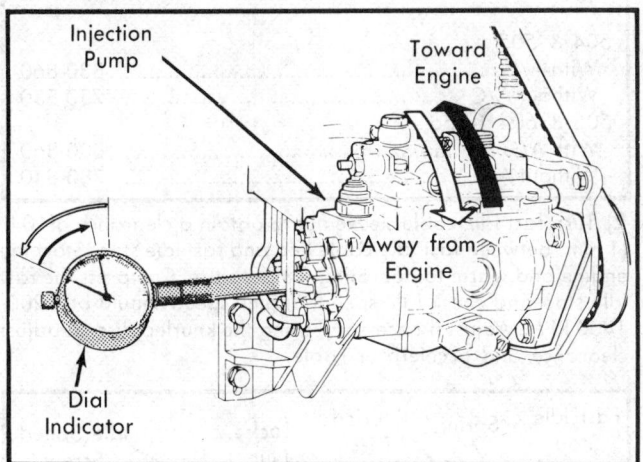

Fig. 11 Timing Volvo Fuel Injection Pump

4) Turn engine clockwise until flywheel "0" mark aligns with arrow. Indicator gauge should now read .0256-.0287" (.65-.73 mm).

NOTE – *These specifications are for checking pump setting. When actually setting pump, reading should be exactly .028" (.70 mm). Also, when making check, if engine is turned too far past "0" mark, it must be turned back approximately ¼ turn and then clockwise again to "0" or settings will be incorrect.*

5) If reading is less than .0256" (.65 mm), loosen injection pump retaining bolts. Turn injection pump inward until .028" (.70 mm) is indicated on gauge. Tighten retaining bolts.

6) If reading is more than .0287" (.73 mm), loosen injection pump retaining bolts. Turn injection pump outward until reading is approximately .0236" (.60 mm) and then turn pump inward until it is at .028" (.70 mm). Tighten injection pump retaining bolts.

CAUTION – *If adjusting allowances in steps 5) and 6) are insufficient, do not tap or knock injection pump to change setting. It may be camshaft is not in proper relationship to crankshaft and/or front or rear drive belts may be improperly tensioned. Correct this and then set injection timing.*

7) After adjusting injection pump setting, turn engine twice and recheck setting. Readjust as necessary. Remove dial indicator and holder. Install rear timing gear cover.

8) Reconnect cold start device, remembering not to turn screw "2". Push lever forward and turn sleeve 90°. Tighten screw "1".

Peugeot – **1)** With pump mounting bolts loose, dial indicator attached to No. 4 cylinder exhaust valve, and engine at 7 mm BTDC, rotate the injection pump body away from the engine.

See Injection Pump Installation. Install dial indicator to pump using suitable adapters (8.0117T, P and S).

2) Turn engine and locate BDC and TDC points on the dial indicator. At BDC the pump dial indicator should have some preload. Zero the pump dial indicator at BDC. Bring piston No. 4 to TDC of compression stroke. Check zero point of engine dial indicator.

3) Turn engine 90° in reverse, and recheck pump dial indicator. Turn engine in normal direction of rotation and bring No. 4 piston to .038" (.97 mm) BTDC for non-Turbo models, and to .016" (.40 mm) BTDC for Turbo models. Rotate the pump towards the engine until the pump dial indicator indicates a pump lift of .020" (.50 mm).

4) Tighten pump mounting bolts, front and rear. Check timing by rotating the engine the normal direction 2 turns. Turn engine back approximately 90°. Rotate engine slowly in normal direction while watching the pump dial indicator. Stop turning the engine when indiator shows a lift of .020" (.50 mm).

5) No. 4 piston should then be at .038" (.97 mm) BTDC for non-Turbo models, and .016" (.40 mm) BTDC for Turbo models. If readjustment is necessary rotate the pump. Remove dial indicators and supports. Reinstall inspection plug with a new gasket. Install springs, washer and half cones of No. 4 exhaust valve and adjust clearance. Reinstall pipes, hoses and controls. Adjust cables and bleed fuel circuit.

VOLVO ENGINE CONTROLS

1) Disconnect cold start device. Disconnect link rod at lever on injection pump. Adjust accelerator cable by turning sheath until cable is stretched, but does not influence pulley position. Pulley should touch idle stop.

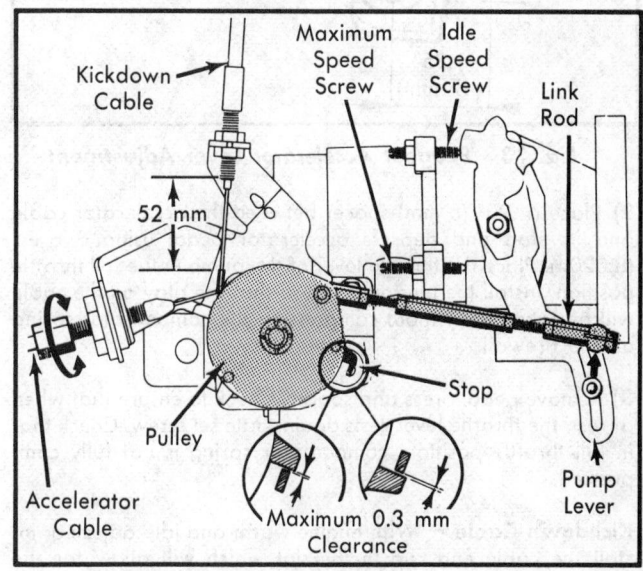

Fig. 12 Adjusting Volvo Control Cables

2) Depress accelerator pedal fully. Pulley should touch full speed stop. Adjust kickdown cable on automatic transmission models. Depress accelerator pedal to floor. Kickdown cable should move approximately 2.05" (52 mm) between end positions. In idle position, kickdown cable should be stretched and distance between kickdown cable clip and cable sheath should be .01-.04" (.25-1.0 mm).

BOSCH DIESEL FUEL INJECTION — PEUGEOT & VOLVO (Cont.)

3) Connect link rod to injection pump lever. Adjust link rod in maximum position by turning pulley to maximum position. Adjust link rod length so injection pump lever touches the maximum speed adjusting screw.

4) Adjust link rod in idle position by returning pulley to idle stop. Move link rod ball joint in oblong hole in injection pump lever until lever touches idle adjusting screw.

5) Readjust link rod by repeating steps **3)** and **4)**. A clearance of .012" (.3 mm) is permitted between pulley and maximum speed stop. Reconnect cold start device.

PEUGEOT ENGINE CONTROLS

Accelerator Cable — 1) With warm engine and idle speed adjusted, position the cable stop within the elongated hole in order to obtain total cable travel of 1.85±.08" (47±2 mm) between idle set screw and maximum RPM stop.

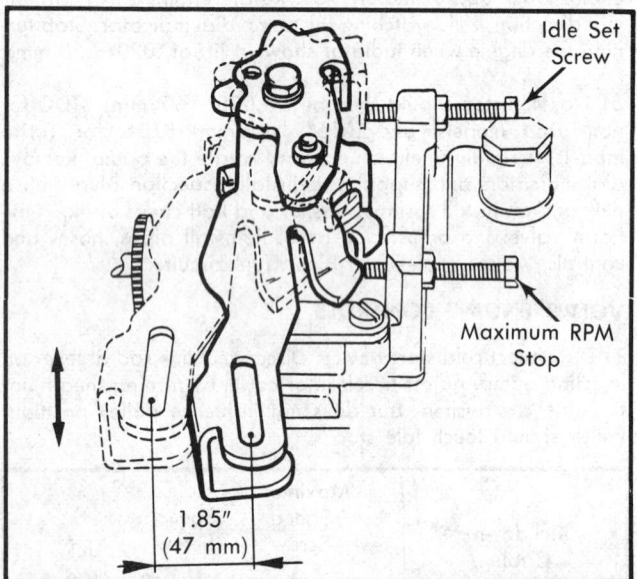

Fig. 13 Peugeot Accelerator Lever Adjustment

2) Place a .20" (5 mm) spacer between the accelerator cable and its stop and depress accelerator pedal using a press (8.0204). Place the throttle lever of the pump in the full throttle position. Install the tensioner clip so that the play on the cable will be taken up without compressing the compensator spring on the firewall.

3) Remove pedal press and spacer. Check to ensure that when at rest, the throttle lever rests against idle set screw. Check that in full throttle position, compensator spring is not fully compressed.

Kickdown Cable — With engine warm and idle adjusted, install the cable end clip in the slot which will allow for the straightest routing of the cable. Loosen locknut of the tensioner. Adjust the tensioner to obtain .004-.020" (0.1-0.5 mm) play between the end clip and the end of the tensioner. Retighten the locknut while immobilizing the tensioner.

IDLE SPEED

Volvo — Run engine to normal operating temperature. Using a Volvo Monotester and adapter (9950), or a photoelectric tachometer, check idle speed. Speed should be 750-850 RPM.

Adjust outer screw to obtain correct speed. Apply tamperproof seal and lock nut after adjustment.

Peugeot — 1) With engine warm, attach tachometer. Check that accelerated idle stop is not in contact with throttle lever and that accelerator cable is released. Adjust set screw to obtain idle speed as listed in table.

Peugeot Idle Speed	
Application	**Idle RPM**
504 & 505	
With A/C	830-860
Without A/C	730-830
505 & 604 Turbo	
With A/C	800-860
Without A/C	780-840

2) Turn fast idle cable sleeve nut to obtain a clearance of .04" (1 mm) between fast idle cable end and fast idle step. Start the engine and warm to operating temperature. Compress the fast idle stop and check idle speed. Engine speed should be 1200-1400 RPM. Adjust if necessary, using the knurled disc. Readjust clearance and accelerator cable.

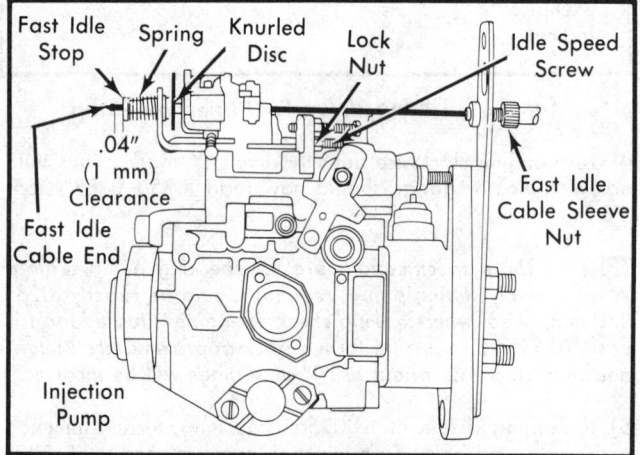

Fig. 14 Peugeot Idle Speed Adjustment Locations

MAXIMUM SPEED

Volvo — Maximum speed setting should be 5100-5300 RPM. Adjust inner screw to obtain setting. Apply tamperproof seal on screw and locknut after adjustment.

NOTE — *Do not race engine any longer than necessary.*

Peugeot — Accelerate engine to full throttle and quickly adjust maximum speed screw to obtain 4800 RPM. Tighten lock nut after adjustment.

TIGHTENING SPECIFICATIONS	
Application	**Ft. Lbs. (N·m)**
Injection Pump Mounting Bolts	15 (20)
Glow Plugs	16 (22)
Fuel Injection Line Unions	18 (25)
Injector Nozzle (Upper-to-Lower Part)	51 (70)
Injector Nozzle-to-Socket	51 (70)

DATSUN DIESEL FUEL INJECTION – PICKUP

Pickup

DESCRIPTION

The diesel injection system includes a fuel injection pump, an injection pump controller system, governor, fuel filter, fuel lines, injector nozzles and glow plug system. The pump controller system consists of a gearing assembly, a control unit and a connecting rod. The purpose of the system is to supply excess fuel for engine firing, and to cut the fuel supply when the ignition is turned off. The glow plug system includes a glow plug timer (in cab, on kick panel below glove box), a glow plug relay (above right shock tower, behind battery) and a water temperature sensor (on front left side of engine block).

OPERATION

FUEL INJECTION PUMP

The injection pump is gear driven off of an idler pulley at the front of the engine. It draws fuel from the tank, pressurizes it, and injects a specific quantity to each cylinder at the proper time. Excess fuel is returned to the tank through another line. In the event of pump failure, the assembly must be replaced as a complete unit.

INJECTION PUMP CONTROLLER

The pump controller system uses a gearing assembly, a connecting rod linking the gearing assembly to the injection pump control lever, and a control unit which is wired to the ignition switch. When the ignition is in the start position, the gears in the assembly rotate, moving the injection pump control lever to an excessive fuel condition. This aids engine starting. When the ignition is turned off, the lever is moved to a position of no fuel delivery, and the engine stops. During normal engine operation, the system maintains a normal mixture.

INJECTION NOZZLES

The injection nozzles spray fuel into a swirl chamber as each compression stroke occurs. Each nozzle has a fuel supply and return line. Nozzles can be disassembled, cleaned and adjusted to correct defective spray patterns. Shims are used to correct nozzle opening pressures. Changing shim size by .002" (.05 mm) will change opening pressure by about 85 psi (6 kg/cm^2).

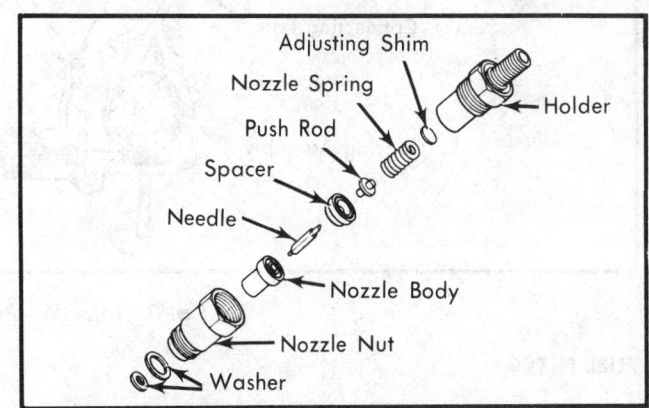

Fig. 2   Exploded View of Fuel Injection Nozzle

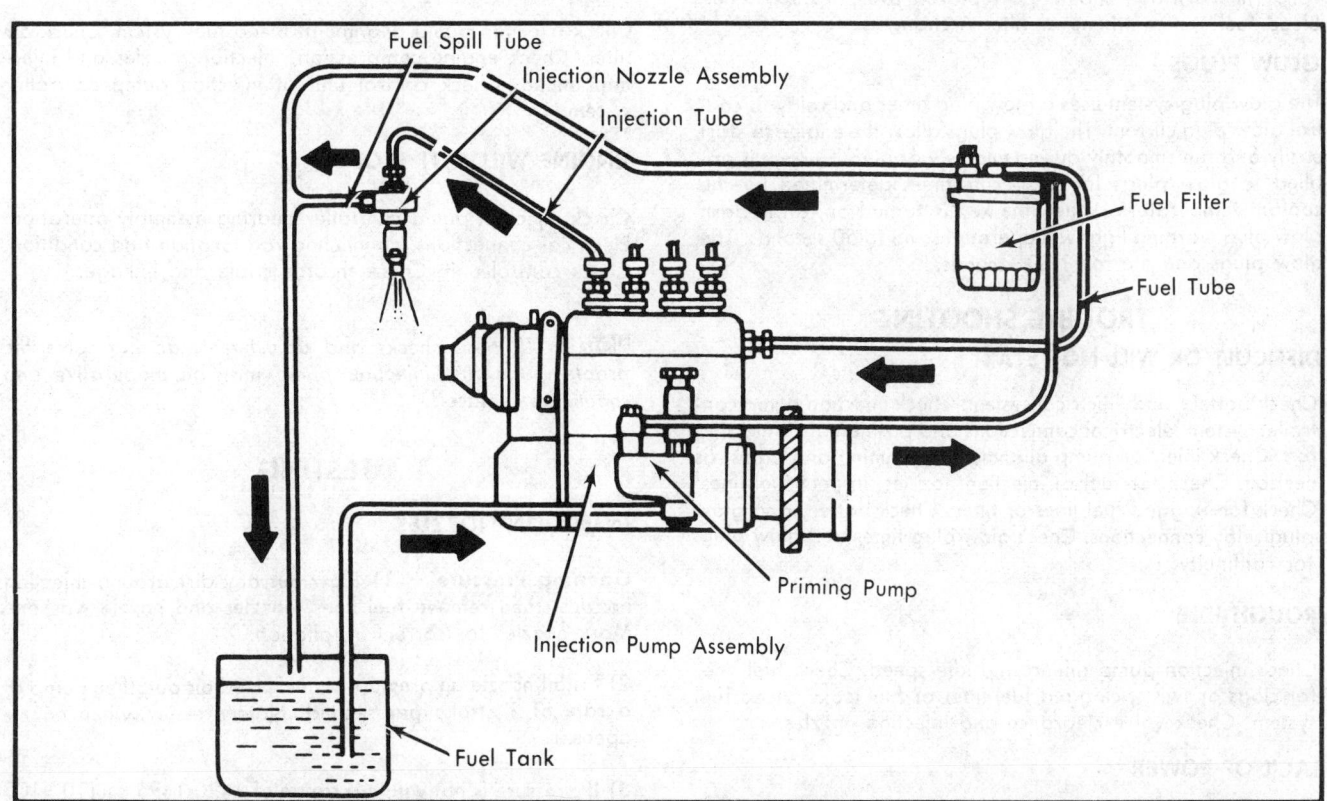

Fig. 1   Datsun Diesel Fuel Injection Components

DATSUN DIESEL FUEL INJECTION — PICKUP (Cont.)

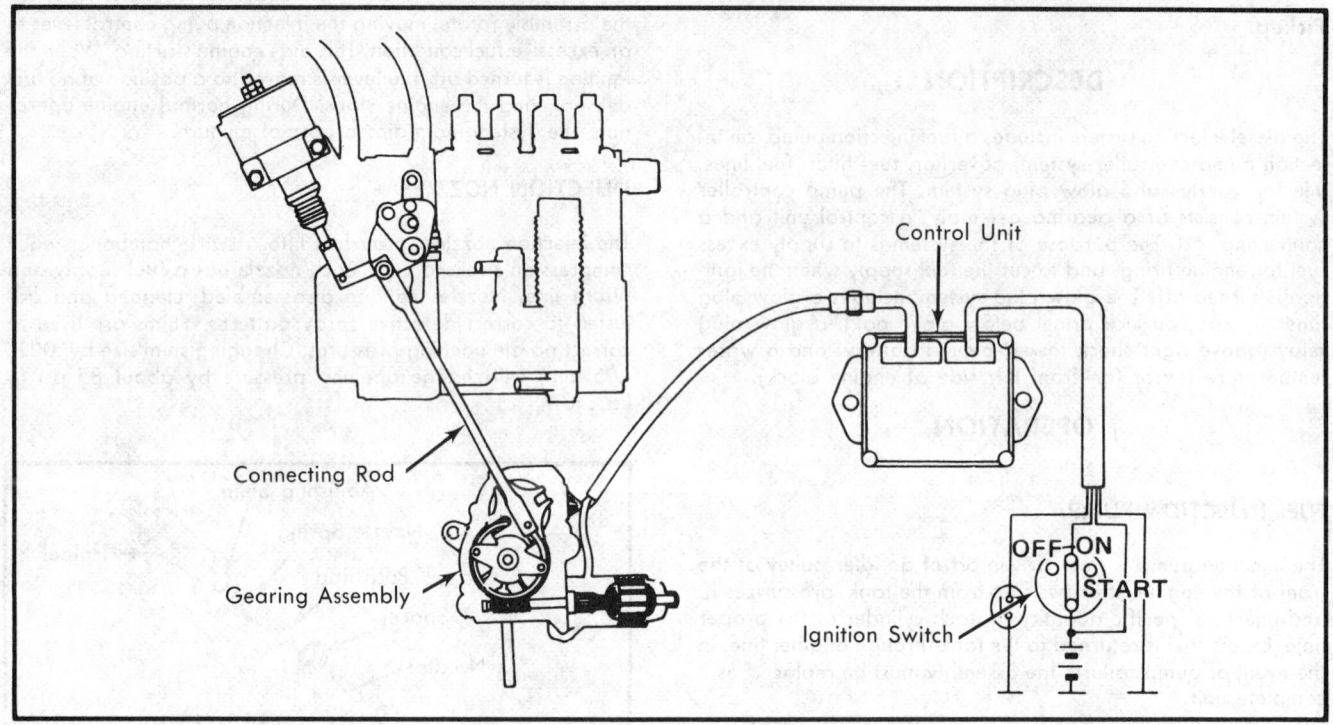

Fig. 3 Injection Pump Controller System

FUEL FILTER

The fuel filter is a sealed cartridge type located on the right side wheel well, just behind the windshield washer fluid reservoir. The cartridge should be replaced every 15,000 miles. Bleed fuel system whenever filter is changed.

GLOW PLUGS

The glow plug system uses a glow plug timer and relay to control glow plug current. The glow plugs allow the engine to start easily and run smoothly during engine warm-up. Current is applied to glow plugs for a specific time, determined by the coolant temperature. When the key is turned on, an in-dash glow plug warning light will operate for up to 50 seconds. The glow plugs operate for 1-30 seconds.

TROUBLE SHOOTING

DIFFICULT OR WILL NOT START

Check battery and electrical system. Check injection pump controller system, electrical connections and position of connecting rod. Check injection pump alignment and timing and adjust as needed. Check for fuel at injection nozzles. Inspect fuel lines. Check for clogged fuel lines or filter. Check battery and glow plug relay connections. Check glow plug timer and glow plugs for continuity.

ROUGH IDLE

Check injection pump timing and idle speed. Check fuel lines for clogs or twists, clogged fuel filter or fuel leaks. Bleed fuel system. Check valve clearance and injection nozzles.

LACK OF POWER

Check venturi valve for proper operation. Check throttle linkage. Check and adjust injection pump timing as needed.

Check fuel lines and clogged fuel or air filters. Bleed fuel system. Check valve clearances and injection nozzles.

EXCESSIVE SMOKE

Check injection pump alignment. Bleed fuel system. Check air filter. Check engine compression, injection nozzles and injection timing. Check control unit of injection pump controller system.

ENGINE WILL NOT STOP

Check injection pump controller gearing assembly operation. Electrical connections, connecting rod location and condition. Check control unit. Check throttle cable and linkage.

NOTE — If these checks and adjustments do not solve the problem, the fuel injection pump may be inoperative and should be replaced.

TESTING

INJECTION NOZZLES

Opening Pressure — 1) Blow out any dirt around injection nozzles, then remove fuel lines, nozzles and nozzle washers. Mark nozzles for correct installation.

2) Install nozzle on pressure tester. Bleed air out, then pump at a rate of 1 stroke per second. Note pressure when nozzle opens.

3) If pressure is not within a range of 1420-1495 psi (100-105 kg/cm²), disassemble and clean nozzle. Change shims as necessary to obtain proper opening pressure.

DATSUN DIESEL FUEL INJECTION – PICKUP (Cont.)

4) Test nozzle again to ensure opening pressure is correct, then check nozzle spray pattern.

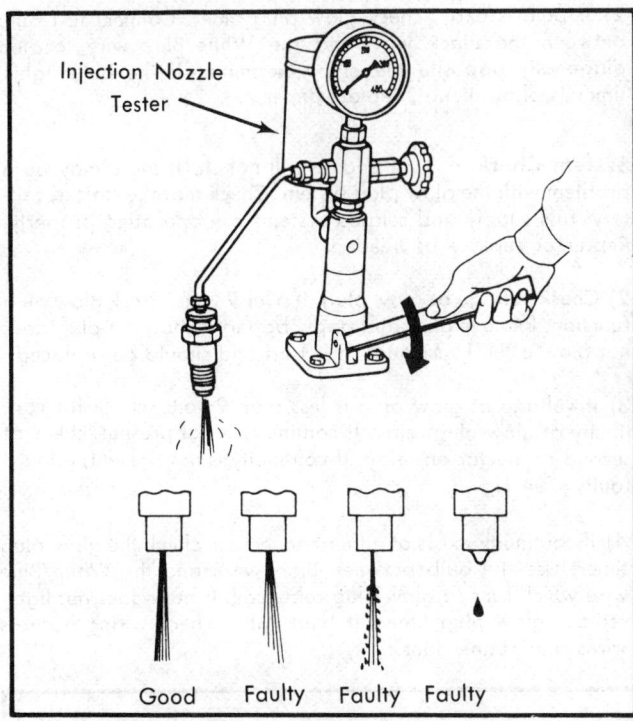

Fig. 4   Injection Nozzle Spray Patterns

Spray Pattern – To test pattern, pump tester handle one time per second. Check spray pattern. If pattern is not correct, clean or replace nozzle.

Nozzle Cleaning – **1)** Disassemble injection assembly. Thoroughly clean all parts in clean solvent. If nozzle needle is damaged, fused, seized or discolored, replace entire nozzle assembly. Check all other parts for excessive wear or damage. Replace as needed.

2) Clean nozzle assembly with a wooden stick and soft brass brush, (Datsun Nozzle Cleaning Kit KV11289004). Be sure to remove all deposits from adjusting shims, spring, push rod, spacer, nozzle body, needle and seat and injection hole.

3) Pull needle about halfway out of body and release. Needle should slide smoothly back into place. Repeat this procedure several times, rotating needle slightly each time. If needle does not slide smoothly, replace nozzle body and needle.

FUEL FILTER

The over-flow valve of the filter housing may be tested for proper opening pressure. Attach a pressure gauge to the discharge port, and pump priming pump until valve opens. If opening pressure is not between 16-21 psi (1.1-1.5 kg/cm²), replace over-flow valve.

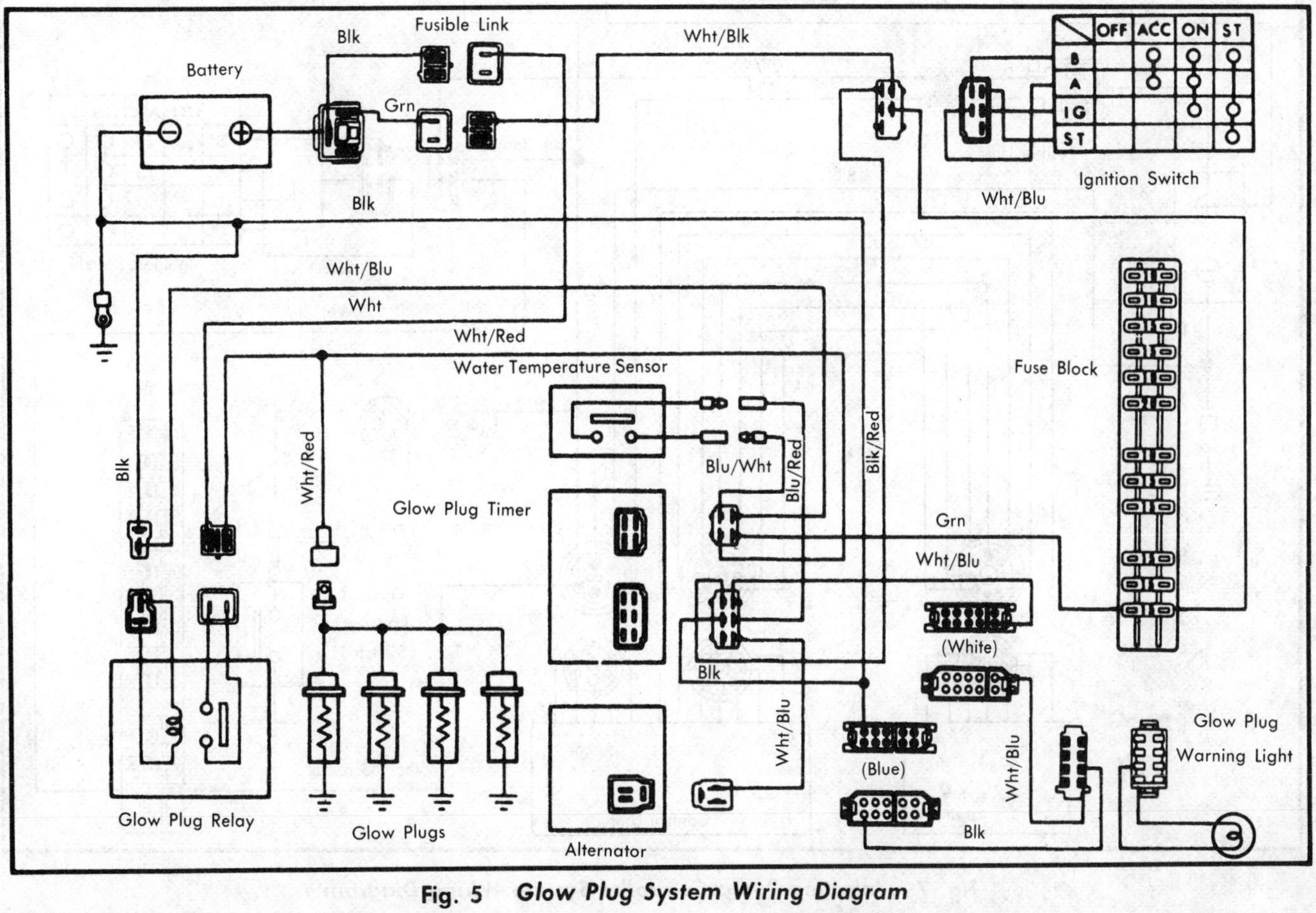

Fig. 5   Glow Plug System Wiring Diagram

1981 Datsun Diesel Fuel Injection

DATSUN DIESEL FUEL INJECTION — PICKUP (Cont.)

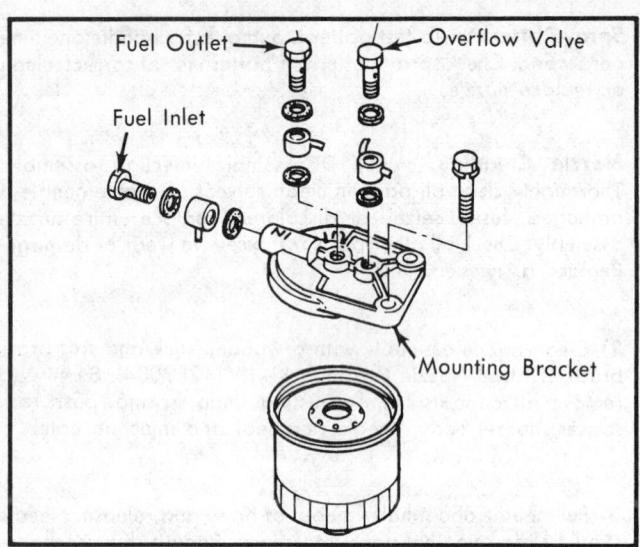

Fig. 6   Exploded View of Fuel Filter Bracket and Valves

GLOW PLUG SYSTEM

Indicator Lamp — 1) Indicator lamp should light when the ignition switch is turned "ON" and remain lighted for up to 50 seconds, depending on coolant temperature. If the bulb does not light, check bulb. Replace as needed.

2) If bulb is okay, check glow plug timer. Connect test bulb between the Black wire and the White/Blue wire located diagonally opposite the empty terminal. If the bulb lights, timer is okay. If not, replace timer.

System Check — 1) If engine will not start, there may be a problem with the glow plug system. Check that the starter, battery, fuel supply and related systems are operating properly. Repair or replace as needed.

2) Check voltage at glow plug. If over 9 volts, check glow plug function. Remove plug and apply battery voltage. If plug does not glow after 15 seconds, it is bad and should be replaced.

3) If voltage at glow plug is less than 9 volts, check for continuity at glow plug relay. If continuity is not present, check at second connector on relay. If continuity is not present, relay is faulty. *See Fig. 8.*

4) If continuity exists at either connection, check the glow plug timer. Use the bulb between Black wire and the White/Blue wire which runs to glow plug relay coil. If bulb does not light, replace glow plug timer. If bulb lights, check wiring harness wires and connections.

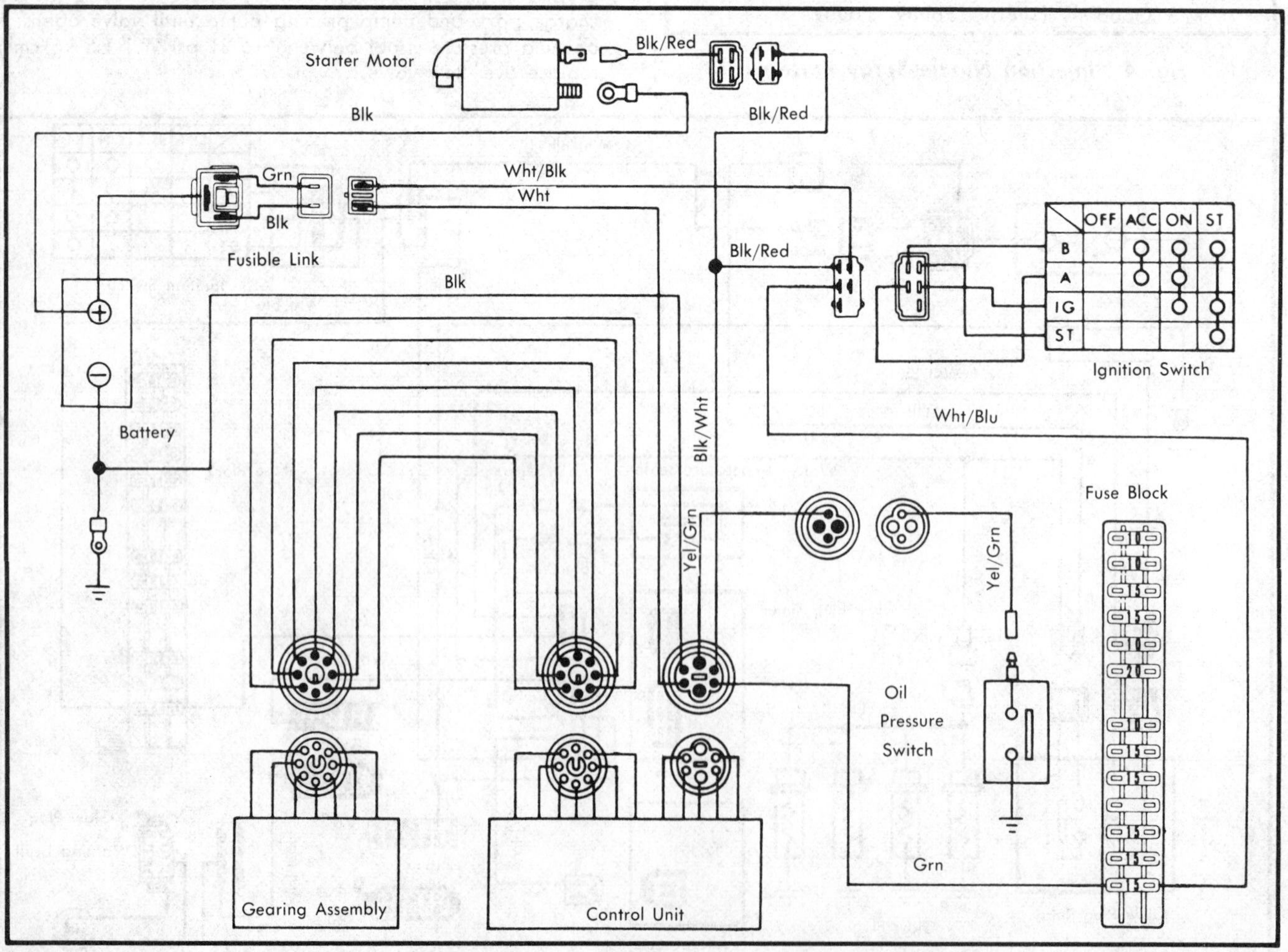

Fig. 7   Injection Pump Controller System Wiring Diagram

DATSUN DIESEL FUEL INJECTION — PICKUP (Cont.)

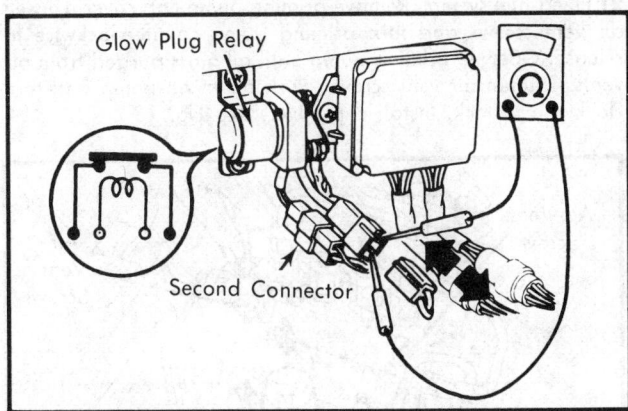

Fig. 8 Checking Continuity at Glow Plug Relay

INJECTION PUMP CONTROLLER SYSTEM

NOTE — *It is important to follow these procedures in the order given if accurate test results are to be obtained. Failure to do so can result in damage to the system.*

System Check — 1) Check control lever position during engine starting and operation. Lever should move smoothly to each position as ignition key position is changed. See *Fig. 9*.

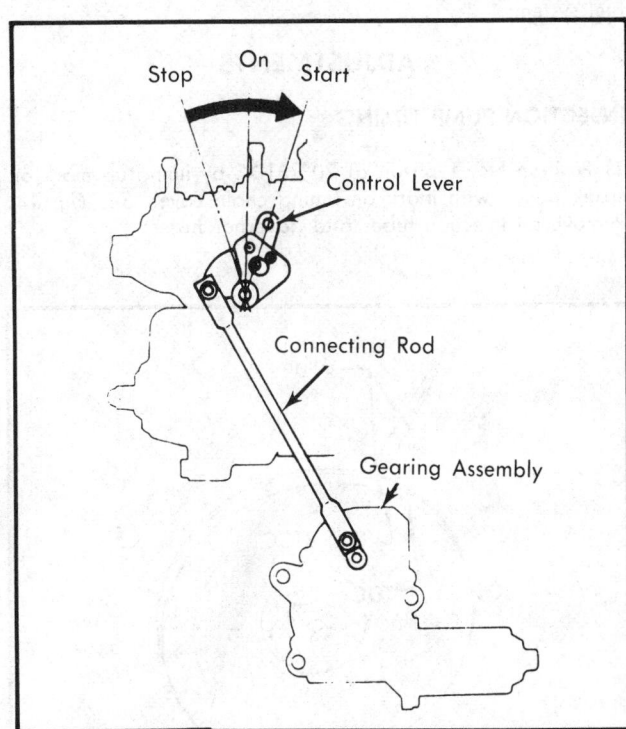

Fig. 9 Control Lever Positions

2) Start engine. Disconnect oil pressure switch connector and ground to engine. Control lever should move to stop position. If not, check control unit and gearing assembly.

Control Unit — 1) With jumper wire from positive side of battery connected to terminal 6 and negative jumper to terminal 5, connect test lamp between terminals 12 and 10, or 12 and

8. Test lamp should light and go out in about 15 seconds. With light between terminals 12 and 11, or 12 and 9, lamp should not light. See *Fig. 10*.

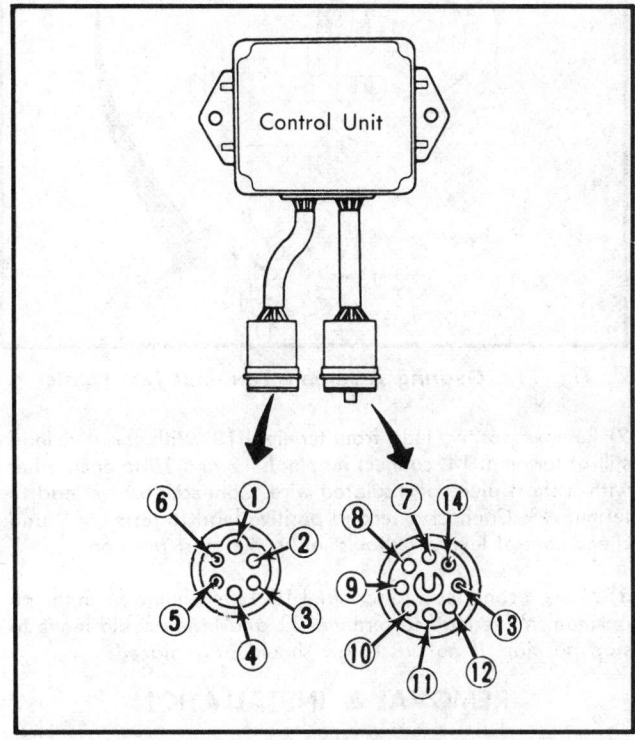

Fig. 10 Control Unit Terminal Test Points

2) Add positive jumper wire connections to terminals 2 and 3, and negative connection to terminal 4. Connect test light between terminals 12 and 9, or 12 and 8. Light should come on and go out in about 15 seconds. With test light between 12 and 11, or 12 and 10, light should not come on.

3) Connect test light between terminals 12 and 9. Remove positive jumper wire from terminal 3, leaving other connections the same. The test light should go out in 10 seconds.

4) At this point, there should be positive jumper wires to terminals 2 and 6 only, and negative jumper wires to terminals 5 and 4. With test lamp between terminals 12 and 10, or 12 and 8, light should come on and go out in about 15 seconds. Lamp should not light when between 12 and 11, or 12 and 9.

5) Disconnect negative wire to terminal 4, leaving only 1 negative wire at terminal 5. With test light between terminals 12 and 11, or 12 and 8, lamp should come on and go out in about 15 seconds. With test light between 12 and 10, or 12 and 9, lamp should not come on.

NOTE — *In all control unit tests, if results are as indicated the unit is good. If not, unit should be replaced.*

Gearing Assembly — 1) With positive battery lead connected to assembly terminal 13, and negative lead to terminal 14, the gearing assembly motor should run. See *Fig. 11*.

DATSUN DIESEL FUEL INJECTION — PICKUP (Cont.)

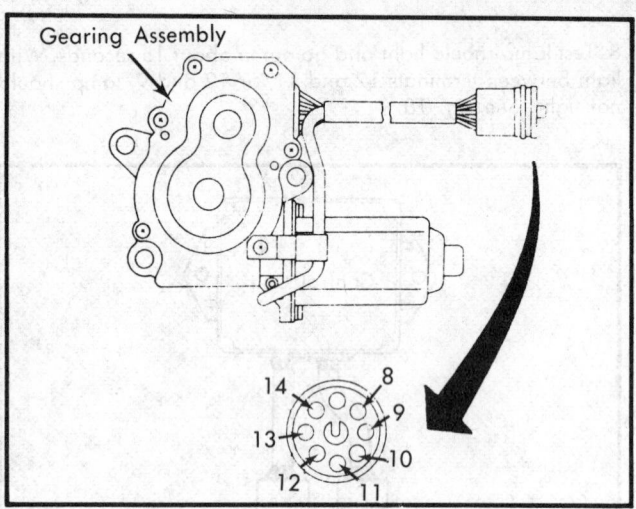

Fig. 11   Gearing Assembly Terminal Test Points

2) Remove positive lead from terminal 13. With negative lead still at terminal 14, connect terminals 12 and 13 to each other with a short piece of insulated wire. Connect positive lead to terminal 8. Connect a second positive lead to terminal 9 and check control lever. It should be in the start position.

3) Move second lead to terminal 10. Lever should be in the on position. Move lead to terminal 11 and lever should move to stop position. If not, assembly should be replaced.

REMOVAL & INSTALLATION

INJECTION PUMP

Removal — 1) Drain coolant and disconnect battery ground cable. Remove radiator, fan and fan clutch. Remove injection tubes. Disconnect governor hose, fuel hose, injection pump controller connecting rod and oil feed pipe bolt.

2) Remove timing gear cover. Remove timer assembly retaining nut. Using special tool (ST19530000), remove timer assembly. Remove injection pump retaining nuts and remove pump.

Installation — 1) With No. 1 cylinder at TDC, hold injection pump loosely in place. Do not tighten retaining nuts. Mesh injection pump drive gear with idler gear, being sure to align the "Y" marks on the gears. See Fig. 12. Align gear to key way of injection pump camshaft while turning crank pulley. Tighten injection pump and timer assembly retaining nuts. Adjust injection timing.

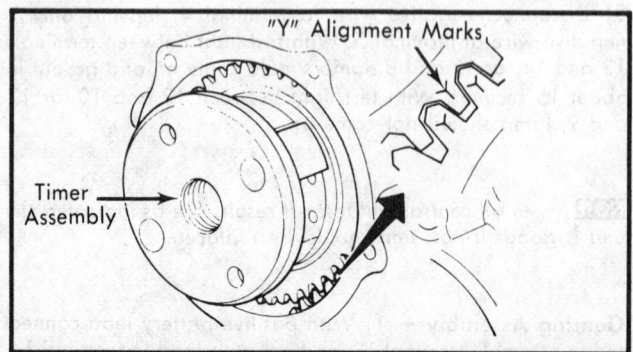

Fig. 12   Injection Pump Drive Gear Installation

2) Bleed fuel system. Remove priming pump cap cover. Loosen air vent screws and turn priming pump counterclockwise to release. Operate priming pump until all air is purged from air vents. Tighten air vent screws. Push down on pump and turn clockwise to lock. Install cap cover. See Fig. 13.

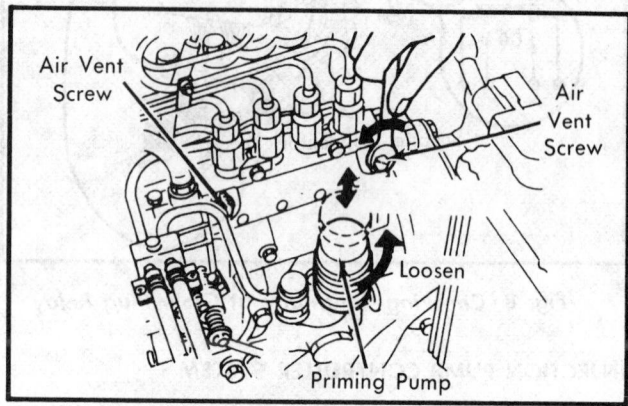

Fig. 13   Bleeding Fuel System

FUEL FILTER

Removal and Installation — Remove fuel filter bracket with filter attached. Remove filter from bracket and install new filter hand tight only, do not use wrench. Install bracket and bleed fuel system.

ADJUSTMENTS

INJECTION PUMP TIMING

1) Position No. 1 piston at 20° BTDC by lining up mark on crank pulley with mark on timing chain cover. See Fig. 14. Remove all injection tubes and governor hoses.

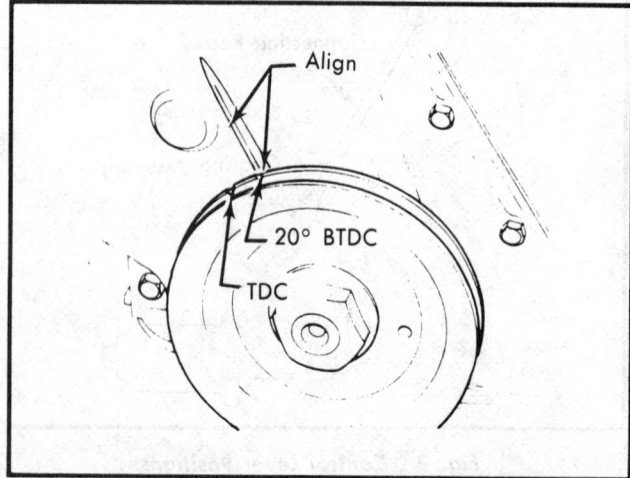

Fig. 14   Alignment for Injection Pump Timing

2) Remove No. 1 delivery valve lock plate and holder, valve stopper and valve spring. Reinstall valve holder and lock plate without the spring or stopper. See Fig. 15. Change fuel line connections so that the priming pump will supply fuel for test.

DATSUN DIESEL FUEL INJECTION — PICKUP (Cont.)

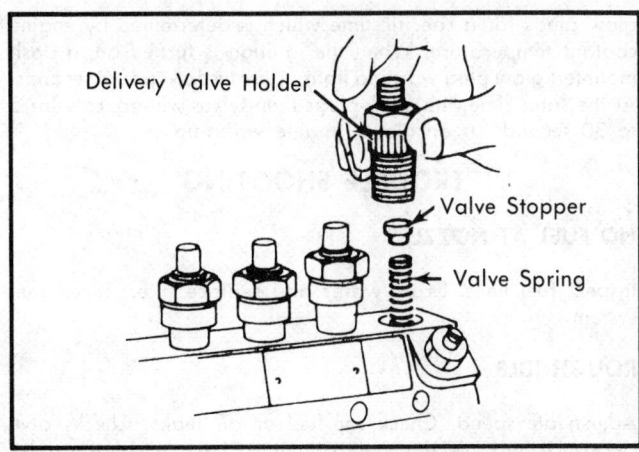

Delivery Valve Holder

Valve Stopper

Valve Spring

Fig. 15 Exploded View of Injection Pump Delivery Valve

3) Connect a short piece of tubing to the No. 1 delivery valve holder. Move injection pump assembly to limit of adjustment towards engine side. With a small container under open end of tubing, operate priming pump while moving injection pump away from engine. Continue to move the pump until fuel flow from the tube stops. Pump is now in proper position.

4) Check the timing marks on the front of the injection pump and the engine front plate. These marks should now be aligned. If not, stamp a new mark on the front plate for future adjustment reference.

5) Remove tubing from delivery valve. Remove valve and reinstall with spring and stopper in proper position. Install injection tubes, fuel line in proper position, and governor hoses. Bleed system.

IDLE SPEED AND DASH POT ADJUSTMENT

1) With transmission in neutral and engine at normal operating temperature, attach tachometer and check engine speed. Idle speed should be 550-700 RPM. If not, make sure that the throttle control knob (in cab, under dash) is pushed all the way in. Loosen the idle adjusting screw lock nut and turn the idle adjusting screw until the proper idle speed is attained. Tighten lock nut. Check to ensure idle speed is correct.

2) Whenever idle speed is adjusted, the dash pot must be adjusted. With engine warm and transmission in neutral, maintain engine speed at 1280-1350 RPM. Loosen dashpot locknut and adjust dashpot so that the control lever tip just touches the dashpot tip. Tighten lock nut and remove test equipment.

TIGHTENING SPECIFICATIONS	
Application	**Ft. Lbs. (N·m)**
Injection Pump-to-Engine	14-18 (19-25)
Pump Delivery Valve Holder	22-25 (31-35)
Timer Assembly Retaining Nut	43-51 (60-71)
Injection Nozzle-to-Engine	43-51 (60-71)
Injection Nozzle-to-Tube	22-25 (31-35)

DATSUN DIESEL FUEL INJECTION — 810

810

DESCRIPTION

The diesel injection system includes a fuel injection pump, fuel filter, fuel lines, injector nozzles and glow plug system. The glow plug system consists of a glow plug control unit (behind left kick panel), 2 glow plug relays and a current flow resistor (on right shock tower) and a water temperature sensor.

OPERATION

FUEL INJECTION PUMP

The injection pump is driven by a belt at the front of the engine. It draws fuel from the tank, pressurizes it, and injects a specific quantity to each cylinder at the proper time. Excess fuel is returned to the tank through another line. In the event of pump failure, the assembly must be replaced as a complete unit. A fuel cut solenoid is used to stop fuel flow when the ignition is turned off.

INJECTION NOZZLES

The injection nozzles spray fuel into a prechamber as each compression stroke occurs. Each nozzle has a fuel supply and return line. Nozzles can be disassembled, cleaned and adjusted to correct defective spray patterns. Shims are used to correct nozzle opening pressures, and are available in 14 sizes from .0197 to .0394" (.5-1.0 mm) in increments of .0016" (.04 mm). Changing one size nozzle shim will change injection pressure by 68 psi (4.8 kg/cm²).

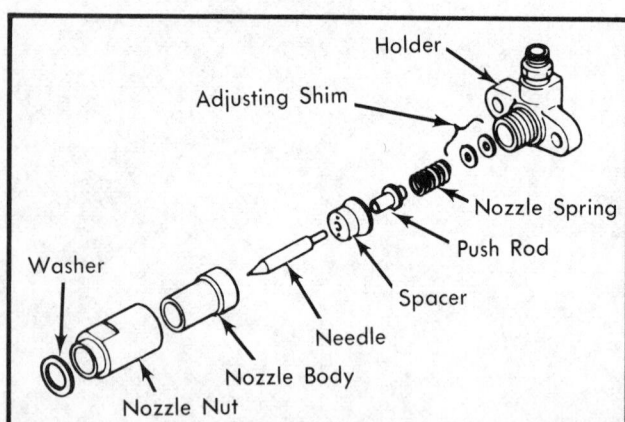

Fig. 1 Exploded View of Fuel Injection Nozzle

FUEL FILTER

The fuel filter is a sealed cartridge type located on the right side wheel well, just behind the battery. The cartridge should be replaced every 30,000 miles. Water should be drained from the filter housing and the fuel system should be bled whenever the cartridge is replaced.

GLOW PLUGS

The glow plug system uses a glow plug control unit, 2 relays and a current flow resistor to control glow plug current. The glow plugs enable the engine to start easily in cold weather and run smoothly during warm-up. Current is applied to the glow plugs for a specific time which is determined by engine coolant temperature. When the ignition is turned on, a dash mounted glow plug warning light operates for up to 8 seconds. At the same time, the glow plugs themselves will operate for 5 to 30 seconds as an aid to engine warm-up.

TROUBLE SHOOTING

NO FUEL AT NOZZLES

Inspect fuel lines. Drain water and replace filter. Bleed fuel system.

ROUGH IDLE

Adjust idle speed. Check for fuel or air leaks. Check valve clearance and injection pump timing. Check injection nozzles and injection pump drive belt. Adjust or replace as needed.

LACK OF POWER

Check and adjust high idle speed screw. Check fuel filter and lines for leaks or clogs. Check throttle valve for proper operation. Bleed fuel system and drain water. Check engine compression. Check and adjust injection nozzles and valve clearances.

EXCESSIVE SMOKE

Check sticky throttle valve. Check clogged injection nozzles, air and fuel filters. Condition of injection pump drive belt. Check injection pump timing.

NOTE — *If the problem remains after the recommended checks, replace injection pump.*

EXCESSIVE FUEL CONSUMPTION

Fuel leakage. Check idle and high idle speed adjustments. Adjust injection timing. Check injection nozzle operation.

ENGINE WILL NOT STOP

Check fuel cut solenoid valve. Check for stuck accelerator linkage.

ENGINE NOISE WHEN WARM

Check idle speed and valve clearance. Check other engine rotating assemblies (water pump, alternator, etc.).

TESTING

INJECTION NOZZLES

Opening Pressure — 1) Blow out any dirt around injection nozzles, then remove fuel lines, nozzles and nozzle washers. Mark nozzles for correct installation.

2) Install nozzle on pressure tester. Bleed air out, then pump at a rate of 1 stroke per second. Note pressure when nozzle opens.

3) If pressure is not within a range of 1780-1920 psi (125-135 kg/cm²), disassemble and clean nozzle. Change shims as necessary to obtain proper opening pressure.

DATSUN DIESEL FUEL INJECTION – 810 (Cont.)

4) Test nozzle again to ensure opening pressure is correct, then check nozzle spray pattern.

Spray Pattern — To test pattern, pump tester handle one time per second. Observe pattern. If not correct, clean or replace nozzle.

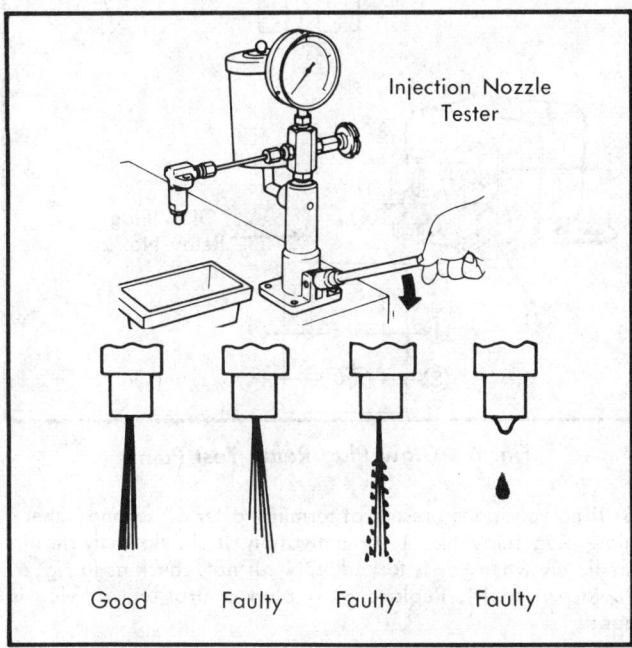

Fig. 2   Injection Nozzle Spray Patterns

Nozzle Cleaning — **1)** Disassemble injection assembly. Thoroughly clean all parts in clean solvent. If nozzle needle is damaged or fused, seized or discolored, replace entire nozzle assembly. Check all other parts for excessive wear or damage. Replace as needed.

2) Clean nozzle assembly with a wooden stick and soft brass brush (Datsun Nozzle Cleaning Kit IV11289004). Be sure to remove all deposits from adjusting shims, spring, push rod, spacer, nozzle body, needle and seat, and injection hole.

3) Pull needle about halfway out of body and release. Needle should slide smoothly back into place. Repeat this procedure several times, rotating needle slightly each time. If needle does not slide smoothly, replace nozzle body and needle.

GLOW PLUG SYSTEM

Indicator Lamp — **1)** Indicator lamp should light when coolant temperature is below 122° (50°C). If not, check bulb. Replace as needed.

2) If bulb is okay, check for battery voltage at terminal 9 of glow plug control unit. If voltage is not present, repair wiring. If present, replace control unit.

System Check — **1)** If engine will not start or is difficult to start, there may be a problem with the glow plug system. Check that the starter, battery, fuel supply and related systems are operating properly.

2) The glow/filter warning light should come on when key is in "ON" position. If not, check for burned out bulb and replace if

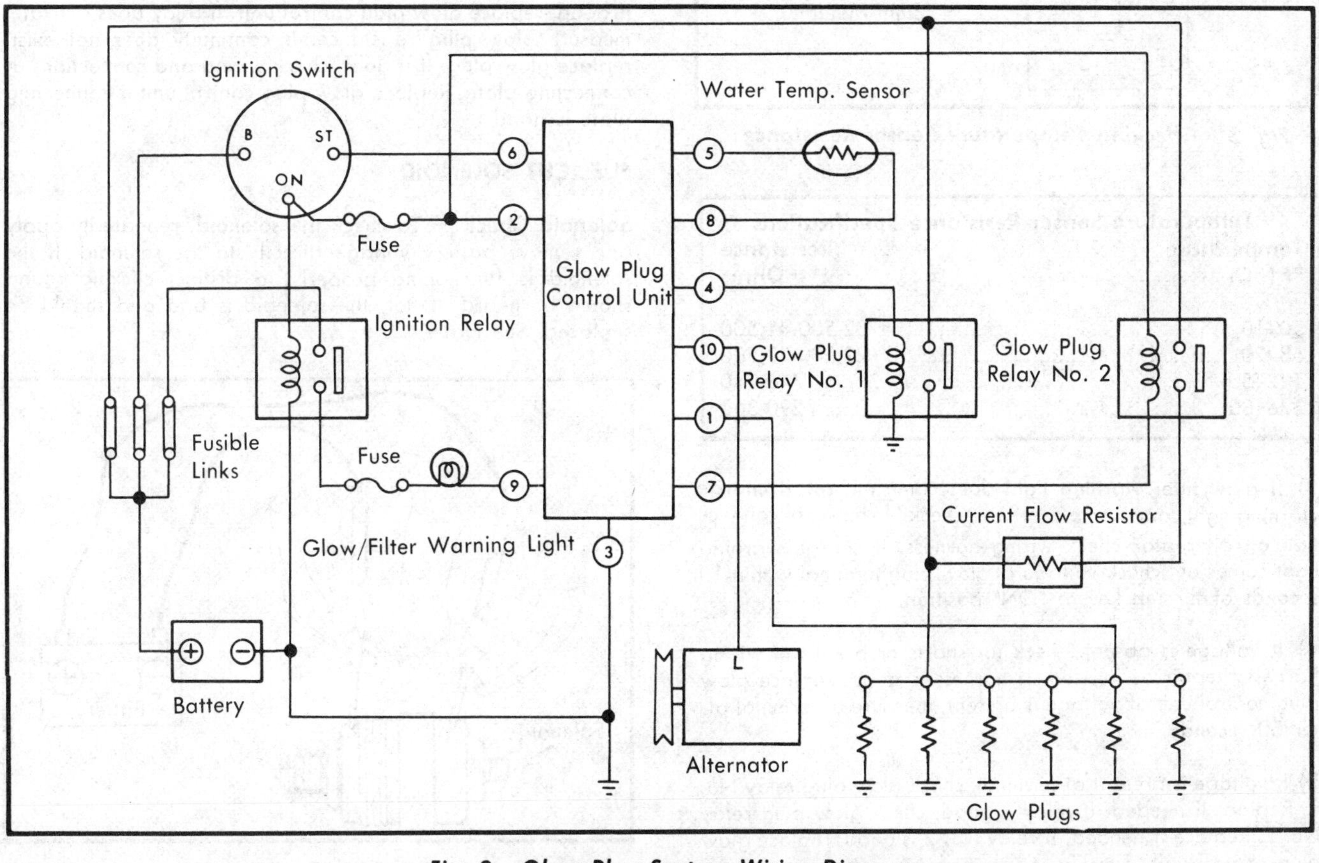

Fig. 3   Glow Plug System Wiring Diagram

DATSUN DIESEL FUEL INJECTION — 810 (Cont.)

needed. If bulb is good, check coolant temperature. If temperature is over 122°F (50°C), re-check starting systems. If below 122°F (50°C) check water temperature sensor and replace if faulty. If sensor is okay, replace glow plug control unit.

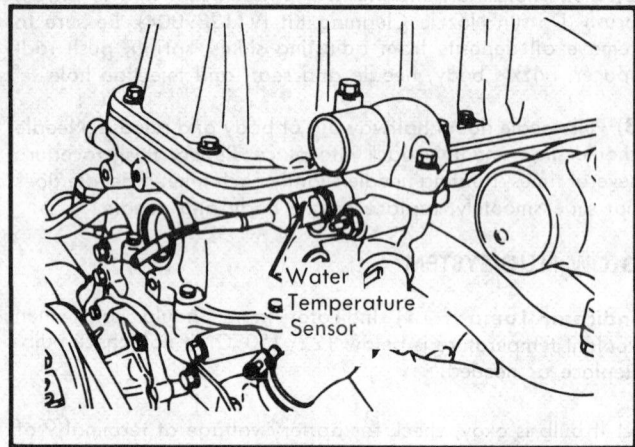

Fig. 4   Location of Water Temperature Sensor

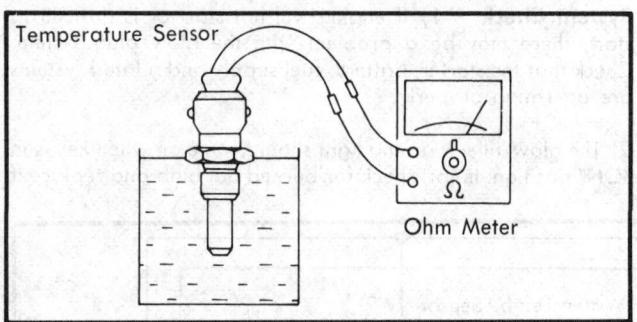

Fig. 5   Checking Temperature Sensor Resistance

Temperature Sensor Resistance Specifications	
Temperature °F (°C)	Resistance Ohms
50 (10)	32,500-41,500
68 (20)	22,500-27,500
122 (50)	740-940
176 (80)	290-360

3) If glow/filter warning light does come on, see if charge warning light comes on also. If not, check "L" terminal connection on alternator check wiring harness. If charge warning light comes on, check voltage at glow plug terminal within 10 seconds of turning key to "ON" position.

4) If voltage is absent, check for shorts or breaks in wiring harness. Repair as needed. If harness is good, replace glow plug control unit. If voltage is present, measure at terminal after 60 seconds.

5) If voltage is present at terminal, check glow plug relay No. 1. Replace if needed. If relay is good, check glow plug relay No. 2. Replace if needed. If relay No. 2 is good, replace glow plug control unit. See *Fig. 6*.

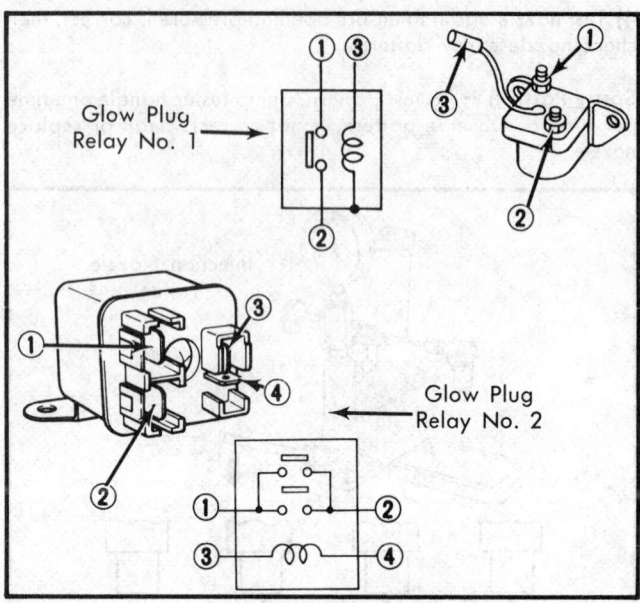

Fig. 6   Glow Plug Relay Test Points

6) If no voltage is present at terminal after 60 seconds, check glow plug relay No. 1 for activation. It should activate immediately when key is turned "ON". If not, check as in *Fig. 6*. Replace if faulty. Replace glow plug control unit if relay is good.

7) If relay No. 1 activates in step **6)**, check to see if relay No. 2 activates as well. If not, check as in *Fig. 6* and replace if faulty. If good, replace glow plug control unit. If relay does activate, measure glow plug resistance. If continuity does not exist, replace glow plug. If it does, check wiring and connections at connecting plate. Replace glow plug control unit if connecting plate is good.

FUEL CUT SOLENOID

Solenoid Check — To check the solenoid, repeatedly apply and remove battery voltage directly to the solenoid. If the solenoid is functioning properly, a distinct clicking sound should be heard. If not, the solenoid is bad and should be replaced. See *Fig. 7*.

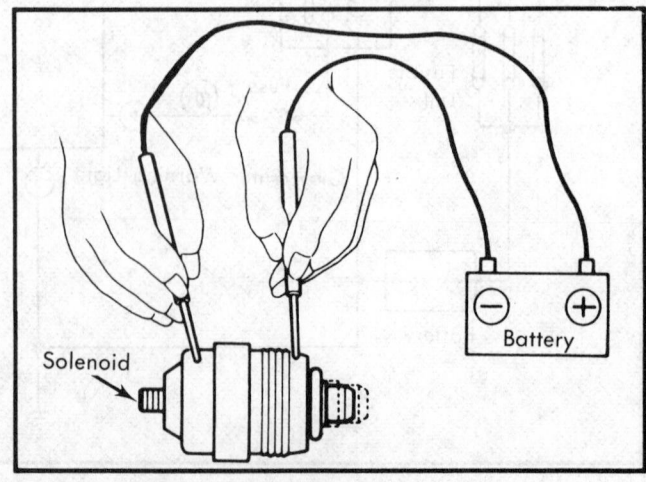

Fig. 7   Checking Fuel Cut Solenoid

DATSUN DIESEL FUEL INJECTION — 810 (Cont.)

REMOVAL & INSTALLATION

INJECTION PUMP

Removal — 1) Drain coolant and disconnect battery ground cable. Remove radiator, shroud and hoses. Loosen pulley nuts and remove alternator, power steering and air conditioning belts. Remove power steering pump.

NOTE — *Do not drain power steering fluid or disconnect hoses from pump during this procedure.*

2) Disconnect remaining wires and hoses from pump. Remove dust cover. Loosen spring set pin and set tensioner pulley to "free tension" position. Re-tighten set pin.

3) Remove injection drive belt. Loosen nut and use a gear puller to remove injection pump drive gear.

4) Disconnect injection tubes from injection nozzles. Remove injection pump nuts and bracket bolt. Remove injection pump assembly and injection tubes.

Installation — 1) With No. 1 cylinder at TDC on the compression stroke, install injection pump. Install drive gear.

NOTE — *There are two grooves and two aligning marks on the drive gear. Use the groove and mark without the "A" marking to position the gear.*

2) With tensioner pulley in free position, install injection drive belt making sure that the timing marks on the belt are in alignment with the marks on the pump drive pulley and the crank damper. If the marks on the belt are not clear, count the number of belt teeth between the timing marks on the two pulleys. There should be 20 teeth between the two marks.

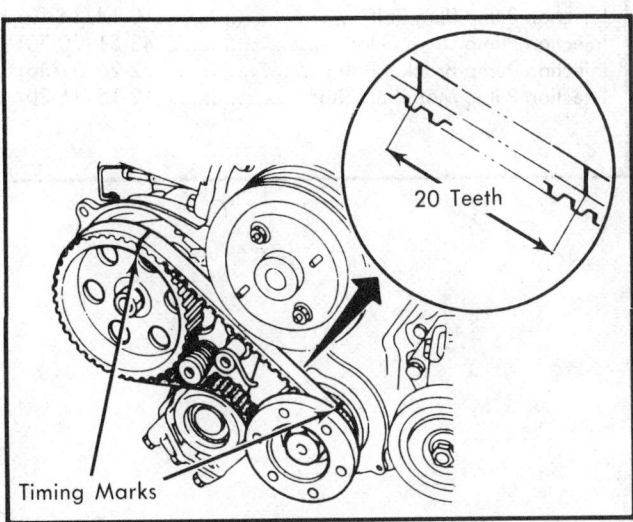

Fig. 8   Injection Pump Drive Belt Installation

3) Loosen the spring set pin and allow tensioner to return to "tension" position. Adjust injection timing, tighten pump and connect injection tubes.

NOTE — *Injection tubes should always be connected in the order: 4, 2, 6, 1, 5, 3 as counted from the front to the rear of the engine.*

4) Bleed fuel system. Loosen the priming pump vent screw on the front of the fuel filter housing. Pump the filter priming pump until fuel begins to flow from the vent hole. Tighten vent screw. Disconnect the fuel return hose and attach a suitable overflow hose to the overflow connector. Place a can or other small container under the hose end and pump priming pump until fuel begins to flow from the hose. Replace overflow hose.

FUEL FILTER

Removal and Installation — Remove fuel filter sensor and drain fuel. Remove fuel filter, replace with new filter. Tighten by hand only, do not use a wrench. Before connecting fuel filter sensor, drain water by pumping priming pump until fuel overflows. Install fuel filter sensor, and bleed fuel system.

ADJUSTMENTS

INJECTION PUMP TIMING

1) With No. 1 cylinder at TDC on the compression stroke, remove fuel injection tubes and loosen fork screw on cold start device. Turn fork 90° and set device in the free position. See Fig. 9.

NOTE — *Do not remove screw on device wire. If removed, pump assembly will require readjusting.*

Fig. 9   Injection Pump Cold Start Device

2) Remove plug bolt from rear of injection pump. Install special timing tool with dial indicator (Datsun Part No. KV11229352) in bolt hole.

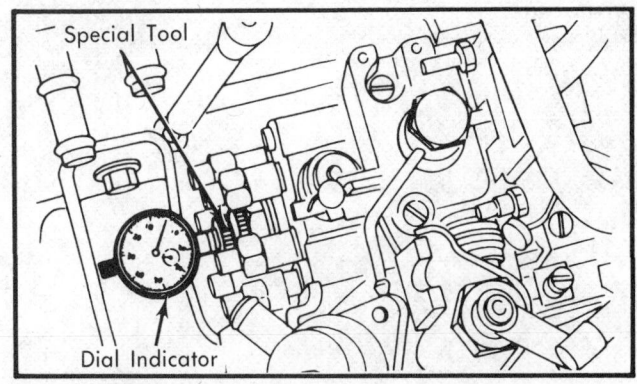

Fig. 10   Injection Pump Timing

DATSUN DIESEL FUEL INJECTION — 810 (Cont.)

3) Turn crank to 15-20° BTDC and zero dial indicator. Rotate clockwise 2 complete turns, then loosen and retighten timing belt tensioner.

4) Rotate clockwise to No. 1 cylinder TDC position, compression stroke, and read dial gauge. Gauge should read .0327-.0351" (.83-.89 mm). If reading is out of this range, turn injection pump body until reading is correct.

5) Tighten pump. Remove tool and replace plug bolt using new washer. Reset fork by pulling on cold start device wire. Tighten fork screw. Connect injection tubes.

IDLE AND HIGH IDLE SPEED

Adjustment should be made with all electrical accessories off and engine at normal operating temperature.

1) Attach tachometer. With transmission in neutral, run engine at 2000 RPM for 2 minutes.

2) Let engine idle for 1 minute. Check idle speed (Auto. Trans. in "D"). Idle should be between 600 and 750 RPM.

3) If adjustment is required, loosen the idle adjusting screw lock nut on idle adjusting screw. Turn screw until proper idle RPM is obtained. Tighten lock nut. See Fig. 11.

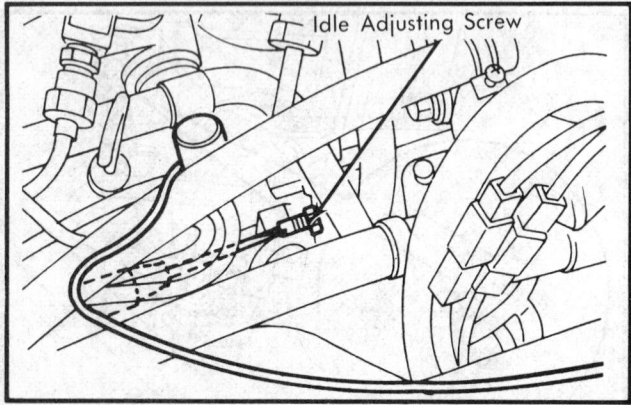

Fig. 11   Location of Idle Adjusting Screw

4) With engine idling and air conditioning turned on, set high idle speed. Locate Fast Idle Control Device (F.I.C.D.) diaphragm and turn adjusting screw on accelerator drum to obtain fast idle speed of 800 RPM. See Fig. 12.

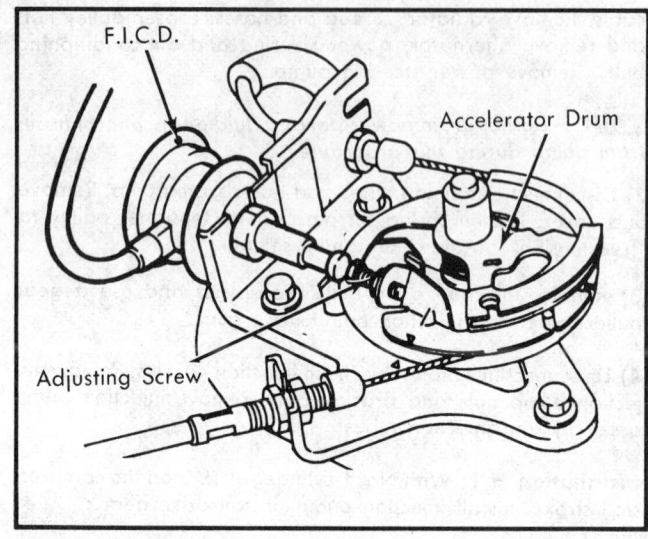

Fig. 12   Fast Idle Adjustment

TIGHTENING SPECIFICATIONS

Application	Ft. Lbs. (N·m)
Injection Nozzle-to-Cylinder Head	12-15 (16-20)
Injection Nozzle-to-Tube	16-18 (22-25)
Injection Pump Plug Bolt	10-14 (14-19)
Injection Pump Drive Gear	43-51 (60-70)
Injection Pump Bracket Bolt	22-26 (31-36)
Injection Pump Mounting Nuts	12-15 (16-20)

DIESEL FUEL INJECTION — ISUZU & LUV

Isuzu
I-Mark
P'UP

LUV
Pickup

DESCRIPTION

Diesel fuel injection system includes the fuel injection pump, injection nozzles, delivery and return lines, fuel filter with water warning light and glow plug system. The thermal glow plug system has a controller, relay unit, thermal switch, dropping resistor, sensing resistor and glow plugs. I-Mark models also have a glow plug timer. Warning lights in the instrument cluster indicate when the glow plugs are operating or the fuel filter is filled with water.

OPERATION

FUEL INJECTION PUMP

The injection pump is located on the lower right side of the engine and driven by a toothed belt. It draws fuel from the tank, pressurizes it, and sends a specific quantity to each cylinder at the proper time. Excess fuel is returned from the injectors and sent back to the tank. A fast idle system is used when coolant is below a specified temperature. A vacuum unit actuates the throttle and increases idle speed. A fuel cut solenoid is actuated by the ignition switch and stops fuel flow at the pump so the engine can be shut down.

INJECTION NOZZLES

The injection nozzles spray fuel into a prechamber as each compression stroke occurs. A fuel return line connects all injectors and returns excess fuel to the pump. Injectors are opened by high pressure in the fuel lines and cannot be adjusted. If spray patterns are incorrect, nozzles must be replaced.

FUEL FILTER & WATER WARNING SYSTEM

The diesel injection system uses an integral fuel filter and water separator. A water sensor is fitted into the bottom of a fuel filter cartridge and lights a warning lamp when water accumulates in the filter. A hand pump is also incorporated into the filter housing to prime the pump after filter replacement.

GLOW PLUGS

I-Mark — The glow plug system uses 4 glow plugs (heaters) to assist in cold starting. When the engine coolant is below 122° F (50°C), the No. 1 relay supplies battery voltage to heat the glow plugs quickly. When the engine starts, relay No. 1 is turned off and relay No. 2 provides a lower voltage to maintain glow plug temperature. The glow plug timer keeps the glow plugs pulsating on and off up to 3 minutes and/or until 10 MPH is attained.

LUV & P'UP — The glow plug system uses 4 glow plugs (heaters) to assist in cold starting. When the engine coolant is below 122° F (50° C), the No. 1 relay supplies battery voltage to heat the glow plugs quickly. When the glow plugs reach maximum temperature, relay No. 1 is turned off and relay No. 2 provides a lower voltage to maintain glow plug temperature. When the engine starts, the glow plug system is turned off. When engine coolant is above 122° F (50° C), only relay No. 2 is operated. This operation provides easy starting but does not drain the battery or overheat glow plugs.

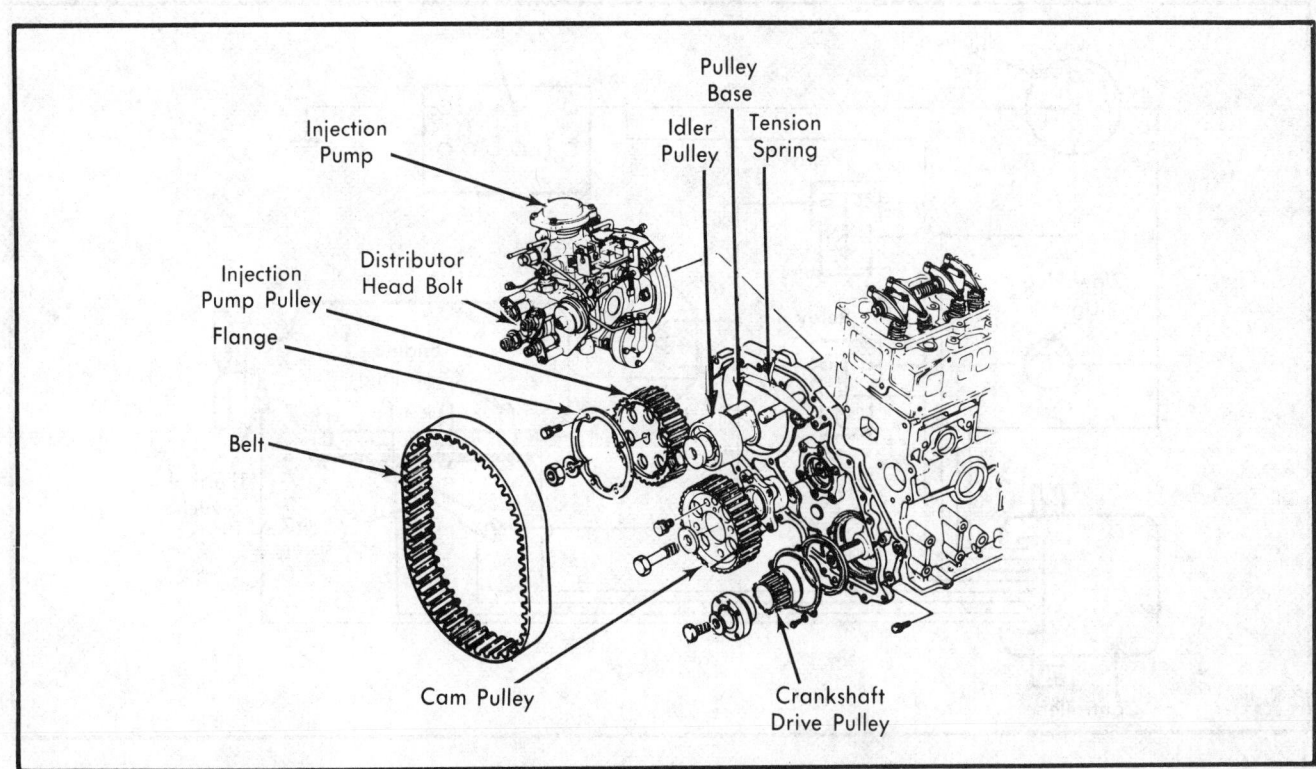

Fig. 1   Exploded View of Injection Pump Drive

1981 Isuzu Diesel Fuel Injection

DIESEL FUEL INJECTION — ISUZU & LUV (Cont.)

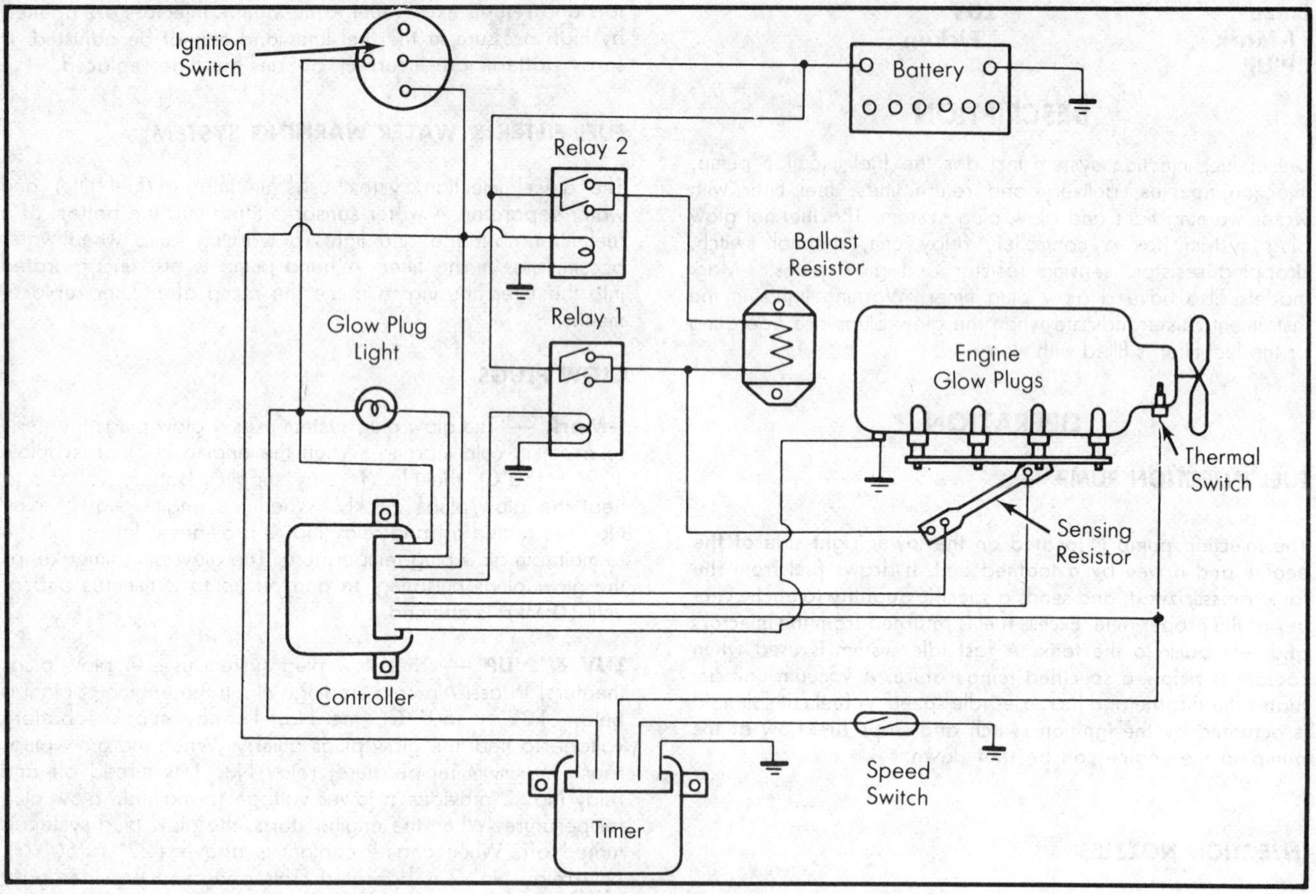

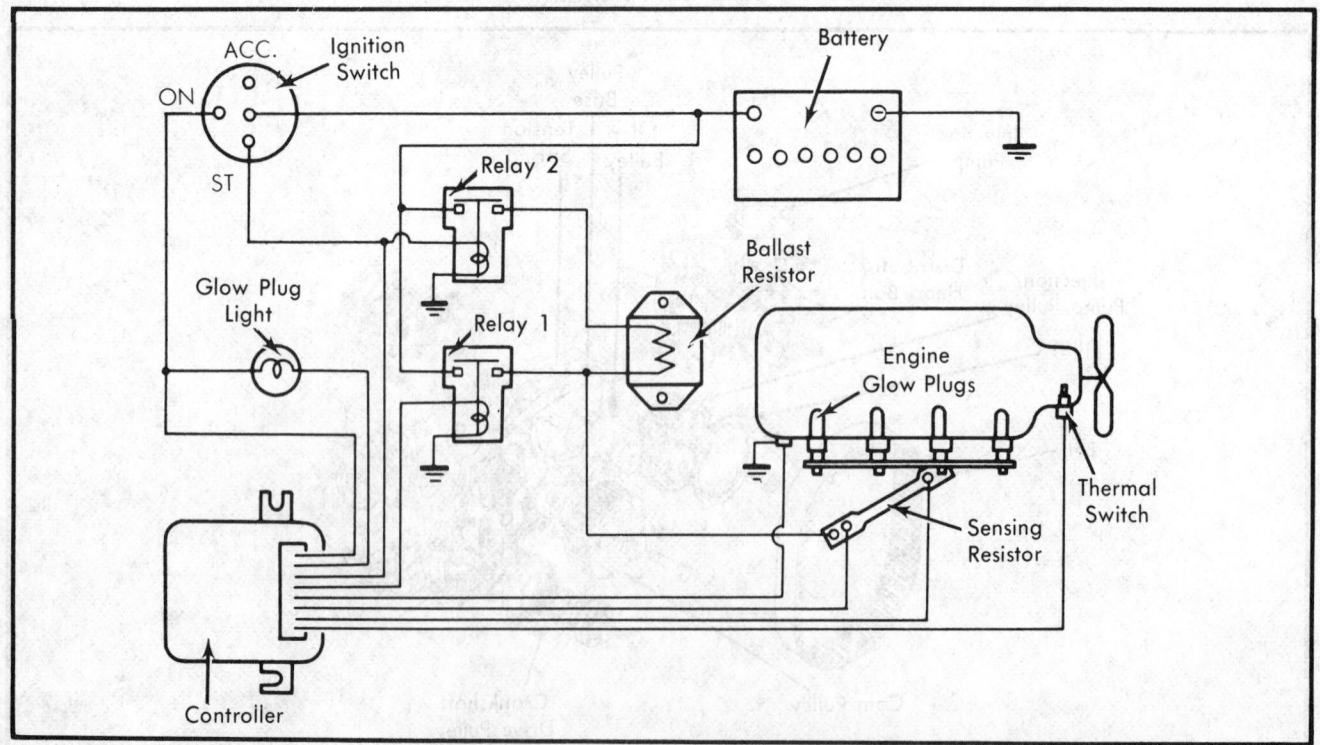

Fig. 2   I-Mark Glow Plug System Wiring Diagram

Fig. 3   LUV & P'UP Glow Plug System Wiring Diagram

F U E L   S Y S T E M S

DIESEL FUEL INJECTION — ISUZU & LUV (Cont.)

TROUBLE SHOOTING

HARD STARTING

Check fuel delivery, injection pump timing and nozzle opening pressures. Check fuel cut solenoid and fuel restrictions. Air leaks.

ROUGH IDLE

Adjust idle speed. Contaminated fuel. Injection timing, nozzle opening pressure or sticking delivery valve in pump.

LACK OF POWER

Air cleaner restriction. Accelerator linkage. Exhaust restriction. Fuel contamination or restriction in lines. Injection timing.

EXHAUST SMOKE

Air cleaner restrictions. Contaminated fuel. Injection timing or nozzle opening pressure.

GLOW PLUG INDICATOR INOPERATIVE

Blown fuse or fusible link. Bad connections at controller. Controller or ignition switch defective.

IMPROPER OPERATION OF GLOW PLUGS

Thermal sensor defective. Controller inoperative. Ignition switch "R" circuit open or intermittent.

TESTING

INJECTION NOZZLES

1) Remove nozzles and connect injection nozzle tester. Pump tester lever about 30 times a minute to observe spray pattern. *See Fig. 4.* If spray is faulty, replace injector.

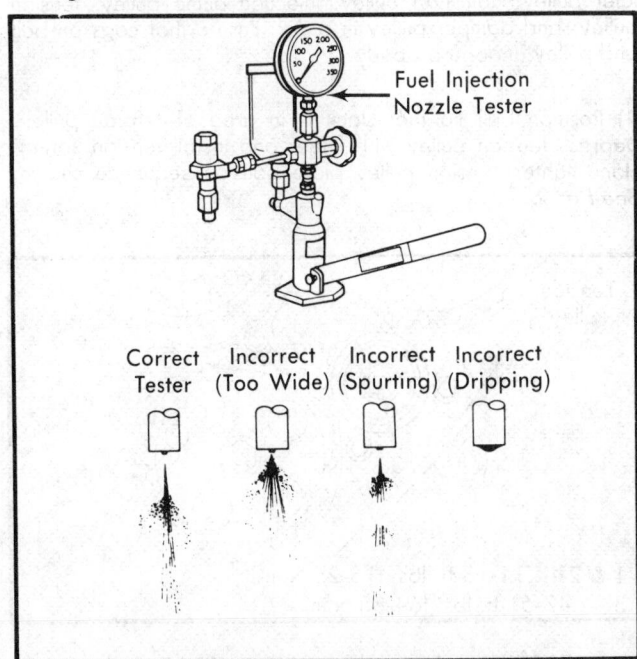

Fig. 4   Injection Nozzle Spray Patterns

2) Pump pressure up slowly to note opening pressure. If not within 1705-1850 psi (120-130 kg/cm²) for I-Mark models or 1495-1635 psi (105-115 kg/cm²) on LUV and P'UP models, injector must be replaced.

NOTE — *When replacing injection nozzles, install parts in this order: ridged washer (with Blue side toward nozzle), gasket, then nozzle holder.*

GLOW PLUG SYSTEM

System Check — 1) Disconnect coolant thermal switch at thermostat housing (front switch). Turn ignition on. Glow plug relay No. 1 (right fenderwell) should make a clicking noise 5-9 seconds after ignition is turned on.

2) Measure voltage between ground and any glow plug terminal. At least 8-9 volts should be present after ignition is turned on.

Glow Plug Relays — No continuity should be present across terminals C and D. With battery voltage applied to terminals A and B, continuity should be present across C and D. If not, replace relay. *See Fig. 5.*

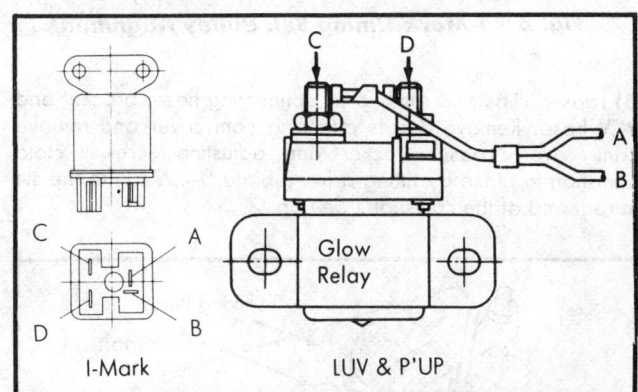

Fig. 5   Glow Plug Relay Testing

Dropping Resistor — Check for continuity across terminals of resistor (in case on fenderwell near battery). If no continuity, replace resistor.

Glow Plugs — Continuity should exist between plug terminal and top. If not, replace glow plugs.

NOTE — *If one glow plug is defective, all must be replaced as a set.*

Thermal Switch — Continuity should exist when switch is at a temperature lower than 109-122° F (43-50° C). No continuity should exist when above 116-127° F (47-53° C). If switch does not operate properly, replace it.

REMOVAL & INSTALLATION

INJECTION PUMP & TIMING BELT

NOTE — *When the timing belt is loosened or removed, it must be replaced. Do not retension or install a used timing belt.*

DIESEL FUEL INJECTION — ISUZU & LUV (Cont.)

Removal (I-Mark) — 1) Disconnect negative battery cable. Remove panel under engine, drain cooling system and remove fan shroud. Remove fan, fan belts and cooling fan pulley.

2) Remove 10 bolts retaining upper dust cover, then remove dust cover and by-pass hose. Turn engine until No. 1 cylinder is at TDC. Align mark on pump pulley with mark on front plate. *See Fig. 6.* Install a bolt (6mm x 1.25) through hole in injection pump pulley into threaded hole in pulley housing.

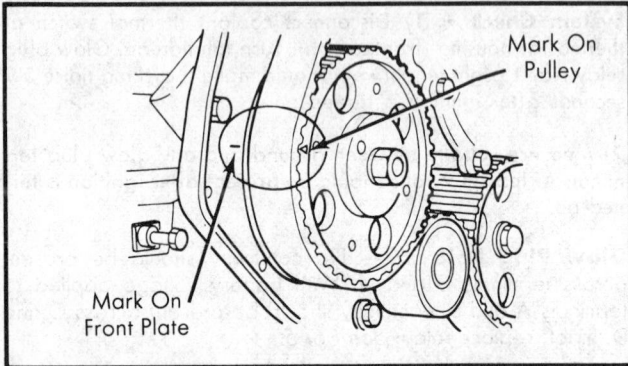

Fig. 6 I-Mark Timing Belt Pulley Alignment

3) Loosen clips and remove air connecting hose, bracket and PCV hose. Remove 3 nuts attaching cam cover and remove cam cover. Loosen rocker arm adjusting screws. Hold camshaft in place by fitting a fixing plate (J-29761) to the slit in rear end of the camshaft. *See Fig. 7.*

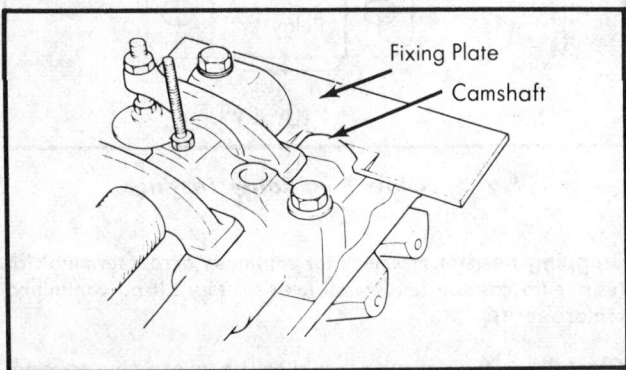

Fig. 7 I-Mark Camshaft Fixing Plate Installation

4) Remove damper pulley, lower dust cover, timing belt holder and tension spring. Loosen tension pulley and plate bolts, then remove timing belt. Remove nut attaching injection pump pulley. Using puller, remove injection pump pulley. Remove lock bolt.

5) Disconnect wiring from fuel cut solenoid valve switch and tachometer pick-up sensor (if so equipped). Disconnect accelerator cable from pump lever. On Auto. Trans. models, disconnect throttle valve control cable from pump lever.

6) On all models, disconnect vacuum hose from actuator of fast idle device and fuel hoses at injection pump. Remove 6 screws attaching injection pipe clips and remove clips. Remove 8 sleeve nuts attaching injection pipe and remove pipe.

7) Remove 4 bolts attaching pump rear bracket and remove bracket. Disconnect control lever spring. Remove 2 nuts attaching injection pump flange. Remove injection pump with fast idle device.

Installation — 1) Install injection pump with fast idle device by aligning notched line on flange with line on front plate. Tighten 4 bolts on rear bracket in sequence. *See Fig. 8.* Ensure that there is no clearance between rear bracket and injection pump bracket.

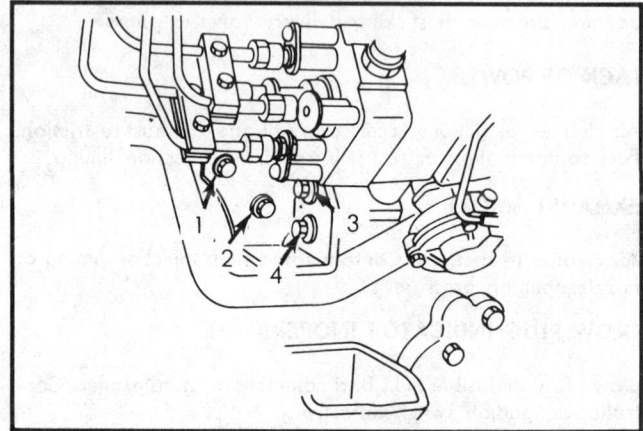

Fig. 8 I-Mark Injection Pump Rear Bracket Bolt Tightening Sequence

2) Install injection pump pulley by aligning it with the key groove. Align mark on pulley with mark on front plate. Using lock bolt, tighten pulley nut. Remove camshaft pulley fixing bolt. Using remover (J-22888), remove pulley from the camshaft, then install pulley on the shaft. Hand-tighten pulley bolts.

3) Install timing belt counterclockwise on crankshaft pulley, idler pulley, camshaft pulley, injection pump pulley, tension pulley, and damper pulley in order. Ensure that cogs on belt and pulley engage properly.

4) Position belt so that slack is in area of tension pulley. Depress tension pulley with finger and install tension spring. Hand-tighten tension pulley plate bolts in sequence shown. *See Fig. 9.*

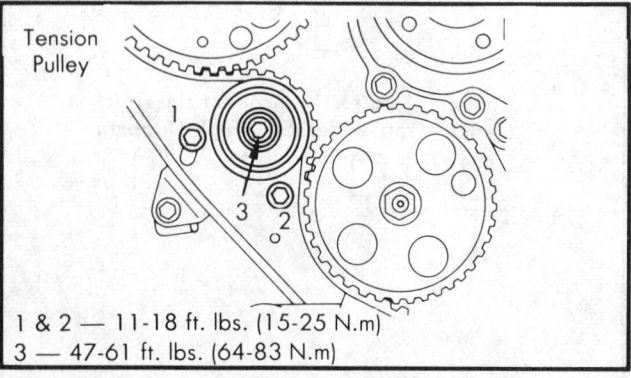

1 & 2 — 11-18 ft. lbs. (15-25 N.m)
3 — 47-61 ft. lbs. (64-83 N.m)

Fig. 9 I-Mark Tension Pulley Bolt Tightening Sequence

DIESEL FUEL INJECTION — ISUZU & LUV (Cont.)

5) Tighten camshaft pulley bolts to 40-47 ft. lbs. (54-64 N.m). Remove injection pump pulley lock bolt and fixing plate on end of camshaft. Install damper pulley on hub. Ensure that No. 1 cylinder is at TDC and that crankshaft is not turned.

6) Tighten tensioner pulley and plate bolts in sequence. *See Fig. 9.* Belt tension between camshaft pulley and injection pump pulley should be 47-64 lbs. (21-29 kg.). Adjust valves and reinstall cam cover. To complete installation, reverse removal procedures.

Removal (LUV & P'UP) — **1)** Disconnect battery cables and remove battery assembly. Remove panel under engine, drain cooling system, disconnect coolant hoses and remove fan and shroud.

2) Remove fan belts, air conditioning compressor and crankshaft pulley. Remove both timing belt covers, then remove tension spring and timing belt tension pulley. Remove timing belt. *See Fig 1.*

3) Remove accelerator cable and wiring from injection pump. Using a back-up wrench, remove fuel lines and injection pipes from pump. Install a bolt (6 mm x 1.25) through hole in injection pump pulley into threaded hole in pulley housing. Remove pulley bolts and use a puller to remove injection pulley.

4) Check position of injection pump scribe line relative to mark on front bracket, then remove bolts and injection pump.

Installation — **1)** Install injection pump, aligning marks on flange and front bracket. Install injection pump pulley, using holding bolt to keep pulley from turning. Turn engine until No. 1 cylinder is at TDC.

2) Align pulleys so marks are together. *See Fig. 10.* Install timing belt on crankshaft pulley, camshaft pulley and injection pump pulley in order. Position belt so slack is in area of idler pulley.

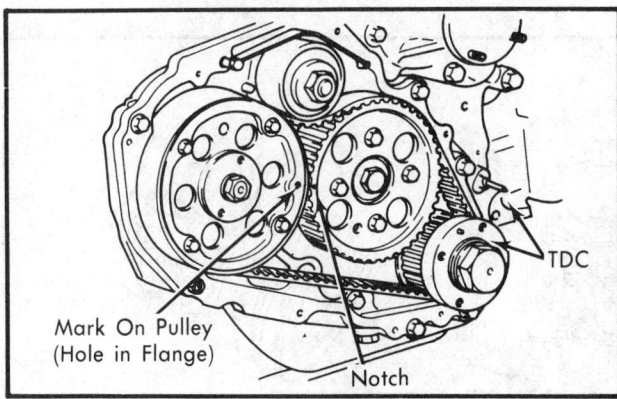

Fig. 10   LUV & P'UP Timing Belt Pulley Alignment

3) Install idler pulley, ensuring base is aligned against 2 pins on timing pulley housing. Hand-tighten pulley nut, then install spring and tighten nut to 22-36 ft. lbs. (30-49 N.m). Turn crankshaft 2 revolutions, then 90° more beyond TDC.

CAUTION — *Always turn engine in firing rotation. Do not rotate in reverse direction.*

4) Loosen tension pulley nut so pulley can take up belt slack, then tighten to specifications. Install injection pump pulley flange so hole in flange is aligned with mark on camshaft

pulley. Turn engine 2 revolutions and check that marks are still aligned when No. 1 cylinder is at TDC.

5) Belt tension between injection pump pulley and crankshaft pulley should be 33-55 lbs. (15-25 kg) when measured with tension gauge. To complete gauge. To complete installation, reverse removal procedure and adjust injection timing.

FUEL FILTER

Removal & Installation — **1)** Disconnect water sensor wiring at connector. Remove filter cartridge and pour out fuel, then remove water sensor. Install sensor on new filter cartridge.

2) Lubricate gasket with fuel, then install filter cartridge. Tighten $2/3$ turn after filter contacts base. Pump hand pump 30-40 times to fill cartridge with fuel. Start engine and check for leaks.

Draining Water — Place container under drain hose. Open drain plug 5 turns and operate pump about 10 times, or until all water is removed from filter. Tighten drain plug and operate pump several times until pressure builds up. Start engine and check that no leaks occur and "FILTER" lamp on dashboard is off.

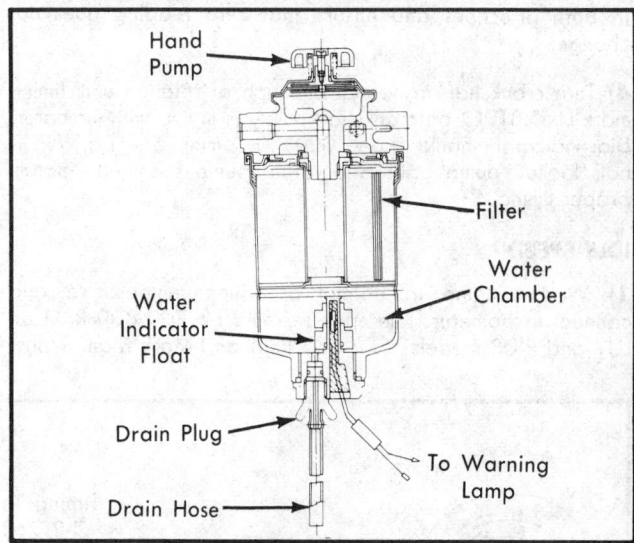

Fig. 11   Fuel Filter and Water Separator

ADJUSTMENTS

INJECTION PUMP TIMING

I-Mark — **1)** Check that notch in pump flange is in line with notched line on front plate. Turn engine to position No. 1 cylinder at TDC. Remove injection pump pulley cover (upper front cover) and see that timing marks are aligned. *See Fig. 6.*

2) Remove cam cover and rear plug. Check that fixing plate fits smoothly into slit at rear end of the camshaft, then remove fixing plate. *See Fig. 7.* Disconnect injection pipe from pump (using back-up wrench) and remove distributor head screw.

3) Install timing gauge tool (GM Part No. J-29763) and set lift approximately .04" (1 mm) from the plunger. Turn engine until No. 1 cylinder is 45-60° BTDC, then calibrate dial indicator to zero.

ISUZU DIESEL FUEL INJECTION – LUV (Cont.)

NOTE — *The crankshaft pulley is provided with a total of 11 notched lines (4 lines in one area and 7 lines in another). The group of 4 is for static timing and should be used for service purposes. The group of 7 is for dynamic timing and used only at the factory.*

4) Turn crankshaft in normal direction of rotation until timing mark (18° BTDC) on crankshaft pulley is in line with indicator. *See Fig. 12.* Dial indicator should show .020" (0.5 mm). If not, loosen pump bolts and rotate pump slightly to obtain proper timing.

LUV & P'UP — **1)** Check that notch in pump flange is in line with notch in front bracket. Turn engine to position No. 1 cylinder at TDC. Remove injection pump pulley cover (right half of timing belt cover) and see that timing marks are aligned. *See Fig. 10.*

2) Disconnect injection pipe from pump (using back-up wrench) and remove distributor head screw. Install timing gauge tool (GM Part No. J-29763) and set lift approximately .04" (1 mm) from the plunger.

3) Turn engine until No. 1 cylinder is 45-60° BTDC, then calibrate dial indicator to zero. Turn crankshaft pulley slightly in both directions and ensure that zero reading does not change.

4) Turn crankshaft in normal direction of rotation until timing mark (15° BTDC) on crankshaft pulley is in line with indicator. Dial indicator should show .020" (0.5 mm). *See Fig. 12.* If not, loosen pump bolts and rotate pump slightly to obtain proper timing.

IDLE SPEED

1) Warm engine to normal operating temperature and connect tachometer. Idle speed should be 700-800 RPM on LUV and P'UP models, 575-675 RPM on I-Mark Man. Trans. models or 675-775 RPM on I-Mark Auto. Trans. models. If not, loosen lock nut and adjust idle speed screw.

2) Disconnect vacuum hoses from vacuum switching valve and connect them together using piece of tubing. Fast idle speed should be 900-950 RPM on all models. If not, loosen adjusting nut and adjust with fast idle nut. *See Fig. 13.* Remove hose jumper and reconnect hoses, then remove tachometer.

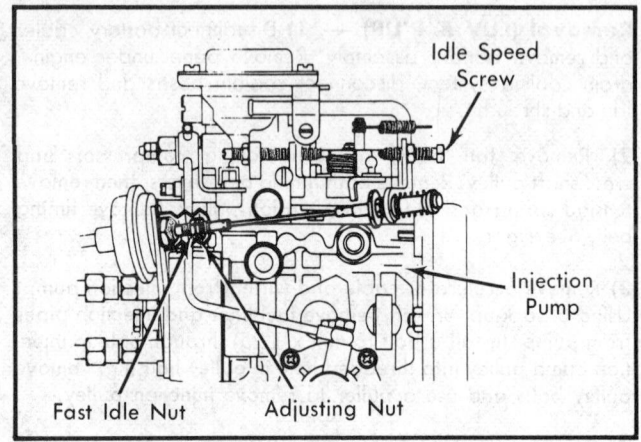

Fig. 13   Idle Speed Adjustments

TIGHTENING SPECIFICATIONS

Application	Ft. Lbs. (N.m)
Injection Pump Pulley Nut	42-52 (57-71)
Timing Belt Cover Bolts	4-7 (5-10)
Injection Nozzles	51-58 (69-79)

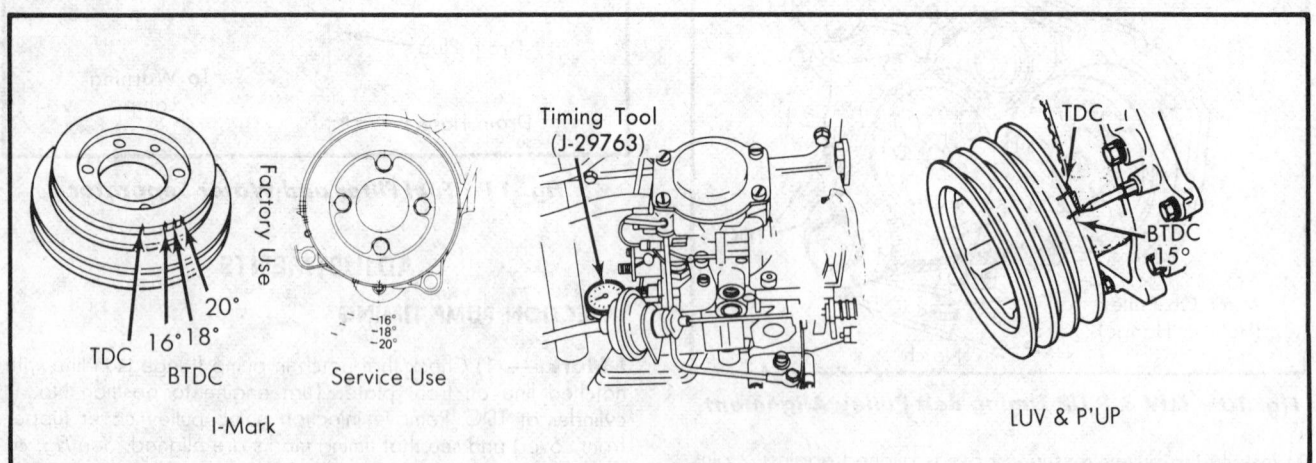

Fig. 12   Injection Pump Timing Adjustment

TOYOTA DIESEL FUEL INJECTION – PICKUP

Pickup

DESCRIPTION

The diesel injection system includes a fuel injection pump, injection nozzles, fuel filter, fuel sediment and water separator/warning device, fuel lines and glow plug system. The glow plug system has a pre-heating timer (behind left kick panel), 2 glow plug relays (one on each fenderwell), a current sensor, register resistor and water temperature sensor.

OPERATION

FUEL INJECTION PUMP

The injection pump is driven by a belt at the front of the engine. If draws fuel from the tank, pressurizes it, and injects a specific quantity to each cylinder at the proper time. Excess fuel is returned to the tank through another line. The injection pump is not serviceable and should not be disassembled.

NOTE – *Air conditioned vehicles have a vacuum unit that increases idle speed when the air conditioning is on.*

INJECTION NOZZLES

The injection nozzles spray fuel into a prechamber as each compression stroke occurs. Each nozzle has a fuel supply and return line. Nozzles can be disassembled, cleaned and adjusted to correct defective spray patterns. Shims are used to correct nozzle opening pressures, and are available in 20 sizes from .039-.076" (1.0-1.95 mm) in increments of .002" (.05 mm). Changing one size nozzle shim will change injection pressure by 71 psi (5 kg/cm^2).

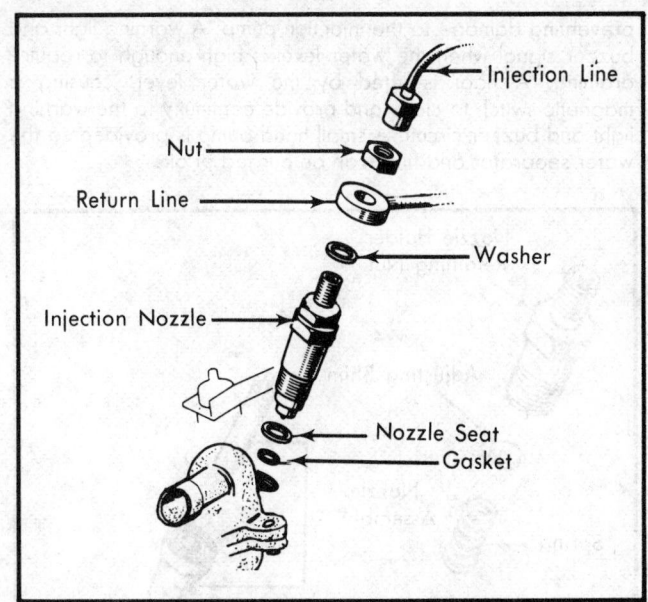

Fig. 2   Fuel Injection Nozzle Installation

FUEL FILTER

The fuel filter is a sealed cartridge type, located on the firewall. The cartridge should be changed at regular intervals and when replaced, should be installed by hand, never with a wrench.

WATER-IN-FUEL WARNING SYSTEM

The fuel injection system includes a water and sediment filter in addition to the sealed cartridge filter. This unit traps water which may be present in the fuel system and holds it,

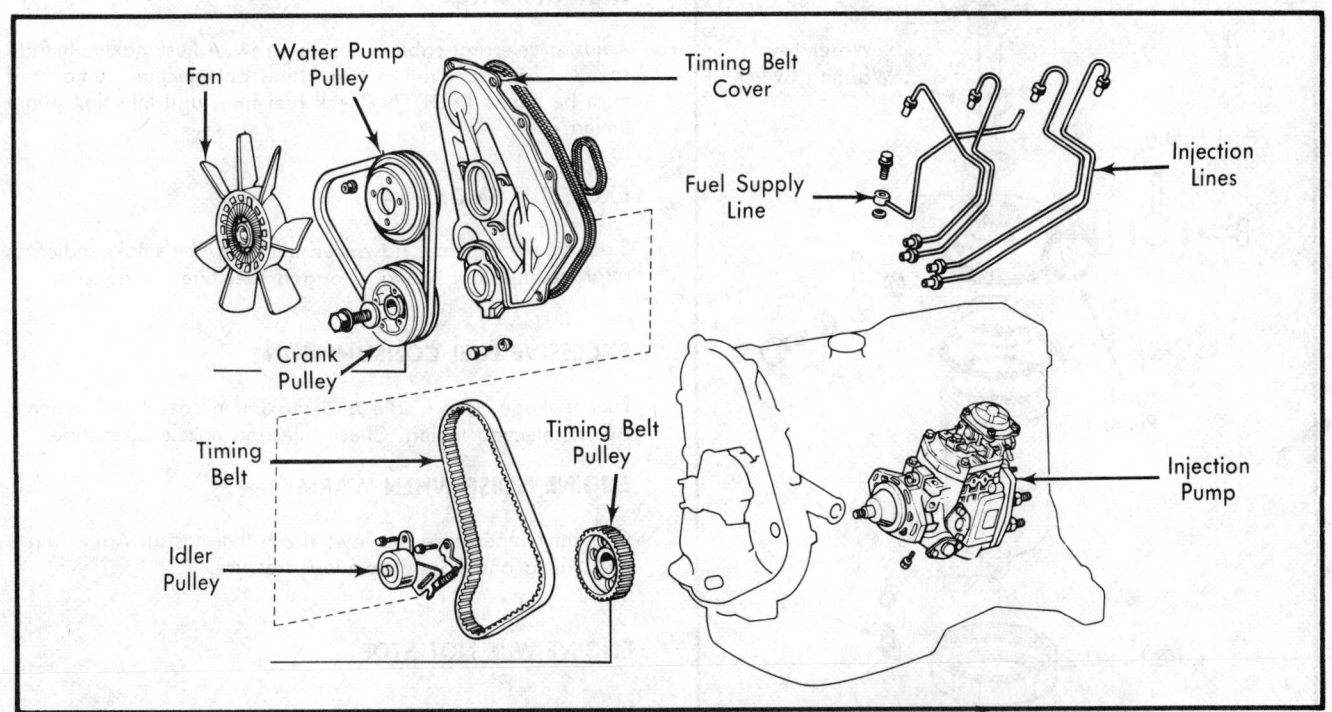

Fig. 1   Toyota Diesel Fuel Injection Components

TOYOTA DIESEL FUEL INJECTION – PICKUP (Cont.)

preventing damage to the injection pump. A warning light and buzzer signal when the water level is high enough to require draining. A float is lifted by the water level, causing a magnetic switch to close and provide continuity to the warning light and buzzer circuit. A small hand pump is provided so the water separator and filter can be purged of air.

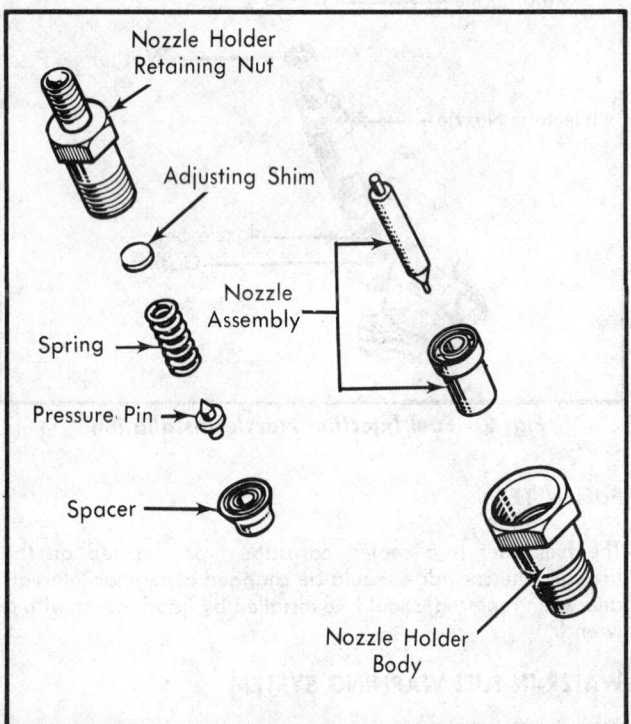

Fig. 3   Exploded View of Fuel Injection Nozzle

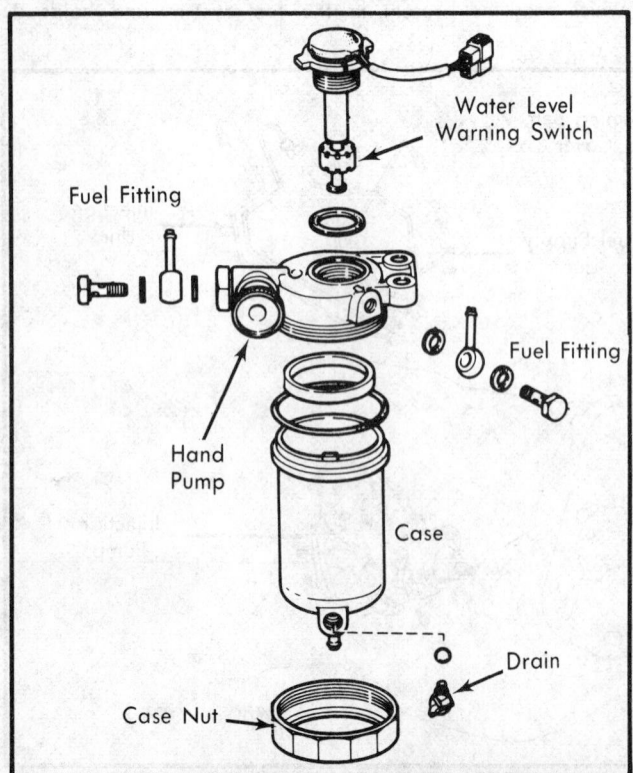

Fig. 4   Water-In-Fuel Warning System

GLOW PLUGS

The glow plug system uses a pre-heating timer and 2 relays to control glow plug current. The glow plugs enable the engine to start easily in cold weather and run smoothly during warm-up. Current is applied to the glow plugs for a specific time which is determined by engine coolant temperature. When the ignition is turned on, a glow plug light operates for 4.5 seconds if coolant is below 104° F (40° C), or .5 second if coolant is above 104° F (40° C).

TIMING BELT WARNING SYSTEM

The timing belt which drives the injection pump must be replaced at 50,000 mile intervals. To ensure maintenance is done at the proper time, the vehicle is equipped with a maintenance warning system. An instrument panel lamp is controlled by a speedometer switch and lights when maintenance is due. After the timing belt is replaced, the lamp is turned off by depressing a reset button (behind grommet in speedometer bezel).

TROUBLE SHOOTING

NO FUEL AT NOZZLES

Check fuel cut solenoid. Inspect fuel lines, drain water and replace filter. Bleed fuel system. Replace injection pump.

ROUGH IDLE

Adjust accelerator cable. Adjust idle speed. Check for fuel or air leaks. Correct injection pump timing. Check injection nozzle opening pressures and adjust or clean nozzles.

LACK OF POWER

Adjust accelerator cable and stop screw. Adjust maximum RPM speed. Check fuel return line fitting on injection pump — it must be marked "OUT". Check fuel filter and injection pump timing.

EXCESSIVE SMOKE

Black smoke indicates advanced timing, white smoke indicates retarded injection timing. Clogged fuel filter or nozzles.

EXCESSIVE FUEL CONSUMPTION

Fuel leakage. Check idle and maximum speed adjustments. Adjust injection timing. Check injection nozzle operation.

ENGINE NOISE WHEN WARM

Coolant temperature too low, check thermostat. Adjust injection timing and nozzle opening pressure.

ENGINE WILL NOT STOP

Disconnect fuel cut solenoid connector. Check for foreign material in fuel cut solenoid or faulty ignition switch.

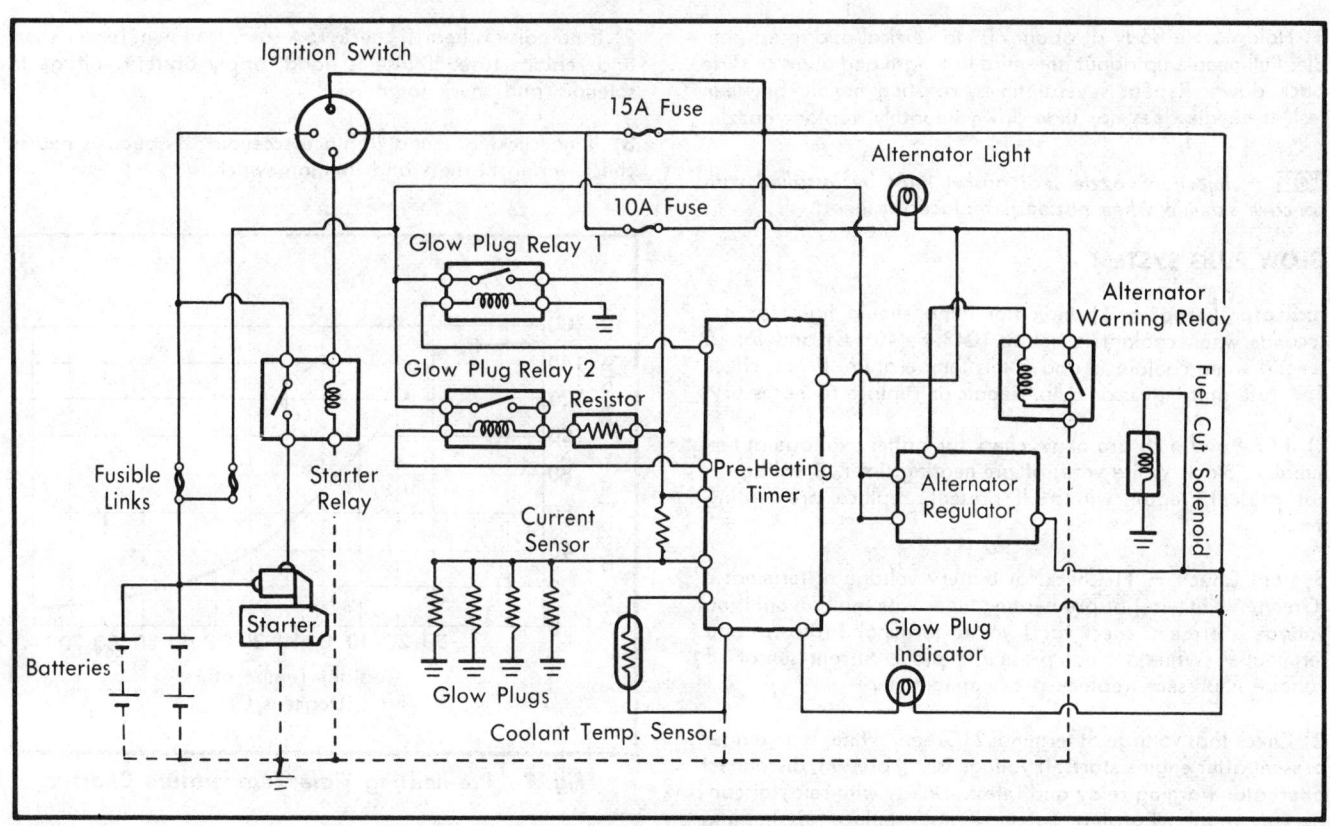

Fig. 5 Glow Plug System Wiring Diagram

TESTING

INJECTION NOZZLES

Opening Pressure — 1) Blow out any dirt around injection nozzles, then remove fuel lines and nozzles. Mark nozzles for correct installation.

2) Install nozzle on pressure tester. Bleed air out, then pump as hard as possible several times to clean out nozzle. Pump up pressure slowly and note when nozzle opens.

3) If pressure is not within 1495-1780 psi (105-125 kg/cm^2), disassemble and clean nozzle. Change shims as necessary to obtain opening pressure of 1635-1780 psi (115-125 kg/cm^2).

NOTE — *Shims are available in 20 thicknesses in increments of .002" (.05 mm). One size change will adjust pressure 71 psi (5 kg/cm^2).*

4) Test nozzle again to ensure opening pressure is correct, then check for leakage.

Leakage Test — Pump pressure slowly until about 142-284 psi (10-20 kg/cm^2) BELOW nozzle opening pressure. Hold pressure for at least 10 seconds; no dripping should occur. If nozzle drips, disassemble and clean, or replace. Check spray pattern.

Spray Pattern — Increase pumping speed to between 15 and 60 times per minute. At certain speeds, nozzle should "shud-

der" when spraying. Check spray pattern at this speed. If pattern is not correct, clean or replace nozzle. See *Fig. 6.*

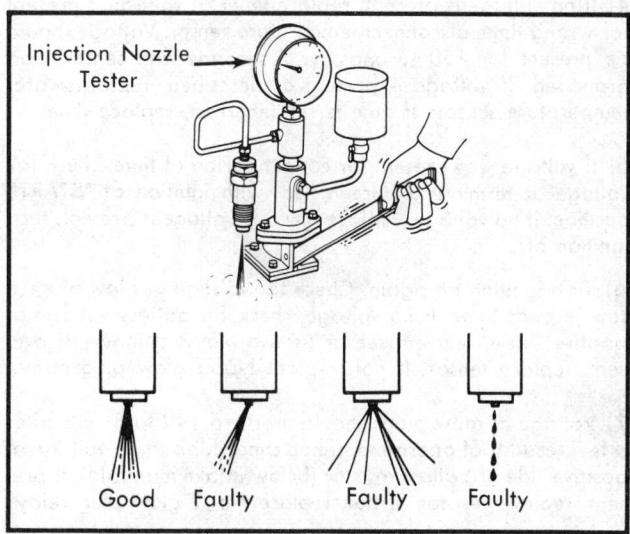

Fig. 6 Injection Nozzle Spray Patterns

Nozzle Cleaning — 1) Disassemble nozzle holder. Wash parts in clean diesel fuel, using a wooden stick and soft brass brush to remove deposits. DO NOT touch nozzle tip with fingers.

2) Inspect nozzle seat and needle tip for damage or corrosion. Replace if either is found.

TOYOTA DIESEL FUEL INJECTION — PICKUP (Cont.)

3) Hold nozzle body at about 60° to vertical and insert needle. Pull needle up about one-third its length and allow to slide back down. Repeat several times, rotating needle between test. If needle does not slide down smoothly, replace nozzle.

NOTE — *Injection nozzle seat gasket must be installed with concave side up when nozzle is replaced in head.*

GLOW PLUG SYSTEM

Indicator Lamp — 1) Indicator lamp should light for 4.5 seconds when coolant is below 104° F (40° C) and for .5 second when coolant is above this temperature. If not, check 15A fuse and indicator bulb. Repair or replace as necessary.

2) If fuse and bulb are okay, check for battery voltage at terminal 7 (Black/White wire) of pre-heating timer. If voltage is not present, repair wiring. If present, replace pre-heating timer.

System Check — 1) Check for battery voltage at terminal 2 (Green/White wire) of pre-heating timer with ignition on. If no voltage is present, check for 1 volt at terminal 3 (Brown) and terminal 9 (White). If not present, replace current sensor. If voltage is present, replace pre-heating timer.

2) Check that voltage at terminal 2 (Green/White) is no longer present after engine starts. If voltage is still present, disconnect alternator warning relay and retest. If okay with relay disconnected, repair charging system. If not, replace pre-heating timer.

3) Turn ignition off and stop engine. Turn ignition on again and check that current flow to terminal 8 (Green/Red) at timer is present according to temperature chart. See *Fig. 7.*

4) If no voltage is present, replace timer. If voltage is present for wrong time, disconnect temperature sensor. Voltage should be present for 150 seconds, or 7 seconds with sensor lead grounded. If voltage is present as described, replace water temperature sensor. If time is still incorrect, replace timer.

5) If voltage was present for correct period of time, check for voltage at terminal 8 (Green/Red) with ignition at "START" position. If no voltage, replace timer. If voltage is present, turn ignition off.

6) Turn ignition on again. Check for voltage at glow plugs a few seconds later. If no voltage, check for battery voltage at positive side of current sensor (above No. 3 cylinder). If present, replace sensor. If not, replace No. 1 glow plug relay.

7) Voltage at glow plugs should drop from 12 to 6 volts after a few seconds of operation. If not, check for battery voltage at positive side of ballast resistor (below intake manifold). If present, replace resistor. If not, replace No. 2 glow plug relay.

8) If all voltage measurements are correct, measure glow plug resistance. Resistance should be close to zero. If infinity, replace glow plug.

FUEL CUT SOLENOID

Solenoid Check — 1) Turn ignition on. Repeatdly connect and disconnect wire at fuel cut solenoid. If a clicking noise is heard, solenoid is okay.

2) If no noise is heard, check 15A fuse. If blown, repair short and replace fuse. If fuse is good, apply battery voltage to solenoid and check for noise.

3) If no clicking sound, replace solenoid. If sound is heard, check wiring harness and ignition switch.

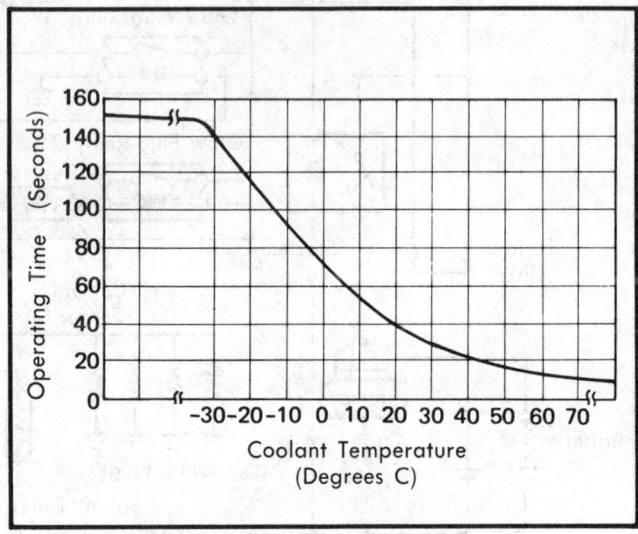

Fig. 7   Pre-heating Time/Temperature Chart

REMOVAL & INSTALLATION

INJECTION PUMP & TIMING BELT

Removal — 1) Drain coolant and disconnect battery ground cable. Remove radiator, shroud and hoses. Remove drive belts, fan and water pump pulley. If equipped with air conditioning, remove compressor and bracket without disconnecting hoses.

2) Pull off crankshaft pulley, then remove timing belt cover and guide. Turn engine to align timing belt pulleys at each position. See *Fig. 8.*

3) Remove tension spring from idler pulley, loosen pulley bolts and remove timing belt. Use puller to remove injection pump pulley.

NOTE — *Pulley will spring off so use care to prevent damage.*

4) Check scribe marks on pump and engine to ensure correct alignment during installation. Remove injection lines, then fuel feed and return lines. Disconnect fuel cut solenoid wire and vacuum hose (if present), then remove mounting bolts and injection pump.

Installation — 1) Install injection pump and connect fuel lines, wiring and vacuum hose (if equipped). Leave mounting bolts loose. Install injection pump pulley.

2) Align pulleys with marks, but place injection pump pulley mark one tooth clockwise from alignment mark. Install timing belt to camshaft gear, then injection pump gear.

TOYOTA DIESEL FUEL INJECTION — PICKUP (Cont.)

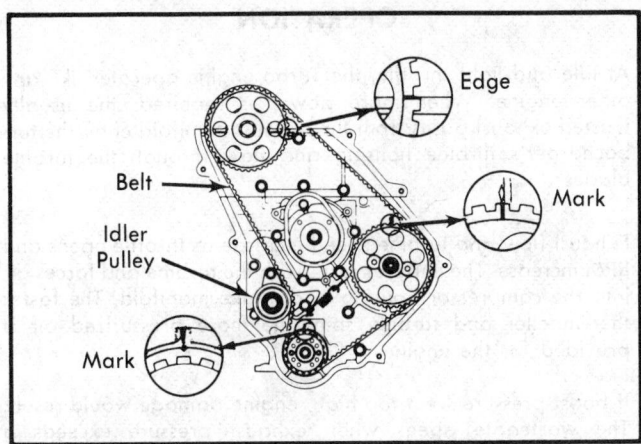

Fig. 8 Injection Pump Pulley Alignment

3) Install timing belt on crankshaft gear. Loosen idler pulley bolts and install spring. Temporarily install crankshaft pulley bolt and turn engine clockwise 2 revolutions to TDC.

4) Check that all alignment marks are in correct position. If not, remove belt and repeat procedure. Tighten idler pulley bolts without moving bracket. Install timing belt guide, cover and crankshaft pulley.

5) Install compressor (if equipped), pulleys, fan and drive belts. Install hoses, radiator and shroud. Connect batteries and refill cooling system, then reset maintenance switch by removing grommet in speedometer bezel and depressing switch button.

NOTE — *Switch will reset only after light has come on. If belt is replaced before light comes on, switch can be reset by removing speedometer and readjusting switch.*

6) Align injection pump with marks made before disassembly, then check injection timing.

FUEL FILTER & WATER SEPARATOR

Removal & Installation — 1) Place a container under water separator drain and open drain valve 2 turns. Turn priming pump knob counterclockwise to loosen, then pump until all water is discharged. Close drain valve.

2) Remove fuel filter, using filter wrench if necessary. Apply a thin film of fuel on new filter gasket and install filter by hand.

3) Pump priming pump 30-40 times to force all air our of filter and separator. Check for fuel leaks, then turn knob clockwise to lock in position.

ADJUSTMENTS

INJECTION PUMP TIMING

1) Remove distributive head bolt on injection pump. Install special alignment tool (Toyota Part No. 09275-54010) and dial indicator to distributive head plug.

2) Set No. 1 or No. 4 cylinder to 45° BTDC on compression stroke. Set dial indicator at zero. Check to see that indicator stays at zero when crankshaft pulley is rocked slightly to left and right.

3) Turn pulley until No. 1 or No. 4 cylinder is at TDC. Dial indicator should read .0394" (1.00 mm). If not, loosen injection pump bolts and all fuel connections. Tilt pump body slightly and recheck injection pump stroke. When correct, tighten bolts and fuel lines, then remove tools and install distributive head bolt and washer.

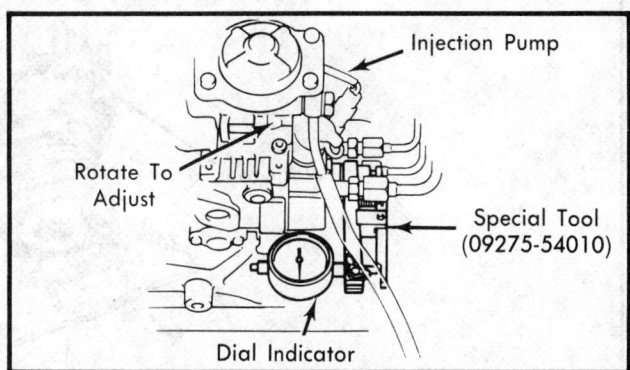

Fig. 9 Injection Pump Timing

IDLE & MAXIMUM SPEED

1) Warm engine to normal operating temperature and turn all accessories off. Check to ensure throttle lever touches full throttle stop screw when accelerator pedal is fully depressed.

2) Install tachometer and check slow idle. Adjust to 700 RPM by turning idle stop screw. Accelerate engine and quickly check maximum speed. Adjust to 4900 RPM with full throttle stop screw. Tighten lock nuts and remove test equipment.

TIGHTENING SPECIFICATIONS	
Application	**Ft. Lbs. (N.m)**
Nozzle Holder-to-Nozzle Body	44-57 (60-78)
Injection Nozzle-to-Cylinder Head	44-57 (60-78)
Injection Pump Pulley Bolt	44-50 (60-68)
Idler Pulley Bolts	11-15 (15-20)
Injection Pump Bolts	11-15 (15-20)

1981 Turbocharging Systems

AUDI TURBOCHARGING SYSTEM

5000 Turbo

DESCRIPTION

The Audi 5000 Turbo uses a KKK turbocharger, mounted directly to the front of the exhaust manifold. A wastegate is attached to the back of the manifold. Other system components include an additional safety switch to prevent excessive boost, an oil cooler mounted behind the front spoiler, and injector cooling fan, dual oil filters and an oil thermostat.

Engine modifications to ensure reliability include a piston cooling system (oil jet spray), low compression pistons, larger piston pins, sodium filled exhaust valves, and increased oil capacity. Automatic transmission, brakes, tires and suspension have also been modified.

OPERATION

At idle and light throttle, the Turbo engine operates like any other engine. When more power is required, the usually wasted exhaust gases from the exhaust manifold enter the turbocharger's turbine housing and flow through the turbine blades.

Exhaust flow and turbine speed increase as throttle opens and RPM increase. The impeller turns with the turbine and forces air into the compressor housing and intake manifold. The faster the impeller and turbine spin, the more pressurized air is provided for the engine.

If boost pressure went too high, engine damage would result. The wastegate opens when exhaust pressure exceeds a predetermined limit and allows exhaust gases to by-pass the

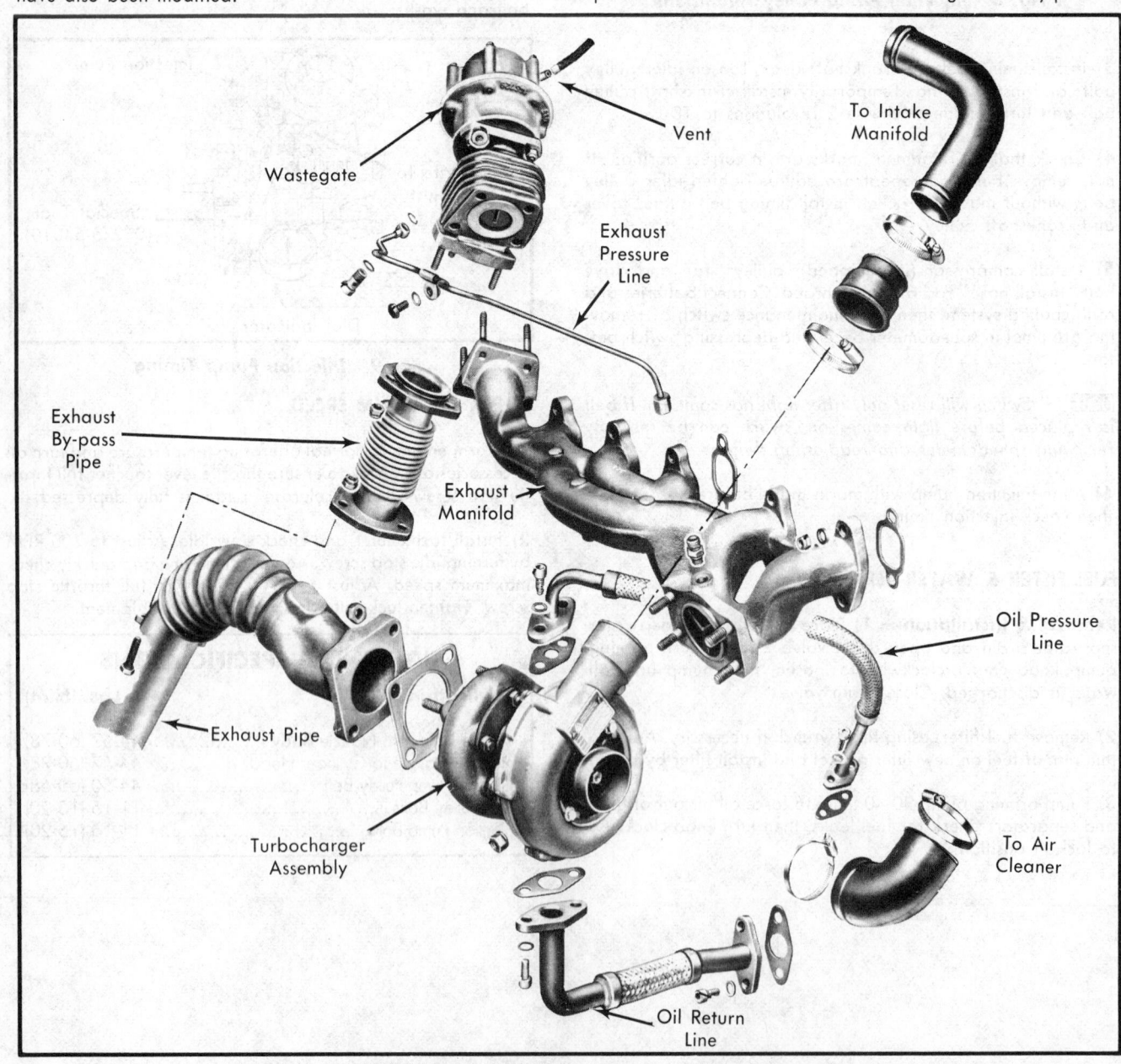

Fig. 1 Exploded View of Audi Turbocharger System Components

AUDI TURBOCHARGING SYSTEM (Cont.)

compressor. A boost pressure safety switch is used for protection in case the wastegate fails. This switch is connected to the intake manifold and serves as the ground for the electric fuel pump. When pressure is higher than 11.6 psi (.82 kg/cm²), the switch opens and the fuel pump stops, slowing the engine.

An electric blower fan is used to cool the injectors and intake manifold and prevent vapor lock. A thermal switch controls fan operation and turns the fan on whenever manifold temperatures exceed 212°F (100°C).

Turbocharger operation requires a large quantity of clean oil to prevent bearing failure. Turbo models have increased oil capacity, an oil cooler, oil thermostat, and special filter. Both the turbocharger filter and the regular engine filter should be changed at regular intervals.

TESTING

1) To test the turbocharging system, use a pressure gauge (VW1397) calibrated in both psi and bar. The gauge is equipped with a valve which locks pressure measurement when closed.

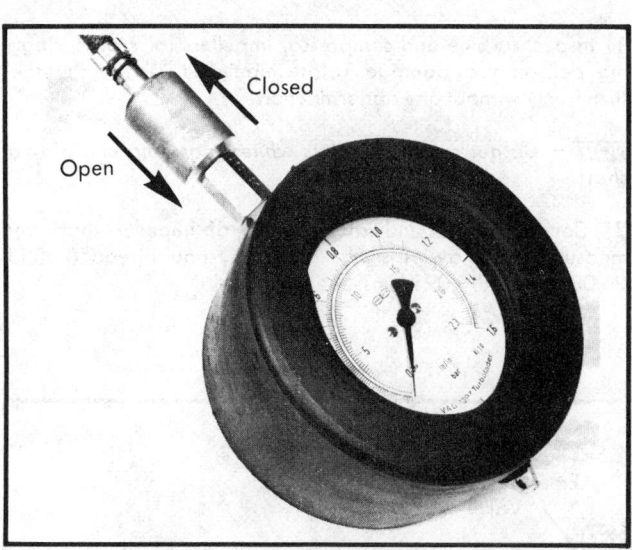

Fig. 2 Turbocharger Boost Gauge (VW 1397)

2) Attach gauge to vacuum advance at distributor, using "T" fitting supplied with gauge. Be sure vacuum advance unit and charcoal canister purge valve are free of leaks. Use hose clamps at all connections to avoid low readings.

3) Boost pressure can only be tested on a chassis dynamometer or through road testing. Carry the gauge inside car by routing the hose out right rear corner of hood and into passenger side vent wing window.

4) Accelerate engine to full throttle in drive position "2". Hold vehicle speed constant with foot brake, when engine speed reaches 4000 RPM. Wait 2 seconds and close gauge valve by pulling sleeve away from dial.

CAUTION — *Testing should not exceed 10 seconds at full boost.*

5) Boost pressure readings will vary with atmospheric pressure, temperature and altitude, but will fall between ranges listed in "Boost Pressure Specifications" table if turbocharger operation is correct.

Boost Pressure Specifications

Ambient Temperature	psi (kg/cm²)
50°F (10°C)	7.0-7.6 (.49-.53)
68°F (20°C)	6.7-7.4 (.47-.52)
77°F (25°C)	6.6-7.3 (.46-.51)
86°F (30°C)	6.4-7.0 (.45-.49)

6) If boost pressure is too high, wastegate is defective. If boost pressure is too low, replace wastegate and perform tests again. If pressure is still too low, replace defective turbocharger.

NOTE — *The boost pressure gauge in the instrument cluster is calibrated to read absolute pressure. When the engine is not running and gauge reads "1", this is normal atmospheric pressure. A reading of over "1" indicates boost pressure in the intake manifold; a reading less than "1" indicates presence of vacuum.*

DATSUN TURBOCHARGING SYSTEM

280ZX

DESCRIPTION

The Datsun 280ZX turbocharger is mounted on the exhaust manifold on the left side of the engine. Components of the turbocharger include turbine and compressor impellers (wheels), impeller shaft, bearings, impeller housings, wastegate controller, and wastegate (exhaust bypass valve). See Fig. 1.

The pressure actuated wastegate, located at the front of the compressor housing, prevents excessive intake boost pressure. If it fails, an emergency relief valve located on the intake manifold releases any excess pressure. Engine oil pressure provides constant lubrication to the impeller bearings.

OPERATION

The turbine impeller of the turbocharger is driven by the exhaust gases expelled from the cylinder combustion chambers. At idle speeds there is no pressurization of intake air and the engine operates like a normally aspirated engine.

With engine under partial load, the throttle valve opens and more fuel-air mixture is drawn into the combustion chambers. The speed and volume of exhaust gases also increases. The increased amount of exhaust gases turns the turbine impeller at a faster RPM. The compressor impeller turns at the same RPM as the turbine impeller because they are mounted on the same shaft. The increased RPM of the compressor impeller boosts the pressure of the intake air.

With engine under full load, the exhaust gases are at maximum pressure and increase the RPM of the turbine and compressor impellers to an extremely high speed. The boost pressure of the intake air reaches a maximum. When the pressure in the intake manifold reaches 6.08-6.85 psi (.43-.48 kg/cm^2), the diaphragm of the wastegate controller pushes against the linkage which opens the wastegate. Part of the exhaust gases are then routed directly into the main exhaust pipe, bypassing the turbine impeller. This maintains the boost pressure of the intake air at a constant 6.19-7.35 psi (.44-.52 kg/cm^2).

If the wastegate fails to function properly, an emergency relief valve located on the intake manifold opens to atmosphere when the intake manifold pressure reaches 7.35-7.73 psi (.52-.54 kg/cm^2). This prevents engine damage from excessive pressure.

TESTING

NOTE – If any turbocharger parts fail inspection or testing, replace entire turbocharger assembly.

TURBINE AND COMPRESSOR IMPELLERS

1) Inspect turbine and compressor impellers for cracks, clogging, deformity, or damage. Rotate impellers to be sure that they turn freely without any abnormal noise.

NOTE – Do not rotate impellers while measuring end play of shaft.

2) Connect a dial indicator to end of impeller shaft and measure end play of shaft. Indicator should read 0.0005-0.0036" (0.013-0.091 mm). See Fig. 2.

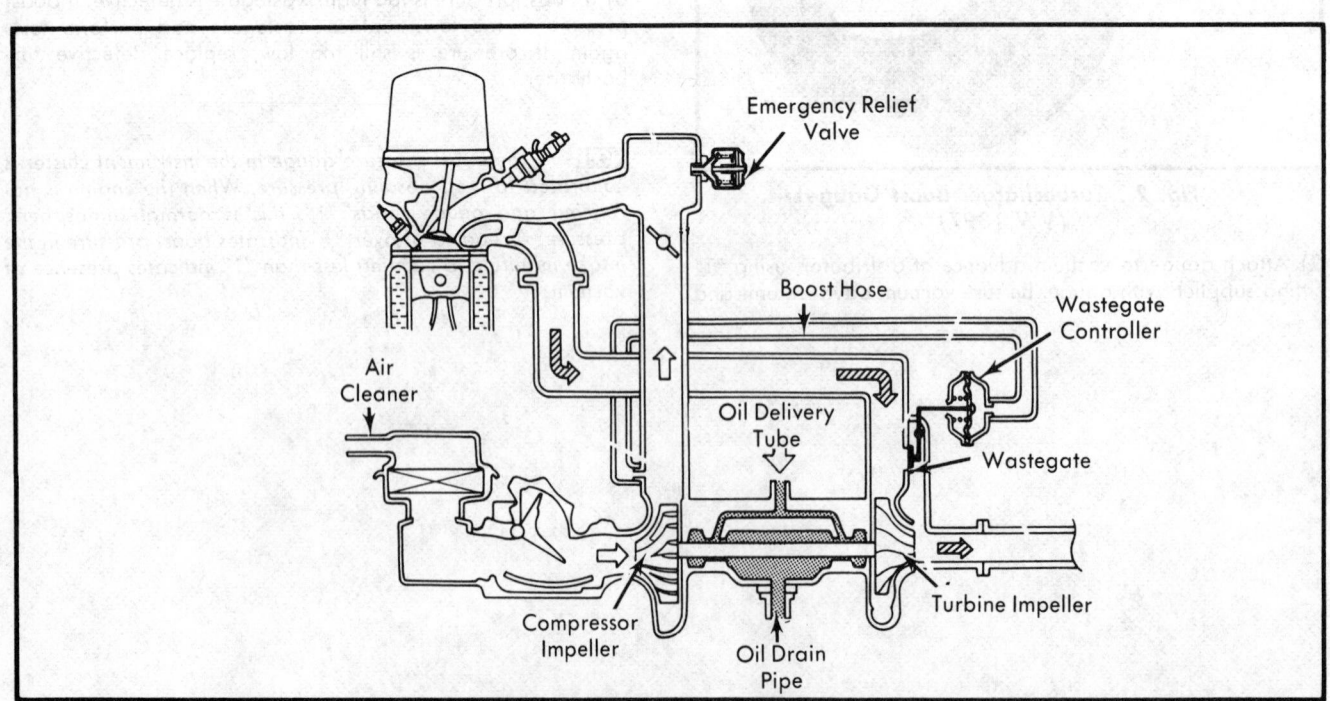

Fig. 1 Cutaway of Datsun Turbocharger

DATSUN TURBOCHARGING SYSTEM (Cont.)

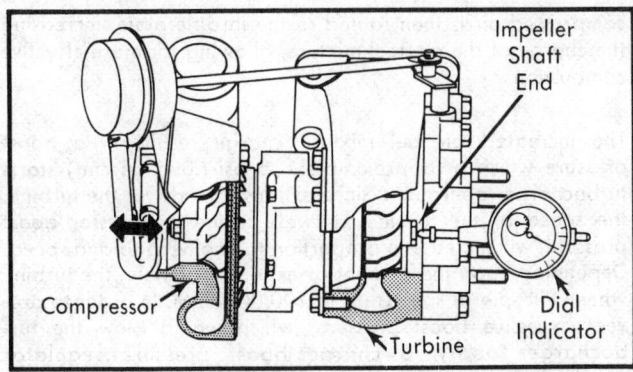

Fig. 2   Measuring Impeller Shaft End Play

WASTEGATE CONTROLLER

CAUTION — *Do not apply more than 9.67 psi (.68 kg/cm²) to wastegate controller diaphragm.*

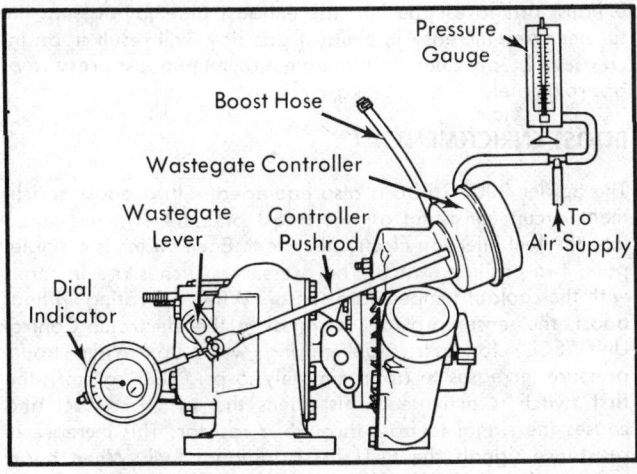

Fig. 3   Testing Wastegate Controller

1) Connect a dial indicator to end of wastegate controller pushrod. See *Fig. 3*. Disconnect boost hose at wastegate controller. Connect a pressure gauge to wastegate controller and apply 6.08-6.85 psi (.43-.48 kg/cm²). Wastegate controller pushrod should move 0.015" (0.38 mm).

2) Disconnect wastegate controller pushrod. Move wastegate lever back and forth and check for binding or sticking.

REMOVAL & INSTALLATION

TURBOCHARGER ASSEMBLY

Removal — **1)** Remove heat insulator, inlet tube, air duct hose, and suction air pipe.

2) Disconnect exhaust gas sensor connector, front tube, oil delivery tube, and oil drain pipe. See *Fig. 4*.

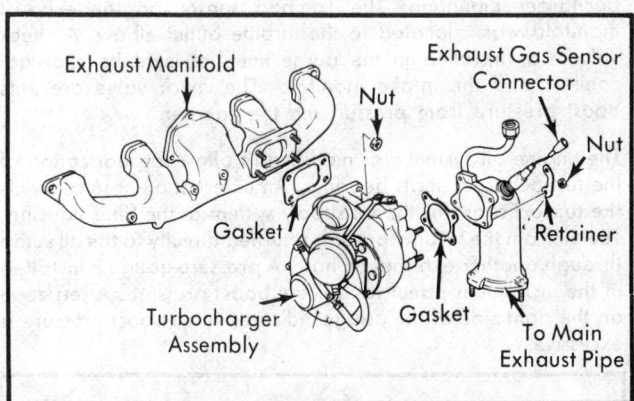

Fig. 4   Datsun Turbocharger Removal

3) Remove 4 nuts securing turbocharger to exhaust manifold. Remove turbocharger and gasket.

Installation — Install components in reverse order of removal. Replace gasket between turbocharger and exhaust manifold.

FIAT TURBOCHARGING SYSTEM

Spider 2000

DESCRIPTION

The turbocharger used on Fiat Spider 2000 Turbo models consists of a turbine wheel, compressor wheel, rotor shaft, wastegate actuator and wastegate. The rotor shaft is supported by two bearings which float on a thin film of oil. The bearings are protected from heat by seal rings and plates. The wastegate actuator operates the wastegate to allow excessive exhaust gas to by-pass the turbine wheel during boost. This limits boost pressure generated by the turbocharger. In addition, two boost enrichment switches, a load enrichment switch and an overboost protection switch are integral with this system.

Modifications have been made to the standard 2000 cc engine to accomodate the turbocharger. These modifications are as follows: The exhaust manifold was changed to provide for turbocharger mounting. The Lambda sensor on the exhaust manifold was relocated to the turbine outlet elbow. A check valve was installed in the purge line between the charcoal canister and the intake manifold. The check valve prevents boost pressure from pressurizing the canister.

The engine oil system was modified to allow for lubrication of the turbocharger shaft bearings. An external oil hose connects the turbocharger to the oil supply system at the filter housing. The oil from the turbocharger is returned directly to the oil sump through another external oil hose. A pressure gauge is installed in the instrument panel to indicate boost pressure. A red zone on the right side of the gauge indicates when boost pressure is excessive.

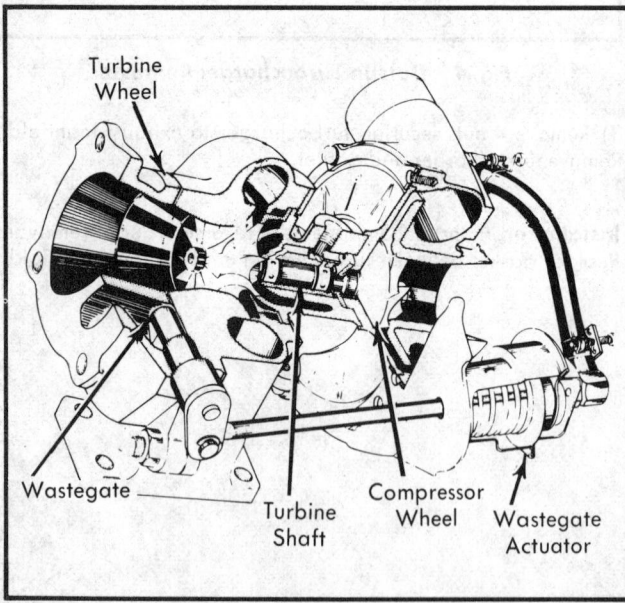

Fig. 1   Cutaway View of Fiat Spider 2000 Turbocharger

OPERATION

The turbocharger is mounted on the exhaust manifold so that all exhaust gases flow through the turbine. The exhaust gas starts the turbine rotating, which in turn causes the compressor wheel to rotate. As the compressor wheel rotates, it draws fresh air in from the air flow sensor and compresses it. The

compressed air is then routed to the throttle plate, increasing the charge of the air/fuel mixture, allowing for more effective combustion.

The increased air/fuel mixture charge results in a boost pressure which at approximately .5 psi (.035 kg/cm^2) starts turbocharger operation. Since exhaust gas drives the turbine, the speed of the turbine, as well as the compressor boost pressure, will increase in proportion to engine load and speed. Depending upon the amount of exhaust gas flow, the turbine wheel will spin at speeds up to 100,000 RPM. In order to prevent excessive boost pressure, which would blow the turbocharger apart, a charge boost pressure regulator (wastegate actuator) is incorporated into the unit.

WASTEGATE ACTUATOR

The wastegate actuator contains a diaphragm and a return spring. The upper chamber of the actuator is connected to the compressor outlet. The boost pressure in the outlet is applied to the diaphragm, and at approximately 6 psi (.42 kg/cm^2) the boost pressure begins to overcome the diaphragm spring pressure. This opens the wastegate valve, allowing some of the exhaust gas to escape into the exhaust pipe, by-passing the turbine. Any increase in exhaust gas flow will result in an increase in by-pass flow to maintain maximum boost pressure at approximately 6 psi (.42 kg/cm^2).

BOOST ENRICHMENT

The Spider 2000 Turbo is also equipped with a boost enrichment circuit consisting of two boost pressure switches wired into the fuel injection electrical system. Each switch is a single-pole, two-position switch. The pressure switches are in series with the coolant temperature sensor. When operating without boost, the sensor provides a signal to the Electronic Control Unit (ECU) for extra fuel during warm-up. When boost pressure increases to approximately .5 psi (.035 kg/cm^2), the first switch is activated. This opens the switch contact and causes the signal to pass through a resistor. This increase in resistance signals the ECU for additional fuel. When boost pressure increases to approximately 5 psi (.35 kg/cm^2) the second switch is activated and an additional resistance is added, signaling for an extra increase in fuel flow.

LOAD ENRICHMENT

A load enrichment switch is also used on Spider 2000 Turbo models. This circuit contains one boost pressure switch wired into the throttle plate switch circuit of the fuel injection electrical circuit. This switch provides a wide open throttle signal to the ECU whenever there is boost pressure. This signals the ECU to provide power enrichment, since the engine is operating under high load.

OVERBOOST PROTECTION

An overboost protection circuit is added in case the wastegate system fails. Boost pressure is applied to a pressure switch, calibrated to open if boost pressure exceeds the set value. This signals the ECU which closes the fuel injectors. The engine slows down and thereby reduces boost pressure. When boost pressure drops below the set value, the switch removes the signal from the ECU and the injectors return to normal operation.

FIAT TURBOCHARGING SYSTEM (Cont.)

TESTING

BOOST ENRICHMENT SWITCHES

1) Disconnect "Y" fitting from switches. Connect an air pressure regulator with a gauge to the "Y" fitting. Disconnect connectors for switches from fuel injection wire harness.

CAUTION — *When operating the regulator with line pressure connected, make sure air pressure to switches does not exceed 12 psi (.84 kg/cm²).*

2) Connect an ohmmeter to pins 1 and 2 of connector for boost enrichment switches. Slowly apply pressure to switches.

3) Check that switch operates (a slight audible click may be heard) at 0.5-1.5 psi (.035-.10 kg/cm²). Ohmmeter should read between 1500 and 2000 ohms.

4) Slowly increase pressure. Check that other switch operates at 4.5-5.5 psi (.31-.38 kg/cm²). Ohmmeter should read between 1750 and 2750 ohms.

LOAD ENRICHMENT & OVERBOOST PROTECTION SWITCH

1) Connect pressure regulator with gauge to "Y" fitting for load enrichment switch. Connect ohmmeter to pins 1 and 3 of connector for load enrichment/overboost switches. Zero ohmmeter.

2) Check that ohmmeter reads infinity. Slowly apply pressure to switch. Check that load switch operates at about 1 psi (.07 kg/cm²). Ohmmeter should read 0 ohms.

3) Connect ohmmeter to pins 1 and 2 of connector. Check that ohmmeter reads infinity.

4) Slowly increase pressure. Check that overboost switch operates at approximately 9 psi (.63 kg/cm²). Ohmmeter should be 0 ohms.

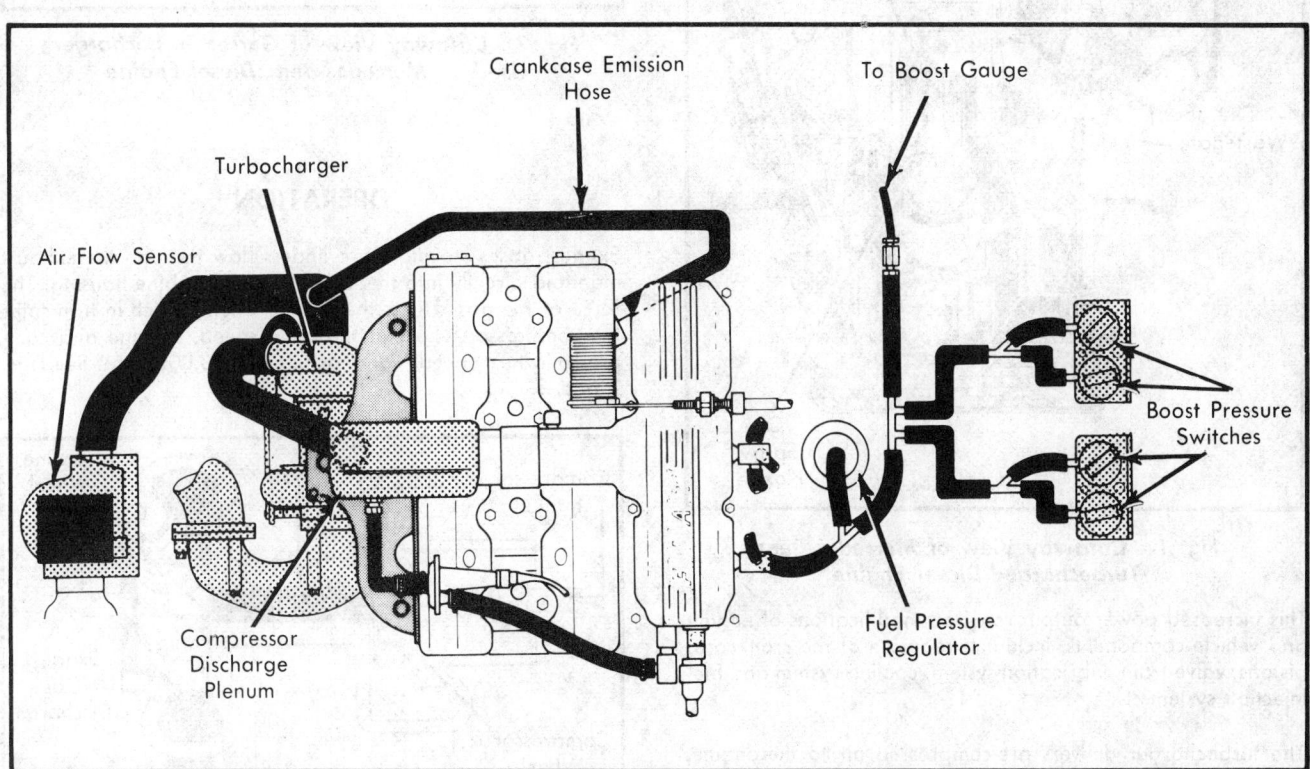

Fig. 2   Turbocharger Layout on Spider 2000 Models

1981 Turbocharging Systems

MERCEDES-BENZ DIESEL TURBOCHARGING SYSTEM

300 SD
300 TD

DESCRIPTION

The diesel turbocharged engine (617.95) is basically the same design as the naturally aspirated diesel engine. See *Fig. 1*. Installation of the Garrett turbocharger produced an increase to 110 SAE net brake horsepower at 4200 RPM.

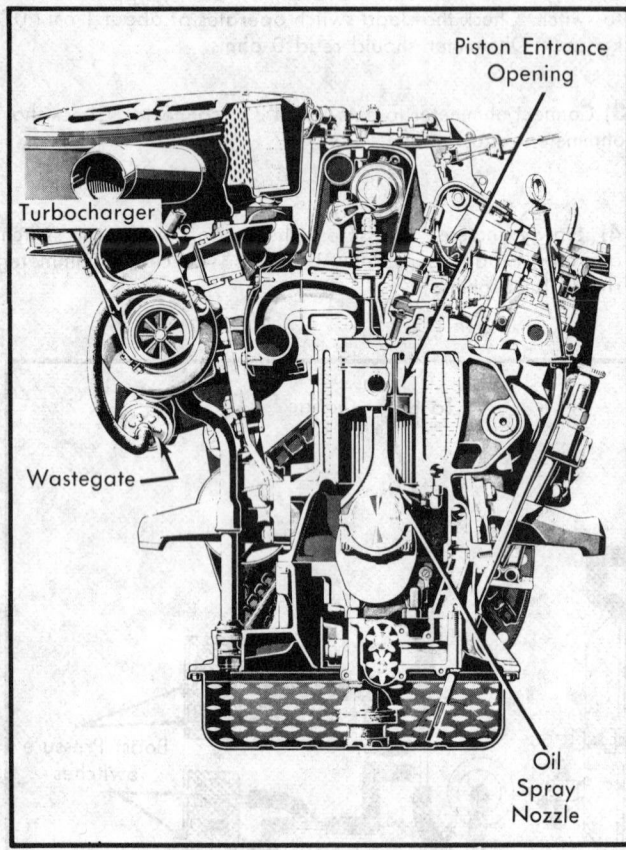

Fig. 1   Cutaway View of Mercedes-Benz Turbocharged Diesel Engine

This increased power output required modifications of engine and vehicle components, including redesign of the crankcase, pistons, valve train, lubrication system, cooling system and fuel injection system.

The turbocharger delivers pre-compressed air to the engine, providing a higher air charge in the cylinders and creating higher pressures and temperatures in the combustion chambers.

The system includes a turbocharger which consists of a turbine, compressor and a wastegate that prevents excessive boost pressures from damaging the engine. See *Fig. 2*.

The turbocharger's turbine wheel and compressor wheel are mounted on a common shaft and turn at the same speed. The turbocharger is mounted between the exhaust manifold and the exhaust pipe and is connected directly to the engine for lubrication and cooling. The wastegate is attached to the turbine housing. Should its boost pressure control valve malfunction, an engine overload protection system will prevent engine damage.

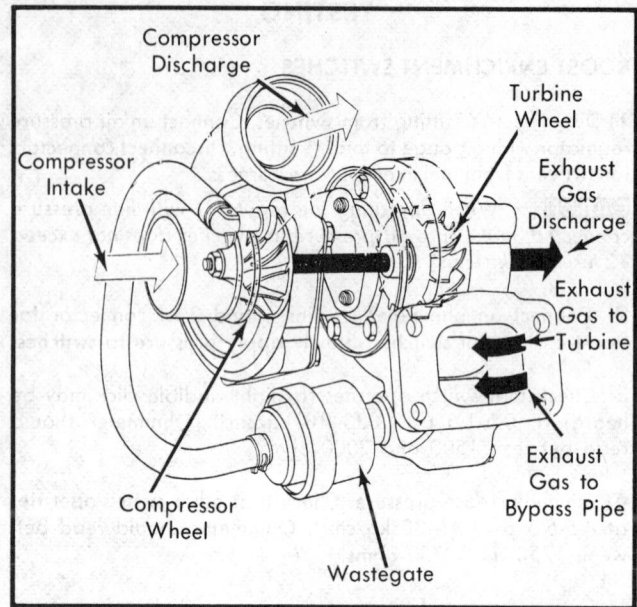

Fig. 2   Cutaway View of Garret Turbocharger Used on Mercedes-Benz Diesel Engine

OPERATION

Exhaust gases leaving the cylinders flow through the exhaust manifold directly into the turbocharger's turbine housing. The force of the gases turns the turbine wheel, which in turn spins the compressor wheel at the same speed. Turbine and compressor wheel speeds can reach up to 100,000 RPM. *See Figs. 2 and 3.*

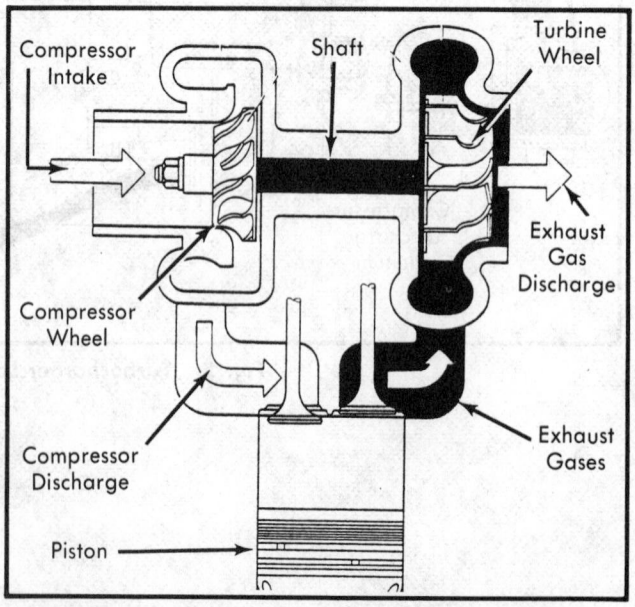

Fig. 3   Airflow Pattern with Garret Turbocharger

The fresh air drawn in by the compressor wheel is compressed and delivered to the combustion chamber above the pistons. At idle speed, the engine operates like any other. However, with

MERCEDES-BENZ DIESEL TURBOCHARGING SYSTEM (Cont.)

increasing load and engine speed, exhaust gases are expelled with increasing velocity. This causes the turbine wheel to turn faster, increasing boost pressure at the compressor wheel. Boost pressure is routed to the intake manifold and to individual cylinders, completing the cycle.

The aneroid compensator on top of the fuel injection pump automatically adjusts the fuel quantity injected into the cylinders depending on existing boost pressure or atmospheric pressure in the intake manifold. Therefore, the correct air-fuel relationship is maintained at all times.

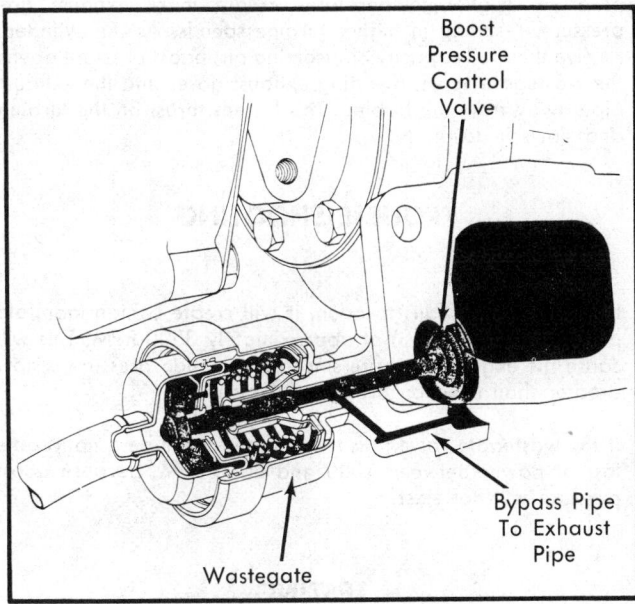

Fig. 4 Cutaway View of Wastegate Valve

Should boost pressure control valve (wastegate) fail, a pressure switch installed in the intake manifold closes an electrical circuit, energizing a switch-over valve. This valve closes the pressure line to the intake manifold and simultaneously opens the aneroid compensator to atmosphere. This reduces the fuel quantity being injected. The pressure switch only functions when intake manifold boost pressure reaches 16 psi (1.125 kg/cm^2). When pressure drops below this figure, the pressure switch opens the electric circuit and venting of the pressure line is stopped.

LUBRICATION

Oil is supplied to the turbocharger for lubrication and cooling from the rear cover of the oil filter. The oil return line runs from the turbocharger back to the upper oil pan housing. Oil spray nozzles for cooling the pistons are connected internally to the engine lubrication system's main oil gallery. See Fig. 1.

TESTING

1) To check turbocharger boost pressure, connect pressure gauge (617 589 02 21 00) to intake manifold after removing plug.

2) Using a dynamometer, drive vehicle in driving range "S" at full load and 4000 RPM. Boost pressure should be 10.1-11.6 psi (.71-.82 kg/cm^2).

3) If boost pressure is too low, check air filter and air intake shroud duct for obstructions. Check turbocharger for leaks between manifold and turbine housing, compressor housing discharge and intake manifold, and between intake or exhaust manifold and cylinder head.

4) Check pressure line between intake manifold and aneroid compensator and overload switch-over valve. To check valve, turn ignition switch to position "2". Disconnect plug on valve and check for battery voltage at black/red wire. If not present, check fuse number 4 or wiring. Check for ground condition of brown/black wire. There should be no ground connection below boost pressure of 16 psi (1.13 kg/cm^2). If ground exists, check pressure switch in intake manifold or its wiring.

5) Other possible causes of low boost pressure would be a defective wastegate, requiring turbocharger replacement, or problems with the fuel injection pump, requiring removal, testing, and repair.

6) If boost pressure control valve (wastegate) does not open, causing boost pressure at full load operation to exceed 16 psi (1.13 kg/cm^2), check hose between compressor housing and wastegate. If hose is leaking or is kinked, replace the hose. If not, replace turbocharger.

NOTE — *When dynamometer test is complete, road test vehicle with tester inside the vehicle. Drive vehicle in driving range "L" or "S" at 4000 RPM. Fully depress accelerator pedal and hold engine speed at 4000 RPM with brakes (short test duration only). Boost pressure should be 10.1-11.6 psi (.71-.82 kg/cm^2). If not, repeat steps 3) through 6).*

REMOVAL & INSTALLATION

TURBOCHARGER ASSEMBLY

Removal — **1)** Remove air filter and disconnect electrical cable from coolant temperature switch.

2) Loosen hose clamp at air intake duct. Remove vacuum line, crankcase breather pipe, air filter housing and air intake duct. Disconnect engine oil supply line to turbocharger. Remove air filter mounting bracket and disconnect exhaust flange.

3) Disconnect and remove exhaust bracket on automatic transmission. Press exhaust pipe to the rear. Remove mounting bracket for intermediate flange and four mounting nuts on the turbocharger.

4) Lift off turbocharger and remove intermediate flange and disconnect oil return pipe at turbocharger.

Installation — **1)** Install all parts in reverse order of removal. Before mounting the turbocharger, install intermediate flange and oil return pipe. Install flange gasket between turbocharger and exhaust manifold with reinforcing bead towards the exhaust manifold.

2) Use only heatproof nuts and bolts when installing turbocharger. Fill center turbocharger housing with approximately ¼ pint of engine oil through the engine oil supply bore, before operating turbocharger. Be sure "O" rings are mounted correctly when installing air intake duct.

PEUGEOT TURBOCHARGING SYSTEM

505 Turbo Diesel
604 Turbo Diesel

DESCRIPTION

The turbocharger used on Peugeot 505 diesel models is mounted on the passenger side of the engine. Components include the turbine, compressor wheel, rotor shaft, bearings and housing. A wastegate valve prevents excessive boost pressure. Modifications made to the XD2 diesel engine to accept the turbocharger are as follows:

New intake and exhaust manifolds were designed. Cylinder heads have new valve seat material, brass valve guides, special swirl chambers and new head bolts. Oil spraying jets were added to cylinder block to help cool inner piston skirts. Crank pin diameter was increased by .19" (5 mm). Connecting rod diameter on both ends was increased. Pistons have a new clover design in the crown and wrist pin diameter was increased by .07" (2 mm). An oil cooler and oil pump with increased output were also added.

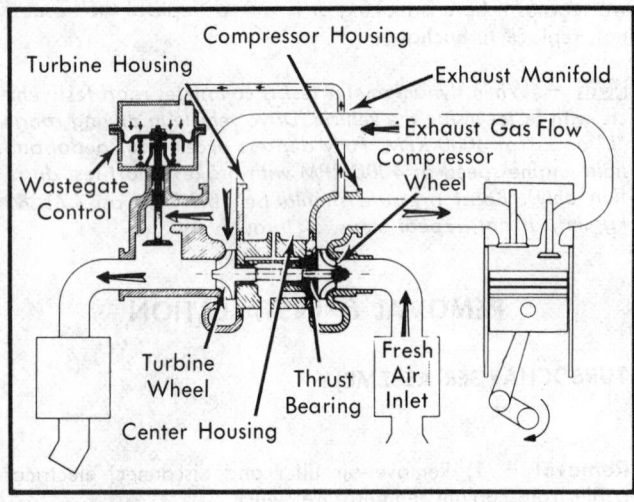

Fig. 1   Peugeot Turbocharging System

OPERATION

The turbocharger is driven by exhaust gases being expelled from the cylinder combustion chambers. At idle speeds there is no pressurization of incoming air and the engine operates like a normally aspirated engine. When the Peugeot diesel engine reaches approximately 1000 RPM, turbo boost begins with approximately 1.45 psi (.10 kg/cm^2). As engine RPM increases, turbo boost pressure increases, depending upon engine load. The greater the load, the higher the boost.

Maximum boost pressure is approximately 8.7 psi (.61 kg/cm^2). Turbine speed depends upon engine RPM and temperature. Higher temperatures create more exhaust gas pressure, resulting in higher turbine speeds. As the cylinders receive their full capacity of incoming air, boost pressure opens the wastegate valve, diverting exhaust gases into the exhaust pipe away from the turbine. This lessens thrust on the turbine and slows it down.

TROUBLE SHOOTING

If the wastegate fails to open, it will create a high manifold pressure (up to 31 psi) at approximately 3500 RPM. This will cause the engine to misfire since compression pressure is now greater than injection pressure (22 psi).

If the wastegate valve fails to close, there will be a noticeable loss of power between 1000 and 2000 RPM, because boost pressure will not exist.

TESTING

NO LOAD PRESSURE TEST

1) Install a suitable pressure gauge in hose between intake manifold and injector pump control unit.

2) Accelerate engine, then run it at a steady 3000 RPM.

3) Pressure gauge should indicate pressure just above idle speed, and read at least 5.8 psi (.40 kg/cm^2) at speeds above 2000 RPM.

4) Full load boost pressure cannot be measured in shop test without a dynamometer.

PORSCHE TURBOCHARGING SYSTEM

924 Turbo

DESCRIPTION

The turbocharger used on the 924 Turbo is mounted on the right side of the engine under the exhaust manifold. Components include the turbine, compressor wheel, rotor shaft, bearings and housings. *See Fig. 1.* A wastegate, located near the right side of the bell housing prevents excessive boost pressure. Should it fail, a boost pressure safety switch turns off the fuel pumps.

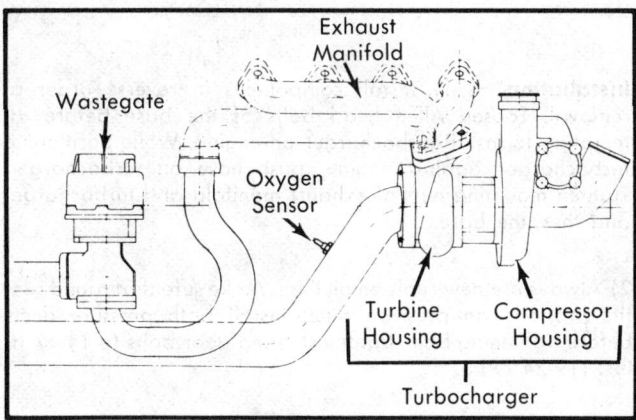

Fig. 1   Porsche Turbocharging System

OPERATION

The turbocharger is driven by exhaust gases being expelled from the cylinder combustion chambers. At idle speeds there is no pressurization of incoming air, and the engine operates like a normally aspirated engine.

At partial load, the throttle valve is open and more fuel-air mixture is drawn into the combustion chamber. Speed and volume of exhaust gases increase, in turn. The increasing volume of exhaust gases causes the turbocharger turbine to turn with greater speed. *See Fig. 2.* The compressor, mounted on the same shaft turns at the same speed as the turbine, producing boost pressure for incoming air. Opening the throttle valve reduces manifold vacuum, closing the pop-off valve located in the compressor housing between the inlet and outlet.

At full load, a large volume of exhaust gases are fed to the turbine, increasing speed of both the turbine and compressor wheels. When boost pressure reaches 6.2-6.8 psi (.43-.47 kg/cm²), the wastegate (boost pressure control valve) opens. Part of the exhaust gases are now routed directly into the main exhaust pipe, by-passing the turbine wheel. The turbocharger speed and boost pressure remain almost constant at 6.2-6.8 psi (.43-.47 kg/cm²).

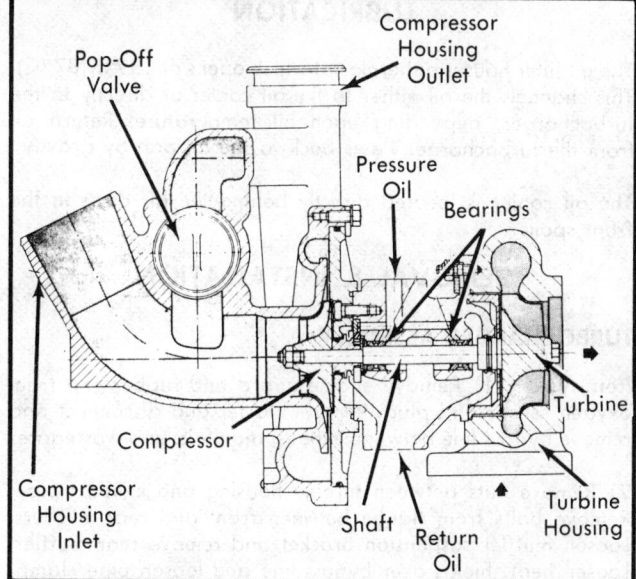

Fig. 2   Cutaway of Porsche Turbocharger

Should the wastegate fail to function properly, an electric boost pressure safety switch located in the compressor discharge pressure duct turns off the electric fuel pumps. This prevents engine damage from excessive pressures.

During deceleration, the throttle valve is closed. The turbocharger now operates against a closed throttle valve, which could damage the turbocharger. To prevent this from occurring, the pop-off valve located between the pressure and intake duct opens due to intake manifold vacuum. This sets up a bypass circuit between pressure and intake ducts. Since the wastegate valve is shut, all exhaust gases are routed to the turbocharger turbine upon acceleration.

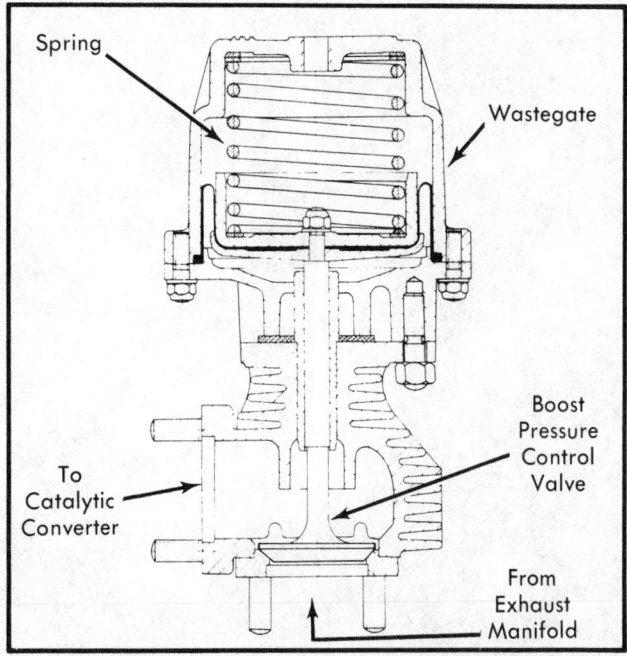

Fig. 3   Cutaway View of Porsche Wastegate

PORSCHE TURBOCHARGING SYSTEM (Cont.)

LUBRICATION

The oil filter houses a thermostat which opens at 189°F (87°C). This channels the oil either to the oil cooler or directly to the turbocharger, depending upon oil temperature. Return oil from the turbocharger flows back to the oil pan by gravity.

The oil cooler is located directly behind the air ducts in the front spoiler.

REMOVAL & INSTALLATION

TURBOCHARGER ASSEMBLY

Removal — 1) Remove engine guard and rubber cap from oxygen sensor and plug. Remove starter and disconnect and remove bypass line between exhaust manifold and wastegate.

2) Remove nuts between turbine housing and exhaust pipe. Remove bolts from flange between front and rear mufflers. Loosen muffler suspension bracket and remove rear muffler. Loosen heat shields over bypass line and loosen pipe clamp.

3) Disconnect control line at wastegate and remove entire exhaust line with wastegate. Be careful not to damage oxygen sensor.

NOTE — *Some vehicles will have a vent line for the wastegate. This can only be removed after lowering exhaust line.*

4) Disconnect oil lines leading to engine oil cooler and oil feed line for turbocharger. Plug oil lines at oil filter flange. Disconnect and remove oil filter flange, catching the escaping oil. Loosen oil clamps and pull out oil lines from the front.

5) Remove pressure duct and take off air cleaner upper and lower sections. Remove mounting nuts from bottom of fuel distributor. Loosen hose clamps on dust cover and move fuel distributor to one side.

6) Unscrew mounting bolt on pressure duct and take off pressure duct. Remove nuts holding exhaust manifold and turbocharger. Unscrew Allen head nuts. Loosen hose clamp. Disconnect both sides of stabilizer. Disconnect steering gear from control arm.

7) Disconnect turbocharger base and remove turbocharger with console toward front. Pull off hose from wastegate connection.

Installation — 1) Install components in reverse order of removal. Loosen Allen head bolts of the base before attempting to install turbocharger on engine. While positioning turbocharger against engine, push hose on turbocharger. Tighten mounting nuts of exhaust manifold and turbocharger and then the base.

2) Always use new seals on oil lines. Make sure that round seal fits properly on pressure duct. Install both pressure ducts before tightening bolt. Tighten steering gear bolts to 14-17 ft. lbs. (19-24 N·m).

3) Before starting engine for first time, prime turbocharger with lubricating oil for 15 seconds by pulling plugs off manifold pressure limiting switch and operating starter.

SAAB TURBOCHARGING SYSTEM

900 Turbo

DESCRIPTION

Saab uses the Garret turbocharger, with turbine and compressor impellers (wheels). See *Fig. 1*. Exhaust gases drive the turbine, which turns the compressor forwarding air under pressure to the throttle valve.

Excessive pressures are prevented by a charge pressure regulator (boost pressure control valve or wastegate). A back-up safety device, a pressure switch, prevents engine damage in case there is failure of the charge pressure regulator.

The Saab Turbo is designed to operate at low engine speeds to provide increased torque at typical vehicle driving speeds. The turbine shaft, which is delicately balanced, is mounted in a floating, sliding-contact bearing having a high oil flow. The shaft actually floats on oil during operation.

Lubrication is supplied by the engine lubrication system. The shaft is sealed against bearing housings with sealing rings installed in shaft grooves.

OPERATION

As engine operation begins, exhaust gases flow through the turbocharger's turbine impeller, causing it to rotate. Gases are expelled through the turbine to the exhaust pipe. As the turbine spins, its shaft turns the compressor impeller, compressing the intake air.

At idle speeds, the air compression has little effect upon its operation. However, as engine speed is increased (partial load), the pressurized air enters the system faster, and exhaust gases are expelled faster. The more exhaust gases passing over the turbine impeller, the faster it turns, and the more pressurized air is delivered to the engine.

At full load, the throttle valve is fully open and charge pressure increases. At 6.4-7.8 psi (.45-.55 kg/cm^2), the valve in the charge pressure regulator opens permitting exhaust gases to flow directly to the exhaust pipe, bypassing the turbine impeller.

In the event the valve sticks and does not open, charge pressure increases to 8.6-11.4 psi (.6-.8 kg/cm^2). This causes a pressure switch to break current flow to the fuel pump, thereby preventing engine damage.

The charge pressure regulator is located on the exhaust side of the engine and its valve is held closed by a spring-loaded diaphragm.

CAUTION — *Never increase the preset charge pressure regulator limit.*

TESTING

CHARGE PRESSURE REGULATOR

1) Connect a pressure gauge (83 92 813) between nipple on inlet manifold and line to pressure switch. Run hose into passenger compartment and place gauge on left hand corner of instrument panel.

2) Warm up engine, and drive vehicle in 3rd gear at an engine speed lower than 1500 RPM. Then accelerate at full throttle by pressing pedal to the floor. As engine speed approaches 3000 RPM, apply brakes while still keeping accelerator pedal pressed down.

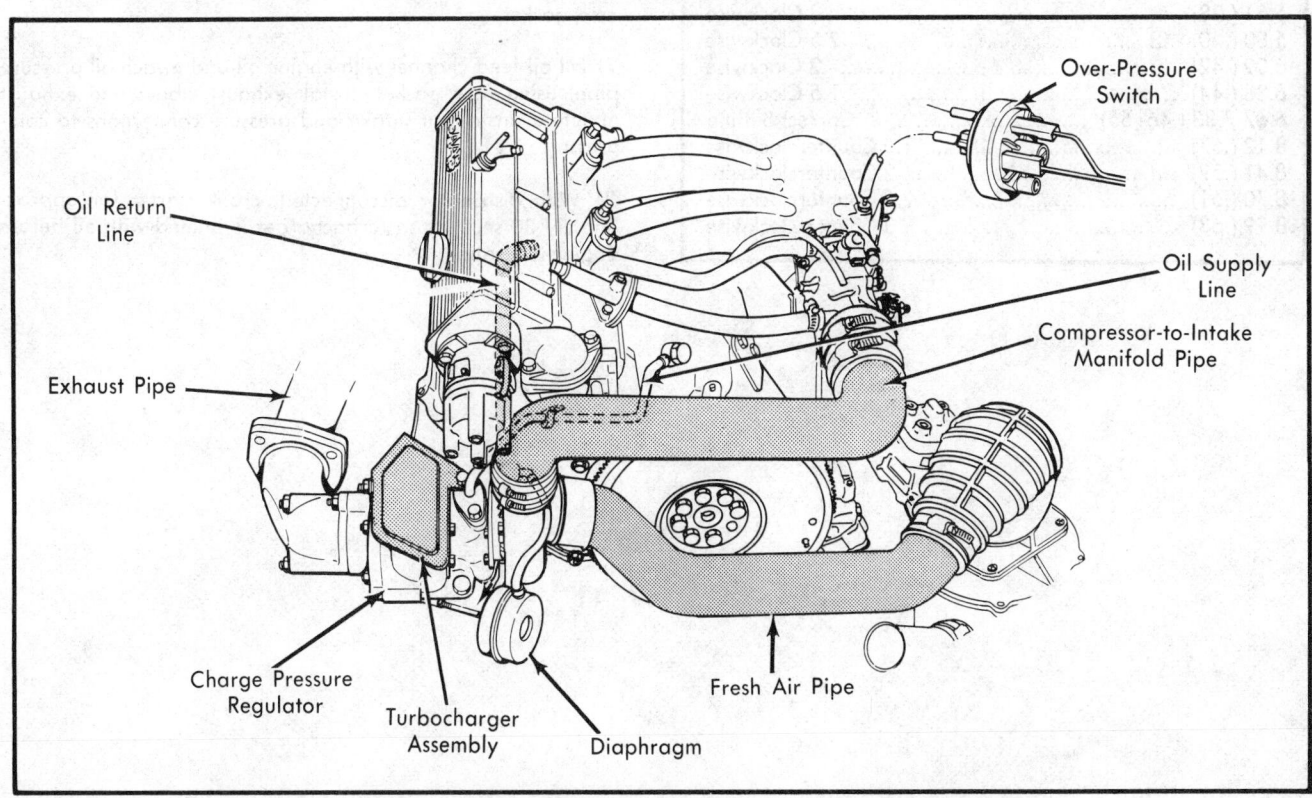

Fig. 1 Components of Saab Turbocharging System

SAAB TURBOCHARGING SYSTEM (Cont.)

3) Note maximum pressure indicated with vehicle under full load at 3000 RPM. Charge pressure should be 6.7-7.8 psi (.46-.55 kg/cm²).

4) To adjust charge pressure, remove wire seal and circlip from charger regulator control arm and detach diaphragm lever. Loosen lock nut on lever and rotate lever end in appropriate direction, according to chart below.

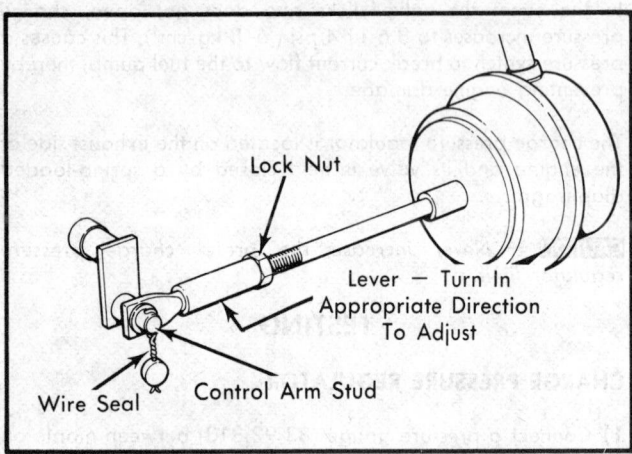

Fig. 2 Adjusting Charge Pressure Regulator

Charge Pressure Adjustment

Gauge Reading While Driving — psi (kg/cm²)	Rotate Lever
5.51 (.38)	3 Clockwise
5.80 (.40)	2.5 Clockwise
6.09 (.42)	2 Clockwise
6.38 (.44)	1.5 Clockwise
6.67-7.83 (.46-.55)	Correct Setting
8.12 (.57)	1.5 Counterclockwise
8.41 (.59)	2 Counterclockwise
8.70 (.61)	2.5 Counterclockwise
8.99 (.63)	3 Counterclockwise

PRESSURE SWITCH

1) Start the engine and run it at idle. Disconnect hose from pressure switch at inlet manifold. Connect pressure gauge and suitable pump (cooling system tester) to pressure switch hose.

2) Increase pressure with pump and check pressure at which engine cuts out. Reading should be 8.6-11.4 psi (.6-.8 kg/cm²). If not, replace pressure switch.

TURBO PRESSURE GAUGE

To check the pressure gauge on the instrument panel, use the same procedure as for the pressure switch. At maximum charge pressure, the needle should be within the wide orange range. At pressure switch actuating pressure, the needle should be in front of the limit between the orange and red zones. If not, replace gauge.

REMOVAL & INSTALLATION

TURBOCHARGER

Removal — 1) Disconnect battery cables. Remove air intake and pressure connections from compressor. Loosen pre-heating hose. Remove exhaust elbow between exhaust manifold and compressor.

2) Disconnect oil supply and return lines at turbocharger. Remove bolts securing turbocharger to exhaust manifold and remove turbocharger. Plug all holes in turbocharger.

Installation — 1) Attach turbocharger to intake manifold, using new gasket. Attach oil return pipe to turbocharger, using new gasket.

2) Fill oil feed channel with engine oil and attach oil pressure pipe, using new gasket. Install exhaust elbow and exhaust manifold. Install air intake and pressure connections to compressor.

3) With distributor disconnected, crank starter for approximately 30 seconds so turbocharger is primed with oil before engine operation.

VOLVO TURBOCHARGING SYSTEM

GLT

DESCRIPTION

The Volvo Turbocharged engine is basically a B21 engine equipped with an exhaust driven turbo-compressor. The turbocharger is mounted on the passenger side of the engine. Components include the turbine, compressor wheel, rotor shaft, bearings, housing and wastegate. In addition, a pressure regulator, pressure switch, overload protection switch and turbo warning light on instrument panel are connected into the turbocharger system.

Engine modifications made to the B21 engine to accept the turbocharger are as follows: Pistons have an increased clearance in the bore to withstand high temperatures generated by turbocharger. Compresson ratio has been lowered to offset some of the increased charge provided by the compressor. Exhaust valves are Stellite coated and Sodium cooled to resist high temperatures. An engine oil cooler is located at side of radiator and has an integral thermostat at the fitting. Heat shields are provided for some components to deflect heat from the turbocharger. The air/fuel control unit for the Continous Injection System is the same as the 6 cylinder engine model, with two of the fuel outlets plugged. These plugged outlets must not be connected to fuel lines. The fuel pump has an increased capacity as does the cold start injectors. The injectors have a larger opening for more fuel injection as required.

OPERATION

The turbine wheel is driven by exhaust gases. A shaft connects turbine wheel with compressor wheel. As exhaust gas flow increases with engine speed, the turbine speed increases and consequently compressor discharge increases. Turbo compressor wheels rotate at a very high speed, requiring that the shaft assembly be carefully balanced. The shaft is supported by bearings using pressurized oil for lubrication. The shaft seals are a piston ring type.

The turbocharger is connected to the standard engine oiling system. Oil supply and pressure must be sufficient to prevent shaft bearing failure. The turbo compressor is designed to provide a relatively high discharge pressure at middle range RPM. In order to prevent excessive pressure at high speeds, several controlling and regulating devices are required.

Pressure Sensor Regulator & Wastegate Actuator — This device monitors discharge pressure from compressor. When pressure reaches 6 psi (.42 kg/cm^2), regulator begins to open wastegate. As pressure increases, the regulator gradually increases wastegate opening. A control rod stroke of approximately $\frac{3}{8}$" (10 mm) is achieved just before maximum pressure switch cuts out fuel pump relay.

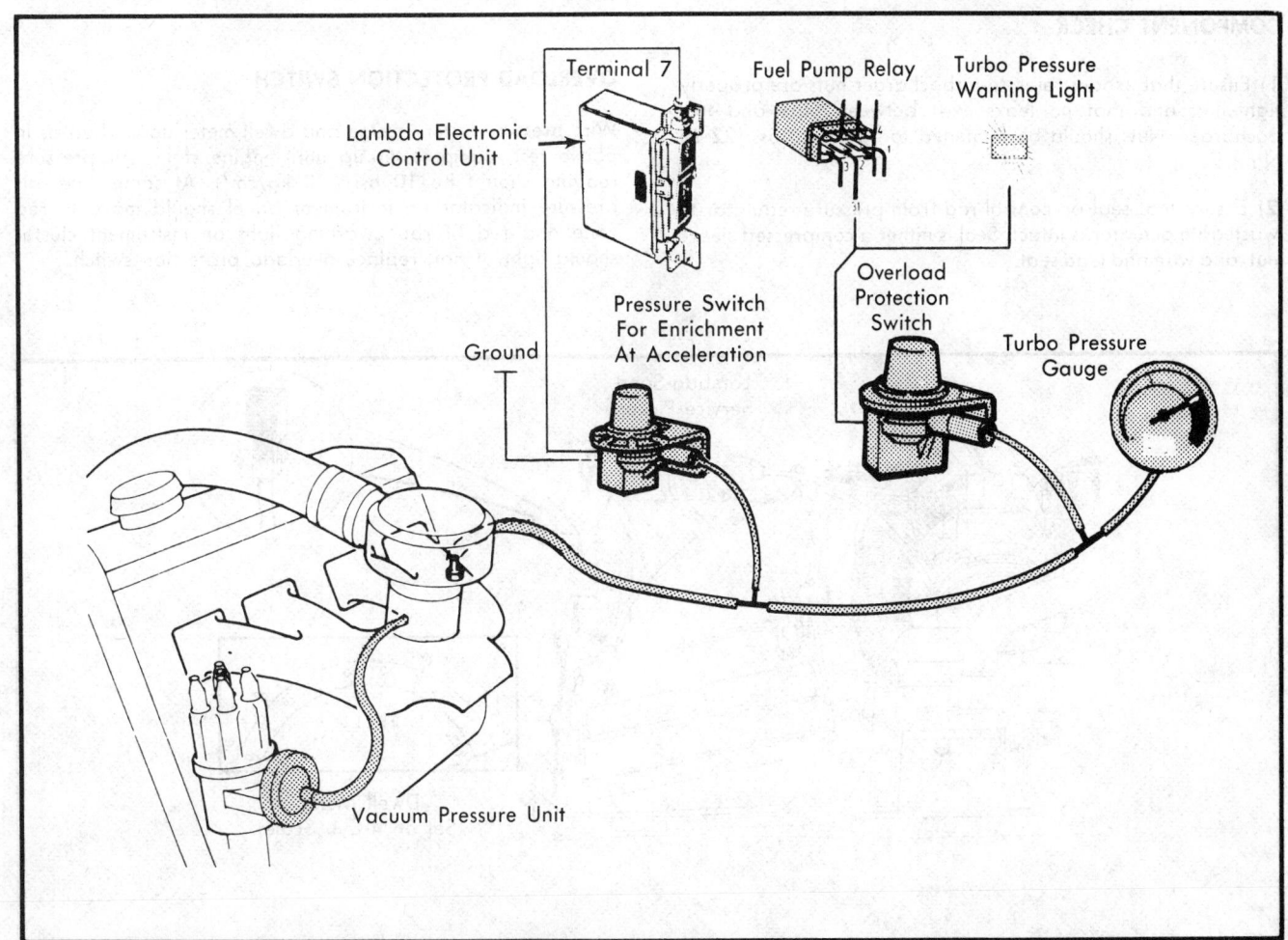

Fig. 1 Controlling Devices for Volvo Turbocharger System

VOLVO TURBOCHARGING SYSTEM (Cont.)

Enrichment Pressure Switch — A pressure switch, located on the firewall, recieves compressor pressure from a fitting on intake manifold. It will close when pressure reaches 2.9 psi (.20 kg/cm²). When it closes, it grounds terminal 7 of the Lambda sond electronic control unit. This will cause Lambda system to operate on a special fixed cycle of 58.5°, allowing for fuel enrichment upon acceleration.

Overload Protection Switch — Excessive compressor pressures may damage engine by inducing an overload, and are normally prevented by pressure sensor and wastegate actuator. In case of failure of that system, a second overload protection switch is activated. The switch receives pressure input from the intake manifold. When pressure reaches 10 psi (.70 kg/cm²) the pressure switch will open a ground circuit for fuel pump relay, momentarily stopping fuel pump flow, resulting in a reduced compressor pressure.

Pressure Control of Spark Timing — The distributor centrifugal advance mechanism provides a spark timing which is too advanced when turbocharger is operating at high load. To counteract this, the pressure control unit at distributor has a double function. Under normal operating conditions it can advance the spark by a maximum 15°. At high pressures it retards the spark timing by a maximum 8°, when compressor pressure reaches 5 psi (.35 kg/cm²).

TESTING

COMPONENT CHECK

1) Ensure that exhaust pipe-to-turbocharger nuts are properly tightened and that no leaks exist between pipe and turbocharger. Nuts should be tightened to 16-18 ft. lbs. (22-25 N·m).

2) Ensure that seal on control rod from pressure regulator to wastegate actuator is intact. Seal is either a compressed sleeve nut, or a wire and lead seal.

TIMING RETARD

1) Connect a standard radiator pump and pressure gauge to distributor air pressure unit. Plug hose removed from distributor.

2) Using a dwell meter with a scale extending to 70°, set on 4-cylinder setting and connect it to the Lambda sond service pick-up of the electronic control unit.

3) Start engine and idle. Note ignition timing. Pump pressure tester up to 5.1 psi (.35 kg/cm²). Ignition timing should retard 6-10°. If not, check distributor and replace distributor pressure unit, if required.

FULL LOAD ENRICHMENT SYSTEM

1) Connect standard radiator air pressure pump and gauge in-line between intake manifold and pressure switch on firewall. Connect dwell meter to Lambda sond service pick-up on electronic control unit.

2) With engine running, pump up air pressure until dwell meter display reads a steady 58.5° (± 2.5°). Air pressure reading at this point should be 2.9 psi (.20 kg/cm²). If reading is not to specification, replace pressure switch and re-check system.

OVERLOAD PROTECTION SWITCH

With pressure tester, gauge and dwell meter hooked up as in above test, pump tester up until engine stalls. Air pressure reading should be 10 psi (.70 kg/cm²). At same time, air pressure indicator on instrument panel should move to red zone and red "Turbo" warning light on instrument cluster should light. If not, replace overload protection switch.

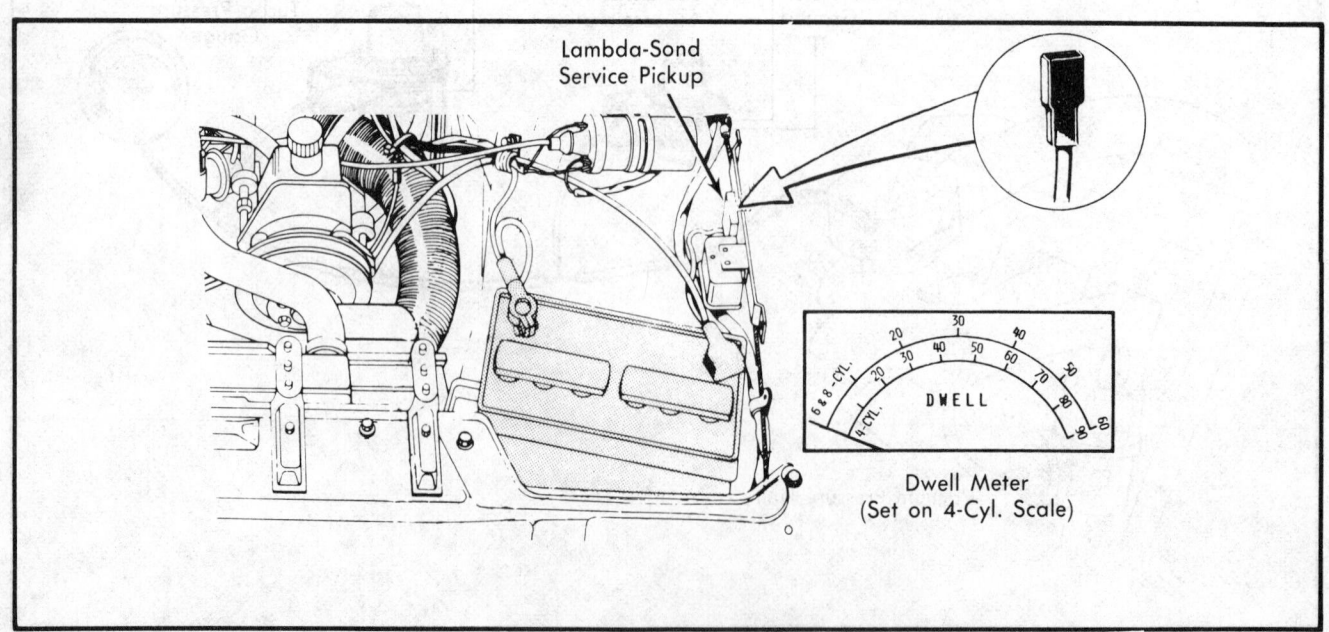

Lambda-Sond Service Pickup

Dwell Meter
(Set on 4-Cyl. Scale)

Fig. 2   Lambda System Connection Point For Dwell Meter

1981 Electric Fuel Pumps

FUEL SYSTEMS

BOSCH ELECTRIC FUEL PUMPS

Audi
 Gasoline Injected Models
BMW
Datsun
 Gasoline Injected Models
Jaguar
Peugeot
 Gasoline Injected Models
Porsche
 Exc. 928
Renault
 18i Wagon Only
Saab
Triumph
Volkswagon
 Gasoline Injected Models
Volvo

DESCRIPTION

Bosch electric fuel pumps are 12 volt, positive displacement roller cell type. Operating pressure is determined by one or more external fuel pressure regulators in the engine compartment. Fuel pumps include an external, replaceable, discharge check valve to prevent fuel from returning to the tank when pump is turned off. Some pumps may also incorporate a damper chamber on the outlet to prevent pulsations in the fuel lines.

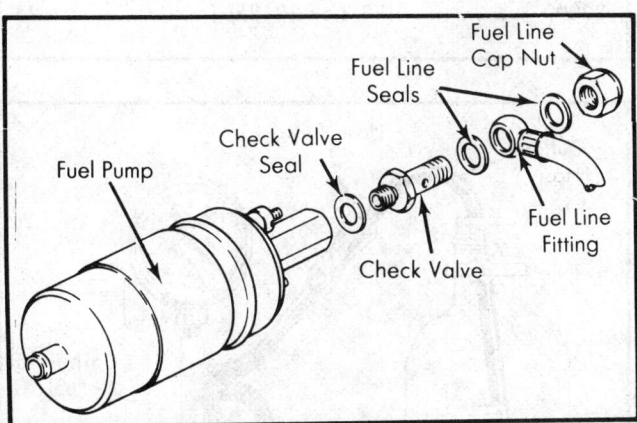

Fig. 1 View of Bosch Electric Fuel Pump

OPERATION

Fuel pumps are actuated by relays when ignition switch is in "START" or "RUN" position, and are protected from circuit overload by fuses and/or fuseable links. Fuel is circulated through pump rotor and brushes to the fuel outlet. Pumps are not serviceable and should be replaced when not operating properly.

REMOVAL & INSTALLATION

FUEL PUMP

CAUTION — *Do not allow smoking, open flame or sparks in area while servicing fuel system components. Disconnect battery ground terminal prior to removing pump. Danger of fire or explosion exists.*

Removal — 1) Fuel pressure must be relieved prior to any component removal. Carefully remove and plug fuel lines to prevent spillage. Disconnect electrical connections.

NOTE —*Depending on make and model, it may be necessary to jack car up or remove carpeting and panels in order to gain access to fuel pump.*

2) Remove mounting bolts and retain rubber insulating grommets for reinstallation. Tip pump as required to clear chassis and remove from car.

Installation — Reverse removal procedure while noting the following:

1) Be sure rubber grommets and insulation are installed correctly or noise and vibration will result.

2) Hook all fuel lines and return lines to proper fittings and be sure they are tight to avoid air and/or fuel leaks.

3) Route fuel lines so they will not vibrate or rub against other body parts.

4) Test system for leaks with engine running.

COURIER & MAZDA ELECTRIC FUEL PUMPS

Courier
 Pickup
Mazda
 626
 RX7
 B2000 Pickup

DESCRIPTION

Pulsating electric powered fuel pump is mounted near fuel tank on frame member.

OPERATION & TESTING

NOTE — *In line fuel filter must be changed within recommended mileage interval before performing tests. If in doubt, install new filter.*

Electrical power is supplied when ignition switch is in "RUN" position. This circuit is protected by a 15 amp fuse (20 amp on RX7) at fuse panel.

Pressure Test — **1)** Remove air cleaner assembly and disconnect fuel line at carburetor. Connect suitable pressure gauge with restrictor and a flexible hose as illustrated in *Fig. 2.*

2) Turn ignition on and briefly vent the system into container by opening hose restrictor. Pressure should stabilize within specifications. If not within specifications and lines and filter are in satisfactory condition, pump must be replaced.

Volume Test — With fuel pressure within limits, open restrictor for one minute and measure fuel expelled. If not within specifications, check for restrictions in tank, line or filter. Replace pump if required.

REMOVAL & INSTALLATION

NOTE — *Negative cable should be disconnected at battery when working on fuel pump.*

1) On 626 and RX7 models, open trunk lid, lift mat and disconnect fuel pump electrical lead. Raise rear of vehicle and support on stands. Remove fuel pump cover attaching bolts and cover.

2) On all models, disconnect inlet and outlet hoses and wiring connector. Remove attaching bolts and nuts and take pump off vehicle. To install, reverse removal procedure.

SPECIFICATIONS

Application	Pressure psi (kg/cm²)	Volume oz./minute
Courier	2.8-3.6 (.20-.25)	32
626	2.8-3.6 (.20-.25)	26
RX7	3.7-4.7 (.26-.33)	37
B2000	2.8-3.6 (.20-.25)	26

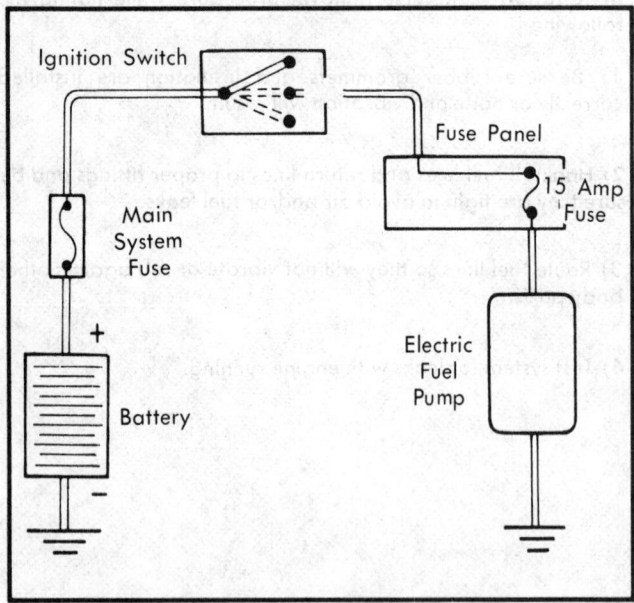

Fig. 1   Fuel Pump Circuit Schematic

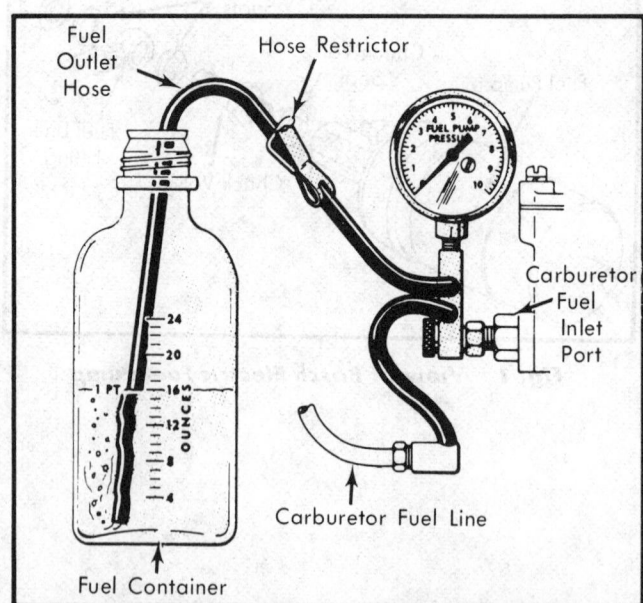

Fig. 2   Fuel Pump Pressure and Volume Test

HONDA ELECTRIC FUEL PUMPS

Accord
Civic
Prelude

DESCRIPTION

Electric fuel pump is located at left rear corner of vehicle on Accord models, left side of fuel tank on Civic hatchback and sedan models, above right rear corner of fuel tank on Civic wagon models, and on left front corner of fuel tank on Prelude models. Fuel pump is a sealed unit and is serviceable as an assembly only.

OPERATION & TESTING

A solid-state relay senses negative pulsations at the ignition coil and switches the pump on when the engne is running or the starter is engaged. Relay is located under dash panel at left side of driver's cmpartment. Circuit is protected by fuse in fuse box as well as main in-line fuse.

Electrical Testing — 1) With ignition switch OFF, connect positive probe of voltmeter to Black/Yellow wire terminal of fuel pump relay connector, and negative probe to ground (Black) terminal. Turn ignition switch on and check for voltage. If no voltage, check fuse and continuity of Black/Yellow wire.

2) If voltage is available, connect the positive probe of voltmeter to Blue wire at pump cut-off relay and negative probe to ground. Turn ignition switch ON and check for battery voltage. If voltmeter does not indicate battery voltage, check Blue wire between connector and negative side of coil. Turn ignition switch OFF.

3) Disconnect relay connector. Attach jumper wire between 2 Black/Yellow wires of connector and turn ignition switch ON. If fuel pressure is now available, replace fuel cut-off relay. If fuel pressure is not available, proceed to fuel pump operational testing.

Fuel Pump Operational Testing — 1) Attach jumper wire between 2 Black/Yellow wires in fuel pump cut-off relay connector. Disconnect fuel hose to carburetor and cap T-fitting. Install pressure gauge to fuel hose. Turn ignition switch ON and check for normal pressure 2-3 psi (.14-.21 kg/cm²).

2) Remove pressure gauge and hold measuring beaker under fuel hose. Turn ignition switch ON and measure amount of fuel flow in 60 seconds. With 10 volts minimum battery voltage, flow should be as indicated in chart.

SPECIFICATIONS

Application	Pressure psi (kg/cm²)	Volume oz./minute
Accord	2-3 (.14-.21)	21
Civic	2-3 (.14-.21)	17
Prelude	2-3 (.14-.21)	23

REMOVAL & INSTALLATION

Raise vehicle and support on jack stands. On Civic Hatchback and Sedan models, remove left rear wheel. On all models, disconnect electrical leads at pump and clamp fuel lines between pump and tank. Remove fuel pump cover bolts and lift off cover and pump as an assembly. Disassemble pump from cover. To install, reverse removal procedure.

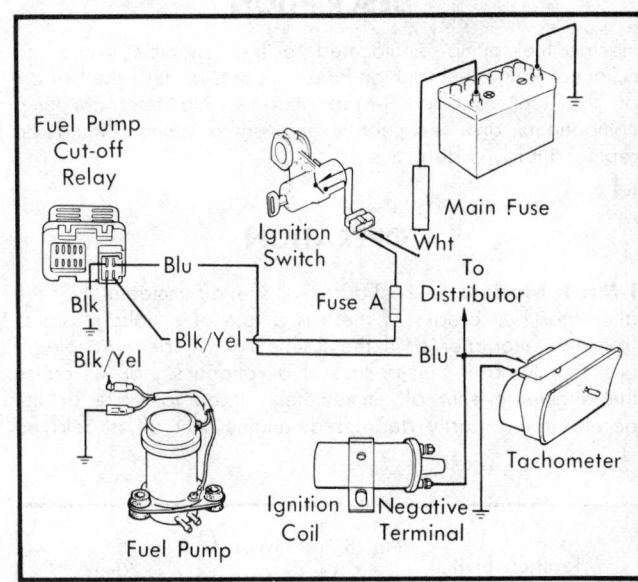

Fig. 1   Fuel Pump Electrical Circuit & Components for Accord Models

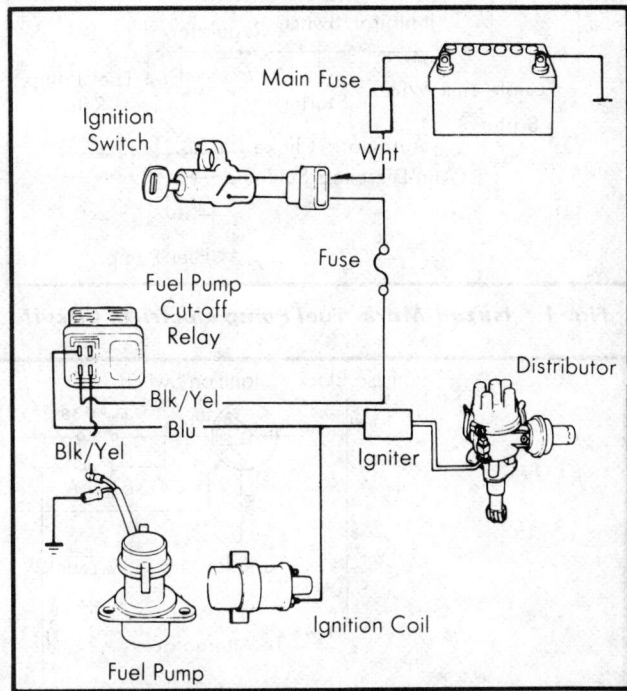

Fig. 2   Fuel Pump Electrical Circuit & Components for Civic & Prelude Models

1981 Electric Fuel Pumps

ISUZU ELECTRIC FUEL PUMPS

Chevrolet LUV
 Gasoline Models Only
Datsun Pickup
 Gasoline Models Only

Isuzu
 I-Mark
  Gasoline Models Only
 P'UP
  Gasoline Models Only

DESCRIPTION

Electric fuel pump is mounted to the left side frame rail adjacent to the fuel tank on Pickup models or near the bottom of the fuel tank on I-Mark models. No internal pump components are serviceable and entire pump should be replaced it found defective.

OPERATION

I-Mark Models — Fuel pump will shut off immediately if the alternator belt breaks, if there is a loss of a voltage signal from the alternator or if the fusible link is open. At idle, a broken alternator belt or loss of a voltage signal will cause the engine to shut off immediately. If on fast idle or the accelerator is partly depressed, engine shut off is delayed

30-45 seconds until the fuel is used up in the carburetor float bowl.

Pickup Models — The 12 volt electrical circuit is protected by fuses and is controlled by a fuel pump relay mounted on the right front inner fender. This relay is controlled by alternator output when engine is running. When engine is off, power is fed through transmission switch (when closed for starting) directly to the fuel pump circuit of the relay.

REMOVAL & INSTALLATION

I-Mark Models — Disconnect fuel return hose from pipe and drain fuel. Remove fuel tank cover. Remove 2 screws from fuel pipe cover and remove cover. Disconnect remaining hose and wiring. Remove fuel pump attaching screws and remove fuel pump. To install, reverse removal procedure.

Pickup Models — Remove electrical lead and fuel lines from tank and carburetor. Remove mounting bolts and nuts and take pump off frame. To install, reverse removal procedure.

Fig. 1 Isuzu I-Mark Fuel Pump Electrical Circuit

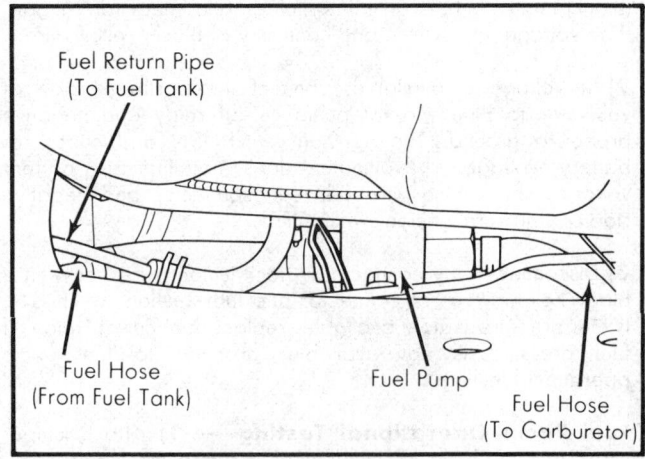

Fig. 3 Typical Fuel Pump Installed Position (Pickup Shown — I-Mark Similar)

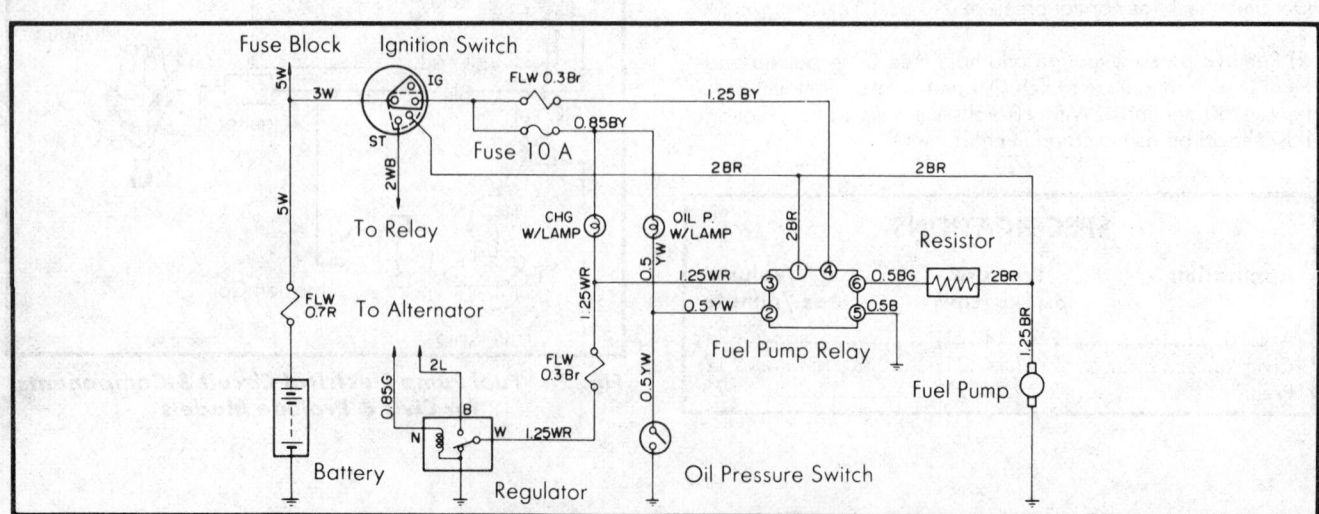

Fig. 2 Isuzu P'UP & LUV Pickup Fuel Pump Electrical Circuit

MITSUBISHI ELECTRIC FUEL PUMP

Datsun
200SX
280ZX
280ZX Turbo
810

DESCRIPTION

The fuel pump is a wet type where the vane rollers are directly coupled to a motor filled with fuel. A relief valve in the pump is designed to open when pressure in the fuel line rises

above 43-64 psi (3.0-4.5 kg/cm²). A check valve on the fuel pump outlet prevents an abrupt drop in pressure in the fuel lines when the engine is stopped.

OPERATION

The fuel pump is actuated by a fuel pump relay when the ignition switch is in the "START" or "ON" position. As fuel goes through the pump, it is routed to a fuel damper mounted near the fuel pump. The damper reduces pulsations in the fuel lines. The fuel pump and damper are mounted just in front of the fuel tank on all models.

REMOVAL & INSTALLATION

Removal — 1) Disconnect negative battery cable at battery. Make sure that there is no pressure in fuel lines. Raise rear of vehicle and support with safety stands. Clamp hose between fuel tank and pump. Remove fuel hose clamps at inlet and outlet hoses on pump.

2) Disconnect fuel hoses from fuel pump. Disconnect harness connector from fuel pump. Remove bolts that attach fuel pump bracket to body. Remove fuel pump and fuel damper from vehicle as an assembly. Separate fuel damper from fuel pump.

Installation — Reverse removal procedures.

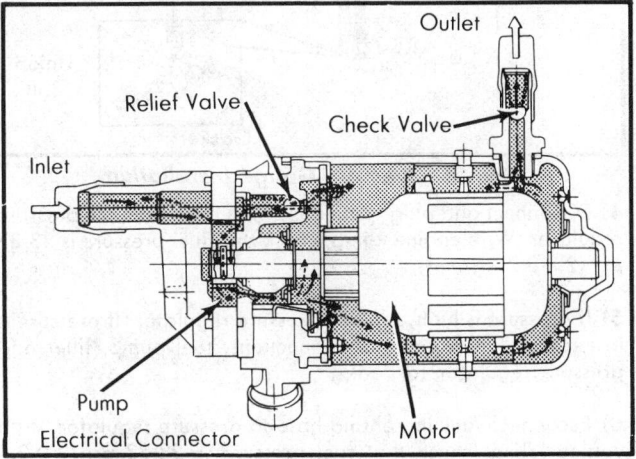

Fig. 1 Sectional View of Mitsubishi Electric Fuel Pump

SUBARU ELECTRIC FUEL PUMP

DESCRIPTION & OPERATION

The Subaru electric fuel pump is an electromagnetic plunger type pump. The pump is located in the engine compartment. It is mounted on a bracket that is attached to the left front strut tower. The fuel pump is actuated when the ignition switch is in the "START" or "ON" position. A check valve, located on the fuel pump outlet, prevents fuel from returning to the fuel tank when engine is turned off.

TESTING

Before performing the following tests, be sure that hose connections are tight and not leaking, be sure that electrical connection is clean and tight. Confirm that pump makes an operating sound when actuated.

Output Pressure — Disconnect fuel hose from carburetor. Connect a pressure gauge to fuel hose. Measure output pressure while operating fuel pump. Pump output pressure should be 1.3-2.0 psi (.09-.14 kg/cm²). If output pressure is not within the specified range, replace the fuel pump.

Suction Pressure — Disconnect fuel hose between fuel filter and pump at the filter. Place finger over end of hose. Suction should be felt when fuel pump is actuated. If no suction is felt, replace fuel pump.

REMOVAL & INSTALLATION

Removal — Disconnect wiring harness from fuel pump. Remove 2 screws that attach fuel pump bracket to left front strut tower. Remove screws that attach fuel pump to fuel pump bracket. Disconnect fuel hoses from fuel pump. Remove fuel pump from vehicle.

Installation — Reverse removal procedures and note the following: Hose from fuel filter goes to the left side of the fuel pump, and the fuel hose from carburetor goes to the right side.

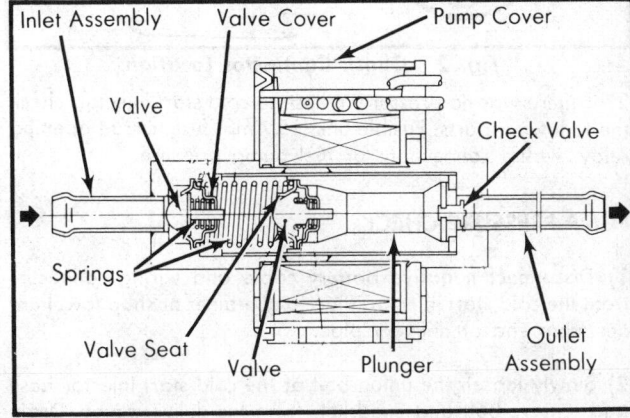

Fig. 1 Sectional View of Subaru Electric Fuel Pump

1981 Electric Fuel Pumps

TOYOTA ELECTRIC FUEL PUMPS

Cressida
Supra

DESCRIPTION

Fuel pump is located at the left rear of vehicle on Cressida models or right rear on Supra models. Internal components include a rotor, check and relief valves, orifice and silencer. See *Fig. 1.* If electric pump becomes defective, it must be replaced as the internal components are not serviceable.

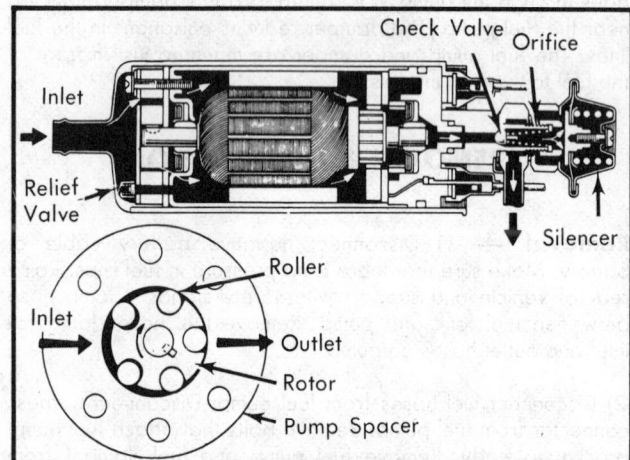

Fig. 1   Cutaway View of Electric Fuel Pump

TESTING

PUMP OPERATION CHECK

1) Turn ignition switch ON. Short both terminals of fuel pump check connector. See *Fig. 2.* Check for pressure in hose to cold start injector. At this time you will hear fuel return noise from pressure regulator.

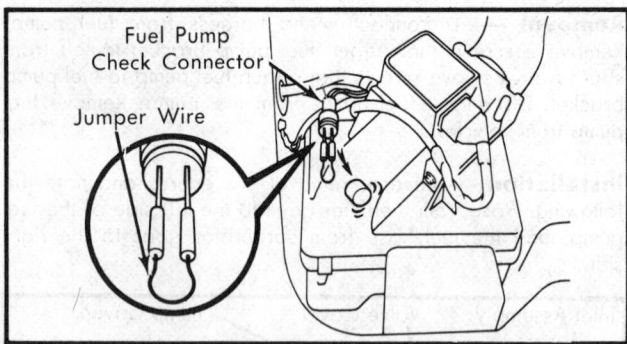

Fig. 2   Check Connector Location

2) If there was no pressure in hose to cold start injector, check the following parts: Fusible link, 15 Amp. fuse, circuit opening relay, wiring connections or fuel pump pressure.

PUMP PRESSURE CHECK

1) Disconnect negative battery cable and wiring connector from the cold start injector. Place a container or shop towel under front end of delivery pipe.

2) Slowly loosen the union bolt of the cold start injector hose and remove bolt and 2 gaskets from the delivery pipe. Drain fuel in delivery pipe.

3) Install gasket, pressure gauge, another gasket and union bolt to delivery pipe as shown in *Fig. 3.* Wipe off any spilled fuel. Reconnect negative battery cable. Start engine.

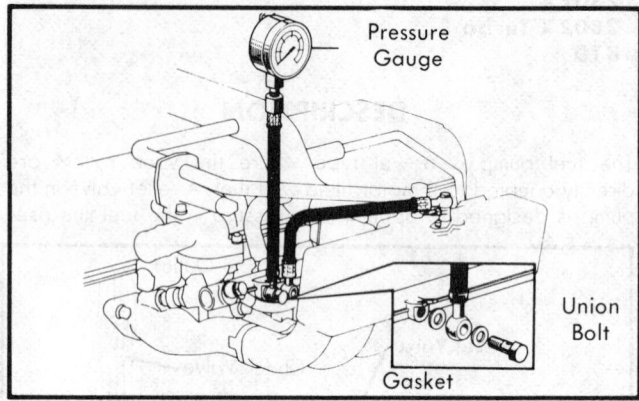

Fig. 3   Pressure Gauge Installation

4) Disconnect and plug vacuum sensing hose from the pressure regulator. With engine idling, check that fuel pressure is 33-38 psi (2.3-2.7 kg/cm^2).

5) If pressure is high, replace pressure regulator. If pressure is low, check fuel hoses and connections, fuel pump, filter and pressure regulator for leaks.

6) Reconnect vacuum sensing hose to pressure regulator. With engine idling, check that fuel pressure is 28-33 psi (2.0-2.3 kg/cm^2). If pressure is high, replace pressure regulator.

7) Turn ignition switch OFF. If pressure drops quickly, check fuel pump, pressure regulator and/or injectors. Disconnect negative battery cable. Carefully remove pressure gauge. Using new gaskets, reinstall removed parts.

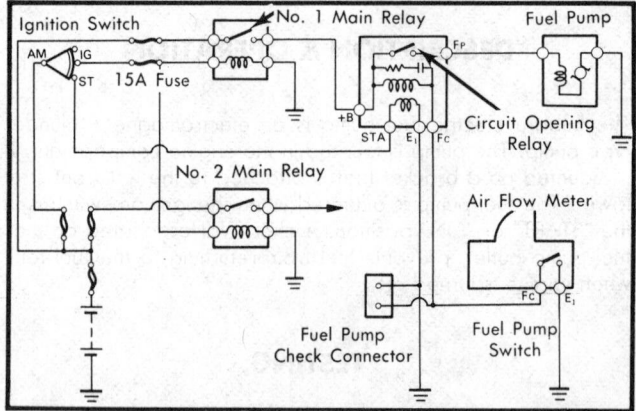

Fig. 4   Cressida Fuel Pump Control System Circuit

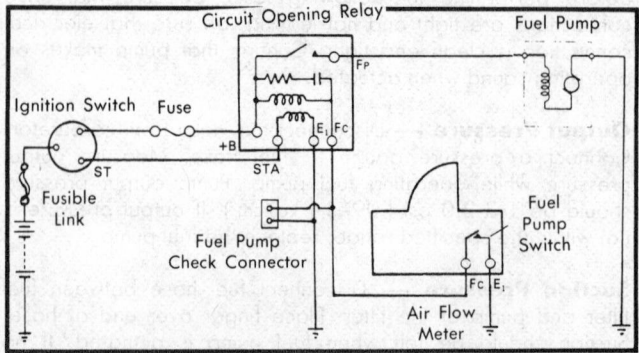

Fig. 5   Supra Fuel Pump Control System Circuit

Section 3
ELECTRICAL

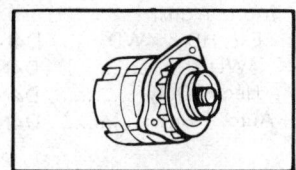

Contents

NOTE — ALSO SEE GENERAL INDEX

DISTRIBUTOR APPLICATION TABLES

AUDI

Application	Fed.	Calif.
Bosch		
4000		
4 Cyl.	049 905 205 Q	049 905 205 Q
5 Cyl.	035 905 206 A	035 905 206 A
5000		
Turbo	035 905 206 J	035 905 206 J
All Others	035 905 206 A	035 905 206 A

BMW

Application	Fed.	Calif.
Bosch		
320i	0237 002 049	0237 002 049
528i	0237 304 006	0237 304 006
633CSi	0237 304 002	0237 304 002
733i	0237 304 002	0237 304 002

CHRYSLER CORP. IMPORTS

Application	Fed.	Calif.
Mitsubishi		
Colt, Champ		
Man. Trans.	T4T62175	T4T62176
Auto. Trans.	T4T62176	T4T62176
D50 & Arrow Pickup		
2.0 Liter		
Man. Trans.	T4T62079	T4T62076
Auto. Trans.	T4T62075	T4T62076
2.6 Liter	T4T62074	T4T62075
Challenger & Sapporo		
2.6 Liter	T4T62078	T4T62077

COURIER

Application	Fed.	Calif.
Mitsubishi①		
2000 cc	E17Z-A	E17Z-A
2300 cc	E17Z-B	E17Z-B

① — Ford basic part number is 12127. Distributor advance specifications not available from manufacturer.

DATSUN

Application	Fed.	Calif.
Hitachi		
200SX		
Man. Trans.	D4N80-12	D4N80-12
Auto. Trans.	D4N80-13	D4N80-13
210		
Man. Trans.	D4K80-01	D4K80-01
	D4K80-03	D4K80-02
Auto. Trans.	D4K80-01	D4K80-04

DATSUN (Cont.)

Application	Fed.	Calif.
310		
Man. Trans.	D4K80-01	D4K80-02
Auto. Trans.	D4K80-01	D4K80-02
510		
Man. Trans.	D4N80-10	D4N80-10
Auto. Trans.	D4N80-11	D4N80-11
810	D6K9-22	D6K9-22
280ZX (Exc. Turbo)	D6K80-03	D6K80-03
280ZX Turbo	D6P80-02	D6P80-02
Pickup		
Man. Trans.		
Exc. HD & 4WD	D4N80-14	D4N80-14
4WD	D4N80-15	D4N80-17
Heavy Duty	D4N80-16	D4N80-16
Auto. Trans.	D4N80-14	D4N80-15

FIAT

Application	Fed.	Calif.
Bosch		
Brava	4430224	4430224
Spider 2000	4430224	4430224
Strada	4430226	4430226
X1/9	4430227	4430227

HONDA

Application	Fed.	Calif.
Hitachi①		
Accord & Prelude		
Man. Trans.	PB2661	PB2661
Auto. Trans.	PB2671	PB2671
Civic		
1300		
Man. Trans.	PA5661	PA5681
Auto. Trans.	PA6912	PA5681
1500 (Exc. 4-Door)		
Man. Trans.	PA6663	②
Auto. Trans.	②	PA6693
1500 (4-Door)		
Man. Trans.	②	PA6912
Auto. Trans.	②	PA6693

① — Honda part number prefix is 30100.
② — Part number not available from manufacturer.

JAGUAR

Application	Fed.	Calif.
Lucas		
XJ6L	45DM6	45DM6

DISTRIBUTOR APPLICATION TABLES (Cont.)

LUV

Application	Fed.	Calif.
Nippondenso		
Man. Trans.		
Exc. 4WD	029100 7260	029100 6900
4WD	029100 6910	029100 6900
Auto. Trans.	029100 6910	029100 6910

MAZDA

Application	Fed.	Calif.
Mitsubishi		
GLC		
FWD	E50818200B	E50818200B
RWD	832518200	832518200
RX7	N2018200	N20118200
626	HE0118200	HE0118200

MERCEDES-BENZ

Application	Fed.	Calif.
Bosch		
280 Series	003 158 01 01	003 158 01 01
380 Series	003 158 02 01	003 158 02 01

PEUGEOT

Application	Fed.	Calif.
Ducellier		
505	525213A	590241

PORSCHE

Application	Fed.	Calif.
Bosch		
911SC	0237 304 016	0237 304 016
924	0237 022 020	0237 022 020
924 Turbo	0237 501 001	0237 501 001
928	0237 405 020	0237 405 020

RENAULT

Application	Fed.	Calif.
Ducellier		
LeCar	525211A	525211A
18i	525198A	525198A

SAAB

Application	Fed.	Calif.
Bosch		
900	0237 009 008	0237 009 008
900 Turbo	0237 013 001	0237 013 001

SUBARU

Application	1600 cc	1800 cc
Hitachi		
4WD Models		D4R80-03
Nippondenso		
2WD Models	029100 7210	029100 7220

TOYOTA

Application	Fed.	Calif.
Nippondenso①		
Tercel	15060	15070
Corolla	28061	28081
Celica	35040	35040
Corona	35040	35040
Pickup	35040	35040
Cressida & Supra	43030	43030
Land Cruiser	61102	61102

① — Nippondenso basic part number is 19100.

TRIUMPH

Application	Fed.	Calif.
Lucas		
TR7	47DE4	47DE4
TR8	35DE8	35DE8

VOLKSWAGEN

Application	Fed.	Calif.
Bosch		
Dasher	049 905 205 Q	049 905 205 Q
Rabbit & Pickup	049 905 205 Q	049 905 205 Q
Jetta & Scirocco	049 905 205 Q	049 905 205 Q
Vanagon		
Breaker Point	022 905 205 S	
Electronic		039 905 205 C

VOLVO

Application	Fed.	Calif.
Bosch		
4 Cyl.	0237 002 038	0237 002 039
6 Cyl.	0237 406 004	0237 402 013

1981 Distributor Specifications

BOSCH DISTRIBUTOR ADVANCE & RETARD SPECIFICATIONS

NOTE – FOR DISTRIBUTOR RPM & DEGREES, DIVIDE SPECIFICATIONS BELOW BY 2

Distributor Part No.	Rot.①	Centrifugal Advance (Engine Degrees @ RPM)	Vacuum Advance (Engine Degrees @ In. of Hg)	Vacuum Retard (Engine Degrees @ In. of Hg)
003 158 01 01	C	....	....	....
003 158 02 01	C	....	....	....
022 905 205S	C	0; 9-14 @ 1600; 21-25 @ 3400	0; 2.9-3.9; 8-12 / 7-1	....
035 905 206A	C	1100; 5-11 @ 1600; 15-20 @ 2200; 22-26 @ 3200; 23-29 @ 6100; 26-30 @ 7000	2.9-3.9; 0; 10-14 / 6.4-7.0; 13.6 / 9.8	8-10 / 4.8-7.5; 1.0-4-4.3
035 905 206J②	C	1175; 1-7 @ 1400; 5-9 @ 2000	2.1-3.5; 0; 11-15 / 4.8-5.9	16-20 / 6.7-8.6; 1.3-4.0
039 905 205C	C	1175; 9-13 @ 1600; 21-25 @ 3400	2.4-4.3; 0; 9-12 / 6.4-7.5	11-13 / 5.4-7.5②; 2.4-4.3②
049 905 205Q	C	0; 15-20 @ 2200; 26-30 @ 5000	3; 0; 10-12 / 7	8-10 / 5.3; 0 / 1.8
0237 002 023	CC	2; 680; 5.2 @ 2500; 9.4 @ 3500; 17 @ 5000	4.9; 7.4 / 13.6; 7.5 / 9.8; 17 / 11.4	....
0237 002 038	C	5; 650; 10 @ 2800; 26 @ 3900; 30	3.1; 5.3 / 10; 6.7; 17	....
0237 002 039	C	4; 650; 10 @ 180; 16 @ 2350; 20 @ 2600	4.1; 4 / 12; 5.3 / 7.3; 8.7 / 17 / 8.8	....
0237 002 049	CC	0; 1000; 10-14 @ 2500; 16-20 @ 2500; 20-24 @ 4000; 22-26 @ 3000	2.7; 3 / 7; 5.4 / 8.0; 10 / 10.7	....
0237 003 014	CC	0-4; 700; 4-8 @ 3000; 10-14 @ 4000; 12-17 @ 5000	1.8; 1-3 / 16; 2.76 / 7.87; 20 / 9.1	3-7 / 5.8②; 0-3 / 4.1②; 3.48②
0237 022 020	C	0; 1000; 8 @ 2000; 13 @ 3000; 20 @ 4000; 23 @ 6000	2.7; 5.4; 8; 10 / 10.7; 9	7; 2.7
0237 304 002	C	9-12 @ 2000; 17-23 @ 2000; 26-32 @ 3500	0; 5.1; 8-12 / 8.6	10.7; 0
0237 304 002③	C	6-9 @ 1000; 14-20 @ 20000; 26-32 @ 3500	5.1; 0; 8-12 / 8.6; 2.75	13-7 / 9.85; 5.4 / 0 / 2.75
0237 304 006	C	13-19 @ 1000; 13.6 @ 4800; 26-32 @ 3000	2.7; 13-17 / 7.7; 7.7; 4.1	13-17 / 9.85; 3 / 0 / 4.1
0237 304 016	C	0; 1500; 15 @ 2400; 20 @ 4800; 13.6 @ 6400	3.3; 5.2 / 7; 4.1 / 4.4	6-10 / 9.1; 3.4
0237 402 013	C	0; 1400; 9 @ 2600; 20 @ 4700; 28 @ 6000; 26	0; 3.2 / 8; 3.8 / 9.0; 2 / 11.8	8 / 5.0; 6 / 4.4; 4.0 / 3.4
0237 405 020	C	700; 15 @ 2400; 13 @ 40000; 18 @ 5100; 23 @ 6200	5.9; 2; 7.7 / 10; 7 / 12.9	3 / 5.9; 1 / 2; 3.7 / 2.2
0237 406 004	C	1000; 10 @ 3100; 13; 22 @ 22; 24 @ 6000	8.6; 9.9 / 11.6; 4 / 16.5; 6.3 / 10.2	12 / 5.9; 10 / 5.1; 4 / 4.7 / 2.4
0237 501 001⑤	C	....	....	....
443 0224④	C	0; 1500; 5 @ 2000; 10 @ 3500; 18	4.0; 9 / 15; 10.0 / 14.0	....
443 0226④	C	5; 1500; 14 @ 3500; 18	3.2; 8 / 14; 9 / 11.0	....
443 0227④	C	5; 1000; 1750; 18 @ 3500; 14	3.2; 8 / 14; 9 / 11.0	....

① – C (Clockwise), CC (Counterclockwise), viewed from rotor end.

② – These figures represent psi because of the turbo boost pressure.

③ – Calif. models only.

④ – Fiat part numbers.

⑤ – Timing is controlled by computer.

DUCELLIER DISTRIBUTOR ADVANCE & RETARD SPECIFICATIONS

NOTE — FOR DISTRIBUTOR RPM & DEGREES, DIVIDE SPECIFICATIONS BELOW BY 2

Distributor Part No.	Rot.①	Centrifugal Advance (Engine Degrees @ RPM)					Vacuum Advance (Engine Degrees @ In. of Hg)				Vacuum Retard (Engine Degrees @ In. of Hg)
525213A	C	0 / 1300	8 / 1800	14 / 3000	28 / 4000	32 / 5000	0 / 3.5	4 / 5.9	9 / 7.9	14 / 9.8	……
590241	C	0 / 1300	8 / 1800	14 / 3000	28 / 4000	32 / 5000	0 / 3.5	4 / 5.9	9 / 7.9	14 / 9.8	……
525211A②	C	0 / 1000	14 / 2200	20 / 3200	25 / 4200	31 / 5000	0 / 2.7	10 / 7.8	……	20 / 12.8	……
525198A②	C	0 / 1100	8 / 1500	16 / 3000	21 / 4000	26 / 4900	0 / 3.5	4.4 / 4.0	13.2 / 8.0	18.6 / 16.0	……

① — C (Clockwise), CC (Counterclockwise), viewed from rotor end.
② — Renault part number.

HITACHI DISTRIBUTOR ADVANCE & RETARD SPECIFICATIONS

NOTE — FOR DISTRIBUTOR RPM & DEGREES, DIVIDE SPECIFICATIONS BELOW BY 2

Distributor Part No.①	Rot.②	Centrifugal Advance (Engine Degrees @ RPM)			Vacuum Advance (Engine Degrees @ In. of Hg)			Vacuum Retard (Engine Degrees @ In. of Hg)		
30100-PA5661	CC	0 / 1000	15 / 3000	18 / 6000	0 / 2.8	5 / 7.9	8 / 11.8	……	……	……
30100-PA5681	CC	0 / 1000	15 / 3000	18 / 6000	0 / 2.0	5 / 5.9	6 / 11.8	……	……	……
30100-PA6663	CC	0 / 1000	15 / 3000	18 / 6000	0 / 2.0	5 / 5.9	6 / 11.8	……	……	……
30100-PA6693	CC	0 / 1500	8.4 / 3000	11.2 / 6000	0 / 2.7	7 / 3.9	7 / 11.8	……	……	……
30100-PA6912③	CC	0 / 1000	15 / 3000	18 / 6000	0 / 2.7	7 / 3.9	10 / 11.8	……	……	……
30100-PA6912④	CC	0 / 1000	15 / 3000	18 / 6000	0 / 2.7	5 / 3.9	6 / 11.8	……	……	……
30100-PB2661	CC	0 / 1500	15 / 3200	13.8 / 6000	0 / 2.8	6 / 4.7	6 / 11.8	……	……	……
30100-PB2671	CC	0 / 1200	9 / 3300	7.8 / 6000	……	……	……	0 / 3.1	6 / 4.7	6 / 11.8

① — Honda part numbers.
② — C (Clockwise), CC (Counterclockwise), viewed from rotor end.
③ — 1500 Calif. Man. Trans.
④ — All except 1500 Calif. Man. Trans.

1981 Distributor Specifications

HITACHI DISTRIBUTOR ADVANCE & RETARD SPECIFICATIONS

NOTE — FOR DISTRIBUTOR RPM & DEGREES, DIVIDE SPECIFICATIONS BELOW BY 2

Distributor Part No.	Rot. ⊖	Centrifugal Advance (Engine Degrees @ RPM)			Vacuum Advance (Engine Degrees @ In. of Hg)				Vacuum Retard (Engine Degrees @ In. of Hg)
D4K80-01	CC	0 / 1200	18 / 3400	23 / 5600	0 / 4.1	......	......	18 / 11.8	......
D4K80-02	CC	0 / 1200	18 / 3400	23 / 5600	0 / 3.9	......	......	13 / 9.8	......
D4K80-03	CC	0 / 1200	18 / 3400	23 / 5600	0 / 3.1	......	......	24 / 9.7	......
D4K80-04	CC	0 / 1200	18 / 3400	23 / 5600	0 / 4.1	......	......	6 / 6.3	......
D4N80-10	CC	0 / 1500	......	10 / 4800	0 / 2.4	7 / 3.5	7 / 4.3	25 / 7.9	......
D4N80-11	CC	0 / 1500	......	10 / 4800	0 / 2.4	7 / 3.5	7 / 4.3	25 / 11.8	......
D4N80-12	CC	0 / 1400	7 / 2200	10 / 3000	0 / 2.8	7 / 3.5	7 / 4.3	10 / 5.9	......
D4N80-13	CC	0 / 1400	7 / 2200	10 / 3000	0 / 2.8	7 / 3.5	7 / 4.3	10 / 5.9	......
D4N80-14	CC	0 / 1500	......	12 / 4000	0 / 3.1	......	8 / 5.9	35 / 15.8	......
D4N80-15	CC	0 / 1500	......	12 / 4000	0 / 3.1	......	8 / 5.9	30 / 13.8	......
D4N80-16	CC	0 / 1500	......	12 / 4000	0 / 3.9	......	3 / 5.9	10 / 9.8	......
D4N80-17	CC	0 / 1500	......	12 / 4000	0 / 3.1	......	4 / 5.9	20 / 10.2	......
D6K9-22	CC	0 / 1300	......	18 / 2700	0 / 3.1	9 / 5.1	9 / 6.3	30 / 11.4	......
D6K80-03	CC	0 / 1000	......	17 / 2800	0 / 3.1	9 / 5.1	9 / 6.3	30 / 11.4	......

⊖ — C (Clockwise), CC (Couterclockwise), viewed from rotor end.

MITSUBISHI DISTRIBUTOR ADVANCE & RETARD SPECIFICATIONS

NOTE – FOR DISTRIBUTOR RPM & DEGREES, DIVIDE SPECIFICATIONS BELOW BY 2

Distributor Part No. ①	Rot. ②	Centrifugal Advance (Engine Degrees @ RPM)			Vacuum Advance (Engine Degrees @ In. of Hg)			Vacuum Retard (Engine Degrees @ In. of Hg)
T4T62074③	C	0 / 1200		12 / 2800	0 / 3.2	12 / 5.9	23 / 11.0	……
T4T62075③	C	0 / 1200		12 / 2800	0 / 3.2	14.4 / 9.8	20 / 14.2	……
T4T62076③	C	0 / 1200		12 / 2800	0 / 5.1	7 / 7.9	15 / 11.8	……
T4T62077③	C	0 / 1200		12 / 2800	0 / 5.1	7 / 7.9	15 / 11.8	……
T4T62078③	C	0 / 1200		12 / 2800	0 / 3.2	8 / 5.9	20 / 14.1	……
T4T62079③	C	0 / 1200		12 / 2800	0 / 2.4	17 / 5.9	28 / 9.5	……
T4T62175③	C	0 / 1000		……	0 / 3.2	12 / 5.9	25 / 11.0	……
T4T62176③	C	0 / 1000		……	0 / 3.2	8 / 5.9	20 / 14.2	……
8387182OO④	C	0 / 1500		10 / 2500	0 / 2.4	……	18 / 11.8	……
8325182OO④	C	0 / 1400		10 / 3000	0 / 2.9	……	14 / 13.7	……
E5081820OB④	C	0 / 1200		10 / 3500	0 / 3.1	……	18 / 13.7	……
HE011820O④	C	0 / 1100		8 / 2500	0 / 2.3	……	18 / 11.8	……
N2011820O④ Leading	C	1.4 / 1000		11 / 2500	0 / 3.9	7 / 7.0	15 / 9.8	……
N2011820O④ Trailing	C	1.4 / 1000		11 / 2500	0 / 3.9	10 / 7.0	30 / 15.7	……

① – No distributor advance specifications are available for Ford Courier from manufacturer.
② – C (Clockwise), CC (Counterclockwise), viewed from rotor end.
③ – Chrysler Corp. Imports.
④ – Mazda part numbers.

BOSCH ELECTRONIC IGNITION SYSTEM

BMW
320i
528i
633CSi
733i
Fiat
  Strada
  X1/9
Mercedes-Benz
  280 Series
  380 Series

Porsche
  911SC
  928
Saab
  900
  900 Turbo
Volvo
  DL
  GL
  GLT Turbo
  GLE
  Coupe

DESCRIPTION

The Bosch electronic ignition system consists of a control module, a breakerless distributor, a single or dual resistor (some models may use a resistor wire, Mercedes-Benz models do not use any resistors), a high output ignition coil, an ignition switch and battery. Standard centrifugal and vacuum advance/retard mechanisms are used. See Figs. 1 and 2.

NOTE — *Volvo MPG models are equipped with the Computer Controlled Electronic Ignition System. See appropriate article in this section.*

NOTE — *Some Strada models are equipped with the Marelli Electronic Ignition system.*

OPERATION

Inside the distributor, a trigger wheel turns with the distributor shaft. The trigger wheel has one tooth or lug for each engine cylinder. As the trigger wheel rotates past the lugs of the magnetic pick-up coil, a magnetic field is built up that continually builds and collapses. This produces a low voltage electrical signal.

This signal passes to the control module, which controls the dwell angle and at the same time interrupts the ignition coil's primary current. This induces the high secondary coil output voltage that fires the spark plugs.

SPECIFICATIONS

Dwell Angle — *Controlled by Electronic Control Module. Not adjustable. See table later in this article.*

Centrifugal & Vacuum Advance (and/or Retard) — *See Specifications Tables in this section.*

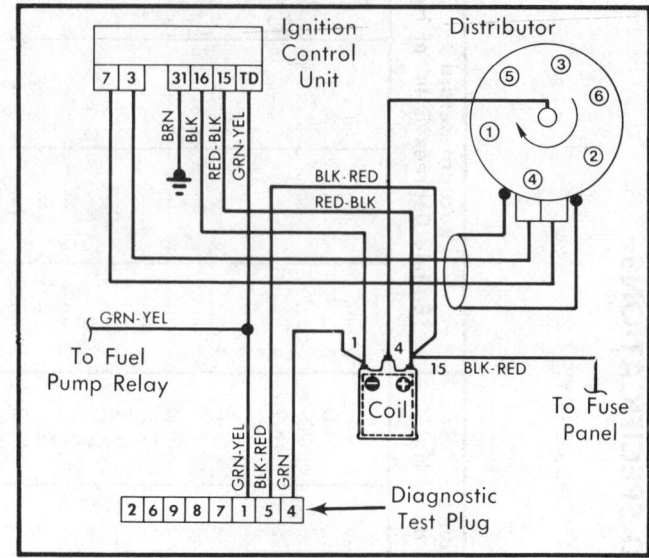

Fig. 2   Wiring Diagram of Mercedes-Benz Bosch Electronic Ignition System

ADJUSTMENT

NOTE — *No adjustment should be attempted on ignition system except spark plug gap and ignition initial timing. Air gap should be visually checked when testing, but if specified clearance does not exist, replace components. Air gap is non-adjustable.*

TESTING

NOTE — *Before testing ignition system, be sure battery is fully charged and in good condition, that all wires are sound and connections are good. Due to high voltage, use care when working on electronic ignition system.*

SYSTEM SPARK TEST

NOTE — *Do not perform this test on Mercedes-Benz vehicles. Use an oscilloscope to check spark results on Mercedes-Benz.*

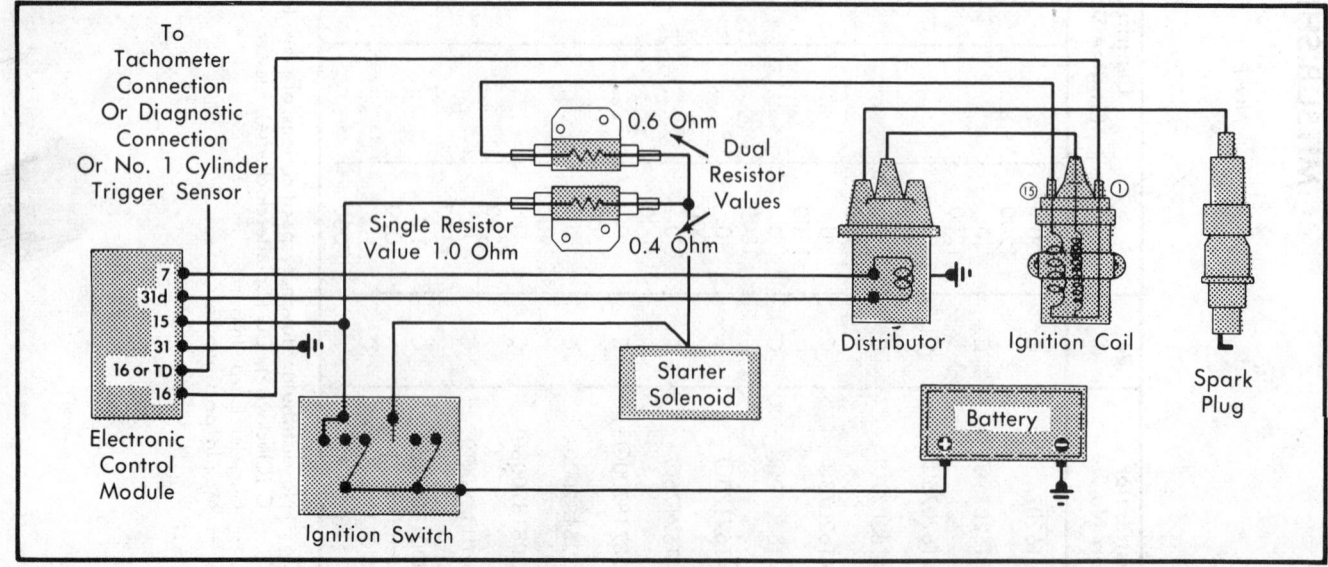

Fig. 1   Wiring Diagram of Typical Bosch Electronic Ignition System

BOSCH ELECTRONIC IGNITION SYSTEM (Cont.)

1) If starter turns, but engine will not start or it fails to develop sufficient power, hold distributor end of coil wire about ⅜" (10 mm) from engine block and crank engine. *See Fig. 3.*

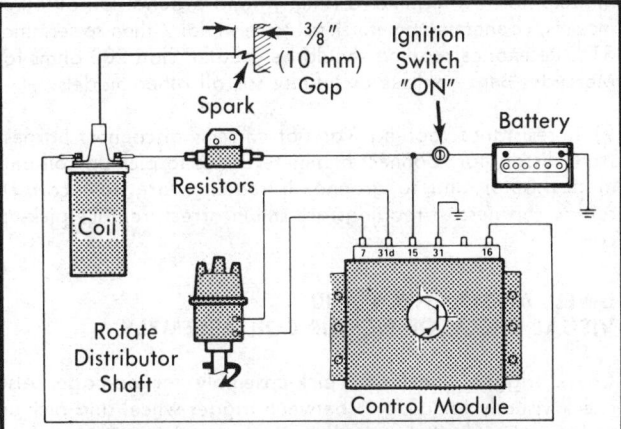

Fig. 3 Coil Wire Hookup For Making an Ignition System Spark Test on All Models Except Mercedes-Benz

2) If spark jumps gap, check distributor cap, rotor, cables and spark plugs. Be sure ignition timing and fuel system are OK. If no sparks occur, perform the following tests

ROTOR RESISTANCE CHECK

Set an ohmmeter to the x1000 scale. With ignition switch off and distributor cap removed, attach ohmmeter leads to rotor. Resistance should be 1000 ohms for Mercedes-Benz or approximately 5000 ohms for all other models.

SPARK PLUG WIRE RESISTANCE

If spark plug connectors have sheet metal jackets carrying the following symbol (▭◀▶▭), they contain "air gap" resistors. Wires cannot then be checked for resistance using an ohmmeter. An oscilloscope must be used.

RESISTOR RESISTANCE CHECK

NOTE — *This test is not performed on Mercedes-Benz vehicles.*

Set an ohmmeter in the low scale. Be sure ignition switch is "OFF". Check resistance of each resistor in the primary circuit. *See Fig. 4.* Some manufacturers use resistor wires instead of ballast resistors. Most use 2 ballast resistors.

Resistor Resistance Specifications	
Application	**Ohms**
BMW	0.4 and 0.6
Fiat Strada & X1/9	.85-.95
Porsche	0.4 and 0.6
Saab	0.4 and 0.6
Volvo	1.0

IGNITION COIL RESISTANCE CHECK

1) Turn ignition switch "OFF". Using an ohmmeter set at the low scale, attach leads to ignition coil primary terminals 1 and 15 (wires removed). *See Fig. 4.* Take primary resistance reading.

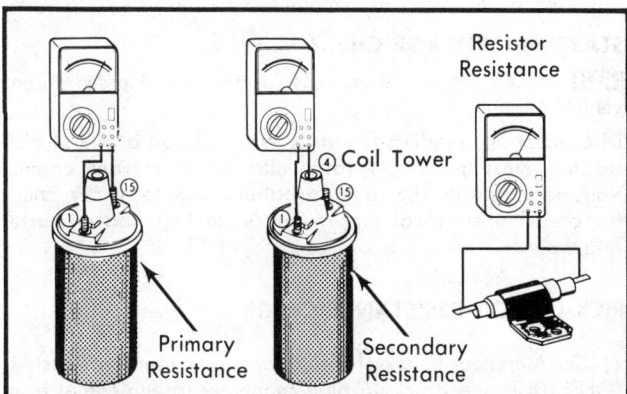

Fig. 4 Ohmmeter Hookup for Ignition Coil Primary and Secondary Resistance Checks, Also Showing Ohmmeter Hookup for Ballast Resistor Check

2) On Mercedes-Benz models, the coil has a pressure relief plug located on top of the coil. Make sure the plug has not popped out. If it has popped out, replace coil.

3) Set ohmmeter to x1000 scale, then connect ohmmeter leads to negative terminal 1 and coil tower terminal 4 (high tension). Take secondary resistance reading. If either the primary or the secondary reading was not within specifications, replace coil.

Ignition Coil Resistance Specification		
Application	**Primary**	**Secondary**
BMW	.4	......
Fiat Strada & X1/9	1.1-1.7	6000-10,000
Mercedes-Benz	.7	8000-11,000
Porsche	.33-.46	7000-12,000
Saab	1.05-1.35	5500-8500
Volvo	1.0-2.0	......

IGNITION COIL VOLTAGE CHECK

1) On Mercedes-Benz vehicles, connect voltmeter positive lead to diagnostic plug terminal 5 (terminal 15 on coil). Connect voltmeter negative lead to ground. Turn ignition switch "ON". Voltage reading should be the same as battery voltage. If voltage reading is not correct, check voltage readings back to battery (checking through ignition switch).

2) On Mercedes-Benz vehicles, connect voltmeter negative lead to diagnostic plug terminal 4 (terminal 1 on coil). Voltage reading should be zero. If reading is not zero, turn ignition switch "OFF" immediately. Replace electronic control unit.

3) On all other models, connect voltmeter negative lead to terminal 1 of coil and positive lead to terminal 15 of coil. Turn ignition switch "ON". Voltage reading should be 4-7 volts. If less, check wires, connections at ignition switch, resistors, coil and control unit to eliminate voltage drop. If more, check for defective resistors.

4) Connect voltmeter positive lead to negative coil terminal 1, and negative lead to a good ground. Reading should be 0.5-2.0 volts (maximum 2.0 volts). If previous tests and pick-up coil

BOSCH ELECTRONIC IGNITION SYSTEM (Cont.)

resistance, starting voltage and control module voltage checks prove OK, substitute a known good control module. If system is now operative, install new module.

STARTING VOLTAGE CHECK

NOTE – *This check is not performed on Mercedes-Benz vehicles.*

Disconnect line leading to starter terminal 15a at the .4 ohm resistor (most models). Attach voltmeter and crank engine. Voltage should be the same as battery voltage. If not, check for break in electrical supply line or contact 15a in starter relay.

PICK-UP COIL RESISTANCE CHECK

1) On Mercedes-Benz vehicles, make sure ignition switch is "OFF". Disconnect pick-up plug connector (green cable) from control module. Attach ohmmeter leads (set to x1000 scale) to center pin (terminal 3) of cable and to larger circular pin (terminal 7) of green cable.

2) On all other models, turn ignition switch off and disconnect connector from control module. Connect ohmmeter leads (set in x100 scale) to terminals 7 and 31d of harness connector. See Fig. 5. Measure pick-up coil resistance.

3) If resistance readings are not to specifications, remove connector from distributor and take reading at pick-up coil pins at distributor. If readings are still not to secifications, replace pick-up coil.

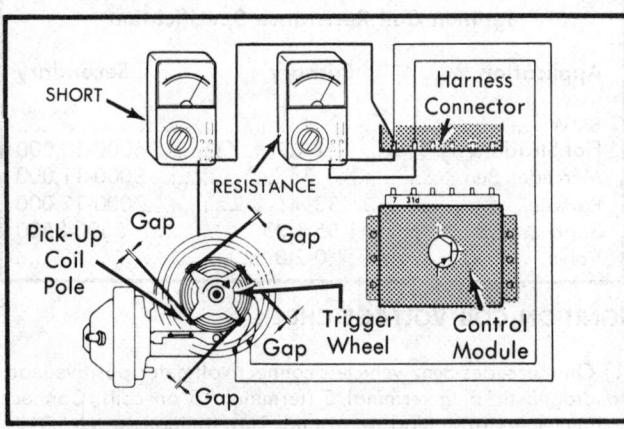

Fig. 5 Ohmmeter Hookups for Pick-Up Coil Resistance and Short Checks

Pick-Up Coil Resistance Specifications

Application	Ohms
BMW	520-700
Fiat Strada & X1/9	890-1285
Mercedes-Benz	500-700
Porsche 928	485-700
Saab	895-1285
Volvo	
4-Cylinder	950-1250
6-Cylinder	540-660

PICK-UP COIL SHORT CHECK

1) On Mercedes-Benz vehicles, connect an ohmmeter to control module harness terminal 3 (then 7) and ground. On all other models, connect ohmmeter lead to terminal 7 then to terminal 31d. Resistance reading should be greater than 200 ohms for Mercedes-Benz vehicles or infinity for all other models.

2) If resistance reading was not correct, disconnect harness from distributor. Connect ohmmeter leads to pick-up coil pins in distributor and to ground. If readings are now correct, replace harness. If readings are still incorrect, replace pick-up coil.

DWELL ANGLE CHECK AND VISUAL CHECK OF PICK-UP COIL ASSEMBLY

Check trigger wheel and pick-upsembly for damage. Also check visually for air gap between trigger wheel and pick-up coil. See Fig. 5. If damaged or if air gap is not to specifications, replace distributor (if components cannot be replaced individualy). Check dwell angle and compare with specifications. If not within specifications, repeat Pick-Up Coil Resistance, Short and Visual Checks. If OK, then replace control module.

Dwell Angle & Air Gap Specifications

Application	Dwell Angle @ RPM	Air Gap In. (mm)
BMW	32-53°@1500	.014-.028 (.36-.72)
Fiat Strada & X1/9	①	.012-.019 (.3-.5)
Mercedes-Benz	7-25°@②	③
Porsche		
911SC	①	①
928	25-39°@1500	①
Saab	60-80°@①	①
Volvo		
4-Cylinder	45-63°@1500	①
6-Cylinder	45-60°@1500	①

① – Specification not available from manufacturer.
② – At cranking speed.
③ – Not adjustable.

CONTROL MODULE VOLTAGE

NOTE – *Test not performed on Mercedes-Benz vehicles.*

Disconnect connector from control module and turn ignition switch "ON". Attach voltmeter positive lead to terminal 15 of control module harness connector. Connect negative lead to ground. Battery voltage should be shown. If not, check for voltage drop in harness between ignition switch and control module.

CONTROL MODULE GROUND CHECK

NOTE – *Test not performed on Mercedes-Benz vehicles.*

Disconnect connector at sontrol module. Turn ignition switch "ON". Connect voltmeter positive lead to terminal 31 of control module (not harness). Connect negative lead to ground.

BOSCH ELECTRONIC IGNITION SYSTEM (Cont.)

Reading should be zero (0) volts. Check module ground wire and repair as necessary if reading is not zero (0).

FINAL CONTROL MODULE OR IGNITION COIL CHECK

NOTE — *Test not performed on Mercedes-Benz vehicles.*

If ignition coil is suspected of being defective, substitute a known good coil and attempt to start vehicle. If it starts, reinstall old coil and start vehicle. If it then fails to start, replace with new coil. If control module is suspected, substitute a known good module and start vehicle. If it starts, reinstall original module. If vehicle fails to start now, install new control module. If system still fails to operate, disconnect tachometer connector at instrument cluster. Attempt to start engine. If engine now starts, replace tachometer.

OVERHAUL

Disassembly — **1)** Remove distributor cap, rotor and dust cover. Remove vacuum unit screws and lock clasp screws. Remove screws securing electrical leads and remove leads by carefully pulling straight out.

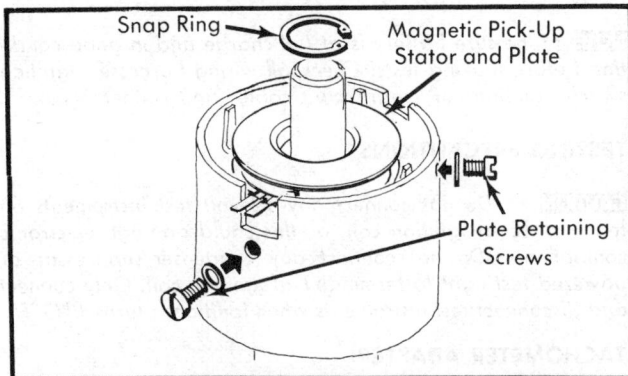

Fig. 6   Removing or Installing Pick-Up Coil, Stator and Carrier Plate

NOTE — *Keep screws with component they attach, as screws are different lengths and damage could result if installed in wrong location.*

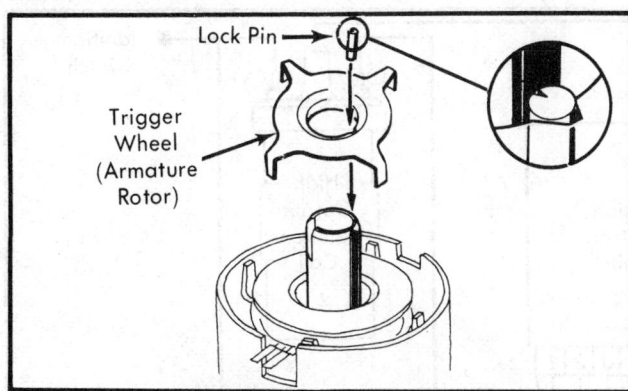

Fig. 7   Installing Wheel and Lock Pin

2) Remove trigger wheel snap ring and then shims. Using 2 screwdrivers, carefully pry upward on trigger wheel. Remove trigger wheel and lock pin. Remove screws securing pick-up coil and stator assembly carrier plate. Remove snap ring and retaining clips. Lift carrier plate and stator straight up off shaft. Remove 3 screws to separate stator winding from carrier plate.

3) Disconnect springs to centrifugal governor. Mark drive shaft relationship to distributor shaft and then secure drive shaft in a soft-jawed vise. Carefully tap on distributor housing with a plastic mallet until circlip releases. If equipped, remove triggering contacts and attaching screws.

4) Remove resilient ring. Mark location of flange to distributor shaft. Support distributor shaft and using a pin punch, remove pin. Remove flange and distributor shaft. Remove lock springs for centrifugal weights and then weights.

Inspection — Springs for weights must not be deformed or damaged. Holes in centrifugal governor weights must not be oval or deformed. Distributor shaft-to-cam clearance should not exceed .004" (.1 mm). Distributor shaft-to-housing clearance should not exceed .008" (.2 mm).

Reassembly — **1)** To reassemble distributor, reverse disassembly procedure, while noting the following: Place a light coat of grease on weights and a couple of drops of oil on felt wick in center of shaft. Do not get grease or oil on pick-up coil and stator assembly.

2) When attaching stator to plate, the connector pins should be positioned opposite and above the attachment ear for carrier plate. Install lock pin with lift facing ridge on distributor shaft. Slot on trigger wheel should be aligned with groove on distributor shaft.

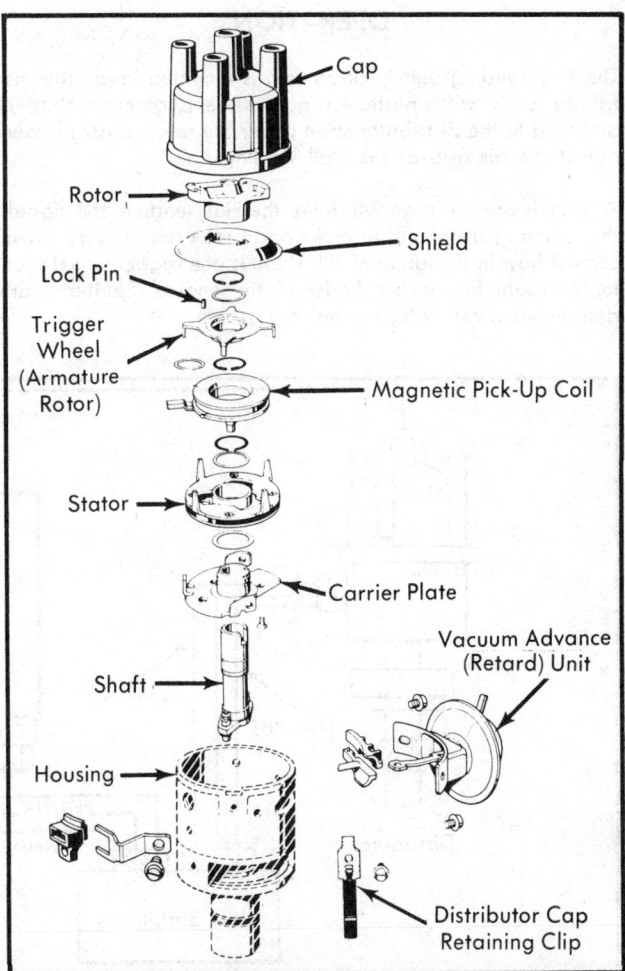

Fig. 8   Exploded View of Bosch Electronic Distributor

BOSCH HALL EFFECT ELECTRONIC IGNITION SYSTEM

Audi
 4000
 5000
Volkswagen
 All Models with CIS
 Vanagon
  Calif. Only

DESCRIPTION

The Bosch Hall Effect electronic ignition system consists of a breakerless Hall Effect distributor, an ignition control unit, ignition coil, ignition switch, and battery.

Closely allied with the ignition system is an idle stabilizer, a solid state control unit located between the ignition control unit and the distributor. It replaces the distributor in sending signals to the ignition control unit when engine speeds fall below 940 RPM.

The Hall Effect distributor has normal centrifugal and vacuum advance mechanisms. *See Figs. 1 and 10.*

NOTE — *On Audi 4000 (with 5-cylinder engines) and 5000 models, an impedance transformer (gray colored) is installed in place of the idle stabilizer. When adjusting ignition timing, DO NOT disconnect the plugs from the impedance transformer.*

OPERATION

The Hall sending unit (pick-up coil) is mounted inside the distributor on a switch plate. A trigger wheel (segmented shutter) attached to the distributor shaft under the rotor, passes in and out of the air gap of the Hall sending unit.

At speeds greater than 940 RPM, the Hall sending unit signals the ignition control unit to make and break the primary circuit current flow in the ignition coil. There is one trigger wheel shutter or tooth for each cylinder of the engine. Shutter width determines dwell, which is not adjustable.

As the ignition control unit breaks the primary circuit through the coil, secondary voltage is released through high tension wiring, distributor cap and rotor to spark plugs. *See Fig. 1.*

If engine speed drops below 940 RPM, the idle stabilizer takes over the duty of producing the signal to the ignition control unit, instead of the Hall sending unit. Mounted between the distributor and the ignition control unit, the idle stabilizer senses engine speed earlier, causing ignition timing to advance. Advancing ignition timing causes idle speed to increase, and the Hall sending unit to resume its normal operation.

SPECIFICATIONS

Centrifugal & Vacuum Advance — *See Specifications Pages in this section.*

ADJUSTMENTS

Hall Effect Air Gap — Air gap is pre-set and cannot be adjusted.

TESTING

NOTE — *Be sure battery is at full charge and in good condition before making tests. Check all wiring harnesses, ignition switch, ignition coil, spark plug cables and connectors.*

TESTING PRECAUTIONS

CAUTION — *Do not connect any 12 volt test instruments on terminal 15 of ignition coil, as this could damage electronic components. Do not connect any condenser/suppressor or powered test light to terminal 1 of ignition coil. Only connect and disconnect test instruments when ignition is turned "OFF".*

TACHOMETER ADAPTER

1) An adapter is necessary when attaching a conventional tachometer into the Hall Effect electronic ignition system. *See Fig. 2.* Tachometer black lead is attached to engine ground. Attach adapter to tachometer red lead.

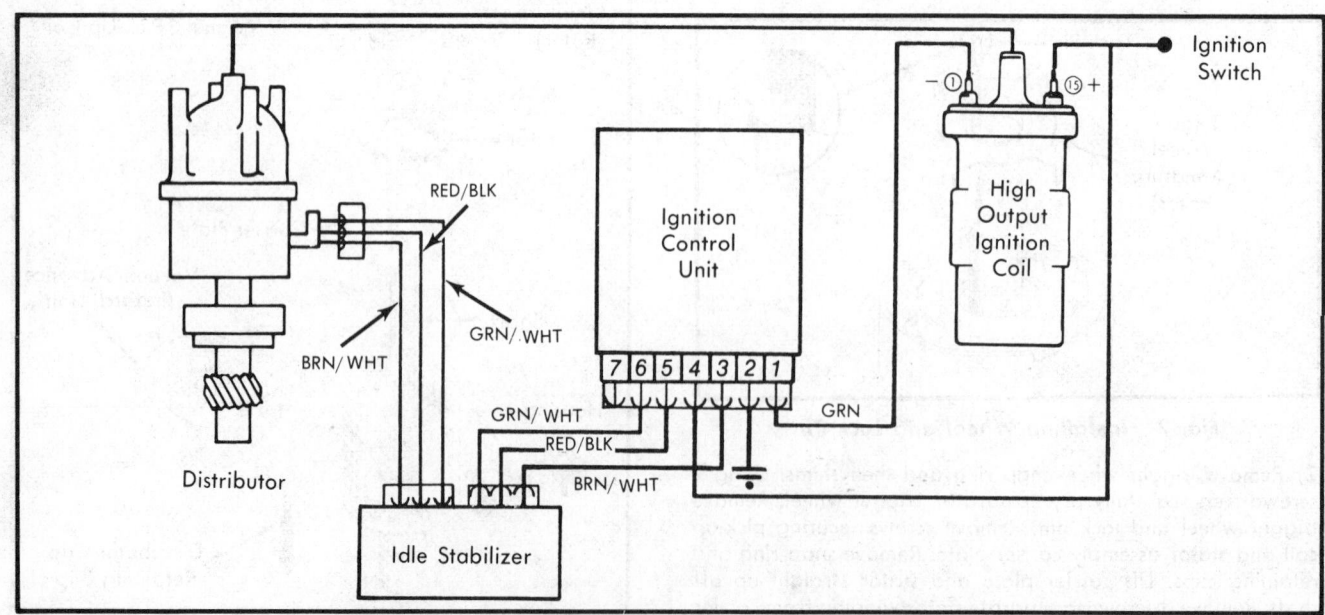

Fig. 1   Schematic Diagram of Bosch Hall Effect Electronic Ignition System

BOSCH HALL EFFECT ELECTRONIC IGNITION SYSTEM (Cont.)

2) Adapter is formed from 2 wires soldered together at one end. One wire (leading to coil terminal 1) must be equipped with a 1000 ohm, 1 watt resistor. The second wire (also leading to engine ground) must be equipped with a 12,000 ohm, 1 watt resistor. Both resistors should be soldered to attaching wires.

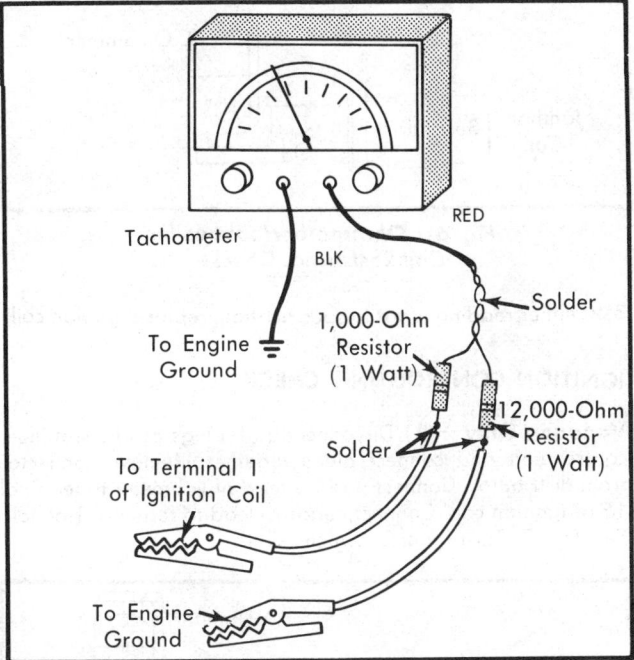

Fig. 2   Assembling Tachometer Adapter

SYSTEM SPARK CHECK

1) If vehicle will not start, check for secondary voltage. Remove coil high tension wire from distributor cap. Hold wire approximately ¼" (6 mm) from engine ground, using insulated pliers.

2) Crank engine and check for a constant blue spark at gap to ground. If there is a good spark, check distributor cap, rotor, spark plug wires, spark plugs, fuel system and engine mechanical components. If there is no spark or only a very weak spark, perform the following checks.

IDLE STABILIZER CHECK

NOTE — On models equipped with the impedance transformer, testing procedures are performed in same way as with idle stabilizer.

1) If engine will not start, check idle stabilizer first. See Fig. 3. Remove both connectors from idle stabilizer and connect them together. This by-passes the idle stabilizer connecting the ignition control unit directly to the distributor. If engine now starts, idle stabilizer is defective.

2) In other cases where engine starts but idle stabilizer is suspected, by-pass the stabilizer by removing the 2 connectors and connecting them together. Turn off all electrical accessories and set idle speed and timing.

3) Then, reconnect the idle stabilizer. Ignition timing at idle may fluctuate, but should be about 3° ATDC (±3°). Turn all

power accessories in step **2)** back on. Ignition timing should be advanced to keep engine speed to specifications. If not, replace idle stabilizer.

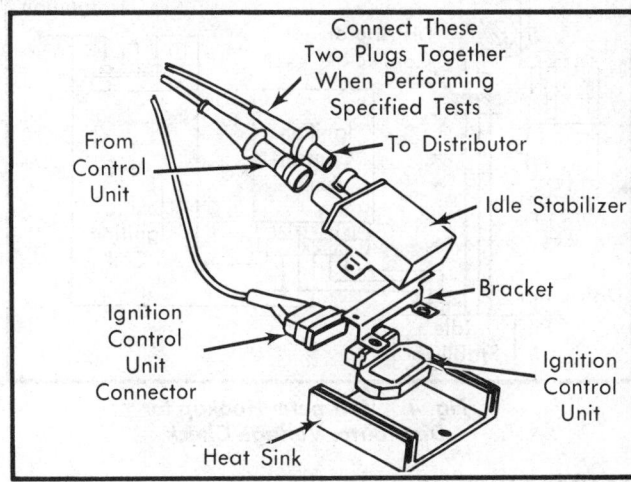

Fig. 3   Idle Stabilizer and Ignition Control Unit

NOTE — An alternative manner of checking idle stabilizer can be used. With engine oil temperature above 140° F (60° C), connect test equipment according to manufacturer's instructions. Start engine and slowly increase engine speed while applying foot brake. Let engine idle. On vehicles with manual transmission, engage 4th gear and release clutch slowly. On vehicles with automatic transmission, move selector into "DRIVE" position. As engine load increases, ignition timing must advance. If not, idle stabilizer control unit is defective and must be replaced.

SPARK PLUG WIRE RESISTANCE

If spark plug connectors have sheet metal jackets carrying the following symbol ( ), they contain "air gap" resistors. Wires cannot then be checked for resistance using an ohmmeter. An oscilloscope must be used.

ROTOR RESISTANCE CHECK

Connect leads of an ohmmeter set in x1000 scale to distributor rotor. Resistance should be approximately 1000 ohms. If not to specification, replace rotor.

NOTE — When replacing rotor, use rotors marked with "R1" only.

DISTRIBUTOR VOLTAGE CHECK

1) Remove connector from distributor and connect voltmeter leads to each of the two outer terminals. See Fig. 4. Turn ignition switch "ON". Battery voltage should be read on voltmeter.

2) If there is no voltage, check wiring harness from distributor to control unit before proceeding to Control Unit Voltage Check.

Distributors & Ignition Systems

BOSCH HALL EFFECT ELECTRONIC IGNITION SYSTEM (Cont.)

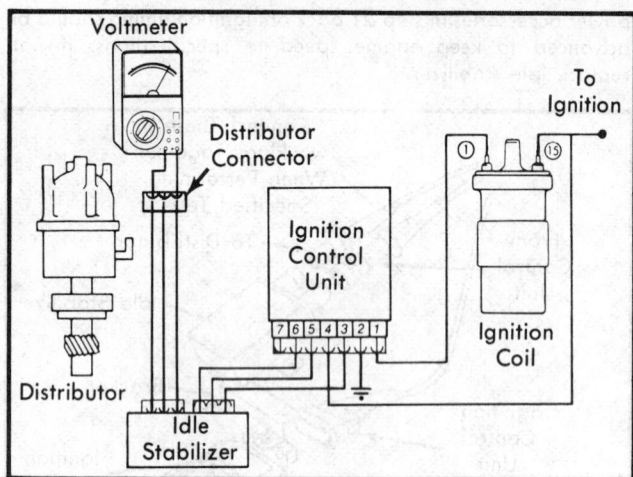

**Fig. 4   Voltmeter Hookup for
Distributor Voltage Check**

CONTROL UNIT VOLTAGE CHECK

1) Disconnect connectors from idle stabilizer and connect them to each other. Reconnect connector to distributor. Remove connector from electronic ignition control unit. *See Fig. 5.* Connect positive voltmeter lead to terminal 4 of control unit harness connector. Attach negative lead to terminal 2 (ground).

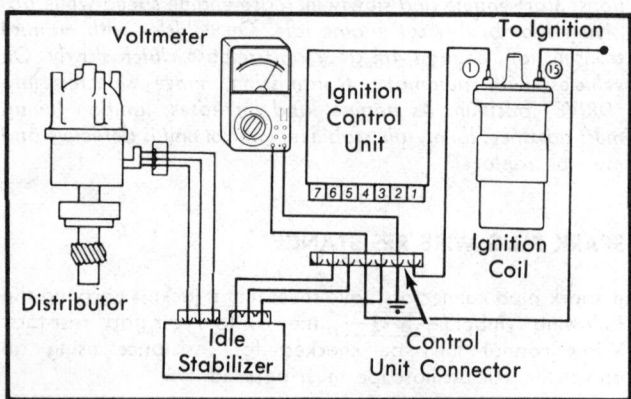

**Fig. 5   Voltmeter Hookup for
Control Unit Voltage Check**

2) Turn ignition switch "ON". Voltmeter should register approximately 12 volts. If reading is not within specifications, check and repair wiring circuit.

IGNITION COIL RESISTANCE CHECK

1) Remove all wires from ignition coil. Set an ohmmeter in the low scale and attach its leads to ignition coil primary terminals 1 and 15. *See Fig. 6.* Coil primary resistance should be .52-.76 ohm.

NOTE — *It may be impossible to check primary resistance with ordinary shop equipment. If electronic ignition checks OK, but there is no spark available at high tension wire, replace ignition coil and retest.*

2) Reset ohmmeter to x1000 scale and connect leads to primary terminal 1 and to coil tower, terminal 4. *See Fig. 6.* Resistance should read 2400-3500 ohms.

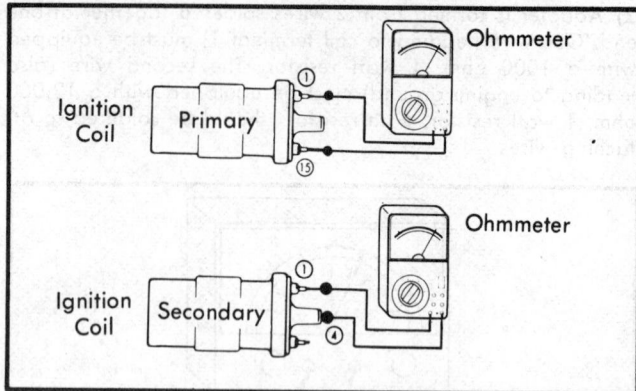

**Fig. 6   Ohmmeter Hookups for
Coil Resistance Checks**

3) If either reading is not to specification, replace ignition coil.

IGNITION CONTROL UNIT CHECK

Vanagon Only — 1) Disconnect both plugs at idle stabilizer control unit and connect plugs together. Remove connector from distributor. Connect positive lead of voltmeter to terminal 15 of ignition coil. Connect negative lead to terminal 1 of coil. *See Fig. 7.* Turn ignition switch "ON".

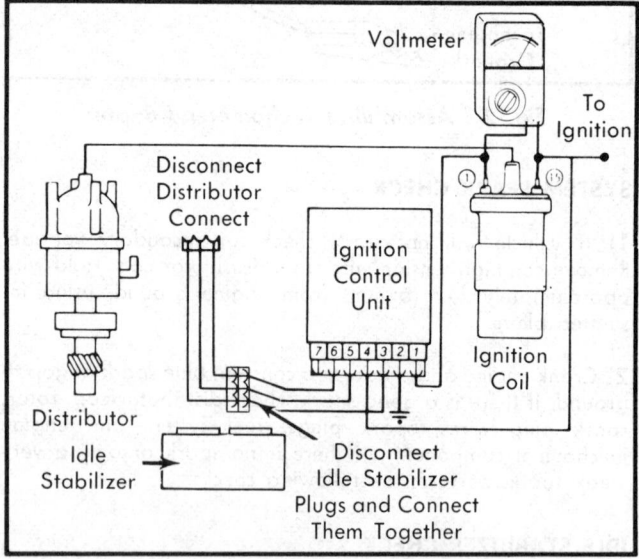

**Fig. 7   Voltmeter Hookup for Ignition Control
Unit Operation Check on Vanagon Models**

2) Voltage should be approximately 5-6 volts. Voltage should drop to zero volts within 1 second. Briefly ground center pin on distributor connector. Voltage should read 5-6 volts briefly, then drop to zero.

3) If control unit did not perform as specified, replace control unit.

NOTE — *If voltage reading does not drop within 1 or 2 seconds, turn off ignition switch immediately.*

All Except Vanagon — 1) Disconnect ignition control unit plug. Connect voltmeter leads between pins 2 and 4 on control

BOSCH HALL EFFECT ELECTRONIC IGNITION SYSTEM (Cont.)

unit plug. See Fig. 8. Turn ignition "ON". Battery voltage should be present. If not, check wiring circuit for breaks.

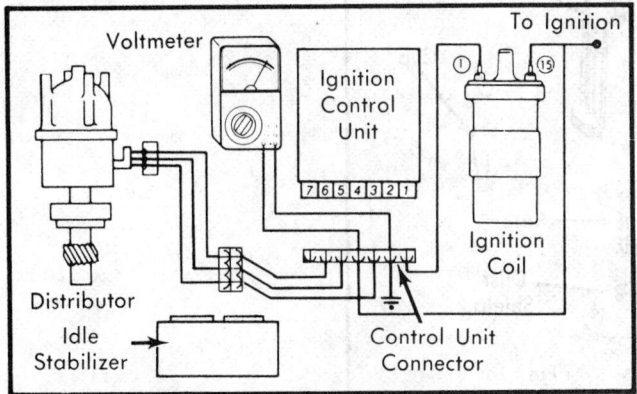

Fig. 8   Voltmeter Hookup for Ignition Control Unit Operation Check on All Models Except Vanagon

2) Turn ignition switch "OFF" and reconnect ignition control unit plug. Disconnect distributor connector plug. Connect the positive lead of voltmeter to terminal 15 of coil and the negative lead to terminal 1 of coil. See Fig. 9.

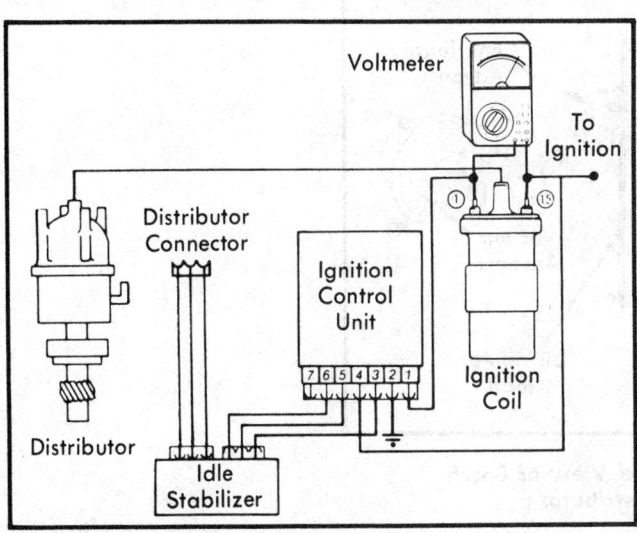

Fig. 9   Voltmeter Hookup for Ignition Control Unit Operation Check at Ignition Coil on All Models Except Vanagon

3) Turn ignition switch "ON". Voltage reading should be a minimum of 2 volts. Voltage reading should last for 1 to 2 seconds and then drop to zero volts.

4) Briefly ground the center pin on the distributor connector. Voltage reading should increase briefly to 5-6 volts. Turn ignition switch "OFF".

5) Connect voltmeter terminals to outer pins of distributor plug connector. Turn ignition switch "ON". Voltage reading should be a minimum of 5 volts. If ignition control unit does not perform as specified, check wiring circuit for broken wires. If wires are not broken, replace ignition coil unit.

HALL SENDING UNIT (GENERATOR) CHECK

1) Reconnect the control unit harness connector to control unit. See Fig. 10. Pull back rubber boot on connector. Attach voltmeter positive lead to connector terminal 6, and negative lead to terminal 3. Be sure connector is securely plugged into control unit.

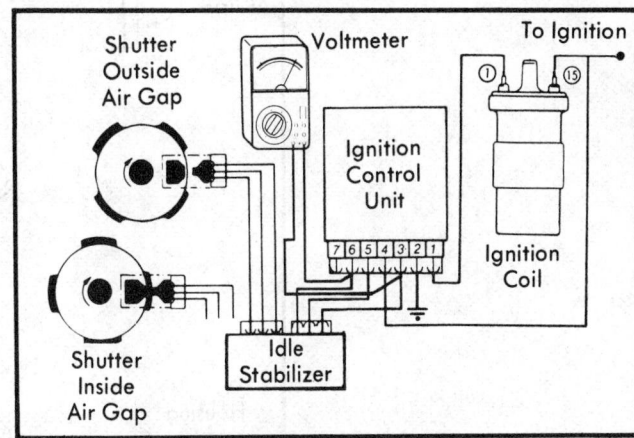

Fig. 10   Voltmeter Hookups for Hall Sending Unit Check

2) Turn ignition switch "ON". With trigger wheel shutter outside Hall sending unit air gap, check voltage reading. It should be 0-.7 volts. See Fig. 10.

3) Now turn distributor until trigger wheel shutter is inside Hall sending unit air gap. See inset in Fig. 10. Voltmeter reading should increase to 1.8-12 volts.

4) If any of the above voltage readings are incorrect, replace the Hall sending unit.

ALTERNATIVE HALL SENDING UNIT OPERATION CHECK

1) Disconnect high tension wire at distributor and connect it to ground. Connect a test light (4-24V) between terminal 1 and 15 of ignition coil. Crank engine with starter for approximately 5 seconds.

2) Test light must flicker. If not, replace Hall sending unit in distributor.

OVERHAUL

Disassembly — 1) Loosen ground strap and remove static shield from distributor cap. See Fig. 11. Remove cap, rotor, carbon brush and spring. Remove dust cover.

2) Remove connector from distributor (Hall generator connector and harness leading to idle stabilizer). Remove retaining snap ring and trigger wheel (segmented shutter). Remove washers. Remove screws and lift out Hall sending unit and connecting socket.

3) Remove base plate and vacuum unit. Remove pin and distributor drive pinion and shims.

Reassembly — To reassemble, reverse disassembly procedure. Replace seals and check components for cracks, corrosion and wear. Clean cap before installing.

BOSCH HALL EFFECT ELECTRONIC IGNITION SYSTEM (Cont.)

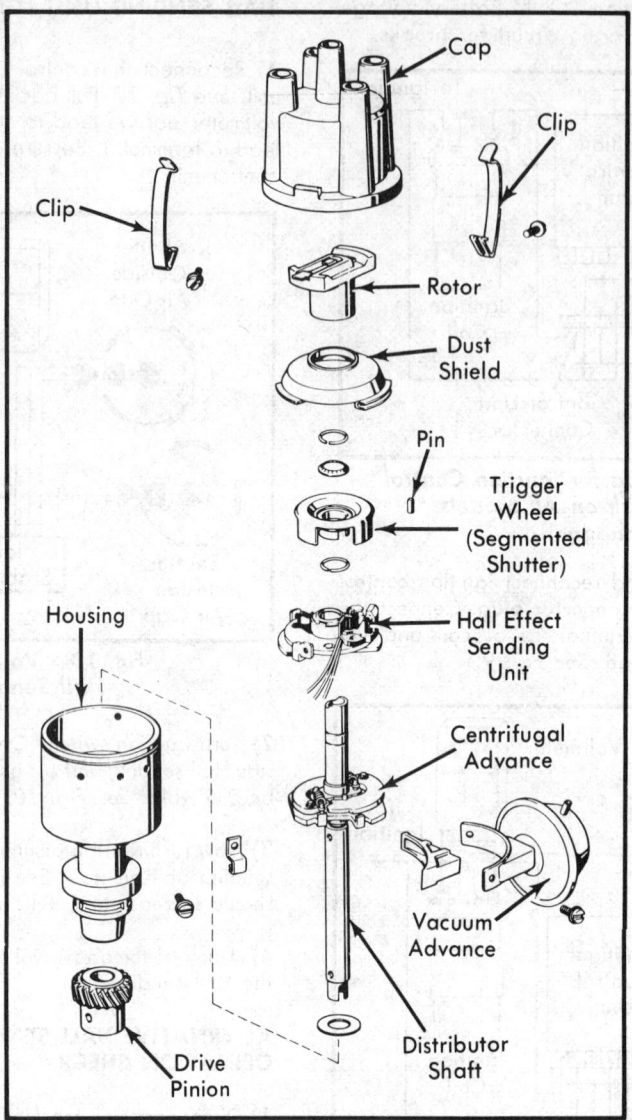

Fig. 11   Disassembled View of Bosch Hall Effect Distributor

BOSCH SINGLE BREAKER DISTRIBUTOR

Audi
4000 (Fed. Man. Trans.)
Volkswagen
Vanagon (Federal)

DESCRIPTION

Conventional single breaker distributor with centrifugal advance and vacuum advance and/or retard unit. Vacuum units may be single or dual diaphragm and are linked to the moveable portion of the breaker plate assembly to advance or retard spark.

NOTE — *Some distributors may use a dual diaphragm unit to provide retard only (vacuum advance side not used.)*

SPECIFICATIONS

Point Gap & Cam Angle — *See Tune-Up Data on Car Model Tune-Up Pages.*

Centrifugal & Vacuum Advance (Or Retard) — *See Specification Tables in this section.*

ADJUSTMENT

Point Gap, Alignment, & Cam Angle — With rubbing block on high point of cam lobe, insert a feeler gauge blade between contacts and check reading against specification. To correct, loosen retaining screw and move stationary contact point until correct gap is obtained, then tighten screw. Align points if necessary by bending stationary contact support only. Check cam angle with a dwell meter; compare indicated reading with specification and correct if necessary.

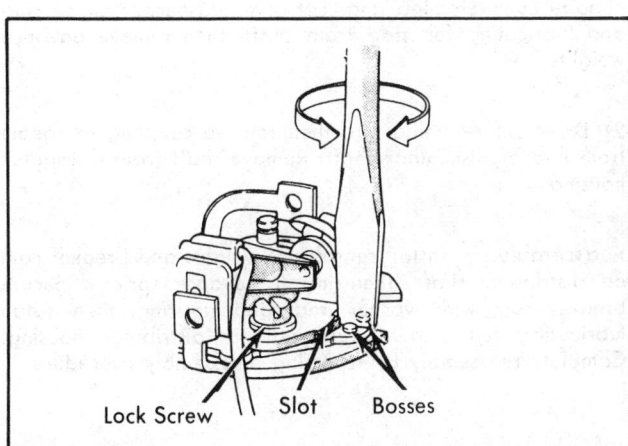

Fig. 1   Adjusting Contact Points

Breaker Arm Spring Tension — To check spring tension, place hook end of spring scale as close as possible to the movable breaker point. Pull scale at a right angle (90 degrees) to the movable arm and note reading just as points begin to open.

Centrifugal Advance — 1) Check distributor in test stand according to test equipment manufacturer's instructions. Operate distributor both up and down the RPM range and check advance at all RPM settings specified. Adjust or replace springs, weights or cam as necessary.

2) If distributor has adjustable driving collar for centrifugal advance, disassemble and lift shaft out. *See Fig. 2.* It is not necessary to remove breaker cam assembly from shaft. To adjust, loosen screws retaining driving collar. If collar is turned in direction of rotation, the advance curve rises. Turning collar in opposite direction of rotation will lower the curve.

CAUTION — *Centrifugal advance curve must not be adjusted by bending spring clamps of driving collar.*

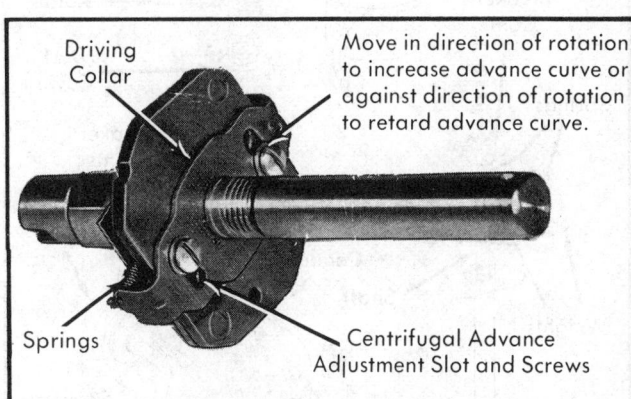

**Fig. 2   Centrifugal Advance Adjustment
(Driving Collar)**

3) If distributor does not have adjustable driving collar, adjustment may be made by bending spring anchor tabs to modify spring tension (see illustration). To adjust for low speed operation, bend primary spring anchor tab outward to decrease advance, and inward to increase advance. For high speed operation, bend secondary spring anchor tab in or out to obtain specified settings.

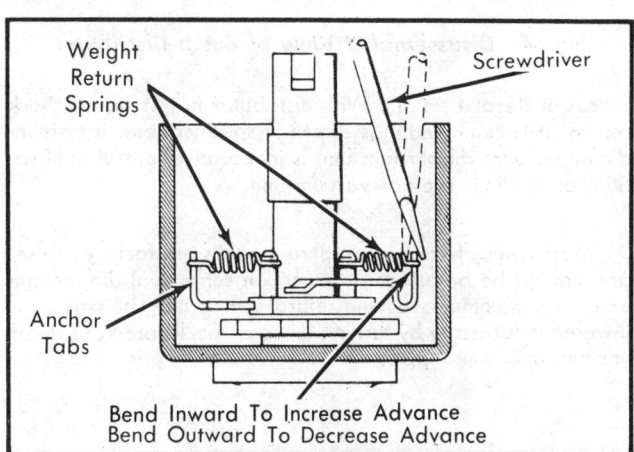

**Fig. 3   Centrifugal Advance Adjustment
(Spring Anchor Tabs)**

Vacuum Advance — 1) With distributor in test stand, check advance at vacuum settings shown in specifications. If tests indicate vacuum diaphragm unit is inoperative, out of calibration, or leaking, replace vacuum unit.

2) Most types of vacuum diaphragm units are factory pre-set and cannot be adjusted. However, on some dual diaphragm vacuum units, the vacuum advance may be increased or decreased by turning an Allen screw located in end of diaphragm unit.

BOSCH SINGLE BREAKER DISTRIBUTOR (Cont.)

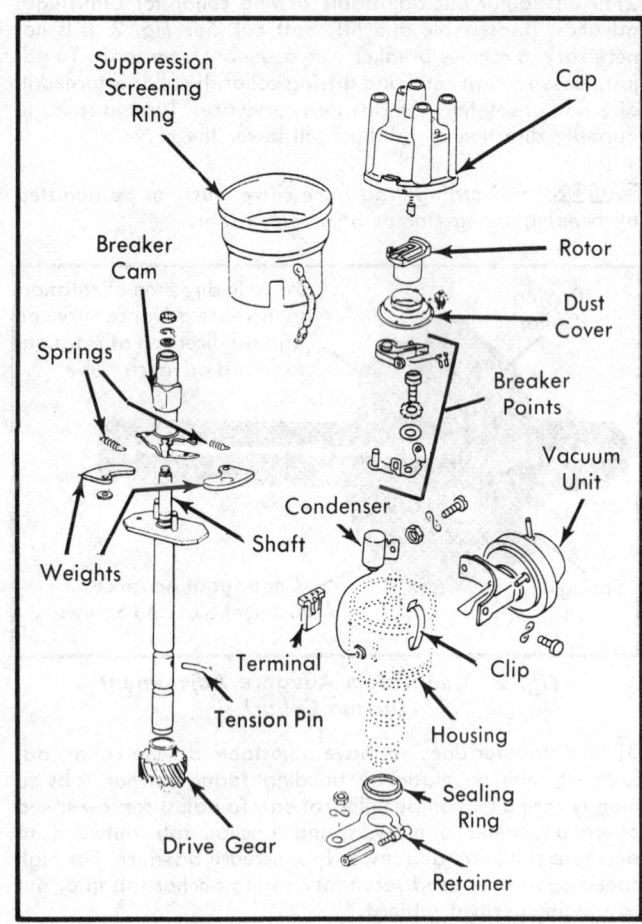

Fig. 4   Disassembled View of Bosch Distributor

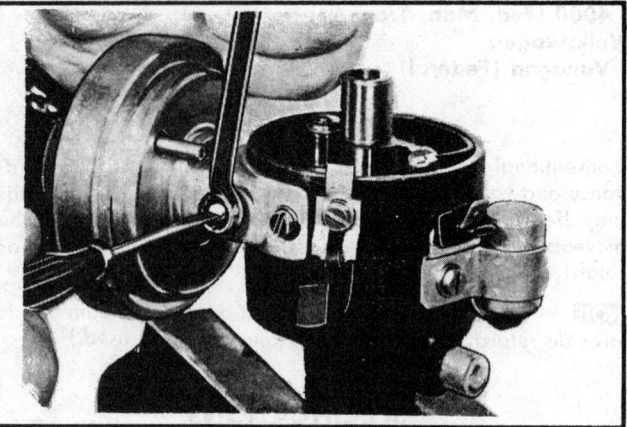

**Fig. 5   Adjusting Maximum Vacuum Retard
(Eccentric Location)**

OVERHAUL

NOTE — *All parts should be marked or set aside separately or in groups so that same combination can be reinstalled. Keep screws with the component they attach, as screws are different lengths and damage could occur if installed in wrong position.*

Disassembly — **1)** Disconnect and remove vacuum unit. Remove breaker points and condenser, then remove breaker assembly. Note positioning of centrifugal advance parts and mark for assembly reference. Disconnect and remove centrifugal advance springs (do not distort). Using 2 screwdrivers, carefully pry upward on the lower edge of breaker cam to disengage cam retaining ring. Lift cam, washer, retaining ring and lubricating felt pad from shaft, then remove advance weights.

2) Drive out retaining pin, then remove coupling (or gear) from end of distributor shaft. Remove shaft from distributor housing.

Reassembly — Install centrifugal weights and breaker cam on distributor shaft, then install advance springs. Secure breaker cam with washer and retaining ring, then install lubricating felt pad. Install shaft in distributor housing. Complete reassembly by reversing disassembly procedure.

Vacuum Retard — **1)** With distributor in test stand, check retard at vacuum setttings shown in specifications. If tests indicate vacuum diaphragm unit is inoperative, out of calibration, or leaking, replace vacuum unit.

2) Most types of vacuum diaphragm units are factory pre-set and cannot be adjusted. However, on some dual diaphragm units, the maximum vacuum retard setting may be raised or lowered if necessary by turning an eccentric, located at side of vacuum unit. See *Fig. 5.*

DATSUN ELECTRONIC CONCENTRATED ENGINE CONTROL SYSTEM

280ZX Turbo

DESCRIPTION

The Electronic Concentrated Engine Control System (ECCS) is a computerized emission, ignition and fuel control system. A single control unit monitors a variety of sensors, including the following:

- Crankshaft Angle Sensor
- Throttle Valve Switch
- Air Flow Meter
- Air Temperature Sensor
- Cylinder Head Temperature Sensor
- Barometric Pressure Sensor
- Oxygen Sensor
- Detonation Sensor
- Vehicle Speed Sensor
- Park/Neutral Switch
- Air Conditioning Switch

The computer processes information from these sensors and controls these engine functions:

- Ignition Timing and Dwell
- Fuel Injectors
- Fuel Pump Operation
- Engine Idle Speed
- EGR Operation

NOTE — *For component location and identification, see Fig. 1.*

OPERATION

ECCS CONTROL UNIT

The control unit is located on the driver's side kick panel. It is not serviceable and should not be opened. A monitor lamp is provided in the lower side of the unit so system operation can be checked. The control unit contains memory and locic circuits that enable it to interpret sensor inputs and control the different engine systems.

ENGINE SENSORS

Crankshaft Angle Sensor — The crankshaft pulley has a disc attached to it which has 90 teeth spaced at 4° intervals. It also has 3 projections at 120° intervals. The crankshaft angle sensor uses magnetic pick-ups (3) to sense the position of these teeth and send a signal to the control unit. Two of the pick-ups work together to ganerate 1 pulse for every 1° of crankshaft rotation. This signal is used for timing and engine speed information. The other pick-up generates a pulse every 120° of rotation and this signal is used to determine piston location (TDC).

Throttle Valve Switch — The throttle valve switch is open when the throttle is being moved and closed when the engine is idling. The switch also contains a set of full-throttle contacts, but these are not used in this system.

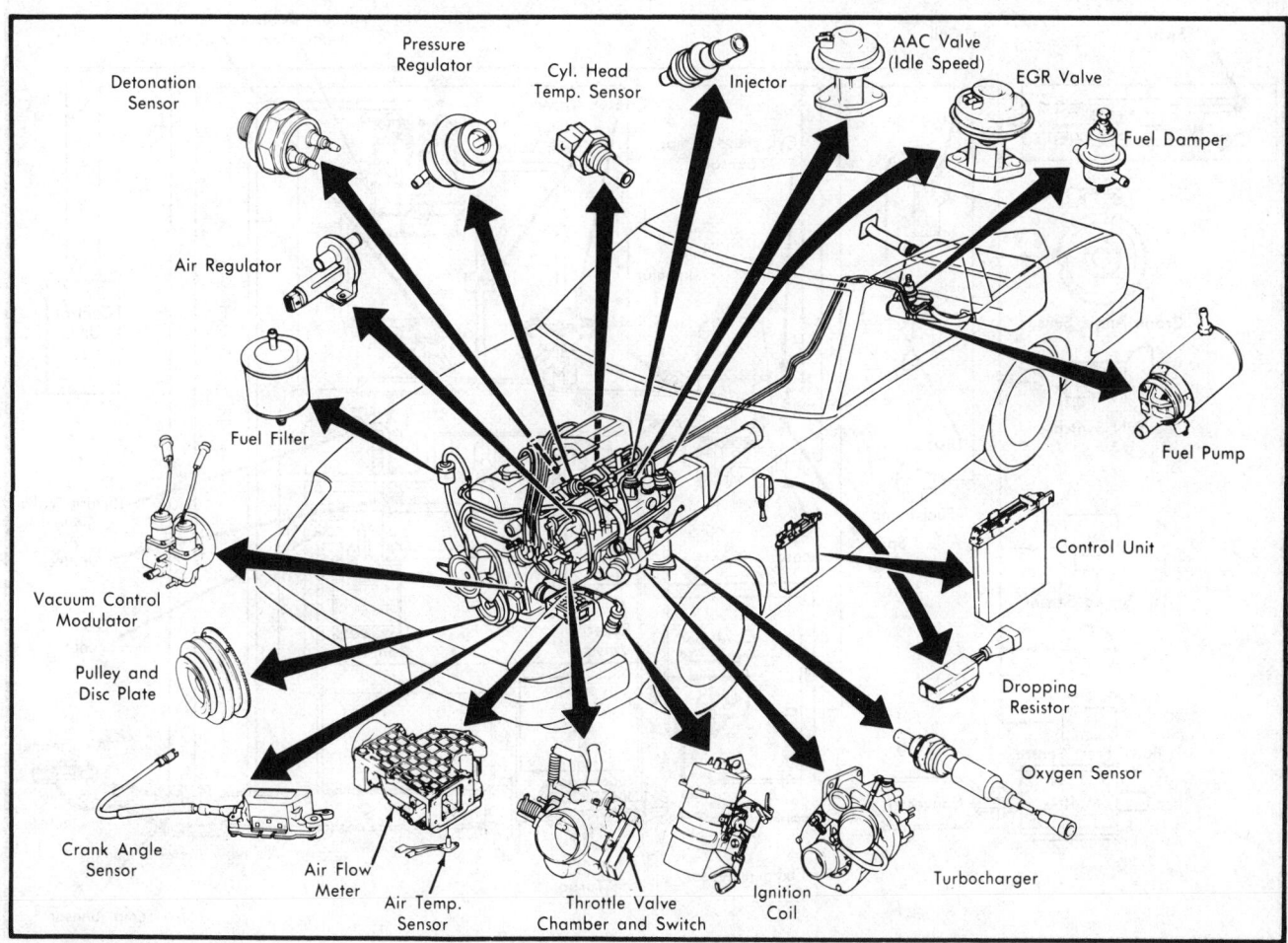

Fig. 1 ECCS Component Locations

DATSUN ELECTRONIC CONCENTRATED ENGINE CONTROL SYSTEM (Cont.)

Air Flow Meter and Temperature Sensor — The air flow meter measures incoming air so fuel mixture can be determined and injection time controlled by the ECCS control unit. It is a standard AFC flow meter, but incorporates a temperature sensor which is also used for ECCS input. The sensor cannot be serviced separately.

Cylinder Head Temperature Sensor — The cylinder head sensor is located in the right rear corner of the head and provides a varying resistance measurement as cylinder head temperature changes.

Barometric Pressure Sensor — This sensor is built into the ECCS control unit and cannot be serviced separately. It allows the control unit to compensate for altitude changes.

Oxygen Sensor — This component measures the amount of unburned oxygen in the exhaust and provides a voltage signal which is used to adjust fuel mixture (amount of injection time).

Detonation Sensor — The detonation sensor is located near the oil dipstick and sends a signal when "knocking" occurs. The control unit modifies ignition timing to reduce detonation.

ENGINE CONTROLS

Fuel Injection — The control unit determines how long voltage is provided to each injector. The injection time will determine how much fuel is injected. *For more information, see the appropriate Bosch AFC Fuel Injection article in FUEL SYSTEMS Section.*

Fuel Pump — The ECCS control unit operates the electric fuel pump. When the ignition is turned to "ON" or "START" position, the fuel pump operates. If the ignition is on and no signal is received from the crank sensor 120° pick-up for more than 1 second, the fuel pump stops. It will operate for 5 seconds before the engine is cranked, and will then stop if the engine is not cranked over at 20 RPM or more.

Ignition Timing — The control unit uses sensor input to determine the correct timing. It sends a signal to a power transistor located on the coil, which permits current to flow through the coil. Timing is advanced and retarded by the control unit based on sensor input, built-in programming and detonation sensor signals.

EGR Operation — Exhaust gas recirculation is controlled by the ECCS. A signal is sent to the vacuum control modulator, which provides a regulated vacuum supply to open the EGR valve. EGR operation is affected by cylinder head temperature, throttle valve position and ignition switch position. Recirculation takes place only when the engine is operating above idle with cylinder head temperature between 135-240° F (57-115° C).

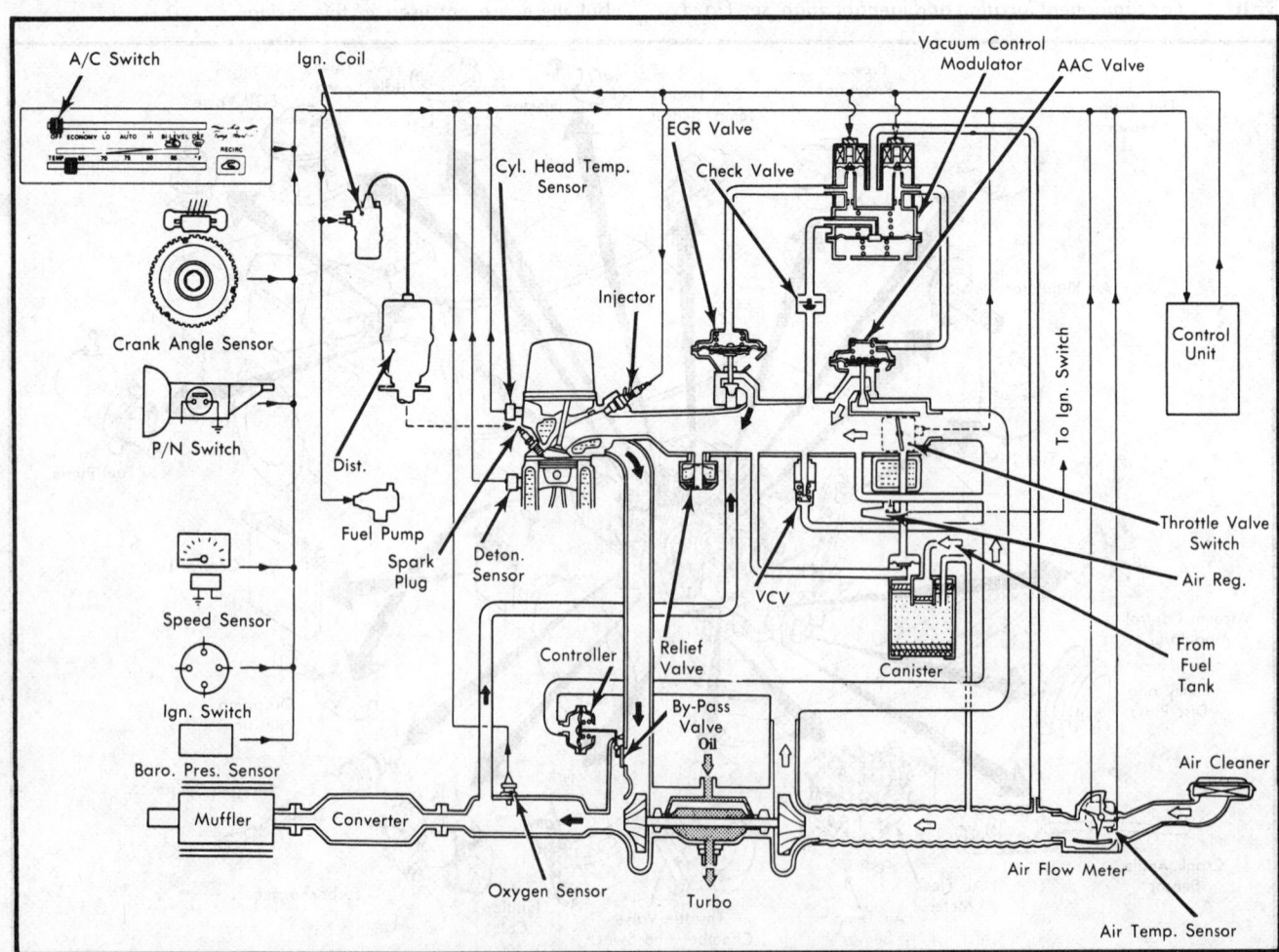

Fig. 2   ECCS Schematic and Vacuum Diagram

DATSUN ELECTRONIC CONCENTRATED ENGINE CONTROL SYSTEM (Cont.)

Idle Speed Control — The Auxiliary Air Control (AAC) valve is used to control idle speed. The valve is operated by a vacuum signal from the vacuum control modulator and wrks much like an EGR valve does. It allows extra air into the throttle chamber, which increases idle speed. The control unit monitors speed with the crankshaft angle sensor and continually corrects idle speed by operating the vacuum control modulator.

TESTING

NOTE — *The Datsun ECCS system requires a special tester (Datsun ECCS Analyzer) to be fully diagnosed. However, some checks of individual components may be made using regular shop test equipment.*

CAUTION — *Be sure ignition switch is off when disconnecting connectors from control unit. While testing, be careful not to bend any pins and do not touch more than 1 pin at a time with meter lead as meter or control unit could be damaged.*

PREPARATION FOR TESTING

1) Turn ignition off. Disconnect battery ground cable and disconnect wire from terminal "S" at starter motor.

2) Remove air cleaner and position air flow meter so flap can be moved by hand from air cleaner side. Disconnect all 3 connectors at control unit.

COMPONENT TESTING

Throttle Valve Switch — 1) Connect ohmmeter across pins 18 and 25 in control unit connectors. With throttle depressed, no continuity should be present. With throttle released, continuity should be present. If not correct, adjust throttle switch. *See Adjustments in this article.*

2) Connect ohmmeter to terminal 18 and ground, then 25 and ground. *See Fig. 5.* No continuity should be present in either position. If present, repair short to ground in harness, or replace throttle valve switch.

Air Flow Meter — 1) Connect ohmmeter across pins 33 and 26 in connectors. Resistance should be 280-400 ohms. If not, check resistance at meter. If not correct, repair harness or replace air flow meter. *See Fig. 4.*

2) Connect ohmmeter across pins 33 and 31 at connector. Resistance should measure any value between infinity and zero. If not, check resistance at meter. If okay at meter, repair harness. If not, replace air flow meter.

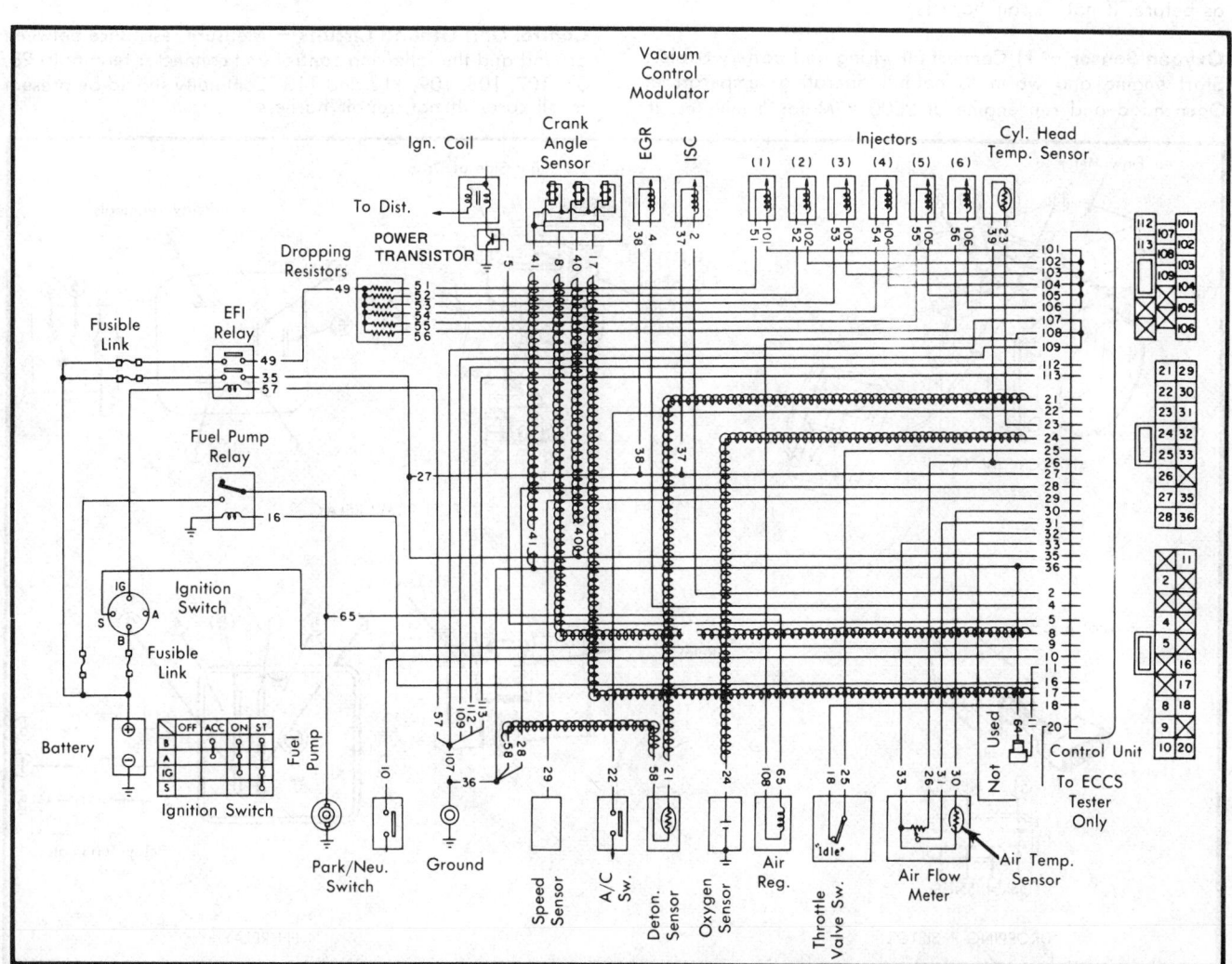

Fig. 3   Datsun ECCS Wiring Diagram

DATSUN ELECTRONIC CONCENTRATED ENGINE CONTROL SYSTEM (Cont.)

3) Connect 1 lead to ground and the other lead of ohmmeter to connector pin 26, then 31, then 33. Infinite resistance should be shown in all cases. If not, repeat check at connector pins or air flow meter. Repair harness or replace meter as necessary.

4) Operate air flow meter flap by hand to ensure it moves smoothly without binding. If okay, meter is functioning properly. If not, replace air flow meter.

Air Temperature Sensor — 1) Connect ohmmeter across pins 30 and 33 in control unit connector. With air temperature at 68° F (20° C), resistance should be 2100-2900 ohms. If not correct, repeat test at air flow meter terminals. Repair harness or replace meter as necessary. See *Fig. 4.*

2) Connect ohmmeter between ground and pin 30 at connector. No continuity should be present. Repeat check at air flow meter terminal and body. Repair harness or replace meter as necessary.

Cylinder Head Temperature Sensor — Remove sensor from head and dip end of sensor into water at 68° F (20° C). Resistance should be 2100-2900 ohms across sensor terminals. Connect harness to sensor and measure between control unit connector pin 23 and ground. Resistance should be the same as before. If not, repair harness.

Oxygen Sensor — 1) Connect all wiring and battery cables. Start engine and warm to normal operating temperature. Open hood and run engine at 2000 RPM for 5 minutes. If

engine does not run smoothly, check air flow meter, cylinder head temperature sensor and air temperature sensor.

2) Accelerate engine several times, then check idle. If not 600-700 RPM in "D", check vacuum control modulator and idle speed control system.

NOTE — *Special ECCS tester is required for idle speed system check.*

3) Check timing. If not 17-23° BTDC, adjust to 20° BTDC with adjustment screw on crankshaft sensor bracket (loosen sensor bolts first).

4) Using a mirror, check that inspection lamp on bottom of control unit goes on and off more than 5 times in 10 seconds with engine running at 2000 RPM in "N". If so, sensor is okay.

5) If not, check oxygen sensor harness. If harness is okay, replace oxygen sensor.

Oxygen Sensor Harness — Disconnect harness from sensor in exhaust pipe and connect to ground with jumper wire. Measure resistance between ground and pin 24 in control unit connector. Zero resistance should be measured. If not present, repair harness.

Control Unit Ground Circuits — Measure resistance between ground and the following control unit connector terminals: 28, 36, 107, 108, 109, 112 and 113. Continuity should be present in all cases. If not, repair harness.

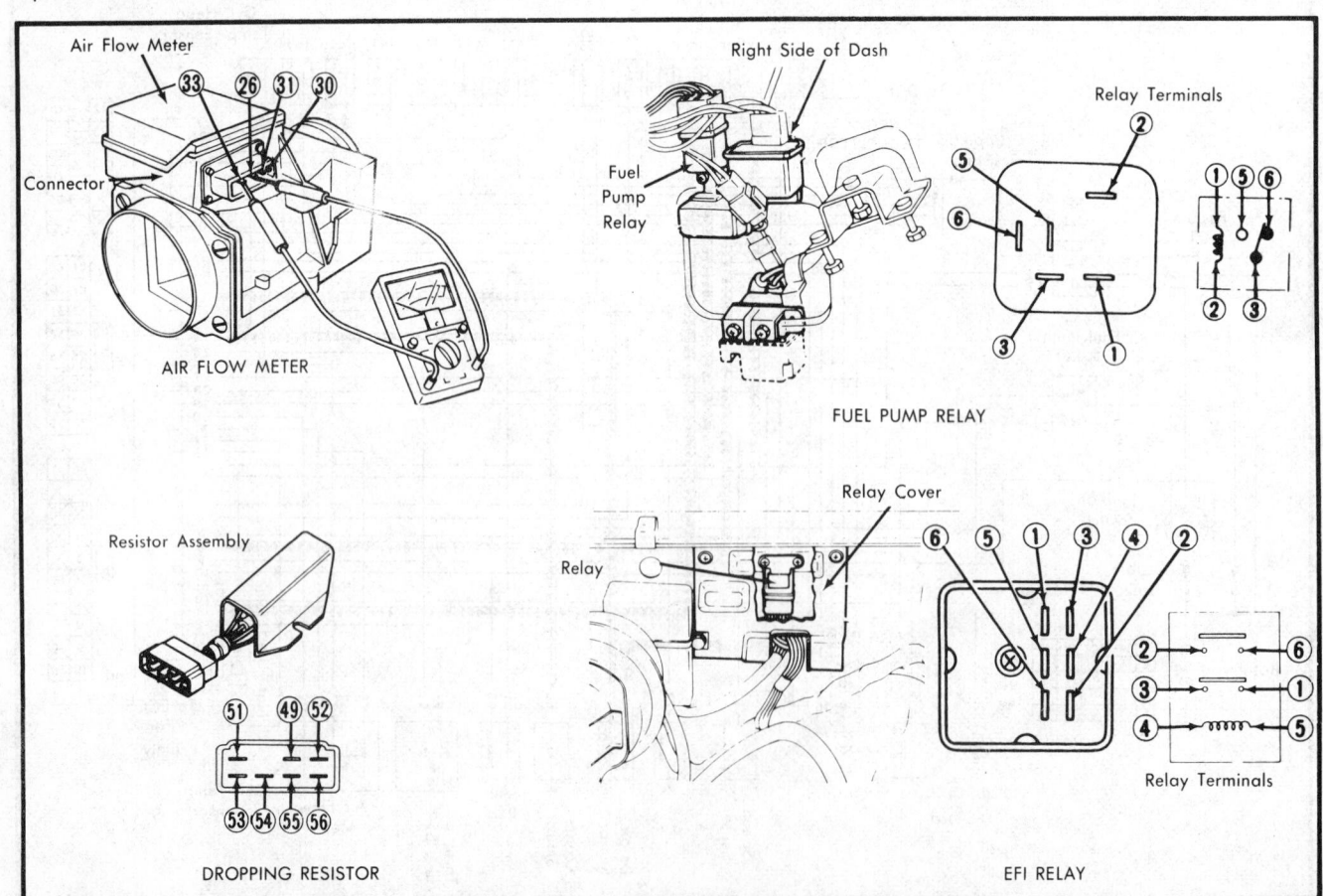

Fig. 4 Datsun ECCS Component Testing Locations

DATSUN ELECTRONIC CONCENTRATED ENGINE CONTROL SYSTEM (Cont.)

Air Regulator — 1) Connect ohmmeter between pin 108 in control unit connector and ground. Resistance should be 25-90 ohms.

2) Connect battery ground cable and leave starter "S" wire disconnected. Turn ignition to "START" position. Using a voltmeter, measure between terminals 108 in control unit connector and ground. Battery voltage should be present. If not, go to next step.

3) Fuel pump should operate for 5 seconds with ignition on and engine not running. If pump is not heard, check pump relay. If pump is heard, go to next step.

4) Start engine and pinch hose between throttle chamber and air regulator. Engine speed should decrease during warm-up but not when engine is at operating temperature. Disconnect hoses from both ends of regulator and see if flap opens. It should move smoothly. Check resistance across terminals on regulator. If continuity exists, regulator is good. If not, replace regulator.

Fuel Pump Relay — Fuel pump relay is mounted on right side of dashboard. Remove relay and check continuity. It should be present between terminals 1 and 2, and terminals 3 and 6. With 12 volts applied to terminals 1 and 2, continuity should be present across terminals 3 and 5. If test is okay, check harness. If not okay, replace relay. *See Fig. 4.*

Injectors — 1) Connect battery ground cable and turn ignition on. Use a voltmeter to measure between ground and the following terminals at control unit connector: 101, 102, 103, 104, 105 and 106. Battery voltage should be present at all terminals. If so, go to step **3)**. If not, go to next step.

2) If battery voltage was not present at terminal, check the appropriate injector. Disconnect battery ground cable and remove connectors at injector. Continuity should exist across terminals on injector. If not, replace injector.

NOTE — *Injector circuits are numbered according to cylinder number. For example, injector power circuit 103 goes to cylinder 3, and dropping resistor circuit 53 goes to cylinder 3.*

3) Check dropping resistor by disconnecting connector at dropping resistor unit and measuring between terminal 49 and all other terminals. Resistance should be about 6 ohms. Replace resistor if any circuit is defective.

EFI Relay — 1) With battery cables connected and ignition on, measure voltage between control unit connector pin 35 and ground. Battery voltage should be present. If not, check EFI relay operation. Relay is located under a cover in engine compartment. *See Fig. 4.*

2) Continuity should exist across terminals 4 and 5. With battery voltage applied to 4 and terminal 5 grounded, continuity should exist across 1 and 3, and 2 and 6. If not, replace relay.

Ignition Signal Circuit — Disconnect starter motor "S" terminal and connect battery ground cable. Turn ignition switch to "START". Measure voltage between control unit connector pin 9 and ground. If battery voltage is not present, check harness and ignition coil.

Vacuum Control Modulator — 1) Connect battery ground cable and turn ignition on. Measure voltage between control unit connector terminal 2 and ground. Battery voltage should be present.

2) Check for battery voltage between terminal 4 and ground. If voltage is present in both checks, modulator solenoid valves are okay. If not, disconnect both connectors at modulator.

3) Check resistance between terminals for each solenoid valve on modulator. Resistance should be 40 ohms for each valve. If not, replace vacuum control modulator.

Park/Neutral Switch — Connect battery ground cable and turn ignition on. Connect voltmeter between control unit connector pin 10 and ground. With transmission lever in "P" or "N", battery voltage should be present. If not, check harness or replace switch.

Air Conditioning Switch — Connect ohmmeter between control unit connector terminal 22 and ground. With switch on, zero resistance should be measured, and with switch off, infinity should be measured. If not correct, check harness or replace switch.

ADJUSTMENTS

THROTTLE VALVE SWITCH

Disconnect throttle valve switch connector. Connect ohmmeter across terminals 18 and 25, ensuring that continuity exists. Allow engine to run at idle and adjust switch so continuity is lost at about 750 RPM.

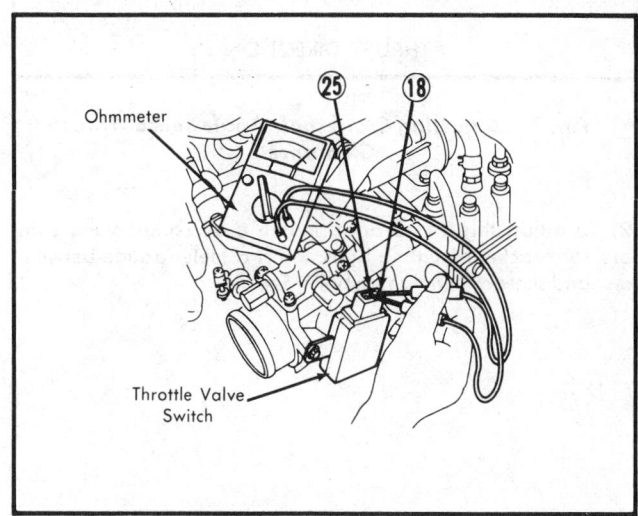

Fig. 5 Adjusting Throttle Valve Switch

CRANKSHAFT ANGLE SENSOR

NOTE — *Remove cover under engine compartment and adjust sensor from beneath vehicle.*

Crankshaft Angle Sensor Clearance — 1) To adjust radial clearance, loosen 2 adjuster mounting bolts (at extreme ends of bracket). Insert feeler gauge between sensor and disc, then press sensor against gauge while tightening bolts. *See Fig. 6.*

DATSUN ELECTRONIC CONCENTRATED ENGINE CONTROL SYSTEM (Cont.)

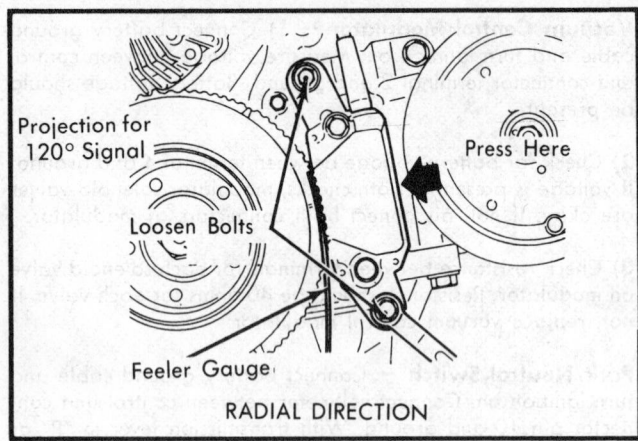

Fig. 6 *Adjusting Crankshaft Angle Sensor Radial Clearance*

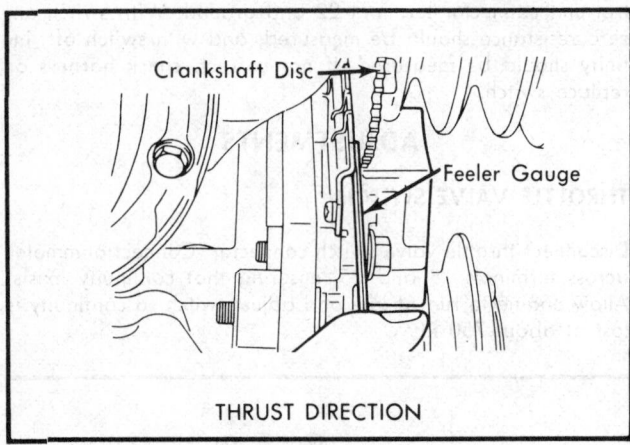

Fig. 7 *Adjusting Crankshaft Angle Sensor Thrust Clearance*

2) To adjust thrust clearance, loosen 4 air conditioning compressor bracket mounting bolts. Insert a feeler gauge between disc and sensor, then tighten bolts. See *Fig. 7*.

Crankshaft Sensor Clearance Specifications

Application	Checking In. (mm)	Adjustment In. (mm)
Radial	.039-.055 (1.0-1.4)	.047 (1.2)
Thrust	.039-.052 (1.0-1.4)	.047 (1.2)

NOTE — *Ignition timing cannot be adjusted by rotating the distributor. The crankshaft angle sensor must be adjusted to change idle speed timing.*

Ignition Timing — **1)** Check ignition timing at idle speed using a timing light. If timing is not 20±3° BTDC, remove cover under engine compartment. Loosen crankshaft angle sensor bolts (2 bolts retaining sensor to adjuster).

2) To advance ignition timing, tighten adjusting screw. This will move crankshaft angle sensor upward. To retard ignition timing, loosen adjusting screw, this will move crankshaft angle sensor downward. See *Fig. 8*.

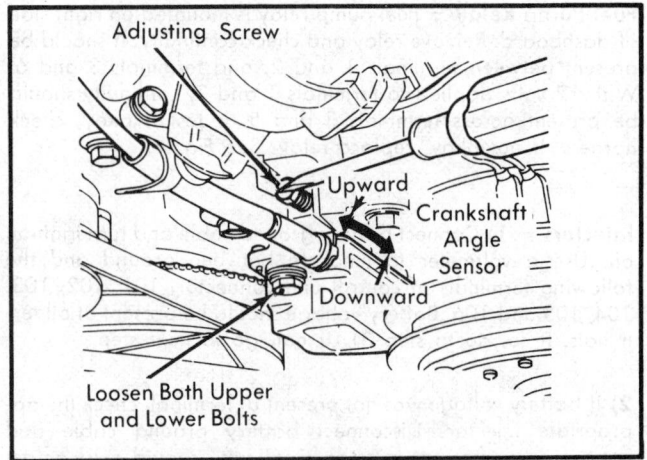

Fig. 8 *Adjusting Ignition Timing by Turning Crankshaft Angle Sensor Adjusting Screw*

3) After adjusting ignition timing, recheck crankshaft angle sensor radial and thrust clearances. Correct if necessary.

DUCELLIER ELECTRONIC IGNITION SYSTEM – PEUGEOT

505

DESCRIPTION

The Ducellier electronic ignition system consists of a Ducellier breakerless distributor, a Delco-Remy ignition coil and amplifier module, an ignition switch and necessary wiring.

The distributor contains both centrifugal and vacuum advance mechanisms, a pick-up coil and a reluctor (polarity wheel). See Fig. 1. The ignition coil and amplifier are both mounted to a common light alloy base that provides both good grounding and cooling of the amplifier module. Silicone grease, which comes with the module and is applied between the module and base, gives improved heat transfer. Since both units are grounded through the common base, all mounting bolts should be snug.

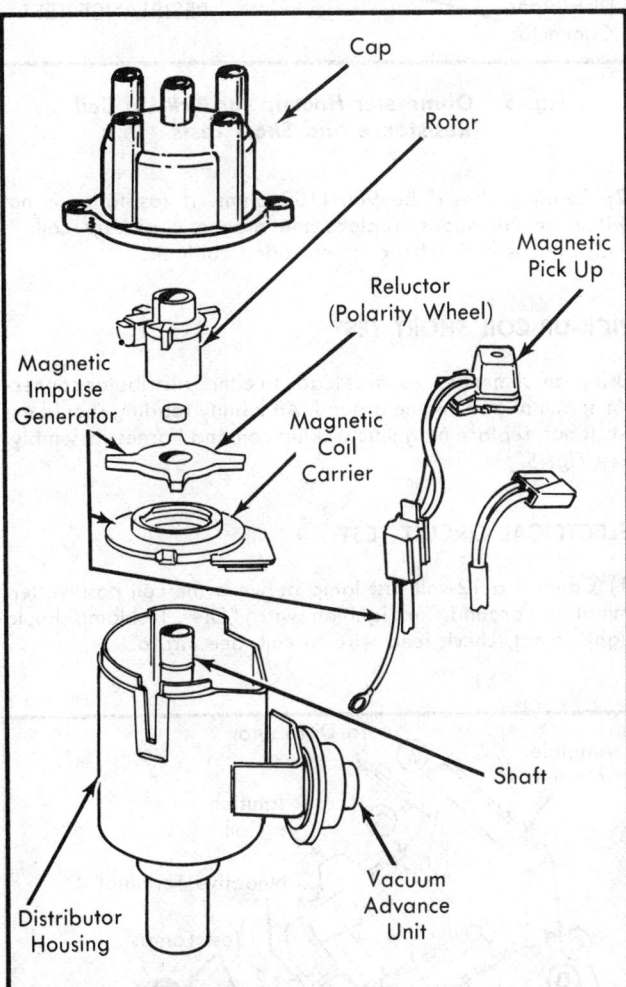

Fig. 1   Exploded View of Ducellier Breakerless Distributor

The ignition coil is encased in epoxy resin instead of oil. The amplifier module receives, amplifies and sends electronic signals to provide proper spark timing.

OPERATION

The distributor contains an electronic pulse generator, consisting of a pick-up coil and a reluctor (polarity wheel). As the distributor shaft turns, the reluctor teeth approach and pass the magnetic pick-up coil. This causes signals to be transmitted to the amplifier module, which in turn opens and closes a transistorized switch in the module. This turns the primary circuit of the ignition coil on and off. When the primary circuit is switched off, a high voltage surge occurs in the secondary circuit, firing the spark plugs.

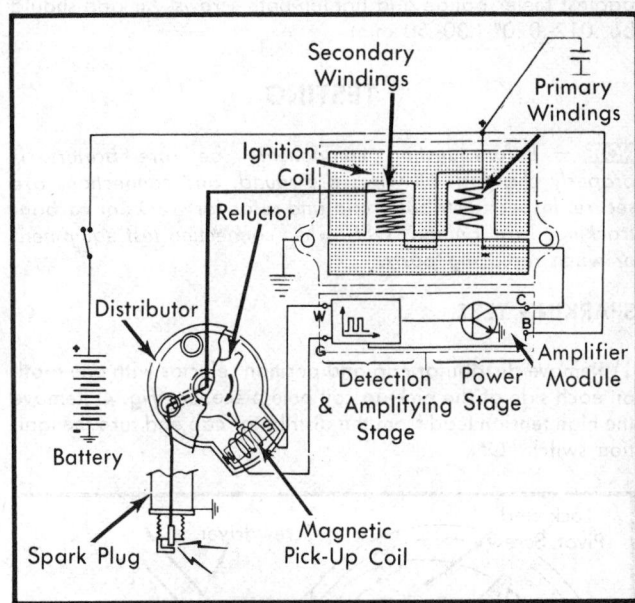

Fig. 2   Schematic of Ducellier Electronic Ignition System

The amplifier module has 4 terminals. Terminals "W" and "G" are connected to the distributor magnetic pulse generator (pick-up coil). Terminal "B" is connected to the coil positive terminal, and terminal "C" to the coil negative terminal. See Fig. 3. The unit is grounded through one of its mounting bolts through the alloy base.

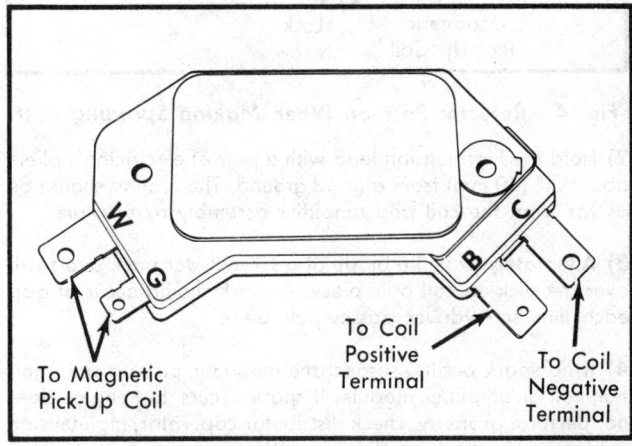

Fig. 3   Amplifier Module Connector Terminals

SPECIFICATIONS

Centrifugal & Vacuum Advance – See Specifications Tables in this section.

DUCELLIER ELECTRONIC IGNITION SYSTEM – PEUGEOT (Cont.)

ADJUSTMENTS

Reluctor-to-Pick-Up Coil Air Gap – Loosen both magnetic pick-up coil mounting screws. See *Fig. 4*. Position reluctor tooth in line with pick-up coil pole piece. Insert a non-magnetic feeler gauge of the proper thickness (.016" or .40 mm) between one reluctor tooth and pole piece. Pivot pick-up coil against feeler gauge and tighten both screws. Air gap should be .012-.020" (.30-.50 mm).

TESTING

NOTE – *Before testing components, be sure battery is properly charged, all wires are sound, and connections are secure. Inspect distributor cap and rotor for cracks or carbon-tracking. Turn ignition "OFF" when connecting test equipment or when replacing parts.*

SPARKING TEST

1) Remove distributor cap and position reluctor with one tooth on each side of the pick-up coil pole piece. See *Fig. 4*. Remove the high tension lead from the distributor cap and turn the ignition switch "ON".

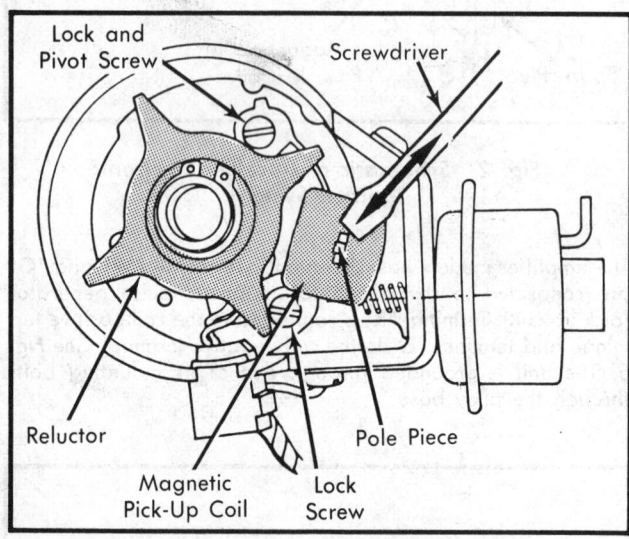

Fig. 4 Reluctor Position When Making Sparking Test

2) Hold the high tension lead with a pair of electrician's pliers about .4" (10 mm) from a good ground. The ground should be as far from the coil and amplifier assembly as possible.

3) Alternately pass the blade of a screwdriver back and forth over the pick-up coil pole piece. A spark should occur at gap each time screwdriver passes pole piece.

4) If no spark occurs, suspect the magnetic pick-up coil, ignition coil or amplifier module. If spark occurs, but engine does not perform properly, check distributor cap, rotor, high tension cables and battery condition.

PICK-UP COIL RESISTANCE TEST

1) Turn ignition switch "OFF". Disconnect connector for terminals "W" and "G" at amplifier module. Using an ohmmeter set in the x100 scale, check the resistance between distributor connector terminals. See *Fig. 5*.

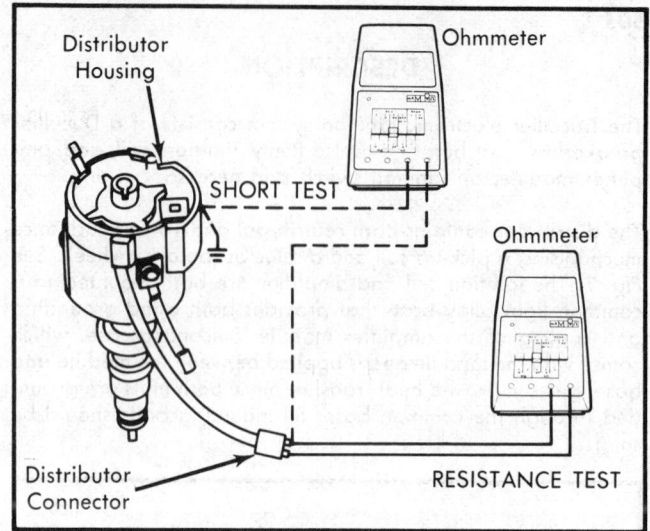

Fig. 5 Ohmmeter Hookup for Pick-Up Coil Resistance and Short Tests

2) Reading should be 900-1100 ohms. If resistance is not within specifications, replace the magnetic pick-up coil. If resistance is high, check for corroded contacts.

PICK-UP COIL SHORT TEST

Using an ohmmeter, connect leads to either distributor connector terminal and engine ground. An infinity reading should exist. If not, replace magnetic pick-up coil and harness assembly. See *Fig. 5*.

ELECTRICAL CIRCUIT TEST

1) Connect a 12-volt test lamp between the coil positive terminal and ground. Turn ignition switch "ON". Test lamp should light. If not, check feed wire to coil. See *Fig. 6*.

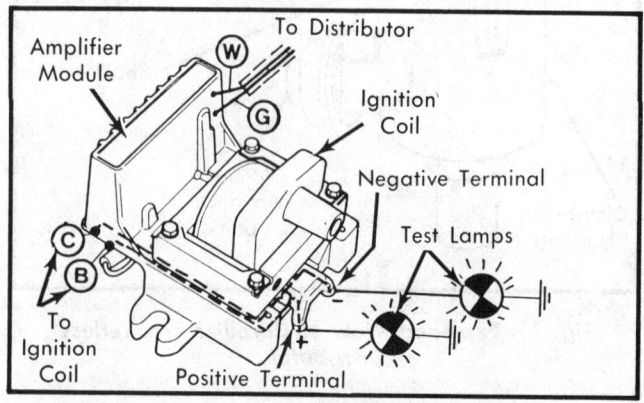

Fig. 6 Test Lamp Hookup for Electrical Circuit Test

2) Connect test lamp between the coil negative terminal and ground. Turn ignition switch "ON". Test lamp should again light. If not, check if coil primary circuit is broken or if amplifier module's power transistor is shorted.

DUCELLIER ELECTRONIC IGNITION SYSTEM — PEUGEOT (Cont.)

IGNITION COIL RESISTANCE TEST

1) Using an ohmmeter set in the low scale, connect leads to coil primary (positive and negative) terminals. Resistance should be .48-.61 ohms. See *Fig. 7*.

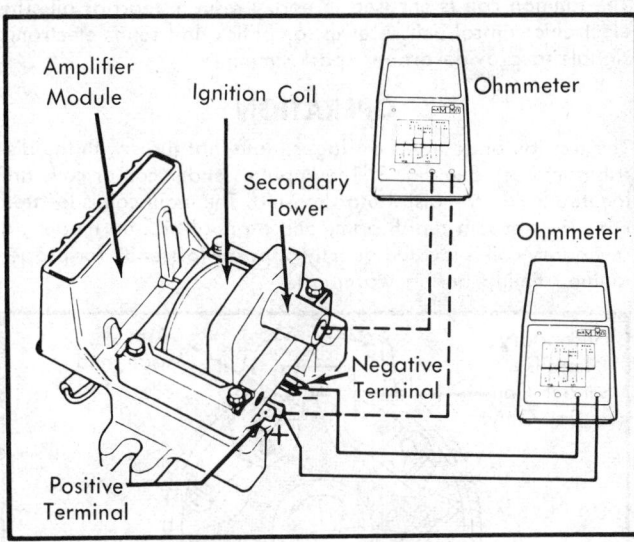

Fig. 7   Ohmmeter Hookup for Making Ignition Coil Resistance Tests

2) Connect ohmmeter set in the x1000 scale to the coil positive terminal and its secondary tower. Reading should be 9,000-11,000 ohms. If either reading is not to specifications, replace ignition coil.

AMPLIFIER MODULE TEST

1) Disconnect distributor harness connector from amplifier module "W" and "G" terminals. Disconnect the high tension lead from distributor cap. Turn ignition switch "ON". Hold high tension lead with a pair of electrician's pliers and position it .4" (10 mm) from good engine ground away from amplifier. The ground should be as far from the coil and amplifier module assembly as possible.

2) Use a jumper wire to feed terminal "G" of amplifier module with successive impulses from battery positive terminal. At each impulse, a spark should jump the gap to ground. If not, repeat same test with a new amplifier module. If spark jumps gap, replace with new module.

OVERHAUL

Disassembly — 1) Remove distributor cap, rotor, and plastic protector. Remove screw in the side of distributor. Pull upward on electrical connector to remove it from distributor housing. Remove 2 screws securing magnetic pick-up coil. See *Fig. 1*.

2) Lift out pick-up coil assembly. Remove reluctor, vacuum advance unit, electromagnetic coil carrier. Remove drive pinion from distributor shaft and pull shaft and centrifugal advance mechanism from housing.

Reassembly — To install, reverse removal procedure.

DUCELLIER ELECTRONIC IGNITION SYSTEM – RENAULT

Le Car
18i

DESCRIPTION

The Ducellier electronic ignition system consists of a Ducellier breakerless distributor, a Delco-Remy ignition coil, an electronic control unit, ignition switch and necessary wiring.

The distributor contains both centrifugal and vacuum advance mechanisms. Dual pick-up versions (Le Car only) have main and secondary impulse sender coils (pick-up coils). Single pick-up versions (18i only) have a single impulse sender (pick-up coil). Distributor also contains trigger (reluctor), seal, rotor and cap.

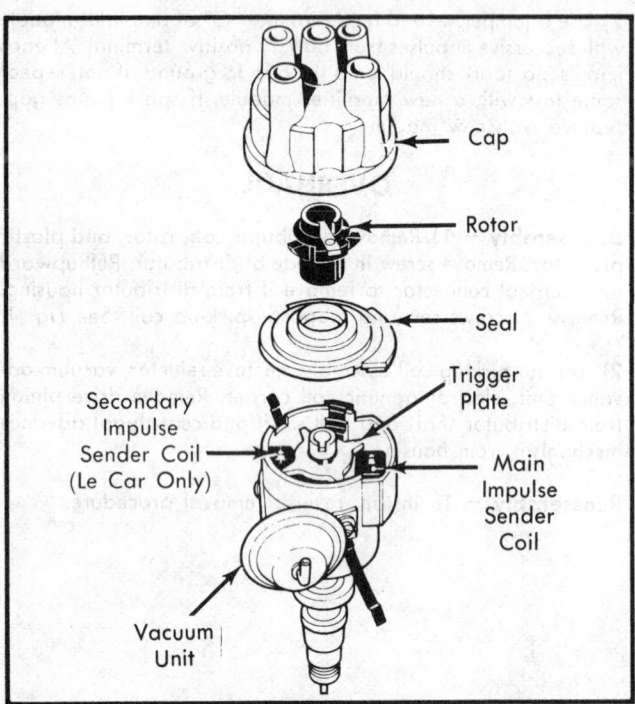

**Fig. 1   Exploded View of Le Car Distributor
(18i Has Main Impulse Sender Coil Only)**

The ignition coil and electronic control unit are mounted to a common support that provides both good grounding and cool-

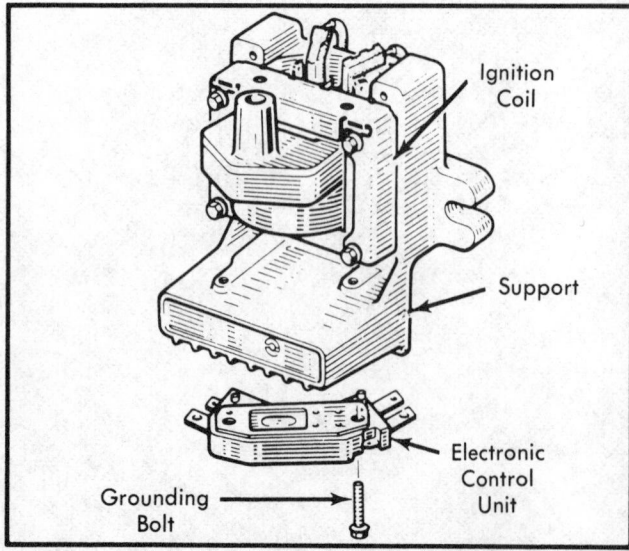

**Fig. 2   Ignition Coil and Electronic
Control Unit Assembly**

ing of the electronic control unit. See Fig. 2. Silicone grease, which comes with each electronic control unit, is applied between the unit and support to provide improved heat transfer. Since both units are grounded through the common support base, all mounting bolts should be snug.

The ignition coil is encased in epoxy resin instead of oil. The electronic control unit receives, amplifies and sends electronic signals to provide proper spark timing.

OPERATION

The distributor contains a trigger plate that turns with the distributor shaft. See Fig. 3. The impulse sender coil or coils are located inside the distributor housing. The main coil is located near the vacuum diaphragm, and on dual pick-up models, a secondary coil is located directly opposite (offset 3° for proper ignition timing during warm-up).

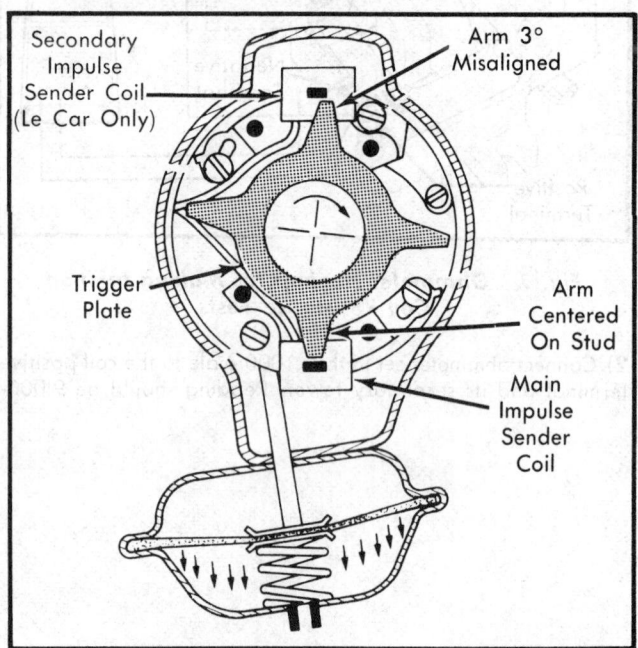

**Fig. 3   Le Car Internal Distributor Components
(18i Has Main Impulse Sender Coil Only)**

On dual pick-up models, when oil temperature is below 59° F (15° C), the secondary impulse sender operates to provide 3° additional advance (6° total). When oil temperature reaches 59° F (15° C), a relay switches operation to the main impulse sender. Ignition timing returns from 6° to 3° BTDC. The 2 impulse senders never operate at the same time.

As the rotating trigger plate approaches and passes the impulse sender coil, a magnetic field builds and collapses, sending a signal to the electronic control unit. This signal opens and closes a transistor in the electronic control unit, turning the primary circuit in the ignition coil on and off.

When the primary coil circuit is turned off, a high voltage surge occurs in the coil secondary circuit, providing spark to the spark plugs through the distributor rotor, cap and secondary wires.

The electronic control unit has 4 terminals. See Fig. 4. Terminals "W" and "G" are connected to the distributor impulse sender coils, terminal "G" through a relay switch that activates either the main or secondary impulse sender coil. Terminal "B" is connected to the coil positive terminal and terminal

DUCELLIER ELECTRONIC IGNITION SYSTEM – RENAULT (Cont.)

"C" to the coil negative terminal. The unit is grounded through one of its mounting bolts to the support shared with the ignition coil.

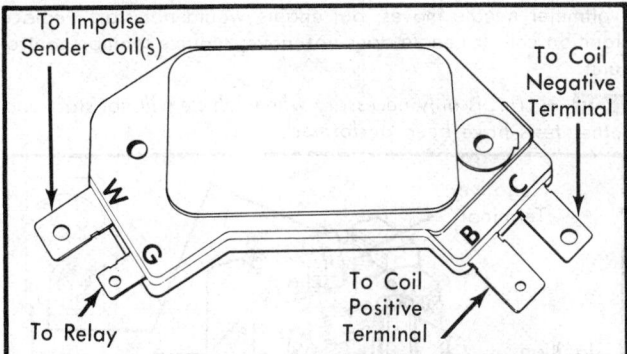

Fig. 4   Electronic Control Unit Terminals

SPECIFICATIONS

Centrifugal & Vacuum Advance – See Specifications Tables in this section.

ADJUSTMENTS

Trigger Plate-to-Impulse Sender Coil Air Gap – Loosen screws "A" and "B". See Fig. 5. Place an .018" (.45 mm) feeler gauge between pick-up coil stud and arm of the trigger plate. See Fig. 6. Move slotted coil base on screw "B" until stud on top of coil touches feeler gauge. Tighten screws "A" and "B".

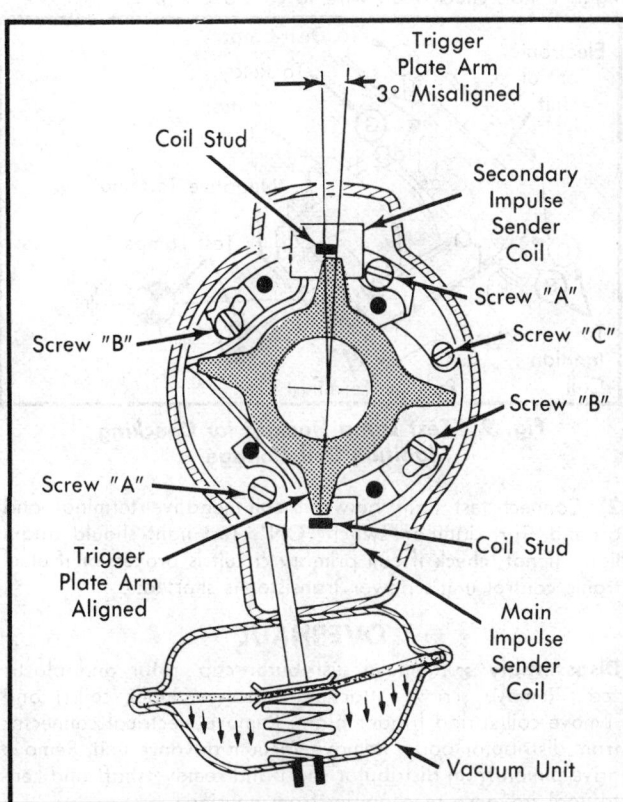

Fig. 5   Adjusting Ignition Timing by Misaligning Trigger Plate Arm 3°

Check air gap at all 4 arms of trigger plate. If gap is not within .012-.024 (.3-.6 mm) range for any arms of trigger plate and cannot be adjusted correctly, replace distributor.

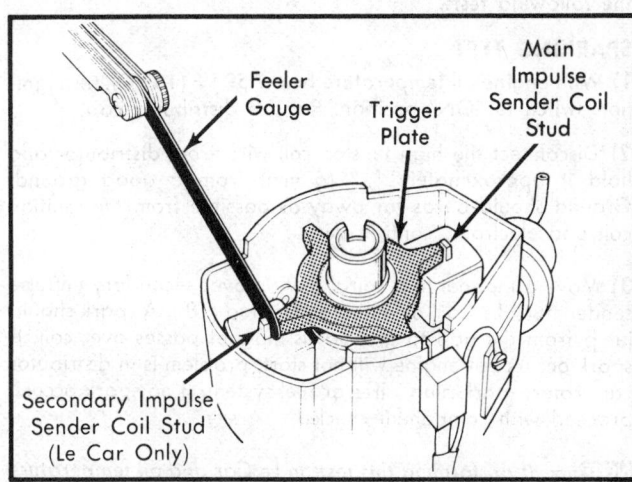

Fig. 6   Checking Distributor Air Gap With Feeler Gauge

Ignition Timing of Secondary Impulse Sender (Le Car Only) – Set trigger plate-to-impulse sender coil air gap. Loosen screw "B" (for secondary sender) and screw "C". See Fig. 5. Align trigger plate arm with main impulse sender coil so that the center of its stud aligns with edge (not center) of trigger plate arm. Tighten screws "B" and "C". This provides 3° additional advance when engine oil temperature is below 59° F (15° C).

DIAGNOSIS & TESTING

NOTE – Before testing components, be sure battery is properly charged, all wires are sound and connections are secure. Inspect distributor cap and rotor for cracks or carbon-tracking. Turn ignition "OFF" when connecting test equipment or when replacing parts.

CAUTION – Before replacing "defective" parts such as the ignition coil, distributor or electronic control unit, check that the electrical system is operative. Particularly check the oil thermoswitch on the right-hand side of the oil pan and the relay which it controls. Also check all wiring and connectors.

ENGINE STARTS WHEN COLD BUT STALLS WHEN IT WARMS UP

NOTE – This applies to Le Car models only.

If engine starts normally and runs well, but stalls when oil temperature reaches 59° F (15° C), the main impulse sender coil is defective. Both impulse coils must be replaced.

IGNITION DEFECT OCCURS DURING ENGINE OPERATION

If ignition defect occurs during normal engine operation, check condition of spark plug wires, coil high tension wire and spark plugs. If engine surges or misfires due to ignition malfunction, and wires and spark plugs are not defective, replace electronic control unit.

NOTE – Never disconnect spark plug wires when engine is running. This may cause high voltage to seek ground through distributor body, causing trigger plate deterioration.

DUCELLIER ELECTRONIC IGNITION SYSTEM — RENAULT (Cont.)

TESTING SYSTEM WHEN ENGINE WILL NOT START

In cold start situations where the engine will not start, perform the following tests.

SPARKING TEST

1) With engine oil temperature below 59° F (15° C), turn ignition switch to "ON" position. Remove distributor cap.

2) Disconnect the high tension coil wire from distributor and hold it approximately ¼" (6 mm) from a good ground. Ground should be as far away as possible from the ignition coil and electronic control unit.

3) Move a magnet in a spiral motion over secondary impulse sender stud (Le Car) or main sender stud (18i). A spark should jump from the gap to ground as magnet passes over coil. If spark occurs but engine will not start, problem is in distributor cap, rotor, spark plug wires or fuel system. If no spark occurs, proceed with component checks.

NOTE — *If performing this test on Le Car and oil temperature is above 59° F (15° C), pass magnet over main impulse sender instead of secondary sender.*

IMPULSE SENDER COIL CHECK

NOTE — *Do not use a test light to check distributor impulse sender coil. High voltage may damage the coil.*

1) Be sure impulse sender coil feed wires have not been cut. Disconnect the 5-wire relay connector and the 3-wire distributor connector (2 black wires, 1 gray). See *Fig. 7.*

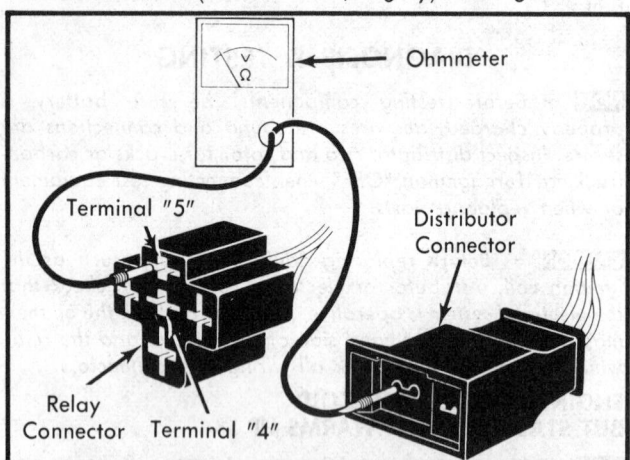

Fig. 7   Ohmmeter Hookup for Checking Impulse Sender Coils

2) Connect lead of an ohmmeter to terminal 5 of the 5-wire relay harness connector. Connect the other ohmmeter lead to the double black wire terminal of distributor connector. The needle should move. If not, replace impulse sender coil or coils.

3) To check impulse sender coil(s) for shorts, connect ohmmeter lead to terminal 5 with second ohmmeter lead connected to distributor body. The needle should not move. If it does, replace impulse sender coil(s).

IGNITION COIL AND ELECTRONIC CONTROL UNIT CHECK

1) Turn the ignition switch to the "ON" position. Connect positive voltmeter lead to ignition coil positive terminal. Con-

nect remaining lead to ignition coil negative terminal. See *Fig. 8.*

2) Quickly move a magnet back and forth over secondary impulse sender coil (Le Car) or main impulse sender coil (18i). If voltmeter needle moves, but engine would not start, replace ignition coil. If needle does not move, replace ignition control unit.

NOTE — *This is only necessary when vehicle will not start and other tests have been performed.*

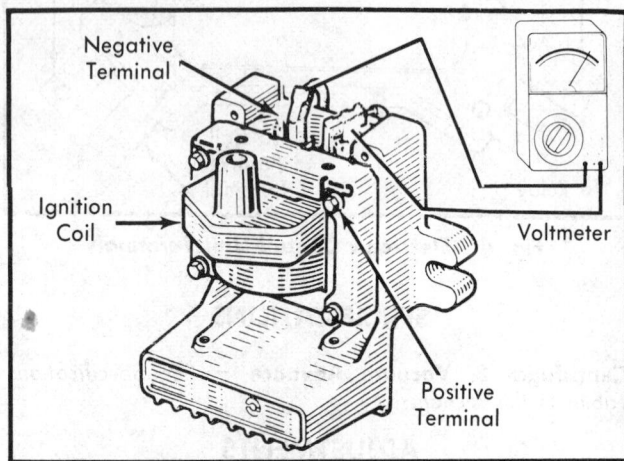

Fig. 8   Voltmeter Hookup for Checking Ignition Coil & Electronic Control Unit

ELECTRICAL CIRCUIT TEST

1) Connect a 12-volt test light between the coil positive terminal and ground. Turn ignition switch "ON". Test light should light. If not, check feed wire to coil. See *Fig. 9.*

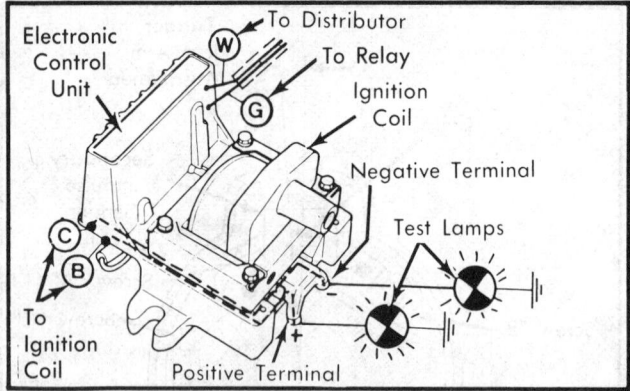

Fig. 9   Test Lamp Hookup for Checking Ignition Coil Voltage

2) Connect test light between coil negative terminal and ground. Turn ignition switch "ON". Test light should again light. If not, check if coil primary circuit is broken or if electronic control unit's power transistor is shorted.

OVERHAUL

Disassembly — Remove distributor cap, rotor and plastic seal. Remove screws attaching impulse sender coil(s) and remove coil(s) and trigger plate. Remove electrical connector from distributor body. Remove vacuum advance unit. Remove drive pinion from distributor shaft and remove shaft and centrifugal advance mechanism from housing.

Reassembly — Reverse disassembly procedure, adjusting air gap. Adjust ignition timing at secondary coil (if equipped).

Distributors & Ignition Systems

HITACHI ELECTRONIC IGNITION SYSTEMS — DATSUN

200SX	510
210	810
280ZX (Exc. Turbo)	Pickup
310	

DESCRIPTION

NOTE — *Datsun 280ZX Turbo models use a computer-controlled ignition system. See DATSUN ELECTRONIC CONCENTRATED ENGINE CONTROL in this section.*

Two different systems are used on Datsun models, however the principle of operation on both systems is the same. Both systems use an electronic distributor, an IC ignition unit, ignition coil(s), battery and wiring harness. *See Figs. 1 through 4.*

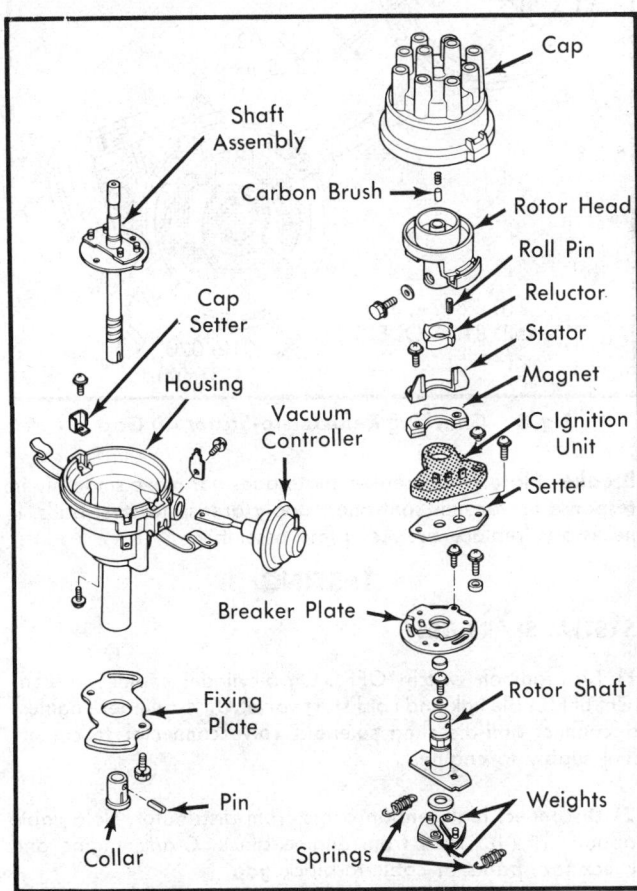

Fig. 1   Dissassembled View of Hitachi Distributor (200SX, 510 and Pickup Models)

The ignition system for 210, 280ZX, 310 and 810 models uses a single coil with a single spark plug for each cylinder. The 200SX, 510 and Pickup models have 4-cylinder engines with 8 spark plugs. These models use a special distributor cap with 8 spark plug wire outlet terminals and 2 coil wire inlet terminals. These models also use 2 ignition coils, one for the spark plugs on the exhaust side of the engine and one for the spark plugs on the intake side.

The 200SX, 510 and Pickup models also differ in that the IC ignition unit is located inside the distributor, stator and magnet assembly has a different shape, IC ignition unit has a 3-pin connector rather than a 2-pin conector, and IC ignition unit contains only 4 internal circuits and 2 transistors, instead of 5 circuits found on other models.

All models except 200SX, 510 and Pickups have IC ignition unit mounted externally on distributor housing. Unit is connected with 2 wires to pick-up coil located inside distributor. These models also have a fusible link between battery and ignition switch. The 280ZX and 810 models, which have 6-cylinder engines, feature reluctors and stators with 6 teeth, while other models have 4-cylinder engines with 4-tooth reluctors and stators.

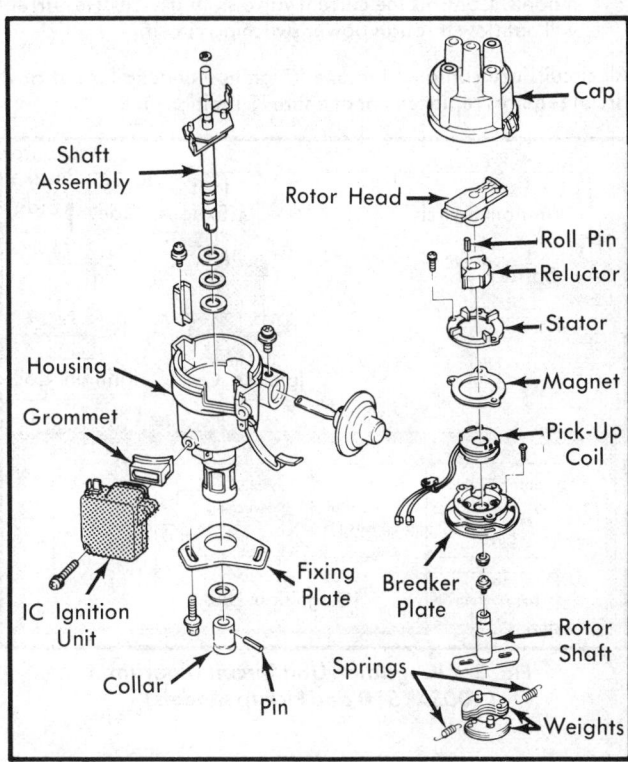

Fig. 2   Disasembled View of Hitachi Distributor on All Models Except 200SX, 510 and Pickups

OPERATION

Regardless of model, all distributors are equipped with a reluctor and stator, although the shapes may differ. The reluctor, which is mounted on the rotor shaft assembly, turns with the distributor shaft inside the stator.

As each reluctor tooth approaches and then passes the stator teeth, the magnetic field changes creating an electrical signal in the pick-up coil. (The pick-up coil is combined with the IC ignition unit on 200SX, 510 and Pickup models.) This signal is received and processed by the IC ignition unit. The IC ignition unit then turns on or cuts off current flow to the ignition coil primary circuit. When current to the primary is turned off, a high voltage surge is created in the secondary circuit which fires the spark plug. Ignition timing is controlled by the relationship of the reluctor to the stator.

The IC ignition unit contains 5 circuits on most models (4 circuits and 2 transistors on 200SX, 510 and Pickup models). These circuits perform the following functions.

- Spark Timing Signal Monitoring Circuit — Monitors and amplifies signal from distributor pick-up coil.

HITACHI ELECTRONIC IGNITION SYSTEMS — DATSUN (Cont.)

- Lock-Preventing Circuit — Cuts off ignition coil primary current when ignition switch is "ON" and engine is not running.
- Duty Control Circuit — Controls the ratio of ignition coil primary current on-off time (equivalent to dwell angle).
- Power Switching Circuit — Makes or breaks the primary circuit current of ignition coil.
- Current Limiting Circuit — Not on 200SX, 510 or Pickup models. Controls the current valve so that excessive current will not flow through power switching circuit.

All circuits are contained in one IC ignition unit. Failure of any circuit requires replacement of entire IC ignition unit.

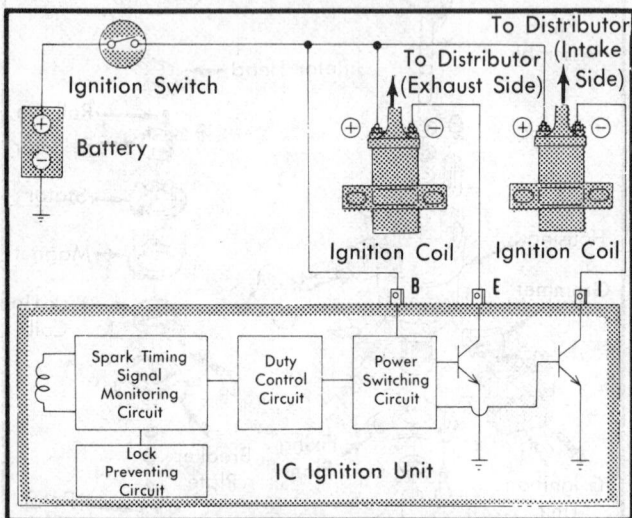

Fig. 3   IC Ignition Unit Circuit Diagram (200SX, 510 and Pickup Models)

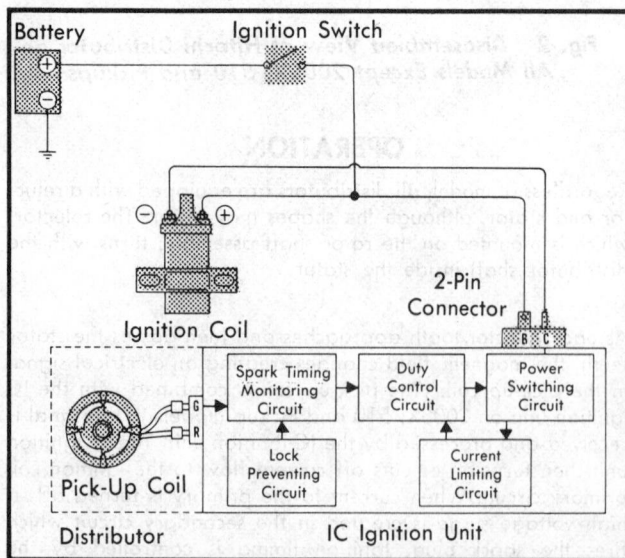

Fig. 4   IC Ignition Unit Circuit Diagram (All Models Except 200SX, 510 and Pickup)

SPECIFICATIONS

Centrifugal & Vacuum Advance — See Specifications Tables in this section.

ADJUSTMENTS

Air Gap — When installing reluctor and stator or checking air gap, loosen screws and center stator around reluctor so that there is equal air gap between each set of reluctor teeth and matching stator teeth. See Fig. 5. Then tighten screws securing stator. Standard air gap is .012-.020" (.3-.5 mm).

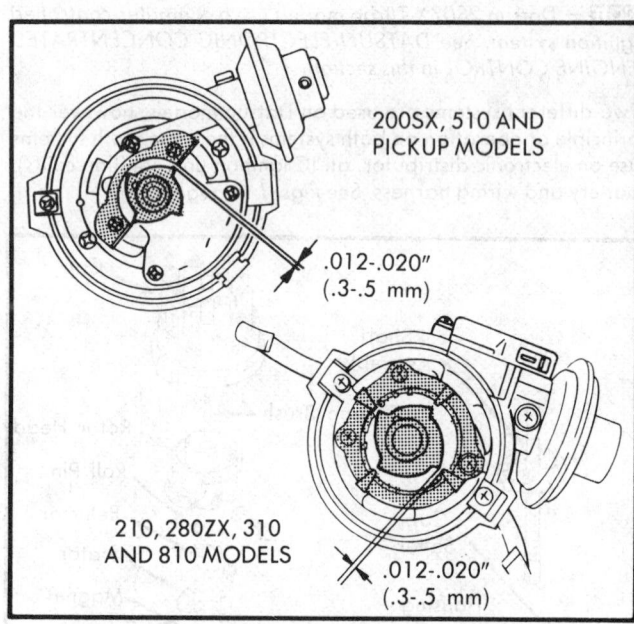

Fig. 5   Checking Reluctor-to-Stator Air Gap

Breaker Plate — If breaker plate does not move smoothly in response to vacuum controller, apply grease to steel balls. If necessary, replace breaker plate assembly.

TESTING

SYSTEM SPARK TEST

1) Turn ignition switch "OFF". On 6-cylinder engines, disconnect EFI fusible link and cold start valve. On 4-cylinder engines, disconnect anti-dieseling solenoid valve connector to cut off fuel supply to engine.

2) Disconnect high tension cable from distributor. Hold cable about ¼" (4-5 mm) from engine block. Crank engine and check for sparks at cable-to-block gap.

3) If sparks occur, the IC ignition system is OK and no further ignition checks are required. If no sparks occur, proceed with tests that follow.

BATTERY VOLTAGE CHECK

1) Turn ignition switch to "OFF" position. Connect positive lead of voltmeter to battery positive terminal. Connect negative lead to battery negative terminal. Read and record battery voltage. If below 11.5 volts, battery charging or starting system is faulty.

2) With ignition switch still "OFF" and voltmeter still hooked to battery, remove coil wire from distributor and connect it to a good ground. Crank engine and record cranking voltage registered on voltmeter. If voltage reading is less than 9.6 volts, battery charging or starting system is faulty.

HITACHI ELECTRONIC IGNITION SYSTEMS — DATSUN (Cont.)

SECONDARY WIRING CHECK

Connect an ohmmeter, in turn, to each spark plug wire. Attach one lead to terminal inside distributor cap and other lead to other end of wire. Resistance reading should be less than 30,-000 ohms. If resistance is higher, replace high tension cables and/or distributor cap.

IGNITION COIL RESISTANCE CHECK

Primary Resistance — **1)** Turn ignition switch "OFF". Remove coil wires to isolate coil from system. See Fig. 6. Set ohmmeter to x1 range. Connect ohmmeter leads to the 2 primary terminals of coil. 200SX, 510 and Pickup models should show a resistance reading of 1.04-1.27 ohms. All other models should read 0.84-1.02 ohms.

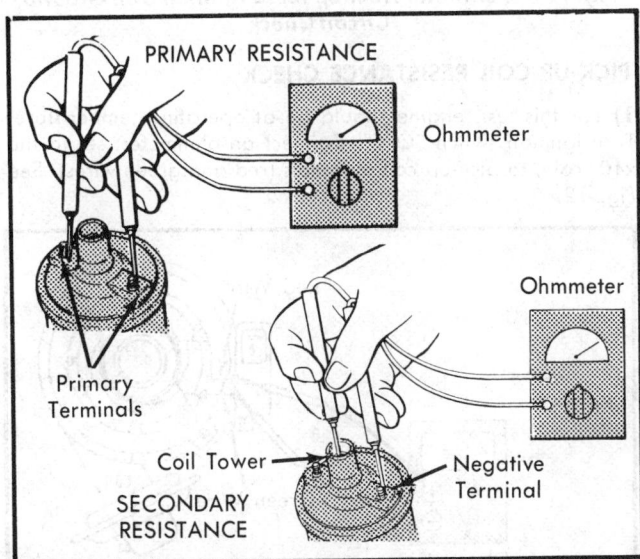

Fig. 6   Ohmmeter Hookup for Coil Resistance Checks

2) If resistance reading is OK, but engine will not start, check ignition switch and wiring from switch to coil and IC ignition unit. If reading is not within specifications, replace ignition coil.

Secondary Resistance — With ignition switch "OFF", set an ohmmeter to the x1000 range. Connect one lead to coil negative terminal and the other lead to coil tower. See Fig. 6. Resistance for 200SX, 510 and Pickup models should be 7,300-11,000 ohms. All other models should be 8,200-12,400 ohms. If not, replace ignition coil.

POWER SUPPLY CIRCUIT CHECK

200SX, 510 and Pickup — Connect a voltmeter positive lead to connector removed from "B" terminal of IC ignition inside distributor. See Fig. 7. Connect voltmeter negative lead to side of distributor. Turn ignition switch "ON". If reading is less than 11.5 volts, check wiring from ignition switch to IC ignition unit.

All Other Models — **1)** Connect voltmeter positive lead to "B" terminal (black and white wire) of IC ignition unit connector. See Fig. 8. Connect negative lead to side of distributor. Turn ignition switch "ON". If below 11.5 volts, check wiring from ignition switch to IC ignition unit.

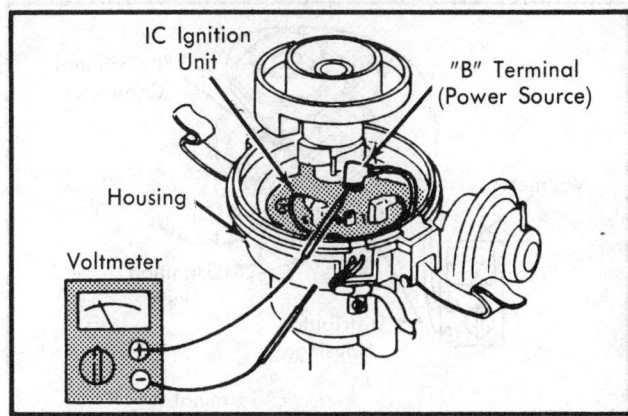

Fig. 7   Voltmeter Hookup for Power Supply Check (200SX, 510 and Pickup Models)

2) To check power supply while cranking engine, remove high tension wire from distributor and ground it. Connect voltmeter positive lead to "B" terminal (black and white wire) of IC ignition unit connector. Connect negative lead to side of distributor. Turn ignition switch to "START" position. Note voltmeter reading.

3) If voltage reading is more than 1 volt below battery CRANKING voltage and/or is below 8.6 volts, check ignition switch and wiring from switch to IC ignition unit.

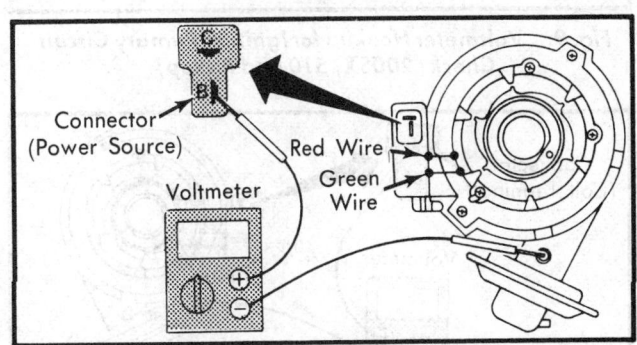

Fig. 8   Voltmeter Hookup for Power Supply Check (All Models Except 200SX, 510 and Pickup)

IGNITION PRIMARY CIRCUIT CHECK

200SX, 510 and Pickup — **1)** Attach a voltmeter negative lead to side of distributor. Connect the voltmeter positive lead to "I" terminal of IC ignition unit connector then to the "E" terminal of IC ignition unit connector. See Fig. 9.

2) Turn ignition switch "ON" after lead has been attached to each terminal. Voltage readings on both terminals should be 11.5-12.5 volts. If reading is below specifications, recheck coil primary resistance. If voltage is correct, proceed to IC Ignition Unit Ground Circuit Check.

All Other Models — **1)** Connect voltmeter positive lead to "C" terminal (blue wire) of IC ignition unit connector. See Fig. 10. Attach negative lead to side of distributor. Turn ignition switch "ON".

HITACHI ELECTRONIC IGNITION SYSTEMS — DATSUN (Cont.)

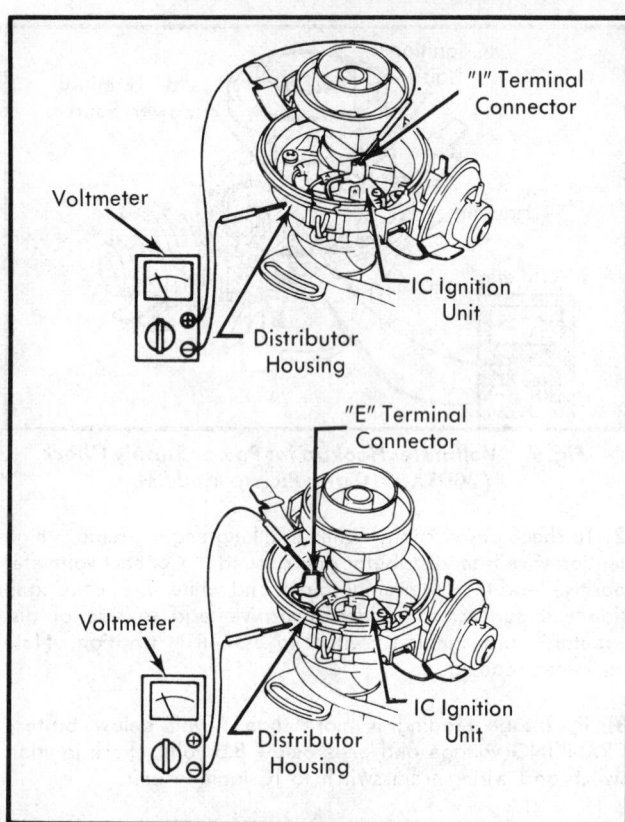

Fig. 9 Voltmeter Hookup for Ignition Primary Circuit Check (200SX, 510 and Pickup)

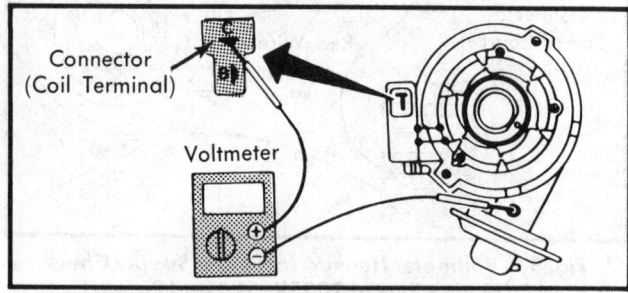

Fig. 10 Voltmeter Hookup for Ignition Primary Circuit Check (All Models Except 200SX, 510 and Pickup)

2) If voltage is 11.5-12.5 volts, proceed to IC Unit Ground Circuit Test. If voltage reading is below 11.5 volts, check Coil Primary Resistance, if not previously done.

IC IGNITION UNIT GROUND CIRCUIT CHECK

1) Connect voltmeter negative lead to battery negative terminal. See Fig. 11. Connect positive lead to exterior of vacuum controller. Pull high tension wire from distributor cap and ground it. Turn ignition switch to "START" position and observe voltmeter reading while cranking engine.

2) If voltage reads 0.5 volts or less, proceed to Pick-Up Coil Resistance Check. If voltage is more than 0.5 volts, check distributor ground wiring from chassis to battery, including battery connections.

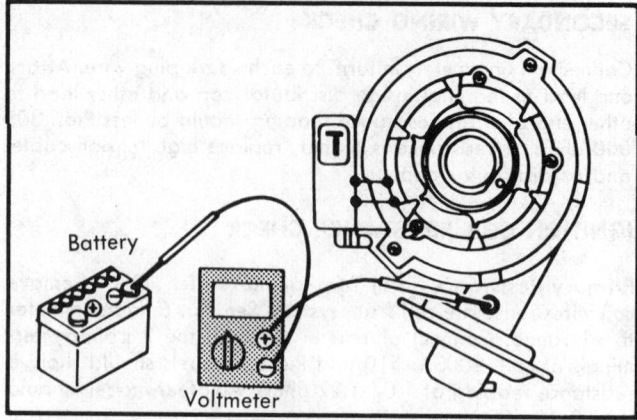

Fig. 11 Voltmeter Hookup for IC Ignition Unit Ground Circuit Check

PICK-UP COIL RESISTANCE CHECK

1) For this test, engine should be at operating temperature. Turn ignition switch "OFF". Connect an ohmmeter, set to the x10 scale, to pick-up coil terminals (red and green wires). See Fig. 12.

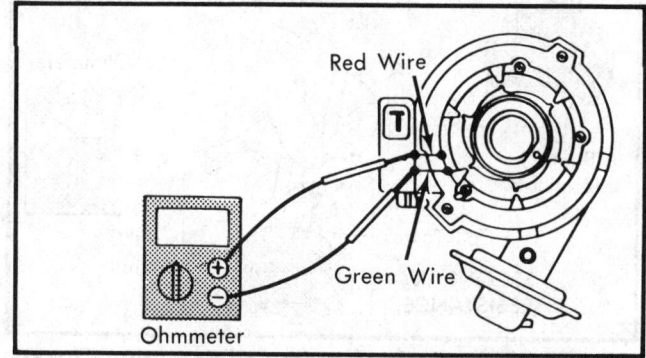

Fig. 12 Ohmmeter Hookup for Pick-Up Coil Resistance Check

2) If ohmmeter reading is approximately 400 ohms, proceed to Pick-Up Coil Output Check. If ohmmeter reading varies widely from 400 ohms, check pick-up coil and wires leading to it.

PICK-UP COIL OUTPUT CHECK

1) Engine should be at operating temperature. Connect a voltmeter, set to the low scale (0-5 volt), with positive lead connected to pick-up coil terminal with red wire. See Fig. 13. Attach negative lead to side of distributor.

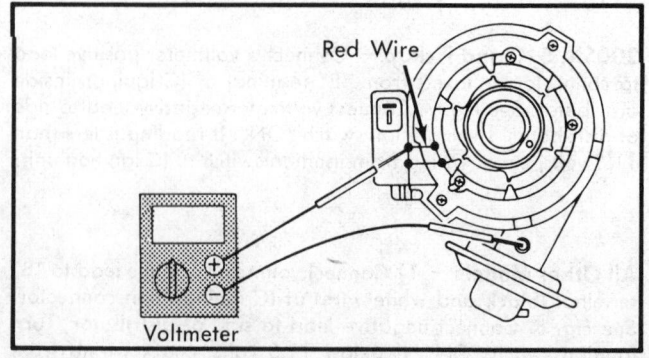

Fig. 13 Voltmeter Hookup for Pick-Up Coil Output Check

HITACHI ELECTRONIC IGNITION SYSTEMS – DATSUN (Cont.)

2) Turn ignition switch to "START" position and check for movement of voltmeter needle while cranking engine. If needle wavers and the no spark condition still exists, replace IC ignition unit.

3) If needle is steady, check physical condition of pick-up coil and reluctor. Check wiring and connector between pick-up coil and IC ignition unit.

OVERHAUL

Disassembly (200SX, 510 and Pickup) – **1)** Remove distributor cap and rotor head. Pry reluctor from rotor shaft assembly. Use care not to damage teeth.

2) Remove IC ignition unit and unit setter. Remove stator and magnet. Remove vacuum controller and breaker plate. Mark housing and fixing plate. Remove fixing plate and collar. Remove rotor shaft and drive shaft. Mark rotor shaft and drive shaft. Remove packing from top of rotor shaft and remove rotor shaft from drive shaft.

3) Mark one governor spring and its bracket and one weight and its pivot pin. Remove springs and weights and apply grease to weights.

Disassembly (All Other Models) – **1)** Remove distributor cap and rotor head. Remove IC ignition unit by disconnecting harness connector, removing screws and disconnecting pick-up coil wires.

2) Remove stator and magnet. Remove vacuum controller and carefully pry reluctor from shaft. Remove roll pin, pick-up coil assembly and breaker plate assembly. Remove pin and pinion gear. Remove rotor shaft and drive shaft assembly.

3) Mark rotor and drive shafts for later assembly. Remove packing and rotor shaft set screw. Mark one of governor springs and its bracket; also one weight and its pivot pin. Remove weights and springs.

Reassembly (All Models) – **1)** To assemble, reverse disassembly procedure. Clean surfaces of IC ignition unit and distributor before assembling. Be sure pick-up coil leads (if equipped) are securely attached to IC ignition unit terminals. See Fig. 14.

2) Align match marks so parts are assembled in original positions. Be sure reluctor is centered in stator, before tightening stator screws. Drive in roll pin with its slit toward outer end of shaft. Grease top of rotor shaft. Check governor operation before installing distributor.

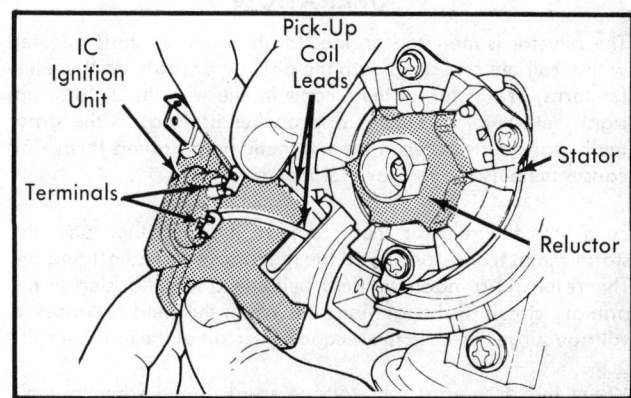

Fig. 14   Connecting Pick-Up Coil Terminals (All Models Except 200SX, 510 and Pickup)

Distributors & Ignition Systems

HITACHI ELECTRONIC IGNITION SYSTEMS — HONDA

Accord
Civic
Prelude

DESCRIPTION

Honda electronic distributors consist of the following: The distributor housing, rotor and the distributor cap. The reluctor, stator, magnets, pulse generator/ignitor and breaker plate assemblies are all located inside the distributor housing. All models use a centrifugal advance system. All Civic models and Accord/Prelude models, with manual transmissions, use a vacuum advance system. Accord/Prelude models, equipped with automatic transmissions, use a vacuum advance/retard system.

OPERATION

The reluctor is mounted on the distributor rotor shaft, secured with a roll pin and turns with the distributor shaft. As the reluctor turns, its 4 external teeth come in line with the 2 stator upright teeth. As the reluctor approaches and passes the stator teeth, variations occur in the magnetic field around them. This causes the pulse generator to signal the ignitor.

Each time the reluctor teeth come in line and then pass the stator teeth, transistors inside the ignitor are turned off and on. This results in a magnetic field building and collapsing in the primary circuit of the ignition coil. When this field collapses, a voltage surge occurs in the secondary circuit of the ignition coil.

When this occurs, a high voltage spark is fed from the coil, through the distributor rotor and cap to the secondary wiring and spark plugs.

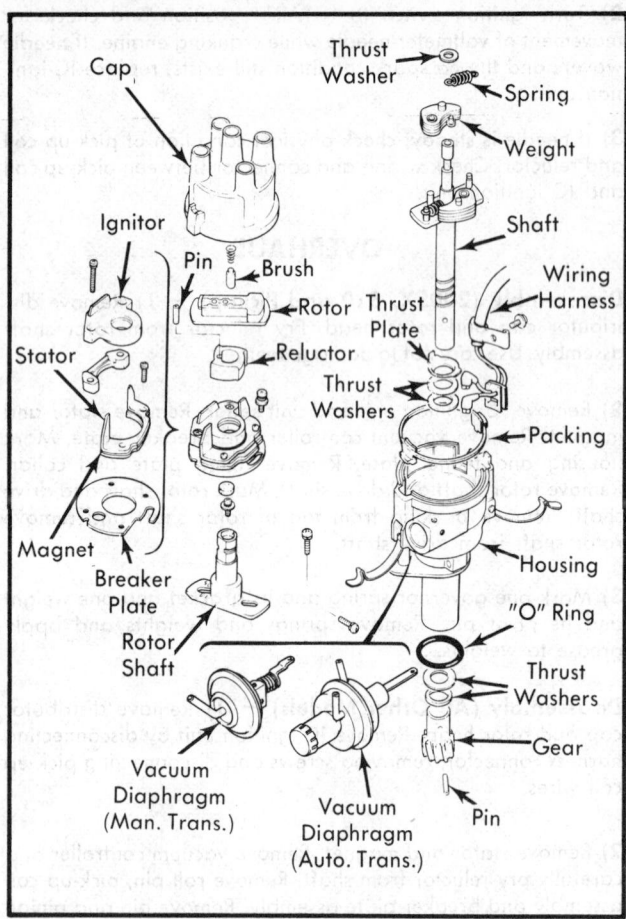

Fig. 2 Disassembled View of Hitachi Distributor (Accord and Prelude Models)

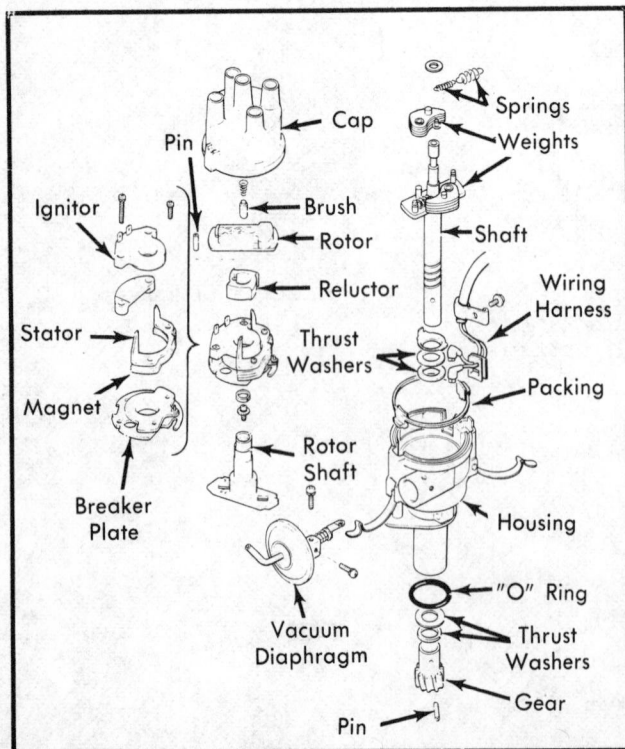

Fig. 1 Disassembled View of Hitachi Distributor (Civic Models)

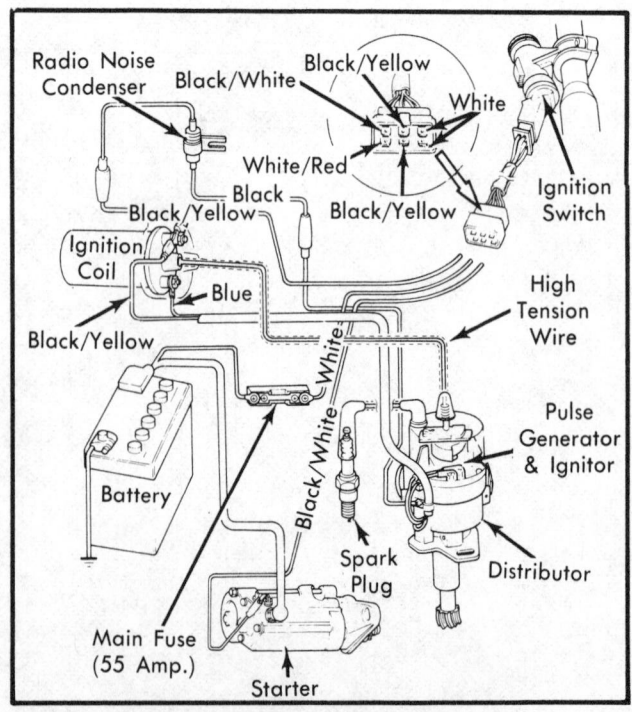

Fig. 3 Schematic of Ignition System (Accord and Prelude Models)

HITACHI ELECTRONIC IGNITION SYSTEMS – HONDA (Cont.)

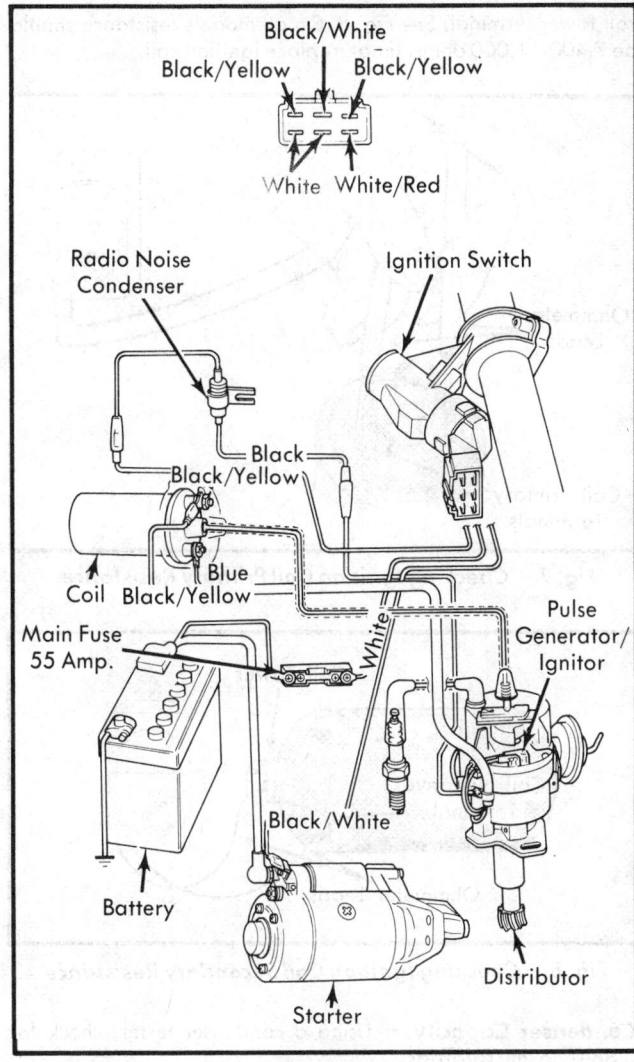

Fig. 4 Schematic of Ignition System (Civic Models)

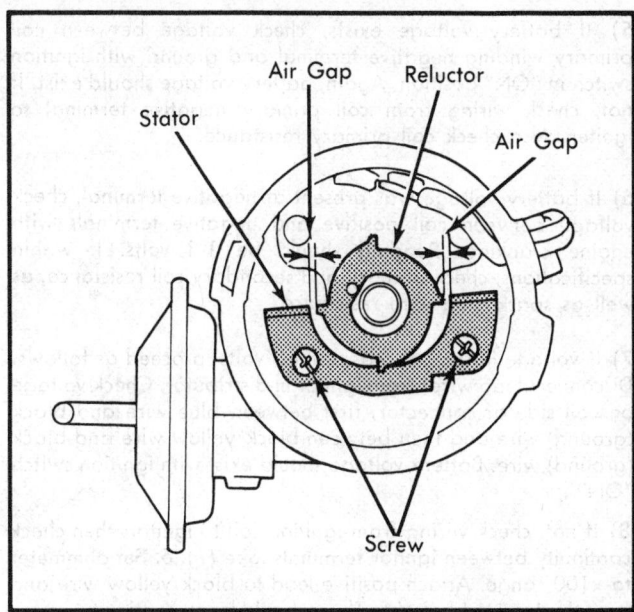

Fig. 5 Adjusting Reluctor-To-Stator Air Gap

Rotor-to-Distributor Cap Terminal — Check occasionally for rough or pitted rotor or cap terminals. Scrape or file off carbon deposits. Smooth rotor terminal with an oil stone or No. 600 sandpaper if roughness exists.

Centrifugal Advance — Disconnect vacuum advance hoses from distributor. Connect timing light and start engine. Increase engine speed. Timing mark (T) should appear to move past pointer toward firewall, indicating an increase in ignition advance. If not, check centrifugal advance mechanism for sticking or binding.

Vacuum Advance — Remove distributor cap. Disconnect vacuum hoses from distributor vacuum advance or advance/retard diaphragm. Connect vacuum pump to diaphragm. Gradually draw a vacuum while watching breaker plate movement. Check for smooth operation without binding. If pump indicates a loss of vacuum, replace diaphragm unit. Turn breaker plate right and left to check for free movement.

SPECIFICATIONS

Centrifugal & Vacuum Advance/Retard — *See Specifications Pages in this section.*

ADJUSTMENT

CAUTION — *To avoid damaging the ignition system, never reverse battery polarity. Do not let pulse generator wires touch ignition wires. Do not do anything that would produce abnormal pulses. Always connect pulse type tachometers to negative terminal of ignition coil. Make sure all wires and cables are connected properly.*

Cam Angle — Cam angle (dwell) is automatically set and manual adjustment is not required.

Reluctor-To-Stator Air Gap — Align 2 teeth of reluctor with 2 teeth of stator and check air gap. Check air gap at all teeth as reluctor is rotated. *See Fig. 5.* There should be equal air gap at all 4 teeth. If necessary to adjust, loosen 2 screws securing stator and reposition stator to provide equal air gaps. Tighten 2 screws.

TESTING

BASIC SYSTEM TEST

1) If engine will not start and starter will not crank engine, check battery, main fuse and electrical wiring. Check starter circuit wiring and ignition switch. If engine will not start, but starter cranks engine, hold coil wire ¼" from coil tower while cranking engine.

2) If there is spark from coil, then hold spark plug wire terminal ¼" from spark plug while cranking engine.

3) If there is no spark at the plug, check spark plug wire condition, inspect distributor cap and rotor, and as a last resort, replace ignitor in distributor. If spark exists at the plug, check fuel system, spark plugs, ignition timing or valve timing.

4) If there was no spark at the coil in step **1)**, check voltage between coil primary winding positive terminal and ground with ignition switch in "ON" position. Battery voltage should be found. If not, check wiring from ignition switch to ignition coil.

HITACHI ELECTRONIC IGNITION SYSTEMS — HONDA (Cont.)

5) If battery voltage exists, check voltage between coil primary winding negative terminal and ground with ignition switch in "ON" position. Again, battery voltage should exist. If not, check wiring from coil primary negative terminal to igniter. Also check coil primary resistance.

6) If battery voltage was present at negative terminal, check voltage between coil positive and negative terminals with engine cranking. Reading should be 1-3 volts. If within specifications, check primary and secondary coil resistance, as well as spark plug wire resistance.

7) If voltage in step **6)** was not 1-3 volts, proceed as follows: Disconnect lead wires from ignitor in distributor. Check voltage on coil side of connector, first between blue wire and black (ground) wire and then between black/yellow wire and black (ground) wire. Battery voltage should exist with ignition switch "ON".

8) If not, check wiring from ignition coil to ignitor, then check continuity between ignitor terminals. See Fig. 6. Set ohmmeter to x100 range. Attach positive lead to black/yellow wire and negative lead to blue wire. There should be no continuity.

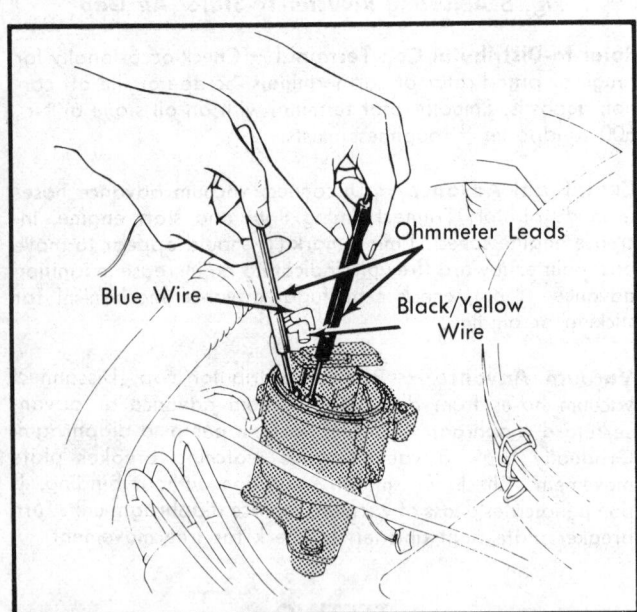

Fig. 6 Checking Continuity at Ignitor Terminals

9) Then, reverse ohmmeter leads (positive lead to blue wire, negative lead to black/yellow wire). There should now be continuity. If incorrect results are obtained, replace ignitor and repeat test.

COMPONENT TESTS

Ignition Coil Primary Resistance — Turn ignition switch "OFF" and remove positive and negative wires from ignition coil terminals. Connect an ohmmeter set in the x1 range with one probe touching each primary terminal. See Fig. 7. On Accord and Prelude models, reading should be 1.06-1.24 ohms. On Civic models, reading should be 1.0-1.3 ohms. If reading is not to specifications, replace ignition coil.

Ignition Coil Secondary Resistance — Turn ignition switch "OFF". Set ohmmeter in x1000 range. Connect ohmmeter probes to ignition coil in negative terminal (wire removed) and

coil tower terminal. See Fig. 8. On all models resistance should be 7,400-11,000 ohms. If not, replace ignition coil.

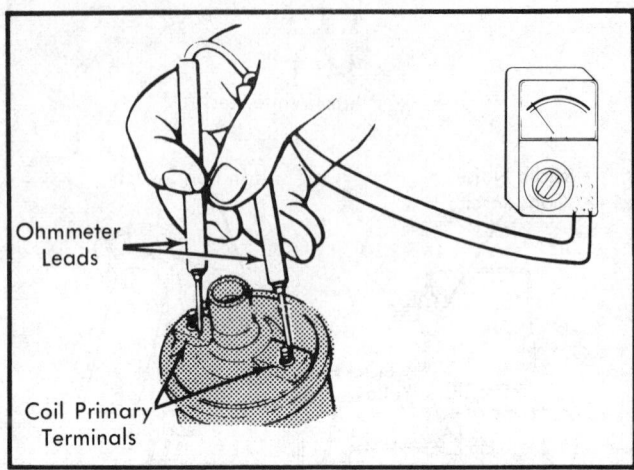

Fig. 7 Checking Ignition Coil Primary Resistance

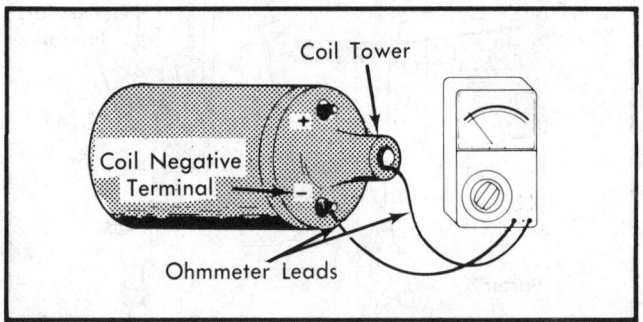

Fig. 8 Checking Ignition Coil Secondary Resistance

Condenser Capacity — Using a condenser tester, check for 0.38-0.56 microfarads.

Ignition Wire Resistance — Carefully remove wires by pulling on their rubber boots. Do not bend wire or conductor may be broken. Check for corroded condition, cleaning if necessary. Connect ohmmeter probes (set in x1000 scale) to each end of ignition wires. Resistance reading should be less than 25,000 ohms. If not, replace wires.

OVERHAUL

Disassembly — 1) Remove spark plug wires and vacuum hoses from distributor. Remove distributor cap. Remove condenser ground wire and disconnect pulse generator/ignitor wire connector from distributor. Remove hold-down bolt, lifting distributor from cylinder head.

2) Carefully pry upward on reluctor with 2 screwdrivers, cushioned with rags to prevent damage to distributor housing. See Fig. 9. Use care not to damage reluctor or stator. When installing reluctor, drive roll pin in place with its gap away from distributor shaft.

3) On Accord and Prelude models with automatic transmission, remove advance/retard diaphragm mount screw. Pull out on diaphragm unit, while pushing down on arm. On Accord and Prelude models with manual transmission and all Civic models, remove advance diaphragm mount screws. Pull diaphragm out of housing, while lifting up on end of arm.

HITACHI ELECTRONIC IGNITION SYSTEMS — HONDA (Cont.)

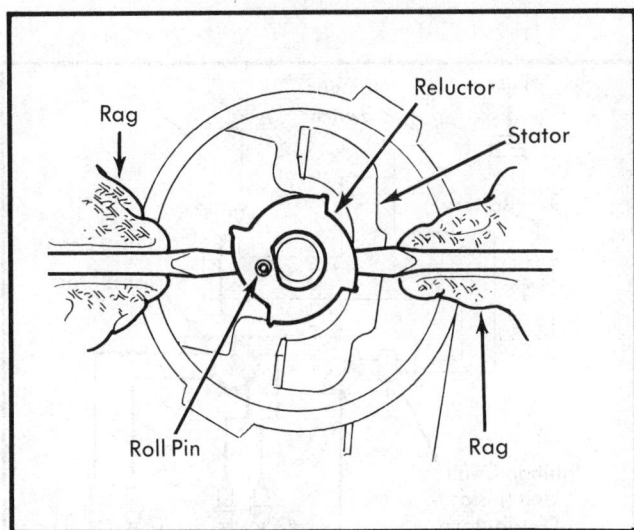

Fig. 9 Removing Reluctor from Shaft

4) On all models, drive roll pin from distributor shaft. Remove shaft and gear from housing. Inspect and replace parts as necessary.

Reassembly — 1) Install centrifugal advance weights and springs. Install thrust plate and 2 washers on shaft. Grease shaft and install in housing. Put 2 washers and gear on lower end of shaft. Line up holes in gear shoulder with hole in shaft. Drive in new roll pin.

2) Rotate gear until mark on gear shoulder lines up with mark on housing. Hold gear in line with mark and install rotor shaft on top of main shaft. Flat surface should face vacuum advance side of housing.

3) Be sure holes in rotor shaft arms fit over pins in centrifugal advance weights. Install screw with lock washer in top of shaft.

4) Align breaker plate in distributor housing. See *Fig. 10*. Check that upper plate moves freely. Be sure diaphragm arm attachment pin does not rotate past end of slot in lower plate.

5) If such condition exists, adjust range of free travel by forcibly rotating plate past its limit in opposite direction. Recheck pin position.

6) Check reluctor-to-stator air gap and rotor-to-terminal surfaces. Install diaphragm assembly. Crank engine until No. 1 piston is at TDC. Install new "O" ring on distributor housing. Line up mark on distributor gear shoulder with mark on housing. Insert distributor straight into final position. Rotor will turn itself to No. 1 firing position.

7) Install hold-down bolt and tighten temporarily. Set ignition timing and tighten hold-down bolt securely. Install distributor cap, aligning mark on cap (near clamp lug) with rotor.

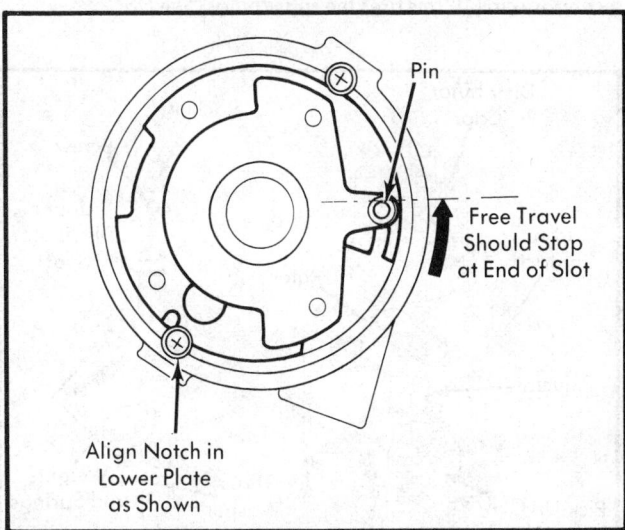

Fig. 10 Installation of Breaker Plate to Distributor Housing

HITACHI ELECTRONIC IGNITION SYSTEM – SUBARU

1800 (4-WD Models)

DESCRIPTION

The Hitachi electronic distributor consists of a housing, rotor and distributor cap. See Fig. 1. A reluctor, mounted on the shaft and governor assembly, combines with the pick-up coil to replace the conventional cam and breaker points. With the ignition switch "ON", the distributor reluctor rotates past the pick-up coil/control unit. As each tooth of the reluctor approaches and passes the pick-up coil/control unit, a signal is sent to the control unit. The control unit then turns the primary circuit in the ignition coil on and off as each tooth passes the pick-up coil. This causes a build-up and collapse of a magnetic field in the coil, resulting in a high voltage surge in the coil's secondary circuit. This fires the spark plugs. See Fig. 2.

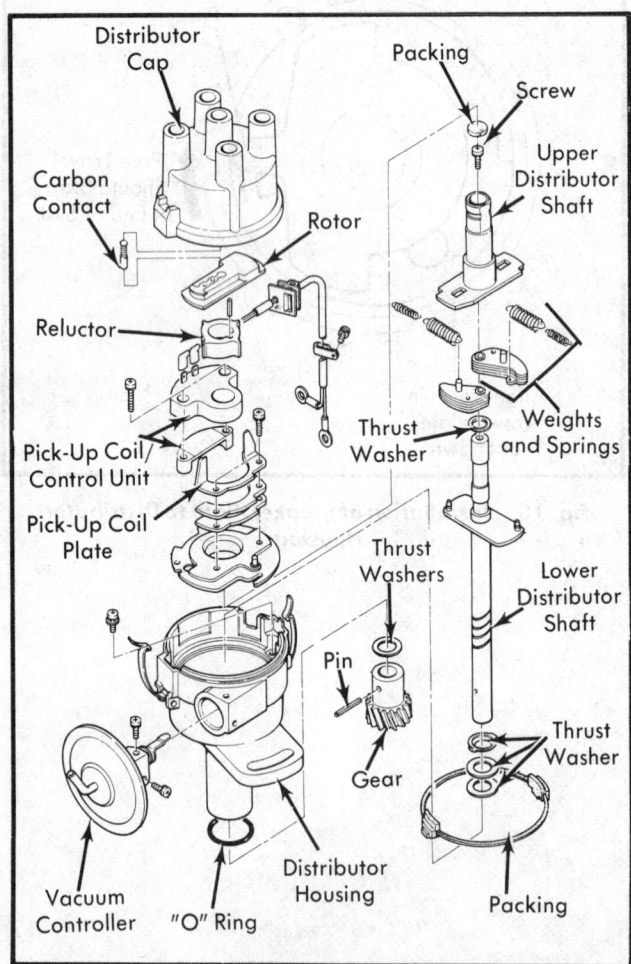

Fig. 1   Disassembled View of Hitachi Distributor for Subaru 4-Wheel Drive Vehicles

SPECIFICATIONS

Centrifugal & Vacuum Advance — See Specification Tables in this section.

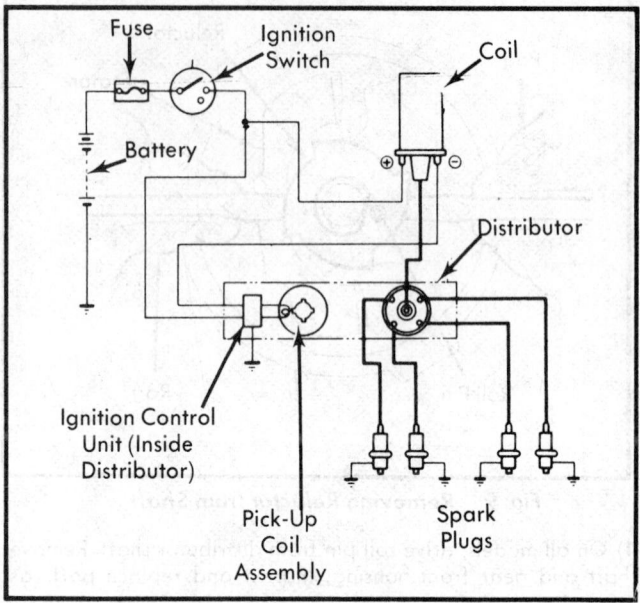

Fig. 2   Schematic of Ignition Circuit for Subaru 4-Wheel Drive Vehicles

ADJUSTMENTS

Air Gap — Align tooth of reluctor with pole piece of pick-up coil. Loosen pick-up coil hold-down screw. Insert a .016" (.4 mm) feeler gauge between tooth and pole piece. Move pick-up coil against gauge and tighten hold-down screw. Air gap should be .012-.020" (.3-.5 mm). See Fig. 3.

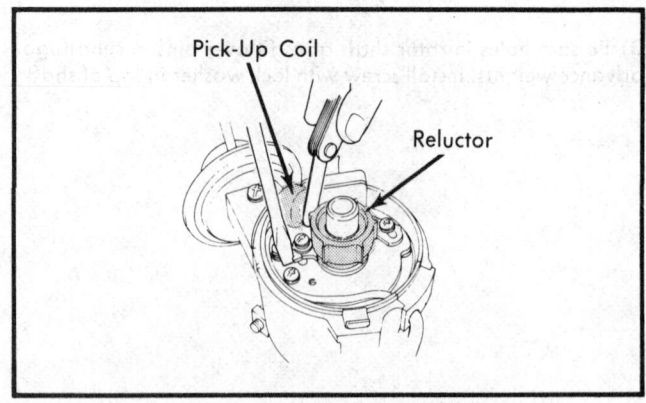

Fig. 3   Adjusting the Air Gap

TESTING

1) Turn ignition switch "ON". Connect negative lead of voltmeter to ground and positive lead to negative terminal of ignition coil. Voltage should be within 1 volt of battery voltage. If not, proceed to step 8).

2) If reading was within 1 volt of battery voltage, turn ignition switch "OFF" and disconnect 2-pole connector. See Fig. 4.

HITACHI ELECTRONIC IGNITION SYSTEM — SUBARU (Cont.)

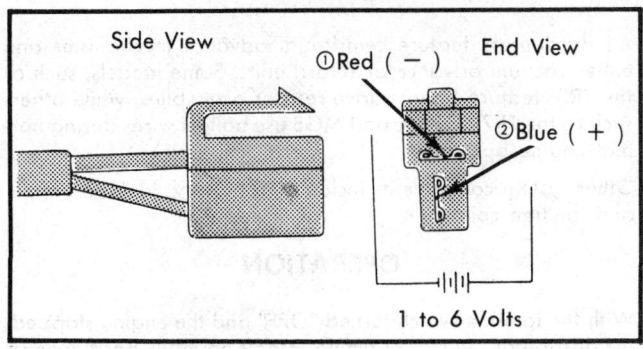

Side View   End View

①Red (−)

②Blue (+)

1 to 6 Volts

Fig. 4 Conducting Tests at 2-Pole Connector

3) Using an ohmmeter set at the x100 scale, measure resistance between the terminals in the distributor side of the 2-pole connector. Reading should be 600-850 ohms. If not, replace pick-up coil.

4) If reading was within specifications, turn ignition switch "OFF". Using an ohmmeter set to the x1 scale, measure resistance between ground and ignition control unit side. Resistance should be less than .5 ohm. If not, check ground wire at regulator mounting screw.

5) If less than .5 ohm, turn ignition switch "OFF" and check air gap between reluctor and pick-up coil. Adjust as necessary.

6) If air gap was originally within specifications, turn ignition switch "OFF" and disconnect 2-pole connector. Disconnect secondary wire from distributor and hold ¼" from engine ground. Turn ignition switch "ON" and check whether spark jumps when a small voltage (1-6 volts) is intermittently applied to terminals 1 and 2 on ignition control unit side of connector.

NOTE — Do not use battery voltage for this test or damage may occur to ignition control unit.

7) If spark occurs, there is no trouble with ignition system. If no spark occurs, replace ignition control unit.

8) If the reading in step 1) was not within 1.0 volt of battery voltage, turn ignition switch "ON" and check voltage at positive terminal of ignition coil. If not equal to battery voltage, check wiring between ignition switch and positive terminal of ignition coil. Repair or replace as necessary. If OK, check connector, switch, fuse and wiring back to the battery.

9) If reading at coil positive terminal was within 1.0 volt of battery voltage, disconnect the lead at negative terminal (coming from ignition control unit). Turn ignition switch "ON". Voltage at negative terminal should be within 1.0 volt of battery voltage.

10) If voltage is within 1.0 volt of battery voltage, but engine will not start, replace ignition control unit. If not within 1.0 volt, remove lead from tachometer (if equipped) at ignition coil. Turn ignition switch "ON" and again check voltage at negative terminal of coil.

11) If reading is now correct, but engine will not start, check wiring harness from negative terminal of coil to tachometer for short circuit. If in step 10), reading was still not within 1.0 volt of battery voltage, replace ignition control unit.

12) If ignition coil is suspected of being defective, check primary and secondary coil resistance. To check primary coil resistance, attach leads of an ohmmeter set in x1 range to coil primary terminals. Reading should be 1.04-1.27 ohms.

13) To check secondary resistance, set ohmmeter to x1000 range and attach leads to coil negative terminal and coil tower. Reading should be 7,360-11,040 ohms. If either reading is not to specifications, replace ignition coil.

OVERHAUL

Disassembly — 1) Remove distributor cap and rotor. Remove vacuum controller by loosening screws and pulling vacuum controller out of distributor housing. Disconnect electrical wires from control unit, then remove wires from distributor housing.

2) Remove gear from distributor shaft by driving out pin. Remove thrust washers with gear. Remove screws attaching pick-up coil plate to distributor housing. Pull pick-up coil with distributor shaft from housing.

3) Remove dust-proof packing from top of distributor shaft. Remove screw from top of shaft, then pull lower distributor shaft out of upper shaft/pick-up coil plate assembly. Remove centrifugal weights and springs from lower distributor shaft.

Reassembly — Reassemble in reverse order of disassembly, noting the following:
- When installing rotor assembly, match notch in pick-up coil base with groove end of housing.
- When installing vacuum controller, tighten only the screw holding the controller to the housing. Tighten screw between lever and pick-up coil base when installing pick-up coil.
- When installing pick-up coil, adjust air gap to specifications.
- Position rotor shaft so flat side is centered on pole piece of pick-up coil. See Fig. 5.
- Align match mark "A" on pinion gear with right side of notch "B" on lower end of housing. See Fig. 5.
- After assembly, check centrifugal advance by using a distributor tester.

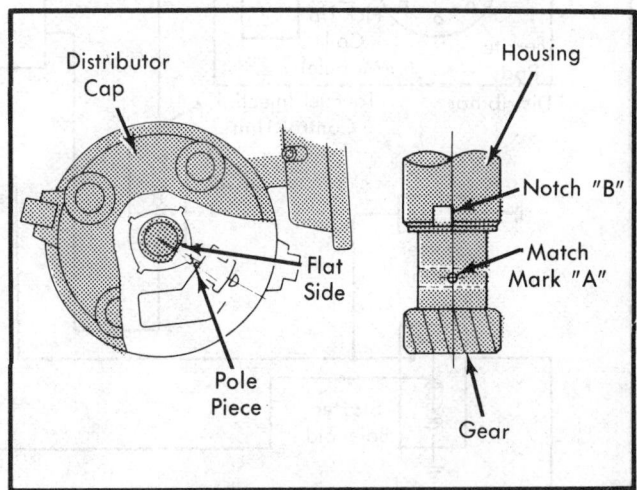

Distributor Cap

Housing

Notch "B"

Match Mark "A"

Flat Side

Pole Piece

Gear

Fig. 5 Aligning Rotor Shaft With Pole Piece and Pinion Gear With Housing

LUCAS "OPUS" ELECTRONIC IGNITION SYSTEM

Jaguar
XJ6
Triumph
TR7
TR8

DESCRIPTION

Although the principle of operation of all Lucas "OPUS" electronic ignition systems is similar, variations do occur between models. *See Fig. 1.*

For example, the XJ6 features a remote electronic control module (amplifier), while the TR8 has the control module mounted inside its distributor. Other models have the module mounted externally on the distributor housing. *See Figs. 4, 5 and 6.*

The XJ6 distributor is equipped with a gear-type reluctor (timing rotor) with one tooth for each cylinder. Other models use a timing rotor with ferrite iron rods (one for each cylinder) imbedded in its outside circumference. In all cases, the reluctor or timing rotor, mounted on the distributor shaft, rotates adjacent to a magnetic pick-up coil (module). The reluctor or timing rotor combines with the pick-up coil to generate signals to the electronic control module (amplifier).

All distributors feature centrifugal advance mechanisms and either vacuum advance or retard units. Some models, such as the TR8, feature ballast-drive resistor assemblies, while others such as the TR7, Spitfire and MGB use ballast wires during normal engine operation.

Other system components include the battery, ignition switch, and ignition coil.

OPERATION

With the ignition switch turned "OFF" and the engine stopped, the distributor reluctor or timing rotor is normally positioned so the teeth or iron rods do not align with the iron core of the pick-up coil. When the ignition switch is turned "ON", a power transistor in the electronic control module (amplifier) completes the ignition coil primary winding circuit.

At the same time a pulsating alternating current voltage is applied by the module to the distributor pick-up coil windings. A small alternating current voltage is produced, and pick-up coil windings are magnetically balanced.

NOTE — *The pick-up coil is magnetically balanced at the factory and the setting must not be changed. The sealed adjusting screw must not be disturbed.*

The voltage at the pick-up coil is applied to the amplifier unit, but is insufficient to affect the transistor controlling the ignition coil primary circuit.

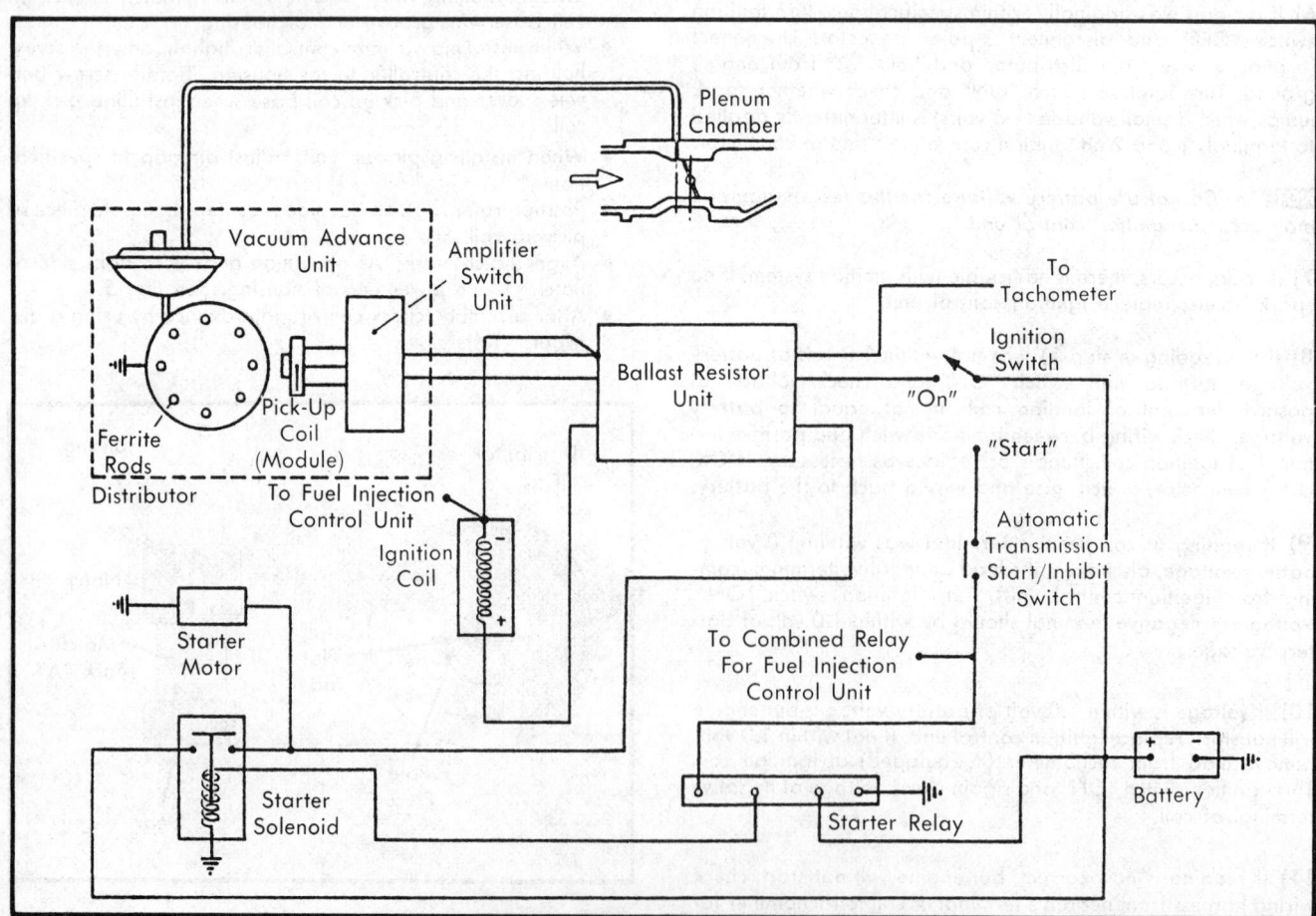

Fig. 1   Typical Lucas "OPUS" Electronic Ignition System
(TR8 Shown, Others Similar)

LUCAS "OPUS" ELECTRONIC IGNITION SYSTEM (Cont.)

As the engine is cranked, the teeth or the iron rods come in alignment with the iron core of the pick-up coil. This causes a magnetic unbalancing and voltage increases to maximum as each tooth or rod passes the pick-up coil. The higher voltage signal is then transmitted to the control module. The transistor is switched off and the coil primary windings' magnetic field collapses.

This results in a high voltage surge in the secondary, which is transmitted to each spark plug by the distributor rotor.

SPECIFICATIONS

Centrifugal and Vacuum Advance (or Retard) — See *Specifications Tables in this section.*

ADJUSTMENT

Reluctor (Timing Rotor)-to-Pick-Up Coil Air Gap — 1) Disconnect battery ground cable. Remove distributor cap and rotor and anti-flash cover, if equipped. Using a non-magnetic feeler gauge, check for .014-.016" (.35-.40 mm) air gap (.006-.008" or .15-.20 mm air gap for XJ6 models). See *Fig. 2.* Measurement should be made between timing rotor at iron rod (or reluctor teeth) and center core of pick-up coil.

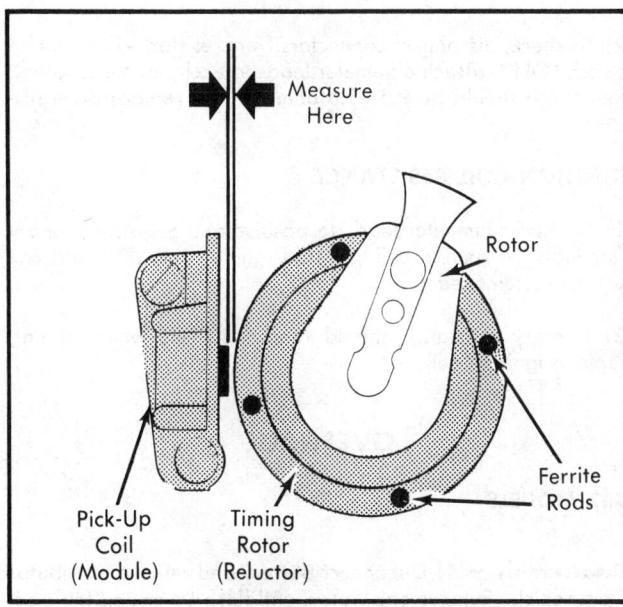

Fig. 2   Adjusting Air Gap (TR7 Shown)

2) To adjust, loosen pick-up coil mounting screws and position coil against feeler gauge being held against reluctor or timing rotor. Tighten screws and recheck air gap.

TESTING (XJ6 MODELS)

IGNITION SYSTEM CHECK

1) Check battery voltage for at least 11.5 volts. If less than 11.5 volts, charge battery. If more than 11.5 volts, attach voltmeter positive lead to coil positive terminal and negative lead to ground. Voltage should be within 1 volt of battery voltage.

2) If incorrect reading is obtained, check wiring between coil positive terminal and ignition switch. If voltage was within 1 volt of battery voltage, attach positive voltmeter lead to coil negative terminal and negative lead to ground. Voltage reading should be more than 2 volts.

3) If voltage is incorrect, disconnect wire leading to control module (amplifier) at coil negative terminal. Again check voltage at coil negative terminal. If less that 2 volts, replace ignition coil. If more than 2 volts, replace control module.

4) If voltage in step **2)** was correct (more than 2 volts), disconnect control module from distributor. Turn ignition switch "OFF" and attach leads of an ohmmeter (set to high scale) to distributor pick-up coil leads. Resistance reading should be 2200-4800 ohms. If not, replace pick-up coil.

5) If pick-up coil resistance is correct, connect control module to distributor. Attach voltmeter positive lead to coil negative terminal and negative lead to ground. Measure voltage. Then crank engine and voltage should fall. If not, replace control module.

6) If voltage fell in step **5)**, but system still is not operating properly, check high tension wires, ignition coil secondary, rotor arms, distributor cap and spark plugs.

CENTRIFUGAL ADVANCE

Check distributor in test stand according to test equipment manufacturer's instructions. Operate distributor up and down the RPM range and check advance at all RPM settings specified.

VACUUM ADVANCE OR RETARD

With distributor in test stand, check advance or retard at all vacuum settings specified. If tests indicate vacuum diaphragm unit is inoperative, out of calibration or leaking, replace vacuum unit.

TESTING (ALL MODELS EXCEPT XJ6)

IGNITION SYSTEM CHECK

1) Remove coil-to-distributor high tension cable from distributor and hold ¼" (6 mm) from engine ground. Turn ignition switch "ON". If equipped, disconnect white/blue lead at drive resistor and check for spark at gap each time connection is broken. On models without drive resistor, crank engine and check for sparks at gap. Reconnect all wires after test.

2) If sparking results, turn off ignition switch. Using a feeler gauge, check air gap between distributor pick-up coil and timing rotor (reluctor). Adjust as necessary. If gap is correct, crank engine to see that distributor shaft rotates.

3) If not, check distributor and drive. If shaft does rotate, replace control module (amplifier). If there was no sparking at gap in step **1)**, check supply voltage at white wire (or at "SW" connector of Ballast Resistor 9BR, if equipped). If less than 11 volts, check battery, wiring and ignition switch.

4) If voltage supply was more than 11 volts, attach voltmeter positive lead to ignition coil positive terminal and negative lead to ground. Voltage should be 11 volts or more (4-8 volts on ballasted models). If voltage is zero (0) or extremely low, check ballast resistor, coil and wires.

LUCAS "OPUS" ELECTRONIC IGNITION SYSTEM (Cont.)

5) If voltage is normal or high, attach voltmeter positive lead to coil negative terminal and negative lead to ground. If voltage reads more than 2 volts, check drive resistor. Turn ignition switch "OFF" and attach ohmmeter leads to drive resistor and check for 9-11 ohms resistance. If not to specifications, replace drive resistor. If OK, check control module and distributor grounds. If OK, but engine does not perform properly, replace control module.

6) If voltage at coil negative terminal was less than 2 volts, disconnect white/blue wire at drive resistor (if equipped). Remove coil negative lead and check voltage at coil negative terminal. If voltage is more than 9 volts, check high tension leads and substitute a new ignition coil. Replace amplifier only if problem is not corrected.

7) If voltage in step **6)**, was less than 9 volts, disconnect coil negative lead and recheck voltage at coil negative terminal. If now less than 9 volts, replace coil. If more than 9 volts, replace control module (amplifier).

BALLAST RESISTOR CHECK (MODEL 9BR)

1) Some models such as the TR8 may be equipped with the Model 9BR Ballast Resistor, a unit consisting of 4 resistors and a printed wiring board mounted in an aluminum heat sink. One side of resistor is connected to (1) starter solenoid ignition terminal, (2) ignition switch and (3) to tachometer. The other side has 2 connections to distributor pick-up coil and 2 connections to primary terminals of ignition coil.

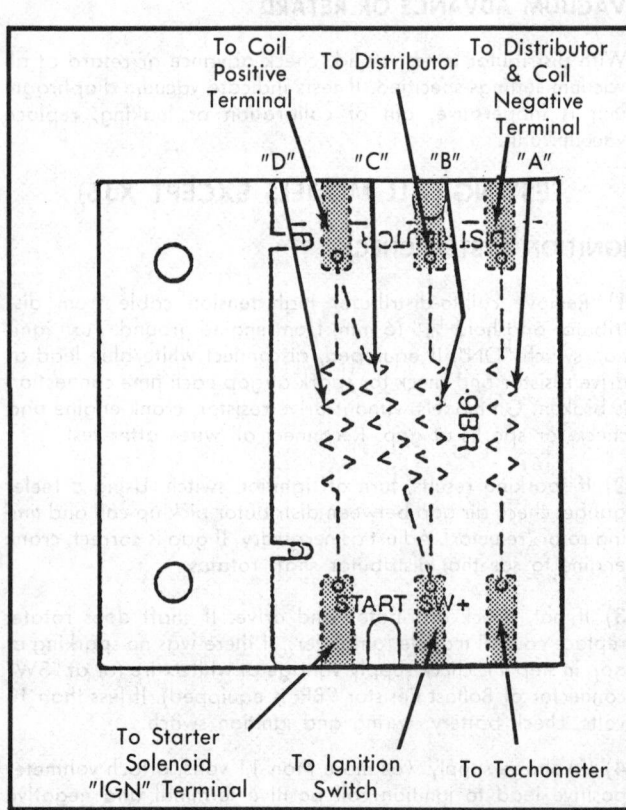

Fig. 3   Model 9BR Ballast Resistor Connections

2) Turn ignition switch "OFF". Connect ohmmeter leads to each set of terminals shown in *Fig. 3*. Resistor reading "A" (tachometer connection) should be 9,000-11,000 ohms. Reading "B" (drive resistor) should be 0.5 ohm; reading "C" (ballast ignition resistor) should be 1.62-1.80 ohms, and reading "D" (ballast resistor) should read 0.25-0.28 ohm. If not, replace ballast resistor assembly.

BALLAST WIRE CHECK

1) On most models, such as the TR7, a pink/white ballast resistance wire is built into the wiring harness leading to the ignition coil. The wire causes a voltage drop so the 12-volt supply may be used to power the 6-volt ignition coil. During engine start, the resistor is bypassed to apply 12 volts reduced by starter load directly to the coil.

2) To check resistor wire, turn ignition switch "OFF" and attach ohmmeter leads to each end of pink/white wire. Resistance should be 1.3-1.5 ohms. If not, replace ballast resistor wire.

DRIVE RESISTOR CHECK

1) A drive resistor is used on some models, such as the TR7, and is mounted externally near the distributor control module (amplifier). This is due to its size and heat dissipating requirements.

2) To check, disconnect connectors from resistor. With ignition switch "OFF", attach ohmmeter leads to each resistor terminal. Resistance should be 9.5-11.5 ohms. If not, replace drive resistor.

IGNITION COIL RESISTANCE

1) Connect ohmmeter leads to positive and negative primary terminals of ignition coil. Be sure ignition is "OFF" and coil wires are removed.

2) Primary resistance should read 1.30-1.45 ohms. If not, replace ignition coil.

OVERHAUL

TR7 MODELS

Disassembly — 1) Disconnect battery and remove distributor from vehicle. Remove cap, rotor, anti-flash cover and felt pad. Remove screws and washers from magnetic pick-up coil (pick-up module). Do not remove pick-up coil at this time.

2) Remove screws securing amplifier to distributor. Hold amplifier while removing screw from bottom of housing. Carefully disengage vacuum unit from movable plate.

3) Remove wire grommet, amplifier housing, and pick-up coil with lead. Remove spring clips. Tap out roll pin securing vacuum unit and remove unit. Remove external snap ring from distributor shaft and carefully remove timing rotor, washer and "O" ring.

4) Remove 2 Phillips head screws and lift out base plate with movable plate attached. Remove springs carefully, noting positions of 2 different springs.

LUCAS "OPUS" ELECTRONIC IGNITION SYSTEM (Cont.)

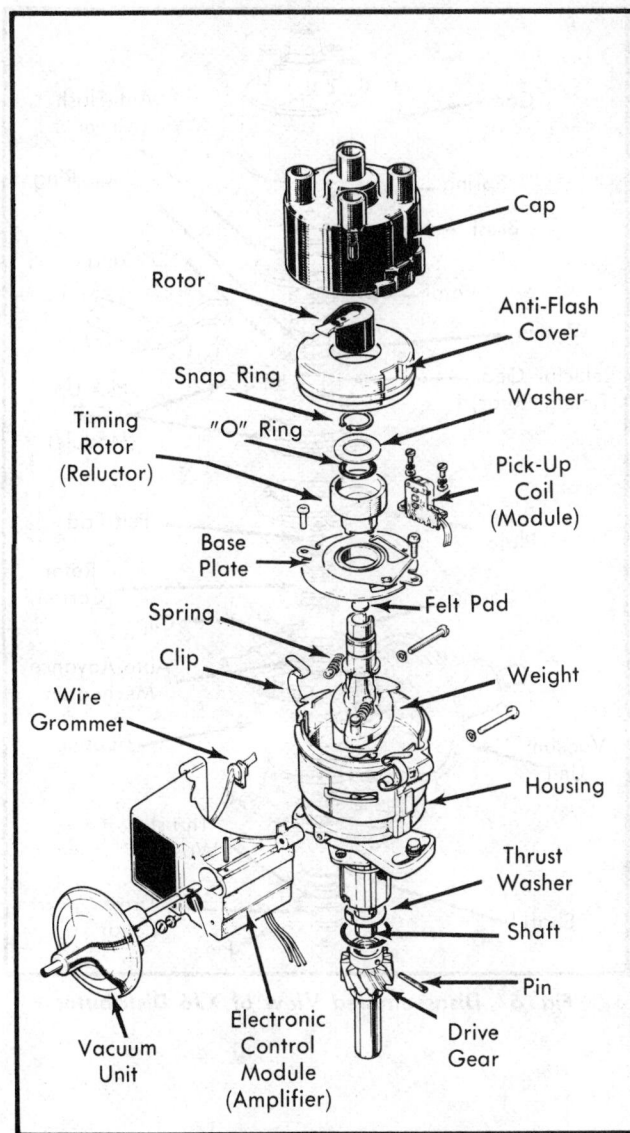

Fig. 4   Disassembled View of TR7 Distributor (MGB and Spitfire Similar)

5) Drive out pin securing drive collar to distributor shaft. Remove drive collar and thrust washer. Remove shaft from housing, along with shim. Detach return springs.

Inspection — Check control springs for proper length. Check pivot holes in weights for wear or deformation. Check distributor shaft for excessive play.

NOTE — *If any part of the distributor body assembly is found to be defective, the complete assembly must be replaced.*

Reassembly — To reassemble distributor, reverse disassembly procedure noting the following. Lubricate weight assembly, shaft and moving plate with Rocol "Moly Pad" or equivalent. Make sure vacuum link is properly attached to moving plate pin. Timing rotor tang must fit into slot on shaft. With distributor assembled and replaced in vehicle, set air gap and ignition timing to specifications.

TR8 MODELS

Disassembly — 1) Remove negative battery cable and then remove distributor from vehicle. Remove cap, rotor, anti-flash cover and felt pad.

2) Remove snap ring, plain washer and rubber "O" ring. Remove timing rotor carefully. Remove 3 screws, spring washers and washer. Remove wire grommet and electronic control module assembly as a unit.

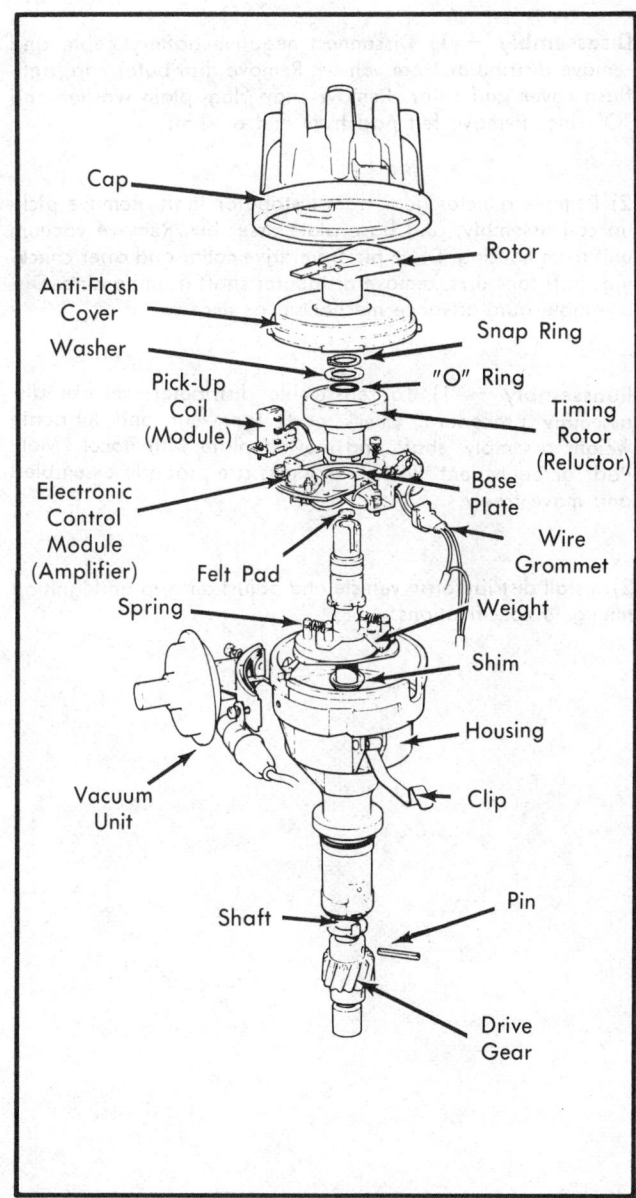

Fig. 5   Disassembled View of TR8 Distributor

3) Remove 2 screws, 2 spring washers and washer to release vacuum unit, rubber gasket and capacitor. Tap out drive gear pin. Remove drive gear and thrust washer. Be sure shaft is free of burrs, and remove shaft from housing.

LUCAS "OPUS" ELECTRONIC IGNITION SYSTEM (Cont.)

4) Remove plastic collar and control springs, but do not attempt to disassemble further.

Reassembly — To reassemble distributor, reverse disassembly procedure, noting the following. Lubricate weight assembly, shaft and moving plate with Rocol "Moly Pad" or equivalent. Make sure vacuum link is properly attached to moving plate pin. Timing rotor tang must fit into slot on shaft. With distributor assembled and installed in vehicle, set air gap and ignition timing to specification.

JAGUAR XJ6 MODELS

Disassembly — **1)** Disconnect negative battery cable and remove distributor from vehicle. Remove distributor cap, anti-flash cover and rotor. Remove snap ring, plain washer and "O" ring. Remove felt pad from end of shaft.

2) Remove reluctor gear from distributor shaft. Remove pick-up coil assembly, and base plate assembly. Remove vacuum unit from housing. Drive pin from drive collar and after checking shaft for burrs, remove distributor shaft from housing. Disassemble auto-advance mechanism as necessary.

Reassembly — **1)** To reassemble distributor, reverse disassembly procedure. Check parts for wear and lubricate weight assembly, shaft and moving plate with Rocol "Moly Pad" or equivalent. Be sure all parts are properly assembled and move freely.

2) Install distributor in vehicle and adjust air gap and ignition timing to specifications.

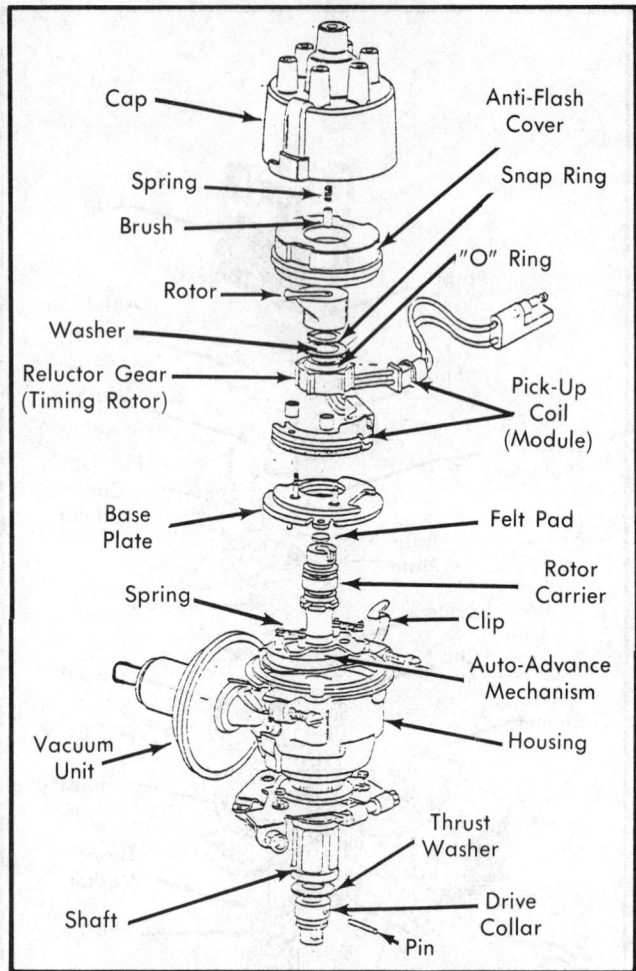

Fig. 6   Disassembled View of XJ6 Distributor

MARELLI ELECTRONIC IGNITION SYSTEM

Fiat
Brava
Spider 2000
Strada

NOTE — *Some Strada models may be equipped with Bosch electronic ignition systems.*

DESCRIPTION

The Marelli electronic ignition system consists of an ignition coil, electronic control module, and a breakerless distributor. See *Fig. 1.*

Marelli distributors are equipped with conventional centrifugal and vacuum advance mechanisms. A 4-tooth trigger (reluctor) is mounted on the distributor shaft and combines with the pick-up coil assembly to provide the control module with electrical signals required.

The control module and ignition coil are mounted on a finned, cast aluminum base which not only cools the units, but also provides a system ground. See *Fig. 2.*

The control module's current limiter provides a constant current flow to the primary circuit, preventing coil damage. The module analyzes the electrical signals from the distributor pick-up coil assembly and provides the coil with proper dwell time and spark timing regardless of engine speed.

OPERATION

Primary voltage is supplied to the ignition coil by the battery, through the ignition switch. There are no resistors in the Marelli system. As the distributor shaft rotates, the teeth of the trigger approach and then pass the stator pole in the pick-up coil assembly.

This creates and collapses a magnetic field, causing an electrical signal or impulse, which is fed to the control module. As this signal is received, the control module opens and closes the ignition coil primary circuit. This causes a high voltage surge in the coil secondary windings, firing the spark plugs.

SPECIFICATIONS

Centrifugal & Vacuum Advance — *See Specifications Pages in this section.*

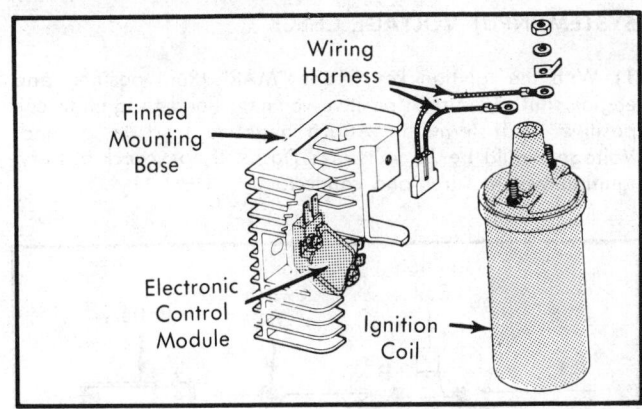

Fig. 2   Ignition Coil, Control Module and Base Assembly

ADJUSTMENT

Trigger-to-Pick-Up Coil Air Gap — Check air gap between trigger and stator pole piece of pick-up coil assembly, using a non-magnetic feeler gauge. Air gap should be .020-.024" (.5-.6 mm). If not to specification, loosen retaining screws and move advance plate to adjust gap. Tighten retaining screws and recheck air gap.

TESTING

CAUTION — *When working around coil, do not ground wire lead to tachometer. Be careful not to disconnect high tension terminal of coil with engine running. Make all resistance checks with the ignition switch "OFF".*

ROTOR RESISTANCE CHECK

Using an ohmmeter set at the x1000 scale, check the rotor resistance for 4,000-6,000 ohms. Replace if resistance varies considerably.

IGNITION SYSTEM CHECK

With ignition system in the "MAR" (Run) position, inspect wiring and connectors. Be sure heat dissipater (module and coil base), power unit, and battery are properly grounded. Be sure coil and distributor connectors are firmly attached to control module terminals.

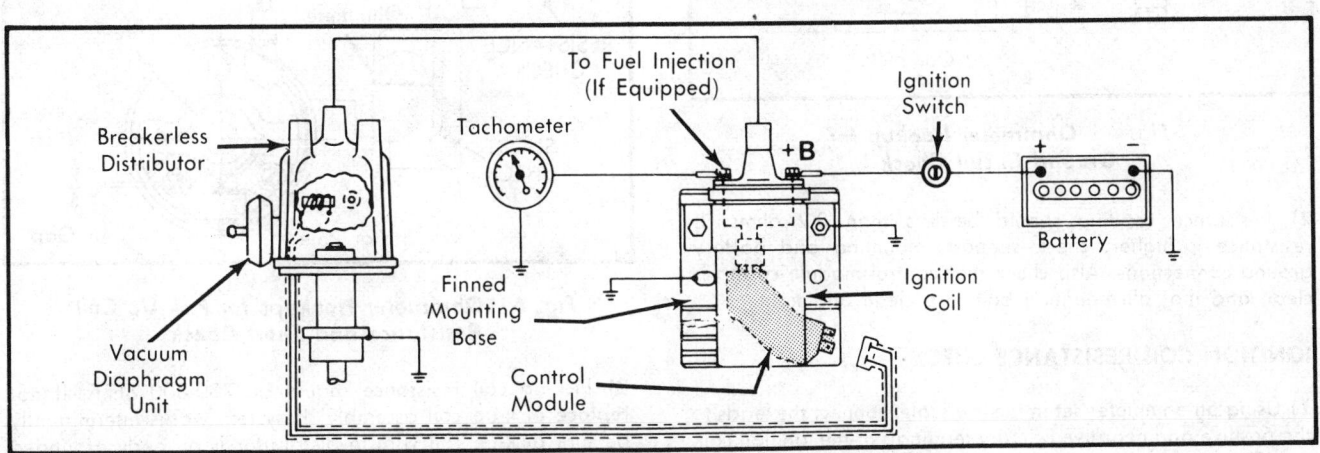

Fig. 1   Schematic of Marelli Electronic Ignition System

MARELLI ELECTRONIC IGNITION SYSTEM (Cont.)

SYSTEM INPUT VOLTAGE CHECK

1) With the ignition key in the "MAR" (Run) position and engine shut off, attach positive voltmeter lead to ignition coil positive (+B) terminal. Attach negative lead to ground. Voltage should be 12 volts. See *Fig. 3*. If not, check battery, ignition switch, wires and connectors.

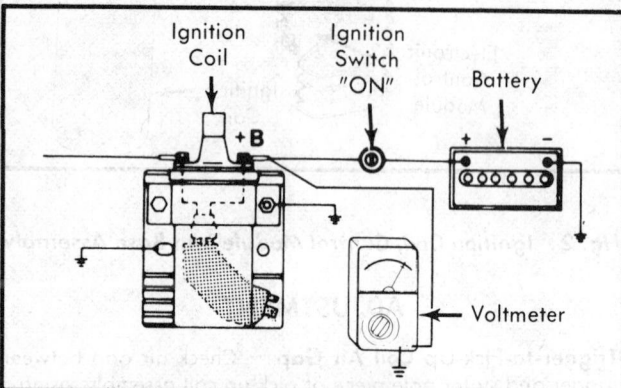

**Fig. 3   Voltmeter Hookup for
System Input Voltage Check**

2) Move positive voltmeter lead to ignition coil negative terminal. Voltage should be within 0.3 volts of voltage recorded at coil positive terminal. If not as specified, make Ignition Coil Resistance Check.

GROUND CIRCUIT CHECK

1) Turn ignition switch "OFF". Connect ohmmeter leads to battery ground terminal and ignition coil ground stud. See *Fig. 4*.

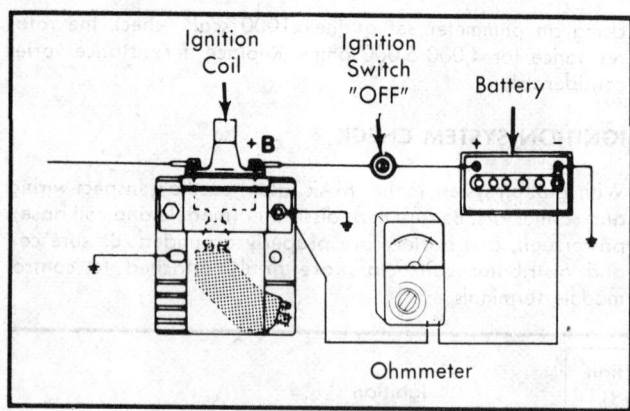

**Fig. 4   Ohmmeter Hookup for
Ground Circuit Check**

2) Resistance reading should be less than 0.2 ohms. If resistance is higher, check support, mounting and battery ground connections. Also check that control module casing is clean and that all mounting bolts are clean and tight.

IGNITION COIL RESISTANCE CHECK

1) Using an ohmmeter set in the low scale, connect the leads to the positive and negative primary terminals of the ignition coil. See *Fig. 5*. Resistance reading should be .75-.81 ohm.

2) Change ohmmeter to the x1000 scale and connect leads to coil negative terminal and coil center tower. See *Fig. 5*. Resistance should be 10,000-11,000 ohms.

3) If either reading is not to specifications, replace ignition coil.

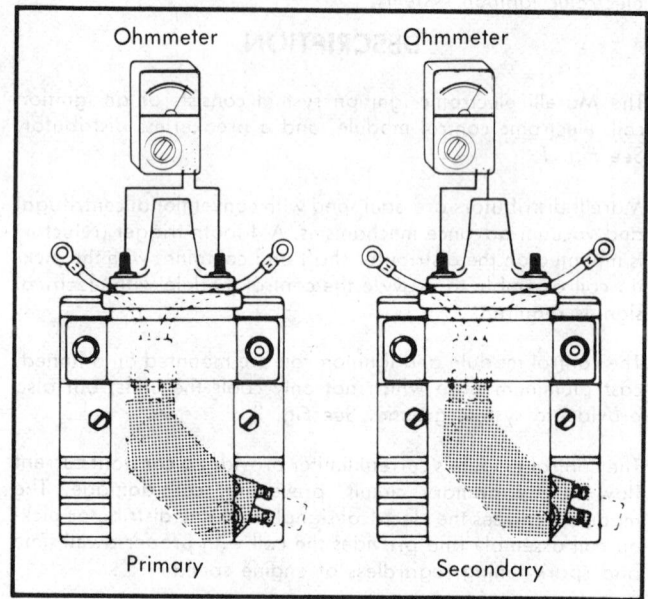

**Fig. 5   Ohmmeter Hookup for Ignition Coil
Primary and Secondary Resistance Check**

PICK-UP COIL RESISTANCE AND SHORT CHECK

1) Turn the ignition switch "OFF". Disconnect 2-wire distributor connector. Connect an ohmmeter set in the x100 scale with one lead touching each terminal of distributor harness connector. See *Fig. 6*.

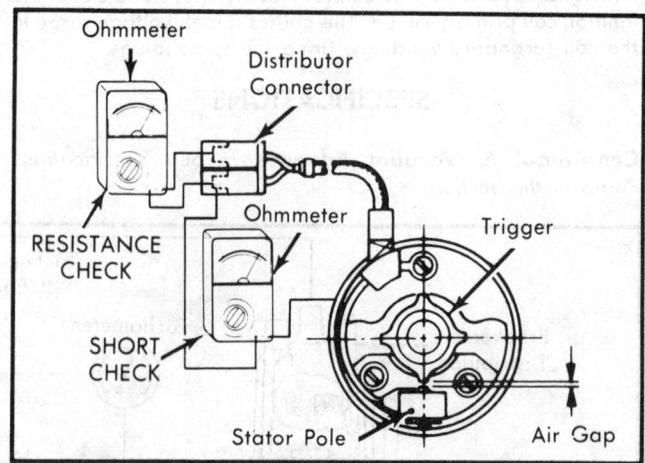

**Fig. 6   Ohmmeter Hookups for Pick-Up Coil
Resistance and Short Check**

2) Pick-up coil resistance should be 700-800 ohms. If not, replace pick-up coil assembly. If system works intermittently, be sure pick-up coil wire in distributor is properly grounded. See *Fig. 7*.

MARELLI ELECTRONIC IGNITION SYSTEM (Cont.)

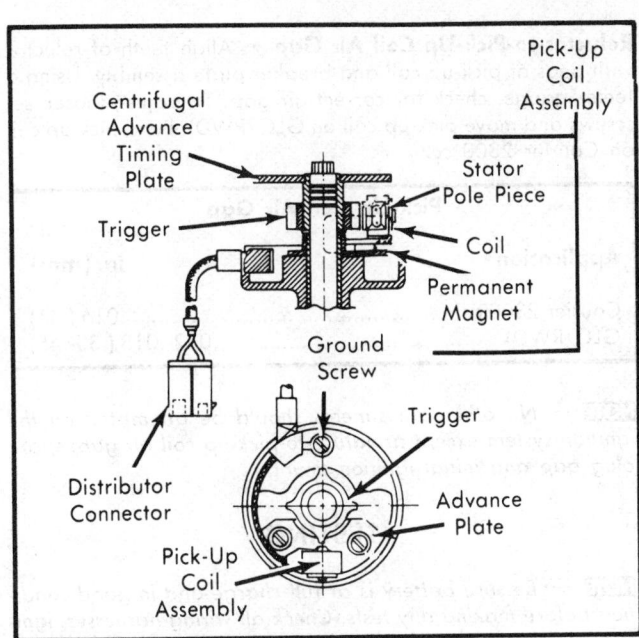

Fig. 7 Interior View of Marelli Distributor

3) Next, attach ohmmeter leads to either terminal of distributor connector and to distributor housing. An infinity reading should exist. *See Fig. 6.* Also check air gap.

CONTROL MODULE CHECK

1) Be sure all ignition system wires and connectors are properly connected. Disconnect coil-to-distributor high voltage wire at the distributor. Hold wire about ¼" (5-6 mm) from a good engine ground, using insulated pliers. *See Fig. 8.*

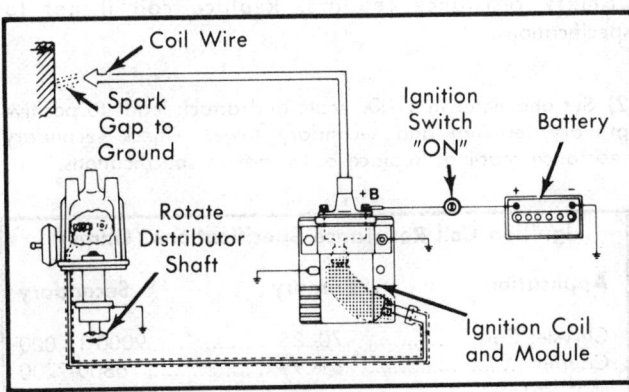

Fig. 8 Coil Wire Hookup for Making Control Module Check

2) Crank engine and check for sparks at gap to ground. If previous tests have disclosed no problem and no spark exists at gap, replace control module.

OVERHAUL

Disassembly — 1) Remove distributor cap and rotor. *See Fig. 9.* Remove pin securing pinion gear and lift shaft and centrifugal advance mechanism (with integral trigger or reluctor) from housing.

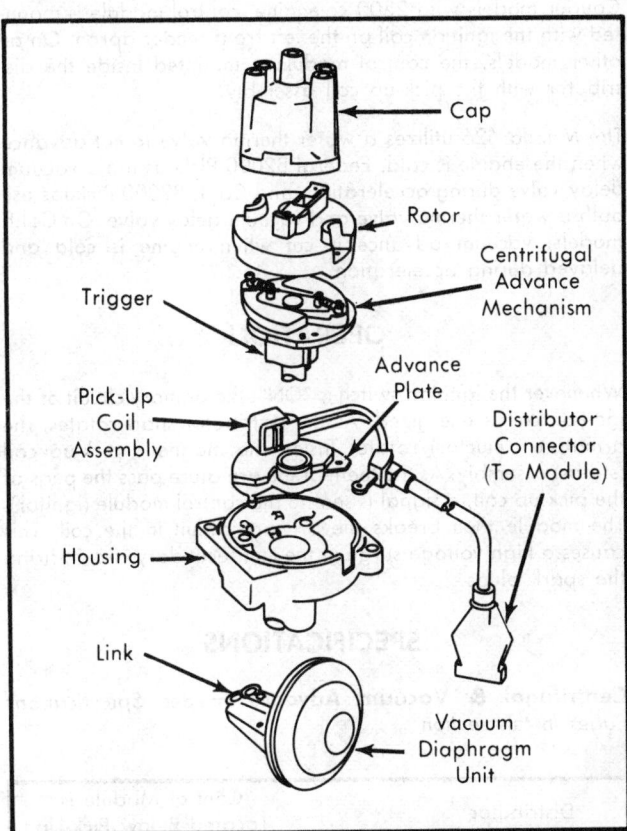

Fig. 9 Disassembled View of Marelli Distributor

2) Remove pick-up coil ground screw and advance plate retaining screws. Disconnect vacuum diaphragm unit from peg on bottom of advance plate. Remove vacuum unit and pick-up coil assembly and advance plate from housing.

Reassembly — Install parts in reverse order of disassembly. Be sure pick-up coil ground screw is tight and that vacuum unit is secured to peg on bottom of advance plate.

Distributors & Ignition Systems

MITSUBISHI ELECTRONIC IGNITION SYSTEM

Arrow Pickup	**Mazda**
Champ & Colt	**GLC**
Challenger	**626**
Courier	**B2000 Pickup**
	Ram-50 Pickup
	Sapporo

DESCRIPTION

Mitsubishi breakerless ignition consists of an electronic control module (ignitor), ignition coil, pick-up coil and distributor. On Courier models with 2300 cc engine, control module is mounted with the ignition coil on the left front fender apron. On all other models, the control module is mounted inside the distributor with the pick-up coil assembly.

The Mazda 626 utilizes a water thermo valve to cut advance when the engine is cold. Federal B2000 Pickups use a vacuum delay valve during acceleration, and Calif. B2000 Pickups use both a water thermo valve and vacuum delay valve. On Calif. models, vacuum advance is cut when engine is cold and delayed during acceleration.

OPERATION

Whenever the ignition switch is "ON", the primary circuit of the ignition coil is energized. As the distributor shaft rotates, the armature (reluctor) rotates inside the magnetic pick-up coil (stator) assembly. As the teeth of the armature pass the pegs of the pick-up coil, a signal is sent to the control module (ignitor). The module then breaks the primary circuit in the coil. This causes a high voltage surge in the coil secondary circuit, firing the spark plugs.

SPECIFICATIONS

Centrifugal & Vacuum Advance — *See Specifications Pages in this section.*

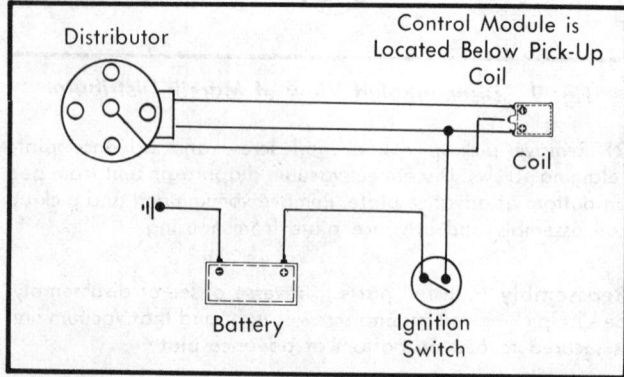

Fig. 1 Wiring Schematic of Mitsubishi Electronic Ignition System With Internal Control Module (All Models Except Courier 2300 cc)

ADJUSTMENTS

NOTE — *Air gap is not adjustable on models not listed in table.*

Reluctor-to-Pick-Up Coil Air Gap — Align teeth of reluctor with pegs of pick-up coil and breaker plate assembly. Using a feeler gauge, check for correct air gap. To adjust, loosen set screws and move pick-up coil on GLC (RWD). Bend pick-up coil on Courier 2300 cc.

Pick-Up Coil Air Gap	
Application	**In. (mm)**
Courier 2300 cc	.016 (.41)
GLC (RWD)	.012-.018 (.30-.45)

NOTE — *No other adjustments should be attempted on the ignition system except armature-to-pick-up coil air gap, spark plug gap and initial ignition timing.*

TESTING

NOTE — *Be sure battery is at full charge and in good condition before making any tests. Check all wiring harnesses, ignition switch, coil and spark plug cables and connectors.*

HIGH VOLTAGE TEST

Connect a remote starter switch in the starting circuit. Remove coil wire from distributor cap. Turn ignition switch "ON" and hold coil wire 1/4" (6 mm) from cylinder block. Crank engine. If no spark or a weak spark results, perform the following tests.

IGNITION COIL RESISTANCE TEST

1) Turn ignition switch "OFF". Set an ohmmeter in the low scale and attach its leads to the coil positive and negative terminals. Coil should be isolated from rest of system. Check primary resistance reading. Replace coil if not to specifications.

2) Set ohmmeter in x1000 scale and attach leads to positive primary terminal and secondary tower. Check secondary resistance reading. Replace coil if not to specifications.

Ignition Coil Resistance Specifications (Ohms)		
Application	**Primary**	**Secondary**
Chrysler Corp.	.70-.85	9000-11,000
Courier	.81-.99	6800-9200
Mazda GLC (FWD)①	Continuity	10,000-30,000
Mazda GLC (RWD)①	1.035-1.265	.....
Mazda B2000①	.90	.....
Mazda 626①	1.035-1.265	.....

① — With coil at normal operating temperature.

MAGNETIC PICK-UP COIL RESISTANCE TEST

Turn ignition switch "OFF". Set an ohmmeter in the x100 scale. Attach leads to pick-up coil's distributor connector terminals. Check resistance against table.

MITSUBISHI ELECTRONIC IGNITION SYSTEM (Cont.)

Pick-Up Coil Resistance

Application	Ohms
Courier①	
2000 cc	945-1155
2300 cc	760-840
Chrysler Corp.	920-1120
Mazda 626①	945-1155

① — Measure resistance at 68° F (20° C).

NOTE — *Specifications for other models were not available from manufacturer.*

IGNITION MODULE TEST

Chrysler Corp. — Connect the ignitor, lamp and battery as shown in *Fig. 2.* Using a dry cell battery or continuity tester, apply voltage to the signal input terminal of the ignitor unit. Lamp should light when voltage is applied and go out when voltage is removed. If not, ignitor is bad.

NOTE — *This test can only determine whether ignitor is bad. Even if ignitor tests out as good, it is not necessarily good.*

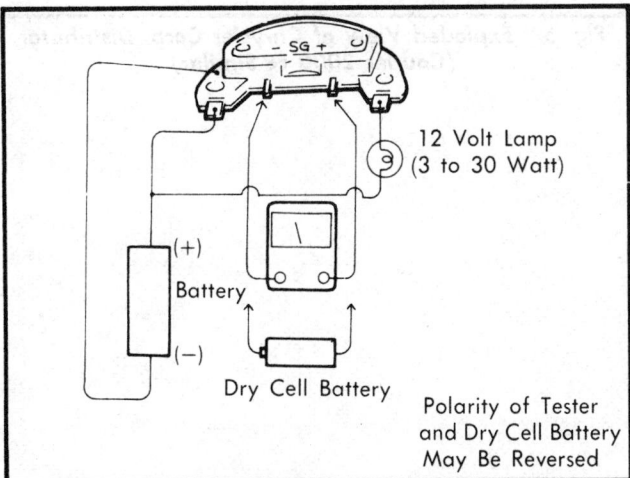

Fig. 2 Checking Chrysler Corp. Ignitor With Battery and Test Lamp

Courier (2300 cc) — 1) Connect a test light (3.4 watts) to the ignition coil positive and negative terminals. See *Fig. 3.* Attach one end of jumper wire to positive terminal of ignition coil. Disconnect the 2-pin connector.

2) Attach other end of jumper wire to the red wire terminal on the module side of the connector. Turn the ignition switch "ON". The test light should come on. The light should go out when the jumper wire is disconnected.

3) If test light does not function as stated, retest to make sure bulb is OK and that all connections are tight. If results are still improper, replace control module and retest.

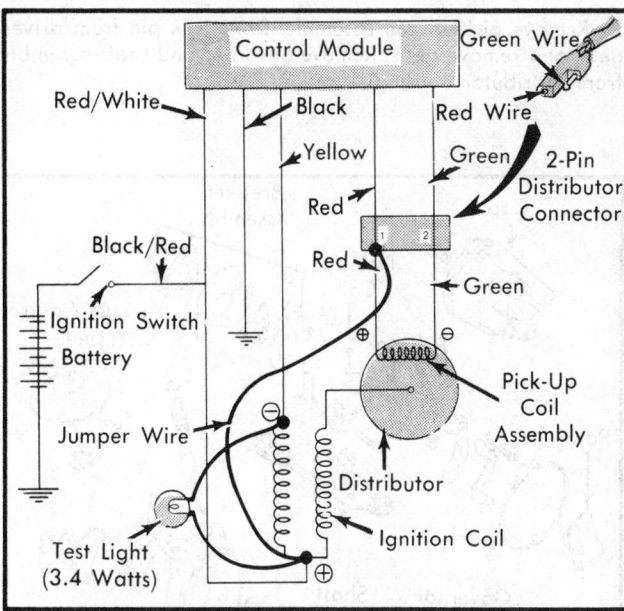

Fig. 3 Courier Ignition Control Module Test Light Should Come On (2300 cc Engine)

SECONDARY WIRE RESISTANCE TEST

Test coil and spark plug cables with an ohmmeter. Do not puncture secondary wires when making the resistance check. Connect leads to each end of the cable. Resistance for Courier should not exceed 570 ohms per inch; for Mazda vehicles, resistance should not exceed 16,000 ohms for each 39" (1 m); and Chrysler Corp. vehicles should not exceed 22,000 ohms per cable.

OVERHAUL

CHRYSLER CORP, COURIER 2000 cc & MAZDA

Disassembly — 1) Remove distributor cap. Remove rotor. Remove governor assembly. Remove attaching screws, then remove pick-up coil and IC ignitor assembly.

2) Pull out the ignitor carefully from pick-up coil (if applicable). Remove the vacuum control unit. Remove the breaker assembly. Remove pin holding gear to shaft and remove gear after marking gear and shaft for reassembly reference.

NOTE — *DO NOT clean grease off back of IC ignitor, as it is necessary for heat transfer.*

Reassembly — Reverse removal procedure. Inspect cap and rotor for cracks and deposits on inside surfaces. Check driven gear for wear and shaft for play in thrust direction.

COURIER 2300 cc

Disassembly — 1) Remove distributor cap and rotor. Remove cover, gasket, and grommet. Remove clips. Drive roll pin from reluctor and remove reluctor. Remove clip holding vacuum diaphragm link. Remove vacuum control unit.

MITSUBISHI ELECTRONIC IGNITION SYSTEM (Cont.)

2) Remove pick-up coil assembly. Drive lock pin from driven gear and remove gear. Remove governor and shaft assembly from distributor housing.

Reassembly — Reverse disassembly procedure. When installing cam, align marks on distributor housing and gear. Align rotor metal end with clip mounting lug on side of distributor with mounting slot.

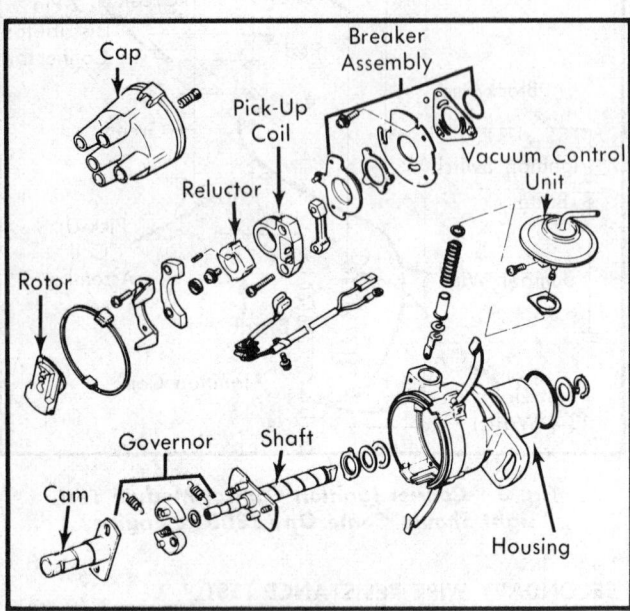

Fig. 4 Exploded View of Mazda Distributor (GLC Shown, Others Similar)

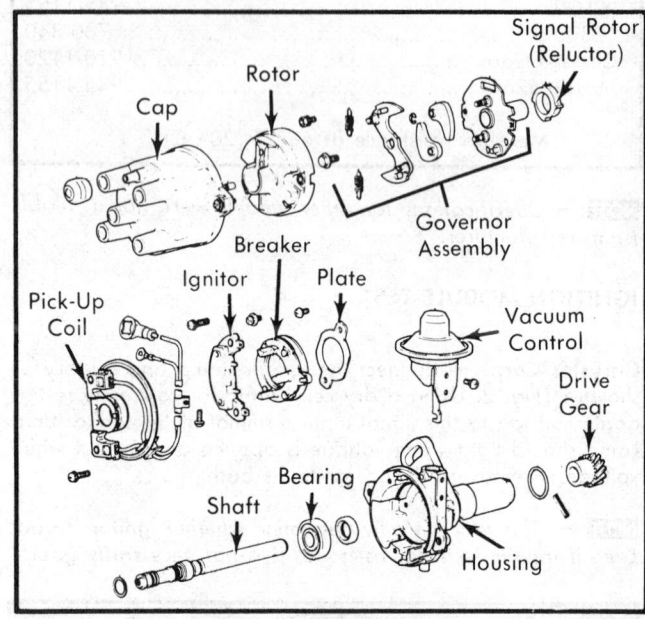

Fig. 5 Exploded View of Chrysler Corp. Distributor (Courier 2000 cc Similar)

MITSUBISHI ELECTRONIC IGNITION SYSTEM — ROTARY ENGINE

**Mazda
RX7**

DESCRIPTION

The Mitsubishi electronic ignition system used on the Mazda RX7 rotary engine is unique in that it has 2 sets of spark plugs (leading and trailing) with one set in the front rotor housing and one in the rear rotor housing. See Fig. 1. There are also 2 ignition coils, 2 pick-up coils in the distributor, and 2 coil-to-distributor high tension wires.

There are 2 separate ignitors mounted on the distributor base. One is for leading side and the other for trailing side. Other system components include a battery, ignition switch, ignition control switches, (water temperature, altitude, etc.), and various relays. All models are equipped with an ignition control system and centrifugal advance mechanisms. All models have vacuum control units for both leading and trailing sides.

OPERATION

A reluctor (signal rotor) is mounted on the rotor shaft and turns inside 2 magnetic pick-up coils, one for the leading side and one for the trailing side. See Fig. 2. As each tooth of the reluctor approaches and then passes the leading pick-up coil, a signal is generated that is sent to the leading ignitor, which breaks the primary circuit in the leading ignition coil. As each tooth passes the leading pick-up coil, the previous passing tooth approaches and becomes aligned with the trailing pick-up coil. This triggers a signal to the trailing ignitor, which breaks the primary circuit in the trailing ignition coil.

Therefore, immediately after the leading spark plug fires, the trailing spark plug also fires, providing more complete and efficient combustion and reducing HC and CO emissions.

As the primary circuit is broken in the leading and trailing ignition coils, a voltage surge occurs in the secondary circuit of the ignition coils. This high voltage is transmitted through the leading and trailing high tension wires to the distributor, rotor and spark plugs.

An emission control unit is also included in the ignition control system along with different sensing switches to provide proper timing under varying engine operating conditions.

SPECIFICATIONS

Centrifugal & Vacuum Advance (or Retard) — See *Specifications Tables* in this section.

ADJUSTMENTS

Reluctor-to-Pick-Up Coil Air Gap — 1) Remove distributor cap and rotor. Turn distributor shaft until the extended tooth of the reluctor (signal rotor) aligns with core of pick-up coil. See *Fig. 2.*

2) Using a feeler gauge, check for .020-.035" (.5-.9 mm) air gap. If gap is incorrect, replace pick-up coil and bearing assembly or distributor drive shaft, if necessary.

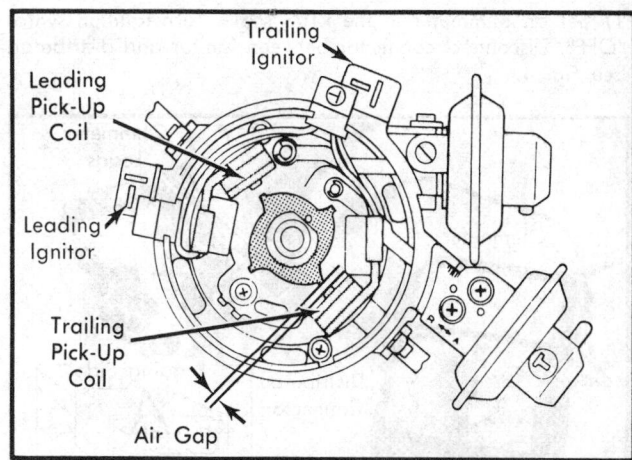

Fig. 2 Adjusting Distributor Air Gap

Ignition Timing — 1) Leading timing is adjusted by loosening distributor lock nut and rotating distributor housing until correct timing is obtained. See *Fig. 3.*

2) Trailing timing is changed by loosening the screws securing the vacuum unit and moving the vacuum unit outward (to advance) or inward (to retard). Retighten screws when correct timing is obtained.

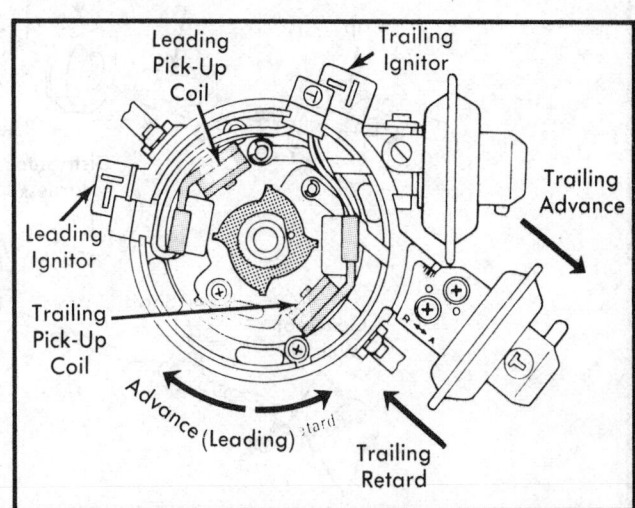

Fig. 3 Adjusting Ignition Timing

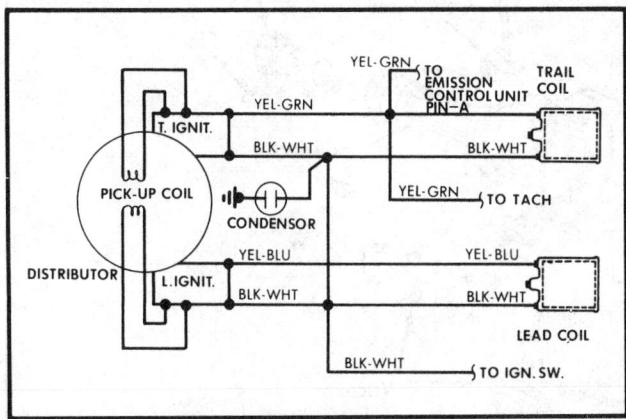

Fig. 1 Schematic of RX7 Ignition System

MITSUBISHI ELECTRONIC IGNITION SYSTEM — ROTARY ENGINE(Cont.)

TESTING

HIGH TENSION WIRE RESISTANCE CHECK

Turn ignition switch "OFF". Connect ohmmeter leads to each end of coil-to-distributor high tension wire. Resistance should not exceed 16,000 ohms (±6,400 ohms) per 39.37" (1 m).

IGNITION COIL RESISTANCE CHECK

Set an ohmmeter in the low scale. With ignition switch turned "OFF", and coil wires disconnected, attach ohmmeter leads to primary terminals of leading coil and then trailing coil. Primary resistance should be 1.22-1.48 ohms for each ignition coil.

PICK-UP COIL RESISTANCE CHECK

1) Set an ohmmeter in the x100 scale. Turn ignition switch "OFF". Disconnect connector between ignitor and distributor. See Fig. 4.

2) Connect ohmmeter leads to leading terminals and then to trailing terminals. Resistance should be 600-700 ohms at 68° F (20° C) for each set of pick-up coils. If not, replace pick-up coil and bearing assembly.

PICK-UP COIL OPERATION CHECK

1) With distributor connector still disconnected, touch ammeter leads to leading terminals and then to trailing terminals.

2) Place a screwdriver against core of pick-up coil being tested. Indicator of meter should move each time screwdriver is taken quickly away from core. If not, replace pick-up coil and bearing assembly.

IGNITOR CHECK

1) Remove ignitor from distributor base. Make a circuit as shown in Fig. 5 with wire and a test bulb. Use 12 volts and a bulb of less than 10 watts.

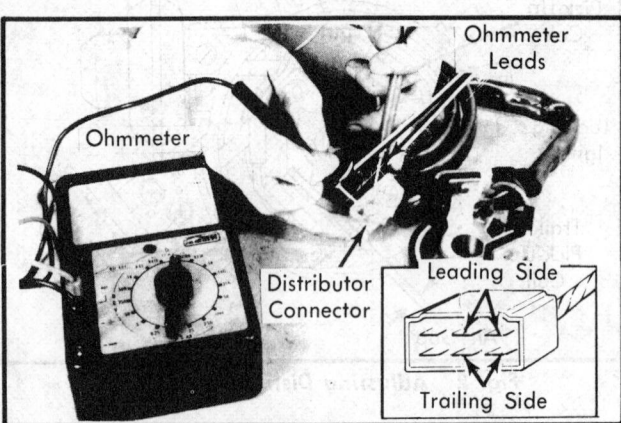

Fig. 4 Ohmmeter Hookup for Pick-Up Coil Resistance Check

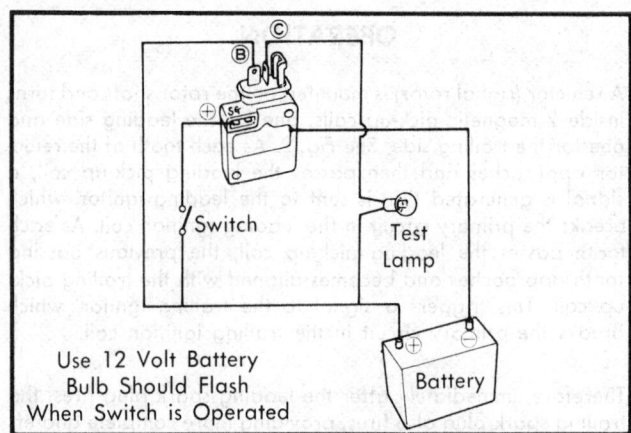

Fig. 5 Test Lamp Hookup for Checking Ignitor Operation — Bulbs Should Flash

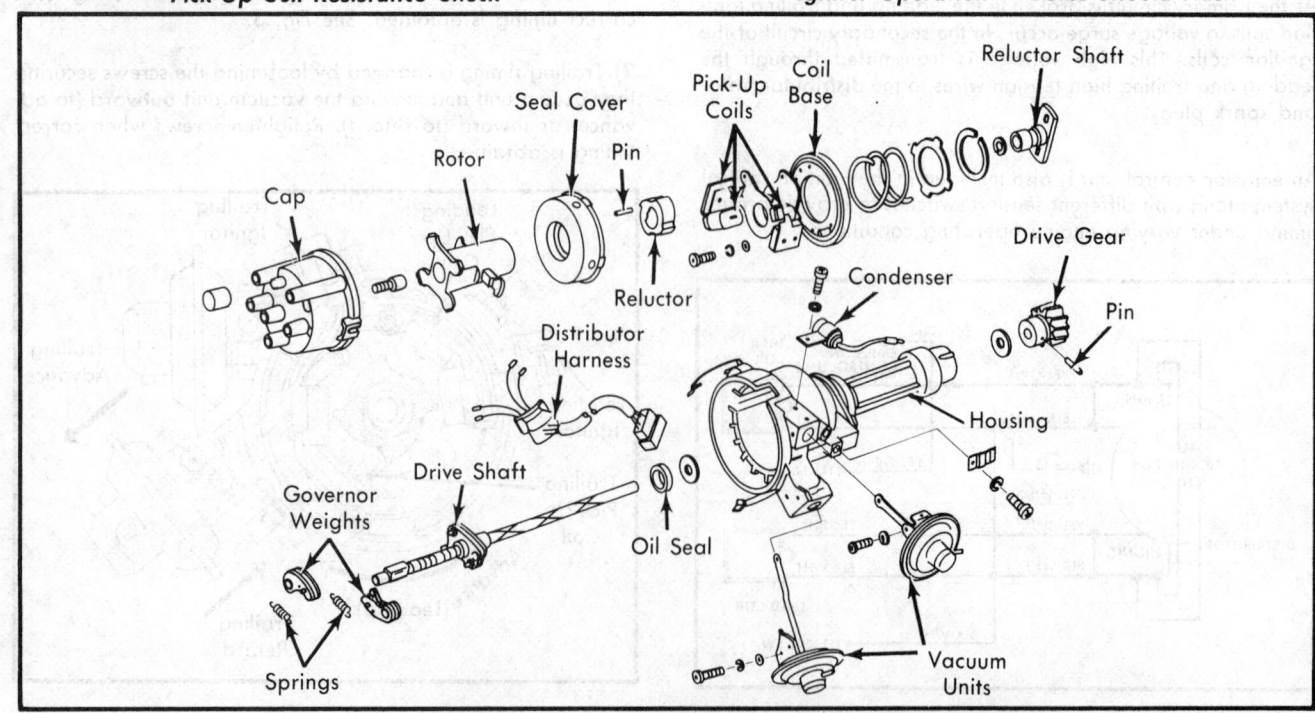

Fig. 6 Disassembled View of RX7 Distributor for Overhaul Purposes

MITSUBISHI ELECTRONIC IGNITION SYSTEM — ROTARY ENGINE(Cont.)

2) Quickly operate switch "ON" and "OFF" and make sure test lamp flashes. If not, replace ignitor.

OVERHAUL

Disassembly — 1) Remove distributor cap, rotor and seal cover. See *Fig. 6.* Remove ignitors and attaching screws from distributor housing. Remove clips holding vacuum diaphragm links. Remove attaching screws and vacuum control units from distributor housing. Remove condenser.

2) Remove reluctor (signal rotor) shaft attaching screw from end of shaft. Remove pick-up coil base bearing attaching screws. Remove reluctor, reluctor shaft, pick-up coils and coil base bearing assembly from top of distributor drive shaft.

3) Remove reluctor from reluctor shaft, using suitable puller. Remove spring pin. Remove governors by removing springs. Drive lock pin out of driven gear, using a small drift. Remove gear and washers. Remove drive shaft through top of distributor housing.

Reassembly — Inspect distributor cap and rotor for cracks, carbon tracks, and burned or corroded terminals. Assemble distributor in reverse order of disassembly, noting the following: Install reluctor shaft onto distributor drive shaft, engaging slots of reluctor shaft and governor pins. Install pick-up coil and coil base bearing assembly and tighten attaching screws. Install reluctor on shaft, driving spring pin in with a suitable punch.

NIPPONDENSO ELECTRONIC IGNITION SYSTEM

Isuzu	1800 (2WD)	Land Cruiser
I-Mark	Toyota	Pickup
P'UP	Celica	Starlet
LUV	Corolla	Supra
Subaru	Corona	Tercel
1600 (2WD)	Cressida	

DESCRIPTION

Nippondenso electronic ignition system includes a breakerless distributor, an ignitor (ignition control unit), a special ignition coil, an ignition signal generating mechanism (pick-up coil assembly) and ignition switch.

The distributor consists of a housing, rotor and cap. It contains a timing rotor (reluctor), magnet, and pick-up coil assembly. A transistorized ignitor is separate from the distributor. See Fig. 1. Distributors contain conventional centrifugal and vacuum advance mechanisms.

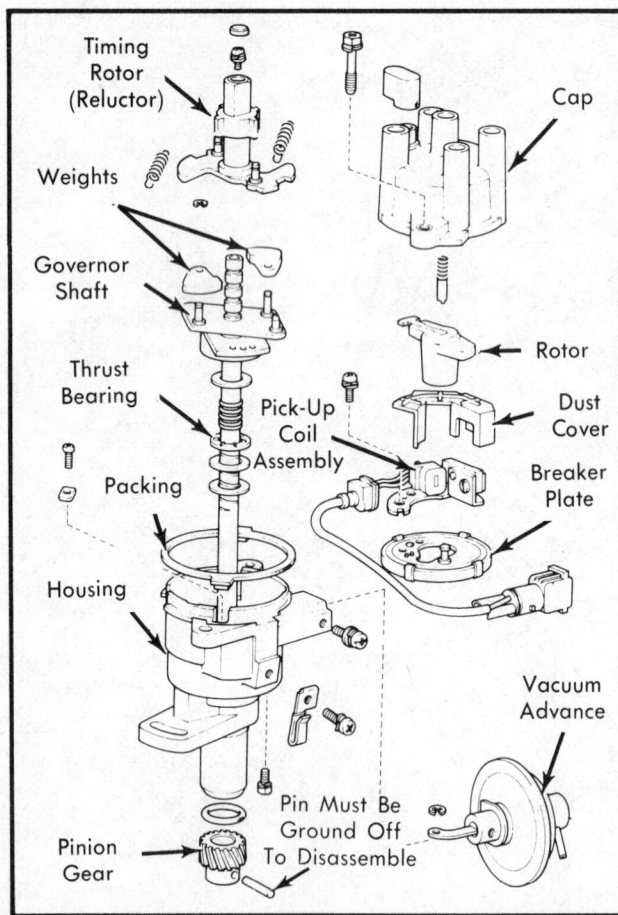

Fig. 1   Exploded View of Typical Nippondenso Distributor (Toyota Model Shown, Others Similar)

OPERATION

As the timing rotor turns with the distributor shaft, its teeth (one for each engine cylinder) pass the pick-up coil assembly. See Fig. 2. As the air gap changes with the approach and passing of each tooth, the magnetic field varies. This creates a signal in the pick-up coil assembly.

The ignitor senses this signal and turns the ignition coil primary circuit on and off. This causes voltage to build and collapse,

resulting in a voltage surge in the secondary that fires the spark plugs.

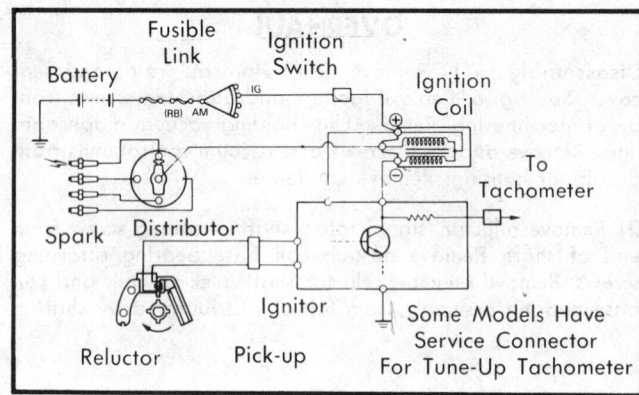

Fig. 2   Schematic of Celica & Corona Electronic Ignition Circuit (Other Models Similar)

SPECIFICATIONS

Centrifugal & Vacuum Advance — See Specifications Tables in this section.

ADJUSTMENT

Timing Rotor (Reluctor)-to-Pick-Up Coil Air Gap — Using a flat feeler gauge, check air gap. Gap should be .008-.016" (0.2-0.4 mm). If not, loosen screws and move pick-up coil against feeler gauge of proper thickness. Tighten screws and recheck air gap.

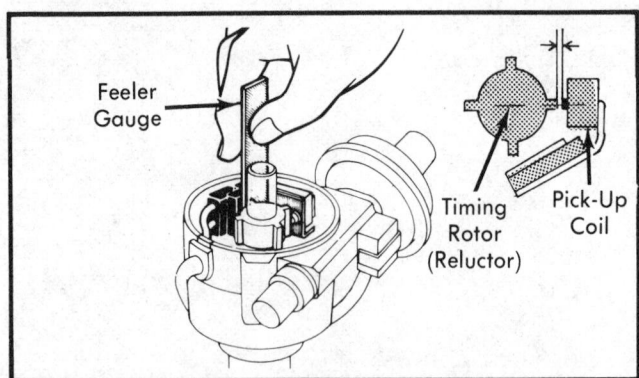

Fig. 3   Checking Timing Rotor-to-Pick-Up Coil Air Gap Using Feeler Gauge

TESTING

CAUTION — Be sure all connections are correct, as reverse battery polarity within the system will damage the ignitor (ignition control unit). Do not disconnect battery while engine is running or transistors may be damaged. Do not allow water to enter ignitor. If a tachometer is connected to system, connect tachometer positive lead to coil negative terminal.

CAUTION — Be especially careful when checking Toyota systems, as a variety of ignition coil, ignitor, and resistor combinations are used. Connectors and wire colors also vary from model to model. Illustrations are for typical systems only.

NIPPONDENSO ELECTRONIC IGNITION SYSTEM (Cont.)

IGNITION COIL TEST

NOTE – *All tests on the ignition coil are made with an ohmmeter with the ignition switch in the "OFF" position. If the resistance for any test is not within specifications, replace ignition coil.*

Primary Coil Resistance – Connect an ohmmeter set in x1 range so leads touch coil positive and negative primary terminals (or connector terminals leading to them). *See Ignition Coil Resistance chart.*

Secondary Coil Resistance – Set an ohmmeter in the x100 range. Connect leads to coil primary terminal and to coil tower (high tension terminal). *See Ignition Coil Resistance chart.*

Resistor Resistance – Connect an ohmmeter, set in the x1 range, so that leads are connected to each side of resistor (or resistance wire), if equipped. *See Ignition Coil Resistance chart.*

Ignition Coil Resistance (Ohms)

Application	Primary Resistance	Secondary Resistance
Isuzu & LUV	1.13-1.53	10,200-13,800
Toyota		
Celica & Corona	0.8-1.1	10,700-14,500
Corolla	0.8-1.1	11,500-15,500
Cressida, Land Cruiser & Supra	0.5-0.7	11,500-15,500
Pickup	0.4-0.5	8,500-11,500
Starlet①	1.3-1.7	10,000-15,000
Subaru②	1.06-1.30	12,150-14,850

① – External resistor resistance 1.1-1.3 ohms.
② – External resistor resistance 1.4-1.6 ohms.

Insulation Resistance – Connect ohmmeter leads between coil positive terminal and mounting bracket of coil. Reading on all models should exceed 10,000 ohms (infinity).

High Tension Wire Resistance — Set ohmmeter to x1000 scale and attach leads to ends of high tension wire. On Isuzu and LUV, resistance should not exceed 73,500 ohms per foot. On all other models, resistance should not exceed 25,000 ohms. If it does, replace wires.

Pick-Up Coil Resistance – Measure pick-up coil resistance at distributor connector with ohmmeter. Check value against table.

Pick-Up Coil Resistance (Ohms)

Application	Resistance
Cressida, Starlet & Supra	140-180
All Other Models	130-190

IGNITOR TESTS

NOTE – *Tests apply to Isuzu, LUV and Toyota models. Two different procedures are used for Toyota, depending on the model.*

Pickup & Starlet Models – 1) Turn ignition switch "ON". On Pickup, disconnect Brown and Yellow wiring harness connectors. Connect voltmeter positive lead to the brown connector on wiring harness side.

2) On Starlet, remove coil cover. Connect voltmeter positive lead to resistor positive terminal and voltmeter negative lead to ground. All readings should be 12 volts.

3) On Pickup, reconnect Brown wiring harness connector. Connect voltmeter positive lead to Yellow connector (ignitor side). Connect negative lead to ignitor body. Reading should be 12 volts. On Starlet, connector voltmeter positive lead to coil negative terminal and negative lead to ground. Voltage should be less than 3 volts.

4) On all models, unplug wiring connector from distributor. Using a 1.5 volt dry cell battery, connect battery positive pole to Pink wire terminal and negative pole to White wire terminal. On Starlet, connect voltmeter positive probe to coil negative terminal and negative probe to ground.

5) On Pickup, connect voltmeter positive probe to Yellow connector (ignitor side) and negative probe to ground. Readings should be 7 volts.

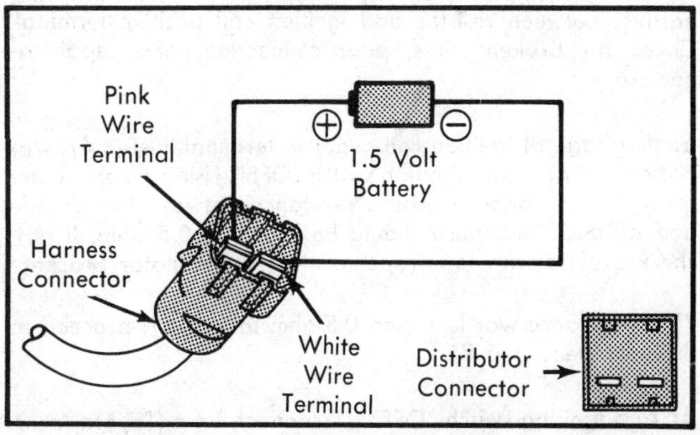

Fig. 4 Checking Ignitor Operation with 1.5 Volt Battery

Other Models – 1) Turn ignition switch "ON". Connect negative voltmeter lead to ground and positive lead to ignition coil postive terminal. Voltage reading should be 12 volts.

2) Connect voltmeter positive lead to ignition coil negative terminal. Negative lead should still be attached to ground. Voltage should read 12 volts. Unplug wiring harness connector from distributor.

3) Using a 1.5 volt dry cell battery, connect battery positive pole to Pink wire terminal and negative pole to White wire terminal. Voltage at negative terminal of coil should read 7 volts for Toyota and 5 volts for Isuzu and LUV. If not, replace ignitor.

CAUTION – *Do not apply voltage for more than 5 seconds.*

IGNITION SYSTEM TEST

NOTE – *Although this information applies basically to Subaru models, the same principle applies to Toyota models with resistors or resistance wires.*

1) Turn ignition switch "ON". Connect negative lead of a voltmeter to ground and positive lead (in turn) to each of the resistor terminals "a" and "b". One reading should be battery voltage, the other reading should be one half that voltage. If so, proceed to step **10)**.

2) If there was no voltage at either terminal in step **1)**, check wiring harness, connector, ignition switch and fuse between

NIPPONDENSO ELECTRONIC IGNITION SYSTEM (Cont.)

battery and resistor. Check for broken wires, poor connections, and battery condition.

3) If there was voltage at only one of the resistor terminals in step **1)**, turn ignition switch "ON" and disconnect lead wire from terminal having no voltage. Check resistor terminal for voltage. If none, replace resistor. If voltage now exists, check wiring harness between resistor and positive terminal of ignition coil for short circuit. Repair or replace as necessary.

4) If there was voltage at both terminals, but one was not about one-half battery voltage, turn ignition switch "ON". Connect voltmeter negative lead to ground and positive lead to ignition coil negative terminal. Reading should be battery voltage.

5) If not, turn ignition switch "ON" and connect voltmeter negative lead to ground and positive lead to ignition coil positive terminal. Reading should be battery voltage. If not, replace ignition coil. If battery voltage is shown, check wiring harness between resistor and ignition coil positive terminal. Check for broken wires, poor connections and repair as necessary.

6) If voltage at ignition coil negative terminal in step **4)**, was battery voltage, turn ignition switch "OFF". Using an ohmmeter set in the x1 range, measure resistance between ignitor side and ground. Resistance should be less than 0.5 ohm. If not, check ground wire for proper contact at regulator bracket.

7) If resistance was less than 0.5 ohm in step **6)**, proceed to the next step, step **8)**.

8) Turn ignition switch "OFF". Disconnect 2-pin (Toyota) or 3-pin (Subaru) distributor connector. Disconnect high tension wire at distributor and hold it about ¼" (6 mm) from engine block. Turn ignition switch "ON". Check if spark jumps when a small voltage (1-6 volts) is applied intermittently on terminals "1" (pink wire) and "2" (white wire) on ignitor side of connector.

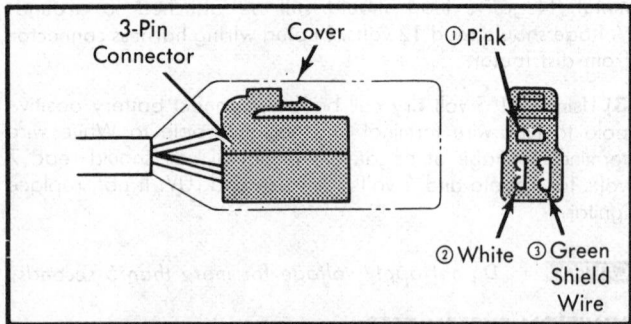

Fig. 5 Conducting Tests at Distributor Connector (Subaru Shown)

CAUTION — *Do not use battery voltage (12 volts) for this test or ignitor may be damaged.*

9) If spark jumps gap, there is no problem with the ignition system. If no spark occurs, replace ignitor.

10) If during step **1)**, the voltage at one resistor terminal was one-half that of the other, turn the ignition switch "ON". Connect negative lead of voltmeter to a good ground and

positive lead to ignition coil negative terminal. If reading is not below 0.5 volt, check wiring harness for shorts, check loose connections at coil negative terminal and repair as necessary. If no problem is found, perform steps **8)** and **9)** again.

11) If in step **10)** reading was below 0.5 volts, turn ignition switch "OFF" and disconnect 2-pin connector. Using an ohmmeter set to x100 range, connect leads to terminals "1" (Pink wire) and "2" (White wire) of distributor connector (distributor side).

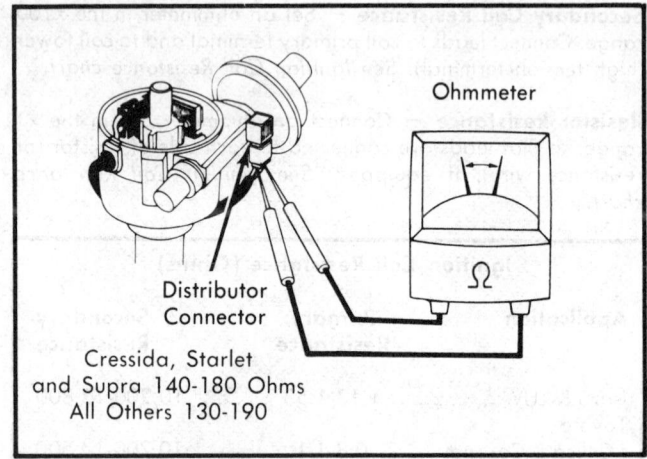

Fig. 6 Check Pick-Up Coil Resistance With Ohmmeter

12) If resistance reading is incorrect, replace pick-up coil assembly. If correct, turn ignition switch "OFF" and check timing rotor (reluctor)-to-pick-up coil air gap. If not .008-.016" (0.2-0.4 mm), adjust as necessary. If air gap is correct, perform steps **8)** and **9)** again.

OVERHAUL

NOTE — *Procedure is general only. Some models may differ slightly.*

Disassembly — **1)** Remove distributor cap rotor, dust cover, and packing. Remove pick-up coil assembly, vacuum advance mechanism, breaker plate and drive pinion.

2) Remove 2 screws from bottom of distributor housing and using a plastic hammer, carefully drive out shaft. Remove thick washer, bearing, thin washer, spring, and blue washer from shaft.

3) Remove governor springs, cam cap, timing rotor (reluctor), weight snap ring and weights.

Reassembly — Assemble in reverse order of disassembly, noting the following:

- Lightly grease timing rotor (reluctor) inner surface. Install on shaft aligning mark on stopper plate ("10.5" on Isuzu and LUV, "15.5" on Subaru, "12" on Celica, Corona and Pickup, "10" on Corolla, "14" on Starlet, "8" on Supra and Cressida, and "11.5" on Tercel).
- When installing breaker plate, align 4 clips of plate with 4 grooves in housing.
- When replacing pinion, replace pin and pinion as a set. Adjust air gap between timing rotor and pick-up coil.

PORSCHE DIGITAL IGNITION TIMING CONTROL

Porsche
924 Turbo

DESCRIPTION

Porsche has developed a computerized engine control system called Digital Ignition Timing Control (DITC) for the 924 Turbo model. Using various engine sensors, the system provides the best ignition timing for optimum engine power, emission control and fuel economy under all operating conditions. The DITC systems consists of the following components: a computer control unit, igntion control unit, pressure sensor (located inside the computer control unit), temperature sensor, throttle switch, crankshaft sensor, distributor and an ignition coil. The crankshaft flywheel has an extra ring of 100 teeth with one tooth being a reference tooth.

OPERATION

As the crankshaft rotates, the crankshaft sensor sends pulses to the computer control unit. From these pulses, the computer control unit determines engine speed and crankshaft (piston position) position. When the engine is running, the computer control unit receives information from the various engine sensors and determines the appropriate time to signal the ignition control unit. The ignition control unit makes and breaks the circuit to the coil, thus firing the spark plug. The computer control unit also controls idle speed, whenever accessories (A/C, lights, etc.) are turned on, by advancing or retarding the ignition timing. With this system, idle speed is adjusted using a timing light.

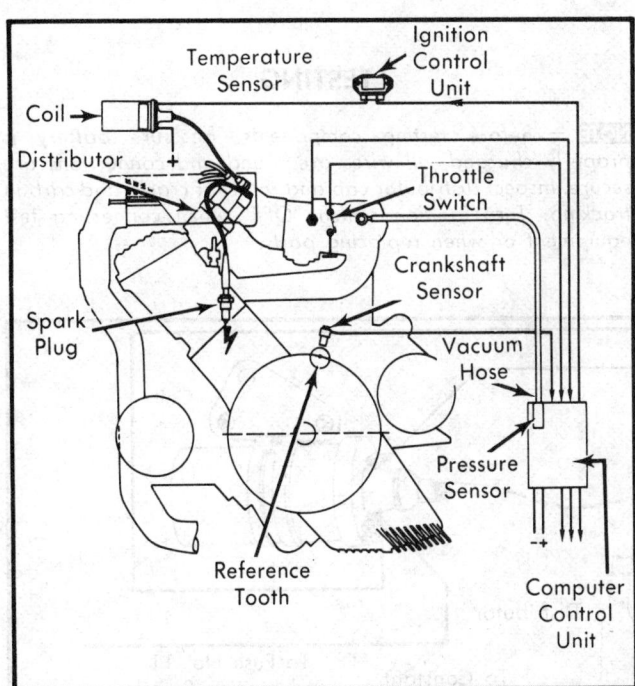

Fig. 1   Porsche Digital Ignition Timing Control Showing Component Location

NOTE — *Testing, Removal & Installation and Overhaul information not available from manufacturer.*

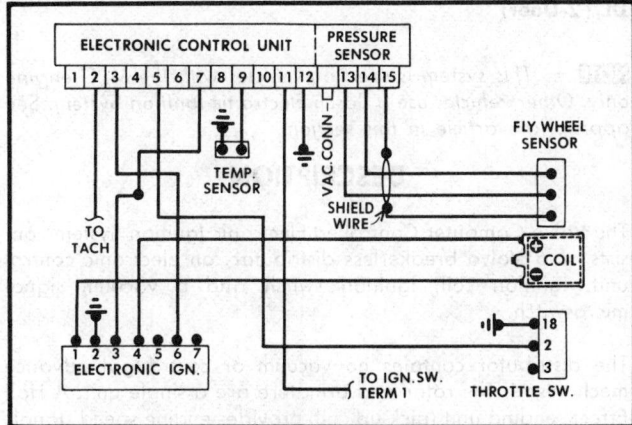

Fig. 2   Porsche Digital Ignition Timing Control Wiring Diagram

ADJUSTMENT

IDLE ADJUSTMENT

NOTE — *The Digital Ignition Timing Control system controls idle speed by varing the ignition timing. Idle speed adjustments are made using an ignition timing light.*

1) With engine off, remove temperature sensor from intake manifold and place it in the fresh air tray behind engine firewall. Leave wire connected to sensor. Install a plug into temperature sensr hole (in intake maifold).

2) Start and run engine until normal operating temperature is reached. Connect a CO tester as per maufacturers instructions. Attach a timing light to engine.

3) Turn the idle control screw (air by-pass screw) until ignition timing mark (dot on flywheel) is fully visible at timing pointer edge. Check idle speed. Speed should be below 900 RPM.

NOTE — *Timing mark (dot) will move around because of the computer regulating timing.*

4) If necessary, adjust CO level at same time idle adjustment is being made. With idle speed (and CO level) adjusted, turn engine off and remove all test equipment. Replace temperature sensor.

REMOVAL & INSTALLATION

DISTRIBUTOR

NOTE — *When removing distributor, crank engine until number 1 cylinder is at TDC (Z1 mark on flywheel will line up with timing pointer edge and mark on camshaft srocket will be opposite valve cover).*

NOTE — *When installing distributor, align distributor so that tab for distributor cap faces flywheel and mounting clips face in same direction as car (front to rear). Also, rotor must align with cylinder number 1 mark on distributor cap.*

NOTE — *Testing, overhaul and other component removal and installation procedures are not available from maufacturer.*

Distributors & Ignition Systems

VOLVO COMPUTER CONTROLLED ELECTRONIC IGNITION SYSTEM

DL (2-Door)

NOTE — *This system is used on vehicles with the MPG engine only. Other vehicles use a Bosch Electronic Ignition System. See appropriate article in this section.*

DESCRIPTION

The Volvo Computer Controlled Electronic Ignition System consists of a Volvo breakerless distributor, an electronic control unit, ignition coil, ignition switch and a vacuum signal microswitch.

The distributor contains no vacuum or centrifugal advance mechanisms. The rotor and armature are a single unit. A Hall Effect sending unit (pick-up coil) provides engine speed signals to the electronic control unit. The distributor also consists of necessary wiring and distributor cap.

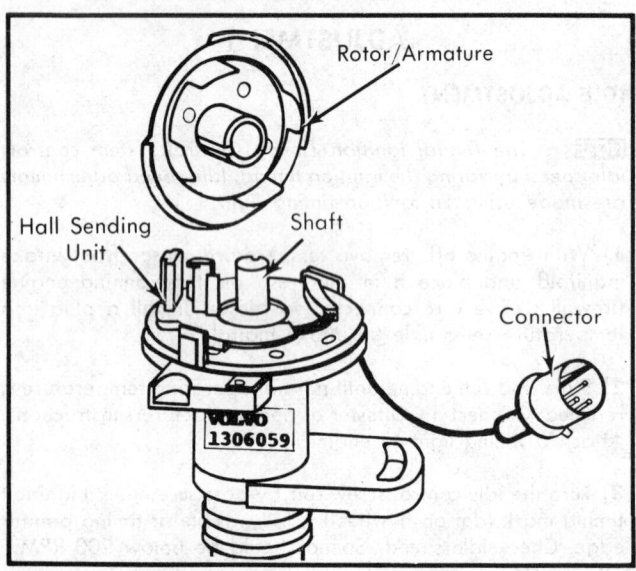

Fig. 1 Exploded View of Volvo Breakerless Distributor

OPERATION

As the engine turns the distributor shaft, the shutter blades of the rotor/armature assembly pass through the Hall Effect pick-up coil. A signal is then sent to the electronic control unit. The electronic control unit receives engine speed information from distributor and engine load information from intake manifold.

Speed and vacuum signals are processed in the electronic control unit to control spark advance and dwell. A throttle position microswitch (located on the airflow meter) provides throttle information. Under normal conditions, the throttle position signal is sent to the electronic control unit. The manifold vacuum signal is also processed by the control unit to control ignition timing. When the throttle is closed, (during deceleration and idle) the circuit is closed and no signal is received at the control unit.

The computer analyzes all information and fires spark plugs at the proper time by interrupting signal to ignition coil primary circuit. This causes a high voltage surge in the secondary circuit, firing the spark plug.

The electronic control unit can operate without the micro-processor in the "LIMP HOME" or "CRANK" mode. When the engine is first started, it runs in the "CRANK" mode until engine speed reaches 1500 RPM. At this point the micro-processor takes over, controlling all engine speeds down to 250 RPM. The vehicle operates at a fixed ignition timing in "LIMP HOME" mode to allow vehicle to be driven to a service facility.

TESTING

NOTE — *Before testing components, be sure battery is properly charged, all wires are sound and connections are secure. Inspect distributor cap and rotor for cracks and carbon tracking. Turn ignition switch "OFF" when connecting test equipment or when replacing parts.*

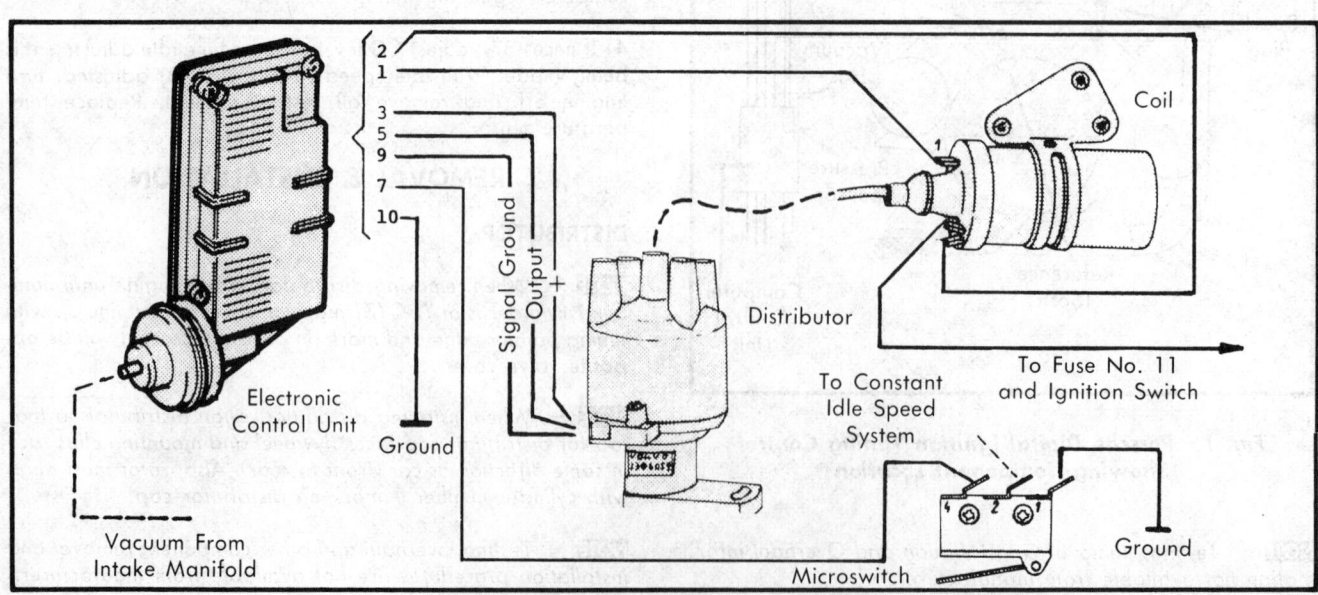

Fig. 2 Schematic of Volvo Computer Controlled Ignition System

ELECTRICAL

VOLVO COMPUTER CONTROLLED ELECTRONIC IGNITION SYSTEM (Cont.)

ENGINE STARTS BUT WILL NOT RUN PROPERLY

1) Check ignition timing with vacuum hose at electronic control unit disconnected. Timing of 10-14° BTDC is acceptable. Check advance by increasing engine speed and observing whether timing advances. If necessary, try a new electronic control unit and re-test.

2) Check vacuum advance. Run engine at approximately 1500 RPM with vacuum hose disconnected. Connect vacuum hose and ensure that timing changes. If not, check vacuum line. If line is ok, try a known good control unit.

TESTING SYSTEM WHEN ENGINE WILL NOT START

In cold start situations where the engine will not start, perform the following test.

SPARKING TEST

1) Disconnect high tension wire at distributor cap and hold approximately ½" (12 mm) from engine block. Crank engine. If spark occurs, check rotor and distributor cap. Ensure spark is reaching spark plugs.

2) If no spark occurs, disconnect connector at distributor. Connect a jumper wire to pin "A" in electronic control unit connector. *See Fig. 3.* With ignition "ON", touch pin "C" with other end of jumper wire and check for spark.

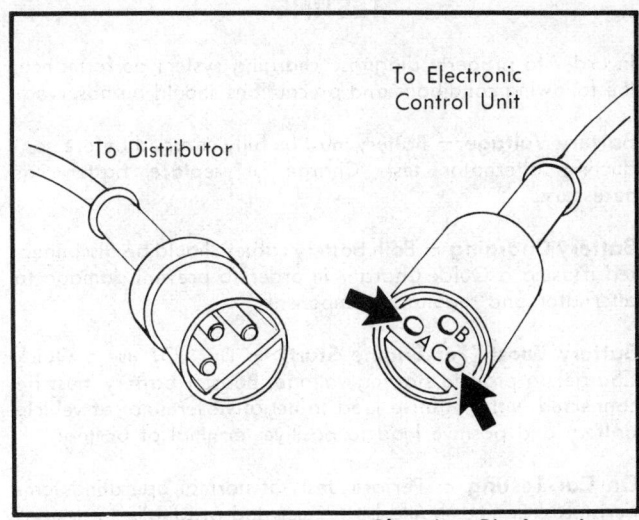

Fig. 3   Distributor Connector Showing Pin Locations

3) If no spark occurs, proceed to step **4)**. If spark occurs, touch a jumper to pin "B" and check for spark. If spark occurs, try a new Hall sender in distributor. If there is no spark, replace electronic control unit.

4) If no spark occured in step **2)**, check wire and connectors carefully. If no fault is found, try a new electronic control unit. If there is still no spark, try a new ignition coil.

Alternators & Regulators

GENERAL SERVICING

TESTING

In order to properly diagnose charging system performance, the following conditions and precautions should be observed:

Battery Voltage — Battery must be fully charged before conducting alternator test. Charge or replace battery as necessary.

Battery Charging — Both battery cables should be disconnected if using a Quick Charger in order to prevent damage to alternator and regulator components.

Battery Boost (For Engine Start) — Do NOT use a Quick Charger to provide starting voltage. Booster battery must be connected with negative lead to negative terminal of vehicle battery and positive lead to positive terminal of battery.

On Car Testing — Perform tests at normal operating temperatures. Engine should be accelerated gradually to desired testing RPM and returned to lower RPM as soon as possible. Do NOT race engine.

CAUTION — *Never disconnect battery or alternator leads while alternator is running. Reverse polarity or excessive voltage will severely damage the charging system.*

Electrical Connections — All electrical connections must be clean and snug for proper system operation. It is recommended that battery cables be disconnected, cleaned and tightened whenever performing charging system maintenance. Regulator must be properly grounded also.

Component Replacement — In order to prevent stray voltage or shorts, always disconnect battery prior to alternator or regulator removal.

Drive Belt — Drive belts must not be cracked, glazed or oily, and must be set at proper tension. A glazed belt may slip even though belt is not loose.

NOTE — *Excessive drive belt tension can cause bearing or case failure. Do NOT overtighten to correct for slippage.*

Disassembly — Case halves and stator should be scribed prior to separation for proper orientation when reassembling.

Diode Test and Replacement — Never use a high voltage source to test diodes. Use a low voltage source to check for one-way current flow. If replacement is required, soldering operations must be performed quickly to prevent diode damage. Diode lead should be pinched with pliers to prevent heat transfer to diode.

Rotor and Stator Testing — Continuity with minimum resistance should be noted between slip rings. No continuity should exist between either slip ring and rotor core or shaft. Stator conduction is normal when there is continuity between leads of stator coil but NOT between stator coil leads and stator core.

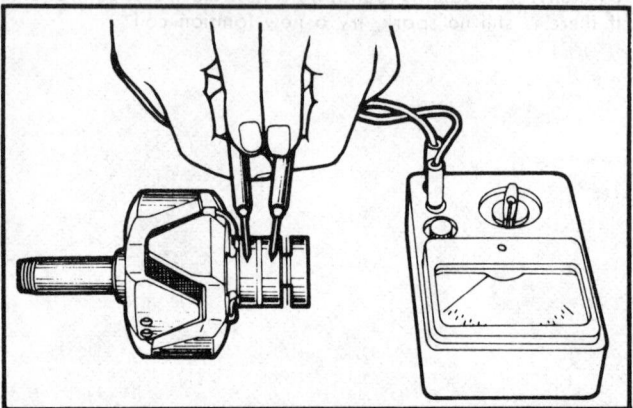

Fig. 1   Rotor Coil Continuity Test

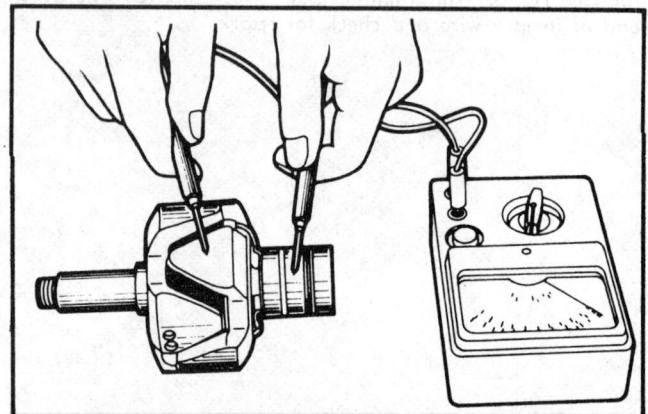

Fig. 3   Rotor Coil Ground Test

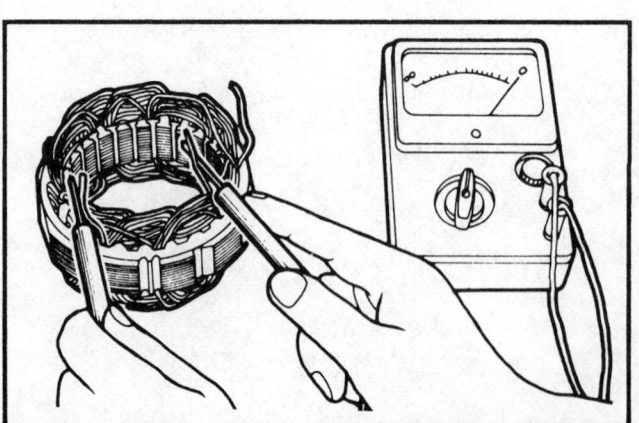

Fig. 2   Stator Coil Continuity Test

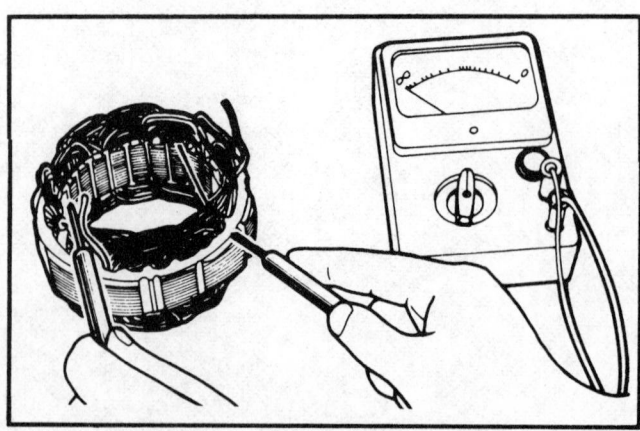

Fig. 4   Stator Coil Ground Test

GENERAL SERVICING (Cont.)
CHARGING SYSTEM TROUBLE SHOOTING

CONDITION & POSSIBLE CAUSE	CONDITION & POSSIBLE CAUSE
No Output • Sticking brushes or brush springs. • Dirty brushes or slip rings. • Loose or dirty wiring connections. • Broken leads. • Open or shorted stator windings. • Open or shorted rotor windings. • Open diodes. • Grounded terminals. • Broken fan belt. • Fuse or warning light defective. **Excessive Output** • Broken neutral wire. • Defective voltage regulator. • Poor ground on alternator and regulator terminals. • Broken ground wire. • Defective battery. **Noisy Alternator** • Loose mounting bracket. • Loose drive pulley. • Defective alternator bearings. • Brushes improperly seated on rotor.	**Low Output** • Loose or worn fan belt. • Sticking brushes. • Low brush spring tension. • Defective voltage regulator. • Dirty slip rings. • Partial short, ground or open in stator windings. • Partial short, ground or open in rotor windings. • Open diode. **Battery Does Not Stay Charged** • Loose or worn drive belt. • Loose or corroded cable connections. • Electrical accessories left on or exceeding charging capacity. • Charging rate too low. • Low speed driving of short duration. **Battery Overcharged** • Defective battery. • Battery overheated. • Excessive alternator output voltage. • Long distance high speed driving.

Alternators & Regulators

BOSCH ALTERNATORS

Audi	Porsche
BMW	Saab
Fiat	Volkswagen
Mercedes-Benz	Volvo

DESCRIPTION

Bosch alternators are conventional 3 phase, self rectifying type alternators. Nine rectifier diodes are connected to stator windings (3 to each phase lead). Diodes change alternator A.C. voltages to D.C. voltages coming out of the "B+" and the "D+" terminals of the alternator.

APPLICATION

Model	Volts/Amps	①Bosch Part No.
Audi		
4000		
Standard	14/55	469 520
Heavy Duty	14/65	489 713
California	14/35	469 502
5000		
Gasoline & Diesel	14/35	469 502
Gasoline Only	14/55	489 653
Gasoline & Diesel	14/65	489 613
All With A/C	14/90	489 514
BMW		
320i	14/65	489 718
528i, 633CSi, 733i	14/65	489 619
Fiat		
Brava & Spider		
Standard	14/55	489 743
With A/C	14/65	489 824
Mercedes-Benz		
240D	14/55	489 556
280 Series	14/35	489 751
300 Series	14/55	489 527
300 Turbo	14/55	489 683
380 Series	14/70	489 898
Porsche 924	14/75	469 502
Saab		
99	14/55	489 783
900	14/55	489 735
Volkswagen		
Dasher		
Gasoline	14/55	489 622
Diesel	14/55	489 520
Calif. & All With A/C	14/65	489 713
Jetta, Rabbit & Scirocco		
Standard	14/45	489 858
With A/C	14/65	489 713
Rabbit Diesel		
Standard	14/35	489 799
With A/C	14/65	489 712
Vanagon	14/65	489 913
Volvo		
Standard	14/55	400 933
Heavy Duty	14/70	450 009
Diesel	14/55	②1257294

① — Bosch part numbers are preceded by 0`120 for alternators. Integral regulator models are numbered 469 and 489, while separate regulator models are numbered 400 and 450.

② — Volvo part number.

ON VEHICLE TESTING

NOTE — Off vehicle testing is included in Overhaul procedures in this article.

WIRING CONTINUITY TEST

Disconnect terminal plug from rear of alternator and connect a voltmeter negative terminal to ground. With ignition "ON", connect positive lead to each of the connector wires in turn. Voltmeter should read battery voltage as each positive connection is made. If proper voltage is not read, trace each wire to find fault.

VOLTAGE DROP TEST — GROUND SIDE

Connect voltmeter between negative terminal of battery and alternator housing. Start engine and run at approximately 3000 RPM. If voltmeter reading exceeds .25 volt, a high resistance in negative side of charging circuit is indicated. If so, check for loose, dirty or corroded connections.

OUTPUT TEST

Disconnect terminal plug from rear of alternator and connect ammeter in series between alternator center terminal and corresponding socket in terminal plug. Connect a jumper lead between the "D+" terminal and its corresponding socket in terminal plug. Start engine and run at approximately 3000 RPM. Turn on headlights and leave on for 5 minutes. Ammeter should read maximum alternator amperage at normal operating temperature.

REGULATOR CONTROL VOLTAGE TEST

Connect voltmeter between battery terminals. Connect ammeter in series between "B+" terminal of alternator and corresponding terminal of connector plug. Connect a jumper lead between alternator "D+" terminal and corresponding terminal of connector plug. Start engine and increase speed to approximately 3000 RPM. Run engine until charging rate falls below 3-5 amps. Voltmeter should then read 13.7-14.4 volts. If these readings are not obtained, replace regulator.

NOTE — Test cables should not be removed or load excessively reduced during testing procedure. Considerable load variations may damage the diodes. Control lamp should not go on at any time during the test.

OVERHAUL

DISASSEMBLY

1) Scribe mark for alignment on front and rear alternator housing. Remove nut, pulley, fan and key. Unscrew brush plate assembly and remove from alternator. Remove frame bolts and separate rear frame from front frame with rotor. Press rotor from frame and bearing from rotor. Remove insulation from wires and cut wires as close to soldered joints as possible.

NOTE — On 4XX 6XX series alternators, lift and secure brushes prior to disassembly.

BOSCH ALTERNATORS (Cont.)

2) Diodes may be tested at this point without further dis-assembly. Use care with insulating bushings under positive diode carrier. To remove negative carrier, extract threaded studs. When one diode has been damaged due to short circuiting, the 3 complementing diodes must also be replaced. Unscrew nuts on both "B+" terminal bolts and lift positive carrier (heat sink) up and back.

TESTING AND REPAIRING

Diode Assemblies — Test diodes with suitable tester before dismantling slip ring and end frame. DO NOT lay positive diode carrier on housing or a false reading will be obtained. Disconnect conductor from "D+" to exciter diodes at heat sink. Unscrew spring and brush holder and remove from alternator. Unsolder stator lead and negative diode connections. Unscrew exciter diodes heat sink and remove together with positive diodes heat sink. Clean all components with trichlorethylene prior to further testing.

Stator — Test stator for short circuits to ground. Tester voltage should be 40V AC. Measure resistance of stator windings between phase connections. Fiesta should indicate .14-.16 ohms, with all remaining models showing .20 to .22 ohms.

Rotor — Test claw pole rotor for short circuits to ground using 40V AC tester. Measure resistance of exciter (field coil) in rotor with ohmmeter across slip rings. Resistance should be 4.0-4.4 ohms. If necessary, turn slip rings in a lathe, noting maximum runout of .001" (.03 mm) and minimum diameter of 1.25" (31.5 mm). Maximum pole wheel runout should not exceed .002" (.05 mm).

Diode Replacement — In case diodes are found to be defective, entire diode plate assembly should be replaced. Care must be exercised in soldering near diodes due to possible damage from excess heat. Use flat jawed pliers as heat sink applied to leads when soldering diode connections.

Drive End Frame — Check ball bearings for wear and replace as necessary. Lubricate ball bearings on one side. Press ball bearing into drive end frame with shielded side downward. Screw on retainer plate. Press ball bearing on slip ring end of rotor and press drive end frame onto drive end of rotor.

Carbon Brushes — Minimum brush length is .2" (5 mm). If replacement is required, grip brush with flat-jawed pliers and unsolder brushes. Do not allow solder to run into strands of brush leads. Brush must be free to slide in holder with normal spring tension of 10-14 ozs. (283-397 g).

REASSEMBLY

1) Solder stator and diode connections using caution not to overheat diodes. Place stator and diode assembly in rear housing and secure with screws.

2) Lubricate new rear bearing and press onto rotor shaft, assuring that shielded side of bearing faces slip rings. Place front bearing in housing with shielded side rearward. Install retainer plate.

3) Place spacer ring on rotor shaft and install rotor assembly into front housing. Press front bearing retaining ring over shaft and into front housing with a socket.

4) Coat bearing bore of rear housing with grease and install spring washer. Assemble front housing with rotor to rear housing, using a turning or twisting motion to seat rear bearing. Line up scribed alignment marks and install screws through housing.

5) Install shaft key, washer, fan, spacer, pulley, lock washer and nut. Install brush and connector plug assembly and retain with screws.

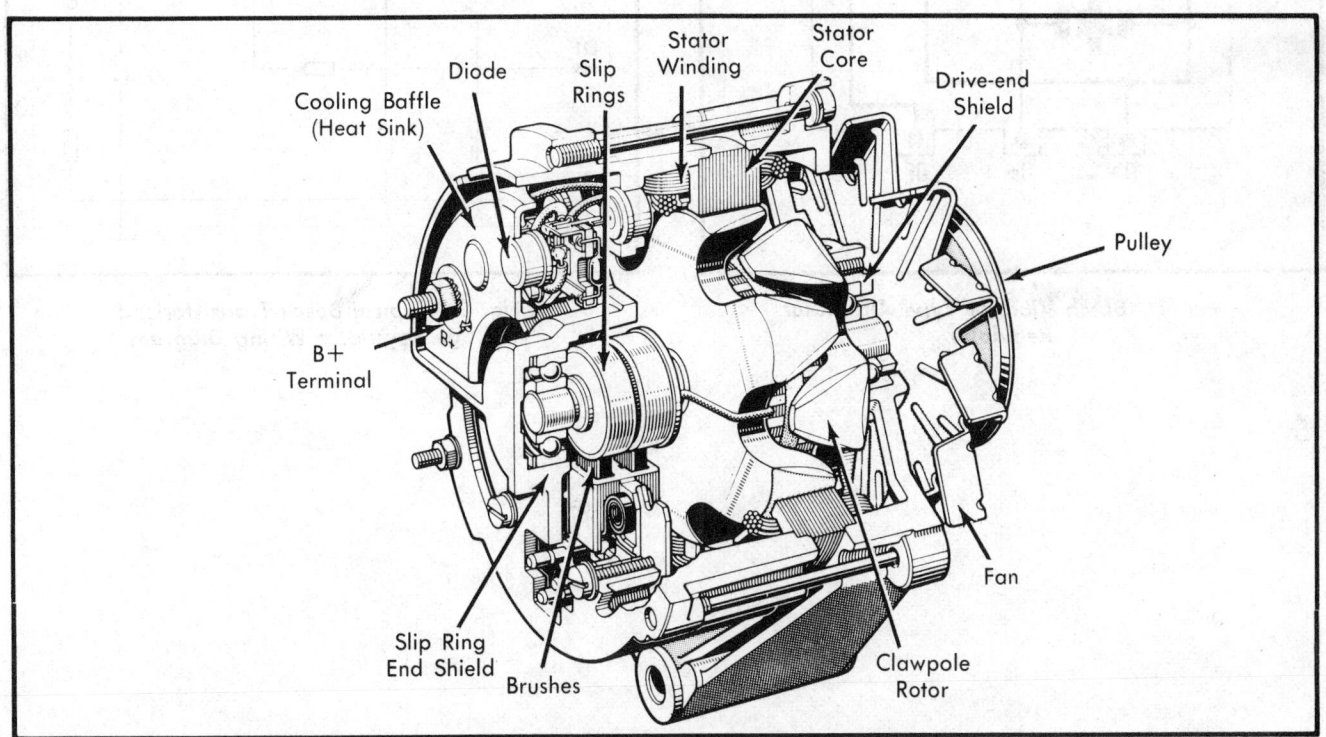

Fig. 1   Cutaway View of Bosch Alternator

Alternators & Regulators

BOSCH REGULATORS

Audi
BMW
Fiat
Mercedes-Benz

DESCRIPTION

Bosch regulators are provided in either transistorized solid state or the vibrating contact type. Vibrating type is mounted separate from alternator. Solid state type may be integral with alternator or separately mounted. Vibrator model is designated "ADN" and externally mounted solid state type is designated "ED". Integral mounted solid state regulator is designated "EE".

NOTE — For Regulator Applications and additional Testing procedures, see Bosch Alternators in this Section.

TESTING

ON CAR TEST

Vibrator Type — Install a battery post adapter at the positive post of the battery. Connect voltmeter across battery. Connect a tachometer to ignition system. Make sure all electrical acessories are turned off. Start engine with battery post adapter switch closed; open switch as soon as engine is started. With engine speed at 4000 RPM, after voltage reading stabilizes, any reading between 13.7 and 14.8 volts is satisfactory.

Transistorized (Solid State) Regulators — All applicable regulators are designed to maintain from 13.7 to 14.5 volts at a load current of 5 to 7 amps. Alternator should be driven at 4000 RPM and load current set at load current rating. Resistance and speed of alternator may be readjusted if necessary. Read voltage within 1 minute. If not within specifications, regulator requires replacement.

ADJUSTMENT

NOTE — If regulator fails to keep voltage within specified limits, it must be replaced. No adjusting procedures are recommended.

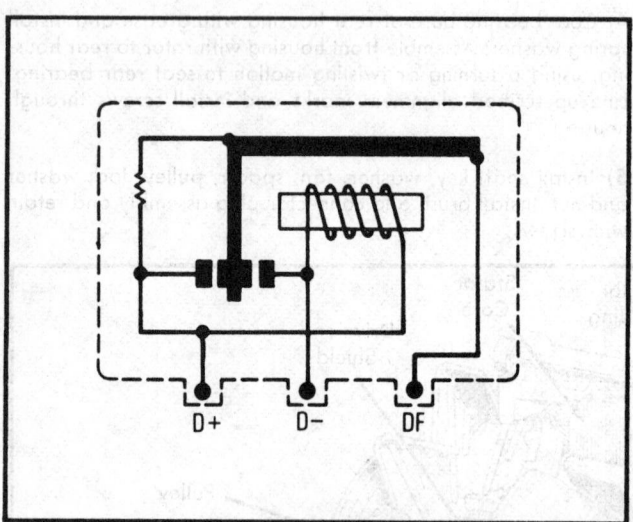

Fig. 1   Bosch Vibrator Type Alternator Regulator

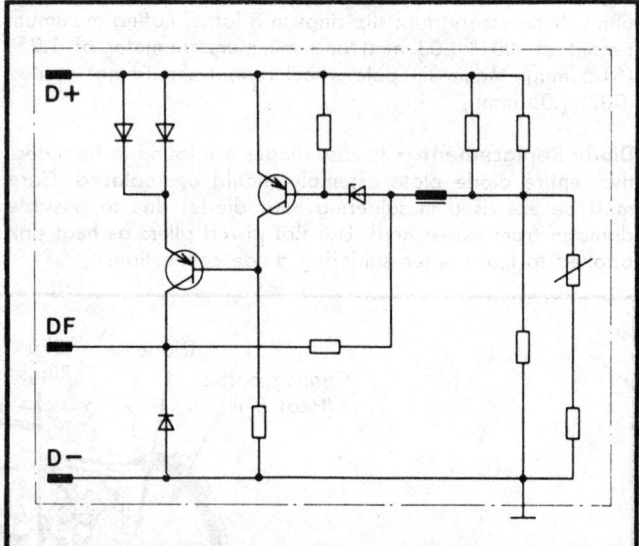

Fig. 2   Typical Bosch Transistorized Voltage Regulator Wiring Diagram

HITACHI ALTERNATORS

Datsun (With IC Regulator)
LUV
Subaru

DESCRIPTION

Hitachi alternators are conventional 3 phase, self rectifying type alternators. Six diodes (3 positive and 3 negative) are used to rectify current.

APPLICATION

Model	Hitachi Type No.
Datsun	
200SX	LR160-78
210	LR150-99
280ZX	LR160-82
310	LR160-125
510	LR150-98
810	LR160-82
Pickup	
2WD	
Standard	LR150-98
Heavy Duty	LR160-78
4WD	
Standard	LR150-52
Heavy Duty	LR160-78
Diesel	LR150-133B
LUV	
Standard	LT140-126
Optional	LT150-144
Optional	LT150-131B
Subaru	
GL Hatchback & Station Wagon (4WD)	LT150-114B
All Other Models	LT150-120

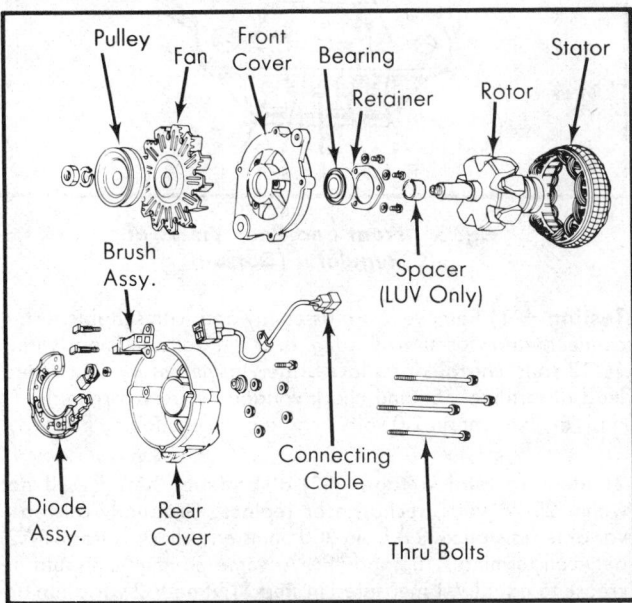

Fig. 1   Disassembled View of Typical Hitachi Alternator

TESTING

NOTE — *Some testing is described as part of Overhaul procedure in this article. The following testing is performed with alternator on the vehicle.*

SPECIFICATIONS

Alternator	Alternator Output	
	Amps@ 2500 RPM①	Amps@ 5000 RPM①
LR150-52	40	50
LR150-98	40	50
LR150-99	40	50
LR160-78	50	60
LR160-82	50	60
LR160-125	42	50
LR160-133B	42	50
LT140-126	30	40
LT150-114B	50	55
LT150-120	42	53
LT150-131B	②17	50
LT150-144	40	50

① — Alternator RPM.
② — At 1250 RPM.

ALTERNATOR TEST ON VEHICLE

Datsun Models — Ensure that battery has a full charge, then connect 30-volt voltmeter as illustrated in *Fig. 2*. Turn ignition switch "ON" and test as follows:

1) If charge light remains OFF, disconnect connector from rear of alternator and ground "L" lead wire. If light remains OFF, replace indicator bulb. If light is ON, reconnect connector and ground "F" terminal by touching brush with grounded wire. If light stays on, replace IC regulator. If light goes out, remove and repair alternator.

2) If light came ON when ignition was turned "ON", start and idle engine. If light is dim, flickers or remains bright, remove and repair alternator. If light went off at idle, run engine at 1500 RPM and turn headlights on high beam. If charge light is on dim, idle engine and measure voltage between terminals "B" and "L". If less than .5 volt, alternator is OK. If more than .5 volt, remove and repair alternator.

NOTE — *Terminals "S", "L", "BAT" and "E" are marked on rear cover of alternator.*

3) If charge light went OFF at 1500 RPM with lights on high beam, measure "B" voltage. If more than 15.5 volts, replace IC regulator. If 13 to 15 volts, idle engine and check indicator light. If OFF, system is OK. If ON, repair faulty alternator.

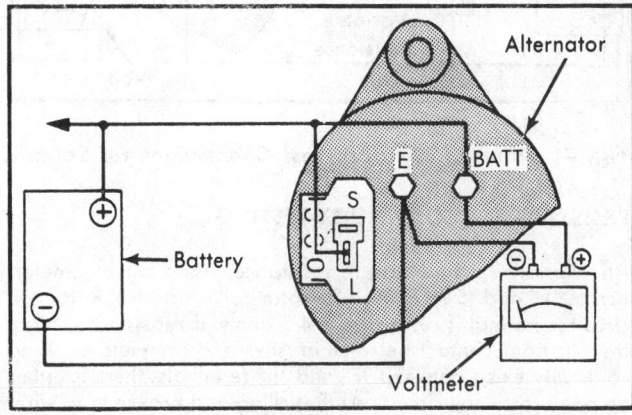

Fig. 2   Alternator Testing Connections for Datsun

Alternators & Regulators

HITACHI ALTERNATORS (Cont.)

Subaru Models — 1) Connect a voltmeter and leads to battery as shown in *Fig. 3*. Operate the alternator and turn off the switch "SW" when alternator speed reaches approximately 800 RPM. Increase speed in small increments while watching voltmeter deflection and read alternator speed when at 14 volts. Speed should be approximately 1000 RPM.

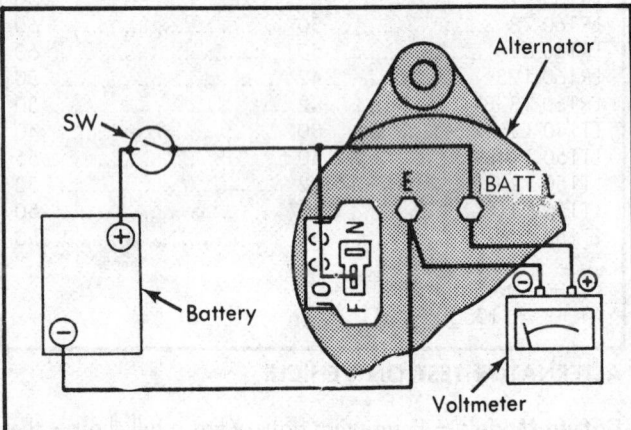

Fig. 3 Alternator Cut-In Speed Test Connections (Subaru)

2) Make test connections using a 30-50 ampere variable resistor, battery, ammeter, and voltmeter as shown in *Fig. 4*. Operate alternator with switch "SW-1" closed. When alternator speed reaches approximately 800 RPM, set the variable resistor to maximum and turn on switch "SW-2". Increase alternator speed while maintaining a constant 14 volts by adjusting resistance. Read current at 2500 RPM and 5000 RPM. Readings should be 37-43 amperes at 2500 RPM and 48-54 at 5000 RPM.

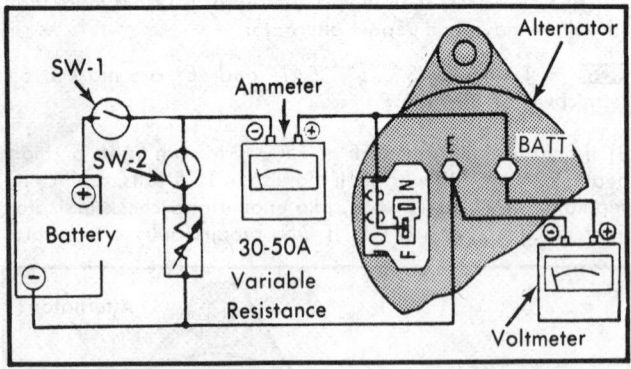

Fig. 4 Alternator Output Test Connections for Subaru

RESISTANCE & CONTINUITY TESTING

All Models — 1) Measure resistance, using an ohmmeter, across "F" and "E" terminals for rotor coil resistance. Rotor coil circuit is normal if resistance is 4-5 ohms. If resistance is high, there is poor contact between brushes and commutator. If no continuity exists between "F" and "E" terminals, there is either an open rotor coil circuit, brush sticking or a broken lead wire. If resistance is low, it indicates a rotor coil layer short or grounded circuit.

NOTE — *The following test will not indicate an open state of the diodes. Tester will indicate continuity regardless of diode conditions if tester leads are connected to the terminals with polarity reversed.*

2) Connect positive lead of tester to alternator "N" terminal, and tester negative lead to alternator "A" terminal. If tester shows continuity, one or more positive diodes are shorted.

3) Next, connect positive lead of tester to alternator "E" terminal, and tester negative lead to alternator "N" terminal. If continuity is indicated, one or more of the negative diodes are shorted.

INTEGRATED CIRCUIT (IC) REGULATOR

An integrated circuit regulator is used on all Datsun models. The voltage regulator is soldered to the brush assembly and mounted inside the alternator.

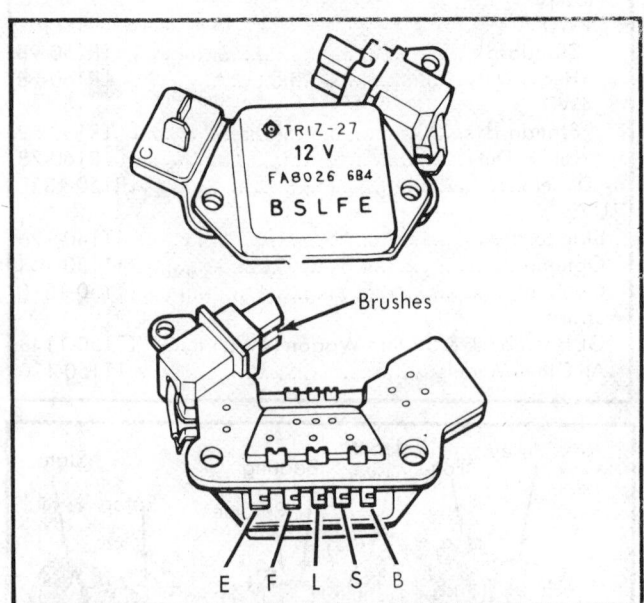

Fig. 5 Front and Rear Views of IC Regulator (Datsun)

Testing — 1) Remove brush assembly and with suitable tester, connect wiring as shown in *Fig. 6*. If V-1 voltage is not within 10-13 volts, charge or replace battery as necessary. Disconnect lead at terminal "S" and check voltage between terminals "F" and "E". If less than 2.0 volts, regulator is functioning properly.

2) Measure total voltage (V-3) of batteries 1 and 2. If not within 20-26 volts, recharge or replace. Gradually decrease variable resistance (Rv) from 300 ohms and check voltage (V-2) between terminals "E" and "F". At some point, V-2 should increase to equal V-1 measured in step 1). If no V-2 variation occurs as described, regulator is defective.

3) Measure voltage (V-4) between center tap of variable resistor (Rv) and terminal "E". With resistance set as in previous step, voltage should be 14.7±.5 volts at 68°F (20°C). At extremely high case temperatures, voltage may be 1 volt lower, while at extremely cold temperatures, voltage may be 1 volt higher.

HITACHI ALTERNATORS (Cont.)

4) Remove test lead from terminal "S" and connect to terminal "B". Repeat steps **2)** and **3)** and check for voltage (V-4) .5-2.0 volts higher than in step **3)**. If testing specifications are not met, it will be necessary to replace the IC regulator/brush assembly.

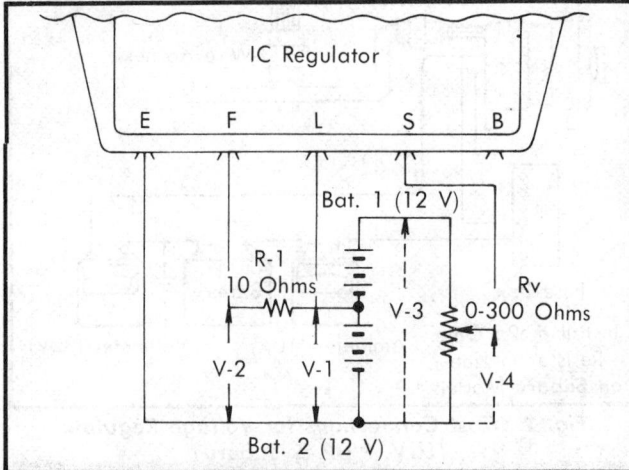

Fig. 6   Regulator Test Arrangement

OVERHAUL

DISASSEMBLY

1) Remove nut and take off pulley, fan, and washers. Pull out spacer. Remove screws securing brush holder and brush holder cover, leaving "N" lead wire connected to stator coil lead.

2) Unscrew through bolts and separate front and rear housings. Remove 3 set screws from bearing retainer and separate rotor from front cover. Pull rear bearing from rotor assembly if replacement is required.

3) Remove diode cover and disconnect stator coil lead wire from diode terminal using a soldering iron. Remove the diode assembly by unscrewing the terminal nut and diode setting nuts. Remove stator from rear cover.

INSPECTION & REPAIR

Rotor — Apply tester to slip rings of rotor. If ohm reading is within 4-5 ohms, rotor continuity is satisfactory. If not, an open connection to the field coil may exist. Next, apply probes to slip ring and rotor core to check for ground. If continuity exists, replace rotor assembly.

Stator — The stator is normal when there is conduction between individual stator core terminals. When there is no conduction between terminals, cable is broken and stator must be replaced. If each lead wire of stator coil (including neutral wire) is not conductive with stator core, condition is satisfactory. If conduction exists, stator is grounded and must be replaced.

Diodes — 1) Perform a conduction test on all diodes in both directions using an ohmmeter. Test the conduction between each terminal and plate. Diode installed on a "+" plate is a positive diode which allows current to flow from terminal to "+" plate only. Current does NOT flow from "+" plate to the terminal. A diode installed on the "−" plate is a negative diode and allows current to flow from the "−" plate to the terminal only. Current does NOT flow from the terminal to the "−"plate.

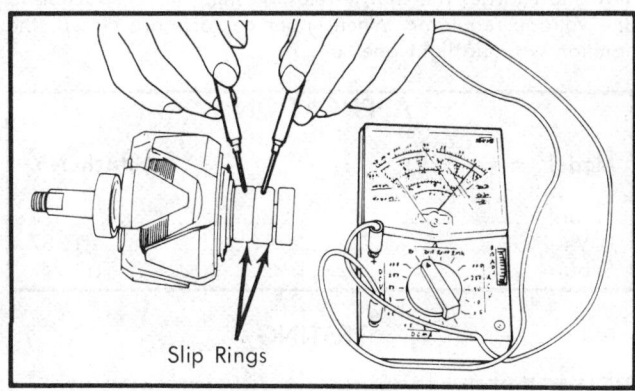

Slip Rings

Fig. 7   Rotor Field Coil Conduction Test

2) If current flows in both directions, the diode is shorted. If current does not flow in either direction, the diode is open. If any diode is defective, replace the entire diode assembly (individual diodes are not serviceable).

Brushes & Brush Springs — Inspect brushes for freedom of movement in holder. Clean brush holder if necessary. Check brushes for cracks and wear; replace if beyond wear limit lines. Check brush springs for corrosion, damage and proper tension. Tension should be 9-12.2 oz. with .08" (2 mm) protrusion from holder. Test brush holder to assure that no continuity exists between holder and brush; replace if required.

REASSEMBLY

Reinstall diode assembly and stator to rear cover. Connect lead wires of stator coil to terminals of diode assembly. Reinstall diode cover. Reinstall rotor to front cover. Place assembly in vise and replace pulley and components. Insert and tighten housing through bolts. Assemble brushes to brush holder and insert holder into alternator.

NOTE — *Soldering must be done quickly to avoid damage to diodes.*

Alternators & Regulators

HITACHI REGULATORS

Isuzu
LUV
Subaru

DESCRIPTION

Regulator system consist of a voltage regulator and a charge relay. The voltage regulator has 2 sets of contact points to control alternator voltage. An armature plate placed between the 2 sets of contacts moves upward, downward, or vibrates. The lower contacts, when closed, complete the field circuit direct to ground. The upper contacts complete the field circuit to ground when closed, through a resistance (field coil), causing the alternator to charge. The charge relay is similar in construction to the voltage regulator. When upper contacts are closed, the ignition warning light goes on.

APPLICATION

Model	Hitachi No.
I-Mark ....
LUV & P'UP	TLIZ-87
Subaru	TLIZ-94E

TESTING

VOLTAGE REGULATOR

I-Mark — 1) Connect a voltmeter between condensor lead and ground with all electrical loads disconnected including blower relay connector. *See Fig. 1.* The voltage relay is working properly when lower side points are closed when engine is off and when upper points are closed when engine is running at idle.

2) If points are not working properly, check coil resistance. If normal, adjust relay. Start engine and increase speed gradually. Voltage should increase with engine speed up to 1400-1850 RPM. Normal condition of regulator is indicated when voltage is 13.8-14.8 volts.

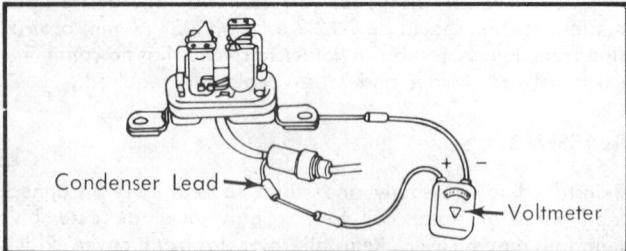

Fig. 1   Regulator Test Connection for I-Mark

LUV, P'UP & Subaru — 1) Connect voltmeter and ammeter as shown in *Fig. 2.* Start and maintain engine speed at 2500 RPM for a few minutes. Check that ammeter reading is 5 amps or less. If reading remains higher than 5 amps, remove battery and substitute with battery known to be fully charged. Recheck to ensure ammeter reading is less than 5 amps.

2) Lower engine speed to idle and again increase it gradually to 2500 RPM, then note voltmeter reading. Function of regulator is normal if measured value is within specified regulating voltage. If voltmeter reading deviates from specified range, regulator is in need of adjustment.

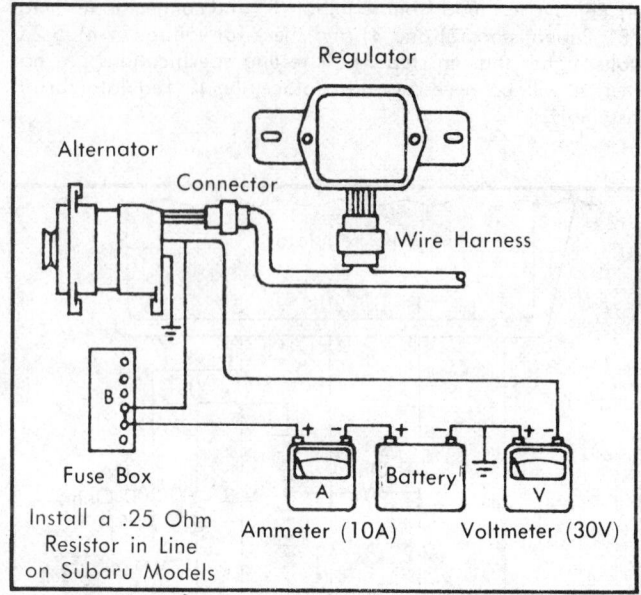

Fig. 2   Test Connections for Voltage Regulator (LUV, P'UP & Subaru)

RELAY

I-Mark — 1) Connect voltmeter between negative terminal and ground and increase engine speed gradually. Voltmeter reading should be 4.0-5.8 volts. If cut-in voltage is too high, adjust by bending coil arm "A" down. Bend up if voltage is too low, *See Fig. 3.*

2) If adjustment of core arm does not correct cut-in voltage, proceed with point gap adjustment. Disconnect battery. Check armature core gap with armature depressed until moving point is in contact with "B" side point.

3) Adjust core gap to .012" (.30 mm) by bending point arm "B". Release armature and adjust gap between "B" side point and moving point to .016-.047" (.40-1.2 mm) by bending point arm "C". After point adjustment, recheck cut-in voltage. If not within 4.0-5.8 volts, repeat cut-in voltage adjustment.

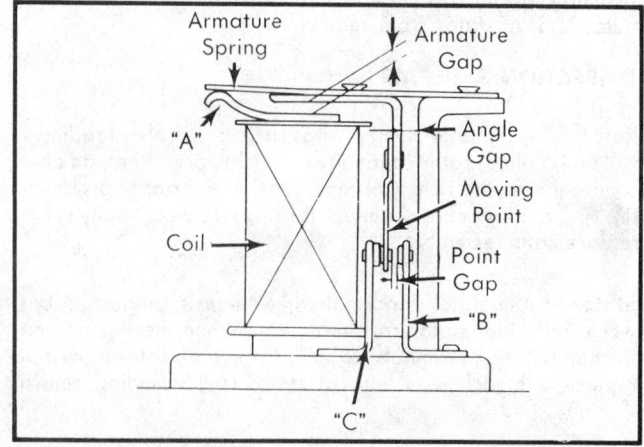

Fig. 3   Voltage Relay Adjustment (I-Mark)

ADJUSTMENT

NOTE — *Charge relay is adjusted in same manner as voltage regulator.*

HITACHI REGULATORS (Cont.)

LUV, P'UP & Subaru — 1) Disconnect and remove voltage regulator from vehicle. If contact points are roughened, smooth with fine sandpaper. Check and adjust core gap first, then point gap. Yoke gap adjustment may be unnecessary on some models.

2) Adjust core gap by loosening screws attaching contact set to yoke. Move contact set upward or downward as required. Adjust point gap by loosening screw attaching upper contact. Move upper contact up or down as required to set gap to specification.

3) Adjust regulated voltage by means of adjusting screw. Turn screw in to increase regulated voltage or out to decrease voltage. When correct voltage adjustment is obtained, secure with lock nut. When adjustment procedure is complete, reinstall regulator and perform on car check.

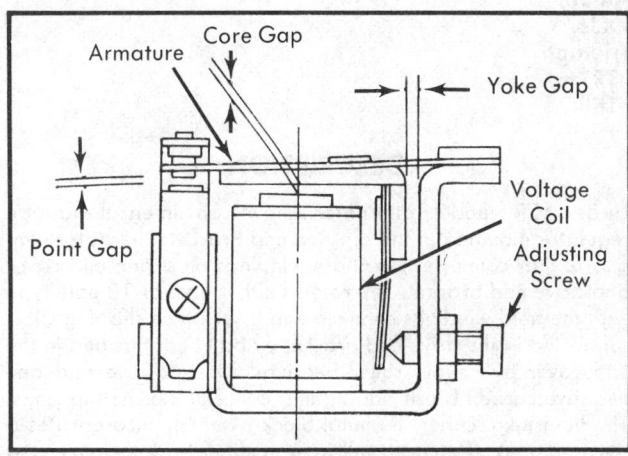

Fig. 4 *Schematic of Voltage Regulator
(LUV, P'UP & Subaru)
Charge Relay Similar*

VOLTAGE REGULATOR SPECIFICATIONS

Regulator	Battery Voltage	Regulated Voltage	Voltage Coil① Resistance (Ohms)	Yoke Gap In. (mm)	Core Gap In. (mm)	Point Gap In. (mm)
TLIZ-87	12	13.8-14.8	10.3	②	.024-.039(.6-1.0)	.012-.016 (.30-.40)
TLIZ-94E	12	14.0-15.0	10.3	.035(.9)	.024-.039(.6-1.0)	.014-.018 (.35-.45)

① — I-Mark resistance 102 ohms.
② — No yoke adjustment required.

VOLTAGE RELAY SPECIFICATIONS

Regulator	Released Voltage	Voltage Coil② Resistance (Ohms)	Yoke Gap In. (mm)	Core Gap In. (mm)	Point Gap In. (mm)
TLIZ-87	5①	31.9	③	.032-.039(.8-1.0)	.016-.024(.41-.61)
TLIZ-94E	8-10	32.1	.035 (.9)	.032-.039(.8-1.0)	.016-.024(.41-.61)

① — Measured at "A" terminal.
② — I-Mark resistance 24 ohms.
③ — No yoke adjustment required.

Alternators & Regulators

LUCAS ALTERNATORS

Jaguar
XJ6
Triumph
TR7
TR8

DESCRIPTION

Lucas ACR model alternators have an integral voltage regulator mounted in the slip ring end bracket. The stator consists of star-connected, 3 phase windings on a ring end cover and drive end bracket. The rotor is either an 8 or 12 pole type with the field windings connected to 2 face-type slip rings. It is supported in the drive-end bracket by ball bearings and in the end cover by needle roller bearings. One positive and one negative carbon brush ride against concentric brass slip rings. The heatsink-rectifier, terminal block assembly incorporates 6 silicon diodes, forming a full wave rectifier bridge circuit, and 3 diodes which supply current to the rotor windings.

APPLICATION

Model	Type. No.
Jaguar XJ6	25 ACR
Triumph	
TR7	
Standard	17 ACR
Heavy Duty	20 ACR
With A/C	25 ACR
TR8	
Standard	17 ACR
With A/C	25 ACR

SPECIFICATIONS

Nominal Output

Alternator	Amps@6000 RPM	Voltage
17 ACR	36	14
20 ACR	66	14
25 ACR	65	14

TESTING

ON CAR TESTING

NOTE — *Alternator drive belt must be properly adjusted, battery and connections in good condition and charge warning bulb and circuit continuous in order to test charging system. Polarity of alternator and battery terminals MUST be observed to prevent system damage. Warm engine 3-4 minutes before testing. (Output may be slightly higher when alternator is cold.) Battery ground cable should be disconnected when attaching jumper wires to alternator and regulator.*

Alternator Output Test — 1) Disconnect multi-socket connector and remove molded cover from rear of alternator. (Cover may be pierced with a probe on some models in order to ground the field winding brush and by-pass the regulator.) Provide a test circuit as illustrated.

2) Start engine and run to give 1,500 alternator RPM (approximately 650-800 engine RPM). Test circuit bulb should be out.

3) Increase engine speed to 2500-3,000 RPM to give 6,000 alternator RPM. Adjust variable resistor so voltmeter reads 14 volts and note ammeter reading equal to the nominal output rating for the appropriate alternator. If readings are not correct, alternator requires overhaul or replacement.

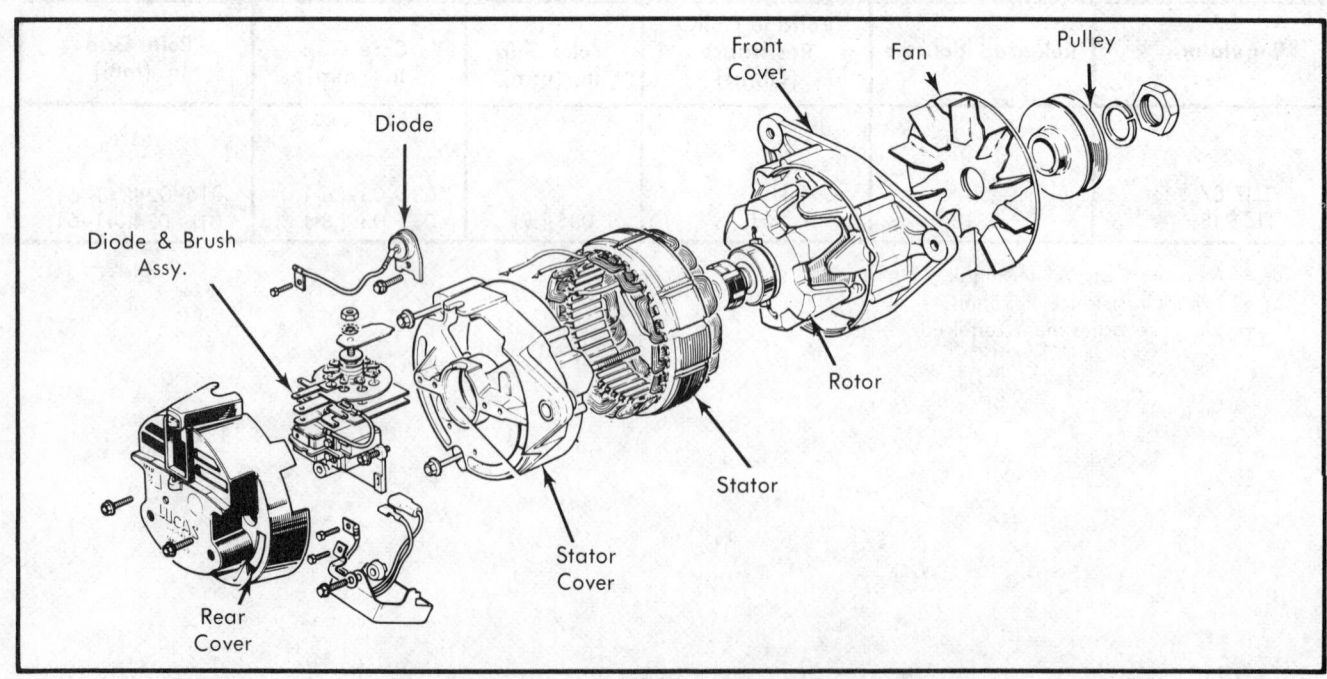

Fig. 1   Exploded View of Lucas 17 ACR Alternator with Integral Regulator

LUCAS ALTERNATORS (Cont.)

NOTE — *Do not connect variable resistor across battery for longer than is necessary to complete the test.*

Regulator Test – 1) Provide Regulator Test Circuit as shown and gradually increase engine speed to approximately 640 RPM (1,550 alternator RPM). Test lamp should go out.

2) Increase engine speed to approximately 2,500 RPM (6,000 alternator RPM). Voltmeter should be steady at 13.6-14.4 volts. If reading is not steady and satisfactory Output Test has been performed, regulator should be replaced.

NOTE — *Up to 10 milliamp battery drain is normal, even with the ignition in the "OFF" position.*

OVERHAUL

DISASSEMBLY

1) Remove end cover and note wire positions and color. Remove screws attaching surge protection diode and brush assembly. Lift out brush assembly and surge protection diode. Regulator may be removed if desired.

2) Unsolder stator wire connections and remove rectifier pack grounding strip. Withdraw rectifier pack. Remove through bolts.

CAUTION — *When necessary to solder or unsolder leads from diodes, use pliers as a heat sink by pinching diode pin with jaws of pliers. Solder connections quickly to prevent heat damage to diodes.*

3) Remove through bolts from alternator frame and carefully slip end bracket and stator off of rotor. (It may be necessary to tap lightly on an extractor or tube placed against outer bearing journal to separate rotor from end bracket.)

4) Complete disassembly, if required, by removing pulley and drive key. Press rotor from drive end bracket and remove screws retaining end bearing in position. Replace as necessary.

NOTE — *Position of all washers, spacers and insulators must be noted for proper assembly.*

TESTING

Rotor — Connect an ohmmeter and read resistance of field coil (across slip rings). Using a 110-volt A.C. supply and a 15-watt test lamp, check for insulation between one of the slip rings and any rotor pole. If lamp lights, rotor is shorted.

Stator — Connect 12-volt battery and 36-watt test lamp to 2 of the stator connections. Repeat test using any other combination of 2 of the 3 connections. If lamp fails to light in either test, stator has an open coil. Using 110-volt/15-watt test lamp, check for insulation between any one of the 3 stator connections and stator laminations. If lamp lights, stator should be relaced.

Diodes — Connect a 12-volt battery and a 1.5-watt test lamp in turn to each of the 9 diode pins and its corresponding heat sink on the rectifier pack, then reverse the connections. Lamp should light (with current flow) in one direction only. If lamp lights in both directions or fails in either, rectifier pack must be renewed.

PARTS REPLACEMENT

Regulator — Aluminum casing of control unit must not make contact with alternator body when installed. (Shorted field circuit could result in maximum alternator output at all times regardless of battery condition.)

Diodes — In event of defective diodes, heatsink and rectifier assembly should be replaced. Protect diodes from excess heat when soldering by using pliers on diode pin as a thermal shunt.

Brushes — Installed brushes must extend at least .2" (5 mm) from housing and springs should indicate 9-13 oz. tension when brush is pushed back flush with housing. If beyond limits, replace brush assembly.

REASSEMBLY

Reverse disassembly procedure and note the following: When intalling slip ring end bearing, ensure that it is fitted with open side facing rotor and that it is seated fully. When replacing rotor to drive end bracket, support inner track of bearing with suitable piece of tubing. DO NOT use drive end bracket as the only support for the bearing when fitting rotor.

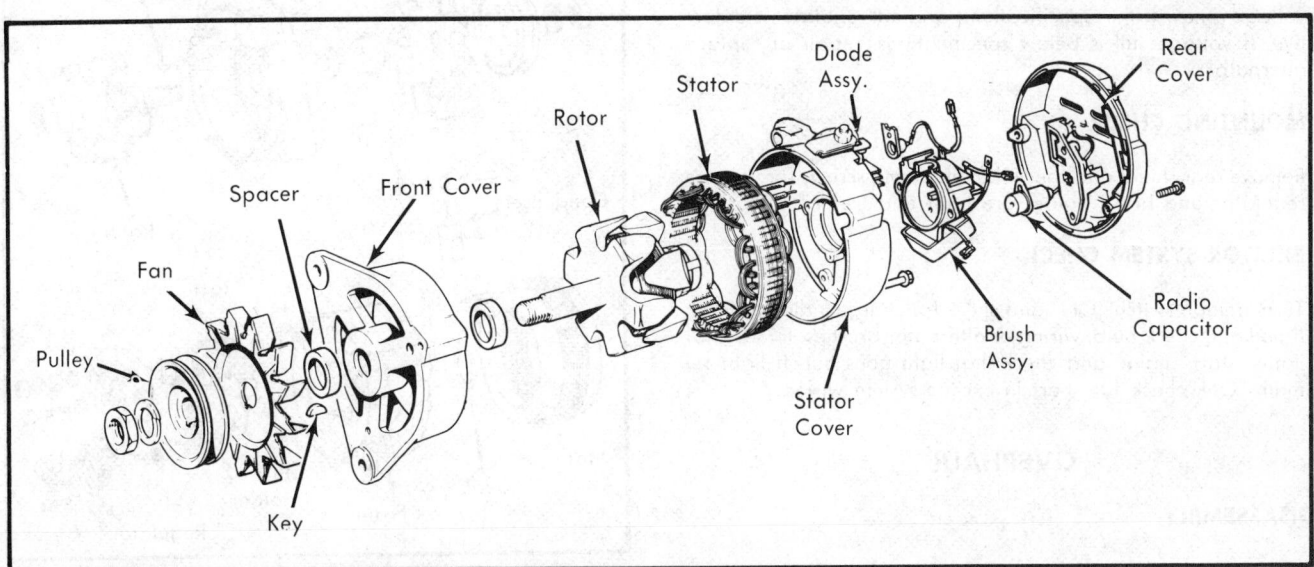

Fig. 2   Exploded View of Lucas 25 ACR Alternator with Integral Regulator

MARELLI ALTERNATORS

Fiat
Strada

DESCRIPTION

Marelli alternators are conventional 3-phase, self-rectifying type alternators. The externally mounted rectifier contains a silicon diode pack connected to form a full-wave, 3-phase rectifying bridge. An integral voltage regulator, also mounted on the rear of the alternator, controls charging rate.

APPLICATION	
Model	**Type**
Strada (W/O Air Cond.)	A125/14V/55A

TESTING

NOTE – *Prior to performing any testing, ensure that alternator drive belt tension is properly adjusted and that battery condition, water level and connections are good. Some testing is done as part of Overhaul procedure.*

ENGINE CRANK TEST

Disconnect distributor connector and connect voltmeter to battery. Crank engine 3 to 4 seconds and note voltmeter reading. A reading of less than 9 volts indicates possible faulty battery.

VOLTAGE TEST

Set engine speed at 2500 RPM with headlights on and heater fan on high speed. Voltmeter should read at least 12.5 but no more than 15.0 volts.

REGULATOR/ALTERNATOR CHECK

If voltage is not as specified, disconnect battery ground cable and remove regulator from alternator. Install known good voltage regulator, connect battery and repeat voltage test. If voltage is now within specifications, original regulator is defective. If voltage still is below specifications, repair or replace alternator.

MOUNTING CHECK

Remove rear shield and check that mounting screws for voltage regulator and brush holder are tight and free of corrosion.

EXCITOR SYSTEM CHECK

Turn ignition switch "ON" and check for charge indicator light. If no light, check bulb, wiring or alternator brushes. If indicator lights, start engine and check that light goes out. If light remains ON, check for short in excitor system wiring.

OVERHAUL

DISASSEMBLY

1) Disconnect battery ground cable and remove rear shield from alternator. Mark electrical leads for identification and disconnect from alternator. Remove alternator from vehicle. Remove voltage regulator and brush holder. Remove pulley, fan, spacers and key.

2) Remove through bolts and separate front frame from rear frame. Remove rectifier cover and disconnect 3 stator wires. Remove rectifier assembly and separate stator assembly from rear frame. Remove screw and lift out condenser.

TESTING (OFF CAR)

With alternator disassembled, perform rotor and stator open, shorts and continuity tests. *See General Servicing in this section.* Disconnect stator leads from rectifier board. Using ohmmeter set to X1 scale, touch one lead to a diode junction and the other to heat sink and note reading. Reverse leads and note reading, then repeat for other diodes. One high and one low reading should be obtained for each diode. Replace diode plate if proper readings are not obtained.

REASSEMBLY

If brushes are worn replace brushes and holder as a complete assembly. Reverse removal procedure and install alternator on vehicle. Adjust belt tension.

SPECIFICATIONS	
Application	**Test Data**
Cut-in Speed	900±50 RPM
Current Flow	55 amps. @ 7000 RPM
Resistance Across Slip Rings	3.1±.1 ohm①
Alternator-to-Engine RPM Ratio	1.75:1
Regulating Voltage	13.8-14.2 volts①

① – At 77°F (25°C).

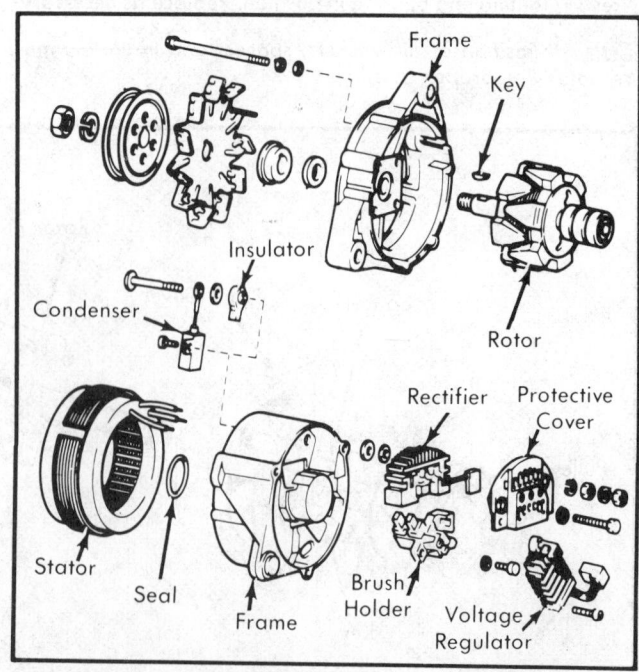

Fig. 1 Disassembled View of Marelli Alternator

MITSUBISHI ALTERNATORS

Chrysler Corp. Imports	Courier
Arrow Pickup	Mazda
Challenger	B2000 Pickup
Champ	GLC
Colt	RX7
Ram-50 Pickup	626
Sapporo	

DESCRIPTION

Mitsubishi alternators are conventional 3-phase, self-rectifying type units containing 6 diodes (3 positive and 3 negative) which are used to rectify current. A case mounted Integrated Circut (IC) regulator is used on all models except Courier, Mazda GLC Wagon and B2000.

APPLICATION

Model	Type or Part No.
Arrow & D-50 Pickups	A2T16471
Challenger & Sapporo	AQ225061
Champ & Colt	AQ2245K1
Courier	①D47Z-10346-A
Mazda	
B2000	0571-18-300A
GLC	8317-18-300
RX7	8841-18-300
626	8356-18-300

① — Ford part number. Check number stamped on housing for individual application.

SPECIFICATIONS

Nominal Output@2500 RPM

Application	Amps.	Voltage
AQ2250G1	41-50	13.5
AQ2245K1	34-37	13.5
A2T16471	37-42	13.5
D47Z-19346-A	35	14
8317-18-300	30	14
8356-18-300	42	13.5
8871-18-300	39	13.5
0571-18-300A	30	14

Brush Wear Limit — Brushes must be replaced when worn to .315" (8.9 mm), to limit line or when 1/3 of original length, whichever is greater.

Brush Spring Pressure — Standard tension should be 12-16 oz. Replace if less than 8 oz. or if springs are corroded.

TESTING

NOTE — *Some testing is done as part of Overhaul procedure.*

ON CAR TEST

CAUTION — *DO NOT short across any alternator terminals nor run vehicle with any wires disconnected.*

Output Test — With ignition switch off and battery ground cable disconnected, connect ammeter between alternator terminal "B" and cable. Connect voltmeter between "B" (+) terminal and ground. Connect ground cable and observe battery voltage. Start engine and turn all lights on. Run engine to produce alternator RPM specified and check ammeter for specified output.

NOTE — *Alternator RPM is approximately twice engine RPM.*

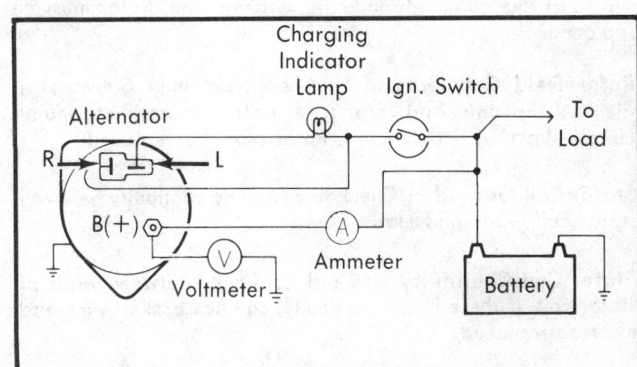

Fig. 1   Alternator Output Test Arrangement

OVERHAUL

DISASSEMBLY

1) Remove brush cover and through bolts. Separate diode end housing from drive housing by tapping front bracket lightly with a soft mallet.

2) Place rotor shaft in padded vise, using caution. Remove pulley nut, pulley, fan, and spacer. Remove rotor drive end housing by lightly tapping end housing with a soft mallet.

3) To separate stator from diode end housing, unsolder three negative diode leads and connections between diodes.

TESTING

Diode Assemblies — Disconnect heat sink and check each diode with tester on continuity in forward or reverse direction. If the diode shows large resistance in one direction and small

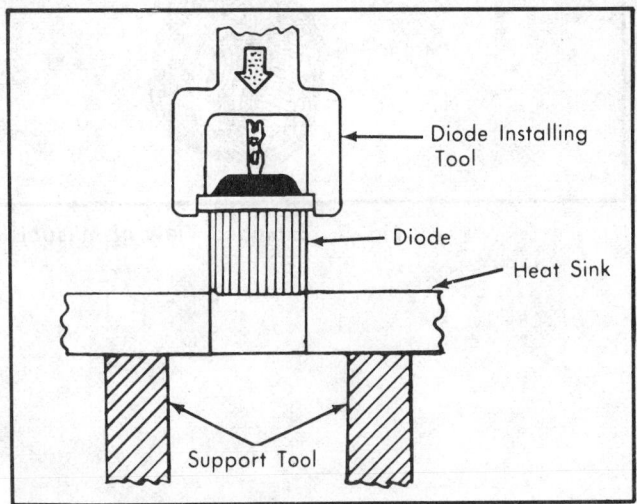

Fig. 2   Using Special Tool to Install Diode

MITSUBISHI ALTERNATORS (Cont.)

resistance in other direction, diode is normal. If it shows small resistance in both directions it is shorted. If large resistance is shown in both directions, diode is open.

CAUTION — *If excessive temperature is allowed, diode will become inoperative.*

Rotor Field Continuity — Check continuity across field coil slip rings. No continuity indicates broken wire. Rotor must be replaced.

Rotor Field Coil Ground — Check continuity between individual slip rings and rotor core/shaft. If there is continuity, coil or slip ring is grounded. Rotor must be replaced.

Stator Coil Ground — Check to ensure no continuity between stator coil leads and stator core.

Stator Coil Continuity — Check continuity between leads of stator coil. If there is no continuity, coil has broken wire and must be replaced.

PARTS REPLACEMENT

Diodes — To remove diode, use a suitable tool to support heat sink and remove diode by use of a suitable press. Press out carefully to avoid damaging mounting bore of heat sink. To install diode, support heat sink as in removal. Select correct type diode (positive diodes have red markings; negative diodes have black markings), and press diode into heat sink.

CAUTION — *Do not strike diodes to remove them since shock may damage other diodes.*

Drive End Bearing — Remove bearing retainer by unscrewing set screws and press out bearing, using a suitable press.

Rear Bearing — Remove rear bearing from housing assembly, using a suitable press or bearing puller.

REASSEMBLY

Reassemble by reversing disassembly procedures, making sure polarity of diodes is correct.

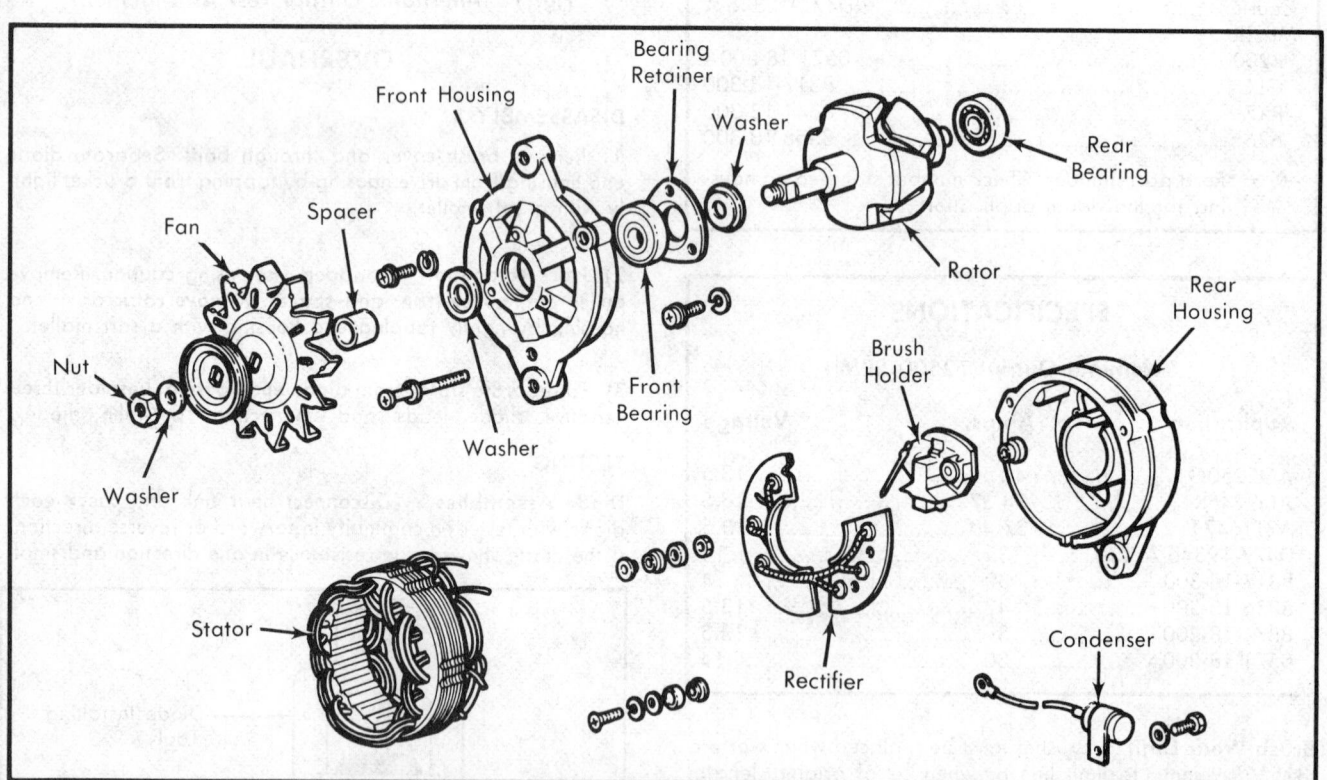

Fig. 3   Exploded View of Mitsubishi Alternator (Courier Application Shown)

Alternators & Regulators

MITSUBISHI REGULATORS

Courier
Mazda

DESCRIPTION

Regulator consists of a constant voltage relay and a pilot lamp relay. Both relays consist of an electromagnet, contacts, frame, moving element and coil side plate. This regulator has a temperature compensation gradient incorporated to automatically lower the adjusted value of the constant voltage relay in warm weather and to increase it in cold temperatures.

APPLICATION	
Model	①**Part No.**
Courier	D97Z-10316-A
Maxda	8914 18 391
① — Vehicle manufacturer part number.	

TESTING

CAUTION — *Ensure that voltage regulator protecting fuse is functional before conducting any charging system diagnosis. Verify condition by substituting known good fuse.*

To check adjusted value of constant voltage relay, connect a voltmeter between terminal "A" and "E" of the regulator. Place alternator at no load by disconnecting positive terminal of battery while engine is idling. Increase alternator speed to approximately 4000 RPM (approximately 2000 engine RPM). Satisfactory voltage is 14-15 volts.

ADJUSTMENT

NOTE — *Adjustment procedures furnished for Mazda, only. Manufacturers recommend installation of new regulator when tolerance not within limits for other models.*

Adjust voltage of the constant voltage relay by bending end of coil side plate up or down as shown in illustration. If plate is bent up, the adjusted value becomes higher. If it is bent down, value becomes lower. Adjust pilot lamp relay by same method.

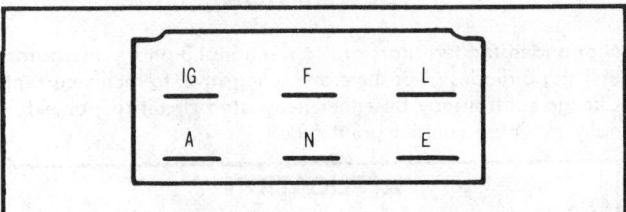

Fig. 1   Regulator Harness Connector

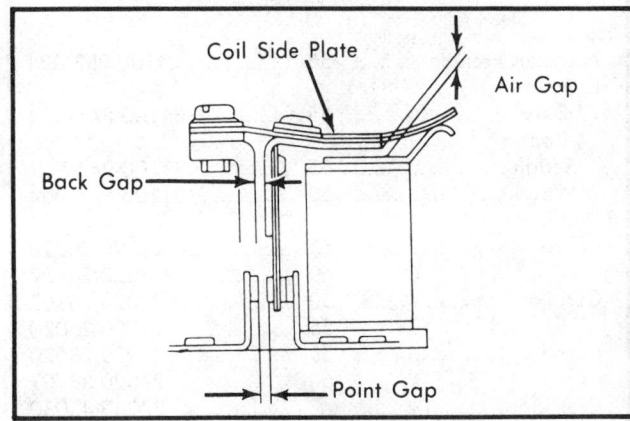

Fig. 2   Voltage Adjustment Point

MITSUBISHI ALTERNATOR REGULATOR SPECIFICATIONS							
	VOLTAGE REGULATOR				PILOT LAMP RELAY		
Reg. No.	Output Volts	Air Gap in. (mm)	Back Gap in. (mm)	Point Gap in. (mm)	Air Gap in. (mm)	Back Gap in. (mm)	Point Gap in. (mm)
891418391	14-15	.028-.051 (.71-1.3)	.028-.059 (.71-1.5)	.012-.018 (.31-.45)	.039-.059 (1.0-1.5)	.028-.059 (.71-1.5)	.020-.035 (.71-1.1)

Alternators & Regulators

NIPPONDENSO ALTERNATORS

Honda
  Accord
  Civic
  Prelude
Toyota
  Celica
  Corolla

Corona
Cressida
Land Cruiser
Pickup
Starlet
Supra
Tercel

DESCRIPTION

Nippondenso alternators are conventional 3-phase alternators utilizing 6 diodes (3 positive and 3 negative) to rectify current. Charge control may be either integrated circuit (IC) or externally mounted contact point type.

APPLICATION

Model	Amps	①Part No.
Honda		
Accord & Prelude	55	31100-PB2-004
Civic		
2-Door	55	31100-PA6-004
4-Door		
Sedan	55	31100-PA6-901
Wagon	50	31100-PA6-004
Toyota		
Celica	55	27020-28020
	60	27020-38102
Corolla	50	27020-26102
	55	27020-28020
Corona	55	27020-28020
	60	27020-38102
Cressida		27060-43030
Land Cruiser	40	27020-61100
	55	27020-61071
Pickup		
Diesel	40	27020-54080
Gas		
Standard	40	27020-35040
I. C. Type	40	27020-35050
Starlet		
Standard	....	27020-13090
I. C. Type	....	27060-13010
Supra	....	27060-43030
Tercel	50	27020-15040

① — Vehicle manufacturer part number.

TESTING

ON CAR TEST

Preliminary Inspection — Check alternator mounting and drive belt tension. Inspect turn signal and gauge fuses. Check alternator and regulator wire connections for tightness. Battery must be fully charged prior to beginning test.

No Load Test — 1) Connect a test meter (09081-00010 alternator tester for models with special connector from regulator) as shown in illustrations. Start engine and increase speed to about 2000 RPM. Read "B" terminal voltage on models with external voltage regulator.

2) On models with external voltage regulators, voltage should be 13.8-14.8 volts. On models with IC type voltage regulators, voltage should be 14.0-14.7 volts. On all models, current draw should be less than 10 amps.

3) If voltage is not steady, dirty regulator points or defective connection at "F" terminal may be responsible. If voltage reading is too high, 1 of the following problems may be indicated: Regulator low speed gap too wide. High speed point gap too wide. High speed point gap resistance too high.

4) Problem could also be due to open in regulator coil or voltage relay coil. Open circuit in regulator "N" terminal of "B" terminal. Low speed contact tension too heavy. Loose regulator ground connection. Faulty IC regulator.

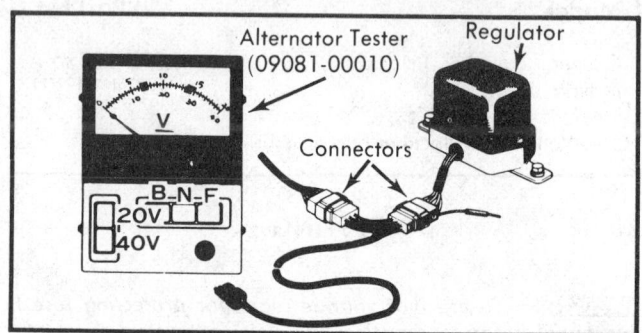

Fig. 1 Connections for Tester 0981-00010

"F" Terminal Voltage (External Regulator) — 1) Disconnect connector from alternator regulator. Turn ignition switch "ON". Check voltage at the red wire terminal. If there is no voltage, check engine fuse and/or ignition switch. Connect connector to voltage regulator. Check voltage at "N" terminal (yellow wire).

2) If voltage is 1-2 volts, check alternator. If battery voltage, turn ignition switch "OFF" and disconnect connector from alternator. Check for continuity between alternator terminals "N" and "F". If there is continuity, replace voltage regulator. If there is no continuity, check alternator.

Regulator Circuit Resistance — Disconnect regulator connector plug and check resistance between regulator "IG" and "F" terminals with an ohmmeter. If any resistance is shown, the low speed contact in the regulator is defective.

Load Test — With regulator tester connected as illustrated, start engine and turn on all lights and accessories. Run engine at 1100 RPM and check amperage and voltage. If reading is low due to fully charged battery, it may be necessary to crank engine (with coil disconnected) for about 15 seconds to discharge battery. If amperage is low when rechecking, rectifiers are open or shorted, or stator coil is open or shorted.

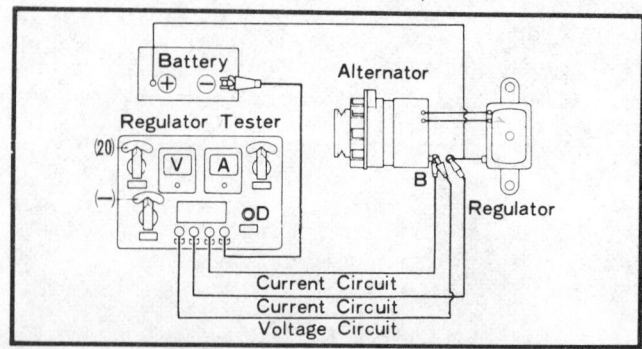

Fig. 2 Connections for Regulator Tester

NIPPONDENSO ALTERNATORS (Cont.)

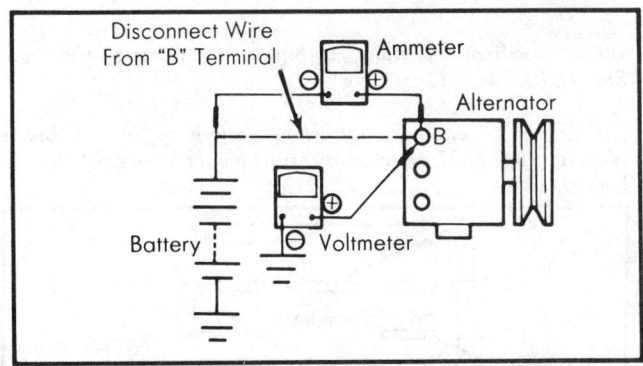

Fig. 3   Test Connections for Alternator With IC Regulator

Performance Test Using Conventional Tester — 1) Attach tester as illustrated and increase engine speed until reverse current (approximately 2.5 amp.) ceases to flow to rotor field coil.

2) Turn off No. 1 switch and increase speed until voltmeter indicates 14V. If speed is under 1000 RPM, alternator performance is satisfactory.

3) Increase load resistance to near maximum so that nearly no current will flow. Close switches 1 and 2 while gradually increasing speed. Rated output should be reached by approximately 5000 RPM with satisfactory alternator.

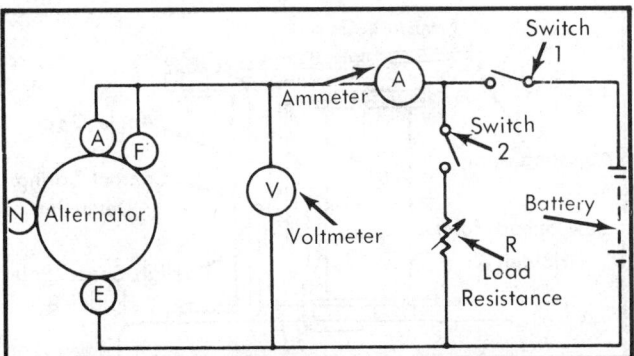

Fig. 4   Conventional Tester Connections

OVERHAUL

DISASSEMBLY

NOTE — *Alternators differ slightly with model application. The following procedures are general only. The procedures can be used if attention is paid to the order of parts during disassembly.*

1) Remove retaining screws and pry drive end frame from stator with screwdriver. If necessary, tap lightly on drive end frame with mallet. Secure rotor core in padded vise and remove pulley attaching nut. Withdraw pulley, fan and spacer. Press rotor from drive end frame. Remove bearing retainer from end frame, then remove bearing, felt cover and felt ring.

2) Remove rectifier holder securing nuts and brush holder attaching screws. Separate stator with rectifier holders and brush holders from rectifier end frame. Remove brush lead terminal and stator coil "N" terminal from brush holder using a small screwdriver. When removing brush holder assembly, DO NOT cut "N" terminal lead or melt the solder.

TESTING

Rotor — Check the rotor for open field windings by using an ohmmeter across the slip rings. Coil resistance should be 3.9-4.2 ohms for external regulator models, and 2.8-3.0 ohms for IC regulator models. Check smoothness of slip rings. Check bearing and replace if necessary.

Stator — Use ohmmeter to check stator coil for ground. To check for open circuit, stator leads must be disconnected from diode leads. To disconnect leads from diodes, unsolder as quickly as possible with a low watt iron. Check 4 leads of stator coil for continuity between each lead. If no continuity or if resistance is noted, stator coil must be replaced.

Diode Test — With diode assembly on bench, contact diode plate with one probe and each of 3 diode leads with other probe. Note ohmmeter reading, then reverse probes and repeat test. Check both positive and negative diodes in this manner. All diodes should show a low reading in one direction and NO reading in the opposite direction. If any rectifier (diode) is defective, replace holder assembly.

NOTE — *Also see General Servicing in this section.*

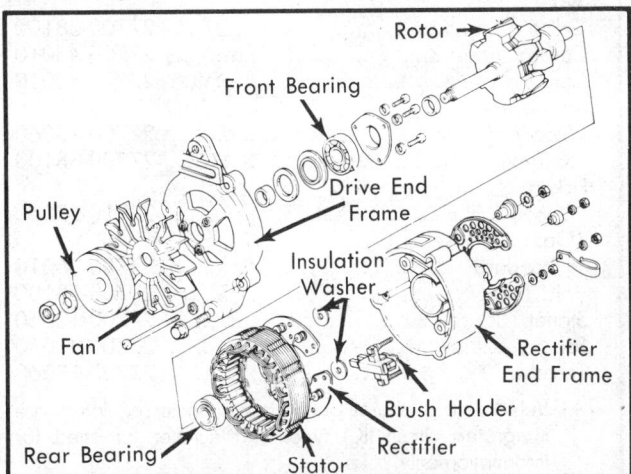

Fig. 5   Disassembled View of Typical Nippondenso Alternator With External Voltage Regulator

PARTS REPLACEMENT

Brushes — Check for cracks and minimum length of .22" (5.5 mm). If damaged or worn beyond limit, replace brushes. Brushes should slide smoothly in holders. Install new springs when replacing brushes. Solder brush wire. New brush protrusion should be .650" (16.5 mm) for Celica, Supra and Tercel, .630" (26 mm) for Cressida, .610" (15.5 mm) for Honda, and .492 (12.5 mm) for all other models.

REASSEMBLY

1) Press brushes into holder against spring tension. Insert a retaining wire through access hole in rectifier and frame and into brush holder to prevent brushes from falling. Remove wire after assembly to end frame is completed.

2) Pack multipurpose grease into rear bearing and press bearing onto rotor shaft. Pack drive end bearing with grease and install in drive end frame. Install felt ring, cover and bearing retainer.

3) Ensure that drive end frame with rotor and rectifier end frame with stator are assembled in original alignment. Tighten body screws and remove brush retaining wire.

Alternators & Regulators

NIPPONDENSO REGULATORS

Honda
  Accord
  Civic
  Prelude
Toyota
  Celica
  Corolla

Corona
Cressida
Land Cruiser
Pickup
Starlet
Supra
Tercel

DESCRIPTION

Nippondenso regulators may be either single or double element type. Single element type has a voltage regulator element only while 2 element type has both voltage regulator and a voltage warning relay. Single element type is normally fitted to units with an ammeter, while double element type normally has a charge warning light.

APPLICATION

Model	Part No.①
Honda (All Models)	31200-PC2-671
Toyota	
Celica	27700-38100
Corolla	27700-43010
Corona	27700-43010
Land Cruiser	
Standard Type	27700-13060
IC Type	27700-38100
Pickup	
Diesel	27700-57060
Gas	
Standard	27700-35010
IC Type	27700-38100
Starlet	27700-13060
Supra	27700-41050
Tercel	27700-13060

① — Vehicle manufacturer part number. Some regulators are integrated circuit (IC) type. Part number furnished for information only.

TESTING

VOLTAGE REGULATOR

NOTE — *Substitution of a known good regulator for one suspected of malfunctioning will frequently save time during testing.*

Toyota — Disconnect wire from "B" terminal of alternator and connect to negative of ammeter. Connect test lead from ammeter positive terminal to "B" terminal of alternator. With engine running at varying speeds from idle to 2000 RPM, voltage should be 13.8-14.8 volts and amperage should be less than 10 amps. If not within specifications, adjust or replace regulator as required. *See ADJUSTMENT.*

NOTE — *If a battery/alternator tester is available, connect and test according to tester manufacturer's instructions.*

Honda — Connect voltmeter across battery terminals and ammeter between positive terminal and main fuse. (Main fuse wire from battery disconnected.) Ensure that all lights and accessories are OFF and disconnect negative cable from battery with engine idling. Vary engine speed from 2000 to 4000 RPM and note voltage reading between 13.5 and 14.5 volts. If not

within specifications, adjust or replace regulator as required. *See ADJUSTMENT.*

CAUTION — *If engine stops when battery negative cable is removed, DO NOT attempt to restart engine until cable is connected.*

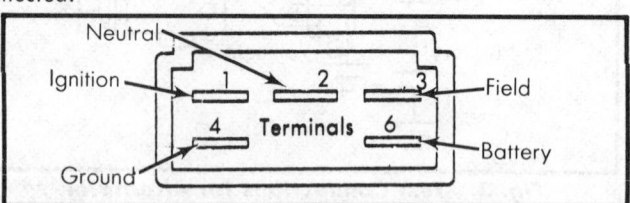

Fig. 1   Terminal Positions for Honda Connector

ADJUSTMENT

NOTE — *Adjustments are not applicable to sealed units. If points are slightly oxidized or pitted, dress contacts with sandpaper (400 grit or finer). If points are oxidized or pitted excessively, replace regulator assembly.*

Voltage Regulator & Relay — 1) For relay, connect voltmeter between "N" terminal (white wire) and ground. Gradually increase engine speed. Voltmeter reading should be 4.0-5.8 volts when indicator light goes out. For regulator, connect voltmeter as described under testing. Adjust regulator and relay by bending adjusting arm as follows.

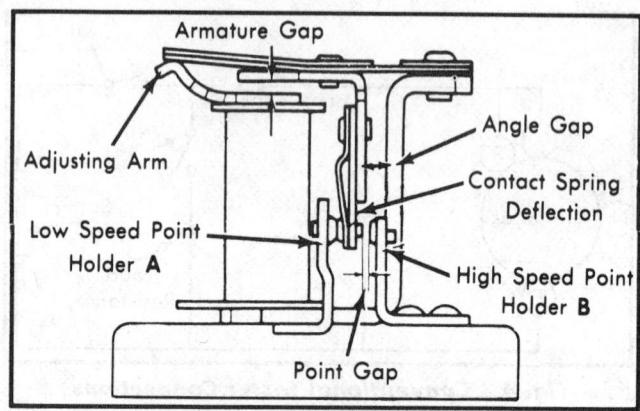

Fig. 2   Adjustments for Voltage Relay. Voltage Regulator Similar.

2) If cut-in or regulated voltage is too high, adjust by bending core adjusting arm down. Bend arm up if voltage is too low. If adjustment of core arm does not correct voltage, proceed with point gap adjustment. Disconnect negative cable from battery.

3) Check armature core gap with armature depressed until moving point is in contact with "B" side point. Armature core gap should be .02" (.5 mm) or more. Adjust by bending point arm "B". Release the armature and adjust the gap between the "B" side point and the moving point by bending point arm "A".

4) Point gap should be .016-.047" (0.4-1.2 mm). Angle gap should be .02" (.5 mm) or more. After adjustment, recheck cut-in or regulated voltage. If not within specifications, repeat voltage adjustment.

NOTE — *Regulator cover must be installed after adjustments prior to further testing.*

SEV MARCHAL ALTERNATORS

Renault
  Le Car
  18i
Volvo
  DL
  GL
  GLT Turbo

DESCRIPTION

Alternator is a conventional three-phase, self-rectifying type. Six silicon rectifier diodes are connected to form a full-wave, three-phase rectifying bridge. Three exciter diodes are connected to stator windings and have a common junction point.

APPLICATION		
Model	**Rating**	**Part No.**
Renault	50	7700 670 257
Volvo	70	1235 908

NOTE — *Specific overhaul procedures are for Volvo models. Procedures for Renault applications are similar.*

OVERHAUL

DISASSEMBLY

1) Remove brush holder attaching screws and carefully remove brush holder. Scribe a mark on end frames for reassembly reference, then remove four through bolts. Separate end frames by inserting two screwdrivers into notches on sides of alternator.

CAUTION — *Do not insert screwdrivers deeper than .08" (2 mm) or damage may occur to stator windings.*

2) Remove nuts and washers for positive and negative diode holders from end frame. Carefully remove stator from end frame. Hold rotor in a vise using special wood blocks so no damage will occur to rotor. Remove nut, washer, pulley, fan, key and spacer.

NOTE — *Check direction spacer under pulley fan faces for assembly reference.*

3) Remove three attaching screws for bearing cap, then push rotor shaft from end frame. Press bearing from end frame. Use a puller to remove bearing from slip ring end of rotor.

BENCH TESTING

NOTE — *Use 40V AC for testing rotor and stator only.*

Rotor — Check rotor winding resistance across slip rings with ohmmeter and insulation between slip rings and rotor with test lamp. Replace rotor if grounded or if resistance is greater than 4.4 ohms.

Stator — Check stator coils for resistance with leads disconnected using an ohmmeter. Check for shorts between core and leads with test lamp. Replace stator if grounded or if resistance is greater than .15 ohm.

Diodes — Use ohmmeter to perform conduction test on diodes. Observe current flow in one direction only from terminal to plate for positive diodes and from plate to terminal for negative diodes. If open or shorted, replace entire diode assembly.

NOTE — *Diodes may be either cylindrical or spherical in construction. Terminals must be disconnected during testing.*

REASSEMBLY

1) Press on inner race of bearing to position bearing on slip ring end of rotor shaft. Press on outer race to press bearing into end frame. Install bearing cap and three attaching screws. Press end frame with bearing assembly firmly onto rotor shaft. Install spacer, key, fan, pulley, washer and nut onto rotor shaft. Tighten nut to 29 ft.lbs. (4 mkg).

2) Install insulating washers and sleeves onto positive diode holder, then install stator to end frame while inserting brush holder through opening in end frame. Install nuts and washers to secure diode holders. Check that "O" ring in end frame bearing seat does not block vent hole.

3) Assemble two end frames along with stator and rotor assemblies together, then secure with four through bolts. Install brush holder attaching screws and tighten.

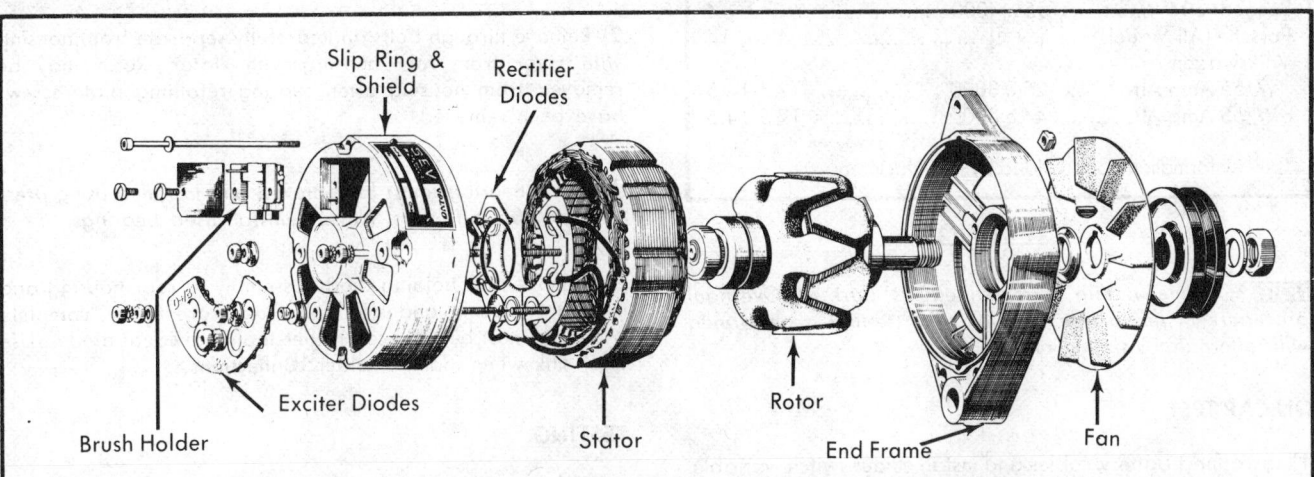

Slip Ring & Shield — Rectifier Diodes — Brush Holder — Exciter Diodes — Stator — Rotor — End Frame — Fan

Fig. 1   Exploded View of Alternator (Volvo Shown, Renault Similar)

Alternators & Regulators

SEV MOTOROLA ALTERNATORS

Peugeot	Volkswagen
604	Dasher
Porsche	Jetta
911SC	Rabbit
924	Rabbit Pickup
928	Scirocco

DESCRIPTION

SEV Motorola alternators are conventional three-phase, self-rectifying type alternators. Six silicon diodes (three positive and three negative) are used to rectify AC current.

NOTE — *Either SEV Motorola or Bosch alternators may be used. Due to the wide variance in application and output for the various models, not all individual part numbers and ratings may be shown. Always check identification plate attached to housing.*

APPLICATION

Model	Amp Rating	①Part No.
Peugeot 604	55	5702.52
Porsche		
911SC	70	911 603 120 02
924	75	063 903 017
928	90	928 603 113 03
Volkswagen (Water Cooled Models)		
Diesel		
W/O Air Cond	55	175 903 017 BX
	65	175 903 017 X
W/Air Cond	65	175 903 017 AX
Gasoline		
W/O Air Cond	55	049 903 015 X
	65	055 903 017 X
W/Air Cond	65	175 903v017 EX

① — Vehicle manufacturer part number.

SPECIFICATIONS

Application	Amps/RPM	Voltage
Peugeot 604	55@4000	14
Porsche (All Models)	①	14
Volkswagen		
W/55 Amp Alt.	25@3000	12.5-14.5
W/65 Amp Alt.	44@3000	12.5-14.5

① — Information not provided by manufacturer.

TESTING

NOTE — *Some testing is described as part of Overhaul procedure in this article. The following testing is performed with alternator installed on vehicle.*

ON CAR TEST

1) Disconnect battery cables and install cutout switch, variable resistance, ammeter and voltmeter as shown. Connect ground cable and check that cutout switch is in closed position.

2) Start engine and run at test RPM. Adjust varible resistance to give the following amperage readings: Models with 65 amp alternators — 45 amps, with 55 amp alternators — 25 amps. Open battery cutout switch to separate battery from test circuit. Load current is now determined by variable resistance.

3) Readjust variable resistance to provide Test Output Amperage. Voltage should be as specified.

CAUTION — *Never run alternator without battery connected unless variable resistor is installed to provide load. Alternator or regulator or both could be severely damaged without providing current load.*

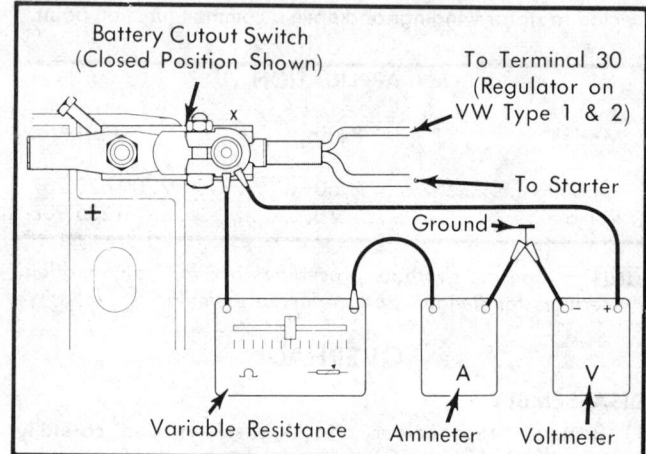

Fig. 1   Alternator Testing Set-Up

OVERHAUL

NOTE — *Since battery current reaches the alternator when the ignition is not on, battery ground strap should be disconnected when removing or installing alternator.*

DISASSEMBLY

1) Remove drive pulley and cooling fan. Remove regulator and brush assembly. Mark front and rear housing along with stator for proper orientation during reassembly.

2) Remove through bolts and carefully separate front housing with rotor from rear housing with stator. Rotor may be removed from housing after bearing retaining plate screws have been removed.

NOTE — *Bearings must be removed and installed using press with suitable adaptors. Never reinstall used bearings.*

3) Remove nuts holding diode assembly to rear housing and separate housing and stator. If diodes are faulty, complete assembly must be replaced rather than individual diodes. Use heat sink when making solder connections.

TESTING

Stator — Check stator for short circuits. If one or more coils are burned, stator shows evidence of shorts. Connect 12 volt,

Alternators & Regulators

SEV MOTOROLA ALTERNATORS (Cont.)

brush holder frame and "—" brush. Lamp should give steady light. If test results are not satisfactory or brush length is less than 3/16" (5 mm), replace brush holder.

CAUTION — *Use only specified test lamp. DO NOT use 110 or 220 volt test lamp on this or any other alternator test procedure.*

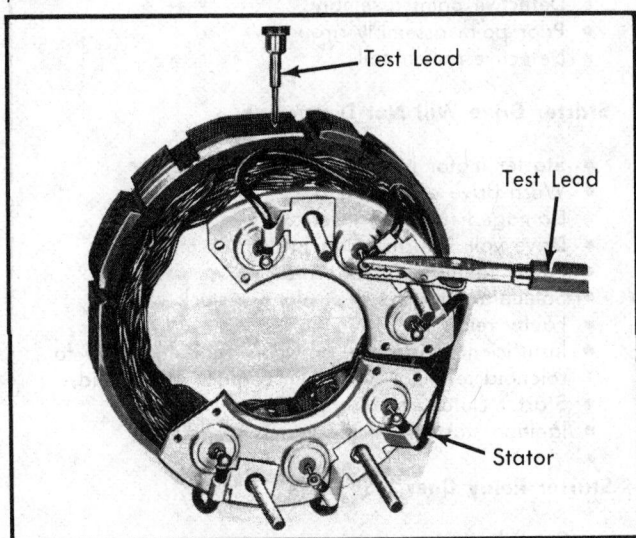

Fig. 2 Checking Stator for Shorts

Diodes — Check diodes with a diode tester for shorts or open circuits. If any diode is defective, entire diode holder with diodes installed must be replaced. If diode tester is not available, diode leads should be quickly and carefully unsoldered and tested with an ohmmeter. Diodes should show low resistance in flow direction and high resistance in reverse direction.

Rotor — Check that slip rings are not dirty or burned. Check winding for breakage or damaged isolation. Measure resistance between slip rings. Normal resistance should be approximately 4.5 ohms. If winding is faulty, rotor must be replaced.

NOTE — *It is recommended that bearings be replaced whenever alternator is disassembled.*

Brush Holder — Connect a test lamp between brushes. Lamp should NOT light. Connect test lamp between "DF" terminal and "+" brush. Lamp should give steady light even if brush and/or terminal cable is moved. Connect test lamp between

2-5 watt test lamp between stator plates and a terminal on stator. If lamp lights, isolation between stator winding and stator plates is defective and stator should be replaced.

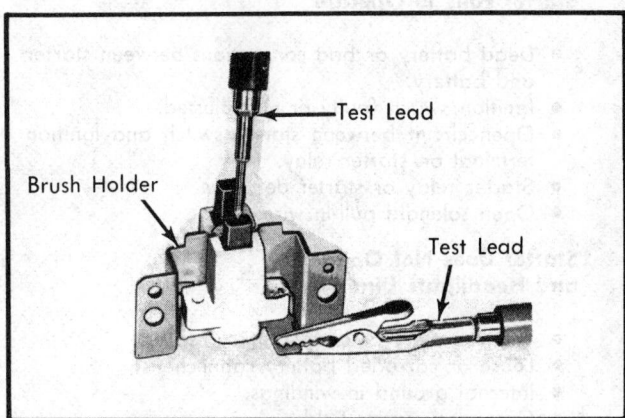

Fig. 3 Checking Brush Holder

NOTE — *Brush length is measured between brush contact surface and holder, with brush resting against spring.*

PARTS REPLACEMENT

Diodes — Mark leads connecting stator to diodes, then quickly and carefully unsolder leads. Place new diode holder in exact position of holder being replaced. Solder new leads while holding with pliers acting as a heat sink. Use minimum 100-watt, well heated soldering iron. Never change places of diode holders. Positive holder is isolated from frame by means of isolation washers and sleeves, and its diodes are marked in red. Negative holder is not isolated and its diodes are marked in black.

CAUTION — *Heat sink must be used during soldering to avoid damage to diodes from overheating.*

REASSEMBLY

Alternator is assembled by reversing disassembly procedures while noting the following: Rotor must be pressed into drive end shield. Connect test lamp between "B+" terminal and alternator frame, then reverse connections. Lamp should light only in one direction. After completion of assembly, test run alternator on bench using same procedure as described for On Car Testing.

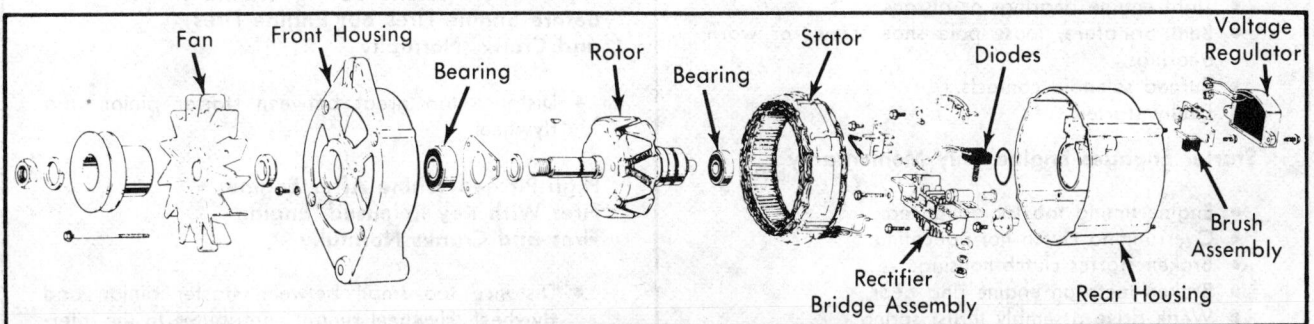

Fig. 4 Disassembled View of SEV Motorola Alternator (Volkswagen Shown)

Starters

STARTING SYSTEMS TROUBLE SHOOTING

CONDITION & POSSIBLE CAUSE	CONDITION & POSSIBLE CAUSE
Starter Fails to Operate • Dead battery or bad connections between starter and battery. • Ignition switch faulty or misadjusted. • Open circuit between starter switch and ignition terminal on starter relay. • Starter relay or starter defective. • Open solenoid pull-in wire. **Starter Does Not Operate and Headlights Dim** • Weak battery or dead battery cell. • Loose or corroded battery connections. • Internal ground in windings. • Grounded starter fields. • Armature rubbing on pole shoes. **Starter Turns but Engine Does Not Rotate** • Starter clutch slipping. • Broken clutch housing. • Pinion shaft rusted or dry. • Engine basic timing incorrect. • Broken teeth on engine ring gear. **Starter Will Not Crank Engine** • Faulty overrunning clutch. • Broken clutch housing. • Broken ring gear teeth. • Armature shaft sheared or reduction gear teeth stripped. • Weak battery. • Faulty solenoid. • Starter spins slowly and draws high current. • Poor grounds. • Engine siezed. • Ignition switch faulty or misadjusted. **Starter Cranks Engine Slowly** • Battery weak or defective. • Engine overheated. • Engine oil too heavy. • Poor battery-to-starter connections. • Current draw too low or too high. • Tight engine bearings or pistons. • Bent armature, loose pole shoe screws or worn bearings. • Burned solenoid contacts. • Faulty starter. **Starter Engages Engine Only Momentarily** • Engine timing too far advanced. • Overrunning clutch not operating. • Broken starter clutch housing. • Broken teeth on engine ring gear. • Weak drive assembly thrust spring. • Weak hold-in coil.	**Starter Drive Will Not Engage** • Defective point assembly. • Poor point assembly ground. • Defective pull-in coil. **Starter Drive Will Not Disengage** • Starter motor loose on mountings. • Worn drive end bushing. • Damaged ring gear teeth. • Drive yolk return spring broken or missing. • Faulty ignition starter switch. • Solenoid contact switch plunger stuck. • Faulty relay. • Insufficient clearance between winding leads to solenoid terminal and main contact in solenoid. • Starter clutch not disengaging. • Ignition starter switch contacts sticking. **Starter Relay Does Not Close** • Dead battery. • Faulty wiring. • Neutral safety switch faulty. • Starter relay faulty. **Starter Relay Operates but Solenoid Does Not** • Faulty solenoid switch, switch connections or switch wiring. • Broken lead or loose soldered connections. **Solenoid Plunger Vibrates When Switch is Engaged** • Weak battery. • Solenoid contacts corroded. • Faulty wiring. • Broken connections inside switch cover. • Open hold-in wire. **Low Current Draw** • Worn brushes or weak brush springs. **High Pitched Whine During Cranking Before Engine Fires but Engine Fires and Cranks Normally** • Distance too great between starter pinion and flywheel. **High Pitched Whine After Engine Fires With Key Released. Engine Fires and Cranks Normally** • Distance too small between starter pinion and flywheel. Flywheel runout contributes to the intermittent nature.

Starters

BOSCH

Audi
BMW
Fiat
Mercedes-Benz
Peugeot

Porsche
Saab
Volkswagen
Volvo

DESCRIPTION

Starter is a brush type, series wound electric motor equipped with an overrunning clutch. Integral solenoid mounted on the starter engages starter pinion gear with flywheel ring gear when starter is engaged. Field frame is enclosed by commutator end frame and drive bushing and carries pole shoes and field coils. A spline on the drive end of the armature shaft carries the overrunning clutch and pinion assembly. Armature shaft is supported in sintered bronze bushings in the commutator end frame and drive end housings.

TESTING

Lock Test— Mount starter in a test stand to allow starter torque measurement (follow manufacturers instructions). With voltage adjusted to specifications, ammeter reading and starter torque should be within specifications.

Free Running Test— With starter in test bench, take readings of starter current, voltage and RPM. Readings should be within specifications.

NOTE — *Starter must be mounted to prevent meshing of pinion and ring gear even in engaged position. If starter has warmed up during previous tests, RPM will be higher.*

APPLICATION

Model	① Bosch Part No.
Audi	
4000	211 218
5000	311 122
5000 Diesel	362 069
BMW	
320i	311 100
528i, 633CSi & 733i	314 025
Fiat Strada & X1/9	212 210
Mercedes-Benz	
240 & 300 Series	362 047
280 & 450 Series	314 018
Peugeot	
504	362 044
505 Diesel	362 045
505 Gasoline	208 211
604	311 124
Porsche	
911SC	312 100
924	311 122
924 Turbo (Standard)	208 221
924 Turbo (Heavy Duty)	311 134
928	312 102
Saab 900 & 900 Turbo	311 108
Volkswagen	
Dasher	
Gasoline	211 218
Diesel	314 014
Jetta, Rabbit & Scirocco (Gasoline)	
Man. Trans.	211 223
Auto. Trans.	212 206
Rabbit (Diesel)	
Man. Trans.	314 012
Auto. Trans.	312 105
Vanagon	
Man. Trans.	211 221
Auto. Trans.	212 208
Volvo	
DL, GL & GLT Turbo	311 103
GLE & Bertone	311 105
Diesel	② 1257325

① — Bosch starter basic part number is 0 001.
② — Volvo part number.

SPECIFICATIONS

Brush Length & Spring Tension

Application	In.(mm)	Lbs. (g)
208 xxx	.52 (13)	2.5-3.1(1150-1350)
211 xxx	.52 (13)	2.5-2.9(1150-1300)
212 xxx	.52 (13)	2.4-2.7(1080-1220)
311 xxx	.39 (10)	2.5-2.9(1150-1300)
312 xxx	.39 (10)	1.8-2.0(800-900)
314 xxx	.52 (13)	2.5-2.9(1150-1300)
362 xxx	.61 (15.5)	2.5-2.9(1150-1300)

OVERHAUL

DISASSEMBLY

1) Clamp starter in vise and remove nut and washer from solenoid main terminal connection. Remove solenoid mounting screws and guide solenoid body away from drive end housing and plunger. Disconnect plunger from actuating lever.

2) Remove screws and cap with rubber seal from commutator end housing. Wipe grease from armature shaft and remove "C" clip with shims. Remove through bolts or nuts from studs and lift off commutator end housing.

3) Lift springs clear of brushes and slide brushes from holders. Remove brush plate from housing. Separate drive end housing and armature assembly from yoke by tapping apart.

4) Remove armature assembly from drive end housing while at the same time uncoupling actuating arm. If necessary to remove actuating arm, first remove rubber insert from drive end housing. Remove pivot arm screw and nut and extract actuating arm.

5) To remove drive pinion assembly from armature shaft, separate thrust collar from over "C" clip. Remove "C" clip from its groove and drive pinion assembly off armature shaft.

BOSCH (Cont.)

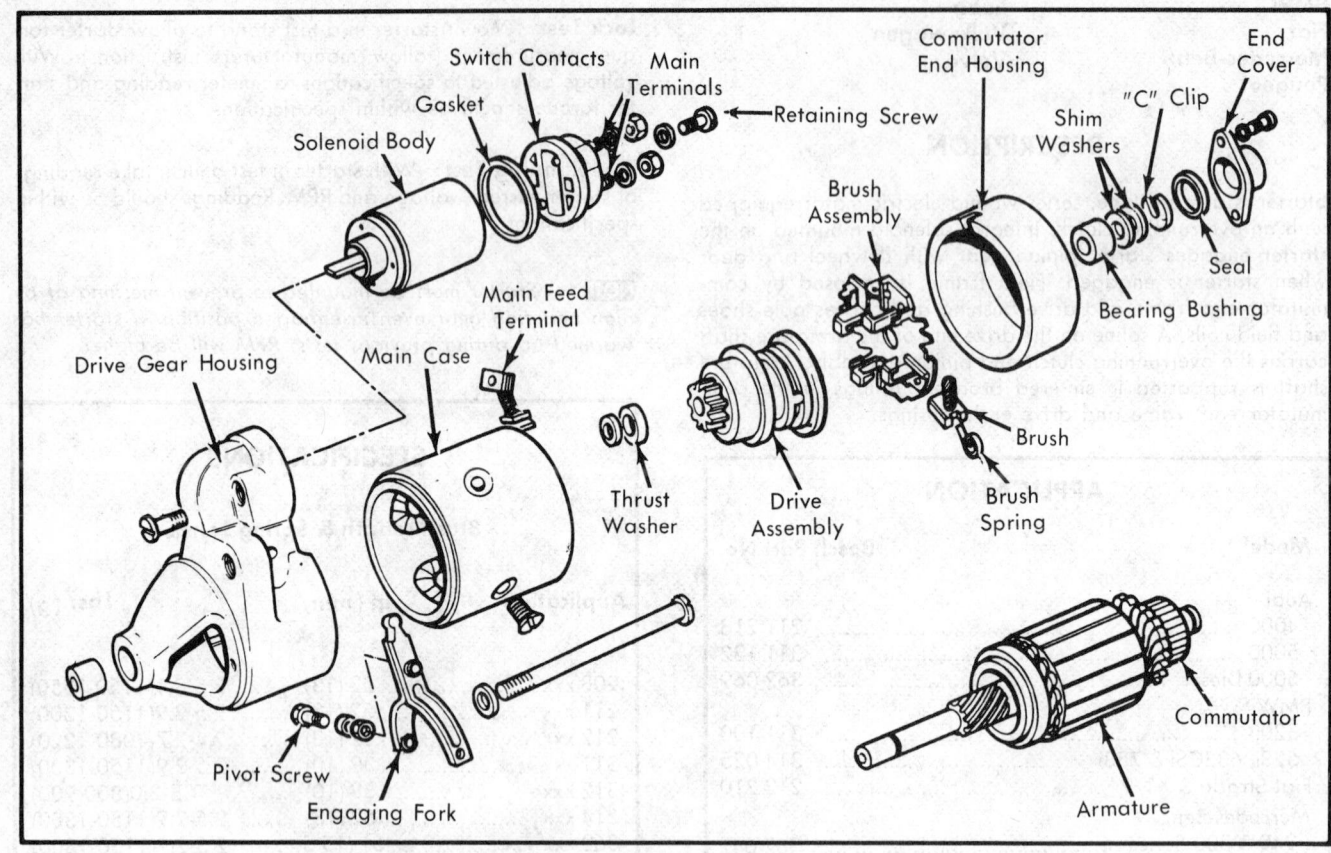

Fig. 1 Disassembled View of Typical Bosch Starter

CLEANING & INSPECTING

Clean all parts with suitable cleaning agent. Inspect for wear or damage, then apply thin coat of oil to running surfaces.

PARTS REPLACEMENT & TESTING

Brushes & Springs —Check brush spring pressure with suitable spring scale. Check brushes for minimum length and freedom of movement in holders. If replacement is necessary, replace all brushes by cutting old brush leads midway between connection and old brush. Solder new brushes to original leads.

Armature — 1) Check commutator to shaft (or core) for short circuit with 110 volt AC test lamp. Test lamp should not light, however slight glow may occur due to dampness. Check armature coils for short circuit between windings using an armature growler.

2) Check commutator for pits, burns or rough surface. If out of round exceeds .002" (.05 mm), or grooves or burned spots cannot be removed with fine crocus cloth, commutator must be tur-

ned. Undercut insulation between commutator bars to a maximum depth of .024" (.6 mm).

NOTE — *Never use emery cloth or a file on commutator; turn on a lathe only.*

Bushings — Self-lubricating bushings should be replaced only when worn or damaged. Force out bushings with suitable mandrel. Clean hole and remove burrs. Before pressing new bushing in place, soak bushing in suitable lubricant for at least 30 minutes.

Drive Assembly — Replace drive when damaged or teeth are worn. *See Disassembly.*

Solenoid Plunger (Armature) — Plunger must move in and out of solenoid body when disconnected from pinion drive lever. If corroded, clean thoroughly before proceeding with tests.

Solenoid Pull-In Coil — Connect jumper wires between a 12 volt battery and the solenoid as shown in *Fig. 2*. Armature should pull in suddenly and return when electrical connection is broken.

BOSCH (Cont.)

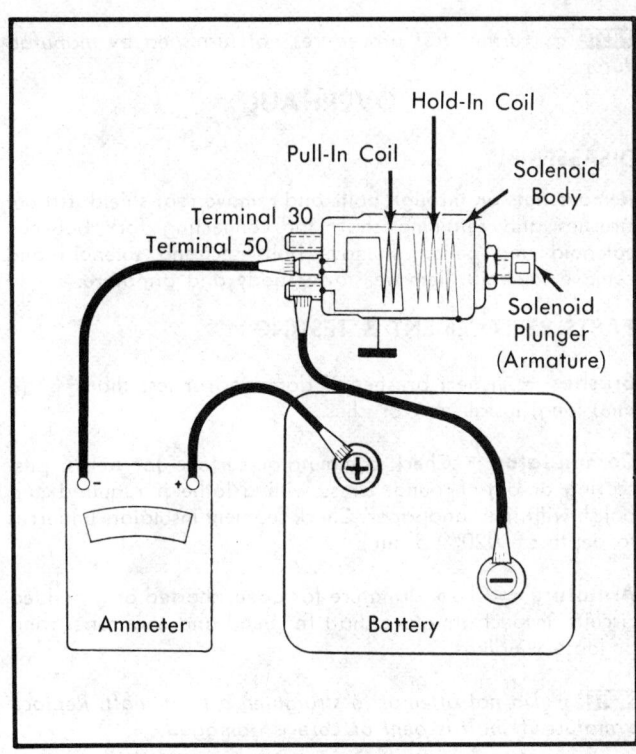

Fig. 2   Typical Connections for Pull-In Test

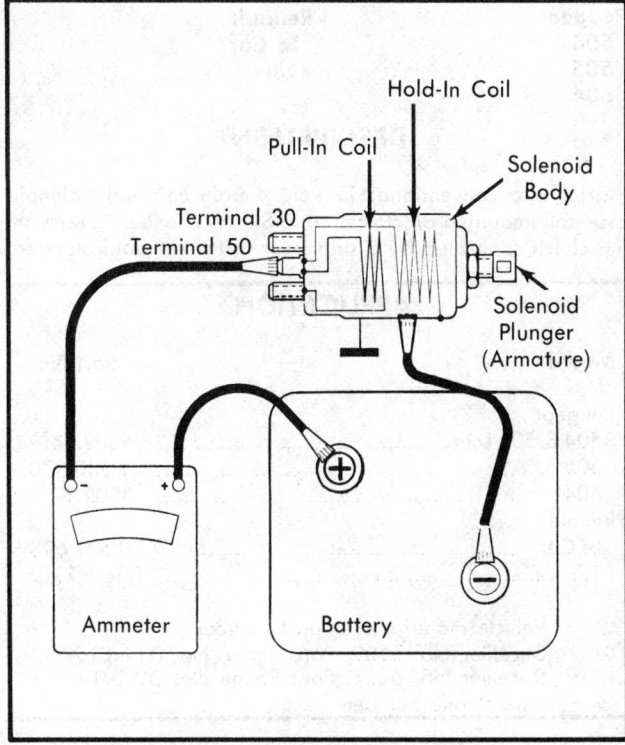

Fig. 3   Typical Connections for Hold-In Test

Hold-In Coil — Connect jumper wires as shown in *Fig. 3* while pressing armature into solenoid by hand. Armature should remain held in. Disconnect jumper terminal 50 and armature should immediately return to its outer position.

NOTE — *Do not attempt to repair solenoid. If either test is unsatisfactory, install new solenoid.*

REASSEMBLY

1) Slide drive pinion assembly and thrust washer onto armature shaft. Install "C" clip into groove in armature shaft and pull thrust washer up over clip. Align fork in drive end housing and insert pivot pin. Slide armature assembly into drive end housing, coupling the shift fork onto the drive pinion flange.

2) Install rubber insert in drive end housing. Guide yoke assembly over armature while aligning notch with rubber insert. Tap yoke into full contact with drive end housing.

3) Install brush assembly noting that cutouts in brush plate slide over through bolts on models so equipped. On models with screws, brush plate cutouts align with loops in field windings. Plates are properly positioned when screws are installed in commutator end housing. Install brushes and springs assuring that field winding brush leads do not contact yoke.

4) Slide commutator end housing into position and secure with nuts and washers or screws, as appropriate. Install drive end housing. Install shims onto armature shaft at commutator end to eliminate end play and install "C" clip in groove.

5) Install bearing cap seal on commutator end housing. Lubricate end of armature shaft with lithium based grease and install bearing cap. Lubricate plunger hook and place in position over shift fork in drive end housing. Install solenoid body with return spring properly positioned, then tighten mounting screws and field connections.

STARTER PERFORMANCE SPECIFICATIONS

Model	No Load Test		Amps.	Lock Test Volts	Torque	Solenoid Pull-In Volts
	Amps.	RPM				
208 xxx	35-55	6000-8000	320-410	8.5	9.4 ft.lbs.	7.5
211 xxx	35-55	6000-9000	340-430	8.5	8.7 ft.lbs.	8.0
212 xxx	35-55	6000-8000	320-410	8.5	9.4 ft.lbs.	7.5
311 xxx	30-50	5500-7500	350-450	8.5	13.0 ft.lbs.	7.5
312 xxx	55-85	8500-10,500	650-730	6.0	13.7 ft.lbs.	8.0
314 xxx	50-80	7300-9300	690-780	6.0	16.6 ft.lbs.	7.5
362 xxx	65-95	6500-8500	1100-1300	7.0	32.5 ft.lbs.	7.5

Starters

DUCELLIER & PARIS-RHONE

Peugeot
504
505
604

Renault
Le Car
18i

DESCRIPTION

Starter is a conventional 12 volt, 4 pole unit with solenoid assembly mounted on starter case. Starters have an overrunning clutch connected by a shift lever to the solenoid plunger.

APPLICATION

Model	①Part No.
Peugeot	
504 & 505 Diesel	5802.04②
505	5802.20
604	5802.17③
Renault	
Le Car	77 00 671 608
18i	D10 E 79④

① — Vehicle manufacturer part number.
② — Ducellier No. 6109, Paris-Rhone No. D11 E159.
③ — Ducellier No. 6237, Paris-Rohne No. D9 E 14.
④ — Paris-Rhone number.

TESTING

Lock Test (Le Car) — Follow instructions and procedures outlined in manual furnished with tester. Use a fully charged battery and carry out the test at a temperature of 77°F. Starter torque should be 9 ft. lbs. at 400 amps.

Operational Test (Peugeot) — Disconnect coil high tension wire (except diesel) and connect tachometer to engine. Connect ammeter between battery and starter and energize starter for maximum of 15 seconds. Gasoline engine should turn at 120 RPM with a maximum draw of 250 amperes. Diesel engine should turn at 120 RPM with a maximum draw of 350 amperes.

NOTE — Further test procedures not furnished by manufacturer.

OVERHAUL

DISASSEMBLY

Remove nuts on through bolts and remove rear shield. Lift out brushes and retaining shaft for connecting fork between solenoid and pinion. Remove bolts securing solenoid and remove solenoid. Remove starter body and armature.

PARTS REPLACEMENT & TESTING

Brushes — Inspect brushes. If damaged or less than 5/16" (8 mm) long, install new brushes.

Commutator — Check commutator surface for burns, pits, scoring or out-of-round. Dress with a lathe if required and polish with fine sandpaper. Check segment insulators undercut to depth of .020" (.5 mm).

Armature — Check armature for open, shorted or grounded circuits. Inspect armature shaft for bend and core for scoring or loose windings.

NOTE — Do not attempt to straighten a bent shaft. Replace armature if shaft is bent or core is damaged.

Bearings — Inspect front and rear bearings for wear and excessive clearance with armature shaft. Replace if damaged or in case of excess clearance.

REASSEMBLY

1) Clean all parts and coat sliding surfaces with multi-purpose grease. Assemble in reverse order of disassembly and check pinion clearance.

2) Disconnect starter field terminal from solenoid and energize solenoid with 12 volt battery. Measure clearance of pinion gear to stop collar. Clearance should be .02-.10" (.5-2.5 mm). Adjust to proper clearance by screwing plunger fork or adjusting screw in or out.

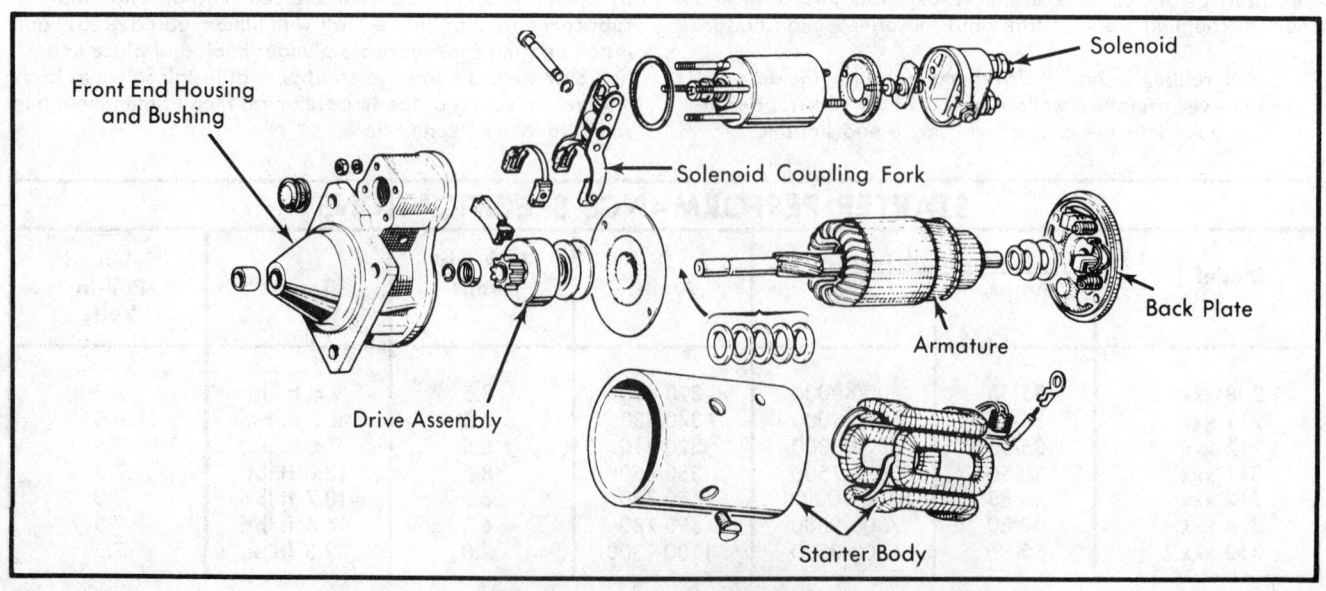

Fig. 1 Disassembled View of Typical Paris-Rhone Starter

FIAT

Brava
Spider 2000

NOTE — *Other Fiat models use Bosch starters.*

DESCRIPTION

Fiat starter is a 12 volt, brush type, 4-pole system with field windings in series. Integral solenoid is mounted on starter housing and causes starter pinion to engage flywheel ring gear when starter is energized. Overrunning clutch pinion drive is mounted directly on drive end of armature shaft.

APPLICATION	
Model	Fiat No.
Brava & Spider 2000	E 100-1.3/12

TESTING

PERFORMANCE TESTS

Mount starter in test stand and perform running test, no load test and stall (lock) test. Starter should develop 31.7-35.1 INCH lbs. (3.6-4.0 N.m) torque while drawing 280 amps and 9.5 volts at 1500-1700 RPM. At 12 volts and 28 amps under no load conditions, armature speed should be 4700-5700 RPM. Stall torque test should produce 143-159 INCH lbs. (16.15-18.05 N.m) torque at 12 volts and 28 or less amps.

OVERHAUL

DISASSEMBLY

1) With metal band (dust cover) removed from commutator end frame, disconnect solenoid terminal lead and remove nuts from solenoid mounting bolts. Remove solenoid. Remove nuts from through bolts and slide off end frame while holding brushes off of commutator.

2) Remove pinion end frame while disengaging shifter fork from overrunning clutch. If pinion drive assembly is to be removed, slide back stop ring and remove lock ring from armature shaft. Remove overrunning cluch/pinion drive assembly.

CLEANING

Use dry compressed air to blow dirt and worn brush dust from starter. Do not immerse starter components in solvent. Use brush dipped in cleaning solvent to clean drive unit, then blow dry with air.

PARTS REPLACEMENT

To replace field coils, mount starter frame in press-type screwdriver stand and remove pole piece attaching screws. Remove pole pieces and field coils. Heat replacement field coils to about 128°F in order to obtain added flexibility and ease in installation. Install pole shoes and tighten screws. Inner diameter of pole shoes should be 2.675-2.677" (67.95-68.00 mm) to assure proper air gap between armature and shoes.

REASSEMBLY

Lubricate inner splined face of drive assembly with SAE 10 motor oil before installing drive on armature shaft. Reverse disassembly procedure to complete overhaul.

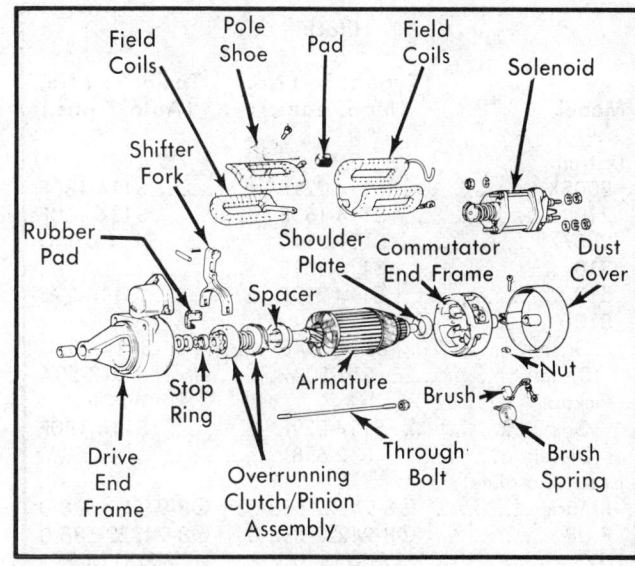

Fig. 1 Disassembled View of Fiat Starter Motor

Starters

HITACHI & MITSUBISHI

Chrysler Corp. Imports
  Arrow Pickup
  Champ
  Challenger
  Colt
  Ram-50 Pickup
Datsun
  200SX
  210
  280ZX
  310
  510
  810

Pickup
Honda
  Civic (Calif.)
Isuzu
  I-Mark
  P'UP
  LUV
Mazda
  626
  GLC
  RX7
  B2000 Pickup

DESCRIPTION

Starter is a conventional 12-volt, 4-pole brush type motor. May be either direct or reduction gear drive. Solenoid mounted on starter shifts overrunning clutch and pinion to flywheel when starter is energized.

APPLICATION

Hitachi

Model	Type or Part No. (Man. Trans.)	Type or Part No. (Auto. Trans.)
Datsun		
200SX	S114-229F	S114-180F
210	S114-163E	S114-160F
280ZX	S114-254D	S1140254D
310	S114-161F	.....
510	S114-229F	S114-295
810		
(Gas)	S114-254D	S114-254D
(Diesel)	512-50A	512-50A
Pickup		
(Gas)	S114-229F	S114-180F
(Diesel)	S12-68B	
Isuzu (Gasoline)		
I-Mark	①8-94222-688-0	①8-94222-688-0
P'UP	①8-94222-688-0	①8-94222-688-0
LUV	②S114-271	②S114-271

Mitsubishi

Model	Type or Part No. (Man. Trans.)	Type or Part No. (Auto. Trans.)
Chrysler Corp. Imports		
Champ & Colt	MD034120	MD27400
Challenger & Sapporo	MD027400	MD27382
Arrow & Ram-50	MD607284	MD07413
Mazda		
626	8088 18 400R	8964 18 400R
RX7	1757 18 400R	N202 18 400
GLC	8131 18 400R	0324 18 400R
B2000 Pickup	8088 18 400R	.....

① — Manufacturers part number.
② — GM part number 94204438.

TESTING

STARTER PERFOMANCE TESTS

No Load Tests — Connect starter in series with a 12 volt battery and an ammeter capable of at least a 1000 ampere reading. Connect voltmeter as shown in *Fig. 1* and compare readings with *Starter Performance Specifications* as shown.

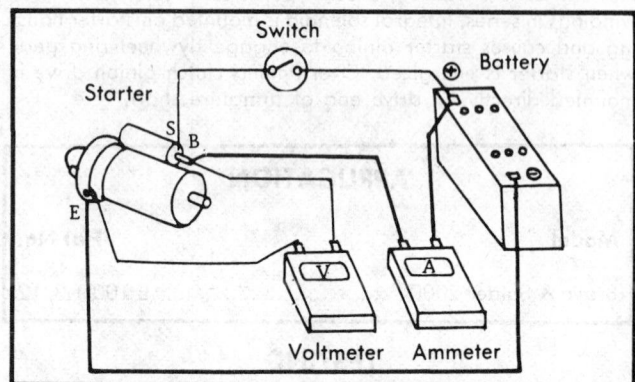

Fig. 1   Connections for No Load Test

Lock (Torque) Test — Mount starter in a test stand to perform torque measurement test. Follow manufacturer's instructions for test stand operation. With voltage adjusted, ammeter reading and torque should be within specifications.

SOLENOID TESTS

NOTE — *Make tests with solenoid removed from starter or remove solenoid lead to starter before testing. Ensure that solenoid plunger and sleeve are clean and dry before performing tests.*

Pull-In Coil Test — Connect jumper between negative post of 12 volt battery and "S" terminal. Connect a second jumper to positive battery terminal and touch "M" (MT) terminal. Plunger should pull in immediately.

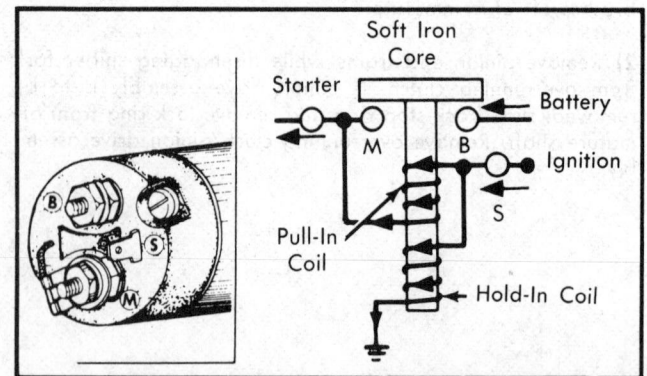

Fig. 2   Starting Circuit Diagram and Solenoid Terminals

Hold-In Coil Test — Connect a ground lead between the "M" (MT) terminal and the solenoid case. Apply 8 volts to the "S" terminal to pull in the plunger. Disconnect lead to "M" (MT) terminal and plunger should remain in.

Return Test — Push plunger into solenoid body by hand. Apply 12 volts between "M" (MT) terminal and the solenoid case. If the case is short circuited, the plunger will be attracted. If nothing happens, the solenoid is satisfactory.

HITACHI & MITSUBISHI (Cont.)

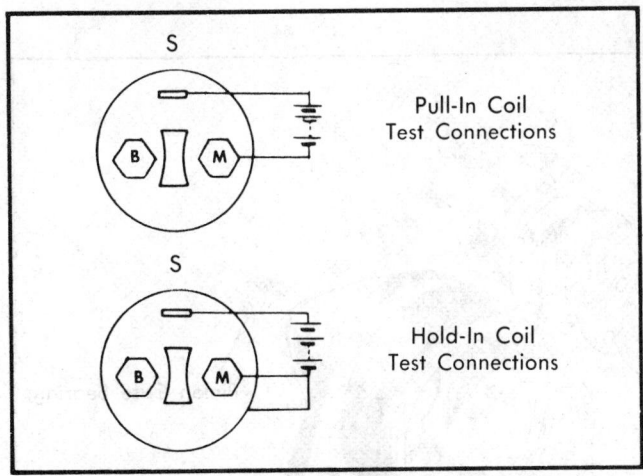

Fig. 3 Test Connections for Pull-In Coil and Hold-In Coil

Pull-In Coil Test Connections

Hold-In Coil Test Connections

OVERHAUL

DISASSEMBLY

1) Loosen nut securing connecting plate to magnetic switch "M" terminal. Remove screws securing magnetic switch and remove switch (solenoid) assembly. Remove through bolts and brush cover assembly, then tap yoke assembly loose with wooden mallet. Remove yoke, armature assembly and pinion shift lever.

2) Remove pinion stop ring from end of armature shaft by pushing stop ring to clutch side. Remove snap ring and overrunning clutch assembly from armature shaft.

PARTS REPLACEMENT & TESTING

Brushes & Springs — Check brush spring tension using a suitable spring scale. Check brush contact surface condition and brush length. Check lead clip and wire conections and condition of brush holders. Replace as required. *See Brush Spring Tension and Brush Length (Minimum).*

Brush Spring Tension	
Application	**Lbs. (kg)**
Chrysler Corp. Imports	3.3 (1.5)
Datsun	
200SX & 810	3.5-4.4 (1.6-2.0)
All Other Models	3.1-4.0 (1.4-1.8)
Honda, Isuzu, LUV & Mazda	3.5 (1.6)

Brush Length (Minimum)	
Application	**In. (mm)**
Chrysler Corp. Imports & Mazda	.45 (11.5)
Datsun, Honda, Isuzu & LUV	.47 (12.0)

Armature — Check external condition of armature for scoring or other damage. Measure shaft distortion with dial indicator. Replace armature if shaft bend exceeds .003" (.08 mm) on Datsun, .006" (.15 mm) on LUV, and .004" (.10 mm) on all other models.

Commutator — Inspect commutator for roughness, grooves, burns or pitting. Sand lightly with 500 grit sandpaper if necessary. Check commutator for out-of-round and mica insulators undercut to a depth of .020-.031" (.5-.8 mm). If necessary, commutator may be turned less than .04" (1 mm) from original size and mica undercut. Replace if excessively worn.

Field Coil — Check field coil continuity by connecting test probe of circuit tester or an ohmmeter to the field coil positive terminal and brush holder. If circuit is open, replace field coil. Check for grounding of field coils by placing one probe of circuit tester on starter housing and other probe to field coil positive terminal. If little or no resistance, field coil is grounded and must be replaced.

Overrunning Clutch Assembly — Inspect pinion assembly and sleeve. Sleeve should slide freely on armature shaft and spline. If damage or resistance is noted, replace assembly. Check pinion and flywheel teeth for excessive rubbing or damaged teeth. Replace as required.

Pinion Gear Clearance — The clearance between the pinion gear and stop collar should be .012-.059" (.30-1.52 mm) on Hitachi and .02-.08" (.51-2.03 mm) on Mitsubishi when solenoid is engaged. Adjust as necessary by changing shims between solenoid and starter yoke. *See Fig. 4.*

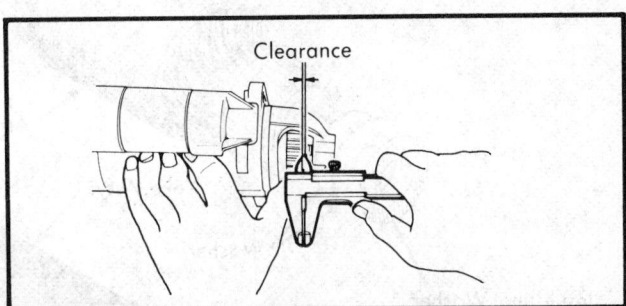

Clearance

Fig. 4 Measuring Pinion Edge-to-Pinion Stopper Clearance

Pinion Case Bearing — Inspect bearing for wear and check side play. If clearance exceeds .008" (.2 mm), replace bearing. New bearing clearance should be .001-.004" (.025-.10 mm) for Hitachi or .002-.004" (.05-.10 mm) for Mitsubishi starters.

NOTE — *Ensure that bearing is installed so that end of bearing is flush with gear case end.*

CLEANING & INSPECTION

Clean all disassembled parts. Do not use grease dissolving solvent on overrunning clutch, armature assembly, solenoid assembly or field coils due to possible damage. Inspect all parts for damage or wear and replace as required.

REASSEMBLY

To reassemble, reverse disassembly procedure. Fill rear case on reduction gear models with grease. Lightly oil pinion and all bearing surfaces.

Starters

HITACHI & MITSUBISHI (Cont.)

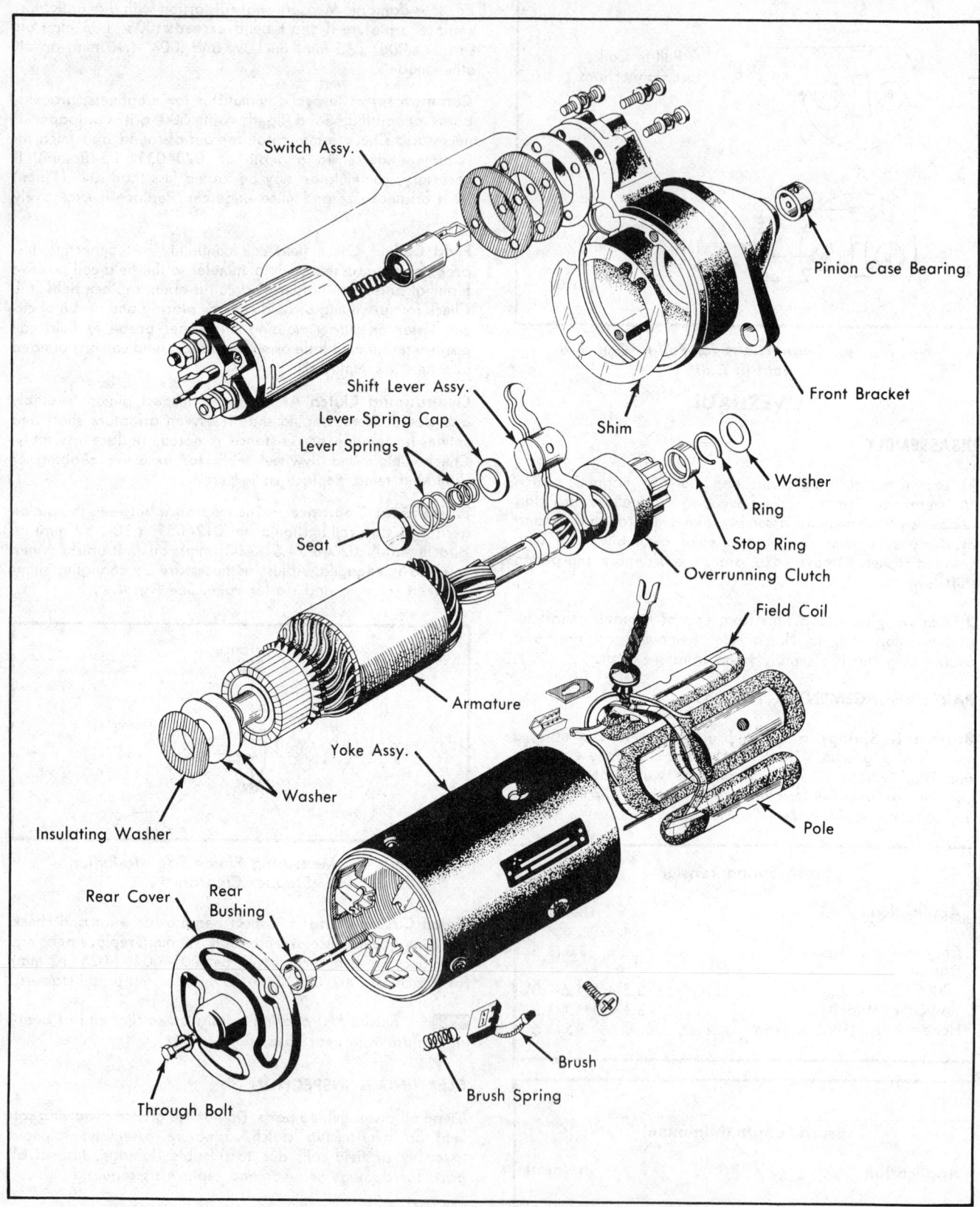

Switch Assy.

Pinion Case Bearing

Front Bracket

Shim

Shift Lever Assy.

Lever Spring Cap

Lever Springs

Washer

Ring

Stop Ring

Seat

Overrunning Clutch

Field Coil

Armature

Yoke Assy.

Pole

Washer

Insulating Washer

Rear Cover

Rear Bushing

Brush

Brush Spring

Through Bolt

Fig. 5 Disassembled View of Typical Mitsubishi Starter

Starters

HITACHI & MITSUBISHI (Cont.)

Type or Part No.	No Load Test		Load Test		
	Amps. (Maximum)	RPM	Amps. (Maximum)	Volts	Torque (Ft. Lbs.) (Maximum)
HITICHI					
S114-160B	60	7000	.....	.....	.....
S114-161F	60	7000	.....	.....	.....
S114-163F	60	7000	.....	.....	.....
S114-170E	60	7000	.....	.....	.....
S114-180F	60	6000	.....	.....	.....
S114-202	60	6000	350	5.0	5.8
S114-229F	60	7000	.....	.....	.....
S114-254D	100	3900	.....	.....	.....
31200PB1-935	70	6000	200	8.0	3.3
MITSUBISHI					
MD034120	50	.....	.....	.....	.....
MD027400	60	.....	.....	.....	.....
MD027382	90	.....	.....	.....	.....
MD027382	60	.....	.....	.....	.....
MD607413	62	.....	.....	.....	.....
O32418400R	53	6800	310	5.0	5.4
1757 18 400R	50	5600	600	5.0	6.9
8088 14 400R	53	6800	310	8.0	5.4
8131 18 400R	93	6800	310	5.0	5.4
8964 18 400R	60	6600	500	5.0	8.3

STARTER PERFORMANCE SPECIFICATIONS

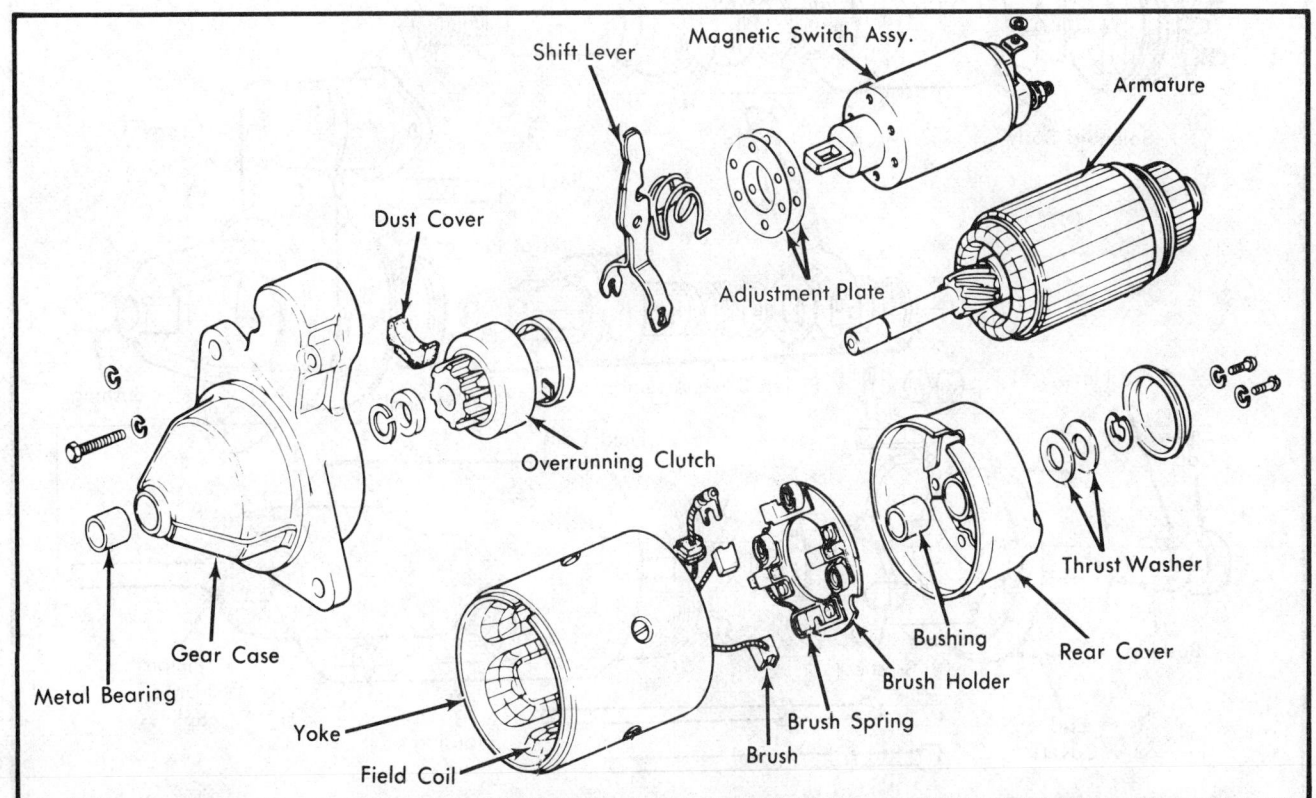

Fig. 6 *Disassembled View of a Typical Hitachi Starter*

LUCAS

Jaguar
XJ6
Triumph
TR7
TR8

DESCRIPTION

Starter is a series wound 4-pole, 4-brush motor, using either wedge shaped or conventional brushes. A housing mounted solenoid shifts the roller type starter clutch and pinion to engage the ring gear when starter is energized.

APPLICATION		
Model	Lucas No.	Type
Jaguar XJ6		3M100
Triumph		
TR7	25703	2M100 PE
TR8	25724	3M100 PE

TESTING

PERFORMANCE TESTS

No Load Test — With starter on bench and using a good 12-volt battery, connect an ammeter in series to starter. Starter should rotate smoothly at specified RPM and current draw.

Lock Test — Use suitable tester and set up according to instructions. With starter locked in test stand and voltage adjusted, ammeter and starter torque readings should be as specified. See Starter Performance Specifications.

OVERHAUL

DISASSEMBLY

1) Disconnect electrical link between solenoid and starting motor. Remove nuts securing solenoid to end bracket and lift off solenoid, leaving plunger attached to engagement lever. Pry off end cap and spire nut (locking washer). Remove through bolts and end cover with brush holder.

2) Carefully remove brushes from holder. Remove seal between drive end bracket and starter housing. Remove engagement lever pivot pin and separate armature with drive assembly from drive end bracket. If removing drive assembly, remove thrust collar and lock ring from armature shaft and take drive assembly off of armature.

PARTS RELACEMENT AND TESTING

Armature — Check armature for open, shorted or grounded circuits. Check for lifted commutator segments and loose turns in armature winding. Check armature for scoring. A scored armature could indicate a loose pole shoe or a bent armature shaft. Do not attempt to true a distorted shaft or machine armature core; replace if damaged.

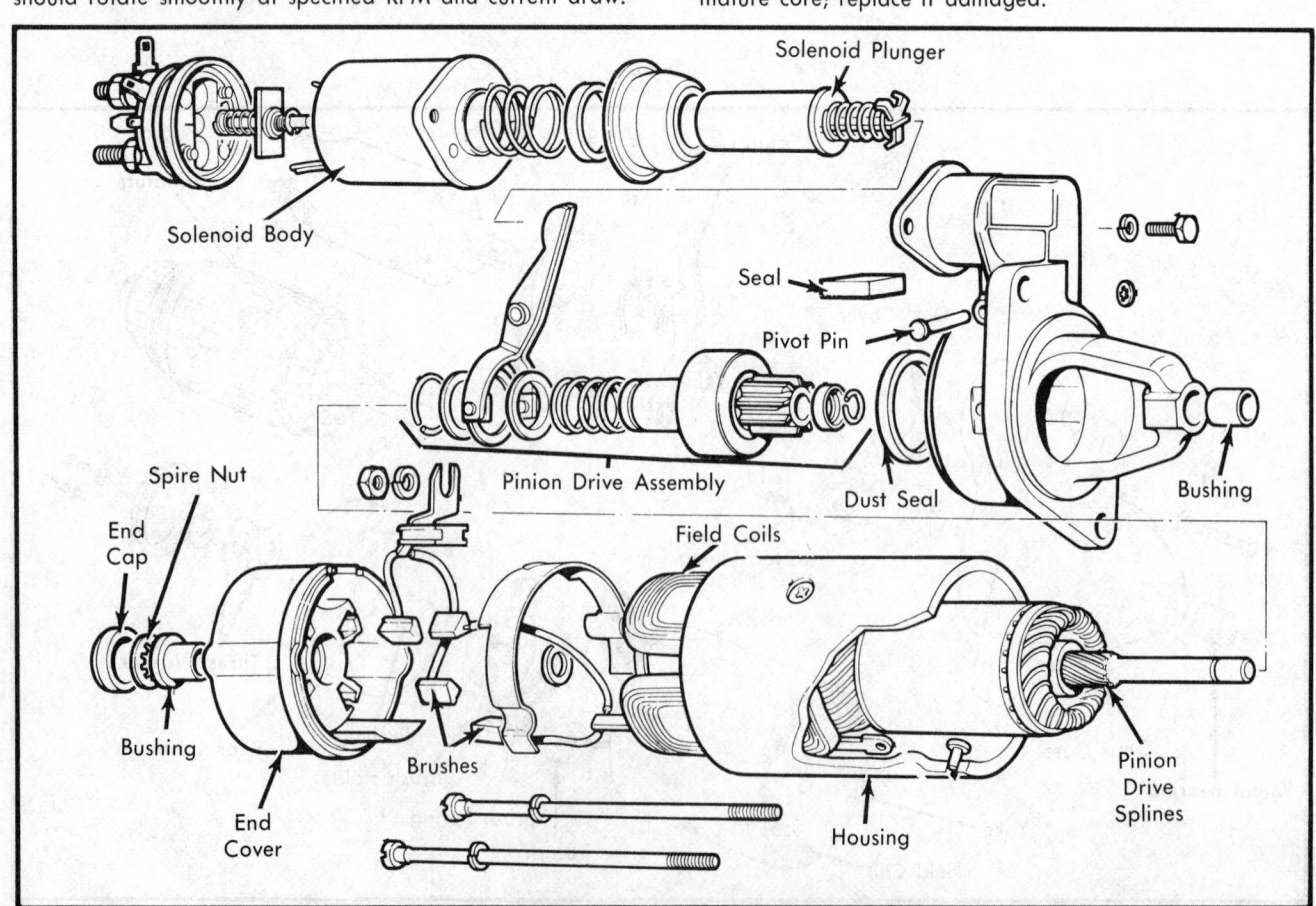

Fig. 1 Exploded View of Lucas 2M100 Starter

LUCAS (Cont.)

Commutator — Clean commutator with cloth moistened in suitable solvent and, if necessary, with fine sandpaper. If further clean up is necessary, turn down in a lathe, removing only as much metal as is absolutely necessary. Do NOT undercut insulators between commutator segments.

Brushes & Springs — Check that brushes move freely in holders by holding back brush springs and pulling gently on connecting wires. If movement is sluggish, remove brush from holder and clean with solvent moistened cloth. Replace brushes if less than 3/8" (9.5 mm) long and springs if tension is less than 36 ozs. (800 g).

Field Coils — Check for open or grounded coils using test lamp or voltmeter and battery connected in series. If any coil is defective, replace all coils. Mark housing and pole shoes for installation in original position. Remove pole piece screws and pry pole shoes, coils and insulation pieces from housing. To install, reverse removal procedure.

Bushings — In event of excessive wear or damage, remove old bushings with suitable mandrel or extractor. Ensure that new porous bronze bushings have been soaked in light engine oil for at least 24 hours and press into position. Fit new bushing using highly polished mandrel .0005" (.013 mm) larger than diameter of shaft.

NOTE — *Do NOT ream bushing after fitting due to possible damage to porosity of new bearing.*

Starter Solenoid — **1)** With all cables and connectors disconnected from solenoid, connect a 12 volt power supply between starter terminal and small unmarked solenoid terminal. Connect a test lamp across main terminals and note test lamp lighted, indicating contacts are closed. Disconnect power from small solenoid terminal and lamp should go out, indicating contacts have been opened.

2) To check winding continuity, connect ohmmeter between starter terminal and ground on solenoid body. Resistance should be 1.01-1.07 ohms. To check pull-in winding, check across small unmarked terminal and starter terminal. Resistance should be .36-.42 ohms for Jaguar and .25-.27 ohms for other models.

3) To check hold in winding, connect ohmmeter between ground on solenoid body and unmarked terminal. Resistance for Jaguar should be 1.49-1.71 ohms and .76-.80 ohms for remaining models.

REASSEMBLY

Ensure that all parts are clean and reverse disassembly procedure, using new lock ring and spire nut. Lightly lubricate bearing surfaces and pivot pin. Armature end play should be adjusted to maximum end play of .010" (.25 mm) by driving retaining ring (spire nut) to proper position.

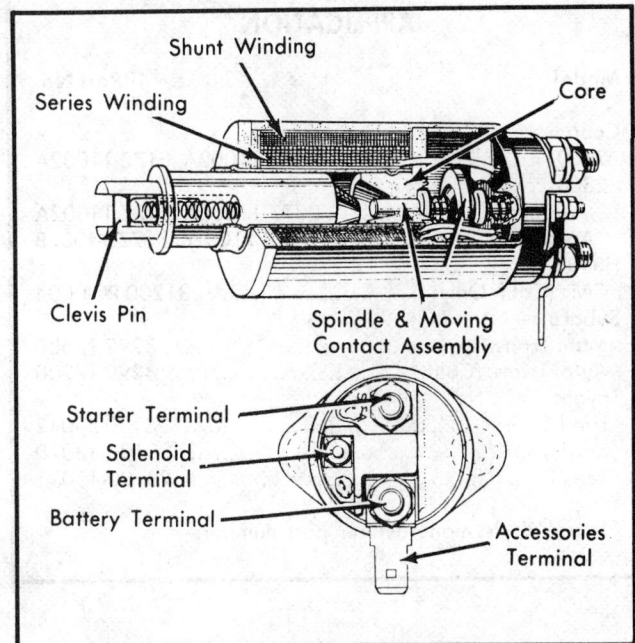

Fig. 2 Lucas Starter Solenoid

STARTER PERFORMANCE SPECIFICATIONS					
	No Load Test ①		Lock Test		
Model	Amps.	RPM	Amps.	Volts	Torque
2M100 3M100	100	6,000	463	①	14.4 ft. lbs.
XJ6	100	5,000-6,000	940	①	29.0 ft. lbs.
TR8	65	6,000	545	①	16.5 ft. lbs.

① — Use 12 volt fully charged battery.

NIPPONDENSO DIRECT DRIVE

Courier
  Pickup
Honda
  Civic (Calif. Only)
Subaru
  Hatchback
  Hardtop

Sedan
  Wagon
Toyota
  Land Cruiser
  Starlet
  Tercel

DESCRIPTION

Nippondenso direct drive starter is conventional 12 volt, 4-pole, brush type starter. Integral solenoid is attached to drive housing and causes starter pinion to engage flywheel ring gear when starter is energized. Overrunning clutch pinion drive is mounted directly on drive end of armature shaft.

APPLICATION

Model	①Part No.
Courier	
2000 cc	D97Z 11002A, E17Z 11002A
2300 cc	
Man. Trans.	D77Z 11002A, E17Z 11002A
Auto. Trans.	D77Z 11002B, E17Z 11002B
Honda	
Civic (Calif. Only)	31200 PC1 004
Subaru	
Man. Trans.	8299 18600
Auto. Trans. (Calif.)	4299 17200
Toyota	
Land Cruiser	28100 60042
Starlet	28100-13020
Tercel	28100-15011

① — Vehicle manufacturer part number.

TESTING

PERFORMANCE TESTS

No Load Test — With starter on bench, and using a fully charged 12 volt battery, make connections as shown in *Fig. 1*. Starter should rotate smoothly at more than 5000 RPM, drawing less than 50 amps at 11 volts.

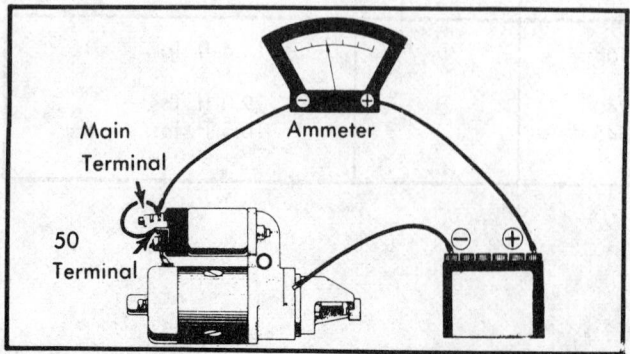

Fig. 1   Circuit for No Load Test

Lock Test — To perform lock test, follow procedures outlined in tester instruction manual. With starter locked in test stand and voltage adjusted as specified, ammeter and torque should be within limits.

SOLENOID TESTS

NOTE — *Tests must be performed with starter assembled and "M" (field) lead from starter disconnected at the solenoid. Plunger and sleeve must be clean and dry.*

Pull-In Test — Connect test equipment as shown in *Fig. 2*. Battery negative is connected to starter body and "C" terminal. Battery positive is connected to terminal "50". If plunger has definitely jumped out, pull-in coil is satisfactory.

Hold-In Test — Connect leads as shown in *Fig. 2*. Disconnect "C" terminal. The pinion should remain projected. If the pinion does not remain projected, hold-in coil is defective and must be replaced.

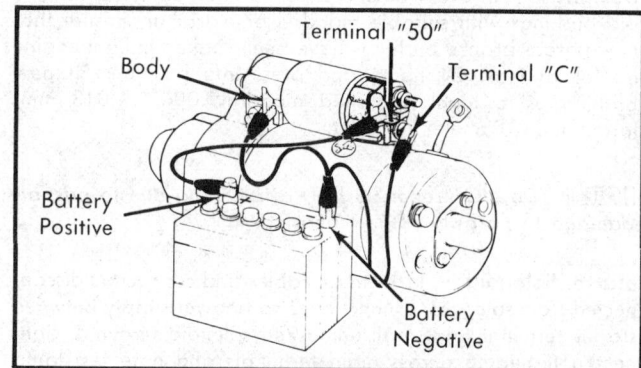

Fig. 2   Solenoid Test Hookup

Plunger Return Test — Connect leads as shown in *Fig. 2*. Disconnect terminal "C" as in Hold-In Test. Disconnect switch body lead. When disconnecting switch body, the pinion should return quickly.

OVERHAUL

DISASSEMBLY

1) Disconnect field coil wire from starter solenoid main terminal and remove solenoid attaching bolts. Remove solenoid by moving it up and down to unhook unit from drive lever.

2) Remove bearing cover and pull out armature shaft lock plate, washer, seal and spring. Remove through bolts, commutator end frame, brush holder and yoke.

3) Remove drive lever set bolt, rubber piece, plate, armature and drive lever from housing. Remove pinion stop collar from armature shaft end and remove starter clutch.

PARTS REPLACEMENT & TESTING

Armature — Check armature for open, shorted or grounded circuits. Check armature shaft for bend. Inspect bushings for condition and maximum clearance of .008"(.20 mm). Replace if required.

Starters

NIPPONDENSO DIRECT DRIVE (Cont.)

NOTE — *Do NOT attempt to straighten a bent armature shaft. Replace if bent.*

Commutator — Clean contact surface and polish with fine sandpaper if required. If surface is scored, burned, out of round or pitted, dress in a lathe only enough to restore smooth concentric surface. Out of round should not exceed .016" (.4 mm) on Subaru and .012" (.3 mm) on all other models. Mica depth should be .016-.031" (.40-.80 mm) standard with a limit of .008" (.20 mm). If beyond limit, undercut with a hacksaw blade to standard depth.

Brushes & Springs — 1) Check brush holder insulation. Connect one lead of ammeter to brush holder positive side and other lead to negative side. If test needle moves, brush holder is shorted and must be replaced.

2) Check brush length. If less than .39" (10 mm) replace brushes. Check spring tension. Minimum tension for Courier is 38 ounces (1077 g), for Land Cruiser and Tercel is 35 ounces (1020 g), and for Subaru is 37 ounces (1050 g). Brushes must move freely in holders.

Field Coils — Connect one prod of circuit tester lead to field coil and other to soldered portion of brush lead. If meter does not register, field coil is open and must be repaired or replaced. Check field coil for ground by connecting one test prod to field coil lead and other to starter housing. If meter registers, coil is grounded and must be repaired or replaced.

REASSEMBLY

Clean all parts and coat sliding surface of armature shaft splines, starter clutch bushing, drive lever and moving stud with multipurpose grease. Reassemble in reverse order of disassembly and note the following: After completing reassembly, between pinion gear and stop collar. If clearance is not .080-.160" (.20-.40 mm) for Courier or .004-.160" (.10-4.0 mm) for all other models, adjust by lengthening or shortening plunger shaft.

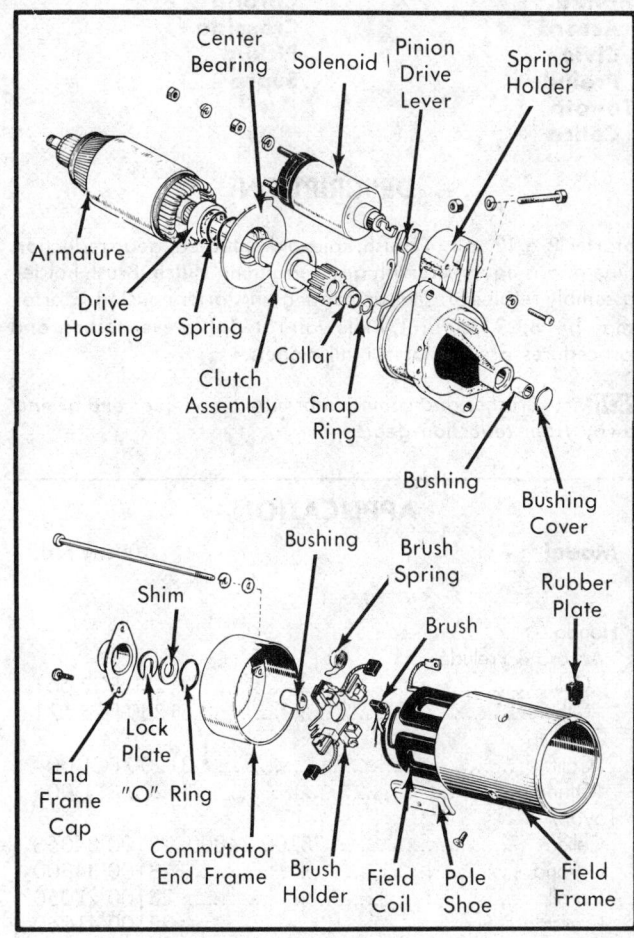

Fig. 3   Disassembled View of Typical Nippondenso Direct Drive Starter Motor

NIPPONDENSO REDUCTION GEAR

Honda	**Corolla**
Accord	**Cressida**
Civic	**Pickup**
Prelude	**Supra**
Toyota	
Celica	

DESCRIPTION

Starter is a 12 volt, 4 brush, solenoid actuated, gear reduction type and is equipped with an overrunning clutch. Brush holder assembly retains brushes and springs in starter housing. Starter may be .8, .9, 1.0 or 1.4 kilowatt rated, however testing and procedures are similar for all models.

NOTE — *Brushes and commutator may be on gear end or end away from reduction gear.*

APPLICATION

Model	①Part No.
Honda	
Accord & Prelude	
Calif.	31200 PC2 661
Others	31200 PC2 671
Civic	
Calif.	31200 PC1 004
Others	31200 PC1 005
Toyota	
Celica	28100 34800, 28100 34053
Corona	28100 34800
Corolla	28100 27050
Cressida & Supra	28100 41060
Pickup (Gas)	28100 34800
Pickup (Diesel)	28100 54090
Tercel	28100 15011

① — Vehicle manufacturer part number.

TESTING

PERFORMANCE TESTS

No Load Test (Toyota)— Connect ammeter in series with starter motor and 12 volt battery as shown in *Fig. 1.* Connect voltmeter in parallel with battery and observe readings. Starter should spin smoothly at no more than 90 amps.

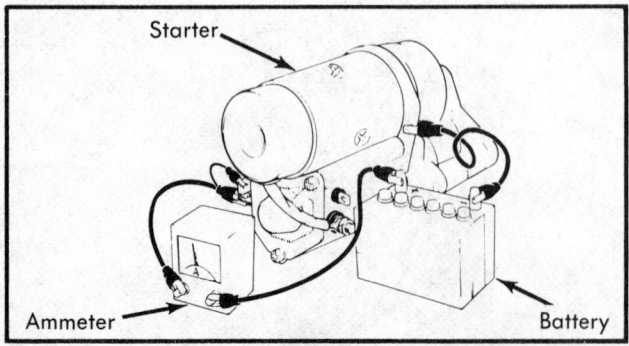

**Fig. 1 Ammeter Hook-Up for No Load Test
(Toyota Shown)**

Cranking Test (Honda) — Hook up voltmeter and ammeter as shown in *Fig. 2.* Disconnect ignition coil secondary wire from coil and ground it. Turn ignition switch to start. Check cranking voltage and current draw. Voltage should be no less than 8.0 volts for Civic, 9.6 volts for Accord and Prelude. Current draw should be no more than 200 amps for Calif. Civics, 230 amps for all other Civics and 160 amps for Accord and Prelude. Cranking speed should be approximately 400 RPM.

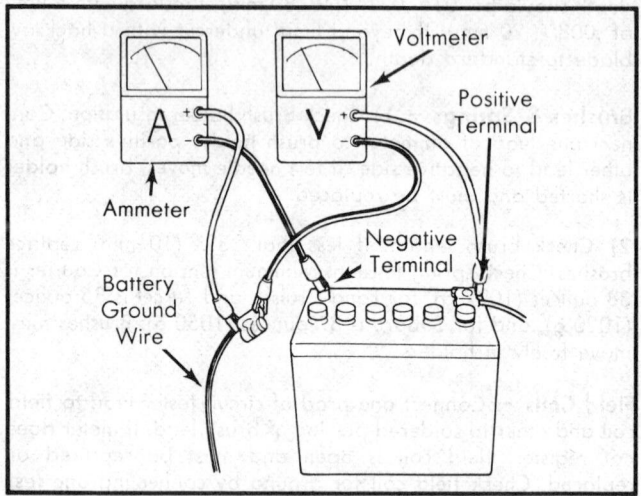

Fig. 2 Cranking Test Hookup

OVERHAUL

DISASSEMBLY

1) With starter removed from vehicle, disconnect wire(s) to magnetic switch. Remove bolts and remove field frame with armature from magnetic switch. Remove "O" ring and felt seal.

2) Remove screws and then remove starter gear housing from magnetic switch. Pull out clutch assembly and gears. Remove ball from clutch shaft hole or from magnetic switch. Remove brushes from brush holder then pull armature out of field frame.

3) Use low pressure air and soft bristle brush to clean brush dust from field frame assembly and armature. Use care to prevent dust from contaminating front and rear bearings or it may be necessary to replace them.

NOTE — *Complete immersion of starter and/or components in solvent is not recommended.*

PARTS REPLACEMENT & TESTING

Brushes & Springs — If brush length is less than .33" (8.5 mm) on Accord and Prelude, or less than .39" (10 mm) on all other models, replace brushes. Replace brush springs if weakened. Check condition of brush holders, spring clip and insulation between positive and negative holders and repair or replace as needed.

Commutator — 1) Inspect commutator for roughness. If surface is pitted or grooved, it should be lightly sanded with No. 500 emery paper. Check commutator for out-of-round. If out-of-round is more than .002" (.05 mm) on Toyota, or

NIPPONDENSO REDUCTION GEAR (Cont.)

.001" (.03 mm) on Honda, turn commutator on lathe until out-of-round is within specification.

2) Insulating mica should be undercut to a depth of approximately .015-.031" (.40-.80 mm) if worn to less than .008" (.20 mm). Wear or cutting limit of commutator is 1.22" (31 mm) for Cressida and Supra, 1.26" (26 mm) for Civic, and 1.14" (29 mm) for all others.

Armature Coil — Check commutator and armature coil core for continuity, if continuity exists, replace armature. Check armature with an armature tester (growler) for shorts, if shorts exist, replace armature. Check for continuity between segments on commutator, if no continuity exists replace armature.

Field Coil — Check field coil for open circuits. There should be continuity between lead wire and field coil brush lead, if not, replace field coil. Check for no continuity between field coil end and end frame, if continuity exists, replace field coil.

Overrunning Clutch Assembly — Inspect gear teeth for wear and damage. Replace gears if damaged. Also, if gears are damaged, check flywheel ring gear. Rotate pinion. Pinion should rotate freely in a clockwise direction and lock up in a counterclockwise direction.

Bearings — Turn each bearing by hand, replace bearings if they stick or have a high resistance to turning.

Solenoid Assembly — Connect a 12 volt battery to solenoid "ST" terminal, main terminal and ground. Plunger should extend firmly. If not, replace solenoid. Disconnect battery from main terminal. Plunger should remain extended. If not, replace solenoid. *See Figs. 3 and 4.*

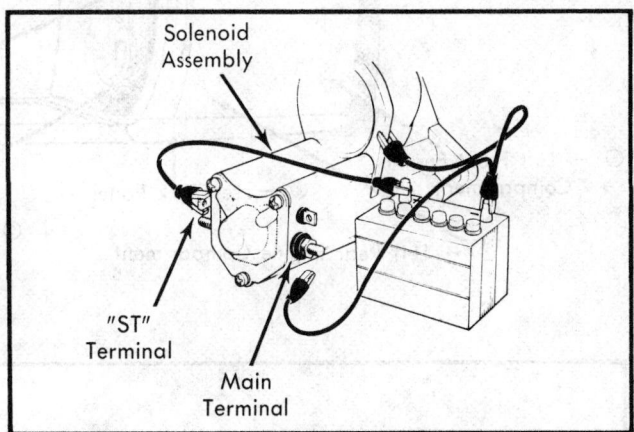

Fig. 4   Solenoid Hold-In Coil Test

REASSEMBLY

To reassemble, reverse disassembly procedures and note the following: Coat all sliding or moving surfaces of shaft splines, bushings and solenoid with multi-purpose grease. Apply grease to clutch assembly cavity to retain steel ball when assembling.

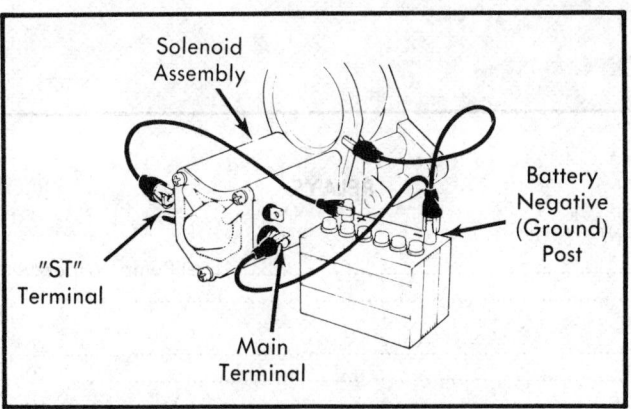

Fig. 3   Solenoid Pull-In Coil Test

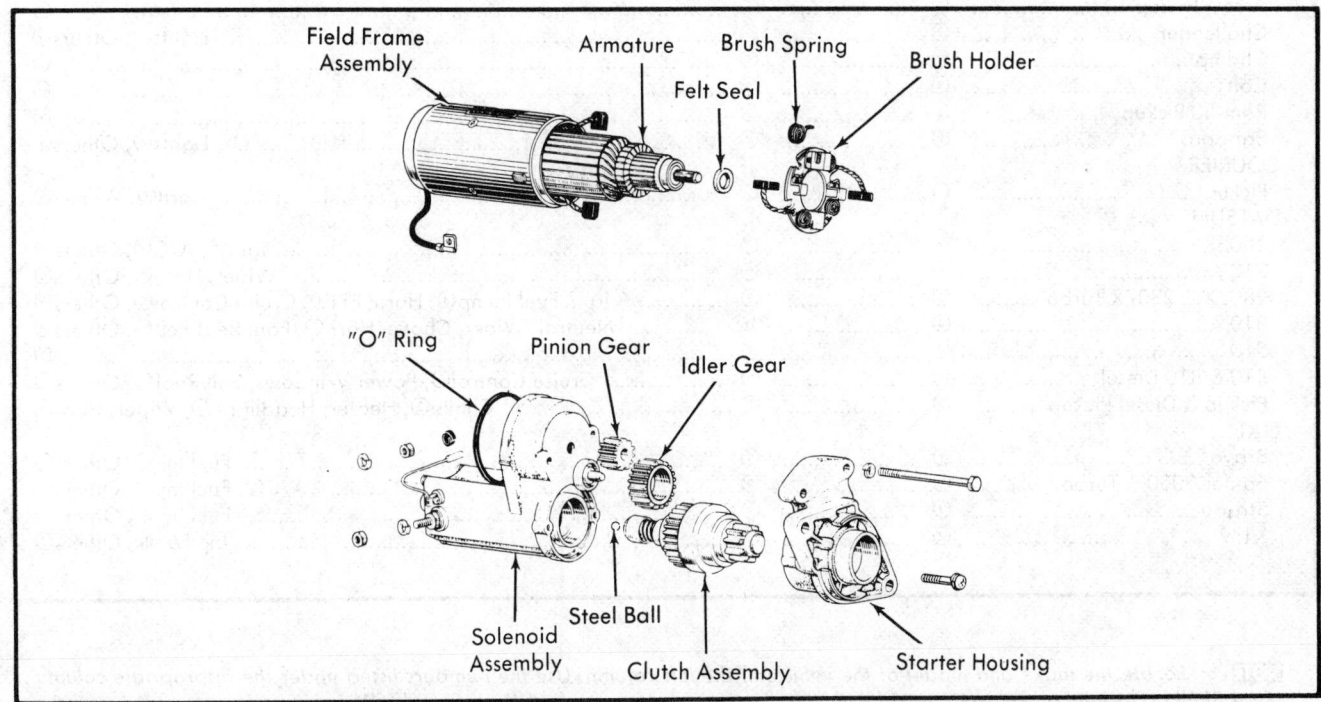

Fig. 5   Exploded View of Nippondenso Reduction Gear Starter.

Fuse Blocks, Flashers & Relays

AUDI — FIAT

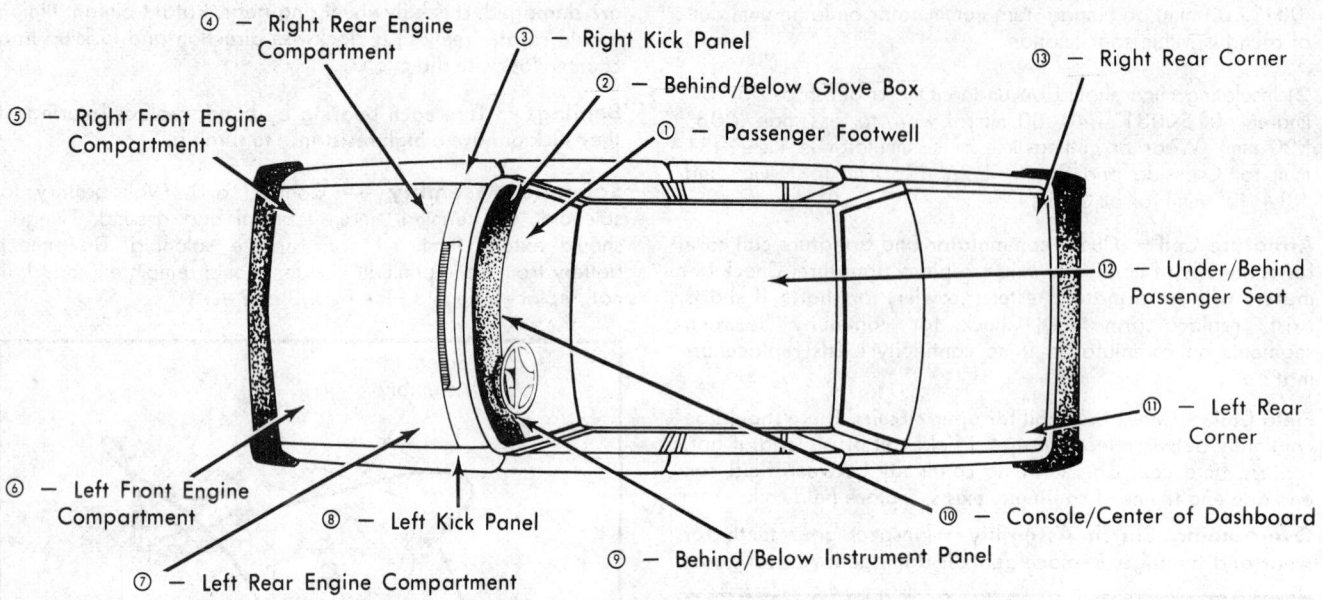

④ — Right Rear Engine Compartment

③ — Right Kick Panel

② — Behind/Below Glove Box

① — Passenger Footwell

⑤ — Right Front Engine Compartment

⑬ — Right Rear Corner

⑫ — Under/Behind Passenger Seat

⑪ — Left Rear Corner

⑥ — Left Front Engine Compartment

⑧ — Left Kick Panel

⑩ — Console/Center of Dashboard

⑦ — Left Rear Engine Compartment

⑨ — Behind/Below Instrument Panel

MAKE — MODELS	FUSE BLOCK	FLASHER	RELAYS
AUDI			
4000	⑨	⑨	Fuel Pump, Wiper⑨
5000	⑦	⑦	⑦
BMW			
320i	⑥	⑥	⑥
528i	⑥	⑥	⑥
633CSi	⑦	⑦	⑦
733i	⑥	⑥	⑥
CHRYSLER CORP. IMPORTS			
Arrow Pickup	⑧	⑨	⑨
Challenger	⑨	⑨	Lights⑥, Others⑨
Champ	⑨	⑨	⑨
Colt	⑨	⑨	⑨
Ram-50 Pickup	⑧	⑨	⑨
Sapporo	⑨	⑨	Lights⑥, Others⑨
COURIER			
Pickup	⑦	⑨	Horn⑥, Wipers⑨
DATSUN			
200SX	②	⑨	Ign.③, A/C④, Others⑤
210	⑧	⑨	Wiper, Horn⑨, Others⑤
280ZX & 280ZX Turbo	③	⑨	Ign., Fuel Pump③, Horn, EFI④, Cruise Control⑫, Others⑤
310	⑧	③⑧	Neutral, Wiper, Choke, Horn⑤, Fan, Seat Belt⑨, Others⑧
510	⑨	⑨	⑤
810 & 810 Diesel	②	⑨	Cruise Control③, Power Windows, Sun Roof⑧, Others⑤
Pickup & Diesel Pickup	⑧	⑨	Choke③, Heater, Headlight ⑧, Wiper, Horn⑨
FIAT			
Brava	②	⑨	Fuel Inj.⑦, Others②
Spider 2000 & Turbo	⑨	⑨	A/C⑤, Fuel Inj.⑨, Others②
Strada	⑨	⑨	Fuel Inj.⑦, Others⑨
X1/9	②	②	Inj. Fan⑫, Others②

NOTE — *Locate the make and model of the vehicle in the left column. Use the numbers listed under the appropriate column (Fuse Blocks, Flashers or Relays) and refer to the illustration above to find the general area where component is located.*

HONDA – RENAULT

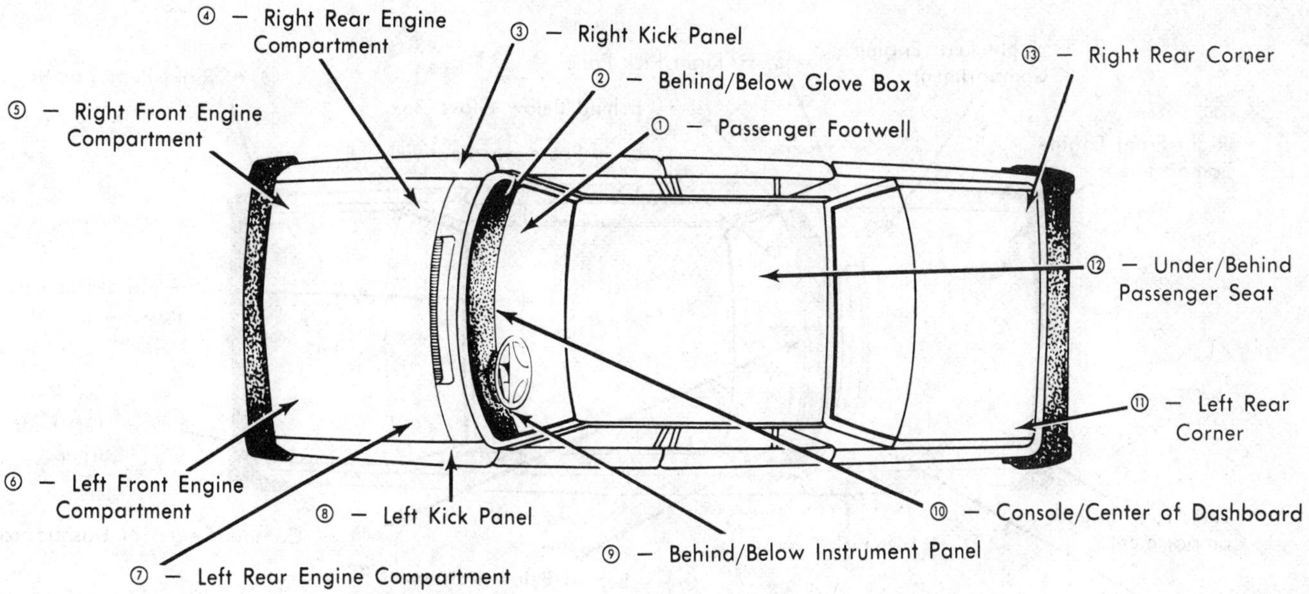

④ — Right Rear Engine Compartment
③ — Right Kick Panel
② — Behind/Below Glove Box
① — Passenger Footwell
⑬ — Right Rear Corner
⑤ — Right Front Engine Compartment
⑫ — Under/Behind Passenger Seat
⑪ — Left Rear Corner
⑥ — Left Front Engine Compartment
⑧ — Left Kick Panel
⑩ — Console/Center of Dashboard
⑦ — Left Rear Engine Compartment
⑨ — Behind/Below Instrument Panel

E L E C T R I C A L

MAKE – MODELS	FUSE BLOCK	FLASHER	RELAYS
HONDA			
Accord	⑨	⑨	⑨
Civic	⑨	⑨	⑨
Prelude	⑨	⑨	⑨
ISUZU & LUV			
I-Mark	⑧	⑨	A/C⑩, Others⑥
Pickups	⑦	⑨	Glow Plugs④, Heater, Fuel Pump⑦, A/C⑩
JAGUAR			
XJ6	②⑨⑤⑥	⑨	Cold Start, Fuel Pump④
MAZDA			
GLC Hatchback	⑨	⑨	Fan, Fast Idle, Horn⑥, Others⑨
GLC Wagon	⑨	⑨	Idle Cut, A/C④, Others⑦
626	⑨	⑧	Door Lock③, Choke⑥, A/C⑩, Others⑧
RX7	⑨	⑨	Hot Start, Choke, A/C⑦, Horn⑧
B2000 Pickup	⑦	⑨	Horn⑥, Others⑨
MERCEDES-BENZ			
380SL & SLC	①	⑨	⑨⑦
All Others	⑦	⑨	⑨⑦
PEUGEOT			
504	⑨	⑩	⑨
505	⑦	⑩	Coil, A/C, Emissions④, Cooling Fan⑥, Defogger, Wiper⑦
604	⑨	⑩	Fan, Coil⑤, Others⑨
PORSCHE			
911SC	⑥⑪	⑨	Heater, Defogger⑪, Others⑥
924 & 924 Turbo	⑨	⑨	⑨
928	①	①	Seat Belt⑩, Rear Wiper⑪, Seat Release⑫
RENAULT			
LeCar	⑩	....	....
18i	⑨	⑨	....

NOTE — *Locate the make and model of the vehicle in the left column. Use the numbers listed under the appropriate column (Fuse Blocks, Flashers or Relays) and refer to the illustration above to find the general area where component is located.*

Fuse Blocks, Flashers & Relays

SAAB — VOLVO

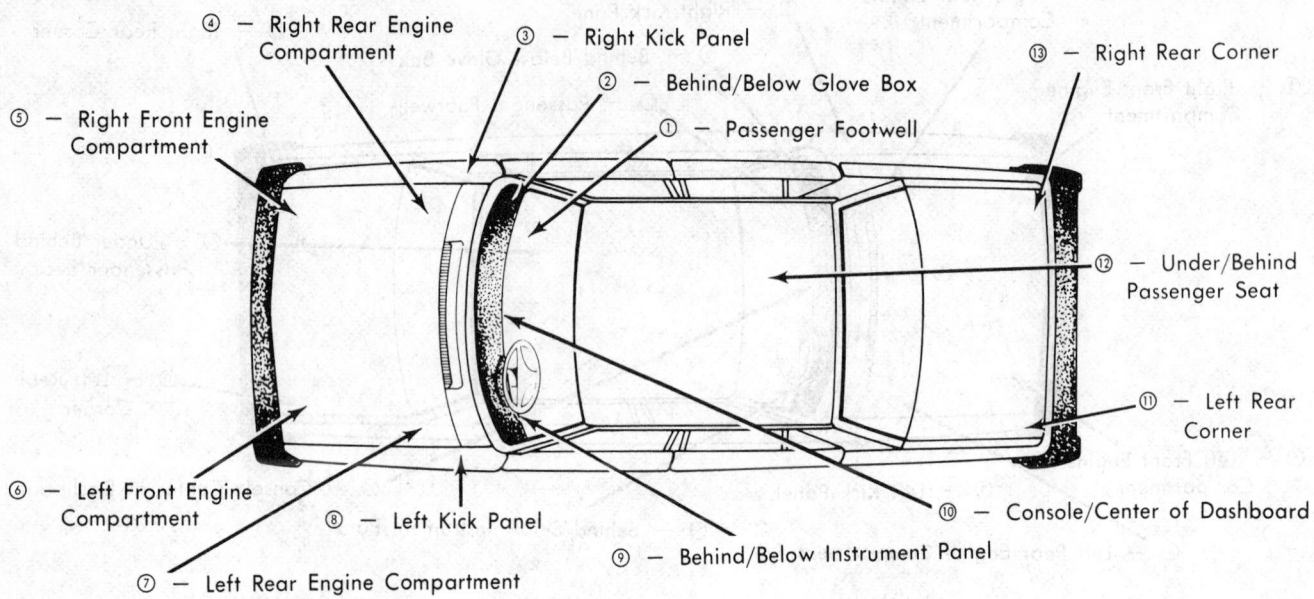

④ — Right Rear Engine Compartment
③ — Right Kick Panel
② — Behind/Below Glove Box
⑤ — Right Front Engine Compartment
① — Passenger Footwell
⑬ — Right Rear Corner
⑫ — Under/Behind Passenger Seat
⑪ — Left Rear Corner
⑥ — Left Front Engine Compartment
⑧ — Left Kick Panel
⑩ — Console/Center of Dashboard
⑦ — Left Rear Engine Compartment
⑨ — Behind/Below Instrument Panel

MAKE — MODELS	FUSE BLOCK	FLASHER	RELAYS
SAAB			
900 & 900 Turbo	⑦	⑦	⑦
SUBARU			
All Models	⑨	⑨	Power Windows⑫
TOYOTA			
Celica	⑨⑥	⑨	Seat Belt, Heater③, Courtesy, O.D.⑨, Choke⑥, Others⑧
Corolla	③⑥⑧	⑨	A/C, Headlight⑥, Heater, Wiper③, Others⑧
Corona	⑨⑤	⑨	Lights, Charging⑤, Others⑨
Cressida	③⑥⑧	⑧	Overdrive⑩, Heater, Wiper, A/C⑧, Others⑥③
Land Cruiser	⑨④	⑨	Others⑨, Charging②
Pickup	⑨	⑨	Wiper, Choke, Seat Belt②, Headlight, Tail Light⑨, Others⑧
Supra	⑨⑤	⑨	Lights, Wiper②, Others⑨
Tercel	⑨⑥	⑨	⑧⑥
Starlet	⑨	⑨	Seat belt③, Cooling Fan⑤, Others⑧
TRIUMPH			
TR7	②	⑨②	②
TR8	②	②	②
VOLKSWAGEN			
Dasher	⑨	⑨	⑨
Jetta	⑨	⑨	⑨
Rabbit	⑨	⑨	⑨
Rabbit Pickup	⑨	⑨	⑨
Scirocco	⑨	⑨	⑨
Vanagon	⑨	⑨	Aux. Heater②, Others⑨
VOLVO			
DL, GL, GLT	⑧	⑩	⑨⑩
GLE, Bertone	⑧	⑩	⑨⑩
Diesel	⑧	⑩	⑨⑩

NOTE — *Locate the make and model of the vehicle in the left column. Use the numbers listed under the appropriate column (Fuse Blocks, Flashers or Relays) and refer to the illustration above to find the general area where component is located.*

AUDI

FUSE BLOCK

4000 — Fuse block is located at left side of dashboard behind storage bin. It contains 15 fuses arranged horizontally. Circuits protected are as follows:

① — 8 Amp. Low Beam Left
② — 8 Amp. Low Beam Right
③ — 8 Amp. High Beam Left
④ — 8 Amp. High Beam Right
⑤ — 16 Amp. Rear Window Defogger
⑥ — 8 Amp. Stop Lights, Hazard Flashers
⑦ — 8 Amp. Cigar Lighter, Radio, Panel Lights
⑧ — 8 Amp. Turn Signals
⑨ — 8 Amp. Back-up Lights, Horn
⑩ — 25 Amp. Fresh Air Fan, Glove Box Light
⑪ — 8 Amp. Windshield Wiper Washer
⑫ — 8 Amp. License Plate Light
⑬ — 8 Amp. Tail, Parking & Side Marker Lights (Right)
⑭ — 8 Amp. Tail, Parking & Side Marker Lights (Left)
⑮ — 25 Amp. Radiator Fan

The following fuses are located behind the fuse panel in in-line holders:
① — 25 Amp. A/C
② — 16 Amp. Fuel Pump

5000 Models — Fuse block is located in engine compartment left rear corner. Fuses are numbered from 1 to 17, with 17 closest to the front of the car and 1 nearest the rear. Circuits protected are:

① — 25 Amp. A/C, Heater Fan, Tachometer
② — Not Used
③ — 8 Amp. High Beam Headlight, Left
④ — 8 Amp. High Beam Headlight, Right
⑤ — 16 Amp. Fuel Pump
⑥ — 8 Amp. Right Marker, Tail Lights
⑦ — 8 Amp. Left Marker Lights, Engine Comp. Light
⑧ — 8 Amp. Instrument Panel, Glove Compartment, License Plate Lights
⑨ — 16 Amp. Gauges, Power Windows, Sunroof, Cruise Control, Radio
⑩ — 25 Amp. Engine Fan
⑪ — 16 Amp. Stop Lights, Horn
⑫ — 16 Amp. Lighter, Radio, Antenna, Clock, Mirrors, Dome Light
⑬ — 8 Amp. Right Low Beam
⑭ — 8 Amp. Left Low Beam
⑮ — 16 Amp. Back-up Lights, Wiper/Washer
⑯ — 25 Amp. Rear Window Defogger
⑰ — 8 Amp. Flashers, Turn Signals

BMW

FUSE BLOCK

320i — Fuse block is located at left front corner of engine compartment. Fuses are arranged in 6 rows of 3, with first row toward battery. Number 1 fuse is next to front relay. Protected circuits are:

① — 8 Amp. Right Fog Light
② — 8 Amp. Left Fog Light
③ — 16 Amp. Fuel Pump
④ — 8 Amp. Right Low Beam
⑤ — 8 Amp. Left Low Beam
⑥ — 8 Amp. Dash Lights, Right Park and Taillights, Hood Light
⑦ — 16 Amp. High Beam
⑧ — 16 Amp. High Beam
⑨ — 8 Amp. Left Park and Taillights
⑩ — 16 Amp. Defogger
⑪ — 25 Amp. Heater Fan, A/C Fan
⑫ — 8 Amp. Brake Lights, Radio, Tachometer
⑬ — 25 Amp. Auxiliary Fan
⑭ — 16 Amp. Back-up Lights, Gauges, Warning Lights
⑮ — 16 Amp. Horn, Wipers, Washer, Power Mirror
⑯ — 16 Amp. Lighter
⑰ — 8 Amp. Turn Signals, Hazard Flashers, Clock, Buzzers
⑱ — Spare

528i, 633CSi and 733i — All models have fuse block at left front corner of engine compartment. Fuses are located in 3 rows with 6 in first row, 8 in second row, and 2 or 3 in third row. Fuses are numbered from center of car toward left side, and protect the following circuits:

① — 8 Amp. (528i), 16 Amp. (633CSi and 733i) Fuel Pump, Emission Controls
② — 8 Amp. Right Low Beam
③ — 8 Amp. Left Low Beam
④ — 16 Amp. Lighter
⑤ — 8 Amp. Clock, Interior Lights, Trunk Light, Warning Buzzer, Locking System, Hazard Lights, Glove Box Light (528i Only), Turn Signals (733i Only)
⑥ — 8 Amp. Warning Lights, Instruments, Back-Up Lights, Transmission Indicator Light, Power Windows, Cruise Control (733i Only)
⑦ — 8 Amp. Right High Beam
⑧ — 8 Amp. Left High Beam
⑨ — 8 Amp. Right Parking and Marker Lights, Instrument Panel and Console Lights
⑩ — 8 Amp. Left Parking and Marker Lights
⑪ — 16 Amp. Wipers, Washers, Power Mirrors, Turn Signals (528i)
⑫ — 8 Amp. Radio, Brake Lights, Clock (Exc. 528i). (733i Only) Safety Check Panel, Speedometer and Cruise Control
⑬ — 16 Amp. Defogger, Sun Roof
⑭ — 25 Amp. A/C, Heater Fan, Auxiliary Fan Relay
⑮ — 8 Amp. Right Fog Light
⑯ — 8 Amp. Left Fog Light
⑰ — 25 Amp. (2 on 633CSi and 733i) Auxiliary Fan

Fuses & Circuit Breakers

CHRYSLER CORP. IMPORTS

FUSE BLOCK

Arrow & Ram-50 Pickups — Fuse block is located beneath instrument panel on left side. Fuses are numbered with first fuse at bottom right and last fuse at top left of block. Protected circuits are:

① — 15 Amp. High Beams
② — 15 Amp. Low Beams
③ — 15 Amp. Heater, Horn, Washer
④ — 15 Amp. Wiper, Radio, Lighter

Next Row
⑤ — 15 Amp. Tail Lights, Panel & Parking Lights
⑥ — 15 Amp. Stop Lights, Courtesy Lights, Buzzers
⑦ — 15 Amp. Flashers
⑧ — 15 Amp. Turn Signals, Back-up Lights, Gauges

Challenger & Sapporo — Main fuse block is on left kick panel. Two 5 Amp. fuses are at battery and high beam fuses are in-line nearby. The fuse block fuses are numbered from front of car toward rear:

① — 20 Amp. Defogger
② — 15 Amp. Flashers

③ — 15 Amp. Stop Lights
④ — 20 Amp. Heater
⑤ — 15 Amp. Tail Lights, Panel Lights
⑥ — 15 Amp. Wiper/Washer
⑦ — 15 Amp. Radio, Lighter, Horn
⑧ — 10 Amp. Turn Signals, Gauges
⑨ — 10 Amp. Back-up Lights
⑩ — 10 Amp. Voltage Regulator

Champ & Colt — Fuse block is located beneath instrument panel on left side. Fuses are numbered from left to right and protect these circuits:

① — 15 Amp. High Beams
② — 15 Amp. Low Beams
③ — 15 Amp. Tail Lights, Panel & Marker Lights
④ — 15 Amp. Stop Lights, Buzzer
⑤ — 15 Amp. Flashers, Courtesy Light, Clock
⑥ — 15 Amp. Heater, Horn, Clock
⑦ — 15 Amp. Lighter, Radio, Mirrors
⑧ — 15 Amp. Turn Signals, Rear Wiper/Washer, Gauges
⑨ — 15 Amp. Front Wiper/Washer
⑩ — 15 Amp. Back-up Lights, Defogger

COURIER

FUSE BLOCK

Fuse is located in engine compartment on left side near windshield. Fuses are numbered with first fuse toward engine in front row, and last fuse toward fender in back row. Fuses and circuits protected are:

① — 15 Amp. Horn, Stop Lights, Hazard Warning Flasher, Interior Light, Cigar Lighter
② — 15 Amp. Hood & Glove Box Light, Electric Rear Window Defroster
③ — 15 Amp. High Beams

④ — 15 Amp. Low Beams
⑤ — 10 Amp. Tail, License, Front Parking, Front Marker and Panel Lights
⑥ — 10 Amp. Wipers/Washers
⑦ — 15 Amp. Blower Motor, Radio
⑧ — Not Used
⑨ — 10 Amp. Front & Rear Turn Signal Lights, Fasten Seat Belt, Oil Pressure & Brake Warning Lights, Fuel Gauge, Temperature Gauge, Back-Up Lights
⑩ — 15 Amp. Engine

DATSUN

FUSE BLOCK

200SX — Fuse block is below glove box on right side of dashboard. The fuses and circuits protected are:

① — 15 Amp. Ignition, Fuel Injection
② — 10 Amp. Turn Signals, Back-up Lights, Cruise Control, Gauges, Kickdown Solenoid
③ — 10 Amp. Ignition, Engine Controls
④ — 20 Amp. Rear Defogger
⑤ — 10 Amp. Radio, Clock Antenna
⑥ — 15 Amp. Wiper/Washer, A/C, Fuel Injection
⑦ — 20 Amp. Heater, A/C
⑧ — 10 Amp. Mirror, Lighter
⑨ — 15 Amp. Tail Lights, Marker & Panel Lights
⑩ — 10 Amp. Courtesy Lights
⑪ — 10 Amp. Clock, Antenna
⑫ — 10 Amp. Hazard Flashers
⑬ — 20 Amp. Stop Lights, Horn
⑭ — 15 Amp. Left Headlight
⑮ — 15 Amp. Right Headlight

210 — Fuse block is located on left kick panel under hood release handle. A single inline fuse of 20 Amp. capacity protects the air conditioner circuit, while 8 fuses in the block protect the following circuits:

① — 10 Amp. Wipers, Washers
② — 15 Amp. Horn, Lighter
③ — 15 Amp. Stop Lights, Courtesy Lights
④ — 15 Amp. Taillights
⑤ — 15 Amp. Heater, Radio
⑥ — 10 Amp. Engine
⑦ — 10 Amp. Flashers, Meter
⑧ — 20 Amp. Defogger

280ZX — Fuse block is located in right kick panel and contains 12 fuses, which protect the following circuits:

① — 10 Amp. Right Headlight
② — 10 Amp. Left Headlight
③ — 20 Amp. Stop Lights, Horn
④ — 15 Amp. Marker Lights, Taillights
⑤ — 10 Amp. Courtesy Lights

Fuses & Circuit Breakers

DATSUN (Cont.)

⑥ — 20 Amp. Flashers, Clock, Lighter, Voltmeter
⑦ — 20 Amp. A/C, Power Mirrors (Turbo)
⑧ — 10 Amp. Radio, Antenna, Mirrors (Exc. Turbo)
⑨ — 15 Amp. Wiper/Washer
⑩ — 10 Amp. Turn Signals, Cruise Control, Back-up Lights
⑪ — 10 Amp. Gauges
⑫ — 20 Amp. Defogger

310 — The main fuse block is on the left kick panel. Relays are also mounted on the panel. Moving from the rear to the front, top row first, the relays control Fuel Cut, Fan, Rear Defogger, A/C, A/C Inhibitor, Hazard Flashers. A front relay panel on the right fenderwell has the Warm-Up Relay, Choke Relay, Neutral Relay, Horn Relay and Wiper Control Unit. The Cooling Fan Timer and Seat Belt Timer are on the pedal bracket. The fuses are numbered from rear of the vehicle toward the front, top row first. The circuits protected are:

① & ② — 10 Amp. A/C Fan
③ — 10 Amp. Radio, Heater, A/C
④ — 10 Amp. Radiator Fan
⑤ — 10 Amp. Choke Heater
⑥ — 10 Amp. Gauges, Back-up Lights, Turn Signals
⑦ — 10 Amp. Emission Controls
⑧ & ⑨ — 10 Amp. Rear Defogger
Next Row
⑩ — Headlights
⑪ — 10 Amp. Horn
⑫ — 10 Amp. Wiper/Washer
⑬ — Not Used
⑭ — 10 Amp. Flashers, Courtesy Lights
⑮ — 10 Amp. Brake Lights, Clock
⑯ — 10 Amp. Tail Lights, Marker Lights

510 — Fuse block is under left side of dashboard. An inline 20 Amp. fuse is used for the air conditioning system. The main fuse block has fuses arranged in 2 rows, protecting the following circuits.

① — 20 Amp. Rear Defogger
② — 10 Amp. Gauges, Backup Lights, Kickdown Switch
③ — 10 Amp. Emission Controls, Engine
④ — 15 Amp. Radio, Heater, Rear Wiper/Washer
⑤ — 15 Amp. Marker & Panel Lights, Tail Lights, Buzzer
⑥ — 15 Amp. Courtesy Lights, Flashers, Brake Lights
⑦ — 15 Amp. Lighter, Clock, Voltmeter, Horn
⑧ — 10 Amp. Front Wiper/Washer

810 — Fuse block is under glove compartment on right side of dashboard. A switch turns off the clock, timer and voice warning system so battery will not discharge during long storage. Fuses are numbered from left to right.

① — 15 Amp. Fuel Injection, Ignition (or Diesel System)
② — 10 Amp. Back-up Lights, Warning Lights, Diesel EGR
③ — 20 Amp. Rear Defogger
④ — 10 Amp. Gauges, Turn Signals, Cruise Control, Antenna, Time Control
⑤ — 15 Amp. Lighter, Antenna, Rear Wiper/Washer
⑥ — 20 Amp. Heater, A/C
⑦ — 15 Amp. Front Wiper/Washer, A/C, Time Control
⑧ — 10 Amp. Radio
⑨ — 10 Amp. Flashers, Courtesy Lights
⑩ — 10 Amp. Horn, Mirrors
⑪ — 15 Amp. Antenna, Clock, Voice Warning, Time Control
⑫ — 15 Amp. Marker Lights, Tail Lights
⑬ — 10 Amp. Stop Lights, Cruise Control
⑭ — 10 Amp. Left Headlight
⑮ — 10 Amp. Right Headlight

Pickup — Main fuse block is located on left kick panel. Fuses are numbered and protect these circuits:

① — 10 Amp. Coil No. 2 (Not Used on Diesel)
② — 15 Amp. Coil No. 1, Fuel Pump, Emissions (Glow Plugs on Diesel)
③ — 15 Amp. Rear Defogger
④ — 15 Amp. Gauges, Backup Lights
⑤ — Not Used
⑥ — 15 Amp. Wiper/Washer, A/C
⑦ — 15 Amp. Radio, Lighter
⑧ — 10 Amp. Clock
⑨ — Not Used
⑩ — 20 Amp. Blower Motor
⑪ — 10 Amp. Horn
⑫ — 15 Amp. Stop Lights, Flashers
⑬ — 15 Amp. Marker Lights, Tail Lights
⑭ — 10 Amp. Left Headlight
⑮ — 10 Amp. Right Headlight

FUSIBLE LINK

All Models — Fusible link is located in wire between battery and alternator near the battery. Its purpose is to protect the alternator and related circuits.

FIAT

FUSE BLOCK

Brava — Fuse block is located in box beneath glove compartment. Fuses are numbered and protect the following circuits:

① — 8 Amp. Stop Lights, Back-up Lights, Turn Signals, Heater Relay, Gauges.
② — 8 Amp. Wiper/Washer
③ — 8 Amp. Left Tail Light, Right Marker Lights, License Light
④ — 8 Amp. Right Tail Light, Left Marker Lights, Panel Lights
⑤ — 8 Amp. Left Low Beam
⑥ — 8 Amp. Right Low Beam
⑦ — 8 Amp. Right High Beam
⑧ — 8 Amp. Left High Beam
⑨ — 16 Amp. Horns, Engine Fan
⑩ — 8 Amp. Clock, Lighter, Antenna, Courtesy Lights

⑪ — 16 Amp. Rear Defogger, Hazard Flashers
⑫ — 16 Amp. A/C Compressor & Evaporator
⑬ — 16 Amp. A/C Condenser Fan
⑭ — 16 Amp. Fuel Injection & Fuel Pump

Spider 2000 — Fuse block is located underneath dash on left side of steering column. Two inline fuses are also used. Fuses in block are numbered from right to left and protect the following circuits:

① — 8 Amp. Dashboard Indicators, Seat Belt Timer & Relay, Stop & Back-up Lights, Gauges, Tachometer, Turn Signals
② — 8 Amp. Wiper/Washer, Heater Fan Switch, Lambda Sensor
③ — 8 Amp. Left High Beam
④ — 8 Amp. Right High Beam

Fuses & Circuit Breakers

FIAT (Cont.)

⑤ — 8 Amp. Left Low Beam
⑥ — 8 Amp. Right Low Beam
⑦ — 8 Amp. Front Right and Left Rear Marker Light, Left Tail Light
⑧ — 8 Amp. Front Left and Right Rear Marker Lights, Right Tail Lights, Panel Lights
⑨ — 8 Amp. Courtesy Lights, Hazard Flashers, Clock, Buzzers
⑩ — 16 Amp. Horns, Engine Fan
⑪ — 16 Amp. Optional Left Power Window
⑫ — 16 Amp. Optional Right Power Window

Strada — Fuse block is under dashboard on left side. Three inline fuses are used. The fuses in the fuse block are numbered from right to left and protect these circuits:

① — 8 Amp. Stop Lights, Back-up Lights, Turn Signals, Heater Relay, Gauges
② — 8 Amp. Wiper/Washer
③ — 8 Amp. Front Right and Left Rear Marker Lights, Left Tail Light
④ — 8 Amp. Front Left and Right Rear Marker Lights, Right Tail Light, Panel Lights
⑤ — 8 Amp. Left Low Beam
⑥ — 8 Amp. Right Low Beam
⑦ — 8 Amp. Left High Beam
⑧ — 8 Amp. Right High Beam
⑨ — 16 Amp. Horns, Engine Fan
⑩ — 8 Amp. Clock, Lighter, Buzzers, Courtesy Lights
⑪ — 16 Amp. Rear Defogger, Flashers
⑫ — 8 Amp. Heater Fan, Panel Lights

Inline Fuses:
① — 16 Amp. Fuel Injection
② — 2 16 Amp. A/C system (Behind A/C control panel)

X1/9 — Fuse block is located in swing-down panel below glove compartment. Two inline fuses are also used. The fuses in the block are numbered from left to right and protect the following circuits:

① — 8 Amp. Turn Signals, Stop Lights, Heater Fan, Defogger Relay, Switch Indicator Lights
② — 8 Amp. Gauges, Dashboard Indicators, Clock Light, Wiper/Washer, Delay Circuit, Back-Up Lights
③ — 8 Amp. Left High Beam, High Beam Indicator
④ — 8 Amp. Right High Beam
⑤ — 8 Amp. Left Low Beam
⑥ — 8 Amp. Right Low Beam
⑦ — 8 Amp. Front Left & Right Rear Marker Lights, Front Left Parking Light, Right Rear Tail Light, License Light, Cigar Lighter, Spot Light
⑧ — 8 Amp. Right Front Parking Light, Left Rear Tail Light, Clock Dimming, Right Front & Left Rear Marker Lights
⑨ — 16 Amp. Right Headlight Motor
⑩ — 16 Amp. Left Headlight Motor
⑪ — 16 Amp. Rear Defogger, Hazard Lights
⑫ — 16 Amp. Horn & Relay, Engine Fan
⑬ — 16 Amp. Spare Fuse
⑭ — 3 Amp. Spare Fuse
⑮ — 3 Amp. Headlight Closing Control Switch
⑯ — 3 Amp. Headlight Raising Control Switch

Inline Fuses:
① — 8 Amp. Lighter, Clock, Courtesy Lights, Buzzers
② — 16 Amp. Fuel Injection, Power Windows

HONDA

FUSE BLOCK

Accord — Fuse block is located in a swing-down panel to left of steering column. Fuses are arranged in 2 rows. Moving from right to left, short row first, protected circuits are:

① — 10 Amp. Right High Beam
② — 10 Amp. Left High Beam
③ — 10 Amp. Right Low Beam
④ — 10 Amp. Left Low Beam
⑤ — 10 Amp. Radio, A/C
⑥ — 15 Amp. Cooling Fan
⑦ — 15 Amp. Wipers, Washer
⑧ — 10 Amp. Regulator, Fuel Pump
⑨ — 10 Amp. Turn Signals, Back-Up Lights, Fuel Gauge
⑩ — 20 Amp. Heater
⑪ — 15 Amp. Defogger
⑫ — 15 Amp. Tail Lights, Gauge Light, License Light
⑬ — 10 Amp. Courtesy Light, Clock, Lighter, Horn
⑭ — 15 Amp. Hazard Flashers, Stop Lights

Civic — Fuse block is located in panel to left of steering column. Circuits protected, from right to left, are:

① — 10 Amp. Inline Radio Fuse
② — 10 Amp. Right Low Beam
③ — 10 Amp. Left Low Beam

④ — 10 Amp. Right High Beam
⑤ — 10 Amp. Left High Beam
⑥ — 15 Amp. Tail Lights, Panel Lights, Marker Lights
⑦ — 10 Amp. Courtesy Lights, Lighter, Clock, Buzzers
⑧ — 15 Amp. Stop Lights, Horn, Flashers
⑨ — 15 Amp. Radio, Rear Defogger
⑩ — 15 Amp. Blower Motor
⑪ — 15 Amp. Engine Fan
⑫ — 10 Amp. Fuel Pump, Emission Controls, Regulator
⑬ — 10 Amp. Turn Signals, Back-up Lights, Gauges, Buzzers, Clock
⑭ — 15 Amp Wiper/Washer

Relays located on the panel are identified from right to left as: Intermittent Wipers, Hazard Flashers, Turn Signals, Fuel Pump Cut-off. The two relays above the panel are the Seat Belt Buzzer and the Brake Warning Light Relay.

Prelude — Fuse block is located in swing-down panel to left of steering column. Fuses are arranged in 2 rows. Moving from right to left, short row first, protected circuits are:

① — 10 Amp. Right High Beam, High Beam Indicator
② — 10 Amp. Left High Beam
③ — 10 Amp. Right Low Beam
④ — 10 Amp. Left Low Beam
⑤ — 15 Amp. Heater Fan

HONDA (Cont.)

⑥ — 15 Amp. Defogger
⑦ — 15 Amp. Engine Fan
⑧ — 15 Amp. Wipers, Washers
⑨ — 10 Amp. Fuel Pump, Engine Controls
⑩ — 10 Amp. Backup Lights, Gauges, Warning Lights, Turn
⑪ — 15 Amp. Radio
⑫ — 15 Amp. Tail, License, Side Marker, Gauge, Glove Box & Switch Lights

⑬ — 10 Amp. Courtesy Lights, Cigar Lighter, Clock, Trunk Light, Door Buzzer
⑭ — 15 Amp. Horn, Stop Lights, Hazard Lights

IN-LINE FUSES

One or two main fuses are installed near the battery to protect entire electrical system. A spare fuse is provided inside fuse block cover.

ISUZU & LUV

FUSE BLOCK

Isuzu I-Mark — Fuse block is located in left kick panel. First fuse is located at the bottom in front, the last fuse is the top rear fuse. Circuits protected are:

① — Not Used
② — 15 Amp. Tail Lights
③ — 15 Amp. Wiper/Washer, Radio
④ — 15 Amp. Heater, Back-up Lights
⑤ — 15 Amp. Instrument Cluster, Emissions Controls
⑥ — Not Used
⑦ — 15 Amp. A/C
⑧ — 15 Amp. Courtesy Light, Lighter

⑨ — 15 Amp. Rear Defogger
⑩ — 15 Amp. Horn, Turn Signals, Stop Lights

Isuzu P'UP & LUV — Fuse block is located in engine compartment on left fenderwell. Fuses are numbered and protect the following circuits:

① — 15 Amp. Tail Lights, Panel Lights, Marker Lights
② — 20 Amp. A/C System, Heater
③ — 15 Amp. Lighter, Stop Lights, Horn, Flashers, Dome Light
④ — 15 Amp. Turn Signals, Gauges, Panel Lights
⑤ — 15 Amp. Fuel Pump, Coil, Regulator
⑥ — 15 Amp. Wiper/Washer, Radio

JAGUAR

FUSE BLOCK

XJ6 Models — Fuse block is located behind instrument panel. Access to fuses is obtained by turning access panel retaining pin counterclockwise until it unlocks. Panel will then drop slightly and bottom edge may be lifted clear of opening. Circuits protected are as follows:

① — 20 Amp. Fog Lights
② — 15 Amp. Hazard Warning System, Electronic Control Unit

③ — 35 Amp. Courtesy Lights, Cigar Lighter, Clock, Trunk Light, Power Antenna
④ — 15 Amp. Back-Up Lights, Gauges, Warning Indicators
⑤ — 35 Amp. Rear Window Defogger
⑥ — 20 Amp. Windshield Wipers
⑦ — Not Used
⑧ — 15 Amp. Instrument Panel Lights
⑨ — 10 Amp. Rear Fog Lights
⑩ — 15 Amp. Turn Signals
⑪ — 35 Amp. Engine Fan, Horn Relay, Windshield Wipers, Stop Lights, Mileage Counter
⑫ — 2 Amp. Cruise Control

MAZDA

FUSE BLOCK

626 — Fuse block is located beneath instrument panel to left of steering column. Capacities and circuits covered are listed on the fuse block cover. Fuses are arranged in 2 rows. Going from top to bottom, left row to right row, circuit information is as follows:

① — 10 Amp. Radio
② — 15 Amp. Sunroof
③ — 10 Amp. Back-up Lights, Gauges, Cruise Control, Kickdown Solenoid
④ — 10 Amp. Emission System, Fuel Pump, Choke Heater
⑤ — 15 Amp. Rear Window Defogger
⑥ — 30 Amp. Power Windows
Next Row
⑦ — 20 Amp. A/C
⑧ — 15 Amp. Headlight Cleaner

⑨ — 15 Amp. Wiper/Washer
⑩ — 15 Amp. Horn, Stop Lights
⑪ — 15 Amp. Clock, Courtesy Lights, Mirrors, Lighter, Trunk Light
⑫ — 10 Amp. Turn Signals
⑬ — 15 Amp. Headlights, Tail, Marker & Panel Lights

GLC Wagon — The fuse block is located under the instrument panel and contains 10 fuses. Circuits protected are as follows, counting from top to bottom, short row first:

① — 15 Amp. Turn Signals, Stop Lights, Horn, Flashers
② — 15 Amp. Clock, Lighter, Courtesy Lights
③ — 15 Amp. Tail Lights, Parking & Marker Lights, Panel Lights
④ — 10 Amp. Rear Defogger, Radio
⑤ — 10 Amp. Front Wiper
⑥ — 15 Amp. Rear Wiper, Heater

MAZDA (Cont.)

⑦ — 10 Amp. Gauges, Back-up Lights, Buzzers, Kickdown Solenoid
⑧ — 15 Amp. Regulator, Emissions

GLC Hatchback — Fuse block is located at the left side of steering column. Fuses are arranged in 2 rows, with 1 fuse to the side of the first row. An inline 15 Amp. fuse is used for the A/C system. Fuses and the circuits protected are:

① — 20 Amp. Cooling Fan, A/C
Next Row
② — 15 Amp. Clock, Tail, Panel & Marker Lights
③ — 15 Amp. Heater, A/C
④ — 15 Amp. Rear Defogger
⑤ — 15 Amp. Front Wiper/Washer
⑥ — 10 Amp. Radio, Rear Wiper/Washer

Next Row

⑦ — 10 Amp. Regulator, Emission Control
⑧ — 10 Amp. Gauges
⑨ — 15 Amp. Lighter, Clock
⑩ — 15 Amp. Stop Lights, Horn
⑪ — 10 Amp. Turn Signals, Flashers, Courtesy Lights, Buzzers

RX7 — Fuse block is located to left side of steering column. Fuses protect, from top to bottom and left to right, the following circuits:

① — 10 Amp. Fuel Pump
Next Row
② — 20 Amp. Heater Fan, Glove Box Light
③ — 15 Amp. Rear Defogger

④ — 20 Amp. Radio, Antenna
⑤ — 10 Amp. Front Washer, Rear Wiper Washer
⑥ — 10 Amp. Front Wiper
⑦ — 30 Amp. Power Windows
⑧ — 10 Amp. Cruise Control
Next Row
⑨ — 20 Amp. Gas Filler Door, Rear Hatch Release
⑩ — 15 Amp. Stop Lights, Horn
⑪ — 15 Amp. Courtesy Lights, Chime, Lighter
⑫ — 10 Amp. Mirrors, A/C, Turn Signals, Flashers
⑬ — 10 Amp. Panel Lights, Headlight Motors
⑭ — 10 Amp. Gauges, Back-up Lights, Clock, Timer Unit
⑮ — 15 Amp. Kickdown Solenoid, Emissions

B2000 — Fuse block is located in left rear corner of engine compartment and contains 2 rows of fuses. Protected circuits include:

① — 15 Amp. Lighter, Clock, Courtesy Light, Stop Lights
② — 10 Amp. Tail Lights, Marker Lights, Panel Lights
③ — 10 Amp. Back-up Lights, Turn Signals, Flashers, Gauges
④ — 15 Amp. Alternator, Emissions
Next Row
⑤ — 15 Amp. Radio, Heater
⑥ — 10 Amp. Wiper/Washer

IN-LINE FUSES

A fuse block containing large in-line fuses is installed in engine compartment near battery. Fuse amperage and circuits protected is printed on fuse block cover.

MERCEDES-BENZ

FUSE BLOCK

380SL & SLC — Main fuse block is located on right kick panel. Fuse capacities and the circuits protected are listed on fuse block cover.

All Other Models — Fuse block is located at left rear corner of engine compartment. Fuse capacites and circuits protected are listed on the fuse block cover.

IN-LINE FUSES

Additional fuses for optional equipment and/or standard extras such as sliding sun roof, heated rear window, radio, automatic antenna, electric windows and air conditioning are located in engine compartment.

PEUGEOT

FUSE BLOCK

504 — Fuse block is located behind lower left corner of instrument panel. Fuses are arranged in a single row and numbered from left to right. Circuits protected are:

① — 15 Amp. Parking, Marker, License & Dashboard Lights
② — 10 Amp. Clock, Courtesy Lights, Trunk Light, Horn, Cigar Lighter, Hazard Flashers, Ignition Buzzer
③ — 10 Amp. Back-Up, Stop & Low Fuel Lights, Preheat Relay, Pre-Heat Indicator Light, Temperature Indicator, Engine Fan, Tailgate Wipers, Seat Belt Buzzer & Light, Fuel Cut-Off
④ — 15 Amp. Rear Window Defogger, Windshield Wiper Motor & Relay, Washer Pump

⑤ — 10 Amp. Warning Indicators, Turn Signals, Gauges, Heater Blower Motor, Radio

505 — Fuse block is located on top of left front fenderwell. Fuses are arranged in 2 rows, and numbered from front to back, starting with row closest to engine.

① — 16 Amp. Fuel Pumps, Emissions
② — 16 Amp. Gauges, A/C, Accessories, Turn Signals, Wiper/Washer
③ — 10 Amp. Left High Beam Headlight & High Beam Indicator
④ — 5 Amp. Spare Fuse
⑤ — 10 Amp. Right Low Beam Headlight
⑥ — 16 Amp. Power Windows & Sunroof
⑦ — 16 Amp. Rear Window Defogger
⑧ — 16 Amp. Heater Blower

Fuses & Circuit Breakers

PEUGEOT (Cont.)

⑨ — 10 Amp. Stop Lights, Back-Up Lights, Engine Fan, Idle Vacuum Switch, Tachometer & Relay, Seat Belt Warning Buzzer

⑩ — 10 Amp. Parking Lights & Indicator, Instrument Panel Lights, License Lights

⑪ — 10 Amp. Right High Beam Headlight

⑫ — 10 Amp. Left Low Beam Headlight

⑬ — 15 Amp. Not Used

⑭ — 10 Amp. Clock, Cigar Lighter, Courtesy Lights, Trunk Light, Glove Box Light, Key Chime

⑮ — 16 Amp. Horns, Hazard Warning Lights

604 — Fuse block is located behind cover on left end of instrument panel. Fuses are arranged in 2 rows and numbered from left to right, top row first. Protected circuits are:

① — 10 Amp. Lighter, Horns, Flashers, Courtesy Light

② — 10 Amp. Stop and Backup Lights, Gauges, Indicator Lights, Starter Switch

③ — 16 Amp. Defogger, Indicator Lights, Accessories

④ — 16 Amp. A/C Fan, Wipers, Washers, Sunroof

⑤ — 10 Amp. Parking and Marker Lights, Dash Lights

⑥ — 16 Amp. Heater Fan and A/C Compressor Relays

⑦ — 16 Amp. Power Windows

⑧ — 16 Amp. Rear Window Lockout

PORSCHE

FUSE BLOCK

924 — Fuse block is located under instrument panel on left of steering column. First row is below relays, second row is above relays. Fuses are numbered from left to right, lower row first.

① — 8 Amp. Left Headlight (Low Beam)

② — 8 Amp. Right Headlight (Low Beam)

③ — 8 Amp. Left Headlight (High Beam)

④ — 8 Amp. Right Headlight (High Beam)

⑤ — Not Used

⑥ — 8 Amp. Courtesy Lights, Headlight Motors

⑦ — 8 Amp. Flashers, Lighter, Clock

⑧ — 8 Amp. Turn Signal Indicators

⑨ — 8 Amp. Backup Lights, Rear Wiper, Mirrors

⑩ — 16 Amp. Fresh Air Blower

⑪ — 8 Amp. Windshield Wipers

⑫ — 8 Amp. License Plate & Luggage Compartment Lights

⑬ — 8 Amp. Side Marker Light (Right)

⑭ — 8 Amp. Side Marker Light (Left)

⑮ — 16 Amp. Fog Lights

⑯ — 8 Amp. Horn

⑰ — 16 Amp. Fuel Pump

⑱ — 16 Amp. Engine Fan, Antenna

⑲ — 25 Amp. Defogger

⑳ — 16 Amp. A/C Condenser Fan

㉑ — 25 Amp. A/C Compressor, Fresh Air Fan

㉒ — Blank

㉓ — 25 Amp. Power Windows

㉔ — Blank

Relays are numbered from right to left, top row first:

① — Cooling Fan

② — Fuel Pump

③ — A/C

④ — Headlight Washer

⑤ — Not Used

⑥ — Rear Defogger

⑦ — Not Used

⑧ — Not Used

⑨ — Horn

⑩ — Wipers

⑪ — Turn Signals

⑫ — Not Used

911SC — Main fuse block is located inside luggage compartment on left side and contains 21 fuses. An additional fuse block is located in engine compartment on left side under regulator cover. Secondary fuse block protects Heater Fan Relay (5 Amp.), Heater Fan (25 Amp.) and Rear Window

Defogger and Wiper Return (25 Amp.). Main Fuses, numbered from front of car to rear, protect the following circuits:

① — 25 Amp. Fog Lamps

② — 5 Amp. License Plate Lights

③ — 5 Amp. Right Front and Rear Parking Lights

④ — 5 Amp. Left Front & Rear Parking Lights

⑤ — 8 Amp. Right Headlight Low Beam

⑥ — 8 Amp. Left Headlight Low Beam

⑦ — 8 Amp. Right Headlight High Beam

⑧ — 8 Amp. Left Headlight High Beam, High Beam Indicator

⑨ — 5 Amp. Right Front Turn Signal

⑩ — 5 Amp. Left Front Turn Signal

⑪ — 16 Amp. Turn Signal Relay, Stop Lights, Back-up Lights

⑫ — 25 Amp. Defogger, Fresh Air Blower

⑬ — 25 Amp. Front Wiper/Washer, Lighter

⑭ — 25 Amp. Sunroof, Mirrors, Rear Wiper/Washer

⑮ — 8 Amp. Brake Lights, Cruise Control

⑯ — 25 Amp. Fuel Pump

⑰ — 16 Amp. Hazard Flasher

⑱ — 5 Amp. Courtesy Lights, Clock, Trunk Light

⑲ — 25 Amp. Headlight Washer

⑳ — 25 Amp. A/C Blower Motor

㉑ — 25 Amp. Power Windows

928 — Fuse block is located in passenger footwell. It contains 34 fuses and 22 relays. Two 400mA inline fuses are located above the fuse panel and protects the security system. Circuits protected by fuses are as follows, from left to right:

① — 16 Amp. Fog Lights

② — Not Connected

③ — 8 Amp. License Light, Engine Compartment Light

④ — 8 Amp. Switch Illumination Light

⑤ — 16 Amp. Cigar Lighter

⑥ — 16 Amp. Windshield Wipers

⑦ — Not Used

⑧ — 16 Amp. Sunroof

⑨ — 8 Amp. Back-up Lights, Mirror, Rear Wiper, A/C

⑩ — 8 Amp. Brake Lights, Automatic Speed Control

⑪ — 8 Amp. Instrument Panel Lights

⑫ — 8 Amp. Instrument Warning Lights

⑬ — Not Connected

⑭ — 25 Amp. Power Seats

⑮ — 16 Amp. Power Antenna, Horn, Rear Wiper

⑯ — 25 Amp. Electric Radiator Fan

⑰ — 25 Amp. Heater, Air Conditioning Blower

⑱ — 15 Amp. Rear Window Defogger

⑲ — 16 Amp. Headlight Motor

⑳ — 16 Amp. Headlight Washer

㉑ — 25 Amp. Power Windows

PORSCHE (Cont.)

㉒ — 16 Amp. Fuel Pump
㉓ — 8 Amp. Interior Lights, Clock
㉔ — 8 Amp. High Beam Headlights Left
㉕ — 8 Amp. High Beam Headlights Right
㉖ — 8 Amp. Low Beam Headlights Left
㉗ — 8 Amp. Low Beam Headlights Right
㉘ — 8 Amp. Left Side Markers
㉙ — 8 Amp. Right Side Markers
㉚ — 8 Amp. Front Left Turn Signal
㉛ — 8 Amp. Rear Left Turn Signal
㉜ — 8 Amp. Front Right Turn Signal
㉝ — 8 Amp. Rear Right Turn Signal
㉞ — Not Connected

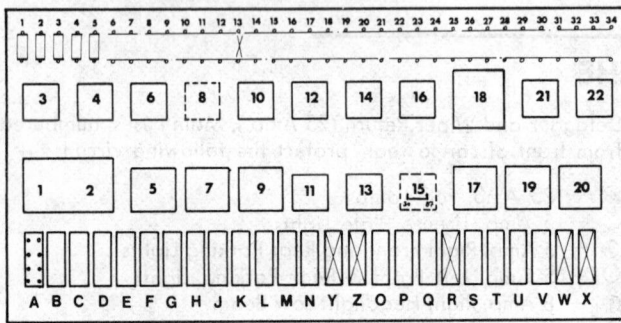

Fig. 1   Porsche 928 Fuse and Relay Block

Relay circuits are below the fuses in the main electrical panel. Other relays include the seat return relay (below seat), the rear wiper relay (at left rear corner behind tool kit tray) and the seat belt relay (behind radio).

①-② — Rear Defogger
③ — Not Used
④ — Not Used
⑤ — Hazard Flasher Unit
⑥ — Window Controls
⑦ — Headlight Washer Pump
⑧ — Not Used
⑨ — Not Used
⑩ — Horns
⑪ — Not Used
⑫ — Fog Lights
⑬ — Intermittent Wiper Speed Control
⑭ — Starter Relay Bridge
⑮ — Washer Pump
⑯ — EFI Control Unit
⑰ — Fuel Pump
⑱ — Extra Cooling Fan for Air Conditioning
⑲ - ⑳ — Retractable Headlight Relay
㉑ — Fresh Air Fan
㉒ — Defroster

RENAULT

FUSE BLOCK

LeCar — Fuse block is located underneath dashboard on right side of steering column. Fuses are numbered from left to right and protect these circuits:

① — 5 Amp. Left Side Parking Lights, Dash Lights
② — 5 Amp. Right Parking Lights
③ — 8 Amp. Wiper/Washer
④ — 5 Amp. Courtesy Lights, Lighter
⑤ — 8 Amp. Heater Fan, Radio
⑥ — 5 Amp. Turn Signals
⑦ — Blank
⑧ — 16 Amp. Backup Lights, Defogger, Brake Lights, Rear Wiper, A/C Relay, Speed Sensor

18i — Fuse panel is located to left of steering column under edge of dashboard. Fuses are numbered from right to left,

with even-numbered fuses in top row, and odd-numbered fuses in bottom row. The circuits protected are:

① — 8 Amp. Turn Signals, Flashers
② — 5 Amp. Wiper Park Circuit
③ — Not Used
④ — Not Used
⑤ — Not Used
⑥ — 8 Amp. Lighter, Courtesy Lights
⑦ — Not Used
⑧ — 16 Amp. Wiper/Washer
⑨ — Not Used
⑩ — 8 Amp. Left Marker Lights, Panel Lights
⑪ — 10 Amp. Left Power Window
⑫ — 5 Amp. Right Marker Lights, Switch Lights
⑬ — 10 Amp. Right Power Window
⑭ — 5 Amp. Gauges
⑮ — 1.5 Amp. Back-up Lights, Intermittent Wiper Relay
⑯ — 1.5 Amp. Auto. Trans.
⑰ — 16 Amp. Heater & A/C Fan
⑱ — 16 Amp. Rear Defogger

SAAB

FUSE BLOCK

900 Models — Fuse block is located in engine compartment near left rear corner. Fuse capacities and circuits protected are as follows:

① — 8 Amp. Right High Beam
② — 8 Amp. Left High Beam
③ — 8 Amp. Right Low Beam

④ — 8 Amp. Left Low Beam
⑤ — 16 Amp. Engine Fan
⑥ — 16 Amp. Defogger
⑦ — 8 Amp. Courtesy Lights
⑧ — 16 Amp. Fuel Pump
⑨ — 8 Amp. Hazard Flashers
⑩ — 5 Amp. Stop Lights
⑪ — 16 Amp. A/C Fan
⑫ — 5 Amp. Right Parking and Taillights

SAAB (Cont.)

⑬ — 5 Amp. Left Parking and Taillights
⑭ — 25 Amp. Horn
⑮ — 8 Amp. Mirrors
⑯ — 16 Amp. Heated Driver's Seat
⑰ — 25 Amp. Heater Fan

⑱ — 8 Amp. A/C
⑲ — 8 Amp. Warning Lights
⑳ — 8 Amp. Turn Signals
㉑ — 8 Amp. Wiper/Washer
㉒ — 16 Amp. Cornering Lights

SUBARU

FUSE BLOCK

All Models — The fuse block is located underneath dashboard on left side. Inline fuses protect the Choke (10 Amp. White), Power Windows (25 Amp. Black), Fuel Pump and Regulator (5 Amp. White), Emissions Computer (5 Amp. Pink) and Rear Defogger (15 Amp. Black). All other circuits are fused through the block. Fuses are numbered from top (toward front of vehicle) to bottom, left row first. Protected circuits are:

① — 25 Amp. Heater Fan Motor

② — 15 Amp. Radio, Lighter, Rear Wiper/Washer
③ — 15 Amp. Front Wiper/Washer, Engine Fan
④ — 15 Amp. Headlight Low Beams
⑤ — 15 Amp. Headlight High Beams
Next Row
⑥ — 15 Amp. Coil, Fuel Pump, Gauges, Warning Lights
⑦ — 15 Amp. Turn Signals, Back-up Lights
⑧ — 15 Amp. Marker Lights, Tail Lights
⑨ — 15 Amp. Horn, Stop Lights, Flashers, Courtesy Lights
⑩ — 25 Amp. Headlight Switch

TOYOTA

FUSE BLOCK

Celica — Main fuse block is located on left side of instrument panel behind cover. In addition, a smaller fuse block is located in engine compartment on left side. Fuses in main block are arranged in three rows. Fuses in engine fuse block are arranged in two rows. Moving from top-to-bottom, and left-to-right, fuses are as follows:

Main Block

① — 5 Amp. Courtesy Lights, Trunk Light, Clock
② — 15 Amp. Tail, Parking, License, Glove Box, Transmission Selector, Instrument Panel, Heater Panel & Marker Lights. Cigar Lighter
③ — Not Used
④ — 15 Amp. Gauges, Back-up Lights, Warning Lights
⑤ — 15 Amp. Turn Signals, Front Wiper/Washer
⑥ — 15 Amp. Alternator Regulator, Emission Controls
⑦ — 7.5 Amp. Radio, Tape Player
⑧ — 15 Amp. Lighter
⑨ — Not Used

Engine Fuse Block

⑩ — 15 Amp. Heater, A/C
⑪ — Not Used
⑫ — 15 Amp. Horn, Flashers, Stop Lights
⑬ — 15 Amp. Right Headlights
⑭ — 15 Amp. Left Headlights

Corolla — Three fuse blocks are used. One is in the engine compartment on left side. The others are under the left side of dashboard and on the left kick panel. Starting from top to bottom and from left to right, protected circuits are:

Kick Panel Block

① & ② — 15 Amp. Rear Defogger
Next Row
③ — 10 Amp. Marker & Panel Lights, Tail Lights
④ — 5 Amp. Courtesy Lights
Next Row
⑤ — 10 Amp. Stop Light

Main Fuse Block
① — 20 Amp. Wiper/Washer (Front & Rear)
② — 5 Amp. Radio
Next Row
③ — Not Used
④ — 10 Amp. Gauges, Back-up Lights, Warning Lights
⑤ — 10 Amp. Lighter, Clock
⑥ — 7.5 Amp. Turn Signals
⑦ — 10 Amp. Main Relay, Choke Relay, Emission Controls, Cooling Fan
Engine Fuse Block
① — 15 Amp. Left Side Headlights
② — 15 Amp. Right Side Headlights
③ — 10 Amp. Hazard Warning Flashers, Horn
④ — 10 Amp. Discharge Warning Light, Charge Light Relay, Choke Relay
⑤ & ⑥ — 15 Amp. Heater, A/C
⑦ — Voltage Regulator, Charge Relay

Corona — Fuse block is next to steering column at left side of instrument panel. A second fuse block is located in engine compartment. Fuses and protected circuits are:
Main Fuse Block
① — 7.5 Amp. Radio
② — 15 Amp. Stop Lights, Cruise Control
③ — 5 Amp. Courtesy Lights
④ — 10 Amp. Left Tail Lights, Left Marker Lights
⑤ — 10 Amp. Right Tail Lights, Right Marker Lights, Panel Lights
⑥ — 15 Amp. Cruise Control Emission Computer, Main & Ignition Relays
⑦ — 10 Amp. Turn Signals
⑧ — 10 Amp. Gauges, Warning Lights, Overdrive Relay, Back-up Lights
Engine Fuse Block
① — 10 Amp. A/C
② — 20 Amp. Wiper/Washer
③ — 10 Amp. Alternator, Choke Heater
④ — 15 Amp. Horn, Hazard Flashers
⑤ — 15 Amp. Right Headlight
⑥ — 15 Amp. Left Headlight
The heater fan, rear defogger and sun roof are protected by circuit breakers.

Fuses & Circuit Breakers

TOYOTA (Cont.)

Cressida — The main fuse block is in the instrument panel. A second block is located in the engine compartment. Fuses are numbered from left to right, top row first. They protect the following circuits:

Main Fuse Block

① — 7.5 Amp. Turn Signals
② — 15 Amp. Cruise Control, Rear Wiper/Washer, Overdrive
③ — 7.5 Amp. Gauges, Heater, A/C, Back-up Lights
④ — 5 Amp. Courtesy Lights, Radio, Clock
⑤ — 7.5 Amp. Fuel Inj., Ignition, Charging Light
Next Row
⑥ — 7.5 Amp. Radio, Clock
⑦ — 15 Amp. Lighter, Antenna

Engine Fuse Panel

① — 7.5 Amp. Charging Relay
② — 15 Amp. Voltage Regulator
③ — 15 Amp. Horn, Flashers
④ — 15 Amp. Panel & Marker Lights, Tail Lights, Clock
⑤ — 15 Amp. Right Headlight
⑥ — 15 Amp. Left Headlight
⑦ — 15 Amp. Fuel Injection
⑧ — 20 Amp. Front Wiper/Washer
⑨ — 15 Amp. Cruise Control, Stop Lights

The rear defogger circuit breaker is on the main panel. It is reset by inserting a pin into the small hole on top. The power windows, door locks and sun roof are protected by one large circuit breaker. Press the button to reset this breaker.

Pickup — Fuse block is located on left side of instrument panel. Fuses are numbered, starting from top to bottom of each row, moving from right to left. Circuits protected are:

① — 10 Amp. Right Headlight
② — 10 Amp. Left Headlight
③ — 15 Amp. Horn, Hazard Flashers
④ — 10 Amp. Turn Signals
⑤ — 10 Amp. Gauges, Heater Relay, Backup Lights
⑥ — 15 Amp. Engine Controls, Fuel Pump
⑦ — 15 Amp. Wipers, Washers
⑧ — 10 Amp. Lighter
⑨ — 10 Amp. Stop Lights
⑩ — 15 Amp. Tail Lights, Dashboard Lights, Marker Lights
⑪ — 15 Amp. Heater, A/C
⑫ — 5 Amp. Radio, Tape Player
⑬ — 5 Amp. Courtesy Light, Clock

Land Cruiser (FJ40) — Main fuse block is under the left side of instrument panel. The Ammeter fuses are near the battery, a 15 Amp. A/C fuse is near heater fan motor, and the 5 Amp. Engine Fan fuse is behind instrument panel. Fuses in the main block protect:

① — 15 Amp. Tail, Parking, Marker, License, Dome & Instrument Panel Lights.
② — 15 Amp. Horn, Stop Lights, Hazard Flashers, Engine Fan
③ — 15 Amp. Headlights
④ — 5 Amp. Radio
⑤ — 15 Amp. Lighter
⑥ — 15 Amp. Engine Controls
⑦ — 20 Amp. Heater Fan, Gauges, Buzzers
⑧ — 20 Amp. Turn Signals, Wiper/Washer

Land Cruiser (FJ60 Station Wagon) — Main fuse block is located at left side of instrument panel. The circuits protected are:

① — 10 Amp. Right Headlight
② — 10 Amp. Left Headlight
③ — 15 Amp. Lighter, Antenna
④ — 5 Amp. Radio
⑤ — 15 Amp. Parking, Marker & Panel Lights, Tail Lights
⑥ — 10 Amp. Brake Lights
⑦ — 10 Amp. Horn, Flashers
⑧ — 10 Amp. Engine Controls, Regulator
⑨ — 10 Amp. Turn Signals
⑩ — 15 Amp. Wiper/Washer, Back-up Lights, Winch Switch
⑪ — 10 Amp. A/C
⑫ — 20 Amp. Rear Defogger
⑬ — 5 Amp. Gauges, Buzzer, Heater Relay
⑭ — 5 Amp. Regulator
⑮ — 5 Amp. Courtesy Light, Engine Fan

Starlet — Fuse block is located at left side of instrument panel. Fuses are arranged in 5 rows of 3. Starting at top left row and going down, then across, fuses protect:

① — 10 Amp. Right Headlight
② — 10 Amp. Left Headlight
③ — Marker, Parking & Panel Lights, Tail Lights
Next Row
④ — 10 Amp. Lighter
⑤ — 5 Amp. Radio
⑥ — 15 Amp. Flashers, Horn, Brake Lights
Next Row
⑦ — 15 Amp. Turn Signals, Back-up Lights, Gauges
⑧ — 20 Amp. Heater, A/C
⑨ — 5 Amp. Courtesy Lights, Clock
⑩ — 10 Amp. Emission Controls, Regulator, Main Relay
⑪ — 15 Amp. Wiper/Washer (Front & Rear)
⑫ — 15 Amp. Rear Defogger
⑬ — 5 Amp. Voltage Regulator
⑭ — 10 Amp. A/C
⑮ — Spare

Supra — Main fuse block is located on left side of instrument panel. An additional fuse block is located on right side of engine compartment. The rear window defogger is protected by a circuit breaker located in right side kick panel. Fuses in block are arranged in three rows. Starting from left-to-right, top-to-bottom, circuits protected are as follows:

Main Fuse Block

① — 5 Amp. Interior Lights, Luggage Compartment Light & Clock
② — 15 Amp. Tail Lights Relay, Tail Lights, Parking Lights, License Lights, Glove Box Light, Lighter, Heater Control Light, Transmission Indicator Light, Map Light, Instrument Panel Lights, Marker Lights
③ — 30 Amp. Power Windows
④ — 15 Amp. Gauges, Warning Indicators, Cruise Control, Defogger Switch, Illuminated Entry Relay, Overdrive Solenoid, Heater Relay, Back-Up Lights
⑤ — 15 Amp. Turn Signals, Wipers, Washer
⑥ — 15 Amp. Alternator, Discharge Warning Light Relay, Electronic Fuel Injection Relay, Emission Control System
⑦ — 7.5 Amp. Radio & Tape Player
⑧ — 15 Amp. Lighter
⑨ — Not Used

TOYOTA (Cont.)

Engine Fuse Block

① — 15 Amp. Stop Lights, Horn, Flashers
② — 15 Amp. Heater, Air Conditioning
③ — 15 Amp. Right Side High & Low Headlights
④ — 15 Amp. Left Side High & Low Headlights

Tercel — Main fuse block is located at left side of dashboard. A second panel is located in the engine compartment. Fuses in main block are numbered starting with the vertical fuse at left, then from top to bottom. Engine compartment fuses are also numbered starting with forward fuse closest to engine.

Main Fuse Block

① — 5 Amp. Radio
② — 10 Amp. Lighter, Clock
③ — Not Used (Inline Circuit Breaker for Defogger)
④ — 10 Amp. Turn Signals, Back-up Lights, Gauges
⑤ — 5 Amp. Engine Controls, Computer

Next Row

⑥ — 10 Amp. Brake Lights
⑦ — 20 Amp. Heater Relay, Heater Blower, A/C
⑧ — 15 Amp. Marker, Panel & License Lights, Tail Lights
⑨ — 5 Amp. Courtesy Lights, Clock

Engine Compartment Block

① — 10 Amp. Right Headlight
② — 10 Amp. Left Headlight
③ — 5 Amp. Charge Light, Choke Heater

Next Row

④ — 15 Amp. Horn, Flashers
⑤ — 20 Amp. Wiper/Washer (Front & Rear)
⑥ — 10 Amp. Voltage Regulator

FUSIBLE LINKS

All Models — A fusible link is located in main battery feed wire near the battery. Protects all circuits except for starter motor.

TRIUMPH

FUSE BLOCK

TR7 & TR8 — Fuse block is located on a relay plate and is accessible after removal of cover panel at front of glove box. Fuses are arranged in two rows of six. Circuits protected, from top left to right are as follows:

① — 25 Amp. Left Headlight Low Beam
② — 25 Amp. Back-Up Lights, Wiper Motor
③ — 25 Amp. Left Headlight High Beam
④ — 35 Amp. Air Conditioning Clutch Relay, Blower Fan

⑤ — 25 Amp. Right Headlight High Beam
⑥ — 25 Amp. Right Headlight Low Beam
⑦ — 35 Amp. Air Conditioning Fan Relay
⑧ — 15 Amp. Rear Window Defogger
⑨ — 50 Amp. Horn, Cigar Lighter, Hazard Warning, Courtesy Lights, Fog Lights, Power Antenna
⑩ — 15 Amp. Front Right Parking & Marker Lights, Instrument Panel Dimmer
⑪ — 15 Amp. Front Left Parking & Marker Lights
⑫ — 35 Amp. Air Conditioning Fan Relay

VOLKSWAGEN

FUSE BLOCK

Dasher, Jetta, Rabbit, Convertible & Scirocco — Fuse block is located under dashboard on left side. Additional inline fuses above the block protect Rear Wipers (8 Amp.), Fuel Pump (16 Amp.), and A/C (25 Amp.). Circuits protected are as follows:

① — 8 Amp. Left Headlight Low Beam
② — 8 Amp. Right Headlight Low Beam
③ — 8 Amp. Left Headlight High Beam and Indicator
④ — 8 Amp. Right Headlight High Beam
⑤ — 16 Amp. Rear Window Defogger (Not Used on Pickup)
⑥ — 8 Amp. Stop Lights, Hazard Warning Flasher
⑦ — 8 Amp. Interior Lights, Clock, Cigar Lighter
⑧ — 8 Amp. Turn Signal System
⑨ — 8 Amp. Back-Up Lights, Horn, Transmission Shift Indicator (Dasher), Choke
⑩ — 16 Amp. Fresh Air Fan
⑪ — 8 Amp. Windshield Wiper & Washer
⑫ — 8 Amp. Luggage Compartment & License Plate Lights
⑬ — 8 Amp. Right Parking, Tail & Side Marker Lights
⑭ — 8 Amp. Left Parking, Tail & Side Marker Lights
⑮ — 25 Amp. Radiator Fan

Rabbit & Rabbit Pickup — Fuse block is located at left side of instrument panel under a cover. The fuses are numbered. Starting at top right corner coming toward front, then from right to left, circuits are:

① — 30 Amp. Radiator Fan
② — 15 Amp. Parking Lights
③ — 20 Amp. Horn
④ — Not Used
⑤ — 4 Amp. Panel Lights
⑥ — 30 Amp. Fuel Pump
⑦ — Not Used

Next Row

⑧ — Not Used
⑨ — 10 Amp. Rear Wiper/Washer
⑩ — 15 Amp. Turn Signals
⑪ — 5 Amp. Radio
⑫ — 10 Amp. Back-up Lights
⑬ — Not Used
⑭ — Not Used

Next Row

⑮ — Not Used
⑯ — Not Used
⑰ — Not Used
⑱ — Not Used
⑲ — 25 Amp. Heater
⑳ — 25 Amp. Rear Defogger
㉑ — 20 Amp. Front Wiper/Washer
㉒ — Not Used
㉓ — Not Used
㉔ — 15 Amp. Stop Lights, Flashers

Fuses & Circuit Breakers

VOLKSWAGEN (Cont.)

㉕ — 15 Amp. Courtesy Lights
㉖ — 10 Amp. Lighter
㉗ — 4 Amp. Horn Relay
㉘ — Not Used

Vanagon — Fuse block is located under dashboard on left side of steering column. Fuse block contains 12 circuits. In addition, a 16 Amp. fuse is located at right side of fuse panel to protect blower fan. Circuits protected in main fuse block are as follows:

① — 8 Amp. Left Tail, Parking & Marker Lights
② — 8 Amp. Right Tail, Parking, Marker & License Lights
③ — 8 Amp. Low Beam Headlight Left
④ — 8 Amp. Low Beam Headlight Right
⑤ — 8 Amp. Left High Beam Headlight & Indicator

⑥ — 8 Amp. Right High Beam Headlight
⑦ — 8 Amp. Accessories
⑧ — 8 Amp. Cigar Lighter, Stop Lights, Interior Lights
⑨ — 16 Amp. Hazard Warning Lights
⑩ — 16 Amp. Windshield Wiper/Washer, Rear Window Defogger
⑪ — 8 Amp. Turn Signals
⑫ — 8 Amp. Horn, Back-Up Lights

Vanagon Changes

Vanagon relays are from left to right: Flasher, Blank, Load Reduction, Key Buzzer, Wipers.

VOLVO

FUSE BLOCK

All Models — Fuse block is located in left kick panel behind cover. Fuses are numbered from top to bottom and space is provided for spare fuses at bottom of block. Circuits protected are as follows:

① — 8 Amp. Lighter, Rear Wipers, Mirrors, Radio, Cruise Control
② — 16 Amp. Horn, Wipers, Washers
③ — 16 Amp. Heater Fan
④ — 8 Amp. Warning Buzzers
⑤ — 8 Amp. Fuel Pump (Feed Pump)
⑥ — 8 Amp. Brake Lights, Courtesy Light Relay

⑦ — 16 Amp. Main Fuel Pump
⑧ — 8 Amp. Courtesy Lights, Power Antenna, Locking System
⑨ — 8 Amp. Hazard Flashers
⑩ — 16 Amp. Power Windows, Heated Driver Seat
⑪ — 16 Amp. Overdrive, Defogger
⑫ — 8 Amp. Backup Lights, Power Window Relay, Heated Driver's Seat, A/C
⑬ — 8 Amp. Gauges, Turn Signals, Belt Warning, Fuel Injection Relay
⑭ — Spare
⑮ — 8 Amp. Left Parking and Marker Lights, License Light
⑯ — 8 Amp. Right Parking and Marker Lights, Headlight Buzzer, Instrument Panel Lights

Section 4

WIRING DIAGRAMS

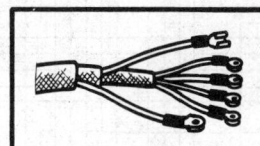

Contents

NOTE — ALSO SEE GENERAL INDEX

1981 Audi

ENGINE COMPARTMENT

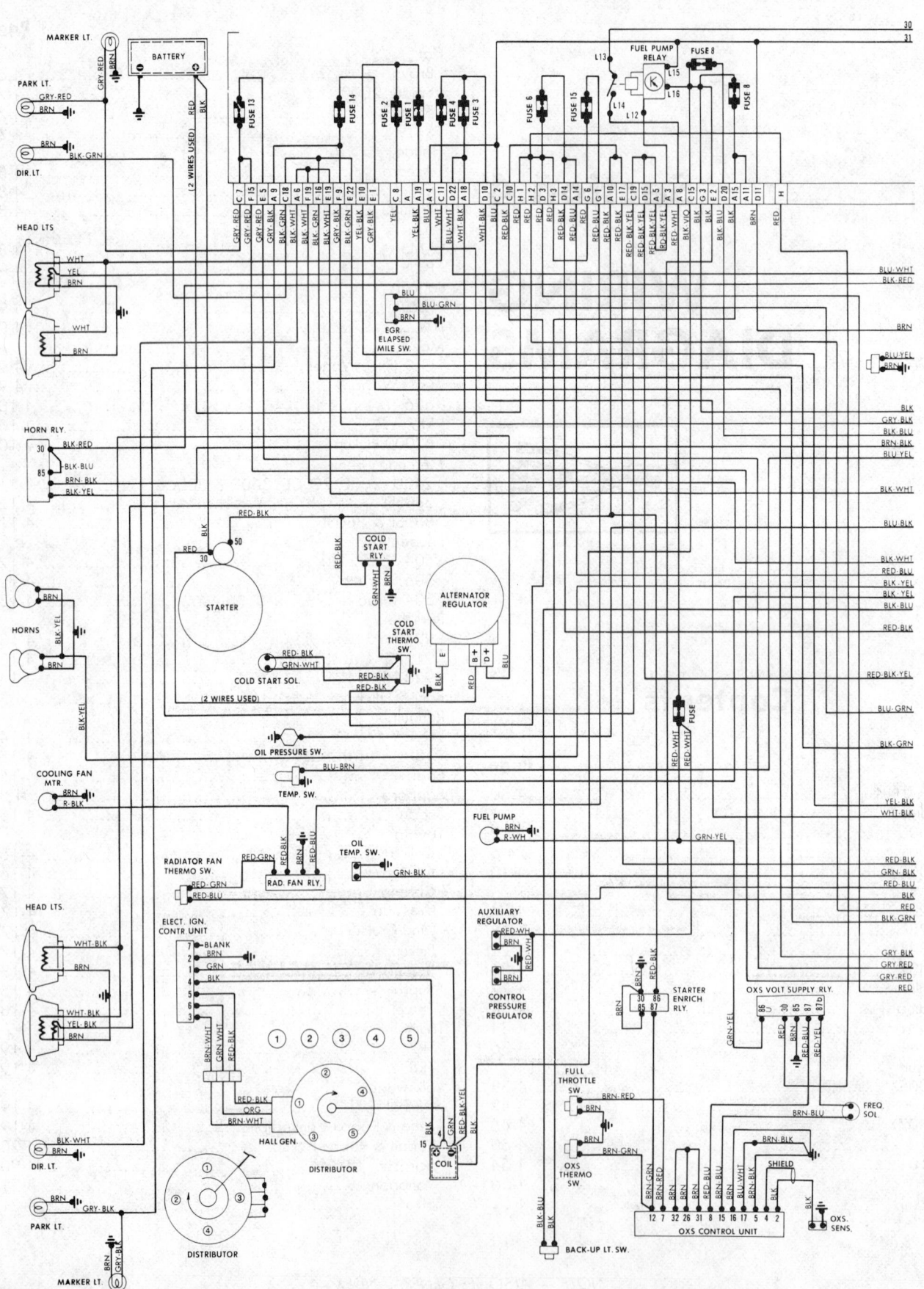

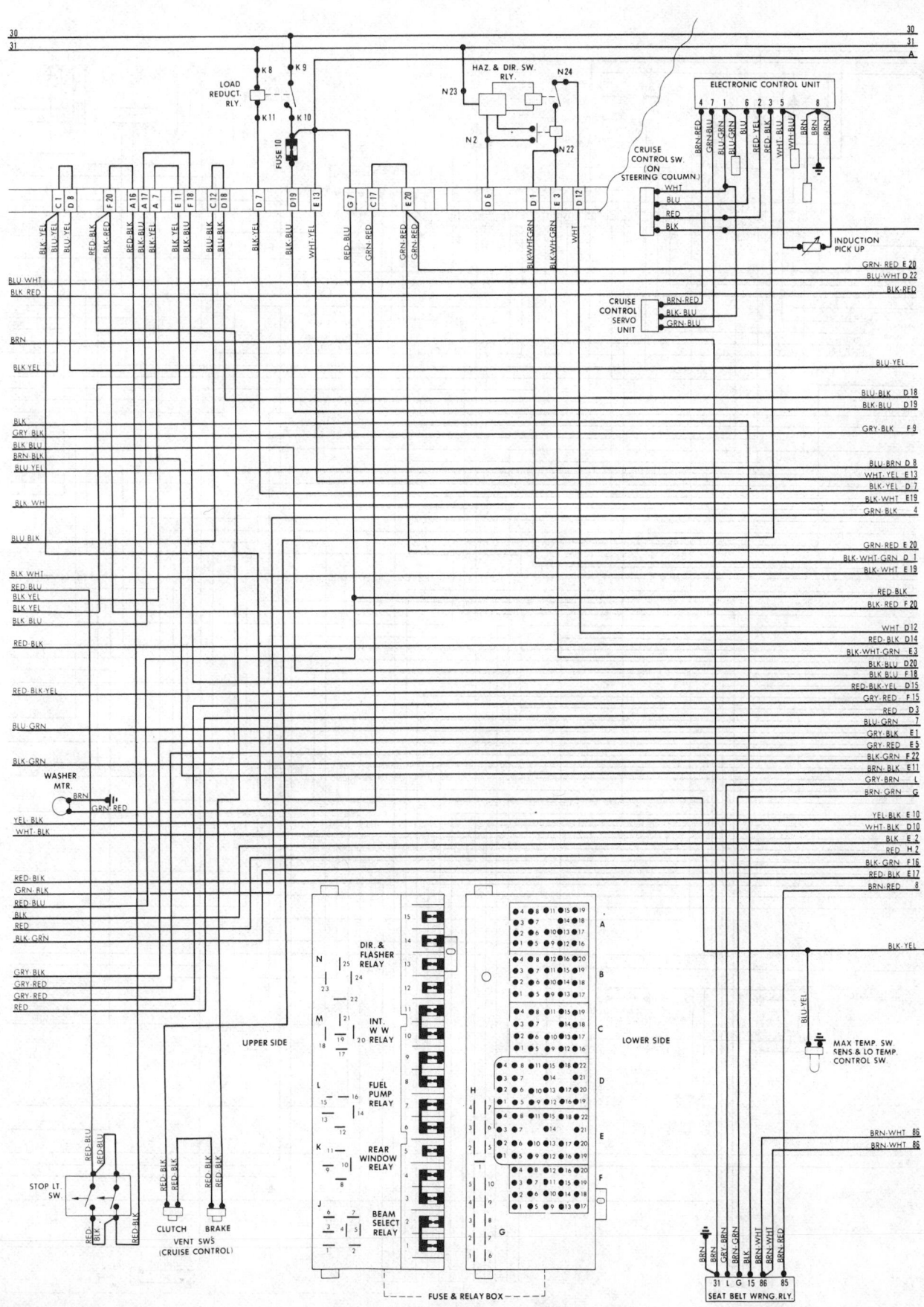

1981 Audi

UNDERDASH

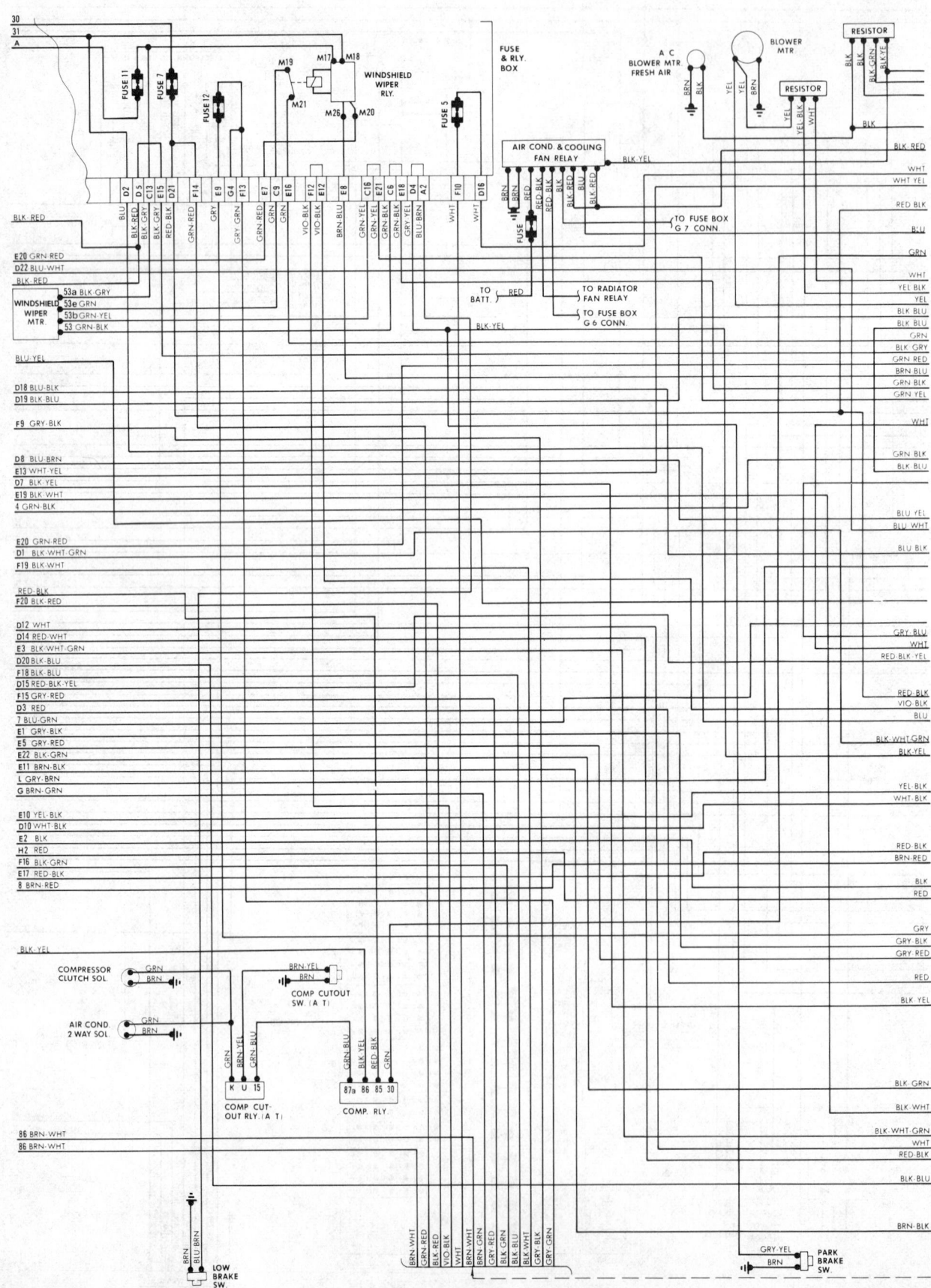

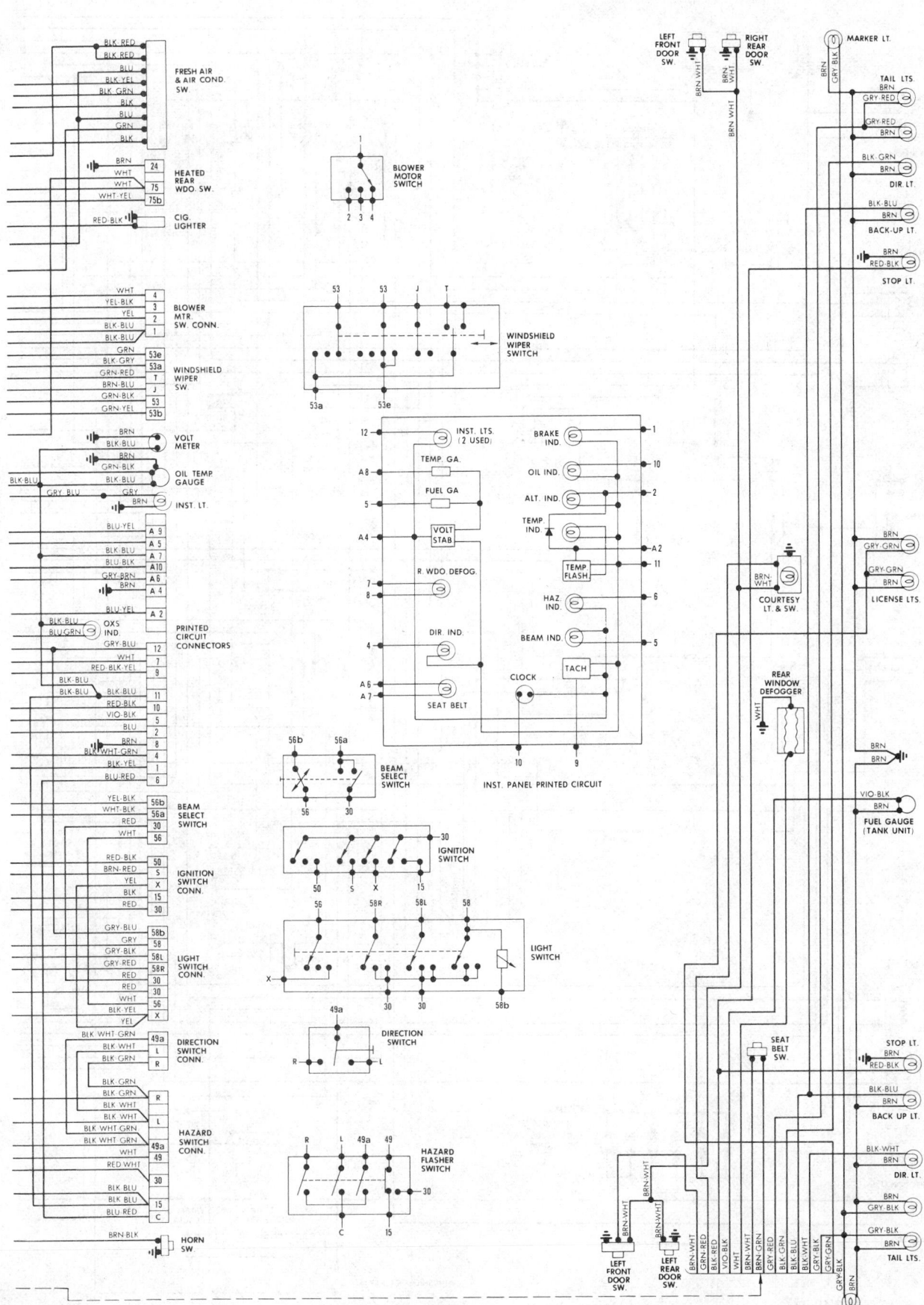

1981 Audi

ENGINE COMPARTMENT & FUSE BLOCK

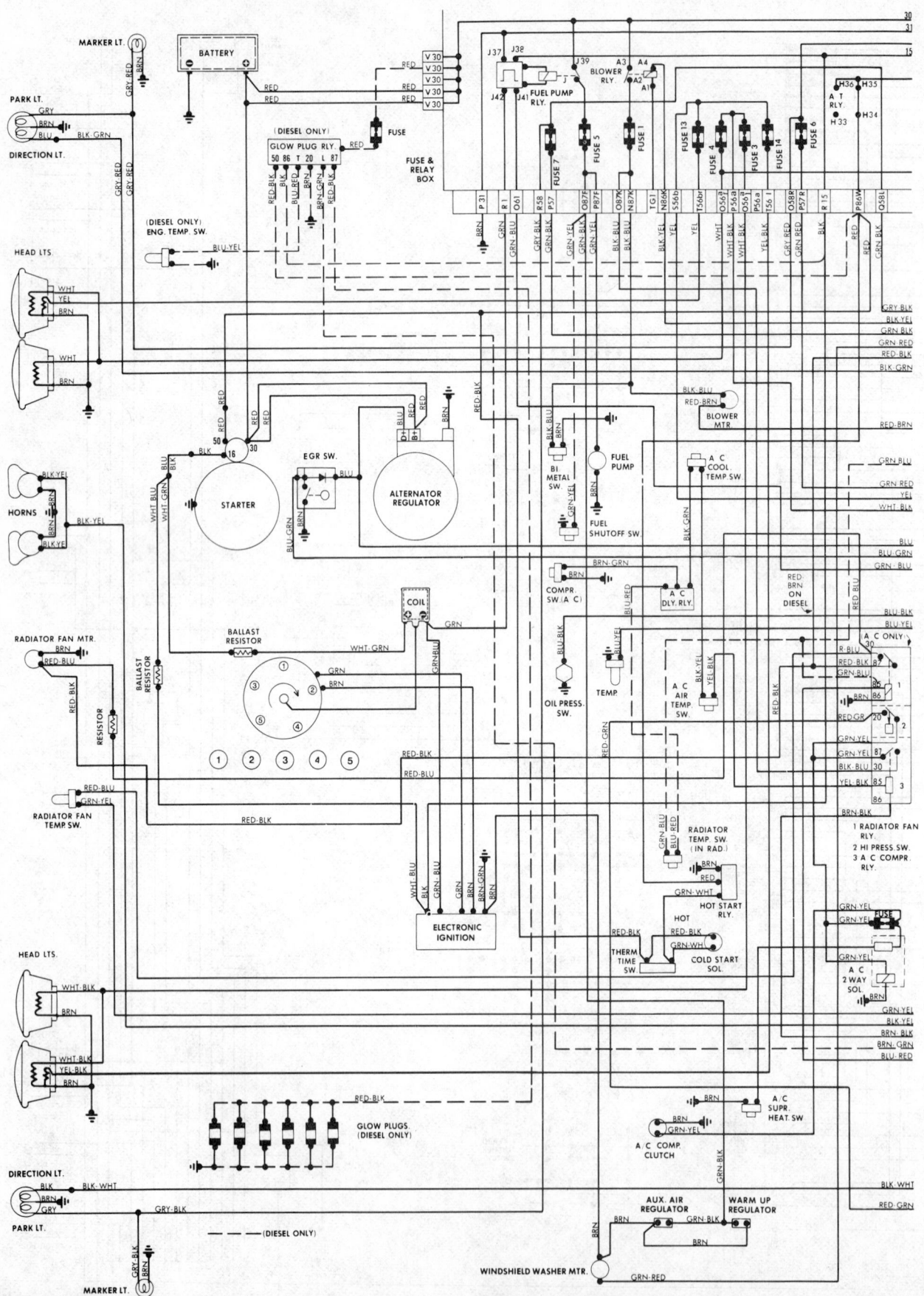

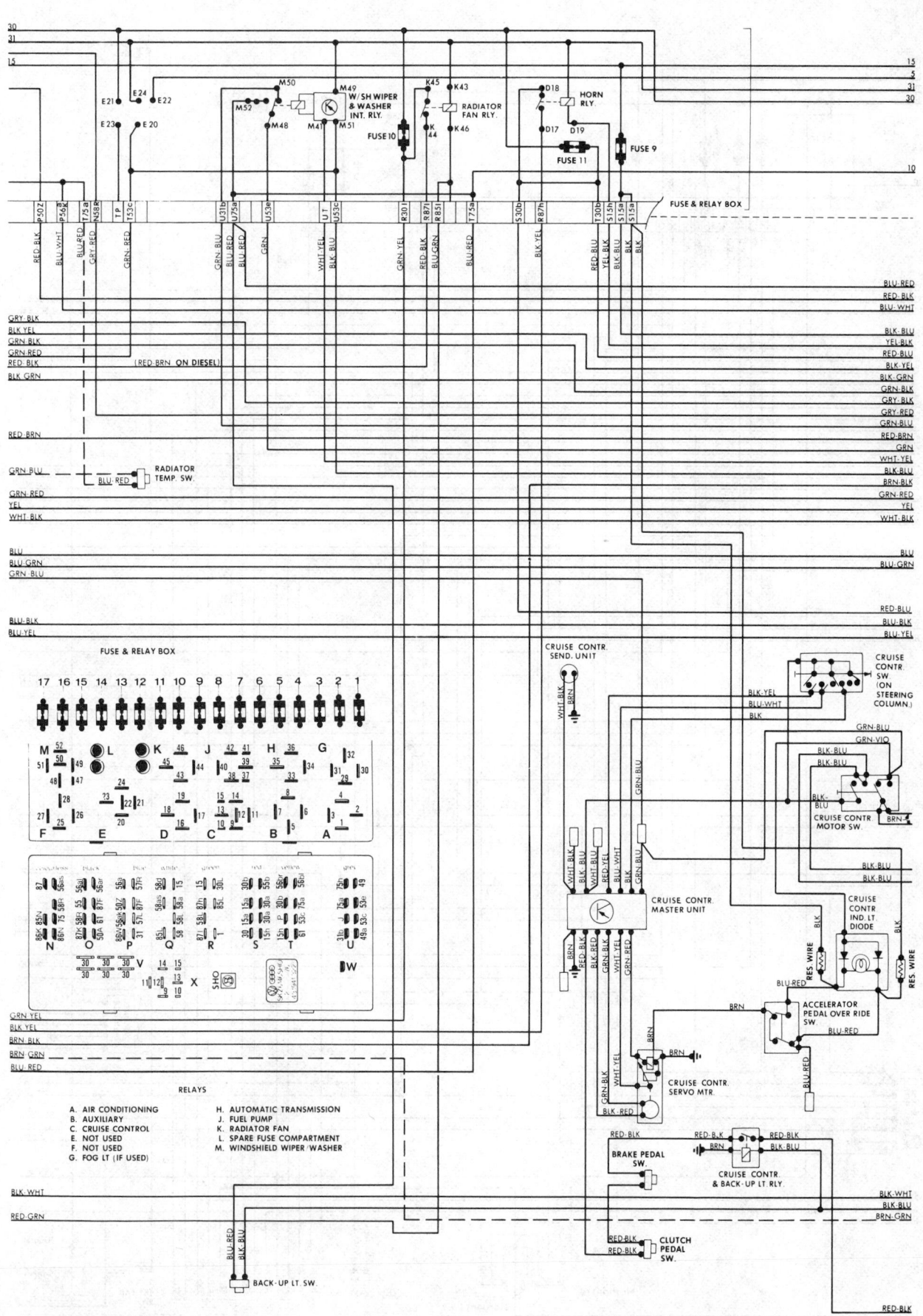

1981 Audi

UNDERDASH & FUSE BLOCK

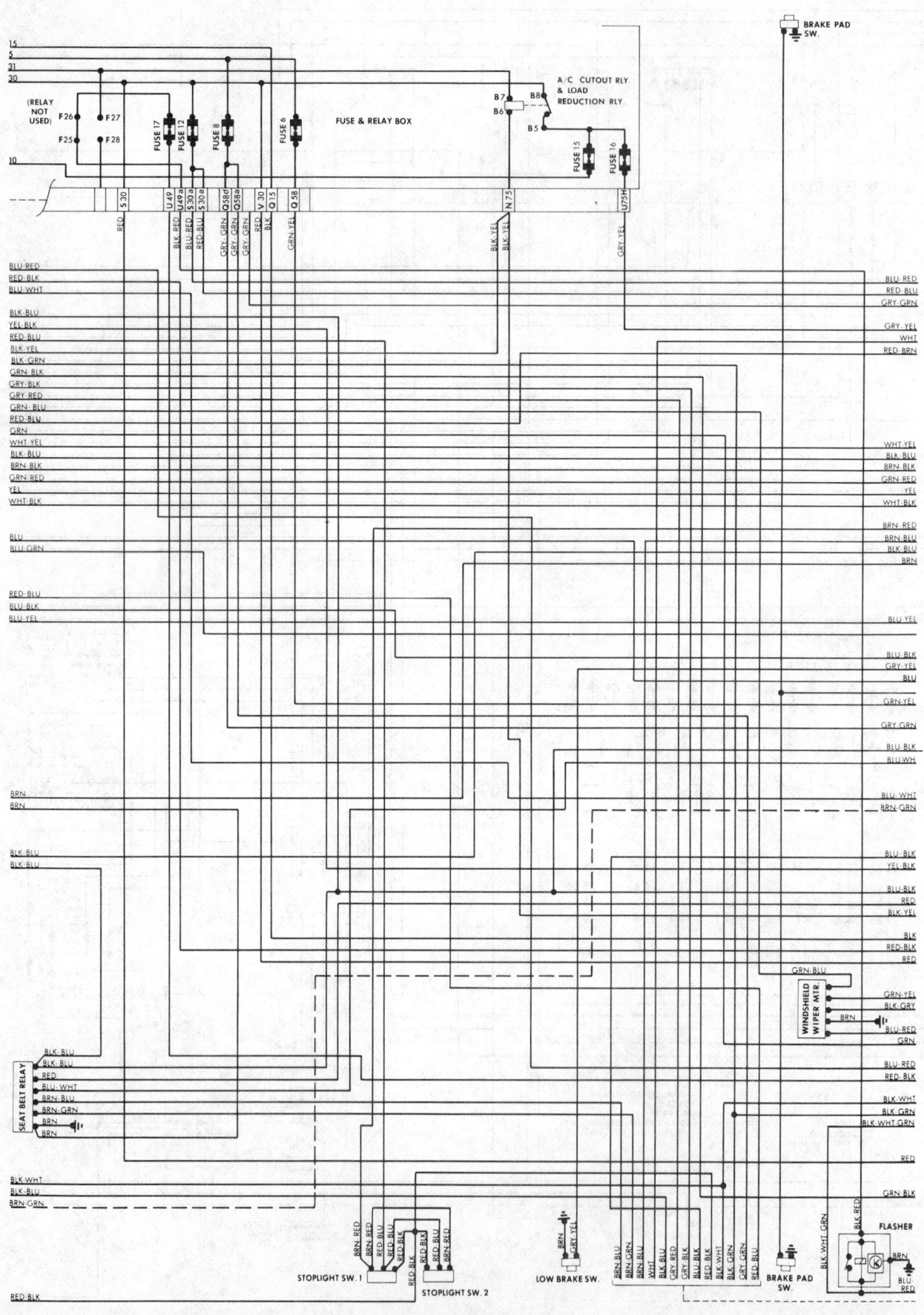

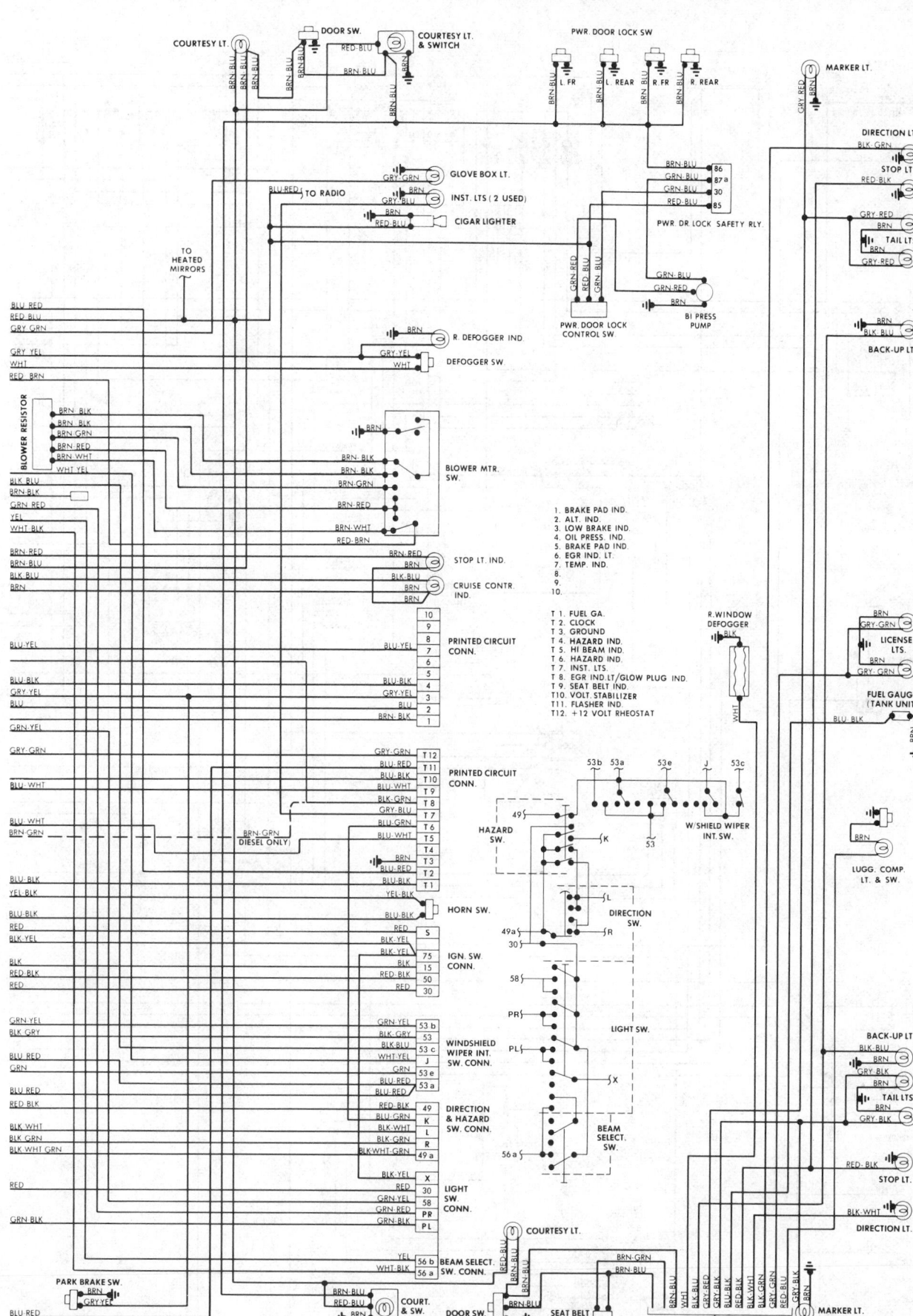

1. BRAKE PAD IND.
2. ALT. IND.
3. LOW BRAKE IND.
4. OIL PRESS. IND.
5. BRAKE PAD IND.
6. EGR IND. LT.
7. TEMP. IND.
8.
9.
10.

T 1. FUEL GA.
T 2. CLOCK
T 3. GROUND
T 4. HAZARD IND.
T 5. HI BEAM IND.
T 6. HAZARD IND.
T 7. INST. LTS.
T 8. EGR IND.LT/GLOW PLUG IND.
T 9. SEAT BELT IND.
T10. VOLT. STABILIZER
T11. FLASHER IND.
T12. +12 VOLT RHEOSTAT

1981 Audi

ENGINE COMPARTMENT

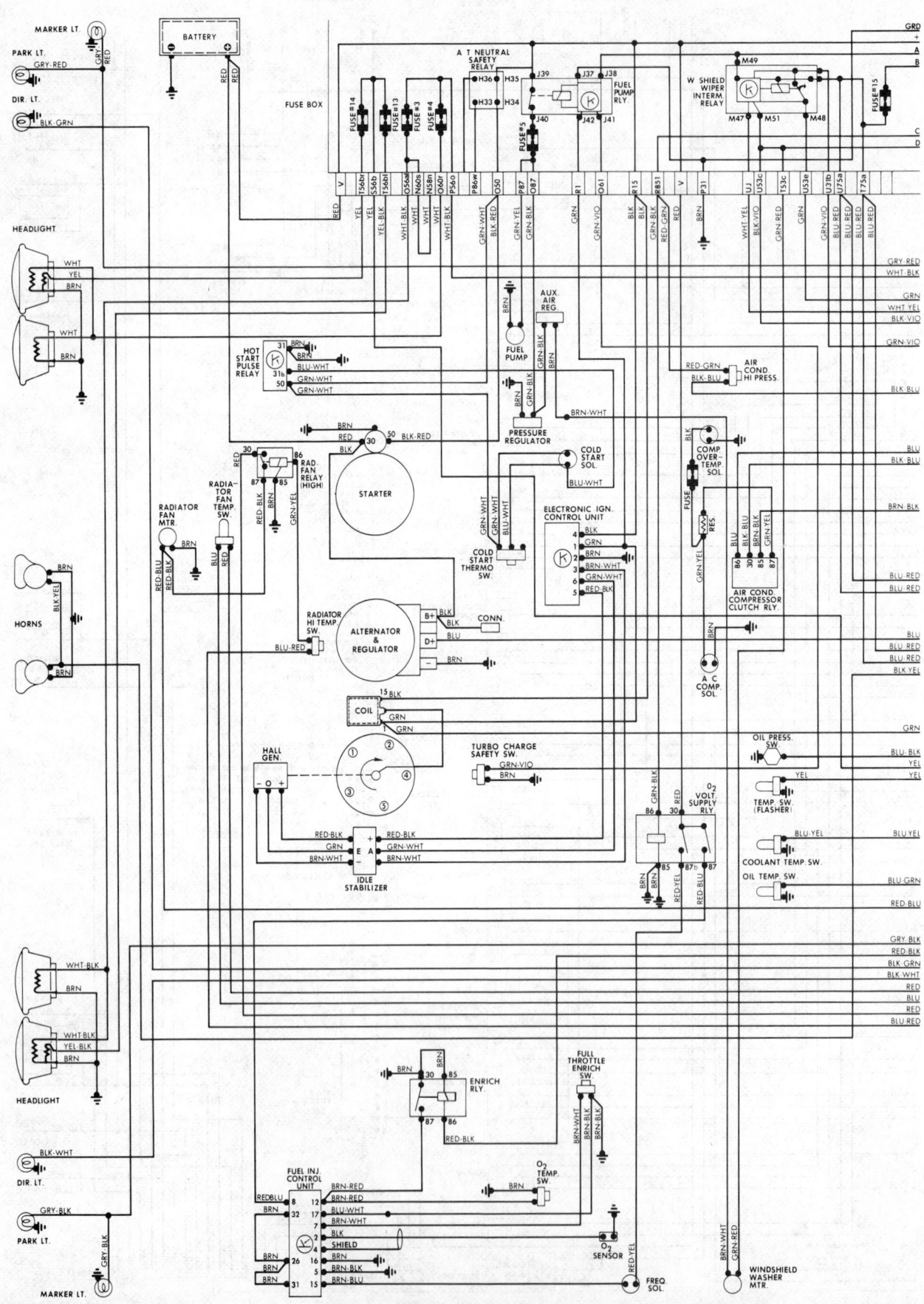

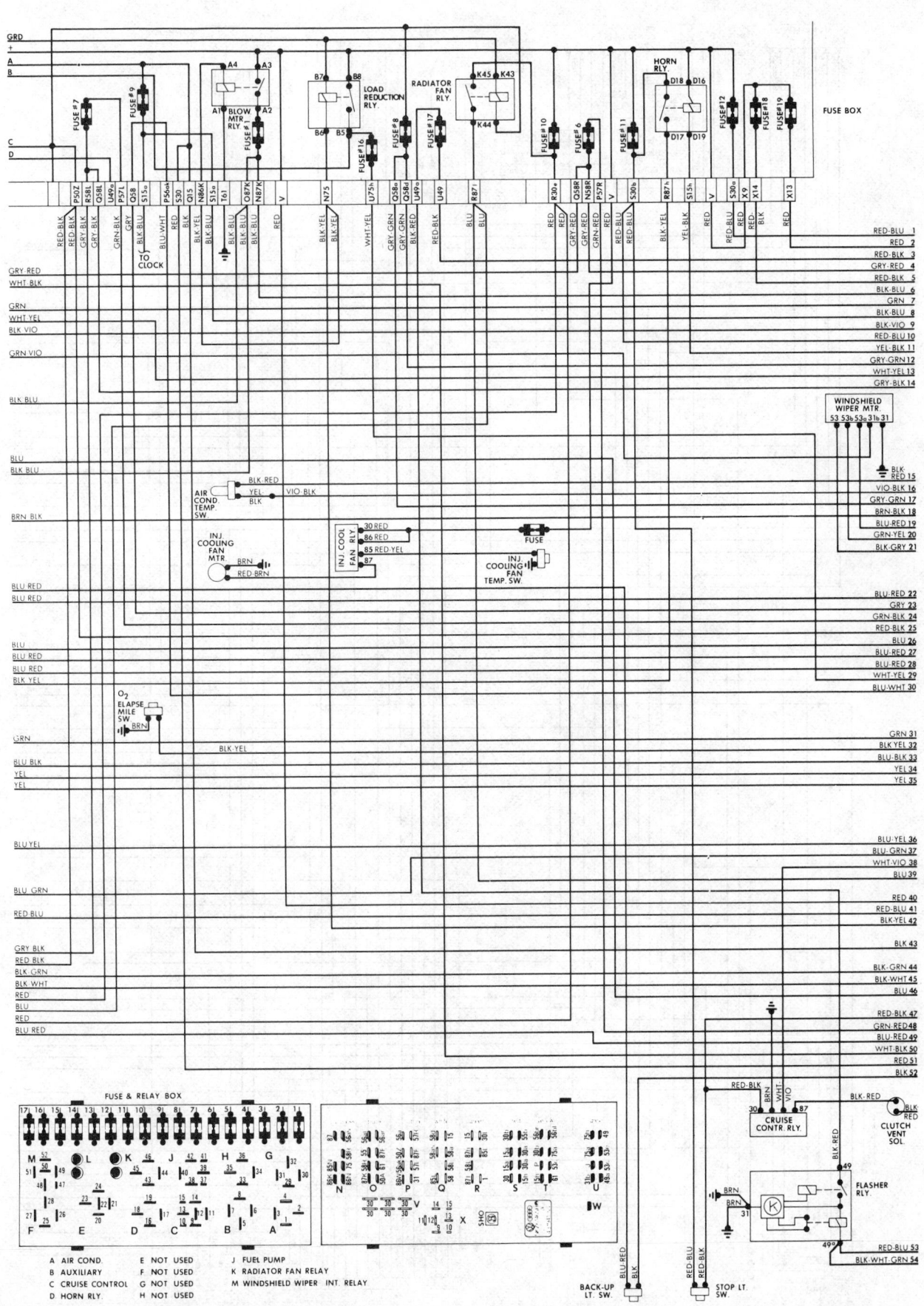

1981 Audi

UNDERDASH

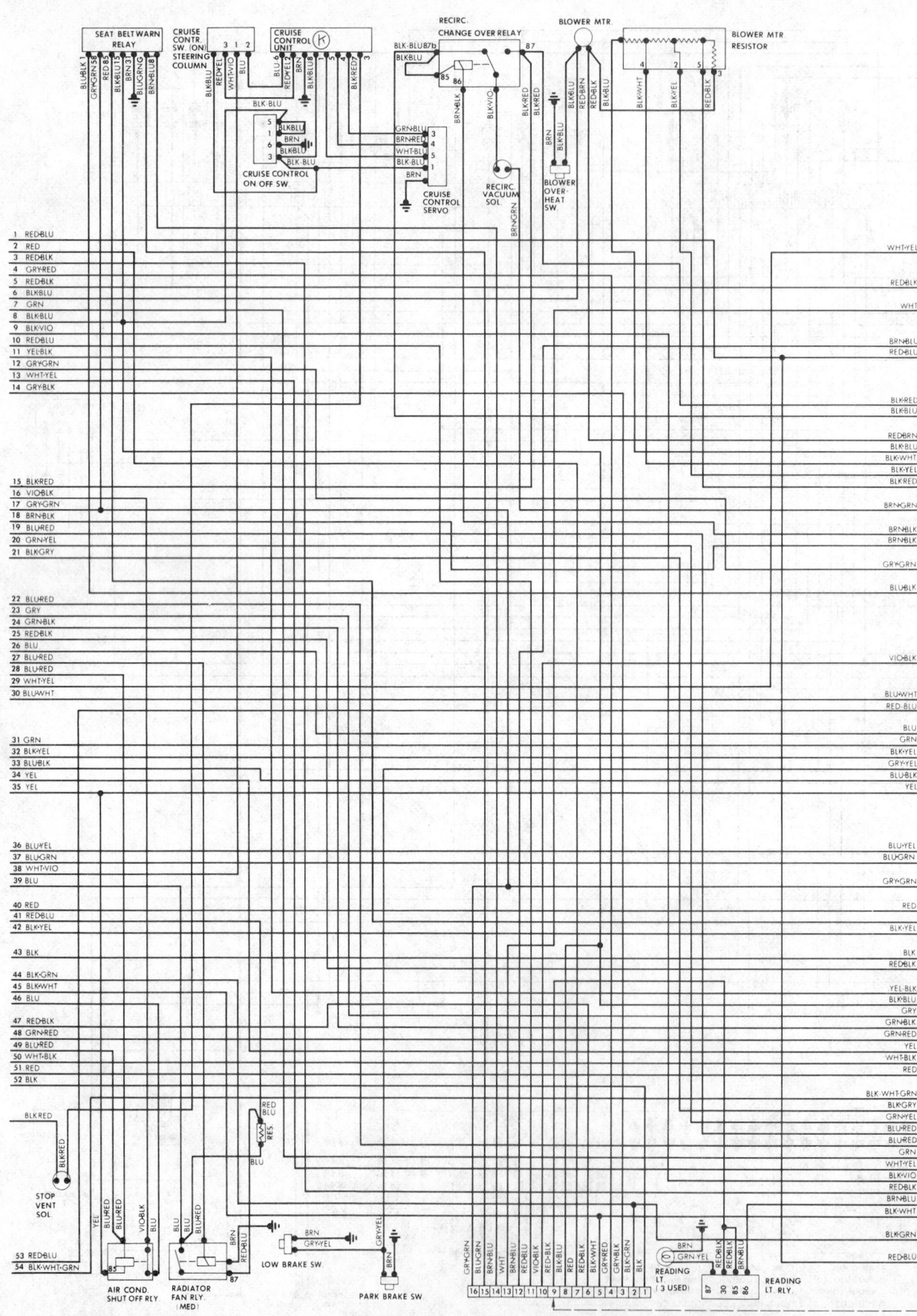

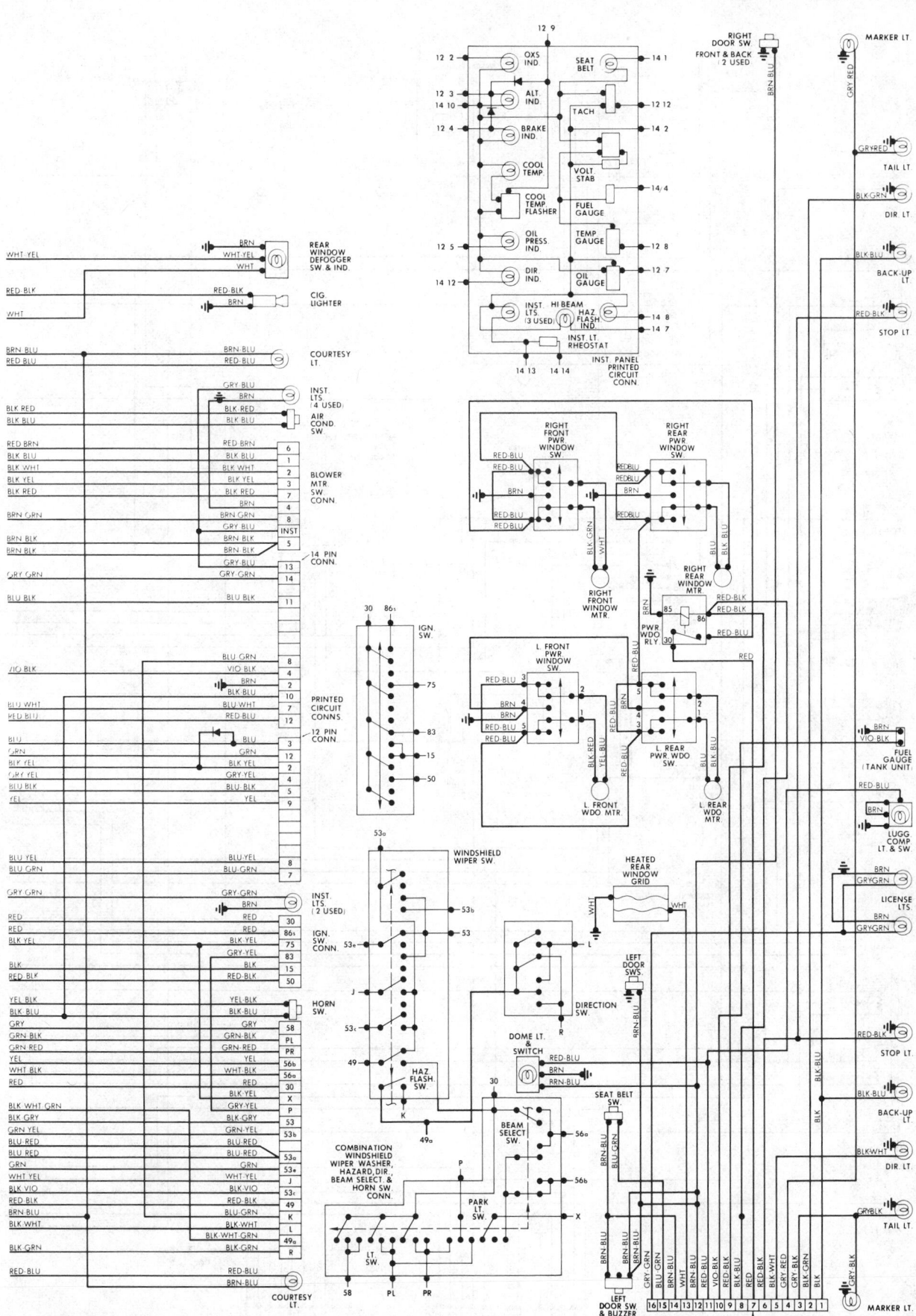

1981 BMW

ENGINE COMPARTMENT

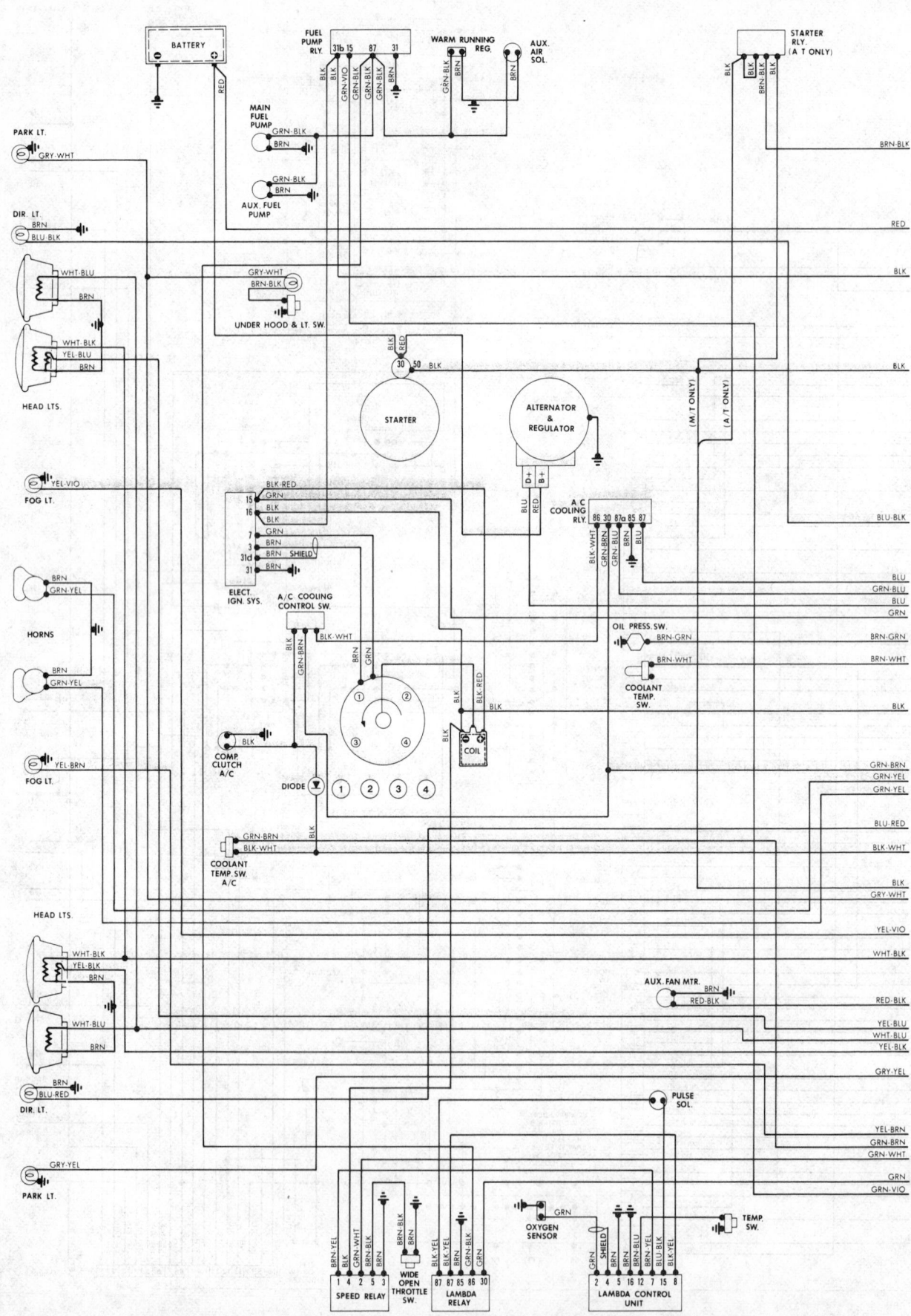

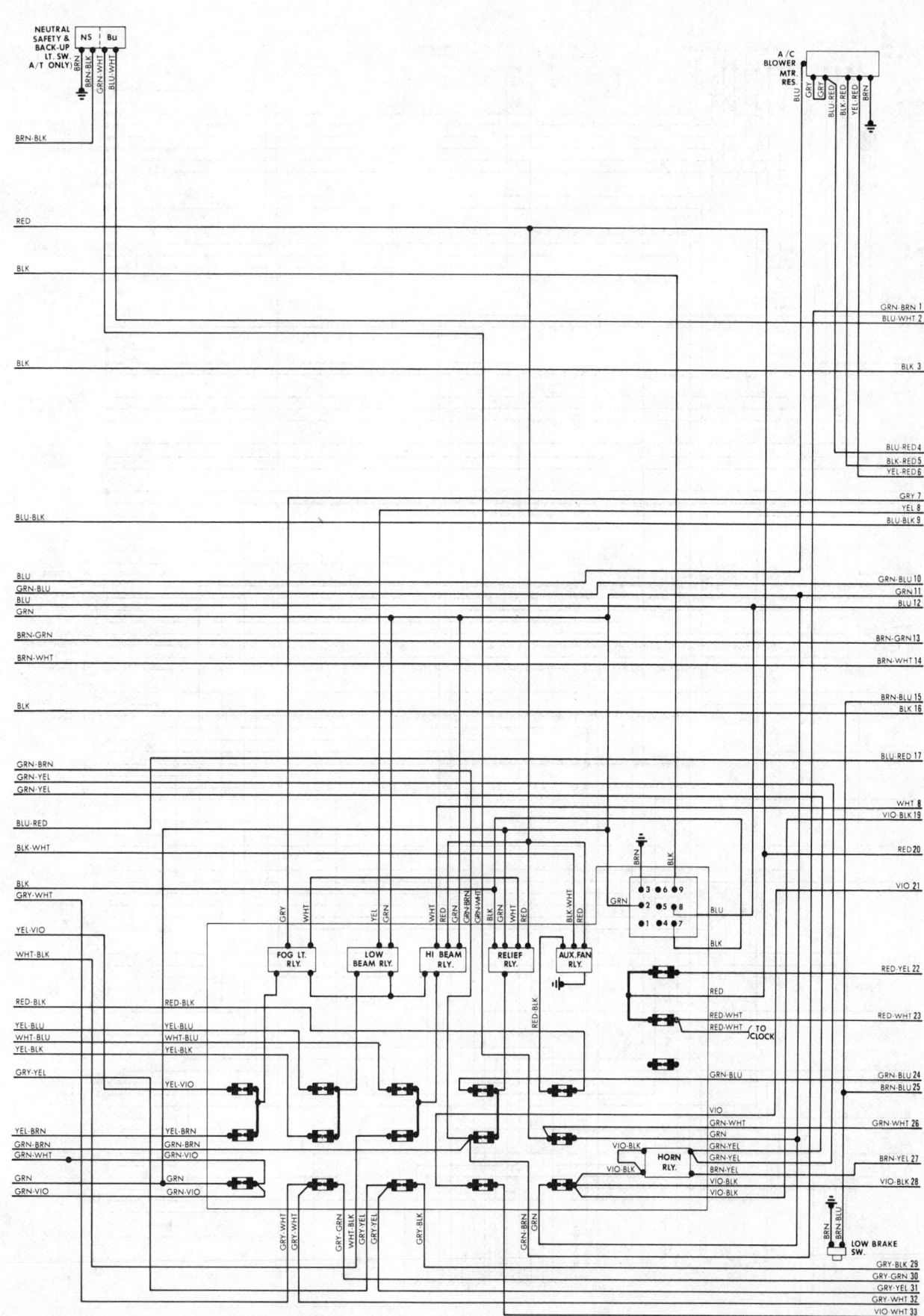

UNDERDASH & INSTRUMENT PANEL

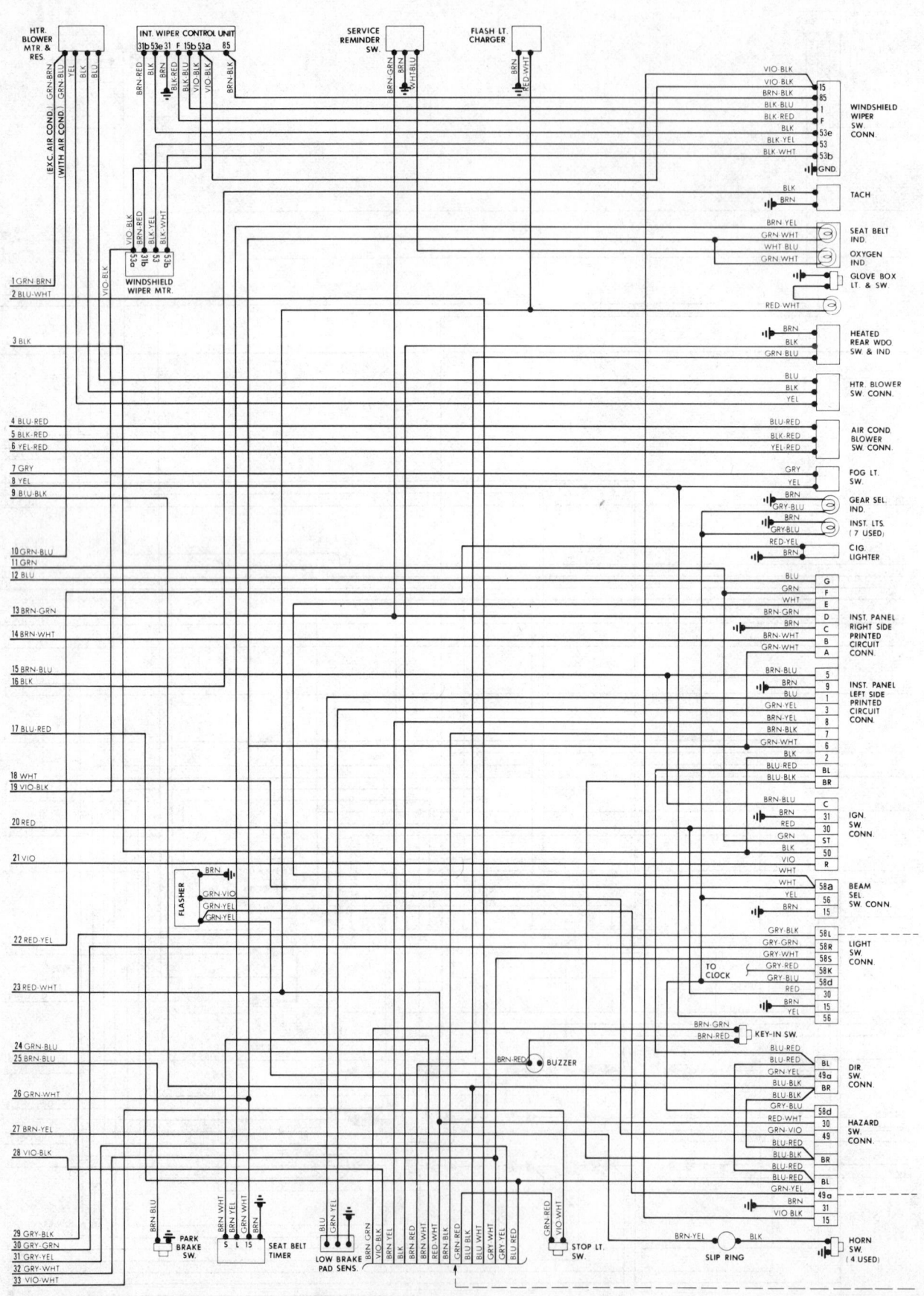

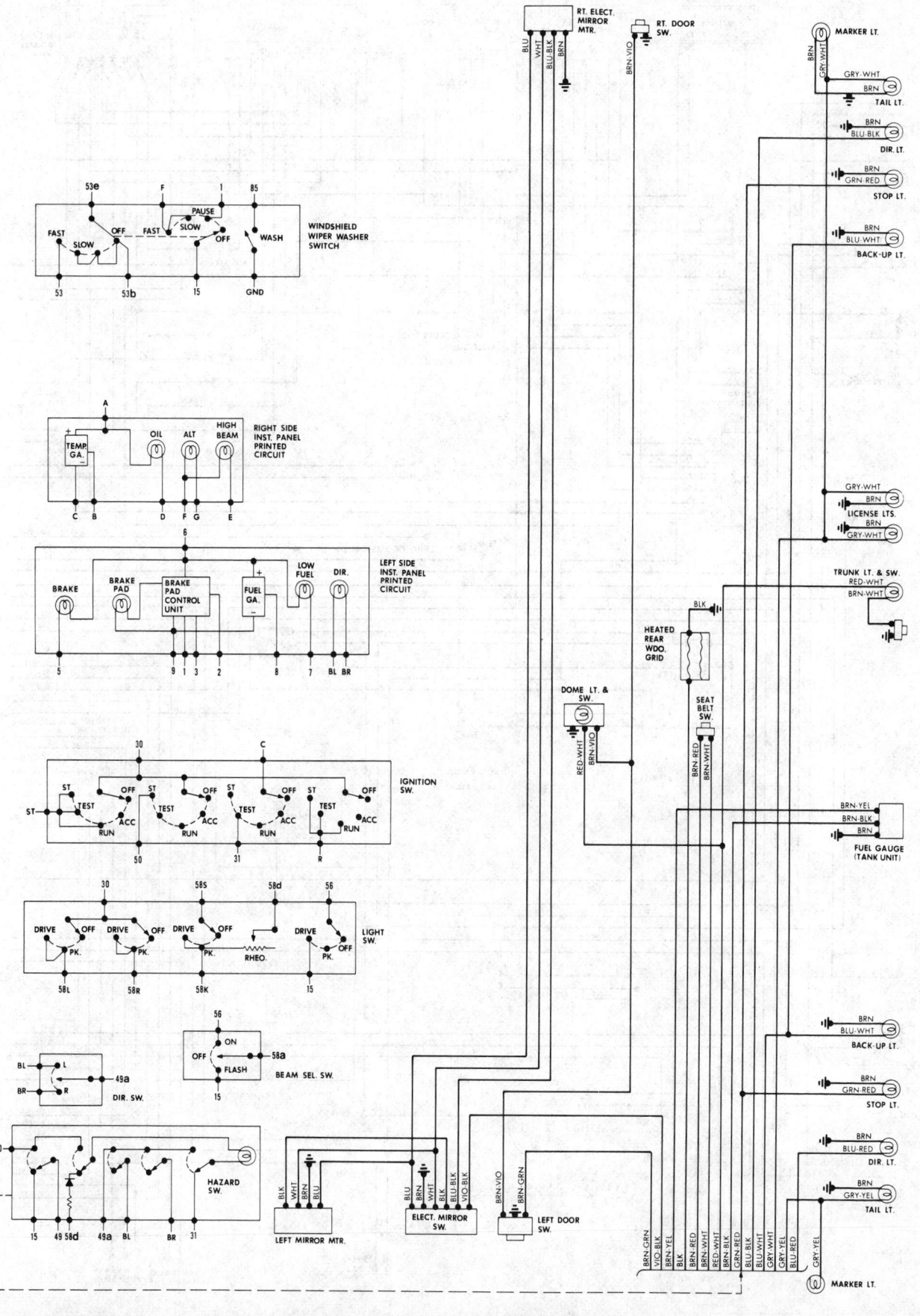

1981 BMW

ENGINE COMPARTMENT

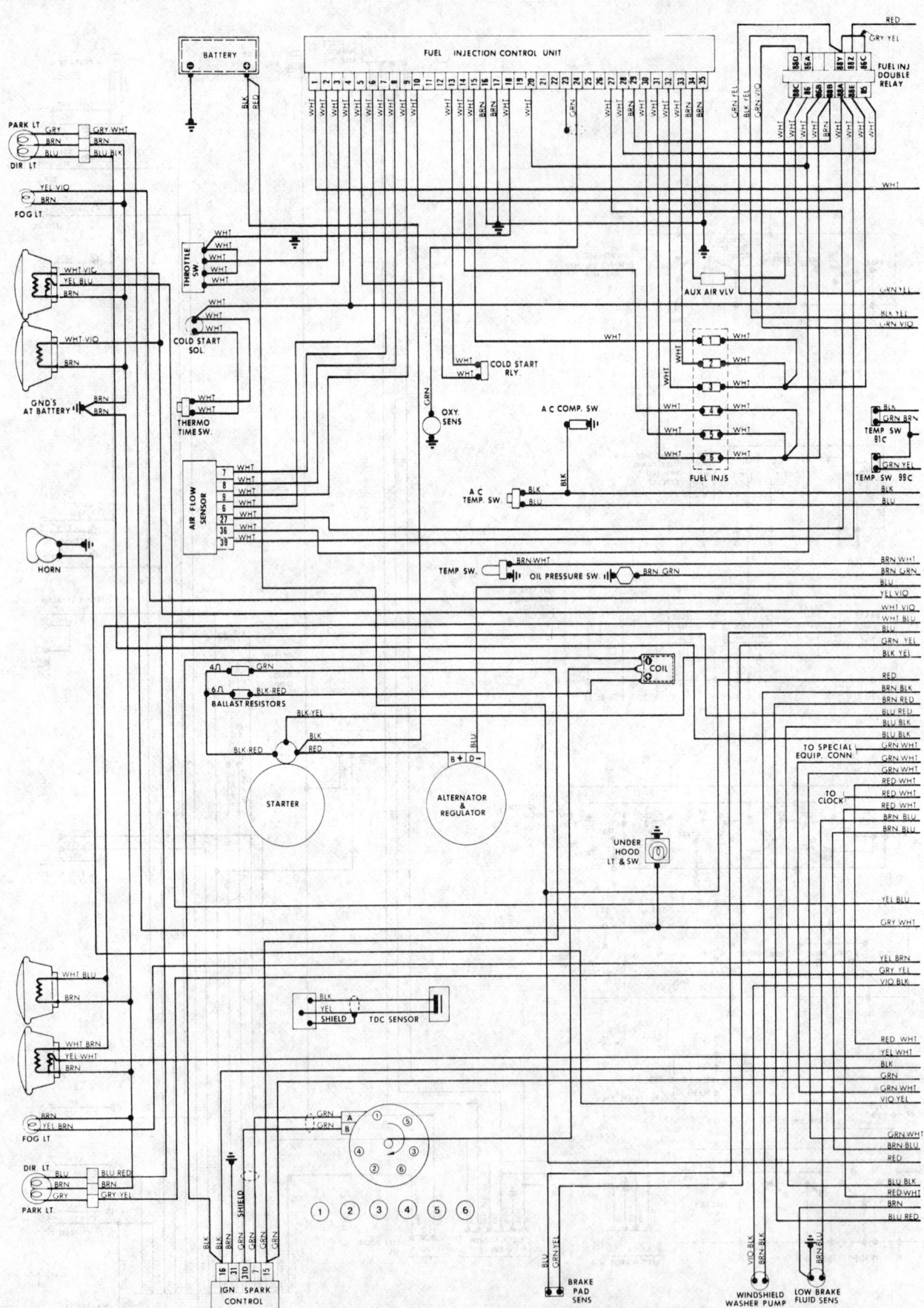

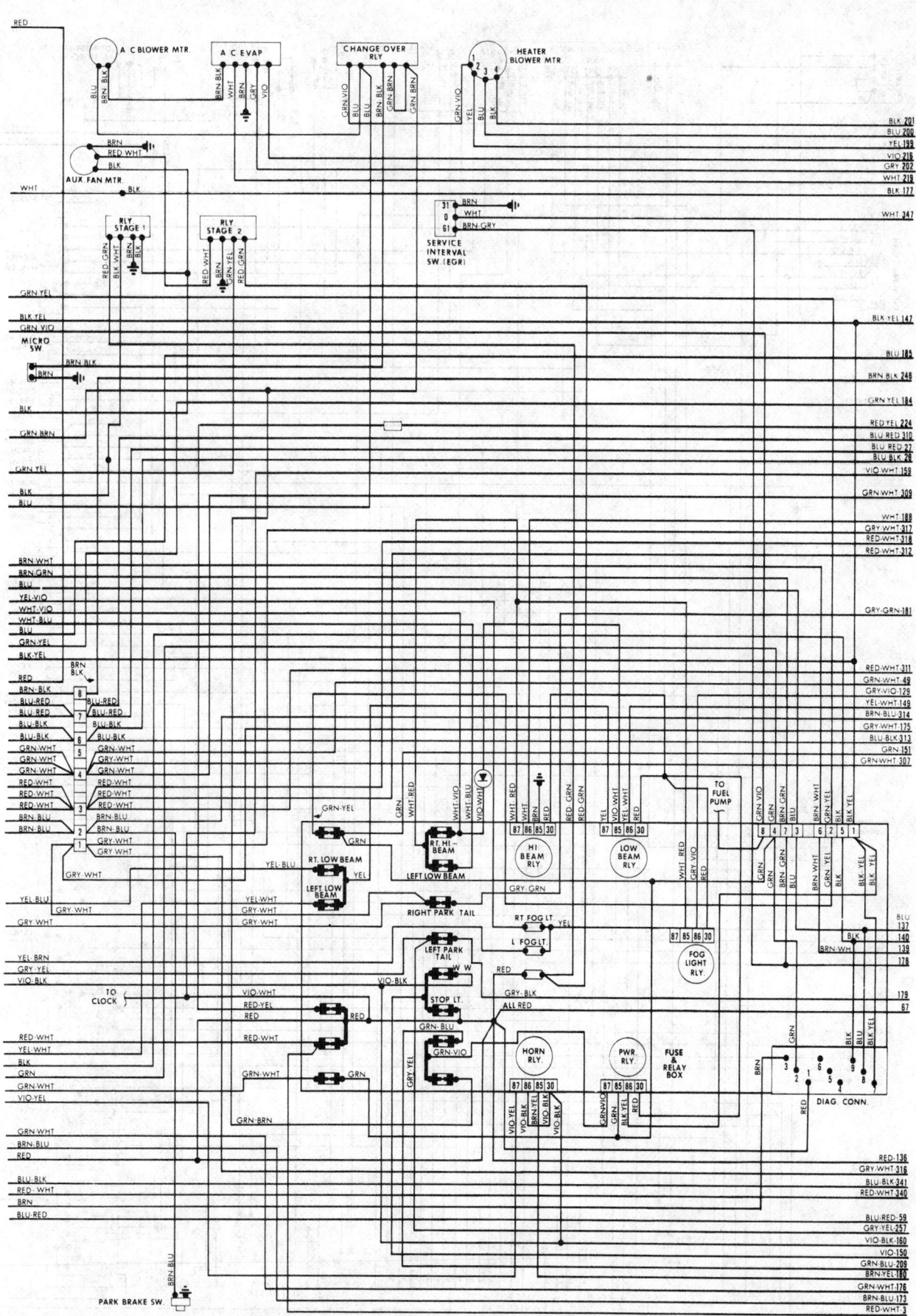

1981 BMW

UNDERDASH & INSTRUMENT PANEL

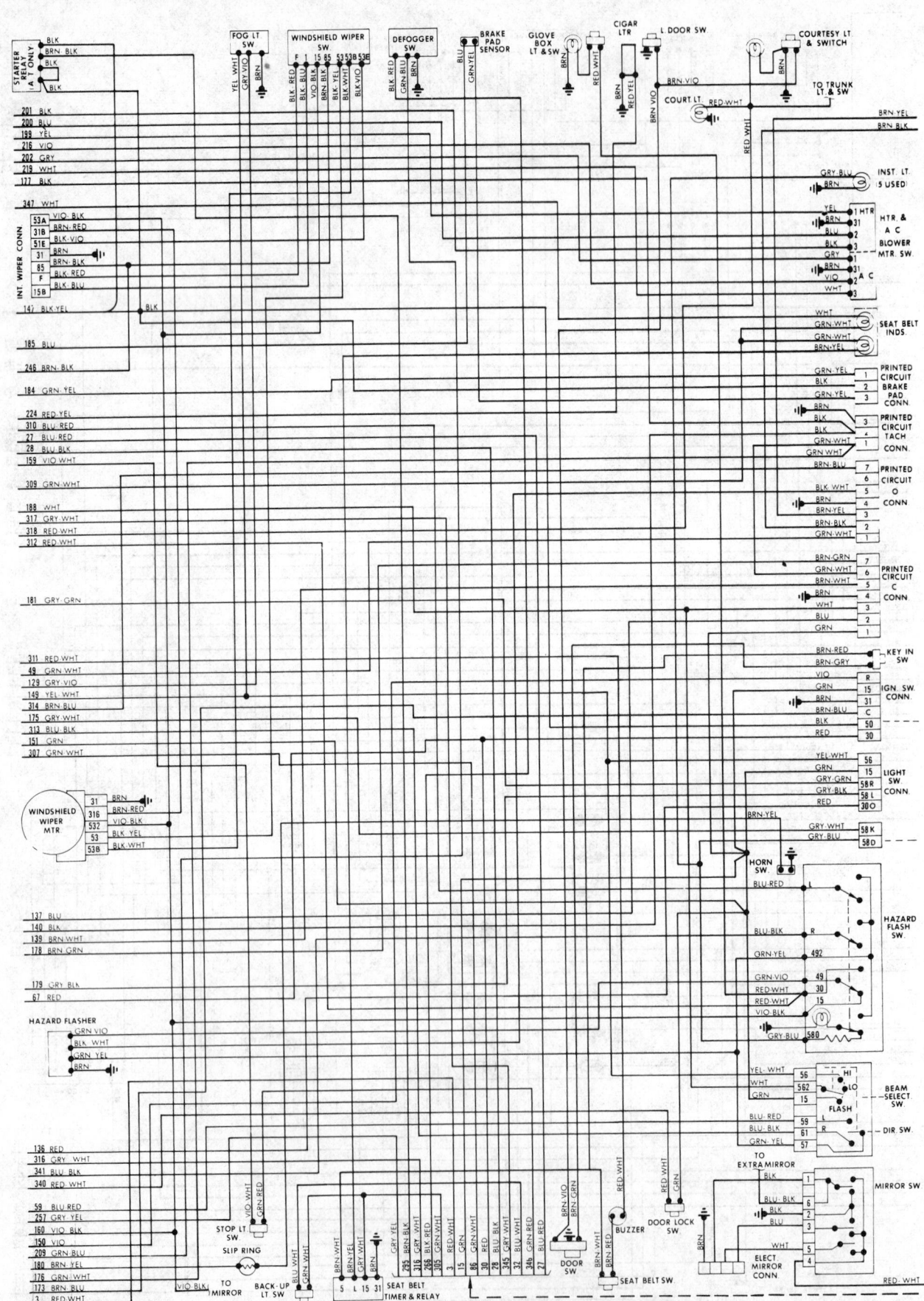

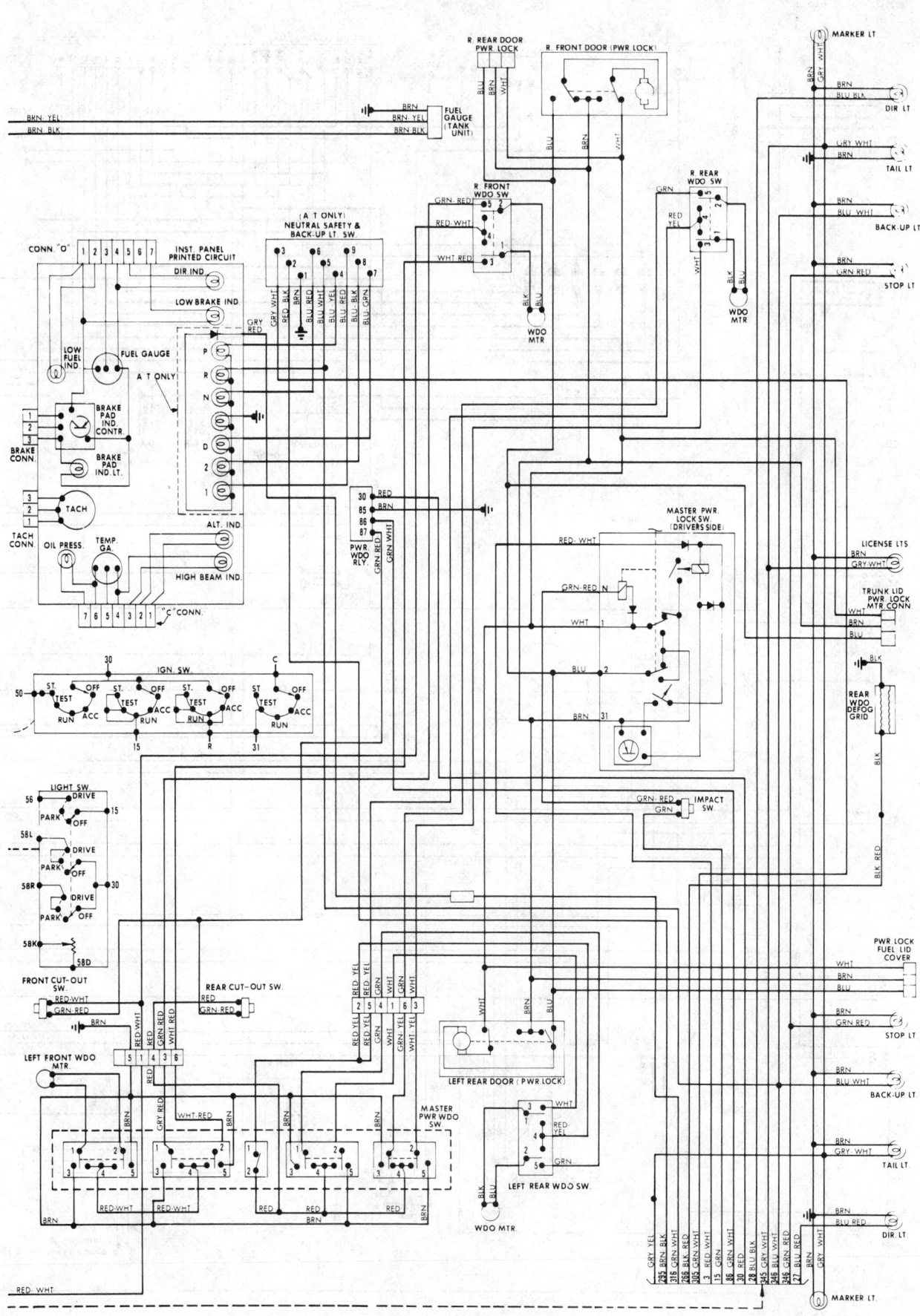

1981 BMW

ENGINE COMPARTMENT

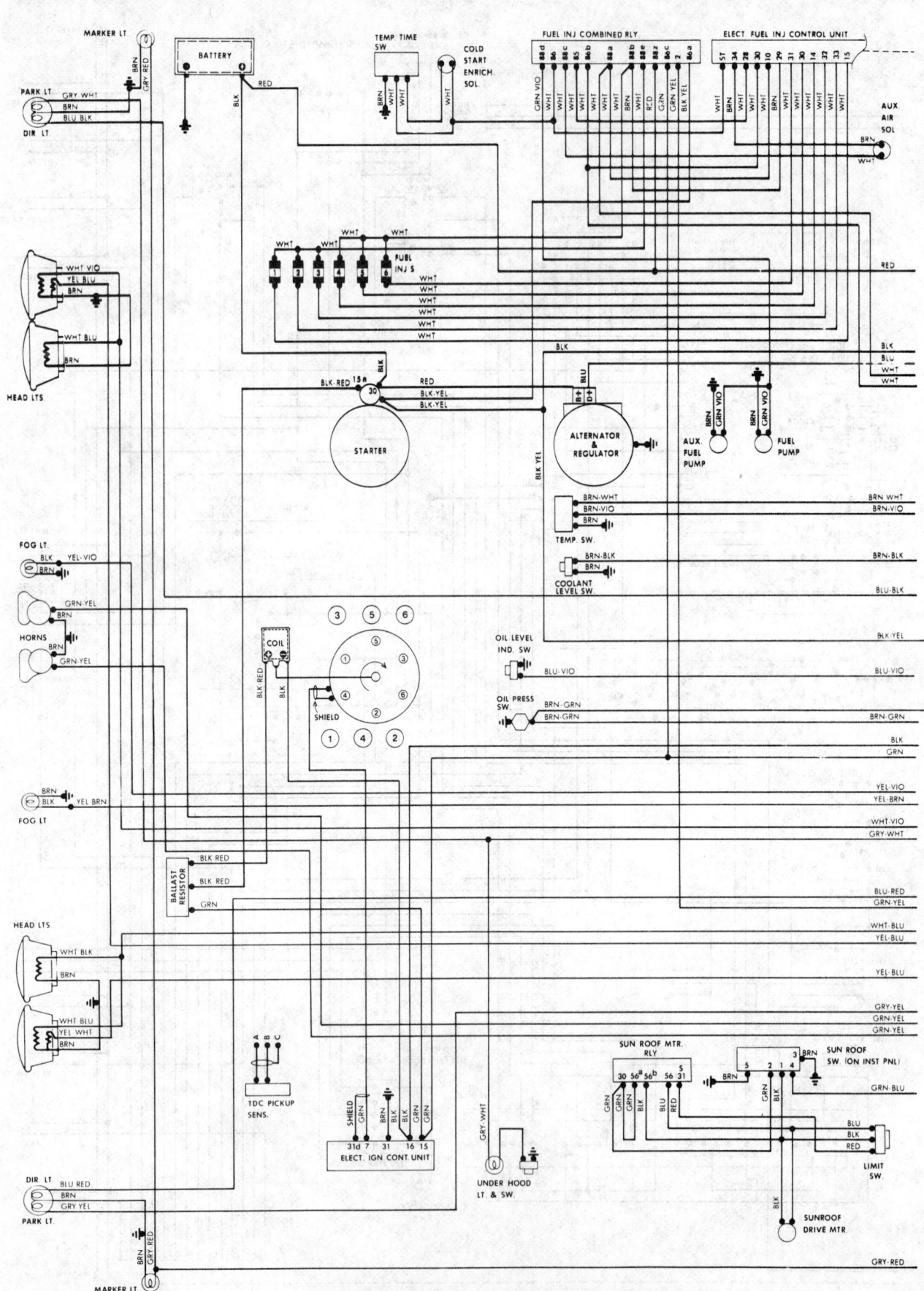

FUSE BLOCK

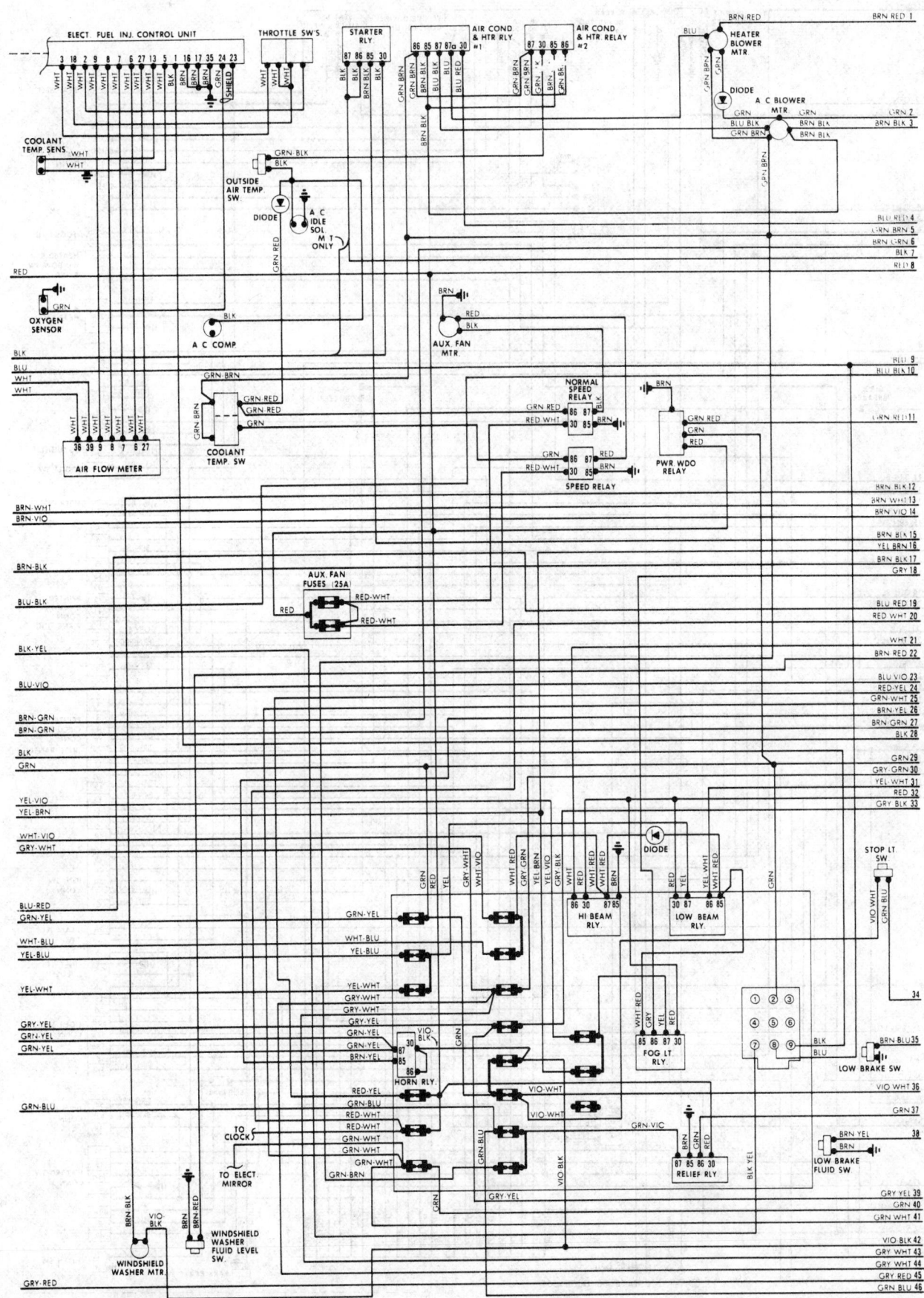

1981 BMW

INSTRUMENT PANEL

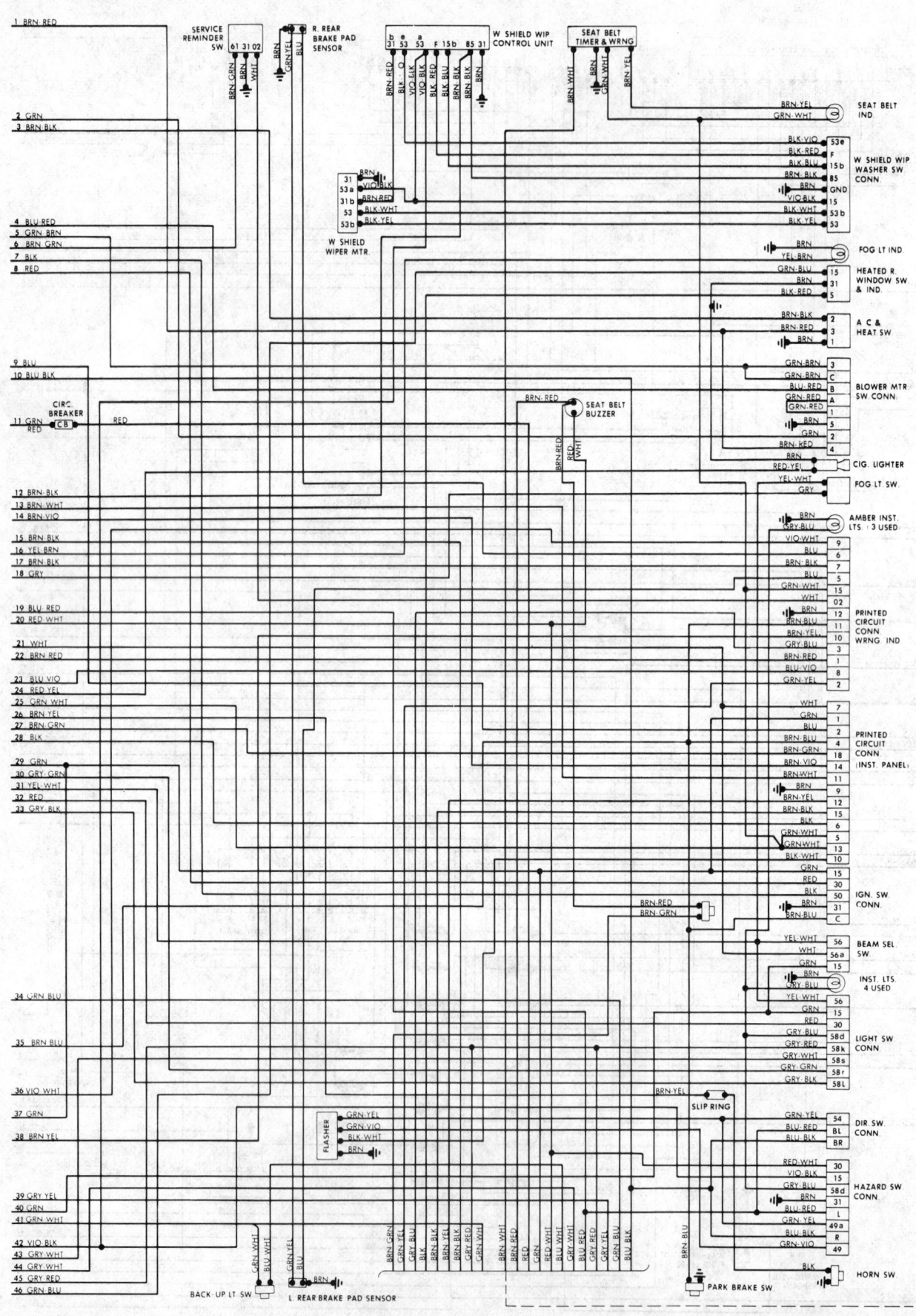

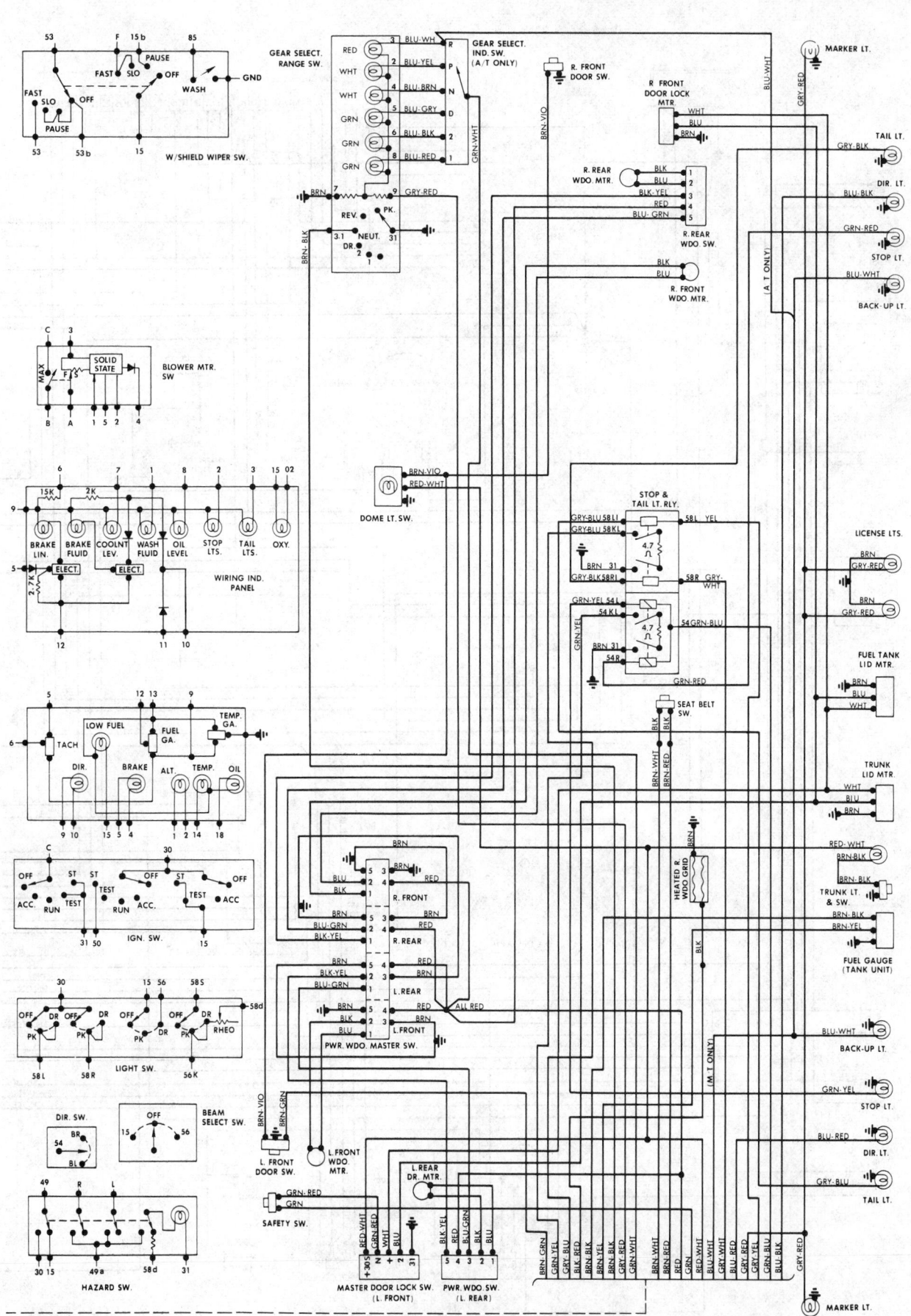

1981 BMW

ENGINE COMPARTMENT

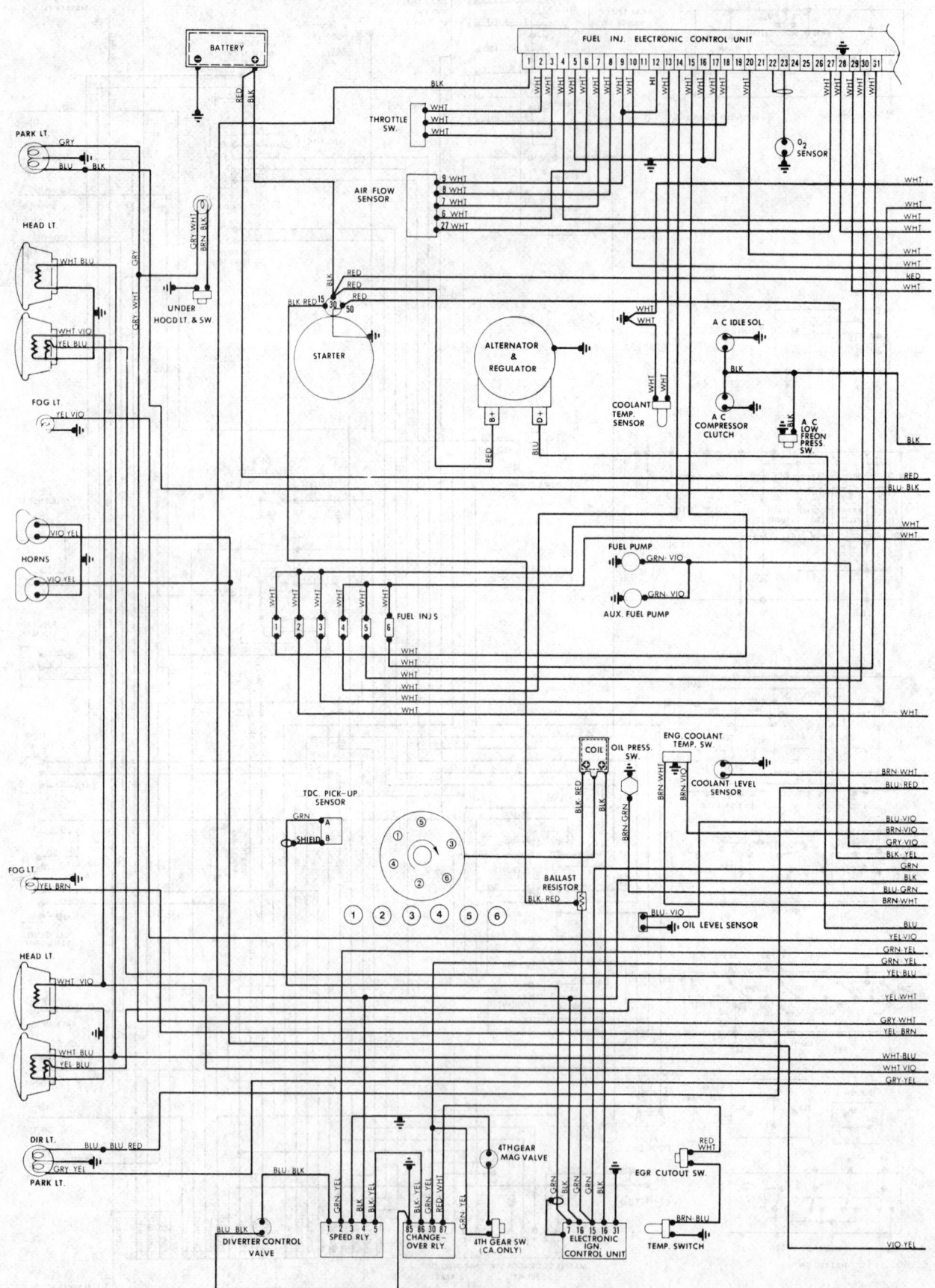

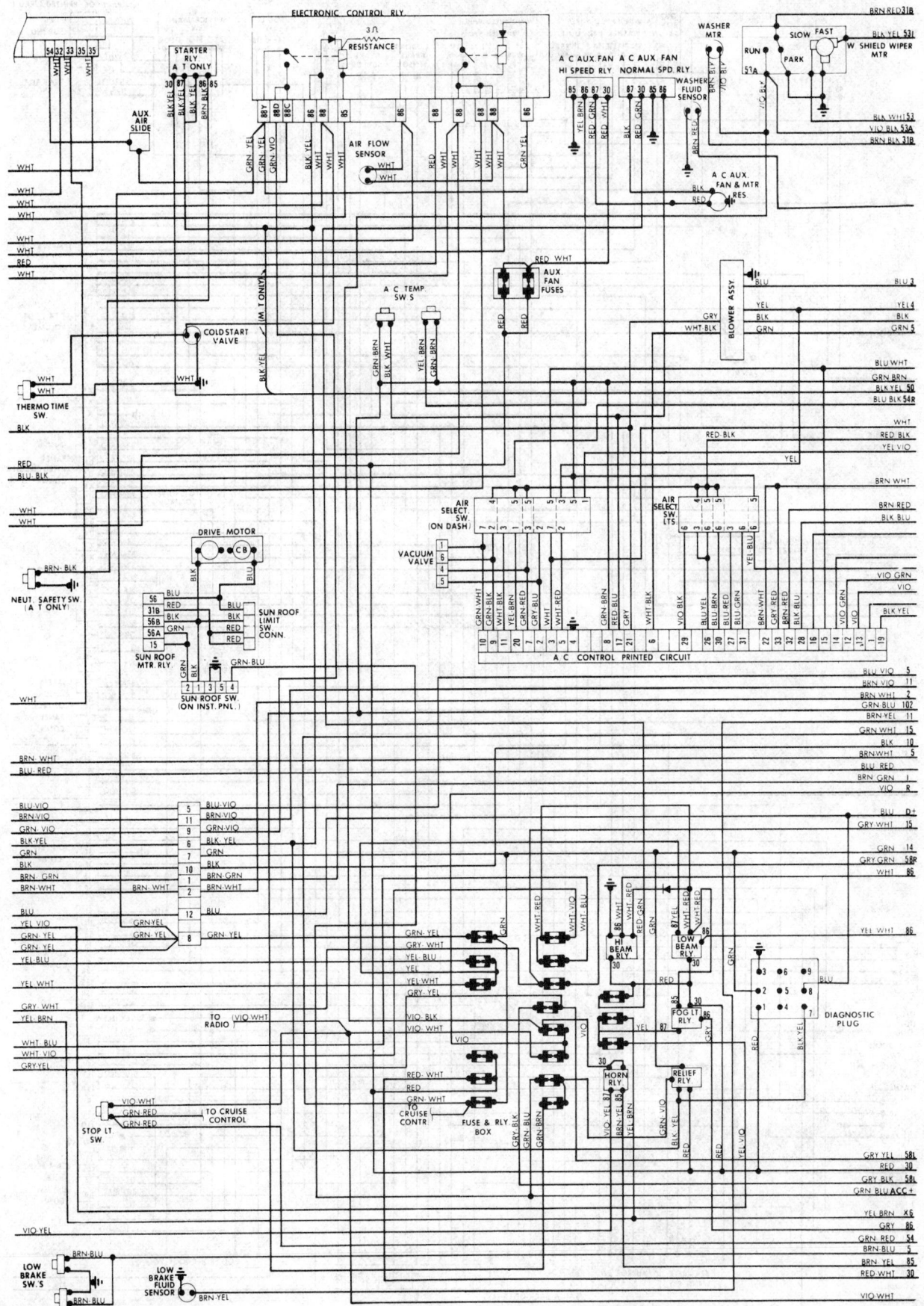

1981 BMW

INSTRUMENT PANEL

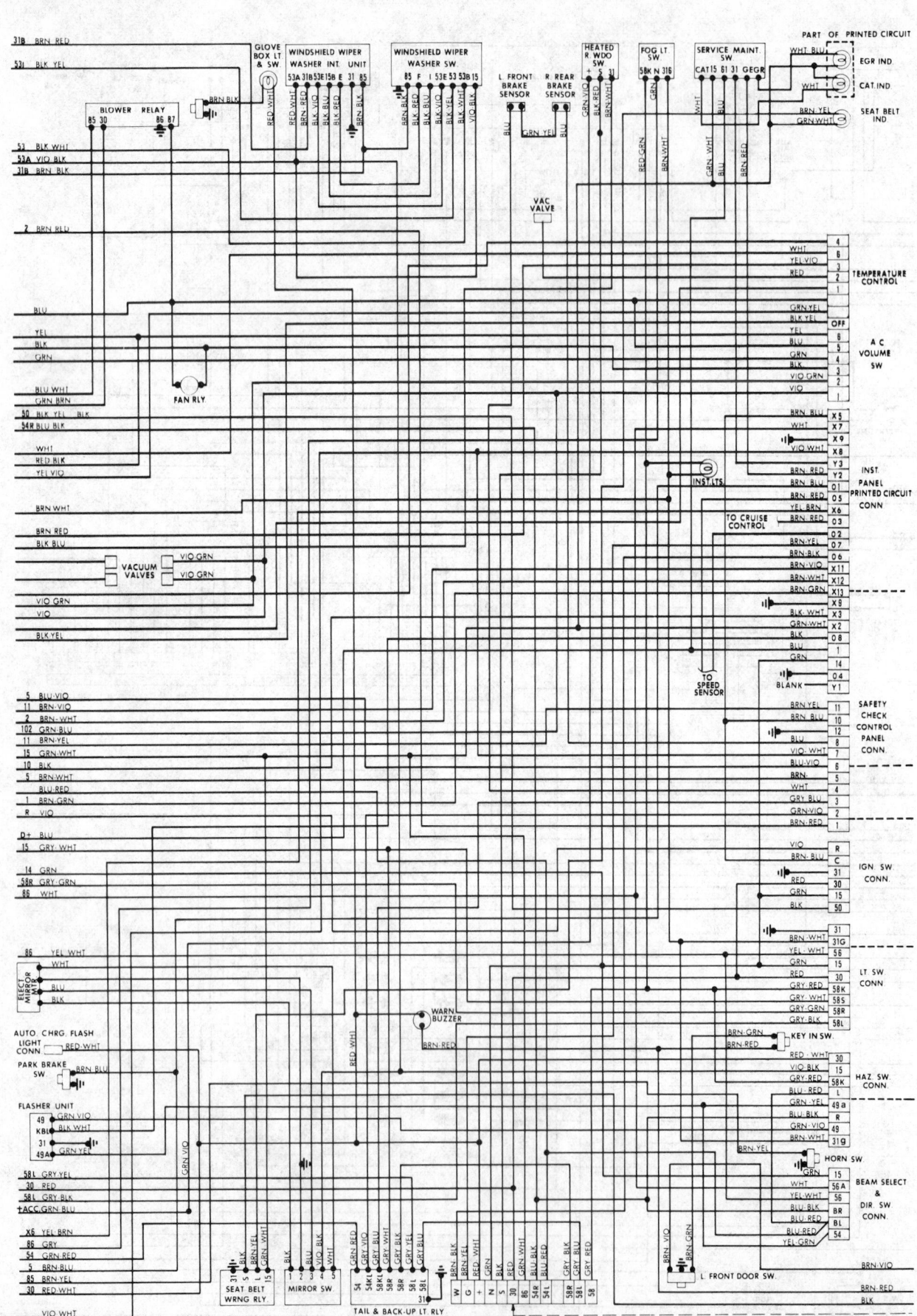

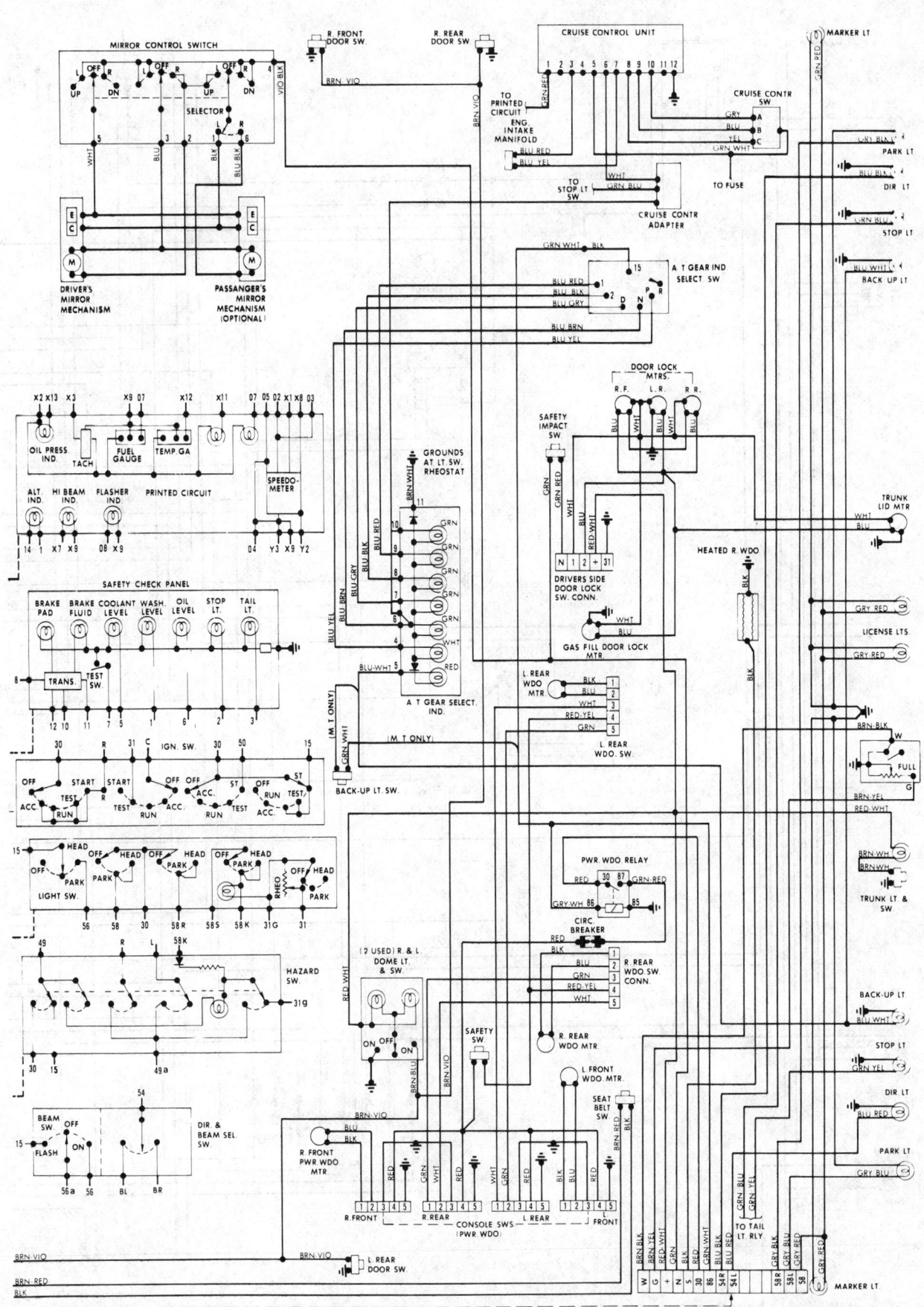

ENGINE COMPARTMENT & FUSE BLOCK

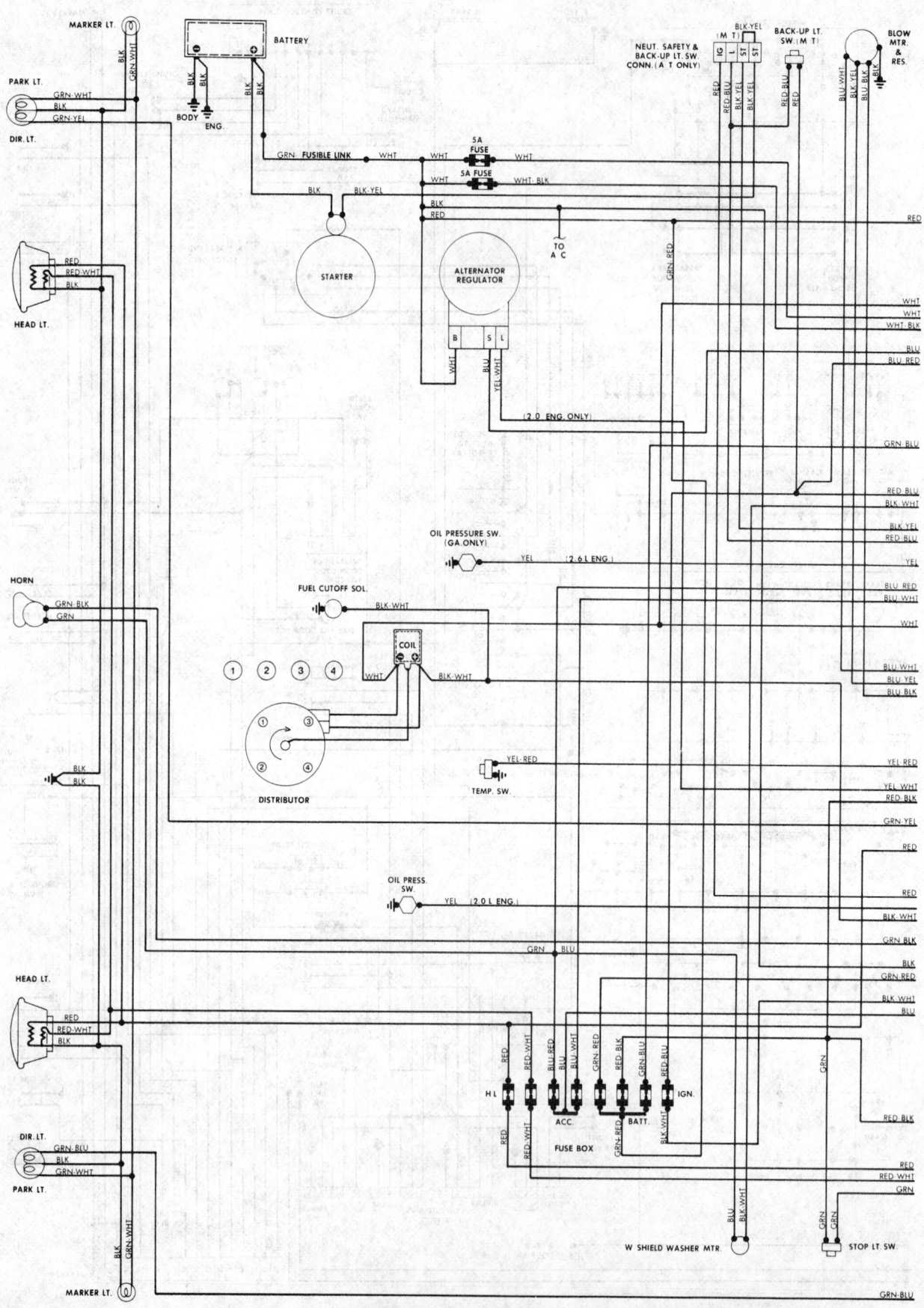

INSTRUMENT PANEL & REAR COMPARTMENT

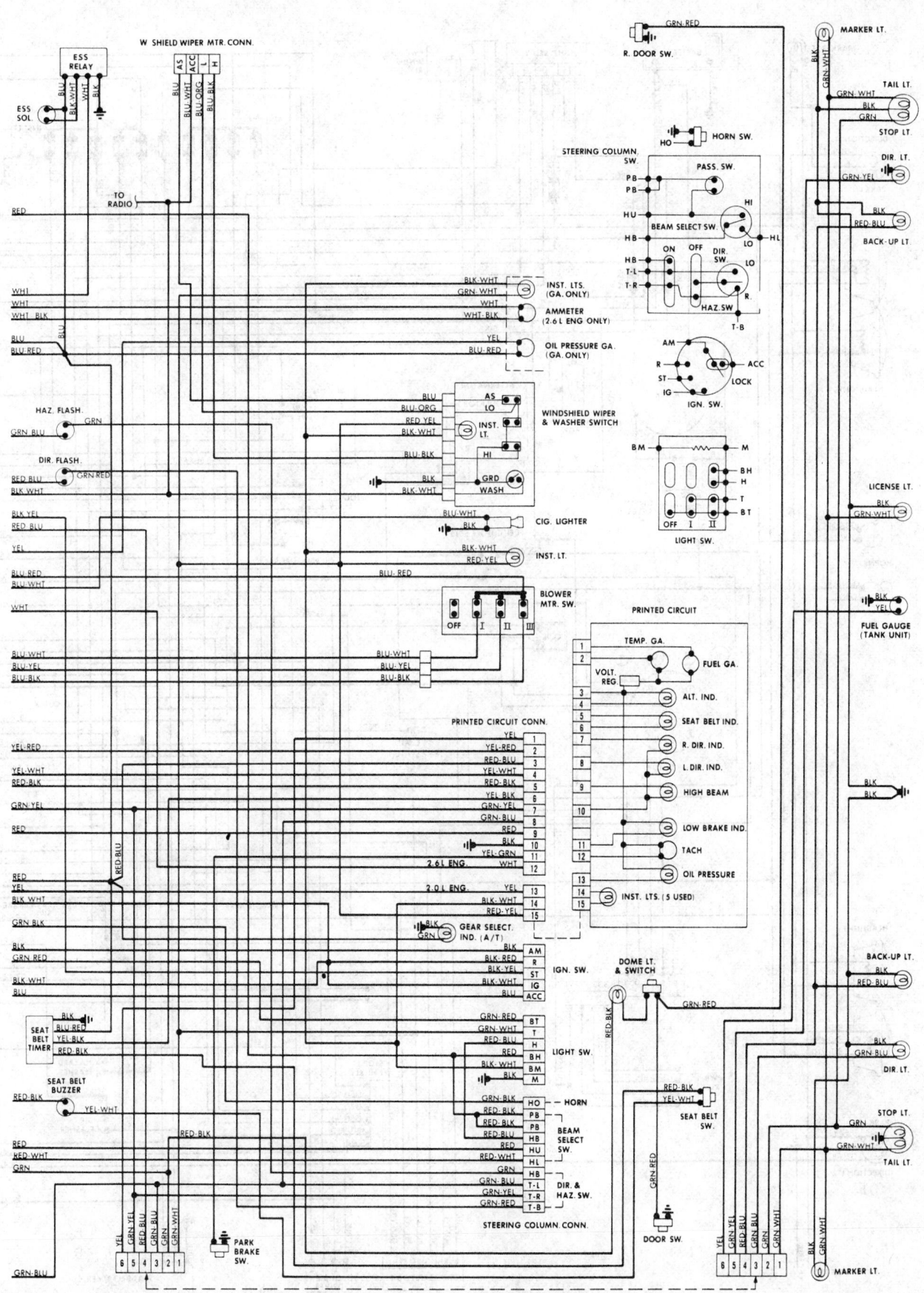

ENGINE COMPARTMENT & FUSE BLOCK

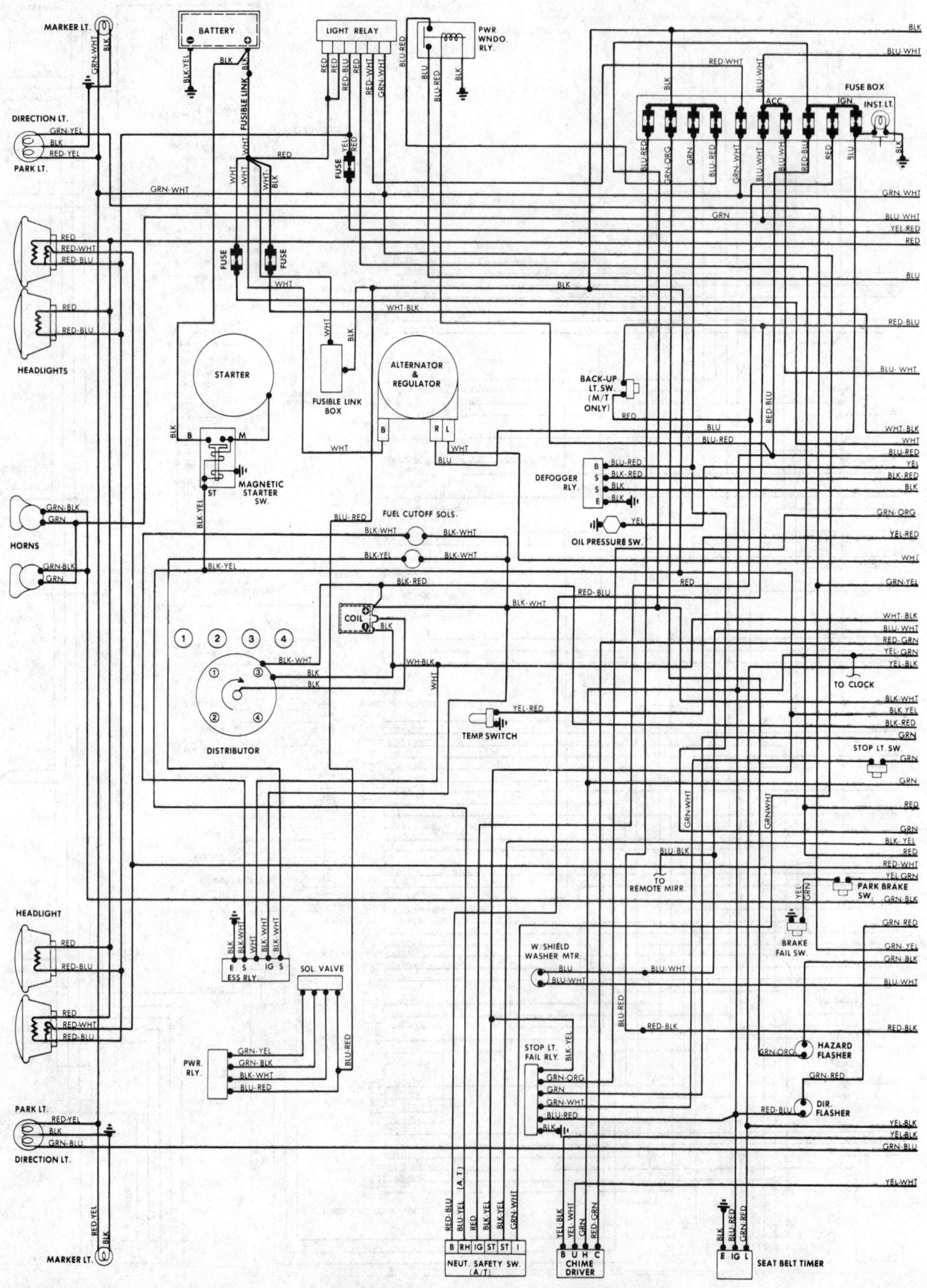

INSTRUMENT PANEL & REAR COMPARTMENT

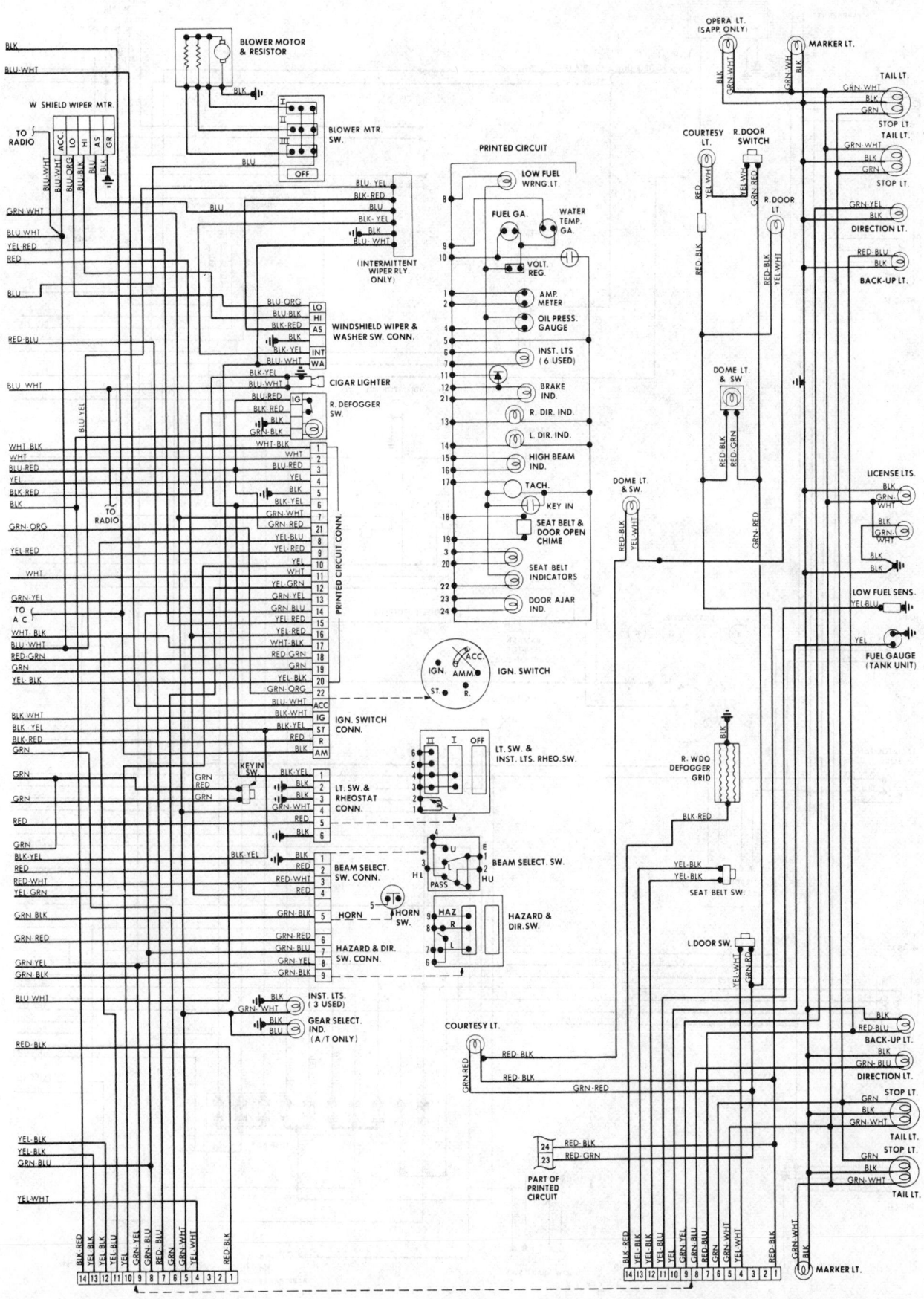

ENGINE COMPARTMENT & FUSE BLOCK

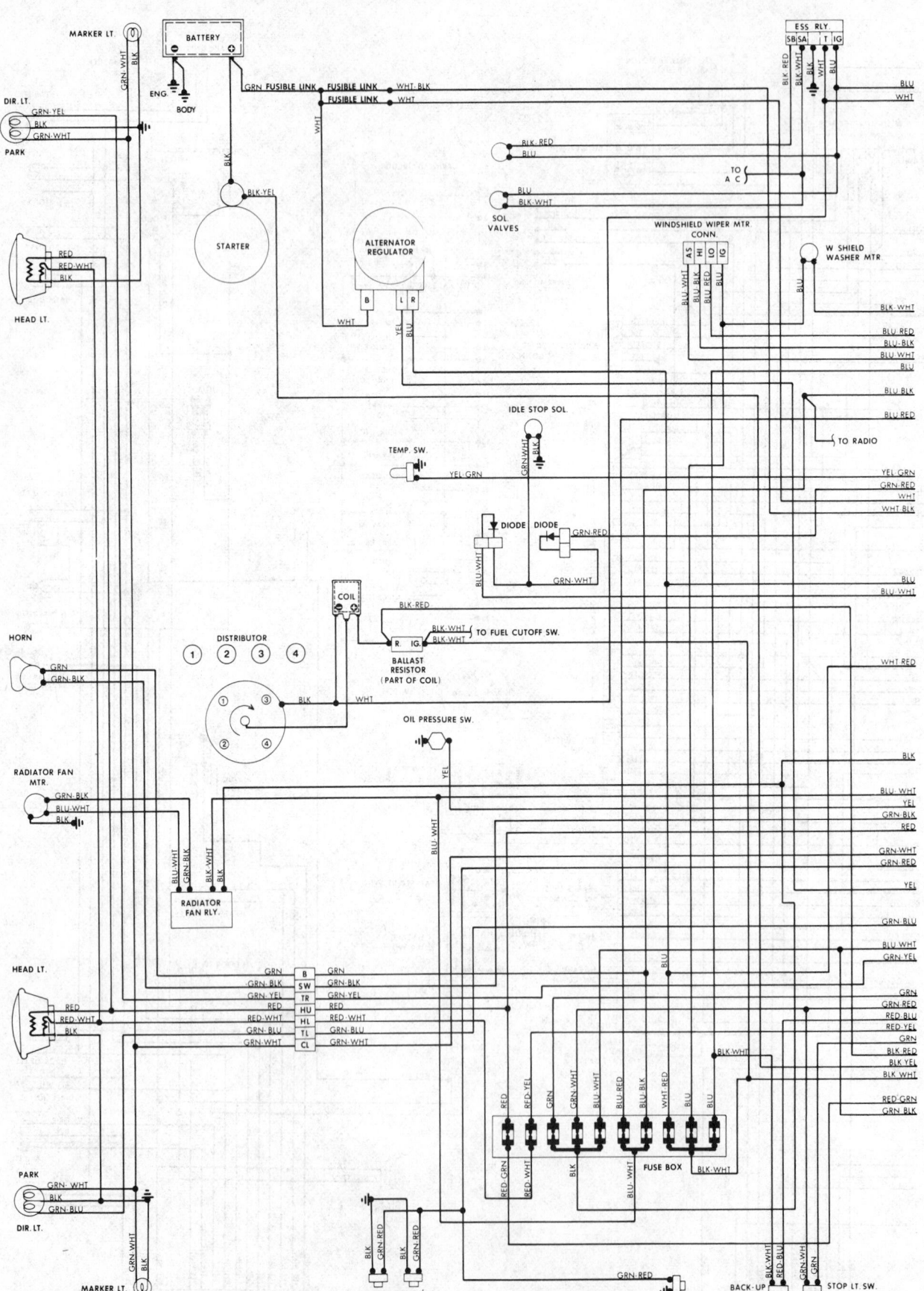

INSTRUMENT PANEL & REAR COMPARTMENT

WIRING DIAGRAMS

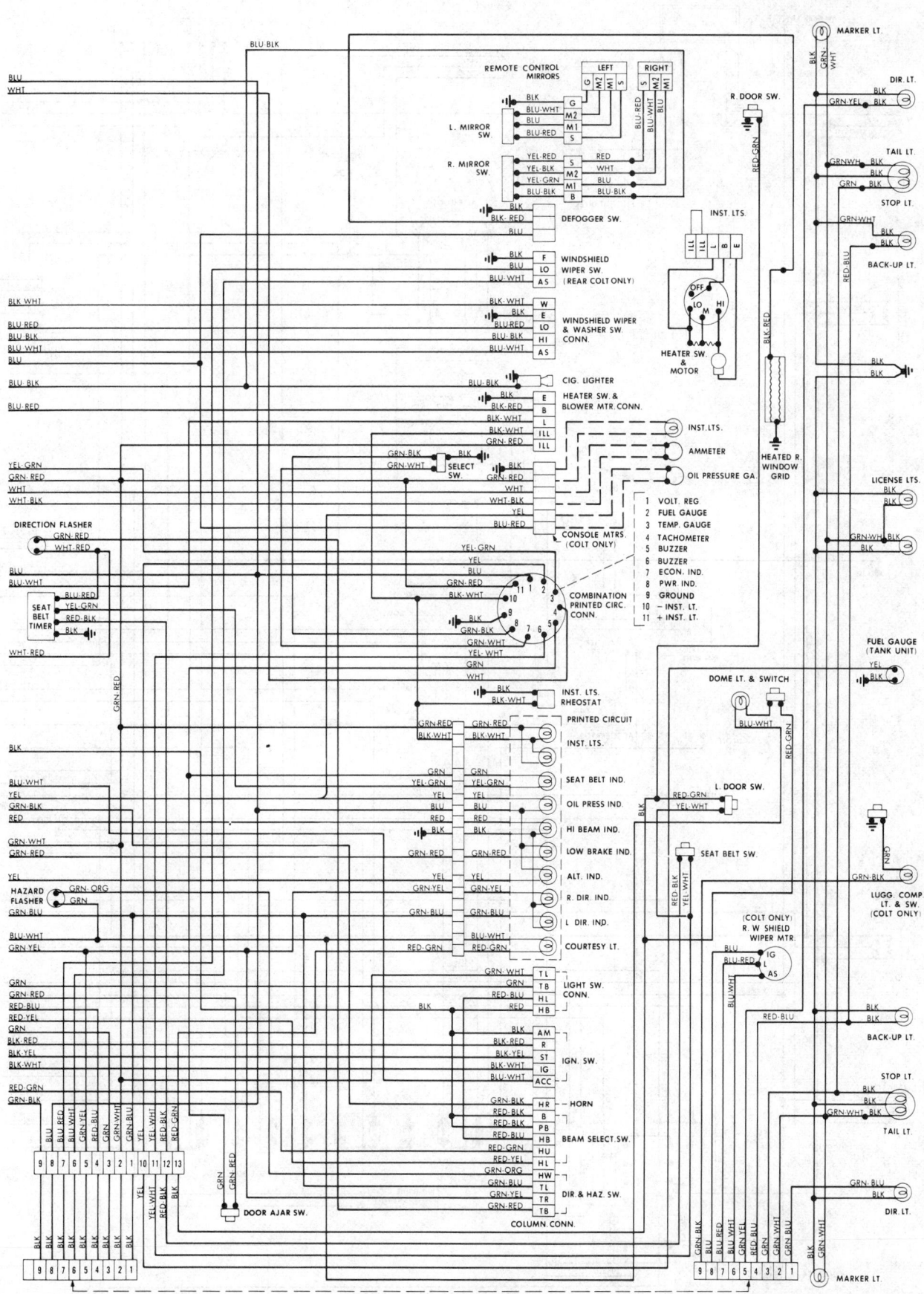

1981 Courier

ENGINE COMPARTMENT & FUSE BLOCK

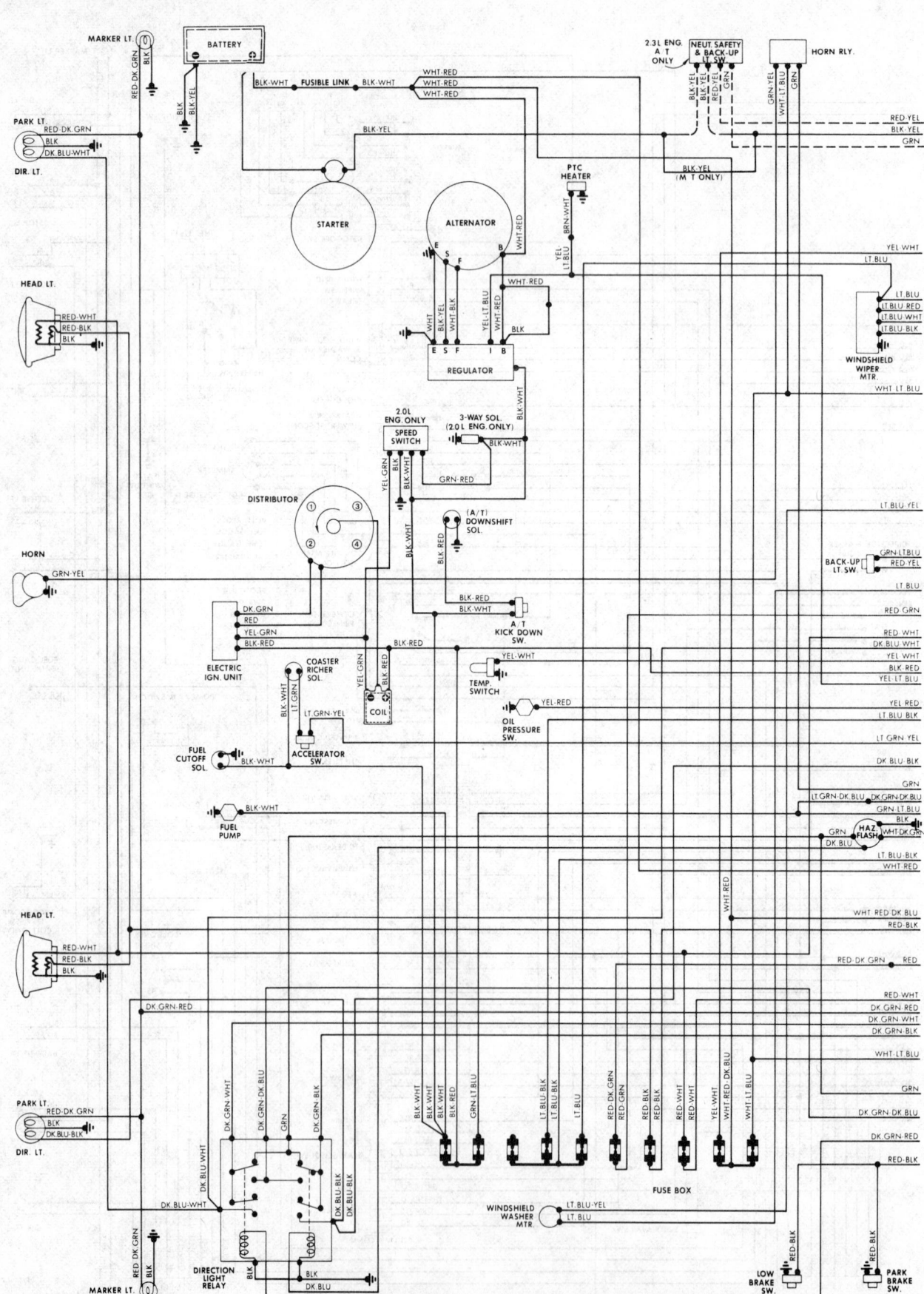

WIRING DIAGRAMS

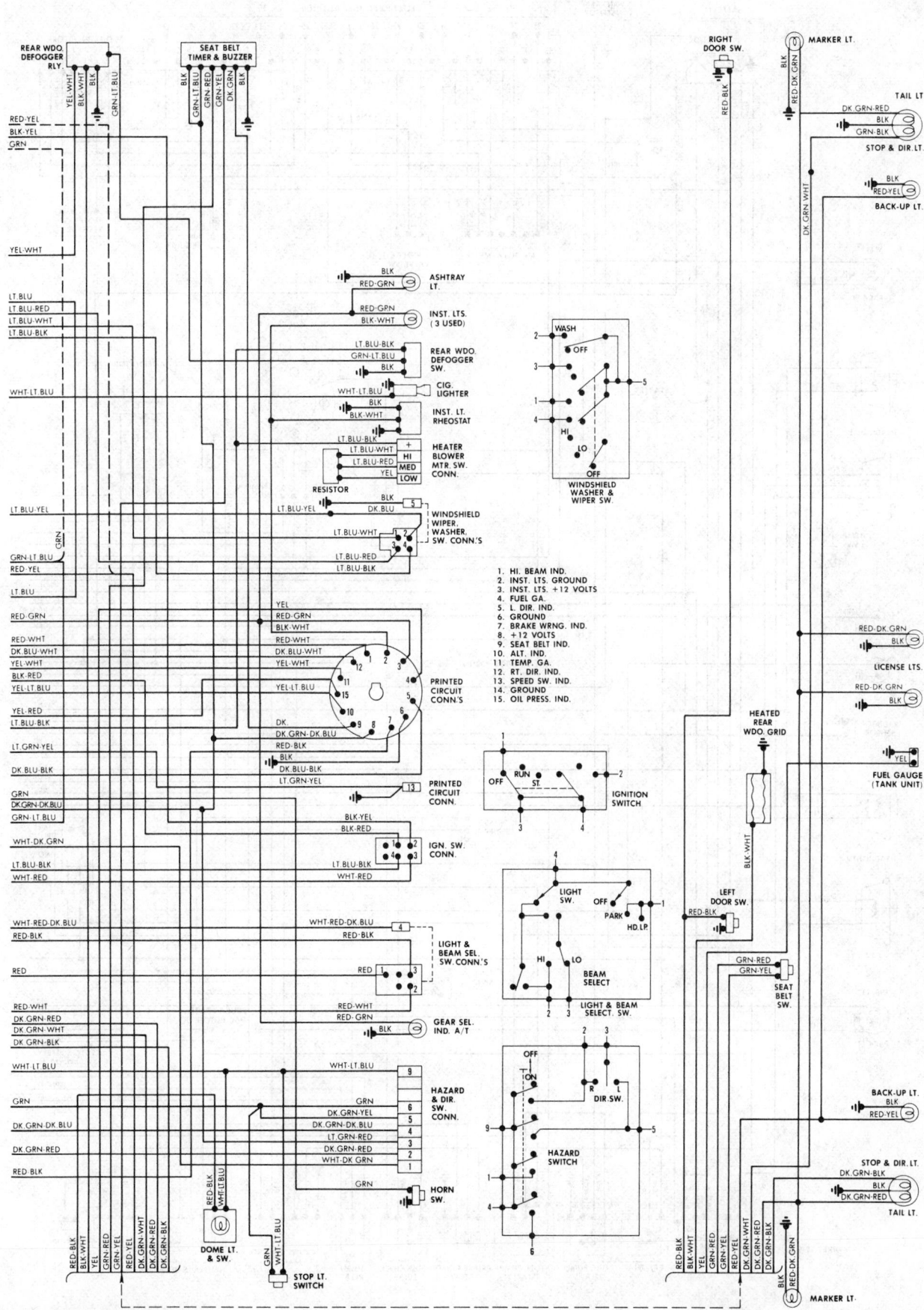

1981 Datsun

ENGINE COMPARTMENT

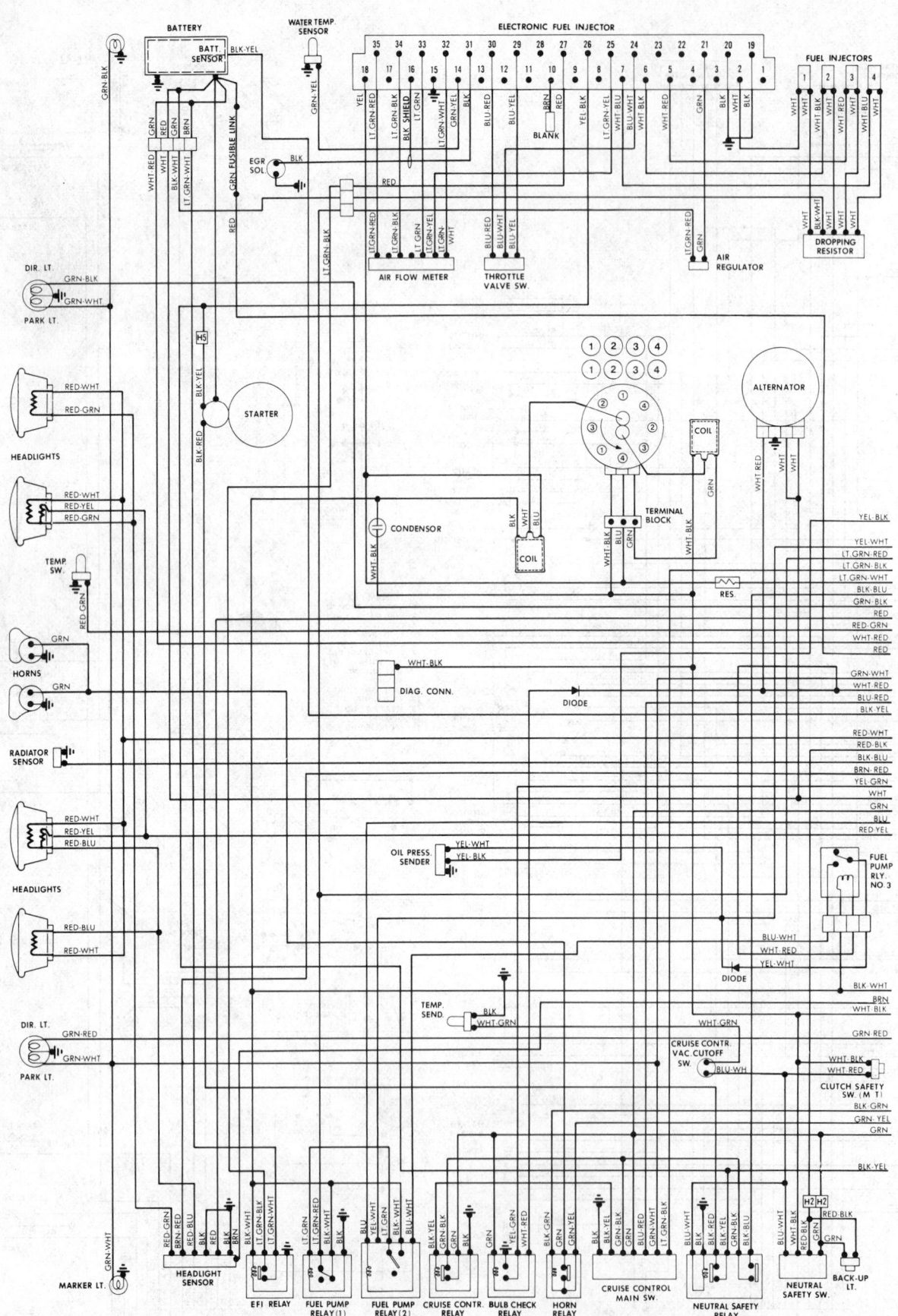

WIRING DIAGRAMS

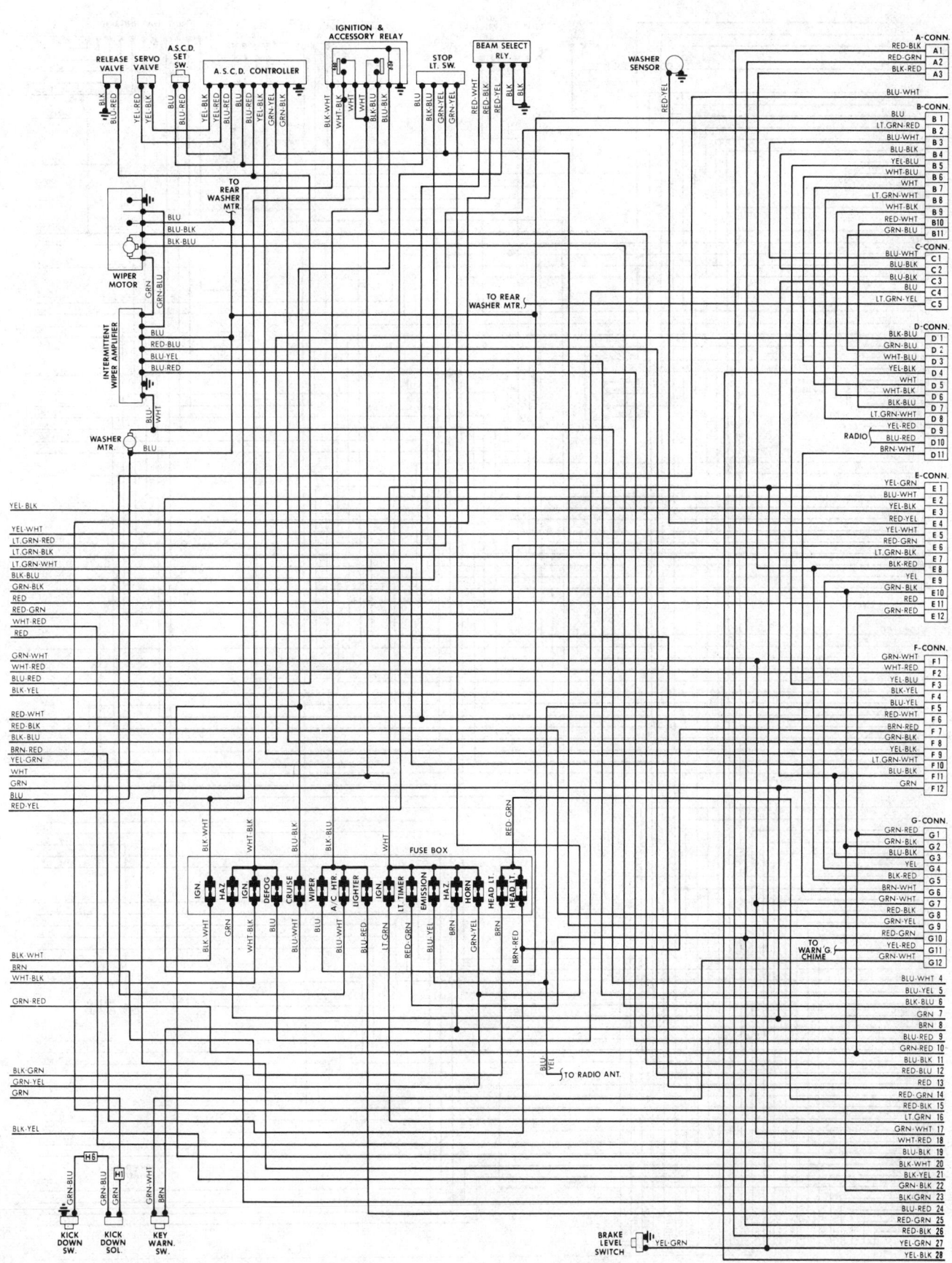

1981 Datsun

UNDERDASH

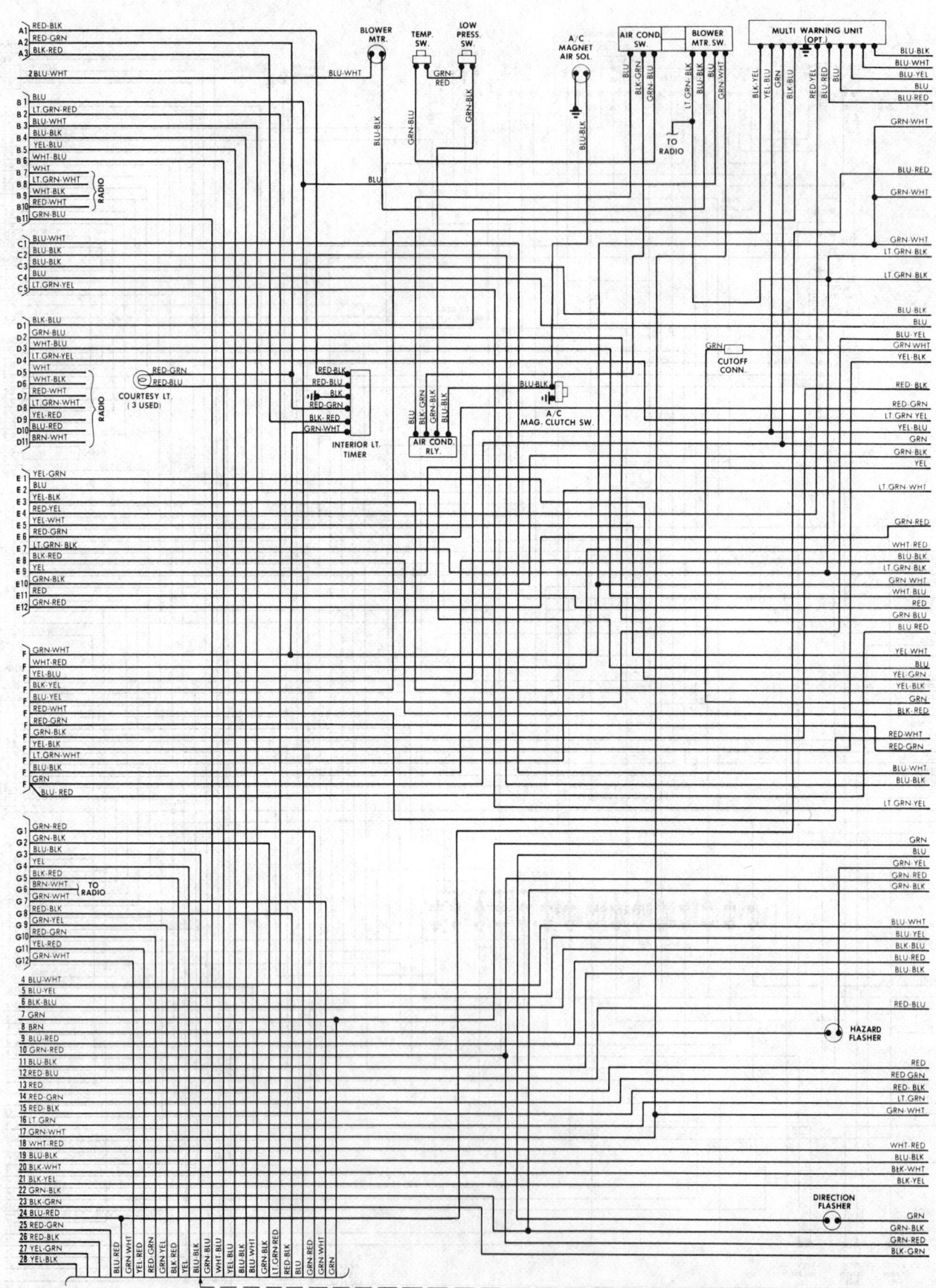

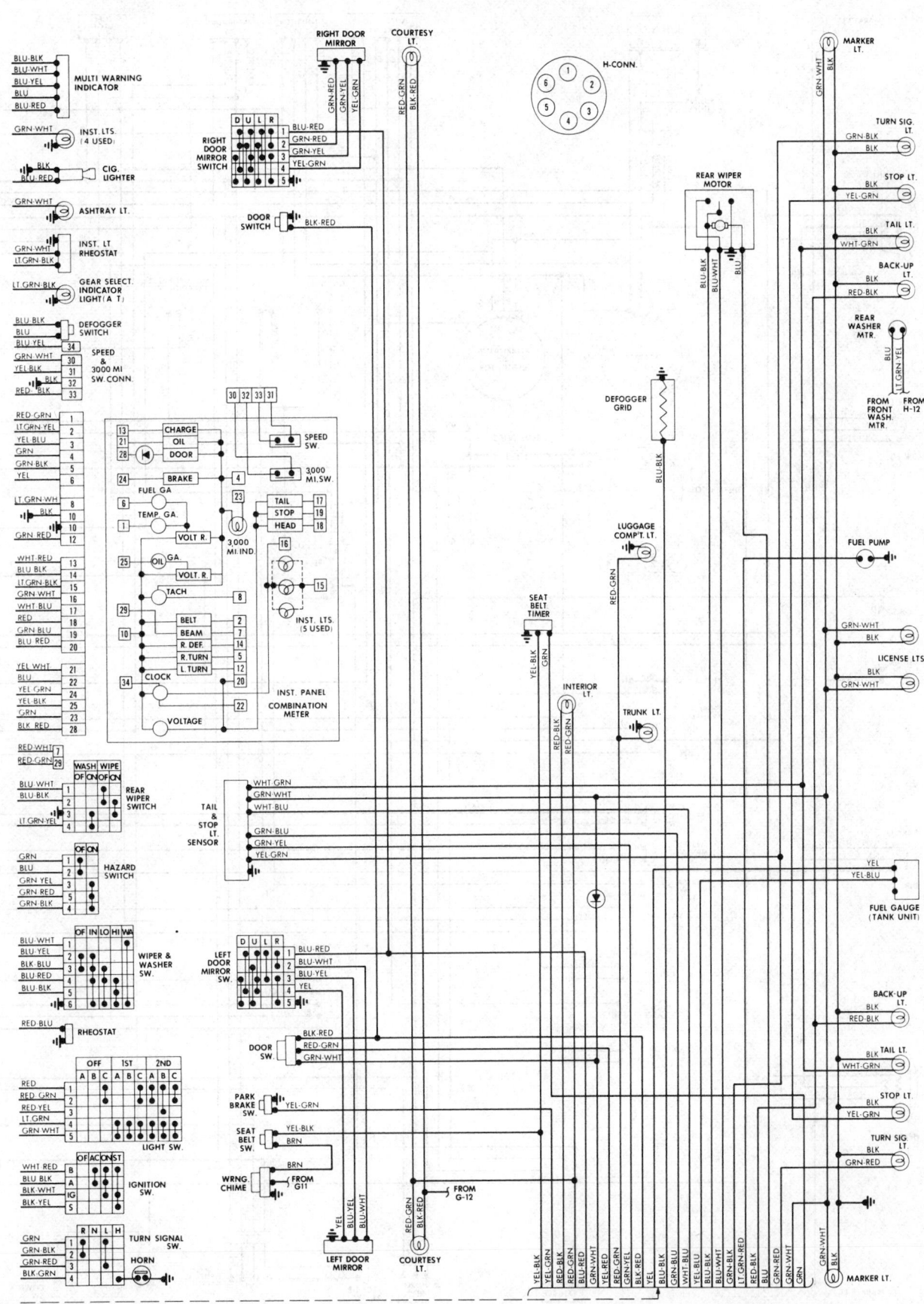

1981 Datsun

ENGINE COMPARTMENT

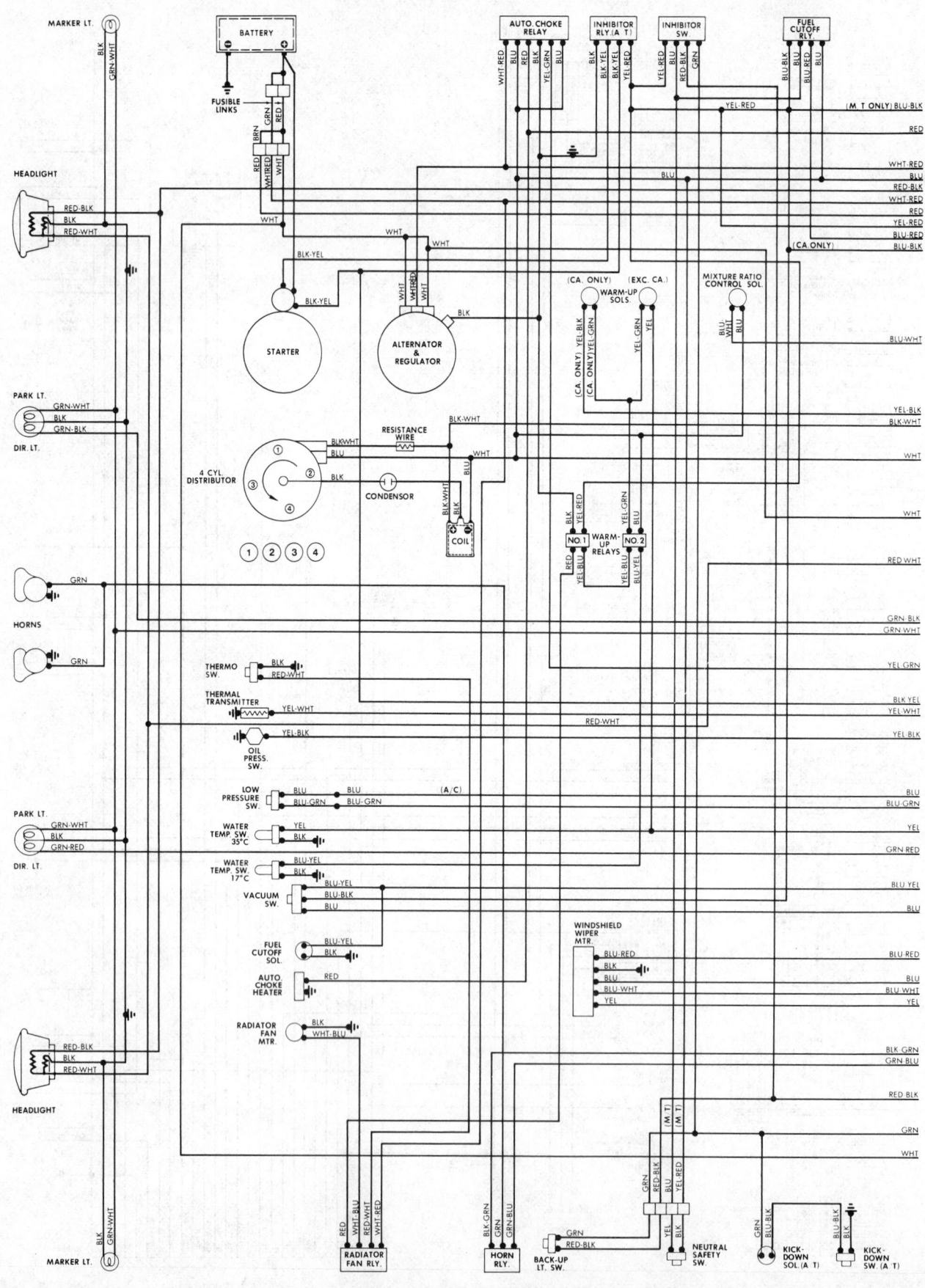

ENGINE COMPARTMENT & FUSE BLOCK

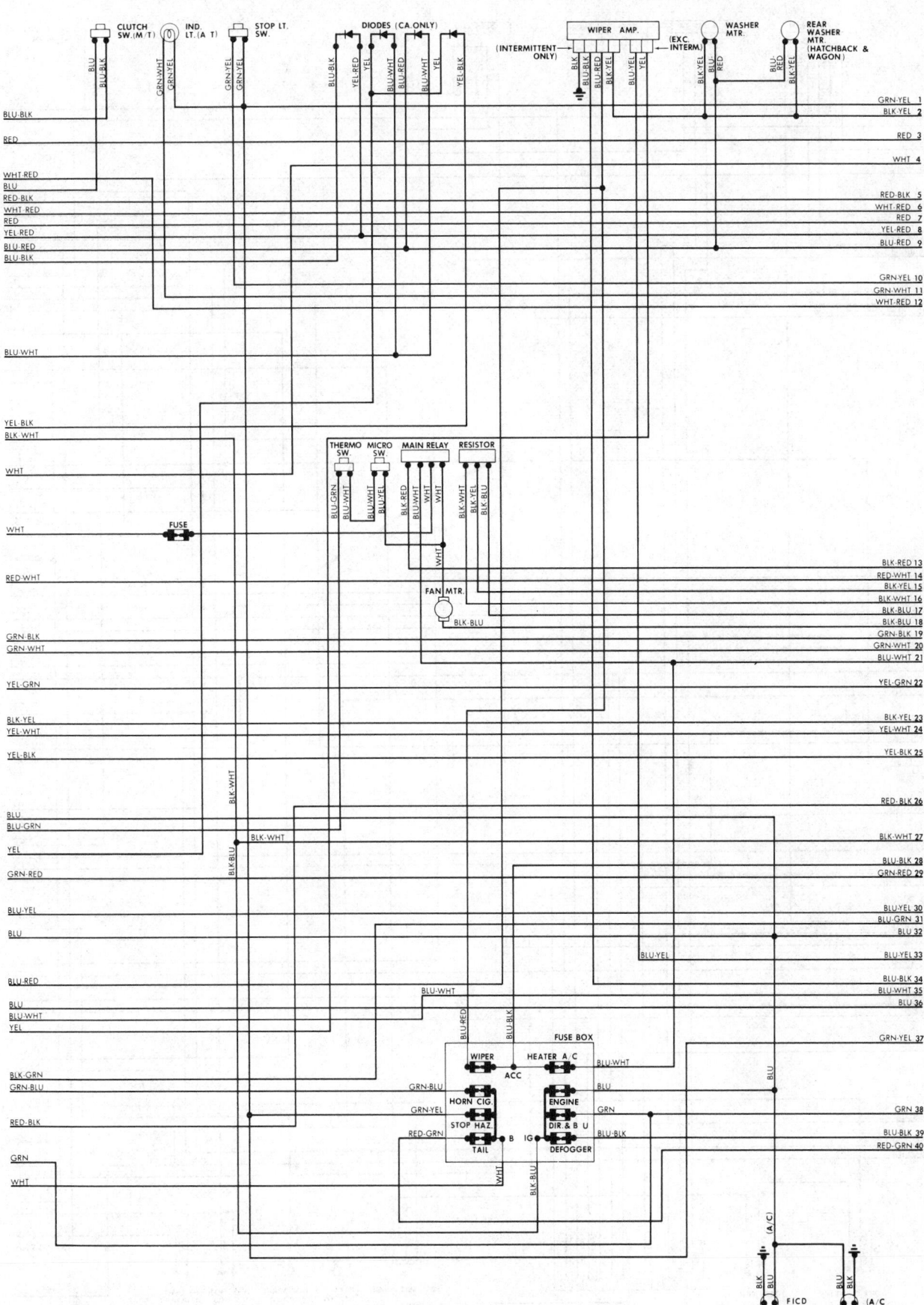

1981 Datsun

UNDERDASH

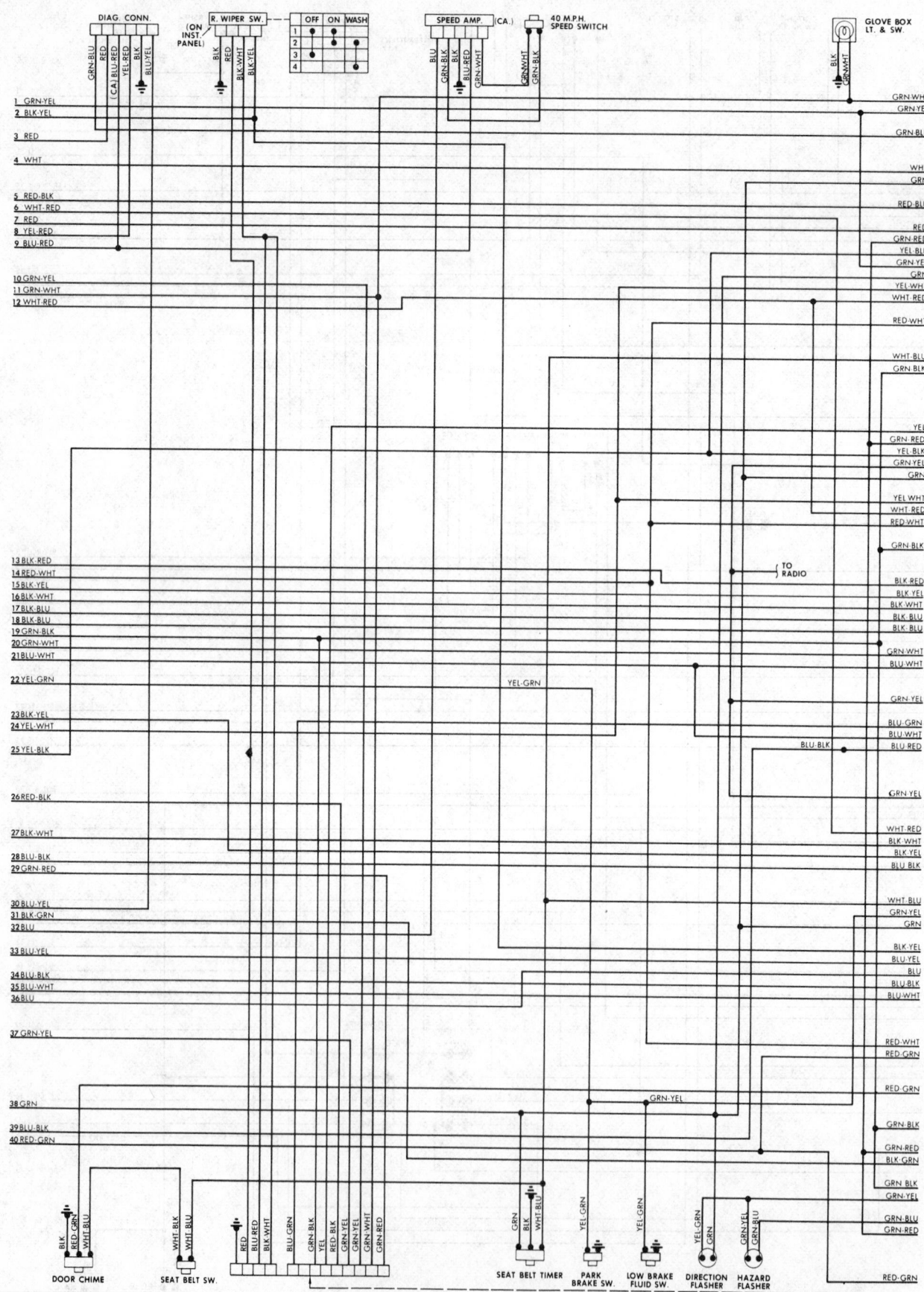

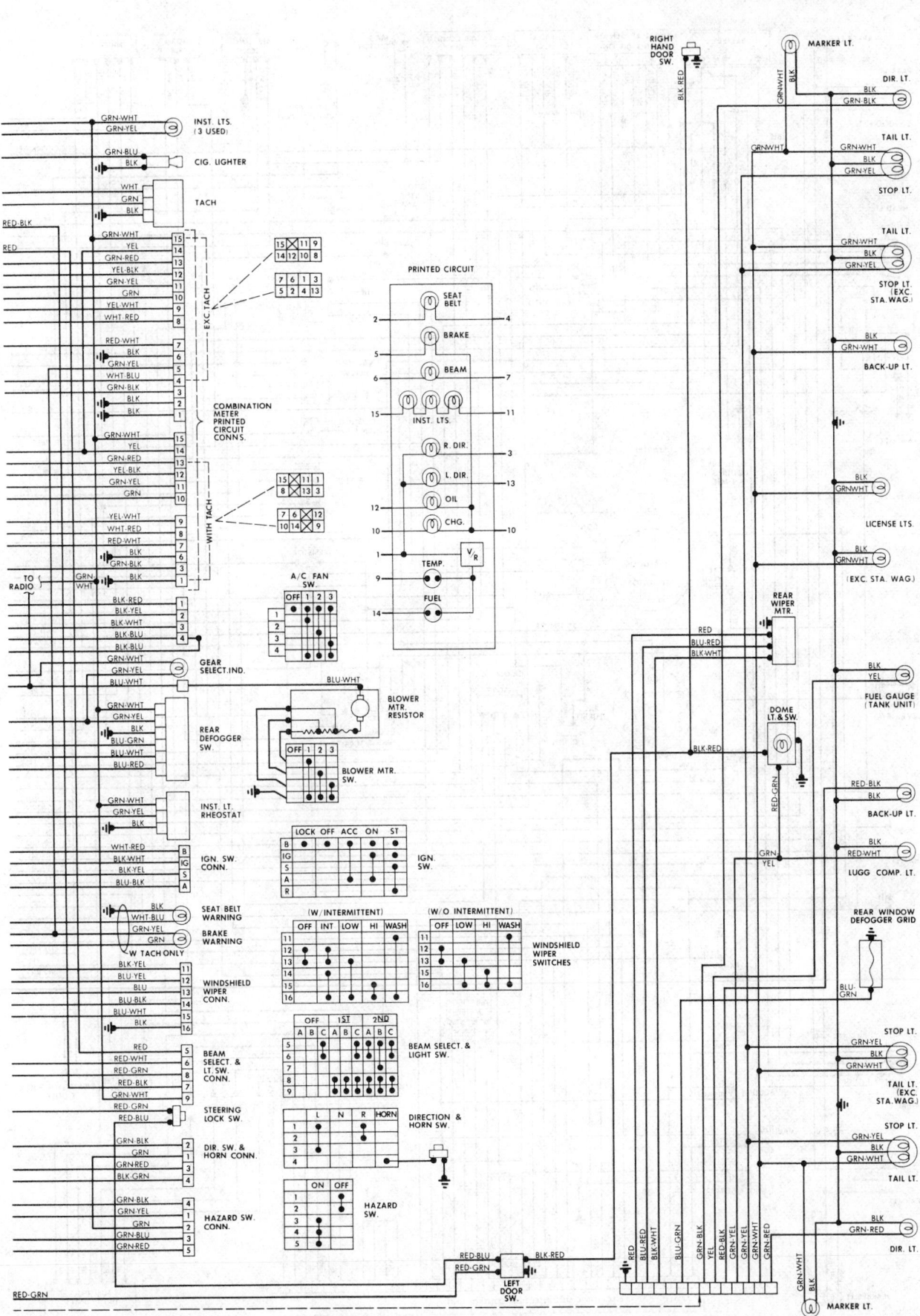

1981 Datsun

ENGINE COMPARTMENT

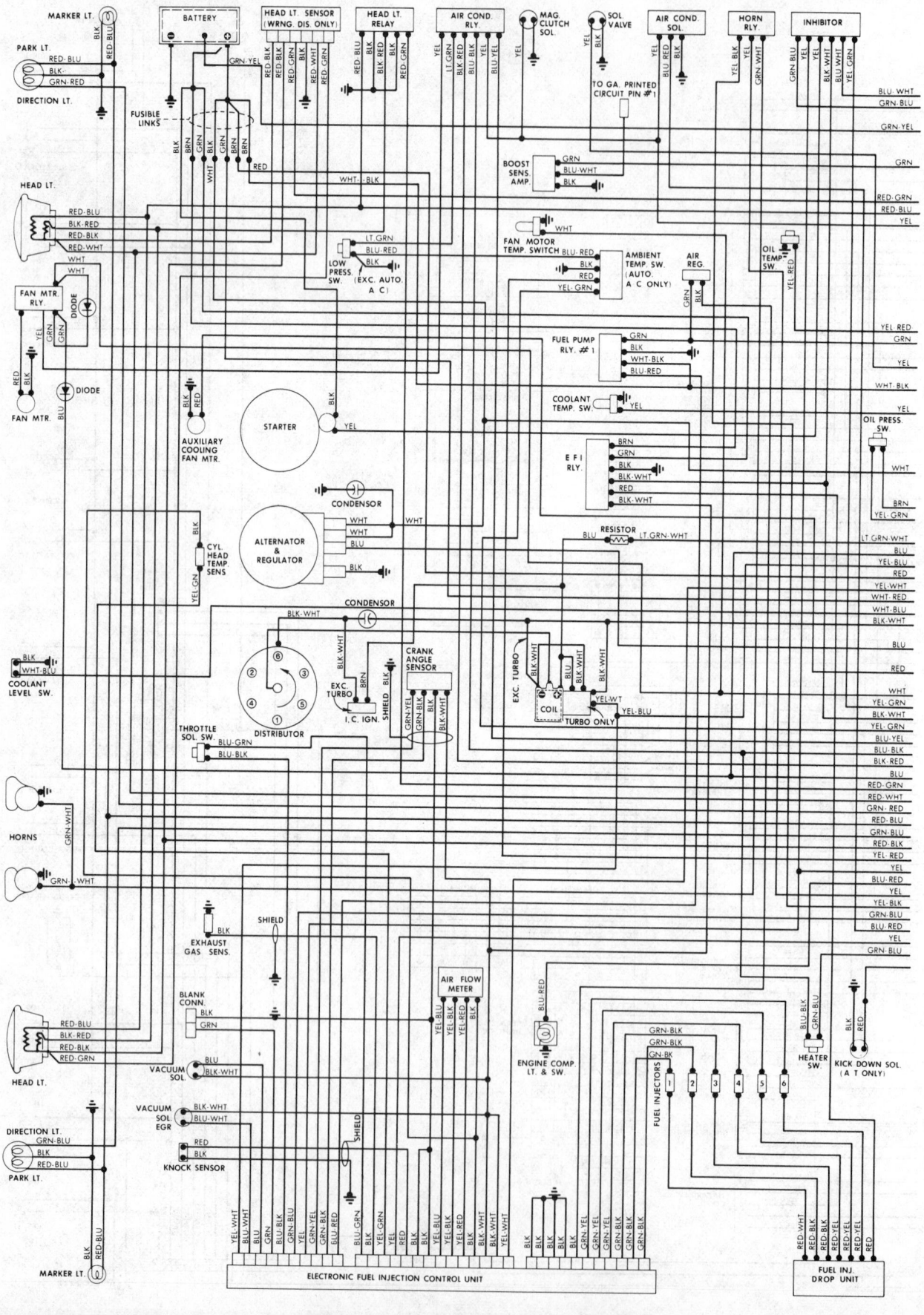

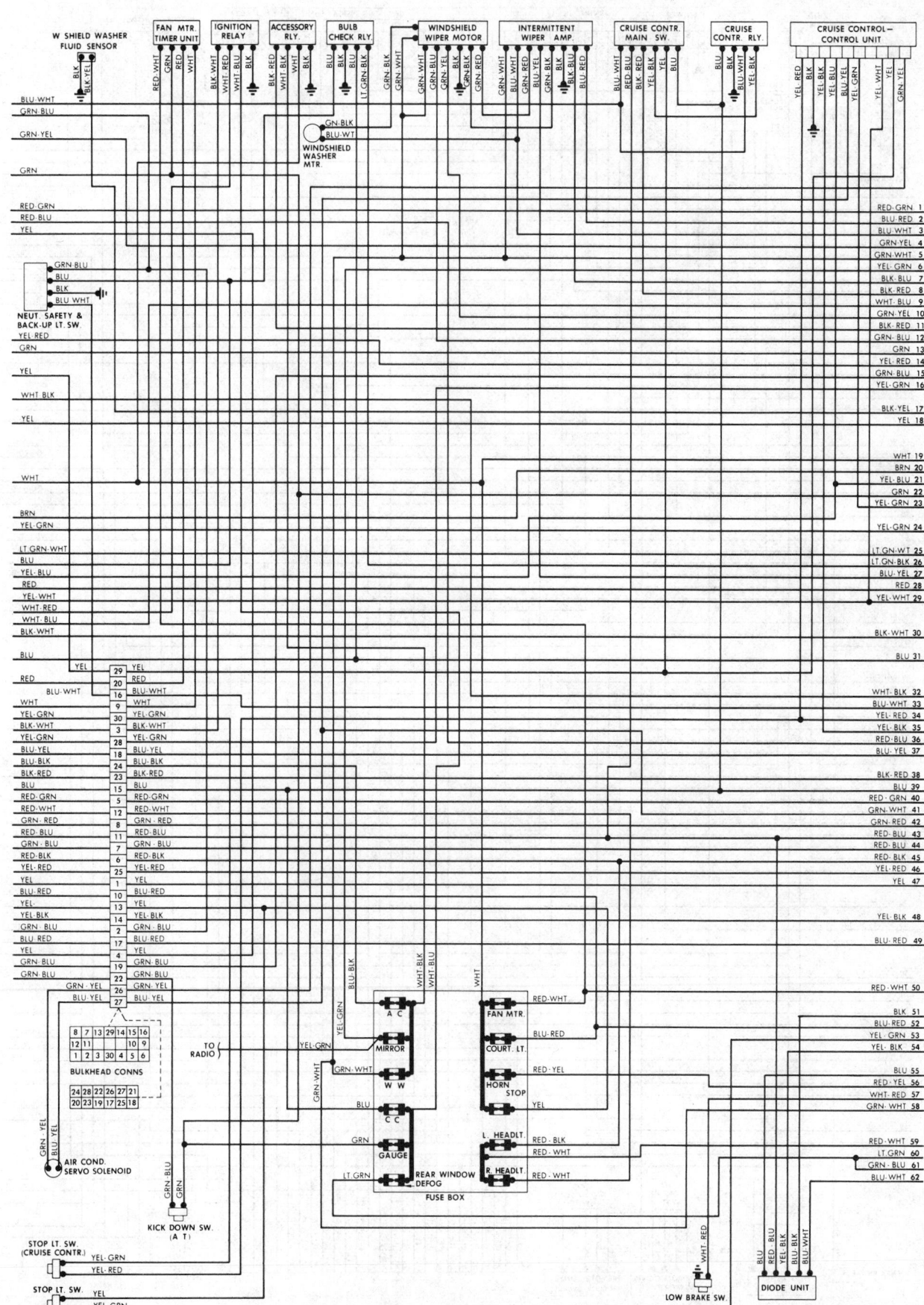

UNDERDASH

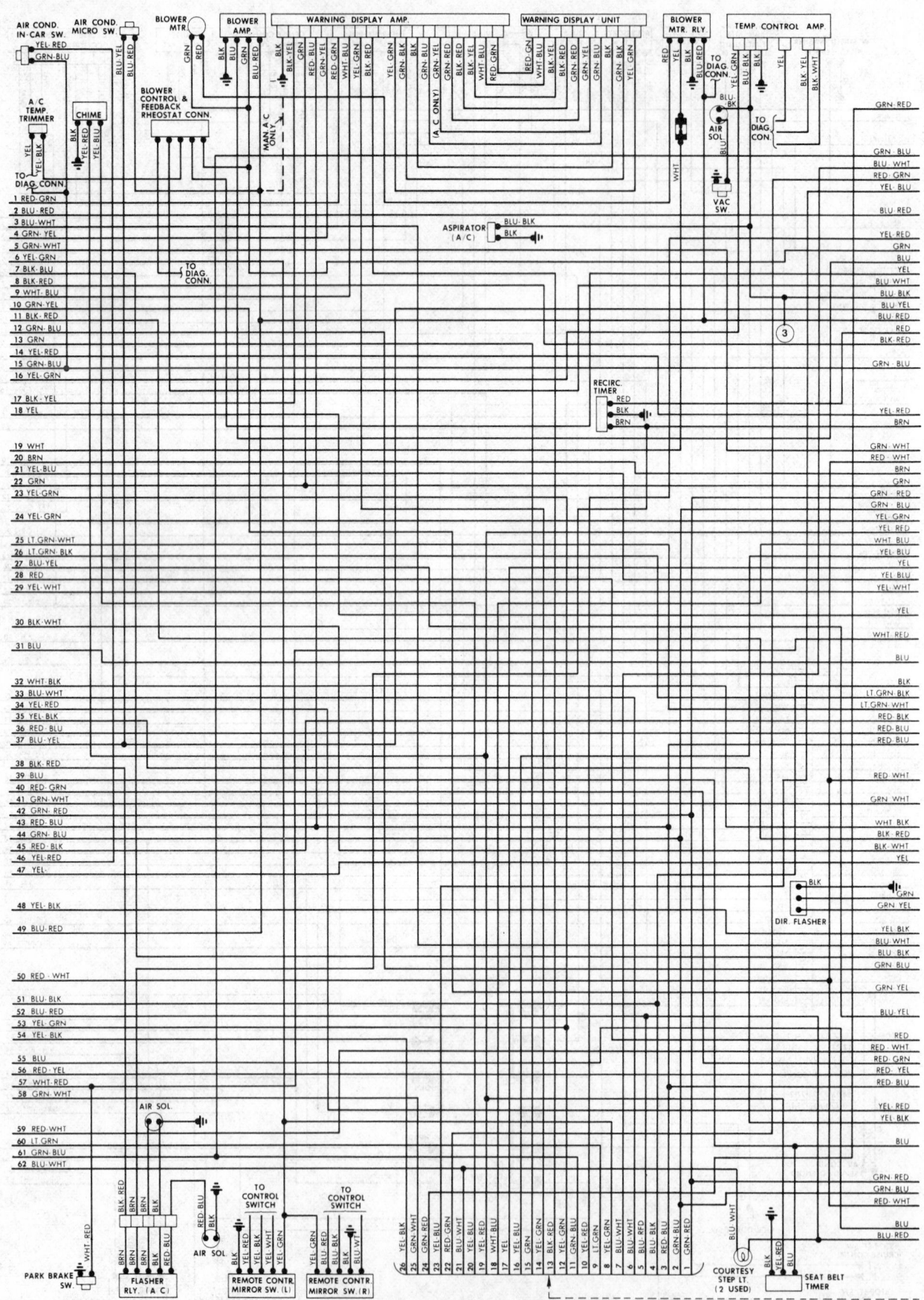

INSTRUMENT PANEL & REAR COMPARTMENT

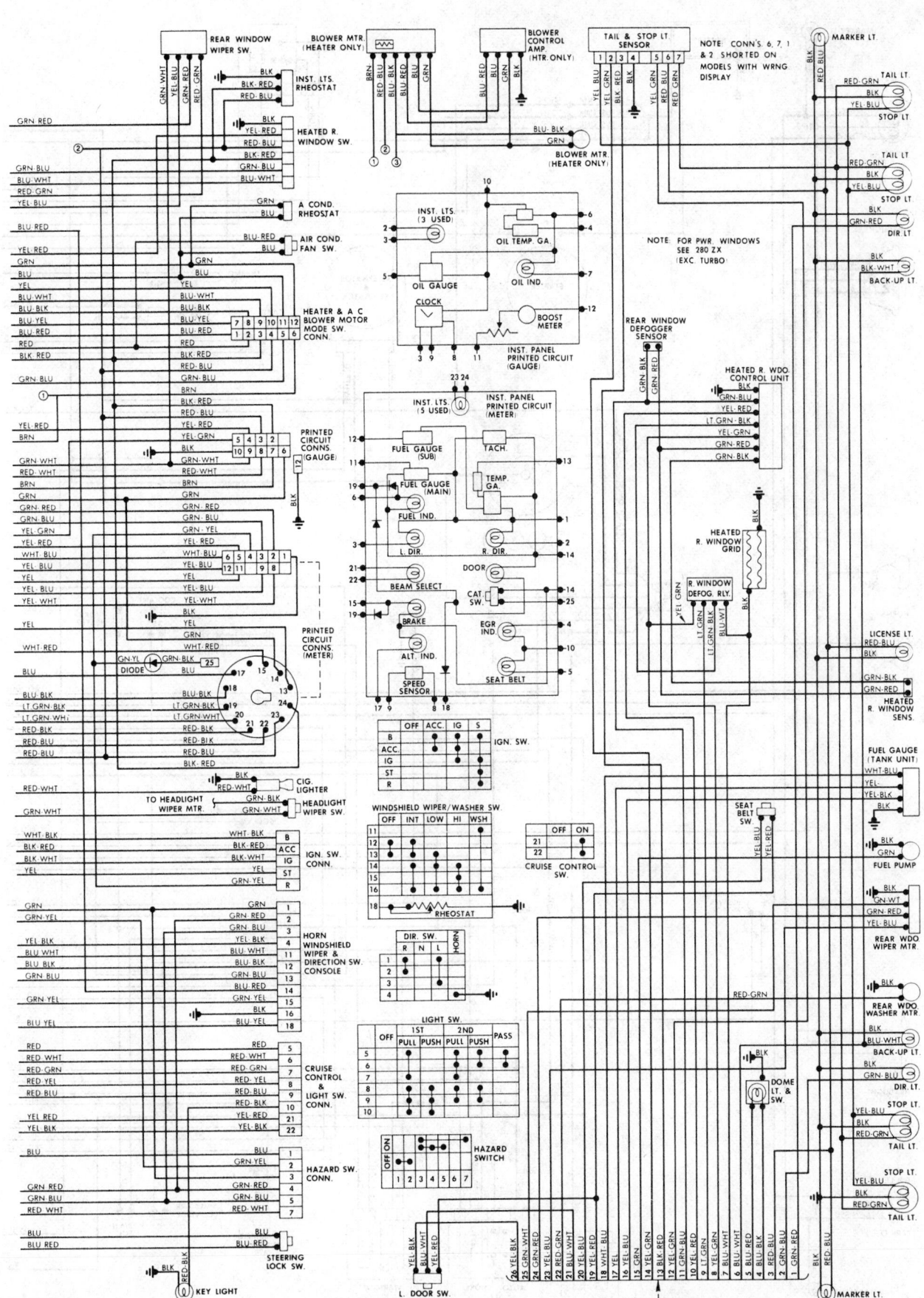

1981 Datsun

ENGINE COMPARTMENT

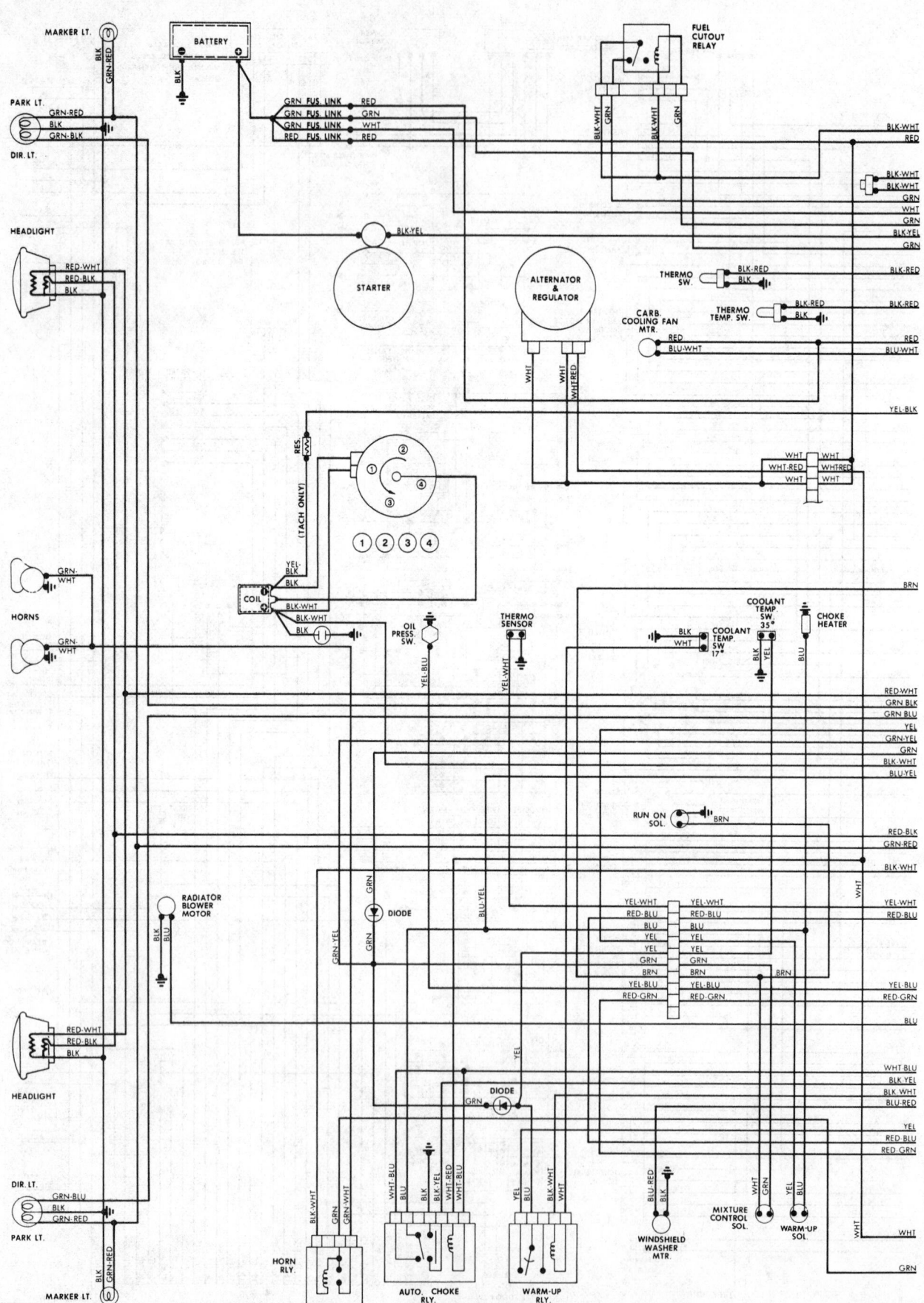

FUSE BLOCK

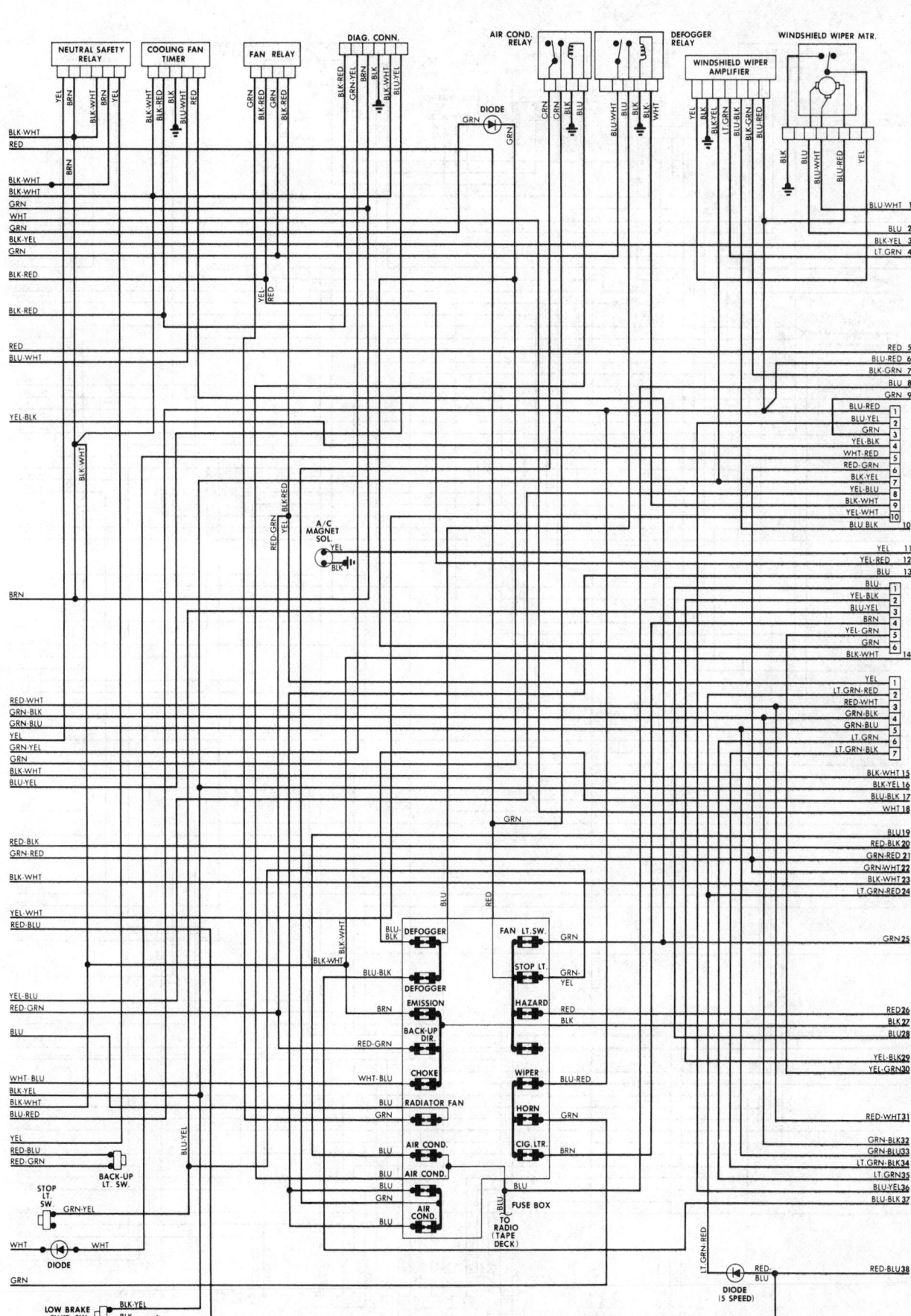

UNDERDASH

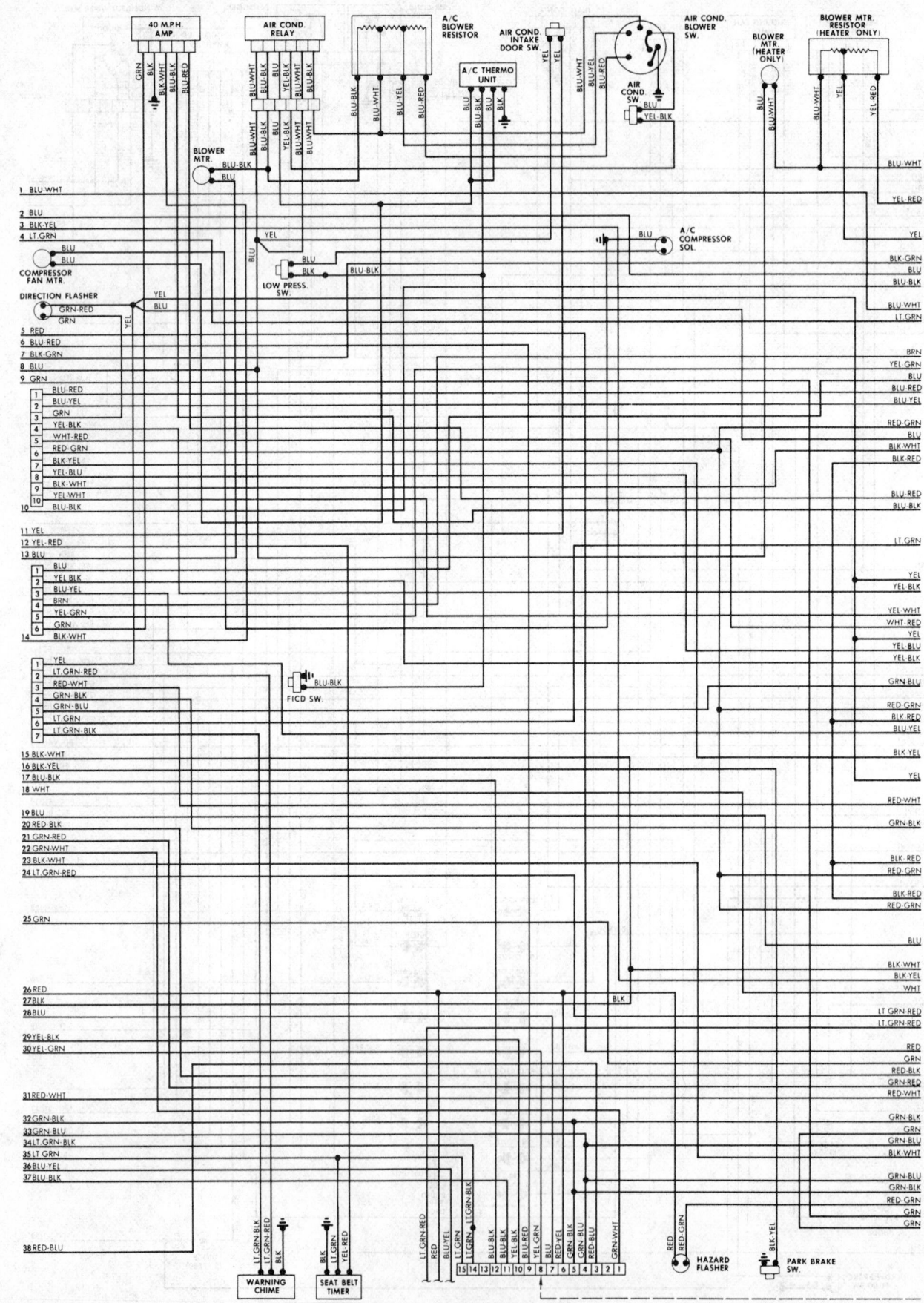

WIRING DIAGRAMS

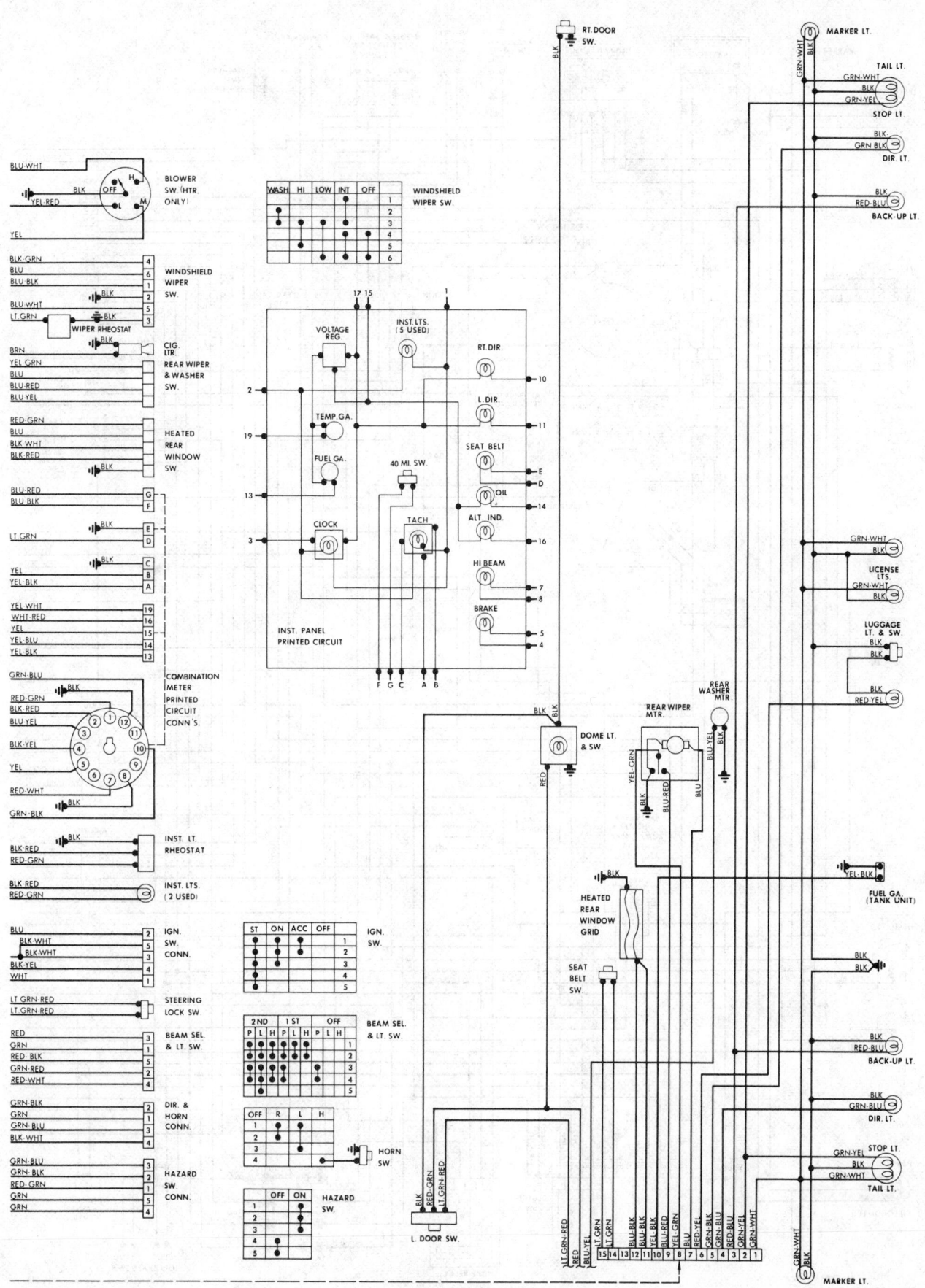

ENGINE COMPARTMENT & FUSE BLOCK

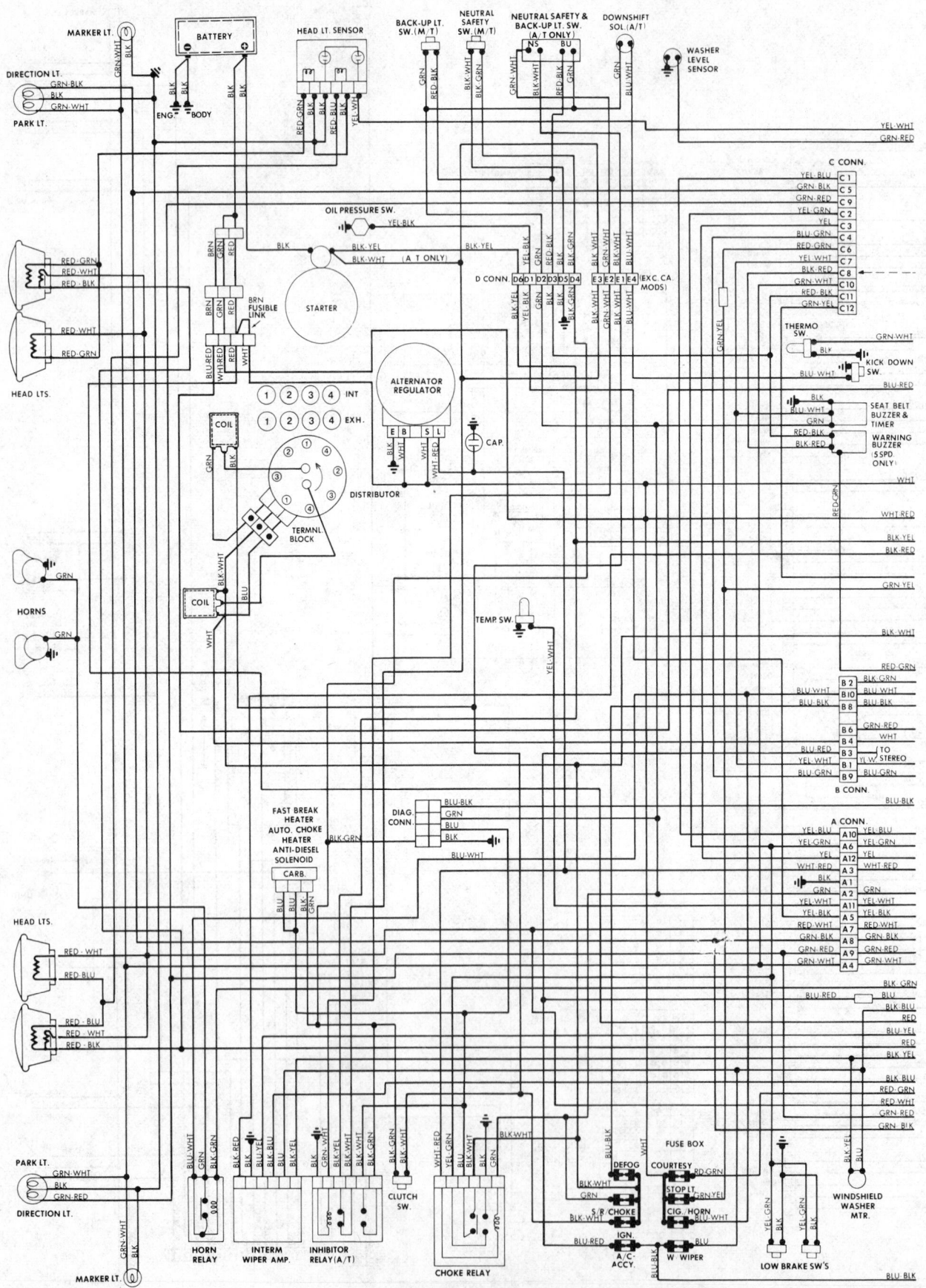

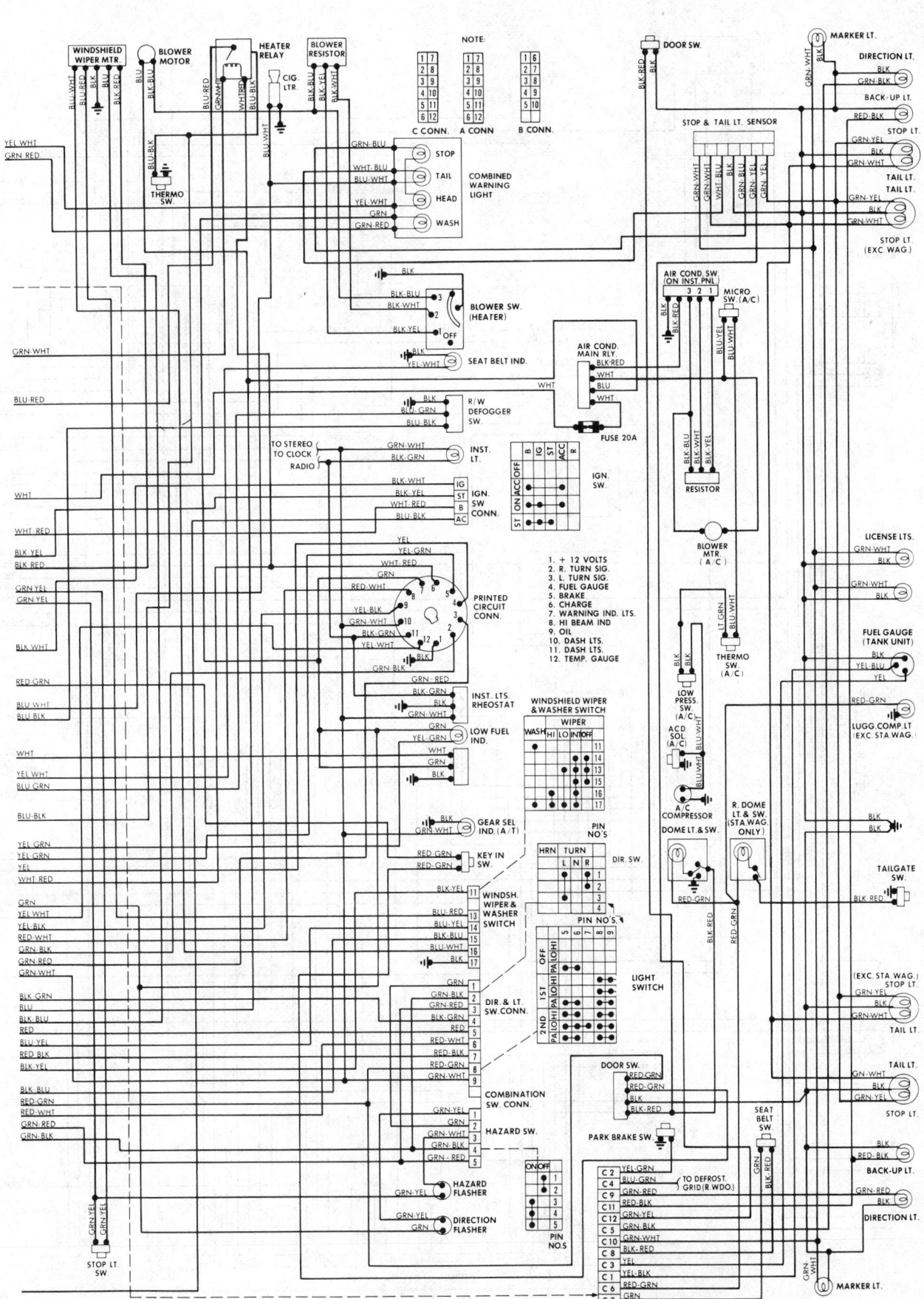

1981 Datsun

ENGINE COMPARTMENT

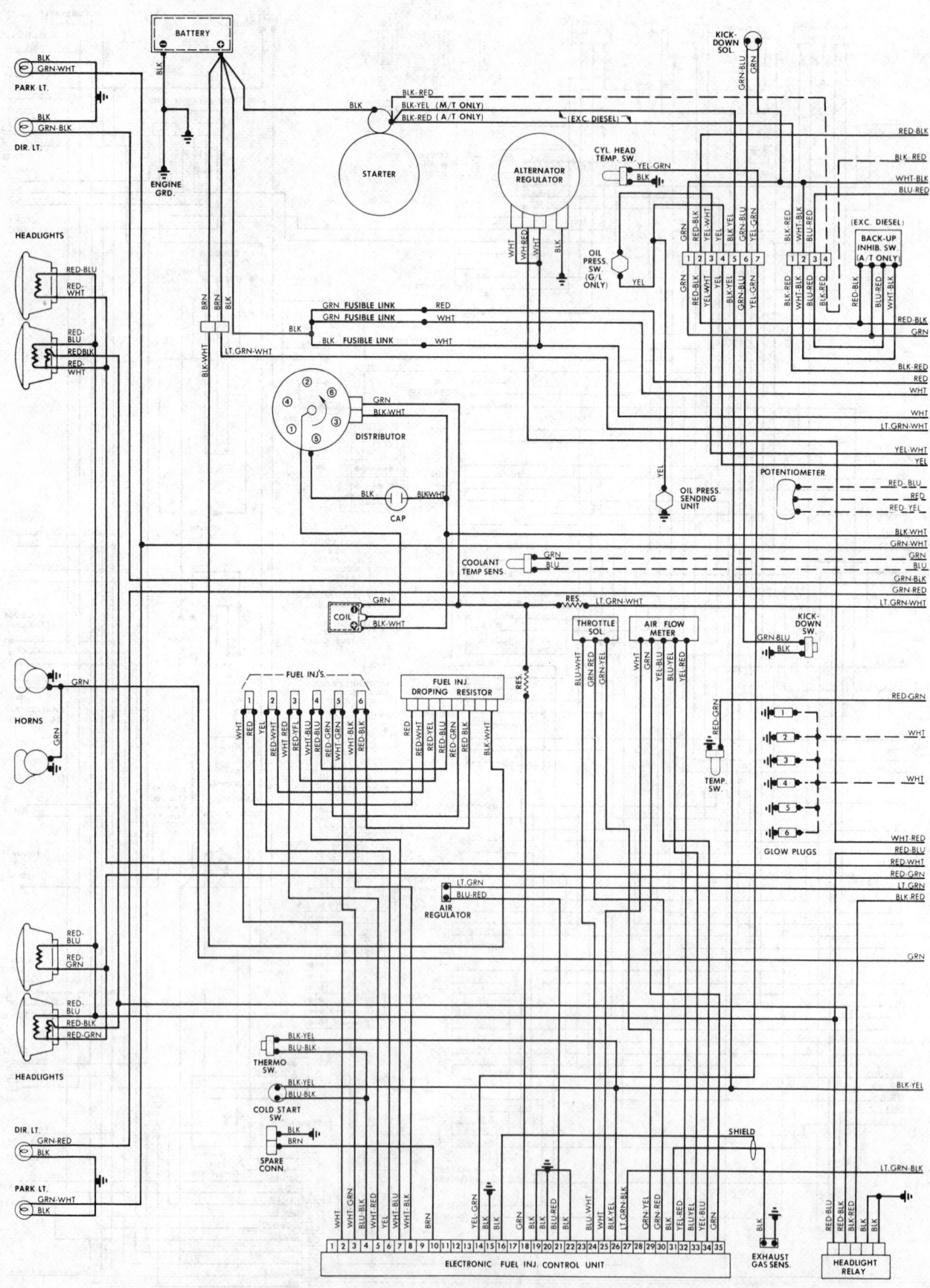

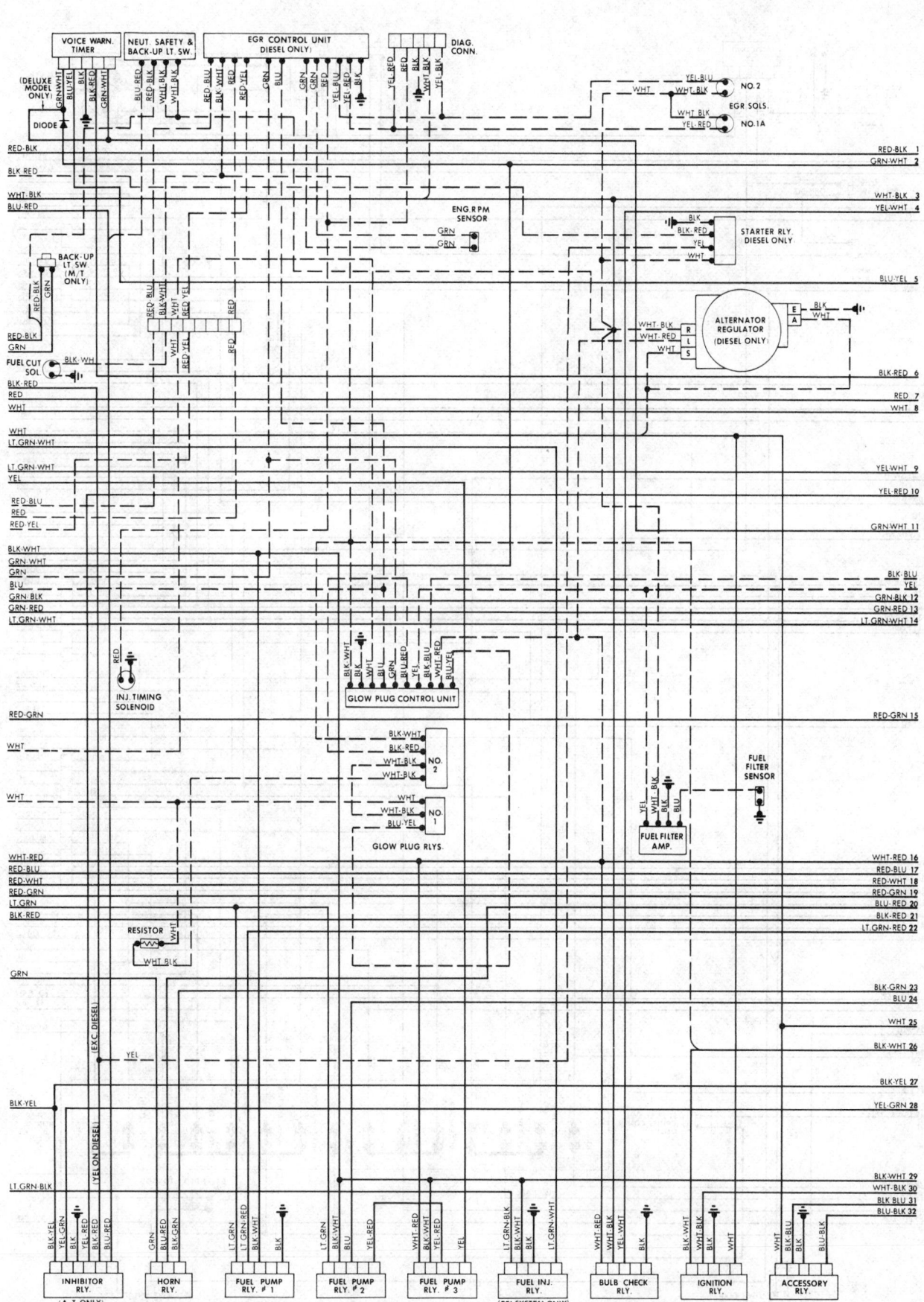

1981 Datsun

ENGINE COMPARTMENT & FUSE BLOCK

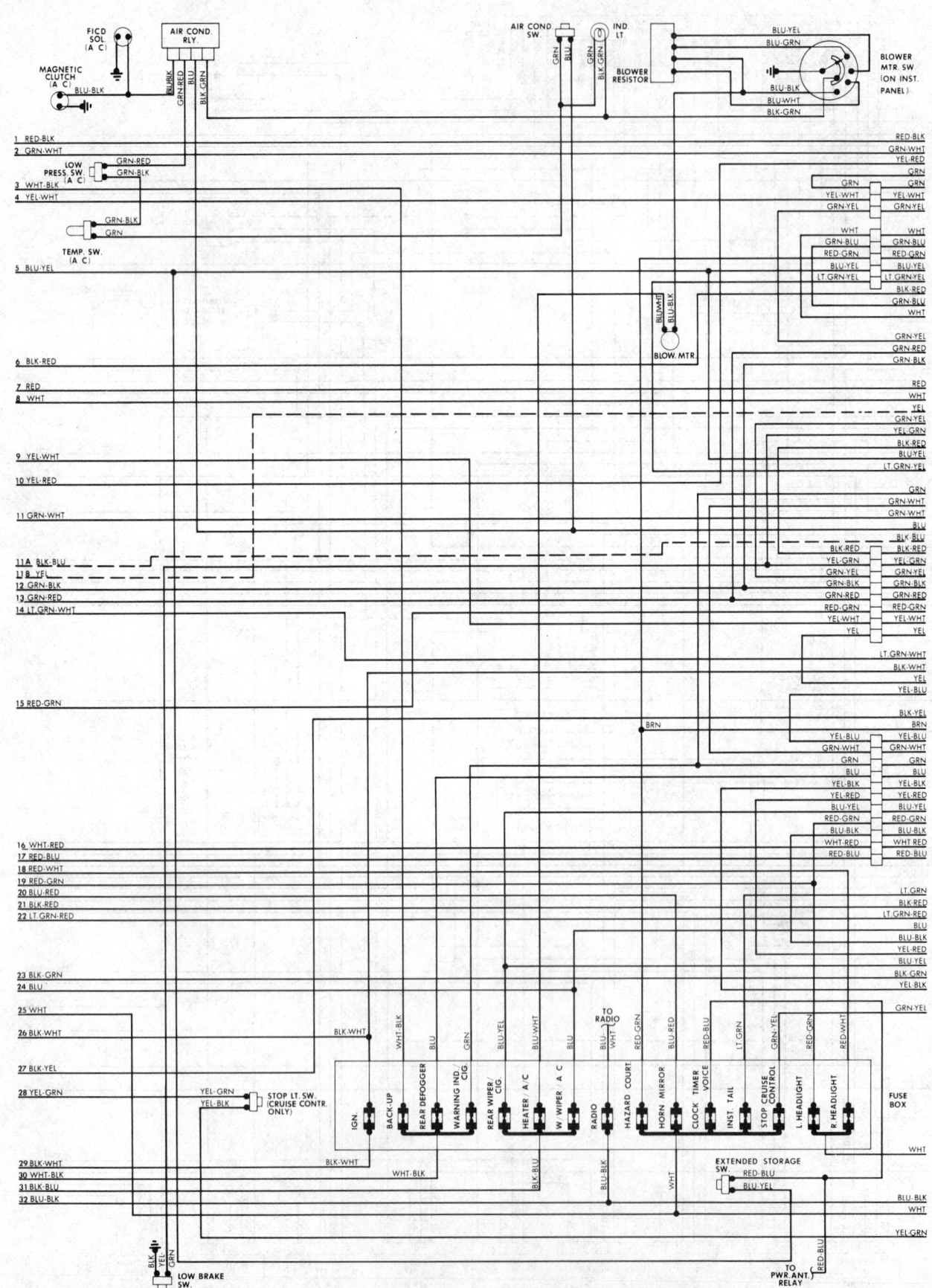

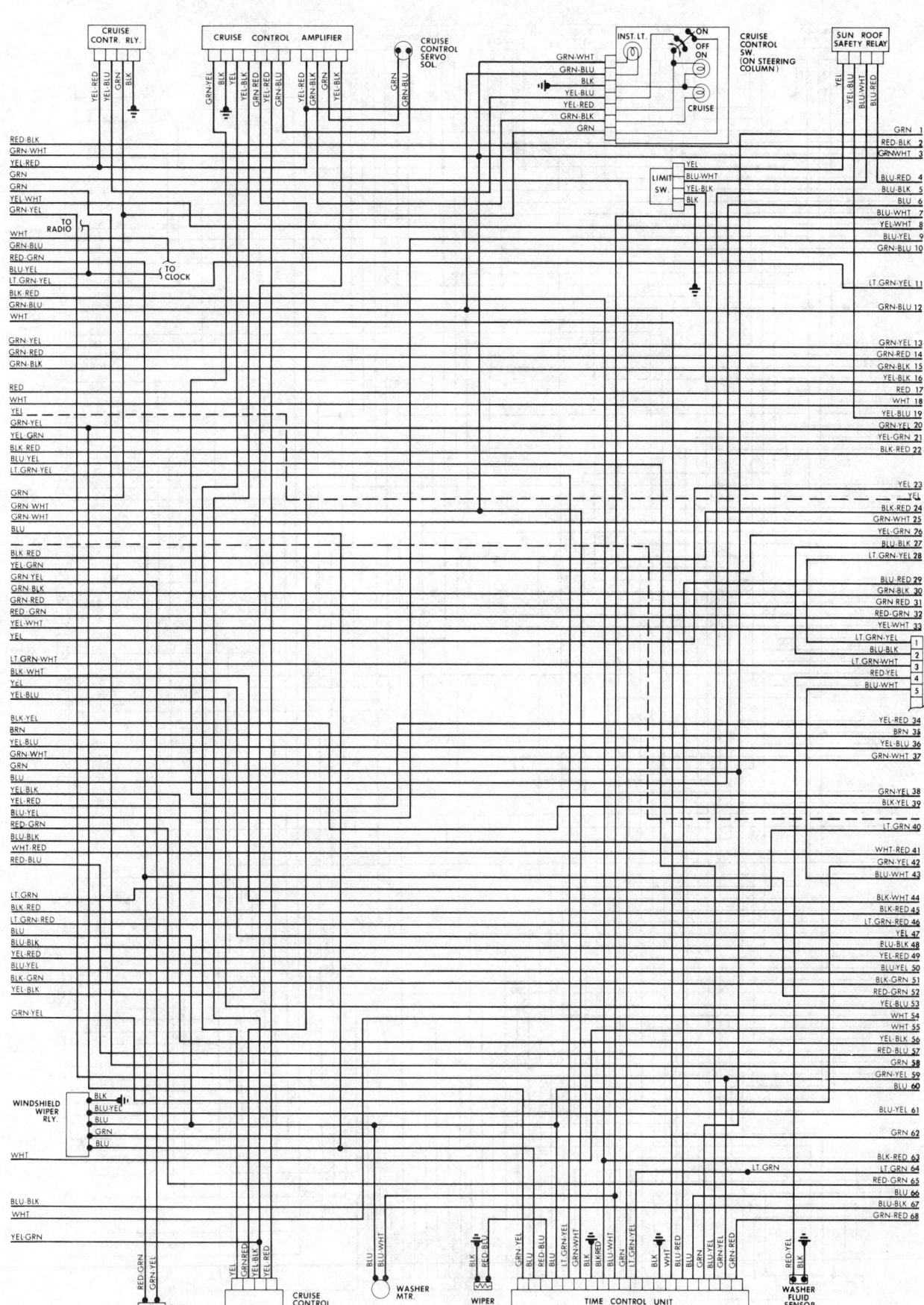

1981 Datsun

UNDERDASH

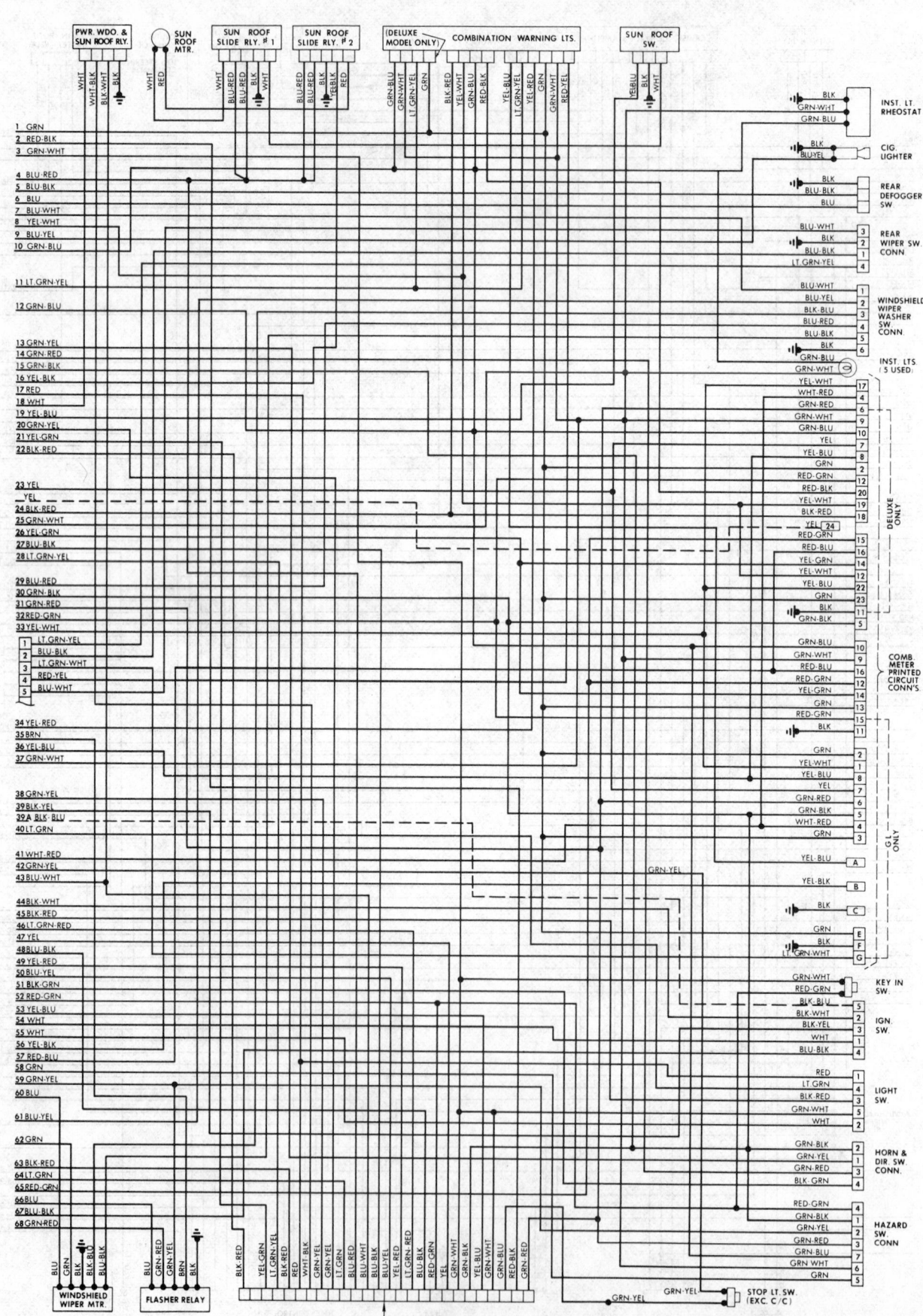

INSTRUMENT PANEL & REAR COMPARTMENT

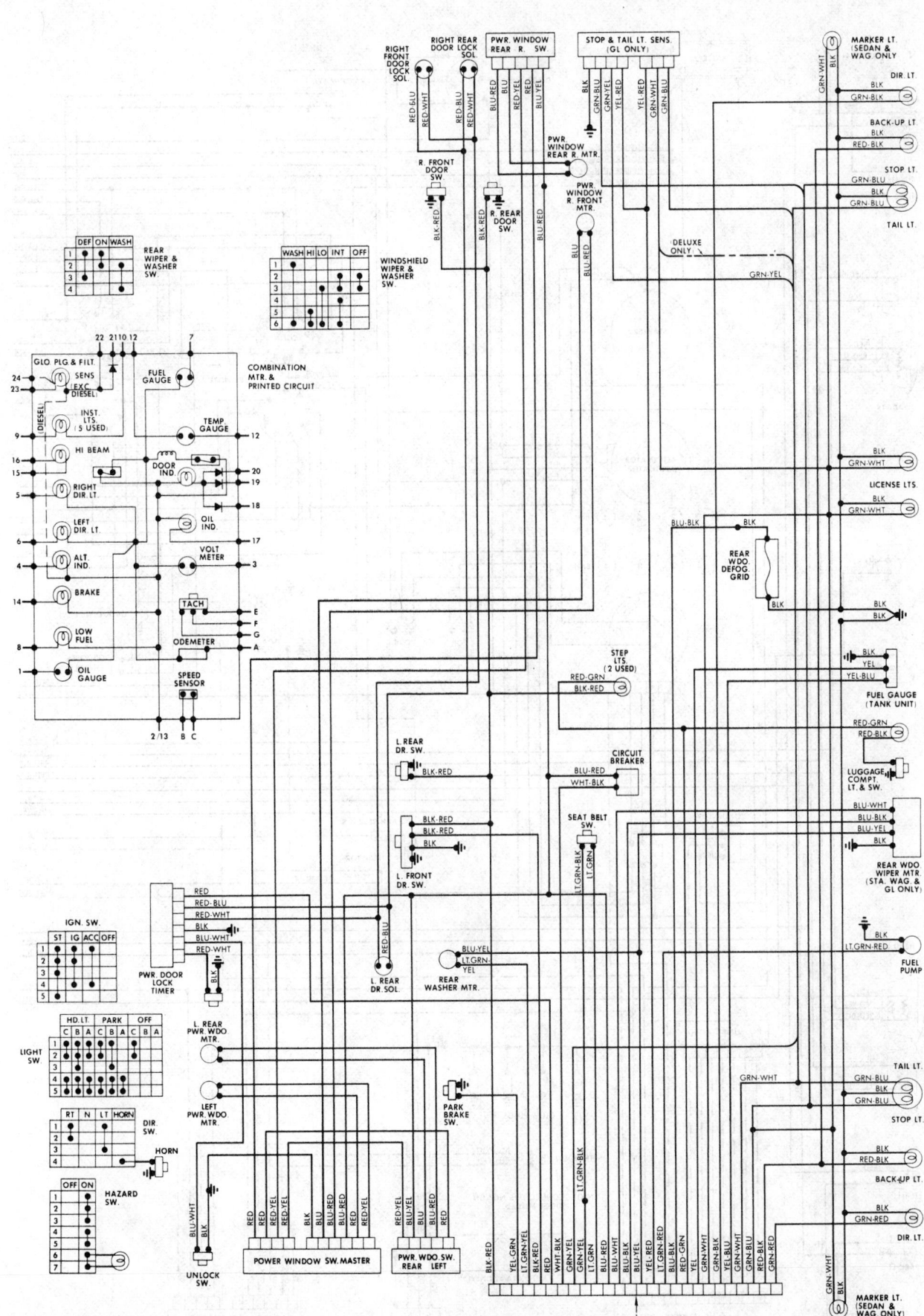

1981 Datsun

ENGINE COMPARTMENT

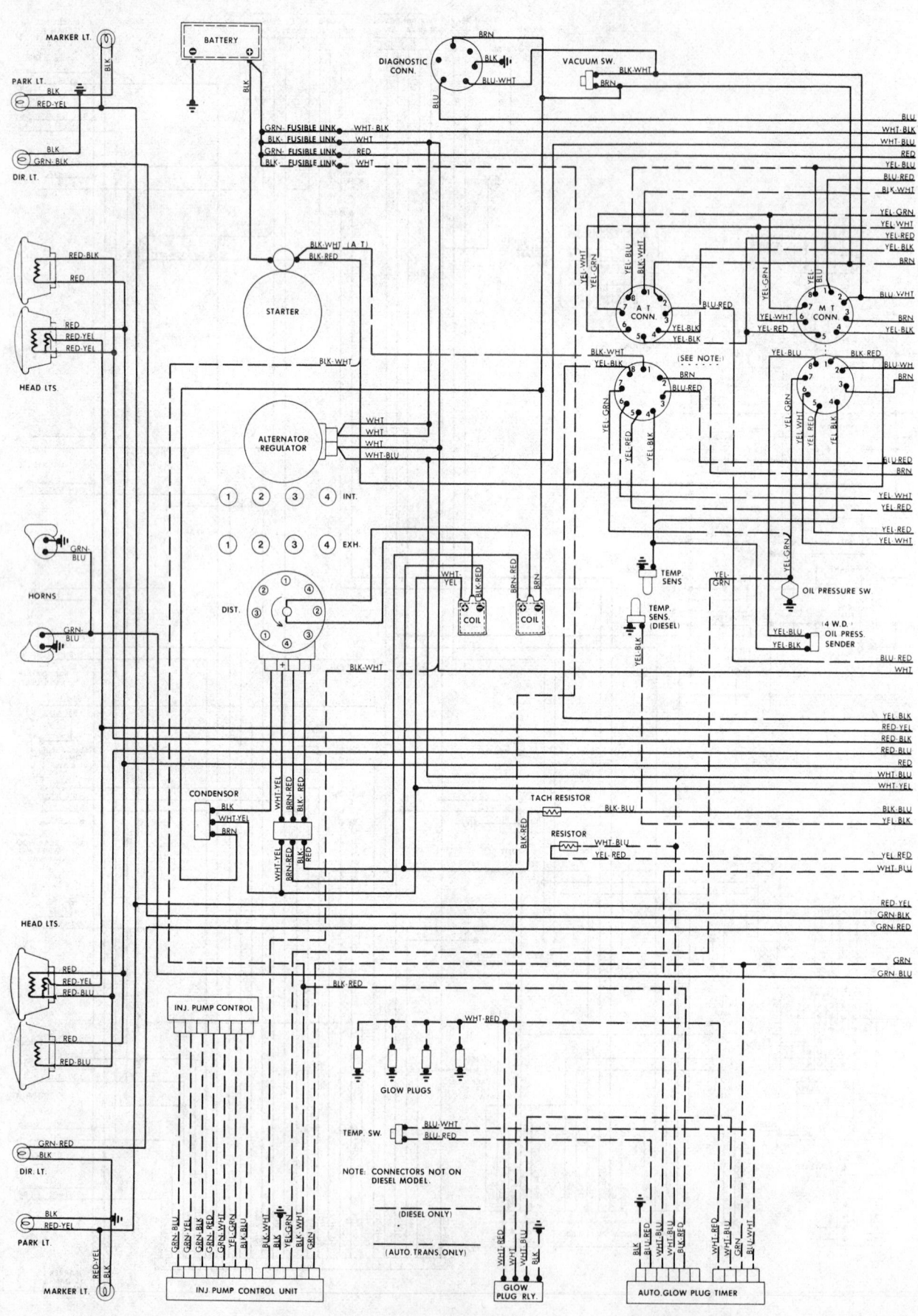

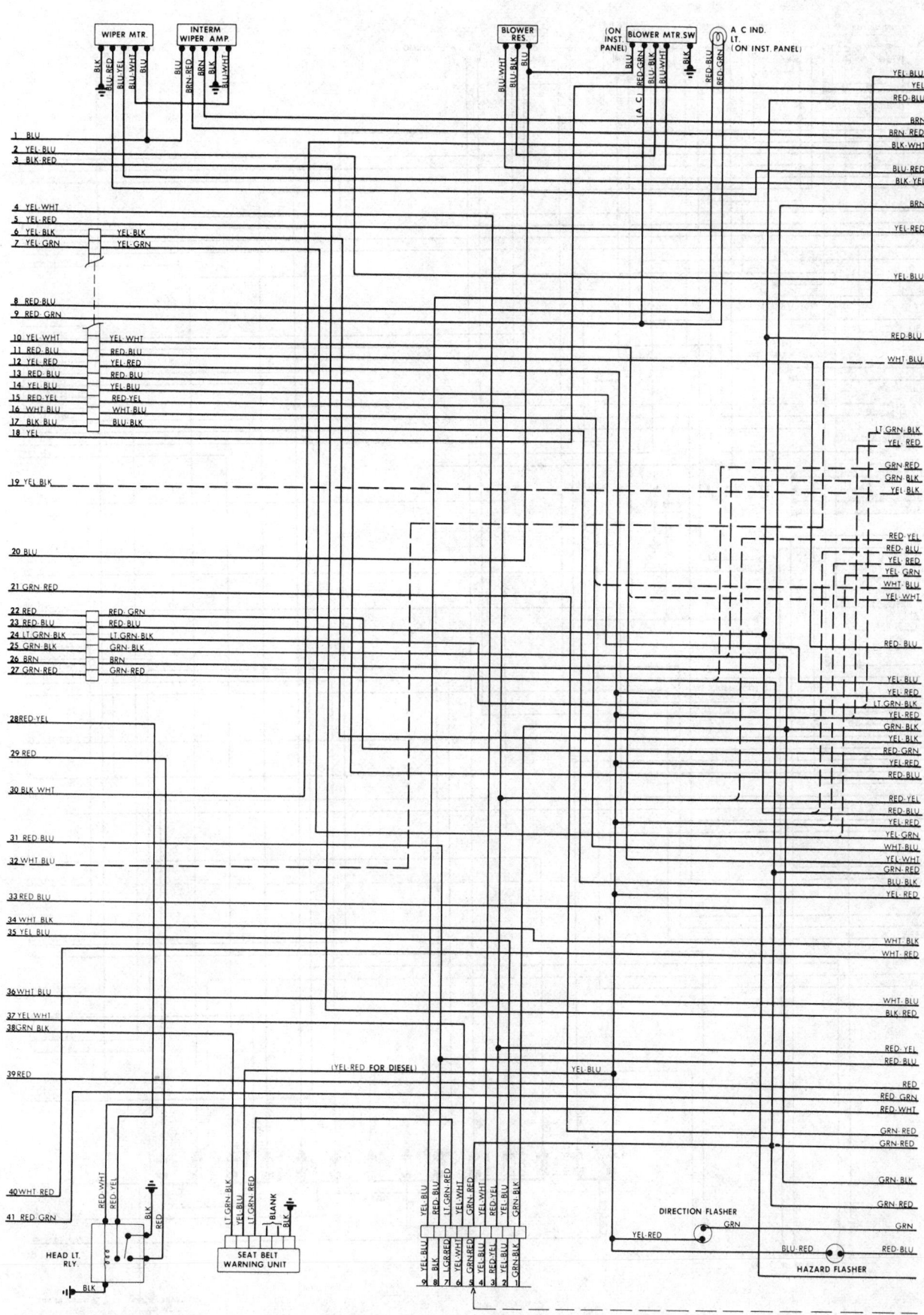

1981 Datsun

UNDERDASH & FUSE BLOCK

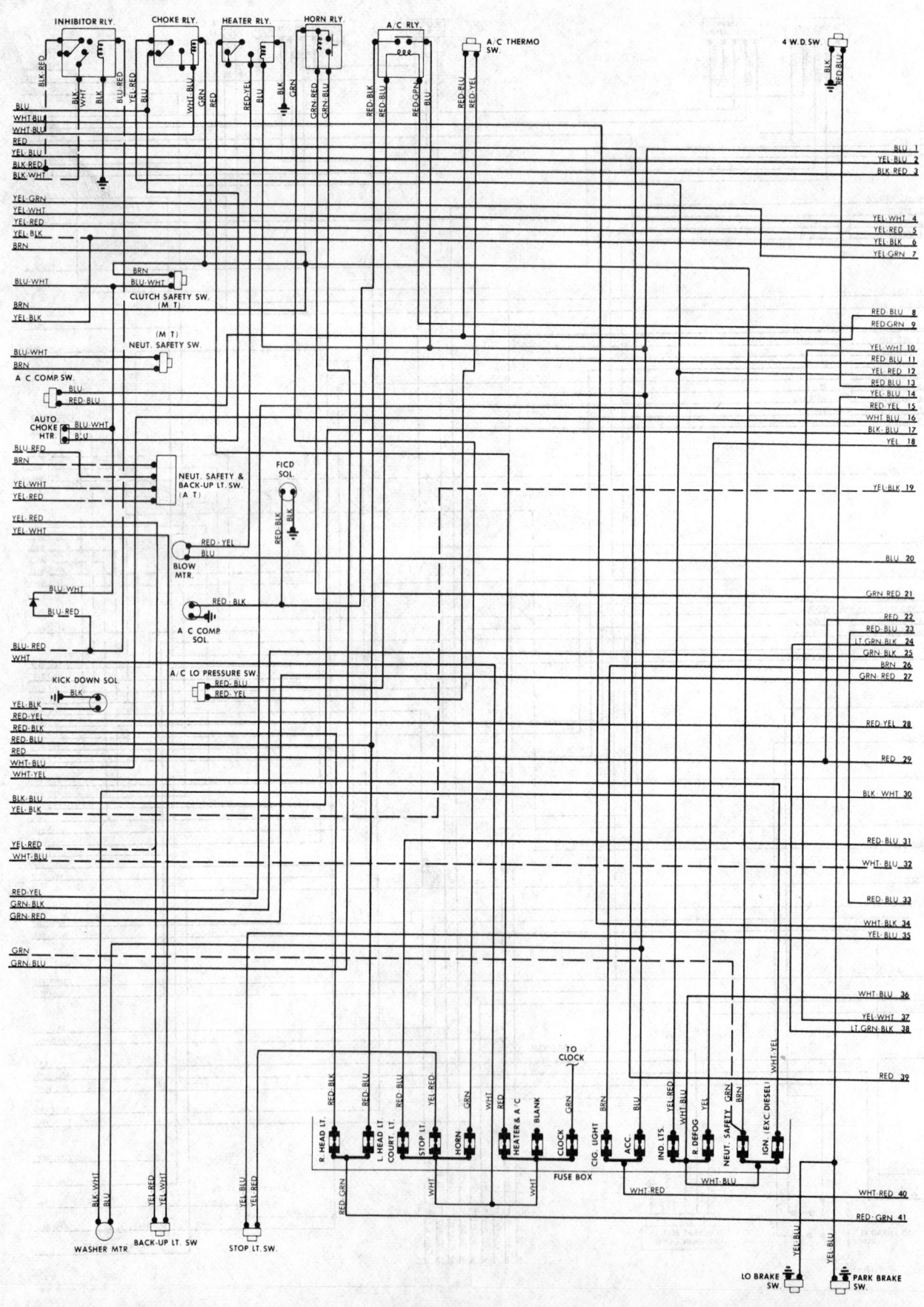

INSTRUMENT PANEL & REAR COMPARTMENT

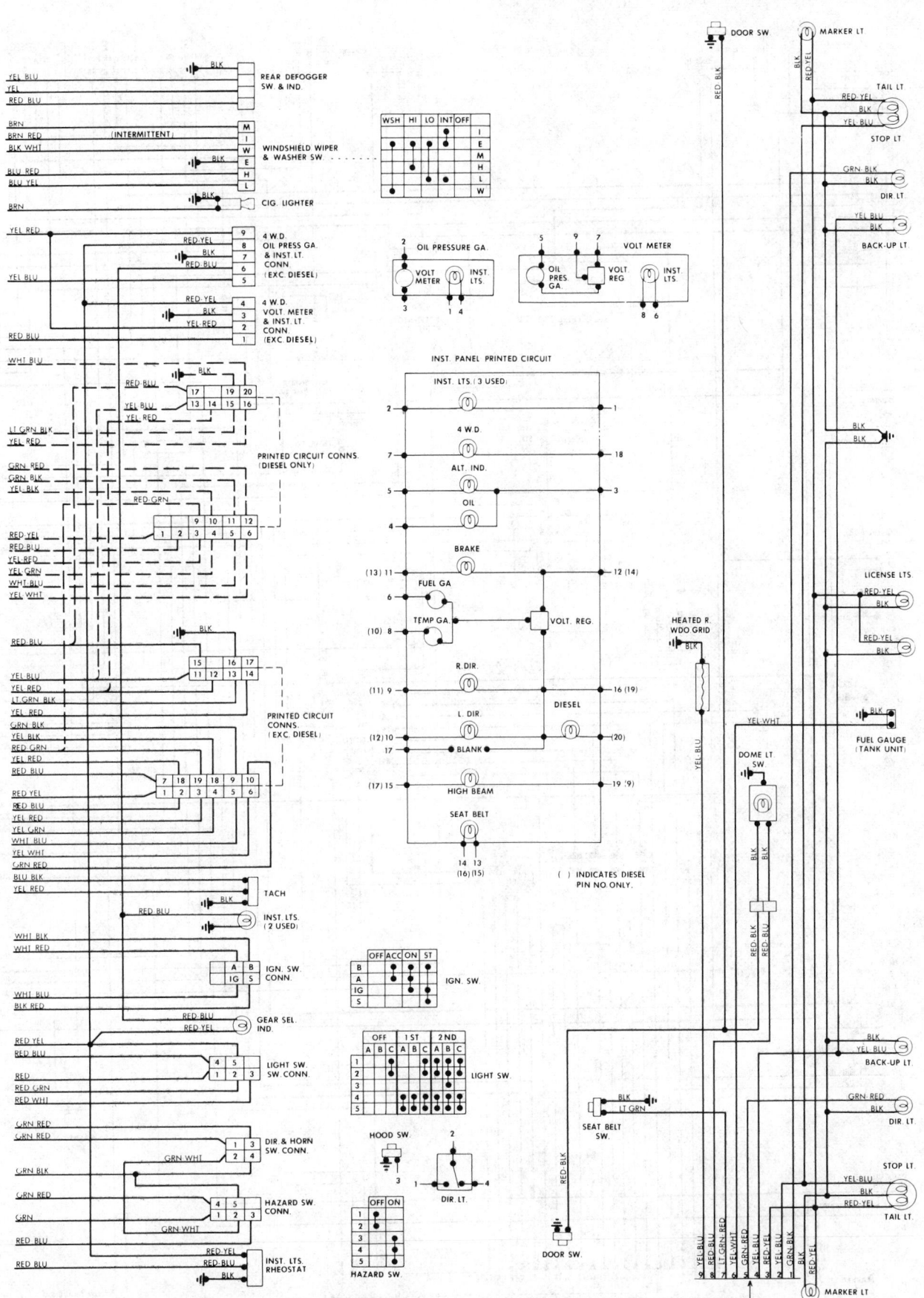

1981 Fiat

UNDERDASH & FUSE BLOCK

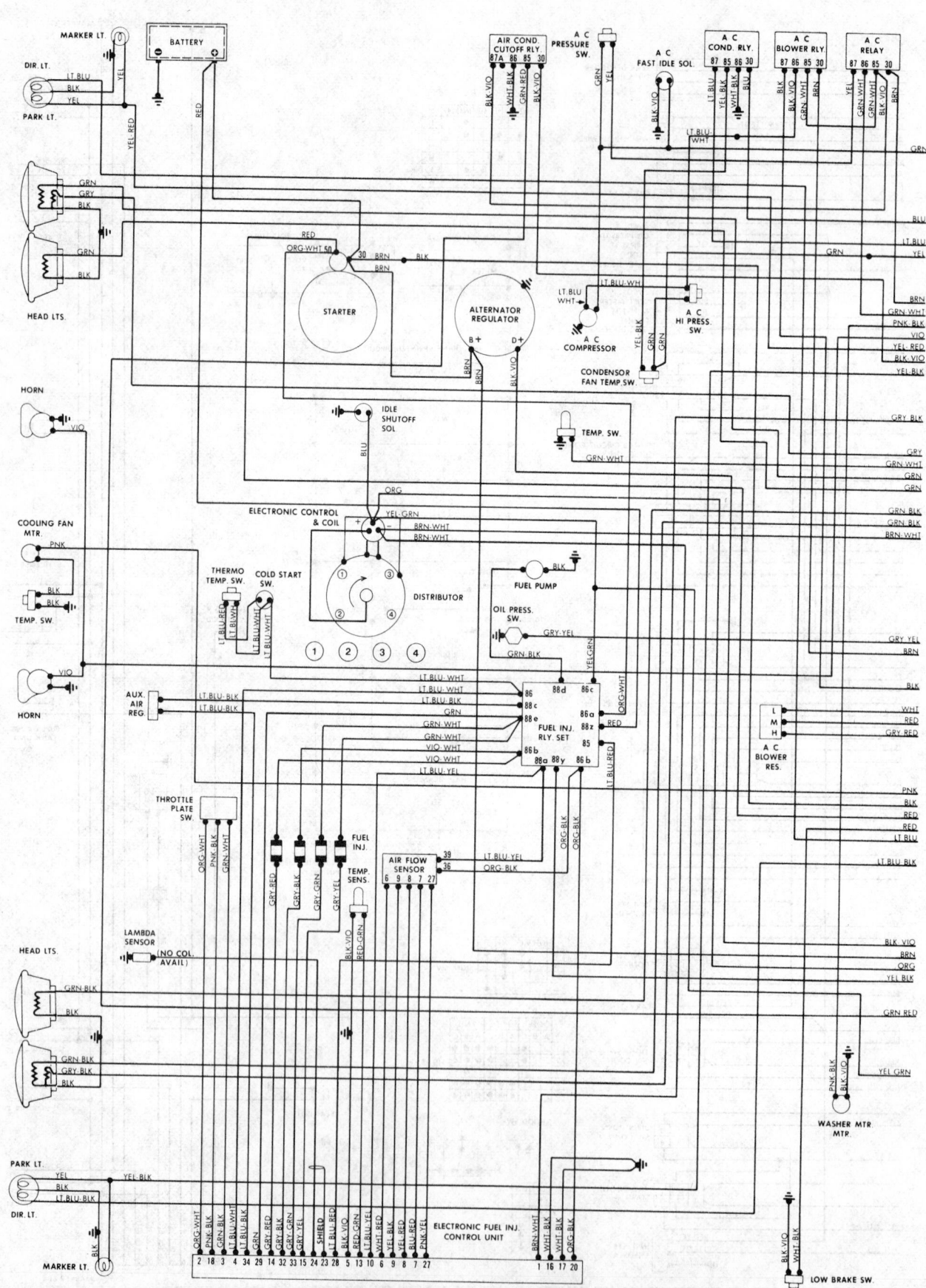

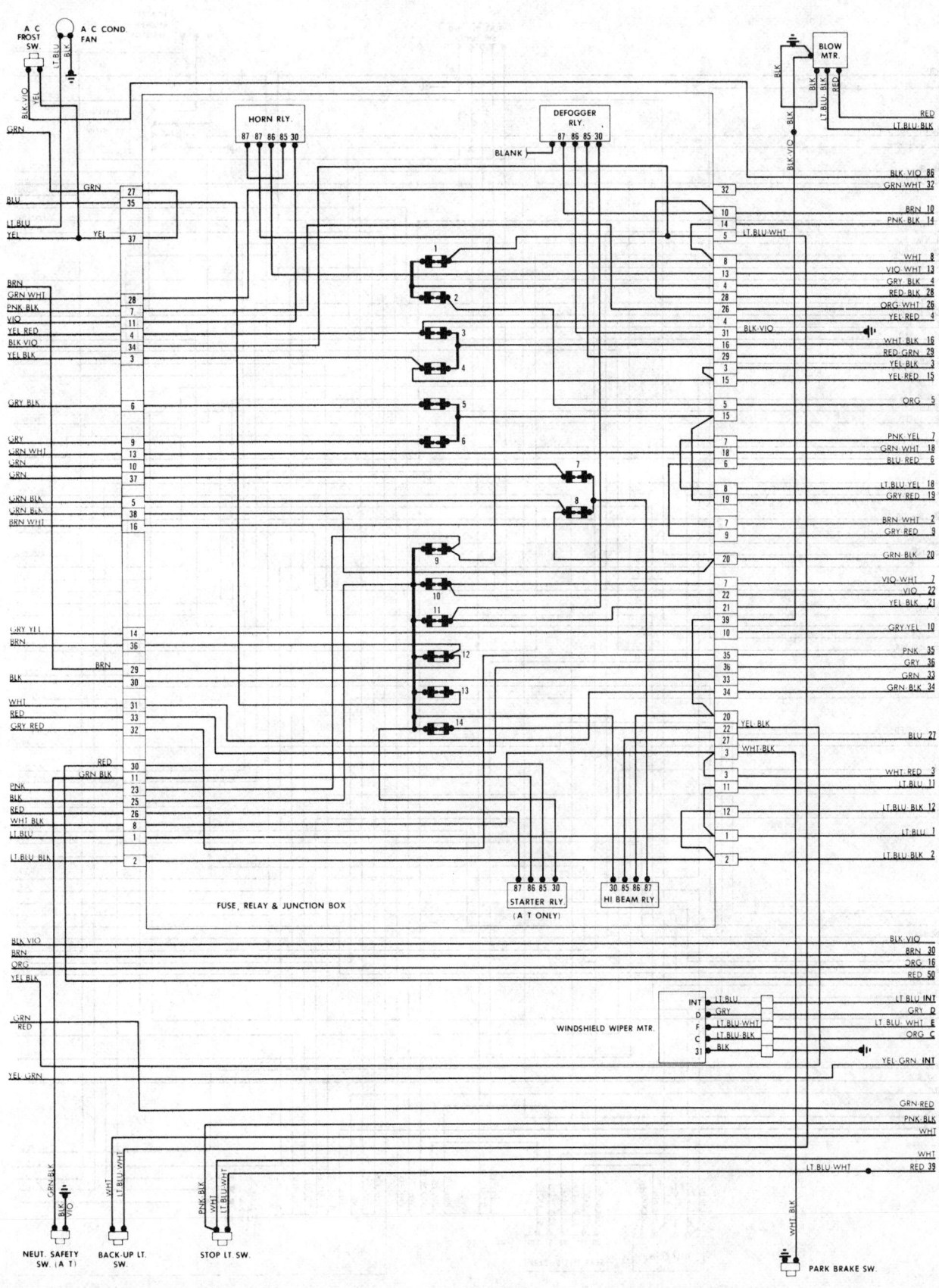

1981 Fiat

UNDERDASH

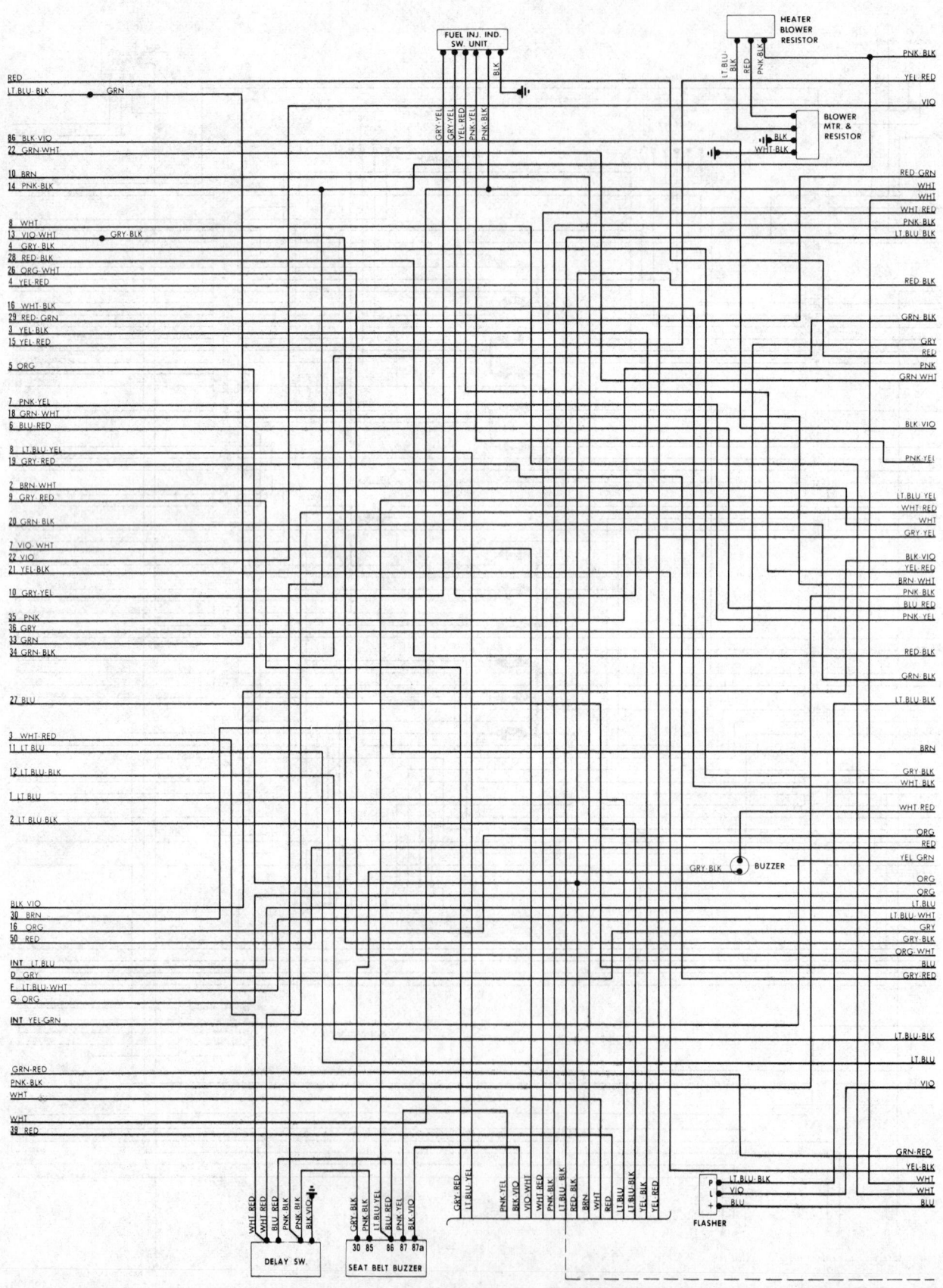

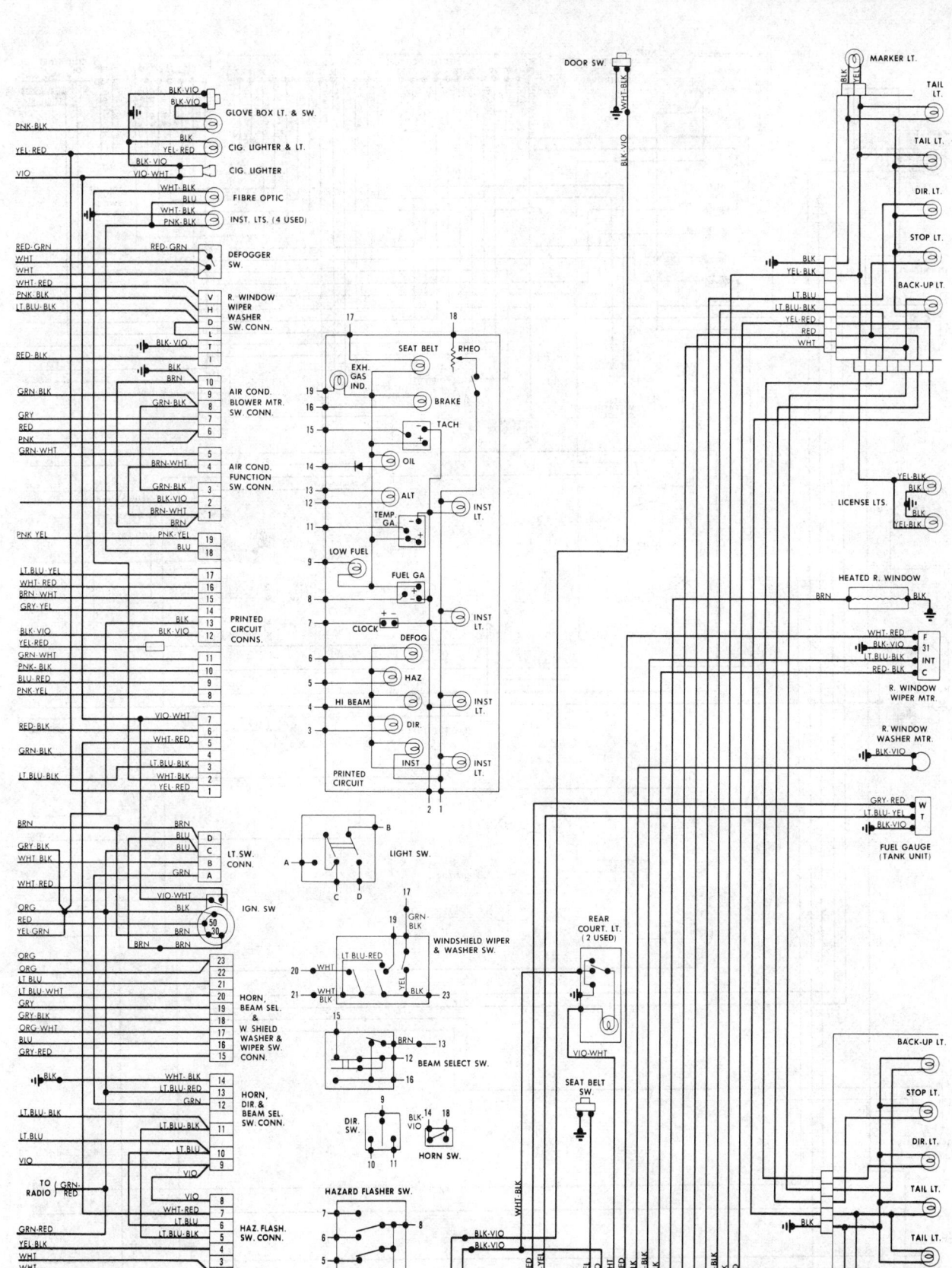

1981 Fiat

ENGINE COMPARTMENT

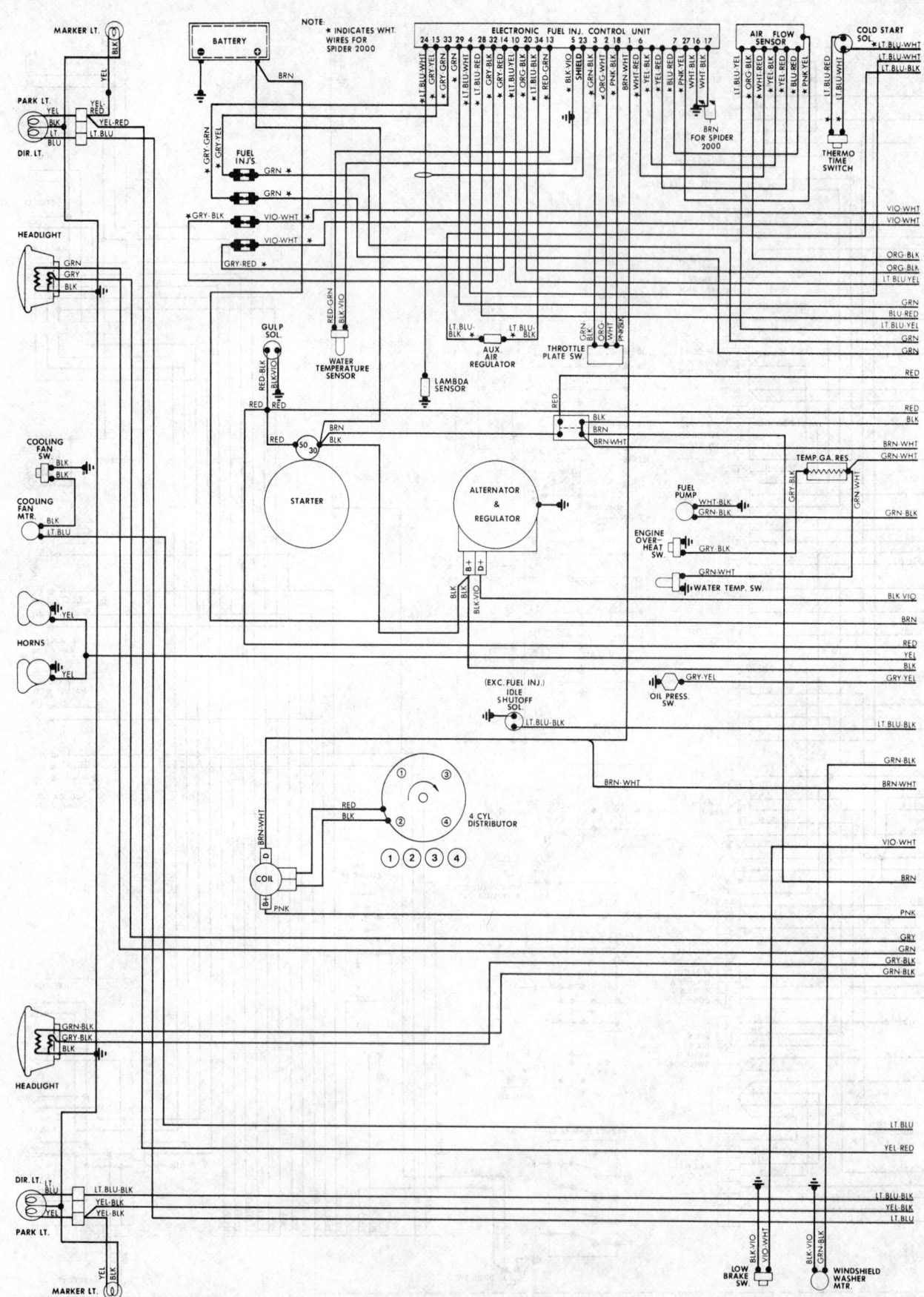

UNDERDASH & FUSE BLOCK

Wiring Diagrams

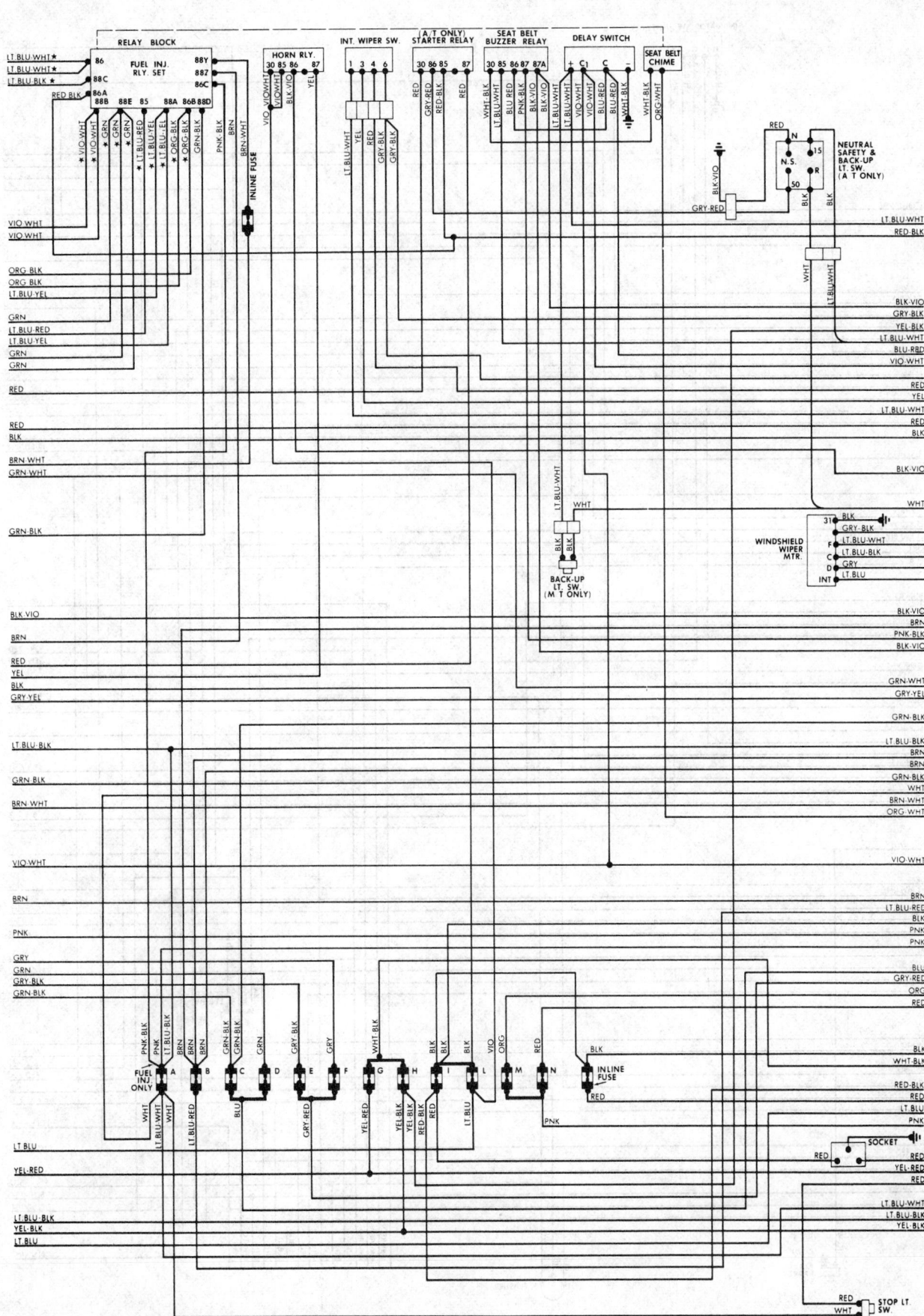

1981 Fiat

UNDERDASH

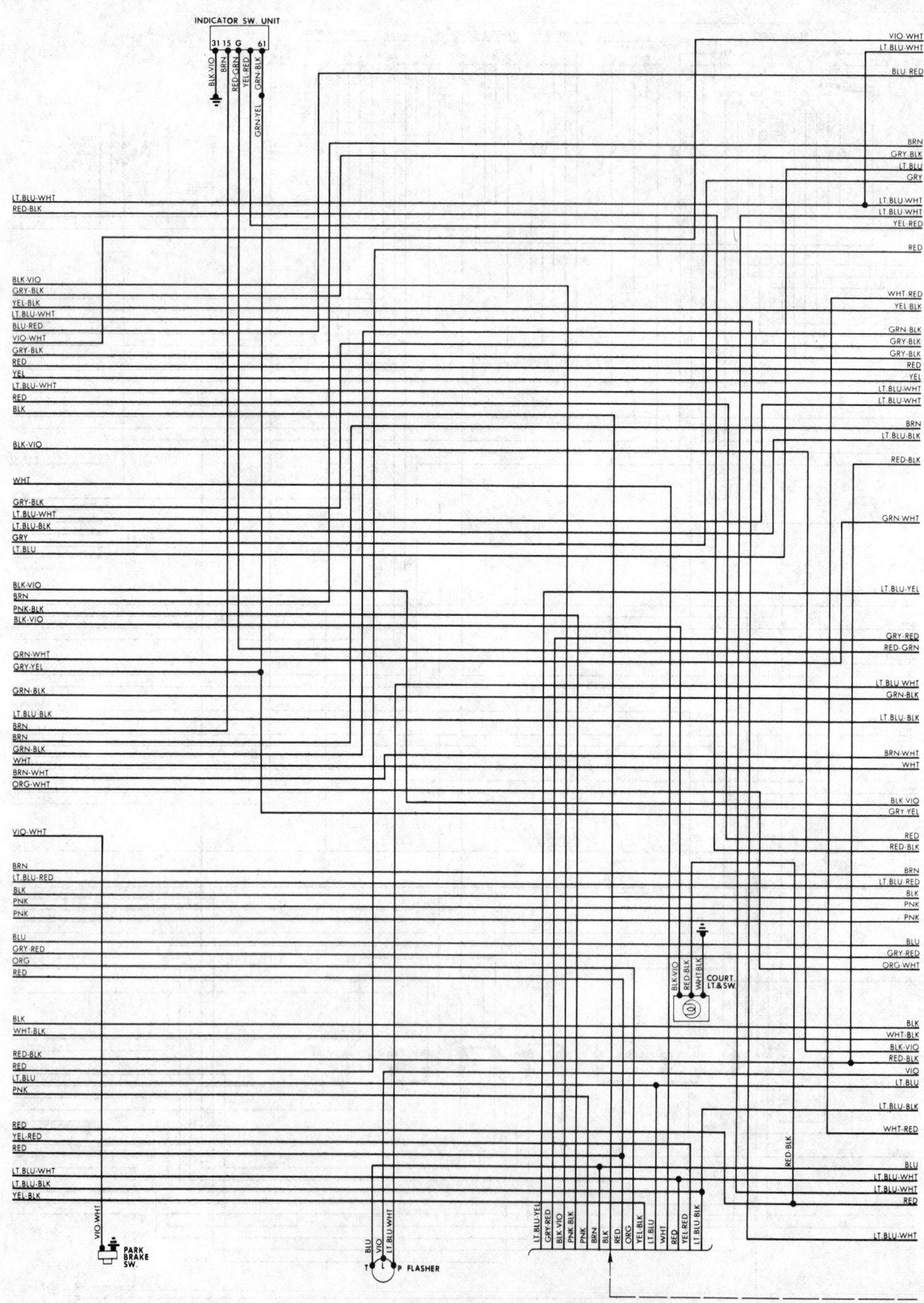

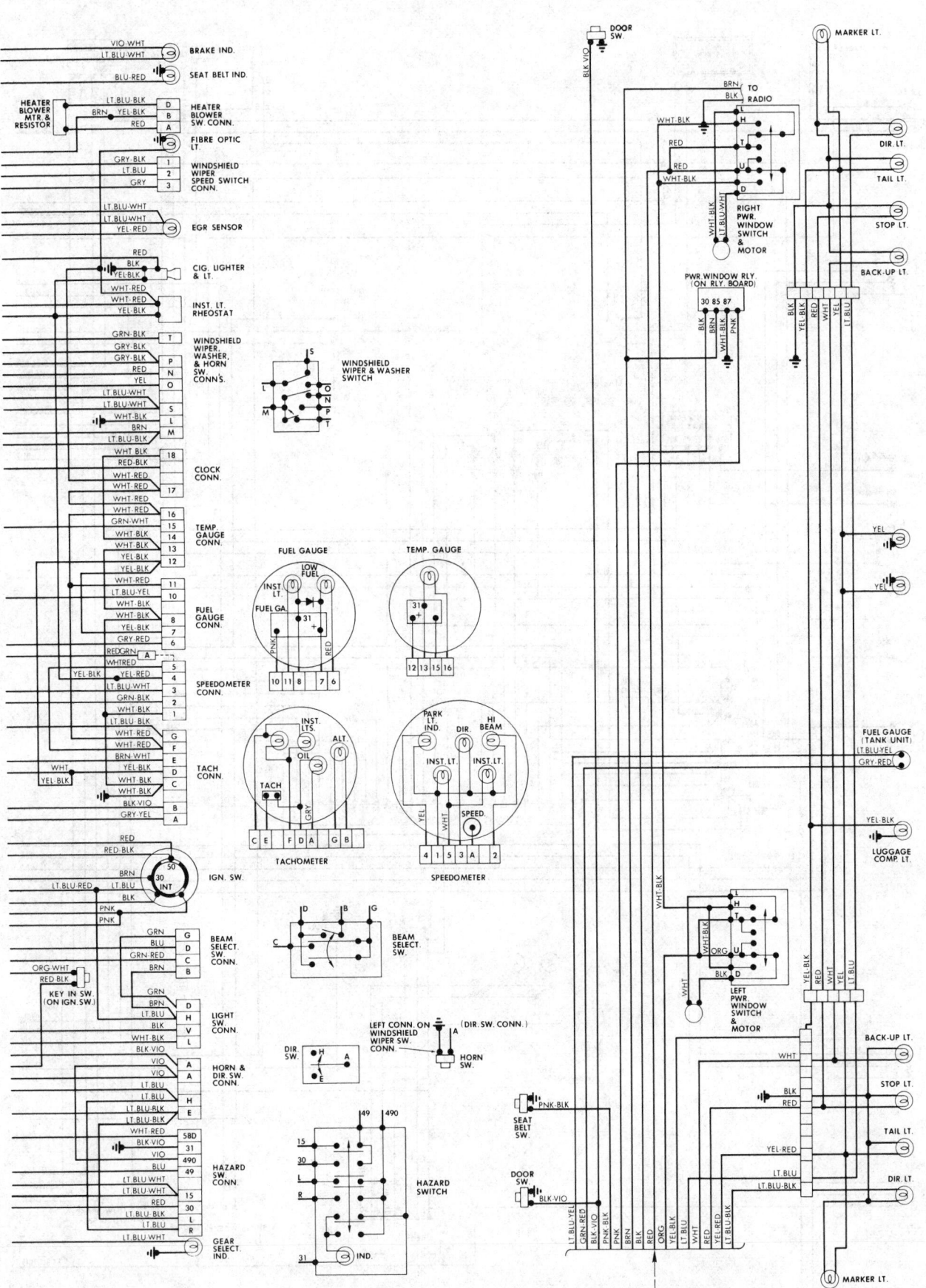

1981 Fiat

ENGINE COMPARTMENT

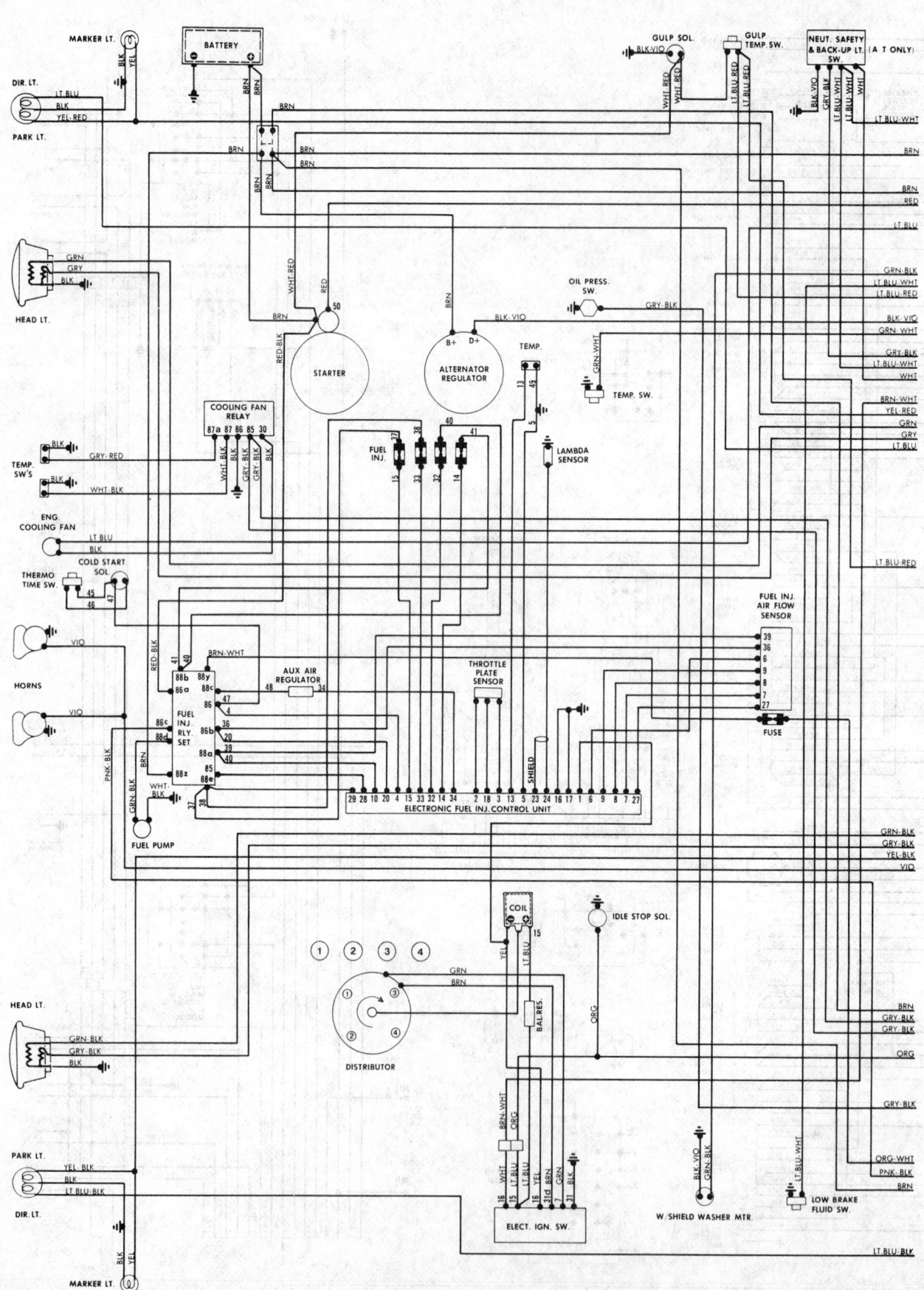

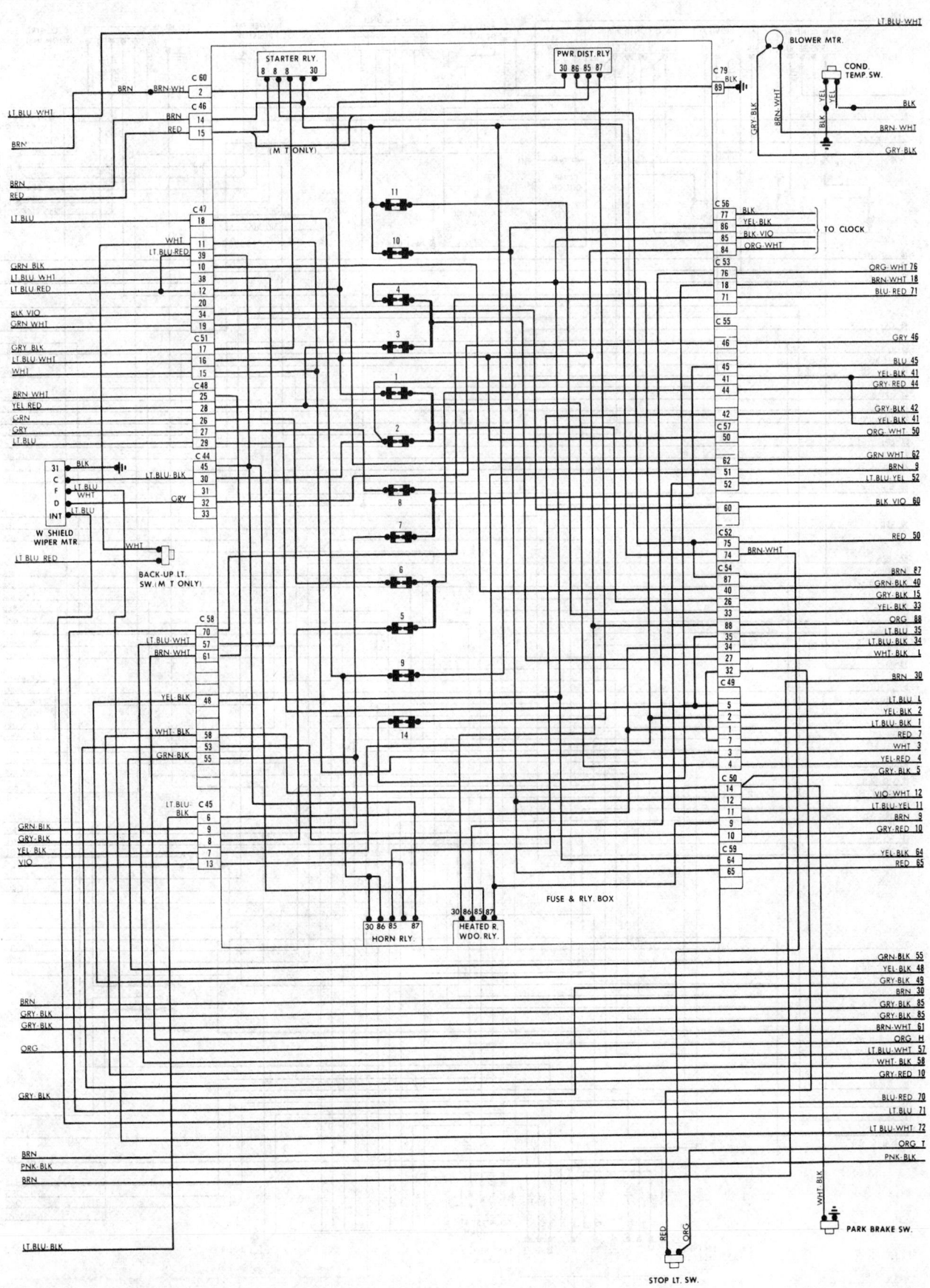

1981 Fiat

UNDERDASH

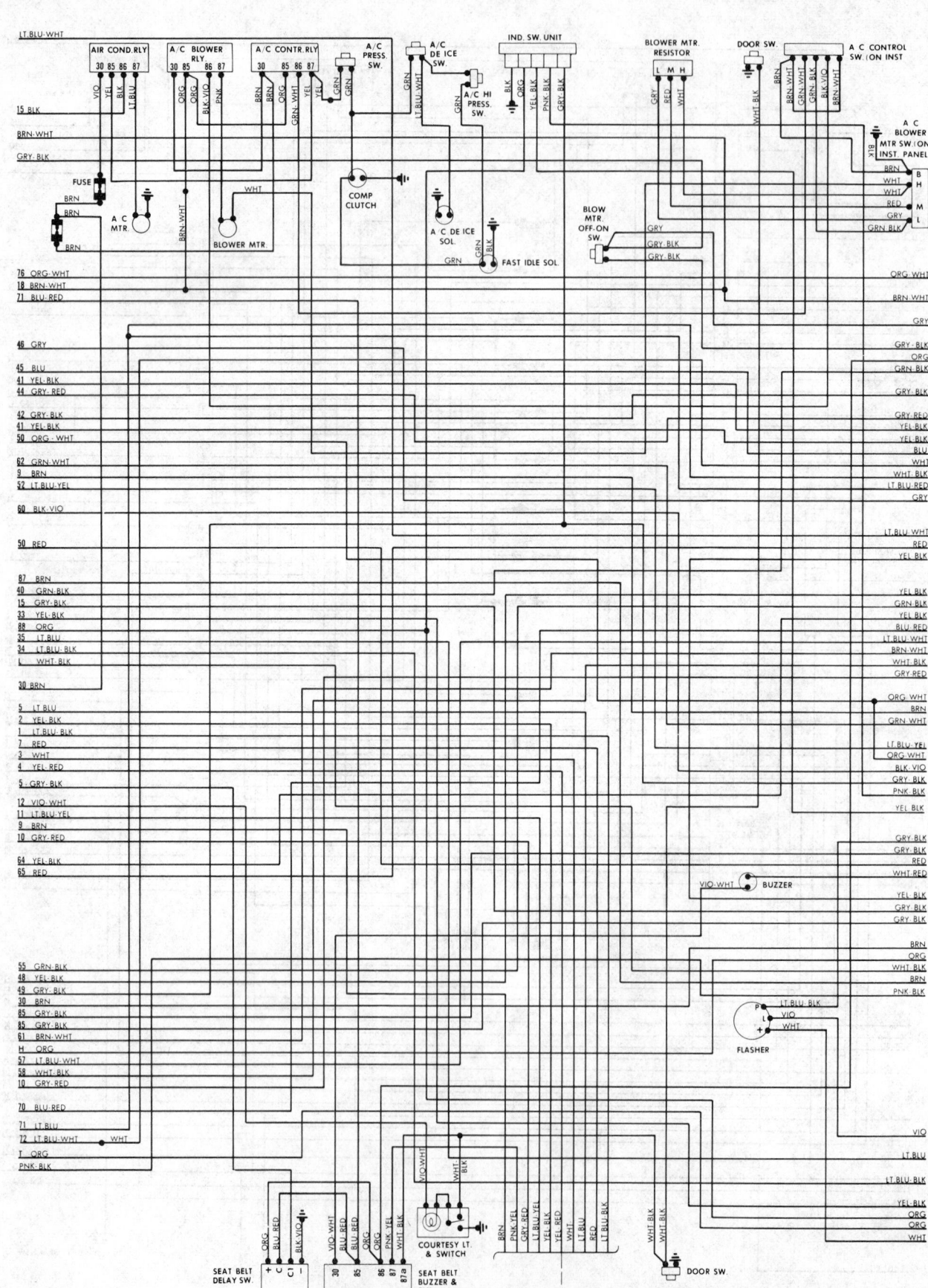

WIRING DIAGRAMS

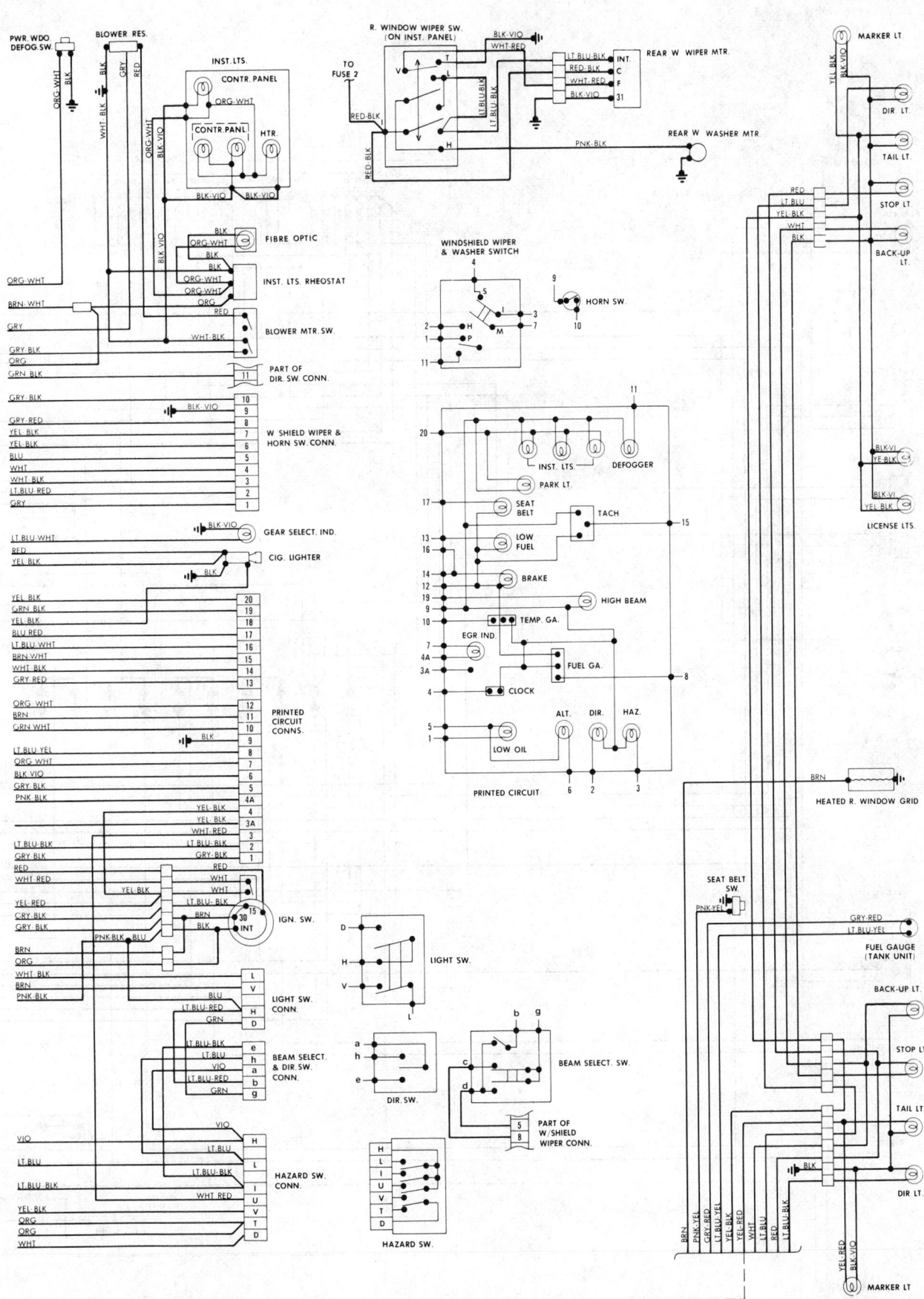

1981 Fiat

FRONT COMPARTMENT & FUSE PANEL

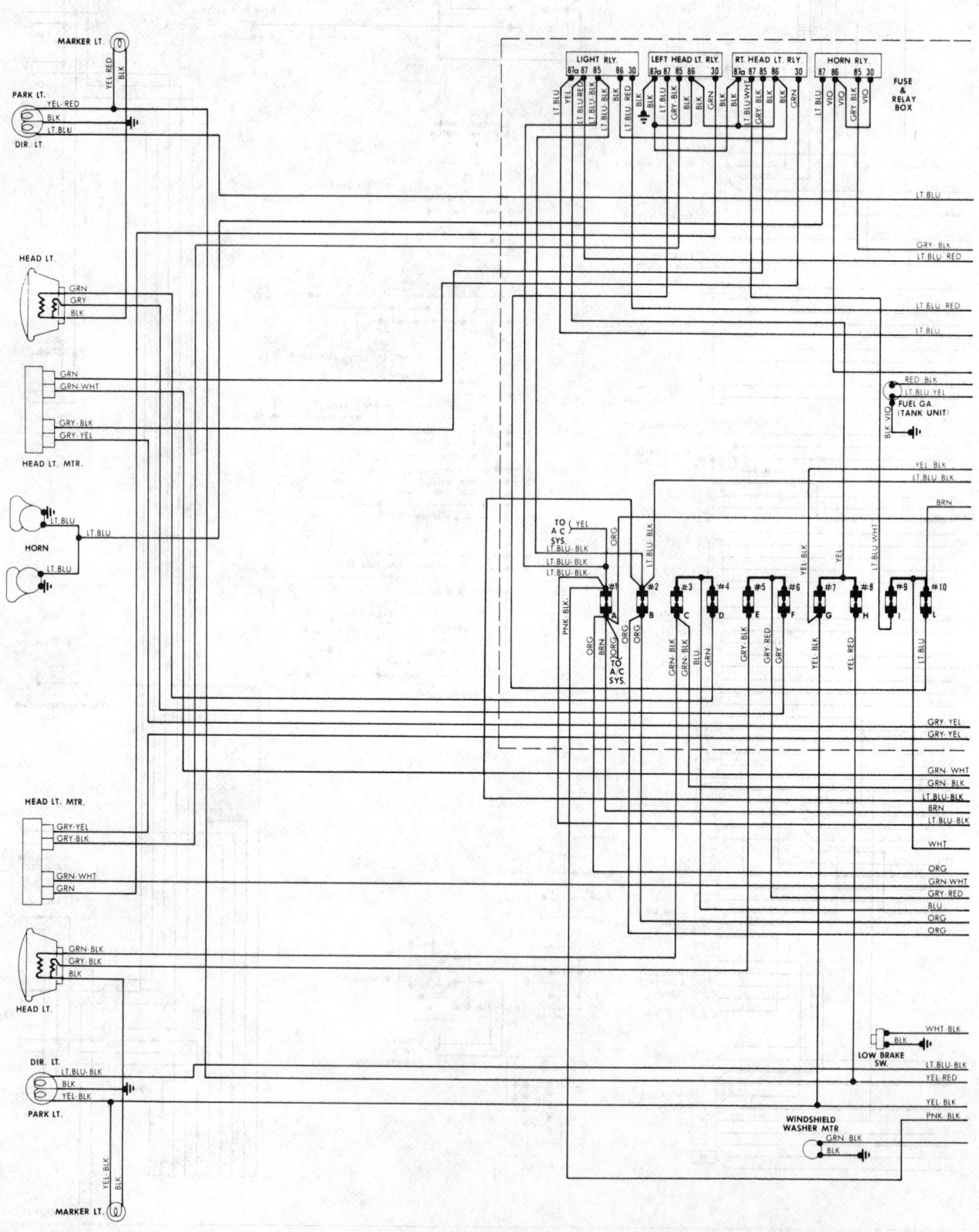

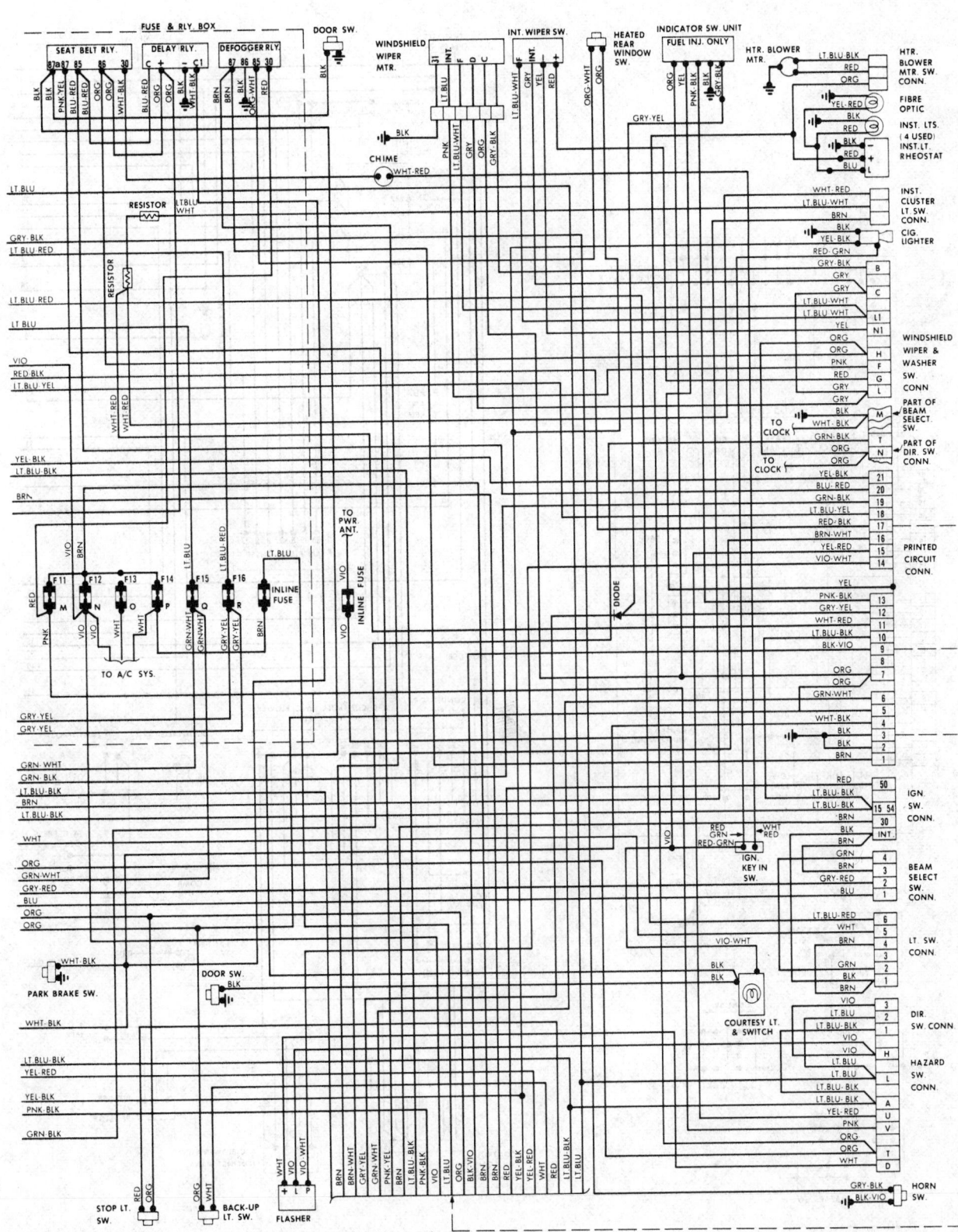

INSTRUMENT PANEL & ENGINE COMPARTMENT

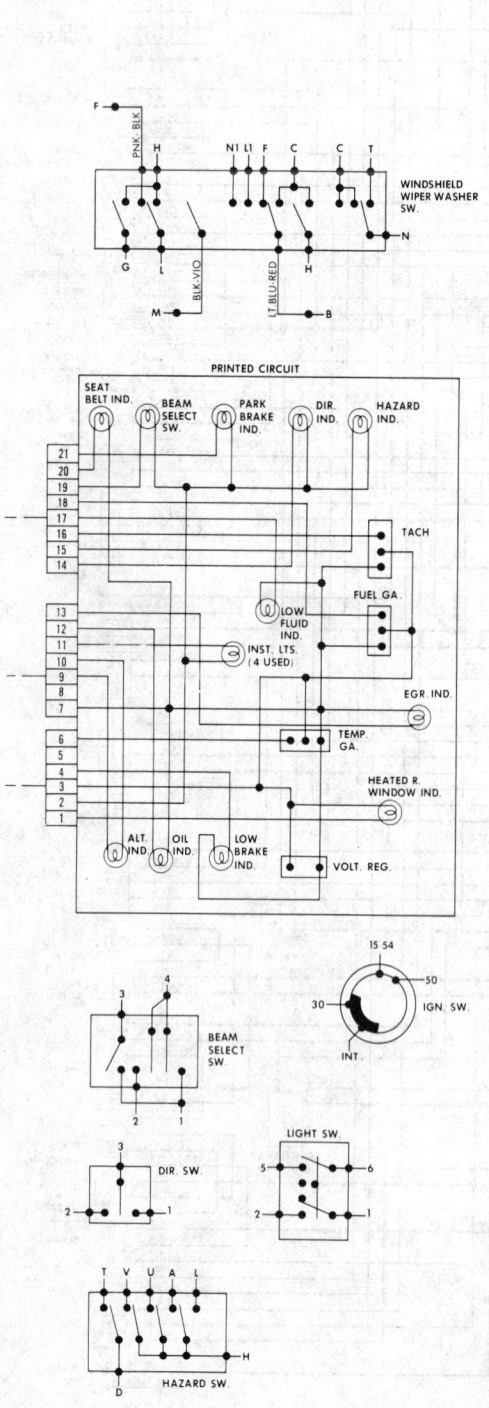

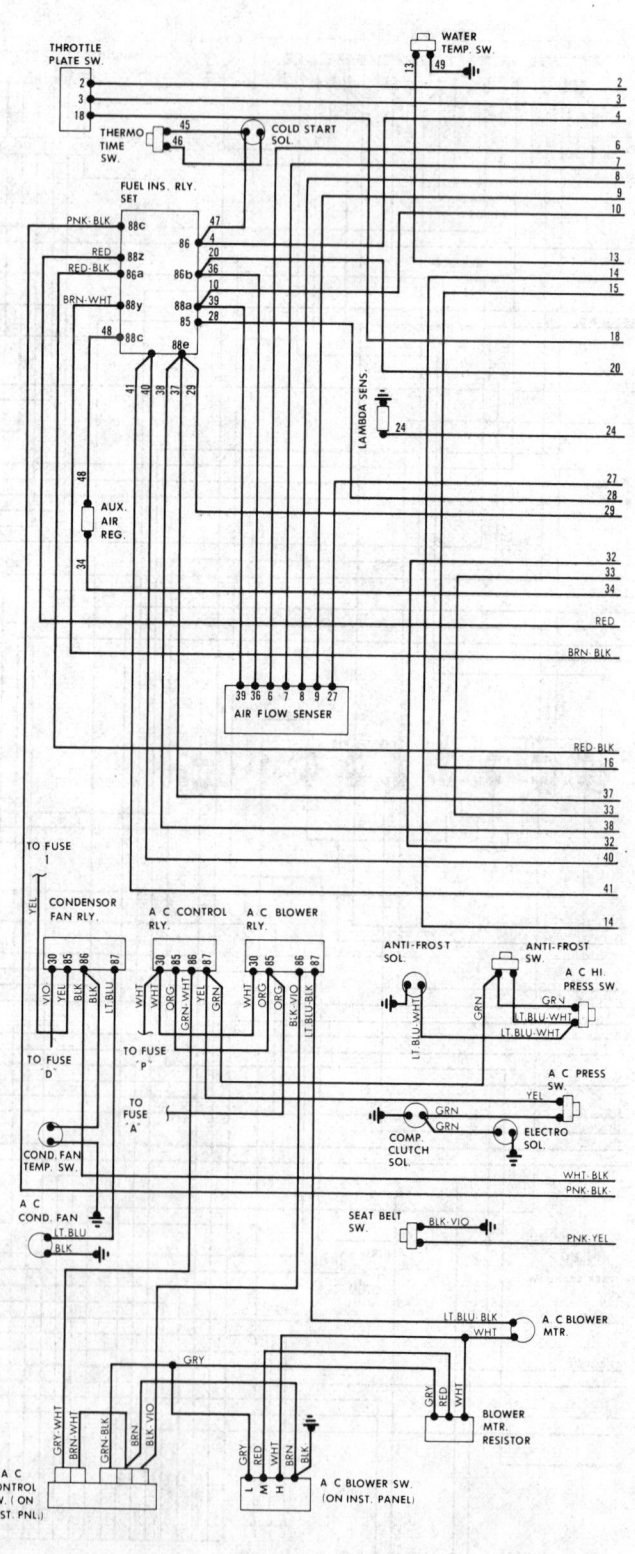

ENGINE COMPARTMENT & REAR COMPARTMENT

WIRING DIAGRAMS

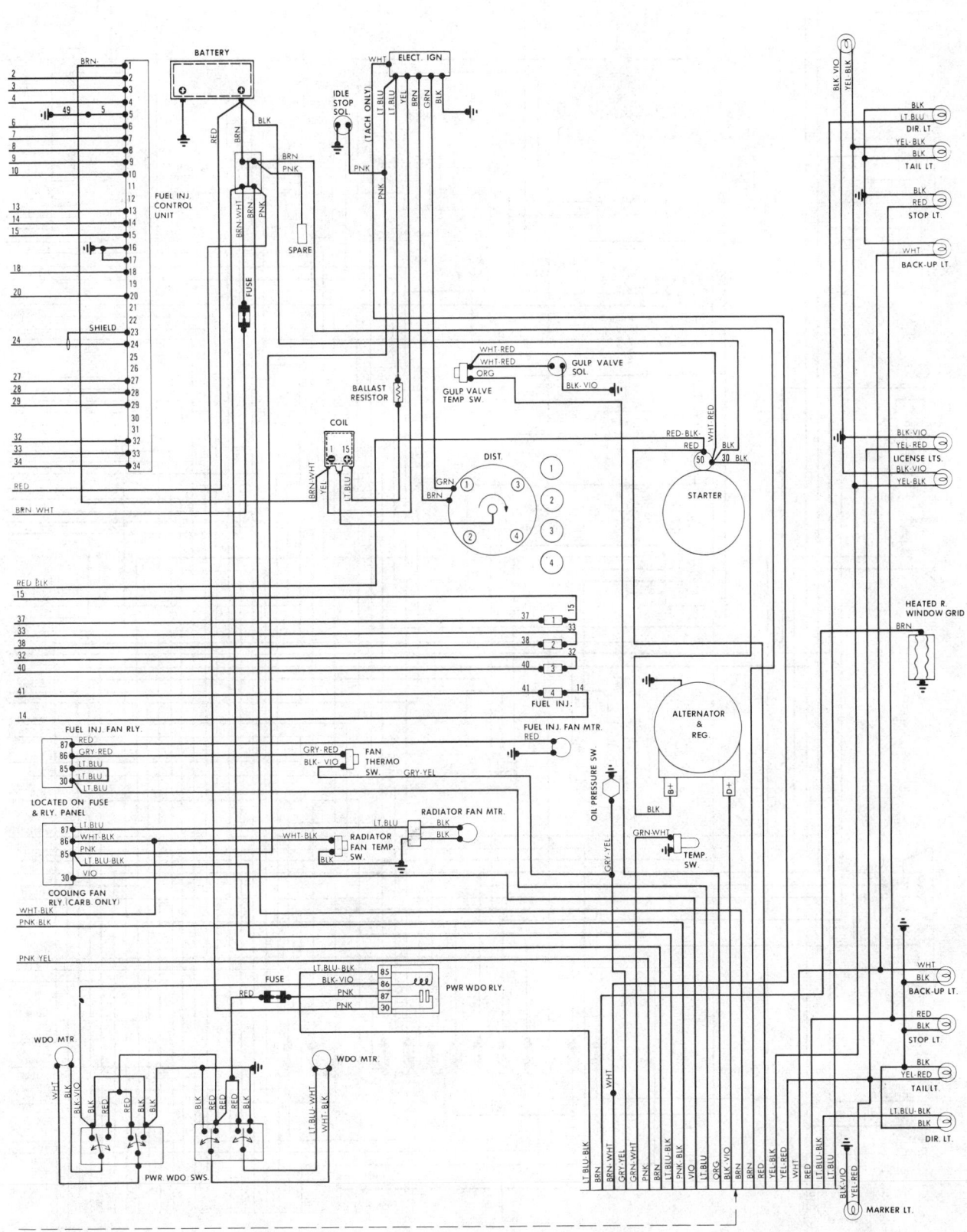

1981 Honda

ENGINE COMPARTMENT & FUSE BLOCK

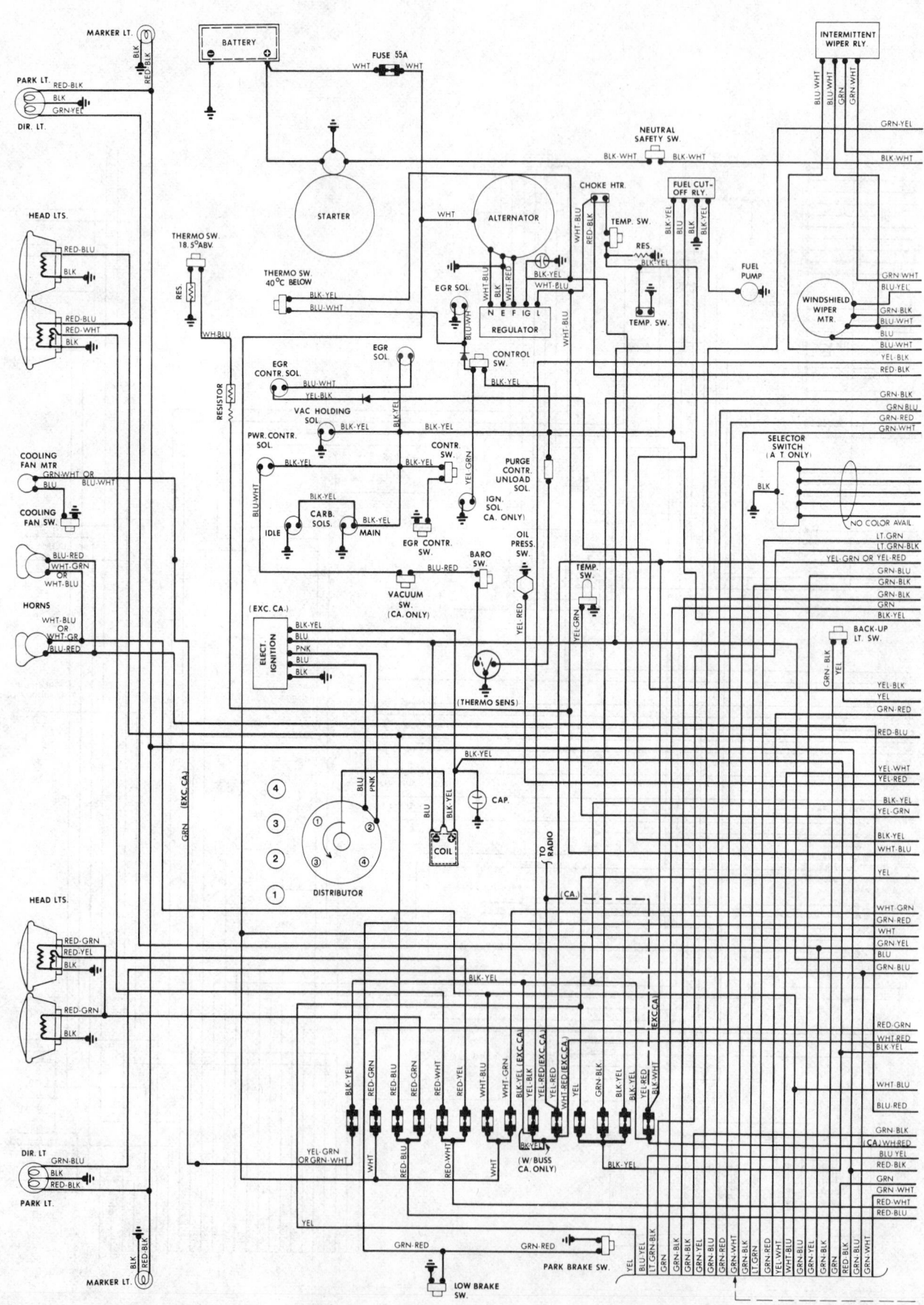

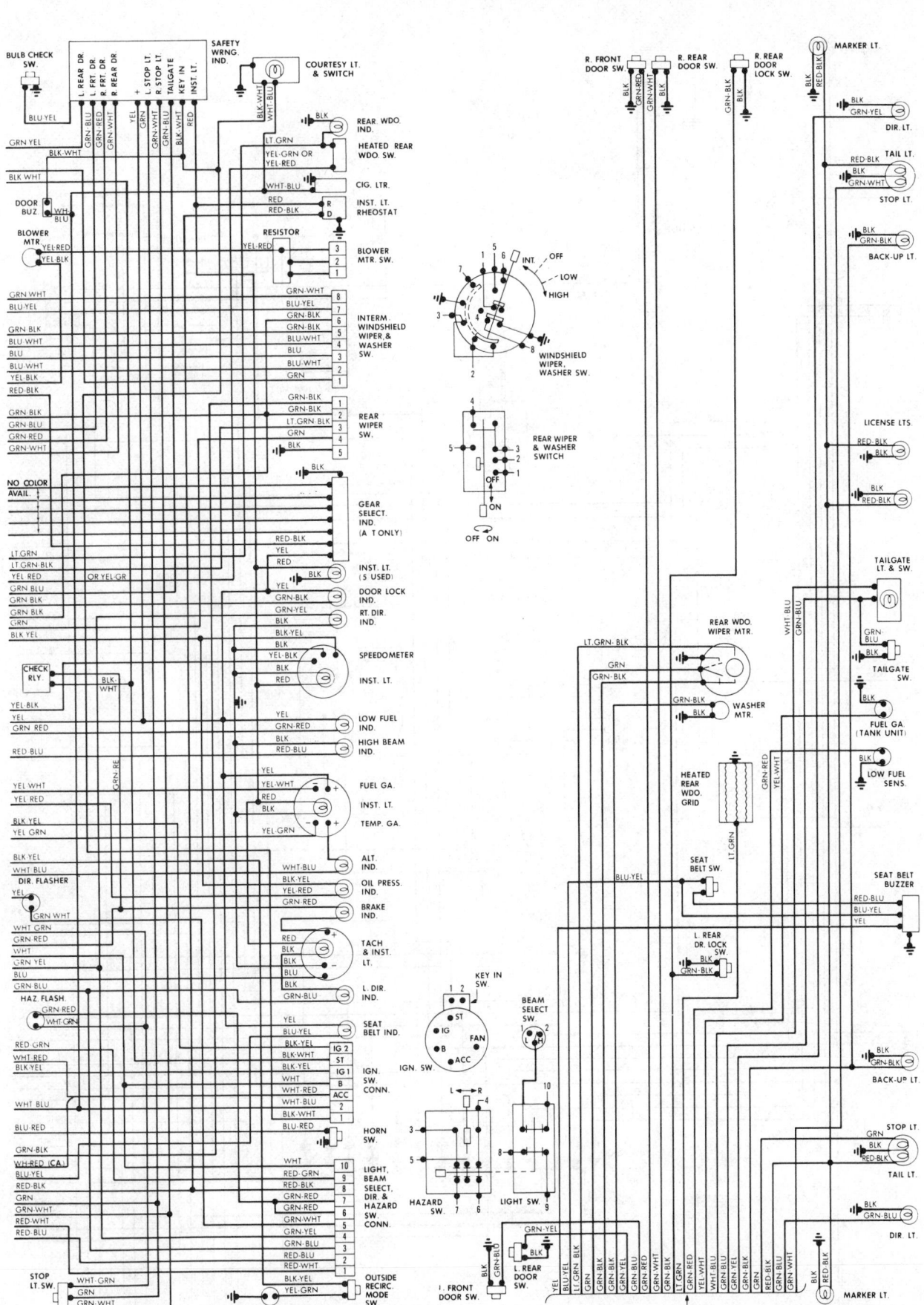

1981 Honda

ENGINE COMPARTMENT & FUSE BLOCK

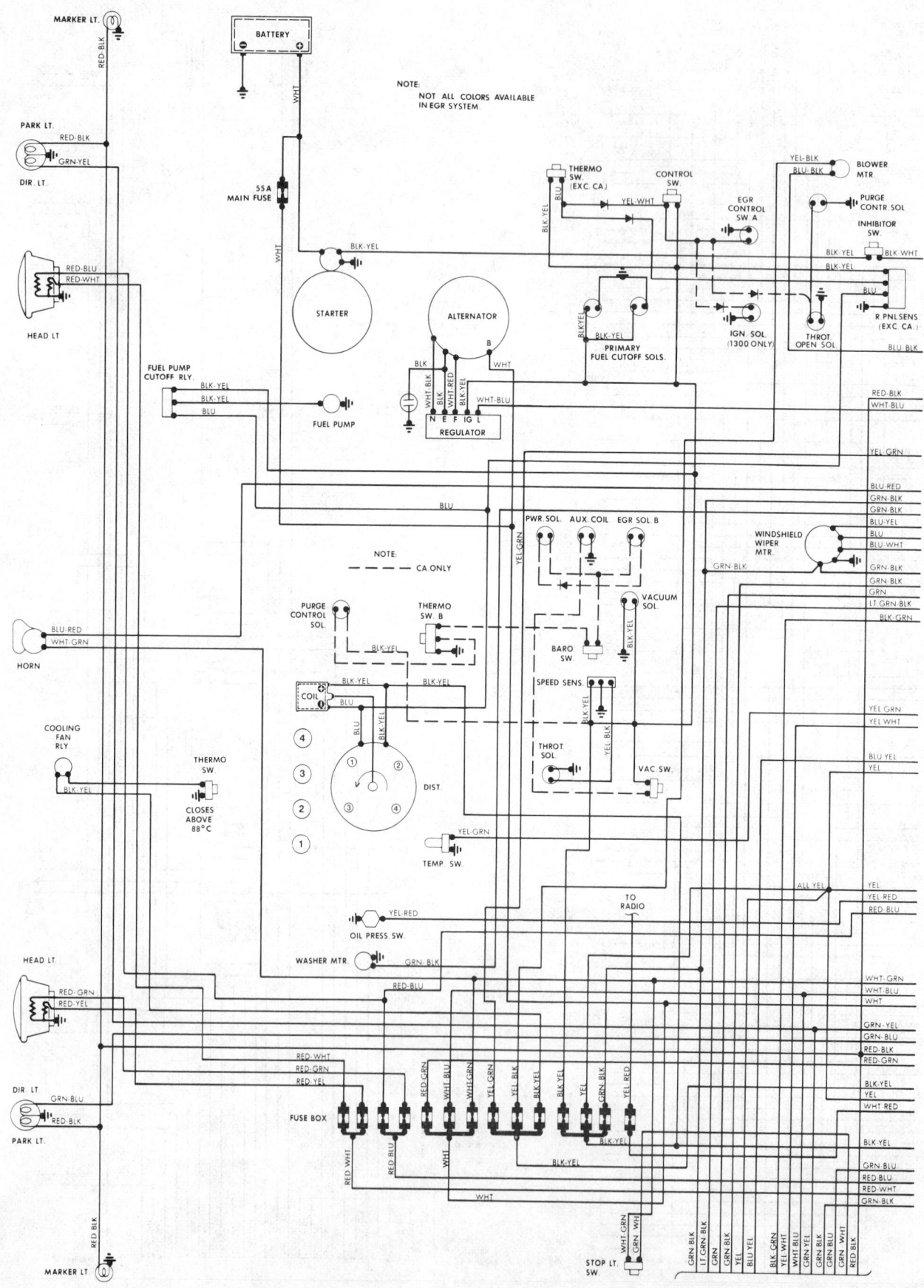

INSTRUMENT PANEL & REAR COMPARTMENT

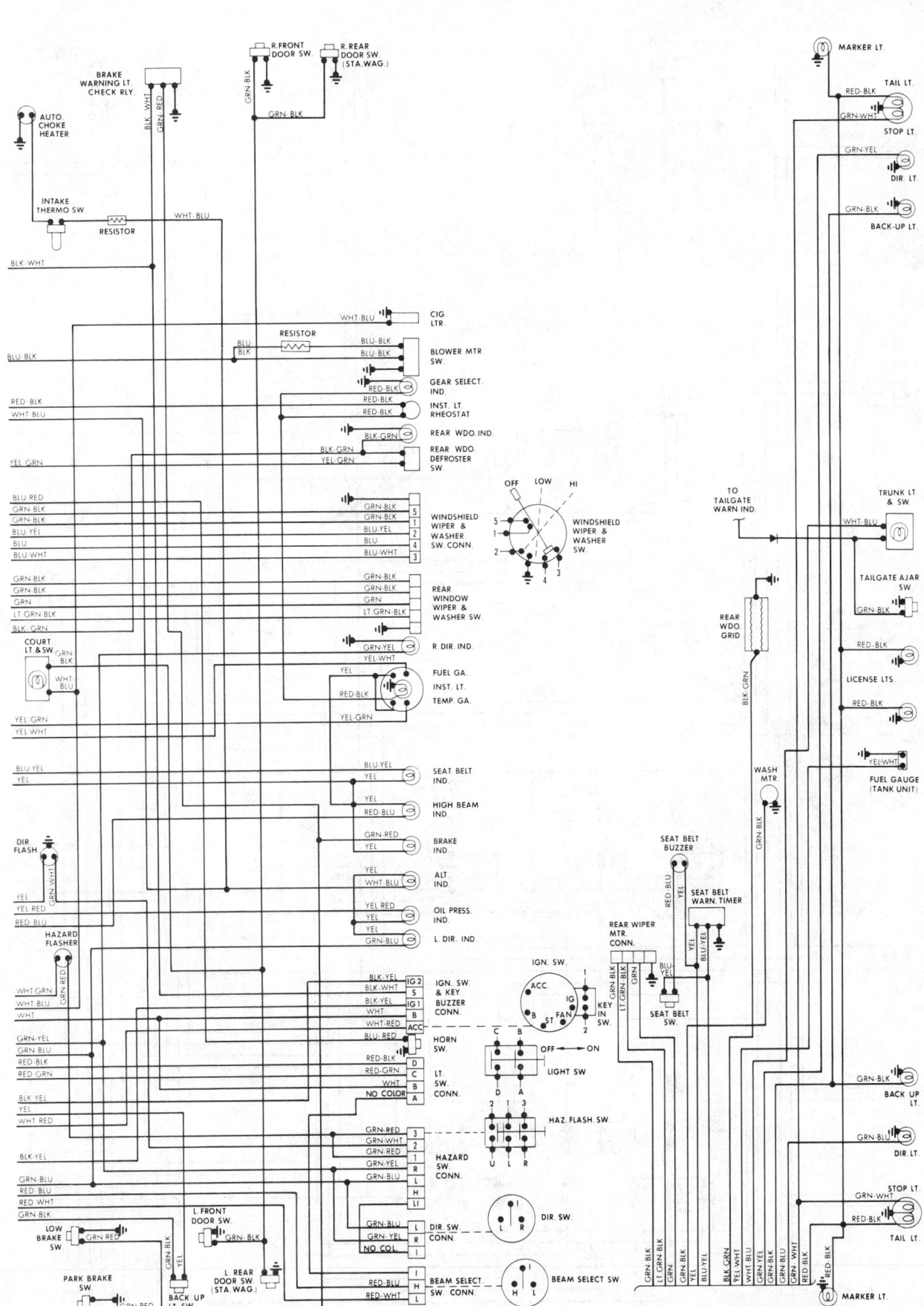

ENGINE COMPARTMENT & FUSE BLOCK

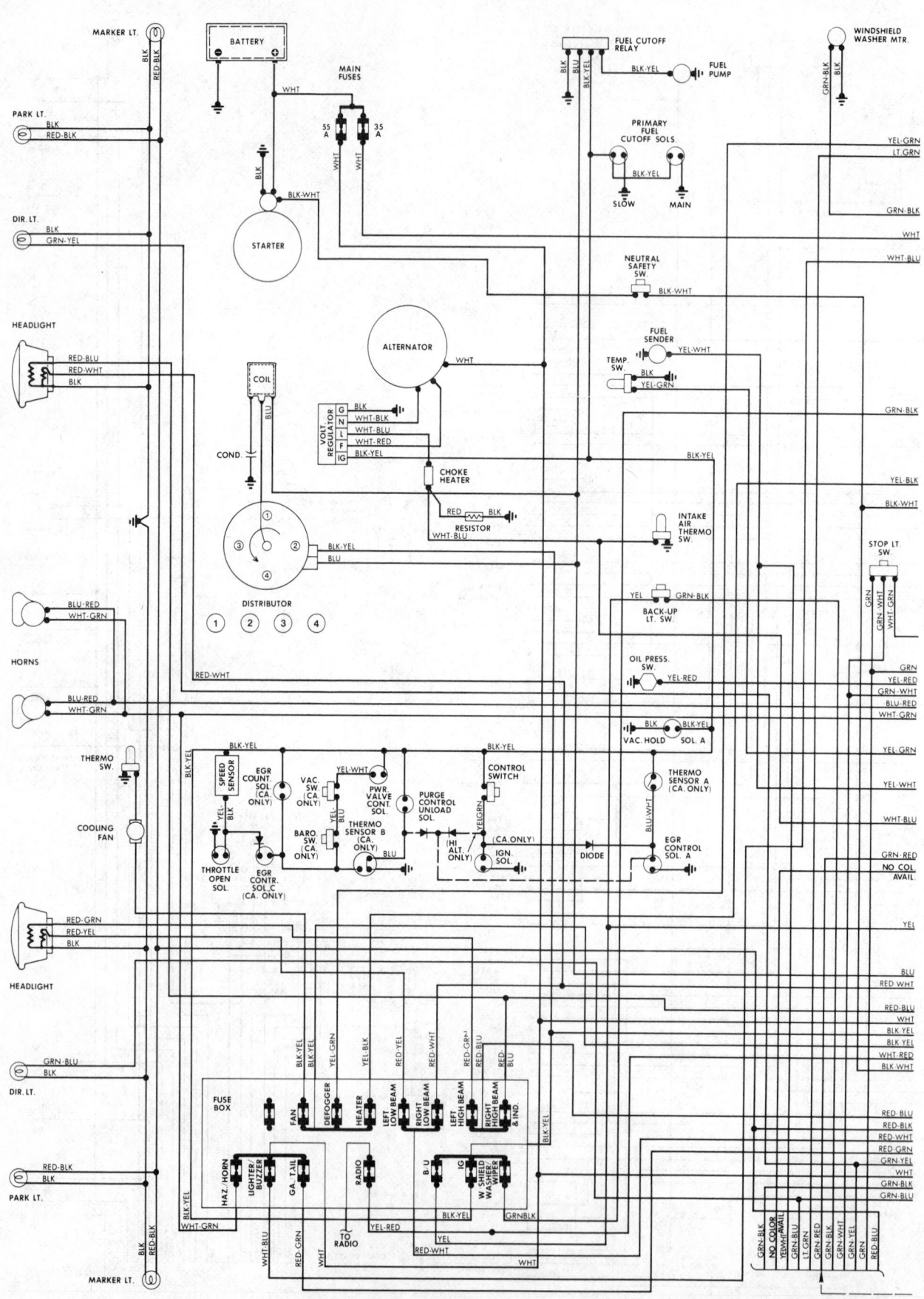

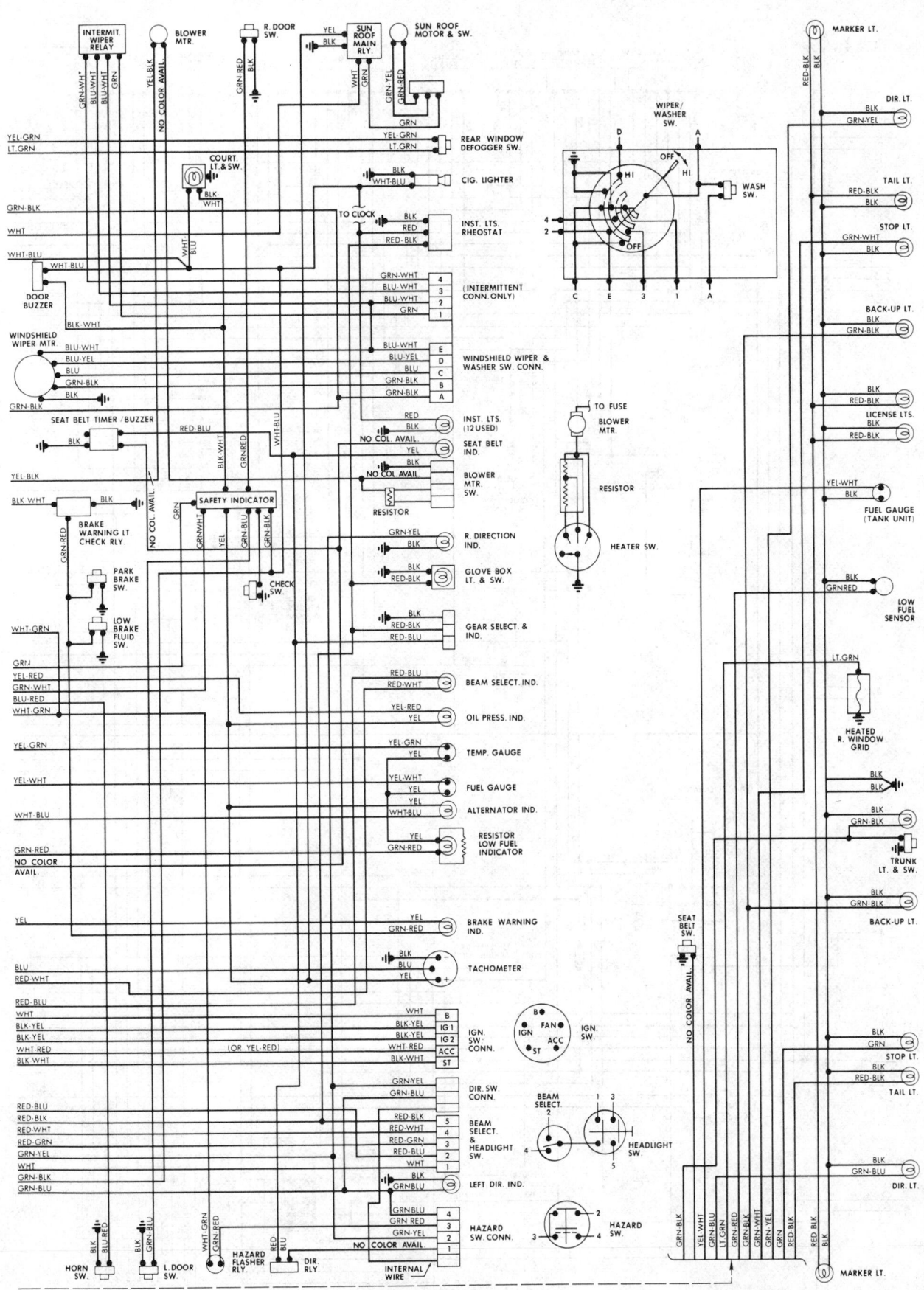

1981 Isuzu

ENGINE COMPARTMENT & FUSE BLOCK

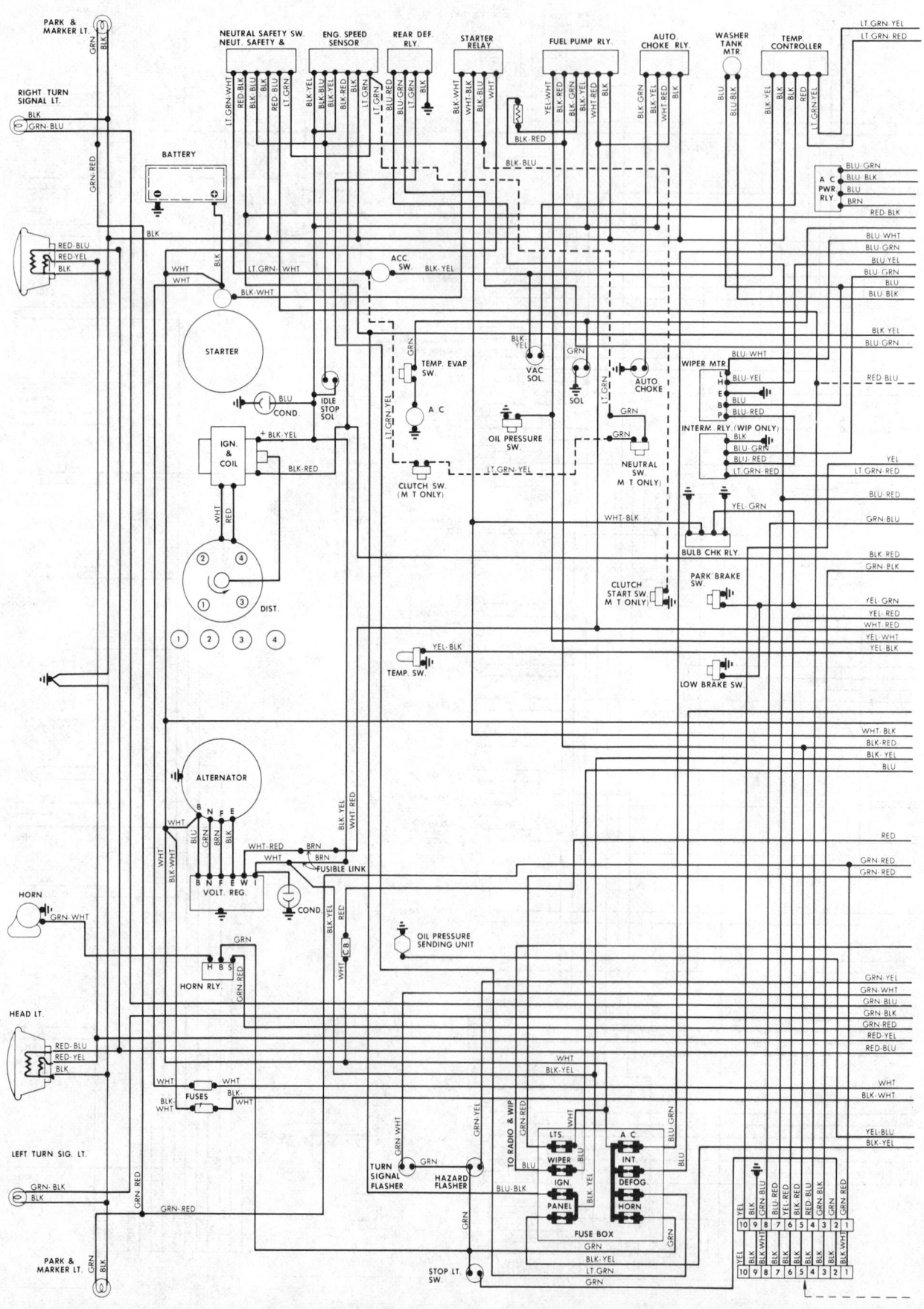

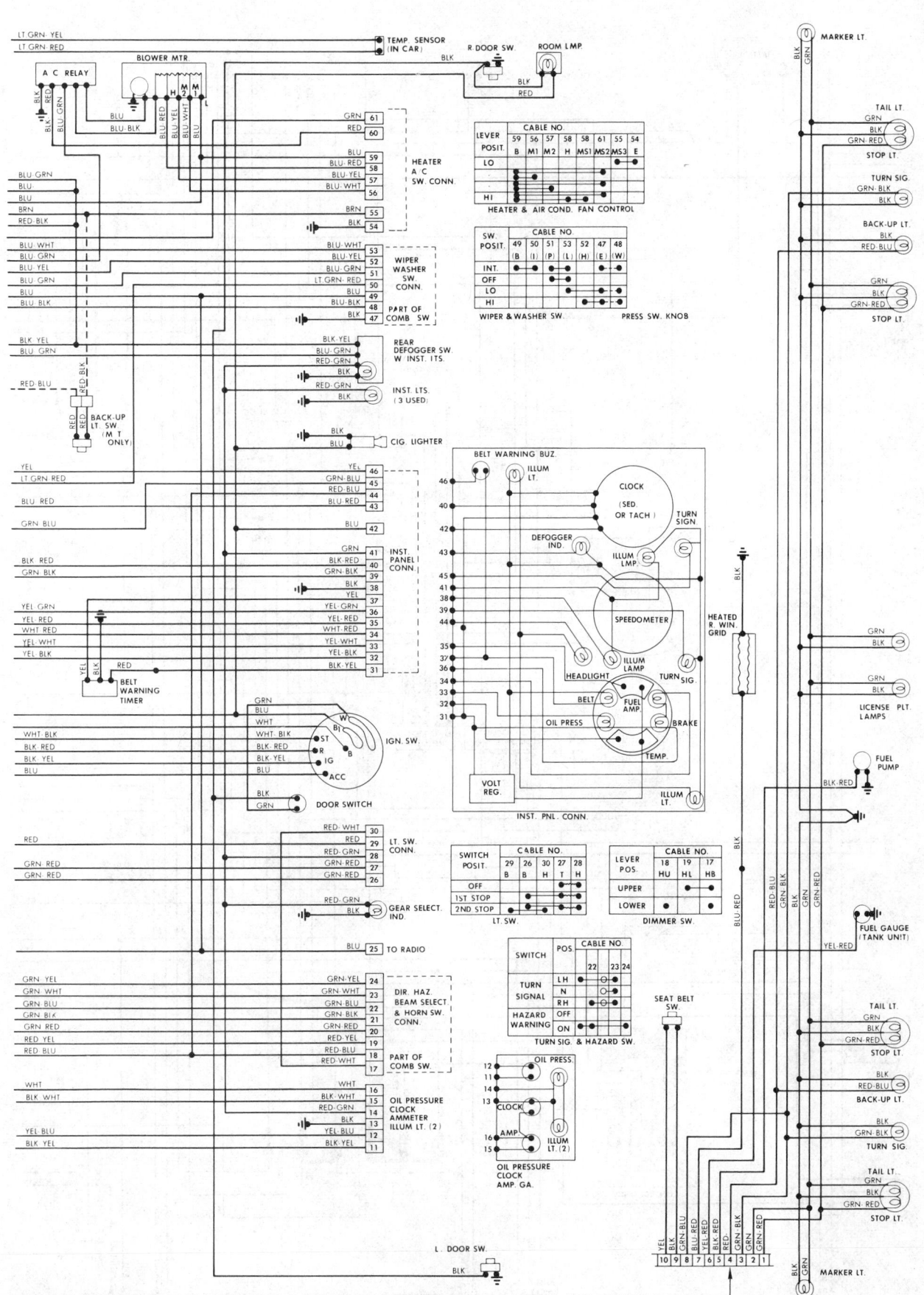

1981 Isuzu & LUV

ENGINE COMPARTMENT & FUSE BLOCK

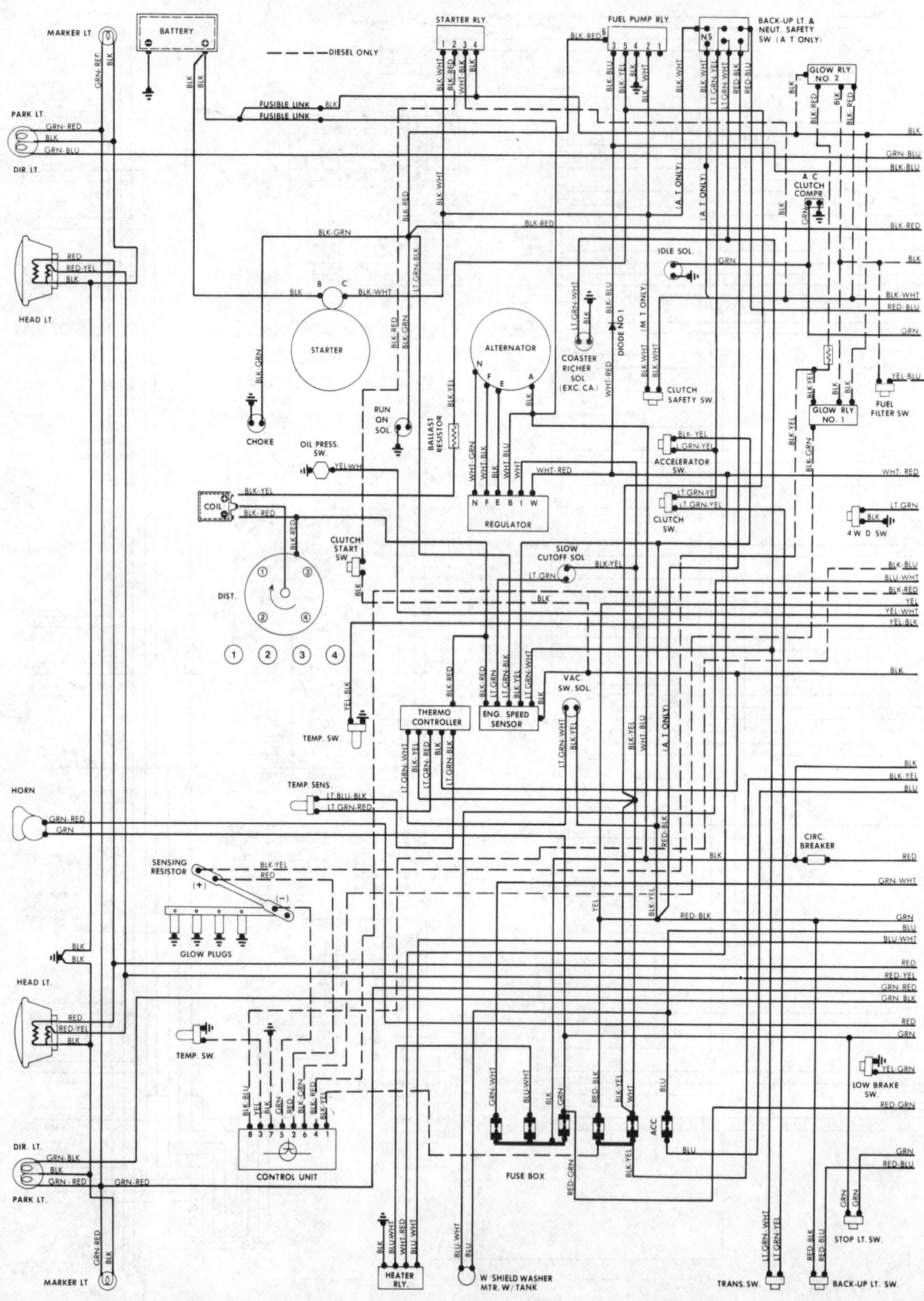

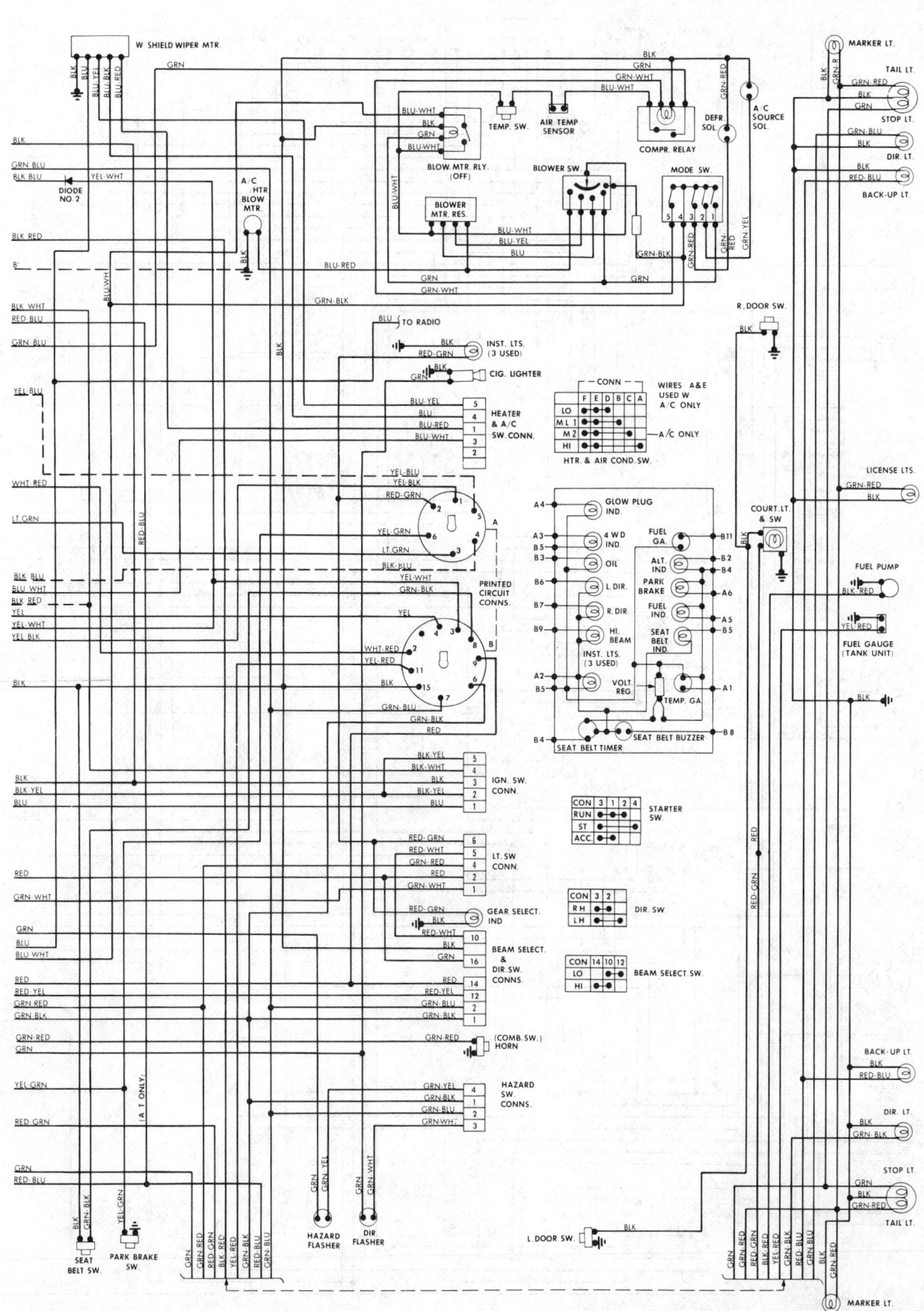

1981 Jaguar

ENGINE COMPARTMENT & FUSE BLOCK

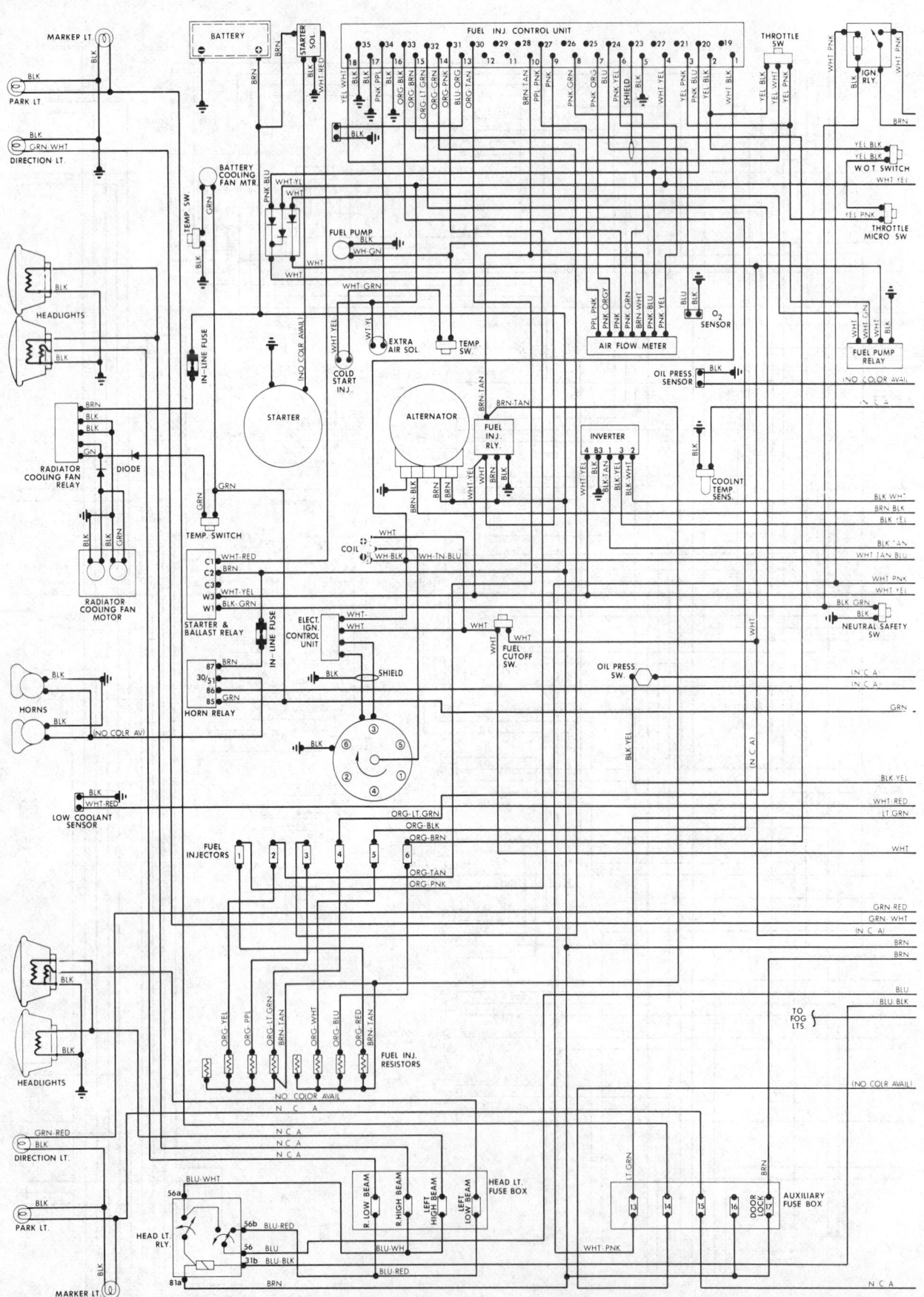

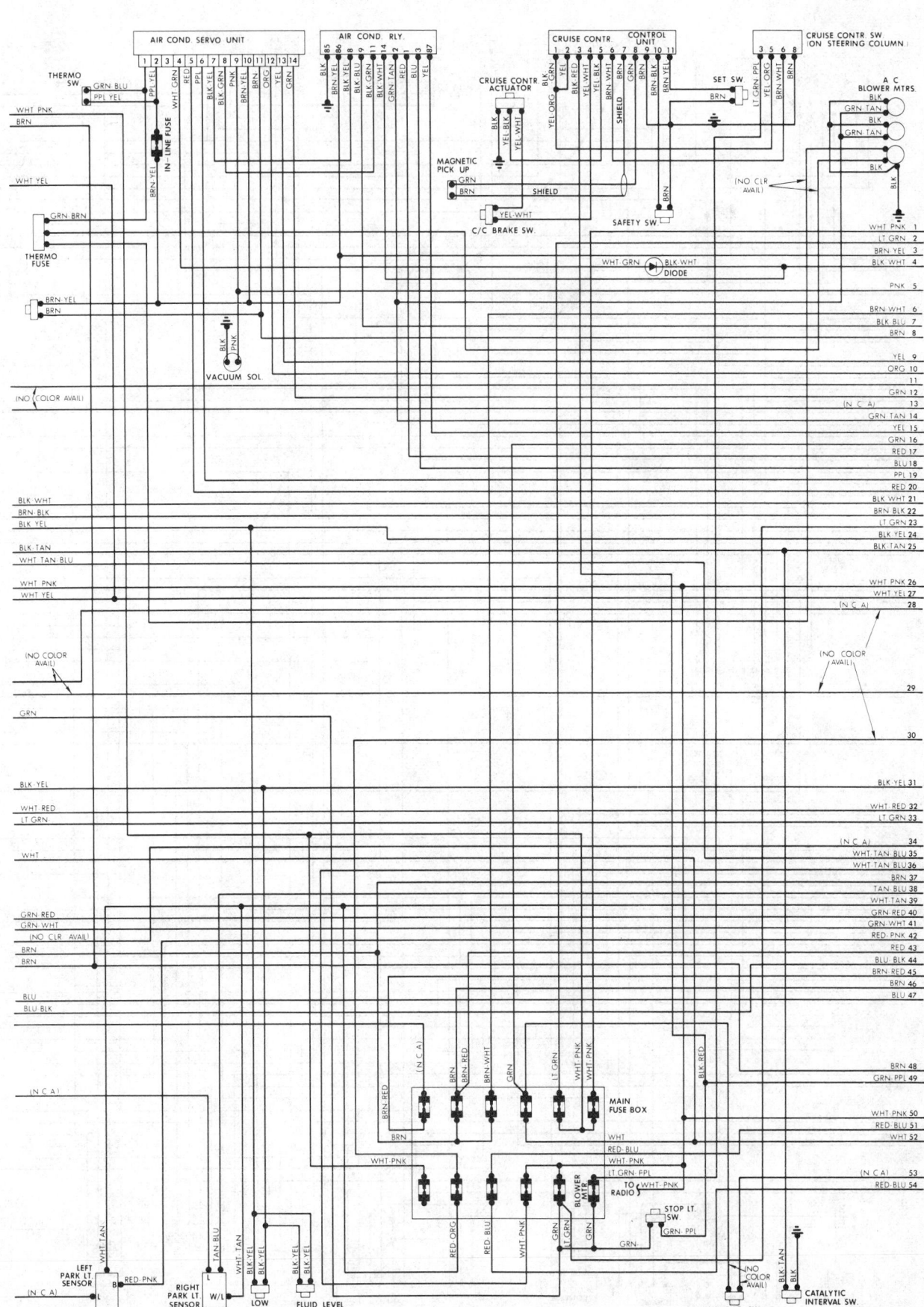

1981 Jaguar

UNDERDASH

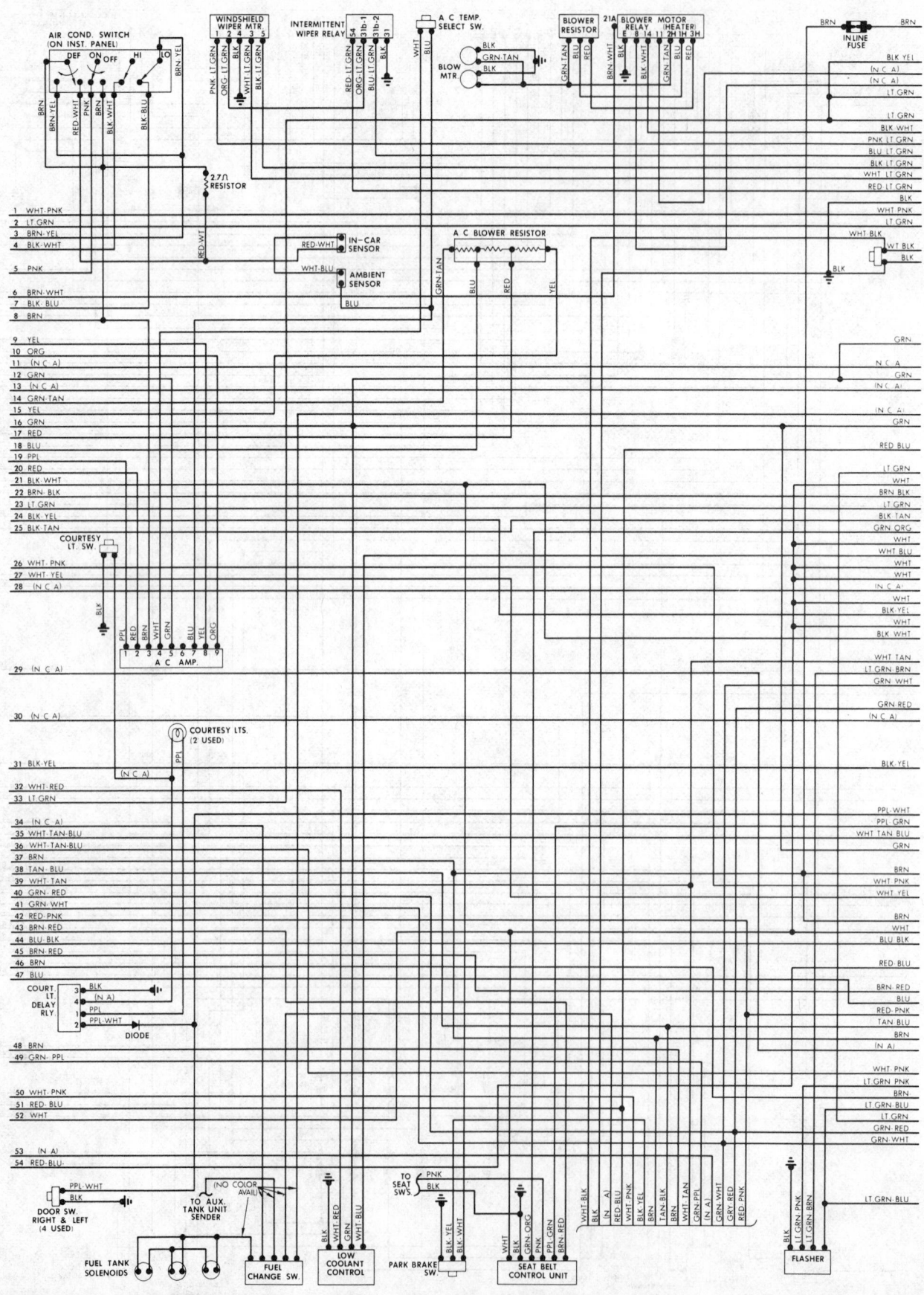

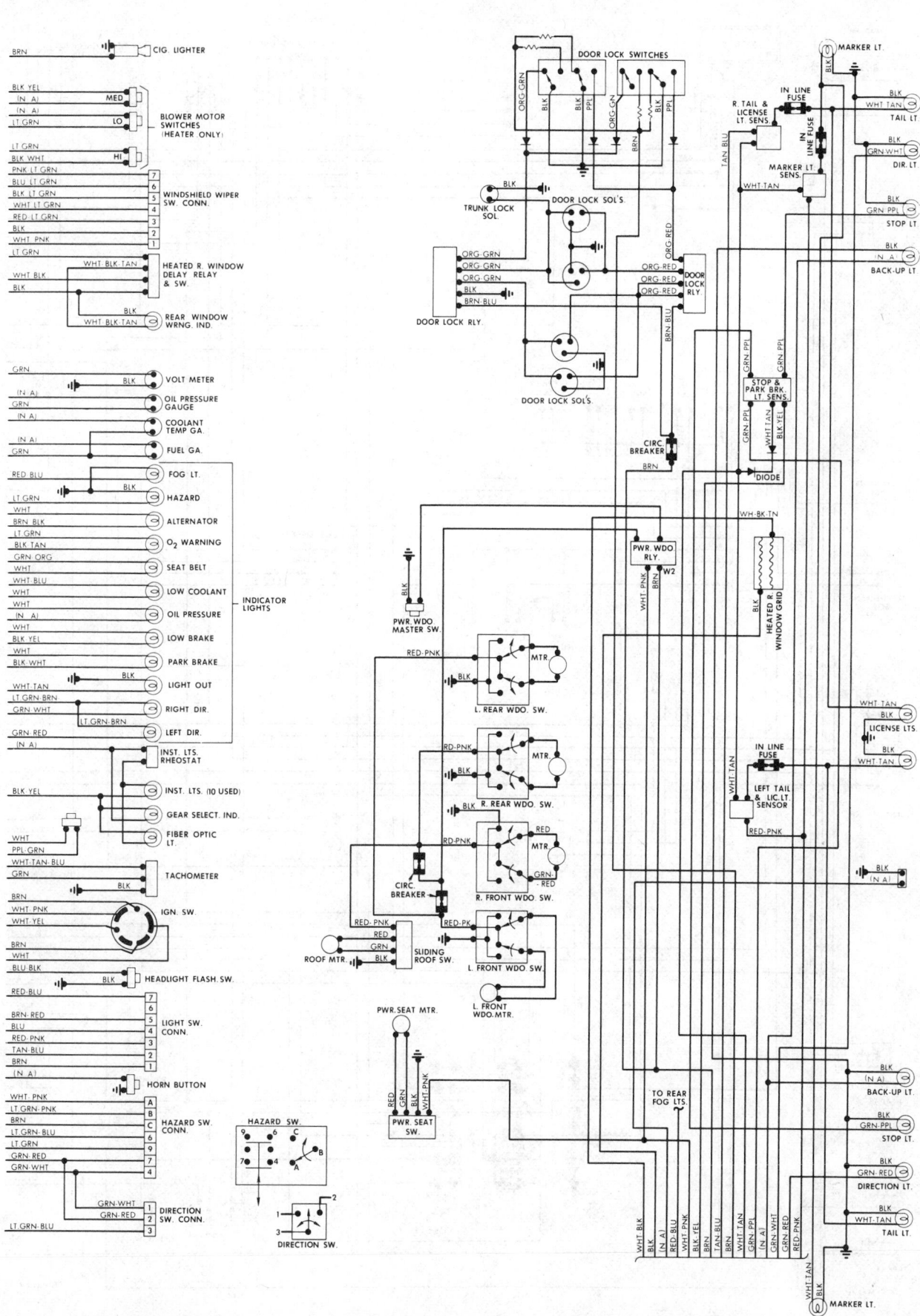

1981 Mazda

ENGINE COMPARTMENT & FUSE BLOCK

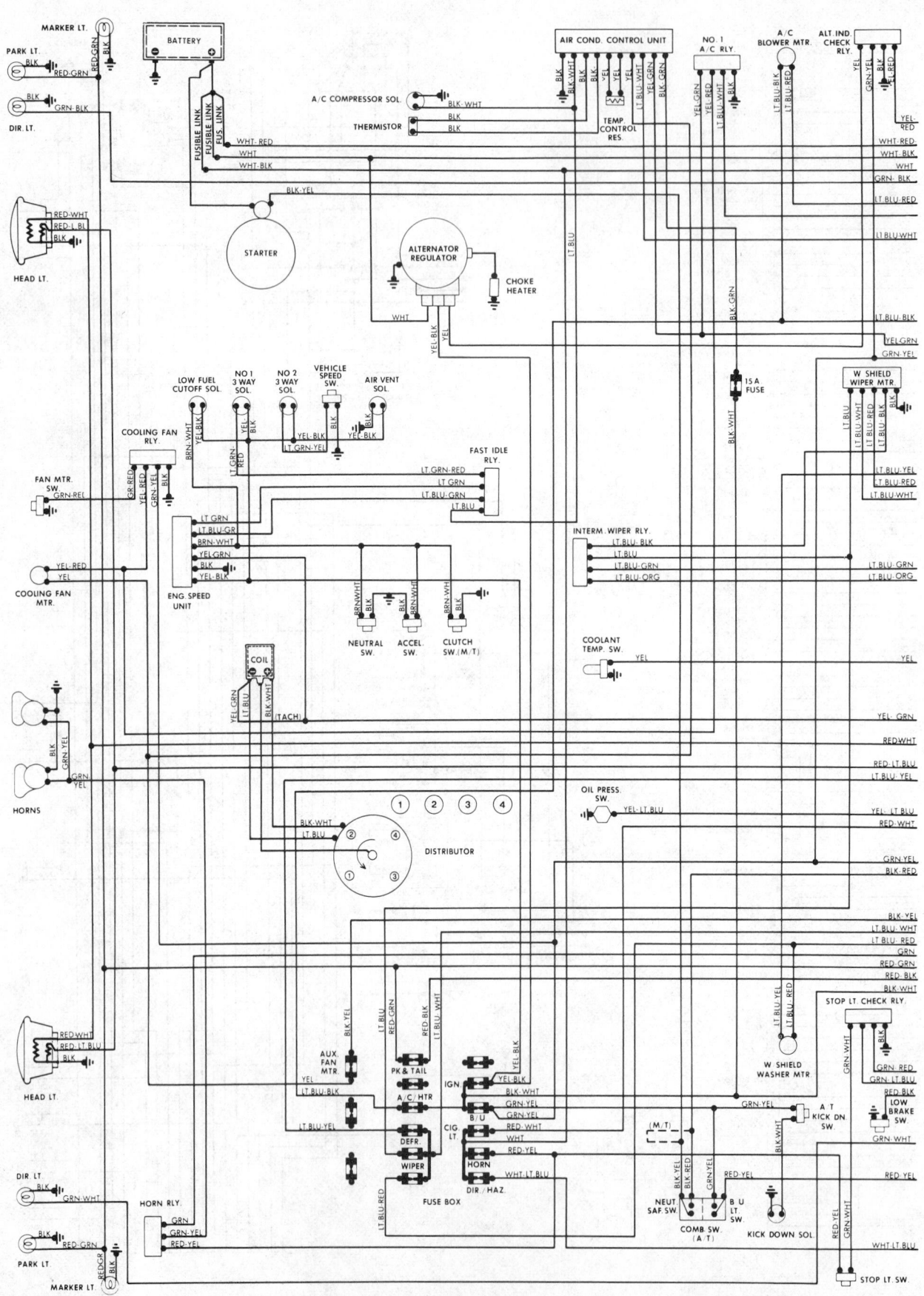

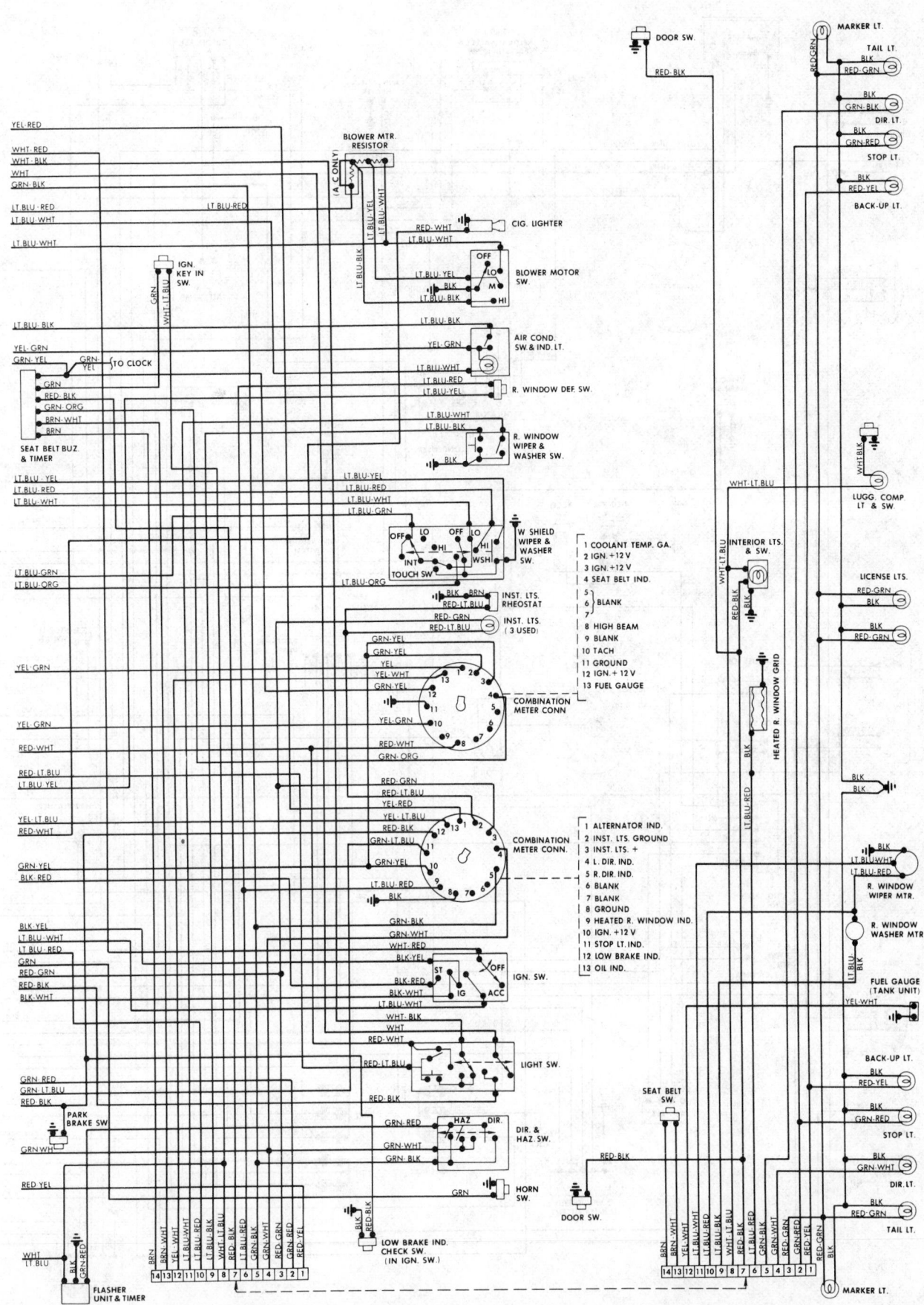

ENGINE COMPARTMENT & FUSE BLOCK

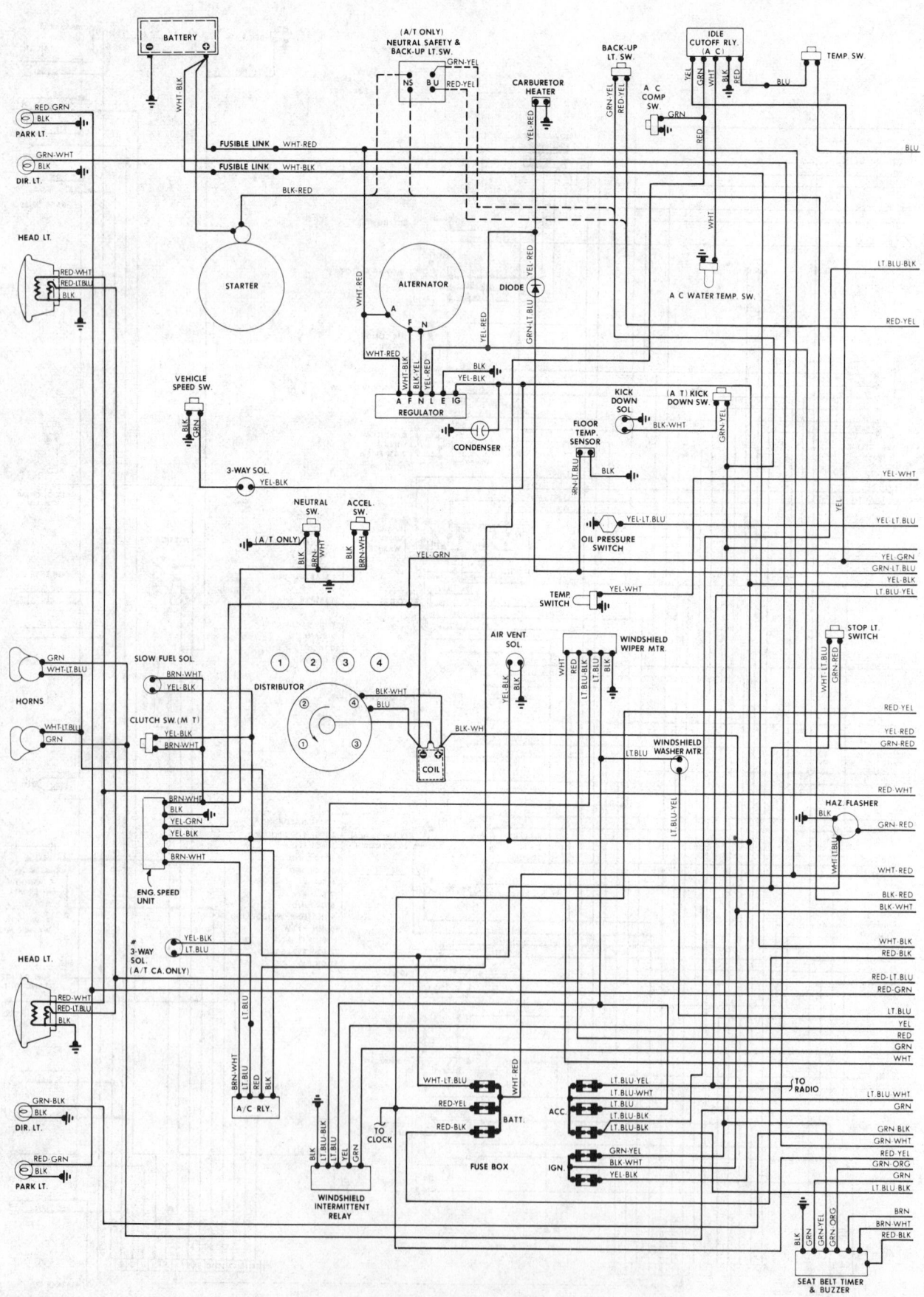

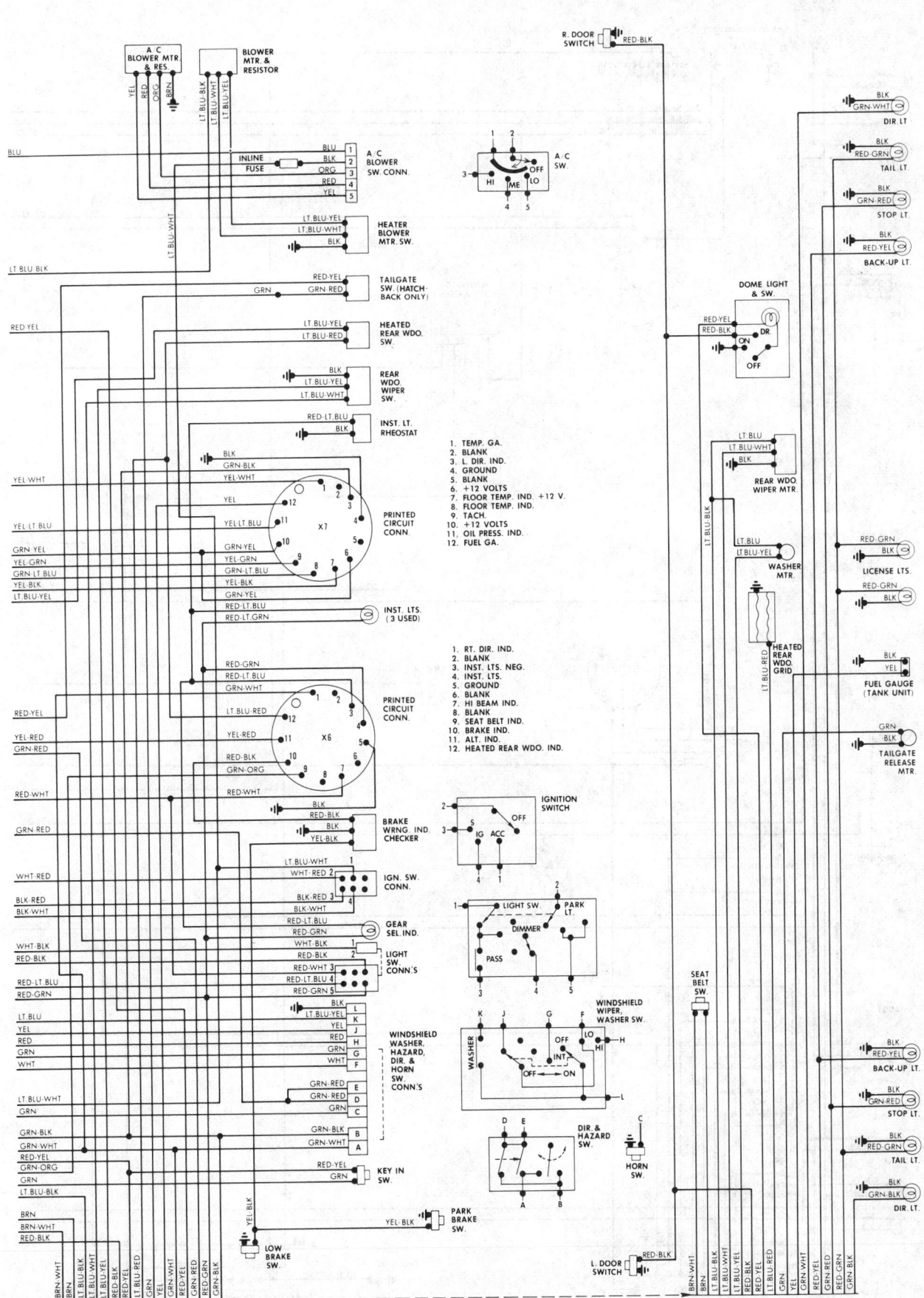

ENGINE COMPARTMENT

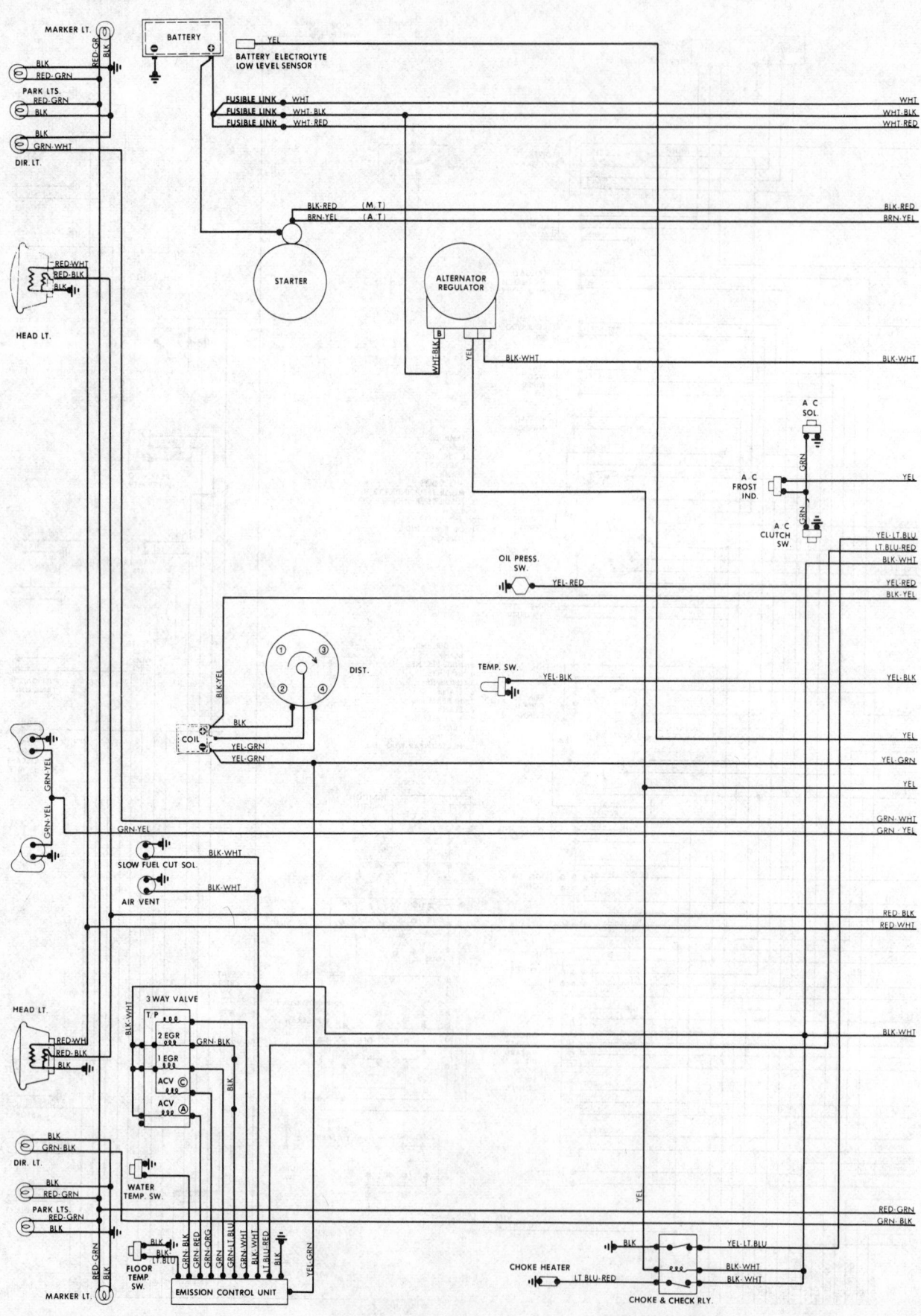

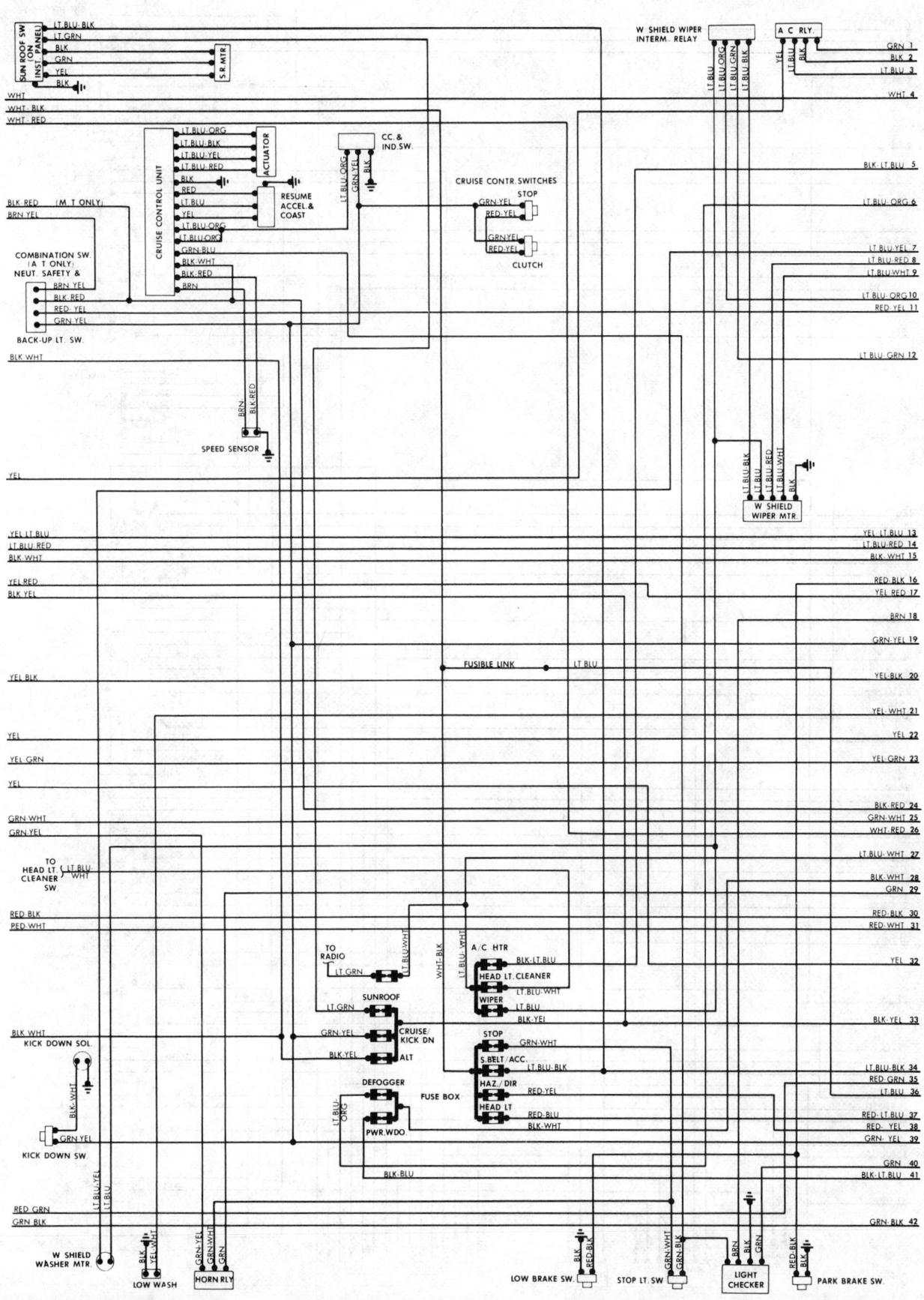

INSTRUMENT PANEL

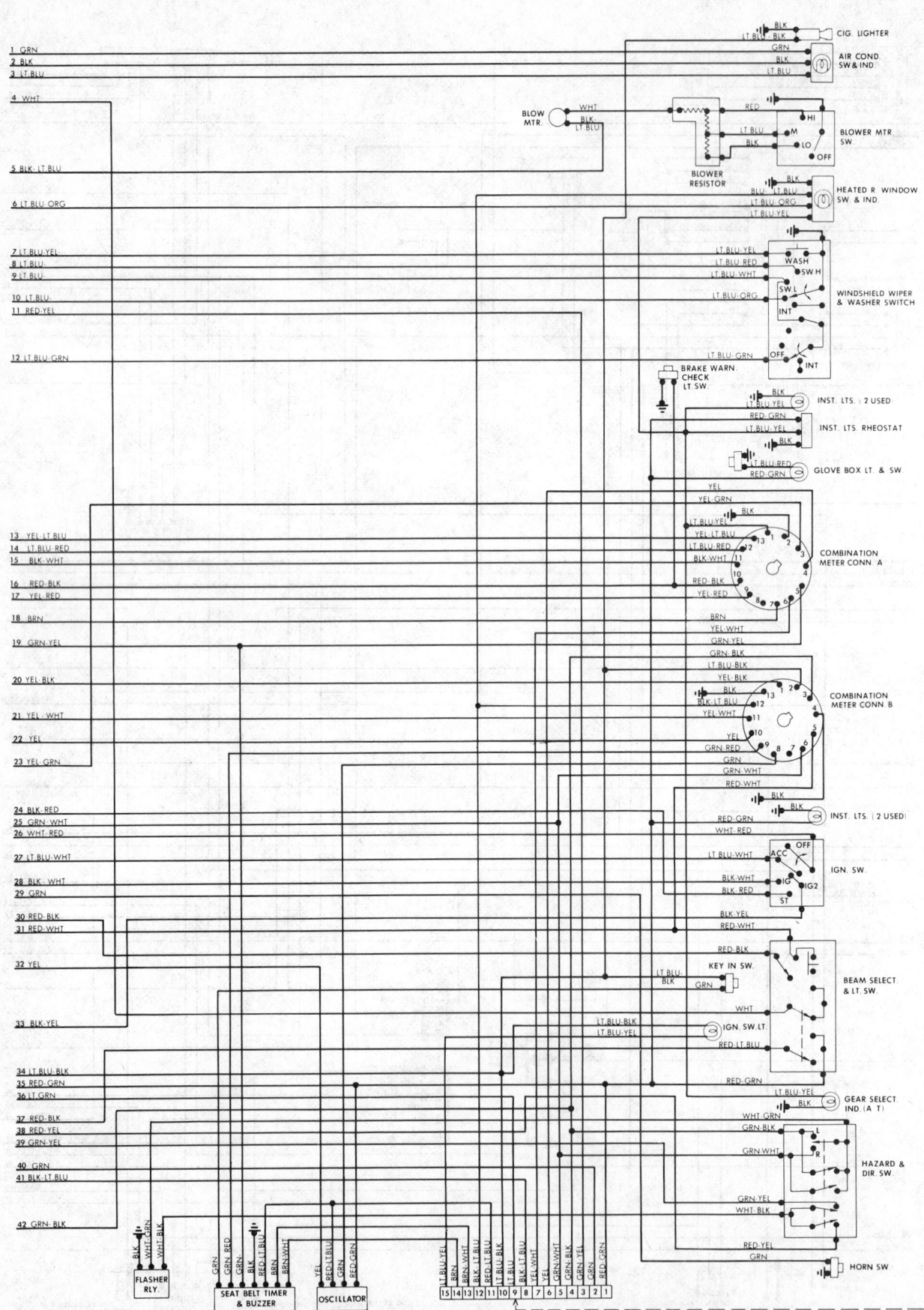

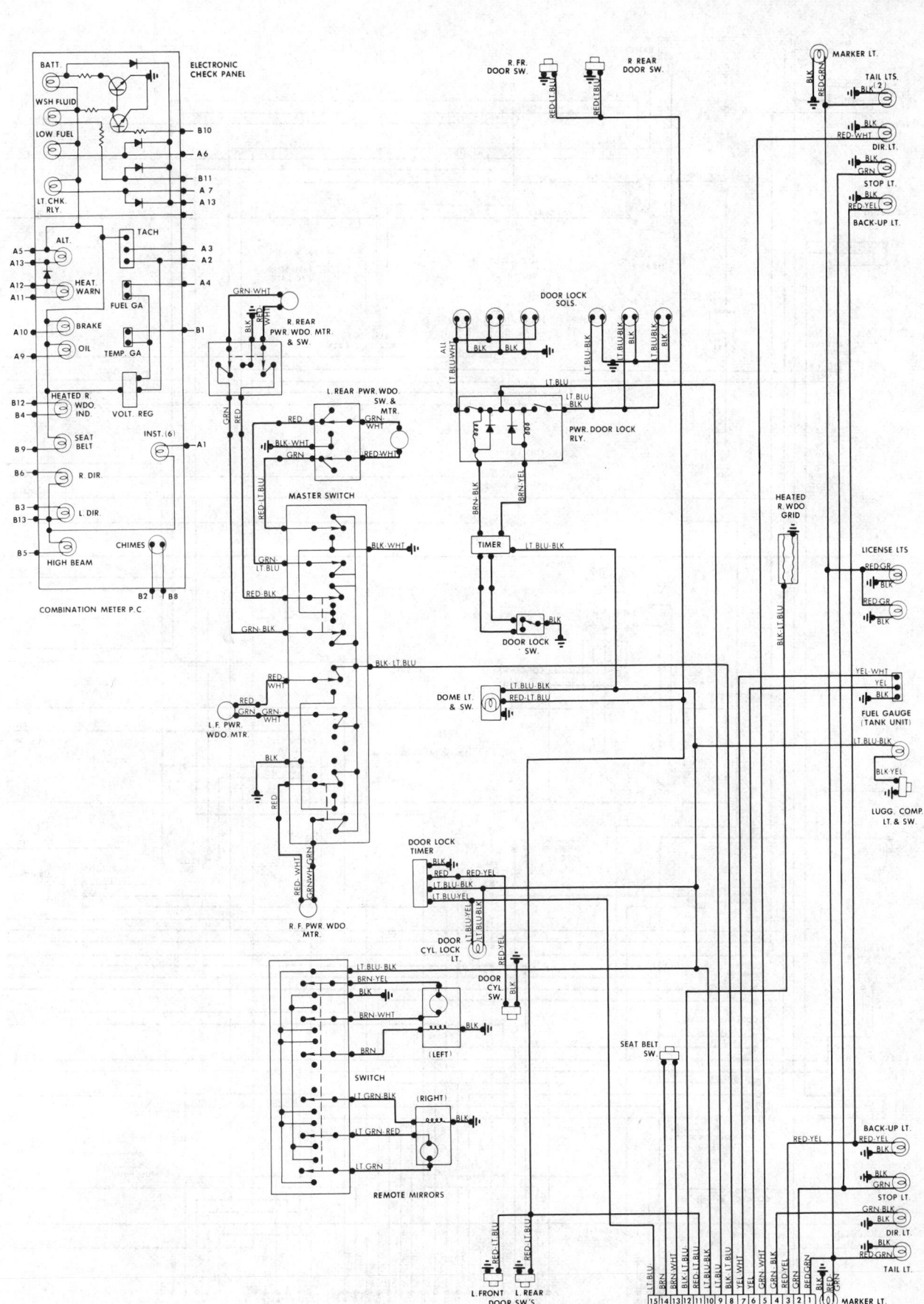

ENGINE COMPARTMENT

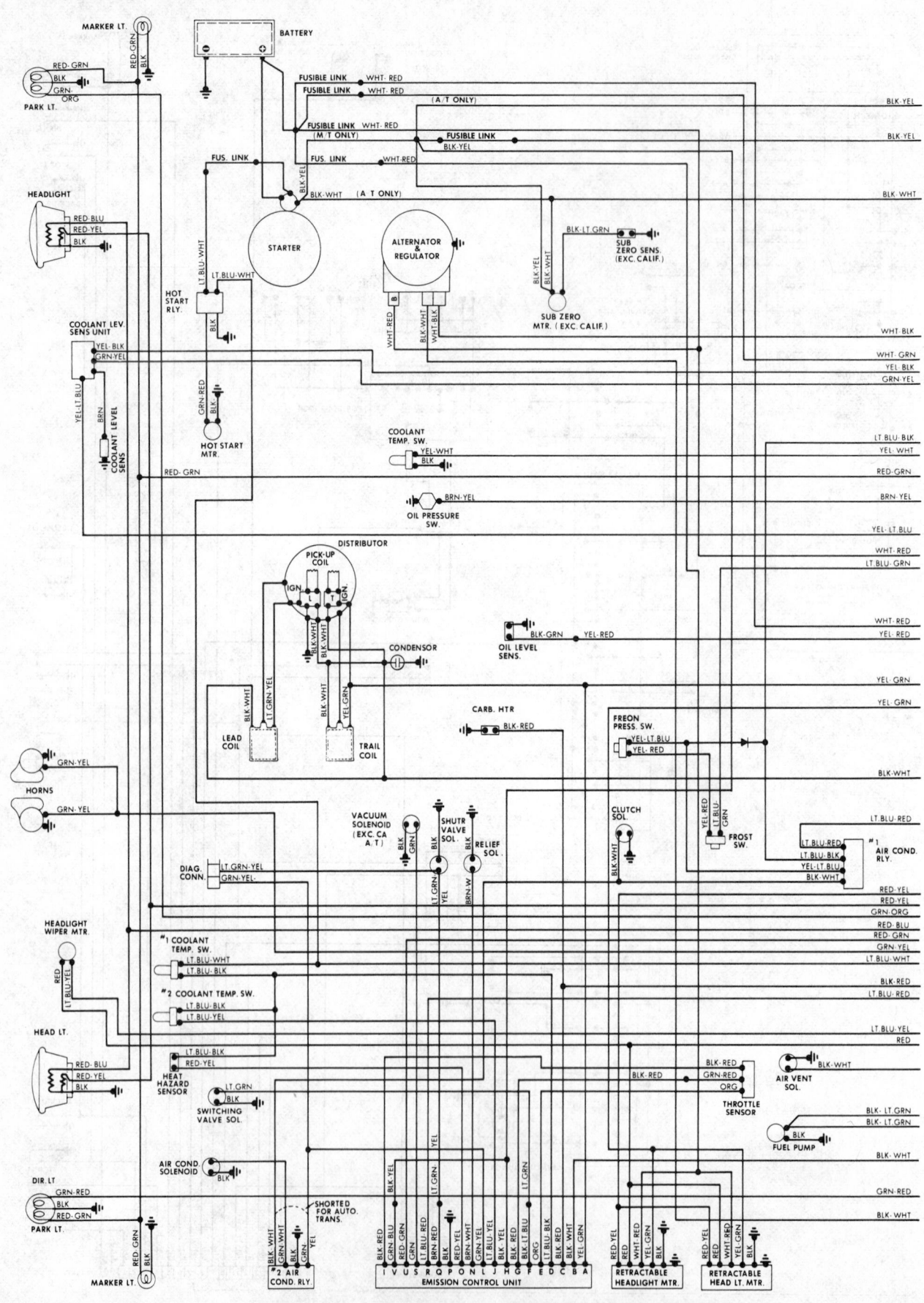

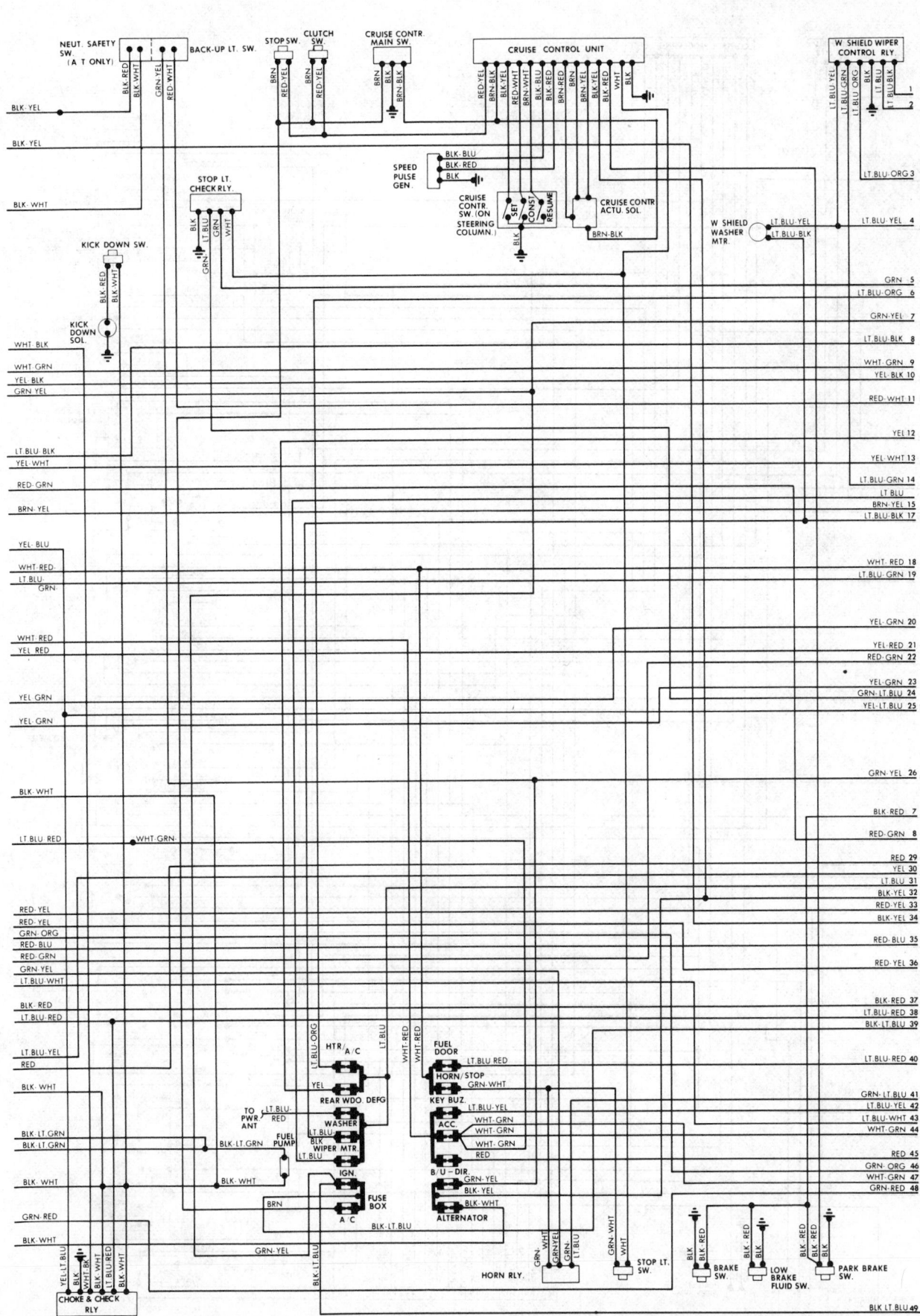

1981 Mazda

UNDERDASH & INSTRUMENT PANEL

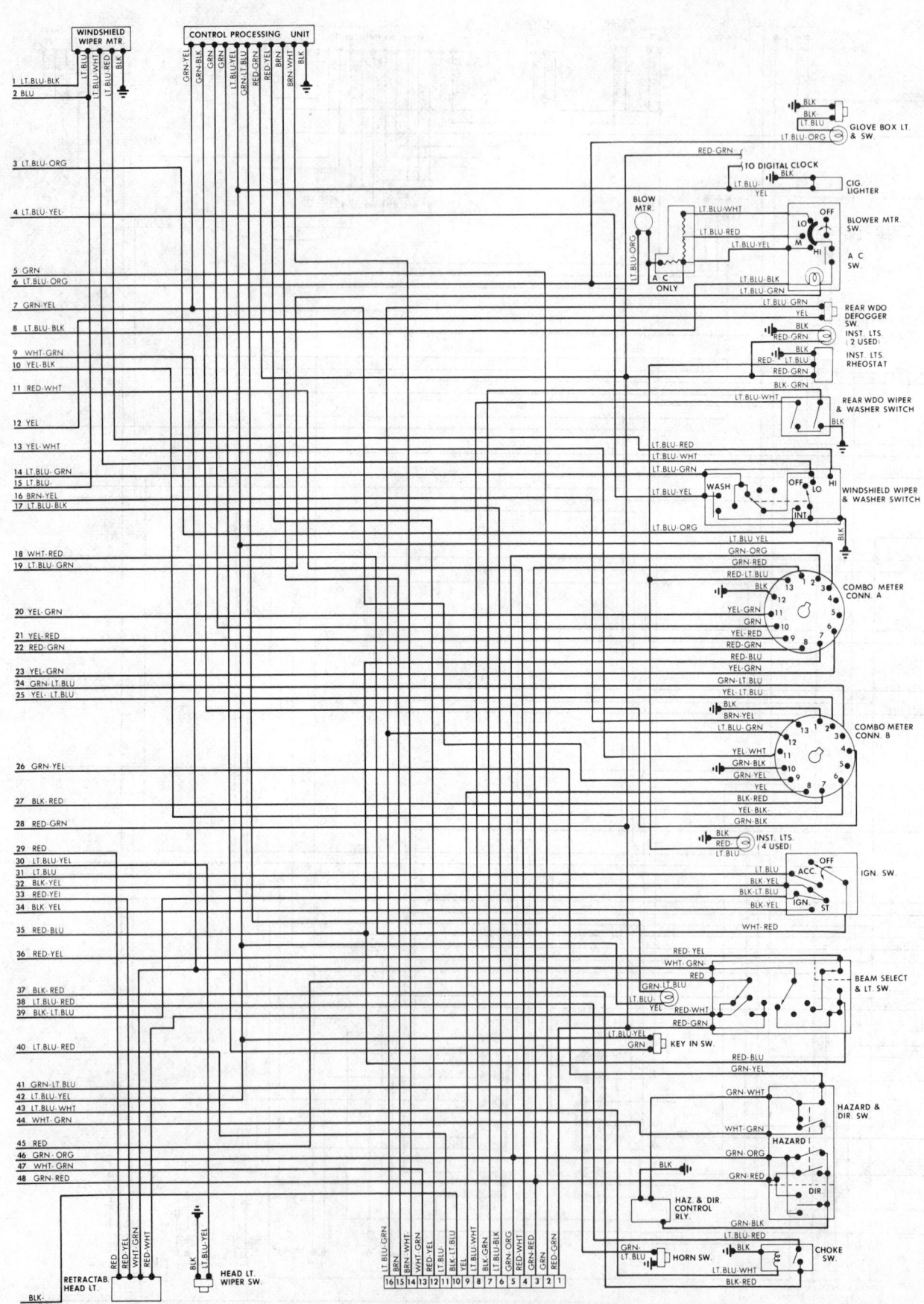

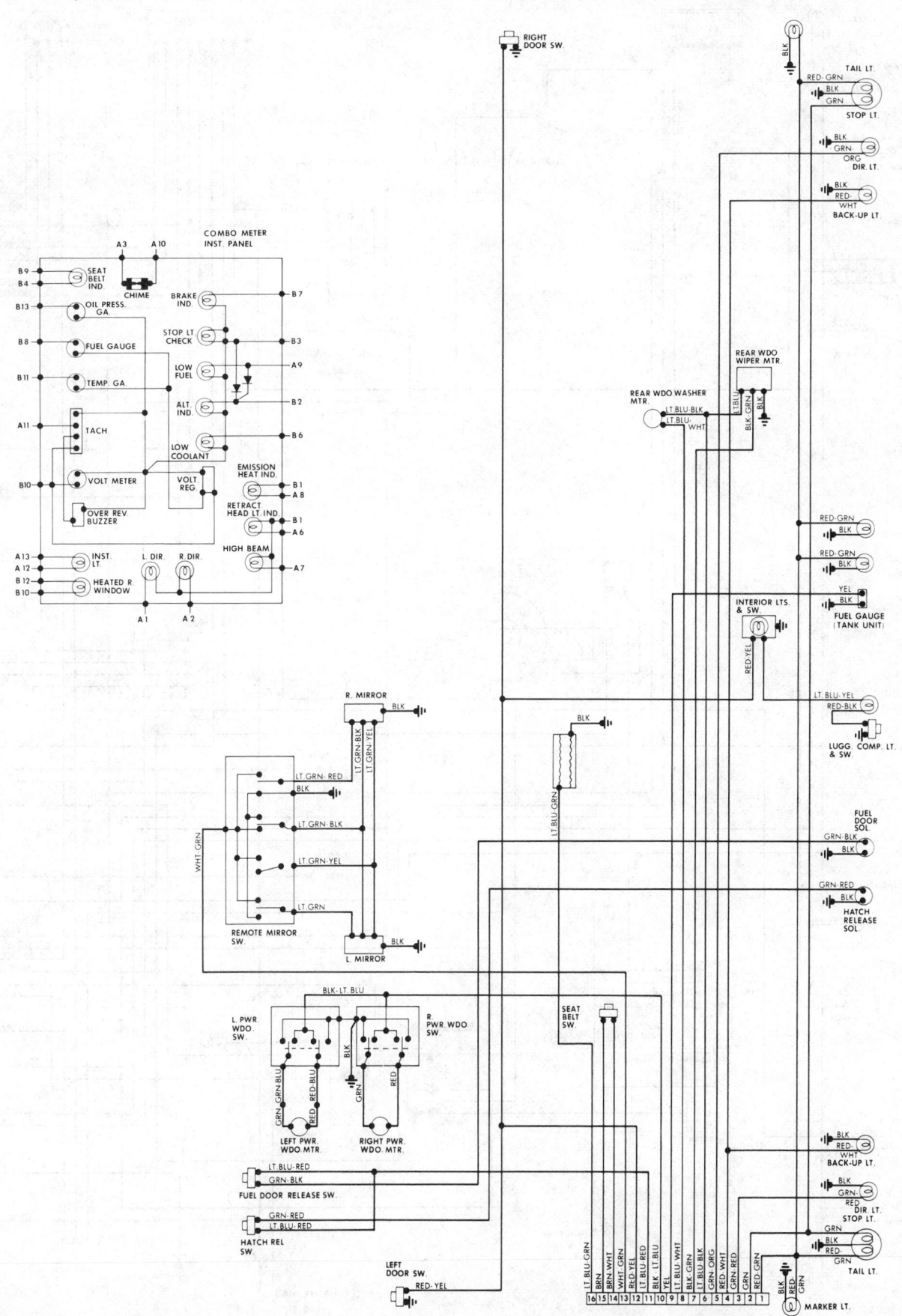

1981 Mazda

ENGINE COMPARTMENT & FUSE BLOCK

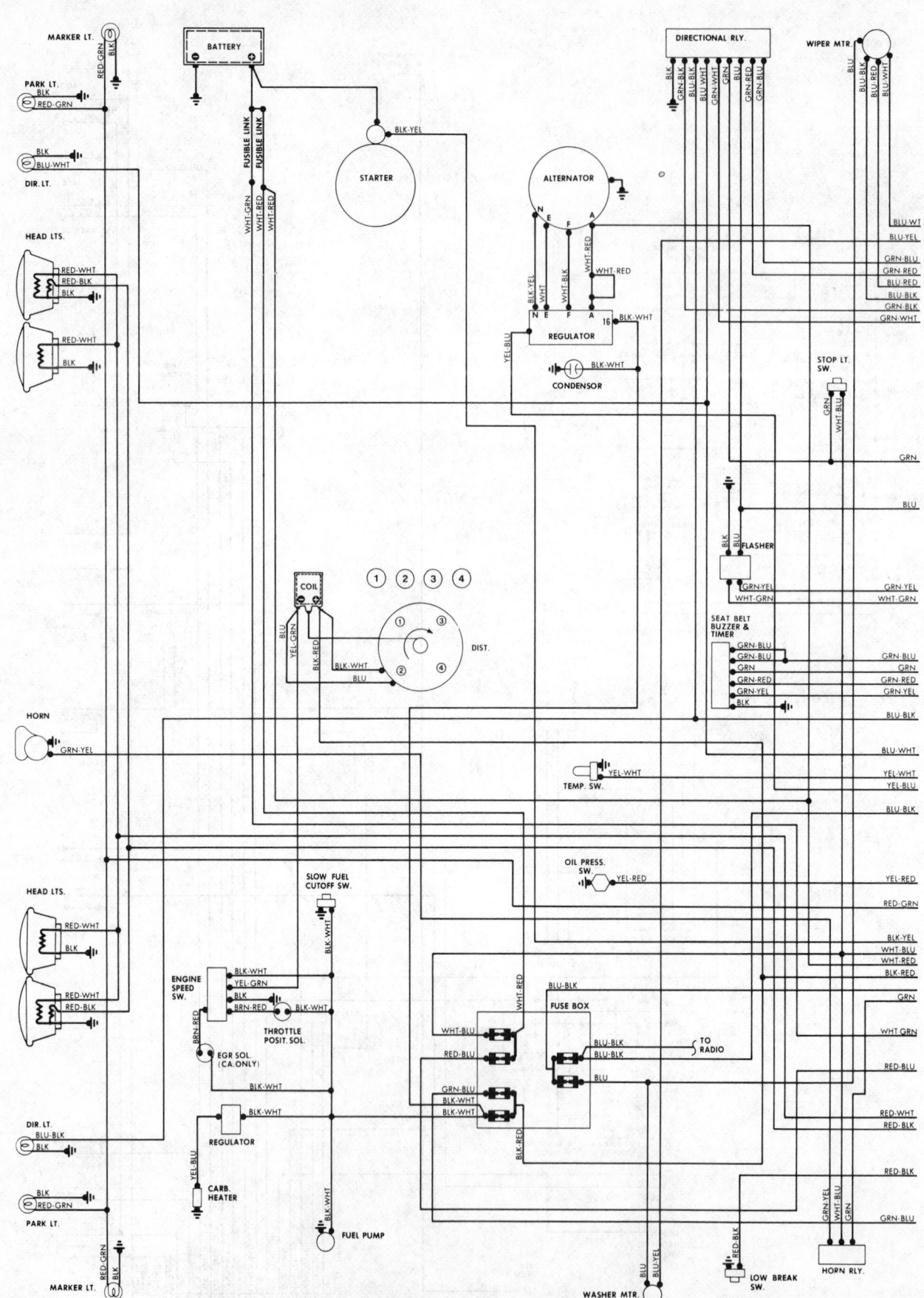

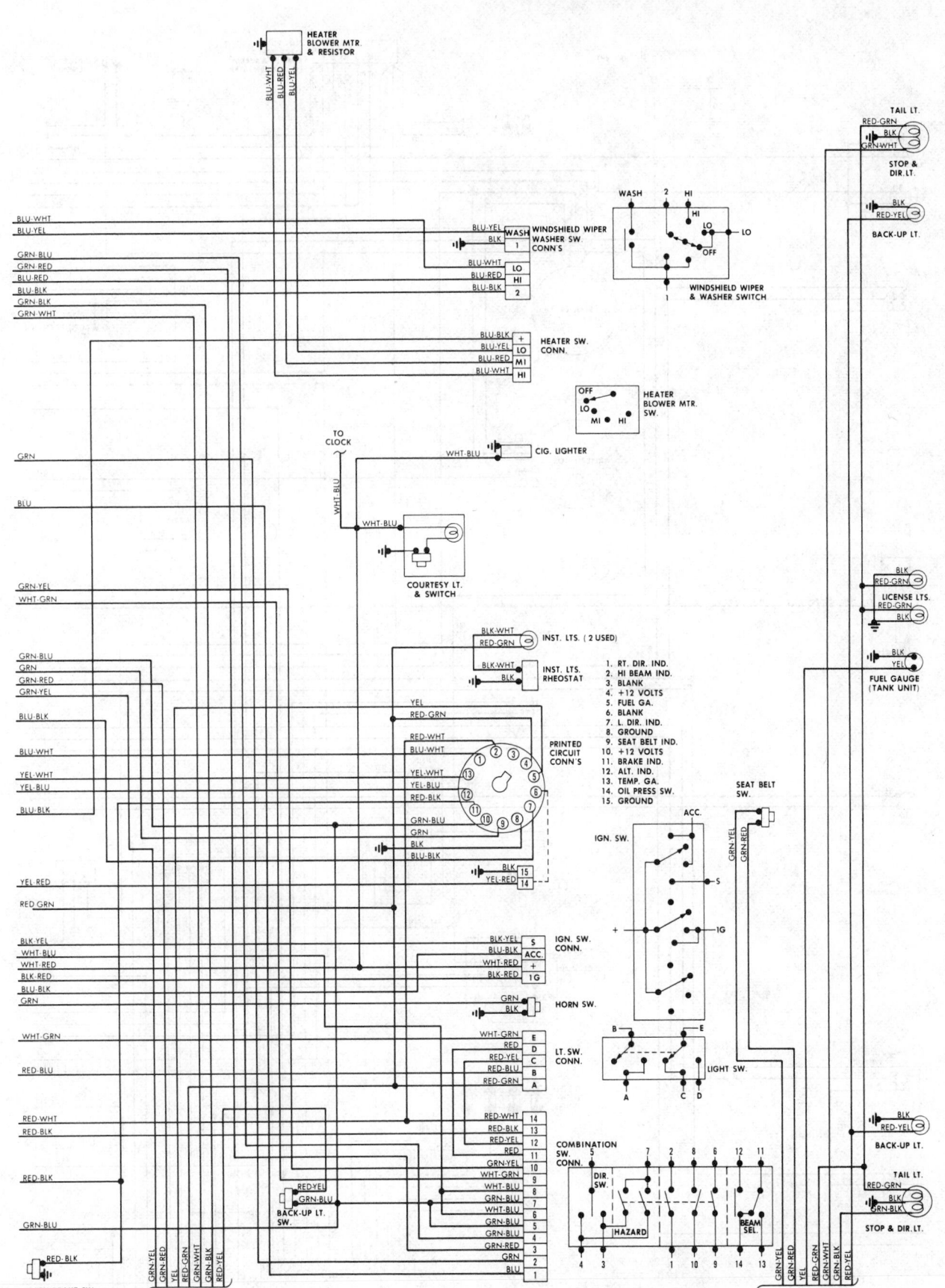

ENGINE COMPARTMENT

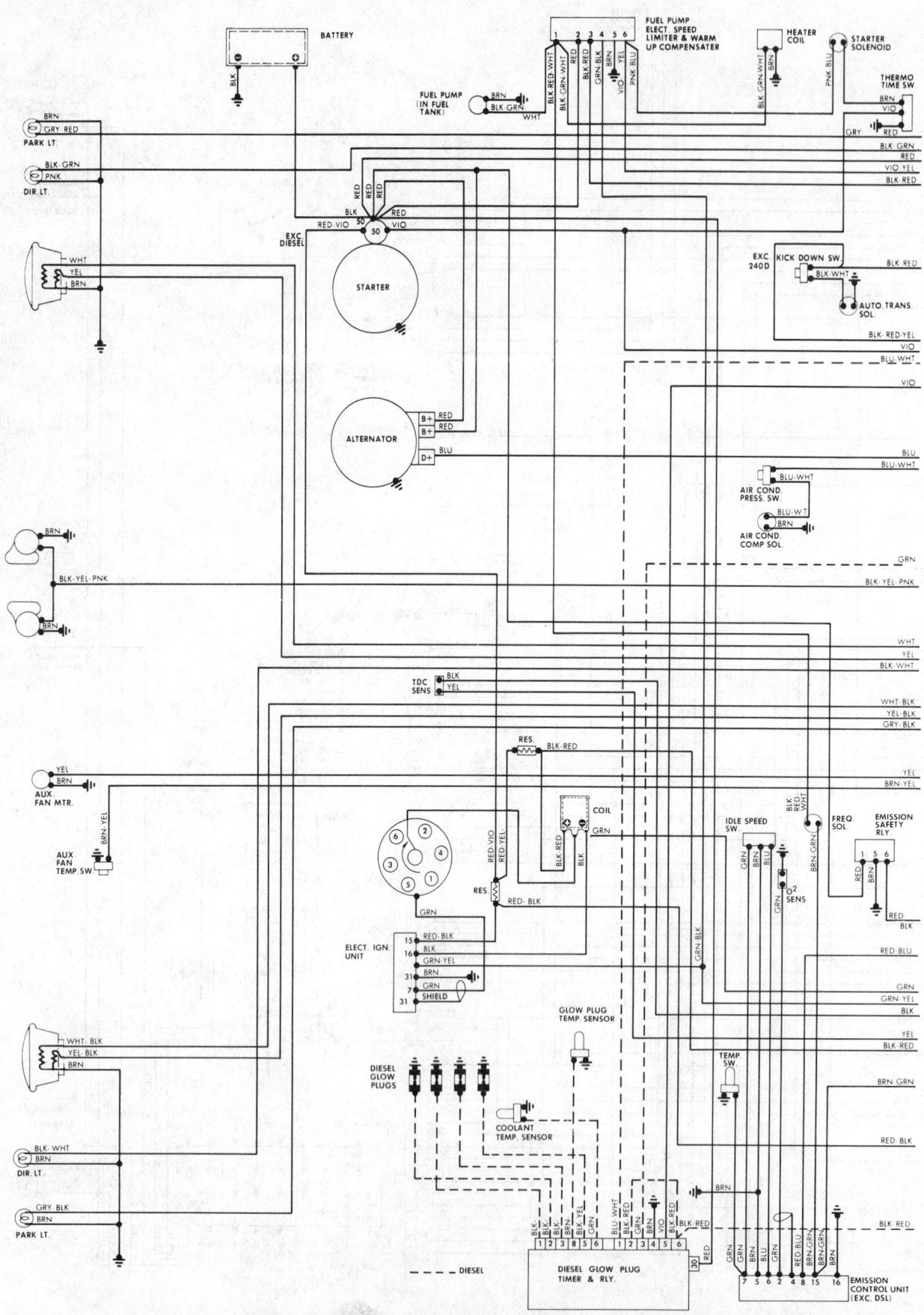

240D
280E

1981 Mercedes-Benz

280CE
300CD
300D

4-111

ENGINE COMPARTMENT & FUSE BLOCK

WIRING DIAGRAMS

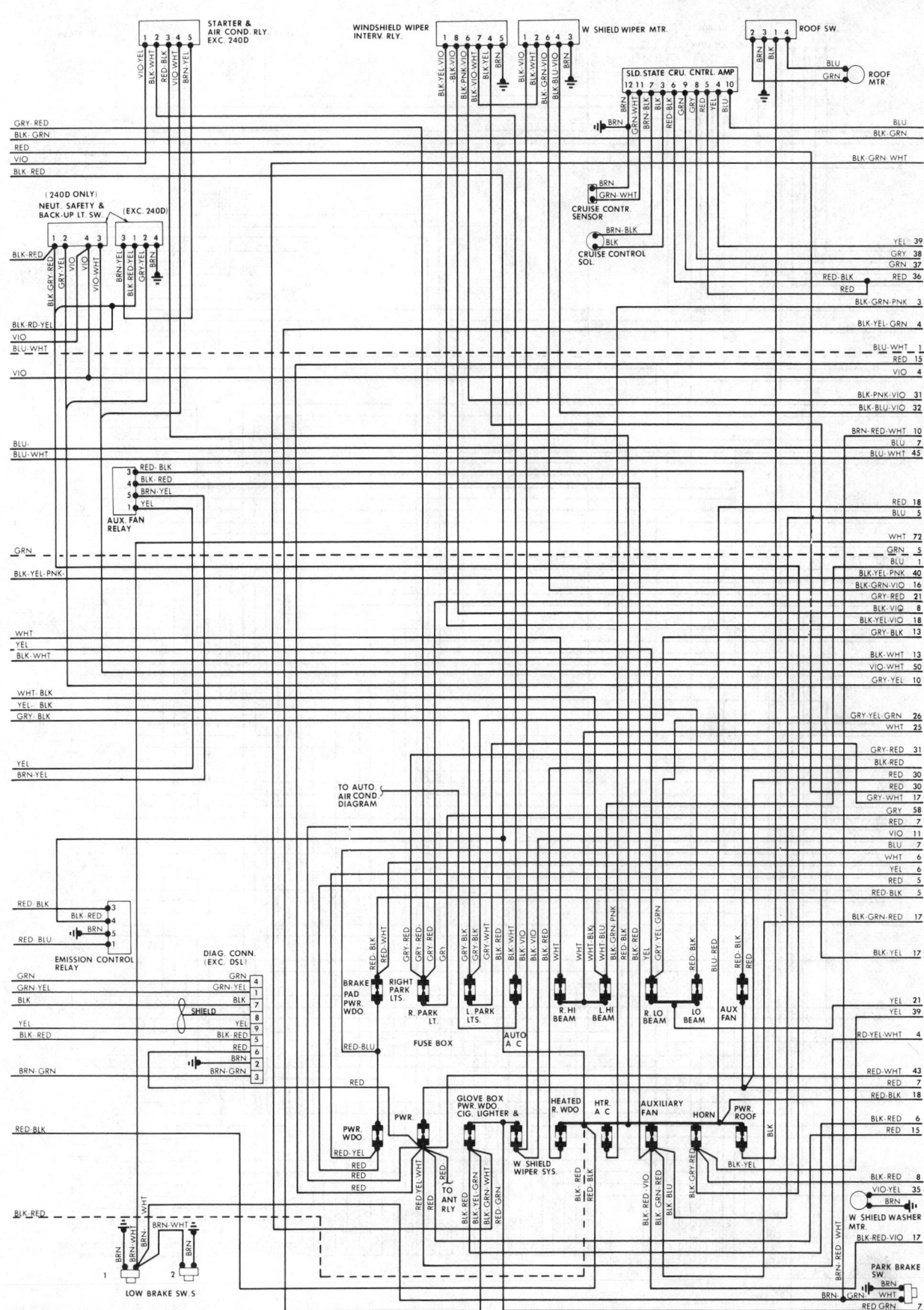

INSTRUMENT PANEL

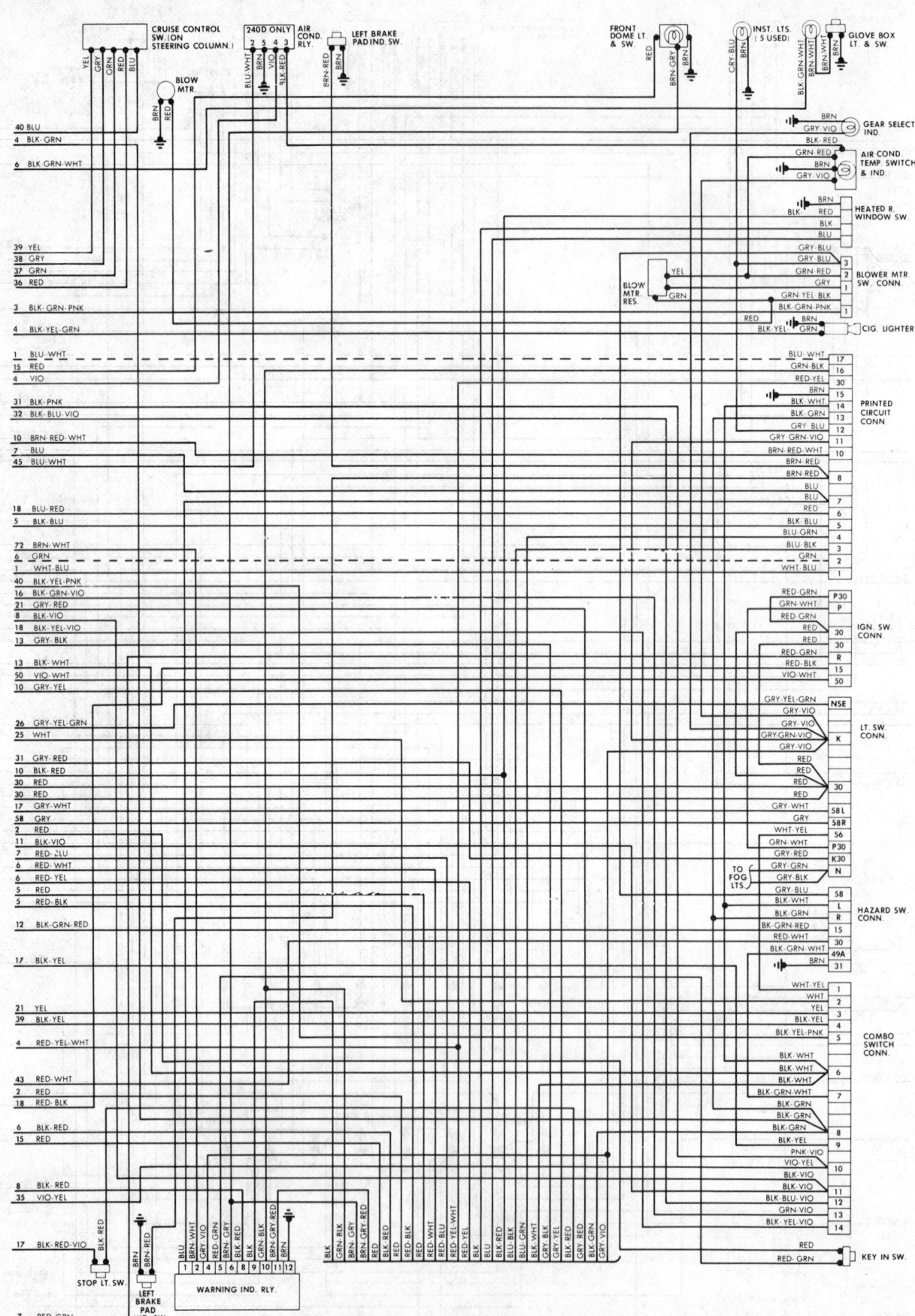

240D
280E
1981 Mercedes-Benz
280CE
300CD
300D
4-113

AIR CONDITIONING

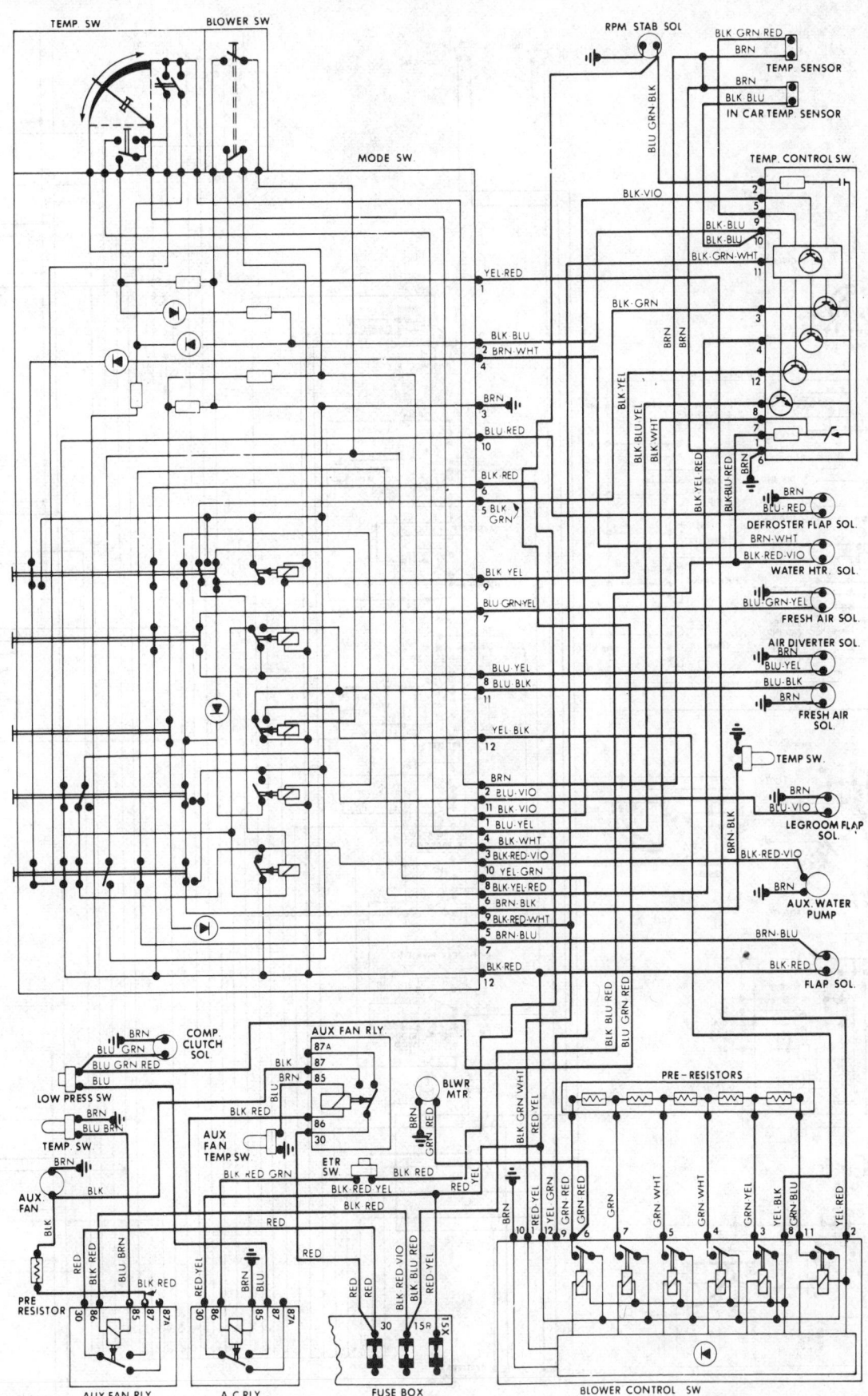

4-114   **240D**   # 1981 Mercedes-Benz   **280CE**
      280E   **300CD**
                                                                   300D

INSTRUMENT PANEL & REAR COMPARTMENT

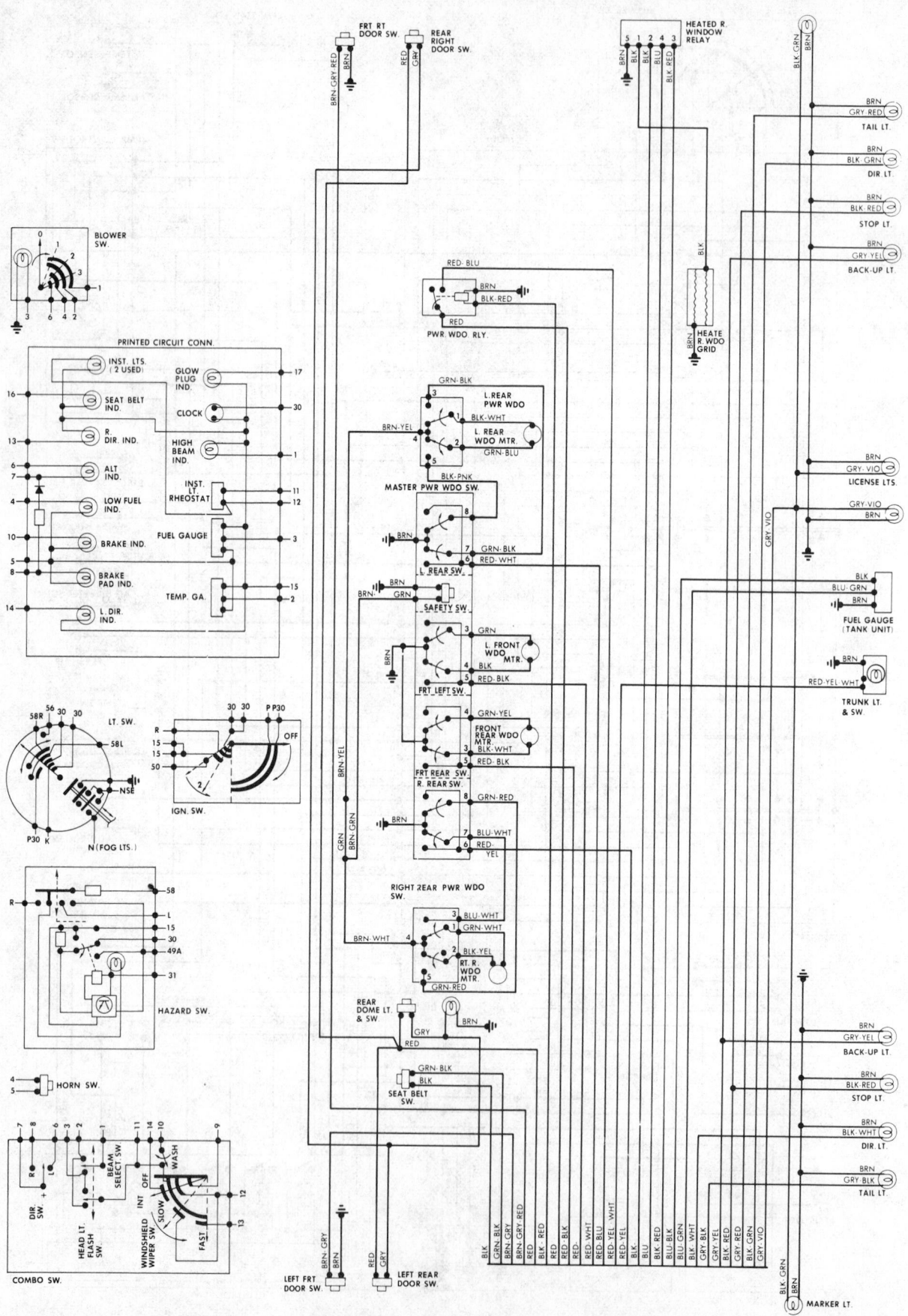

ENGINE COMPARTMENT

WIRING DIAGRAMS

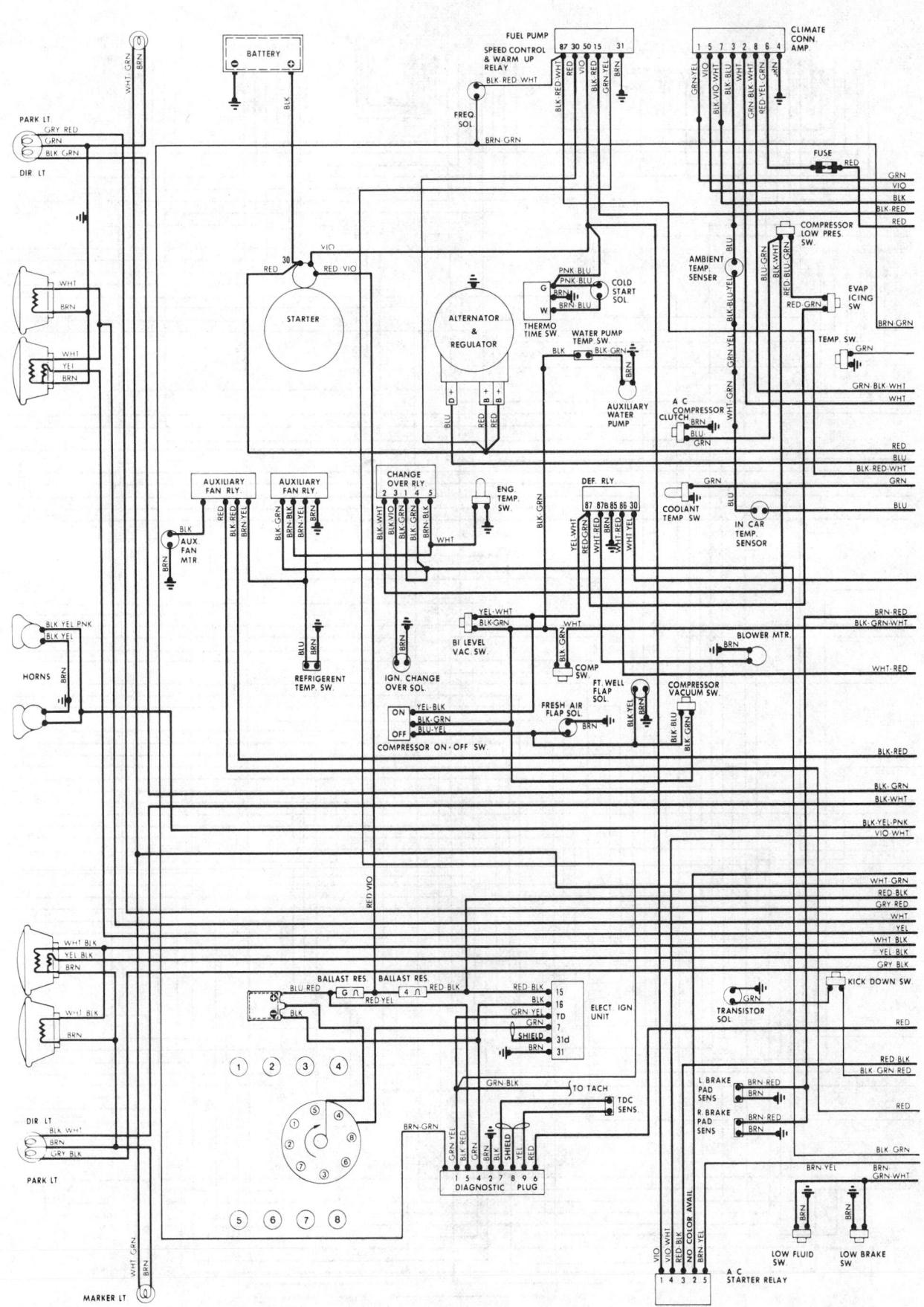

UNDERDASH

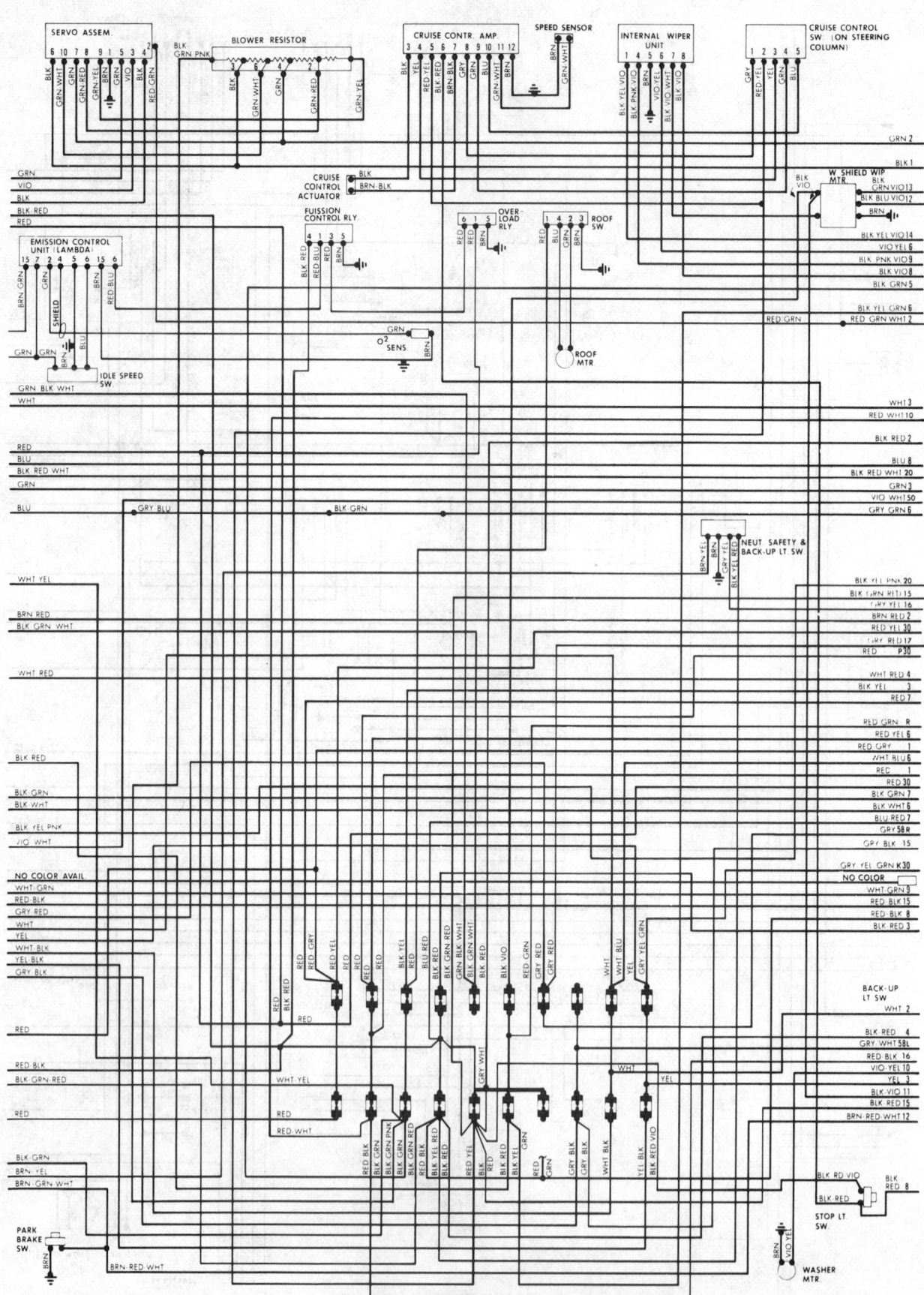

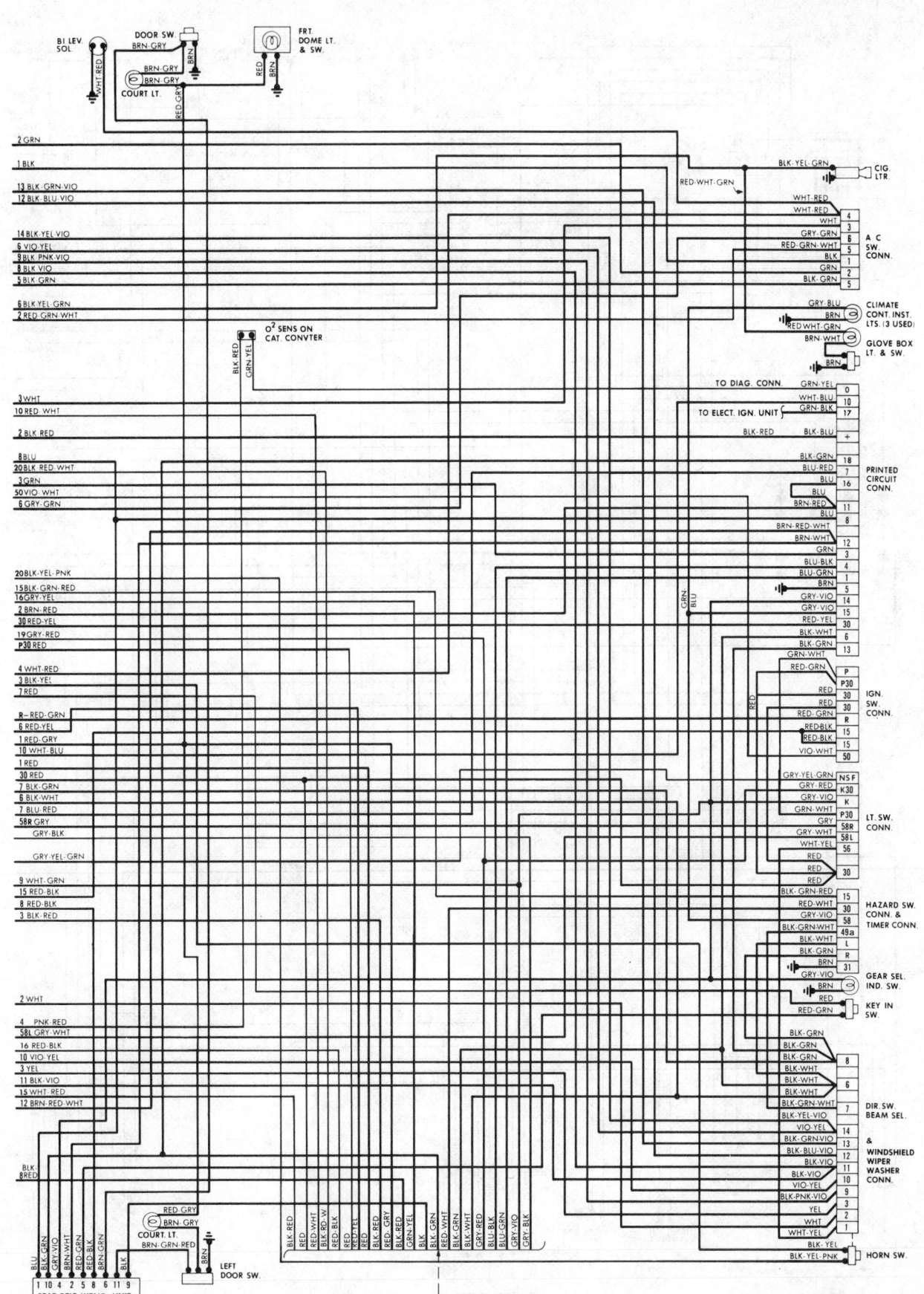

1981 Mercedes-Benz

AIR CONDITIONING

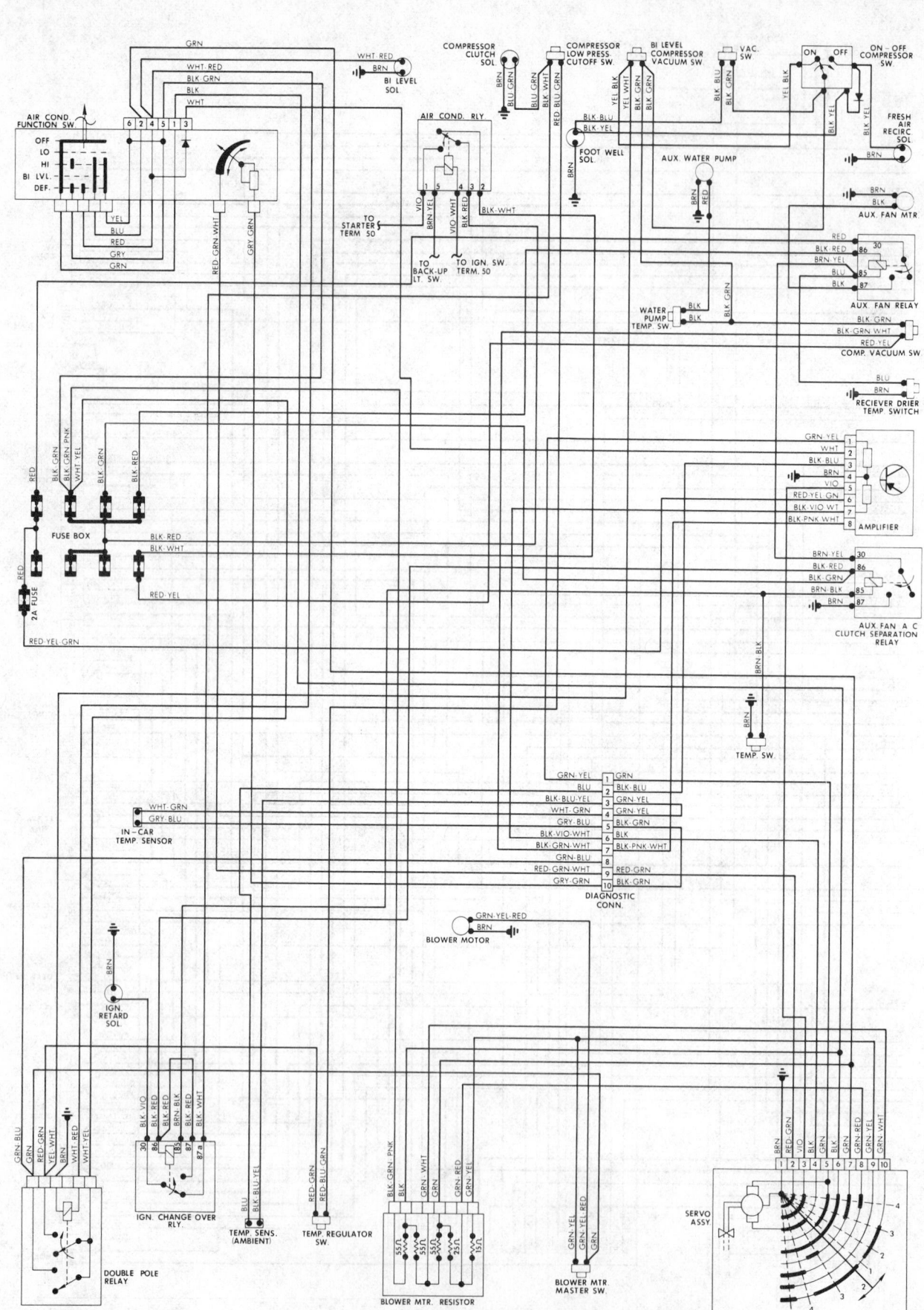

ACCESSORIES & REAR COMPARTMENT

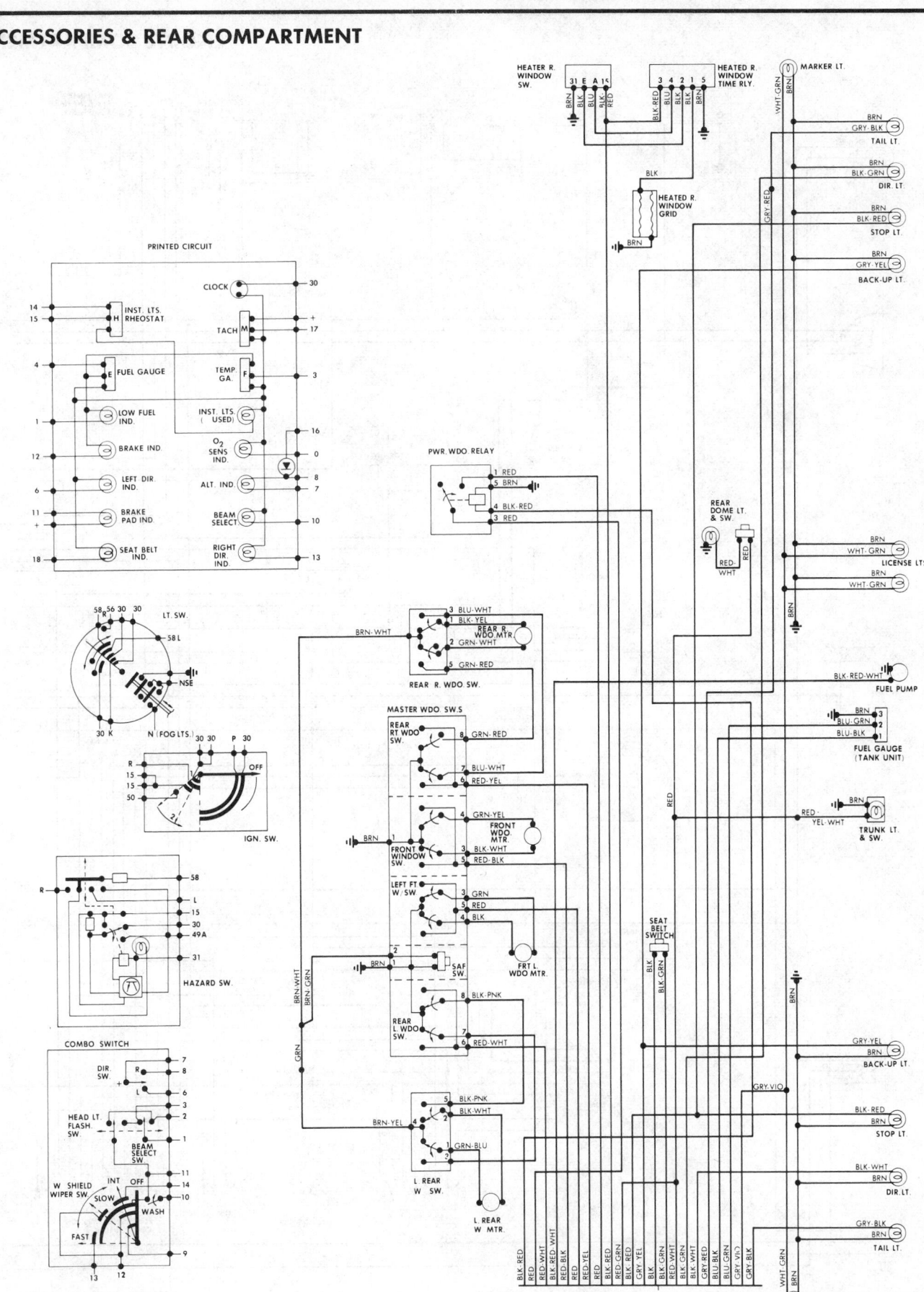

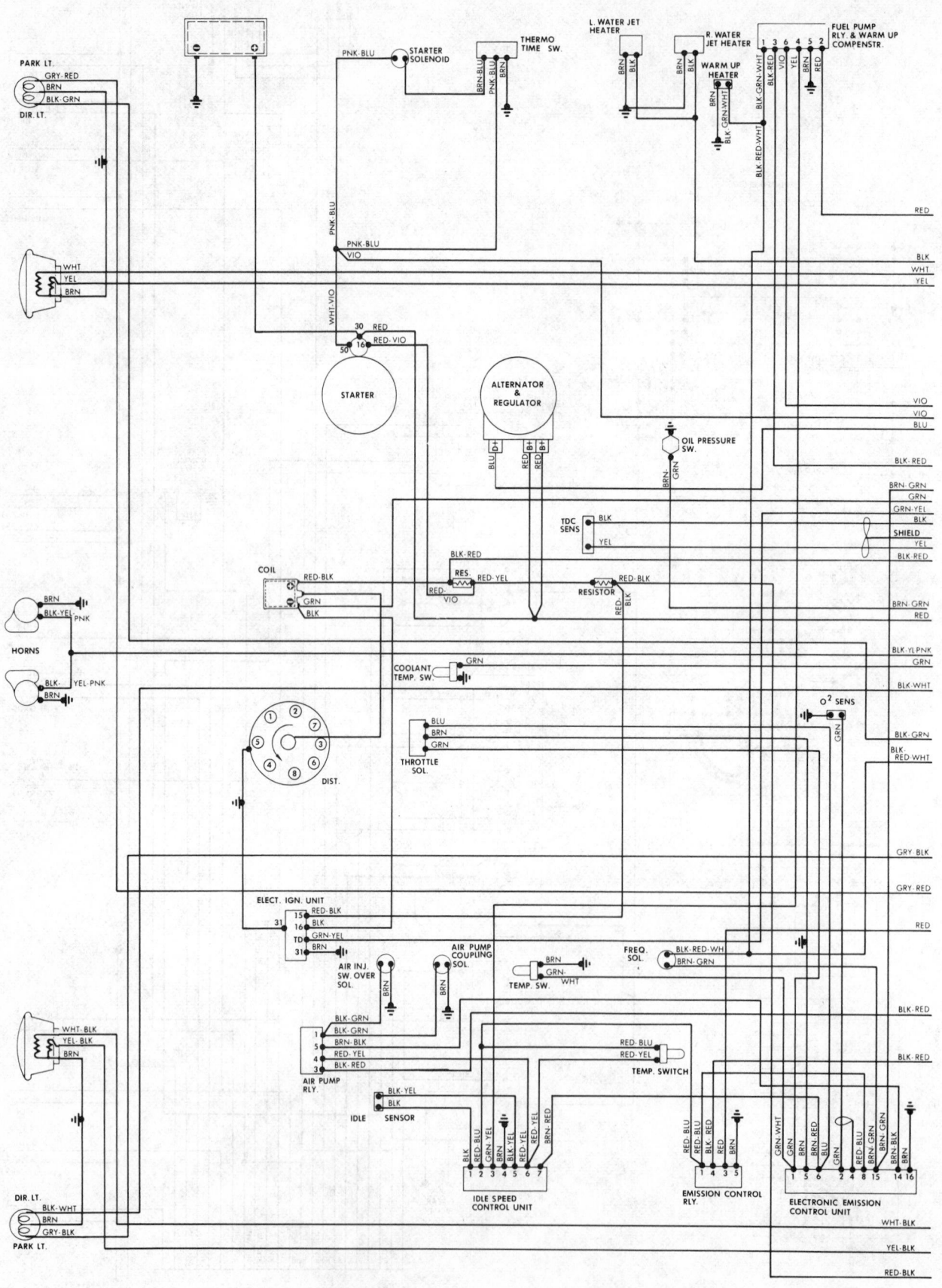

ENGINE COMPARTMENT & FUSE BLOCK

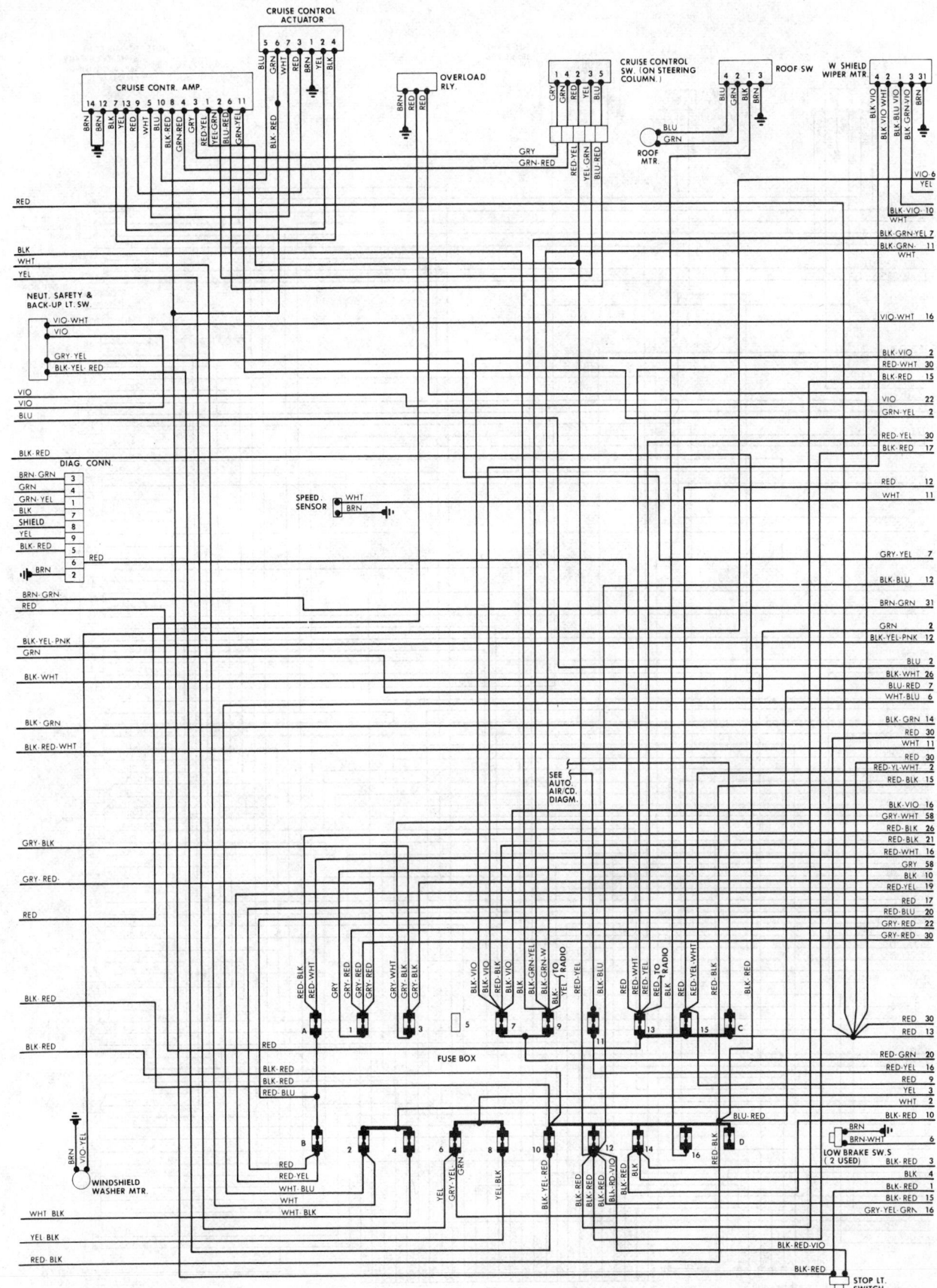

UNDERDASH & INSTRUMENT PANEL

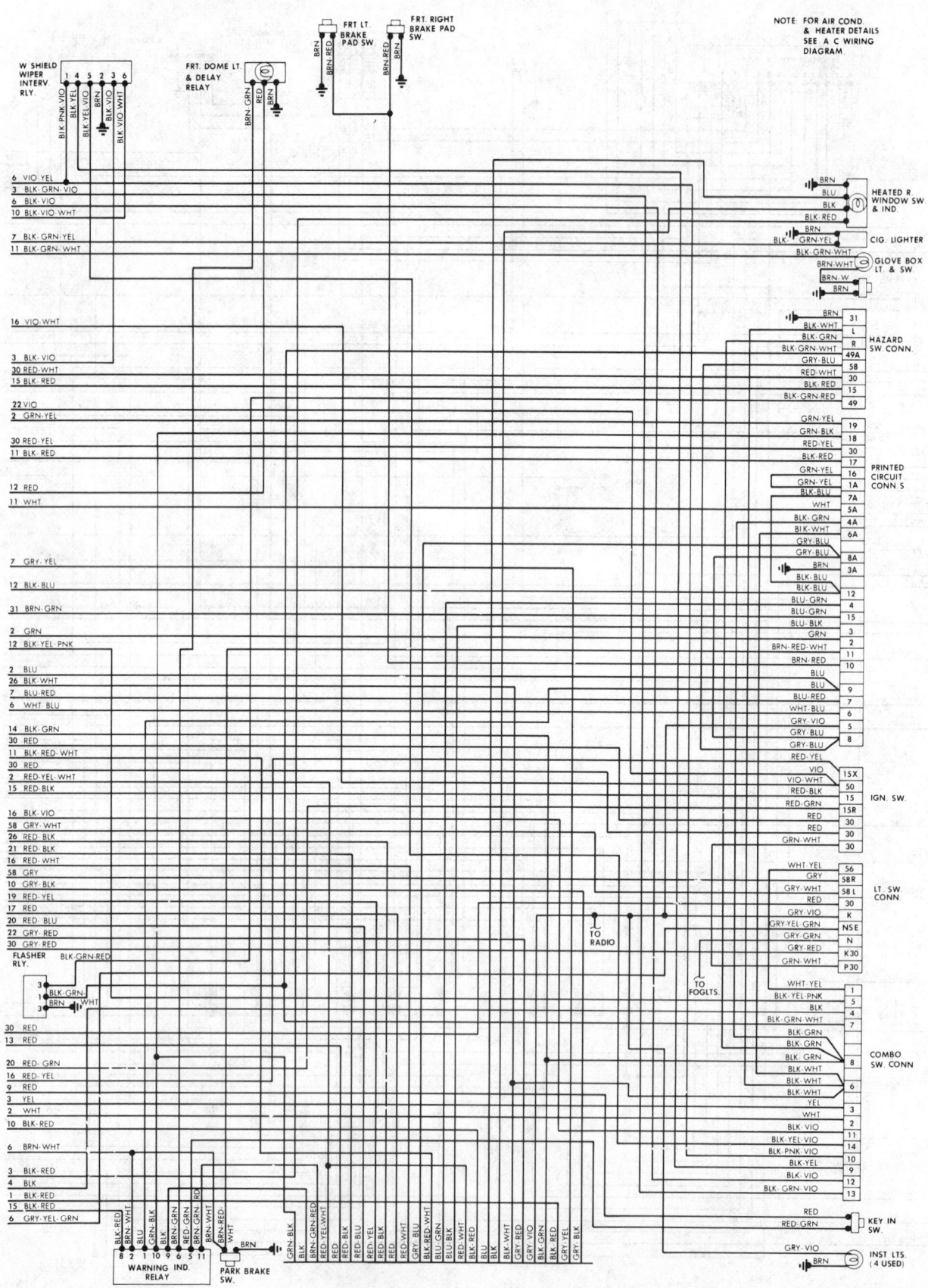

ACCESSORIES & REAR COMPARTMENT

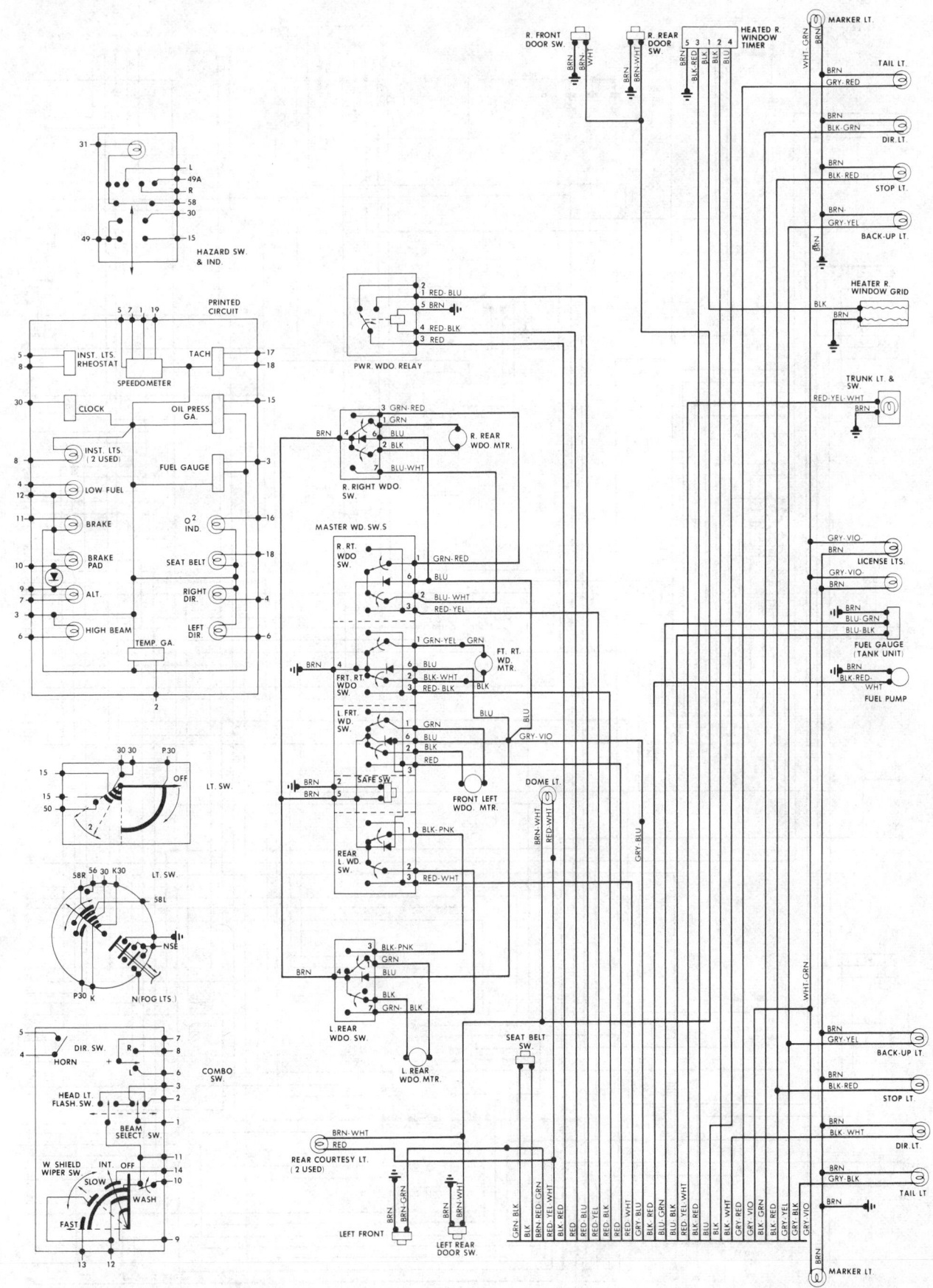

1981 Peugeot

ENGINE COMPARTMENT & FUSE BLOCK

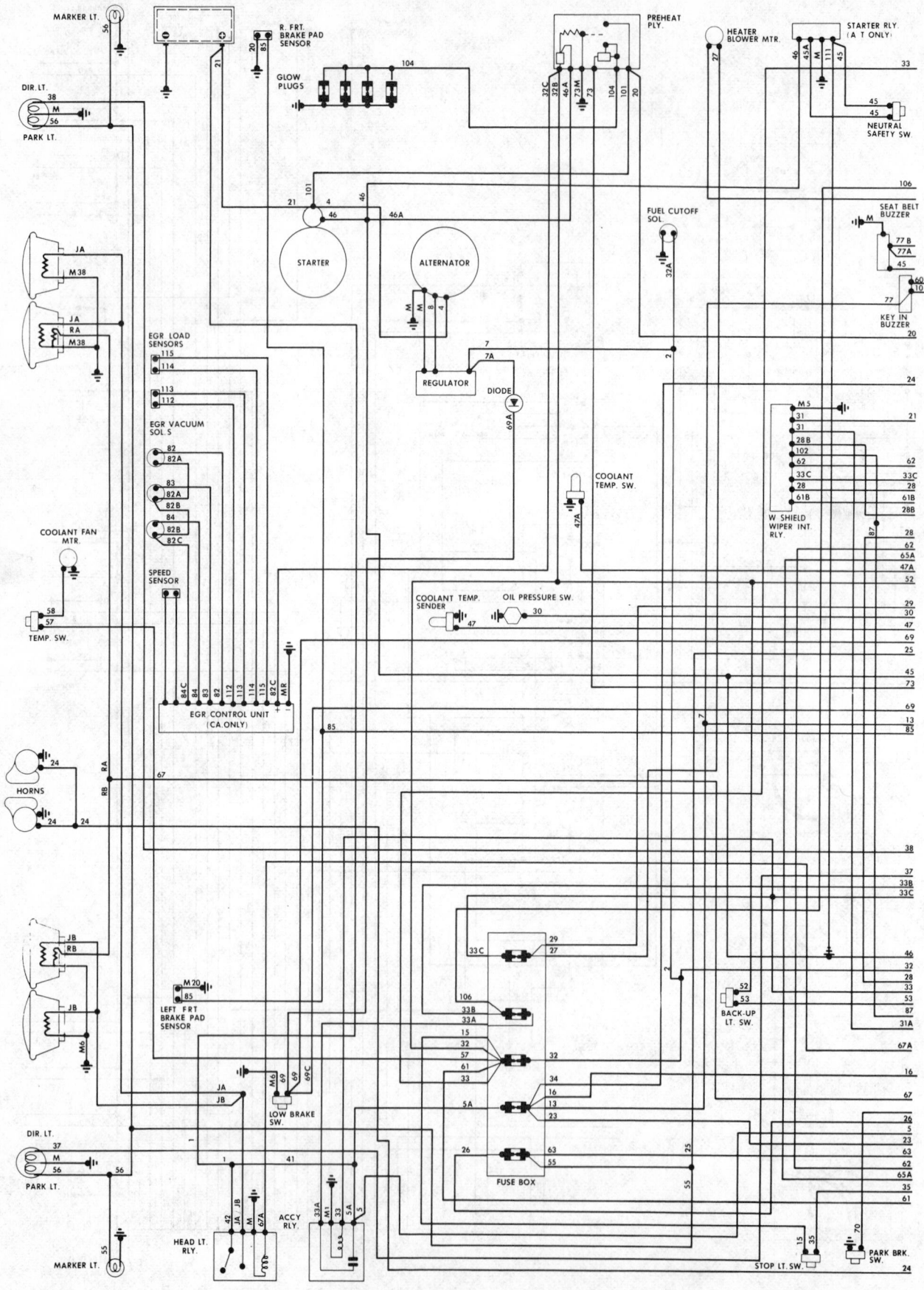

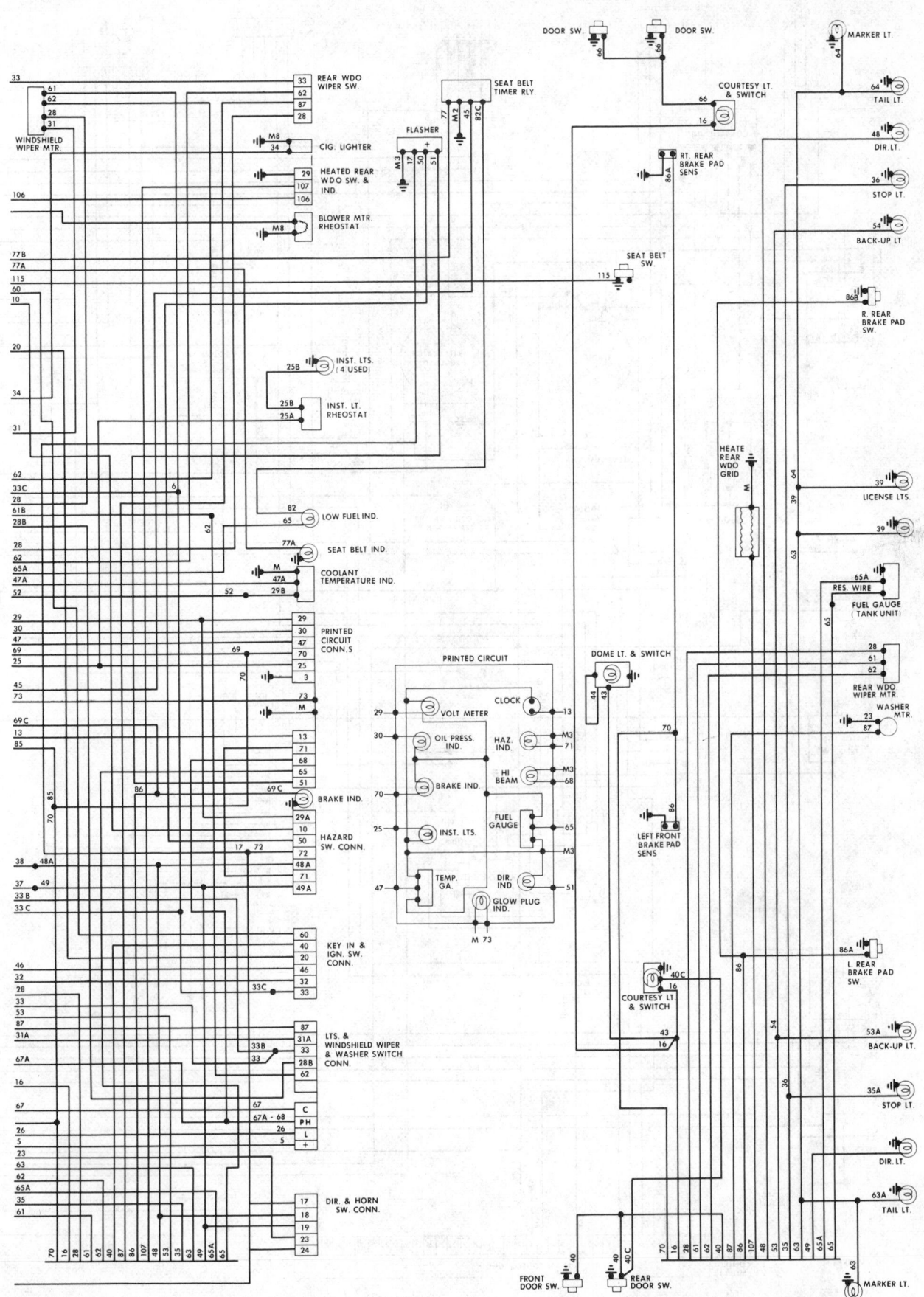

1981 Peugeot

ENGINE COMPARTMENT

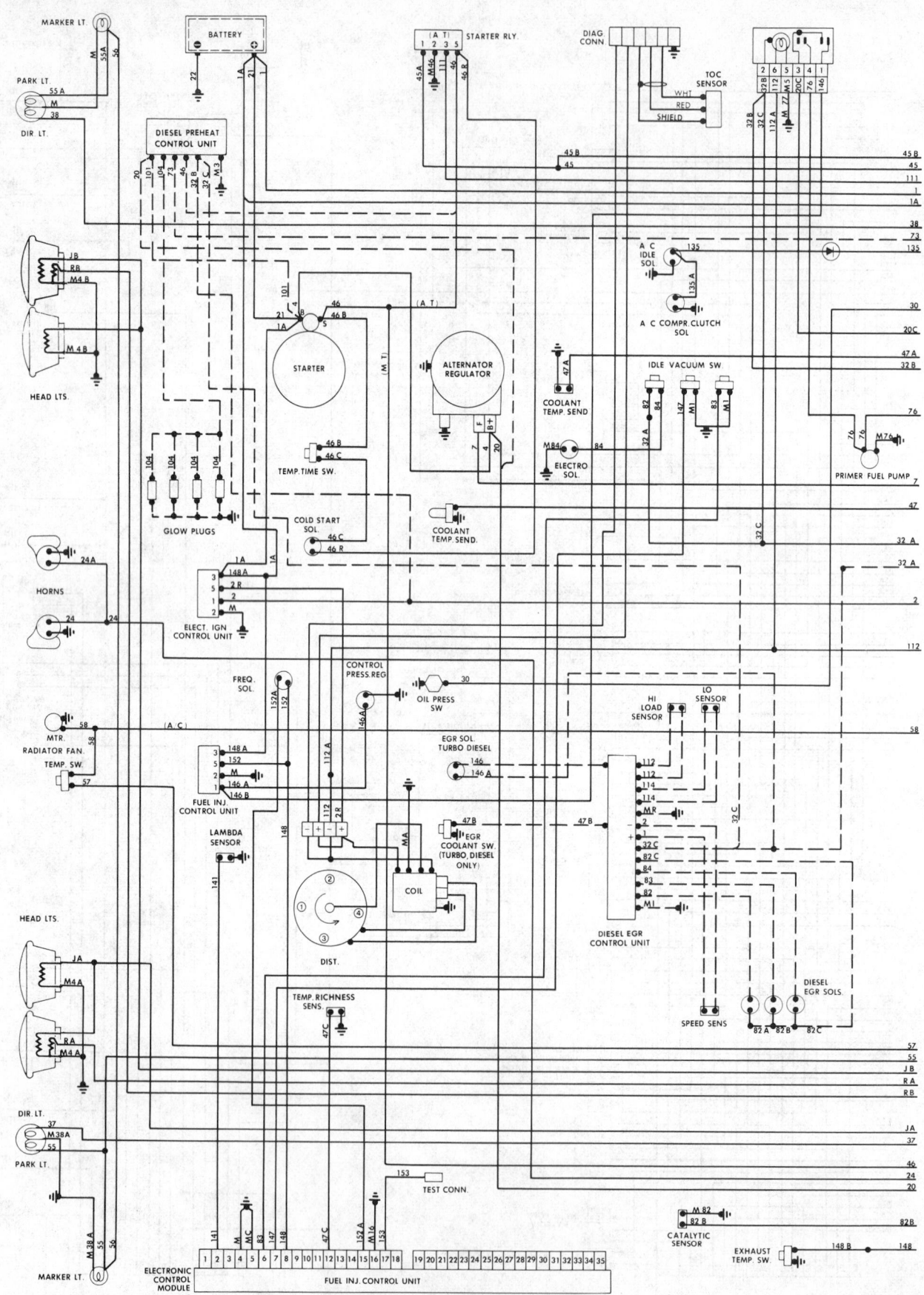

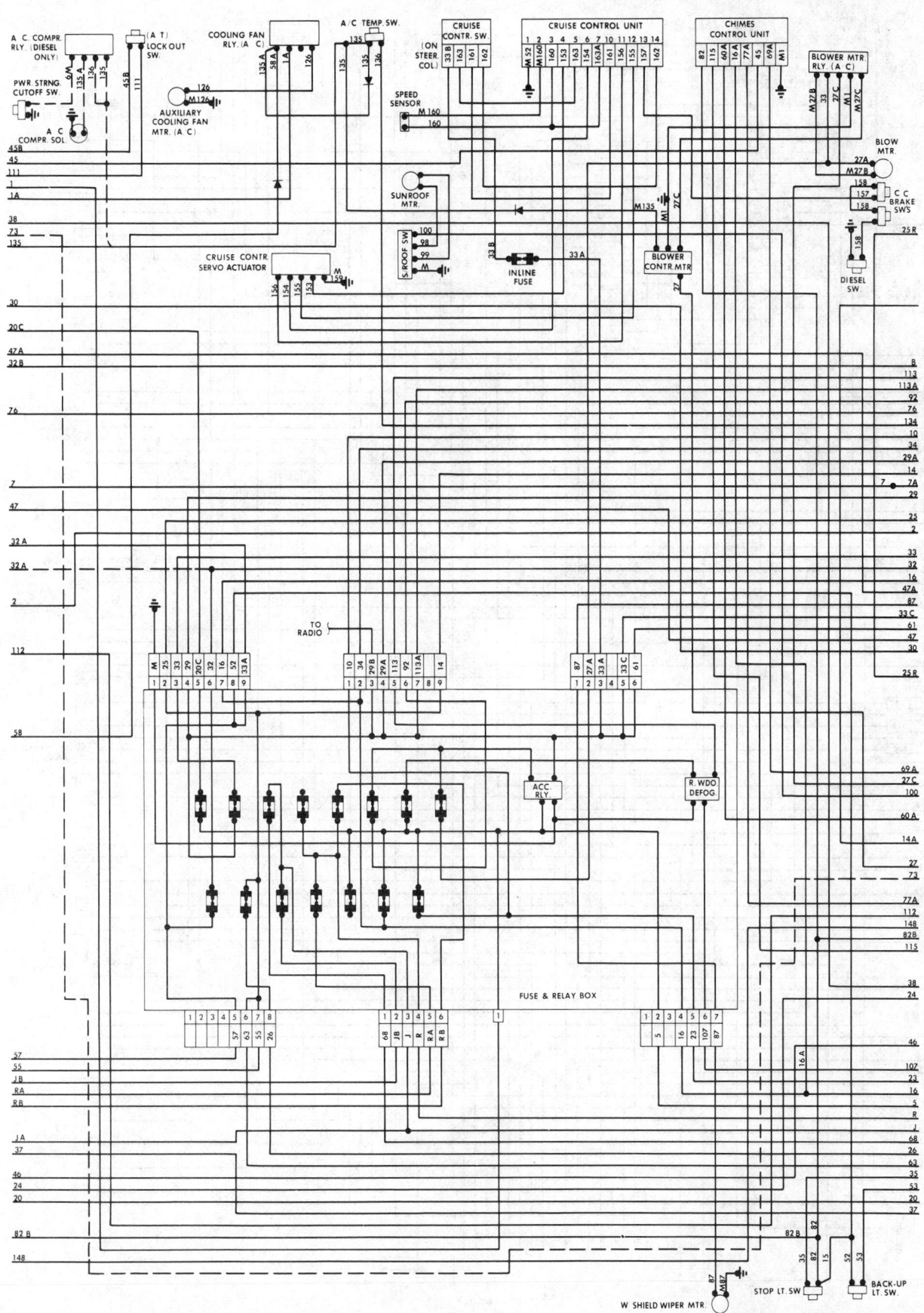

1981 Peugeot

UNDERDASH

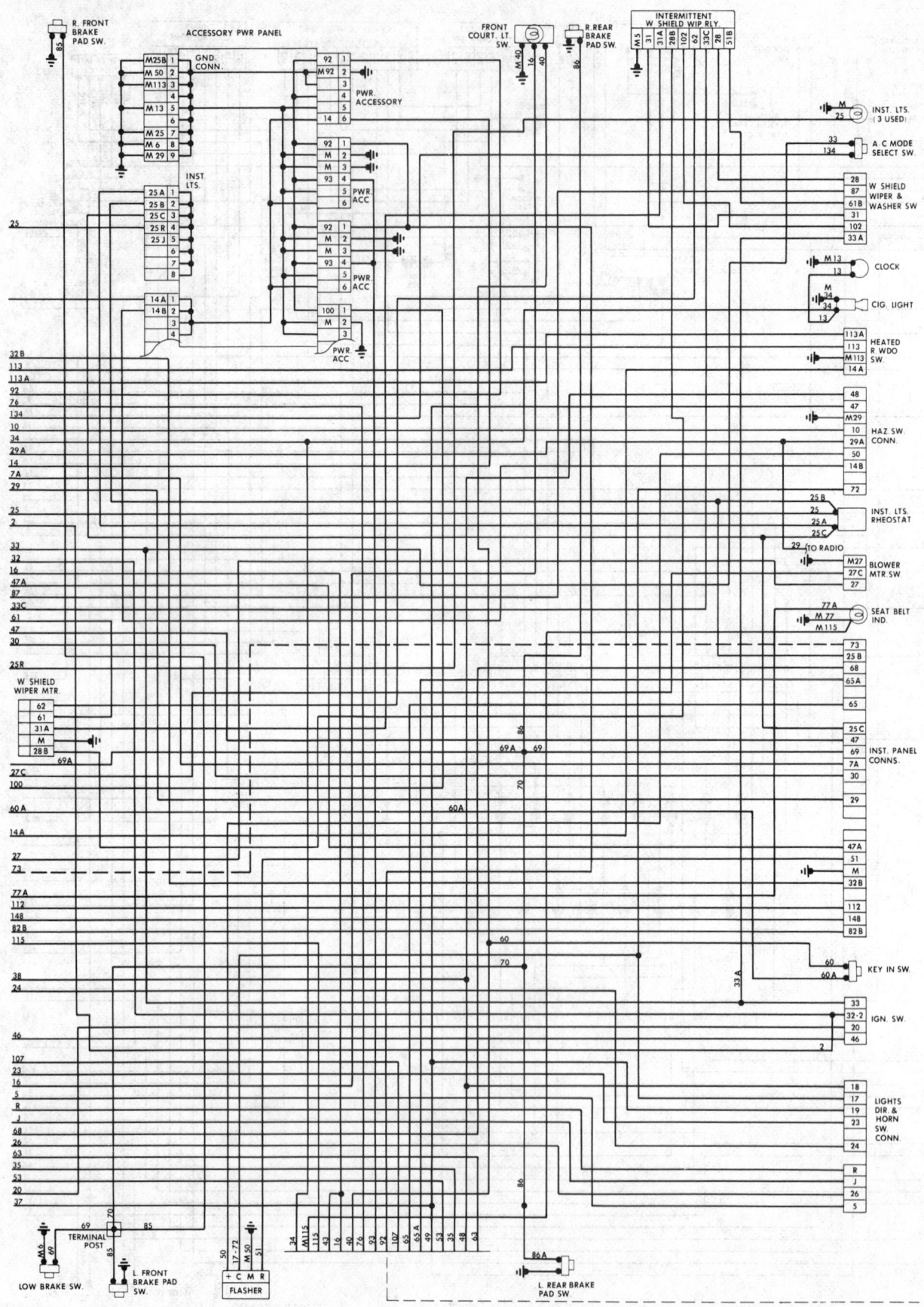

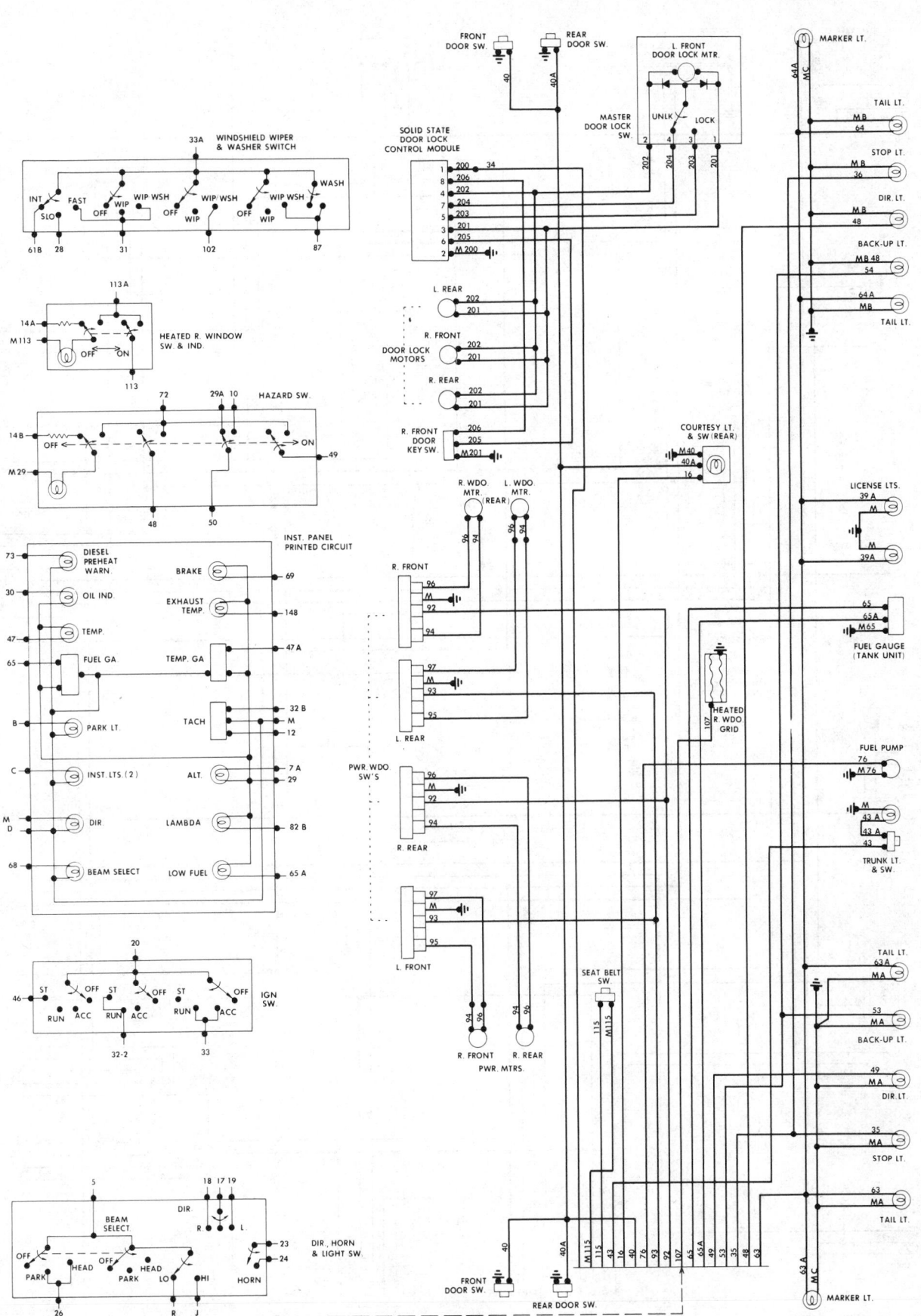

1981 Peugeot

ENGINE COMPARTMENT

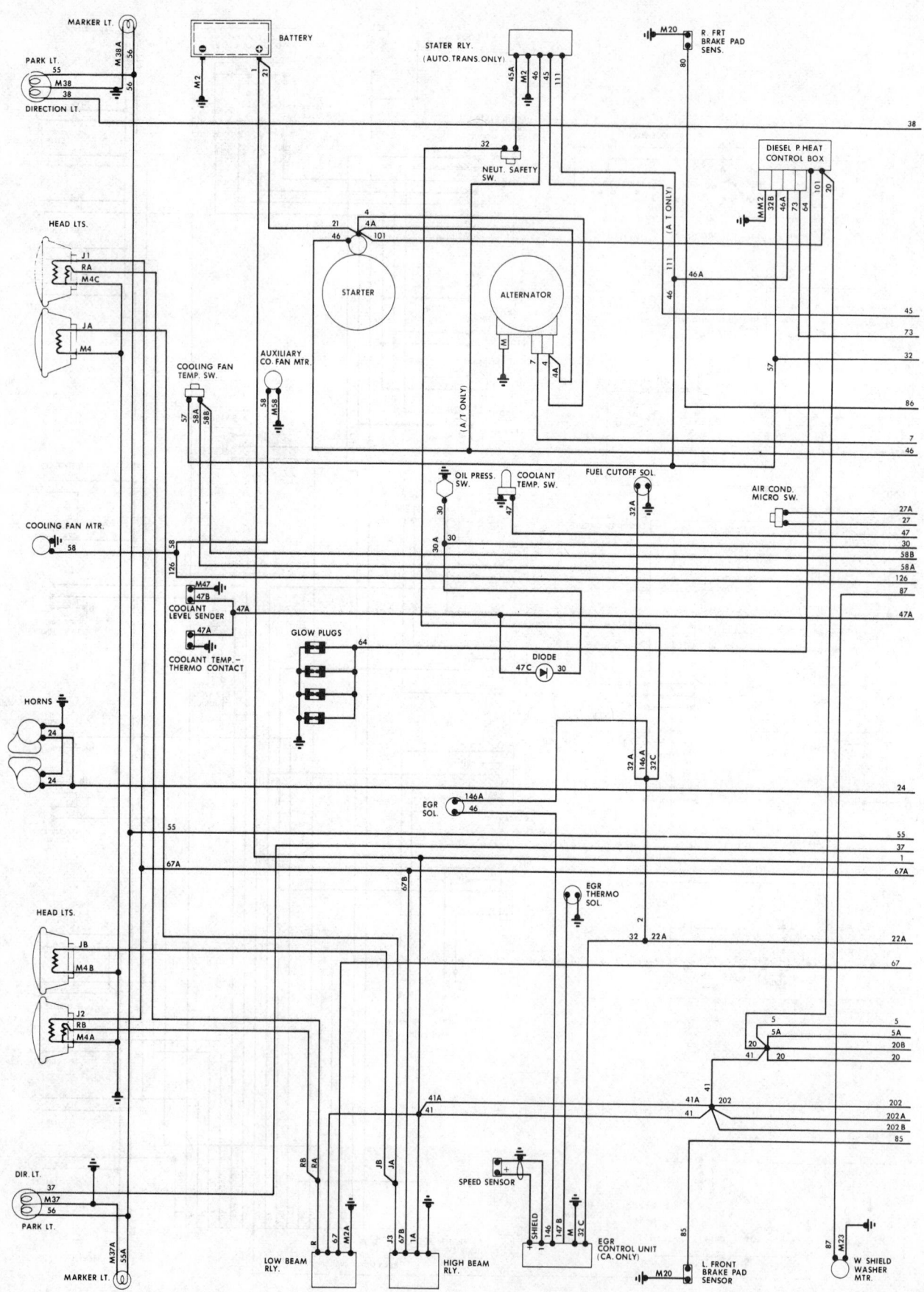

ENGINE COMPARTMENT & FUSE BLOCK

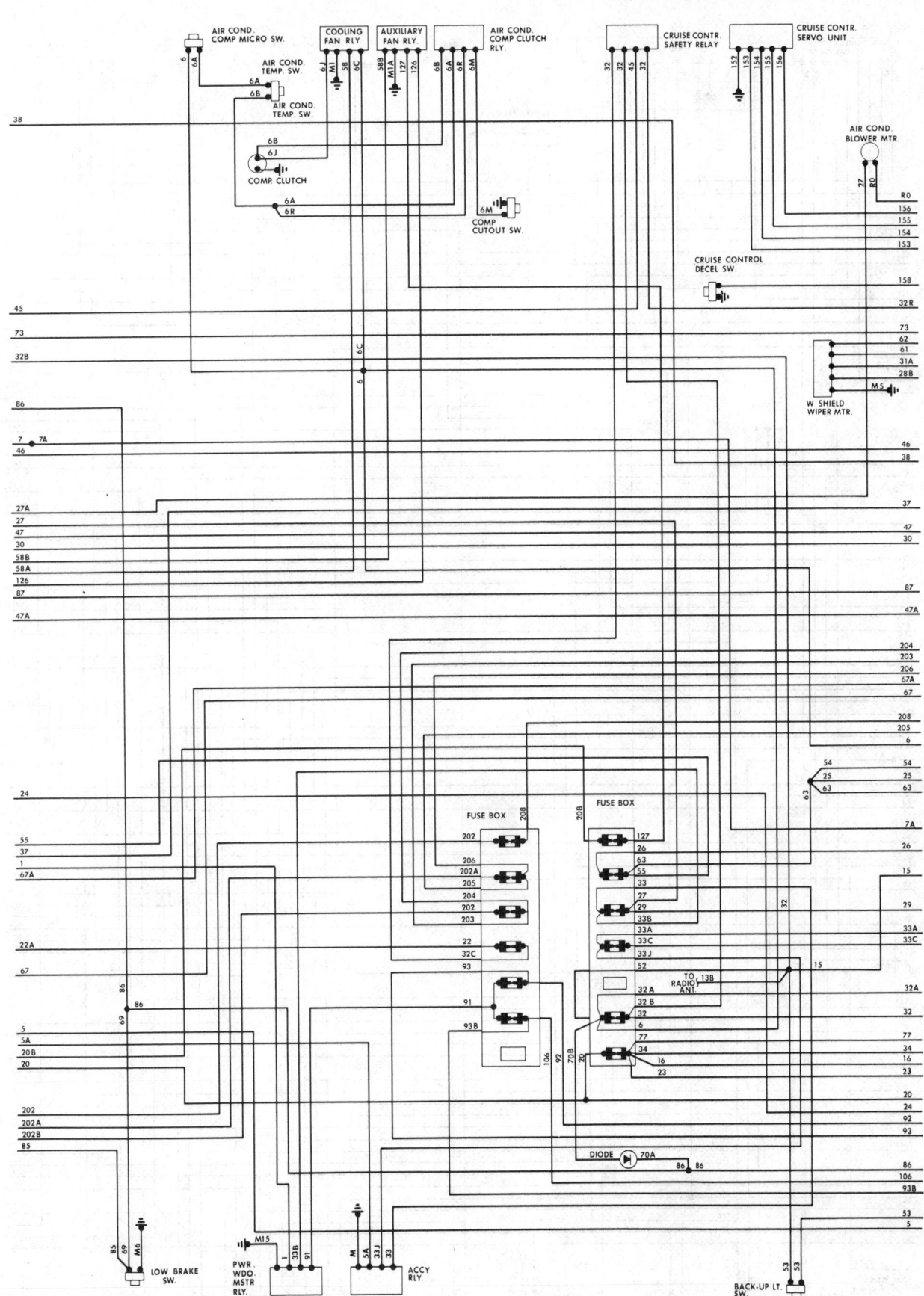

1981 Peugeot

UNDERDASH

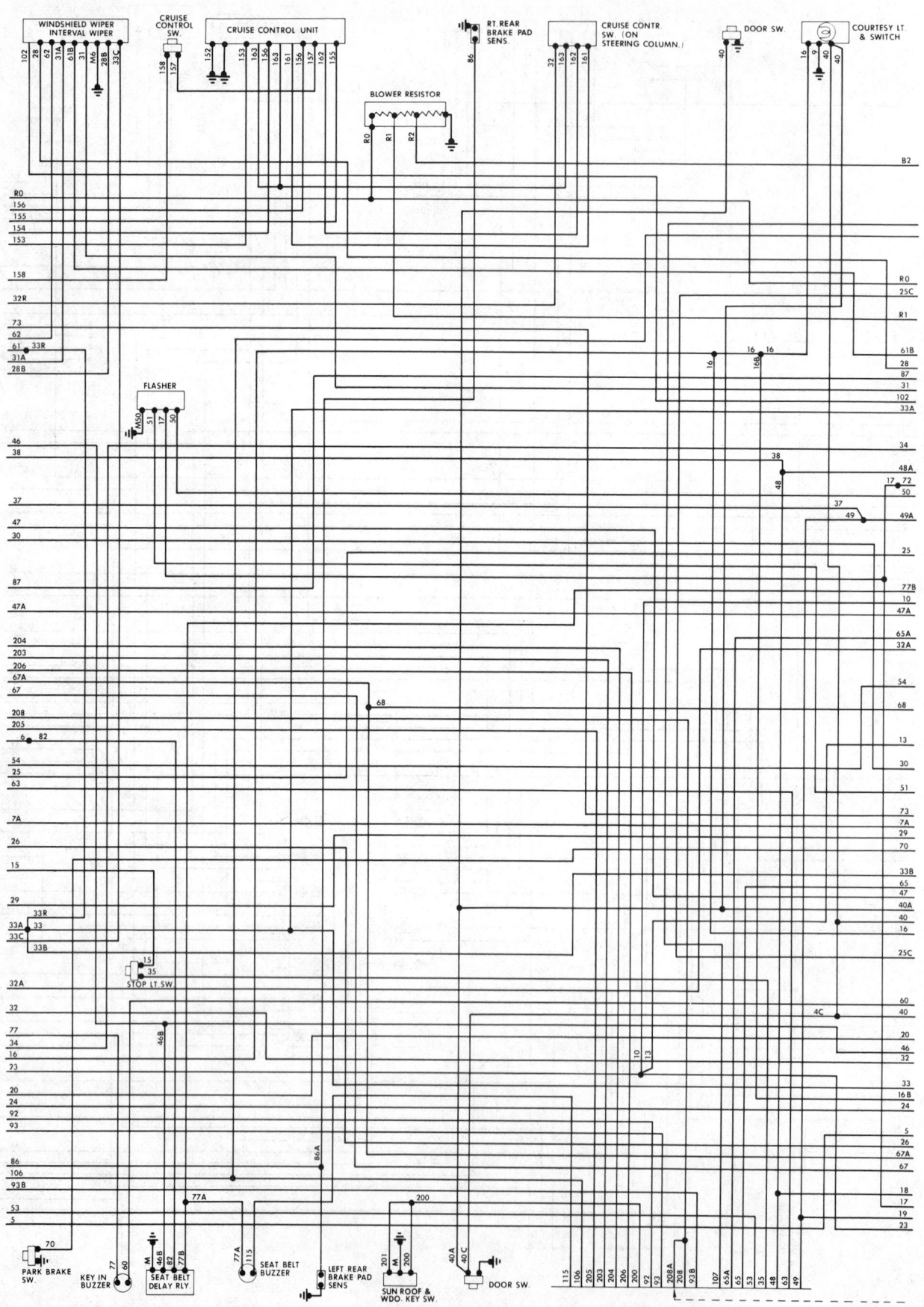

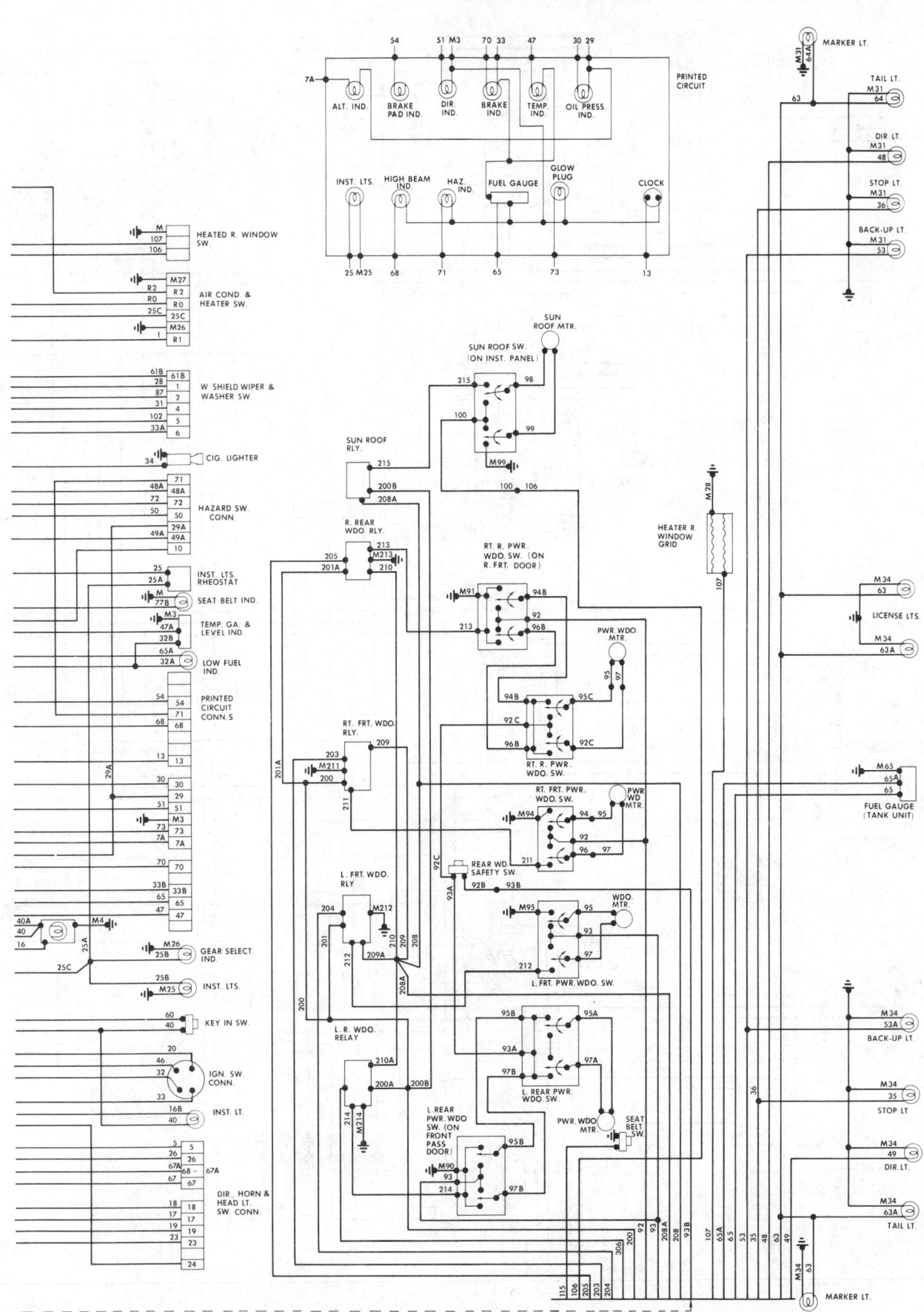

ENGINE COMPARTMENT & FUSE BLOCK

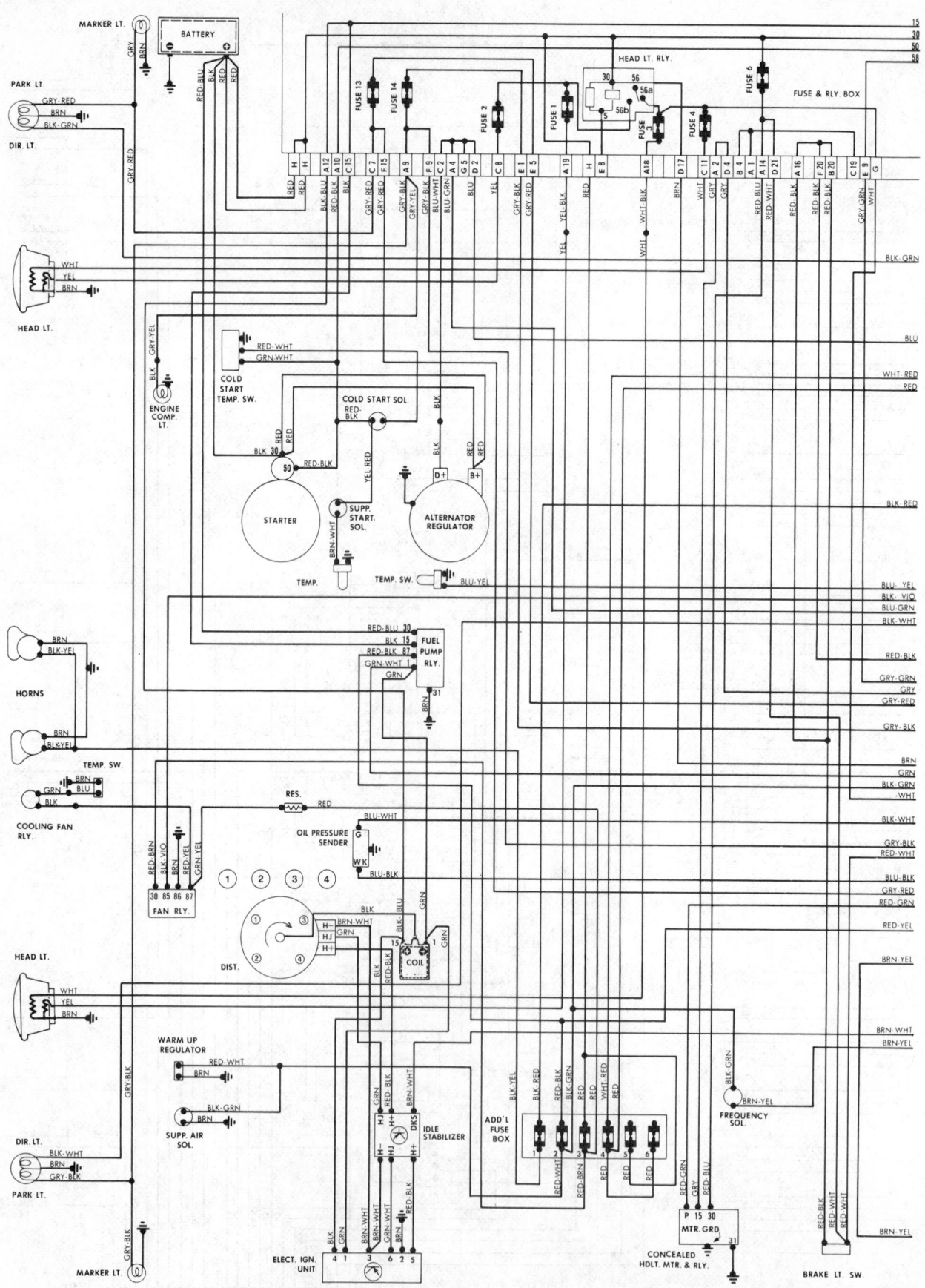

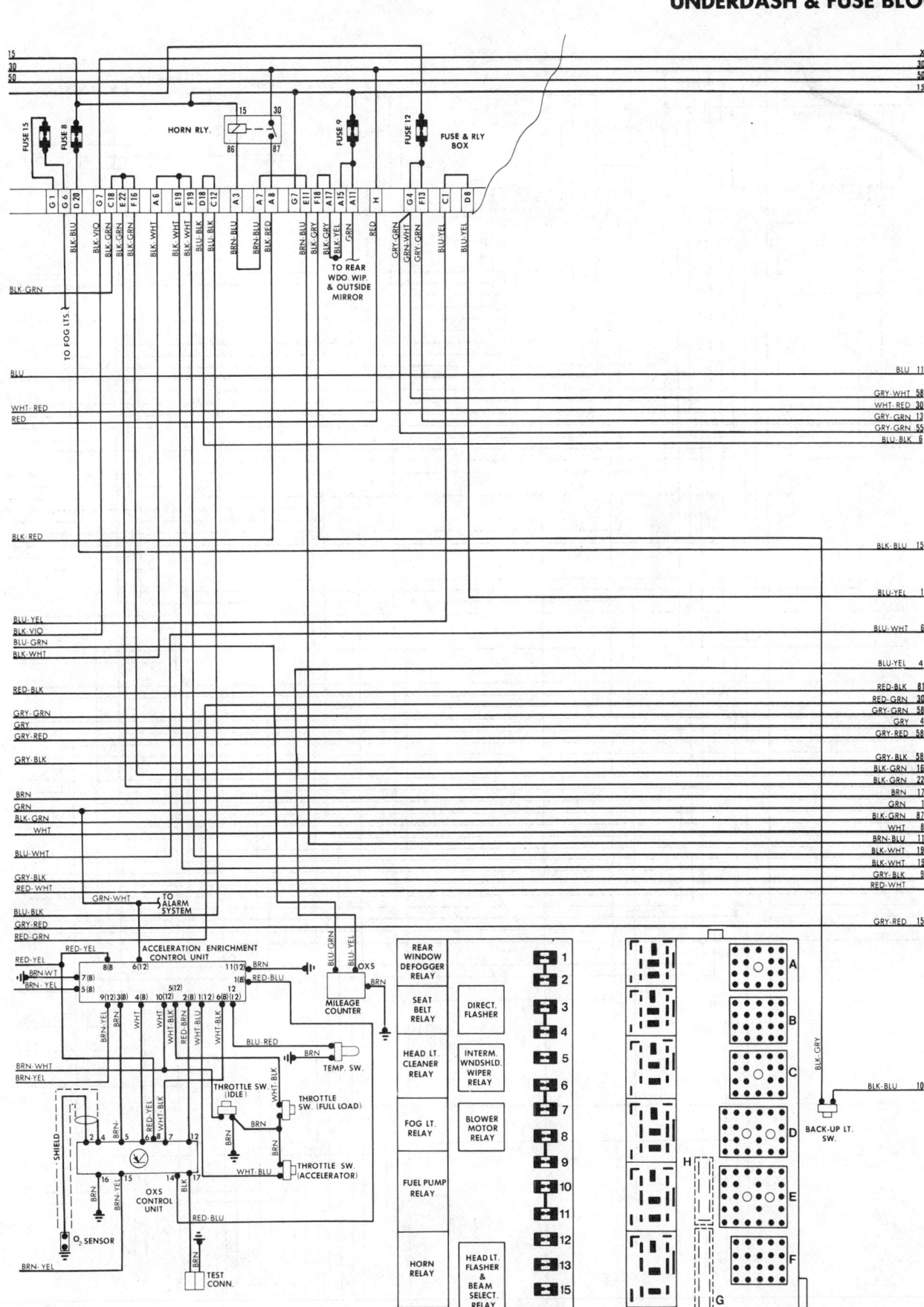

UNDERDASH

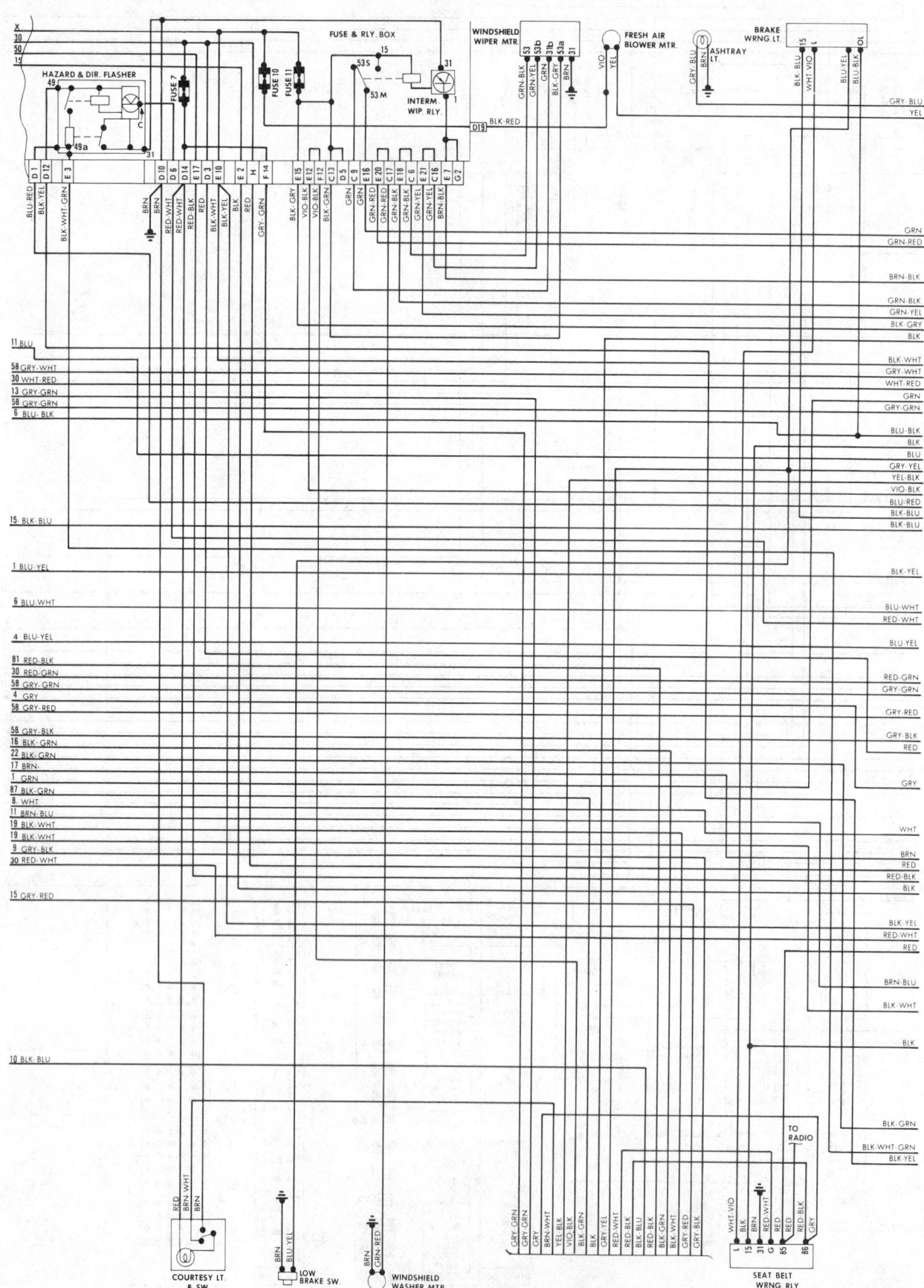

INSTRUMENT PANEL & REAR COMPARTMENT

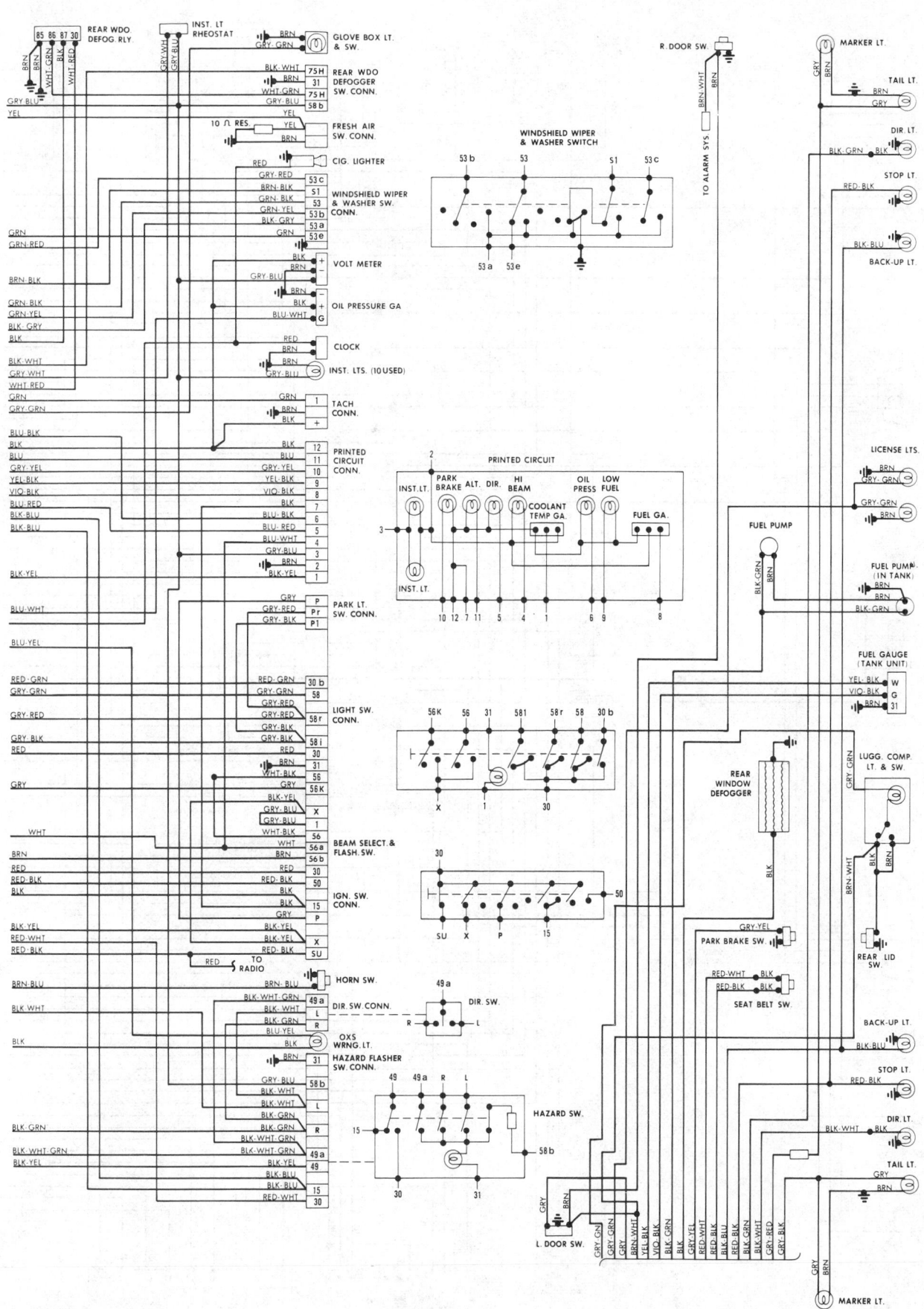

1981 Porsche

FRONT COMPARTMENT & FUSE BLOCK

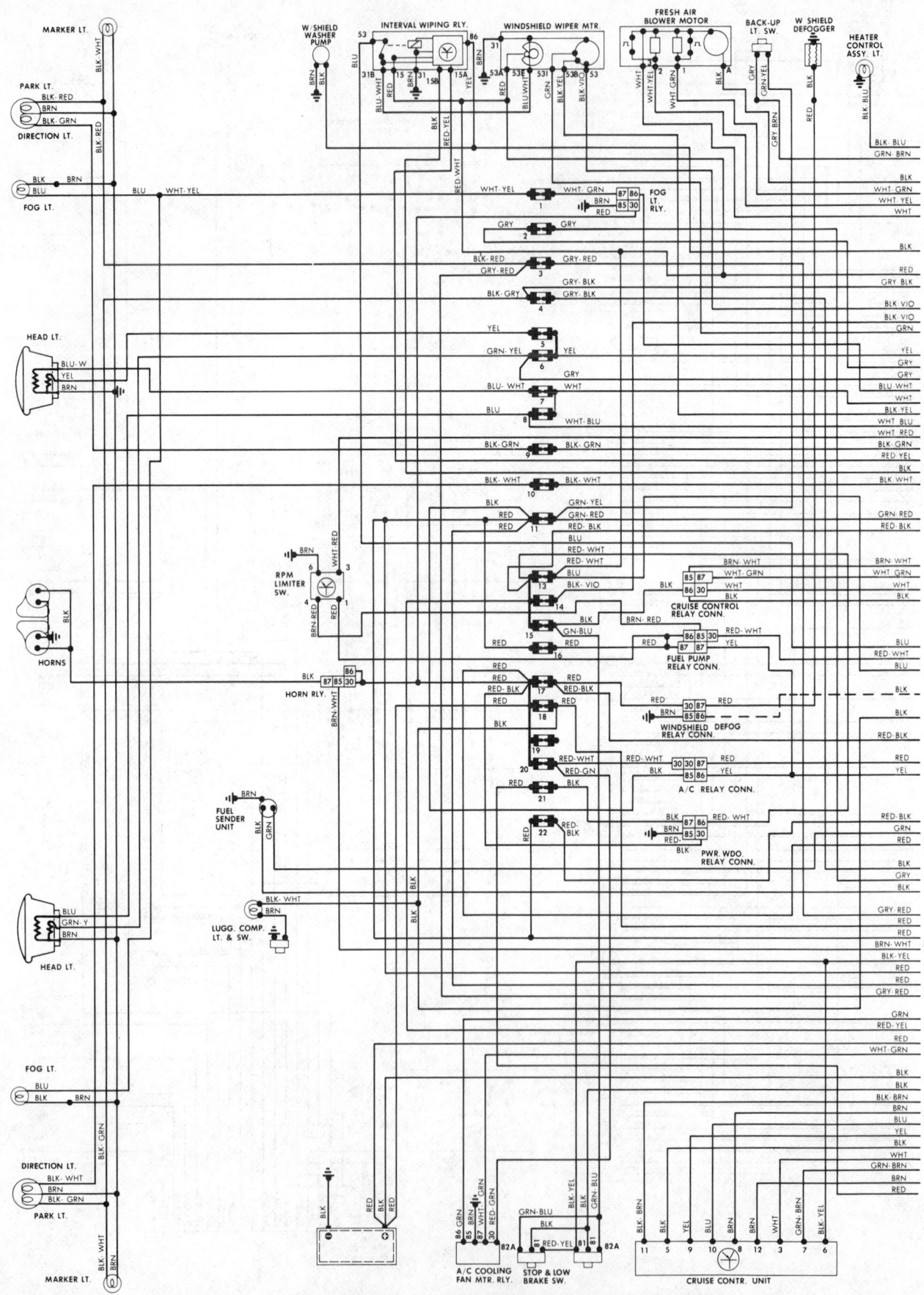

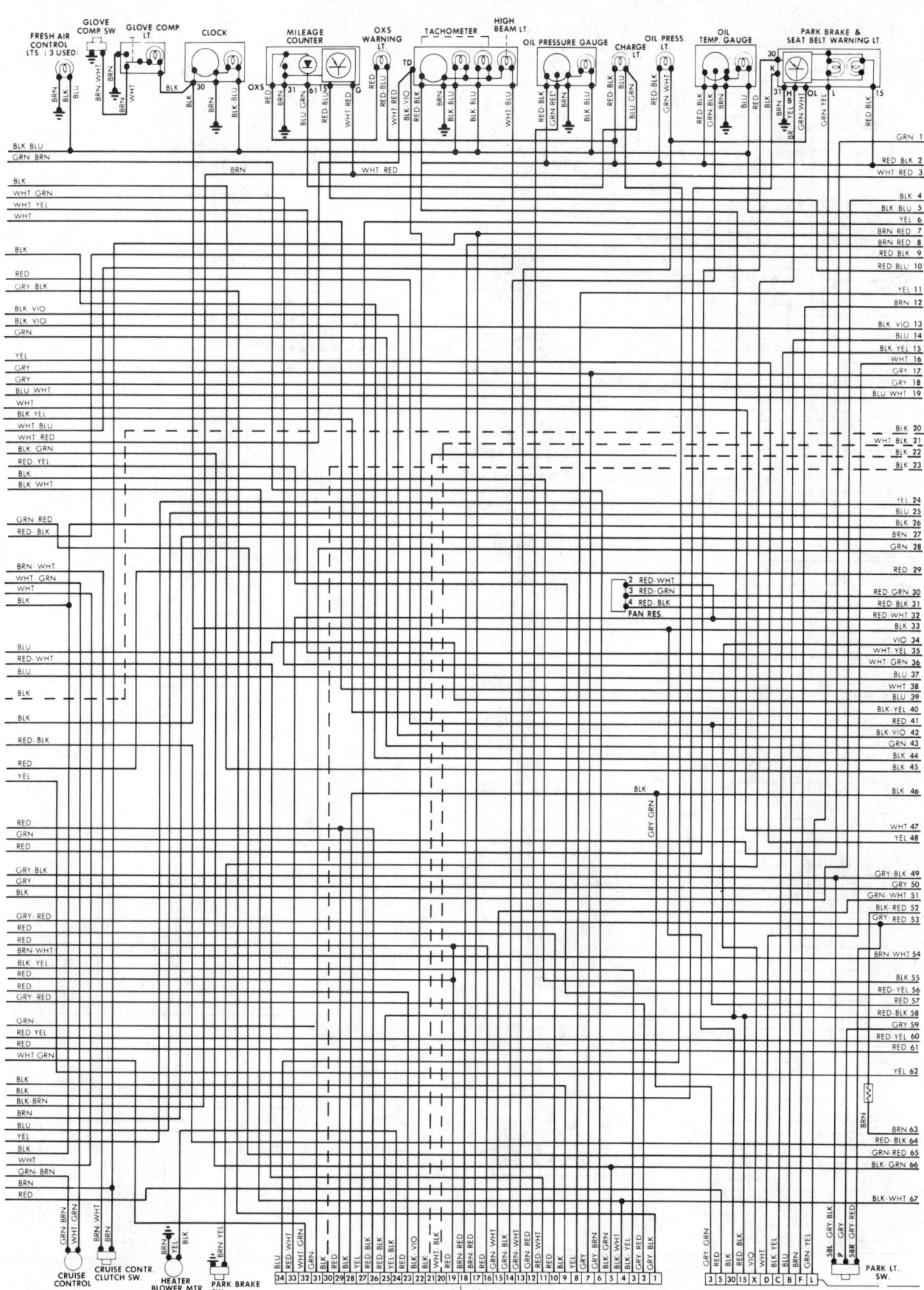

1981 Porsche

INSTRUMENT PANEL & ACCESSORIES

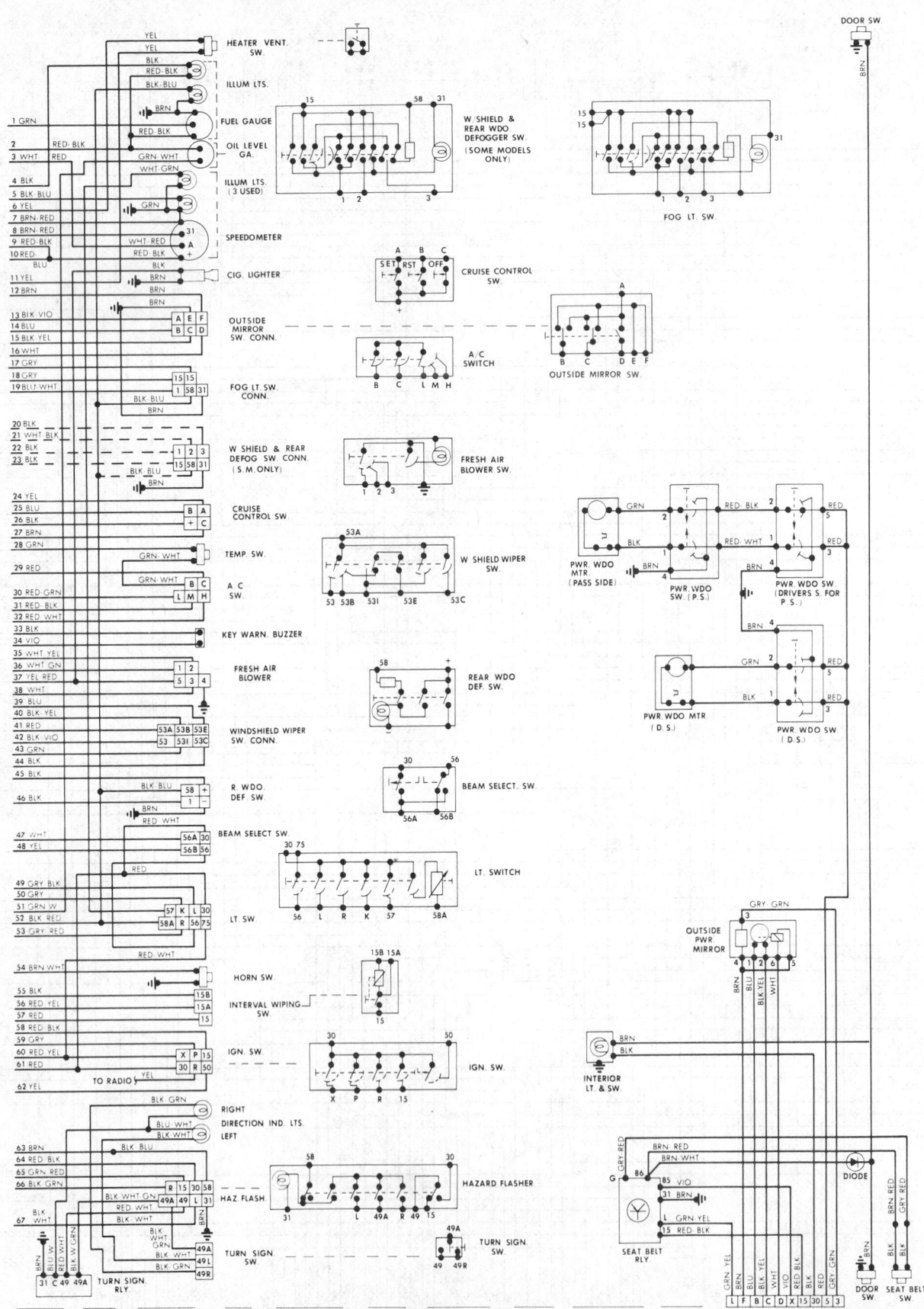

ENGINE COMPARTMENT & REAR COMPARTMENT

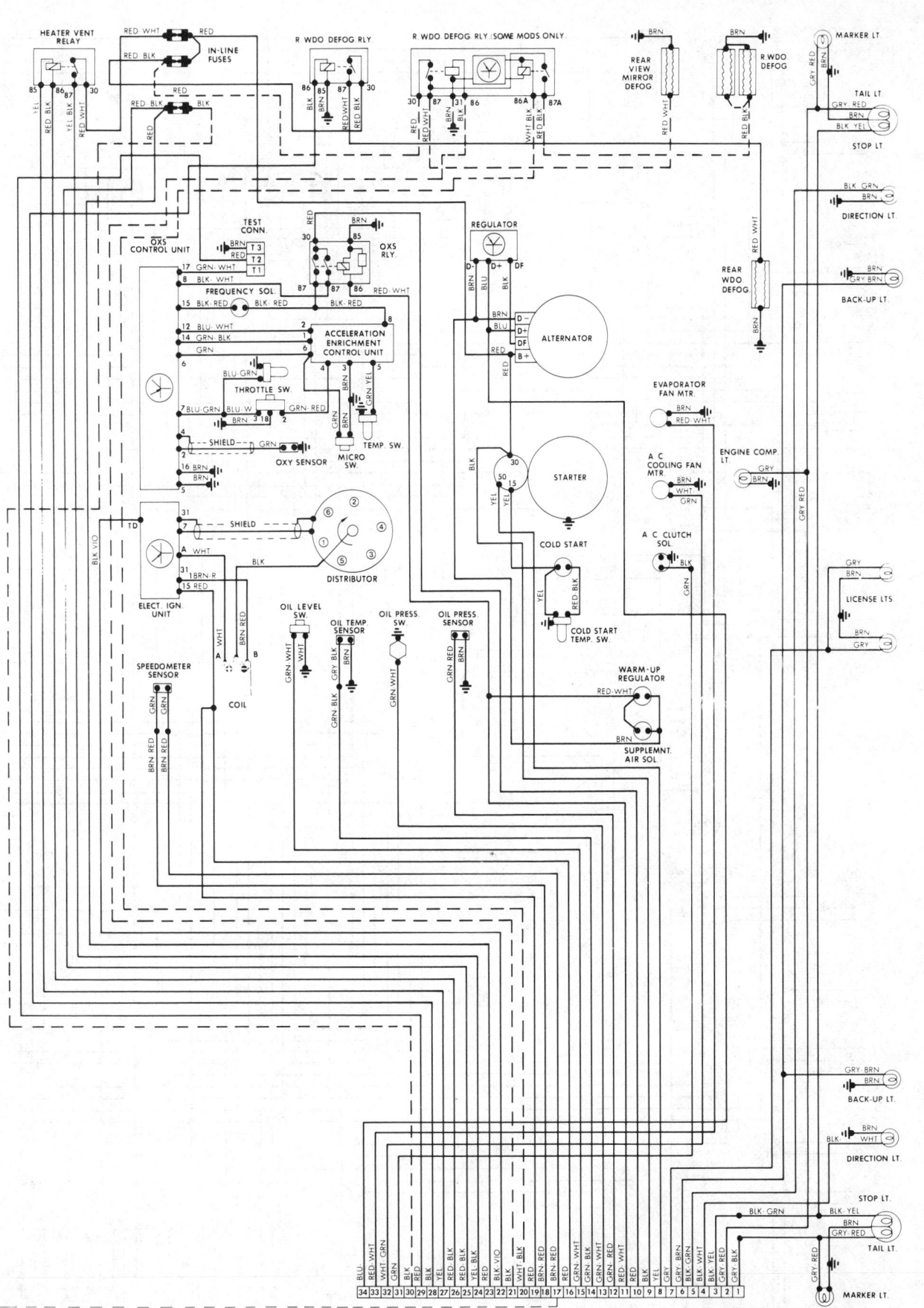

1981 Porsche

ENGINE COMPARTMENT & FUSE BLOCK

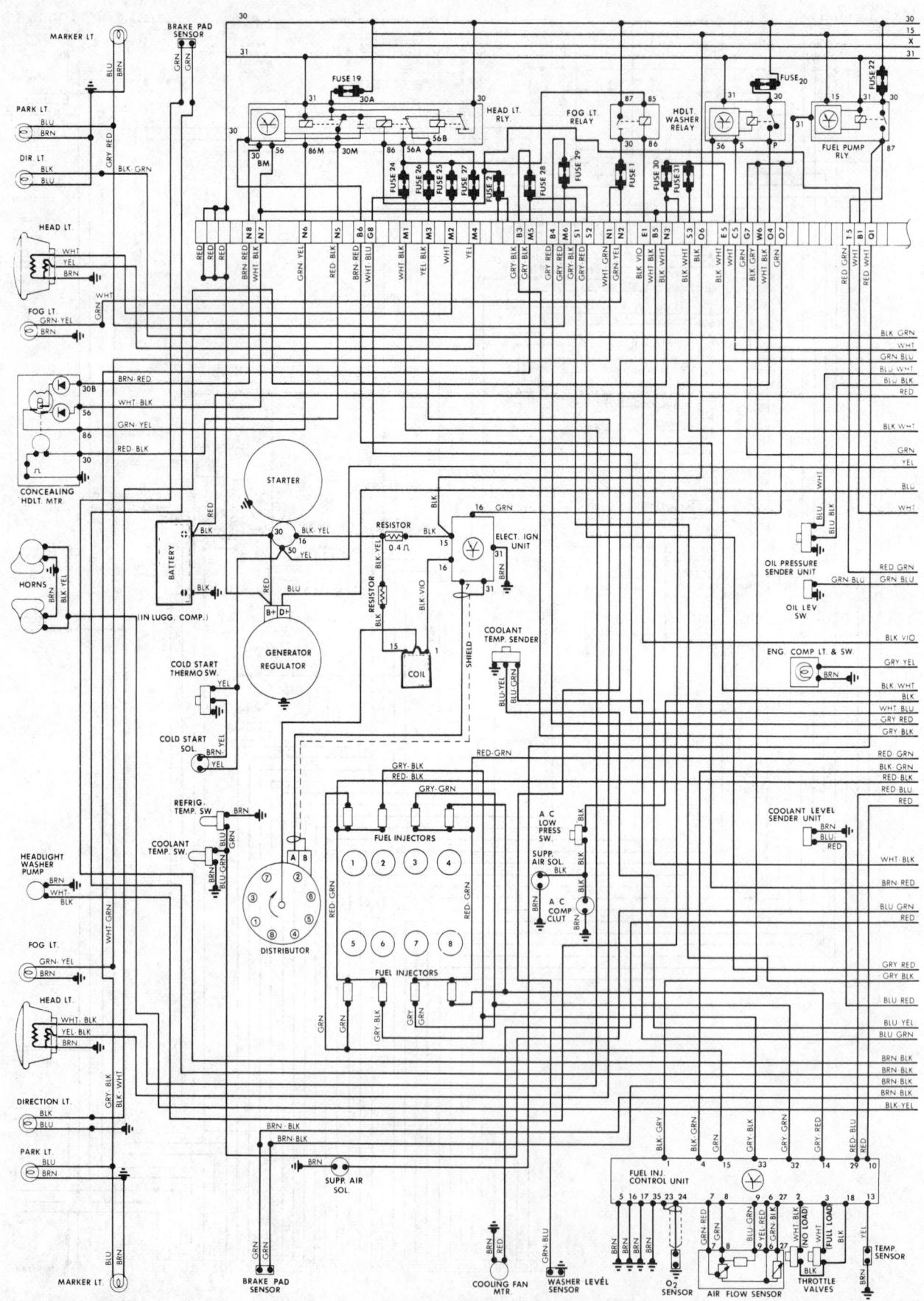

UNDERDASH & FUSE BLOCK

WIRING DIAGRAMS

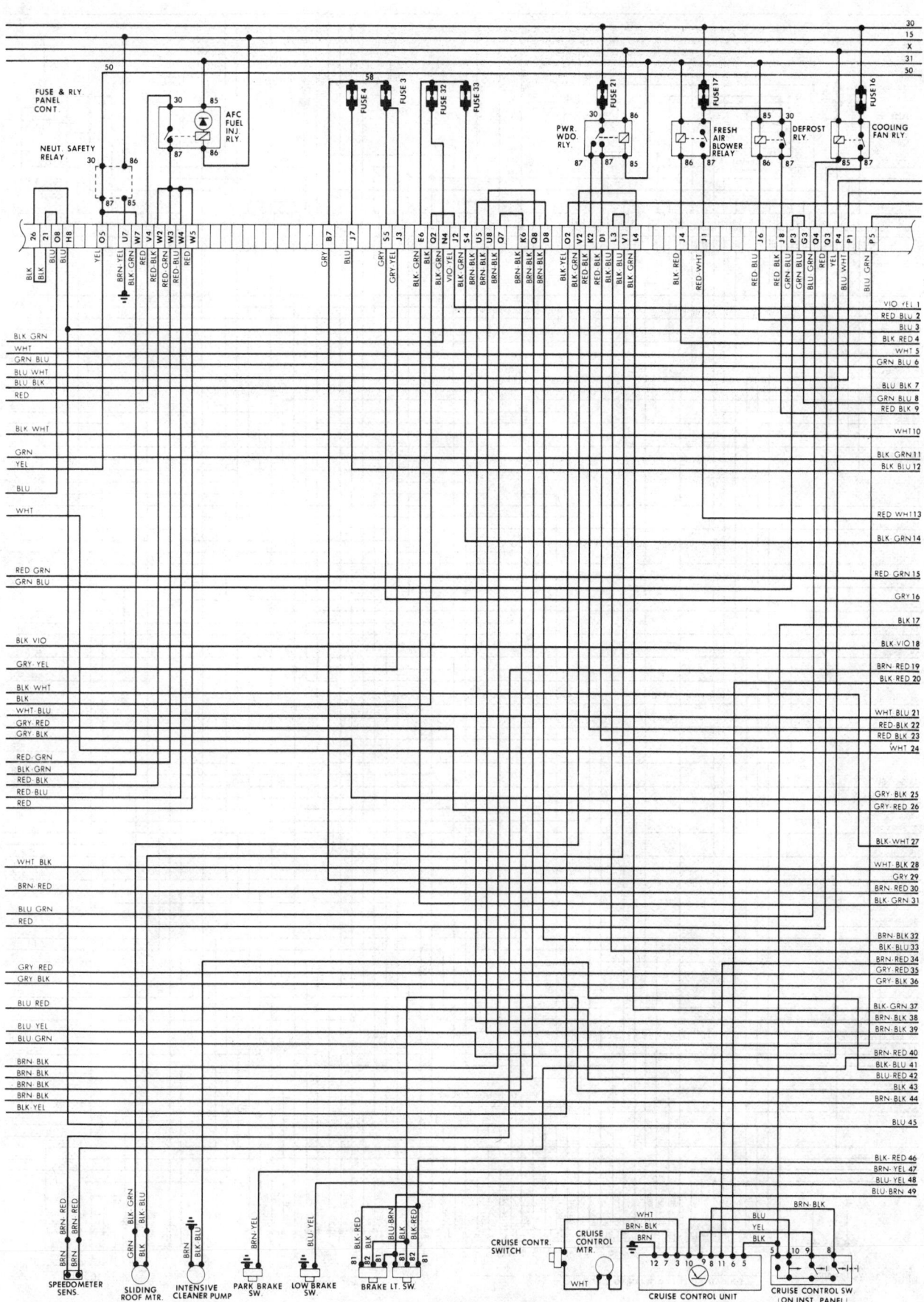

1981 Porsche

UNDERDASH & FUSE BLOCK

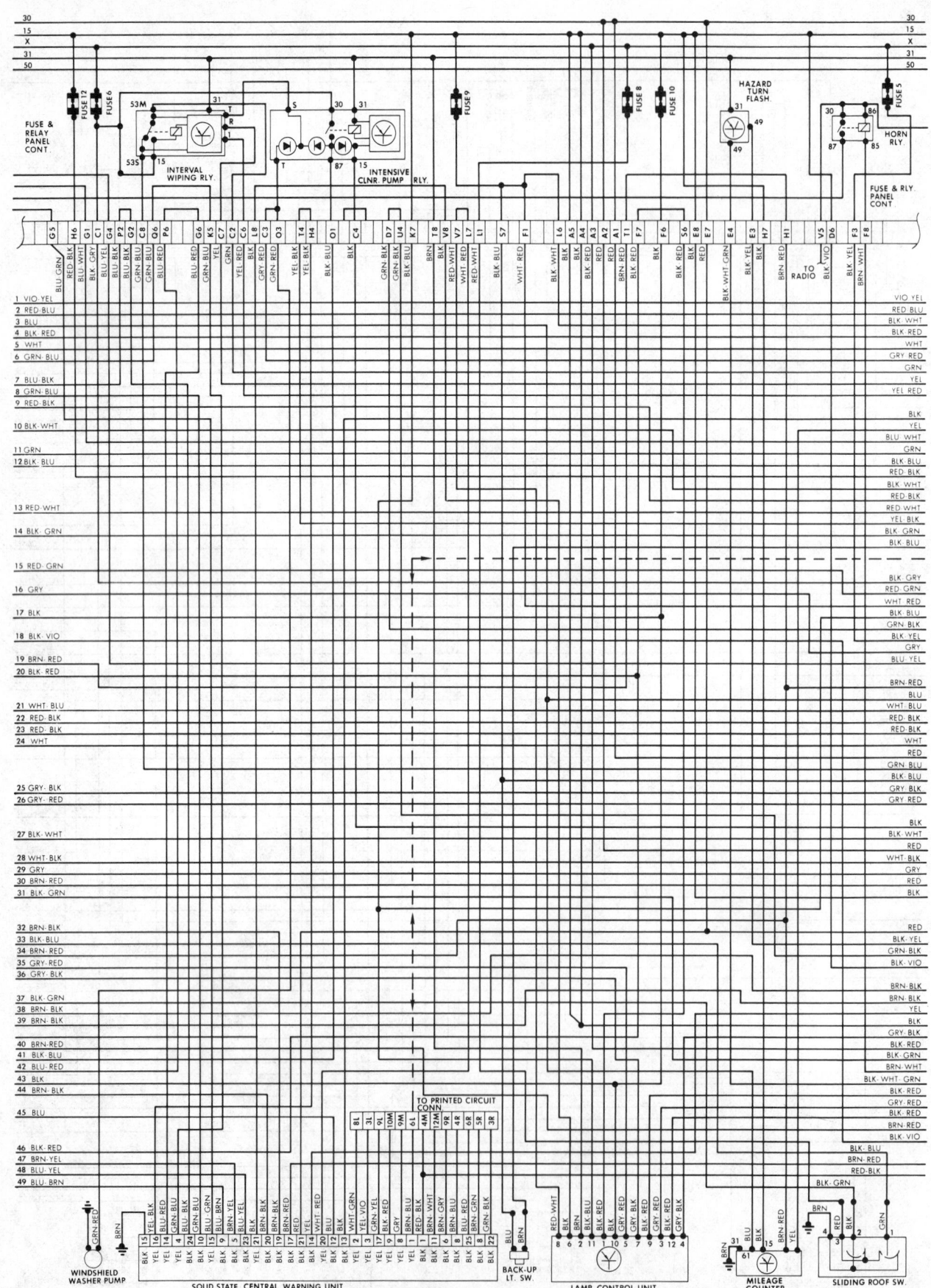

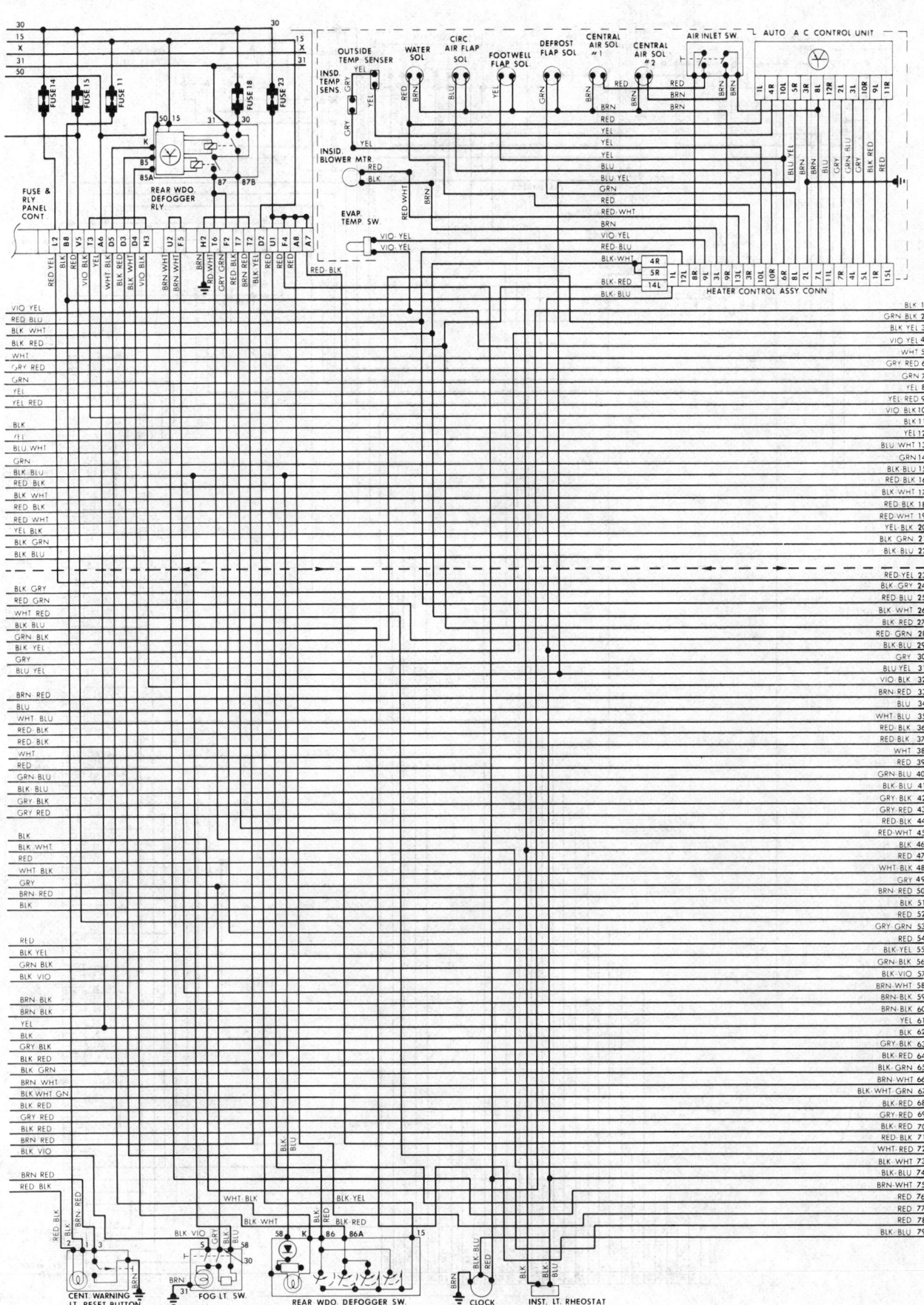

1981 Porsche

INSTRUMENT PANEL

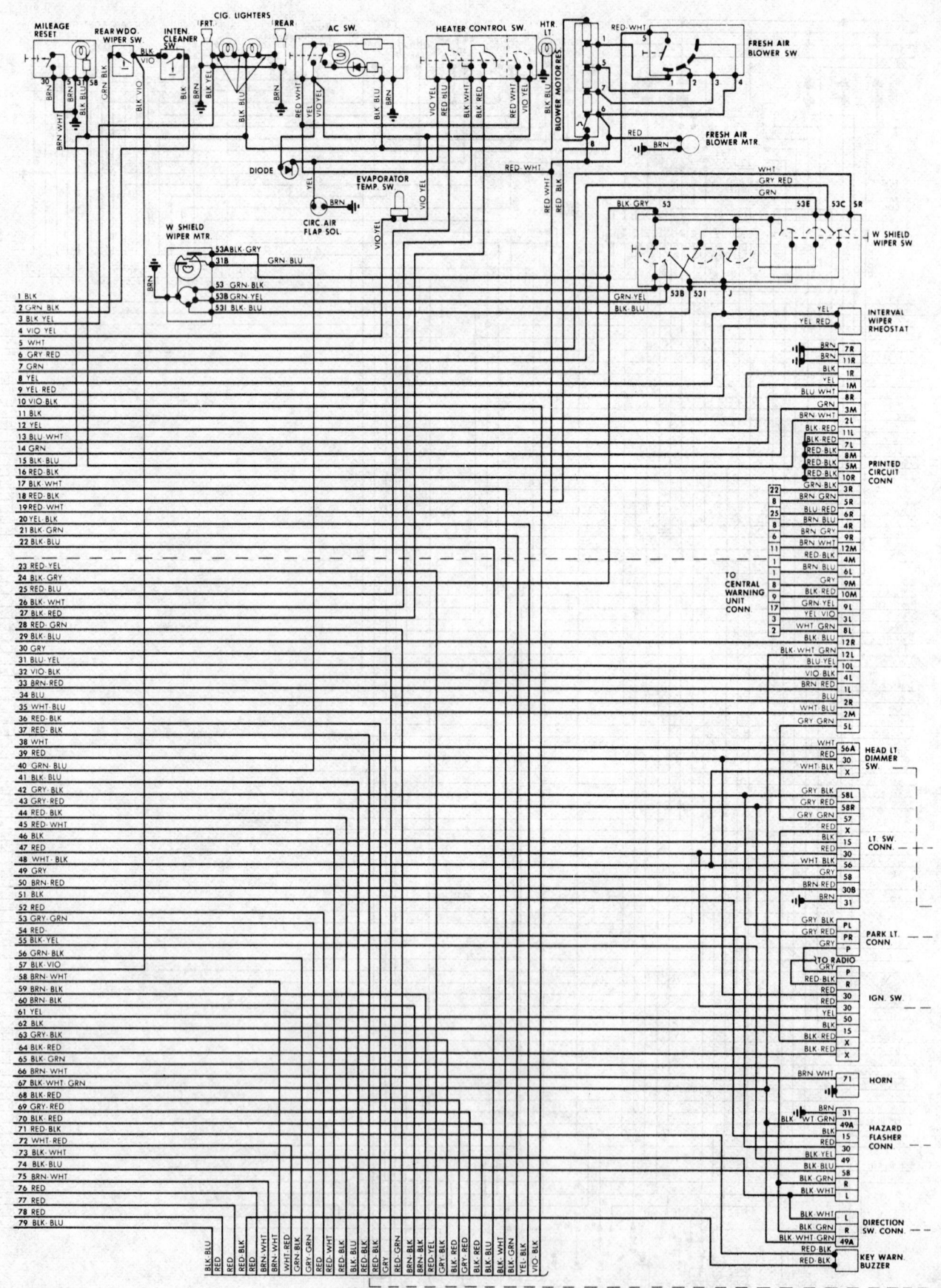

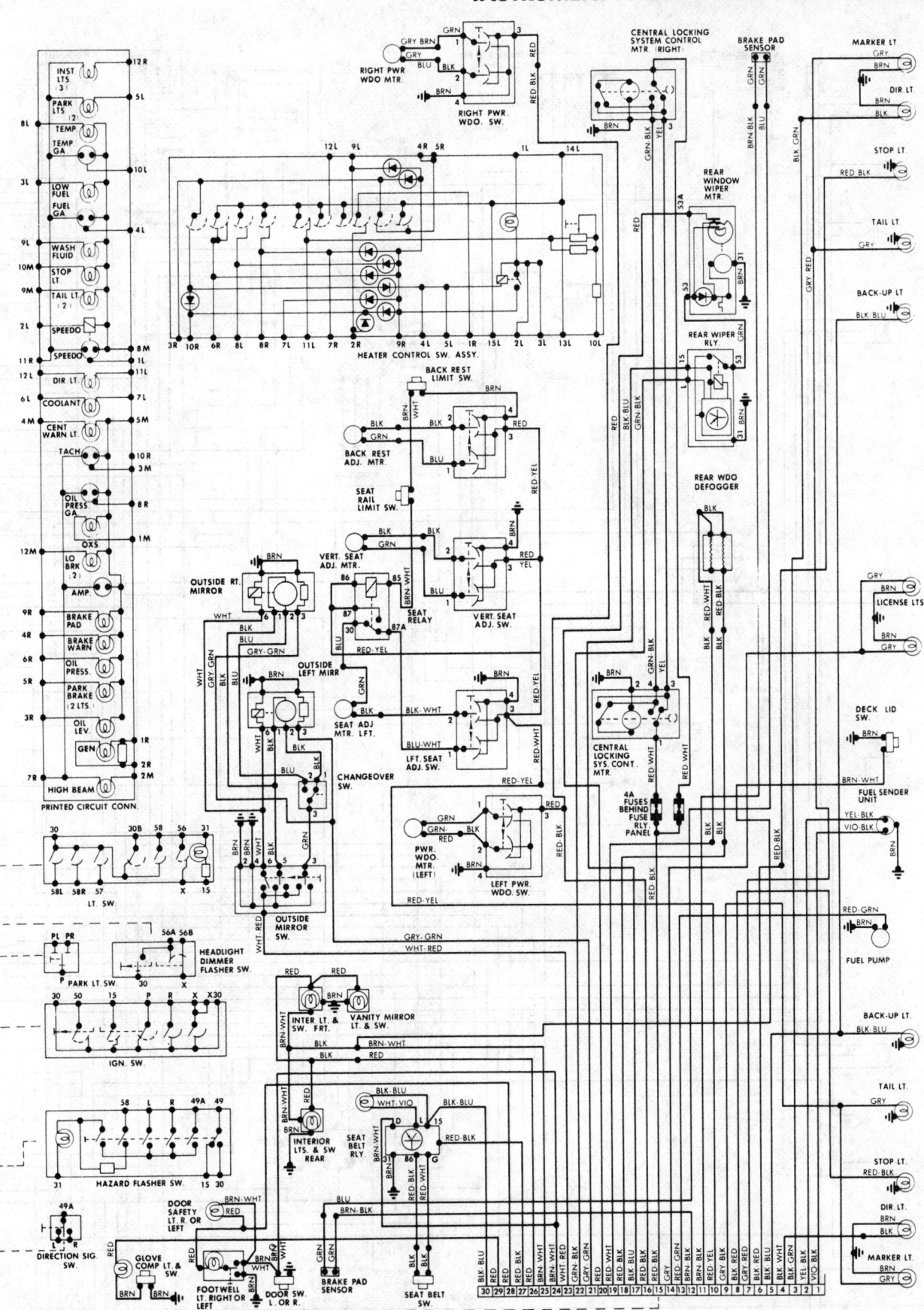

1981 Renault

ENGINE COMPARTMENT & FUSE BLOCK

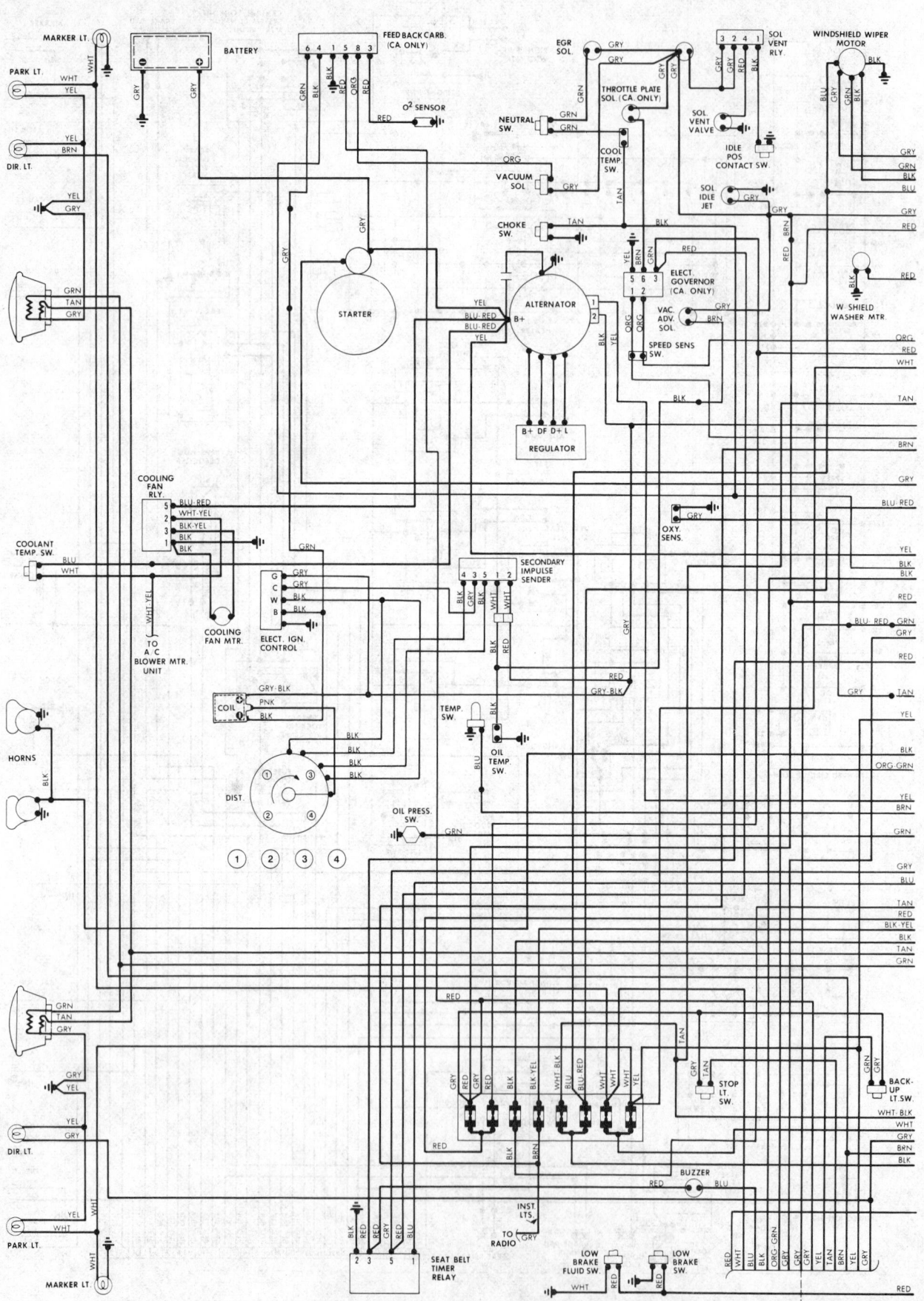

INSTRUMENT PANEL & REAR COMPARTMENT

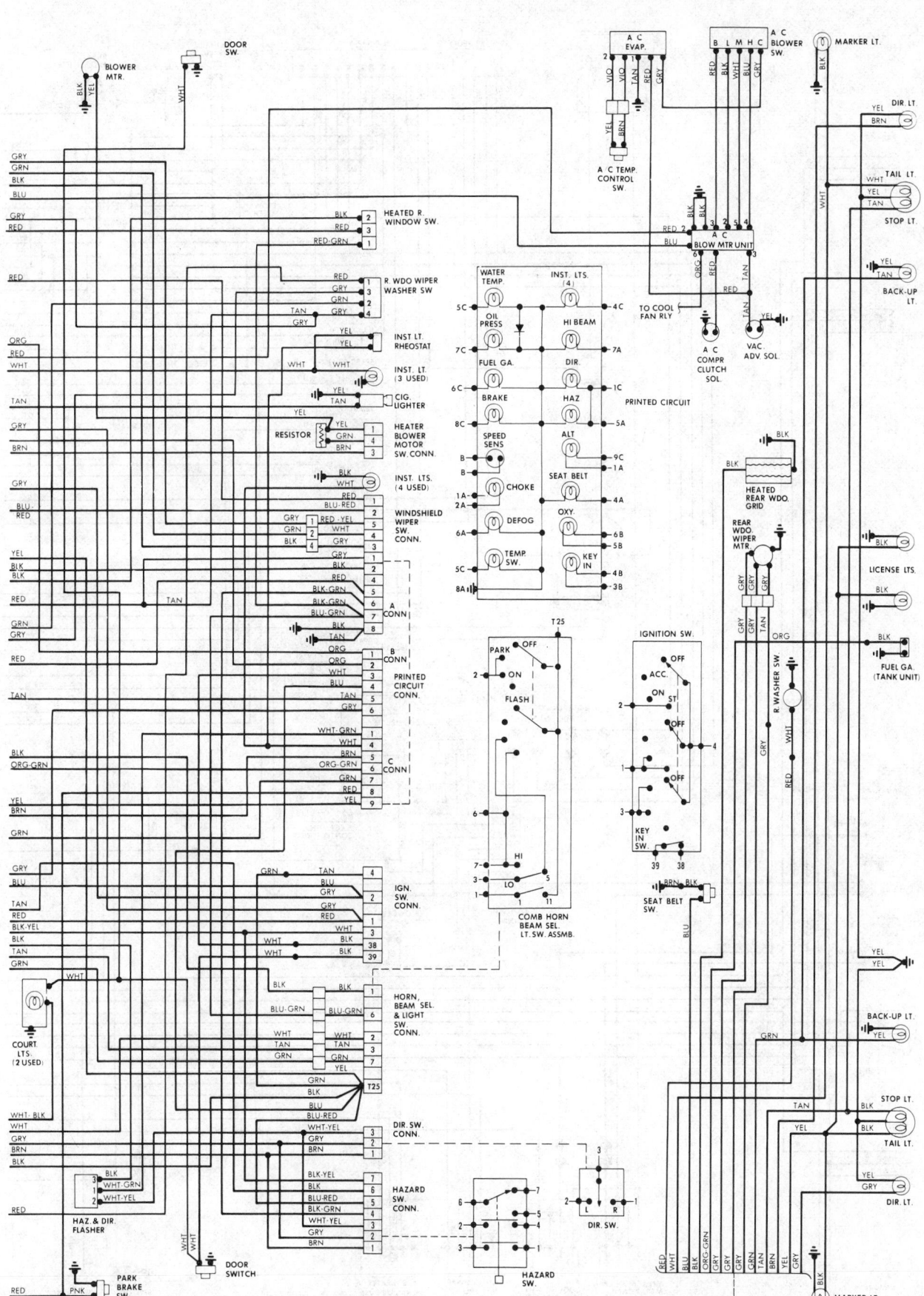

1981 Renault

ENGINE COMPARTMENT

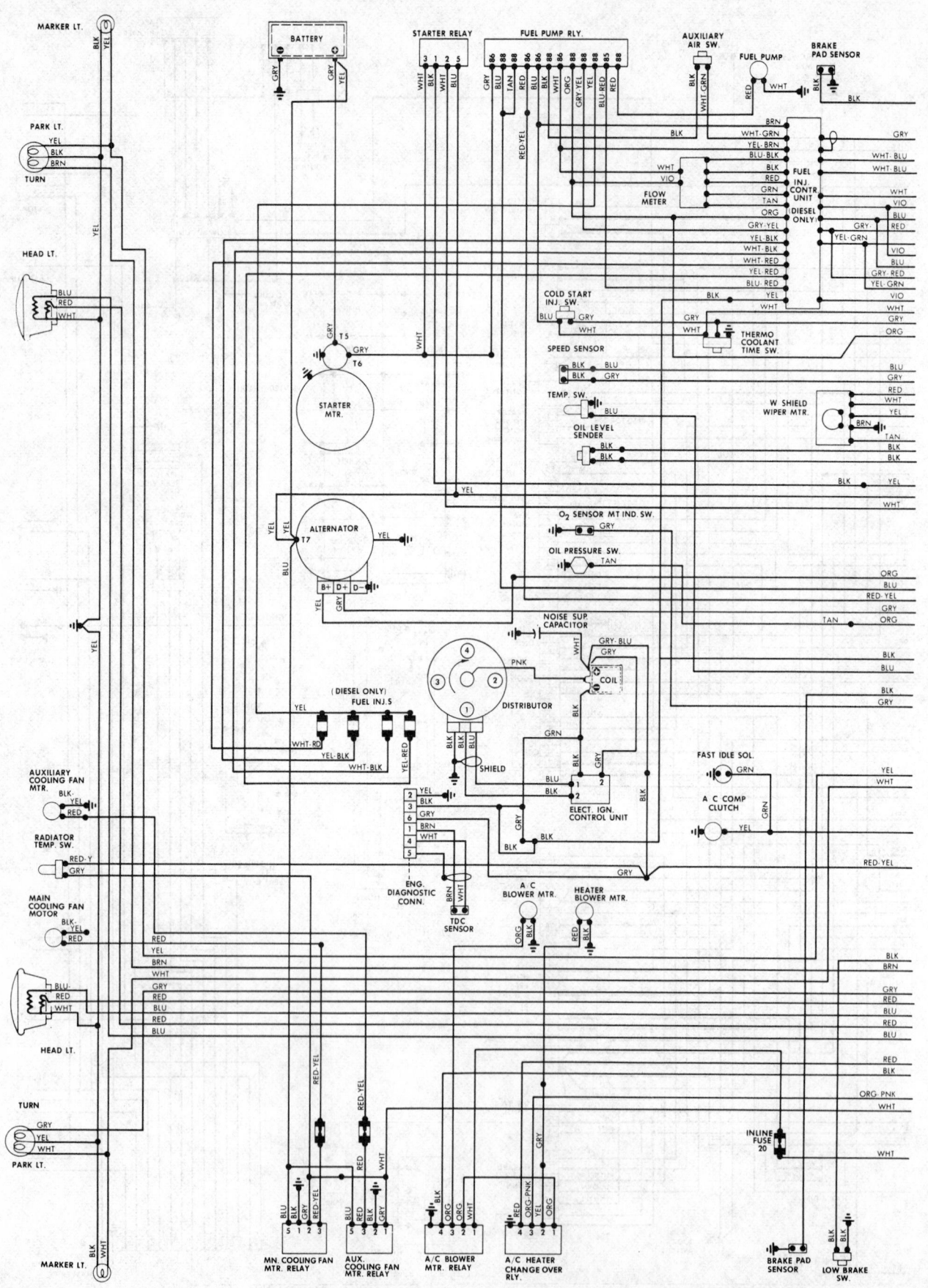

ENGINE COMPARTMENT & FUSE BLOCK

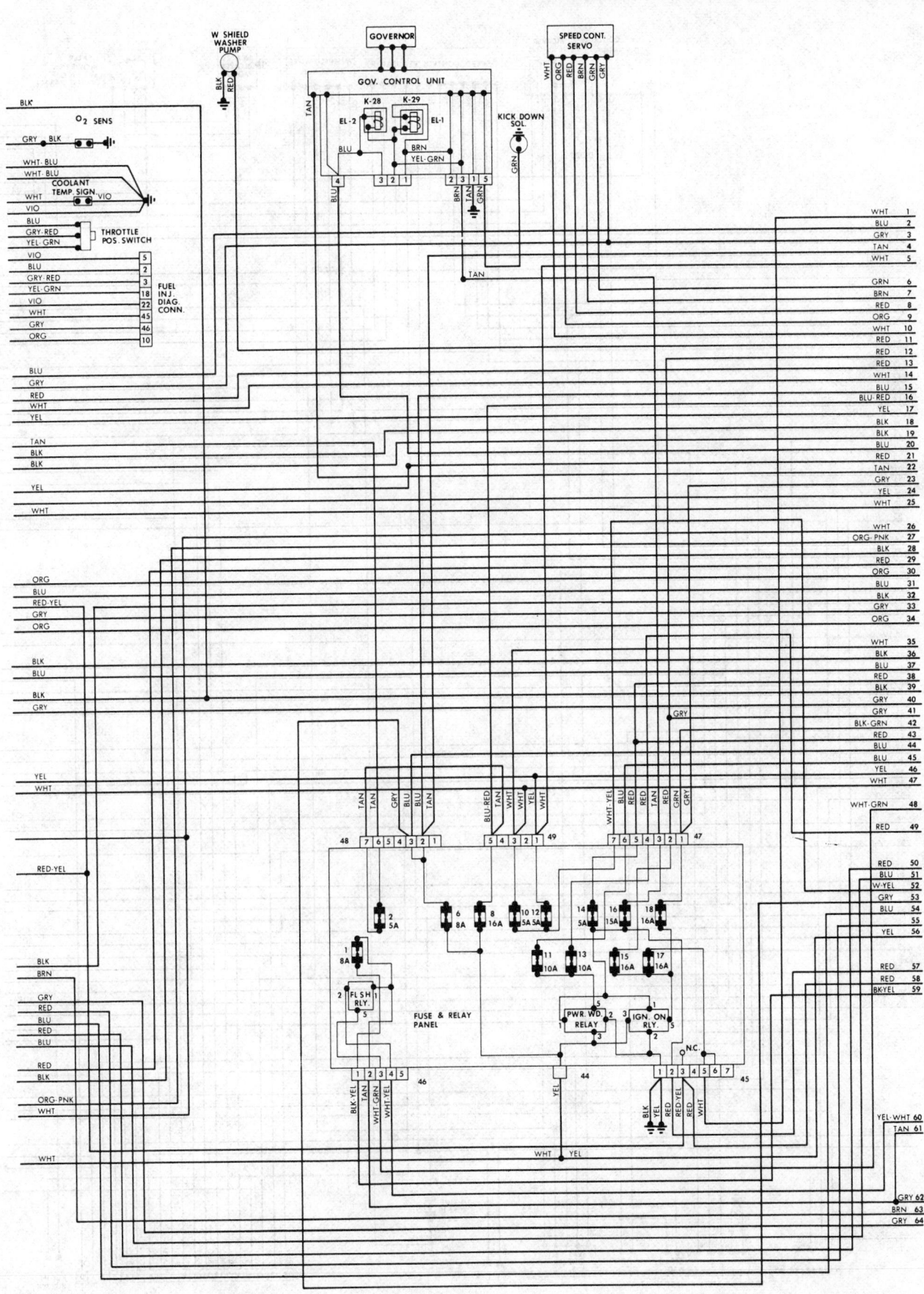

1981 Renault

UNDERDASH

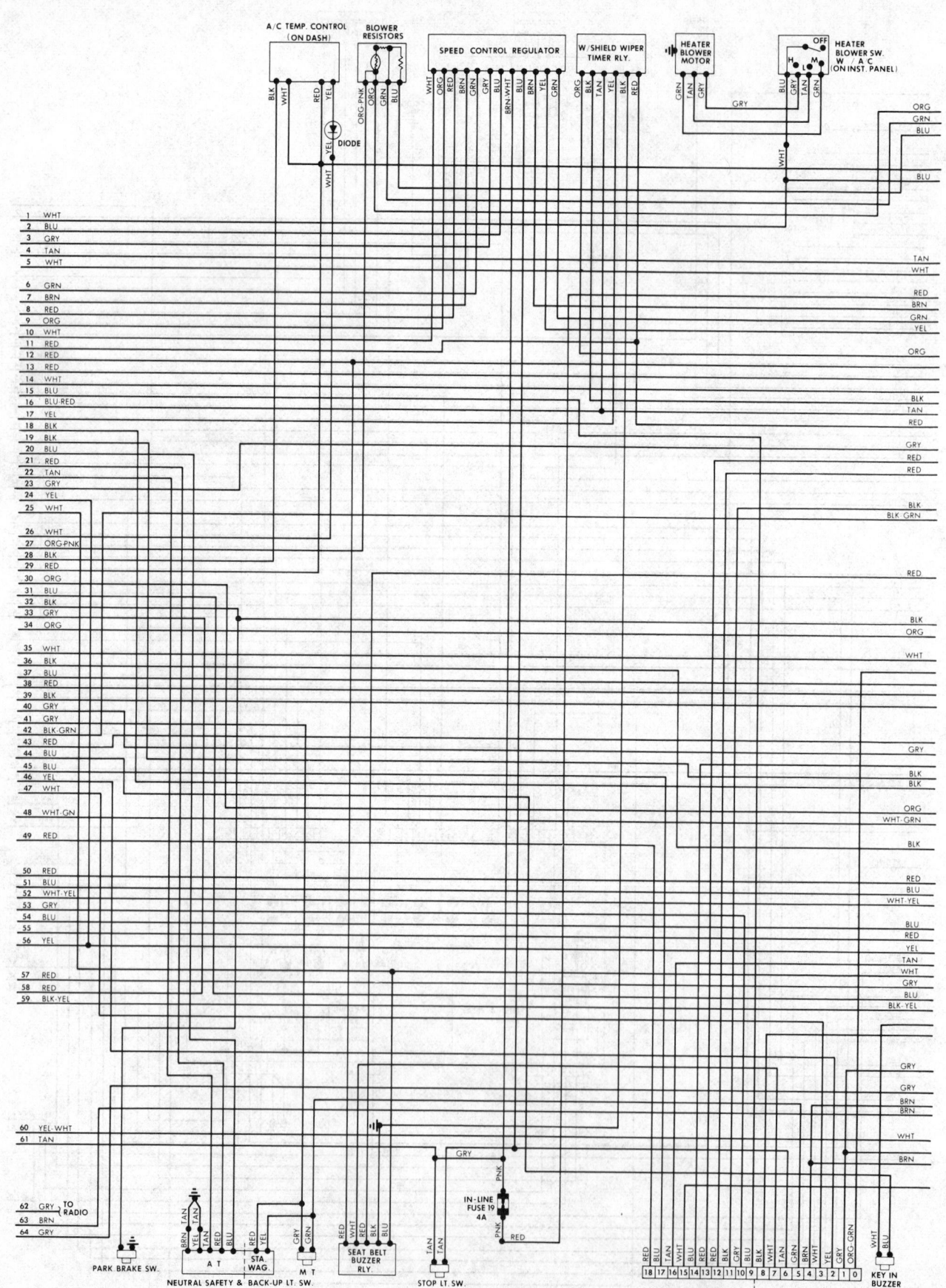

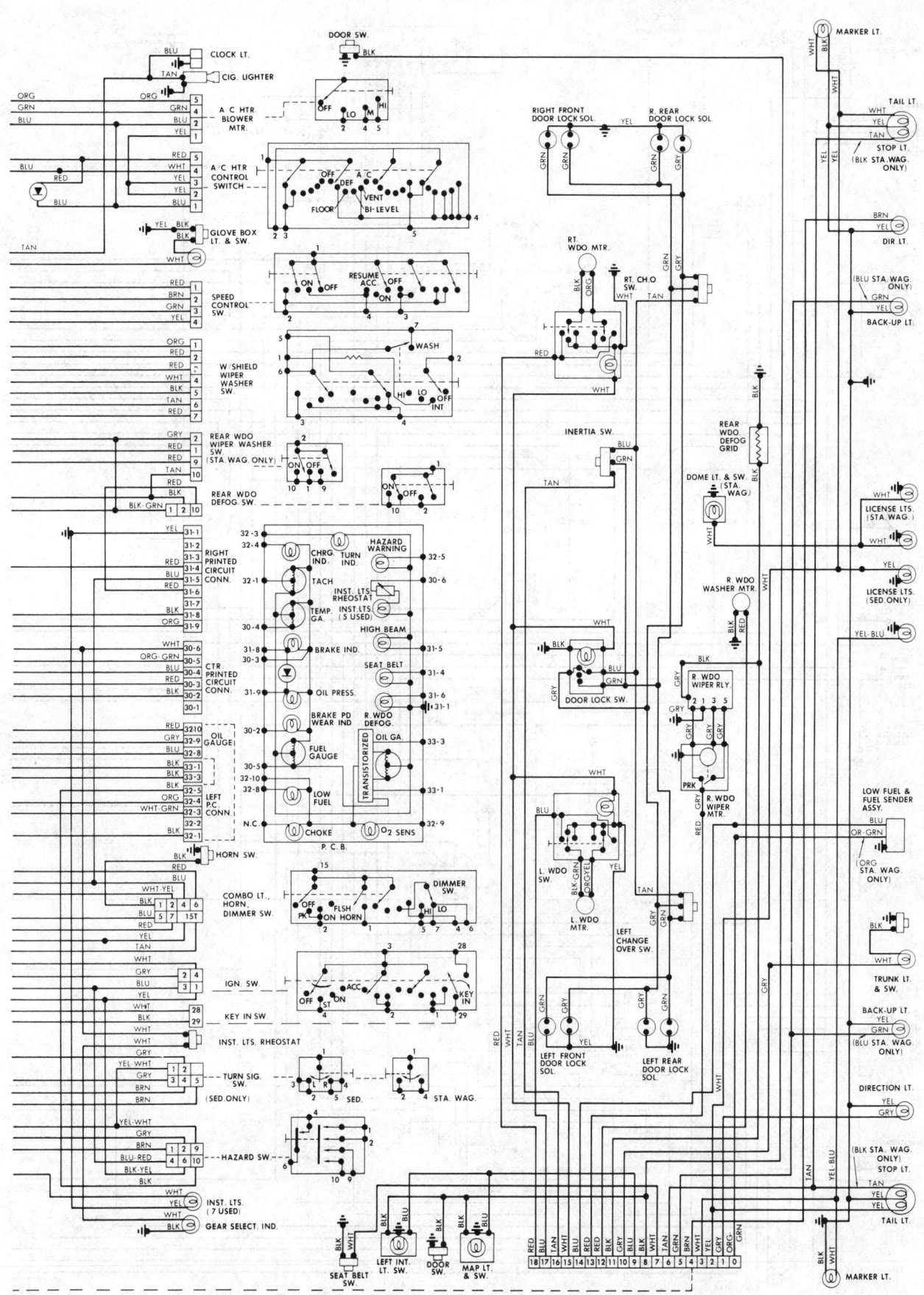

ENGINE COMPARTMENT

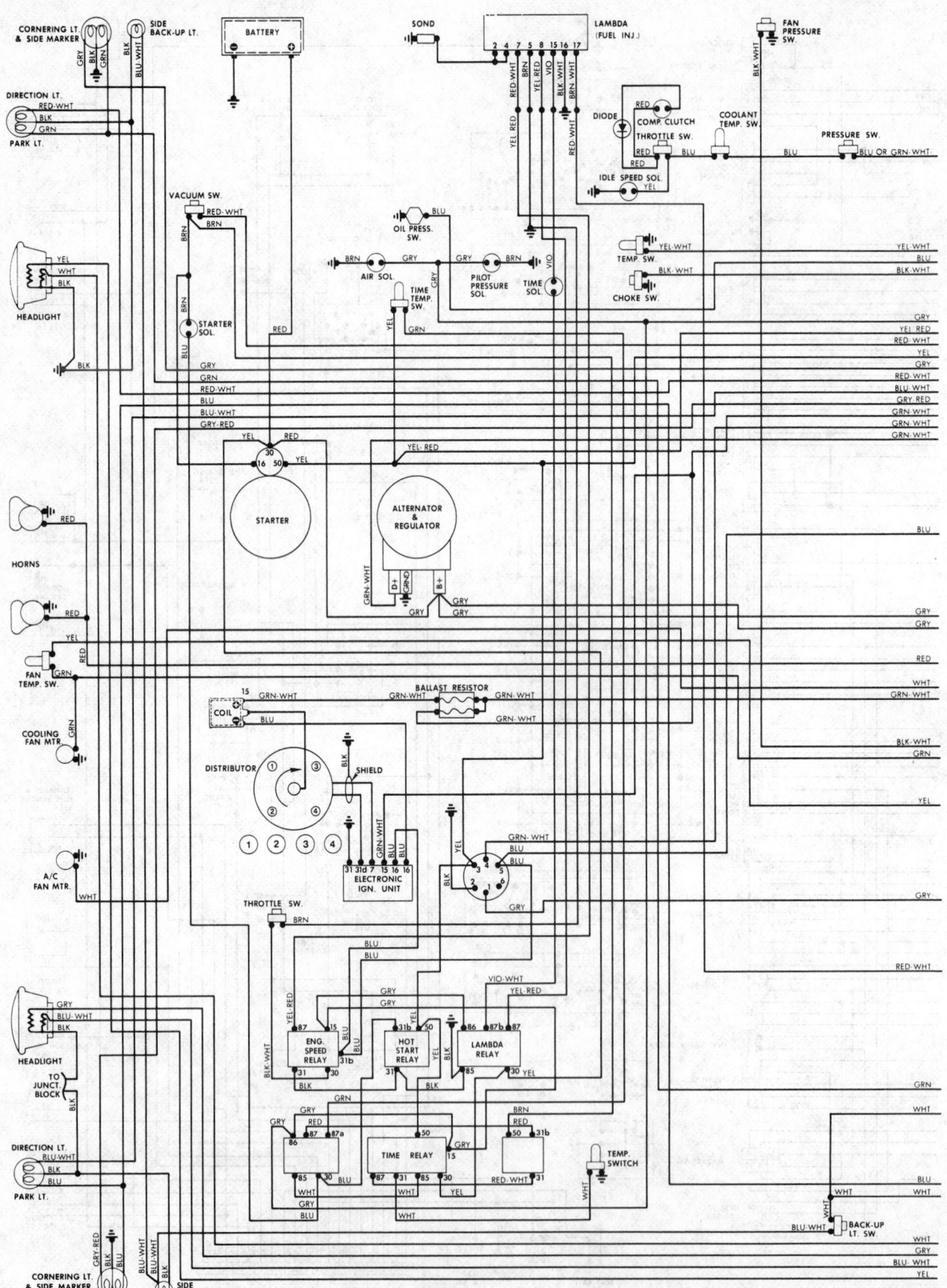

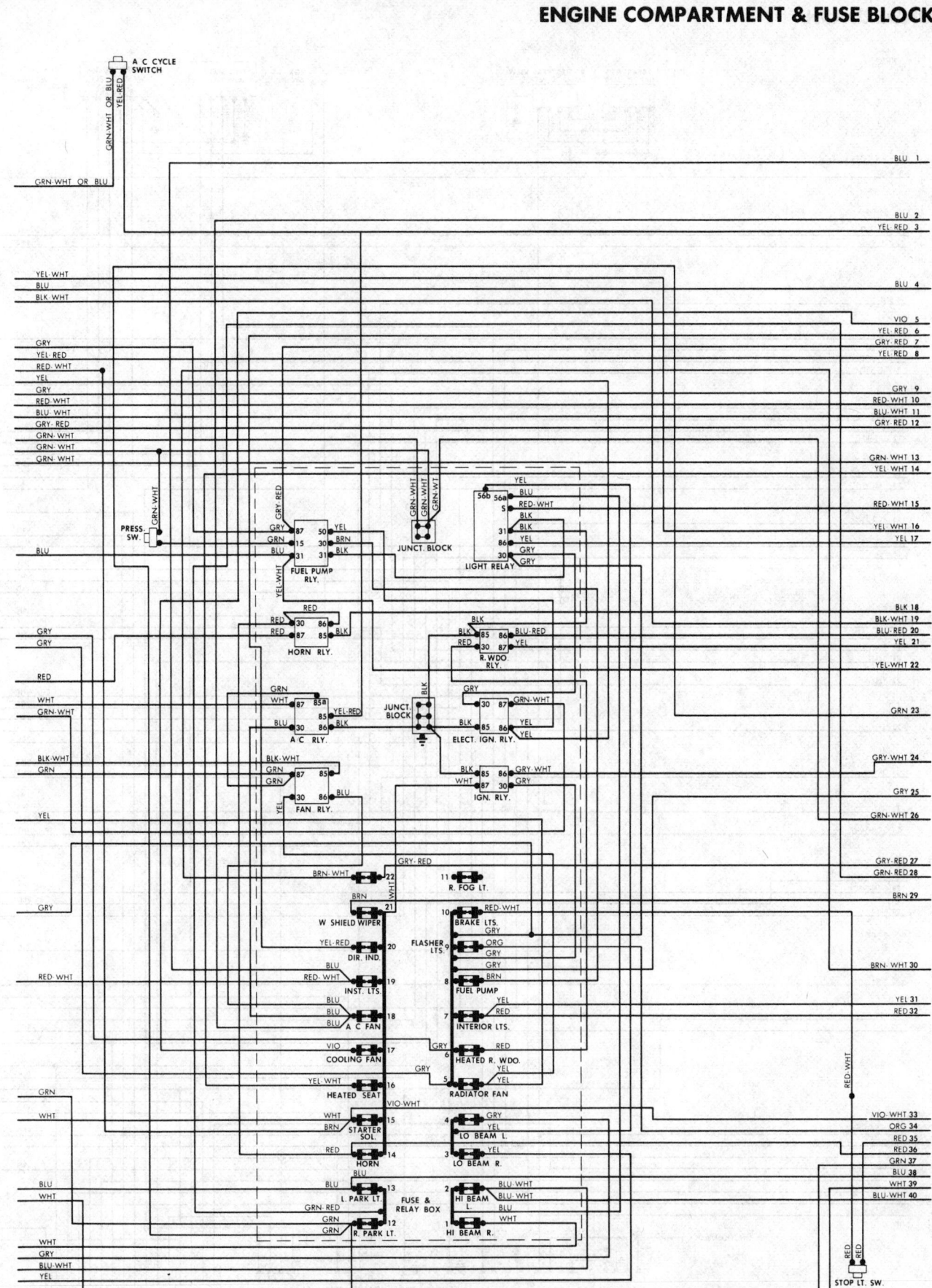

UNDERDASH

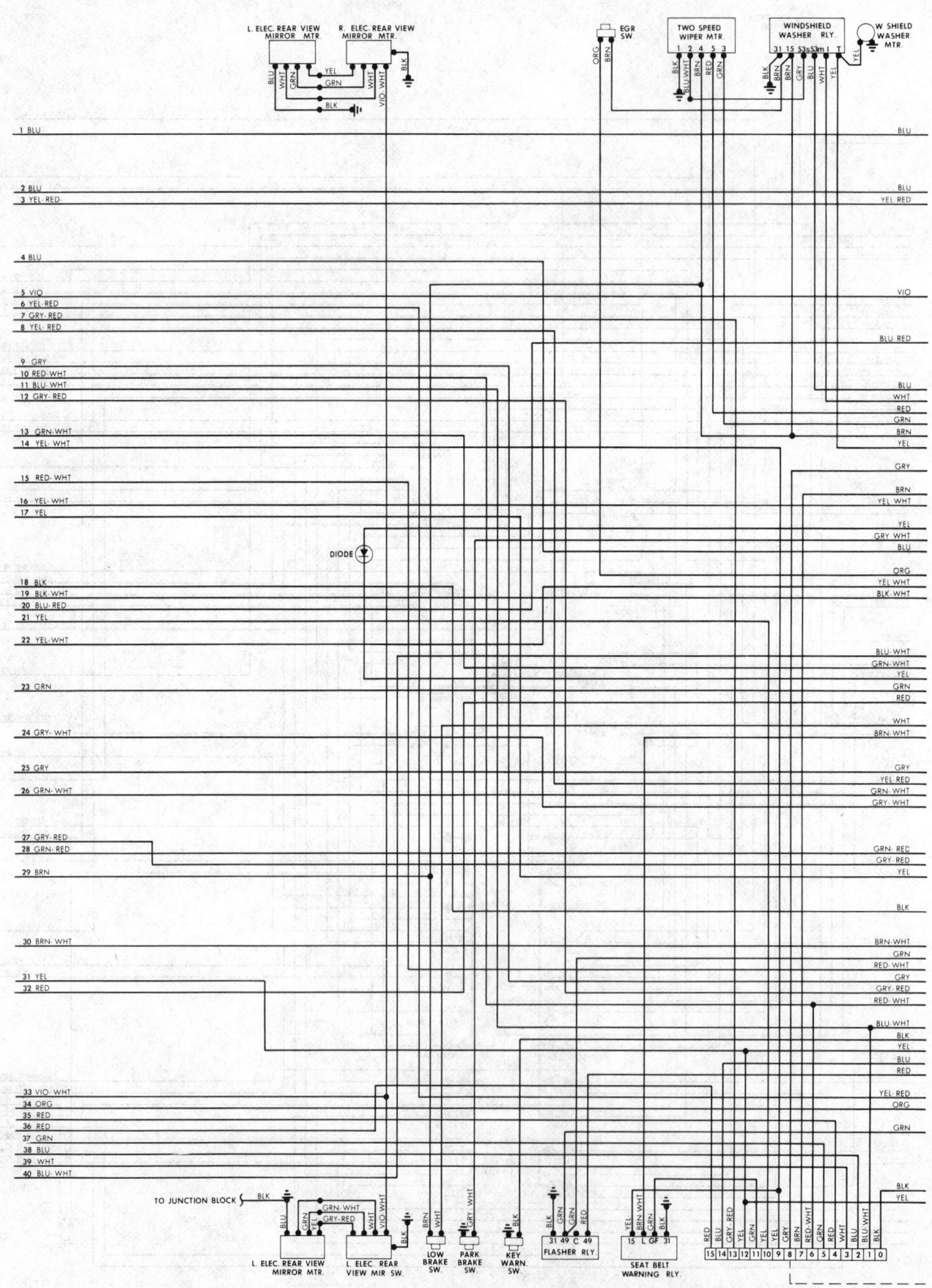

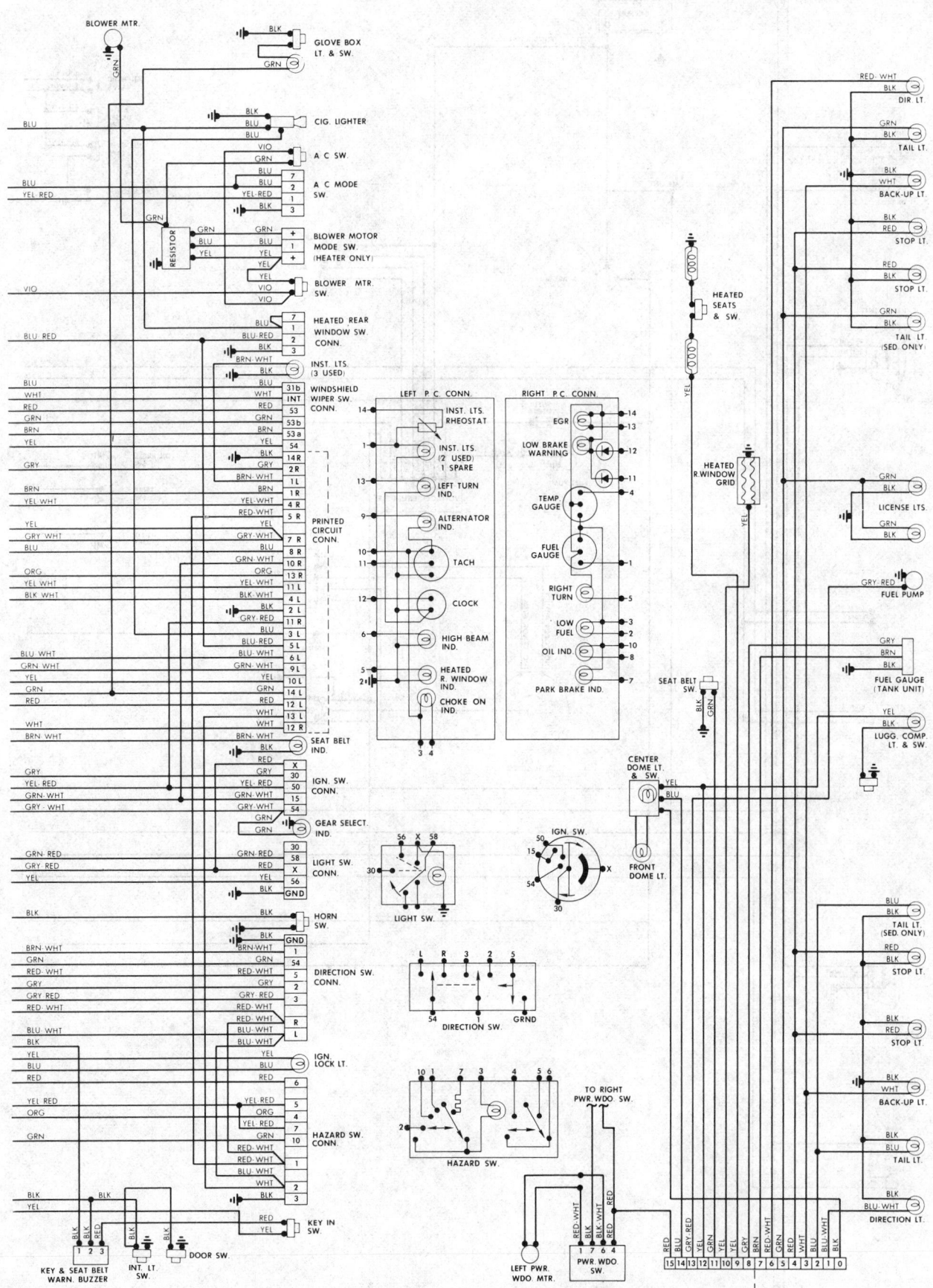

ENGINE COMPARTMENT

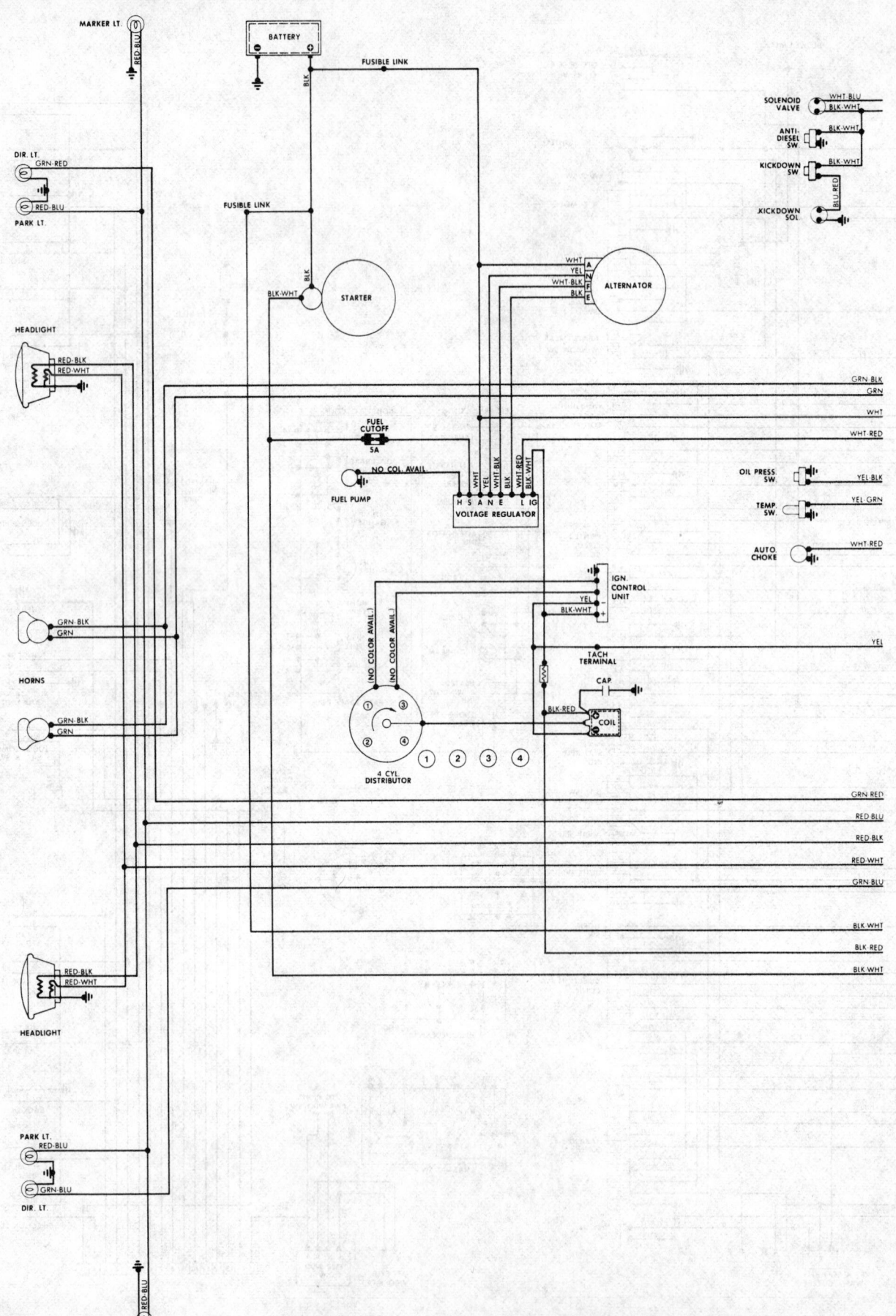

Hardtop
Hatchback

1981 Subaru

Sedan
Wagon

4—159

UNDERDASH & FUSE BLOCK

WIRING DIAGRAMS

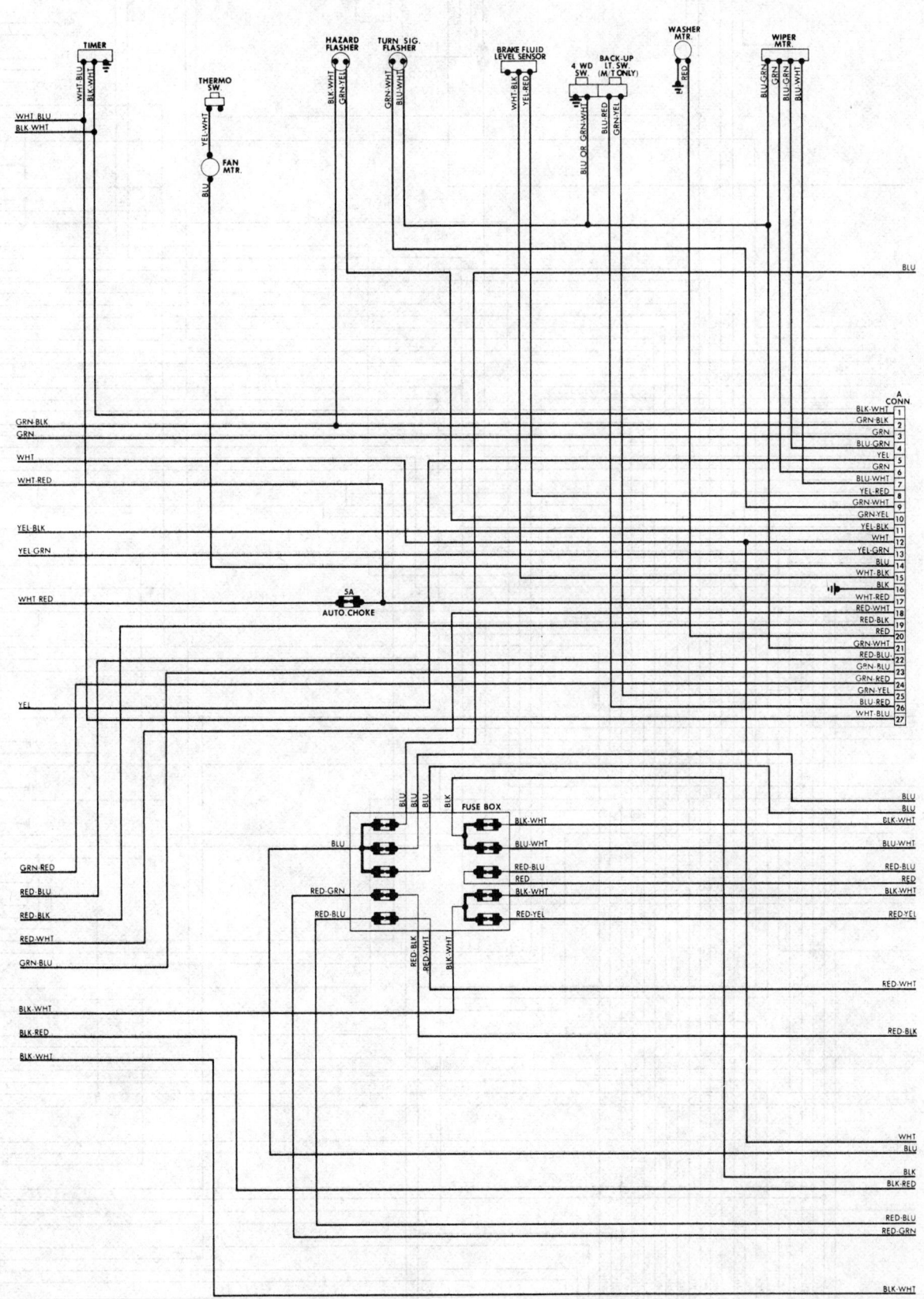

UNDERDASH

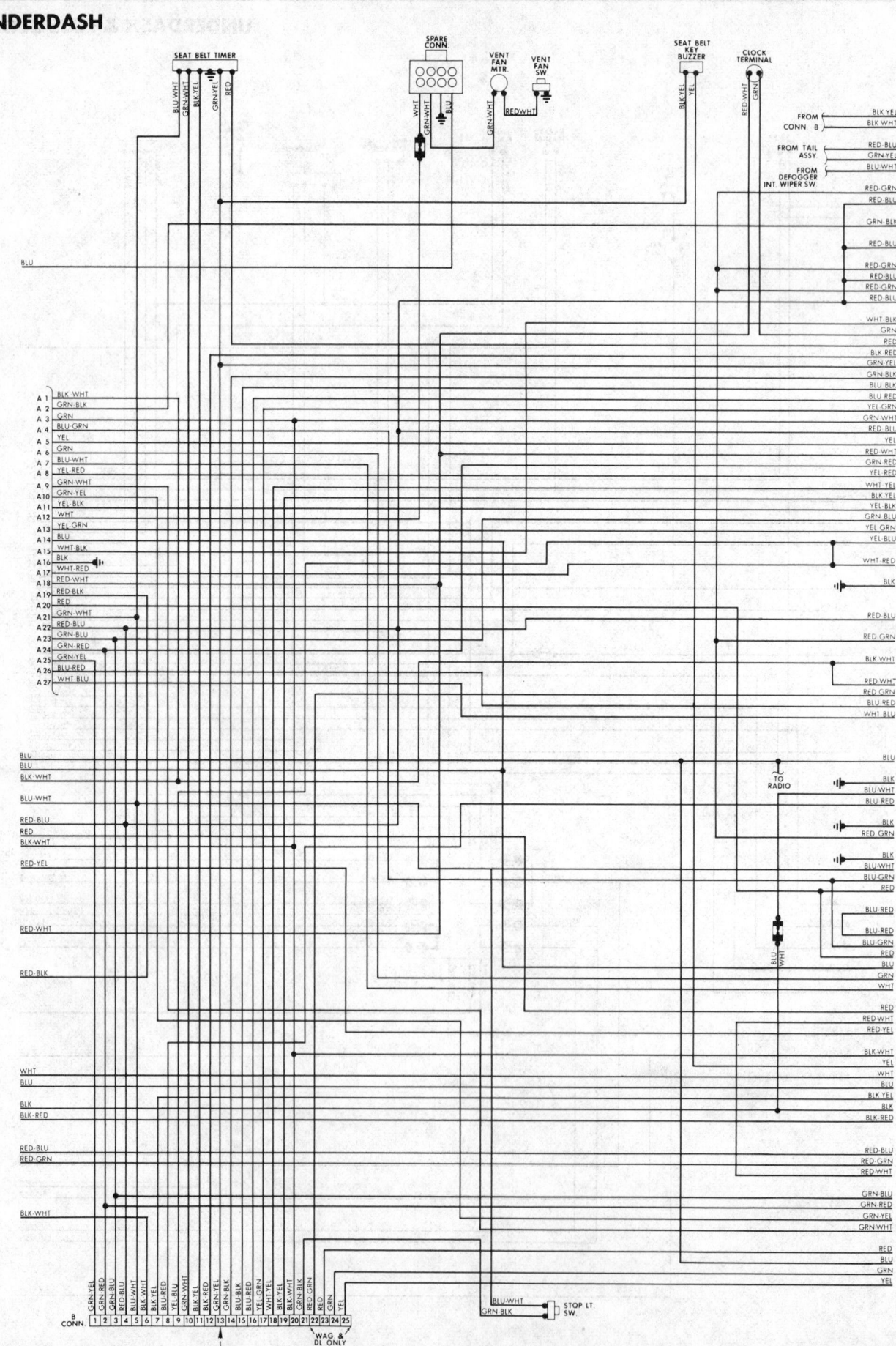

INSTRUMENT PANEL & REAR COMPARTMENT

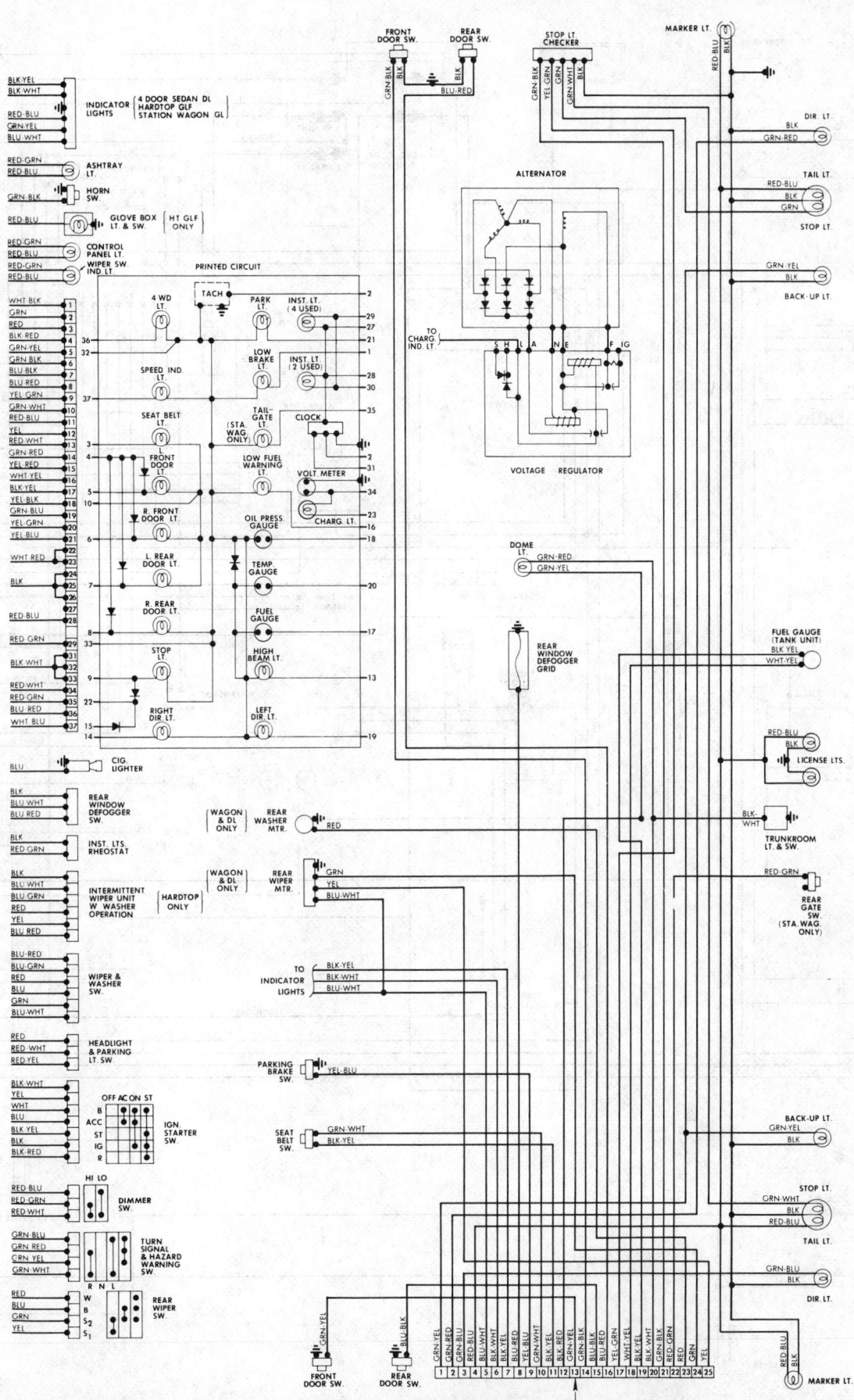

1981 Toyota

ENGINE COMPARTMENT & FUSE BLOCK

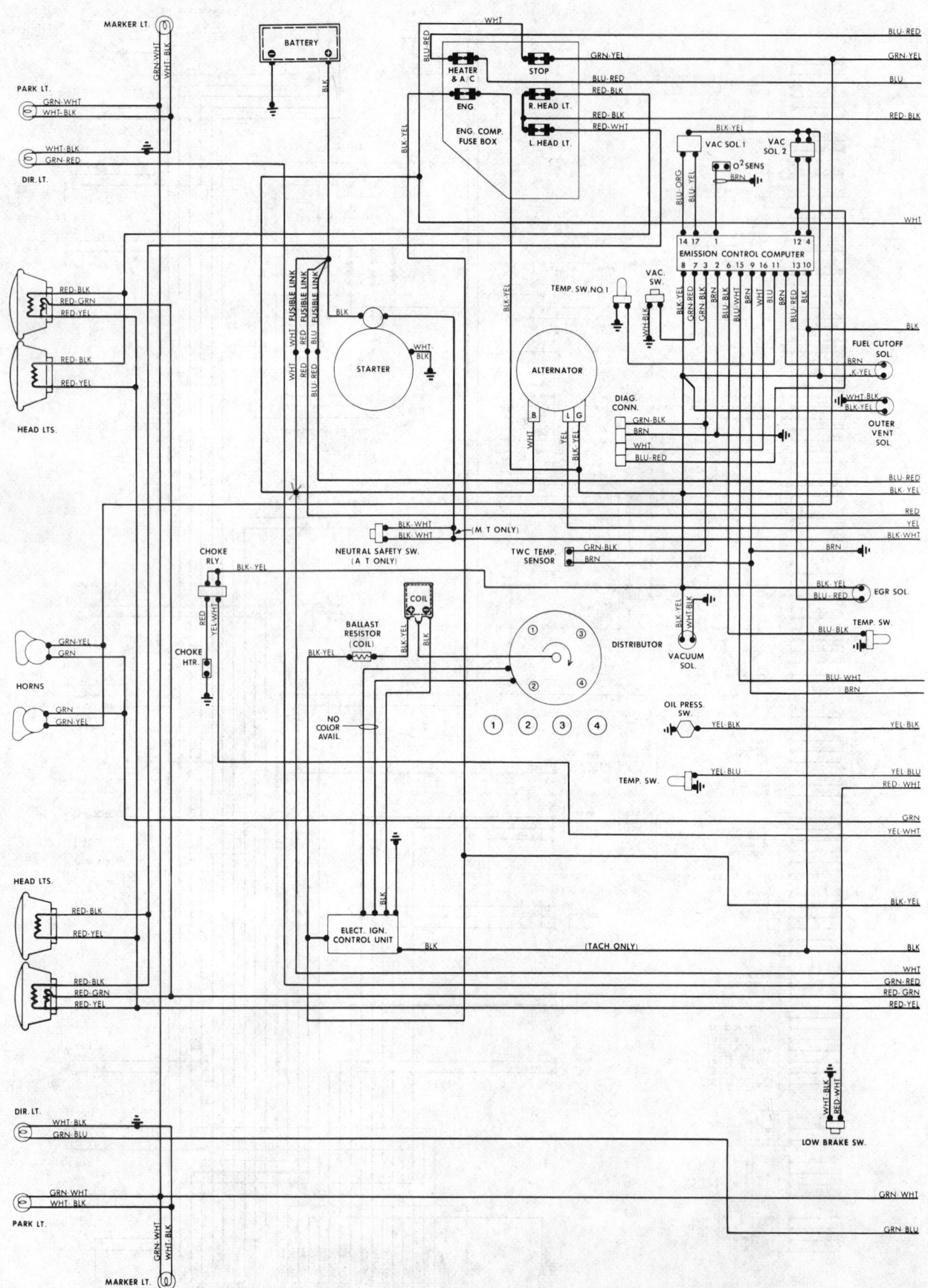

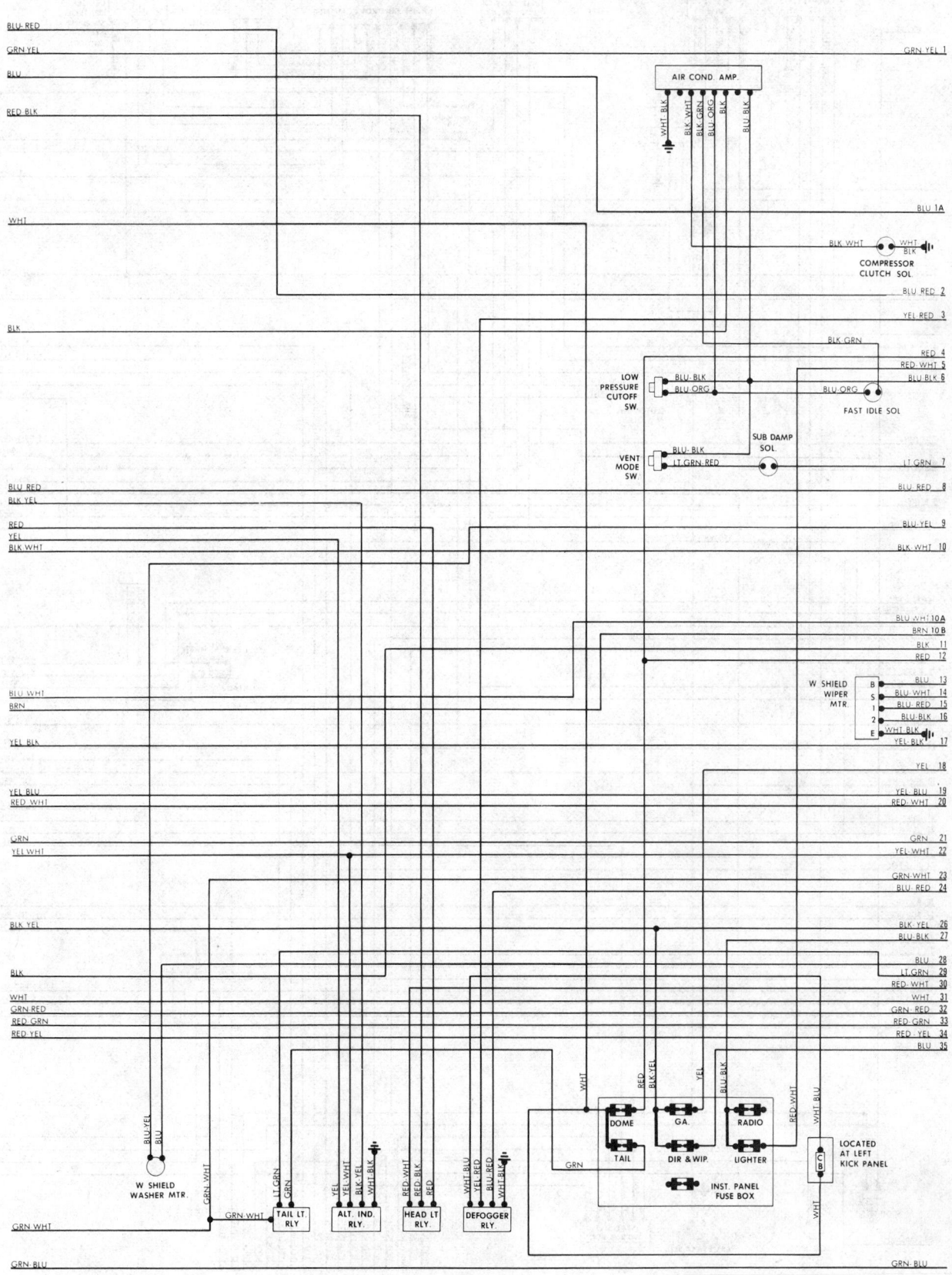

1981 Toyota

UNDERDASH

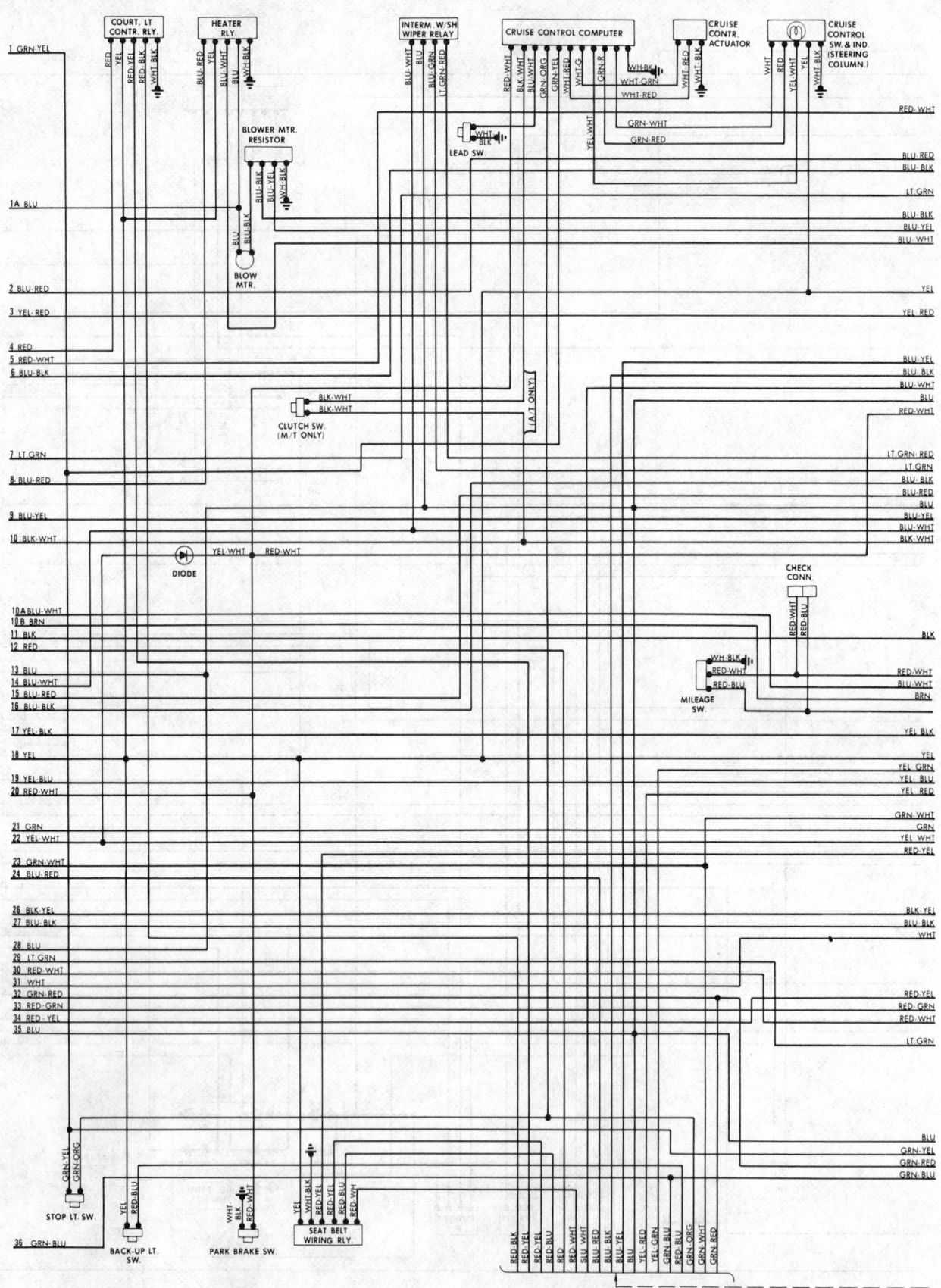

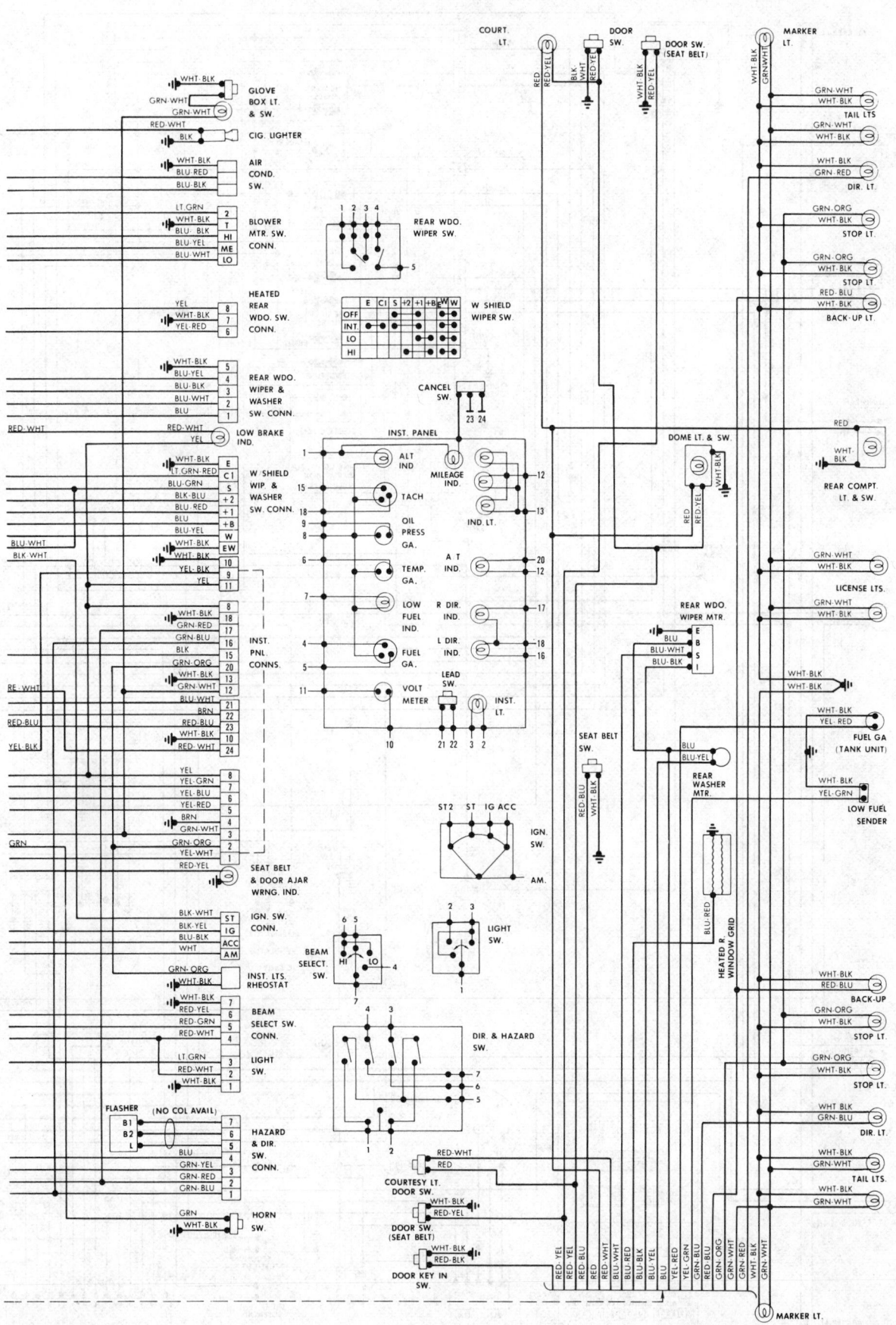

1981 Toyota

ENGINE COMPARTMENT & FUSE BLOCK

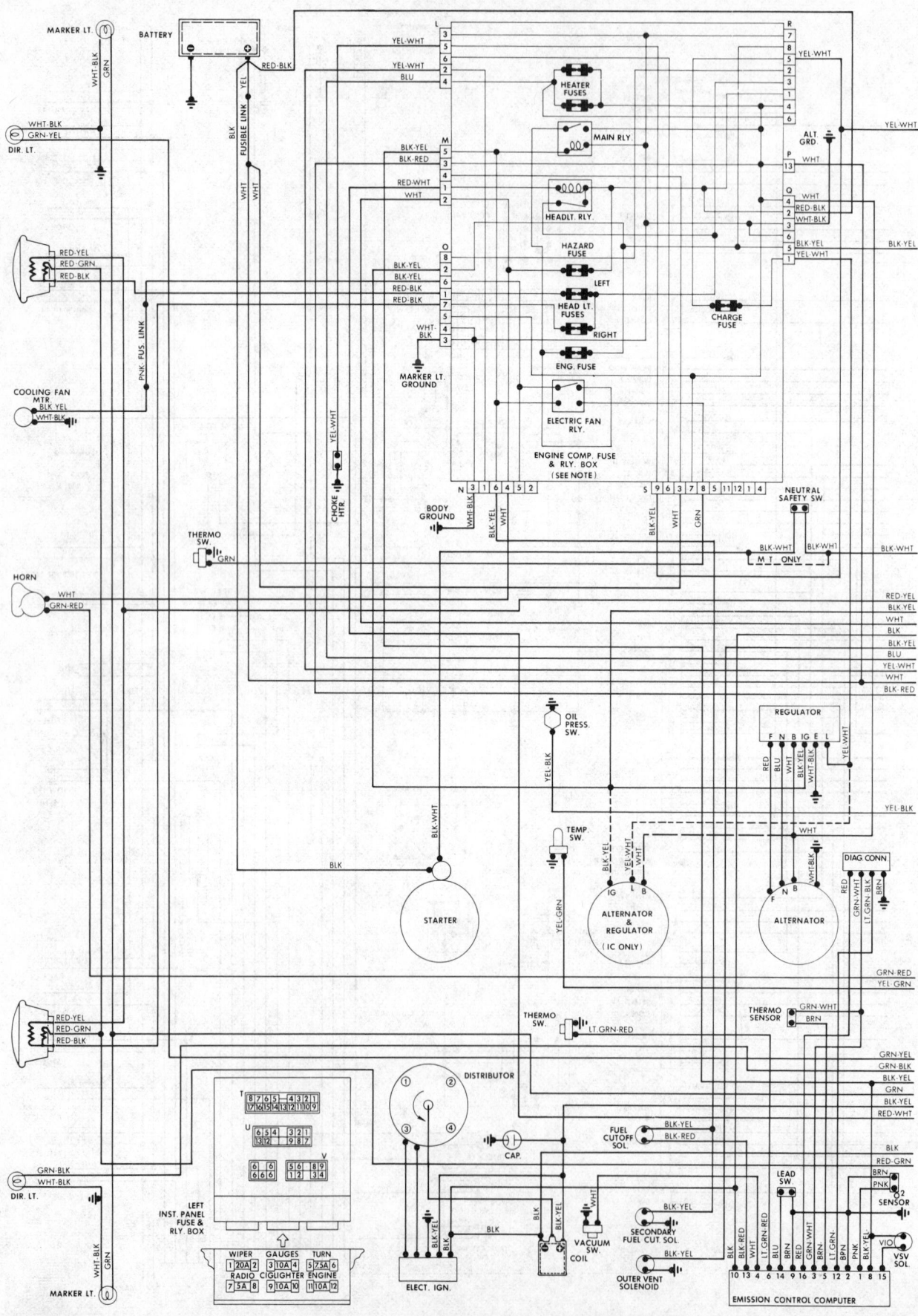

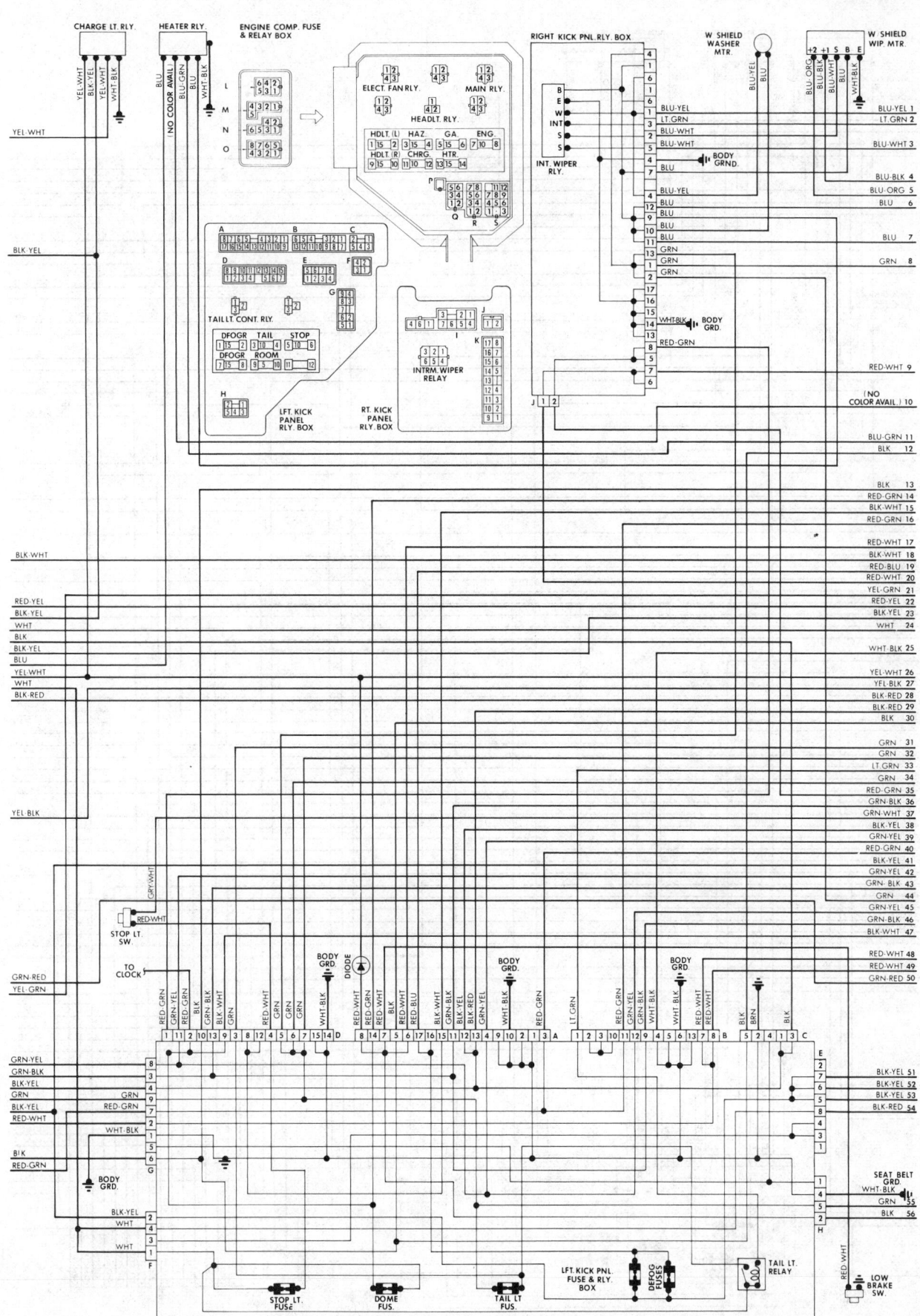

1981 Toyota

UNDERDASH

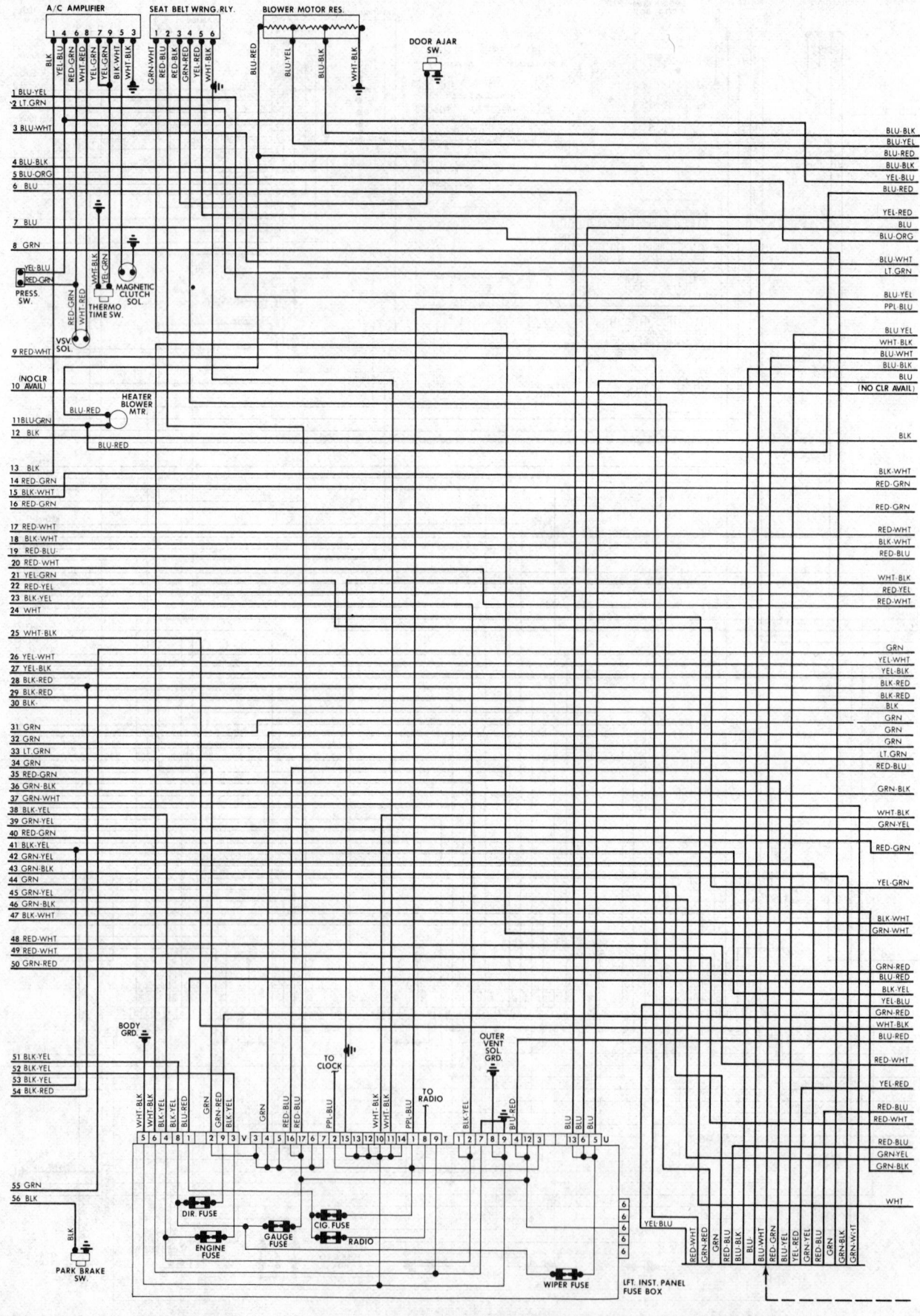

INSTRUMENT PANEL & REAR COMPARTMENT

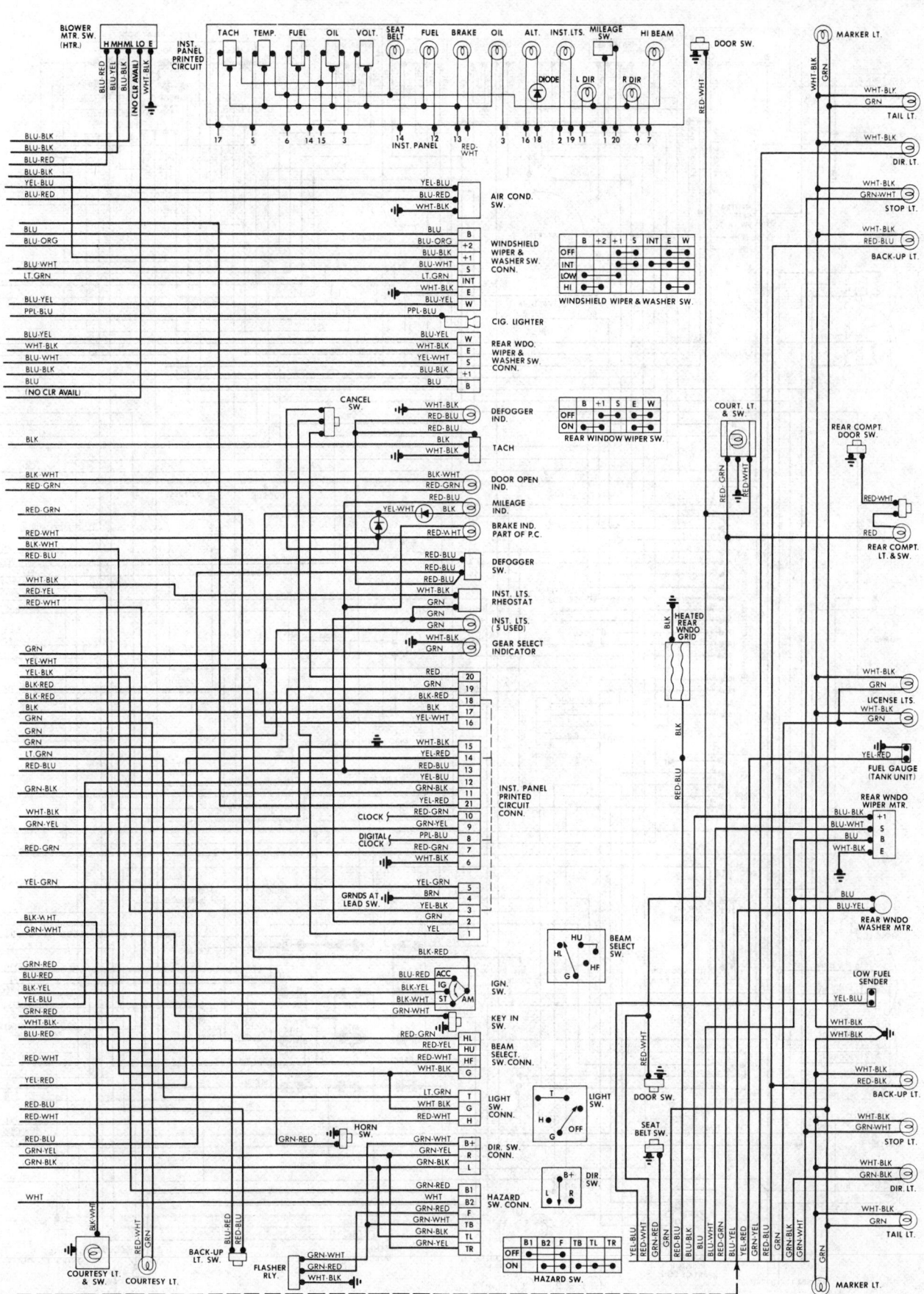

1981 Toyota

ENGINE COMPARTMENT & FUSE BLOCK

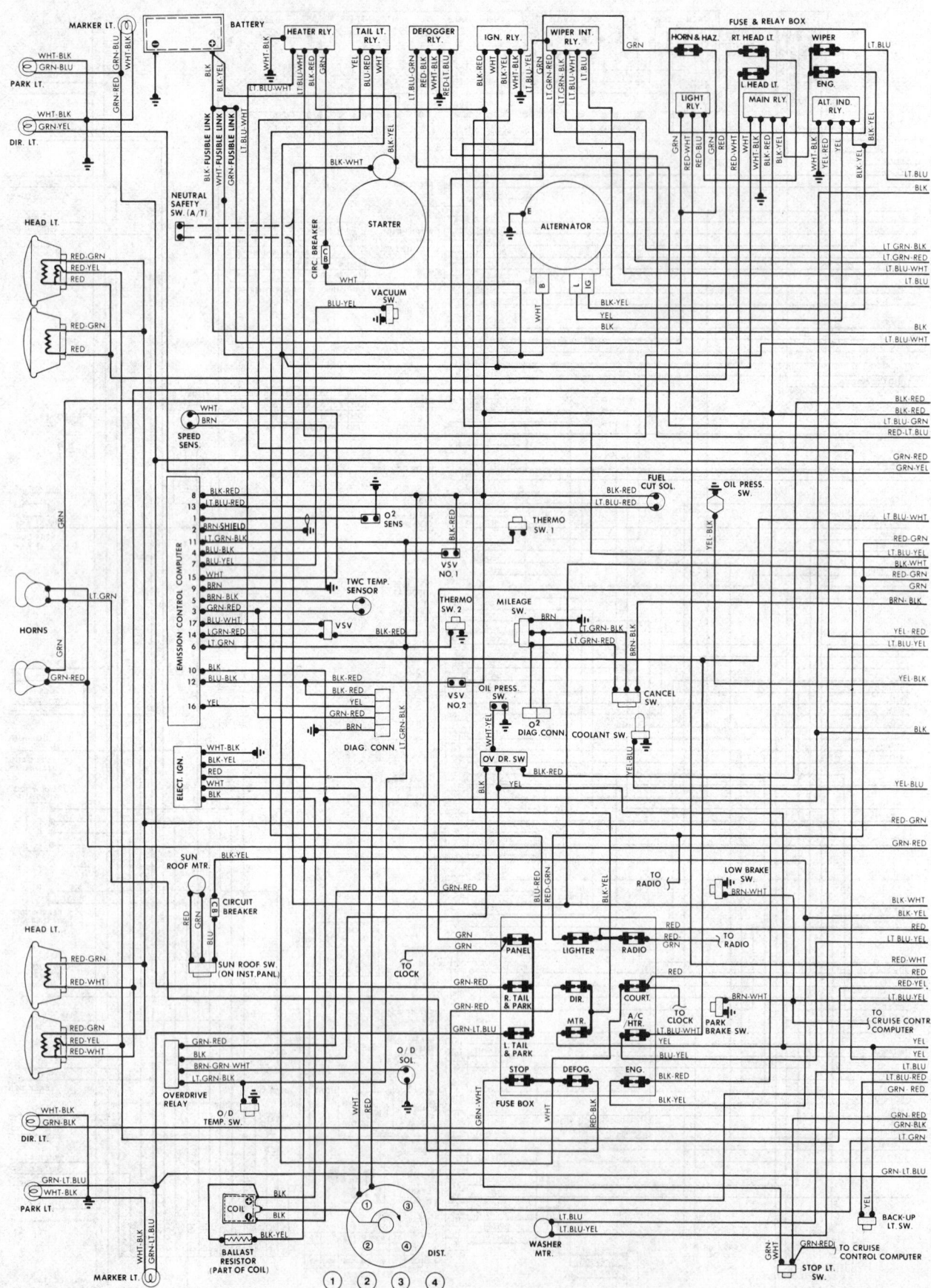

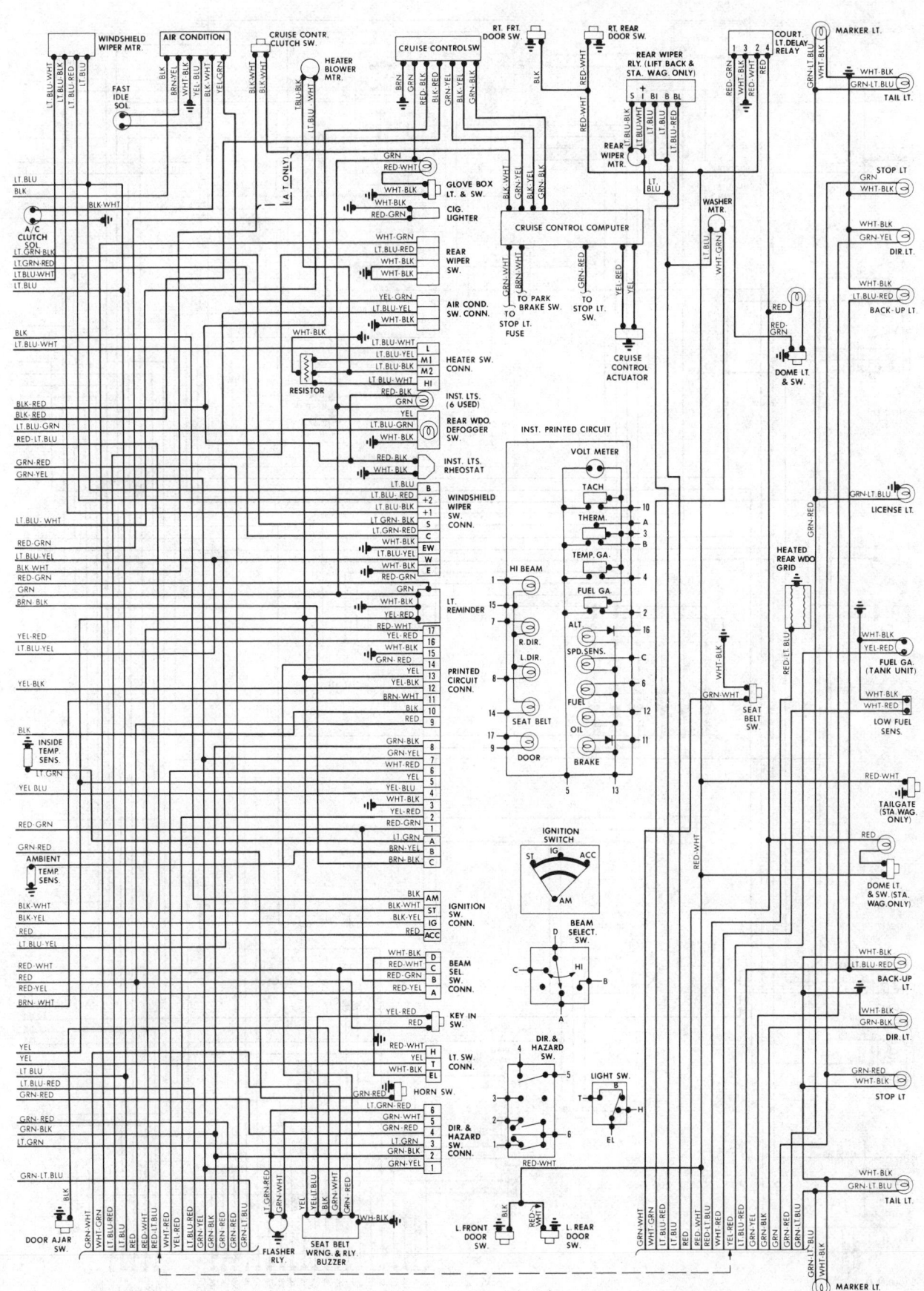

1981 Toyota

ENGINE COMPARTMENT

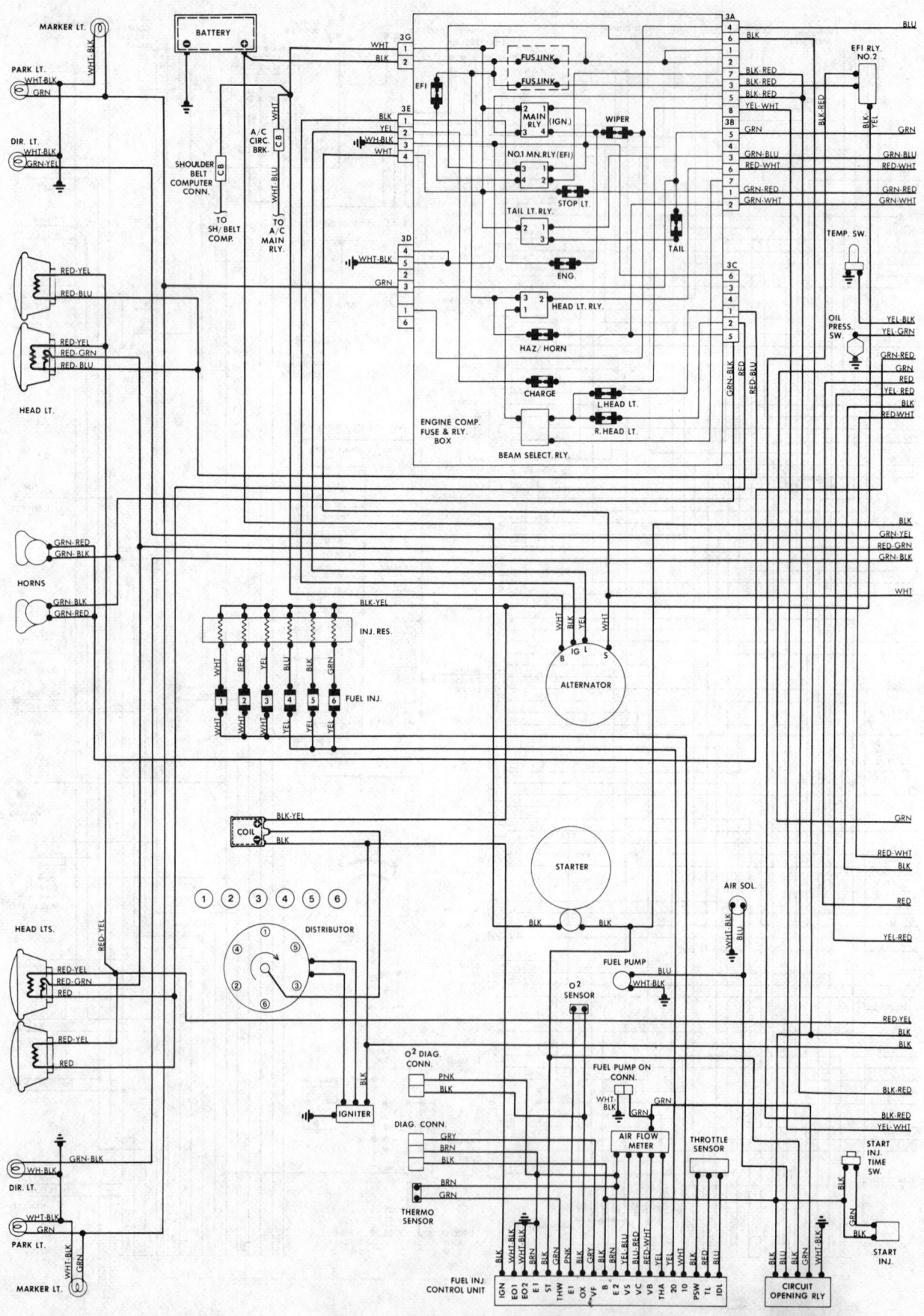

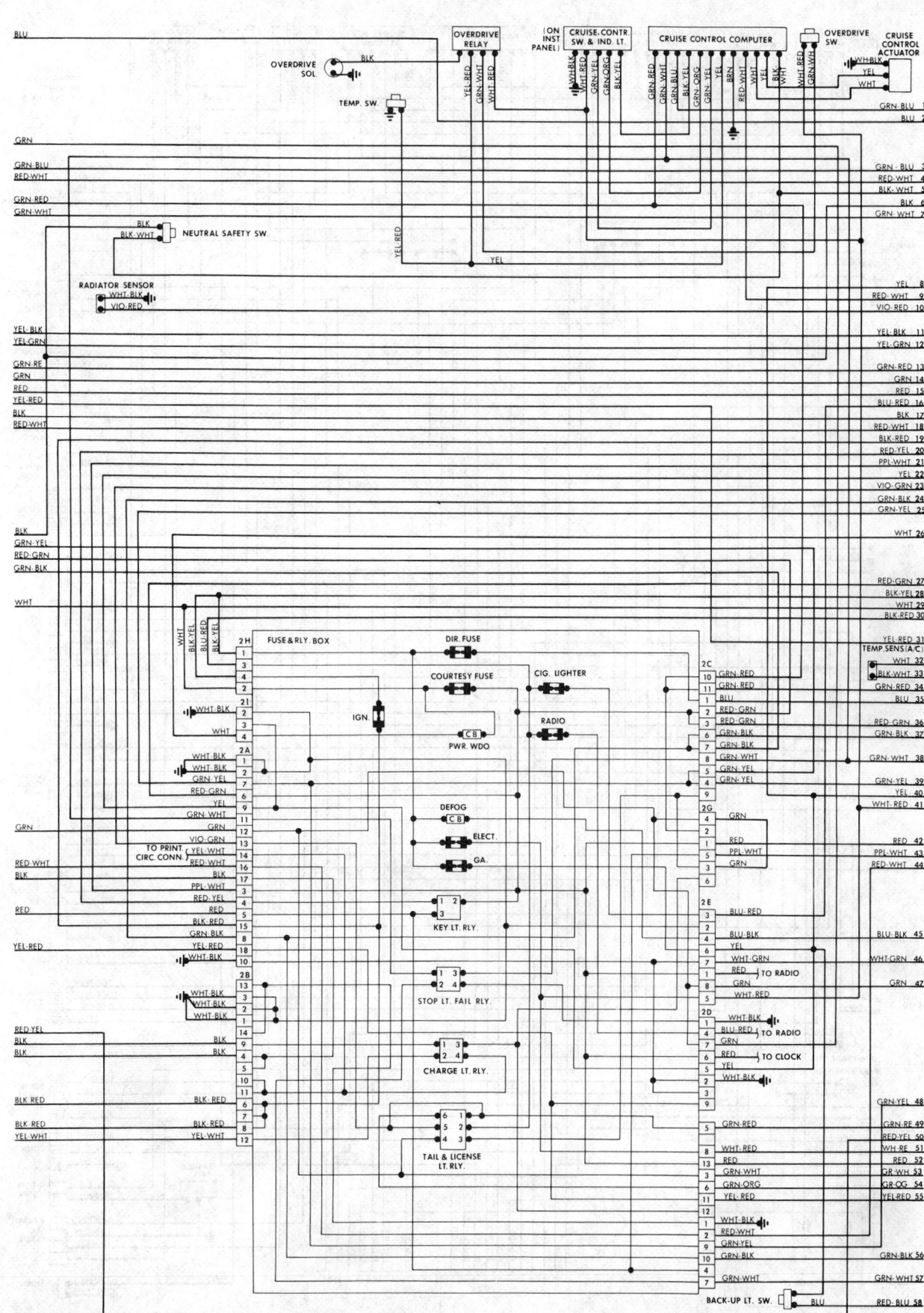

1981 Toyota

UNDERDASH

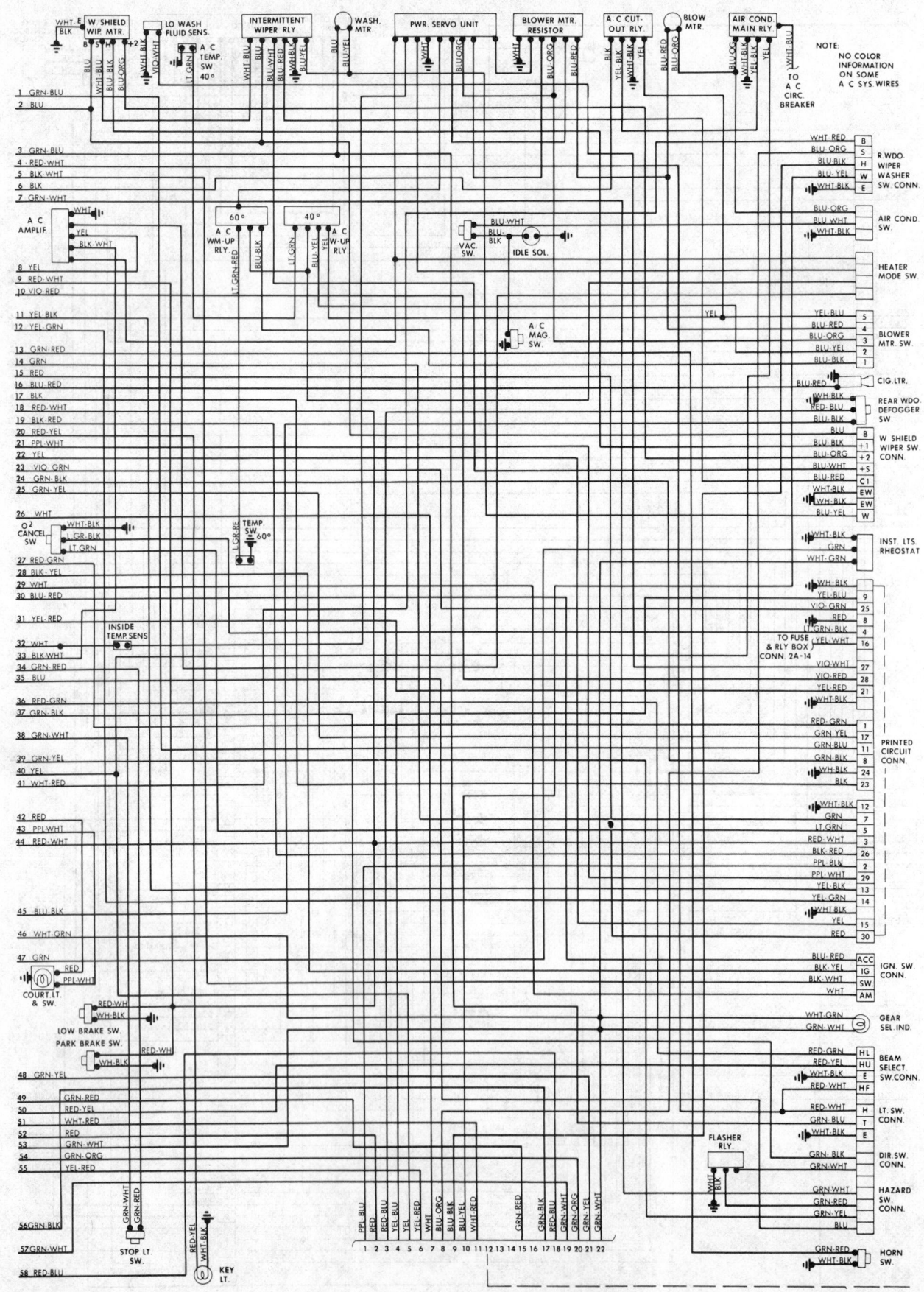

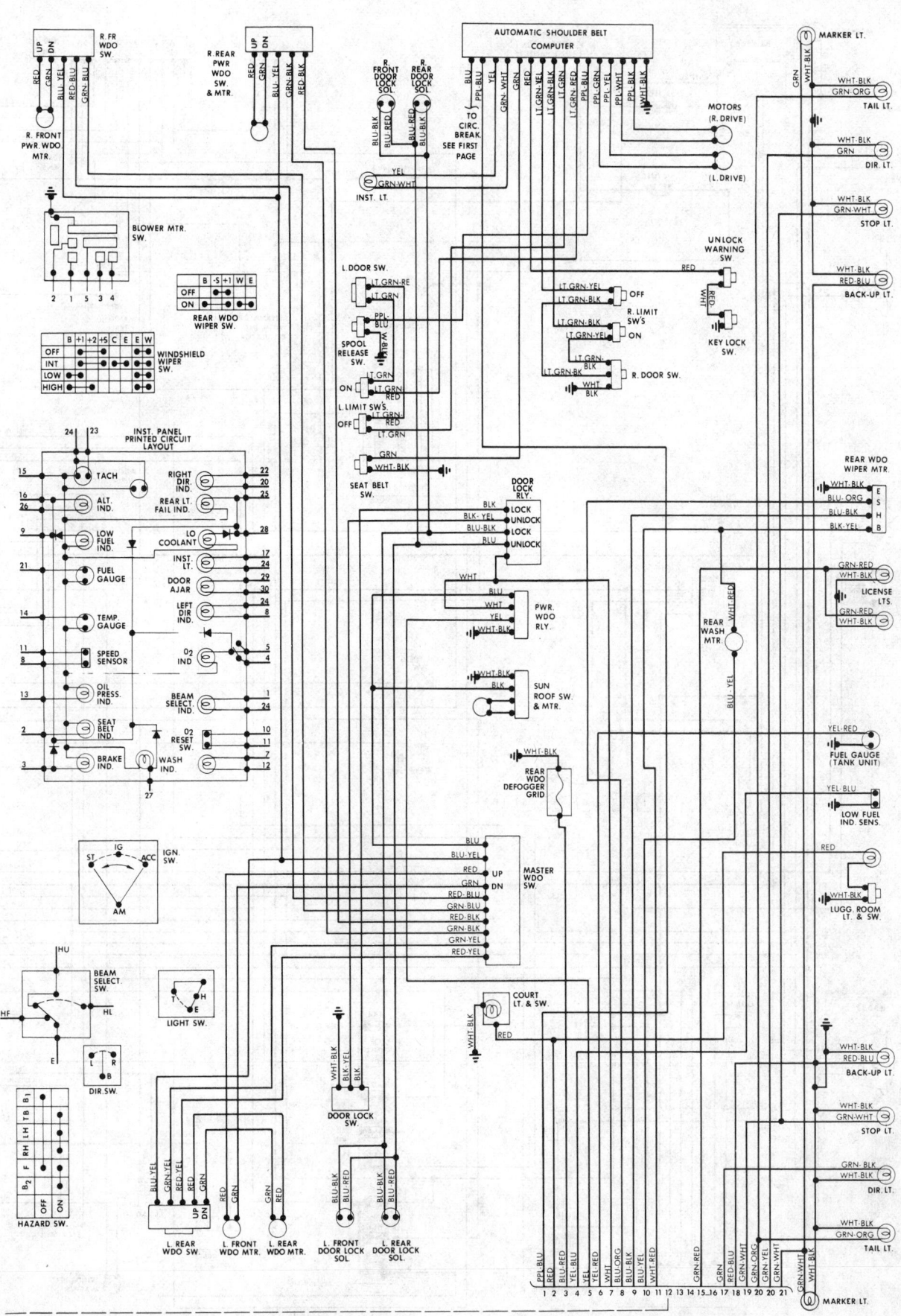

1981 Toyota

ENGINE COMPARTMENT & FUSE BLOCK

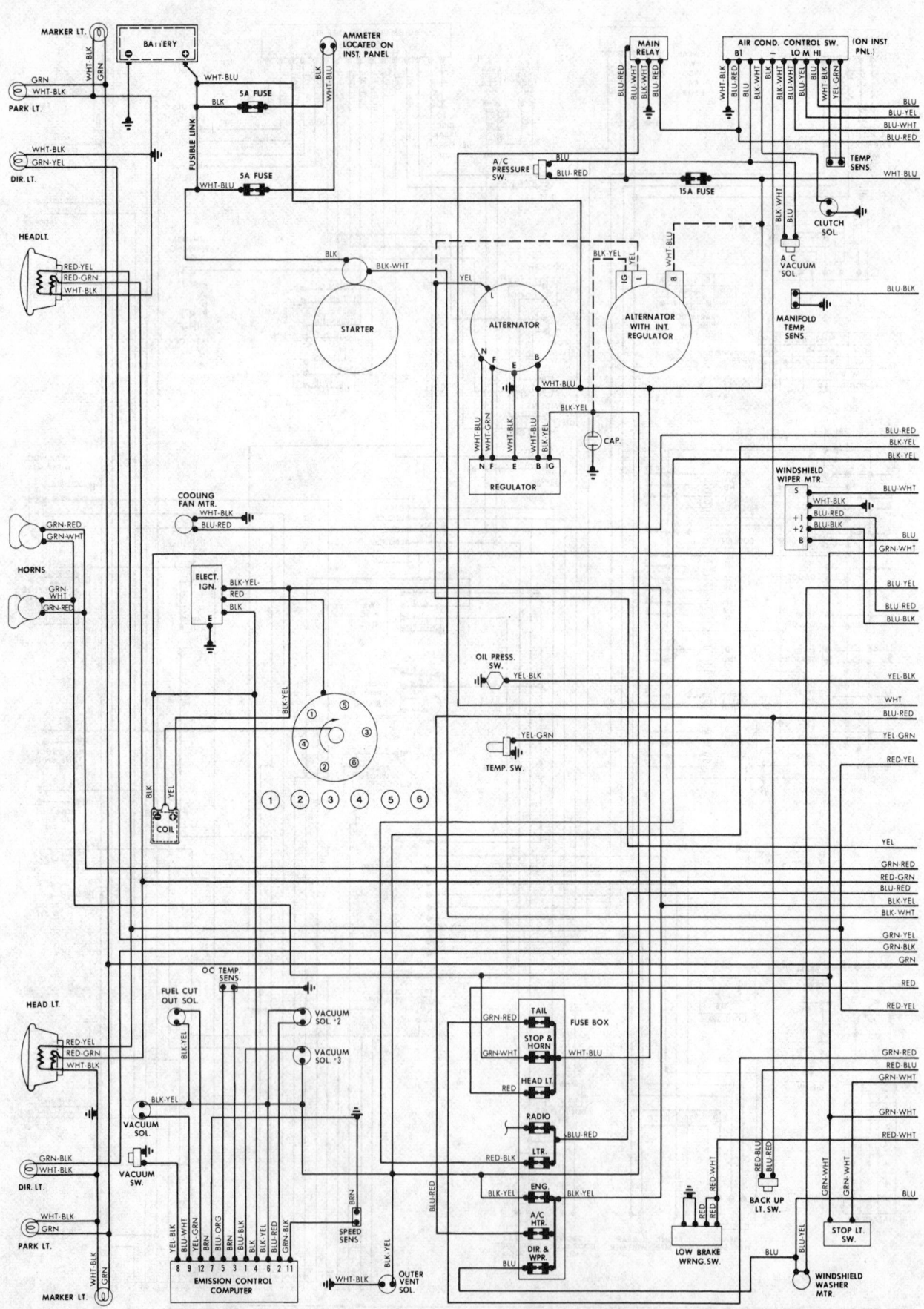

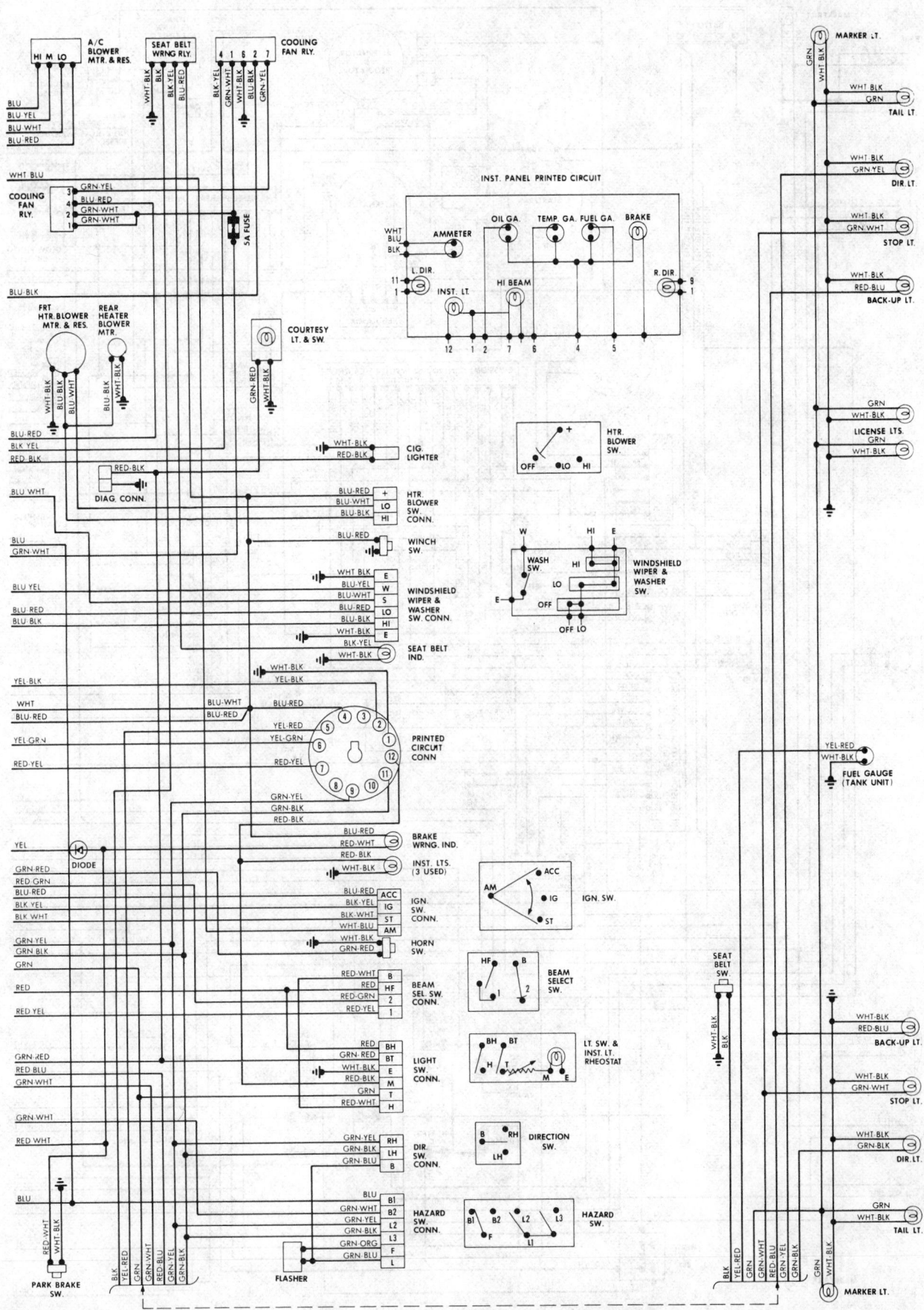

1981 Toyota

ENGINE COMPARTMENT & FUSE BLOCK

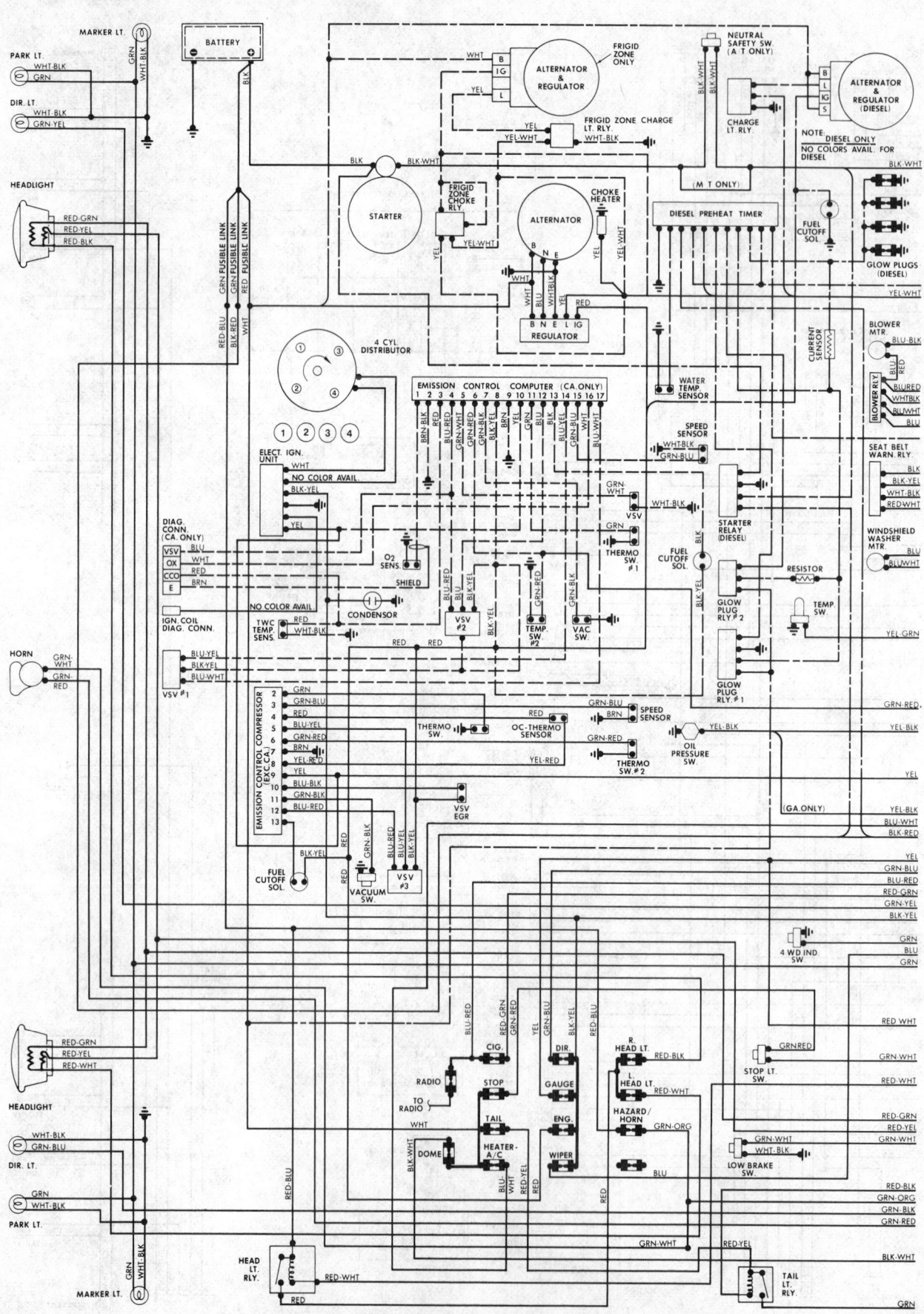

INSTRUMENT PANEL & REAR COMPARTMENT

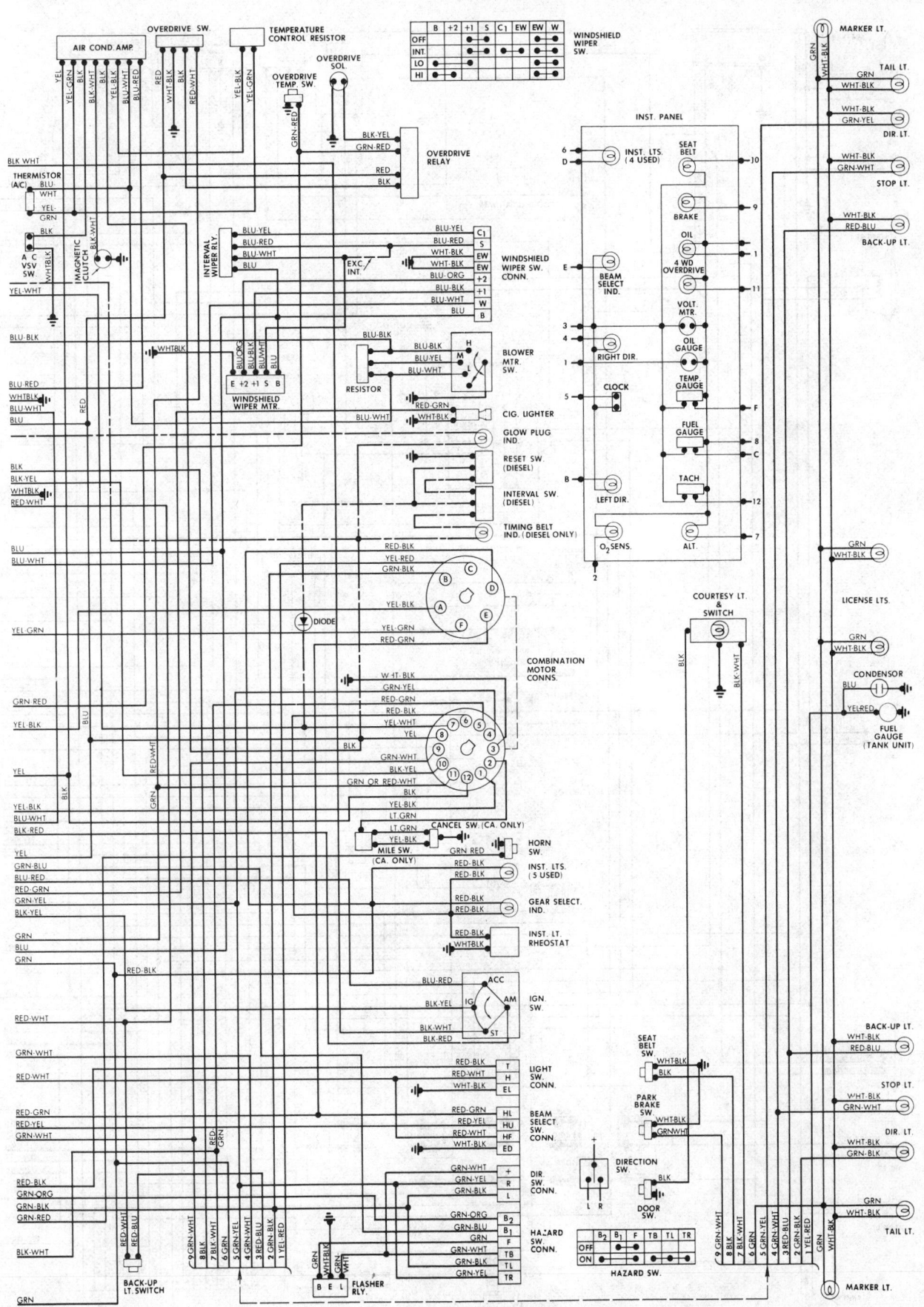

1981 Toyota

ENGINE COMPARTMENT & FUSE BLOCK

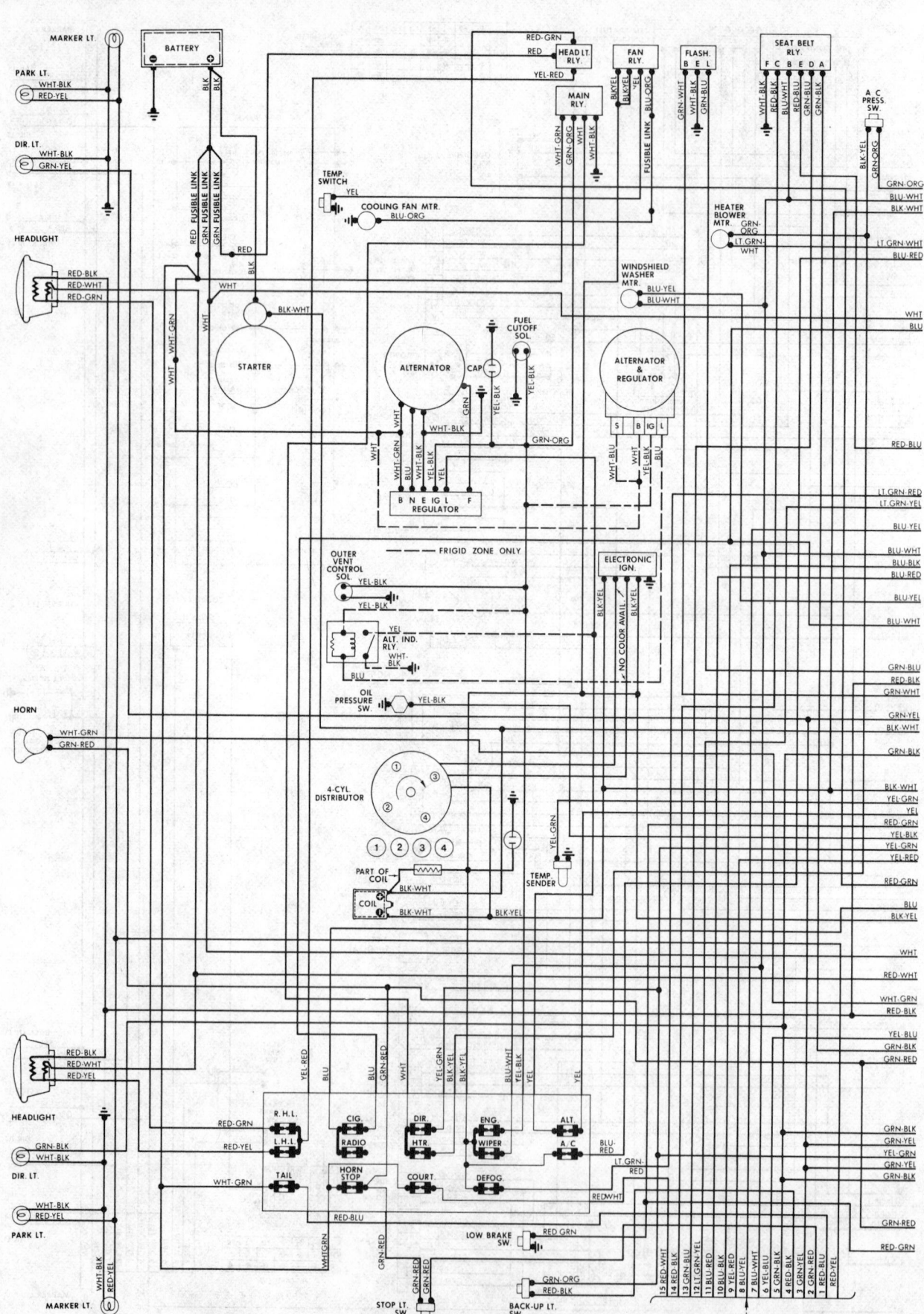

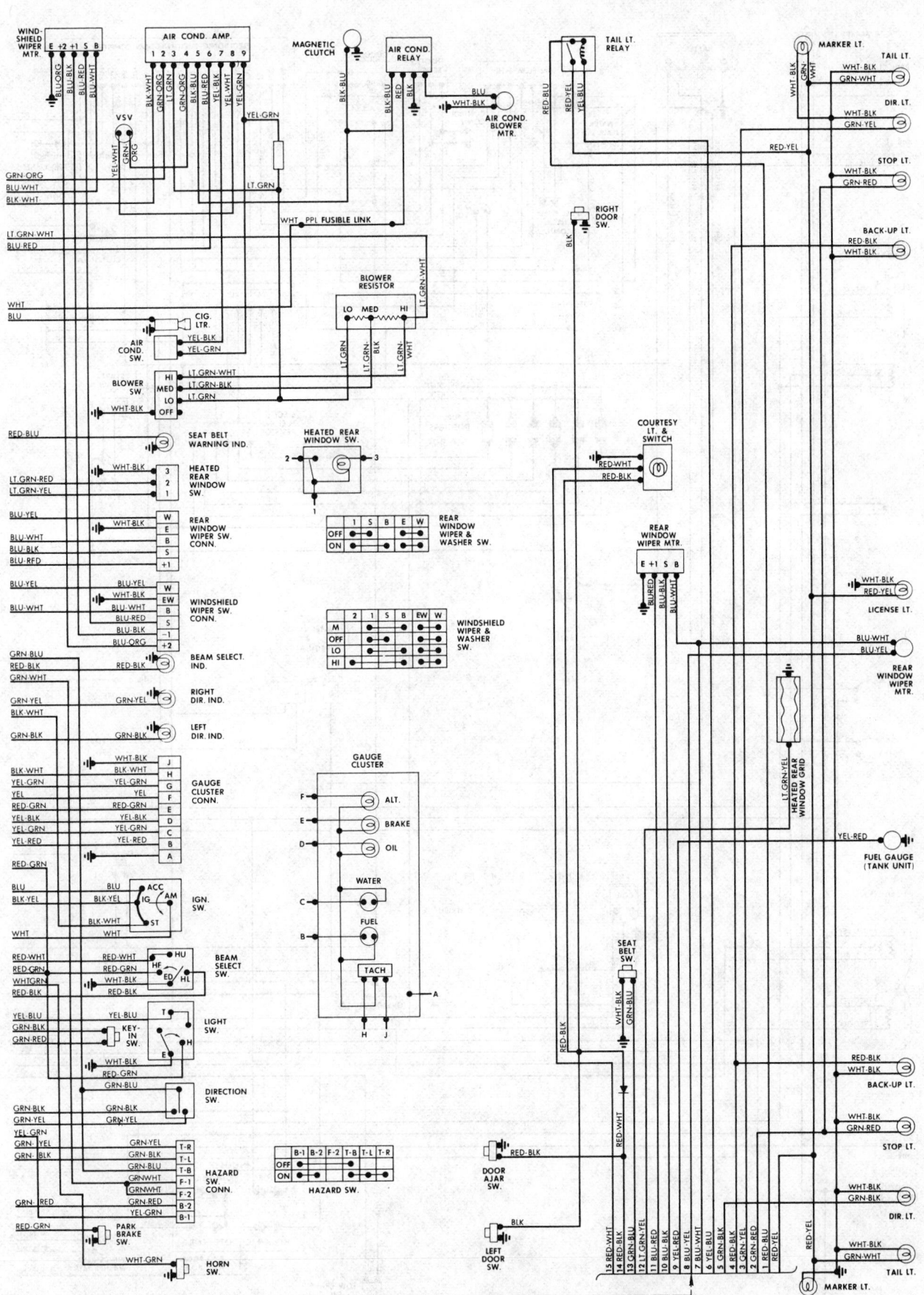

1981 Toyota

ENGINE COMPARTMENT & FUSE BLOCK

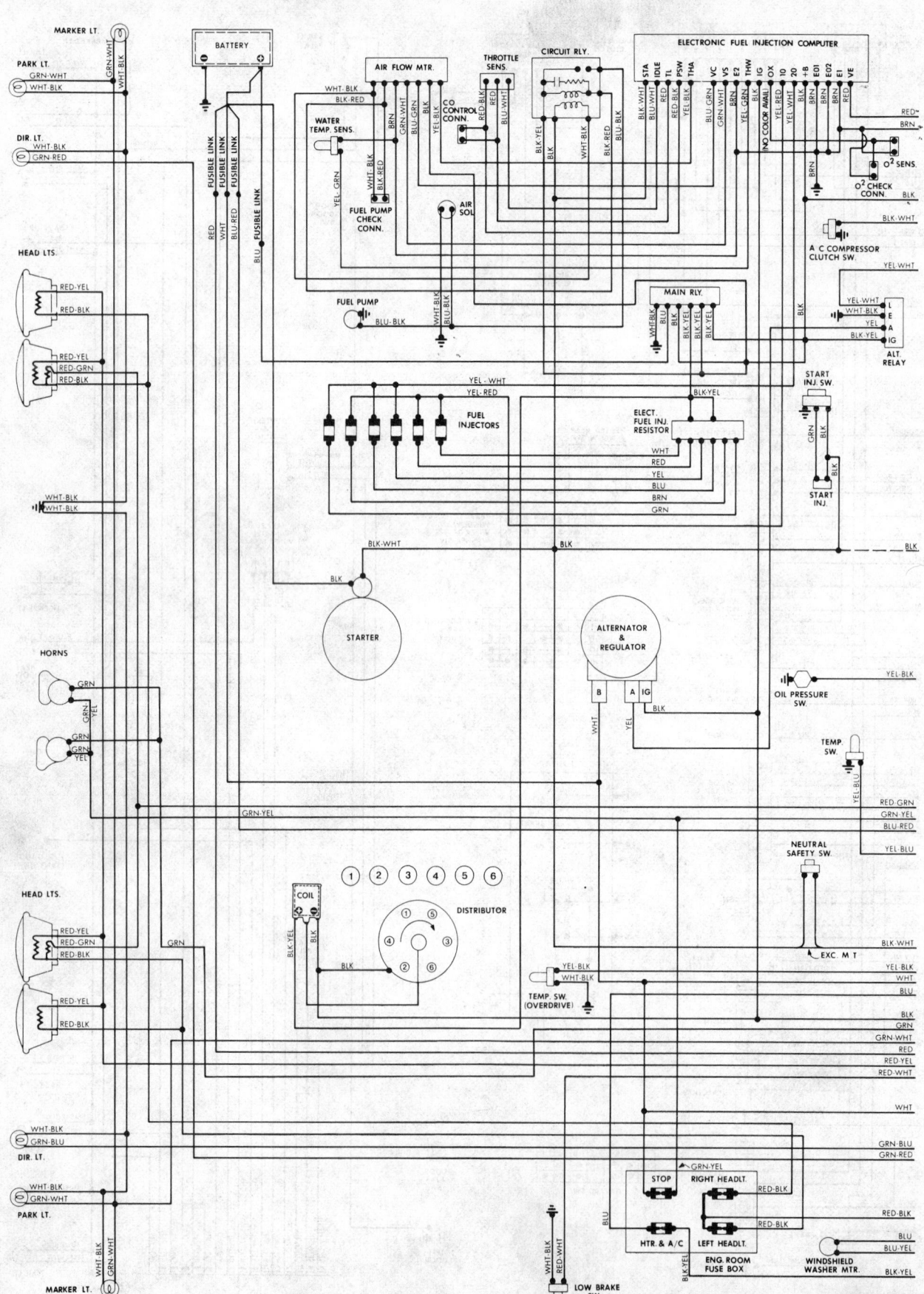

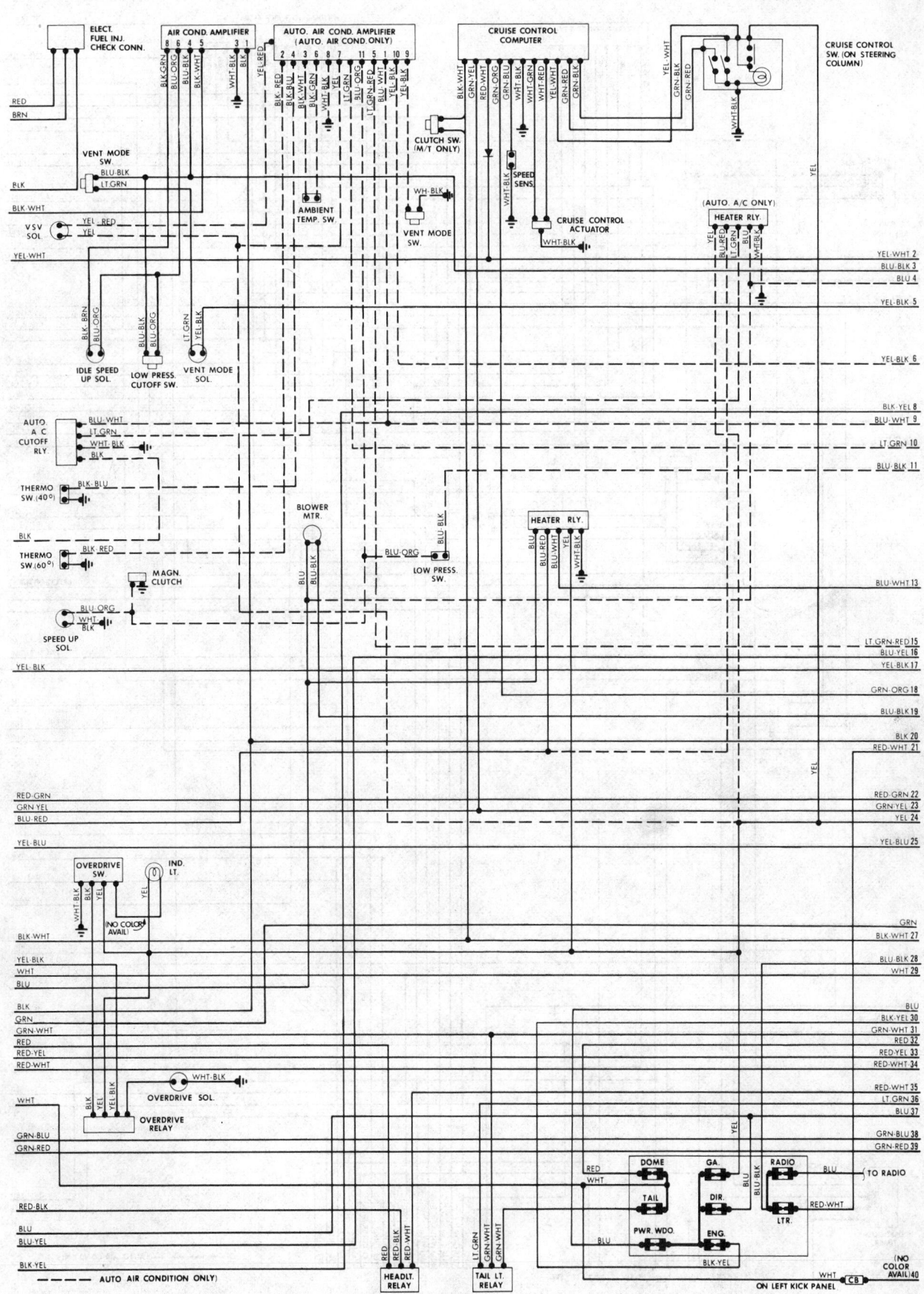

UNDERDASH

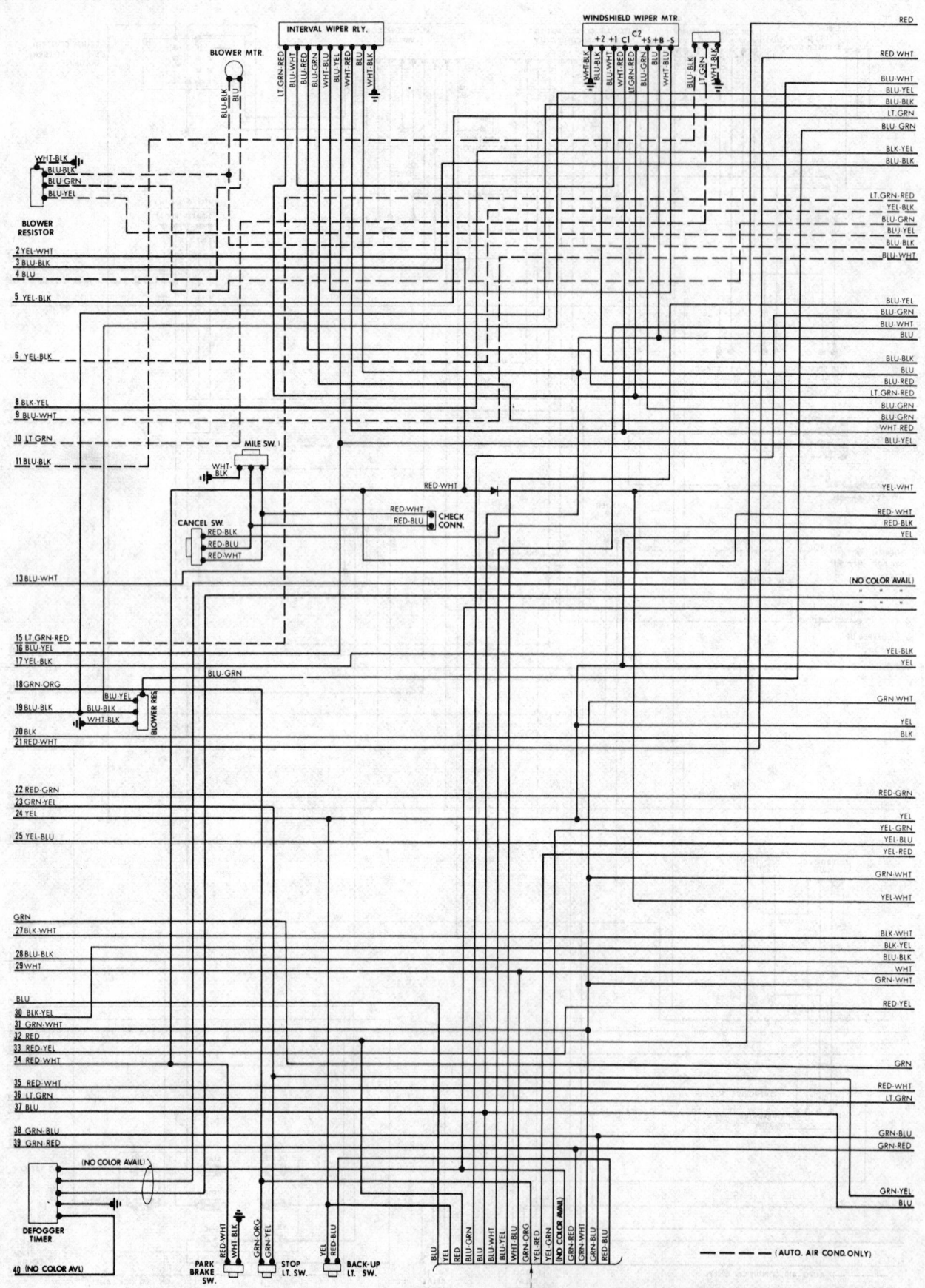

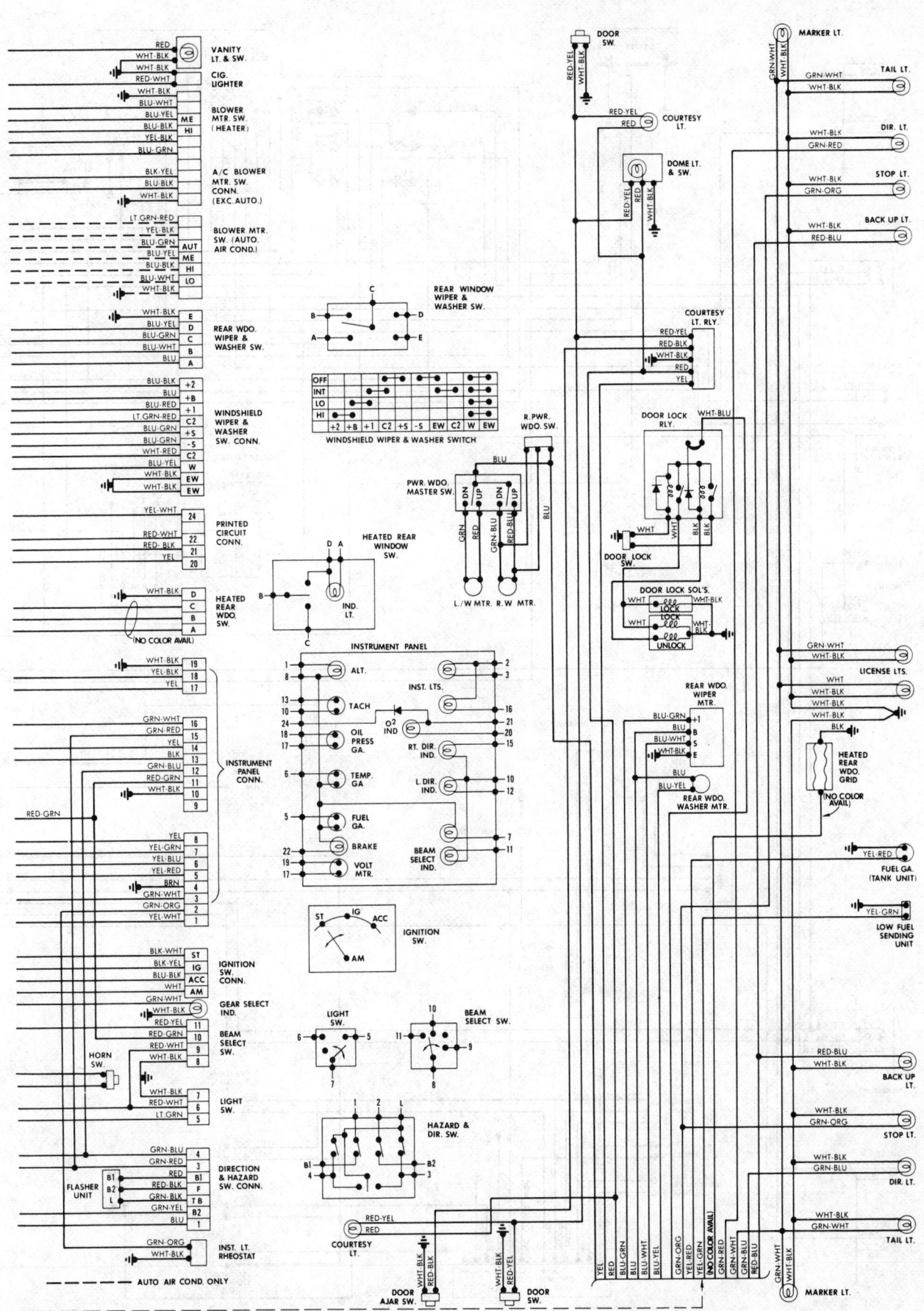

1981 Toyota

ENGINE COMPARTMENT & FUSE BLOCK

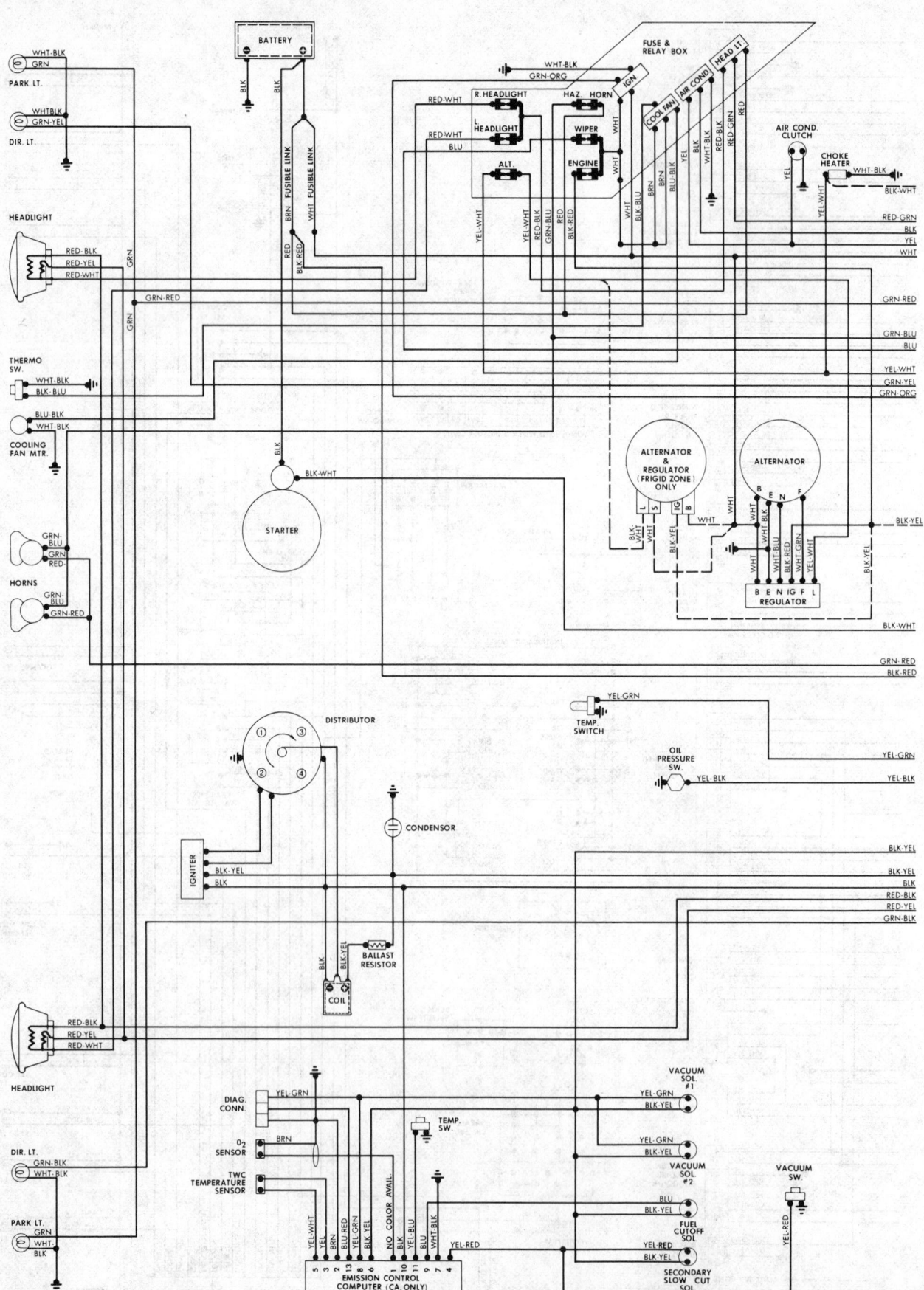

ENGINE COMPARTMENT & UNDERDASH

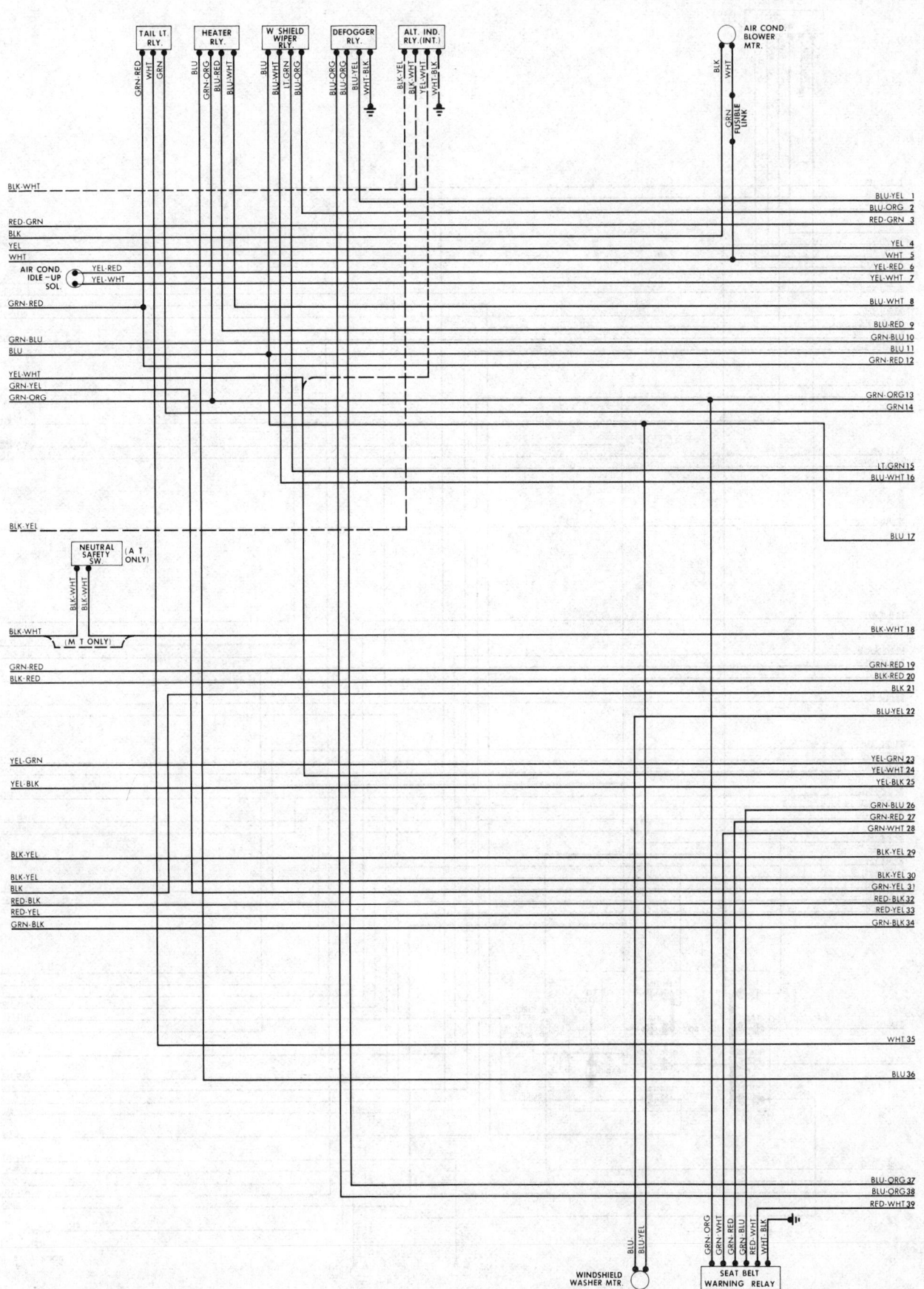

UNDERDASH

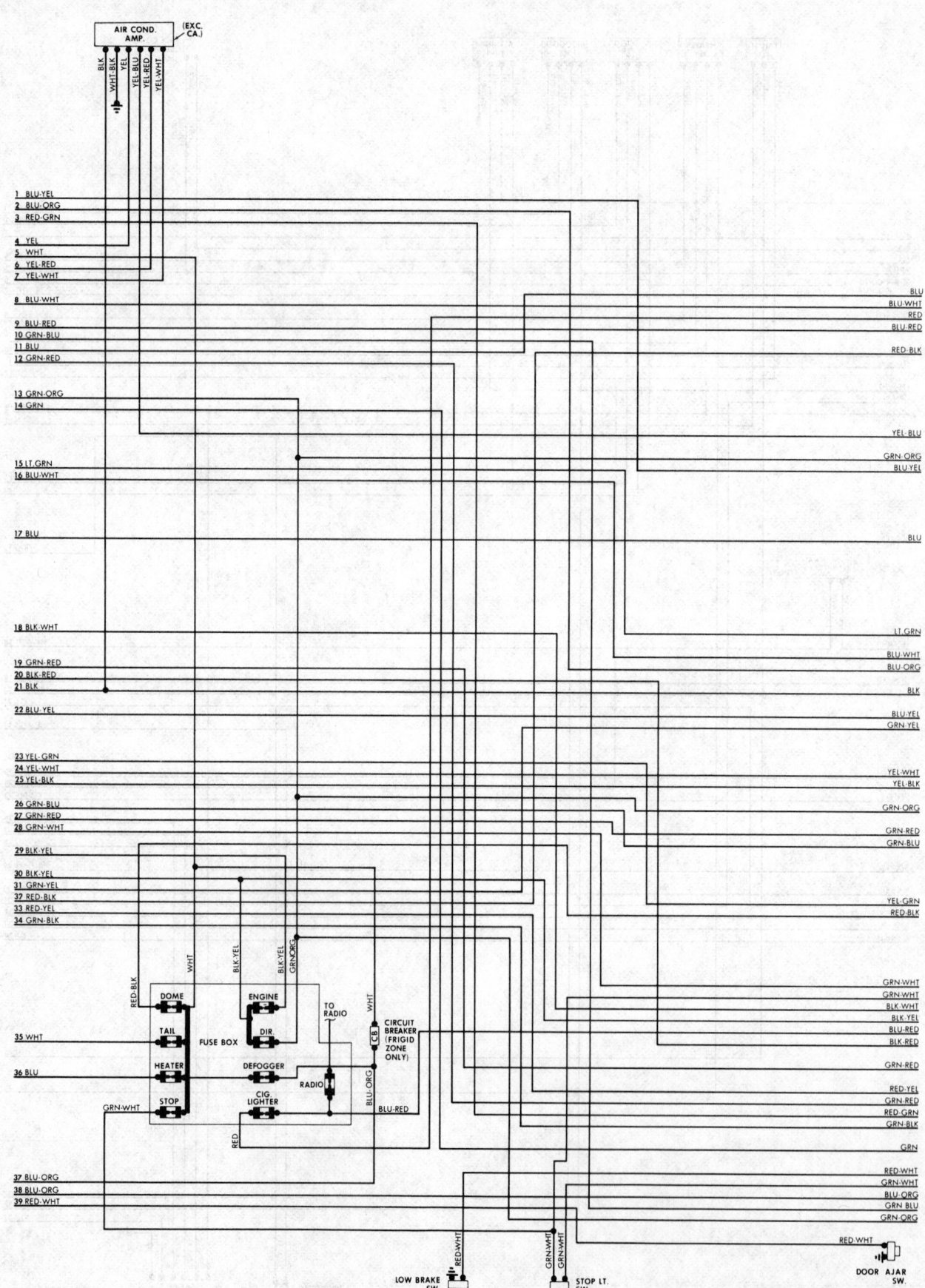

INSTRUMENT PANEL & REAR COMPARTMENT

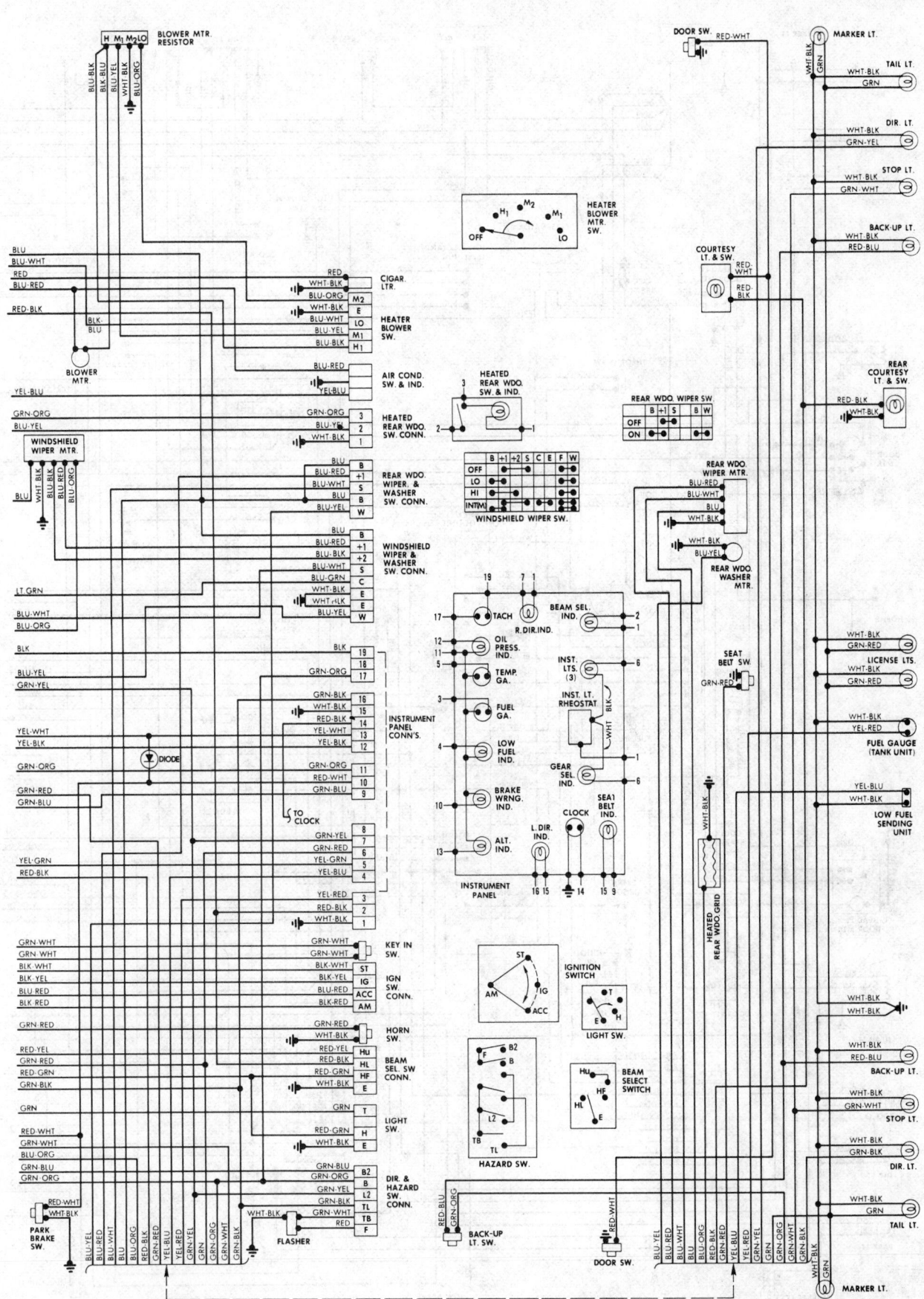

1981 Triumph

ENGINE COMPARTMENT & FUSE BLOCK

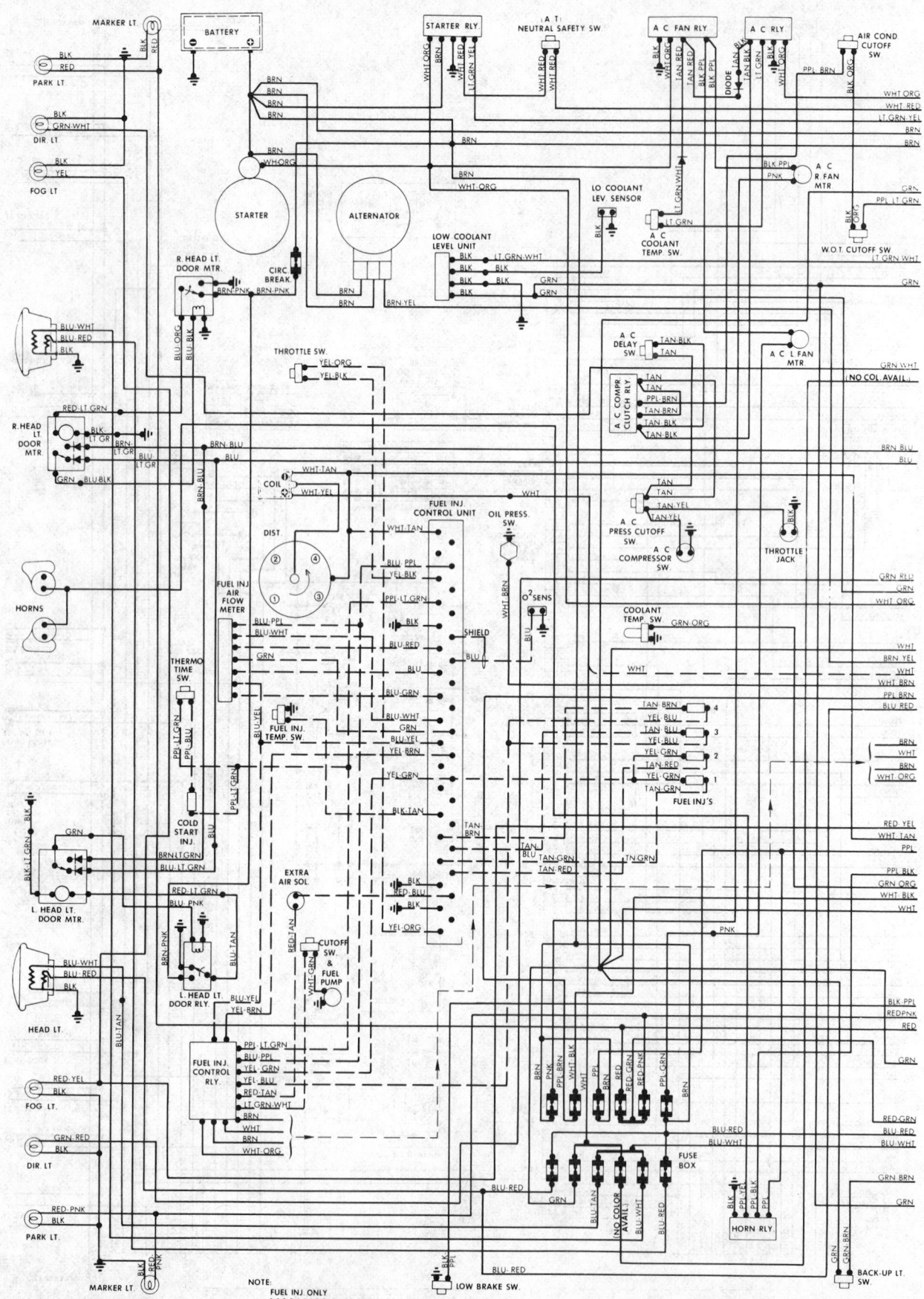

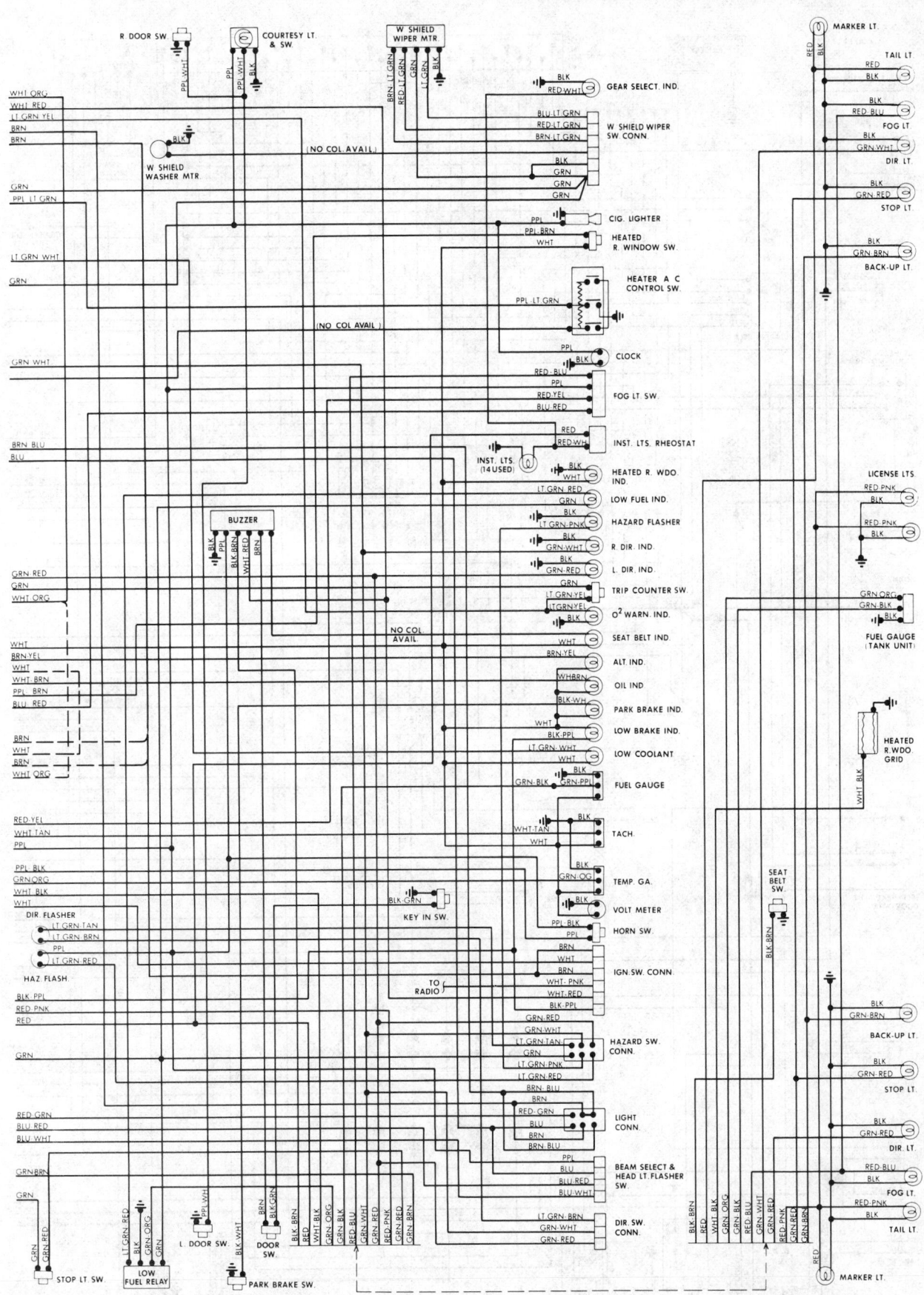

1981 Triumph

ENGINE COMPARTMENT

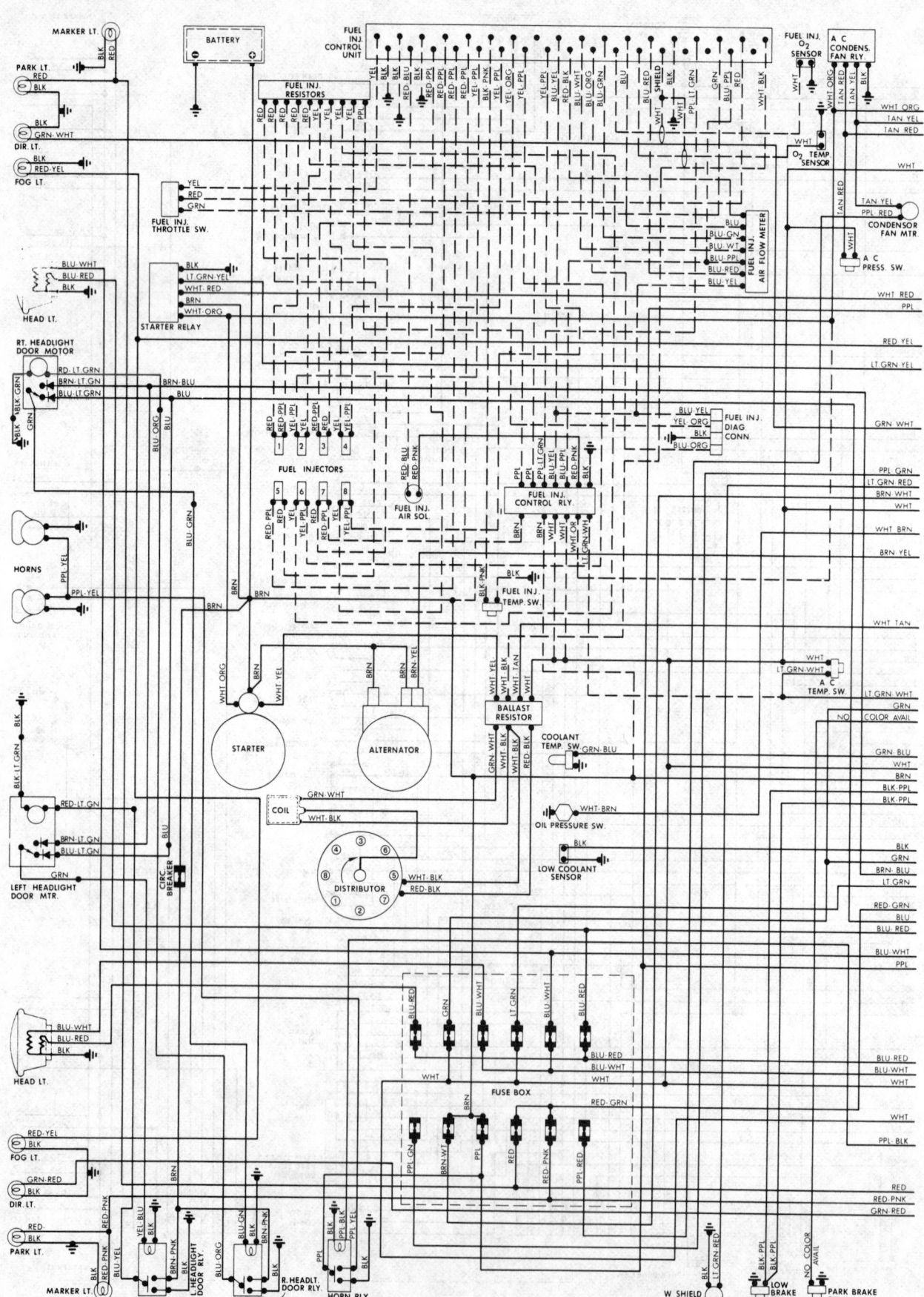

INSTRUMENT PANEL & REAR COMPARTMENT

WIRING DIAGRAMS

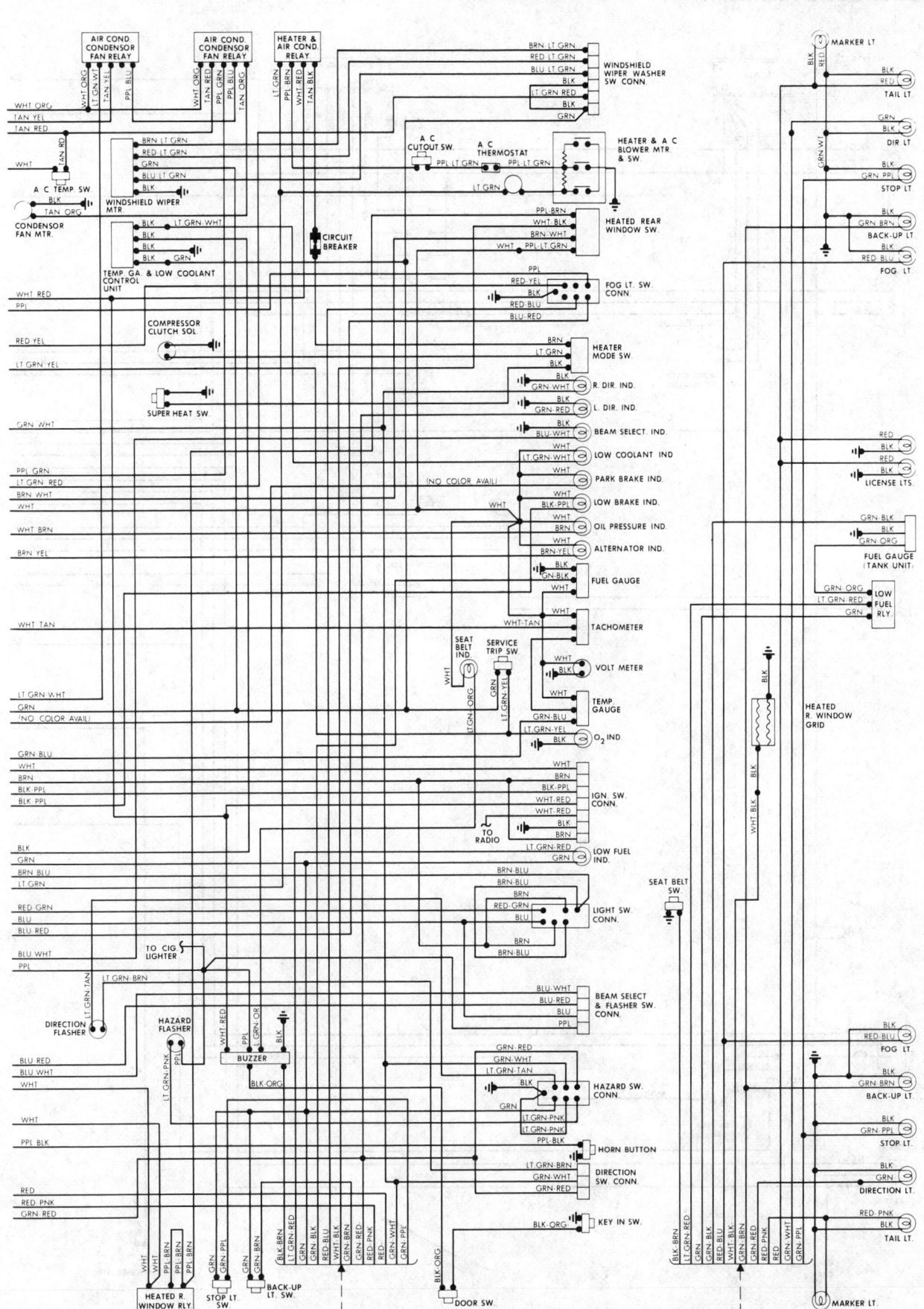

1981 Volkswagen

ENGINE COMPARTMENT

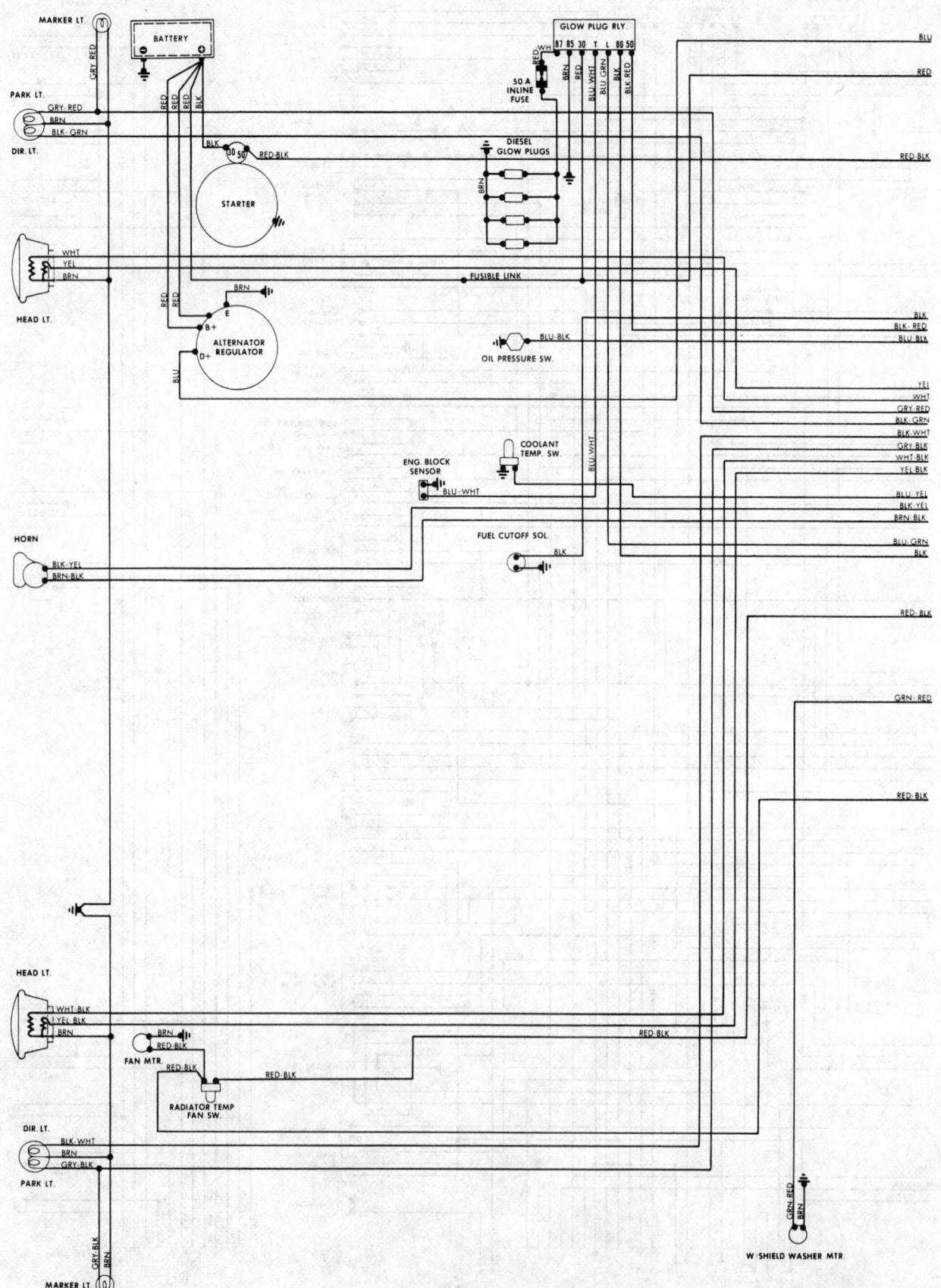

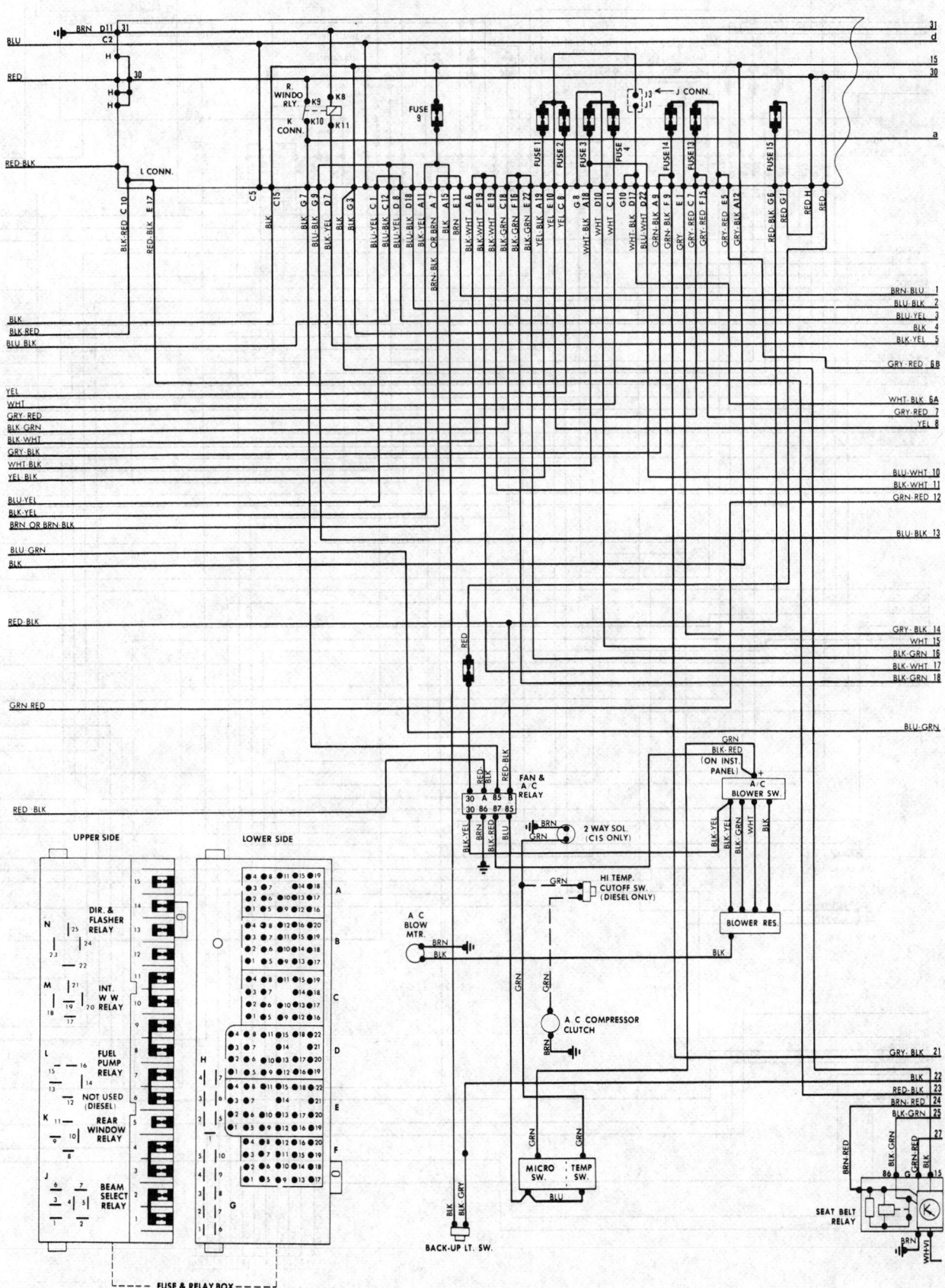

1981 Volkswagen

UNDERDASH

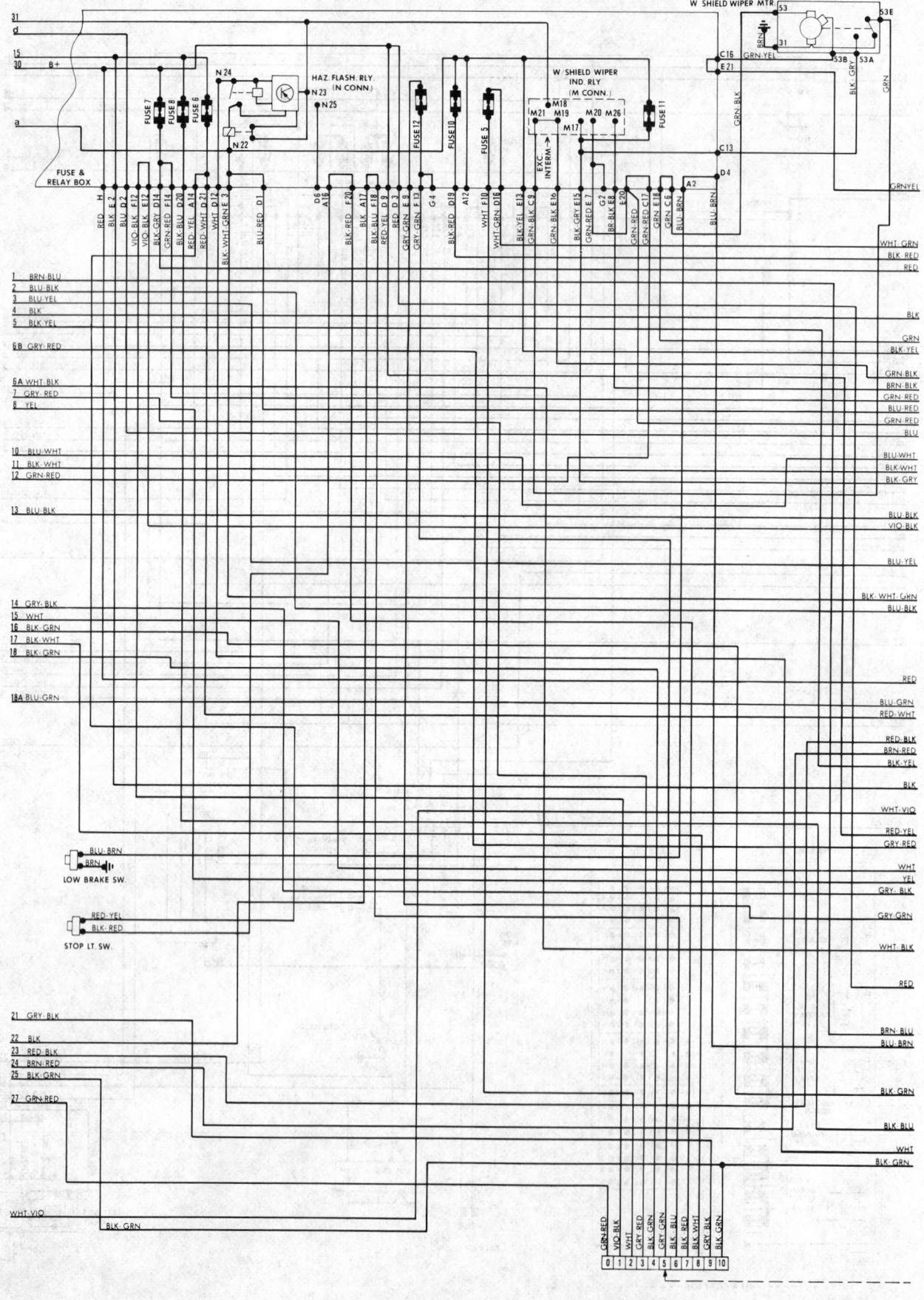

INSTRUMENT PANEL & REAR COMPARTMENT

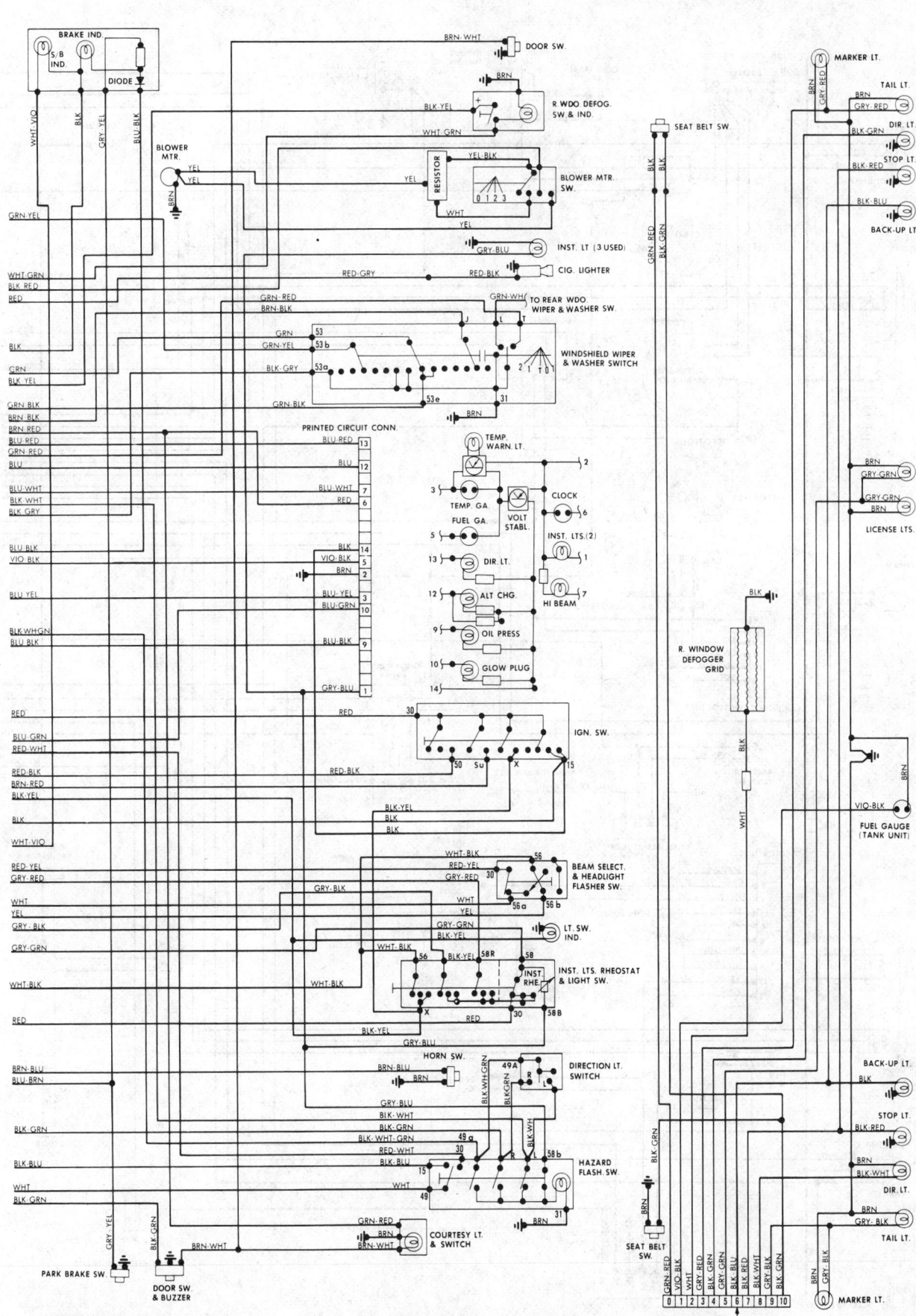

ENGINE COMPARTMENT

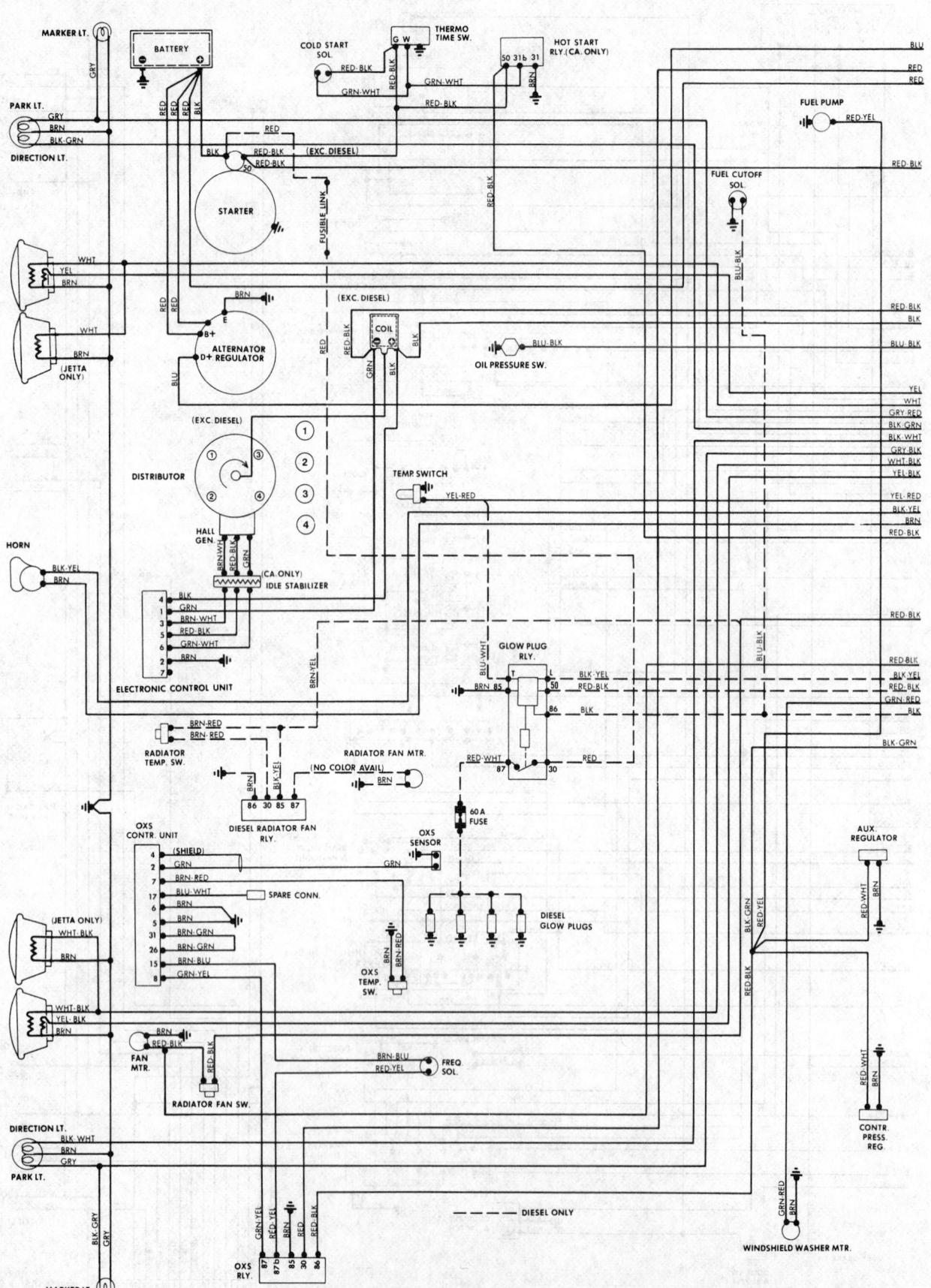

1981 Volkswagen

Jetta
Rabbit Convertible

4-199

ENGINE COMPARTMENT, FUSE BLOCK &
UNDERDASH

WIRING DIAGRAMS

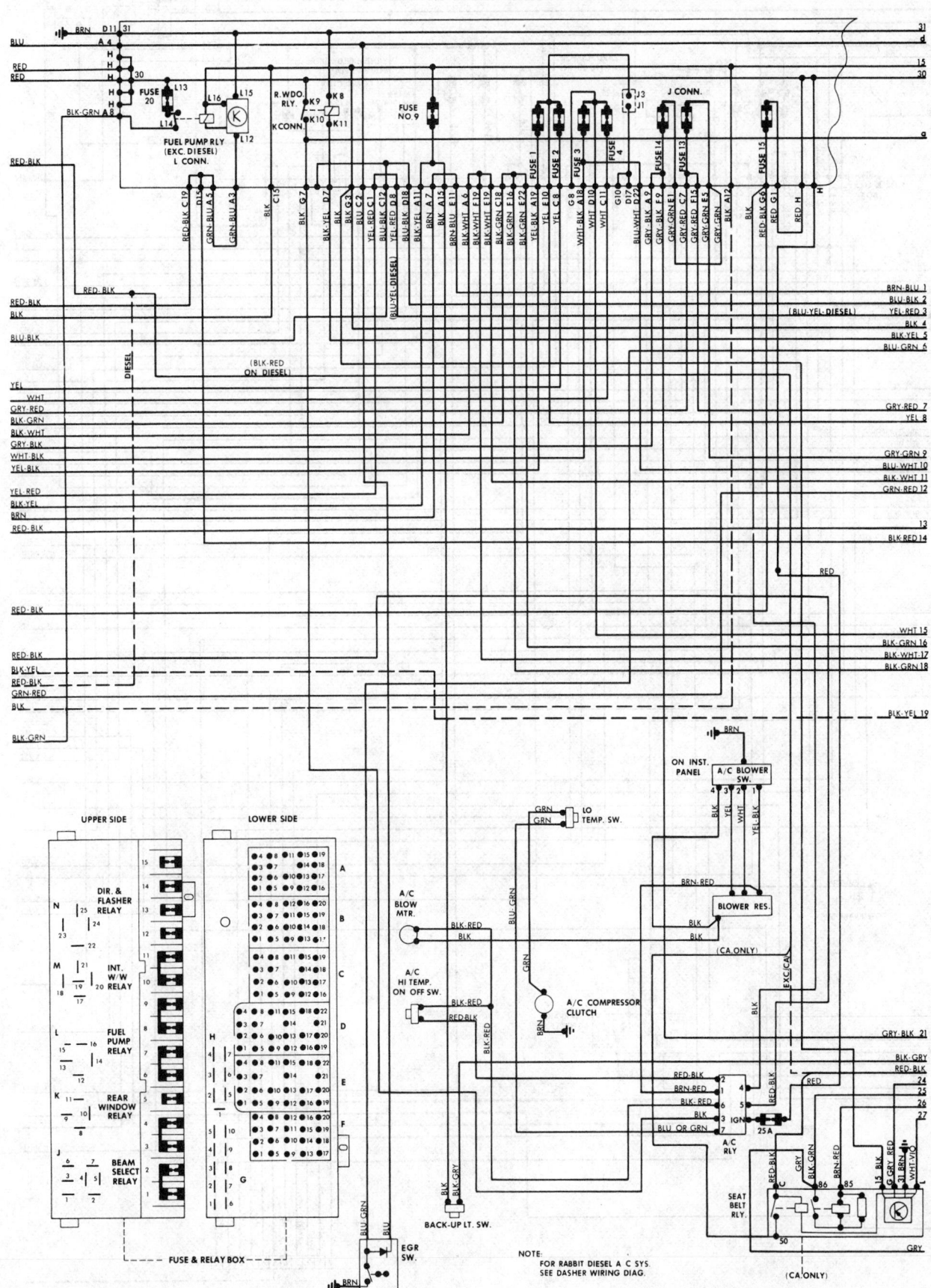

UNDERDASH

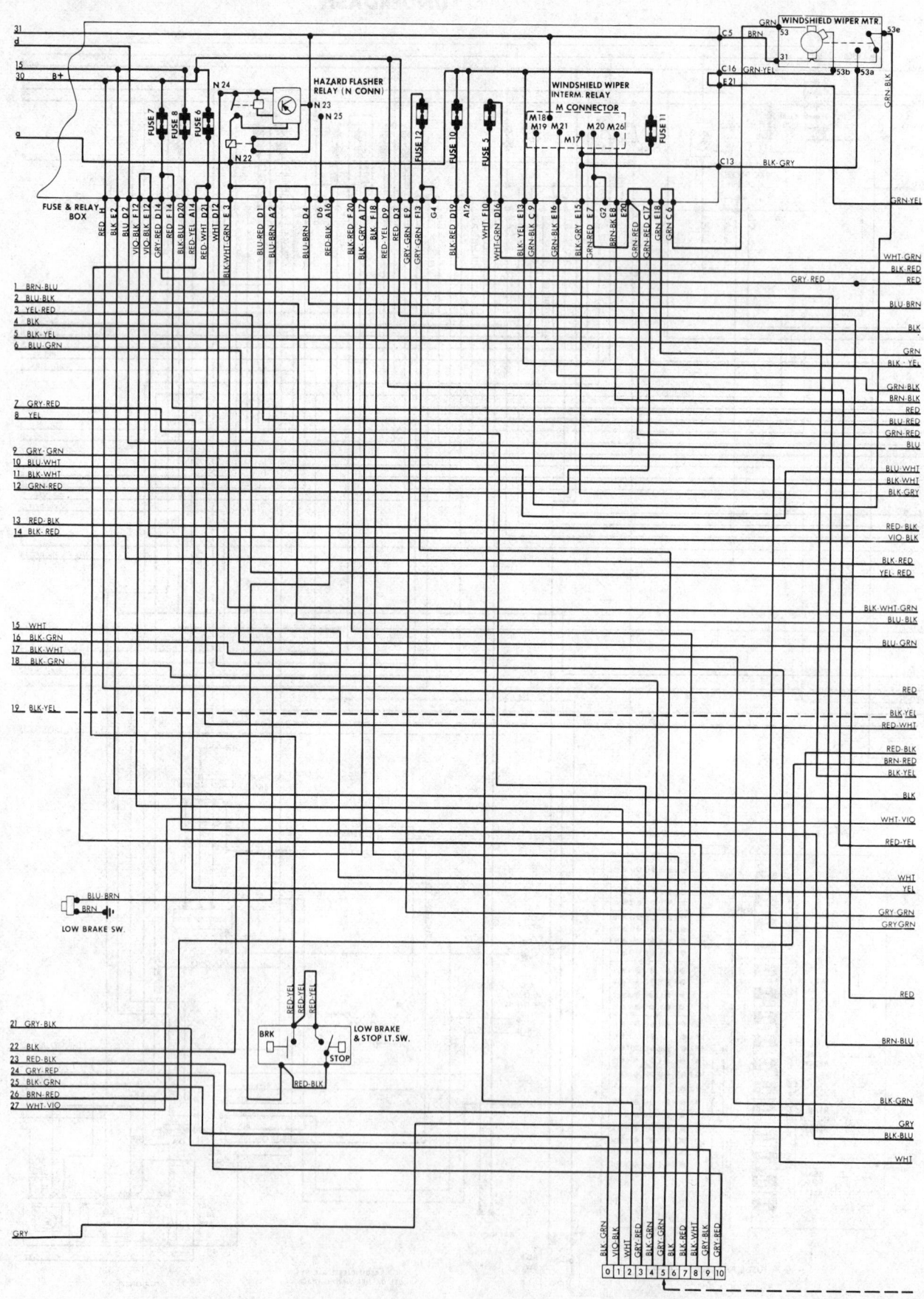

INSTRUMENT PANEL & REAR COMPARTMENT

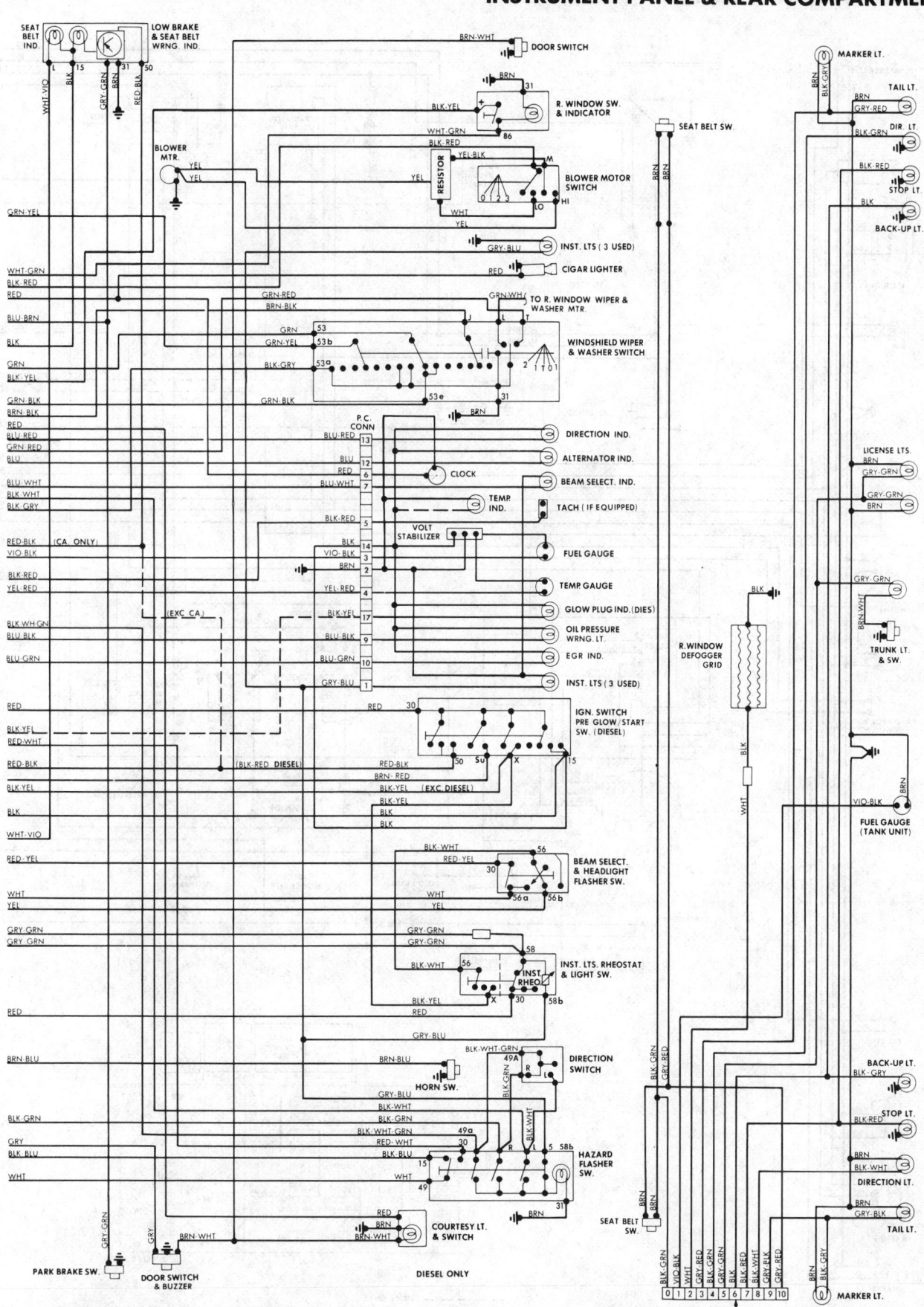

ENGINE COMPARTMENT

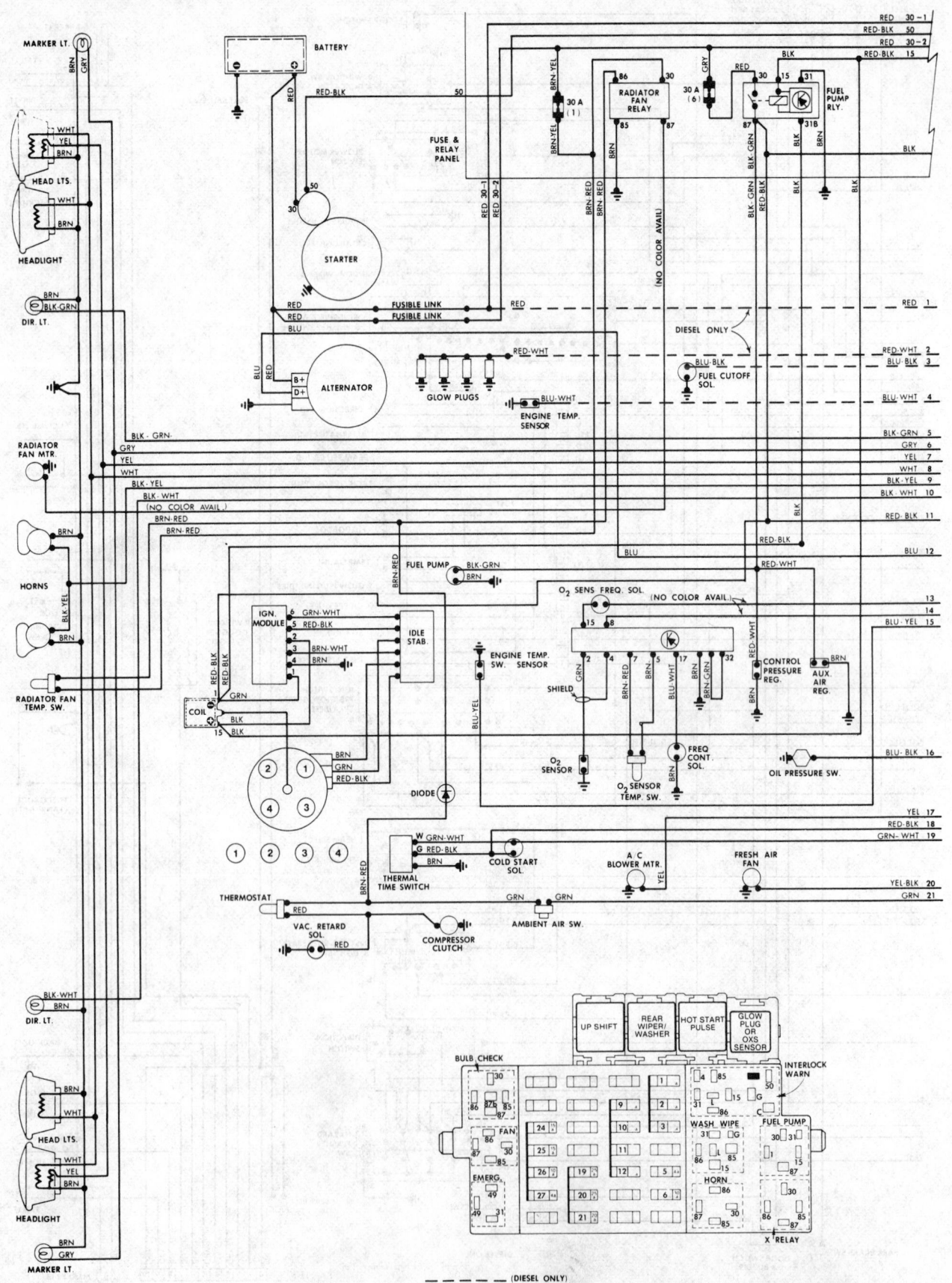

WIRING DIAGRAMS

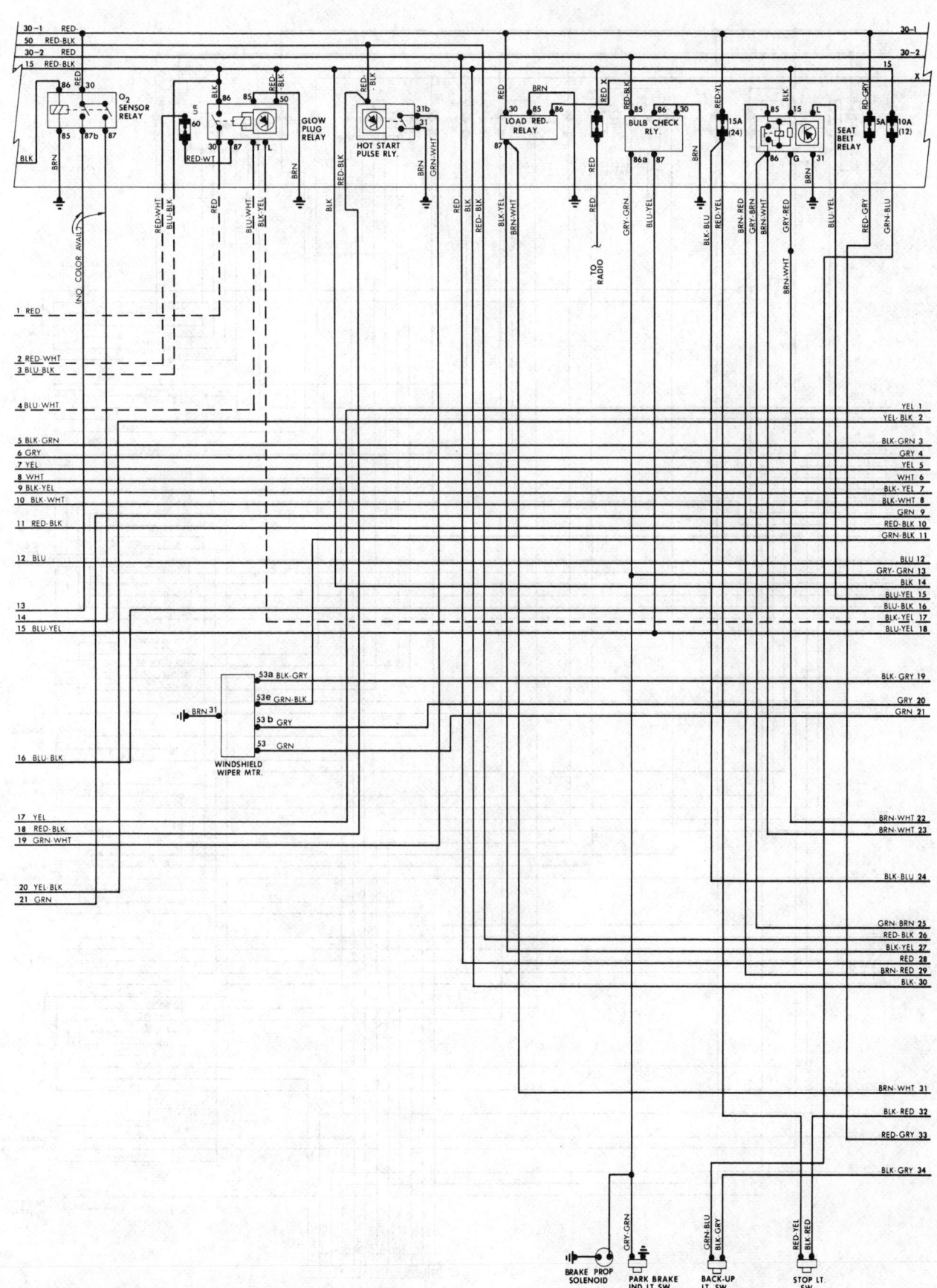

INSTRUMENT PANEL

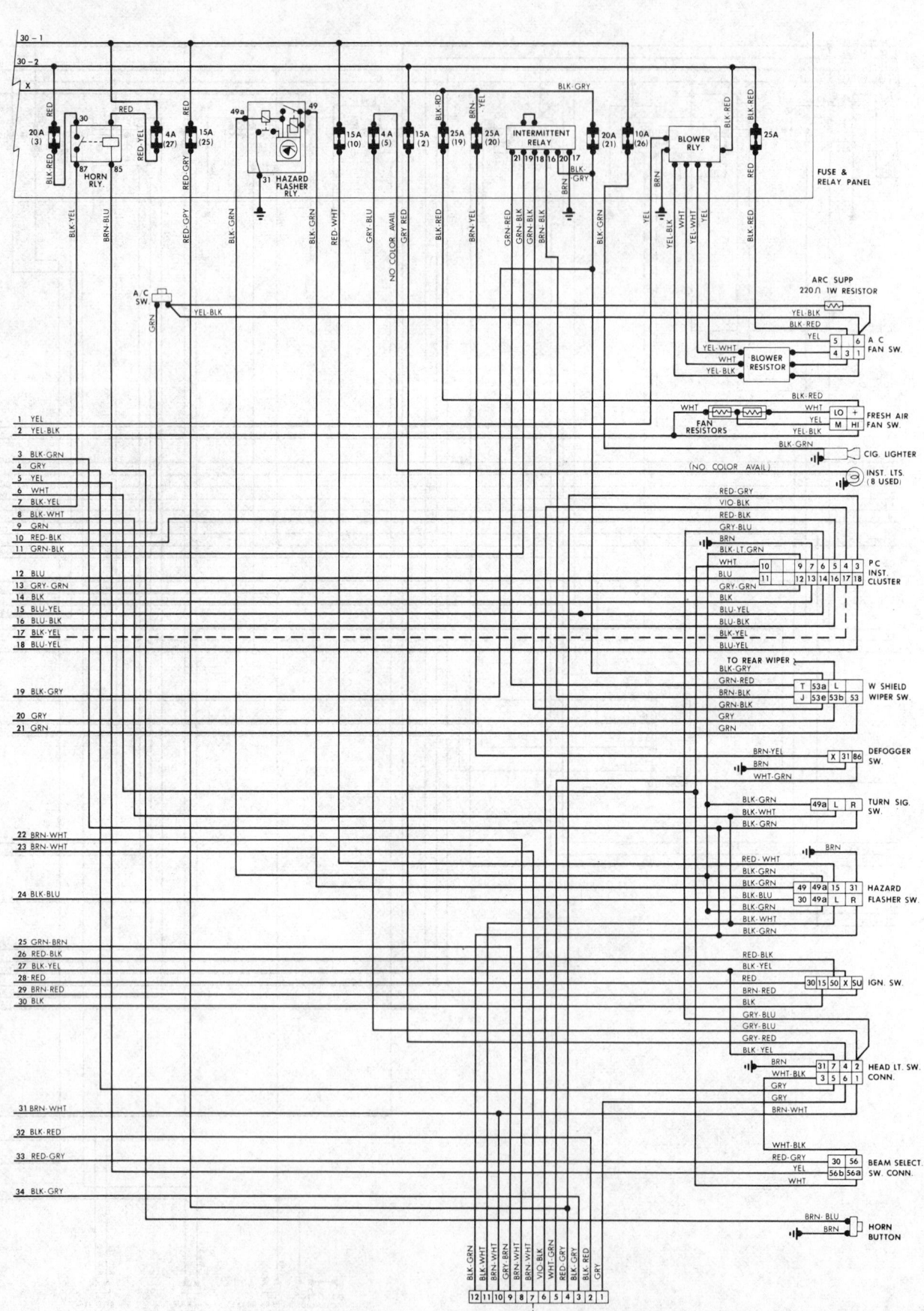

REAR COMPARTMENT

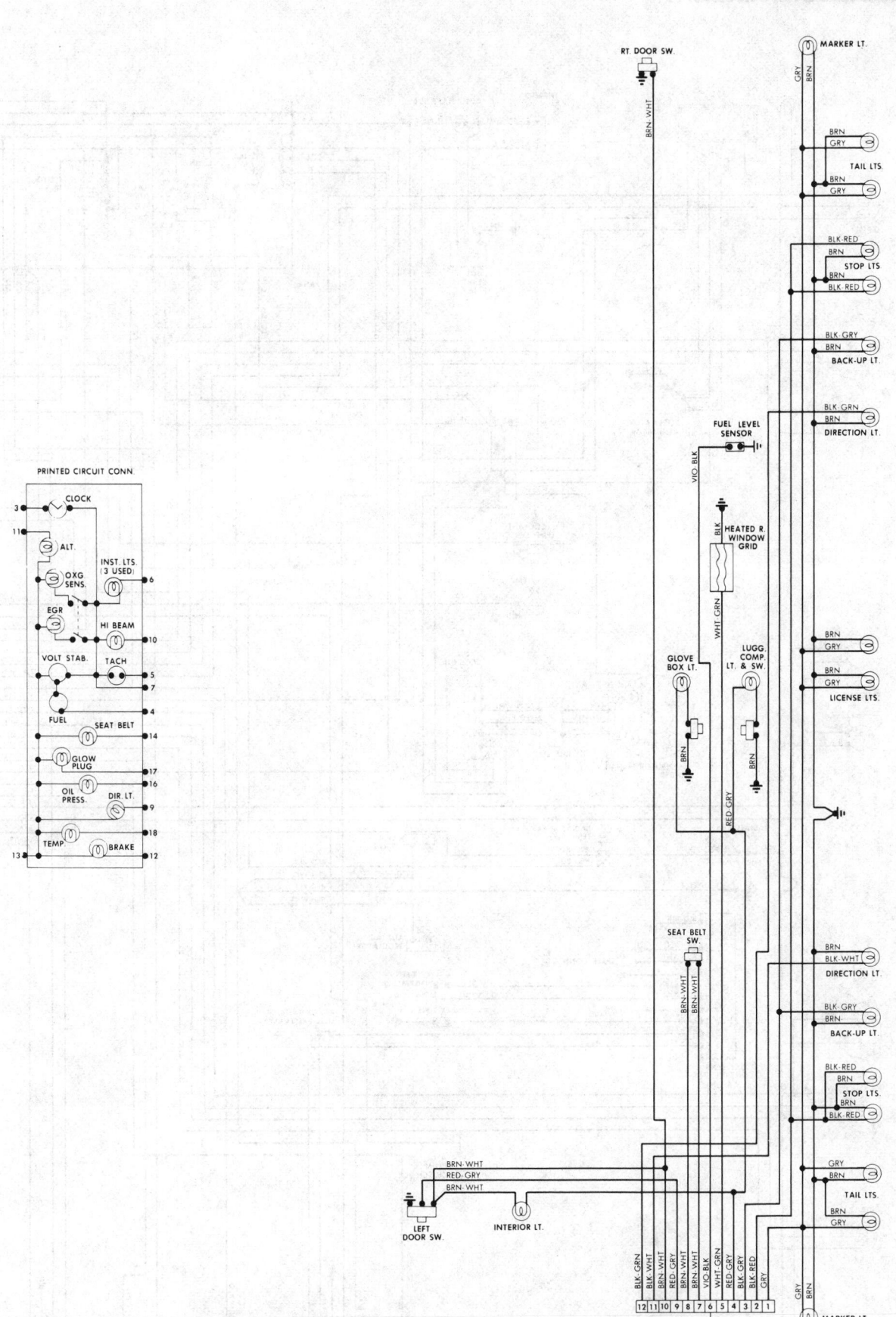

1981 Volkswagen

ENGINE COMPARTMENT

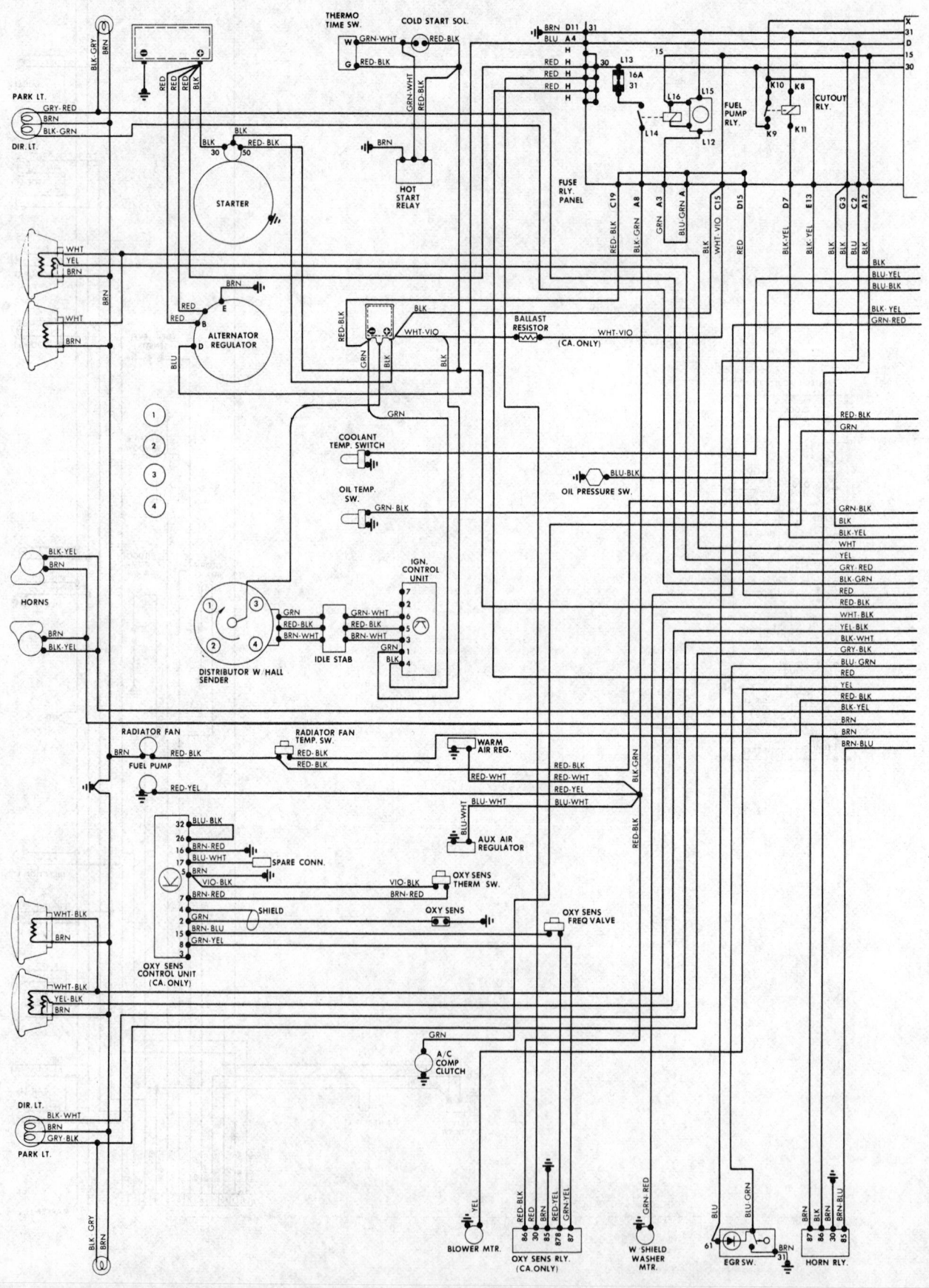

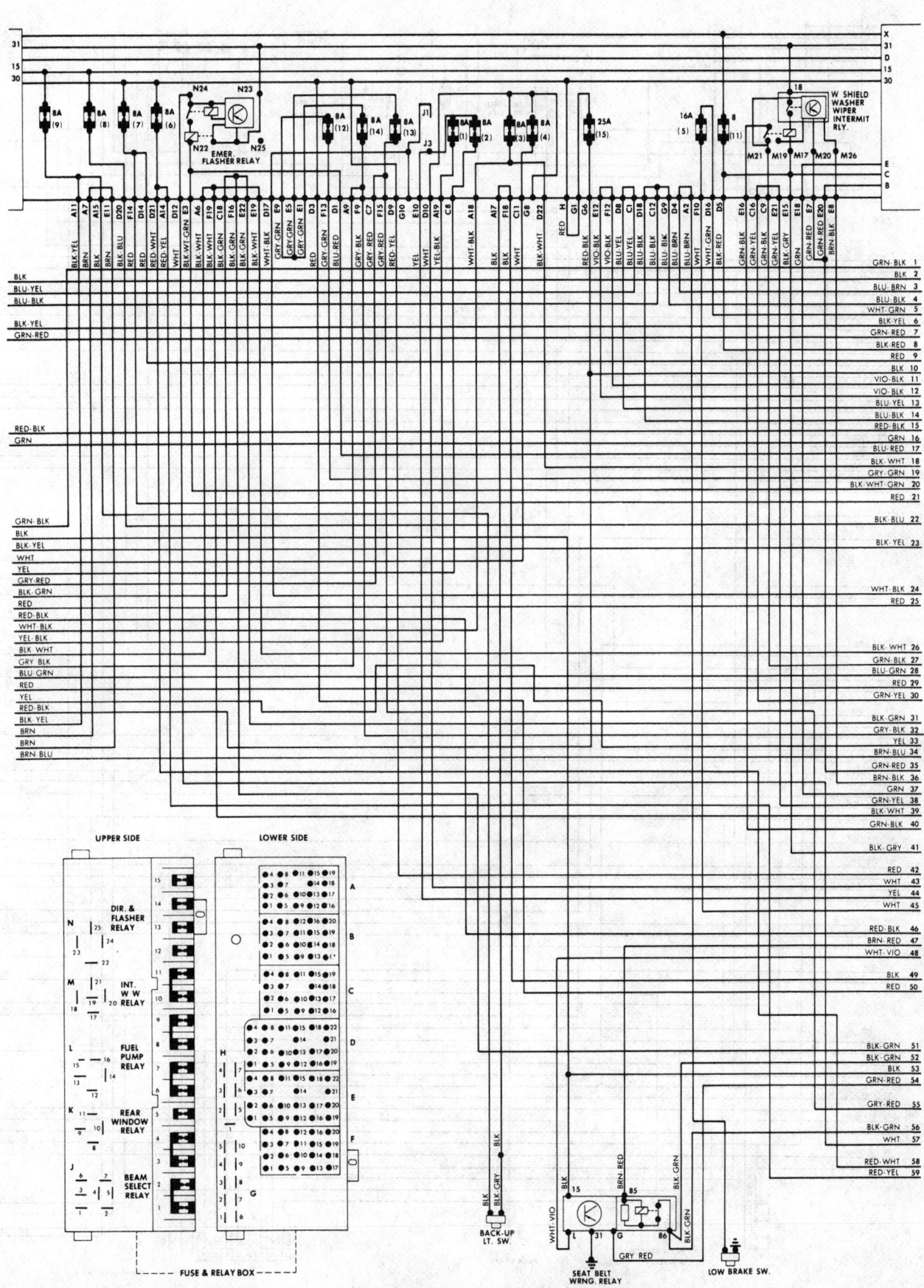

UNDERDASH

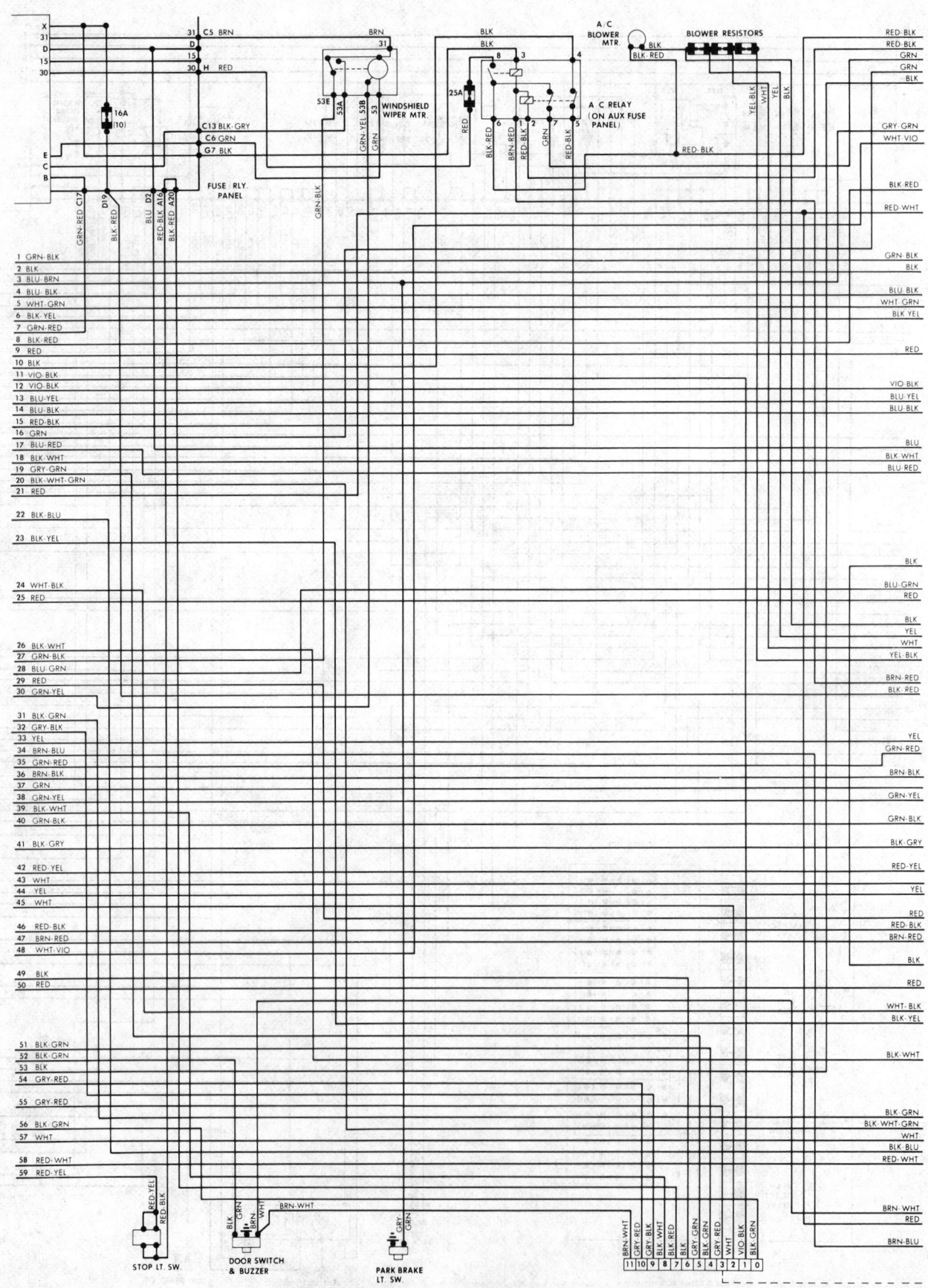

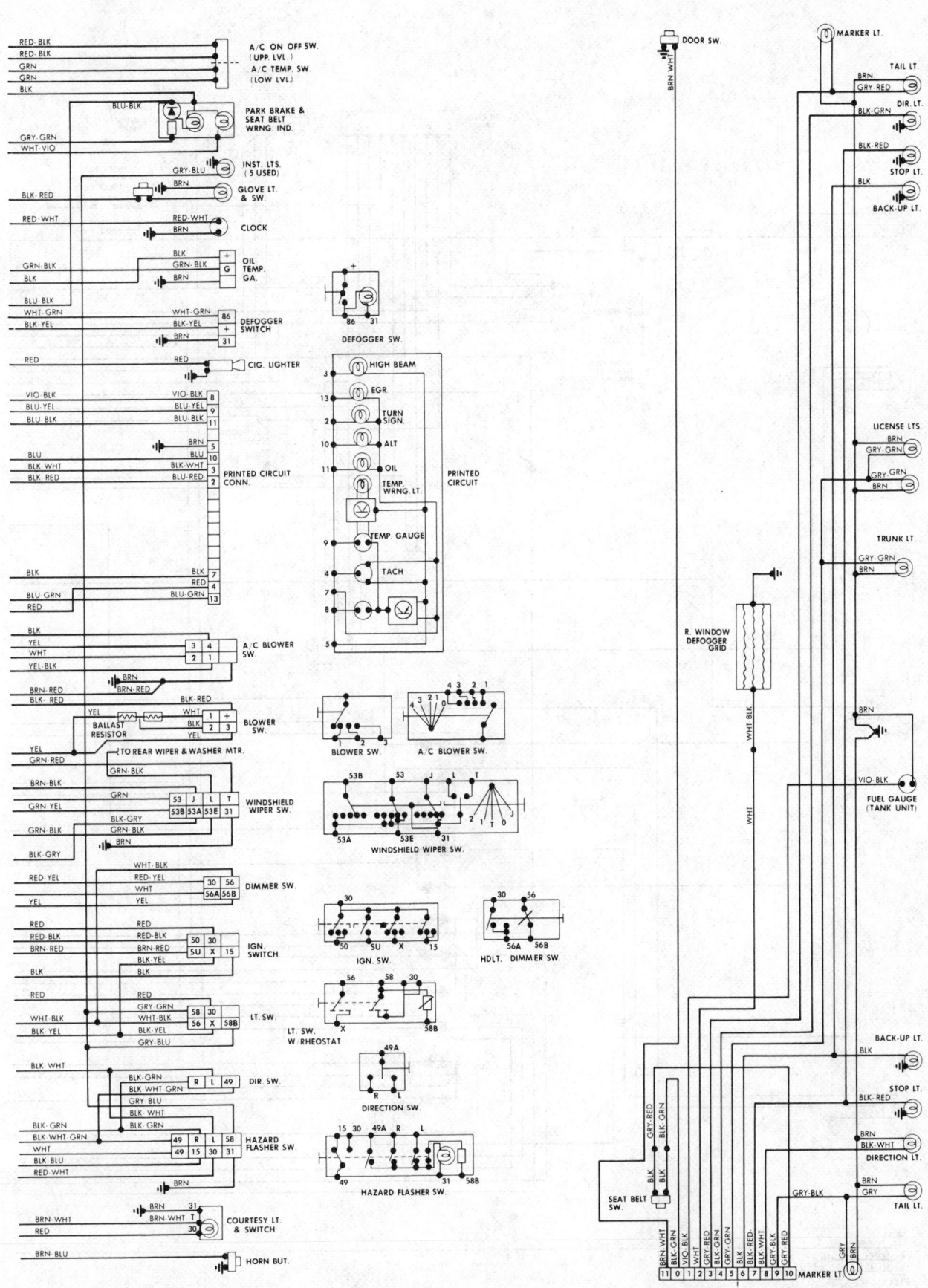

1981 Volkswagen

FRONT COMPARTMENT & FUSE BLOCK

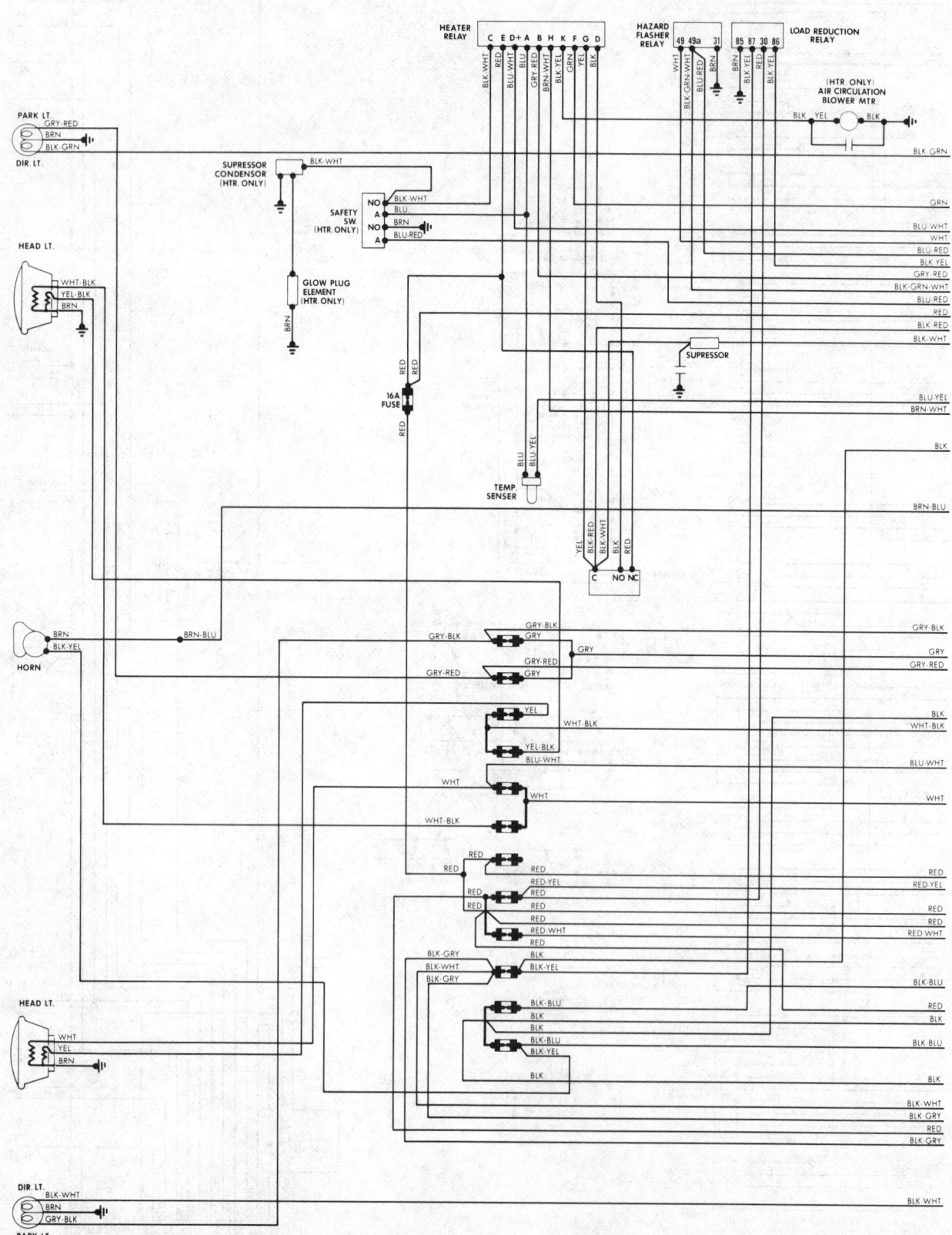

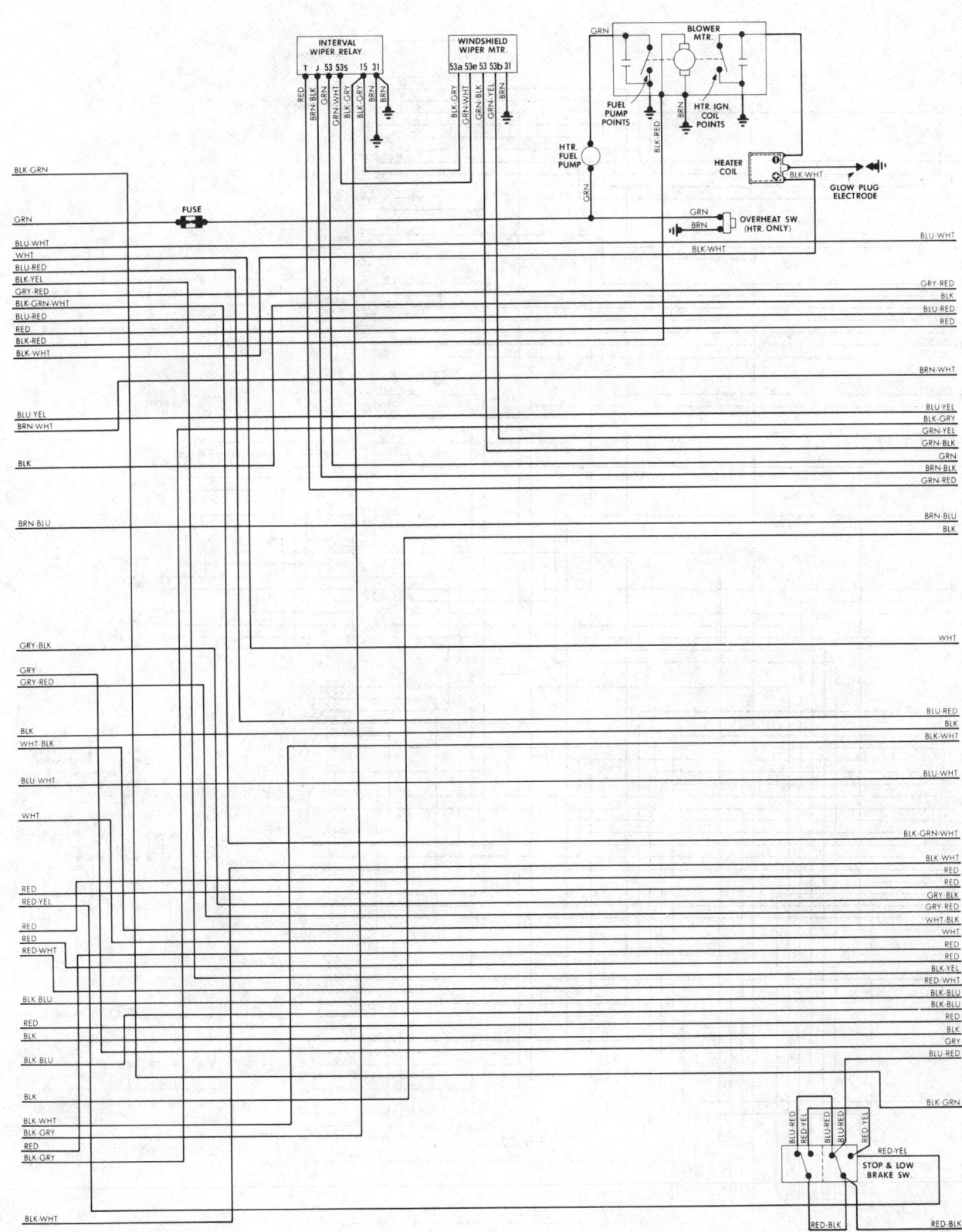

1981 Volkswagen

INSTRUMENT PANEL

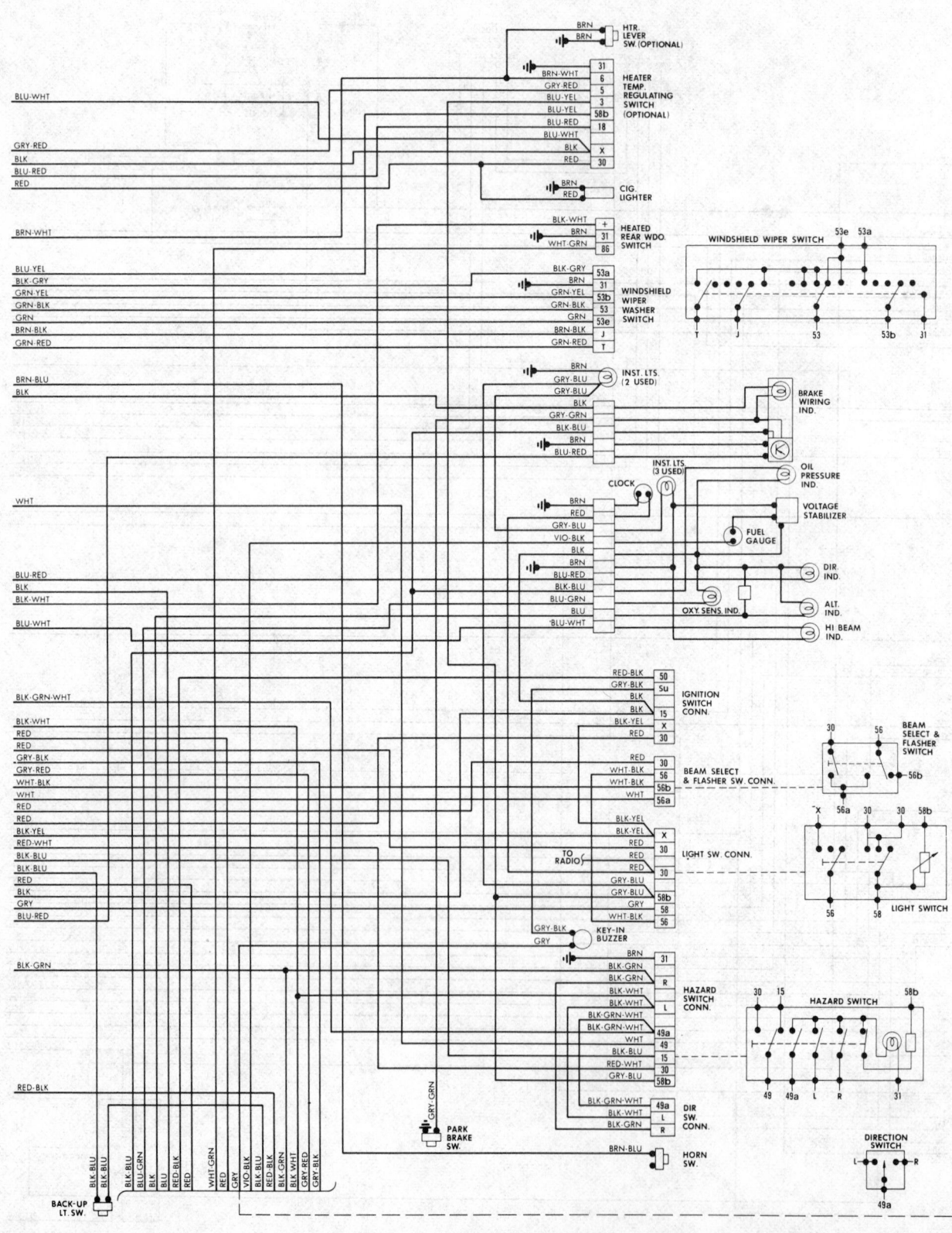

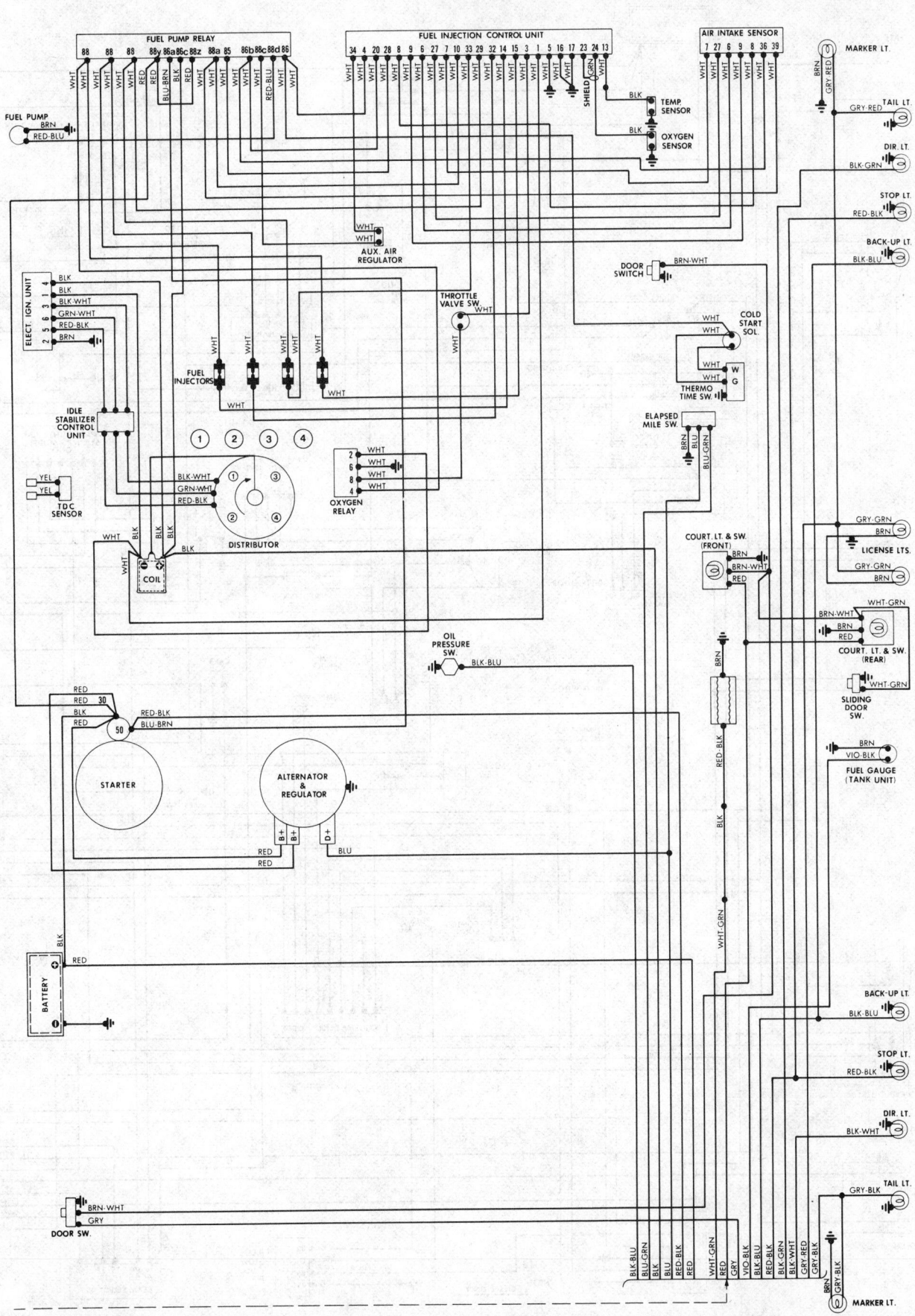

ENGINE COMPARTMENT

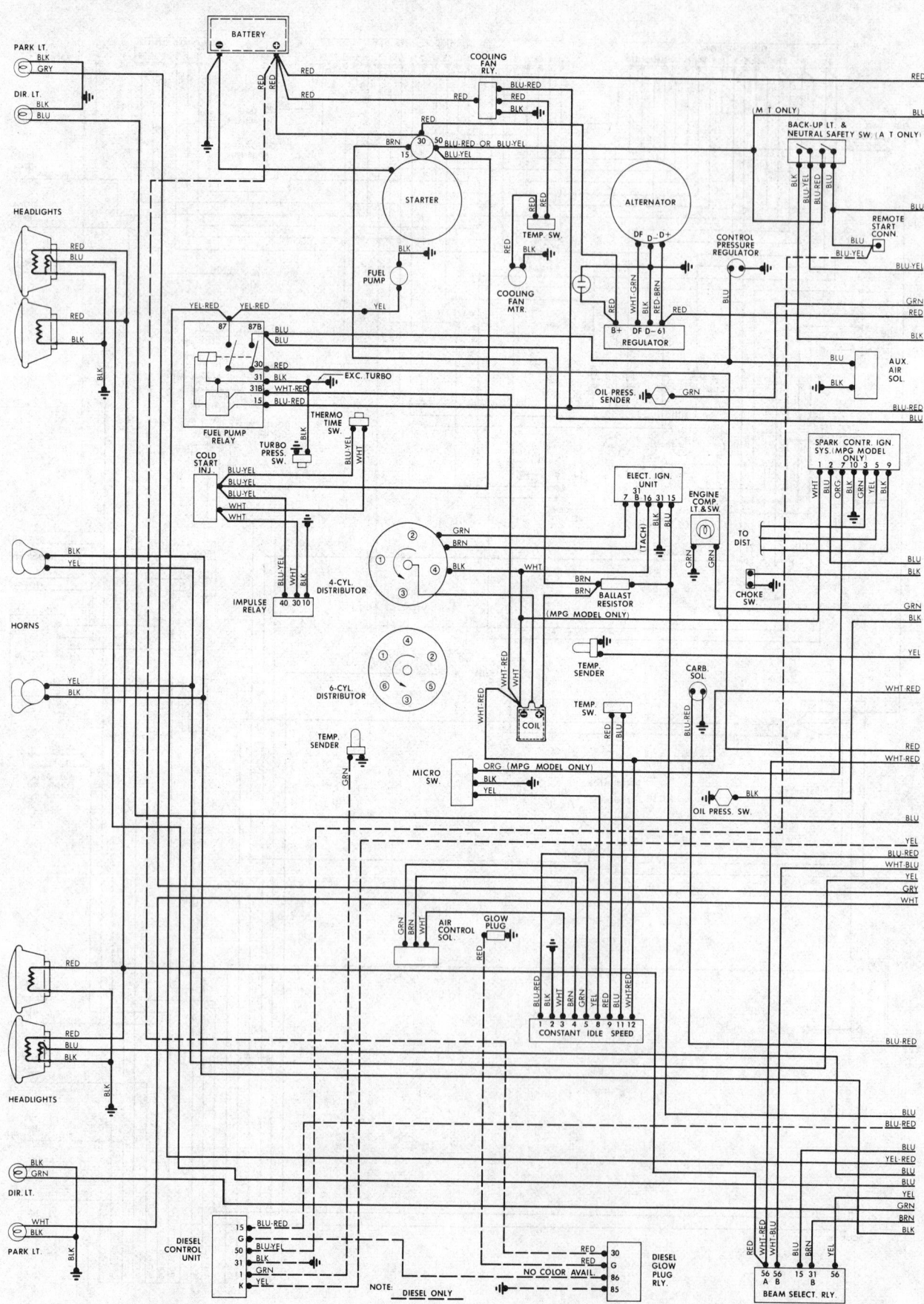

DL
GL
GLT Turbo

1981 Volvo

GLE
Bertone
Diesel

4-215

UNDERDASH & FUSE BLOCK

Wiring Diagrams

4-216 DL
       GL
       GLT Turbo

1981 Volvo

GLE
Bertone
Diesel

INSTRUMENT PANEL

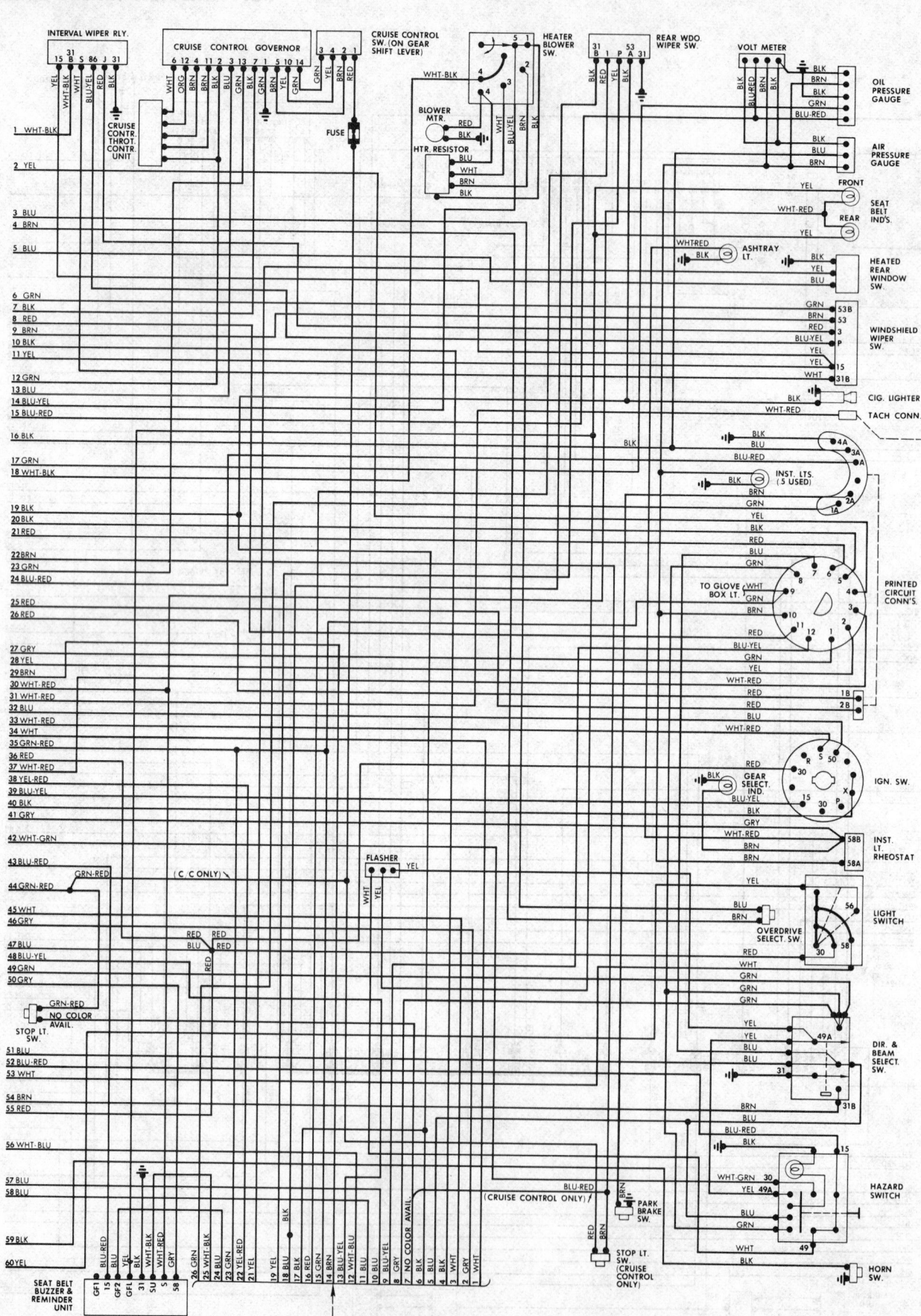

DL
GL
GLT Turbo

1981 Volvo

GLE
Bertone
Diesel

4–217

ACCESSORIES & REAR COMPARTMENT

WIRING DIAGRAMS

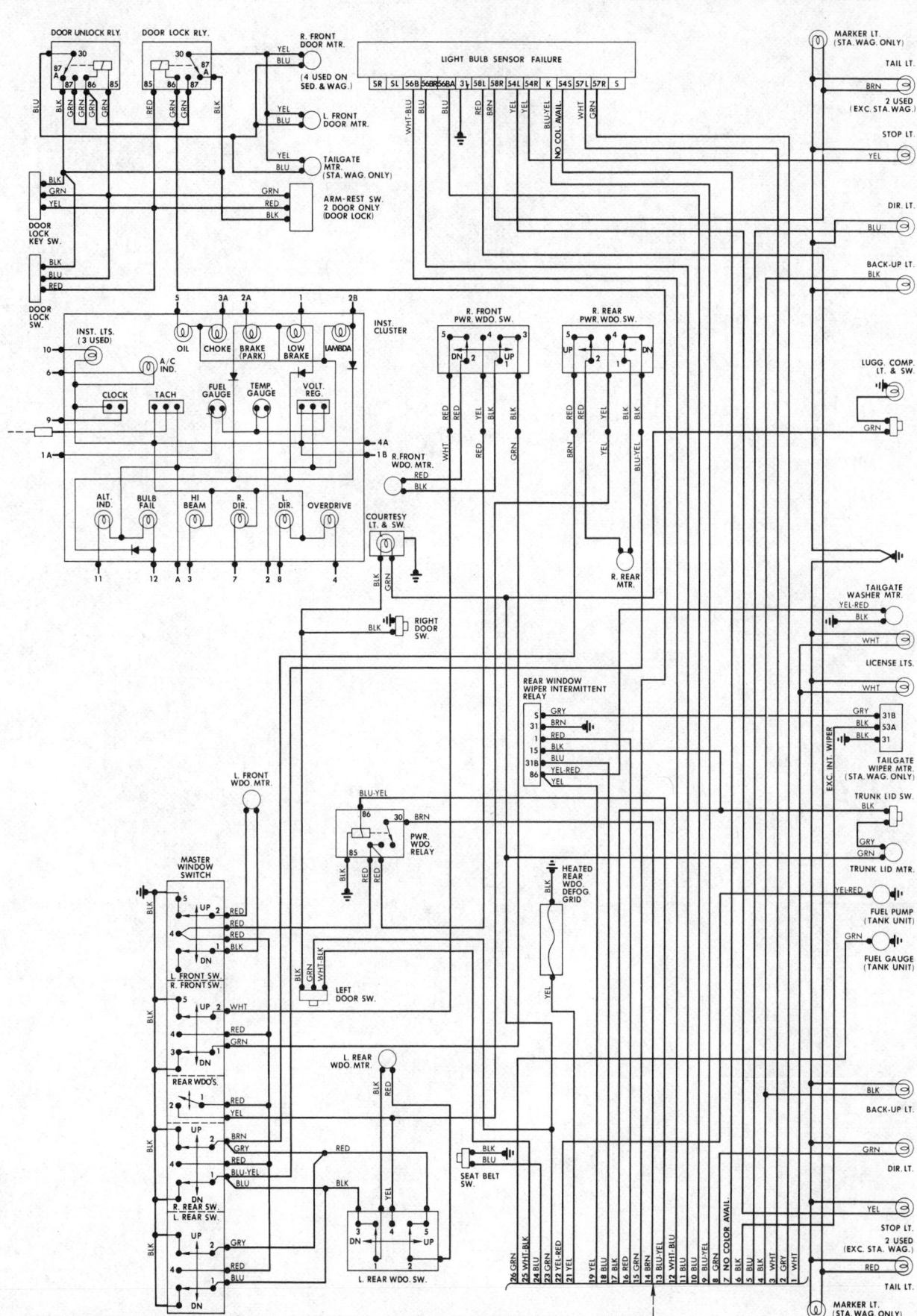

Section 5

ACCESSORIES & EQUIPMENT

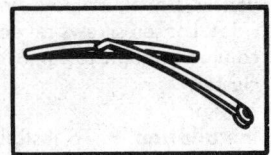

Contents

NOTE — ALSO SEE GENERAL INDEX

BMW

320i
528i
633CSi
733i

DESCRIPTION

All models have an instrument cluster with speedometer, tachometer, fuel gauge and temperature gauge. The headlight switch is located on the instrument panel. High beam, turn signals and wiper switch are on steering column levers. The 633CSi and 733i models have a safety check panel at the lower left side of the instrument panel.

The gauges use variable resistance sending units. No voltage limiter is used. On 733i models, the speedometer is electronically operated, with a sending unit on the rear axle.

TESTING

TEMPERATURE GAUGE

Disconnect sending unit wire and connect it to ground. Turn on ignition briefly. Gauge needle should move into red zone on gauge. If it does, temperature sending unit may be defective. If not, check continuity of sending unit wire. If wiring is good, gauge is inoperative.

FUEL GAUGE

Remove rear seat and tank access cover. Unplug sending unit wire and connect it to ground. Turn ignition on briefly. Gauge needle should move to Full. If it does, sending unit may be defective. If not, check sending unit wire continuity. If wire is good, gauge is inoperative.

RESISTANCE CHECK

NOTE — *Most models have a combination temperature sending unit that includes a resistance sender and a temperature switch. The smaller terminal is the resistance sender. Temperature values for the sending unit are stamped in the body of the sender.*

1) Connect test resistor between sending unit wire and ground. Turn ignition on. Gauge readings should match those shown in "Gauge Resistance Check" chart.

Gauge Resistance Check		
Model & Gauge	Gauge Reading	Resistance (Ohms)
528i		
Fuel Gauge	Full	3
	Half	32
	Empty	68
Temperature		
Gauge	122° F (50° C)	195
	176° F (80° C)	64
	230° F (110° C)	30
733i		
Fuel Gauge	Full	5
	Half	50
	Empty	82
Temperature		
Gauge	104° F (40°C)	288
	140° F (60° C)	125
	240° F (115° C)	26

2) Remove sending unit and check resistance at position or temperature specified in "Gauge Resistance Check" chart. Resistance should be close to specifications in chart. If not, replace sending unit.

NOTE — *Resistance values were not available for 320i or 633CSi models.*

REMOVAL & INSTALLATION

INSTRUMENT CLUSTER

Removal (320i & 528i) — **1)** Disconnect battery ground cable. Remove steering wheel. Remove insulation panel under left side of dashboard. Disconnect speedometer cable at middle joint. Do not lose felt ring.

2) Unscrew knurled nut below instrument cluster. Pull out instrument cluster. Unplug wiring from cluster and transmission gear indicator (if equipped). Remove cluster.

Installation — To install, reverse removal procedure.

Removal (633CSi) — **1)** Disconnect battery ground cable. Remove steering wheel. Remove insulation panel under left side. Pry cover off test panel and remove 3 screws. Pull panel out, but leave wires connected.

2) Unscrew headlight switch knob and remove switch. Pull off left air control knob, then remove trim cover at left edge of heater panel. Remove instrument cluster screws (2 on each side). Loosen screws on each side of steering column and lower column enough to remove cluster. Unplug wiring and remove cluster.

Installation — To install, reverse removal procedure.

Removal (733i) — Disconnect battery ground cable. Remove insulation panel below left side of dashboard. Remove 3 screws across top of instrument cluster hood. Move steering column down and out as far as possible. Disconnect wiring, then pull cluster out toward center of vehicle.

Installation — To install, reverse removal procedure.

COMBINATION SWITCH

Removal (All Models) — Disconnect battery ground cable. Remove steering wheel and lower column cover. Remove screws from switch. Cut cable clips, unplug wiring, and remove switch.

Installation — To install, reverse removal procedure.

HEADLIGHT SWITCH

Removal (320i, 528i & 633CSi) — Disconnect battery ground cable. Remove insulation panel below left side of dashboard. Pull out headlight knob. Insert a pin through shaft to keep it from turning, then unscrew knob. Remove switch nut and pull switch out from rear. Unplug wiring and remove switch.

Installation — To install, reverse removal procedures.

Removal (733i) — Disconnect battery ground cable. Remove insulation panel below left side of dashboard. Remove knurled nut on back of headlight switch. Unplug wiring and remove switch.

Installation — To install, reverse removal procedure.

Switches, Gauges & Instrument Panels 5-3

CHRYSLER CORP. IMPORTS

Arrow Pickup   Colt
Challenger   Ram-50 Pickup
Champ   Sapporo

DESCRIPTION & OPERATION

All models have an instrument cluster with speedometer, fuel gauge and temperature gauge. The fuel gauge has a built-in voltage limiter to keep the supply voltage to the gauges at 7 volts. Some models may also have a shunt type ammeter, oil pressure gauge and tachometer. The pressure gauge is the bimetal type and uses full battery voltage. Control switches are located on the steering column for Challenger and Sapporo. Champ, Colt and Pickup models use dashboard switches.

TESTING

VOLTAGE LIMITER

Unplug the fuel or temperature sending unit connector. Connect a voltmeter between the sending unit wire and ground. With the ignition on, voltage should should swing between 1 to 7 volts. If not, fuel gauge/limiter must be replaced.

CAUTION — Voltage limiter must be securely grounded or it will be ruined when vehicle is started. Ensure ground connection is tight when installing fuel gauge.

FUEL GAUGE

1) Disconnect fuel gauge sending unit wire. On Colt and Champ models, connect a 17 ohm resistor between wire and ground. On all other models, ground sending unit wire. Fuel gauge should read full.

CAUTION — Keeping the wire grounded too long can damage coils in gauge. Perform test as quickly as possible.

2) On Colt and Champ models, connect a 120 ohm resistor between sending wire and ground. On all other models, connect a 95 ohm resistor between sending wire and ground. Gauge should read empty.

FUEL SENDING UNIT

Connect ohmmeter between gauge terminals. On Colt and Champ models, resistance should be 17 ohms with tank full, or 120 ohms with tank empty. On all other models, resistance should be 1-5 ohms with tank full and 103-117 ohms with tank empty. If not, replace sending unit.

TEMPERATURE GAUGE

Unplug temperature sender wire at sending unit. Connect a 70 ohm resistor between wire and ground. Gauge should indicate about 176° F (80° C). DO NOT connect sender wire directly to ground. If gauge tests okay, remove sending unit and place in hot water. Resistance should measure 70 ohms with water at 176° F (80° C).

OIL PRESSURE GAUGE

Unplug sending unit wire. Battery voltage should be present between wire and ground with ignition on. If not, check fuse.

Connect a 120 ohm resistor between wire and ground. Gauge should indicate about 85 psi (6 kg/cm²).

AMMETER

On Challenger and Sapporo, check ammeter fuse in box at left front fender panel. On all models, remove ammeter. Connect a 3.4 watt bulb (or 60 ohm resistor) in series with a battery and ammeter. If ammeter indicates about 6 amps, it is working correctly.

CAUTION — Ammeter is a shunt type that normally passes one-thirtieth of the current being used in vehicle. Do not allow more than 1 amp to pass through ammeter.

REMOVAL & INSTALLATION

INSTRUMENT CLUSTER

Removal (Arrow & Ram-50 Pickups) — 1) Disconnect battery ground cable. Remove heater and radio knobs. Remove 2 screws under upper edge of cluster. Remove 2 screws inside ashtray opening. Remove instrument cluster bezel. Remove 4 screws at corners of cluster. Unplug wiring and speedometer cable and remove cluster.

2) To remove console gauges, remove console floor screws on each side. Pull console back. Remove console gauge mounting screws from inside console. Push gauges toward front of vehicle, unplug wiring and remove.

Installation — To install, reverse removal procedure.

Removal (Challenger & Sapporo) — Disconnect battery ground cable. Remove 4 cluster hood screws. Remove 4 cluster screws. Pull cluster out slightly, then unplug wiring and speedometer cable. Remove cluster.

Installation — To install, reverse removal procedure.

Removal (Champ & Colt) — 1) Remove instrument cluster hood mounting screws. Leave switch connectors plugged in. Remove lower left corner panel of dashboard. Pull out instrument cluster hood main connector and unplug it. Remove cluster hood and switches.

2) Remove instrument cluster screws and pull cluster back. Unplug wiring, remove speedometer cable and remove cluster.

Installation — To install, reverse removal procedure.

COMBINATION SWITCH

Removal (Challenger & Sapporo) — 1) Disconnect battery ground cable. Remove steering wheel. Tilt wheel to lowest position and remove column cover. Remove column switch screws. Take off wiring clamp, unplug wiring and remove switch.

Installation — To install, reverse removal procedure. Ensure that turn signal cancel cam pins fit into steering wheel holes.

ACCESSORIES & EQUIPMENT

COURIER

Pickup

DESCRIPTION & OPERATION

The instrument cluster contains a speedometer and fuel gauge. The XLT package adds a temperature gauge and ammeter. A voltage regulator in the fuel gauge provides a constant 7 volt supply to operate the gauges.

A combination switch on the steering column operates the headlights, turn signals, hazard flashers and wipers. This switch must be replaced as a complete assembly.

TESTING

AMMETER (XLT ONLY)

Turn on the headlights with the engine stopped. If the pointer moves toward the "D" end of scale, ammeter is working. If pointer moves toward "C", reverse connections at ammeter.

FUEL GAUGE & TEMPERATURE GAUGE (XLT ONLY)

1) Remove cluster far enough to reach rear connections with test leads. Connect a jumper wire between cluster ground terminal and a good chassis ground. See *Fig. 1*.

2) Ensure main connector is tight. Turn ignition on. Use a non-powered test lamp for the tests. Connect test lamp between "F"

and "J" terminals, "I" and "J" terminals and "E" and "J" terminals. The lamp should come on in each case.

3) Connect test lamp between "G" and "J" terminals, then "D" and "J" terminals. The test lamp should flash in each case.

NOTE — *Testing procedure for non-XLT models was not available.*

REMOVAL & INSTALLATION

INSTRUMENT CLUSTER

Removal — Disconnect battery ground cable. Remove meter hood. Remove 4 screws and pull cluster back slightly. Unplug wiring and speedometer cable. Remove instrument cluster.

Installation — To install, reverse removal procedure.

COMBINATION SWITCH

Removal — 1) Disconnect battery ground cable. Remove steering wheel. Remove steering column cover. Unplug connectors at base of steering column. Pull headlight switch knob off shaft.

2) Remove snap ring and pull turn signal cam off the shaft. Remove retaining bolt at bottom of switch. Pull switch off column.

Installation — To install, reverse removal procedure.

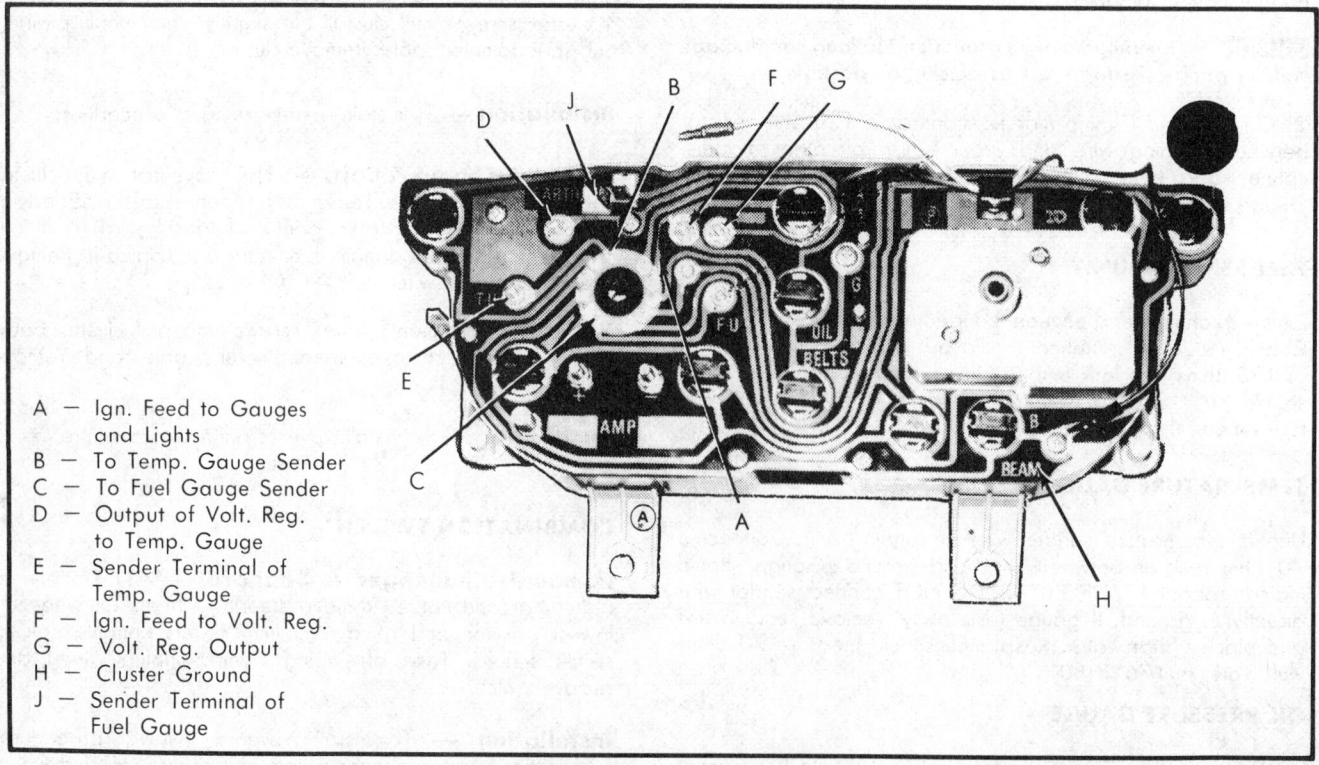

A — Ign. Feed to Gauges and Lights
B — To Temp. Gauge Sender
C — To Fuel Gauge Sender
D — Output of Volt. Reg. to Temp. Gauge
E — Sender Terminal of Temp. Gauge
F — Ign. Feed to Volt. Reg.
G — Volt. Reg. Output
H — Cluster Ground
J — Sender Terminal of Fuel Gauge

Fig. 1 Connection Points for Testing Courier XLT Instrument Cluster

DATSUN

200SX	510
210	810
280ZX	Pickup
310	

DESCRIPTION

All models have an instrument cluster that contains the main instrument assembly. This cluster can be removed with all the gauges installed. A combination switch on the steering column includes the wiper switch, lighting switch and turn signals. Other control switches are located on the instrument panel or console.

TROUBLE SHOOTING

GAUGES NOT WORKING

Blown fuse. Faulty voltage regulator. Loose sender connections. Defective sending unit. Loose connections in instrument cluster.

WARNING LIGHTS NOT WORKING

Burned out bulb. Loose connections. Broken printed circuit. Defective sending unit.

HORN NOT WORKING

Blown fuse. Faulty horn switch. Horn relay inoperative. Loose connection or open circuit. Defective horn.

TESTING

Use an ohmmeter to check sensor switch, and gauge operation as shown in "Datsun Switch and Gauge Testing" chart. If sensor, switch or gauge does not operate as described, replace it.

Datsun Switch & Gauge Testing	
Component	**Test Result**
Fuel Gauge	①With 32 ohm resistor reads half tank
Temperature Gauge	①With 116 ohm resistor reads 120°F (50°C)
Brake Fluid Sensor	Float raised, 250 ohms; float lowered, 0 ohms
Windshield Washer Sensor	Float raised, infinity; float lowered, 0 ohms
Coolant Sensor	Float raised, infinity; float lowered, 0 ohms
Stop Lamp Switch	Continuity with plunger in
Parking Brake Switch	Continuity with plunger out
① — Insert resistor between sender wire and ground.	

REMOVAL & INSTALLATION

COMBINATION SWITCH

Removal (All Models) — Disconnect battery ground cable. Remove horn pad and steering wheel. Remove column covers. Unplug connectors, remove mounting screw and slide switch off column.

Installation — To install, reverse removal procedures.

INSTRUMENT PANEL ASSEMBLY

Removal (200SX) — **1)** Disconnect battery ground cable. Remove steering wheel. Remove steering column covers and combination switch.

2) Remove cover below instruments and disconnect air duct. Remove lower left switch assembly. Remove 8 screws on console (2 inside rear ashtray). Slide box rearward. Remove parking brake handle. Lift console out.

3) Disconnect wiring at junction block. Disconnect speedometer cable and antenna. Remove heater control screws and 2 center floor bolts. Remove defroster grille. Remove 4 screws across top of panel and 2 screws at each end. Remove instrument panel assembly from vehicle.

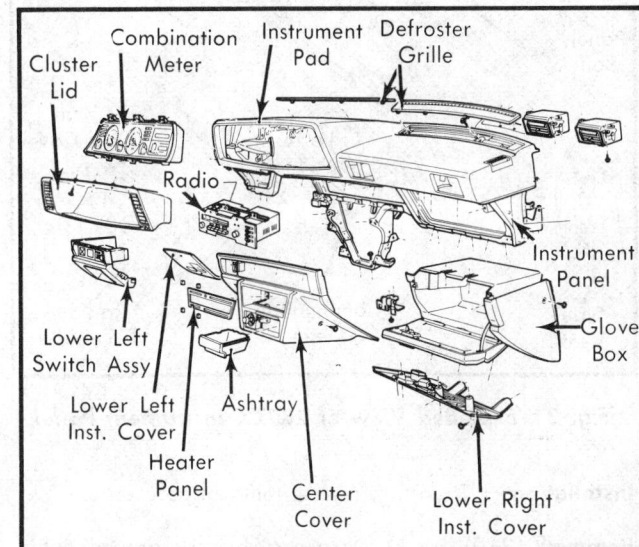

Fig. 1   Exploded View of 200SX Instrument Panel

Installation — To install, reverse removal procedure.

Removal (210) — **1)** Disconnect battery ground cable. Remove steering wheel pad and wheel. Remove steering column cover. Remove panel light dimmer. Pull out heater knob and remove heater bezel. Remove heater screws.

2) Pull off radio knobs and remove shaft nuts. Pull out ashtray and remove holder screws. Remove 3 screws above instruments, 1 screw on each side of column (under dash) and 1 screw at left edge of panel. Unplug all wiring and speedometer cable.

3) Remove left half of instrument panel. Remove retaining screws and lift off combination meter assembly. Gauges can be removed after front bezel and mask are taken off.

Installation — To install, reverse removal procedure.

Removal (280ZX) — Disconnect battery ground cable. Remove horn pad, steering wheel and column covers. Remove combination switch. Remove lower instrument panel covers.

DATSUN (Cont.)

2) Disconnect wiring harness for courtesy lamp. Unplug air conditioner vacuum tube. Remove console bracket covers. Remove 4 screws on each side of radio console and remove console. Remove center ventilation duct cover (5 screws).

3) Remove heater control screws. Disconnect speedometer cable at middle joint. Remove glove box cover and glove box. Remove plugs near windshield and remove 4 instrument panel screws. Remove panel bolts at outer edges. Disconnect wiring and pull panel back and out.

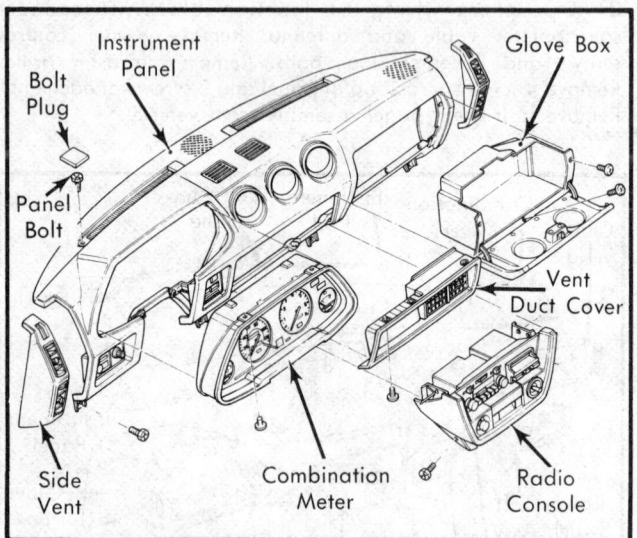

Fig. 2 Exploded View of 280ZX Instrument Panel

Installation — To install, reverse removal procedure.

Removal (310) — 1) Disconnect battery ground cable. Remove horn pad, steering wheel and column cover. Remove lower left cover. Disconnect speedometer cable. Unplug wiring harness connectors.

2) Remove choke knob and nut. Remove heater control knobs and heater control panel screws. Remove 2 bolts at each end of instrument panel. Remove 2 bolts below center of instrument panel.

3) Insert a thin wire between cluster lid and edge below windshield. Pull off cluster mask with wire. See Fig. 3. Remove bolts attaching center of panel to firewall. Remove steering column bracket bolts. Pull panel up and back to remove from vehicle.

Installation — To install, reverse removal procedure.

Removal (510) — 1) Disconnect battery ground cable. Remove steering column covers. Disconnect hazard warning switch. Remove wiper switch. Remove ashtray, heater knobs and heater panel bezel (carefully pry out).

2) Remove plug to left of glove box door. Remove radio knobs and nuts. Remove side defroster control knob. Remove cluster lid screws. See Fig. 4. Unplug wiring for center dash light, rear defogger, lighter, clock and turn signal switch. Remove left cluster lid. Disconnect speedometer cable and remove combination meter.

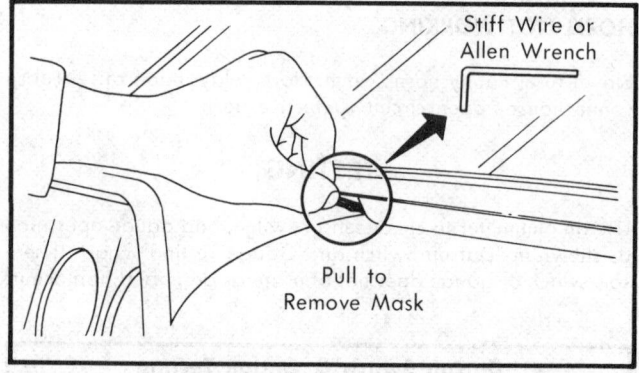

Fig. 3 Inserting Wire to Remove Instrument Panel Mask on 310

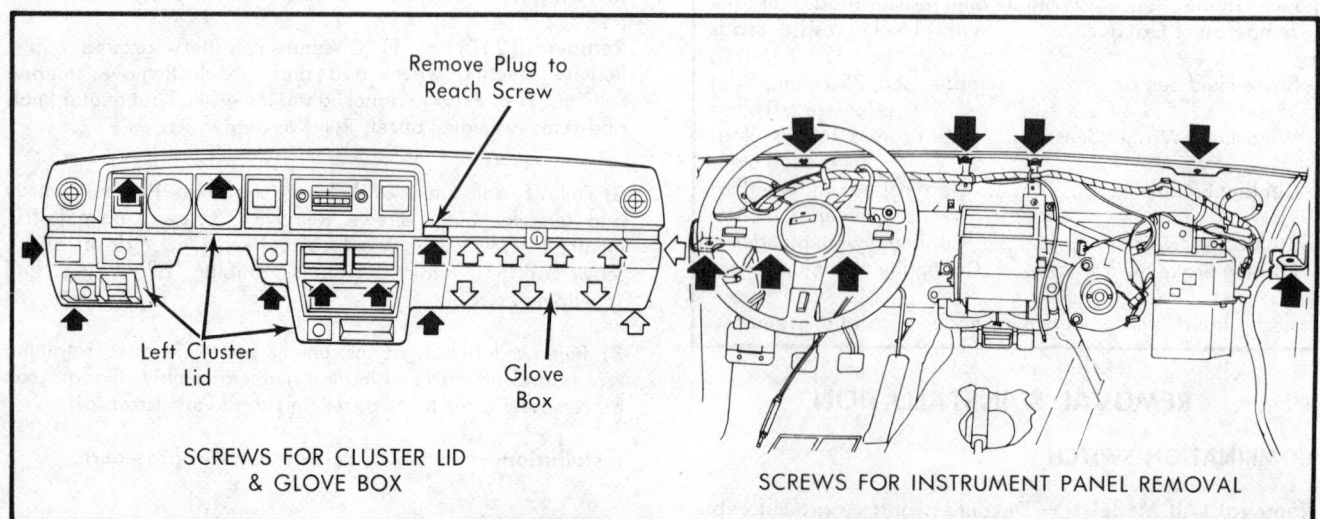

SCREWS FOR CLUSTER LID & GLOVE BOX

SCREWS FOR INSTRUMENT PANEL REMOVAL

Fig. 4 Remove Screws from Locations Shown by Arrows to Remove Cluster Lid and Instrument Panel On 510

DATSUN (Cont.)

3) Open glove box and remove latch screw. Remove glove box screws and remove glove box. Disconnect antenna cable. Unplug instrument connectors at left end of dashboard.

4) Disconnect heater control cables. Unplug heater ground connector. Remove instrument panel mounting screws and remove panel.

Installation — To install, reverse removal procedure.

Removal (810) — **1)** Disconnect battery ground cable. Remove left lower cover. Remove fuse block and unplug wiring from junction block. Remove steering wheel. Remove column covers and combination switch.

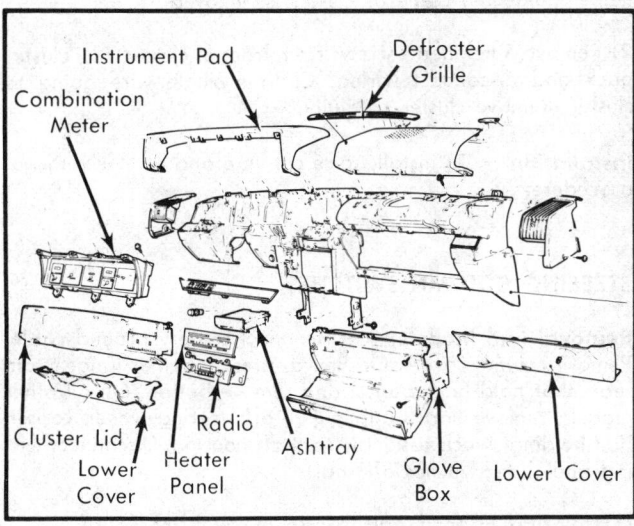

Fig. 5 Exploded View of 810 Instrument Panel Assembly

Labels: Instrument Pad, Defroster Grille, Combination Meter, Cluster Lid, Lower Cover, Heater Panel, Radio, Ashtray, Glove Box, Lower Cover

2) Loosen tilt lever and lower column. Disconnect speedometer cable and antenna cable. Remove choke knob. Remove 5 screws under top edge of cluster pad and 2 screws at bottom ends. Remove pad and cluster bezel.

3) Open console box and remove mat. Remove screw inside box. Remove console. Remove heater contol bezel. Remove heater panel screws and radio. Remove defroster grille and heater nozzle on left side. Remove mounting screws for instrument panel and removal panel.

Installation — To install, reverse removal procedure.

Removal (Pickup) — **1)** Disconnect battery ground cable. Remove steering column cover. Remove package tray (if equipped). Disconnect speedometer cable.

NOTE — *Cluster lid and combination meter can be removed at this point if necessary.*

2) Unplug wiring for center light, rear defogger, lighter, clock and turn signal switch. Remove 3 instrument panel top bolts (under plugs). Remove bolt above parking brake and bolt in glove box.

3) Remove 2 bolts at each end of instrument panel. Remove panel from vehicle.

Installation — To install, reverse removal procedure.

FIAT

Brava
Spider 2000
Strada
X1/9

DESCRIPTION & OPERATION

All models have gauges mounted in a removable cluster. The cluster contains a speedometer, fuel gauge, temperature gauge and tachometer (except on Brava and Strada with automatic transmission). A voltmeter is also included on X1/9 models. A clock and warning lights may be included in the instrument cluster.

Steering column switches are used for the wipers, high beams and turn signals. The other switches are located on the dash panel or console. Most switches snap in and out of the panel.

REMOVAL & INSTALLATION

INSTRUMENT CLUSTER

NOTE — *All models may have a single wire leading to the cluster which does not have a connector. Cut this wire to remove cluster, then splice wire together when cluster is installed.*

Removal (Brava) — Snap out trim plate on left and right sides of cluster. Remove 2 screws holding cluster to panel. Reach under dashboard and release speedometer cable by pulling on cable ring. Disconnect wiring and remove cluster. Snap out switch panel and remove.

Installation — To install, reverse removal procedure.

Removal (Spider 2000) — Reach under dashboard and remove thumb screws which hold cluster. Disconnect speedometer cable. Pull cluster forward and remove. Steering wheel may have to be removed for access.

Installation — To install, reverse removal procedure.

Removal (Strada) — Open hood. Disconnect battery, then remove spare tire and jack. Reach into spare tire well and remove bolt which retains cluster. Remove steering wheel. Release tabs on back of cluster and push cluster out. Unplug wiring and speedometer cable. Remove cluster carefully.

Installation — To install, reverse removal procedure.

Removal (X1/9) — 1) Open hood. Remove left cowl grille. Disconnect speedometer cable at coupling. Remove cable grommet and push cable into firewall opening, or have a helper guide the cable as cluster is removed.

2) Remove 5 hex-head screws from front of cluster. Pull cluster back and disconnect wiring. Cut the single wire going to cluster. Remove cluster carefully.

Installation — To install, spice cut wire and reverse removal procedure.

STEERING COLUMN SWITCHES

Removal (All Models) — Disconnect battery ground cable. Remove column covers. On Brava, press together tangs (from rear) that hold horn button and remove button. On all other models, remove horn buttons. Pull off steering wheel. Loosen bolt holding switch assembly to shaft housing. Disconnect wiring and slide switches off shaft.

Installation — To install, reverse removal procedure.

HONDA

Accord
Civic
Prelude

DESCRIPTION & OPERATION

All models have an instrument cluster that contains a speedometer, fuel gauge and coolant temperature gauge. All models except Civic Hatchback and Wagon have a tachometer. A combination switch on the steering column controls headlights, high beams, turn signals, hazard flashers and wipers. Other switches are located on the instrument cluster edge or instrument panel.

REMOVAL & INSTALLATION

INSTRUMENT CLUSTER

Removal (Accord) — Remove lower cover from beneath steering column. Remove the 2 screws from bottom of gauge housing. Squeeze plastic tab on speedometer cable and pull cable out. Unplug wiring and remove gauge assembly.

Installation — To install, reverse removal procedure.

Removal (Civic Hatchback and Wagon) — 1) Disconnect battery ground cable. Remove steering wheel. Disconnect column wiring harness. Remove bolts from upper bracket and lower bracket of column. Remove lower bolt on universal joint (at steering gear) and remove column.

2) Remove bulb access cover at top of cluster. Remove 2 mounting screws through access cover opening. Remove lower cluster bolt and screw. Pull cluster out part way. Disconnect speedometer cable and tachometer cable (if equipped). Unplug connectors and remove instrument cluster with switches

Installation — To install, reverse removal procedure.

Removal (Civic Sedan) — 1) Remove cover below steering column and remove 2 nuts from upper bracket. Remove 1 screw and coin box/vent. Remove heater control lever knobs and carefully pull off heater panel.

2) Remove 3 heater control bracket mounting screws. Remove 8 instrument panel mounting screws and remove panel. Remove 4 cluster mounting screws and pull gauge assembly part way out. Pull out speedometer and tachometer cables, then unplug connectors. Remove cluster.

Installation — To install, reverse removal procedure.

Removal (Prelude) — Remove 4 instrument cluster cover screws and lift off cover. Remove 4 instrument cluster screws. Squeeze tab on speedometer cable and pull cable out. Unplug wiring connectors. Remove instrument cluster and place speedometer cable out of the way.

Installation — To install, reverse removal procedure.

COMBINATION SWITCH

Removal (All Models) — Remove steering wheel. Pull turn signal cancel sleeve and washer off steering column. Remove column covers. Unplug wiring connectors and remove clamp screw. Remove combination switch.

NOTE — *Steering column can be lowered to improve access if necessary.*

Installation — To install, reverse removal procedure.

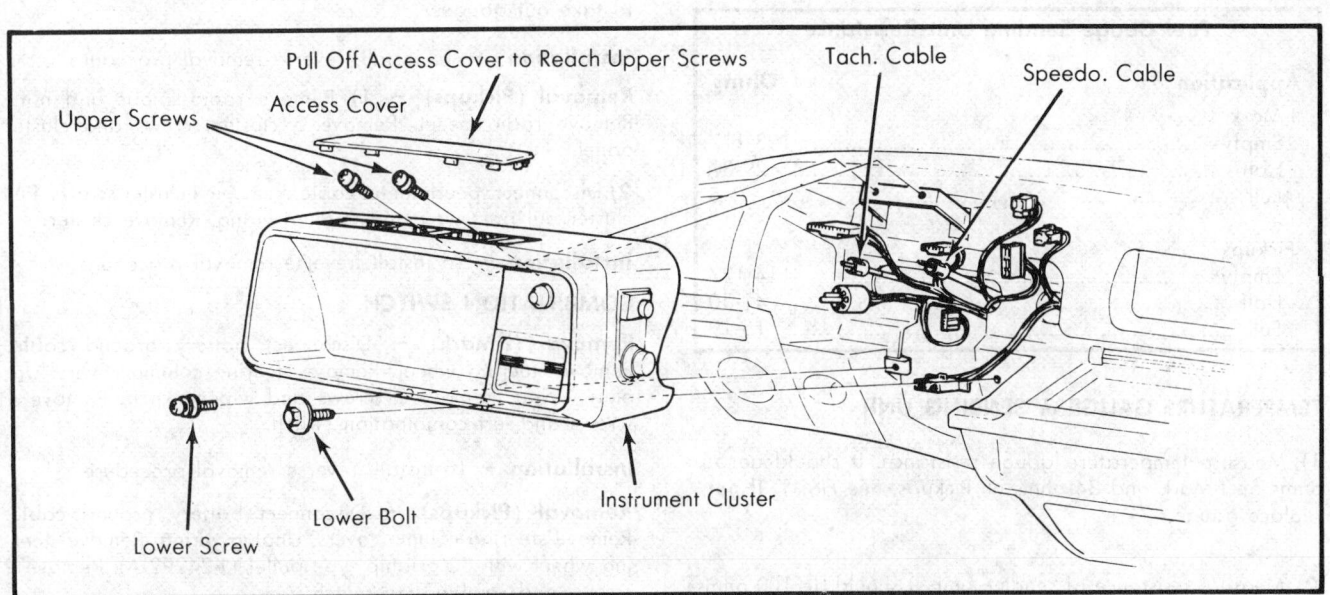

Fig. 1   Removing Instrument Cluster Assembly.

ISUZU & LUV

Isuzu
  I-Mark
  P'UP
LUV

DESCRIPTION & OPERATION

All models have an instrument cluster with speedometer, fuel gauge and temperature gauge. The gauges use variable resistance sending units. A voltage regulator in the cluster ensures readings stay constant when charging voltage varies.

The hazard flashers, windshield wiper/washer and turn signals are controlled by steering column levers. The I-Mark uses 2 combination switches. Pickup models have one switch which controls all functions. All models have a panel-mounted light switch.

TESTING

VOLTAGE REGULATOR

1) The regulator is built into the fuel gauge. Remove gauge cluster and measure resistance of regulator. I-Mark regulator should have 65-75 ohms resistance. Pickup models should measure 110 ohms.

2) Connect voltage regulator to battery and check output. Voltmeter at output terminal should swing above and below 7 volts on Pickup models. It should swing between 0-12 volts on I-Mark. See *Fig. 1*.

FUEL GAUGE & SENDING UNIT

1) Connect ohmmeter to fuel gauge terminals. Resistance should be 50-60 ohms on I-Mark and 25 ohms on Pickups. See *Fig. 1*. If not, replace gauge.

2) Connect ohmmeter to fuel tank sending unit. As float is moved, resistance reading should change smoothly. Check resistance at 3 positions. If readings are not correct, replace sending unit.

Fuel Gauge Sending Unit Resistance	
Application	**Ohms**
I-Mark	
Empty	103-117
Half	29-37
Full	1-5
Pickups	
Empty	114-127
Half	41-50
Full	15-19

TEMPERATURE GAUGE & SENDING UNIT

1) Measure temperature gauge resistance. It should be 55 ohms on I-Mark and 34 ohms on Pickups. See *Fig. 1*. If not, replace gauge.

2) Measure resistance of sending unit. It should be 100 ohms for I-Mark (at room temperature). Resistance on Pickups should be 50 ohms at 176° F (80° C). If not, replace sending unit.

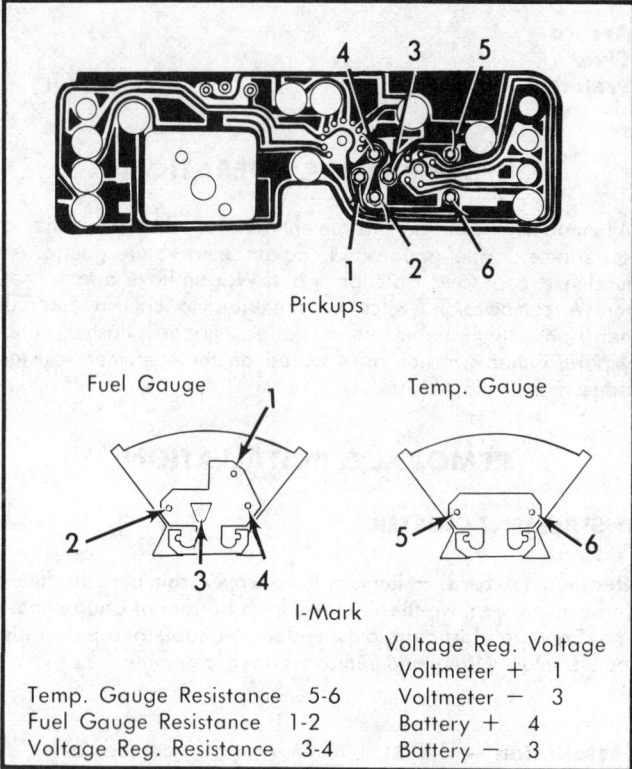

Pickups

Fuel Gauge   Temp. Gauge

I-Mark

Temp. Gauge Resistance	5-6
Fuel Gauge Resistance	1-2
Voltage Reg. Resistance	3-4

Voltage Reg. Voltage
Voltmeter +	1
Voltmeter −	3
Battery +	4
Battery −	3

Fig. 1 Connection Points for Testing Gauges. Be Sure to Use Correct Terminals While Testing.

REMOVAL & INSTALLATION

INSTRUMENT CLUSTER

Removal (I-Mark) — 1) Disconnect battery ground cable. Remove steering wheel. Disconnect speedometer cable and remove wing nut. Remove instrument cluster screws.

2) Rotate left end of cluster out and unplug wiring. Remove cluster. Remove bezel screws and lens. Remove screws or nuts to take out gauges.

Installation — To install, reverse removal procedure.

Removal (Pickups) — 1) Remove radio knobs and nuts. Remove radio bezel. Remove 5 cluster screws and cluster panel.

2) Disconnect speedometer cable. Remove 4 cluster screws. Pull cluster out part way and unplug wiring. Remove cluster.

Installation — To install, reverse removal procedure.

COMBINATION SWITCH

Removal (I-Mark) — Disconnect battery ground cable. Remove steering wheel. Remove steering column covers. Unplug wiring. Remove 2 screws and wiper switch. Remove 4 screws and left combination switch.

Installation — To install, reverse removal procedure.

Removal (Pickups) — Disconnect battery ground cable. Remove steering column covers. Unplug wiring. Remove steering wheel with "C" clamp type puller (J-24292-A). Remove 2 screws and combination switch.

Installation — To install, reverse removal procedure.

MAZDA

GLC
626
RX7
B2000

DESCRIPTION & OPERATION

All models have a steering column combination switch to control turn signals, headlights and wipers. The instrument cluster contains a speedometer, fuel gauge and water temperature gauge. Some models also have a tachometer, voltmeter and oil pressure gauge. The fuel and temperature gauge operate on 7 volts, supplied by a cluster-mounted voltage regulator. The sending units are variable-resistance type and have the same resistance values on all models.

TESTING

GAUGES

1) Turn ignition on. If gauge needles do not move at all, check for blown fuse or broken power wire. If both gauges are inoperative, voltage regulator may be the cause. If only one gauge does not work, the gauge, sending unit, or connecting wiring may be at fault.

2) To test temperature gauge, disconnect sending unit wire. Connect a resistor between wire and ground, then check gauge reading. Change resistance and recheck. If gauge readings are as shown in "Mazda Gauge Testing" chart, replace sending unit. If not, repair wiring or replace gauge.

3) To test fuel gauge, disconnect wire to sending unit at fuel tank (GLC Hatchback, RX7 and B2000) or unplug connector behind left kick panel (GLC Wagon and 626). Connect resistor between Yellow wire and ground. Check gauge reading.

NOTE — *Allow 2 minutes for gauge reading to stabilize. It should be within 1 pointer width of line on gauge face. See Fig. 1.*

4) If gauge readings are incorrect, replace gauge. If readings are okay, test in-tank sending unit before replacing it. Resistance should measure 0-5 ohms with float raised, and 103-117 ohms with float lowered. If not, replace sending unit.

Mazda Gauge Testing		
Gauge	**Needle Position**	**Test Resistor**
Fuel	Fuel Line	7 ohms
	Half Tank	33 ohms
	Empty Line	95 ohms
Temperature①	Hot Line	16 ohms
	Cold Line	233 ohms

① — On GLC Hatchback, resistors should be 12 ohms and 164 ohms.

REMOVAL & INSTALLATION

INSTRUMENT CLUSTER

NOTE — *Removal and installation procedures were not available for B2000 models.*

Removal (GLC Hatchback) — Disconnect battery ground cable. Remove steering wheel. Remove meter hood by moving it up and down with bare hands. Disconnect speedometer cable and remove 4 cluster screws. Pull cluster back and unplug wiring.

Installation — To install, reverse removal procedure.

Removal (GLC Wagon) — 1) Disconnect battery ground cable. Place a strip of masking tape along edge of instrument panel under cluster to protect finish. Remove 2 screws and meter hood.

2) Remove 1 screw at left end of center panel, then unsnap panel. Remove 3 screws under edge of dashboard cover and remove cover. Remove 3 cluster screws, disconnect speedometer cable and wires and remove cluster.

Installation — To install, reverse removal procedure.

Removal (626) — Disconnect battery ground cable. Remove steering wheel and column cover. Disconnect speedometer cable. Remove cluster hood and mounting bolts. Pull cluster back, unplug wiring and remove cluster.

Installation — To install, reverse removal procedure.

Removal (RX7) — Disconnect battery ground cable. Remove steering wheel. Remove 2 screws and cluster cover. Remove attaching screws, disconnect speedometer cable and pull cluster back. Unplug wiring and remove cluster.

Installation — To install, reverse removal procedure.

COMBINATION SWITCH

Removal (All Models) — Disconnect battery ground cable. Remove steering wheel. Remove column covers and snap ring at top of column (if equipped). Unplug wiring connectors. Loosen combination switch screw. Remove switch.

Installation — To install, reverse removal procedure.

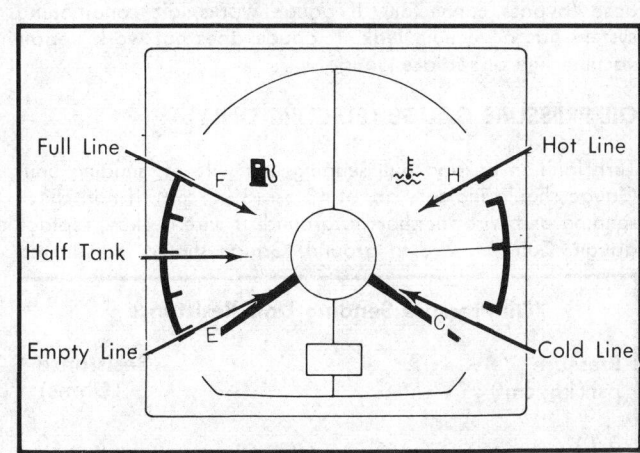

Fig. 1 Gauge Testing Needle Locations. Needle Should Indicate Proper Reading When Test Resistor is Connected

MERCEDES-BENZ

240D
280 Series
300 Series
380 Series

DESCRIPTION

All models have an instrument cluster with speedometer, clock, fuel gauge, oil pressure gauge and temperature gauge. Some models have a tachometer and 380 models have a vacuum gauge. The headlight switch is located on the instrument panel. A combination switch on the steering column lever controls the high beams, turn signals and wipers. Additional switches on the console operate other electrical options.

OPERATION

The speedometer on 300SD and 380SEL models is electronic, with a sending unit in the rear of the transmission. All other models use a cable-driven speedometer. The 300SD and 380SEL models also use an electric oil pressure sending unit, while all other models have an oil pressure line to the instrument cluster. Fuel and temperature gauges on all models use variable resistance sending units. Vacuum gauges are connected directly to the intake manifold by a vacuum line.

TESTING

ELECTRONIC SPEEDOMETER

1) Remove screw and pull sender out of transmission tail housing. Turn ignition on. Place a large screwdriver blade across sender tip. Move blade quickly off and on sender. Speedometer needle should move slightly. If not, remove instrument cluster and unplug connector at back of cluster.

2) Connect negative lead of voltmeter on pin 3 and positive lead on pin 5. Repeat test of sender. If voltage is indicated, speedometer is defective. If no voltage, replace sender and harness.

VACUUM GAUGE

Locate vacuum source hose at 4-way connector near engine. Check for vacuum. If not present, clean vacuum port or repair hose. If vacuum is present, connect directly to vacuum gauge hose (bypass connector). If gauge works, air conditioning system has a vacuum leak. If gauge does not work, repair vacuum line or replace gauge.

OIL PRESSURE GAUGE (ELECTRIC ONLY)

Turn ignition on and pull sending unit wire off sending unit. Gauge should indicate about 43 psi (3 kg/cm²). If not, check sending unit wire for short to ground. If wire is okay, replace gauge. Connect wire to ground. Gauge should indicate no

Oil Pressure Sending Unit Resistance	
Pressure psi (kg/cm²)	Resistance (Ohms)
0 (0)	10
14 (1)	70
28 (2)	130
43 (3)	185

pressure. If reading remains high, sending unit wire is broken. Check resistance of sending unit as indicated in "Oil Pressure Sending Unit Resistance" chart.

FUEL GAUGE

Connect ohmmeter between terminal "G" and 31 on fuel gauge sender. Resistance should be between 2 and 70 ohms, depending upon level of fuel in tank. The higher the fuel level, the lower resistance will be. Connect ohmmeter across terminal "W" and 31. Continuity should exist only if tank is empty (low fuel warning contacts). If sender is okay and wire is good, replace fuel gauge.

REMOVAL & INSTALLATION

INSTRUMENT CLUSTER

Removal (380SL & 380SLC) — Pry out steering wheel center cap. Remove and discard screw. Remove steering wheel. Push top of cluster hood up and insert tool to pull cluster out. Unplug wiring, disconnect speedometer cable and remove oil pressure line. Remove cluster.

Installation — To install, reverse removal procedure. Install new steering wheel screw and tighten to 60 ft. lbs. (80 N·m).

Removal (240D, 280E, 280CE, 300D, 300CD & 300TD) — Push top of hood up and slide in pulling hook. Move hook over to right side of cluster (3 o'clock position) and pull cluster out slightly. Loosen speedometer cable clamp (in engine compartment). Pull cluster back, unplug wiring and remove oil pressure line. Disconnect speedometer cable and remove cluster.

Installation — To install, reverse removal procedure.

Removal (300SD & 380SEL) — Pry out steering wheel center cap. Remove and discard screw. Remove steering wheel. Insert pulling hook at left side of cluster and pull cluster out of spring clips. Unplug wiring and remove cluster.

Installation — To install, reverse removal procedure. Use new steering wheel screw and tighten to 60 ft. lbs. (80 N·m).

HEADLIGHT SWITCH

Removal (All Models) — Pull switch knob off. Remove nut and push switch shaft into panel. Remove cover below instrument panel. Disconnect wiring and remove switch.

Installation — To install, reverse removal procedure.

COMBINATION SWITCH

Removal (300SD & 380SEL) — Pry out steering wheel center cap. Remove and discard screw. Remove steering wheel. Remove cover below instrument panel. Unplug combination switch wiring. Remove screws from switch and pull switch out.

Installation — To install, reverse removal procedure. Install new steering wheel screw and tighten to 60 ft. lbs. (80 N·m).

Removal (All Other Models) — Remove rubber sleeve on switch lever. Remove 2 screws and pull switch out slightly. Remove 2 horn wires. Take off lower instrument panel cover and unplug wiring. Remove switch.

Installation — To install, reverse removal procedure.

PEUGEOT

504
505
604

DESCRIPTION & OPERATION

All models are equipped with an instrument cluster that contains a speedometer, fuel gauge, temperature gauge and tachometer (or clock). Some models are also equipped with a voltmeter. Steering column switches control the lights, wipers, turn signals and cruise control.

The gauges use variable-resistance sending units. When resistance is high, the gauge reads low. When resistance is near zero, the gauge reads high (or full).

TESTING

GAUGES

With ignition turned on, gauge needle should move. Disconnect sending unit wire. Gauge should read low. Connect wire to ground. Gauge should read high. If gauge works as indicated, replace sending unit. If not, check wiring and/or replace gauge.

REMOVAL & INSTALLATION

INSTRUMENT CLUSTER

Removal (505) — Disconnect battery ground cable. Remove steering wheel. Pull instrument cluster out of place. Disconnect speedometer cable and unplug wiring. Remove cluster.

Installation — To install, reverse removal procedure.

Removal (604) — Disconnect battery ground cable. Pull sharply on speedometer cable to disconnect it from cluster. Pull release handle under left side of cluster and unhook right side. Unplug wiring and remove cluster. See *Fig. 1.*

Installation — To install, reverse removal procedure, ensuring that cable clicks into place.

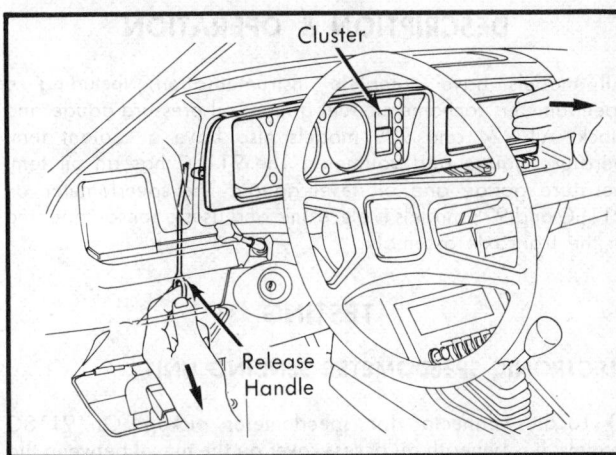

**Fig. 1 Removing 604 Instrument Cluster.
Pull Release Handle and Unhook Right Side.**

COMBINATION SWITCHES

Removal — Remove steering wheel. Remove column covers and unplug wiring. Remove switch screws (if equipped) and remove switch.

Installation — To install, reverse removal procedure.

PORSCHE

911SC
924
924 Turbo
928

DESCRIPTION & OPERATION

All models have complete instrumentation, including a speedometer, tachometer, fuel gauge, oil pressure gauge and clock. All 924 and 928 models also have a coolant temperature gauge and voltmeter. The 911SC has an oil temperature gauge and oil level gauge. The speedometer on 911SC and 928 models is electronic and uses a sensor mounted in the transaxle assembly.

TESTING

ELECTRONIC SPEEDOMETER SENDING UNIT

1) Locate connector for speedometer pickup. On 911SC models, it is beneath an access cover on the tunnel between the rear seats. Connect a test buzzer or voltmeter across the 2 wires.

2) Lift vehicle and rotate right rear wheel, while holding left rear wheel. Buzzer should sound 8 times for each 2 revolutions of the wheel. If vehicle has a limited slip differential, buzzer should sound 8 times for every 1 revolution of the rear wheel. If not, replace sending unit.

3) Make and break the wire connections (between sender and speedometer) as rapidly as possible. Speedometer needle should fluctuate. If not, replace speedometer assembly.

REMOVAL & INSTALLATION

SPEEDOMETER AND GAUGES

NOTE — *Procedure was not available for 911SC models.*

924 & 924 Turbo — Gauges are retained by rubber mounting ring. To remove, press from behind until gauge slides forward out of hole. Remove tachometer and combination gauge, then reach through the openings and pry out speedometer.

Installation — To install, reverse removal procedure.

INSTRUMENT CLUSTER

928 — Disconnect battery ground cable and remove steering wheel. Remove column switch, cover screws, rear wiper switch and defroster switch. Disconnect both 12-pin plugs at cluster. Remove bolt and screw under cluster, then lift and tilt cluster towards rear. Remove mounting bolt on right side and remove cluster.

Installation — To install, reverse removal procedure.

STEERING COLUMN SWITCH

NOTE — *Procedure was not available for 911SC models.*

924 & 924 Turbo — Remove steering wheel. Remove 4 screws and turn signal switch, then pull off wiper switch. Remove snap ring and bearing to access ignition switch housing.

Installation — To install, reverse removal procedure.

928 — Remove steering wheel. Remove cover under steering column switch. Loosen switch mounting screw and cluster cover screws. Lift cluster cover, unplug wiring, and slide off column switch.

Installation — To install, reverse removal procedure.

RENAULT

Le Car
18i

DESCRIPTION

Le Car models have an instrument cluster with speedometer and fuel gauge. All warning lights are also in the cluster. The headlights, turn signals, and wipers and controlled by 3 steering column levers. The 18i can be equipped with 2 different instrument clusters. One contains a clock, speedometer, fuel and temperature gauge (Custom model). The other has a speedometer, tachometer, temperature gauge, fuel gauge, and an oil level gauge (Deluxe model). Three steering colunm levers are used on all models to control lights, turn signals and wipers. Other switches are on the console or instrument panel.

OPERATION

OIL LEVEL SENSOR

The oil level sensor uses a probe whose resistance changes when it is in a liquid. When the ignition is on and there is no oil pressure, the sensor and a control box compute the oil level and display it on a gauge. As soon as the oil light goes off, the sensor turns off. The sensor can be removed from the side of the crankcase. The control box is behind the instrument cluster.

REMOVAL & INSTALLATION

INSTRUMENT CLUSTER

Removal (Le Car) — Disconnect battery ground cable. Remove speedometer cable clip in engine compartment so cable will be slack. Pull off instrument cluster trim. Press side retaining clips back and pull cluster out. Remove speedometer cable and wiring plugs from cluster. Remove cluster.

Installation — To install, reverse removal procedure.

Removal (18i Custom) — Disconnect battery ground cable. Remove steering column covers. Remove 2 screws under lower front edge of cluster. Unplug wiring and speedometer cable. Carefully insert a screwdriver at top of cluster and pry out at top, while pushing in at the bottom of cluster. Tilt top of cluster out and remove.

Installation — Insert panel so notches pivot on the pins at each side of cluster opening. Tilt cluster back and install 2 screws. Connect wiring and speedometer cable, then install column covers.

Removal (18i Deluxe) — Disconnect battery ground cable. Remove trim covers from each side of cluster. Remove screw at each side. Remove cluster hood. Disconnect switches. Squeeze panel clips and pull cluster out. Unplug wiring and remove cluster.

Installation — To install, reverse removal procedure. Push cluster in hard enough to snap speedometer cable into place.

COMBINATION SWITCH

Removal (Le Car) — Disconnect battery ground cable. Remove instrument cluster screws and column lower cover. Remove 4 switch screws, unplug wiring and remove switch.

Installation — To install, reverse removal procedure.

Removal (18i) — Disconnect battery ground cable. Remove steering wheel and column covers. Remove holding bolt and screw. Unplug wiring and pull switch off. Light switch can be separated from the wiper/turn signal assembly by driving out the pivot pin.

Installation — To install, reverse removal procedure.

ACCESSORIES & EQUIPMENT

SAAB

900
900 Turbo

DESCRIPTION & OPERATION

The instrument cluster contains a speedometer, tachometer, fuel gauge, temperature gauge and clock. Turbo models also have a boost gauge. The control switches are located on the steering column or the instrument panel. The ignition switch is located between the front seat on the floor.

NOTE — *The speedometer cable and most instrument cluster bulbs can be changed by removing the left speaker/defroster grille.*

REMOVAL & INSTALLATION

INSTRUMENT PANEL & HEADLIGHT SWITCH

Removal — 1) Disconnect battery ground cable. Remove steering wheel. Remove 4 screws under edge of instrument panel. Tilt instrument panel back.

CAUTION — *The screws are different lengths. Note positions of screws as instrument panel will be damaged by installing screws in the wrong places.*

2) Remove left speaker/defroster grille. Reach in opening and unplug wiring connectors. Disconnect speedometer cable. Remove instrument panel with switches. Remove cluster screws and remove cluster.

INSTRUMENT PANEL LOWER PAD

Removal — Remove lower steering column cover. With engine hood open, remove nut at each edge of lower pad. Remove ashtray. Remove screw inside ashtray opening and remove lower pad.

Installation — To install, reverse removal procedure.

COMBINATION SWITCH

Removal — Remove steering column lower cover. Remove screws under steering column and slide switch bracket off column. Unplug wiring and remove switch.

Installation — To install, reverse removal procedure.

SUBARU

DL
GL
GLF

DESCRIPTION

Subaru models may be equipped with either of 2 dashboards. The DL models have a speedometer with fuel and temperature gauges. The GL and GLF models also have a tachometer, oil pressure gauge and voltmeter. The steering column lever operates the turn signals and headlight dimmer. Rotary switches on either side of the instrument cluster control the lights and wipers.

OPERATION

Fuel and temperature gauges use a regulated 7 volt supply to ensure accurate readings. The voltage regulator is in the fuel gauge. The oil pressure gauge does not have a regulated voltage supply and operates on 12 volts. All the gauges use variable-resistance sending units.

TESTING

FUEL GAUGE

1) Turn ignition off. If gauge does not drop below "E", replace it. Turn ignition on. Check temperature gauge operation. If temperature gauge does not work, check fuel and wiring to terminal 21 on the back of instrument cluster.

2) Unplug fuel tank sender. Connect a 7 ohm resistor between sending unit wire and ground. Fuel gauge should read "F". If so, replace fuel tank sending unit. If not, check for 7 volts at sending unit wire.

3) If voltage is present at sending unit wire, replace fuel gauge. If not, check for 7 volts at terminal 9 (Black/Yellow wire) at back of instrument cluster. If voltage is present, repair wiring to fuel sending unit. If no voltage, replace temperature gauge.

TEMPERATURE GAUGE

1) Turn ignition off. If gauge needle does not drop below "C", replace it. Turn ignition on and check fuel gauge operation. If fuel gauge does not work check fuse and wiring to terminal 21 on back of instrument cluster.

2) Unplug temperature sending unit wire at sending unit. Connect a 52 ohm resistor between wire and ground. Temperature gauge should indicate about 190° F (86° C). If so, replace sending unit. If not, check for 7 volts at sending unit wire.

3) If voltage, is present, replace temperature gauge. If no voltage is present at sending unit wire, check for 7 volts at terminal 8 of 12-pin connector on instrument cluster (Yellow/Green wire). If voltage is present, repair wiring to sending unit. If no voltage, replace temperature gauge.

OIL PRESSURE GAUGE

1) Turn ignition off. Gauge needle should drop. If not, replace gauge. Turn ignition on. Check for power at terminals 29 (Black/White wire) and 32 (Yellow/Black wire) at back of cluster. If voltage is not present, repair fuse or wiring.

2) If voltage is present, check gauge operation. If inaccurate, unplug wire from sending unit. Connect a 140 ohm resistor bet-

ween wire and ground. Gauge should indicate about 55 psi. If so, replace sending unit. If not, replace gauge.

VOLTMETER

1) Turn ignition off. If voltmeter needle does not drop, replace voltmeter. Turn ignition on. If needle does not rise, check fuse. If fuse is good, check for battery voltage at terminal 35 (Black/White wire) at back of cluster. If no voltage, repair wiring to cluster.

2) If voltage is present at meter, turn off all accessories and connect a fully-charged battery. If meter does not indicate 11.5-12.5 volts, replace it.

REMOVAL & INSTALLATION

INSTRUMENT CLUSTER & SWITCHES

Removal — 1) Disconnect battery ground cable. Remove steering column bracket bolts and drop column down. Remove screws from cluster cover. On GL and GLF models, screws are hidden inside vents on either side of cluster.

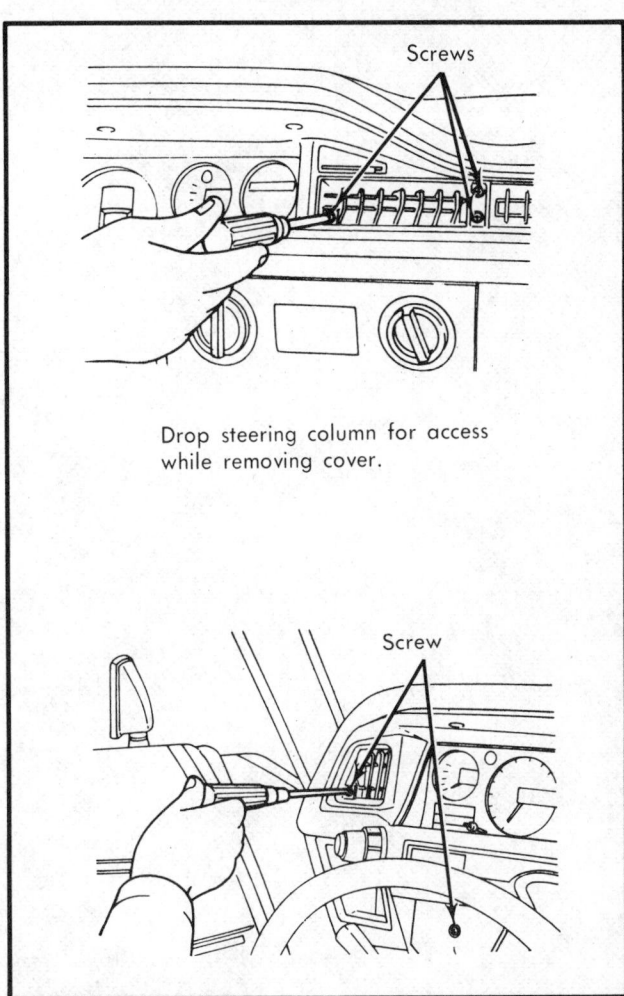

Drop steering column for access while removing cover.

Fig. 1 Screw Locations for Removing GL & GLF Instrument Cluster Cover

2) Pull off ventilation knobs and remove passing light switch (if equipped). Unplug electrical wiring from cover and remove cover, with switches.

SUBARU (Cont.)

3) Remove cluster screws. Pull cluster forward and disconnect wiring and speedometer cable. Remove cluster.

Installation — To install, reverse removal procedure.

COMBINATION SWITCH

Removal — Remove steering column bracket screws and pull down steering column. Remove horn pad and steering wheel. Remove steering column cover screws. Unplug wiring connectors. Remove combination switch.

Installation — To install, reverse removal procedure.

Subaru Gauge Sending Unit Resistance		
Gauge	Reading	Resistance (Ohms)
Fuel①	Empty	95
	Half Tank	33
	Full	7
Temperature①	190° F (86° C)	52
	230° F (110° C)	24
Oil Pressure	55 psi	140
① — Internal resistance of gauge is 45 ohms.		

TOYOTA

Celica
Corolla
Corona
Cressida
Land Cruiser

Pickup
Starlet
Supra
Tercel

DESCRIPTION & OPERATION

GAUGES

All models have a cluster which includes a speedometer, temperature gauge and fuel gauge. The fuel gauge may also have a low fuel warning light. Some models are equipped with a tachometer, oil pressure gauge and voltmeter. A low brake fluid warning light is used on most models.

Gauges may be either the bimetal type or coil type. Testing procedures for the two types vary slightly. All sending units for gauges are variable resistance type.

SWITCHES

All models have a combination switch on the steering column. The switch controls the headlights, turn signals, wipers, hazard flashers and high beams. The switch can be removed and component switches replaced.

TESTING

FUEL GAUGE & WARNING LIGHT

1) Unplug connector at fuel tank sending unit. Connect a 3.4 watt test lamp between Yellow/Red wire and ground. Turn ignition on. Bulb should start flashing and needle should vibrate.

2) Connect ohmmeter to sending unit terminal and ground. Move sender arm and check that resistance varies smoothly. Pointer of gauge should move when sender is connected to it and float arm is moved.

Fuel Sending Unit Resistance		
Model	Float Position	Resistance (Ohms)
Land Cruiser	Full	15-19
	Half	35-45
	Empty	113-127
All Other Models	Full	1-5
	Half	28-37
	Empty①	102-118

① — Pickup models are 92-108 ohms.

3) With gauge connector in place and ignition on, check for voltage at gauge terminals. At one terminal, 2-7 volts should be present. Check gauge resistance by measuring across terminals. Be sure ignition is off and connector unplugged.

4) To check low fuel warning light sensor, remove fuel sender from tank. Connect battery voltage to sensor terminal. Connect a 3.4 watt test lamp between body of sending unit and ground. With sensor dry, light should come on within 40 seconds. With sensor in gasoline or water, light should not come on.

Fuel & Temperature Gauge Internal Resistance			
Model	Terminal Conn.	Fuel (Ohms)	Temp. (Ohms)
BIMETAL GAUGE (2 Term.)			
Celica, Corolla, Tercel			
Starlet & Supra		55	55
Land Cruiser & Pickup		25	25
COIL GAUGE (3 Term.)			
Corolla	IG-U	80	65
	U-E	220	21
	IG-E	300	46
Corona	IG-S	60	125
	S-E	160	160
	IG-E	220	285
Cressida	IG-U	60	95
	U-E	160	110
	IG-E	220	205
Tercel	IG-U	87	91
	U-E	242	90
	IG-E	328	182

TEMPERATURE GAUGE

1) Unplug connector at coolant temperature sender. Connect a 3.4 watt test lamp between wire and ground. Turn ignition on. Bulb should start flashing and needle of gauge should vibrate.

2) Connect ohmmeter between sender terminal and body of sender. Check resistance at several coolant temperture. Replace sender if inaccurate.

Coolant Temperature Sender Resistance		
Model	Temperature °F (°C)	Resistance (Ohms)
Cressida	176 (80)	72
	212 (100)	37
Land Cruiser	122 (50)	226
	240 (115)	26
Tercel	176 (80)	64-84
	212 (100)	36-45
All Other Models	176 (80)	48-52
	212 (100)	27-28

3) Check gauge resistance by measuring across terminals with ohmmeter. Ignition must be off and connector unplugged. Resistance should be as shown in "Fuel and Temperature Gauge Internal Resistance" chart.

OIL PRESSURE GAUGE

1) Unplug connector at oil pressure sender. Connect a 3.4 watt test lamp between connector and ground. Turn ignition on. Bulb should come on and gauge needle should move.

2) Connect one end of test lamp to sender terminal and other end to battery voltage. With engine running, test lamp should flash. Lamp should not light when engine is stopped.

NOTE — Bulb may come on briefly when engine is stopped, but should not remain lit.

TOYOTA (Cont.)

REMOVAL & INSTALLATION

COMBINATION SWITCH

Removal (All Models) — **1)** Disconnect battery ground cable. On Corolla, remove instrument cluster bezel. On Corona, remove fuse block cover and hood release lever. On all models, remove trim under steering column. Remove column covers.

2) Remove horn button and pull off steering wheel. Press in locking tabs on connector and unplug it. Remove mounting screws and combination switch.

3) Remove 2 screws and retainer on light switch. Remove nut and set screw. Be careful not to lose ball and spring from light switch lever. Note position of leads and remove leads from connector.

4) Remove wiper switch, hazard flasher switch and dimmer switch. See Fig. 1. Hazard flasher/turn signal switch cannot be removed on Celica.

Installation — **1)** Install dimmer, hazard flasher and wiper switches. Insert spring in end of arm on light switch. Install nut and screw. Use a small amount of grease to hold ball on end of switch arm, then install retainer.

2) To complete installation, reverse removal procedure.

INSTRUMENT CLUSTER

Removal (Celica & Supra) — **1)** Disconnect battery ground cable. Remove fuse box cover. Remove heater and radio knobs, then pry off heater bezel. Remove cluster bezel and disconnect warning light wires.

2) Remove 3 screws and instrument cluster. Disconnect wiring and speedometer cable.

Installation — To install, reverse removal procedure.

Removal (Corolla) — **1)** Disconnect battery ground cable. On sedan and station wagon models, remove radio knobs. On coupe and liftback models, remove lower cluster trim panel by grasping top and pulling back. Disconnect warning light wiring.

2) On all models, remove instrument cluster trim cover. Unplug wiring and disconnect speedometer cable. Remove screws and instrument cluster.

Installation — To install, reverse removal procedure.

Removal (Corona) — Disconnect battery ground cable. Remove instrument cluster trim panel. Remove screws and pull instrument cluster back. Disconnect speedometer cable and wiring.

Installation — To install, reverse removal procedure.

Removal (Cressida) — **1)** Disconnect battery ground cable. Remove trim panel under cluster. Remove rear wiper switch, antenna switch and instrument light dimmer knob.

2) Remove cluster cover panel. Disconnect speedometer cable. Remove cluster screws and pull cluster out. Unplug wiring and remove cluster.

Installation — To install, reverse removal procedure.

Removal (Land Cruiser) — Disconnect battery ground cable. Remove cluster screws and pull cluster out. Disconnect speedometer cable and wiring. Remove cluster.

Installation — To install, reverse removal procedure.

Removal (Pickup) — Disconnect battery ground cable. Remove steering column covers. Remove 5 screws and cluster finish panel. Remove screws and pull cluster out. Disconnect wiring and speedometer cable. Remove cluster.

Installation — To install, reverse removal procedure.

Removal (Starlet) — Disconnect battery ground cable. Remove instrument cluster hood. Disconnect speedometer cable. Remove cluster screws, pull cluster back and unplug wiring. Remove cluster.

Installation — To install, reverse removal procedure.

NOTE — Removal and installation procedures for Tercel were not available.

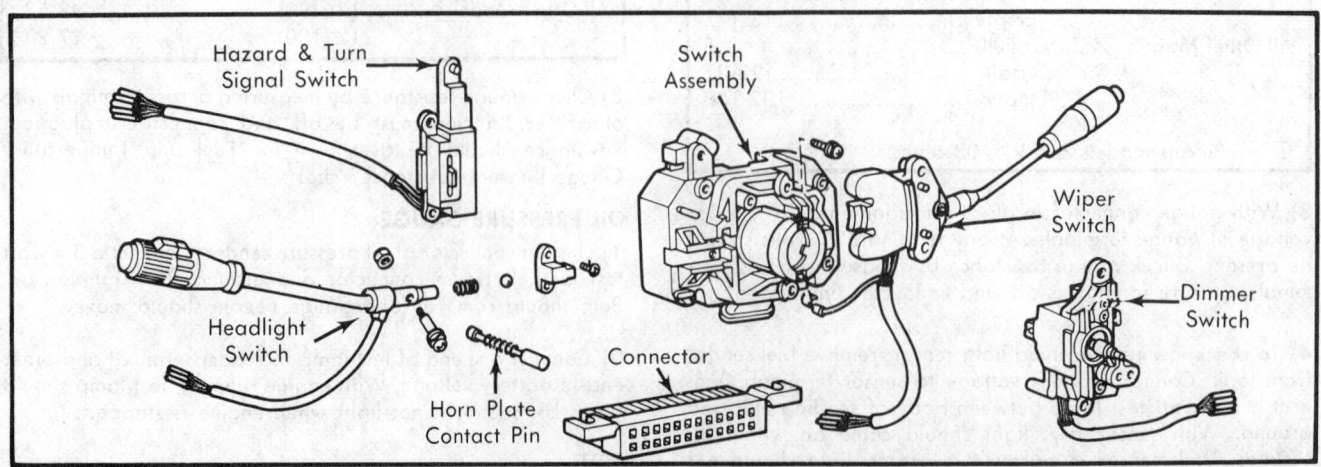

Fig. 1 Exploded View of Combination Switch

TRIUMPH

TR7
TR8

DESCRIPTION & OPERATION

The instrument cluster contains a speedometer, tachometer, clock, voltmeter, temperature gauge and fuel gauge. The instruments use a magnetic coil system and do not have a voltage limiter. Variable resistance sending units are used with the temperature and fuel gauges. The fuel block and most relays are located behind the glove compartment. Control switches are located on 2 steering column levers and the center of the instrument panel.

REMOVAL & INSTALLATION

INSTRUMENT CLUSTER

Removal — 1) Carefully pry the center dashboard grille up out of dashboard. Remove 4 screws along top of cluster hood. Remove the screw which holds the hood to bracket above switch panel. *See Fig. 1.* Remove screw at each end of hood and lift hood up and off.

2) Remove steering column covers. Loosen nuts on odometer trip reset and clock reset cables. Slide cables out of bracket slot under instrument cluster. Disconnect speedometer cable. Remove 4 cluster screws and pull panel out slightly. Unplug wiring and remove cluster.

NOTE — *Instruments can be removed by taking out 3 screws at top of cluster, then sliding out the lens and bezel. Remove instrument screw on back of panel and lift out instrument.*

Installation — To install, reverse removal procedure.

COMBINATION SWITCH

Removal — Disconnect battery ground terminal. Remove steering column covers. Pull off horn pad and remove steering

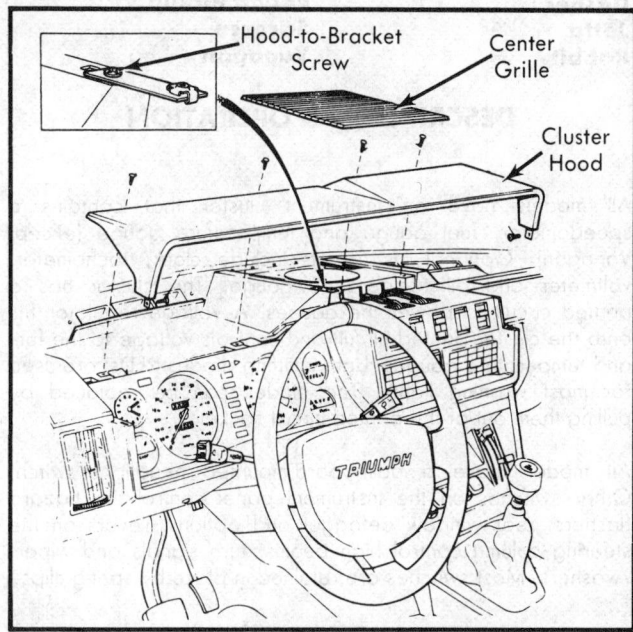

Fig. 1   Removing Instrument Cluster Hood.
Remove 4 Screws at Top, 2 at Ends and 1 at Center

wheel. Note wiring location, then unplug connectors and unclip wiring. Remove switch screw and pull switch off column.

Installation — To install, reverse removal procedure. Ensure that arrow on turn signal cancelling cam is aligned with turn signal lever.

SWITCH PANEL

Removal — Remove screws at each end of panel. Remove cluster hood screw at right end of hood. Push hood up slightly and pull switch panel out. Note wiring connections, then unplug and remove switches.

Installation — To install, reverse removal procedure.

VOLKSWAGEN

Dasher	Rabbit Pickup
Jetta	Scirocco
Rabbit	Vanagon

DESCRIPTION & OPERATION

All models have an instrument cluster that contains a speedometer, fuel gauge and temperature gauge (except Vanagon). Optional instruments include clock, tachometer, voltmeter and oil temperature gauge. The cluster has a printed circuit to power the gauges. A voltage regulator fits onto the cluster printed circuit and controls voltage to the fuel and temperature gauges. Light emitting diodes (LEDs) are used for most warning lights. The diodes can be replaced by pulling them out of the printed circuit socket.

All models have a dashboard-mounted headlight switch. Other switches on the instrument panel control the hazard flashers, rear window defogger and options. Levers on the steering column control high beams, turn signals and wiper-/washers. Most switches are retained in place by spring clips.

TESTING

VOLTAGE REGULATOR

1) If both fuel and temperature gauges are inoperative, voltage regulator may be faulty or have a bad ground connection. If only one gauge is inoperative, regulator is not the problem.

2) Partially remove instrument cluster. Position cluster so regulator can be reached with voltmeter probes, but leave chassis harness connected. Check to ensure ground screw on regulator is tight.

3) Turn ignition on. Connect voltmeter negative lead to center terminal of regulator. Connect positive lead to each of the other terminals. Battery voltage should be present at one terminal and 9.5-10.5 volts at the other. If not, replace voltage regulator.

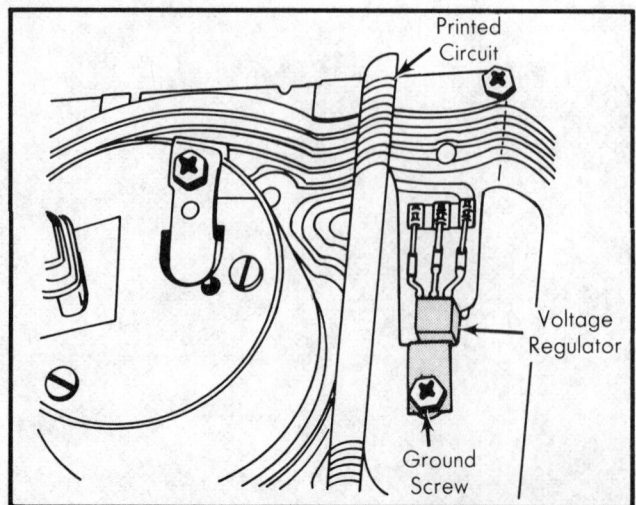

Fig. 1 Testing Voltage Regulator. Place Negative Lead on Center Terminal. Check Voltage on Each Side Terminal. (Vanagon Shown)

FUEL GAUGE

1) Unplug wire fuel tank sending unit. Connect VW tester 1301 between wire and ground. Turn ignition on. With tester set at 60, gauge should show a full tank. With tester at 560 (Vanagon) or 350 (all other models), gauge should show empty.

NOTE — *Tester settings do not indicate resistance in ohms. Resistance values were not available.*

2) If gauge needle does not move at all, check continuity between sender wire and gauge. If needle moves but does not match specifications, replace gauge. If gauge works correctly with tester but not sending unit, replace sending unit.

TEMPERATURE GAUGE

1) Unplug sending unit wire. Connect VW tester 1301 between wire and ground. Turn ignition on. With tester set at 500, gauge should indicate cool. With tester at 60, gauge should indicate hot.

NOTE — *Tester settings do not indicate resistance in ohms. Resistance values were not available.*

2) If gauge needle does not move at all, check continuity between sender wire and gauge. If needle moves but does not match specifications, replace gauge. If gauge works correctly with tester but not sending unit, replace sending unit.

REMOVAL & INSTALLATION

INSTRUMENT CLUSTER

Removal (Dasher) — **1)** Disconnect battery ground cable. Remove radio, pull knobs off heater controls and remove heater panel. Remove 6 screws from instrument panel. Pull panel out slightly and remove headlight, flasher and defogger switches.

NOTE — *Instrument cluster bulbs can be changed without removing cluster. Remove left storage bin and reach through opening above it. Twist bulb holders to remove.*

2) Unplug heater control wiring. Remove instrument panel, leaving cluster in panel support. Remove 2 cluster screws. Disconnect speedometer cable, wiring and indicator lights from cluster. Remove cluster.

Installation — To install, reverse removal procedure.

Removal (Vanagon) — Disconnect battery ground cable. Reach behind cluster hood and pull back of hood up. Pull hazard flasher switch forward. Pull brake warning light housing toward front of vehicle. Remove 4 mounting screws and remove cluster.

Installation — To install, reverse removal procedure.

Removal (All Except Dasher & Vanagon) — **1)** Disconnect battery ground cable. Remove left radio speaker grille and speaker. Pull headlight switch knob out. Reach through speaker grille opening and press button on headlight switch, then pull off headlight knob.

VOLKSWAGEN (Cont.)

2) Remove radio knobs. Remove 6 screws and pull off cluster bezel. Remove 4 screws and pull instrument cluster back. Disconnect speedometer cable and wiring. Remove cluster.

Installation — To install, reverse removal procedure.

COMBINATION SWITCH

Removal (All Models) — Pull off horn pad and remove steering wheel nut. Remove steering wheel. Remove column cover. Unplug wiring and remove 3 switch screws. Remove switches.

Installation — Install switches on column. Place steering wheel on column and check that clearance between wheel and turn signal switch is about $\frac{1}{16}$-$\frac{1}{8}$" (2-4 mm). If not correct, move spacer sleeve up or down. Tighten steering wheel nut to 36 ft. lbs. (50 N.m) and replace pad.

VOLVO

DL
GL
GLT Turbo

GLE
Bertone
Diesel

DESCRIPTION & OPERATION

All models are equipped with an instrument cluster containing a speedometer and combined temperature/fuel gauge. A tachometer or clock is installed in the left side of the cluster. Additional instruments (depending on model) are mounted to the right of the cluster. Warning lights are at the bottom of the instrument cluster.

TESTING

TEMPERATURE AND FUEL GAUGE

NOTE — *Gauge needle should be horizontal ± one needle width in the following tests.*

Both gauges can be checked with a test resistor. Be sure terminal pins are inserted and mounting nuts are tight before testing gauges. Before replacing gauge, check voltage stabilizer, gauge and sender.

Voltage Stabilizer — If one gauge is not working, disconnect the sending unit wire from the other (working) gauge. Connect a 100 ohm 1 watt test resistor (Volvo Part. No. 9995158-4) between gauge and ground. With ignition on, gauge pointer should be horizontal. If not, voltage stabilizer is faulty.

Gauges — Disconnect sending unit wire from suspected gauge. Connect 100 ohm test resistor between gauge terminal and ground. Gauge needle should be horizontal. If so, sender is bad. If not, gauge is faulty.

Fuel Gauge Sending Unit — Fuel tank sender should have a variable resistance between 230-330 ohms (empty tank) and 35-45 ohms (full tank). Resistance should vary smoothly as float is moved.

Temperature Sending Unit — Heat sensor in water and check resistance. It should measure 260-310 ohms at 122° F (50° C) and 55-65 ohms at 212° F (100° C).

SPEEDOMETER

If speedometer works and odometer does not, or odometer works and speedometer does not, the unit is faulty and must be replaced. If both stop working at the same time, speedometer drive gear or cable is usually the cause.

REMOVAL & INSTALLATION

INSTRUMENT CLUSTER

Removal — 1) Disconnect battery ground cable. Remove steering column covers. Remove bracket screws and slide bracket down column. Remove cluster screws. Disconnect speedometer cable. Hold speedometer from rear and press up and out until cluster comes loose. Disconnect wiring and remove cluster.

2) To remove instruments, remove retaining screws and carefully pull off. Voltage stabilizer is removed by pulling straight out.

Installation — To install, reverse removal procedure.

IGNITION SWITCH

Removal — Remove hush panel and console side panel. Disconnect switch wiring. Use a short screwdriver to remove switch.

Installation — Reverse removal procedure.

TURN SIGNAL/DIMMER SWITCH

Removal — Remove steering column covers. Remove 2 retaining screws and lift switch out. Mark wires for installation and remove wires.

Installation — To install, reverse removal procedure.

HEADLIGHT SWITCH

NOTE — *Removal procedures not available from manufacturer.*

Wiper/Washer Systems

AUDI

4000
5000

DESCRIPTION & OPERATION

All models have a 2-speed wiper system with intermittent cycle. The washer pump is located in the side of the fluid reservoir. The system is controlled by the right steering column lever. On 5000 models, moving the lever to the first position selects the intermittent cycle. The second position operates the low speed, and the third selects high speed. On 4000, the lever operates the intermittent feature when it is moved down from rest position. Moving the lever up selects the two constant speeds. Pulling the lever toward the wheel (on all models) operates the washer pump.

REMOVAL & INSTALLATION

WIPER MOTOR

Removal (All Models) — Open hood. Remove cowl cover if necessary. Pry linkage rods off motor crank arm. Remove crank arm nut and 3 motor bolts. Remove crank arm from shaft, then remove motor.

Installation — Install motor on bracket and connect wiring. Run motor and allow it to park. Install crank arm on 4000 models as shown. *See Fig. 1.* On 5000 models, crank arm should be pointing to right side of motor, at a right angle to motor centerline. Install crank arm and motor shaft nut, then slip linkage rods onto crank arm joint.

WIPER SWITCH

Removal (4000) — Remove steering wheel. Remove steering column cover. Remove 3 screws on turn signal switch. Pull turn signal switch and wiper switch from column.

Installation — To install, reverse removal procedure.

Removal (5000) — Remove steering wheel. Insert Phillips screwdriver into slot at bottom of column cover and loosen screw. Pull switch and top of cover assembly off column. Remove 2 screws inside cover to remove switch from cover.

Installation — To install, reverse removal procedure.

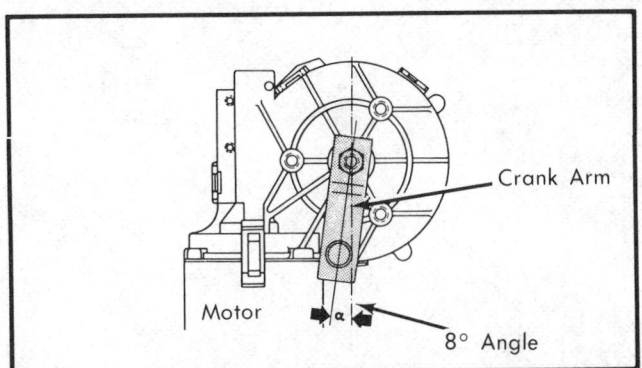

Fig. 1 Wiper Motor Crank Arm Position (4000 Models)

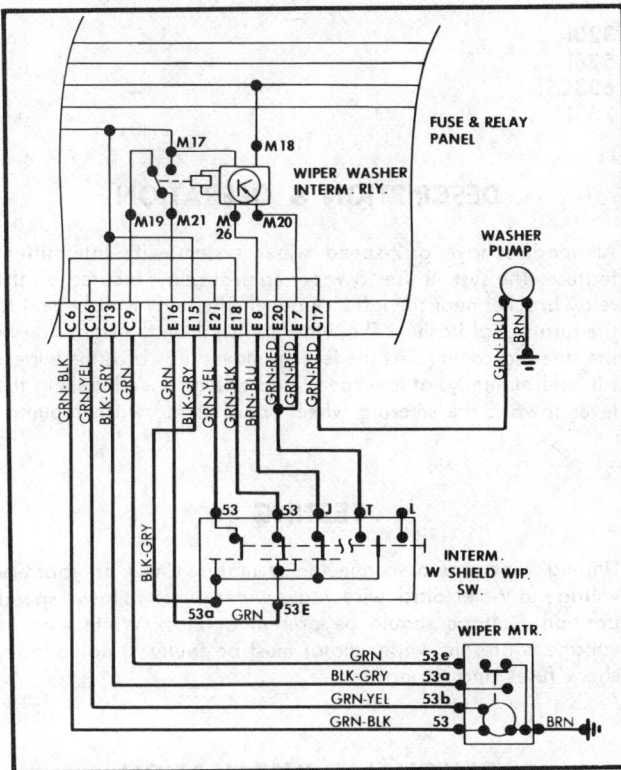

Fig. 2 Audi 4000 Wiper Wiring Diagram

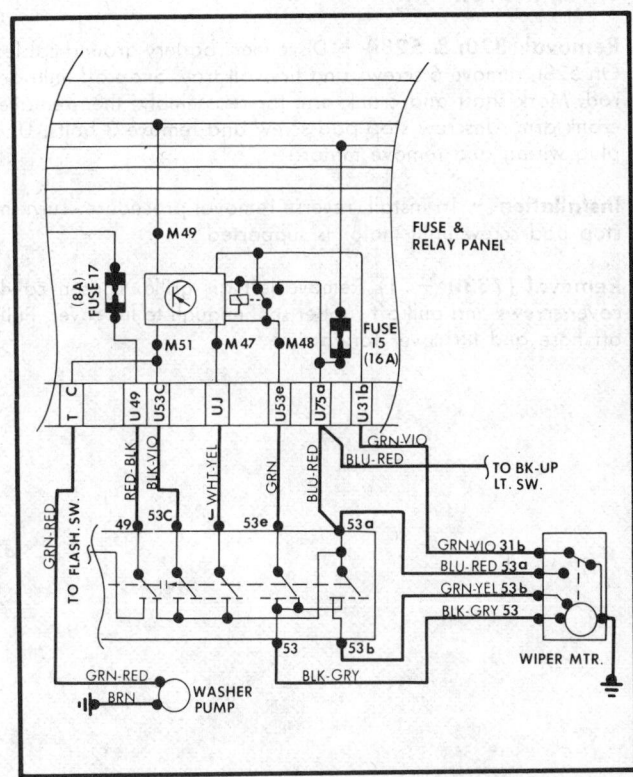

Fig. 3 Audi 5000 Wiper Wiring Diagram

BMW

320i
528i
633CSi
733i

DESCRIPTION & OPERATION

All models have a 2-speed wiper system with intermittent feature. The system uses a wiper control relay, located on the relay bracket near the left kick panel. The relay is right next to the turn signal flasher. The wiper switch is on the right side of the steering column. As the lever is moved upward, the wipers run intermittently, at low speed and at high speed. Pulling the lever toward the steering wheel operates the washer pump.

TESTING

Unplug wiper motor connector at motor. Check for battery voltage at Violet/Black wire. Move wiper switch to lower speed position. Voltage should be present at Black/White wire. If voltage is present, wiper motor must be faulty. If no voltage, check fuses and wiring.

REMOVAL & INSTALLATION

WIPER MOTOR

Removal (320i & 528i) — Disconnect battery ground cable. On 528i, remove 6 screws and firewall tray. Snap off linkage rod. Mark shaft and crank arm for reassembly, then remove crank arm. Unscrew stop pad screw and remove 3 bolts. Unplug wiring and remove motor.

Installation — To install, reverse removal procedure. Turn in stop pad screw until motor is supported.

Removal (733i) — 1) Remove left air grille. Loosen cowl cover screws and pull off rubber seal enough to lift cover. Pull off hose and tilt cover forward.

2) Remove motor cover and unplug wiring. Remove both wiper arms. Unscrew shaft nuts. Turn stop pad screw out. Disconnect linkage to right wiper. Loosen 2 screws at center of cowl and pull linkage apart.

3) Mark shaft and crank arm for reassembly. Remove motor crank arm. Remove 3 screws and wiper motor.

Installation — To install, reverse removal procedure, ensuring that linkage fits properly and stop pad is turned in to support motor.

NOTE — *Procedures were not available for 633CSi models.*

WIPER SWITCH

Removal (All Models) — Remove steering wheel. Remove lower column cover. Remove screws on right side of column and pull switch free. Cut off wiring clips and unplug wiring. Remove switch.

Installation — To install, reverse removal procedure.

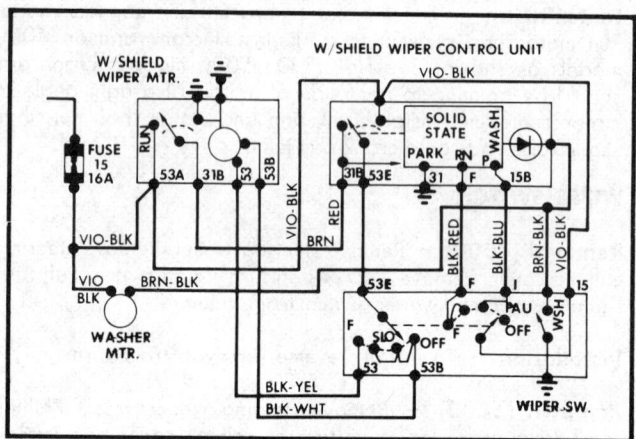

***Fig. 1 BMW Wiper/Washer Wiring Diagram
(All Models)***

CHRYSLER CORP. IMPORTS

Arrow Pickup　　　　**Champ**
Colt　　　　　　　　**Ram-50 Pickup**
Challenger　　　　　**Sapporo**

DESCRIPTION

All models have a 2-speed wiper motor. The washer system uses an electric pump mounted under the fluid reservoir. Challenger and Sapporo models have an intermittent wiper system. Champ and Colt models may be equipped with a rear wiper/washer. On these models, only one washer fluid reservoir is used, but a separate pump under the reservoir is provided for the rear washer.

OPERATION

The wiper systems are operated by a dash-mounted switch on Champ, Colt and Pickups, and by a column-mounted switch on Challenger and Sapporo. The intermittent system cycles the washers every 6 seconds. If the washer switch on this system is held for about 5 seconds, the wipers make 2-4 sweeps and turn off.

TESTING

FRONT WIPER MOTOR

Raise wiper arms so they do not touch windshield. Unplug motor connector. Connect jumper wires as shown in Front Wiper Motor Testing Terminal Connections chart. Replace motor if it does not run smoothly.

Front Wiper Motor Testing Terminal Connections		
Model	Low Speed	High Speed
Arrow & Ram-50		
Pickup	Blue/Wht=12v ...	Blue/Wht=12v
	Blue/Org=Gnd	Blue/Blk=Gnd
Challenger & Sapporo ..	+=12v	+=12v
	1=Gnd	2=Gnd
Champ & Colt	Blue=12v	Blue=12v
	Blue/Red=Gnd	Blue/Blk=Gnd

REAR WIPER MOTOR

Raise wiper arm so motor can operate without load. Connect battery voltage to the Blue wire terminal and connect the Blue/Red wire terminal to ground. Replace motor if it does not run smoothly.

INTERMITTENT RELAY

1) If wipers do not park or operate properly in intermittent position, turn wipers on to intermittent. Insert positive lead of voltmeter into rear of relay connector at terminal 3 and check voltage. Battery voltage should be present when wipers are stopped and no voltage when wipers are operating. If not, replace relay.

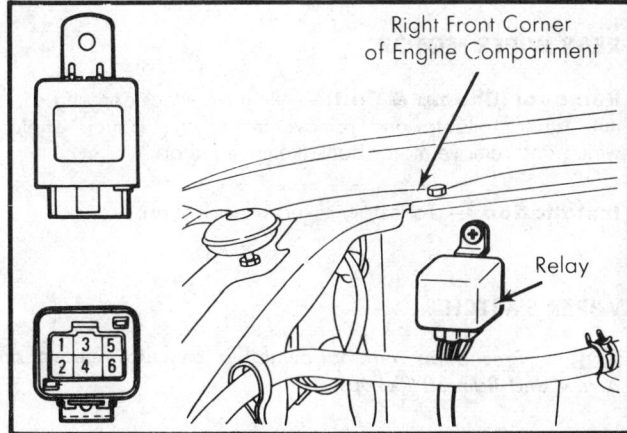

Fig. 1 Intermittent Wiper Relay Location

2) If wipers do not operate at all in intermittent position, connect a voltmeter to relay. Place the positive lead on terminal 1 and negative lead on terminal 4. If battery voltage should be present. Check voltage between terminal 6 and 4, then between 3 and 4. No voltage should be present. If readings are not correct, replace relay.

3) If wipers do not operate with washer switch on, check for voltage between terminal 1 (+) and terminal 4 (-). Battery voltage should be present. With the washer switch on, no voltage should be present at terminal 5. Terminal 3 should have battery voltage for 0.6-1.5 seconds, then drop to zero while wipers operate, then return to 12 volts when wipers stop. If readings are not correct, replace relay.

REMOVAL & INSTALLATION

FRONT WIPER MOTOR

CAUTION — *Do not separate crankshaft and motor unless necessary. Be sure to scribe matching marks on shaft and crank arm before disassembly.*

Removal (Arrow & Ram-50 Pickups) — Remove wiper arm. Remove shaft nut and push shaft into body. Remove wiper access panel on right side of firewall. Remove motor bolts and connector. Snap motor free from linkage.

Installation — To install, reverse removal procedure.

Removal (Challenger & Sapporo) — Lift wiper arm cover and remove shaft nut. Remove wiper arm, seal and nut. Push shaft into body. Unplug motor wiring and remove mounting bolts. Pull motor out and snap free from linkage. Remove motor and linkage. Remove access cover and pull linkage out.

Installation — To install, reverse removal procedure, ensuring that motor is grounded.

Removal (Champ & Colt) — Disconnect wiring at motor. Remove motor bolts and snap motor free from linkage. Remove motor.

Installation — To install, reverse removal procedure.

CHRYSLER CORP. IMPORTS (Cont.)

REAR WIPER MOTOR

Removal (Champ & Colt) — Remove wiper arm and shaft nut. Open tailgate and remove innner trim panel. Unplug wiring and remove motor bolts. Remove motor.

Installation — To install, reverse removal procedure.

WIPER SWITCH

NOTE — *Procedures were not available for switch removal on Arrow and Ram-50 Pickups.*

Removal (Challenger & Sapporo) — Disconnect battery ground cable. Remove steering wheel. Tilt column to lowest positionand remove column cover. Remove column switch screws. Unplug wiring, remove wiring clip and remove switch.

Installation — To install, reverse removal procedure, ensuring that cancel cam pins are aligned with holes in back of steering wheel.

Removal (Champ & Colt) — Remove instrument cluster hood screws. Remove 5 screws holding lower left panel of dashboard. Unplug wiring harness and remove corner panel. Unplug instrument cluster hood wiring and remove hood. Remove switch knob and switch from hood.

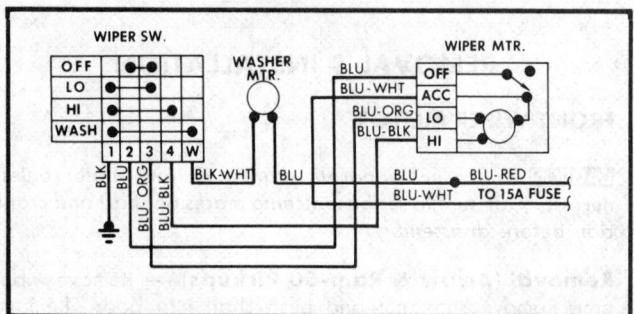

Fig. 2   Arrow & Ram-50 Pickups Wiring Diagram

Installation — To install, reverse removal procedure. Do not overtighten switch screws.

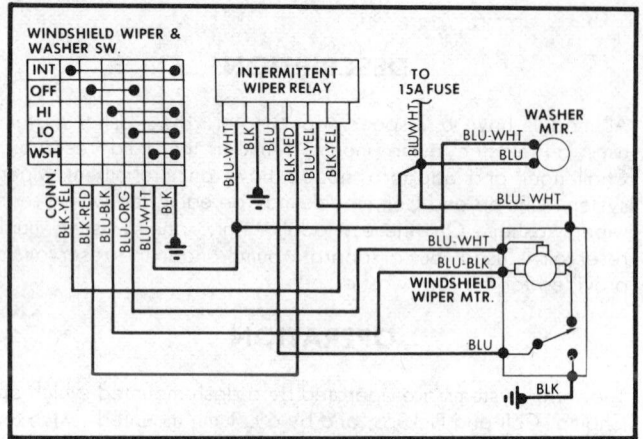

Fig. 3   Challenger & Sapporo Wiring Diagram

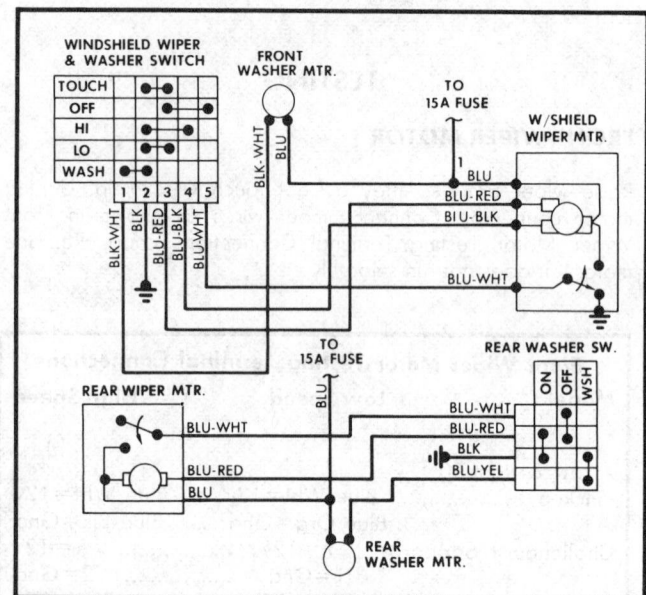

Fig. 4   Champ & Colt Wiring Diagram

COURIER

Pickup

DESCRIPTION

The wiper system includes a 2-speed motor and separate washer pump. The control switch is located on a lever on the left side of the steering column. A 10 amp fuse protects the wiper system.

OPERATION

The wipers are turned on by rotating the control lever. Pushing in on the end of the lever will start the washer pump. The pump should stop as soon as the lever is released.

TESTING

WIPER MOTOR

1) Use a test lamp to check for power at the Blue wire in harness side of main wiring connector. Ignition must be on. If no power is present, check fuse or wiring.

2) Connect a jumper wire between battery voltage and Blue wire in motor side of main connector. When Blue-White wire is grounded, motor should operate at low speed. With Blue-Red wire grounded, motor should operate at high speed. Disconnect ground wire so blades stop in the middle of windshield.

3) Connect a jumper wire between Blue-Black and Blue-White wires. Wipers should move to park position and stop. If motor does not work properly, check ground connection. If it is good, replace wiper motor.

WIPER/WASHER SWITCH

1) Unplug the 2 wiper/washer connectors at base of steering column. Connect one probe of a self-powered test lamp (or ohmmeter) to the Black wire in the 2-pin switch connector.

2) With switch off, no continuity should be present between Black wire and any others. With switch on low, lamp should light at White wire. With switch on high, lamp should light at Red wire. With washer on, lamp should light at Blue wire.

3) If switch does not work as described, replace it.

WIRING TEST

1) Disconnect 4-pin wiper switch connector at base of steering column. Turn ignition on. Connect one end of a jumper wire to ground, then touch the other end to each wire in the harness side of connector.

2) With Blue-White grounded, wipers should operate at low speed. With Blue-Red grounded, wipers should operate at high speed. With Blue-Yellow wire grounded, washer should spray.

3) If motor operates correctly, unplug 2-pin connector and check for continuity with ground on the Black wire (male terminal). If a good ground connection is present and wipers do not function properly, repair wiring harness or replace switch.

REMOVAL & INSTALLATION

WIPER MOTOR & LINKAGE

Removal — 1) Disconnect battery ground cable. Remove wiper arm nuts and wiper arms. Remove cap, nut, spacer and grommet from each wiper arm pivot shaft. Remove 2 wiper motor bracket screws.

2) Unplug wiring and remove wiper motor assembly. Note position of rubber and ground washers. Remove motor link retaining clip. Note position of motor-to-bracket washers, then remove motor.

Installation — To install, reverse removal procedure, ensuring that all washers are placed in their original locations.

COMBINATION SWITCH

Removal — 1) Disconnect battery ground cable. Remove steering wheel. Remove steering column cover. Unplug connectors at base of steering column. Pull off headlight switch knob.

2) Remove snap ring at top of column and pull off turn signal cam. Remove retaining bolt at bottom of combination switch. Remove switch.

Installation — To install, reverse removal procedure.

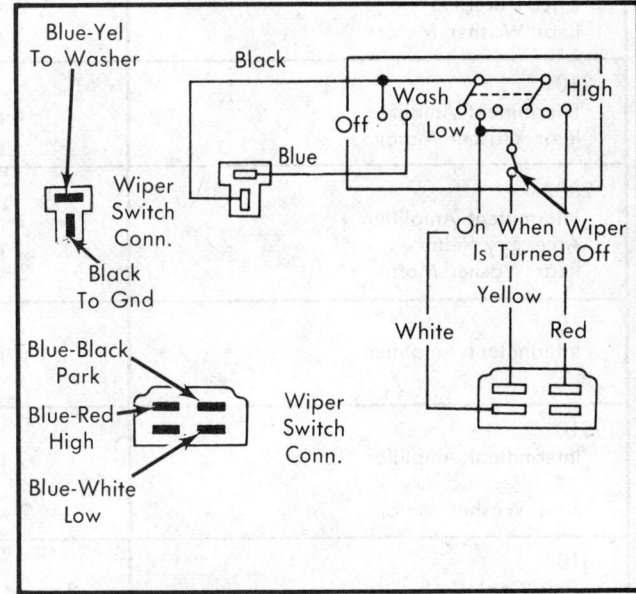

Fig. 1 Courier Wiper/Washer System Wiring Diagram

Wiper/Washer Systems

DATSUN

200SX	510
210	810
280ZX	Pickup
310	

DESCRIPTION & OPERATION

All models are equipped with either 2-speed or intermittent wipers. Hatchback and station wagon models have a rear wiper/washer system, operated by a dashboard mounted switch. All front wiper/washer systems are operated by a steering column lever.

WIPER MOTOR

All wiper motors include an integral park switch inside the motor housing. The motor cover can be removed and the switch adjusted if wipers do not park correctly. Some models have a circuit breaker (mounted externally) to protect the wiper motor.

INTERMITTENT AMPLIFIER

All models except 810 use an intermittent amplifier to control the delayed wiper cycle. The amplifier is a solid-state unit which interrupts current flow to the motor. The time delay is either fixed or adjustable with a knob at the end of the wiper stalk.

All 810 models have a Time Control Unit which controls the delayed wiper cycle. This unit also operates the clock, turn and hazard flashers, seat belt chimes and other circuits.

WASHER

All models have washer systems. A separate pump is used for the rear washer. A rear-mounted reservoir is used on 510 models. All others share a common reservoir for both washer systems.

DATSUN WIPER SYSTEM COMPONENT LOCATIONS		
Model & Component	**Connector**	**Location**
200SX		
Intermittent Amplifier	8-pin	Rear of relay bracket at right front corner engine compartment
Ignition/Accessory Relay	6-pin & 1-pin	Right kick panel
Circuit Breaker	2-wire	Wiper motor connector at cowl
Rear Washer Motor	2-pin	Right front shock tower
210		
Intermittent Amplifier	6-pin	Brake pedal bracket
Rear Washer Motor	2-pin	Behind right front shock tower
280ZX		
Intermittent Amplifier	6-pin	Brake pedal bracket
Accessory Relay	5-pin	Right kick panel top rear
Rear Washer Motor	2-wire	Left front shock tower
310		
Intermittent Amplifier	7-pin	Front of relay bracket at right front corner engine compartment
510		
Intermittent Amplifier	7-pin	Relay bracket at right front corner engine compartment
Rear Washer Motor	2-wire	Left rear corner of car
810		
Time Control Unit	8-pin & 11 pin	Right kick panel at top
Wiper Relay	5-pin	Rear outside corner of relay bracket at right front corner engine compartment
Accessory Relay	4-pin	Front outside corner of relay bracket
Pickup		
Intermittent Amplifier	5-pin	Steering column bracket

DATSUN (Cont.)

FRONT WIPER MOTOR TESTING

Model	Continuity (Motor Off)	Slow Speed Connections	High Speed Connections	Park Switch (On-Off with Motor Running)
200SX	B & L, B & H	B +12v L Gnd	B +12v H Gnd	P & E
210	1 & 2, 2 & 3, 2 & 4,	2 + 12v 3 Gnd	2 +12v 4 Gnd	1 & 5
280ZX	1 & 4, 1 & 5	1 +12v 4 Gnd	1 +12v 5 Gnd	2 & 3, 2 & 6, 7 & 8
310 & Pickup	1 & 4 1 & 5	1 +12v 4 Gnd	1 +12v 5 Gnd	2 & 3
510	1 & 2, 2 & 3, 2 & 4	2 +12v 3 Gnd	2 +12v 4 Gnd	1 & 5
810	B & L B & H	B +12v L Gnd	B +12v H Gnd	P & E

REAR WIPER MOTOR TESTING

Model	Continuity (Motor Off)	Motor Connections	Park Switch (On-Off with Motor Running)
200SX & 810	B & S	B +12v S Gnd	P & E
210 & 510	P & E, S & E	S +12V E Gnd	P & B
280ZX	1 & 4	1 +12v 4 Gnd	2 & 3, 2 & 4
310	1 & 4	4 +12v 1 Gnd	2 & 3, 2 & 4

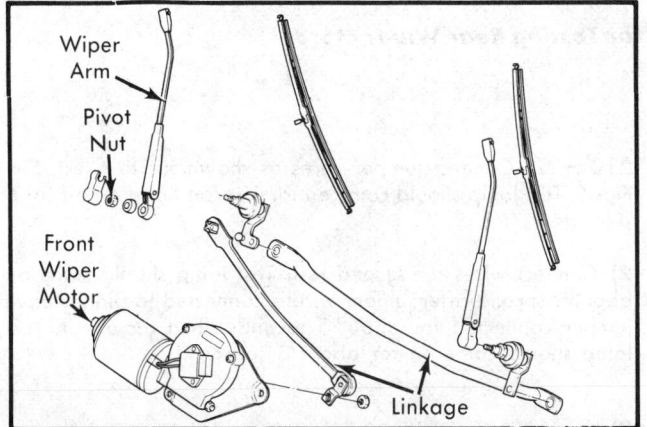

Fig. 1 Typical Datsun Wiper/Washer Components

TESTING

FRONT WIPER MOTOR

Motor can be tested on the car. Unplug connector and use ohmmeter to check continuity with motor stopped. Using jumper wires, test both motor speeds by applying voltage to terminals shown in "Front Wiper Motor Testing" chart. Finally, check park switch operation by connecting ohmmeter across park terminals while motor is running. Switch should open and close. *See Fig. 2.*

REAR WIPER MOTOR

Motor can be tested on the car. Unplug wiring and use ohmmeter to check continuity with motor stopped. Use jumper wires to operate motor by applying voltage to terminals shown in "Rear Wiper Motor Testing" chart. Check park switch operation by connecting ohmmeter across park terminals while motor is running. Switch should open and close. *See Fig. 3.*

Wiper/Washer Systems

DATSUN (Cont.)

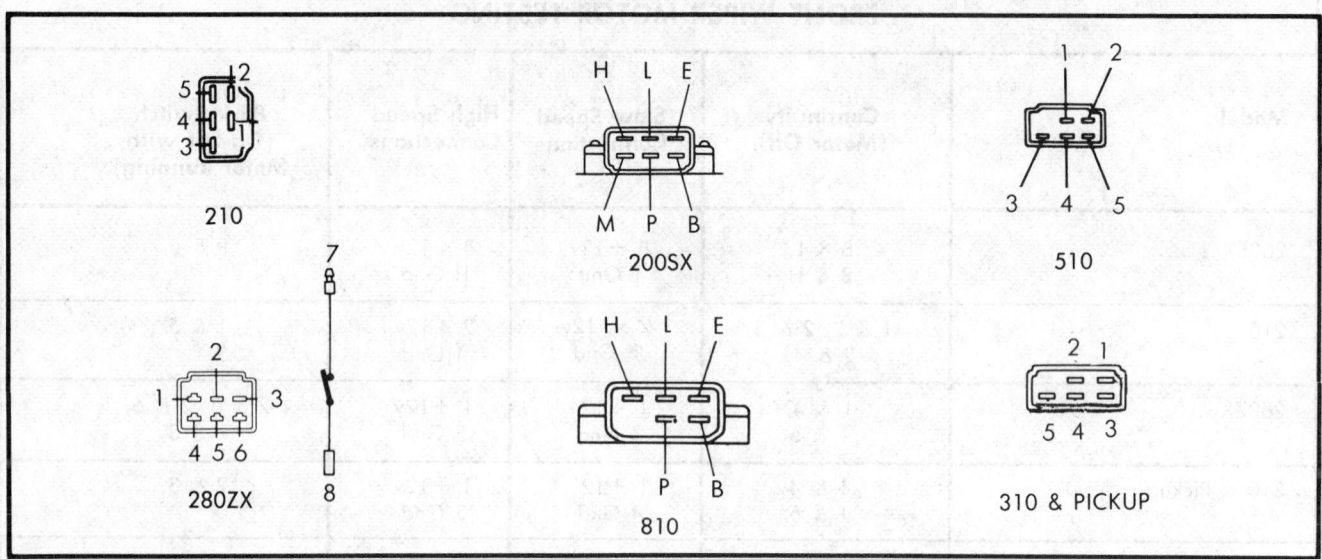

Fig. 2   Terminal Identification for Testing Front Wiper Motor

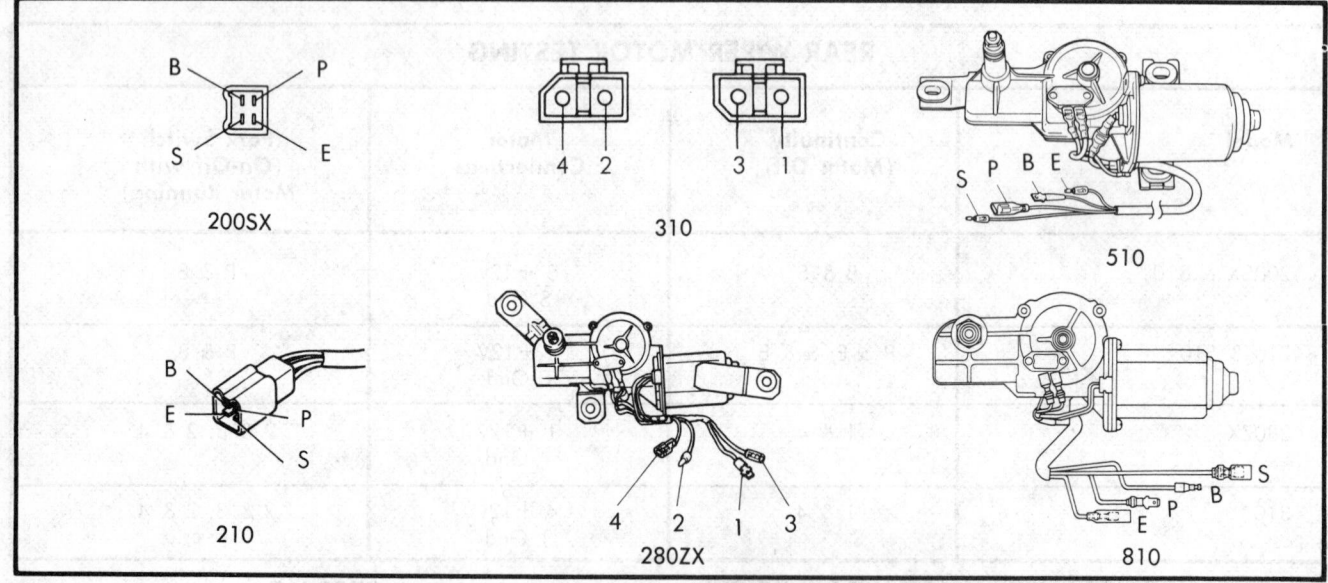

Fig. 3   Terminal Identification for Testing Rear Wiper Motor

INTERMITTENT AMPLIFIER

Remove amplifier from vehicle or position so jumper wires can be connected to terminals. Use care to prevent improper connections since amplifier can be ruined. Connect test lamp and battery as shown in Figs. 4,5,6 & 7. Be sure to use correct test procedures for the vehicle being tested.

200SX & 280ZX — Connect jumper wires to amplifier. See Fig. 4. When wire "A" is connected, test lamp should come on. Disconnect wire "B". Test lamp should go off, then come back on after a few seconds. If not, replace amplifier.

210 — 1) Connect jumper wires as shown for first test. See Fig. 5. Test lamp should come on for 1 second and go off for 6 seconds.

2) Connect wires for second test. Test lamp should come on about 1 second after jumper wire is connected to pin 2. Leave jumper connected for about 5 seconds, then remove it. Test lamp should come on for about 3 seconds.

3) If amplifier fails either test, replace it. Check system operation in all models.

DATSUN (Cont.)

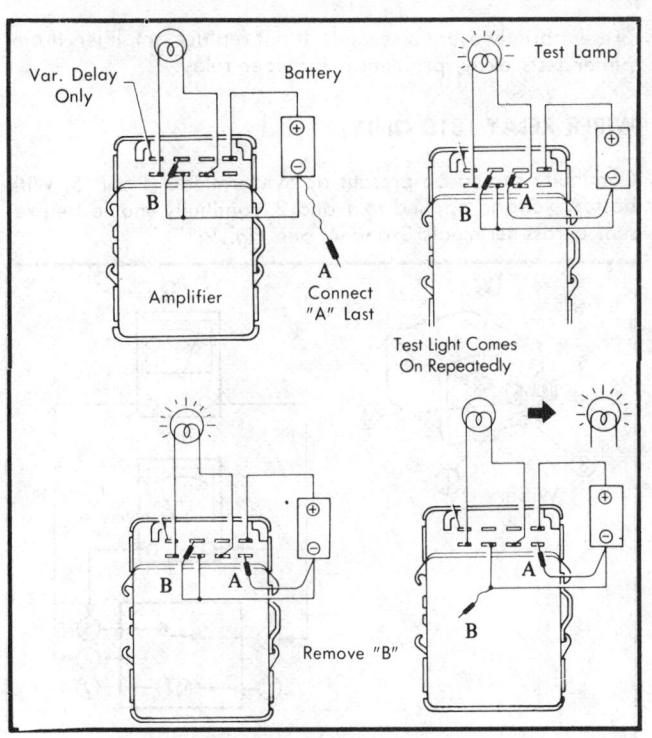

Fig. 4 Jumper Wire Connections for Testing 200SX & 280ZX Intermittent Amplifier

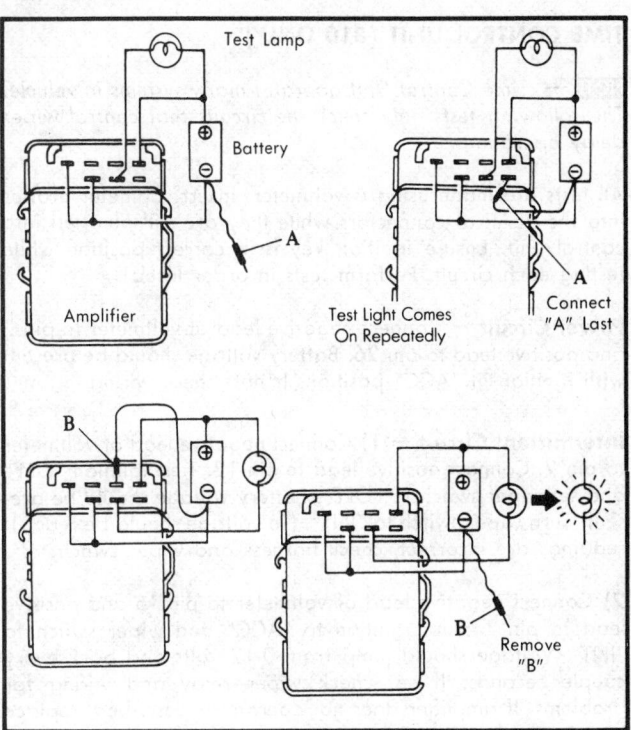

Fig. 6 Jumper Wire Connections for Testing 310 & 510 Intermittent Amplifier

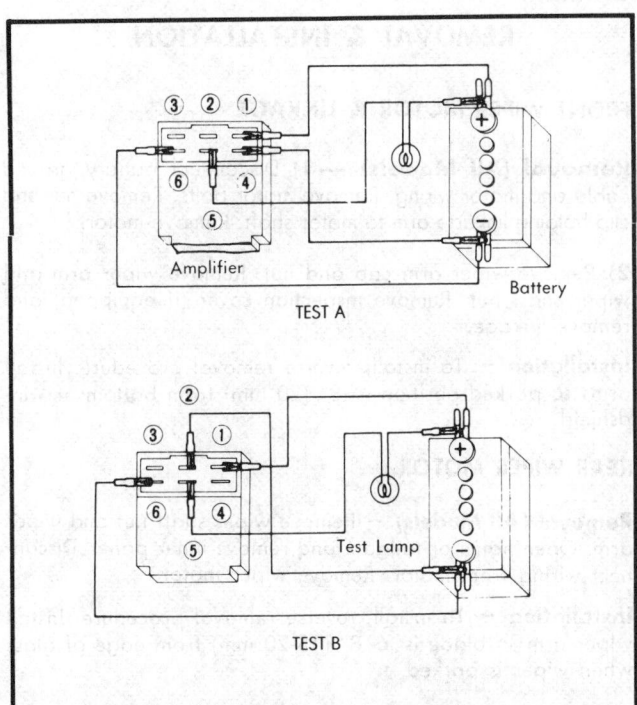

Fig. 5 Jumper Wire Connections for Testing 210 Intermittent Amplifier

Pickup — Connect jumper wires to amplifier. See *Fig. 7.* Test lamp should come on when wire is connected to pin 3. Disconnect jumper wire from pin 2. Test lamp should go off, then come back on after 6 seconds. If not, replace amplifier.

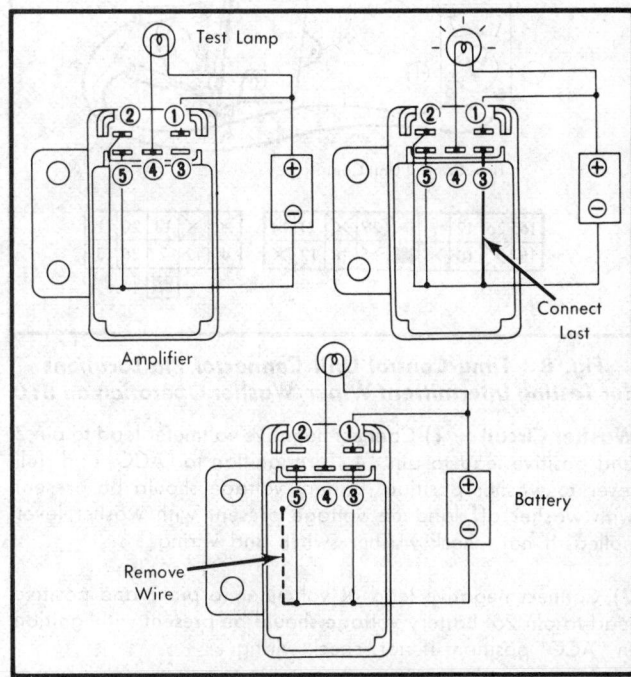

Fig. 7 Jumper Wire Connections for Testing Pickup Intermittent Amplifier

310 & 510 — Connect jumper wires to amplifier. See *Fig. 6.* When wire "A" is connected, test lamp should come on. Disconnect wire "B". Test lamp should go off, then come back on after a few seconds. If not, replace amplifier.

DATSUN (Cont.)

TIME CONTROL UNIT (810 ONLY)

NOTE — *Time Control Unit operates many systems in vehicle. The following tests only check the circuits that control wiper delay operation.*

All tests are made using a voltmeter. Insert voltmeter probes into the REAR of connectors while they are still plugged into control unit. Ensure ignition key is in correct position while testing each circuit. Perform tests in order listed.

Power Circuit — Connect negative lead of voltmeter to pin 2 and positive lead to pin 26. Battery voltage should be present with ignition in "ACC" position. If not, check wiring.

Intermittent Circuit — 1) Connect negative lead of voltmeter to pin 2. Connect positive lead to pin 12. Turn ignition "OFF" and set wiper switch to "OFF". Battery voltage should be present. Turn wiper switch to "INT". No voltage should be read. If readings are incorrect, check harness and wiper switch.

2) Connect negative lead of voltmeter to pin 15 and positive lead to pin 1. Turn ignition to "ACC" and wiper switch to "INT". Voltage should jump from 0-12 volts and back every couple seconds. If so, check wiper relay and wiring for problems. If amplifier does not operate as described, replace it.

3) Connect negative lead of voltmeter to pin 2 and positive lead to pin 16. Turn ignition to "ACC" and wiper switch "ON". Rotate delay adjustment knob at end of wiper lever. Voltage should vary from 0 (short delay) to 8 volts (long delay). If wiper delay cannot be adjusted, but voltage is as described, replace amplifier. If voltage readings are incorrect, check harness and wiper switch.

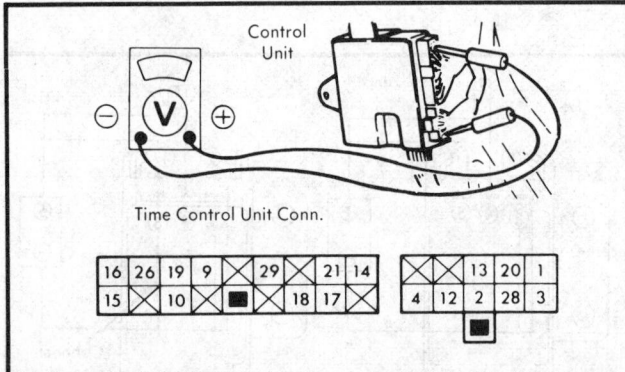

Fig. 8 Time Control Unit Connector Pin Locations for Testing Intermittent Wiper/Washer Operation on 810

Washer Circuit — 1) Connect negative voltmeter lead to pin 2 and positive lead to pin 14. Turn ignition to "ACC" and pull lever to washer position. Battery voltage should be present with washer off, and no voltage present with washer lever pulled. If not, check washer switch and wiring.

2) Connect negative lead of voltmeter to pin 2 and positive lead to pin 26. Battery voltage should be present with ignition in "ACC" position. If not, check wiring.

3) Connect negative lead of voltmeter to pin 15 and positive lead to pin 1. Rotate lever switch fully counterclockwise, with ignition switch at "ACC" position. Battery voltage should be

present briefly every 3 seconds. If not replace amplifier. If amplifier tests okay, problem is in wiper relay.

WIPER RELAY (810 ONLY)

Continuity should be present across terminals 3 and 5. With battery voltage applied to 1 and 2, continuity should be present across terminals 3 and 4. See Fig. 9.

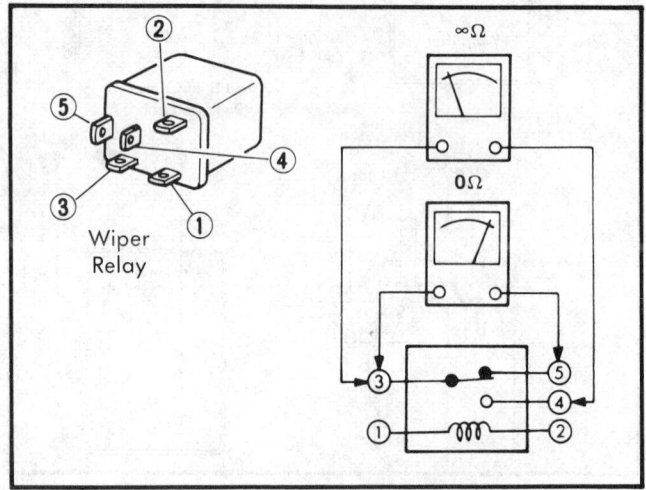

Fig. 9 Wiper Relay Terminal Identification for Testing (810 Only)

REMOVAL & INSTALLATION

FRONT WIPER MOTOR & LINKAGE

Removal (All Models) —1) Disconnect battery ground cable and motor wiring. Remove motor bolts. Remove nut and clip holding linkage arm to motor shaft. Remove motor.

2) Remove wiper arm cap and nut. Remove wiper arm and wiper shaft nut. Remove inspection cover (if equipped) and remove linkage.

Installation — To install, reverse removal procedure. Install arms so parked position is .8" (20 mm) from bottom of windshield.

REAR WIPER MOTOR

Removal (All Models) — Remove wiper shaft nut and wiper arm. Open hatch or tailgate and remove inner panel. Disconnect wiring from motor. Remove wiper motor.

Installation — To install, reverse removal procedure. Install wiper arm so blade is .6-.8" (15-20 mm) from edge of glass when wiper is parked.

COMBINATION SWITCH

Removal (All Models) — Remove steering wheel pad and steering wheel. Disconnect all wiring. Remove retaining screw and pull switch off column.

Installation — To install, reverse removal procedure. Align tab on switch with hole in column.

DATSUN (Cont.)

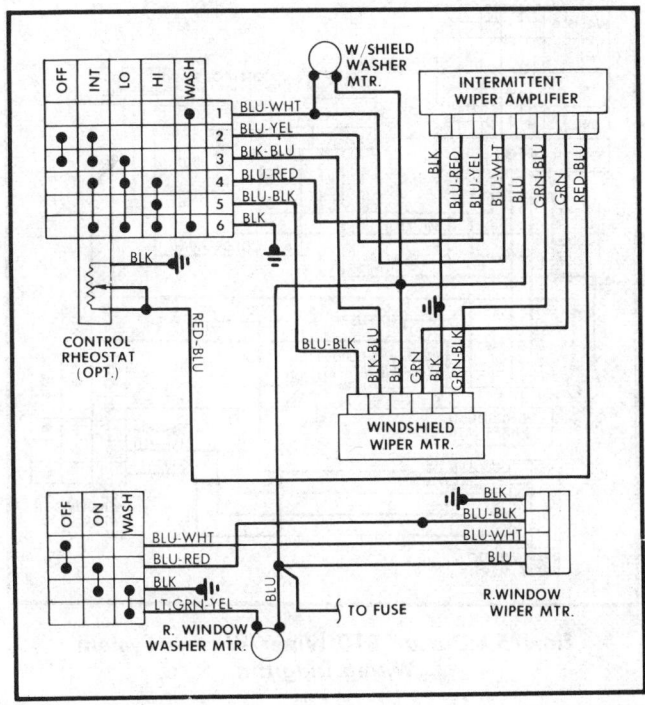

Fig. 10   Datsun 200SX Wiper/Washer System Wiring Diagram

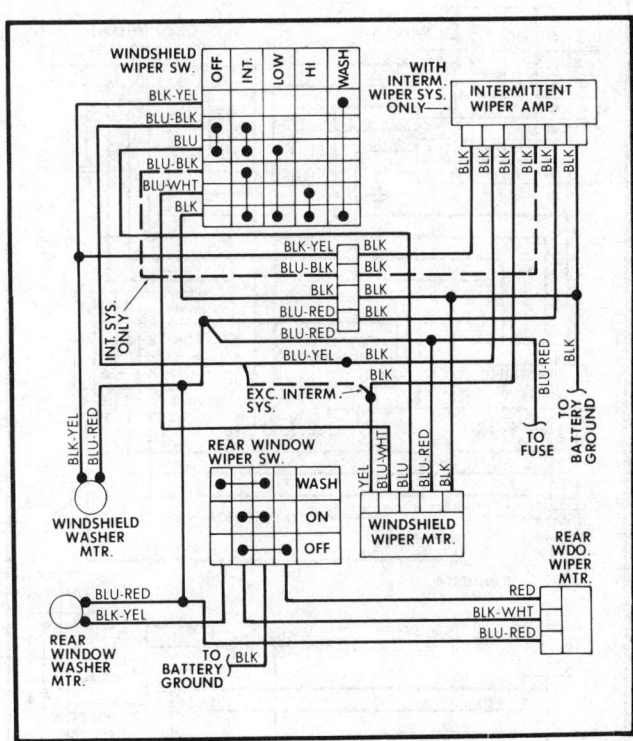

Fig. 11   Datsun 210 Wiper/Washer System Wiring Diagram

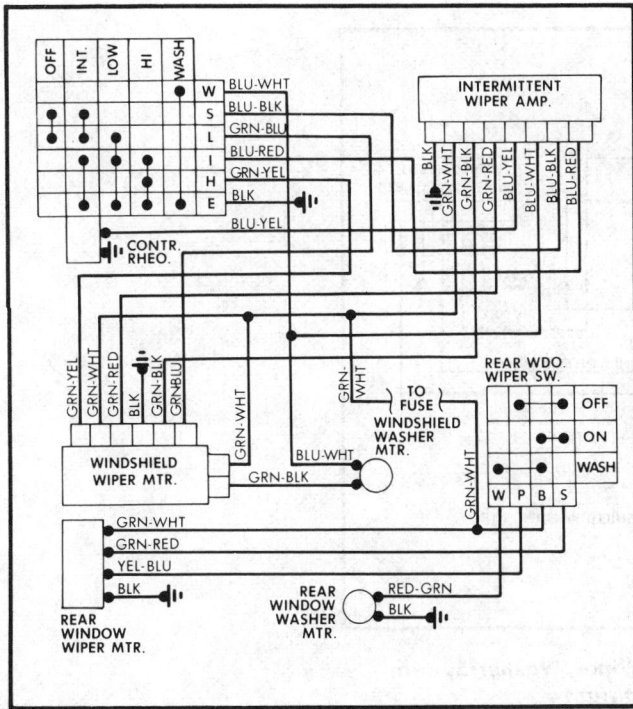

Fig. 12   Datsun 280ZX Wiper/Washer System Wiring Diagram

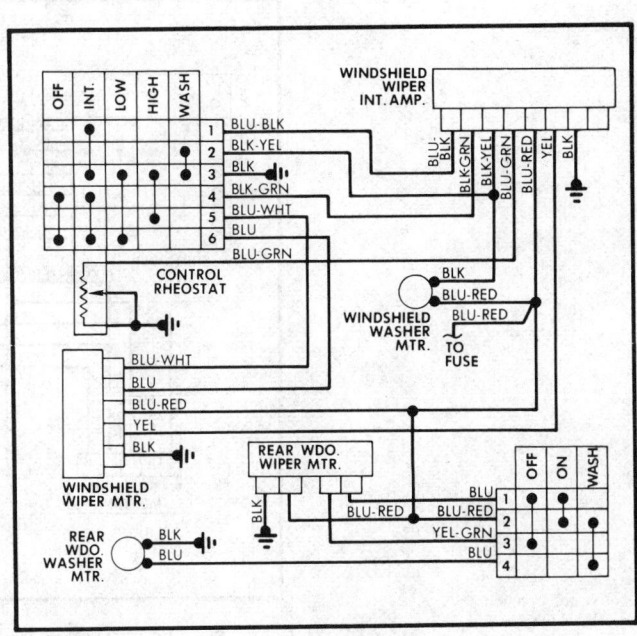

Fig. 13   Datsun 310 Wiper/Washer System Wiring Diagram

Wiper/Washer Systems

DATSUN (Cont.)

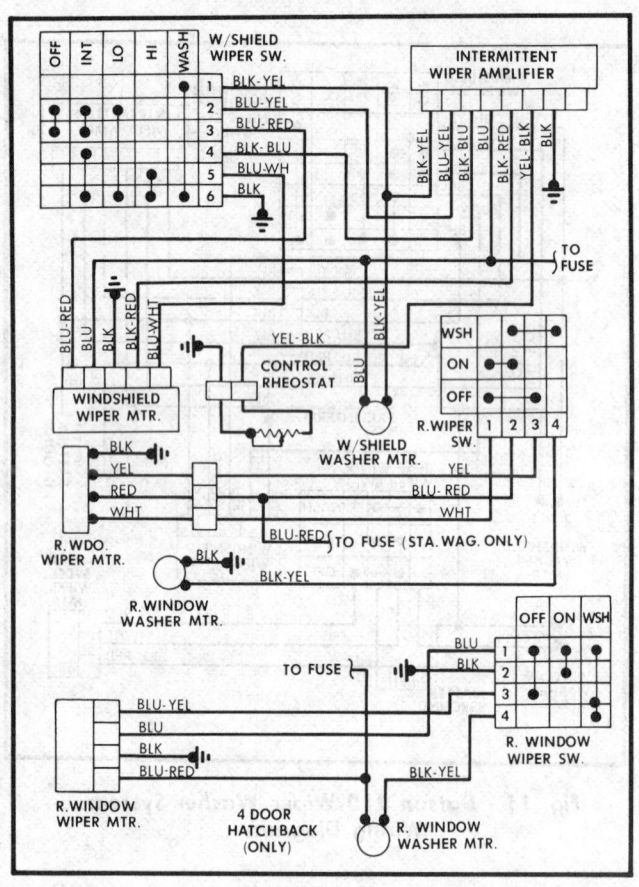

**Fig. 14   Datsun 510 Wiper/Washer System
Wiring Diagram**

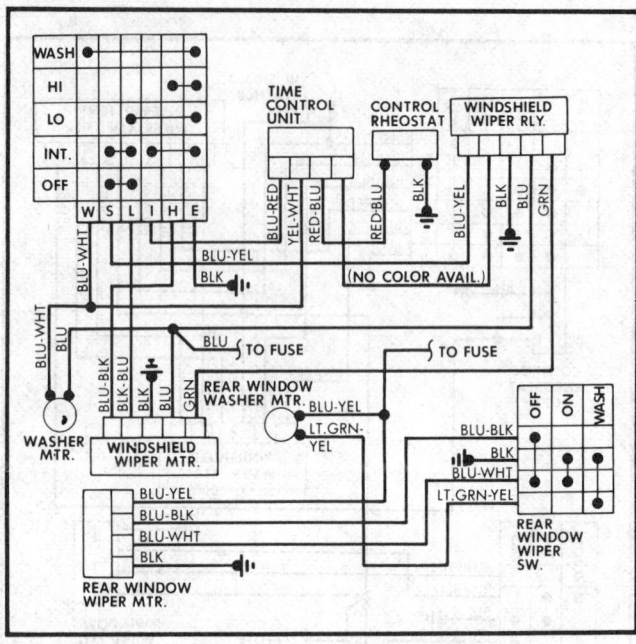

**Fig. 15   Datsun 810 Wiper/Washer System
Wiring Diagram**

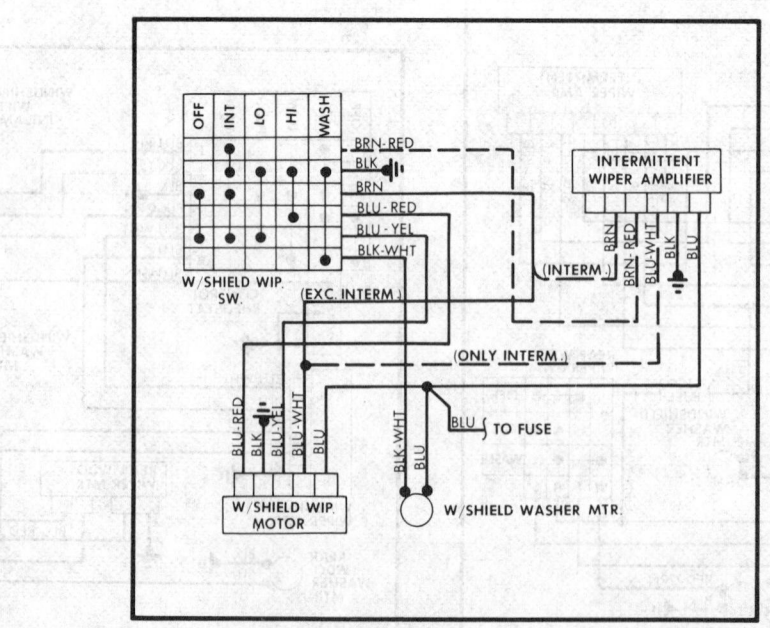

**Fig. 16   Datsun Pickup Wiper/Washer System
Wiring Diagram**

FIAT

Brava
Spider 2000
Strada
X1/9

DESCRIPTION & OPERATION

All models have electric wipers with washer. The Spider 2000 and Strada have a wiper lever on the steering column that selects off, intermittent and constant speeds. A second dashboard knob on the Spider 2000 selects high or low speed. Brava models have a 2-speed system without intermittent feature, while X1/9 models have a slow and fast speed plus intermittent. Lifting the lever toward the steering wheel operates the washers on all models.

Strada models may be equipped with a rear wiper/washer system. The control switches are on the dashboard. The rear washer pump and reservoir are located at the left rear corner of the vehicle.

REMOVAL & INSTALLATION

FRONT WIPER MOTOR

Removal (Brava) — 1) Remove weatherstrip from top of cowl. Unclip hood release cable. Remove 4 top bolts and loosen lower bolt that holds protection panel to firewall. Remove panel.

2) Run wipers and stop in straight-up position. Reach under cowl and remove retaining clip, washers and linkage from left wiper pin. Run wipers and stop in park position. Remove left wiper arm and shaft nuts.

3) Remove linkage bracket bolts, then remove motor/linkage assembly from cowl. Unplug wiring. Scribe marks on motor shaft and crank arm, then remove crank arm. Remove bolts and rubber cushions, then lift motor from linkage bracket.

Installation — To install, reverse removal procedure.

NOTE — *Procedures for Spider 2000 were not available.*

Removal (Strada) — Place wipers in park position. Disconnect wiring. Remove motor shaft nut. Remove 3 mounting bolts and wiper motor.

Installation — To install, reverse removal procedure.

Removal (X1/9) — 1) Open hood. Disconnect wiring, remove cowl grommet bolts and push connector through to rear side of cowl panel. Remove left wiper arm and shaft nuts and spacers.

2) Remove motor crank arm nut. Remove motor bracket bolts and move bracket around inside cowl to access motor-to-bracket bolts. Remove wiper motor.

Installation — To install, reverse removal procedure.

REAR WIPER MOTOR

Removal (Strada) — Lift wiper arm and pull it off. Remove shaft nut. Remove motor bolt and disconnect wiring. Remove motor.

Installation — To install, reverse removal procedure.

WIPER SWITCH

Removal (All Models) — Disconnect battery ground cable. Remove horn button and steering column covers. Remove steering shaft nut and pull off steering wheel. Loosen switch bolt and pull column switch assembly off column shaft. Disconnect wiring and remove switch.

Installation — To install, reverse removal procedure.

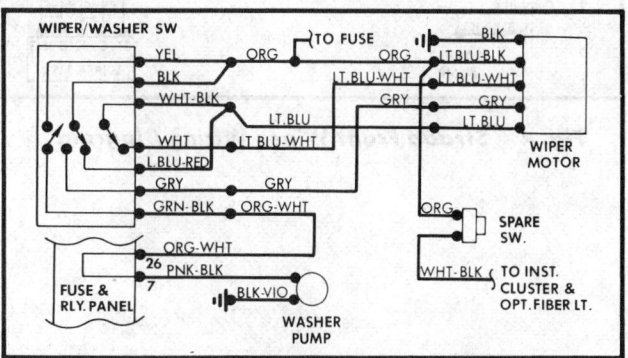

Fig. 1   Brava Wiper Wiring Diagram

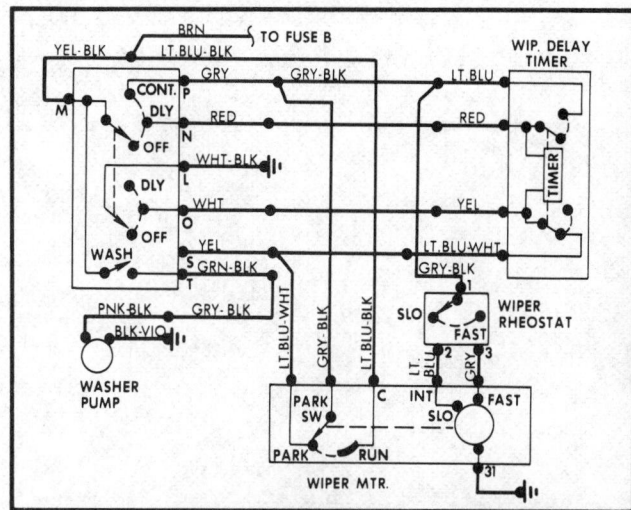

Fig. 2   Spider 2000 Wiper Wiring Diagram

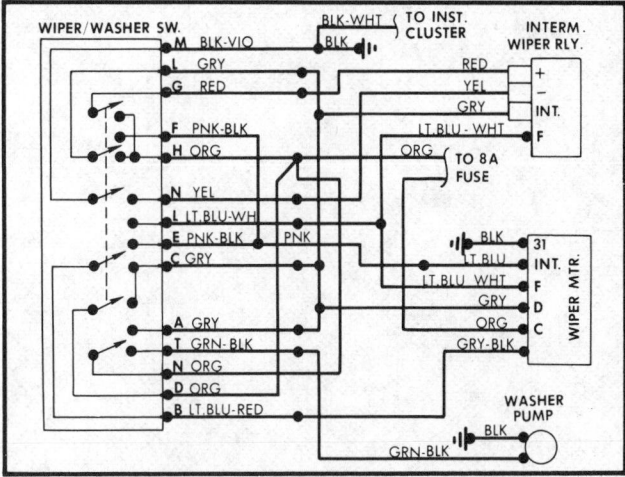

Fig. 3   X1/9 Wiper Wiring Diagram

Wiper/Washer Systems

FIAT (Cont.)

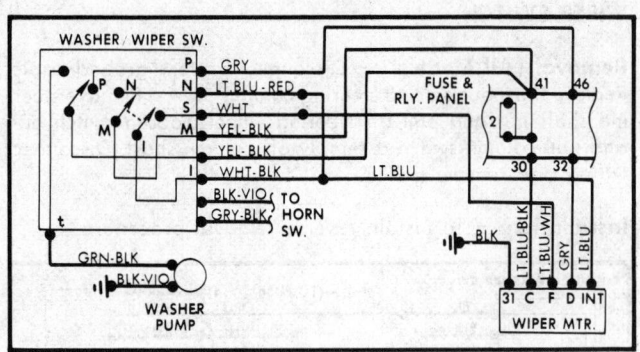

Fig. 4 Strada Front Wiper Wiring Diagram

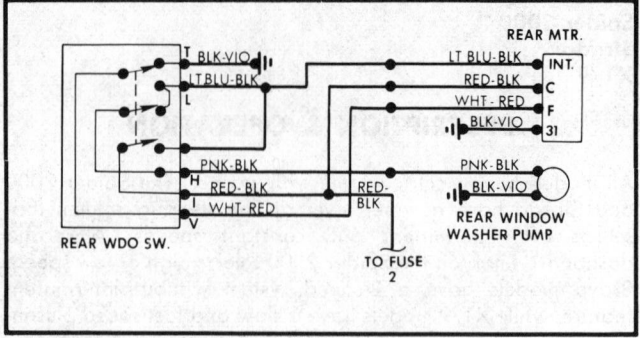

Fig. 5 Strada Rear Wiper Wiring Diagram

HONDA

Accord
Civic
Prelude

DESCRIPTION & OPERATION

All models are equipped with a 2-speed front wiper motor with intermittent feature. The washer system uses a small electric pump to spray fluid on the windshield. The wiper switch is part of the combination switch on the steering column. A rear wiper/washer system is used on Accord and some Civic models. A dashboard switch controls the rear wiper and washer pump. The pump and reservoir are located at rear of vehicle.

TESTING

FRONT WIPER MOTOR

1) Remove cowl air scoop and grille. Unbolt motor to gain access to connector. Unplug connector. Disconnect wiper motor linkage from motor.

2) Connect a jumper wire to the motor Green/Black wire and ground. Connect a jumper wire from battery voltage to Blue wire to test low speed, and to the Blue/Yellow wire to test high speed. If motor does not operate smoothly, replace it.

REAR WIPER MOTOR

Remove rear wiper motor. Connect a jumper wire between ground and the Green wire in motor connector. Connect a jumper wire between battery voltage and the Green/Black wire in motor connector. If motor does not run smoothly, replace it.

WASHER PUMP MOTOR

Connect battery voltage and ground to the pump terminals. Washer pump should operate and spray on window. If not, repair fluid lines or replace pump.

REMOVAL & INSTALLATION

FRONT WIPER MOTOR

Removal (All Models) — Remove cap on wiper arm, then remove nut and pull arm off. Remove pivot cap, nut, washer and cushion. Remove air scoop and hood seal. Remove linkage nut or clip. Remove motor bolts, unplug wiring and remove motor.

Installation — To install, reverse removal procedure. Operate motor once and allow to park, then install wiper arms.

REAR WIPER MOTOR

Removal (All Models) — Remove tailgate inner trim panel. Remove wiper arm cover and nut from wiper shaft. Remove wiper arm, nut and bushings. Remove wiper motor bolts, unplug connector and remove motor.

Installation — To install, reverse removal procedure.

COMBINATION SWITCH

Removal (All Models) — Disconnect battery ground cable. Remove steering wheel and column covers. Remove turn signal cancelling sleeve and washer. Remove screws holding combination switch and remove switch.

Installation — To install, reverse removal procedure.

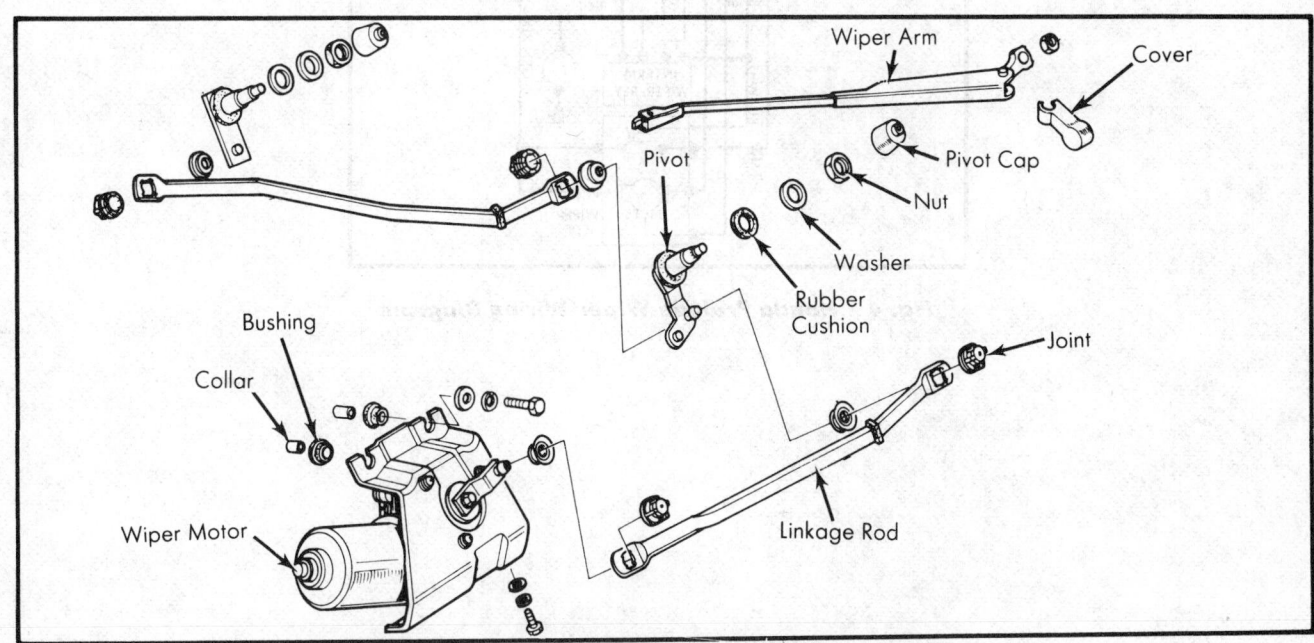

Fig. 1 Exploded View of Honda Wiper Linkage
(Accord Shown, Others Similar)

Wiper/Washer Systems

HONDA (Cont.)

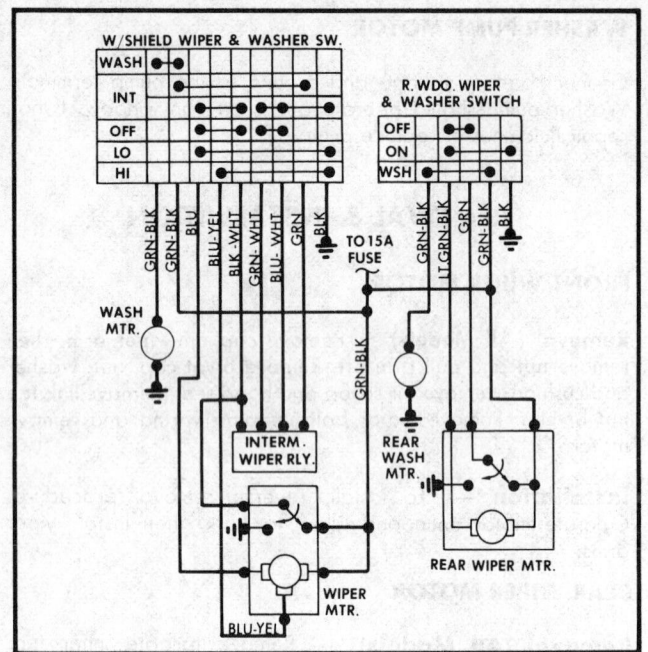

Fig. 2 Honda Accord Wiper Wiring Diagram

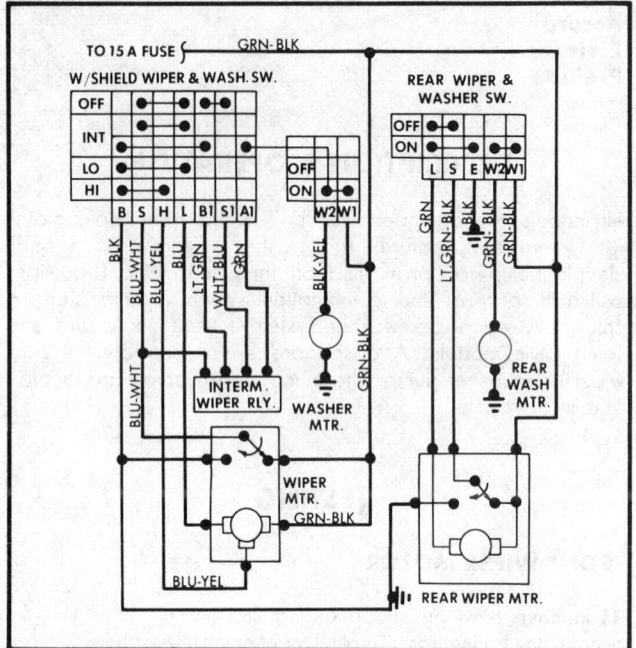

Fig. 3 Honda Civic Wiper Wiring Diagram

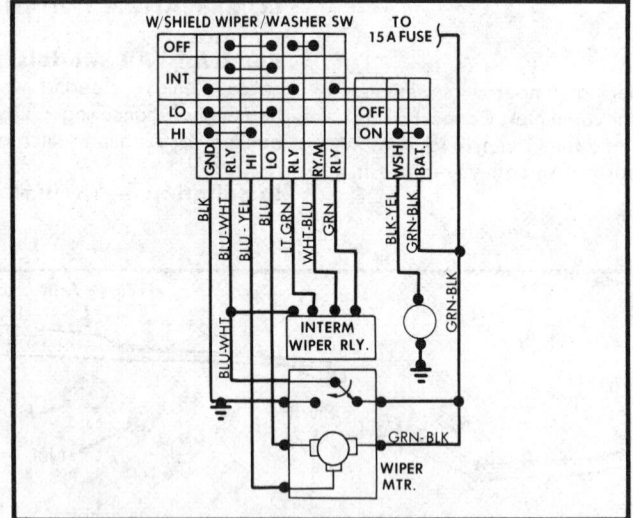

Fig. 4 Honda Prelude Wiper Wiring Diagram

ISUZU & LUV

Isuzu
I-Mark
P'UP
LUV

DESCRIPTION & OPERATION

All models have a 2-speed wiper system with washer. The control switch is on a steering column lever. I-Mark models may have an intermittent system which gives a short delay between wiper cycles. The delay relay is mounted in a box near the windshield washer reservoir. It cannot be serviced. If defective, the relay must be replaced.

TROUBLE SHOOTING

WIPER ACTION SLUGGISH OR UNEVEN

Worn or binding linkage. Poor ground connection. Worn motor brushes.

WIPER DOES NOT PARK OR DOES NOT STOP

Dirty contact points in park switch at motor. Shorted or open wiring. Bad wiper switch.

WIPER DOES NOT OPERATE

Blown fuse. Open wiring circuit. Bad wiper switch. Defective wiper motor.

TESTING

WIPER MOTOR

I-Mark — Remove motor from vehicle. Connect jumper wires and ammeter to measure current flow with motor in high speed. Current draw should not exceed 3 amps. If it does, loosen adjusting nut at end of armature.

NOTE — *Testing procedures were not available for other models.*

REMOVAL & INSTALLATION

WIPER MOTOR

Removal (I-Mark) — Disconnect battery ground cable. From underneath instrument panel, remove nut and crankarm from motor. Unplug wiring. Remove 3 nuts and motor assembly.

Installation — To install, reverse removal procedure.

Removal (LUV & P'UP) — Remove 4 motor mounting bolts. Unplug wiring. Pull motor out part-way and remove shaft nut. Remove motor.

Installation — To install, reverse removal procedure.

WIPER LINKAGE

Removal (I-Mark) — **1)** Disconnect battery ground cable. Remove wiper arm nuts and wiper arms. Remove steering wheel. Remove instrument cluster. Reach through cluster opening and pry linkage arm from shaft assembly. Remove 3 screws and left shaft assembly.

2) Remove glove box. Pry linkage arm from shaft assembly. Remove 2 screws and right shaft assembly.

Installation — To install, reverse removal parocedure.

Removal (LUV & P'UP) — **1)** Remove wiper arm covers, nuts and wiper arms. Remove pivot shaft nuts and push shafts into cowl. Remove access covers on cowl (in engine compartment).

2) Remove wiper motor bolts. Unplug wiring. Remove motor complete with linkage. Disengage finger on link retainer from hole in link. Disconnect link by turning retainer clockwise.

Installation — To install, reverse removal procedure.

WIPER SWITCH

Removal (I-Mark) — Disconnect battery ground cable. Remove steering wheel. Remove steering column covers. Unplug wiring. Remove 2 screws and wiper switch.

Installation — To install, reverse removal procedure.

Removal (LUV & P'UP) — Disconnect battery ground cable. Remove steering column covers. Unplug wiring. Remove steering wheel, using "C" clamp type puller (GM No. J-24292-A). Remove 2 screws and combination switch.

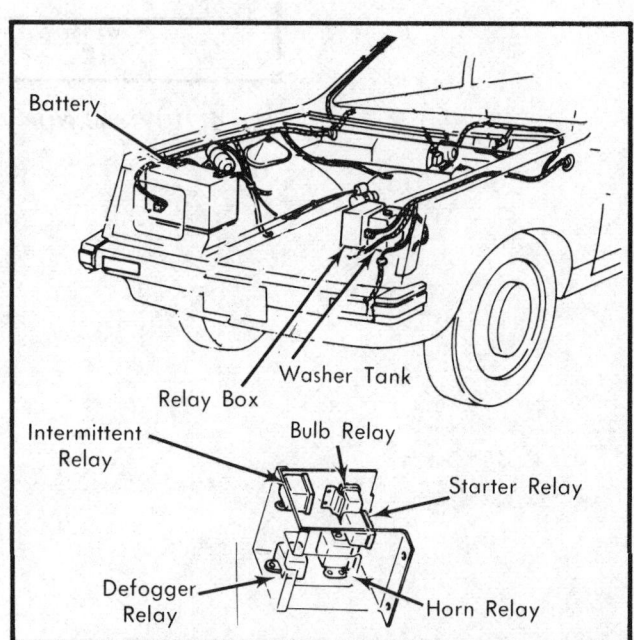

***Fig. 1** Location of I-Mark Intermittent Wiper Relay. Remove Relay Box to Gain Access*

Wiper/Washer Systems

ISUZU & LUV (Cont.)

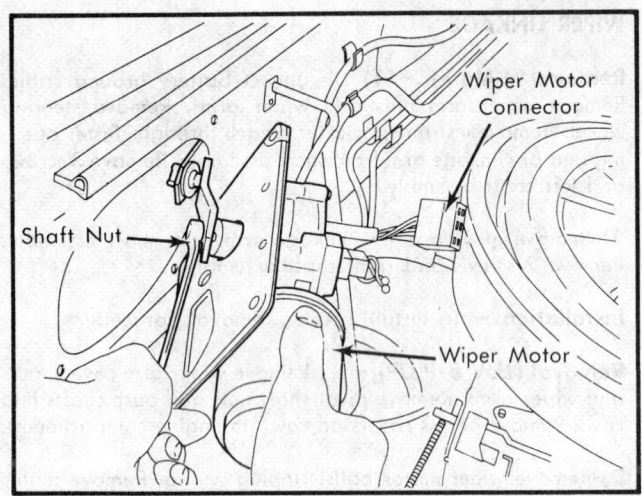

Fig. 2 Removing Wiper Motor on LUV and P'UP. Do Not Bend Linkage While Removing Shaft Nut

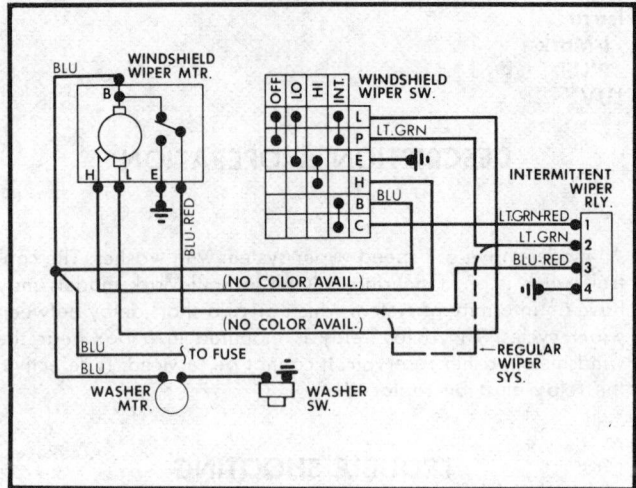

Fig. 3 I-Mark Wiper/Washer Wiring Diagram

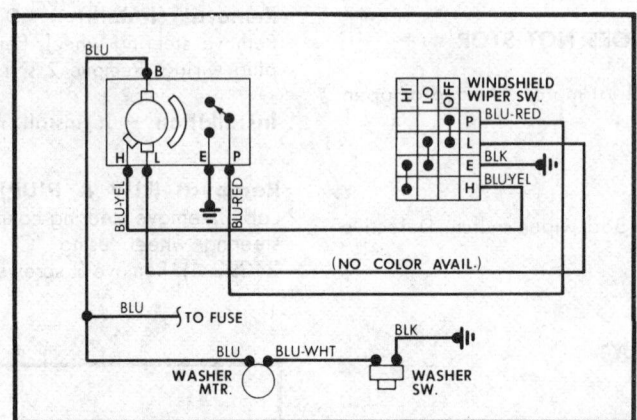

Fig. 4 LUV and P'UP Wiper/Washer Wiring Diagram

Wiper/Washer Systems

JAGUAR

XJ6

DESCRIPTION & OPERATION

Jaguar models have a 2-speed wiper system with intermittent feature. The wipers are controlled by a lever on the right side of the steering column. Moving the lever downward runs the wipers on the intermittent cycle, while moving the lever up operates the low and high speeds. Pressing the button on the lever operates the washers. When the lever is pulled toward the steering wheel, the wipers work until it is released.

The wiper system uses a relay to control the intermittent cycle. The relay is located under the right side of the instrument panel.

REMOVAL & INSTALLATION

WIPER MOTOR

Removal — Remove battery. Lift spring clip on wiper arms and remove arms. Disconnect cable from motor. Remove 2 nuts from motor clamp. Tilt motor towards engine and unplug wiring. Remove motor and drive assembly.

Installation — To install, reverse removal procedure. Run motor and allow wipers to park, then install wiper arms.

WIPER SWITCH

Removal — 1) Disconnect battery ground cable. Remove steering column lower cover. Remove clamp bolt (beneath column) that holds adaptor. Loosen lock nut and back out set screw 2 turns. Remove steering wheel.

2) Remove insulation panel under left side of dashboard. Remove upper column cover. Loosen clamp and remove switch assembly. Unplug wiring, remove 2 screws and separate wiper switch.

Installation — To install, reverse removal procedure.

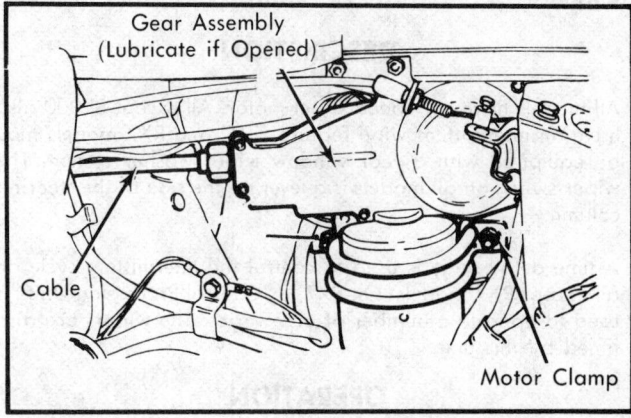

Fig. 1   Removing Wiper Motor Assembly. Remove Battery, Cable and Motor Clamp.

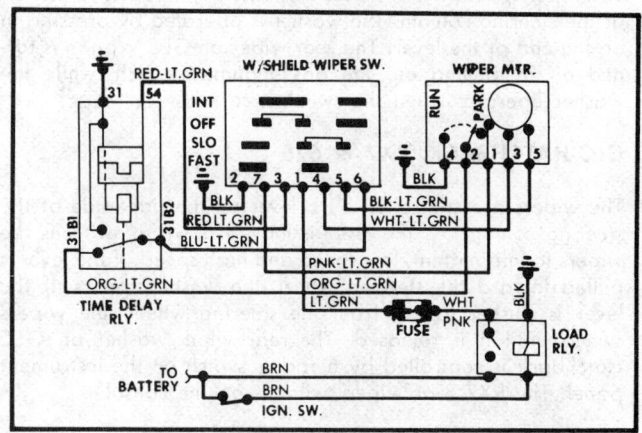

Fig. 2   Jaguar Wiper/Washer Wiring Diagram

Wiper/Washer Systems

MAZDA

GLC
626
RX7
B2000

DESCRIPTION

All models have a 2-speed wiper motor. All except B2000 also have an intermittent wipe feature. GLC and RX7 models may be equipped with a rear window wiper/washer system. The wiper switch on all models is a lever on the side of the steering column.

A time delay relay is used to control the intermittent cycle on all except RX7 models. On RX7, a "Control Processing Unit" is used to operate a number of accessories. The wipers are also timed by this unit.

OPERATION

GLC WAGON & B2000

The wiper speeds are controlled by twisting the lever to the left of the steering column. The washer is operated by pressing in on the end of the lever. The rear wiper on GLC Wagon is turned on by pulling out the dash-mounted switch, while the washer operates when the switch is turned.

GLC HATCHBACK, RX7 & 626

The wipers are controlled by a lever on the right side of the steering column. As the lever is moved down, it switches the wipers to intermittent, low speed and high speed. If the lever is pulled toward the steering wheel, the washer sprays. If the lever is pushed away from the steering wheel, the wipers sweep until it is released. The rear wiper/washer on GLC Hatchback is controlled by a rocker switch on the instrument panel. The RX7 rear wiper switch is on the console.

TESTING

WIPER MOTOR

1) Remove wiper motor from vehicle. Connect jumper wires to connector at motor to check both speeds. For low speed, connect battery voltage to Blue wire terminal and ground the Blue/White terminal. For high speed, ground the Blue/Red terminal instead.

2) To check the park switch, apply battery voltage to the Blue wire terminal. Connect a jumper wire between Blue/White and Blue/Black. Ground the Black wire. Motor should run briefly and stop.

Mazda Intermittent Wiper Relay Locations		
Model	**Connector**	**Location**
GLC	6-pin	Left of instrument cluster
RX7①	17-pin	Left kick panel
626	6-pin (4 wires)	Left kick panel, Top front relay
① — Time delay is controlled by "Control Processing Unit".		

3) To check rear wiper motor, apply battery voltage to Blue/Red wire and ground the Blue/White wire. Motor should run steadily.

REMOVAL & INSTALLATION

FRONT WIPER MOTOR ASSEMBLY

Removal (All Except B2000) — 1) Run wipers until they are in vertical position, then turn ignition off. Remove wiper arms and shaft nuts.

2) Remove cowl grille or access panel. Unplug connector at motor. Remove mounting bolts and wiper motor.

Installation — To install, reverse removal procedure.

NOTE — *Removal procedures were not available for B2000 models.*

REAR WIPER MOTOR ASSEMBLY

Removal — Disconnect battery ground cable. Remove wiper arm and shaft nuts. Remove light and service cover on rear hatch. Disconnect wiring and remove rear wiper motor.

Installation — To install, reverse removal procedure.

WIPER SWITCH

Removal — Disconnect battery ground cable. Remove steering wheel. Remove column covers and snap ring at top of column (if equipped). Unplug wiring connectors. Loosen combination switch screw. Remove combination switch.

Installation — To install, reverse removal procedure.

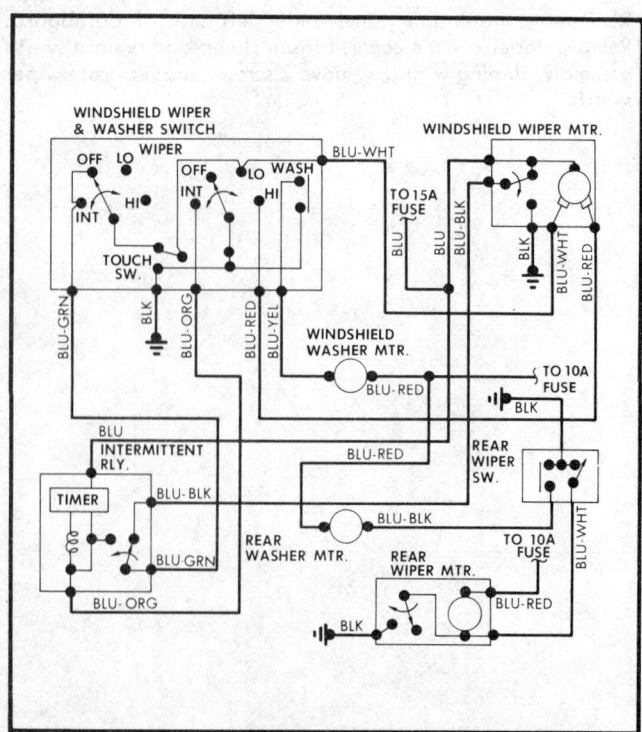

Fig. 1 Mazda GLC Hatchback Wiring Diagram

MAZDA (Cont.)

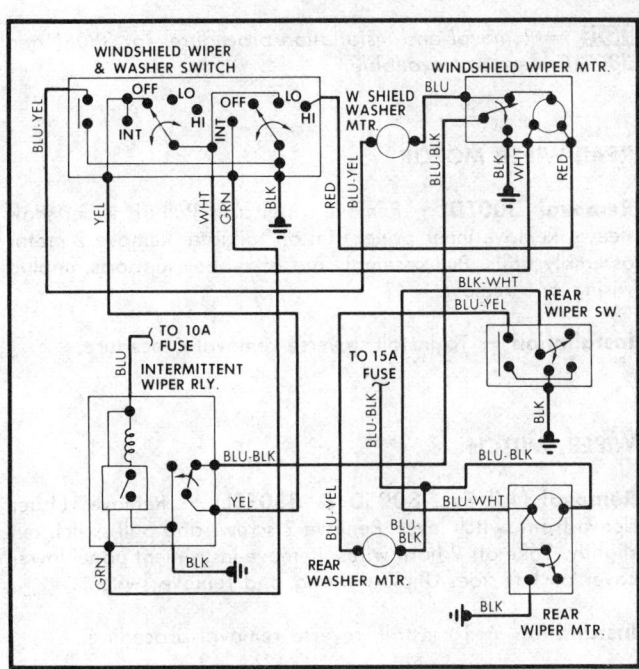

Fig. 2   Mazda GLC Wagon Wiring Diagram

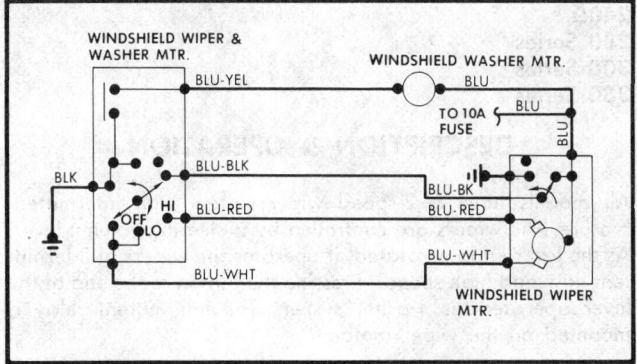

Fig. 4   Mazda B2000 Wiring Diagram

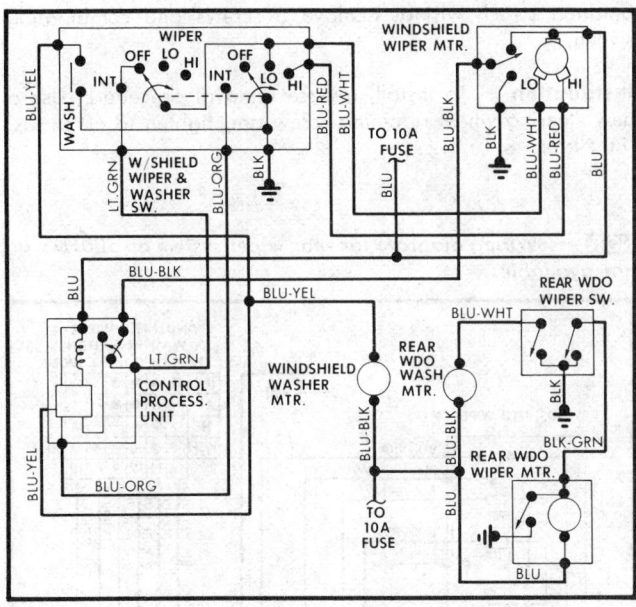

Fig. 3   Mazda RX7 Wiring Diagram

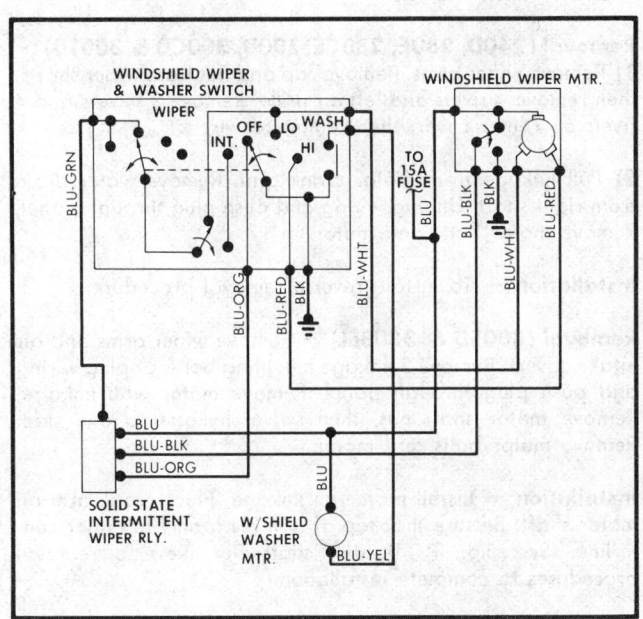

Fig. 5   Mazda 626 Wiring Diagram

ACCESSORIES & EQUIPMENT

MERCEDES-BENZ

240D
280 Series
300 Series
380 Series

DESCRIPTION & OPERATION

All models have a 2-speed wiper system with intermittent feature. The wipers are controlled by a steering column lever. As the lever knob is rotated, it operates the wipers at intermittent, low and high speeds. Pressing the button at the end of the lever operates the washer system. The intermittent relay is mounted on the wiper motor

Station wagon models have a rear window wiper/washer system. This system has a low speed, intermittent speed and washer. It is controlled by 3 push buttons at the top left corner of the console. Pressing the washer button operates the washer and wiper until it is released. Pressing either of the other buttons operates the low speed or intermittent speed until the button is pressed a second time.

REMOVAL & INSTALLATION

FRONT WIPER MOTOR

Removal (240D, 280E, 280CE, 300D, 300CD & 300TD) — 1) Remove wiper arms. Remove cap and nut from wiper shafts, then remove 4 rivets and left air grille. Remove 2 screws and 4 rivets on center cover, then remove cover.

2) Pull linkage from motor crank arm. Remove water drain from right shaft. Unplug wiring and push plug through panel. Remove motor bolts and motor.

Installation — To install, reverse removal procedure.

Removal (300SD & 380SEL) — Remove wiper arms and air intake covers. Remove 3 linkage mounting bolts. Unplug wiring and push plug through panel. Remove motor with linkage. Remove motor shaft nut, then swivel linkage to one side. Remove motor bolts and motor.

Installation — Install motor on linkage. Place crank arm on motor shaft. Be sure that top of arm is parallel to motor centerline. *See Fig. 1.* Tighten shaft nut. Reverse removal procedures to complete installation.

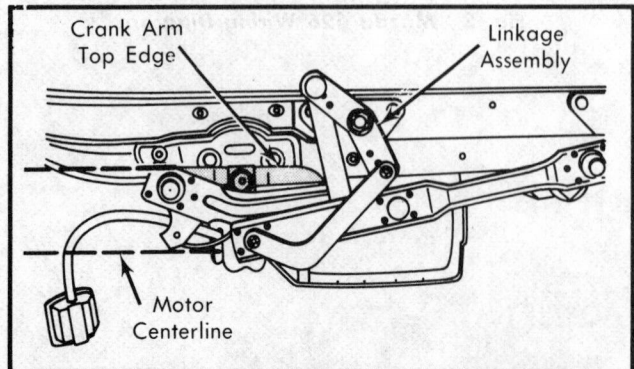

Fig. 1 Installing Motor Crank Arm Nut Crank Arm Must Be Parallel To Motor Centerline

NOTE — *Removal and installation procedures for 380SL and 380SLC were not available.*

REAR WIPER MOTOR

Removal (300TD) — Remove wiper arm. Pull off wiper shaft sleeve. Remove inner panel trim on tailgate. Remove 2 motor assembly bolts. Pull assembly out of rubber supports, unplug wiring and remove.

Installation — To install, reverse removal procedure.

WIPER SWITCH

Removal (All Exc. 300SD & 380SEL) — Remove rubber sleeve from switch lever. Remove 2 screws and pull switch out slightly. Take off 2 horn wires. Remove instrument panel lower cover on left side. Unplug wiring and remove switch.

Installation — To install, reverse removal procedure.

Removal (300SD & 380SEL) — Pry out steering wheel center emblem. Remove screw and discard. Remove steering wheel. Remove cover under left side of instrument panel. Unplug combination switch wiring. Remove 3 screws and combination switch.

Installation — To install, reverse removal procedure. Use a new steering wheel retaining screw and tighten to 60 ft. lbs. (80 N·m).

NOTE — *Wiring diagram for rear wiper system on 300TD was not available.*

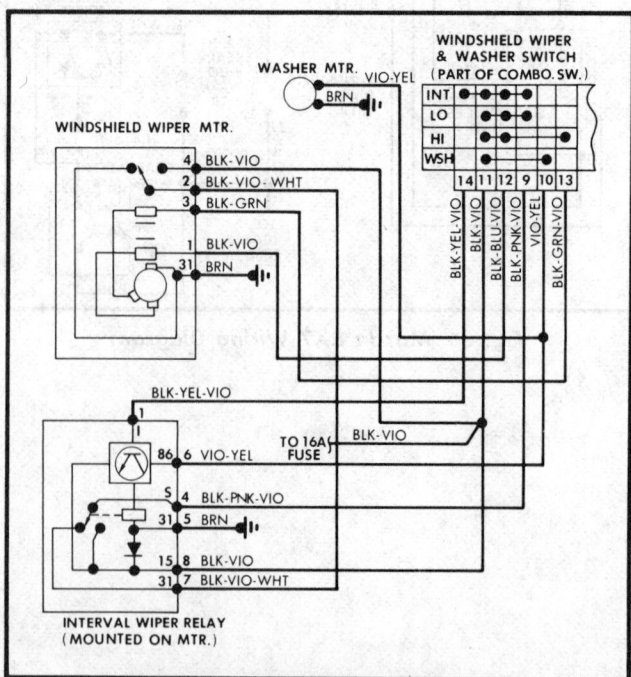

Fig. 2 Mercedes Wiper System Wiring Diagram (All Models)

PORSCHE

911SC
924
924 Turbo
928

DESCRIPTION

Porsche 911SC and 928 models have a 3-speed wiper motor. The 924 models use a 2-speed motor. All models have an intermittent cycle. A rear wiper may be installed on all models. A steering column lever is used to control the main wiper system, with a dashboard-mounted switch to vary the intermittent cycle (not used on 924). All models may be equipped with headlight washer. On 928, a special tank of concentrated washer fluid is provided to ensure good windshield cleaning.

OPERATION

FRONT WIPERS

Moving the steering column lever upward selects the wiper speed. Moving the lever downward operates the intermittent feature on 924 and 928. A switch near the clock selects intermittent on the 911SC. The interval on the 928 can be varied by rotating a thumbwheel under the right side of the instrument cluster.

REAR WIPERS

The rear wiper on 924 and 928 is controlled by a console switch. On 911SC, the switch is on the cluster. No rear washer is used. Be sure window glass is wet to prevent scratches.

WINDSHIELD WASHER

The washer sprays when the wiper lever is pulled toward the steering wheel. 928 models also have a special container of solution which ensures good cleaning. This washer is operated by a button under the right side of the cluster (by the intermittent adjustment thumbwheel).

HEADLIGHT WASHER

All models may have a headlight washer. This unit sprays fluid under high pressure directly onto the headlights. It operates only when the headlights are raised (924 and 928) and on. It uses the windshield washer reservoir. A separate pump is provided, which is operated by the wiper lever on 928 and a special button on 911SC and 924. The button is on the instrument cluster on 911SC, and on the console for 924 models.

REMOVAL & INSTALLATION

FRONT WIPER MOTOR

Removal (All Models) — Remove motor cover (if equipped). Remove crank arm nut and unplug wiring. Remove motor bolts. If necessary, loosen motor bracket bolts to slip motor out.

Installation — Install motor on bracket and connect wiring. Let motor run and return to park position, then install crank arm so wiper arms are parked at bottom of windshield. Replace motor cover.

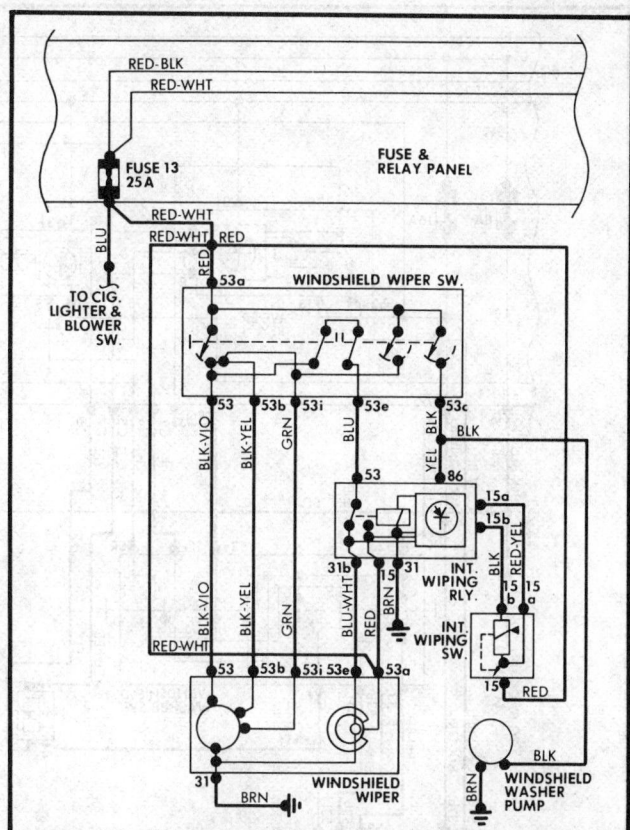

Fig. 1   911SC Wiper System Wiring Diagram

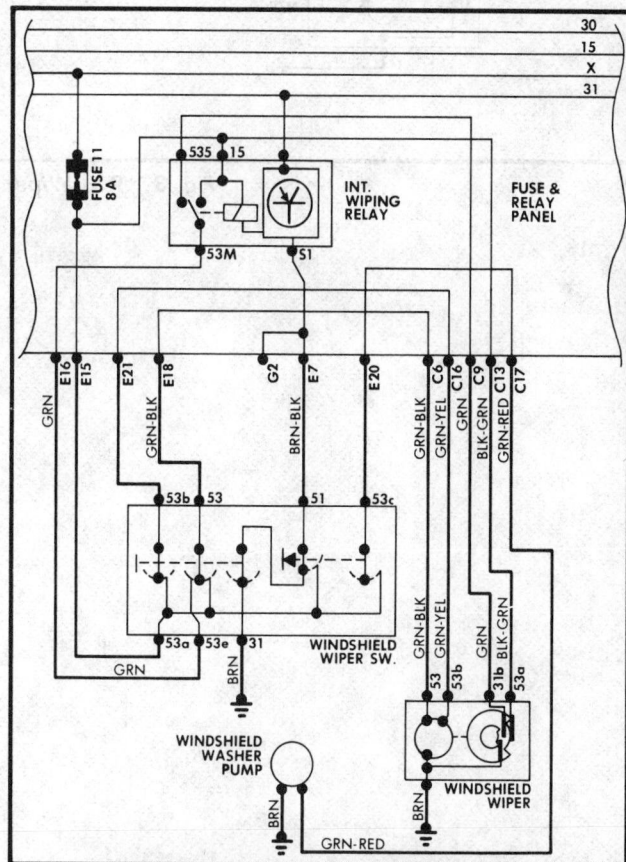

Fig. 2   924 & 924 Turbo Wiper System Wiring Diagram

Wiper/Washer Systems

PORSCHE (Cont.)

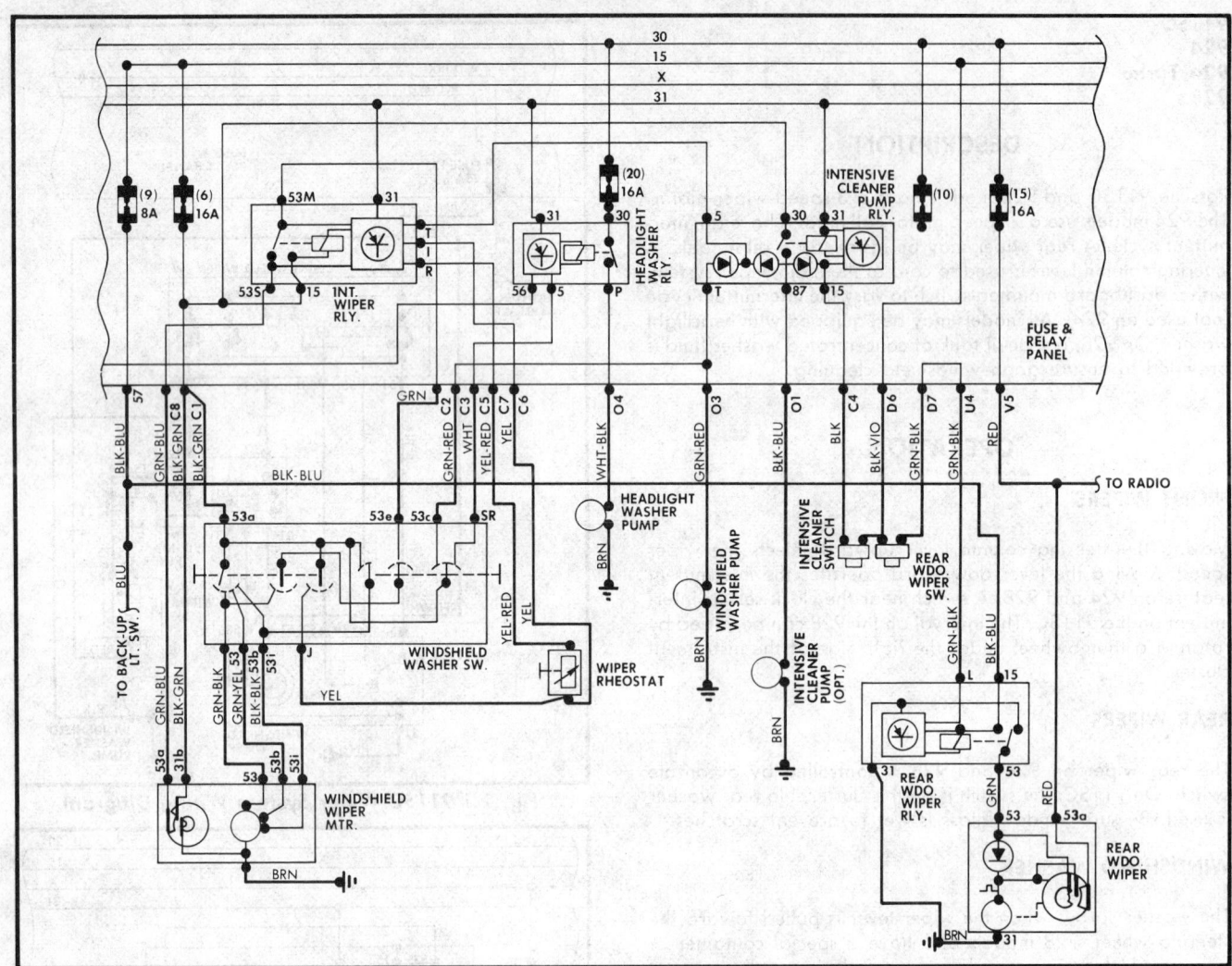

Fig. 3   928 Wiper System Wiring Diagram

Wiper/Washer Systems

RENAULT

Le Car
18i

DESCRIPTION

All models are equipped with 2-speed wiper motors. The 18i model also has an intermittent cycle. A rear wiper/washer is available on Le Car and 18i Station Wagon models. The Le Car rear washer has a reservoir in the rear of the car, while the 18i uses the front fluid reservoir. The 18i rear pump is inside the pillar behind the left rear door.

OPERATION

The wipers are controlled by the right column lever. Pulling the lever toward the steering wheel operates the washers. Moving the lever downward operates the intermittent cycle (18i only), low speed and high speed. The rear wiper is controlled by a push button switch. Hold the switch to operate the washer and wiper.

TESTING

WASHER MOTOR

If motor does not operate, connect a jumper wire from battery to the motor pink wire. If motor still does not work, check pump motor ground connection. If it does not operate, replace motor. If motor now operates, but not with switch, check wiring or replace switch.

REMOVAL & INSTALLATION

FRONT WIPER MOTOR

Removal (Le Car) — 1) Raise base of wiper arm and remove nut. Pull off wiper arms and remove shaft nuts. Remove electrical box, 2 motor plate bolts and pull motor assembly out to the side.

2) Remove motor crank arm nut. Remove motor mounting bolts and pull motor from bracket.

Installation — Place motor on bracket and tighten bolts. Crank arm must be in line with linkage when motor is in park position. *See Fig. 1.* Reverse removal procedure to complete installation.

Removal (18i) — 1) Remove wiper arms and shaft nuts. Remove electrical box, ground wire and motor plate bolt. Push shafts into body and slide motor assembly to the right.

2) Remove crank arm nut and motor bolts. Remove motor from linkage assembly.

Installation — Install motor on linkage assembly. Motor crank arm must be in line with linkage arm when motor is in park position. Reverse removal procedure to complete installation. *See Fig. 1.*

REAR WIPER MOTORS

Removal (All Models) — Remove inner trim panel. Disconnect motor wiring. Remove wiper blade, arm and shaft nuts. Remove motor bolts and motor assembly.

Installation — To install, reverse removal procedure.

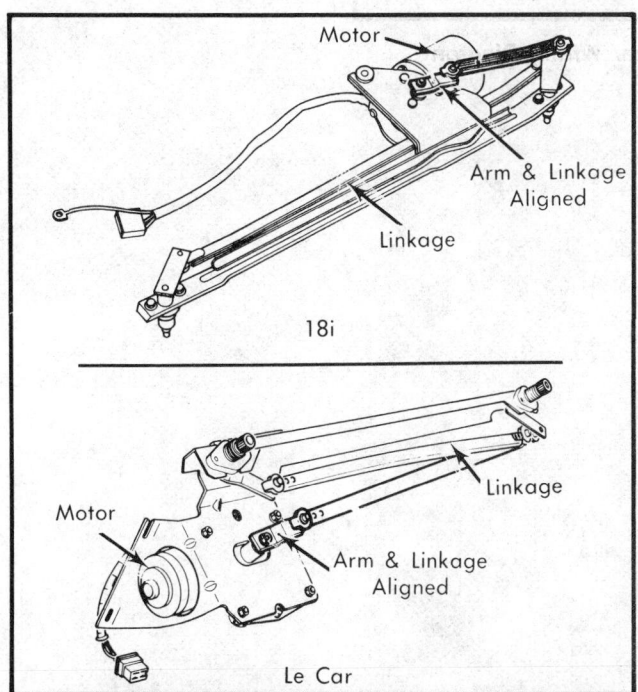

Fig. 1 Wiper Motor Crank Arm Position.
Motor Must Be In Park Position When Nut is Tightened.

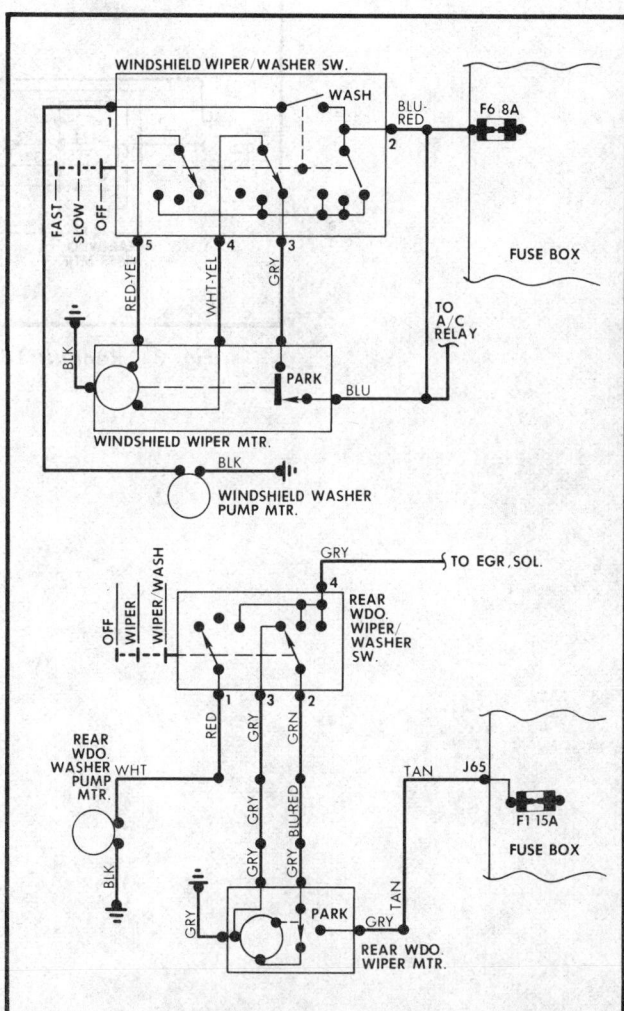

Fig. 2   Renault Le Car Wiper Wiring Diagram

RENAULT (Cont.)

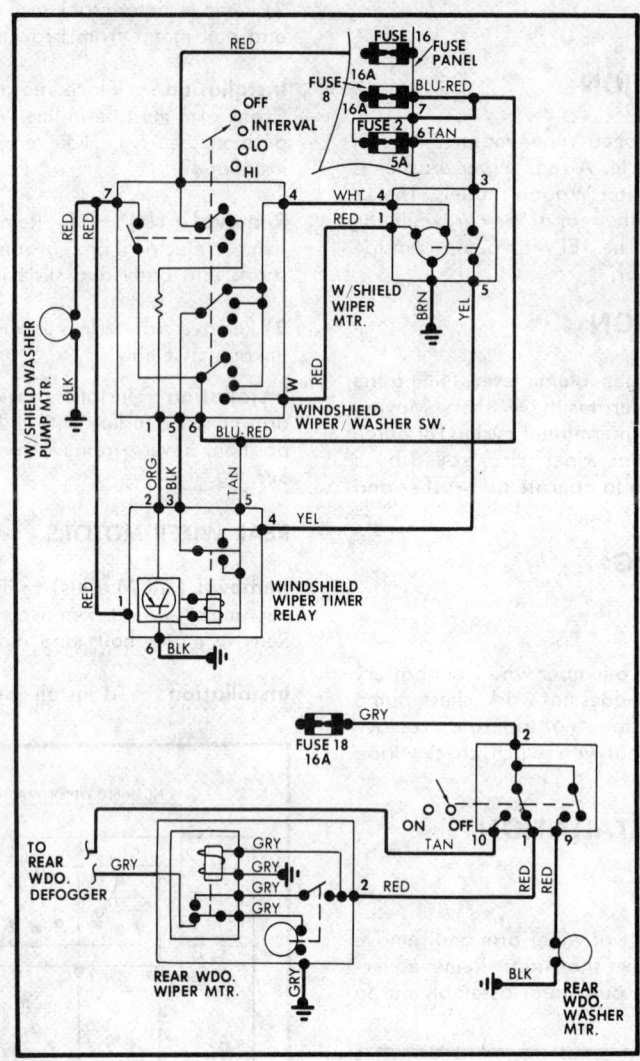

Fig. 3   Renault 18i Wiper Wiring Diagram

SAAB

900
900 Turbo

DESCRIPTION & OPERATION

All models have a 2-speed wiper motor that operates the wiper arms through a cable and linkage. The wiper control switch is a steering column lever. The intermittent control relay is located next to the turn signal flasher (on relay bracket under left side of dashboard). The wiper switch operates the washers when it is pulled toward the steering wheel. As the lever is moved down, the wipers operate intermittently, at low speed and at high speed.

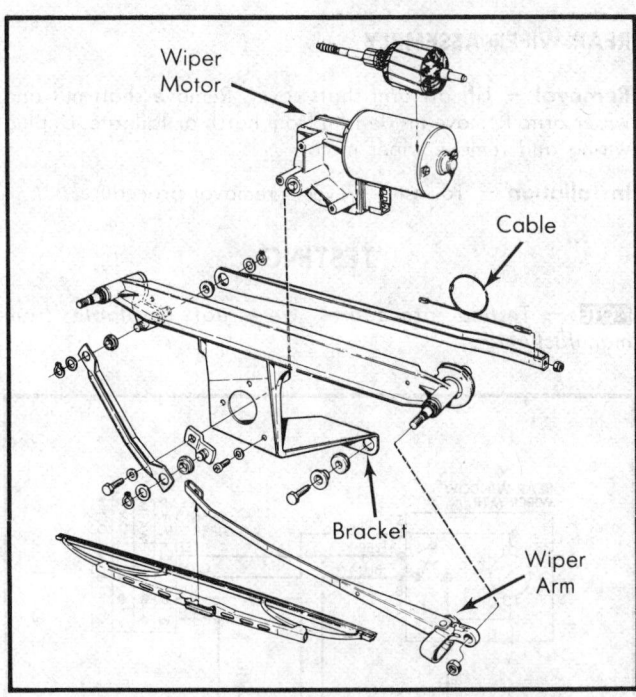

Fig. 1 Saab 900 Wiper Motor Assembly. Remove Wiper Arms and 4 Bolts to Remove

REMOVAL & INSTALLATION

WIPER MOTOR

Removal — Lift wiper arm. Fold cap up and remove wiper shaft nut. Remove wiper arms and rubber shaft covers. Remove bolts at wiper bracket and one bolt at each shaft. Unplug wiring and remove motor assembly with bracket.

Installation — To install, reverse removal procedure.

WIPER SWITCH

Removal — Remove lower steering column cover. Remove screws under steering column and slide switch bracket off steering shaft. Unplug wiring and remove switch.

Installation — To install, reverse removal procedure.

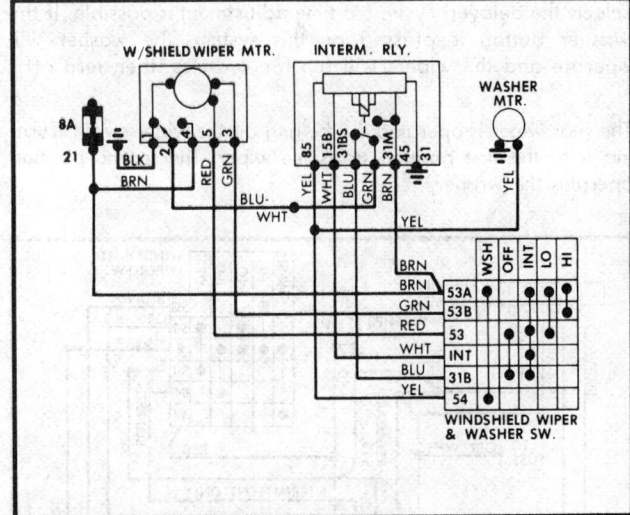

Fig. 2 Saab 900 Wiper/Washer System Wiring Diagram

SUBARU

DL
GL
GLF

DESCRIPTION

The wiper/washer system includes a 2-speed motor, separate washer pump and rotary switch. The switch is located at the right side of the instrument cluster. GL and GLF models have an intermittent system. Hatchback and Station Wagon models may be equipped with a rear window wiper/washer.

OPERATION

The standard wiper system has 2 speeds. The washer is operated by pushing in the button at the end of the wiper switch. The intermittent system has a third switch position that selects the delayed cycle. No time adjustment is possible. If the washer button is pressed on this system, the washer will operate and the wipers will run for 4 cycles, then turn off.

The rear wiper is operated by the ring on the wiper switch. Turning it to the first position starts the wiper. The second position operates the washer.

REMOVAL & INSTALLATION

FRONT WIPER ASSEMBLY

Removal — 1) Pull up arm shaft covers and remove shaft nut. Pull off wiper arms. Unplug wiring at motor. Remove 5 cowl panel screws and lift off cowl panel.

2) Cut a short section of metal tubing the same inner diameter as the outer diameter of the plastic joint on motor shaft. Press tubing down over joint to disconnect rod from wiper motor. Remove wiper motor bolts and motor.

Installation — To install, reverse removal procedure. Place wiper arm with red mark on driver's side. Adjust arms so blades stop about 0.6" (15 mm) above bottom of glass.

REAR WIPER ASSEMBLY

Removal — Lift off arm shaft cover. Remove shaft nut and wiper arm. Remove inside trim from hatch or tailgate. Unplug wiring and remove wiper motor.

Installation — To install, reverse removal procedure.

TESTING

NOTE — *Testing procedures were not available from manufacturer.*

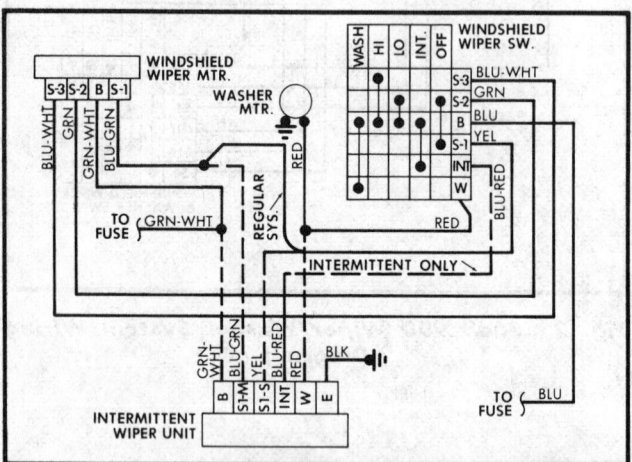

Fig. 1 Subaru Front Wiper/Washer Wiring Diagram

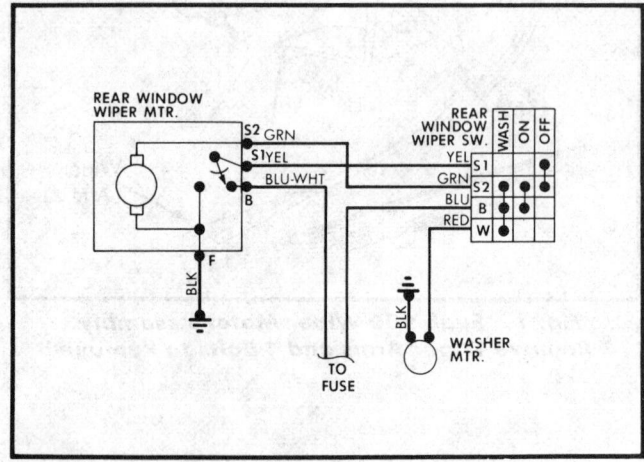

Fig. 2 Subaru Rear Wiper/Washer Wiring Diagram

TOYOTA

Celica   Pickup
Corolla   Starlet
Corona   Supra
Cressida   Tercel
Land Cruiser

DESCRIPTION & OPERATION

All models have a 2-speed front wiper motor that operates the wipers through a linkage system. Most models are equipped with an intermittent feature on the front wiper system. An wiper control relay is used on those systems to allow the delayed wiping action. All models except Pickup may be equipped with a rear wiper/washer system. Corona models have a rear wiper relay located at the rear wiper motor.

The control switch for the front wiper/washer system is a steering column lever. It is part of the combination switch but can be replaced separately on all models except Celica, Starlet and Tercel. All front wiper motors are protected by an internal circuit breaker. The rear wiper/washer system is controlled by a dash or console switch.

TESTING

FRONT WIPER MOTOR

1) Unplug connector at wiper motor. Use an ohmmeter to check continuity between motor case and ground. If not present, repair motor ground. Make sure motor is in park position, then check that continuity exists between terminals "+1", "+2" and "S". No continuity should exist between "B" and all other connector terminals. See Fig. 1.

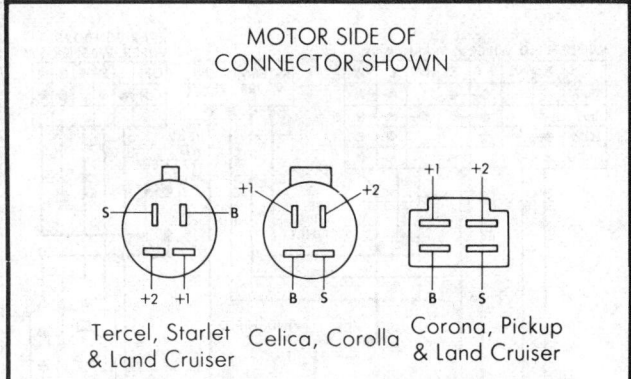

Fig. 1   Front Wiper Motor Terminal Locations for Jumper Wires and Continuity Checks

2) Turn ignition on. Use harness side of connector for this test. Battery voltage should be present at terminal "B". If not, check fuse and wiring.

3) Connect a jumper wire from battery voltage to terminal "+1" on motor connector to run motor at low speed, and to terminal "+2" for high speed.

REAR WIPER MOTOR

1) Unplug connector at wiper motor. Use an ohmmeter to check for continuity between motor case and ground. Be sure motor is in park position, then check for continuity between terminals "+1", "S" and ground. See Fig. 2.

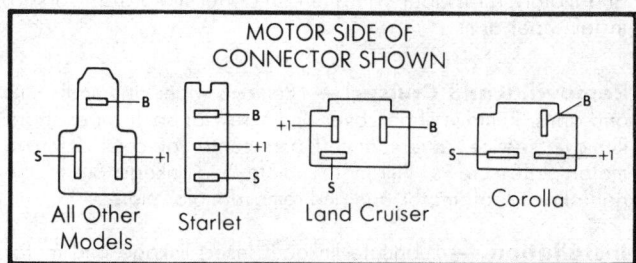

Fig. 2   Rear Wiper Motor Terminal Locations for Jumper Wires and Continuity Check

2) With ignition on, voltage should be present at terminal "B". Connect a jumper wire from battery voltage to motor connector terminal "+1" to check motor operation.

WIPER CONTROL RELAY

Ensure wiper system is operating correctly except for the intermittent wipers. Check that battery voltage is available at wiper relay. If voltage is available and intermittent wipers do not operate properly, replace relay.

Wiper Control Relay Location		
Model	**Connector**	**Location**
Celica	4-Pin	Left kick panel
Corolla	4-pin	Right kick panel
Corona	4-pin	Left kick panel
Cressida	6-pin	Right kick panel
Land Cruiser	5-pin	Under instru. cluster
Pickup	4-pin	Right kick panel
Starlet	4-pin	Left kick panel
Supra	9-pin	Right kick panel
Tercel	4-pin	Left kick panel

REMOVAL & INSTALLATION

FRONT WIPER MOTOR REMOVAL

Removal (Pickup & Starlet) — Remove wiper arm shaft nuts and arms. Use screwdriver to pry wiper linkage from motor arm. Disconnect wiring and remove wiper motor. Scribe alignment marks on motor shaft and arm before removing arm. Remove pivot shaft nuts and remove linkage.

Installation — Grease linkage joints and install linkage and motor. Turn wipers on, then off. After motor has parked, install wiper arms.

Wiper/Washer Systems

TOYOTA (Cont.)

Removal (Corolla, Corona & Cressida) — Remove wiper arm shaft nuts and arms. Remove cowl grille panel and access covers. Disconnect wiring and remove wiper motor bolts. Pry wiper arm from linkage. Remove wiper motor. Scribe alignment marks on motor shaft and arm before removing arm. Pry linkage from pivot shaft. Remove arm shaft screw, then remove pivot and linkage.

Installation — Grease linkage joints and install linkage and motor. Turn wipers on, then off. After motor has parked, install wiper arms.

Removal (Land Cruiser) — Remove wiper arm shaft nuts and arms. Remove shaft cover and screw at each wiper shaft. Remove service covers at left and center of cowl. Remove motor plate screws. Pull motor, plate and linkage out to the right. Pry link off motor arm and remove motor plate.

Installation — Lubricate linkage. Insert linkage and motor into cowl opening. Guide link under cowl reinforcement. Run motor and allow to stop in park position, then install wiper.

NOTE — *No procedures were available for Tercel models.*

Removal (Celica & Supra) — Remove wiper arm shaft nuts and wiper arms. Remove cowl grille panel and access hole covers. Pry linkage from wiper motor arm. Unplug wiring and remove wiper motor. Pry linkage from pivot shaft. Remove arm shaft screw, then remove pivot and linkage.

Installation — To install, lubricate linkage points and reverse removal procedure. Run motor and allow it to stop in park position, then install wiper arm.

REAR WIPER MOTOR REMOVAL

Removal (All Models) — Remove wiper arm shaft nut and wiper arm. Remove shaft bushings. Open rear door and remove inner trim panel. If motor is attached to linkage, disconnect wiper motor arm from linkage. Remove motor.

Installation — To install, reverse removal procedure. Before installing wiper arm, run motor and allow it to stop in park position. Install wiper arm.

WIPER SWITCH

Removal (All Models) — **1)** Disconnect battery ground cable. On Corolla, remove instrument cluster bezel. On Corona, remove fuse block cover and hood release lever. On all models, remove trim panel under steering column. Remove column covers.

2) Remove horn button and pull off steering wheel. Press in locking tabs on connector and unplug it. Remove mounting screws and combination switch. On models with multi-piece switch, remove wiper switch screws. Mark wire terminals and remove from connector.

Installation — To install, reverse removal procedure.

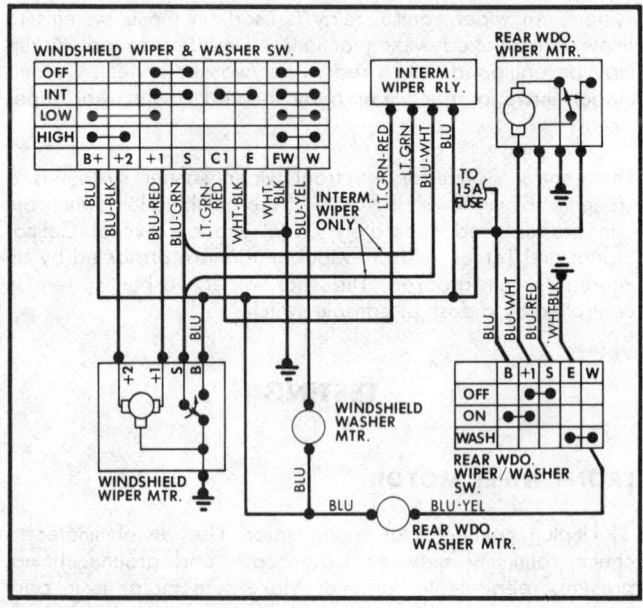

Fig. 4   Celica Wiper Wiring Diagram

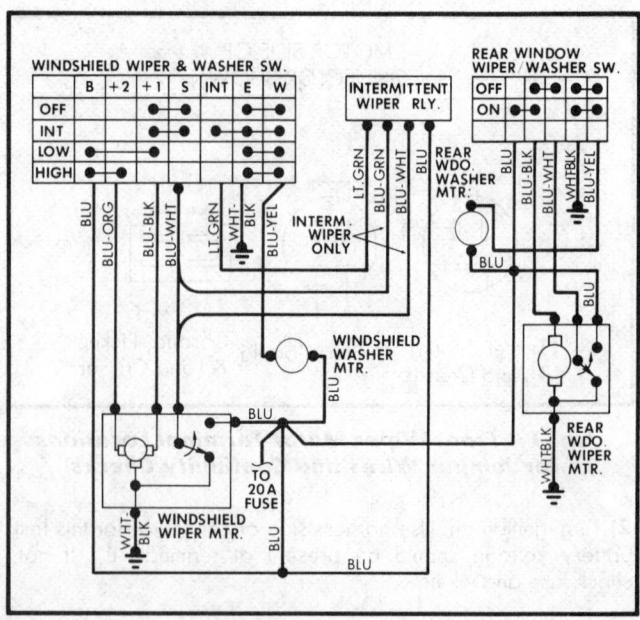

Fig. 5   Corolla Wiper Wiring Diagram

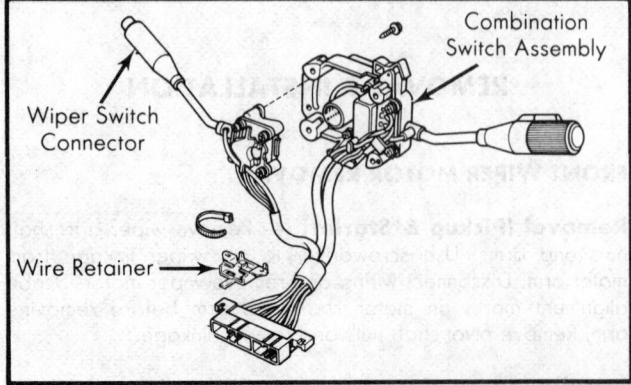

Fig. 3   View of Toyota Combination Switch Showing Wiper Switch Removal

TOYOTA (Cont.)

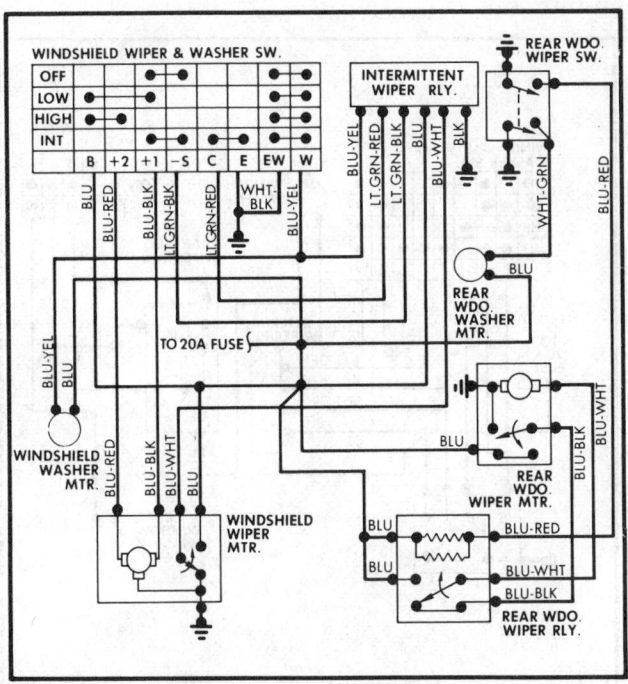

Fig. 6   Corona Wiper Wiring Diagram

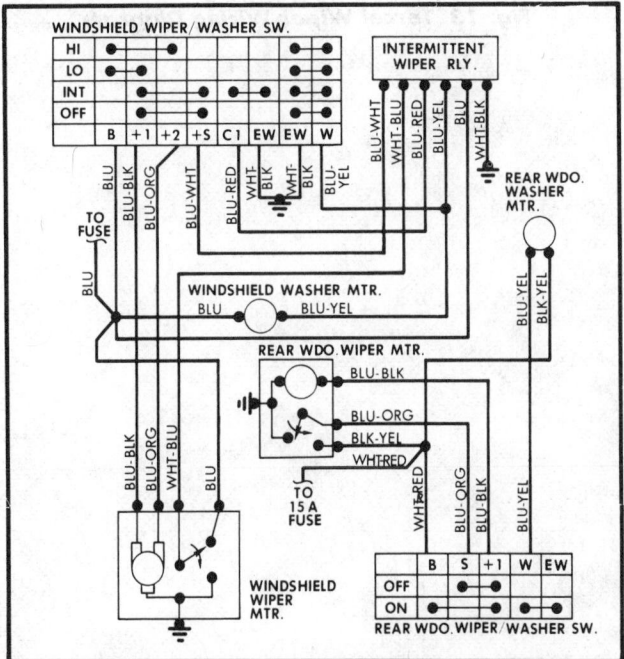

Fig. 7   Cressida Wiper Wiring Diagram

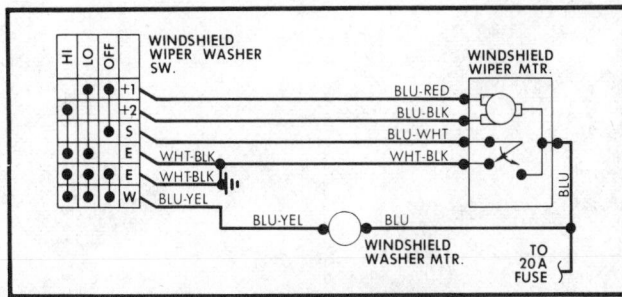

Fig. 8   Land Cruiser FJ40 Wiper Wiring Diagram

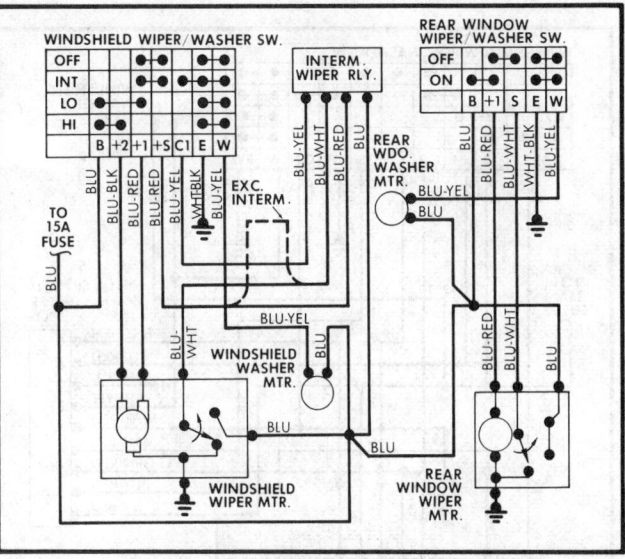

Fig. 9   Land Cruiser FJ60 Wiper Wiring Diagram

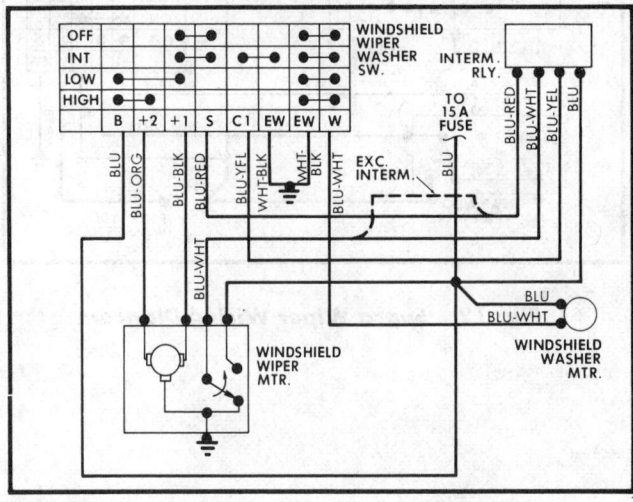

Fig. 10   Pickup Wiper Wiring Diagram

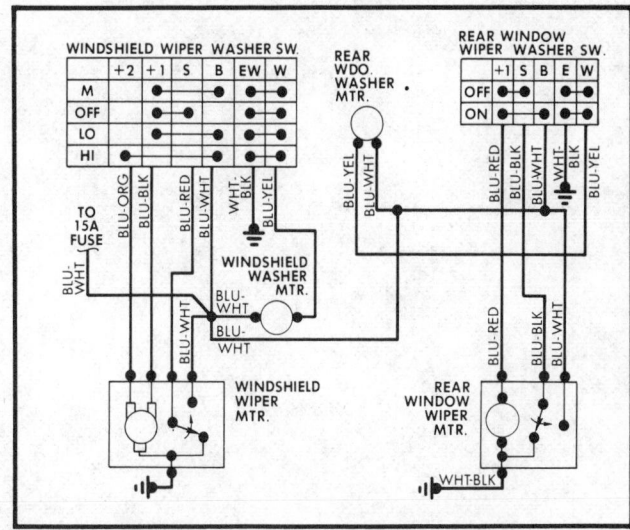

Fig. 11   Starlet Wiper Wiring Diagram

Wiper/Washer Systems

TOYOTA (Cont.)

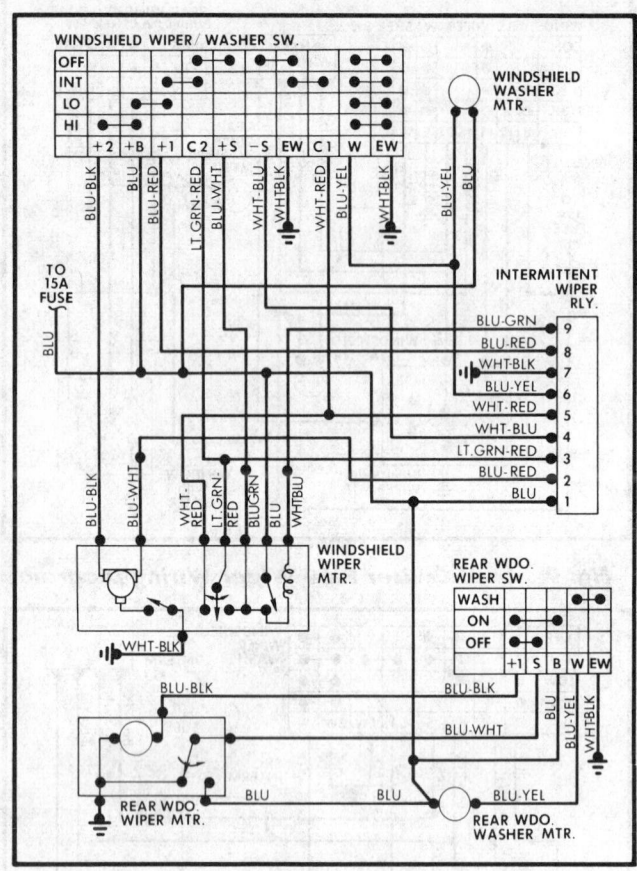

Fig. 12 Supra Wiper Wiring Diagram

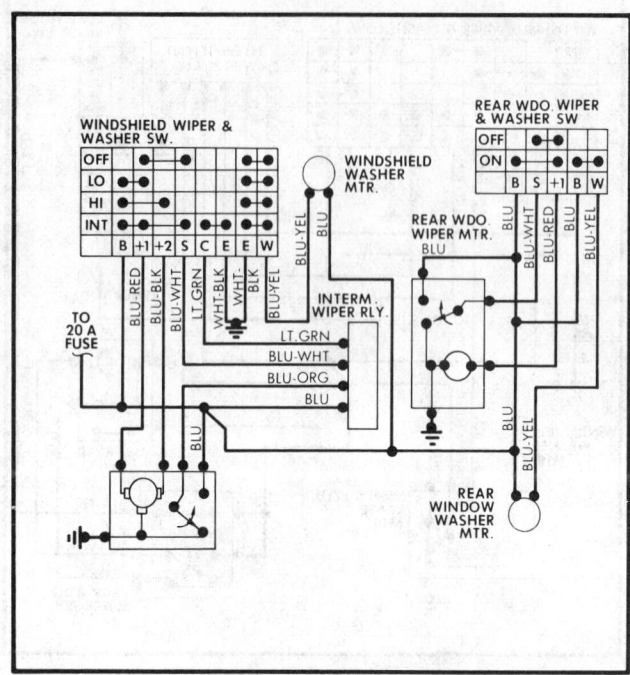

Fig. 13 Tercel Wiper Wiring Diagram

Wiper/Washer Systems

TRIUMPH

TR7
TR8

DESCRIPTION & OPERATION

Triumph models have a 2-speed wiper system. The wiper motor drives a gear and cable system to power the wiper arms. A lever on the steering column operates the wipers. When the lever is pulled down, the wipers cycle until it is released. As the lever is pushed up through the 2 detents, the wipers run at low speed and high speed. The button on the end of the lever operates the washer. The washer pump is located beneath the fluid reservoir.

REMOVAL & INSTALLATION

WIPER MOTOR

Removal — 1) Lift the passenger wiper arm and pry off wiper arm from shaft. Leave driver's side arm on glass and pry off arm with screwdriver. Remove nut and spacer, then pull off pivot plate and arm. Remove cowl fresh air duct and washer reservoir.

2) Unplug motor wiring. Remove screw from motor strap and unhook strap from body. Remove 2 screws and access plate near brake master cylinder. Remove rubber gasket on left wiper shaft. Remove nut, spacer and gasket from right wiper shaft. Remove motor and drive assembly.

3) Remove 5 screws and gearbox cover. Remove circlip, washer, connecting shaft and washer. Lift out rack and tube assembly.

Installation — Lubricate gears and sliding surfaces in motor assembly. Reverse removal procedures to complete installation. Before installing wiper arms, run motor and allow it to return to park position.

WIPER SWITCH

Removal — 1) Disconnect battery ground cable. Remove 2 long screws and steering column cover. Remove steering wheel. Note wiring harness routing, then remove clips and unplug wiring. Loosen switch clamp screw and slide combination switch off column.

2) To service the wiper switch, drill out the 2 rivets. Do not remove screws near center hole in switch. Remove the switch lever pivot screw, then remove switch. *See Fig. 2.*

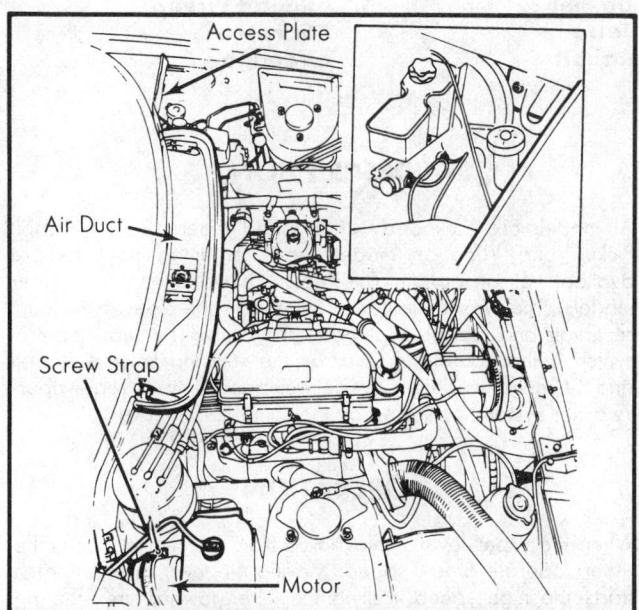

Fig. 1   Removing Wiper Motor on Triumph TR8. TR7 Models are Similar.

Installation — Position new switch and install 2 bolts where rivets were drilled out. Insert pivot screw and tighten slightly so lever is still free to move. Place switch on column and tighten clamp screw. Before installing steering wheel, ensure that arrow on turn signal cam aligns with turn signal lever. Reverse removal procedures to complete installation.

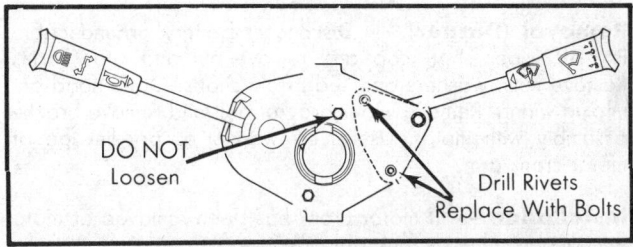

Fig. 2   Removing Wiper Switch From Combination Switch. Remove Screws and Rivets as Shown.

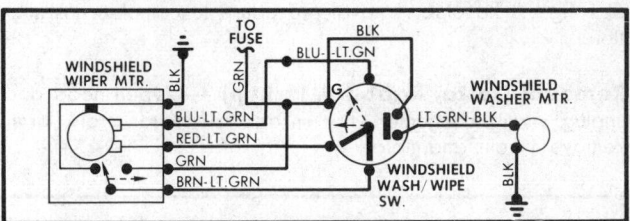

Fig. 3   Triumph Wiper/Washer Wiring Diagram

Wiper/Washer Systems

VOLKSWAGEN

Dasher	Rabbit Pickup
Jetta	Scirocco
Rabbit	Vanagon

DESCRIPTION

All models are equipped with 2-speed wipers. Rabbit, Rabbit Pickup and Vanagon models have an intermittent feature available as an option. This feature is standard on all other models. The washer motor is located in the side of the fluid reservoir and can be replaced separately. The wiper control switch is the right-hand lever on the steering column. Rabbit and Scirocco models may be equipped with a rear wiper-/washer system, operated by the same column lever.

OPERATION

When the wiper lever is moved up from the rest position, the wipers operate at low speed. Moving the lever another notch starts the high speed. Pulling the lever toward the steering wheel operates the washer. Pushing the lever toward the dashboard starts the rear system (if equipped). Pulling the lever down from the rest position selects the intermittent wiper cycle (if equipped). The wipers operate once every 6 seconds.

REMOVAL & INSTALLATION

FRONT WIPER MOTOR

Removal (Dasher) — Disconnect battery ground cable. Pry off wiper shaft cap and remove nut and wiper arms. Remove nuts, washers and seals from shafts. Open hood and unplug wiring. Remove wiper bracket bolt and remove bracket assembly with motor. Use a screwdriver to pry linkage off motor crank arm.

Installation — If motor crank has been removed or motor is changed, check crank arm alignment. Connect wiring plug and allow motor to run briefly. Stop motor and allow it to park. Crank arm should be at 90° angle to motor centerline. See Fig. 1. Reverse removal procedure to complete installation.

Removal (Jetta, Rabbit & Pickup) — Open hood and unplug wiring connector. Pry linkage off motor crank arm. Remove 4 bolts and motor.

NOTE — Do not remove motor bracket when removing motor.

Installation — Check crank arm alignment by running motor and allowing it to park. Crank arm should be at 20° angle to motor centerline. See Fig. 1. To complete installation, reverse removal procedure, installing left linkage rod first.

Removal (Scirocco) — Remove connecting linkage from motor crank arm. Unplug wiring. Remove wiper motor crank arm and 3 motor bolts. Slide motor out from beneath bracket and remove motor.

Installation — Check crank arm alignment by running motor and allowing it to park. Crank arm should be in line with the motor centerline, and linkage ball should point away from motor. See Fig. 1. Reverse removal procedure to complete installation.

Removal (Vanagon) — Remove wipers arms and shaft nuts. Remove glove box and instrument cluster. Remove wiper linkage rods by extending fully to passenger side. Remove wiper bracket bolts and bracket. Remove crank arm, 3 bolts and wiper motor.

Installation — Connect motor wiring, run motor and allow it to park. Align crank arm and linkage rod as shown. See Fig. 1. Reverse removal procedure to install.

REAR WIPER MOTOR

Removal — Remove inner trim panel on rear hatch. Unplug wiring and pry linkage off motor crank arm. Remove motor crank arm, motor bolts and motor.

Installation — Check crank arm alignment by running motor and allowing it to park. Install crank arm in correct position. See Fig. 2. Reverse removal procedure to complete installation.

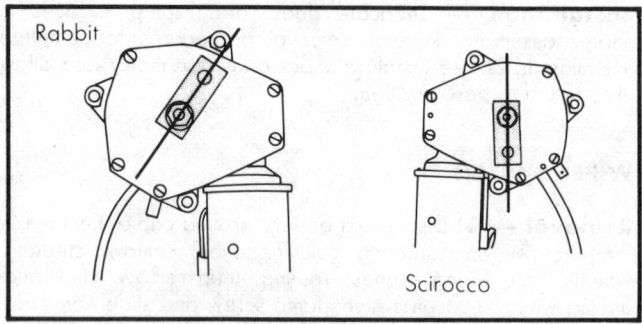

Fig. 2   Aligning Rear Motor Crank Arm During Installation. Motor Must Be in Park Position.

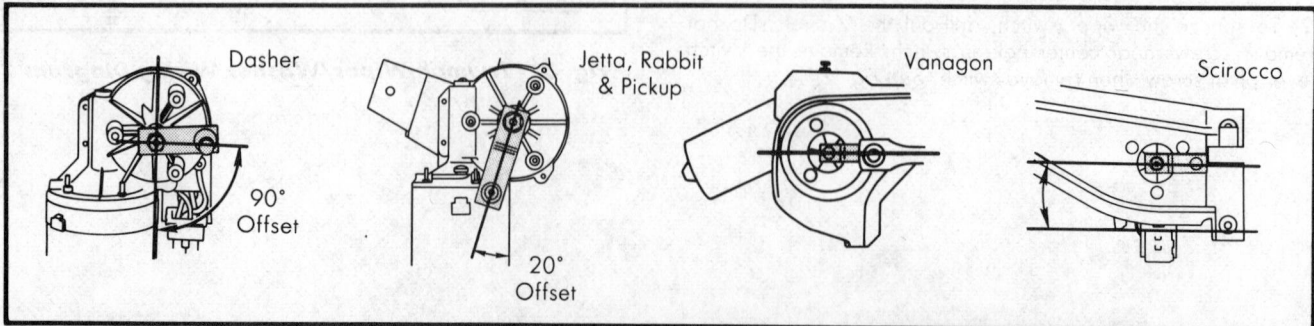

Fig. 1   Aligning Front Motor Crank Arm During Installation. Motor Must Be in Park Position.

VOLKSWAGEN (Cont.)

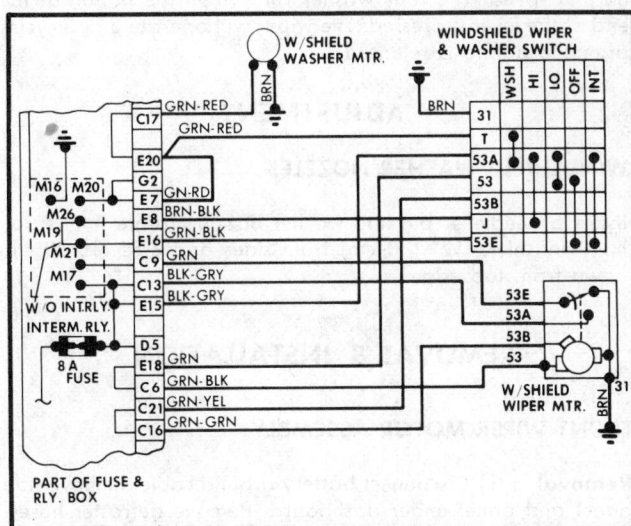

Fig. 3 Dasher, Jetta & Rabbit Convertible Wiper System Wiring Diagram

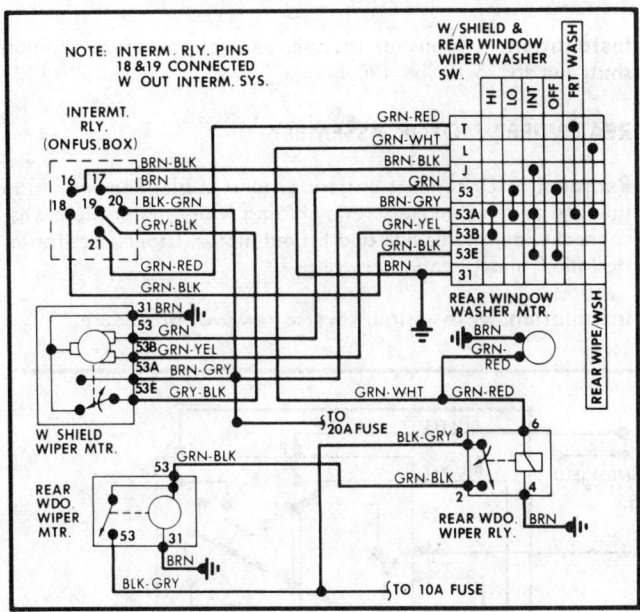

Fig. 4 Rabbit & Rabbit Pickup Wiper System Wiring Diagram

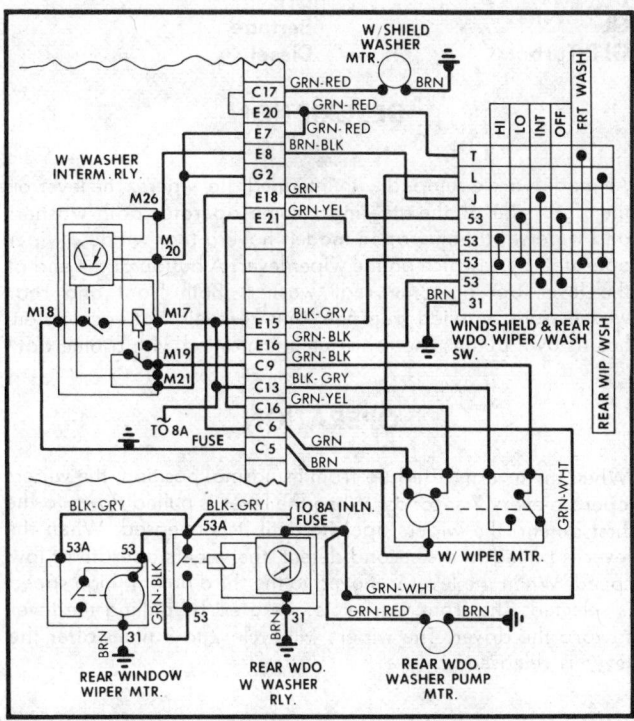

Fig. 5 Scirocco Wiper System Wiring Diagram

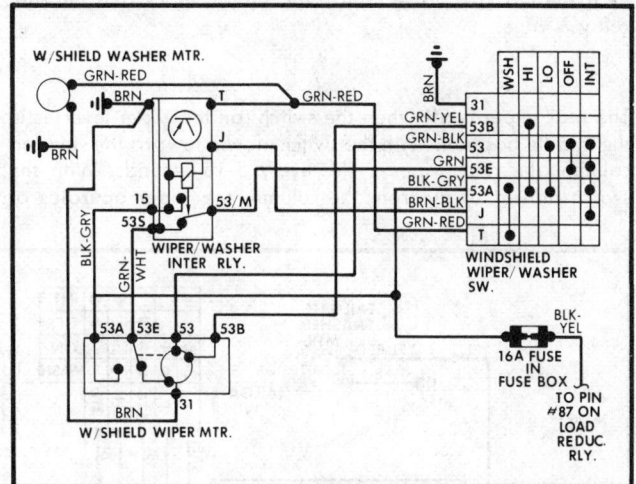

Fig. 6 Vanagon Wiper System Wiring Diagram

Wiper/Washer Systems

VOLVO

DL   GLE
GL   Bertone
GLT Turbo   Diesel

DESCRIPTION

All models are equipped with intermediate wipers. The lever on the right side of the steering column operates both washers and wipers. Station wagon models have a rear window wiper operated by a switch on the wiper lever. A button at the end of the lever operates the rear washer. Both front and rear washers are supplied from the same resevoir, but each system has its own pump. The rear pump is marked with a blue dot.

OPERATION

When the lever is lifted up from its normal position, the wipers operate every 7 seconds. When the lever is pulled down to the first detent, the wipers operate until it is released. When the lever is pulled to the second detent, the wipers operate at low speed. When the lever is moved to the third detent, high speed is selected. The front washer is operated by pulling the lever toward the driver. The wipers will cycle 2 to 3 times after the lever is released.

NOTE — *The interval relays are located under a footplate near the left kick panel. The front relay is black and the rear relay is blue.*

The rear wiper is off when the switch (on the wiper lever) is in the middle position. With the switch moved toward the steering column, the rear wiper cycles every 5-15 seconds. With the switch moved away from the column, the wiper operates at normal speed. The rear washer runs when the button at the end of the lever is pressed. The wiper will operate 2 or 3 cycles after the button is released.

ADJUSTMENT

WINDSHIELD WASHER NOZZLES

Insert a needle or pin into washer nozzle. Rotate until spray hits windshield 12" (30 cm) from sides and 4-8" (10-20 cm) down from top edge.

REMOVAL & INSTALLATION

FRONT WIPER MOTOR ASSEMBLY

Removal — 1) Disconnect battery ground cable. Remove side panel and panel under dashboard. Remove defroster hoses. Remove glove box.

2) Lift wiper arm pivot cover and remove shaft nut. Remove wiper arm. Disconnect wiper arm assembly and lift out through glove box.

Installation — To install, reverse removal procedure. Tighten shaft nut to 15 ft. lbs. (20 N·m).

REAR WIPER MOTOR ASSEMBLY

Removal — Disconnect battery ground cable. Remove inside tailgate panel. Remove screws holding wiper motor plate. Disconnect wiper motor link and lift out motor. Label wires for installation and disconnect wiring.

Installation — To install, reverse removal procedure.

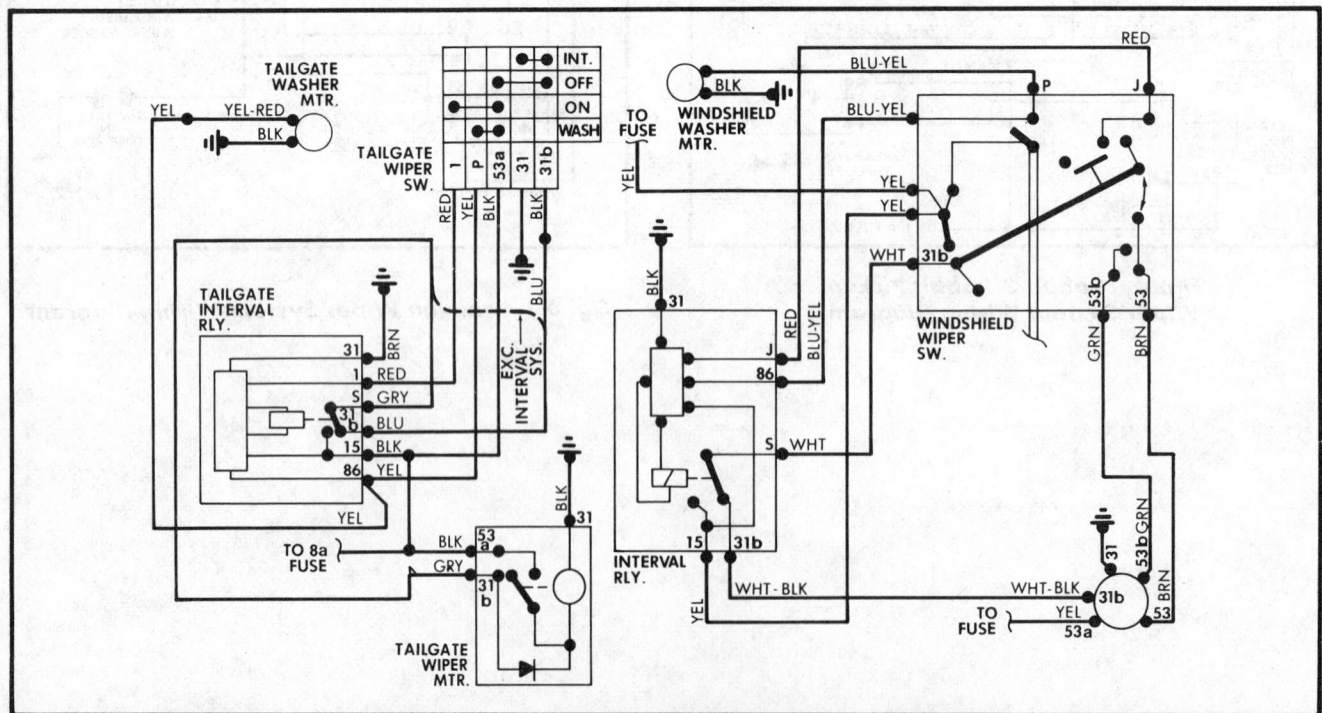

Fig. 1   Volvo Wiper/Washer System Wiring Diagram

Section 6
ENGINES

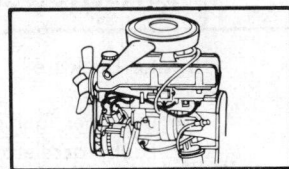

Contents

NOTE — ALSO SEE GENERAL INDEX.

Engine Trouble Shooting

GASOLINE ENGINE TROUBLE SHOOTING

The following Trouble Shooting guide covers all mechanical problems which relate to all engines in general. For specific Trouble Shooting problems relating to Diesel engines, see Diesel Engine Trouble Shooting in this section. For Carburetor or Ignition problems in all engines, see Tune-Up Trouble Shooting in Section 1.

CONDITION & POSSIBLE CAUSE	CONDITION & POSSIBLE CAUSE

Engine Lopes While Idling

- Intake manifold-to-head leaks.
- Blown head gasket.
- Worn timing gears, chain or sprocket.
- Worn camshaft lobes.
- Overheated engine.
- Blocked crankcase vent valve.
- Leaking EGR valve.
- Faulty fuel pump.

Engine Has Low Power

- Leaking fuel pump.
- Sticking valves, weak valve springs, incorrect valve timing or worn camshaft lobes.
- Excessive piston-to-bore clearance.
- Blown head gasket.
- Improper power steering glow control valve operation.
- Clutch slipping on manual transmission.
- Engine overheating.
- Improper pressure regulator valve operation on automatic transmission.
- Improper automatic transmission fluid level.
- Improper operation of diverter valve.
- Vacuum leaks.
- Leaking piston rings.

Faulty High Speed Operation

- Low fuel pump volume.
- Leaking engine valves, or faulty valve springs.
- Incorrect valve timing.
- Intake manifold restricted.
- Worn distributor shaft.

Faulty Acceleration

- Improper fuel pump stroke.
- Incorrect basic ignition timing.
- Inoperative pump discharge check ball or needle.
- Faulty elastomer valve.
- Worn or damaged pump diaphragm or piston.
- Leaking engine valves.

Intake Backfire

- Improper ignition timing.
- Faulty accelerator pump discharge.
- Improper choke operation.
- Defective EGR valve.
- Too lean fuel mixture.
- Initial choke valve clearance too large.

Exhaust Backfire

- Vacuum leak.
- Faulty diverter valve.
- Faulty choke operation.
- Exhaust system leak.

Engine Detonation

- Overadvanced timing or faulty ignition system.
- Spark plugs loose or cracked.
- Fuel lines, fuel filter or fuel pump clogged or faulty.
- EGR valve inoperative.
- PCV system inoperative.
- Vacuum leaks.
- Excessive combustion chamber deposits.
- Leaking, sticking or broken valves.

External Oil Leakage

- Improperly seated fuel pump, or worn gasket.
- Improperly seated or broken push rod cover gasket.
- Improperly seated or broken oil filter gasket.
- Improperly seated or broken oil pan gasket, or bent oil pan gasket surface.
- Improperly seated or broken timing chain cover gasket.
- Improperly seated or worn rear main bearing oil seal.
- Loose oil line plugs.
- Improperly seated oil pan drain plug.
- Obstructed camshaft rear bearing drain hole.
- Loose rocker arm cover, or broken cover gasket.
- Oil pressure sending switch leaking.

GASOLINE ENGINE TROUBLE SHOOTING (Cont.)

CONDITION & POSSIBLE CAUSE	CONDITION & POSSIBLE CAUSE

Excessive Oil Consumption

- Intake or exhaust valve "O" ring seal damaged or has excessive looseness.
- Worn valve stems or guides.
- Plugged oil drain back holes.
- Improper PCV valve operation.
- Engine oil level too high.
- Engine oil too thin.
- Valve stem oil deflectors missing or damaged.
- Piston rings improperly installed or incorrect size.
- Piston rings out-of-round, broken or scored.
- Piston ring gaps not staggered.
- Piston ring tension insufficient due to engine overheating.
- Piston ring grooves or oil return slots clogged.
- Piston rings sticking in ring grooves.
- Ring grooves worn excessively.
- Compression rings installed upside down.
- Excessively worn or scored cylinder walls.
- Mismatch of oil ring expander and rail.
- Intake gasket dowels too long.
- Excessive main or connecting rod bearing clearance.

No Oil Pressure

- Low oil level.
- Oil pressure gauge or sending unit broken.
- Oil pump malfunction.
- Oil pressure relief valve sticking.
- Oil passages on pressure side of pump blocked.
- Oil pickup screen or tube blocked.
- Loose oil inlet tube.
- Excessive clearance at main or connecting rod bearing.
- Loose camshaft bearings.
- Internal leakage at oil passages.

Low Oil Pressure

- Low engine oil level, or engine oil too thin.
- Oil pressure relief spring weak or stuck.
- Oil pickup tube and screen blocked, or has air leak.
- Excessive oil pump clearance.
- Excessive main, rod or camshaft bearing clearance.

High Oil Pressure

- Improper grade of oil.
- Oil pressure gauge or sending unit inaccurate.
- Oil pressure relief valve sticking closed.

Noisy Main Bearings

- Inadequate oil supply.
- Excessive main bearing clearance.
- Excessive crankshaft end play.
- Loose flywheel or torque converter.
- Loose or damaged vibration damper.
- Eccentric or out-of-round crankshaft journals.
- Excessive belt tension.

Noisy Connecting Rods

- Inadequate oil supply.
- Excessive bearing clearance or missing bearing.
- Crankshaft connecting rod journal out-of-round.
- Misaligned connecting rod or cap.
- Improperly tightened connecting rod bolts.

Noisy Pistons and Rings

- Excessive piston-to-cylinder wall clearance.
- Cylinder walls excessively tapered or out-of-round.
- Piston ring broken.
- Piston pin loose or seized.
- Connecting rods misaligned.
- Piston ring side clearance excessively loose or tight.
- Excessive carbon build-up on piston.

Noisy Valve Train Components

- Insufficient oil supply.
- Worn or bent push rods.
- Worn rocker arms, or bridged pivots.
- Dirt or chips in hydraulic valve lifters.
- Excessive valve lifter leak down.
- Valve lifter face worn.
- Broken or cocked valve springs.
- Excessive valve stem-to-guide clearance.
- Valve bent.
- Loose rocker arms.
- Excessive valve seat runout.
- Missing valve lock.
- Push rod rubbing or contacting cylinder head.

Engine Trouble Shooting

GASOLINE ENGINE TROUBLE SHOOTING (Cont.)

CONDITION & POSSIBLE CAUSE	CONDITION & POSSIBLE CAUSE
Noisy Valve Train Components (Cont.) • Excessively worn camshaft lobes. • Plugged valve lifter oil feed holes. • Faulty valve lifter check ball. • Rocker arm retaining nut installed upside down. • Valve lifters incorrectly fitted to bore size. • Faulty valve lifter plunger, or push rod seat. **Noisy Valves** • Improper valve lash. • Excessively worn, dirty or faulty valve lifters. • Worn valve guides. • Excessive runout of valve seat or valve face. • Worn camshaft lobes. • Loose rocker arm studs. • Bent push rods. • Broken valve springs. **Burned, Sticking or Broken Valves** • Weak valve springs. • Improper valve lifter clearance. • Improper valve guide clearance, or worn guides.	• Out-of-round valve seats, or improper valve seat width. • Deposits or gum formation on valve stems, seats or guides. • Warped valves or faulty valve forgings. • Exhaust back pressure. • Improper spark timing. **Broken Pistons and/or Rings** • Undersize pistons. • Wrong type or size of rings. • Tapered or eccentric cylinder bore. • Improper connecting rod alignment. • Excessively worn ring grooves. • Improperly assembled piston pins. • Insufficient ring gap clearance. • Engine overheating. • Incorrect ignition timing. **Excessive Exhaust Noise** • Leaks at exhaust pipe joints. • Burned or blown out muffler or exhaust pipe. • Exhaust pipe leaking at manifold flange. • Exhaust manifold cracked or broken. • Leak between manifold and cylinder head. • Obstruction in muffler or tail pipe.

DIESEL ENGINE TROUBLE SHOOTING

Diesel engine mechanical diagnosis is the same as that for gasoline engines for such items as noisy lifters, rod bearings, main bearings, valves, rings and pistons. The following trouble shooting guide cover those items which apply only to diesel engines.

CONDITION & POSSIBLE CAUSE	CONDITION & POSSIBLE CAUSE
Engine Does Not Crank • Loose or corroded battery cables, or dead batteries. • Loose starter connections or faulty starter. **Engine Cranks Slowly but Does Not Start** • Loose or corroded battery cables, or batteries do not have a sufficient charge. • Wrong weight engine oil in engine.	**Engine Cranks Normally but Does Not Start** • Glow plugs not functioning. • Glow plug control system not functioning. • Fuel not being injected into cylinders. • No fuel going to injection pump. • Fuel filter blocked. • Fuel tank filter blocked. • Fuel pump not operating. • Fuel return system blocked. • No voltage to fuel solenoid. • Incorrect or contaminated fuel.

DIESEL ENGINE TROUBLE SHOOTING (Cont.)

CONDITION & POSSIBLE CAUSE	CONDITION & POSSIBLE CAUSE

Engine Cranks Normally but Does Not Start (Cont.)

- Incorrect injection pump timing.
- Low compression.
- Injection pump malfunction.

Engine Starts but Will Not Run at Idle

- Incorrect slow idle adjustment.
- Fast idle solenoid not functioning.
- Fuel return system blocked.
- Glow plugs turning off too soon.
- Injection pump timing incorrect.
- Insufficient fuel going to injection pump.
- Incorrect or contaminated fuel.
- Low compression.
- Injection pump malfunction.
- Fuel solenoid closes in "RUN" position.

Engine Starts and Idles Rough Without Abnormal Smoke or Noise

- Incorrect slow idle adjustment.
- Injection line fuel leaks.
- Fuel return system blocked.
- Air in fuel system.
- Incorrect or contaminated fuel.
- Injector nozzle malfunction.

Engine Starts and Idles Rough Without Abnormal Smoke or Noise, but Clears After Warm-Up

- Injection pump timing incorrect.
- Engine has not fully broken in.
- Air in fuel system.
- Injector nozzle malfunction.

Engine Misfires Above Idle but Idles Correctly

- Blocked fuel filter.
- Injection pump timing incorrect.
- Incorrect or contaminated fuel.

Engine Will Not Return to Idle

- External linkage binding or adjusted wrong.
- Fast idle adjustment incorrect.
- Internal injection pump malfunction.

Fuel Leaking on Ground

- Loose or broken fuel line or connection.
- Internal injection pump seal leak.

Knocking Noise from Cylinders

- Injector nozzles sticking open.
- Very low nozzle opening pressure.

Noticeable Loss of Engine Power

- Restricted air intake.
- EGR valve malfunction.
- Restricted or damaged exhaust system.
- Blocked fuel tank filter
- Blocked fuel filter, or fuel tank vacuum vent in gas cap.
- Restricted fuel supply from tank to injection pump.
- Restricted fuel return system.
- Incorrect or contaminated fuel.
- External compression leaks.
- Blocked injector nozzles.
- Low compression.

Excessive Black Smoke and Loud Engine Noise

- Basic timing incorrect.
- EGR valve malfunction.
- Injector pump housing pressure not to specifications.
- Internal injection pump malfunction.

Engine Overheating

- Cooling system leaks.
- Belt slipping or damaged.
- Thermostat stuck closed.
- Head gasket leaking

Oil Light On at Idle

- Oil cooler, or oil cooler line restricted.
- Low oil pump pressure.

Engine Will Not Shut Off

- Injector pump fuel solenoid doesn't return fuel valve to "OFF" position.

VACUUM PUMP DIAGNOSIS

Excessive Noise

- Loose screws between pump and drive assembly.
- Loose tube on pump assembly.
- Valves not functioning properly.

Oil Leakage

- Loose end plug.
- Bad crimp.

4000 4-CYLINDER

ENGINE CODING

ENGINE IDENTIFICATION

Engine number is stamped on side of engine block near distributor. Number prefix indicates the following application:

Engine Identification Codes	
Application	Engine Code
Federal	YG
Calif.	YK

ENGINE & CYLINDER HEAD

ENGINE

NOTE — *Unless otherwise specified, leave all fuel injection lines connected to components.*

Removal — 1) Disconnect battery ground strap. Remove grille, condenser from radiator, and air duct from throttle valve housing. Remove hose from air duct to auxiliary air regulator. Remove fuel distributor, air flow sensor, fuel injectors, and air cleaner as one unit. Remove cold start valve.

NOTE — *Cap or plug fuel injectors and cold start valve.*

2) Remove front engine mount. Loosen nuts on outer half of crankshaft pulley and remove "V" belt. Discharge refrigerant from air conditioning system and remove air conditioning lines from compressor. Support bracket and plug all open connections.

3) Disconnect wire to compressor clutch. Remove crankcase vent hose connection from valve cover and move air conditioning hoses to one side, away from engine. Remove upper compressor mounting bolts and 3 lower compressor mounting bolts. Remove compressor from vehicle.

4) Open heater control valve fully. Remove cap from coolant expansion tank. Drain coolant from engine by removing hoses, saving coolant for later installation. Remove upper radiator hose from engine, lower radiator hose from radiator, and plug from radiator fan.

5) Disconnect plug from radiator thermo switch. Remove both rubber mounts and lift radiator, fan and fan shroud out of vehicle as an assembly.

6) Disconnect clutch cable. Disconnect wiring. Remove control pressure regulator, leaving fuel lines connected. Remove air hose, if equipped. Unplug blue wire from alternator at plug between battery and rear of engine. Remove charcoal filter hose at intake air duct.

7) Disconnect wiring on oil pressure switch and coolant temperature gauge sender. Remove wires from ignition coil. Remove heater hoses.

8) Remove throttle cable. Remove vacuum hoses from the following:

- Ignition distributor retard unit (clear hose).
- Ignition distributor advance unit (violet hose), leading to charcoal filter.

- Throttle valve housing (gray hose) leading to vacuum amplifier.
- EGR temperature control valve (blue angled connection) to vacuum amplifier.
- Throttle valve housing stage 1 (red hose) to vacuum amplifier.
- Intake manifold (hose leading to brake booster).

9) Pull out fuel injectors. Remove 3 upper engine-to-transmission bolts. Remove right and left engine mount nuts. Remove exhaust pipe attaching nuts from manifold and remove pipe. Remove cover plate.

10) Remove front engine mount. Disconnect starter cables and label for later installation. Remove starter. Remove 2 lower engine-to-transmission bolts. Loosen right and left engine mount nuts on subframe. Through starter hole, remove torque converter bolts.

11) Remove bolt for front exhaust pipe support. Install transmission support tool. Install engine lift chain (US 1105). Lift engine until weight is taken off engine mounts. Adjust support bar to contact transmission.

12) Pry engine apart from transmission. Carefully lift engine out of engine compartment, using caution not to damage transmission mainshaft, clutch and body. Mount engine on stand.

Installation — To install engine, reverse removal procedure. When tightening engine mount and subframe bolts, run engine at idle speed. Tighten mount bolts. Adjust throttle and clutch cables, align exhaust system components and refill coolant expansion tank.

CYLINDER HEAD

Removal & Installation — 1) Disconnect battery ground cable. Drain coolant system and disconnect hoses which are connected to cylinder head. Disconnect exhaust pipe and electrical wires. Disengage accelerator linkage and disconnect at holder. Loosen alternator tensioner and remove "V" belt and camshaft drive belt.

2) Loosen head bolts in reverse order or tightening sequence shown in *Fig. 1*. To install, ensure that cylinder head and block cylinder head mating surfaces are clean. Install cylinder head gasket DRY, using no sealant. Use only polygon cylinder head bolts. Install bolts 8 and 10 first to center cylinder head. Tighten head bolts in sequence illustrated.

NOTE — *DO NOT torque polygon cylinder head bolts after first 1000 miles, nor after 1000 miles following repair.*

3) When installing "V" belt, adjust tension so that thumb pressure permits 3/8-9/16" (10-15 mm) deflection of belt inward, midway between alternator and crankshaft belt pulley. When installing camshaft timing belt, adjust tensioning arm until belt can be turned 90° with thumb and index finger at a point midway between camshaft sprocket and intermediate sprocket.

4000 4-CYLINDER (Cont.)

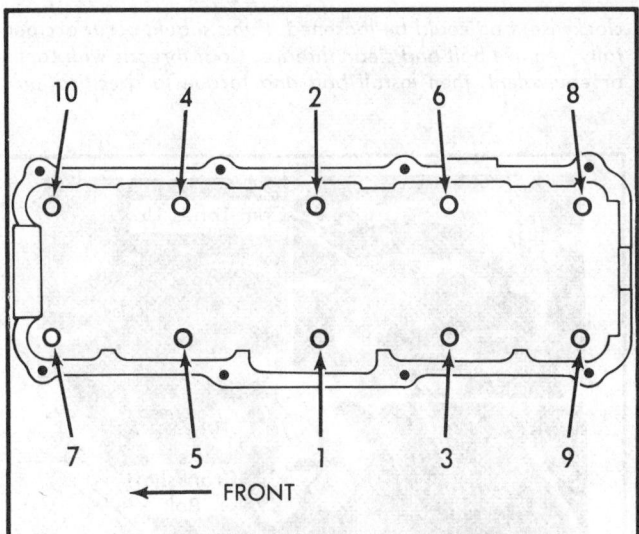

Fig. 1   Cylinder Head Tightening Sequence (Reverse Sequence When Removing)

CAMSHAFT

TIMING BELT

1) Remove radiator grille. Loosen alternator mounting bolts and remove "V" belt. Remove camshaft belt guard. Loosen mounting nut of camshaft belt tensioner arm and remove tension from belt. Slide belt forward off camshaft sprocket.

2) Install new belt and adjust tensioner arm until belt can be turned 90° with thumb and index finger at a point midway between camshaft sprocket and intermediate sprocket. Check valve timing.

CAMSHAFT

Removal – Remove bearing caps 1, 3, and 5. Diagonally loosen bearing caps 2 and 4 in steps. Remove caps and lift out camshaft.

Installation – To install, lubricate bearing shells, journals and contact faces of caps. Install caps 1, 3, and 5, observing off-center bearing position. See Fig. 2. Numbers on bearing caps are not always on same side. Tighten bearing caps diagonally. Install caps 2 and 4 and tighten diagonally.

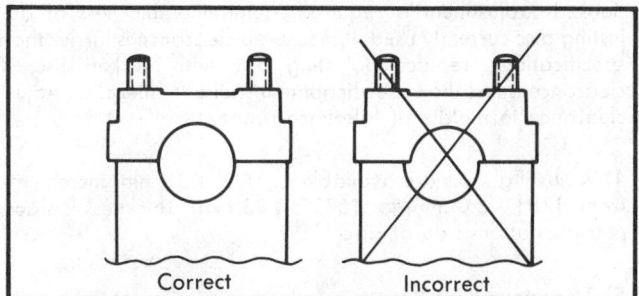

Fig. 2   Checking Bearing Cap Alignment

CAMSHAFT OIL SEAL

Removal – Remove upper drive belt cover. Set crankshaft to TDC on cylinder 1. Loosen drive belt and remove camshaft

sprocket. Remove Woodruff key. Using special tool (10-219), remove oil seal.

Installation – Install protective sleeve (10-203) over camshaft. Push seal over sleeve, and using remainder of special tool (10-203), press seal in until flush. Check camshaft end play with cam followers removed. Maximum end play is .006" (.15 mm). Reinstall cam followers.

VALVE TIMING

1) Turn camshaft sprocket until punch mark on rear of camshaft sprocket is aligned with upper edge of lower drive belt cover (arrow) or valve cover gasket on left side of engine. See Fig. 3.

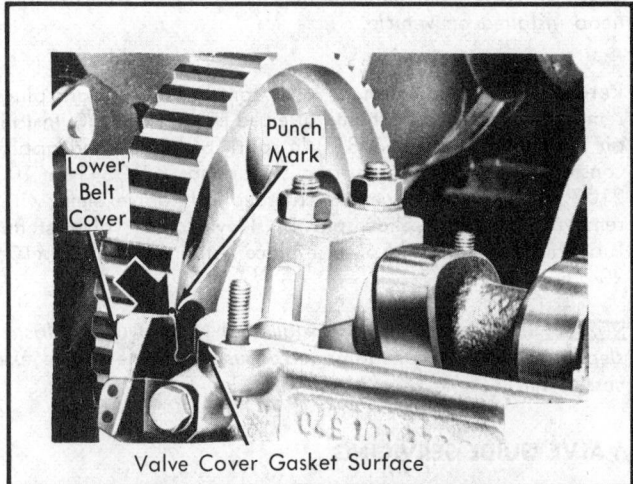

Fig. 3   Camshaft Drive Sprocket Timing Mark Alignment

2) Turn crankshaft pulley and intermediate shaft sprocket until notch in crankshaft pulley is aligned with punch mark on intermediate shaft sprocket. See Fig. 4. Slide camshaft drive belt in place and adjust tension, as previously described.

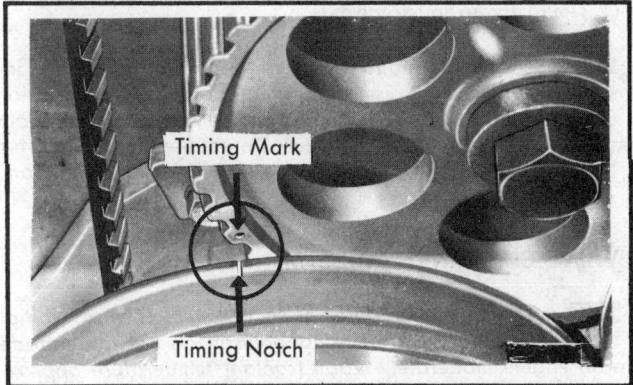

Fig. 4   Intermediate Shaft Sprocket Aligned with TDC Notch in Crankshaft Pulley

VALVES

VALVE ARRANGEMENT

E-I-E-I-I-E-I-E (front to rear).

Audi Engines

4000 4-CYLINDER (Cont.)

VALVE SPRINGS

With cam followers removed, install valve spring compressor tool (10-210). Compress springs and remove valve keepers and collar. Lift out valve springs. To install, reverse removal procedure.

MECHANICAL VALVE LIFTER ASSEMBLY

With camshaft and adjusting discs removed, lift out cam followers. Inspect for wear or damage. Replace as necessary. Lightly oil cam followers and replace in original location.

VALVE STEM OIL SEALS

NOTE — *Valve stem oil seals may be replaced with cylinder head installed on vehicle.*

Removal & Installation — With camshaft and spark plug removed, turn crankshaft until affected piston is at BDC. Install air hose adapter (VW 653/3) in spark plug hole and apply constant pressure. Using spring compressor (VW 541 or 10-210), remove valve keepers. Lift seal off valve stem with remover (10-218). Slide plastic sleeve onto valve stem. Lubricate new seal and push in place with installing tool (10-204).

NOTE — *Do not attempt to install seal without using plastic sleeve, or seal will be damaged, causing engine to use excessive oil.*

VALVE GUIDE SERVICING

1) Before taking measurements, clean valve guides with a cleaning broach. To measure, attach a suitable device with a dial indicator (VW 387 or US 4420A) to mounting surface of cylinder head. Insert a new valve into valve guide until stem is flush with end of guide. Rock valve against dial indicator and check amount of guide-to-stem clearance. Maximum valve rock should not exceed .039" (1.0 mm) for intake valves or .051" (1.3 mm) for exhaust valves.

2) Use suitable press and adaptor (10-206) to remove and install valve guides. Press worn guides out from combustion chamber side. Coat new guide with oil and press into cold cylinder head from camshaft side. Do not use more than 1 ton of pressure or guide shoulder may break. Ream guide by hand to proper size.

VALVE CLEARANCE ADJUSTMENT

NOTE — *Cold settings are given for reference as initial settings after engine work. Final adjustments are to be made with engine moderately warm (coolant temperature approximately 95° F (35° C).*

1) Remove accelerator linkage, upper drive belt cover and cylinder head cover. Turn crankshaft pulley bolt in a clockwise direction until cam lobes of cylinder to be adjusted point upward. See Fig. 5.

NOTE — *Do not turn camshaft by mounting bolt as this will stretch drive belt. If crankshaft sprocket bolt is turned counter-*

clockwise, bolt could be loosened. If this should occur accidentally, remove bolt and clean threads. Coat threads with Loctite or equivalent, then install bolt and torque to specification.

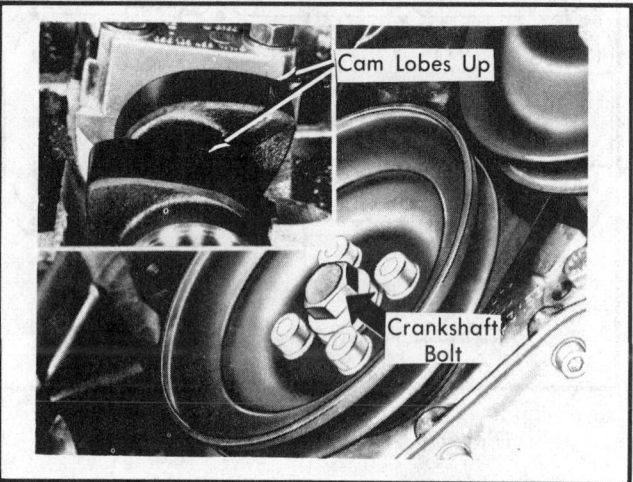

Fig. 5   Adjusting Valve Clearance

2) Adjust valve clearances in firing order (1-3-4-2). Using a feeler gauge, measure valve clearance of each cylinder in turn. If clearance is within .002" (.05 mm) of specification, no adjustment is necessary.

Valve Clearance Specifications	
Application	**In. (mm)**
Intake	
Hot	.008-.012 (.20-.30)
Cold	.006-.010 (.15-.25)
Exhaust	
Hot	.016-.020 (.40-.51)
Cold	.014-.018 (.36-.46)

3) Compare measured clearance for each valve to specifications. If adjustment is required, determine thickness of adjusting disc currently used. If measured clearance is larger than specifications, replace adjusting disc with thicker disc. If clearance is less than specification, install a thinner disc. Adjust clearance to middle of tolerance range.

4) Adjusting discs are available in .002" (.05 mm) increments from .1181" (3.0 mm) to .1673" (4.25 mm). Thickness is stamped on bottom side of disc.

5) To remove discs from cam followers, turn cam followers so that they are adjacent to each other between cam lobes. Insert cam follower tool (VW 546) and depress cam followers. Remove adjusting discs with special tool (US 4476 or 10-208). To install discs, depress cam followers and slip discs into place with side indicating thickness downward. Remove tool. Repeat procedure until all valves are properly adjusted.

Audi Engines

4000 4-CYLINDER (Cont.)

PISTONS, PINS & RINGS

OIL PAN

Drain engine oil. Attach a suitable lifting device to engine and apply supporting tension to engine. Remove front sub frame attaching bolts at left and right. Remove cover plate. Unscrew oil pan bolts and remove pan. When installing, use a new gasket, installing it dry without adhesive. Install oil pan bolts and tighten in a crisscross pattern.

PISTON & ROD ASSEMBLY

1) Before removing connecting rods, mark rod, cap and piston for proper installation. Remove nuts from connecting rod bolts, remove caps, and carefully push piston and rod assemblies out top of cylinders.

2) On reassembly of piston and rod assemblies, forged marks on rod and cap, as well as locating projections on bearing inserts, should face toward timing gear at front of engine. See Fig. 6. All connecting rods must be of same weight class. Weight class numbers are stamped on bottom of connecting rod caps. Using a ring compressor tool (US 1008A), install piston and rod assemblies with arrow on top of piston facing timing gear (front of engine).

Forged Marks on Bosses Point to Timing Gear

Bosses

Nuts

Fig. 6   Identification Marks on Connecting Rod Bosses

FITTING PISTONS

1) Measure cylinder at three points: .39″ (10 mm) from top and bottom, and at center of cylinder bore. Take measurements in line with thrust face and at 90° to thrust face.

2) Measure piston diameter at .39″ (10 mm) from bottom of piston skirt (measuring at 90° to pin bore). Combining this measurement with measurement of corresponding cylinder bore, if piston-to-cylinder clearance exceeds .003″ (.07 mm), oversize pistons must be installed.

NOTE — *Top of piston is marked with an arrow, denoting direction piston is to be installed in cylinder, and with a 4-digit number indicating piston diameter in millimeters (for example, 79.48).*

3) Place piston rings squarely in top of cylinder bore (above ring ridge) and measure end gap; replace as necessary. Measure ring side clearance; replace rings and/or pistons if clearance exceeds .006″ (.15 mm). Install rings on piston with end gaps 120° offset to each other and stamped word "TOP" on rings facing upward.

PISTON PINS

Use pin-drift to lift circlip from piston groove. Use tool (VW 207c) to remove and install piston pins. If pins are too tight it may be necessary to warm pistons to about 140°F (60°C) for removal and replacement.

CRANKSHAFT MAIN & CONNECTING ROD BEARINGS

MAIN & CONNECTING ROD BEARINGS

1) Push crankshaft toward one end and measure crankshaft end play at No. 3 (thrust) bearing. Main bearing caps are stamp-numbered "1" to "5" from timing gear end to flywheel end. They must be installed in original positions upon reassembly. Measure connecting rod side play. Remove rod and main bearing caps and check bearing clearance, using Plastigage method.

2) Measure crankshaft journals with a micrometer to determine if crankshaft is out-of-round. Maximum ovality permissible is .0012″ (.03 mm). Install main inserts with bearing half having oil groove into block. Lubricate bearings and install caps.

Crankshaft Journal Diameters		
Size	Main Bearing Inches (mm)	Connecting Rod Inches (mm)
Standard	2.124 (53.97)	1.809 (45.97)
1st US	2.114 (53.72)	1.799 (45.72)
2nd US	2.104 (53.47)	1.789 (45.47)
3rd US	2.094 (53.22)	1.779 (45.22)

REAR MAIN BEARING OIL SEAL

Rear main bearing oil seal may be replaced with engine in vehicle, if transmission and flywheel are removed. Carefully pry oil seal from crankcase. Install guide tool (2003/2A) on crankshaft and press seal into position as far as possible by hand. Press seal in until properly seated with installing tool (2003/1).

INTERMEDIATE SHAFT OIL SEAL

Press seal out of flange. Coat new seal lips with oil and press new seal into flange, using suitable tool (10-203). Press until flush.

FRONT MAIN BEARING OIL SEAL

1) Remove "V" belt and upper drive belt cover. Set crankshaft to TDC. Remove "V" belt pulley from crankshaft and loosen

Audi Engines

4000 4-CYLINDER (Cont.)

drive belt sprocket. To remove drive belt sprocket bolt, engage 4th gear and apply foot brake. Have assistant remove water pump pulley and lower drive belt cover. Then loosen drive belt and remove drive belt sprocket.

2) Pry old seal out of front cover with extractor tool (10-219). Using installation tool (10-203), press new seal into place after coating seal lips with oil. Press in until flush and then to a depth of .080" (2 mm) below outer edge of cover.

NOTE — *When pressing seal into place, install washer from socket bolt between tool (10-203) and bolt head.*

3) To install remaining components, reverse removal procedure and check valve timing.

ENGINE OILING

Crankcase Capacity — 3.2 qts. (3.7 qts. with filter).

Oil Filter — Replaceable, spin-on type. Hand-tighten.

Normal Oil Pressure — 28 psi (1.97 kg/cm²) at 2000 RPM with oil temperature at 176° F (80° C).

ENGINE OILING SYSTEM

Oiling system is a pressure feed system. A gear type oil pump lifts oil from oil pan and pressure feeds it to crankshaft journals, camshaft bearings and intermediate shaft. Other parts of system receive oil mist or splash for lubrication.

OIL PUMP

Removal & Installation — Remove oil pan and two oil pump mounting bolts. Pull pump straight down and out of engine.

Remove two pump cover bolts and separate cover from pump body. Ensure that oil pump gear end clearance is not more than .006" (.15 mm). Remove pump drive shaft and gears. Bend up metal edges and remove filter screen. To reassembly, reverse disassembly procedures.

ENGINE COOLING

Cooling System Capacity — With air conditioning — 7.4 qts.; without air conditioning — 6.5 qts.

Thermostat — Arrow should point toward fender when installed. Begins to open at 194°F (90°C); opening ends at 216°F (102°C).

Expansion Tank Cap — Pressure relief valve opens at 17-19 psi (1.20-1.33 kg/cm²)

Cooling Fan — Begins to operate at 199-208° F (93-98° C); shuts down at 190-199° F (88-93° C). Switch located in radiator.

WATER PUMP

1) Drain coolant and remove alternator. Remove camshaft belt guard, hose clamps and pump hoses. Remove water pump mounting bolts and lift out pump by turning slightly.

2) Remove pulley and pump body mounting screws. Separate pump assembly from housing. To reassemble, reverse diassembly procedure using new gasket and pump-to-block seal.

ENGINE SPECIFICATIONS

GENERAL SPECIFICATIONS										
Year	Displ.		Carburetor	HP at RPM	Torque (Ft. Lbs. at RPM)	Compr. Ratio	Bore		Stroke	
	cu. ins.	cc					in.	mm	in.	mm
1981	97	1588	Fuel Inj.	76@5500	83@3200	8.2:1	3.13	79.5	3.15	80.0

VALVES							
Engine & Valve	Head Diam. In. (mm)	Face Angle	Seat Angle	Seat Width In. (mm)	Stem Diameter In. (mm)	Stem Clearance In. (mm)	Valve Lift In. (mm)
1588 cc Intake	1.338 (34)	45°	45°	.079 (2.0)	.314 (7.98)	.008-.012 (.20-.30)	.....
Exhaust	1.220 (31)	45°	45°	.094 (2.4)	.313 (7.95)	.016-.020 (.40-.51)	.....

4000 4-CYLINDER (Cont.)
ENGINE SPECIFICATIONS (Cont.)

PISTONS, PINS, RINGS						
	PISTONS	PINS		RINGS		
Engine	Clearance In. (mm) ①	Piston Fit In. (mm)	Rod Fit In. (mm) ③	Rings	End Gap In. (mm) ④	Side Clearance In. (mm) ⑤
1588 cc	.0011 (.028)	②	.0011-.0034 (.028-.086)	Comp.	.012-.018 (.30-.46)	.0008-.002 (.02-.05)
				Oil	.010-.016 (.25-.40)	.0008-.002 (.02-.05)

① — Wear limit .003″ (.07 mm). ② — Push fit at 140°F (60°C). ③ — Wear limit .004″ (.12 mm).
④ — Wear limit .040″ (1.0 mm). ⑤ — Wear limit .006″ (.15 mm).

CRANKSHAFT MAIN & CONNECTING ROD BEARINGS							
	MAIN BEARINGS				CONNECTING ROD BEARINGS		
Engine	Journal Diam. In. (mm)	Clearance In. (mm) ①	Thrust Bearing	Crankshaft End Play In. (mm) ②	Journal Diam. In. (mm)	Clearance In. (mm) ③	Side Play In. (mm)
1588 cc	2.125 (53.97)	.001-.003 (.025-.076)	No. 3	.003-.007 (.077-.178)	1.810 (45.97)	.0011-.0034 (.028-.086)	.015 (.38)

① — Wear limit .007″ (.17 mm). ② — Wear limit .010″ (.25 mm).
③ — Wear limit .004″ (.12 mm).

VALVE SPRINGS			
	Free Length In. (mm)	PRESSURE Lbs. @ In. (kg @ mm)	
Engine		Valve Closed	Valve Open
1588 cc Inner	.....	.....	46-51@.72 (21-23@18.3)
Outer	.....	.....	96-106@.92 (44-48@22.3)

TIGHTENING SPECIFICATIONS

Application	Ft. Lbs. (N·m)
Head Bolts (Cold Only)	
Step 1	29 (40)
Step 2	43 (60)
Step 3	①54 (75)
Main Bearing Caps	47 (65)
Connecting Rod Caps	33 (45)
Flywheel (Use Loctite)	54 (75)
Intermediate Shaft Sprocket	58 (80)
Crankshaft Drive Belt Sprocket	58 (80)
Intake Manifold	18 (25)
Camshaft Bearing Caps	14 (20)
Camshaft Sprocket	58 (80)
Engine-to-Transmission Bolts	40 (55)
Drive Belt Tension Nut	33 (45)
Crankshaft "V" Belt Pulley	14 (20)

① — After torque to 54 ft. lbs. (75 N·m), turn 90° more.

Audi Engines

4000 4-CYLINDER DIESEL

ENGINE CODING

Engine Identification—Code for Audi diesel engine is stamped on cylinder block below mating surface of head, near fuel injection pump. Left side of block.

Engine Identification	
Application	**Code**
All Models	CR

ENGINE & CYLINDER HEAD
ENGINE

Removal — 1) Disconnect battery, remove engine cover plate and cover plate on transmission. Open heater control valve, open cap on expansion tank and drain coolant by detaching hose from thermostat and bottom radiator hose. If equipped with air conditioning, do not loosen any air conditioning system hoses. Detach radiator cowl from radiator and remove complete with both fans. Remove front grille and detach condensor from radiator.

2) Disconnect plugs from fan and thermoswitch. Remove radiator nuts and remove radiator with fan. Remove fuel supply line and fuel return line from injector pump. Disconnect accelerator cable from pump lever and detach bracket from pump body. Disconnect cold start cable at pin and detach retaining washer from bracket. Disconnect wire from fuel shut-off solenoid. Remove gear shift light switch complete with wiring from bracket.

3) Disconnect wiring from oil pressure switch, coolant temperature sensors, glow plugs and thermoswitch. Detach coolant hose and loosen clutch cable from bracket and unhook from clutch lever. Loosen right and left engine mounts at top and detach vacuum hose to vacuum pump at reservoir. Remove alternator. Remove front engine stop bolts. If equipped with air conditioning, detach compressor belt after removing pulley nuts. Remove compressor bracket at top and bottom of engine. Remove compressor with bracket, place on side and tie in place so that hoses are not under tension.

4) Remove exhaust pipe from manifold and disconnect starter cable and remove from intermediate plate. Remove exhaust pipe from front transmission support. Remove starter and place on carrier. Remove 2 transmission-to-engine bolts from below. Remove flywheel cover plate. Install transmission support bar (VW 785/1B). Attach lifting unit (US 1105) to engine and lift engine and transmission with crane until transmission housing touches steering rack. Adjust support bar (VW 785/1B) to contact transmission. Remove 3 transmission-to-engine bolts from above. Pry engine apart from transmission. Lift engine and guide out of engine compartment.

Installation—Place starter on engine carrier before installing engine and connect starter cable so it can not touch engine. Do not interchange fuel supply and return line. Return line is marked OUT on screw head. To install engine, reverse removal procedure. Adjust throttle and clutch cables, align exhaust system components and refill coolant expansion tank.

CYLINDER HEAD

Removal & Installation — 1) Remove expansion tank cap and disconnect lower radiator hose to drain coolant. Disconnect battery. Remove radiator fan, pulleys and fan belts. Remove drive belt for power steering. Remove valve cover and front timing belt cover. Disconnect all wires to cylinder head.

2) Remove air cleaner and attached hoses. Disconnect vacuum pump and move to wheel housing. Remove vacuum pump plunger from cylinder head. Remove and plug fuel delivery pipes and disconnect cold start device. Set No. 1 piston to TDC. Loosen water pump retaining bolts to relieve tension on timing gear belt.

3) Hold rear camshaft drive gear in place, and remove center retaining bolt. Camshaft must not rotate, or damage could result to valves and pistons. Tap gear loose from camshaft tapered end. Remove injection pump drive belt by loosening retaining bracket bolts. Hold rear camshaft sprocket, and remove center retaining bolt. Tap gear loose from camshaft. Remove injectors and glow plugs before removing head.

4) When replacing head gasket make sure gasket thickness is the same by matching notches on side of head gasket. Markings on head gasket must face up. Reverse removal procedure. To install, ensure that cylinder head and block mating surfaces are clean. Install cylinder head gasket dry, using no sealant. Install bolts 8 and 10 first to center cylinder head. Tighten head bolts in sequence illustrated in *Fig. 1*.

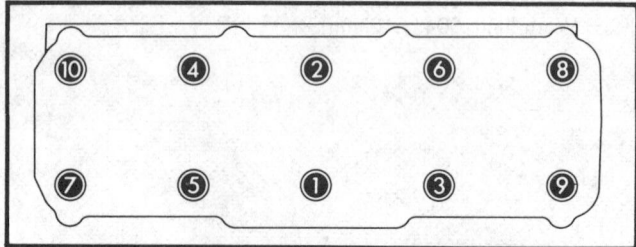

**Fig. 1   Cylinder Head Tightening Sequence
(Reverse Sequence When Removing)**

NOTE—*Every time head is removed, cylinder head bolts must be torqued, and again after about 1000 miles as described in specifications. Piston height must be measured when installing new pistons or short block. Head gasket is then selected according to measurement.*

CAMSHAFT
TIMING BELT

Removal & Installation — 1) Remove belt cover and valve cover, turn engine to TDC on cylinder No. 1 and fix camshaft in position with tool (2065A). Align tool as follows; turn camshaft until one end of tool touches cylinder head. Measure gap at other end of tool with feeler gauge. Take half of measurement and insert feeler of this thickness between tool and cylinder head. Turn camshaft so that tool rests on feeler. Insert second feeler of same thickness between other end of tool and cylinder head.

2) Lock injection pump sprocket in position with pin (2064). Check that marks on sprocket, bracket and pump body are aligned (engine at TDC). Loosen tensioner and remove V-belt pulley from crankshaft, remove drive belt. To install, reverse

4000 4-CYLINDER DIESEL (Cont.)

removal procedure. Check belt tension between camshaft sprocket and injection pump sprocket with tool (VW210), scale should read 12-13. Turn crankshaft 2 turns in direction of engine rotation, strike belt with rubber hammer one time between camshaft sprocket and injection pump. Recheck tension.

CAMSHAFT

1) To remove camshaft, first remove camshaft drive belt and vacuum pump drive belt and sprockets. Remove outer bearing caps 1, 5, and 3 first. Then, diagonally loosen bearing caps 2 and 4 and lift off camshaft. To install, reverse removal procedure and lubricate bearing shells, journals and contact faces of caps. Position cap 5 by tapping end of camshaft with soft-faced hammer. Lightly tighten bearing caps 2 and 4 diagonally.

2) To check camshaft end play, camshaft followers must be removed and camshaft must be free of tension. Only camshaft bearing caps 1 and 5 should be installed. With dial indicator and mounting tool (VW 387) in place on end of camshaft, check for maximum end play of .006" (.15 mm).

VALVE TIMING

See *TIMING BELT* procedure in this article.

INJECTION PUMP TIMING

1) To check injection pump timing, set crankshaft to TDC on No. 1 cylinder. Push in cold start device completely when checking or adjusting injection timing. Remove plug from injection pump cover. Install adaptor and dial gauge 0 to .118" (0 to 3 mm), in place of plug and preload gauge to approximately .097" (2.5 mm). Turn engine slowly counterclockwise (opposite to normal rotation) until dial gauge needle stops moving.

2) Zero gauge and turn engine clockwise until TDC mark on flywheel is aligned with boss on bell housing. Check that gauge reads .031-.035" (.78-.88 mm). If necessary, loosen bolts on mounting plate and support. Set lift by turning pump until gauge reads .034" (.86 mm). Tighten pump mounting bolts and recheck injection pump timing.

NOTE — *To avoid fuel leaks, always replace seal for center plug.*

VALVES

VALVE ARRANGEMENT

E-I-E-I-I-E-I-E (front to rear).

VALVE GUIDE SERVICING

1) With head disassembled, insert new valve in guide which has been cleaned of carbon deposits. With end of stem flush with end of guide, check back and forth travel of head with dial indicator. Maximum reading for intake valve is .039" (1.0 mm) and for exhaust valve is .051" (1.3 mm).

2) Before replacing worn guides, ensure that valve seats can be resurfaced and that head is not cracked. Use tool (10-206) and press worn guides out from combustion chamber side. Do not use more than 1 ton pressure or guide shoulder may break. Ream guides by hand and reface valve seats.

VALVE STEM OIL SEALS

Removal & Installation — 1) Seals may be replaced with cylinder head installed or removed from engine. Remove camshaft, adjusting disc and followers. Turn crankshaft until piston of cylinder concerned is at TDC. Remove valve springs, allowing valve to rest on piston crown.

2) Using special pliers (10-218), pull valve stem seals off. To install new seal, slide plastic sleeve from gasket set onto valve stem. Lubricate new seal and place in installer tool (10-204). Push seal carefully onto valve guide and reverse removal procedure.

VALVE SPRINGS

Removal & Installation — With camshaft and followers removed, compress spring with suitable tool (US 1020 and 1020/1 or 2037) and remove valve locks (keepers). Lift off valve springs. Valve spring seats may be removed with pliers (10-218) if required. To install, reverse removal procedure.

CAM FOLLOWERS (TAPPETS)

Removal & Installation — With camshaft removed, lift off followers and adjusting disc. Mark all components for installation in original position and inspect for wear or damage. To install, coat with oil and replace in original position.

VALVE CLEARANCE ADJUSTMENT

1) With cylinder head cover removed, turn crankshaft so that cam lobes of cylinder to be checked point upward. Check for specified clearance. If not within tolerances given, replace adjusting disc to mid-point of clearance range. Adjusting discs are available in .0019" (.05 mm) increments from .1181" (3.0 mm) to .1673" (4.25 mm).

2) To replace disc, turn crankshaft so piston is not at TDC so that valves do not contact pistons when cam followers are pressed down. Use follower depressor tool (VW546) to press follower down, then remove adjusting disc with etched marking downward (toward cam follower).

3) Rotate crankshaft so that lobes point upward and recheck clearance. Start and run engine until coolant temperature is warmed to approximately 95°F (35°C) and recheck clearance.

NOTE — *Valve clearances must be checked and readjusted after 1000 miles following cylinder head, camshaft or valve replacement or grinding.*

Valve Clearances		
Application	**Hot** In. (mm)	①**Cold** In. (mm)
Intake	.008-012 (.20-.30)	.006-.010 (.15-.25)
Exhaust	.016-.020 (.40-.50)	.014-.018 (.35-.45)

① — Cold setting are given for reference as initial setting after engine rework.

Audi Engines

4000 4-CYLINDER DIESEL (Cont.)

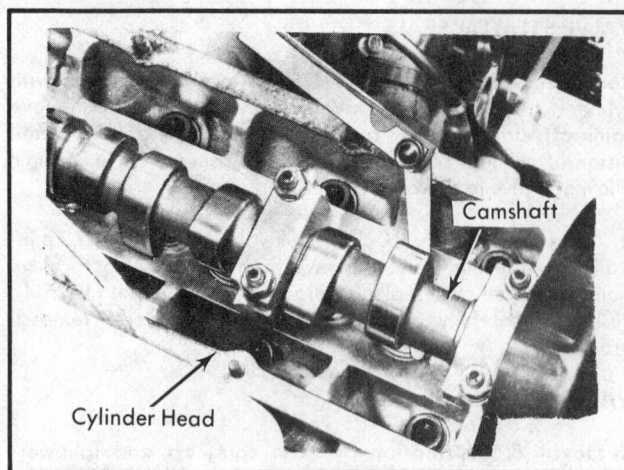

Fig. 2   Adjusting Valve Clearance

PISTON, PINS & RINGS

OIL PAN

Removal & Installation — Oil pan may be removed while engine is installed. Support engine with bar (10-222). Remove cover plate under engine and drain engine oil. Remove 4 bolts from subframe and lower subframe. Remove oil pan. To install, use new oil pan gasket and tighten pan bolts in a criss-cross pattern.

PISTON & ROD ASSEMBLY

Removal & Installation — Note that rod caps and rods are not marked for reassembly, mark each cap and rod before removing from block. Remove cap nuts and push piston/rod assembly out top of cylinder. When assembling, note that arrow on piston top points to crankshaft pulley (front of engine). Valve detents will be at left side of block. Raised casting marks on connecting rod and cap must face oil filter side of engine.

FITTING PISTONS

1) Measure cylinder at 3 points: 3/8" (10 mm) from top and bottom, and at center of bore. Measure in line with and at 90° to thrust face.

NOTE — *Do not measure when block is mounted in repair stand with adapter (VW 540) due to possible distortion.*

2) Measure pistons at 9/16" (15 mm) from bottom of piston skirt, 90° to pin bore. Subtract this measurement from that of corresponding cylinder bore and note piston-to-cylinder clearance. If clearance exceeds .027" (.07 mm), oversize pistons must be installed.

3) Place each piston ring squarely into bottom of cylinder about 9/16" (15 mm) and measure end gap. Measure ring side clearance in pistons with feeler gauge.

4) Install rings on pistons with "TOP" mark facing piston crown. Ring gaps should be spaced 120° apart. Use suitable compressor (US 1008A or equivalent) and install piston/rod assemblies.

PISTON PINS

Removal & Installation — Use pin type drift to pry circlip from pin boss. Press out pin with suitable driver (10-508). If pin is too tight, heat piston to approximately 140° F (60° C) prior to removal. Assemble piston/connecting rod assembly so that arrow on piston top faces forward when assembly is correctly installed. Use new circlips to retain pins.

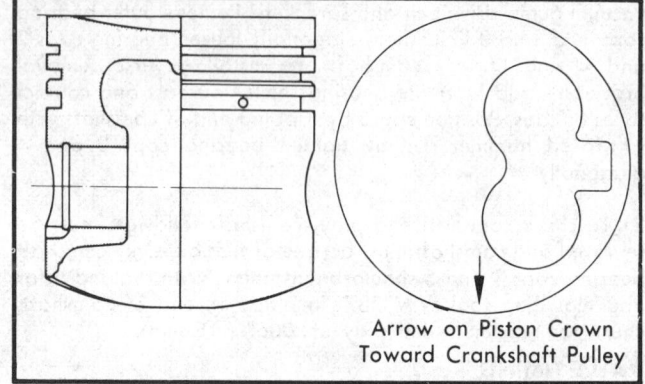

Arrow on Piston Crown
Toward Crankshaft Pulley

Fig. 3   Side and Top View of Diesel Piston

CRANKSHAFT MAIN & CONNECTING ROD BEARINGS

MAIN & CONNECTING ROD BEARINGS

Check crankshaft end play at number 3 main bearing with feeler gauge. Check main and connecting rod bearing clearance using Plastigage method. Main bearings are numbered 1 through 5 with 1 at drive belt end and 5 at flywheel end. Install bearing shells with grooves in block and shells without grooves in bearing caps. All bearing shells must be installed in original position if they are not being replaced. Use new connecting rod cap nuts.

NOTE — *Bearing clearance may be checked with engine installed in vehicle. Do not turn crankshaft when checking with Plastigage.*

CRANKSHAFT REAR OIL SEAL

Removal & Installation — With flywheel removed, use tool (2086) to pry oil seal from sealing flange. Coat lips and outer edge of new seal with oil. Push seal into position by hand, then use installing tool (2003/1) to press in until properly seated.

CRANKSHAFT FRONT OIL SEAL

Removal & Installation — Lubricate threaded head of oil seal extractor tool (2085). Set in position and screw it as far as possible into oil seal by pushing firmly in. Loosen knurled screw and turn inner part against crankshaft until oil seal is pulled out. Clamp extractor in a vise and remove oil seal with pliers. Install seal flush with front cover.

NOTE — *When installing crankshaft pulley bolt, coat threads and contact surface of bolt head with loctite 573 or equivalent.*

ENGINE OILING

Crankcase Capacity — 3.7 qt. with filter change; 3.2 qt. without filter change.

Audi Engines

4000 4-CYLINDER DIESEL (Cont.)

Oil Filter — Replaceable spin-on type filter is mounted on right side of engine block.

Normal Oil Pressure — Minimum of 28 psi (1.97 kg/cm²) at 2000 RPM with engine at normal operating temperature.

OIL PUMP

Gear-type pump is mounted at front of engine and is driven by the crankshaft. The oil suction tube extends from the oil pump base to the oil pan. The pump is non-serviceable, and must be replaced as an assembly if defective.

Removal — With oil pan removed, remove oil suction pipe and unbolt pump from engine.

Installation — Ensure that driving dog on crankshaft engages pump gear properly and reverse removal procedure. Align drive belt sprocket with Woodruff key and apply Loctite 573 (or equivalent) to threads and contact surface of pulley bolt before installing.

ENGINE COOLING

Cooling Capacity — 7.4 qts.

Thermostat — Opens at 185° F (85° C).

Expansion Tank Cap — Relieves pressure at 15 psi. (1.06 kg/cm²).

Radiator — Diesel models use a main and an auxiliary radiator, both cross flow type, and a coolant expansion tank. An electric cooling fan is actuated by a thermoswitch at temperatures above 200°F (93°C) and turned off at lower temperatures.

WATER PUMP

Removal & Installation — Allow engine to cool, then drain cooling system. Remove "V" belts, timing belt covers. See Timing Belt procedures in this article. Remove retaining bolts and water pump. To install, use new "O" ring on pump and reverse removal procedure.

TIGHTENING SPECIFICATIONS

Application	Ft. Lbs. (N·m)
Head Bolts	
Step 1	29 (40)
Step 2	43 (60)
Step 3	①54 (75)
Camshaft Bearing Caps	14 (20)
Main Bearing Caps	47 (65)
Connecting Rod Caps	33 (45)
Flywheel (Loctite)	54 (75)
Crankshaft Pulley (Loctite)	250 (350)
Camshaft Sprocket Bolt	
Front	33 (45)
Rear	72 (100)
Intake Manifold	22 (30)
Injectors	51 (70)
Injector Pipes	18 (25)
Engine Mounting Bolts	25 (35)
Engine-to-Transmission	40 (55)

① — Turn bolt in sequence with breaker bar ½ turn (180°) further. Run engine until it reaches normal operating temperature, stop engine and retighten head bolts in sequence ¼ turn (90°) further with breaker bar without loosening them.

At 1000 miles (with engine warm or cold) retighten bolts with breaker bar, turning bolts in sequence ¼ turn (90°) without loosening them.

ENGINE SPECIFICATIONS

GENERAL SPECIFICATIONS

Year	Displ. cu. ins.	cc	Carburetor	HP at RPM	Torque (Ft. Lbs. at RPM)	Compr. Ratio	Bore in.	Bore mm	Stroke in.	Stroke mm
1981	96.9	1588	Fuel Inj.	52@4800	71@3000	23:1	3.01	76.51	3.4	86.40

VALVES

Engine & Valve	Head Diam. In. (mm)	Face Angle	Seat Angle	Seat Width In. (mm)	Stem Diameter In. (mm)	Stem Clearance In. (mm)	Valve Lift In. (mm)
1588 cc Int.	1.338 (34.0)	45°	45°	.078 (2.0)	.314 (7.97)	.039 (1.0)	.....
Exh.	1.220 (31.0)	45°	45°	.096 (2.4)	.313 (7.95)	.051 (1.3)	.....

Audi Engines

4000 4-CYLINDER DIESEL (Cont.)

ENGINE SPECIFICATIONS (Cont.)

PISTONS, PINS, RINGS						
	PISTONS	PINS		RINGS		
Engine	Clearance In. (mm)①	Piston Fit In. (mm)	Rod Fit In. (mm)	Rings	End Gap In. (mm)②	Side Clearance In. (mm)
1588 cc	.011 (.03)	Push Fit	.....	Upper	.012-.020 (.30-.50)	.002-.004③ (.06-.09)
				Center	.012-.020 (.30-.50)	.002-.003③ (.06-.08)
				Oil	.010-.016 (.25-.40)	.001-.002④ (.03-.06)

① — Wear Limit — .027" (.07 mm).
② — Wear Limit — .040" (1.0 mm).
③ — Wear Limit — .008" (.2 mm).
④ — Wear Limit — .006" (.15 mm).

CRANKSHAFT MAIN & CONNECTING ROD BEARINGS						
	MAIN BEARINGS				CONNECTING ROD BEARINGS	
Engine	Journal Diam. In. (mm)	Clearance In. (mm)①	Thrust Bearing	Crankshaft End Play In. (mm)②	Journal Diam. In. (mm)	Clearance In. (mm)	Side Play In. (mm)②
1588 cc	2.124 (53.96)	.001-.003 (.03-.08)	No. 3	.003-.007 (.08-.18)	1.88 (47.77)	.0011-.0034 (.028-.088)	.015 (.37)

① — Wear Limit .007" (.17).
② — Wear Limit .015" (.37).

4000 & 5000 5-CYLINDER

ENGINE CODING

ENGINE IDENTIFICATION

Engine number is stamped on left side of block near control pressure regulator.

Engine Identification Codes	
Application	Code
2144 cc	
Federal CIS	WD
Calif. CIS	WE
Turbo	WK

ENGINE & CYLINDER HEAD

ENGINE

Removal (5000) — 1) Disconnect battery ground cable. Remove coolant expansion tank cap. Disconnect hose from bottom of expansion tank and drain. Place temperature lever in "COLD" position if vehicle is equipped with air conditioning.

2) Disconnect coolant hoses and drain coolant. DO NOT disconnect any fuel lines. Remove control pressure regulator, cold start valve, and fuel injectors. Loosen air duct and vacuum hoses from throttle valve assembly. Remove air cleaner cover with filter.

3) Pull hood latch cable guide from bracket. Remove radiator cowl, shroud, electric fan and radiator. On air conditioned vehicles, remove grille and tilt condenser outward.

4) Remove power steering pump, leaving hoses connected. Remove vacuum amplifier, ignition coil and EGR control valve. Remove windshield washer and power steering reservoirs from holders. Remove distributor cap, rotor and ignition wires.

5) Remove circlip to remove throttle cable (manual transmission). Remove throttle push rod (automatic transmission). Disconnect electrical connections on distributor. Disconnect wiring to oil pressure and water temperature senders.

6) Remove air conditioning compressor, leaving hoses connected. Tie back compressor with wire. Remove exhaust pipe from manifold and from transmission bracket. Remove front engine mount, starter and alternator.

7) Remove torque converter mounting bolts (automatic transmission) from drive plate, doing so through starter mounting hole. Remove lower engine-to-transmission bolts. Install transmission support tool (VW 785/1). Remove upper engine-to-transmission bolts.

8) Remove left engine bracket and loosen right engine bracket from engine mount. With engine lifting device securely attached, lift engine until "V" belt pulley is behind grille opening. Lift transmission with support tool. Detach engine from transmission.

9) Lift engine upward, turning front of engine toward right as engine is lifted. Remove engine, using care that all wires, hoses and vacuum lines are free. Mount engine on stand (VW 540).

Installation — 1) To install engine, reverse removal procedure, noting the following: Tighten starter cable, so cable cannot touch engine. Metal lip of gasket between exhaust manifold and exhaust pipe faces exhaust pipe. Adjust power steering pump, alternator, and air conditioning compressor belt tension.

2) Attach vacuum hoses to EGR control valve with straight adapter installed to EGR valve and angled adapter to vacuum amplifier. Refill coolant expansion tank. Adjust accelerator cable.

3) Tighten engine mounting bolts with engine running at idle speed.

Removal (4000) — 1) Disconnect battery ground cable. Open heater control valve fully. Open cap on coolant expansion tank and drain coolant. Remove engine-to-transmission bolt holding coolant pipe. Remove upper coolant hose from pipe on left side of engine.

2) Remove upper radiator cover and upper radiator hose from engine. Remove vacuum hose at brake booster and at cruise control unit. Remove power steering pump and place in cowl.

3) Detach coolant hose at thermostat housing. Disconnect wires from oil pressure switch and control pressure regulator. Remove throttle push rod and control pressure regulator, leaving fuel lines connected.

4) Remove remaining coolant hose. Remove alternator adjusting bolt and mounting bolt and place alternator into lower radiator cover. Remove alternator bracket from engine block and remove front stop.

5) Loosen clamps and remove air duct. Disconnect plugs from frequency valve and ground point. Remove distributor vacuum unit hoses. Disconnect plugs at cold start valve, auxiliary air regulator and throttle switch. Remove coil high tension wire at ignition coil.

6) Pull out fuel injectors and remove cold start valve. Leave all fuel lines connected, protecting injectors and valve with caps. Remove fuel distributor with air flow sensor plate. Disconnect fuel feed and return lines. Pull PCV valve hose from valve cover.

7) Loosen upper air filter housing clips and housing bolt. Disconnect oxygen sensor, thermo switch, thermo-time switch, temperature sending unit, and ignition distributor connectors.

8) On air conditioned vehicles, remove coolant hoses at oil cooler. Remove heater hoses. Remove hose flange from engine block and remove cover for right engine mount. Loosen left and right engine mounts. Detach ground strap from mounting bracket. Remove upper engine-to-transmission bolts, leaving one easy-to-reach bolt installed.

9) Loosen "V" belt adjusting bolts for air conditioner compressor. Disconnect wire from oil temperature switch. Remove compressor clamping bolt, bracket from engine block, and wire from compressor clutch. Remove upper compressor mounting bolt and wire compressor out of way, leaving hoses connected.

10) Disconnect starter cables. Remove both front subframe bolts. Remove exhaust pipe attaching nuts from manifold. Remove bolt from exhaust pipe support. Remove starter.

Audi Engines

4000 & 5000 5-CYLINDER (Cont.)

11) Working through starter mounting hole, remove 3 torque converter mounting bolts from drive plate. Remove lower engine-to-transmission bolts. Unhook shift rod clip. Install transmission support tool (VW 785/1).

12) Attach engine sling (US 9019 and US 1105) to engine. Adjust support bar to contact transmission. Remove upper engine-to-transmission bolt, left in earlier. Lift engine slightly and pry engine away from transmission. Continue to lift engine, while turning it toward the left.

13) Use care when guiding engine out of engine compartment. Be sure all wires, hoses, and vacuum lines have been removed. Secure torque converter so it does not fall out. Mount engine on stand (VW 540).

Installation — To install engine, reverse removal procedure, noting the following: Attach starter cable so that it does not touch engine, causing a short circuit. Align exhaust system and refill coolant tank. Tighten engine mounting bolts while engine is running at idle speed.

CYLINDER HEAD

Removal — 1) Disconnect battery ground strap and drain cooling system. Disconnect coolant hoses from head and exhaust pipe from manifold. Remove electrical and vacuum leads from distributor. Disconnect accelerator linkage, fuel and vacuum lines and air filter from manifold.

2) Remove valve cover and timing belt cover. Rotate crankshaft so that number 1 cylinder is at TDC on firing stroke. Remove drive belt sprocket from camshaft, but do NOT separate from timing belt. Loosen head bolts in reverse order of tightening sequence and lift off head.

Installation — 1) Install head gasket DRY (no adhesive) with part number facing upward. Guide pins may be used at opposite corners of head to ease alignment. Be sure cylinder head and block mating surfaces are clean.

2) Install head using only polygon cylinder head bolts. Install bolts 9 and 11 to center head, then tighten bolts in sequence shown in *Fig. 1*.

NOTE — *Do not retorque polygon cylinder head bolts after first 1,000 miles nor after first 1,000 miles following repairs.*

3) Complete assembly in reverse order of removal and ensure that all timing marks are properly positioned.

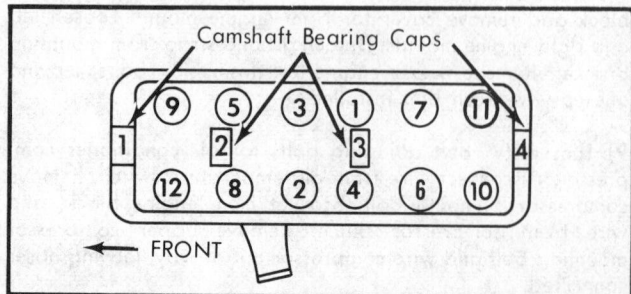

**Fig. 1   Tighten Cylinder Head in Sequence Shown
(Loosen in Reverse Order)**

CAMSHAFT

DRIVE (TIMING) BELT

Remove "V" belts and take off drive belt cover. Engine should be in number 1 cylinder firing position (TDC). Loosen water pump bolts and turn pump counterclockwise to loosen belt. Install new belt and adjust by turning water pump clockwise to tighten. Ensure that valve timing is correct. Belt is properly adjusted when it can just be twisted 90° with thumb and index finger between camshaft and water pump sprockets.

CAMSHAFT

Diagonally loosen bearing caps 2 and 4 and remove caps. Diagonally loosen bearing caps 1 and 3 and remove caps. Remove camshaft from head. When installing, caps must be installed in original position. Lubricate bearings and journals and install caps with off-center position properly aligned. See *Fig. 2*. Tighten caps 2 and 4 diagonally and then caps 1 and 3.

CAUTION — *Front oil seal must not be installed beyond flush position or oil return will be blocked.*

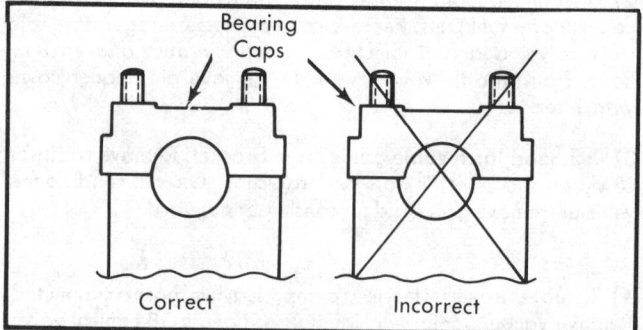

**Fig. 2   Camshaft Bearing Caps with Proper
Off-Center Position**

VALVE TIMING

Rotate crankshaft until notch on "V" belt pulley aligns with mark on oil pump housing (engine out of vehicle) or TDC "O" mark on flywheel aligns with lug cast on clutch housing (engine installed). Fully loosen drive belt tension by loosening and turning water pump clockwise. Turn camshaft sprocket so that punch mark on rear aligns with valve cover gasket (upper edge of belt cover) on left side of engine. Install and adjust belt by turning water pump counterclockwise to tighten.

VALVES

VALVE ARRANGEMENT

E-I-E-I-I-E-I-E-I-E (front to rear).

VALVE GUIDE SERVICING

1) With head disassembled, insert new valve and check for wear with dial indicator. See *Fig. 3*. If wear exceeds .039" (1.0 mm) for intake, or .051" (1.3 mm) for exhaust valve, guides should be replaced.

4000 & 5000 5-CYLINDER (Cont.)

2) Press worn guides out of head from combustion chamber side with suitable tool (10-206). Coat new guides with oil and press into cold head from camshaft side. Press guides in as far as they will go, but DO NOT use more than 1 ton pressure once shoulder is seated. Ream guide by hand to proper size.

VALVE STEM OIL SEALS

NOTE — *Valve stem seals may be replaced with cylinder head installed on vehicle.*

With camshaft and followers removed, remove spark plug and turn crankshaft until piston of cylinder concerned is at BDC position. Install pressure hose (VW 653/3) in spark plug hole and apply low pressure air to keep valve seated. Remove valve springs with compressor (VW 451/1 or 2036) and lift off seal with pliers (10-218). Place seal protector over valve stem, lubricate seal and push seal in place with installing tool (10-204).

VALVE SPRINGS

With camshaft and followers removed, compress spring with suitable tool (US 1020 and 1020/1 or 2037) and remove valve locks (keepers). Lift off valve springs. If required, valve spring seats may be removed using pliers (10-218). To install, reverse removal procedure.

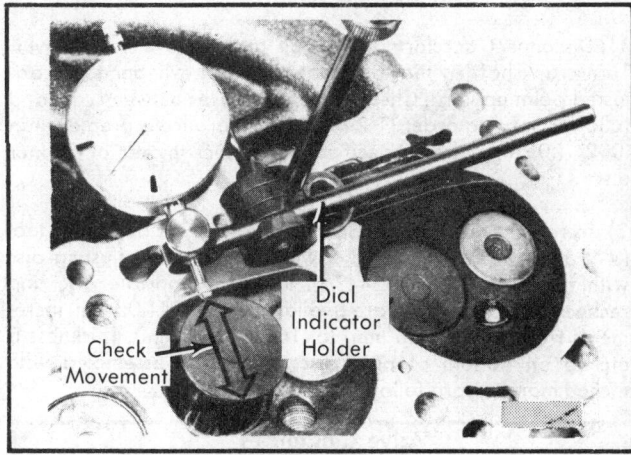

Fig. 3   Checking Valve Guide for Wear

CAM FOLLOWERS (TAPPETS)

With camshaft removed, lift off followers and adjusting discs. Inspect for wear or damage and replace as necessary.

NOTE — *Cam followers and valve system components must be kept in order and installed in original positions. Coat with oil when installing.*

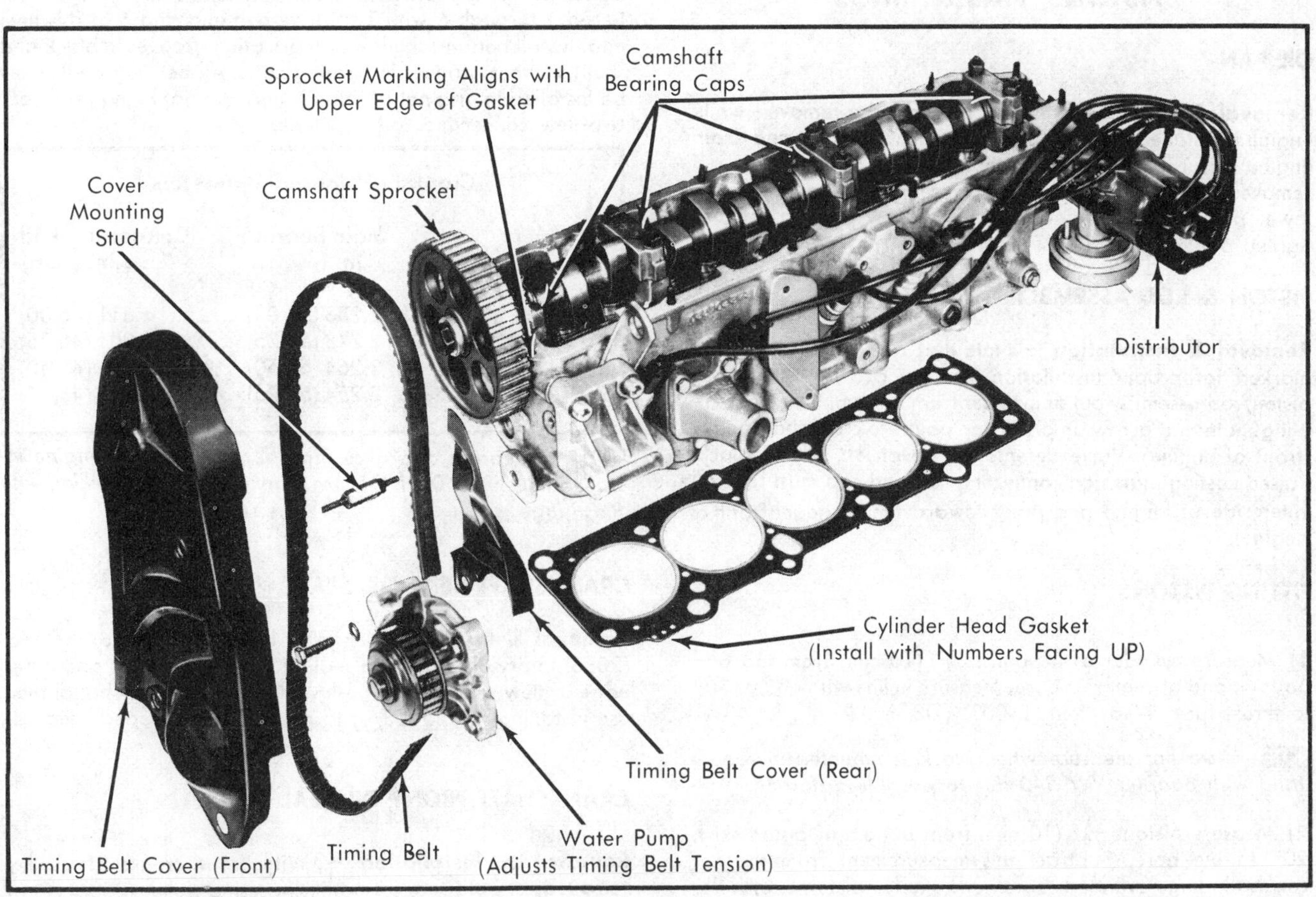

Fig. 4   Cylinder Head and Camshaft Assembly with Drive (Timing) Belt and Cover

Audi Engines

4000 & 5000 5-CYLINDER (Cont.)

VALVE CLEARANCE ADJUSTMENT

1) Disconnect accelerator linkage and remove valve cover. Turn crankshaft so that both cam lobes of cylinder to be adjusted point upward. Check valve clearances between cam and follower in firing order (1-2-4-5-3). If clearance is greater than .002" (.05 mm) from specifications, select thicker or thinner disc.

2) To replace valve adjusting disc, use follower depressor tool (VW 548) to press follower down, then remove adjusting disc with tool (10-028 or US4476). Insert appropriate disc and recheck clearance. Discs are available in .0019" (.05 mm) increments from .1181" (3.0 mm) to .1673" (4.25 mm). Thickness is etched on bottom of disc; discs should be assembled with etched mark toward follower (DOWN).

Valve Clearances		
Application	Hot In. (mm)	Cold In. (mm)
Intake	.008-.012 (.20-.30) ...	.006-.010 (.15-.25)
Exhaust	.016-.020 (.40-.50) ...	.014-.018 (.35-.45)

NOTE — *Cold settings are given for reference as initial setting after engine rework. Final adjustments are to be made after engine is warm (at least 95 °F or 35 °C), and checked again after 1000 miles.*

PISTONS, PINS & RINGS

OIL PAN

Removal & Installation — Oil pan may be removed while engine is installed. Remove 2 front bolts in subframe and drain engine oil. Turn flywheel so that recesses point down and remove both rear pan bolts. Remove remaining pan bolts and lower pan from engine. To install, use new pan gasket and tighten pan bolts in a criss-cross pattern.

PISTON & ROD ASSEMBLY

Removal & Installation — Note that rod cap and rod are marked for proper installation. Remove cap nuts and push piston/rod assembly out of cylinder from bottom. When assembling, note that arrow on piston top points to crankshaft pulley (front of engine). Valve detents will be at left side of block. Raised casting marks on connecting rod and cap must face oil filter side of engine and point toward timing gear (front of engine).

FITTING PISTONS

1) Measure cylinder at 3 points: ⅜" (10 mm) from top and bottom, and at center of bore. Measure in line with and at 90° to thrust face. Wear limit is .003" (.08 mm).

NOTE — *Do not measure when block is mounted in repair stand with adapter VW 540 due to possible distortion.*

2) Measure pistons ⅜" (10 mm) from bottom of piston skirt, 90° to pin bore. Subtract this measurement from that of corresponding cylinder bore and note piston-to-cylinder clearance. If clearance exceeds .003" (.08 mm), oversize pistons must be installed.

3) Place each piston ring squarely into bottom of cylinder about ⅝" (16 mm) and measure end gap. Reading should be .010-.020" (.25-.50 mm). Measure ring side clearance in pistons using a feeler gauge. Ring clearance should be .0008-.0030" (.02-.08 mm) with a wear limit of .004" (.1 mm)

4) Install rings on pistons with "TOP" mark facing piston crown. Recessed edge on outside of center ring must face toward piston pin. Oil scraper ring with spring can be placed in either way. Ring gaps should be spaced 120° apart. Use suitable compressor (US 1008 A) and install piston and rod assemblies.

PISTON PINS

Removal & Installation — Use pin type drift to pry circlip from pin boss. Press out pin with suitable driver (VW 207 C). If pin is too tight, heat piston to approximately 140° F (60° C) prior to removal. Assemble piston and connecting rod assembly so that arrow on piston top faces forward when installed. Use new circlips to retain pins.

CRANKSHAFT MAIN & CONNECTING ROD BEARINGS

MAIN & CONNECTING ROD BEARINGS

Check crankshaft end play at number 4 main bearing with feeler gauge. Check main and connecting rod bearing clearance using Plastigage method. Main bearings are numbered 1 through 6 with 1 at drive belt end and 6 at flywheel end. Install bearing shells with lubrication grooves in block and shells without grooves in bearing caps. All bearing shells must be installed in original position if they are not being replaced. Use new connecting rod cap nuts.

Crankshaft Journal Diameters		
Size	Main Bearing In. (mm)	Connecting Rod In. (mm)
Standard	2.283 (58.00)	1.811 (46.00)
1st US	2.273 (57.75)	1.801 (45.75)
2nd US	2.264 (57.50)	1.791 (45.50)
3rd US	2.254 (57.25)	1.781 (45.25)

NOTE — *Bearing clearance may be checked with engine installed in vehicle. DO NOT turn crankshaft when checking with Plastigage.*

CRANKSHAFT REAR OIL SEAL

Removal & Installation — With flywheel removed, use tool (2086) to pry old seal from sealing flange. Coat lips and outer edge of new seal with oil push seal into position by hand, then use installing tool (2003/1) to press in until properly seated.

CRANKSHAFT FRONT OIL SEAL

Removal & Installation — With front crankshaft pulley removed, pry old seal from housing using puller (2086). Coat seal lip and outer edge lightly with oil and start into position. Use pulley bolt and tool (2080 A) to press seal in until seated.

Audi Engines

4000 & 5000 5-CYLINDER (Cont.)

ENGINE OILING

Crankcase Capacity — All models 4.3 US quarts (4.8 US quarts with filter change).

Oil Filter — Replaceable, spin-on type.

Normal Oil Pressure — 14 psi (.98 kg/cm²) at idle speed or 85 psi (5.98 kg/cm²) at 5500 RPM measured with oil temperature at 176°F (80°C).

OIL PUMP

1) Gear type pump is mounted at front of engine, driven by crankshaft with oil suction pipe extending into oil pan. To remove, loosen pulley bolt, take off timing belt cover, loosen

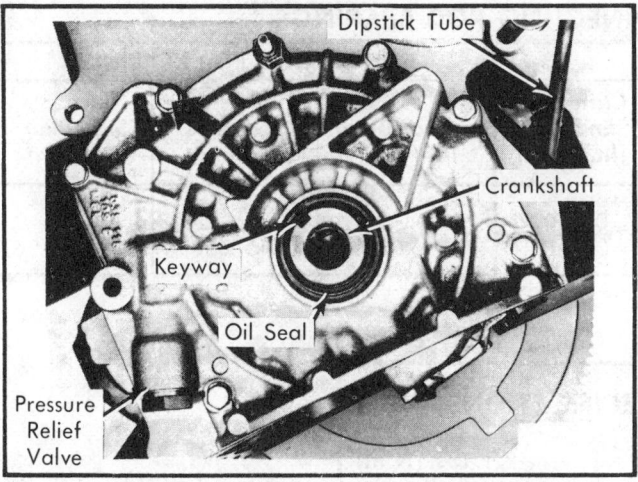

Fig. 5 Engine Oil Pump with Crankshaft Oil Seal

water pump bolts and turn pump counterclockwise, and remove front "V" belt pulley and drive belt sprocket. Drain engine oil and remove oil pan and oil suction pipe.

2) Unbolt pump and remove from front of engine. Inspect end cover, housing and gears for wear or scoring. Replace pump gears in pairs only, with triangle marking toward end cover (rear). To install, reverse removal procedure.

ENGINE COOLING

Cooling System Capacity — 9 U.S. quarts.

Thermostat — Begins to open at 194° F (90° C). Opening ends at 216° F (102° C).

Expansion Tank Cap — Relief valve opens at 17-19 psi (1.20-1.33 kg/cm²).

Radiator — Cross flow type with electric cooling fan and coolant expansion tank. Fan cuts in at 194-203° F (90-95° C) and cuts off at 185-194° F (85-90° C). Switch controlling fan is located in radiator. On air conditioned vehicles, temperature switch in supply hose controls compressor. It cuts in at 223-232° F (106-111° C) and cuts off at 244-253° F (118-123° C).

WATER PUMP

Water pump is driven by timing belt and is mounted at lower left front of engine block. To remove, drain cooling system and remove timing belt cover. Loosen and remove water pump mounting bolts. Remove pump and check for wear. To install, use new "O" ring and reverse removal procedure. Add coolant mixture until tank is full and replace cap. Run engine until cooling fan turns on. Check coolant level and top off if necessary.

ENGINE SPECIFICATIONS

GENERAL SPECIFICATIONS										
Year	Displ.		Carburetor	HP at RPM	Torque (Ft. Lbs. at RPM)	Compr. Ratio	Bore		Stroke	
	cu. ins.	cc					in.	mm	in.	mm
1981 Turbo	130.8	2144	Fuel Inj.	130@5400	142.0@3000	7.0:1	3.13	79.5	3.40	86.4
Others	130.8	2144	Fuel Inj.	103@5300	112.4@4000	8.0:1	3.13	79.5	3.40	86.4

VALVES							
Engine & Valve	Head Diam. In. (mm)	Face Angle	Seat Angle	Seat Width In. (mm)	Stem Diameter In. (mm)	Stem Clearance In. (mm)①	Valve Lift In. (mm)
2144 cc Intake	1.496 (38.0)	45°	45°	.079 (2.0)	.314 (7.97)	.039 (1.0)	.....
Exhaust	1.220 (31.0)	45°	45°	.094 (2.4)	.313 (7.95)	.051 (1.3)	.....

① — Maximum allowable clearance.

Audi Engines

4000 & 5000 5-CYLINDER (Cont.)

ENGINE SPECIFICATIONS (Cont.)

PISTONS, PINS, RINGS						
	PISTONS	PINS		RINGS		
Engine	Clearance In. (mm)	Piston Fit In. (mm)	Rod Fit In. (mm)	Rings	End Gap In. (mm)②	Side Clearance In. (mm)③
2144 cc	.001-.003 (.025-.080)	①	.....	All	.010-.020 (.25-.50)	.0008-.003 (.02-.08)

① — Push fit at 140°F (60°C).   ② — Wear limit .040" (1.0 mm).   ③ — Wear limit .004" (.1 mm).

CRANKSHAFT MAIN & CONNECTING ROD BEARINGS							
	MAIN BEARINGS				CONNECTING ROD BEARINGS		
Engine	Journal Diam. In. (mm)	Clearance In. (mm)	Thrust Bearing	Crankshaft End Play In. (mm)	Journal Diam. In. (mm)	Clearance In. (mm)	Side Play In. (mm)
2144 cc	2.283 (58.00)	.0006-.003② (.016-.075)	No. 4	.003-.007 (.07-.08)	1.811 (46.00)	.0006-.002① (.015-.620)	.016 (.40)

① — Wear limit .005" (.12 mm).
② — Wear limit .006" (.16 mm).

TIGHTENING SPECIFICATIONS

Application	Ft. Lbs. (N·m)
Head Bolts	
Step 1	29 (40)
Step 2	43 (60)
Step 3	①54 (75)
Main Bearing Cap	47 (65)
Connecting Rod Cap	36 (50)
Flywheel (Drive Plate) Loctite	54 (75)
Crankshaft Pulley	235 (350)
Intake Manifold	18 (25)
Camshaft Bearing Cap	14 (20)
Camshaft Sprocket	58 (80)
Engine Mounting Bolts	33 (45)

① — After 3rd step, tighten polygon socket head bolts ¼ turn (90°) past specified torque DO NOT retighten after 1,000 miles.

5000 5-CYLINDER DIESEL

ENGINE CODING

ENGINE IDENTIFICATION

Engine number is stamped on a raised pad at the top of the block on the left side between number 2 and 3 cylinder.

Engine Identification	
Application	Code
1986 cc	CN

ENGINE & CYLINDER HEAD

ENGINE

NOTE — *Engine is removed from car with hood and transmission remaining installed.*

Removal — **1)** Disconnect battery ground strap and remove air cleaner. Remove front grille and cover plates under engine/transmission. Detach and lay aside windshield washer reservoir and hydraulic fluid reservoir. Drain cooling system and disconnect water hoses attached to engine.

2) Remove power steering pump with hoses connected and lay aside. If equipped with A/C, loosen condenser and tilt outward. Remove auxiliary radiator. Disconnect wiring harness, overheating fuse connector, temperature sender wire, and wires connected to starter.

3) Remove upper part of fuel filter and loosen fuel return pipe on injection pump. Detach accelerator cable and disconnect idle speed control cable from injection pump lever. Remove right engine mount cover plate and remove front engine mount from crossmember. If equipped with A/C, remove compressor from engine leaving hoses attached.

4) Remove alternator mounting bracket and remove exhaust pipes from manifold and transmission bracket. Remove body ground strap and lower engine/transmission bolts. Remove flywheel cover plate from transmission and install supporting tool (VW785/1) with slight preload. Install engine lifting tool (US 1105 or equivalent).

5) Loosen right engine bracket from engine mount and remove left engine bracket. Lift engine/transmission up until transmission housing touches steering housing. Turn disc of supporting tool until it touches transmission housing and remove upper engine/transmission bolts.

6) Pry engine/transmission apart and turn engine to right while lifting. Turn engine 90° so that left side of engine is toward front of car and lift out. Use caution not to damage transmission main shaft, clutch and body.

Installation — To install engine, reverse removal procedures and note that metal lip on exhaust manifold flange gasket must face exhaust pipe. After installing upper transmission/engine bolts, remove supporting tool (VW785/1). It is recommended that engine mountings be tightened while engine is running at idle speed.

CYLINDER HEAD

Removal — **1)** Disconnect battery ground strap and drain cooling system. Disconnect coolant hoses from head and exhaust pipe from manifold. Remove feed pipes from injectors and disconnect wire to glow plug feed. Disconnect temperature sender wire and any other wires which could interfere with removal of cylinder head.

2) Remove valve cover and front timing belt cover. Remove vacuum pump "V" belt at rear of engine. Remove injection pump belt cover and set crankshaft to TDC on number 1 cylinder. Align marks on flywheel/clutch housing and injection pump sprocket mounting plate.

3) Lock injection pump sprocket in position with tool (2064). Hold vacuum pump pulley and injection pump drive sprocket with tool (3036) and remove retaining bolt. Remove "V" belt pulley and injection pump sprocket along with drive belt. Note number and position of spacer washers on "V" belt pulley.

4) Remove front camshaft sprocket and timing belt but DO NOT separate sprocket from belt. Loosen and remove head bolts in reverse order of tightening sequence. Lift off cylinder head with camshaft installed.

Installation — **1)** Ensure that mating surfaces of engine block and cylinder head are clean. Use gasket with same identification notches as original if installing on original piston and block assembly. To determine proper gasket for new assemblies, measure piston height above top surface of engine block and select gasket from following table:

Available Cylinder Head Gaskets		
Piston Projection in Inches (mm)	Gasket Number	Identification Notches
.026-.031 (.67-.80)	069 103 383	1
.032-.035 (.81-.90)	069 103 383A	2
.036-.040 (.91-1.02)	069 103 383B	3

2) Install guide pins in right front and left rear cylinder head bolt holes and place dry gasket in position with numbers facing up. Do not use sealer. Install head bolts and tighten in thrree steps following the sequence illustrated in *Fig. 1*. Run eninge to operating temperature of 122°F (50°C). Stop engine and repeat tightening sequence, again torquing bolts to specifications.

NOTE — *After approximately 1000 miles, retorque cylinder head bolts in sequence, loosening them one at a time 30°, and then retightening to specifications.*

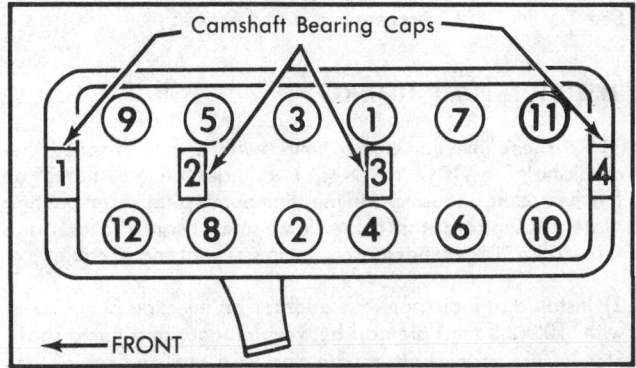

Fig. 1 Cylinder Head Tightening Sequence (Loosen in Reverse Order)

Audi Engines

5000 5-CYLINDER DIESEL (Cont.)

CAMSHAFT

TIMING BELTS

Removal — 1) Remove alternator "V" belt and outer half of vacuum pump pulley and "V" belt. Remove drive belt covers and cylinder head cover. Set crankshaft at TDC on No. 1 cylinder and align marks on flywheel/clutch housing and injection pump sprocket mounting plate.

2) Lock injection pump sprocket with pin (2064) and hold inboard half of vacuum pump pulley and injection pump drive sprocket with tool (3036). Remove center retaining bolt and pulley half along with pump sprocket and injection pump drive belt.

3) Lock camshaft with tool (2065 A) and loosen drive belt by loosening water pump. Remove crankshaft pulley, camshaft drive belt and drive belt sprocket.

Installation — 1) Ensure that crankshaft is still at TDC on No. 1 cylinder and install injection pump drive sprocket with drive belt. Tighten injection pump drive retaining bolt until it is just possible to turn sprocket on camshaft by hand. Check belt tension and adjust by moving mounting plate and injection pump.

2) Tighten drive sprocket bolt and remove setting pin from injection pump. Attach crankshaft pulley, camshaft drive belt and camshaft sprocket. Tension belt by moving water pump. To complete installation, reverse removal procedure.

NOTE — *Belt should be tensioned so that scale on tool (VW 210) reads 12 to 13. Tension may also be checked by twisting belt 90° between pulleys using thumb and index finger. If belt twists more than 90°, tension is too loose. If belt will not twist 90°, tension is too tight.*

CAMSHAFT

To check camshaft end play, camshaft followers must be removed and camshaft free of tension. Check for maximum end play of .006" (.15 mm) with dial indicator. To remove camshaft, first remove camshaft drive belt and injecton pump drive belt. Remove outer bearing caps (1 and 4) first, loosen nuts of caps 2 and 3 alternately and diagonally, and lift off cam shaft. To install, reverse removal procedures, installing bearing caps 2 and 3 first, then caps 1 and 4.

VALVE TIMING

See *TIMING BELT* procedures in this article.

INJECTION PUMP TIMING

1) To check injection pump timing with engine installed. Set crankshaft to TDC on No. 1 cylinder. Align marks on flywheel/clutch housing and injection pump sprocket/ mounting plate. Loosen cold start cable clamp screw nearest to lever and turn clamp 90°. Do not loosen clamp screw at end of cable.

2) Install dial indicator with adaptor on injection pump cover with .10" (2.5 mm) preload between plunger and pump shaft. Slowly turn crankshaft counterclockwise until indicator stops moving, then zero the dial indicator with about .04" (1 mm) preload.

3) Turn crankshaft clockwise so TDC mark is aligned with reference mark. Dial indicator should show lift of .033" (.85 mm). If necessary, loosen injection pump bolts and turn pump to set .033" (.85 mm) lift. Tighten mounting bolts and turn clamp on cold start device cable back 90° to tension cable. Tighten screw. Remove dial indicator and replace plug on injection pump.

VALVES

VALVE ARRANGEMENT

E-I-E-I-I-E-I-E-I-E (front to rear).

VALVE GUIDE SERVICING

1) With head disassembled, insert new valve in guide which has been cleaned of carbon deposits. With end of stem flush with end of guide, check back and forth travel of head with dial indicator. Maximum reading for intake and exhaust valve is .051" (1.3 mm).

2) Before replacing worn guides, ensure that valve seats can be refaced and that head is not cracked. Use tool (10-206) and press worn guides out from combustion chamber side. Oil new guides and press in up to shoulder from camshaft side. DO NOT use more than 1 ton pressure or guide shoulder may break. Ream guides by hand and reface valve seats.

VALVE STEM OIL SEALS

Removal & Installation — 1) Seals may be replaced with cylinder head installed or removed from engine. Remove camshaft drive belt and injection pump drive belt. Remove camshaft and cam follower. Turn crankshaft until piston of cylinder concerned is at TDC. Remove valve springs, allowing valve to rest on piston crown.

2) Using special pliers (10-218), pull valve stem seals off. To install new seal, slide plastic sleeve from gasket set onto valve stem. Lubricate new seal and place in installer tool (10-204). Push seal carefully onto valve guide and reverse removal procedure.

VALVE SPRINGS

Removal & Installation — With camshaft and followers removed, compress spring with suitable tool (VW541/1 and 2036) and remove valve locks (keepers). Lift off valve springs. Valve spring seats may be removed with pliers (10-218) if required. To install, reverse removal procedure.

CAM FOLLOWERS (TAPPETS)

Removal & Installation — With camshaft removed, lift off followers and adjusting discs. Mark all components for installation in original position and inspect for wear or damage. To install, coat with oil and replace in original position.

VALVE CLEARANCE ADJUSTMENT

1) With cylinder head cover removed, turn crankshaft so that cam lobes of cylinder to be checked point upward. Check for specified clearance. If not within tolerances given, replace adjusting disc to mid-point of clearance range. Adjusting discs are available in .0019" (.05 mm) increments from .1181" (3.0 mm) to .1673" (4.25 mm).

5000 5-CYLINDER DIESEL (Cont.)

2) To replace disc, turn crankshaft so piston is NOT at TDC so that valves do not contact pistons when cam followers are pressed down. Use follower depressor tool (2078) to press follower down, then remove adjusting disc with tool (10-208 or US 4476). Insert required disc with etched marking downward (toward cam follower).

3) Rotate crankshaft so that lobes point upward and recheck clearance. Start and run engine until coolant temperature is warmed to approximately 95°F (35°C) and recheck clearance.

NOTE — *Valve clearances must be checked and adjusted after 1000 miles following cylinder head, camshaft or valve replacement or grinding.*

Valve Clearances

Application	Hot In. (mm)	Cold In. (mm)
Intake	.008-.012 (.20-.30)	.006-.010 (.15-.25)
Exhaust	.016-.020 (.40-.50)	.014-.018 (.35-.45)

NOTE — *Cold settings are given for reference as initial setting after engine rework.*

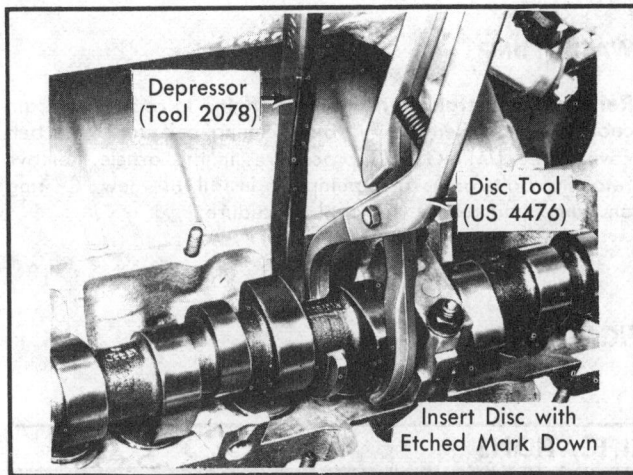

Fig. 2 Adjusting Valve Clearance

labels: Depressor (Tool 2078), Disc Tool (US 4476), Insert Disc with Etched Mark Down

PISTONS, PINS & RINGS

OIL PAN

Removal & Installation — Oil pan may be removed while engine is installed. Remove 2 front bolts in subframe and drain engine oil. Turn flywheel so that recesses point down and remove both rear pan bolts. Remove remaining pan bolts and lower pan from engine. To install, use new pan gasket and tighten pan bolts in a criss-cross pattern.

PISTON & ROD ASSEMBLY

Removal & Installation — Note that rod cap and rod are marked for proper installation. Remove cap nuts and push piston/rod assembly out top of cylinder. When assembling, note that arrow on piston top points to crankshaft pulley (front of engine). Valve detents will be at left side of block. Raise casting marks on connecting rod and cap must face oil filter side of engine.

FITTING PISTONS

1) Measure cylinder at 3 points: 3/8" (10 mm) from top and bottom, and at center of bore. Measure in line with and at 90° to thrust face.

NOTE — *Do not measure when block is mounted in repair stand with adapter VW 540 due to possible distortion.*

2) Measure pistons at 9/16" (15 mm) from bottom of piston skirt, 90° to pin bore. Subtract this measurement from that of corresponding cylinder bore and note piston-to-cylinder clearance. If clearance exceeds .027" (.07 mm), oversize pistons must be installed.

3) Place each piston ring squarely into bottom of cylinder about 9/16" (15 mm) and measure end gap. Measure ring side clearance in pistons with feeler gauge.

4) Install rings on pistons with "TOP" mark facing piston crown. Ring gaps should be spaced 120° apart. Use suitable compressor (US 1008 A or equivalent) and install piston/rod assemblies.

PISTON PINS

Removal & Installation — Use pin type drift to pry circlip from pin boss. Press out pin with suitable driver (10-508). If pin is too tight, heat piston to approximately 140°F (60°C) prior to removal. Assemble piston/connecting rod assembly so that arrow on piston top faces forward when assembly is correctly installed. Use new circlips to retain pins.

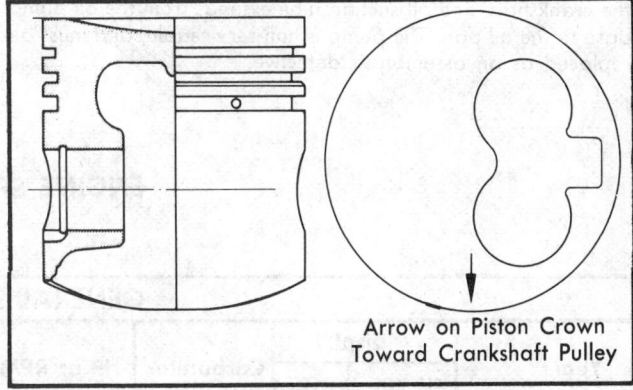

Fig. 3 Side and Top View of Diesel Piston

label: Arrow on Piston Crown Toward Crankshaft Pulley

CRANKSHAFT MAIN & CONNECTING ROD BEARINGS

MAIN & CONNECTING ROD BEARINGS

Check crankshaft end play at number 4 main bearing with feeler gauge. Check main and connecting rod bearing clearance using Plastigage method. Main bearings are numbered 1 through 6 with 1 at drive belt end and 6 at flywheel end. Install bearing shells with lubrication grooves in block and shells without grooves in bearing caps. All bearing shells must be installed in original position if they are not being replaced. Use new connecting rod cap nuts.

NOTE — *Bearing clearance may be checked with engine installed in vehicle. DO NOT turn crankshaft when checking with Plastigage.*

Audi Engines

5000 5-CYLINDER DIESEL (Cont.)

CRANKSHAFT REAR OIL SEAL

Removal & Installation — With flywheel removed, use tool (2086) to pry old seal from sealing flange. Coat lips and outer edge of new seal with oil. Push seal into position by hand, then use installing tool (2003/1) to press in until properly seated.

CRANKSHAFT FRONT OIL SEAL

Removal & Installation — With front crankshaft pulley removed, pry old seal from housing using puller (2086). Coat seal lip and outer edge lightly with oil and start into position. Use pulley bolt and tool (2080 A) to press seal in until seated.

NOTE — *When installing crankshalt pulley bolt, coat threads and contact surface of bolt head with Loctite 573 or equivalent.*

ENGINE OILING

Crankcase Capacity — 5.3 quarts with filter; 4.8 quarts without filter change.

Oil Filter — Replaceable spin-on type filter is mounted on right side of engine block.

Normal Oil Pressure — Minimum of 28 psi (1.97 kg/cm²) at 2000 RPM with engine at normal operating temperature.

OIL PUMP

Gear-type pump is mounted at front of engine and is driven by the crankshaft. The oil suction tube extends from the oil pump base to the oil pan. The pump is non-serviceable, and must be replaced as an assembly if defective.

Removal — Remove front crankshaft pulley and "V" belts. Remove camshaft drive belt and cover. Drain engine oil and remove oil pan and oil suction pipe. Unbolt pump and remove from engine.

Installation — Ensure that driving dog on crankshaft engages pump gear properly and reverse removal procedure. Align drive belt sprocket with Woodruff key and apply Loctite 573 (or equivalent) to threads and contact surface of pulley bolt before installing.

ENGINE COOLING

Cooling System Capacity — 9.9 quarts.

Thermostat — Opens at 188°F (87°C).

Expansion Tank Cap — Relieves pressure at 18 psi (1.27 kg/cm²).

Radiator — Diesel models use a main and an auxiliary radiator, both cross flow type, and a coolant expansion tank. An electric cooling fan is actuated by a thermoswitch at temperatures above 200°F (93°C) and turned off at lower temperatures.

WATER PUMP

Removal & Installation — Allow engine to cool, then drain cooling system. Remove "V" belts, timing belt and drive belt covers. See *TIMING BELT* procedures in this article. Remove retaining bolts and water pump. To install, use new "O" ring on pump and reverse removal procedure.

ENGINE SPECIFICATIONS

GENERAL SPECIFICATIONS

Year	Displ.		Carburetor	HP at RPM	Torque (Ft. Lbs. at RPM)	Compr. Ratio	Bore		Stroke	
	cu. ins.	cc					in.	mm	in.	mm
1981	121	1986	Fuel Inj.	67@4800	90@3000	23.0:1	3.01	76.5	3.40	86.4

VALVES In. (mm)

Engine & Valve	Head Diam.	Face Angle	Seat Angle	Seat Width	Stem Diameter	Stem Clearance	Valve Lift
1986 cc Diesel							
Intake	1.417 (36.0)	45°	45°	.078 (2.0)	.314 (7.97)	.051 (1.3)	.....
Exhaust	1.220 (31.0)	45°	45°	.096 (2.4)	.313 (7.95)	.051 (1.3)	.....

5000 5-CYLINDER DIESEL (Cont.)
ENGINE SPECIFICATIONS (Cont.)

PISTONS, PINS, RINGS

Engine	PISTONS Clearance In. (mm)①	PINS Piston Fit In. (mm)	Rod Fit In. (mm)	RINGS Rings	End Gap In. (mm)②	Side Clearance In. (mm)
1986 cc Diesel	.011 (.03)	Push Fit	.....	Upper	.012-.020 (.30-.50)	.002-.004③ (.06-.09)
				Center	.012-.020 (.30-.50)	.002-.003③ (.05-.08)
				Oil	.010-.016 (.25-.40)	.001-.002④ (.03-.06)

① — Wear Limit — .027" (.07 mm).
② — Wear Limit — .040" (1.0 mm).
③ — Wear Limit — .008" (.2 mm).
④ — Wear Limit — .006" (.15 mm).

CRANKSHAFT MAIN & CONNECTING ROD BEARINGS

Engine	MAIN BEARINGS Journal Diam. In. (mm)	Clearance In. (mm)①	Thrust Bearing	Crankshaft End Play In. (mm)②	CONNECTING ROD BEARINGS Journal Diam. In. (mm)	Clearance In. (mm)	Side Play In. (mm)
1986 cc Diesel	2.28 (57.96)	.0006-.003 (.016-.075)	No. 4	.003-.007 (.07-.18)	1.88 (47.77)	.0005-.0024 (.015-.06)	.016 (.40)

① — Wear Limit .006" (.16 mm).
② — Wear Limit .01" (.25 mm).

TIGHTENING SPECIFICATIONS

Application	Ft Lbs. (N·m)
Head Bolts	
Step 1	35 (48)
Step 2	50 (69)
Step 3	①65 (90)
Camshaft Bearing Caps	14 (20)
Main Bearing Caps	47 (65)
Connecting Rod Caps	33 (45)
Flywheel (Use Loctite)	54 (75)
Crankshaft (Use Loctite)	250 (350)
Camshaft Sprocket Bolt	
Front	33 (45)
Rear	72 (100)
Injectors	51 (70)
Injector Pipes	18 (25)
Engine Mounting Bolts	33 (45)
Engine-to-Transmission	43 (60)

① — After 1000 miles, with engine either cold or warm, retighten cylinder head bolts in numerical order shown by loosening bolts (one at a time) 30° and then retightening to 65 Ft. Lbs. (90 N·m).

320i 4-CYLINDER

ENGINE CODING

ENGINE IDENTIFICATION

Engine identification number is on engine block at left hand side above starter motor.

ENGINE & CYLINDER HEAD

NOTE — *Transmission must be removed prior to removing engine.*

MANUAL TRANSMISSION

Removal — 1) Remove all mounting bolts accessible from above. Remove exhaust support and exhaust pipe at manifold. Tighten compressing strap (261012) around front rubber coupling until bolts attaching rubber coupling to transmission output flange can be removed.

2) Detach center bearing bracket from body after removing heat shield to gain access. Pull down on propeller shaft at center bearing to disengage shaft from transmission flange. Remove speedometer cable and disconnect back-up light switch.

3) Remove center console from transmission, remove circlip and washer, pull out selector rod. Remove clutch slave cylinder, support transmission with jack or stand. Remove crossmember and remaining transmission mounting bolts. Remove transmission towards rear of vehicle.

Installation — To install, reverse removal procedure and note the following: When installing propeller shaft, push center bearing bracket forward .08" (2 mm) to preload center bearing and tighten nuts.

AUTOMATIC TRANSMISSION

Removal — 1) Remove accelerator cable. Remove all mounting bolts accessible from above. Remove oil filler neck and drain oil. Remove exhaust support and exhaust pipe at manifold. Remove speedometer drive cable. Remove bolts from transmission output flange and detach coupling.

2) Detach center bearing bracket from body after removing heat shield to gain access. Pull down on propeller shaft at center bearing to disengage shaft from transmission flange.

3) Remove drive plate bolts from torque converter. Remove transmission oil cooler lines. Support transmission with jack or stand, then remove crossmember at body. Remove remaining transmission mounting bolts. Remove transmission and torque converter from vehicle.

Installation — To install, reverse removal procedure, ensuring that torque converter is properly positioned on drive plate. When installing propeller shaft, push center bearing bracket forward .08" (2 mm) to preload center bearing and tighten nuts.

ENGINE

Removal — 1) Remove transmission. Drain cooling system and disconnect hoses. Remove fan shroud and radiator. Disconnect and remove battery. Remove intake cowl and disconnect wires and fuel lines to injection system. Detach and suspend A/C compressor (if equipped). DO NOT disconnect hoses.

2) Disconnect wires, fuel and coolant lines and control cables between engine and chassis. Install engine sling (110000) to eyes at front and rear of engine. Detach left engine mount and upper engine damper. Detach right engine mount and lift engine from vehicle.

Installation — To install, reverse removal procedure and note the following: When filling with coolant, set heater control to "warm" and fill radiator slowly. Bleed system after engine is warm by turning cap to catch 1, then remove cap and fill radiator.

CYLINDER HEAD

Removal — 1) Pull off breather tube, then pull hose with connector out of tube. Dismantle air cleaner assembly. Disconnect ground lead from battery. Drain cooling system. Disconnect accelerator cable. Remove cylinder head cover (rocker arm cover).

2) Remove lines to injection valves (mark for reassembly). Remove pressure converter hoses, water hoses at cylinder head and crankcase hoses at throttle housing and thermo valve (marking for reassembly). Remove upper timing case cover, disconnect plug connectors and ignition coil wires. Remove distributor cap and pull plugs off cold start valve, auxiliary air valve and timing valve. Disconnect oil pressure switch wire.

3) Set piston of No. 1 cylinder at TDC, (rotor points to notch in distributor housing, indicator points to notch in pulley). Remove timing chain tensioner and timing chain sprocket. Remove exhaust pipe at manifold and holder to transmission. Remove cylinder head bolts in reverse sequence of tightening, remove cylinder head.

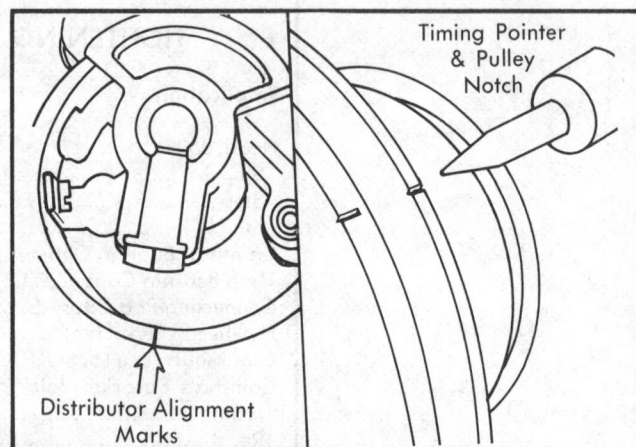

Fig. 1   Correct Procedure to Set No. 1 Piston at TDC

Installation — 1) Measure dowel (installation guide) projection above cylinder head mounting surface. See *Fig. 3.* Maximum projection should not exceed .197" (5 mm). Ensure that there is no oil in cylinder head bolt blind holes or head bolts will not be able to exert required holding force on head.

2) Replace cylinder head and components in reverse order of removal procedure. Tighten head bolts in sequence. See *Fig. 2.* Start engine and run until normal operating temperature is reached. Allow to cool to about 95° F (35° C) and tighten to final torque.

320i 4-CYLINDER (Cont.)

NOTE — *Head bolts should be re-checked for final torque after 600 miles. Always check torque with engine cool.*

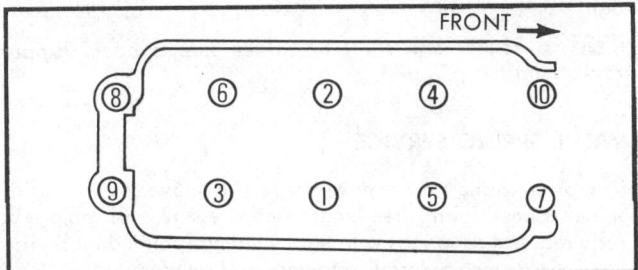

**Fig. 2   Tighten Cylinder Head in Sequence Shown
(Remove in Reverse Sequence)**

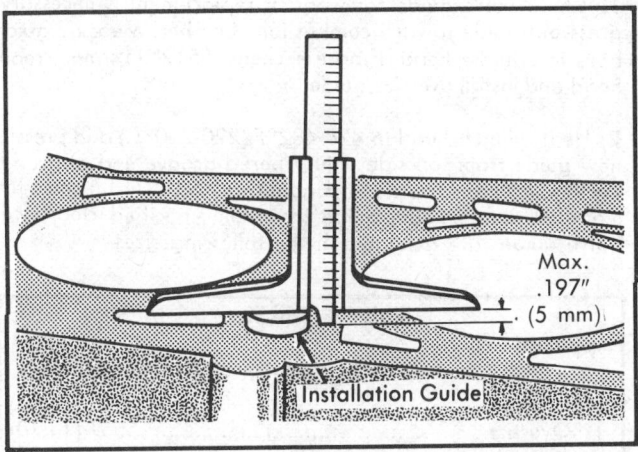

Fig. 3   Measure Dowel Projection as Shown

CAMSHAFT

CAMSHAFT

Removal — 1) With cylinder head removed, loosen clamping screw and pull out distributor. Attach head assembly to a suitable holding tool (No. 11 1 040). Remove oil line and cold start valve.

2) Adjust valve clearance to maximum possible. Attach a suitable compression frame to preload the rocker assembly. Check end play between guide plate and camshaft. Remove guide plate and carefully withdraw camshaft.

Installation — 1) When replacing camshaft, note the following: After guide plate has been installed, it must be possible to easily rotate the camshaft. Make sure that notch in flange aligns with cast tab on cylinder head. Adjust valve clearances, note position of oil pipe sealing rings.

2) When replacing distributor, turn rotor counterclockwise by about 1.4" (35 mm) from notch in distributor housing, bring distributor drive into mesh with camshaft drive. Ensure vacuum advance has been located in original position. Adjust ignition timing.

ENGINE FRONT COVER

Upper Cover — Remove cylinder head cover and detach EGR check valve pipe from exhaust manifold. Take out bolts (8) at-

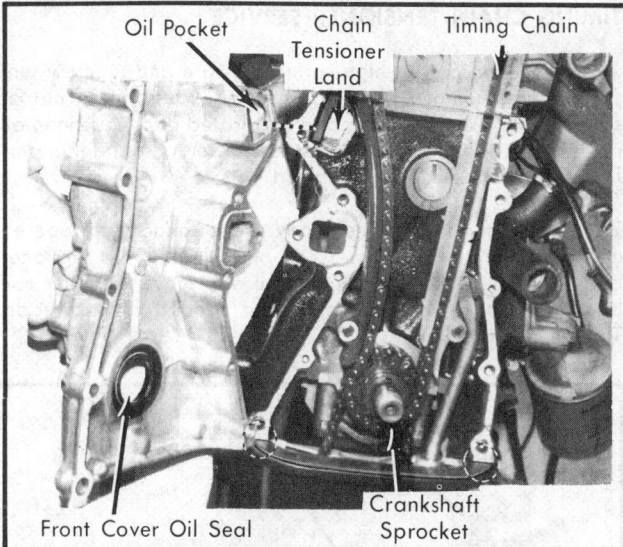

Fig. 4   Timing Chain with Lower Case and Cover

taching cover to head and block. Remove, clean and inspect cover. To install, use new gasket and apply suitable sealant to mating surfaces. Place cover in position and insert all bolts, tightening lower bolts at block slightly. Tighten bolts evenly to specifications starting at lower head and finishing with bolts fastening cover to block.

Lower Timing Case Cover — 1) Disconnect battery ground cable and remove water pump. Remove upper timing case cover and chain tensioner piston. Remove alternator with bracket and tensioning bar. Remove air pump and bracket with tensioning bar.

2) Take off front pulley and remove bolts on timing case cover and front of oil pan. Carefully separate oil pan gasket from timing case cover with knife blade and remove lower cover.

3) To install, apply sealant and new gaskets. Ensure that chain tensioner take-up land is in oil pocket and reverse removal procedures.

TIMING CHAIN REPLACEMENT

Removal & Installation — 1) Remove distributor cap, set piston of No. 1 cylinder at TDC. Remove upper and lower timing case covers. Remove sprocket. Remove circlip and unscrew pivot pin until guide rail rests on cylinder head gasket. Remove timing chain from sprocket and crankshaft. Remove guide rail by pulling down and swinging to the right.

2) If timing chain sprockets need replacing, remove timing chain, oil pan and oil pump sprocket. Remove Woodruff key and oil pump drive chain. Using puller (11 2 000), remove sprocket. Heat sprocket and install. To complete installation, reverse removal procedure.

VALVE TIMING

Rotate engine to TDC of No. 1 piston. Position camshaft so that timing mark on camshaft flange is straight up and locating pin hole is straight down. Without moving crankshaft or camshaft, install camshaft sprocket so that it engages locating pin hole in camshaft flange.

320i 4-CYLINDER (Cont.)

TIMING CHAIN TENSIONER SERVICE

1) Use caution due to high spring pressure and unscrew tensioner plug. Remove piston and spring. Press piston out of sleeve, remove ball bearing and perforated disc, and clean all parts thoroughly. Reassemble parts in order, ensuring that perforated disc does not block bleed slots.

2) Install piston in tensioner body. Place spring with tapered end facing tensioner plug. Screw plug slightly into tensioner body. Fill oil pocket with engine oil and move tensioner rail back and forth until oil comes out around plug threads. Tighten tensioner plug.

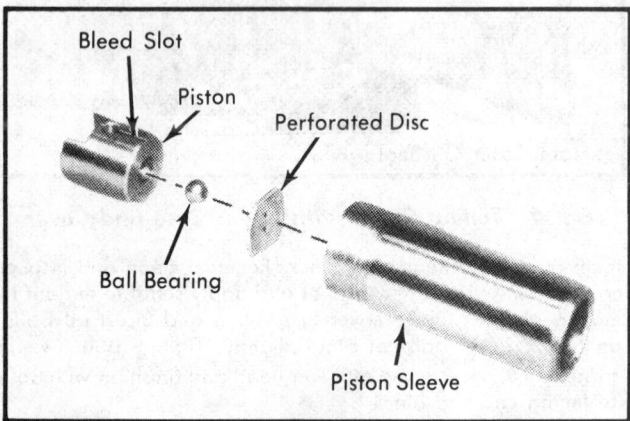

Fig. 5   Exploded View of Chain Tensioner Piston Assembly

VALVES

VALVE ARRANGEMENT

Right Side — All exhaust.

Left Side —All intake.

ROCKER ARM ASSEMBLY

Removal — With camshaft removed, push back thrust ring and rocker arm so rocker shaft circlip may be removed. Remove distributor mounting flange. Drive out rocker arms from rear using drift (11 3 040). Retain all springs, washers, rocker arms and thrust rings in proper order for assembly.

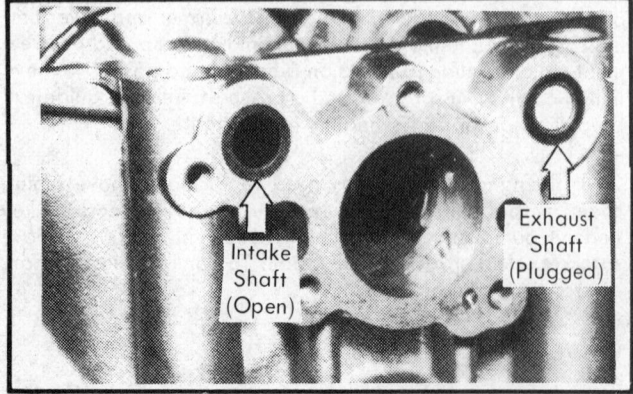

Fig. 6   Rear View of Head Showing Plug in Exhaust Rocker Shaft

Installation — Install all parts in original location. Replace worn rocker arms and shafts, and any rocker arms with loose

contact pads. When installing rocker arm shafts, notches must be aligned to allow cylinder head bolts to fit in openings. Install circlip and ensure that plug in exhaust side rocker shaft is tight.

NOTE — *Rocker arm shaft on intake side is open. Exhaust rocker shaft is plugged.*

VALVE SPRING SERVICE

Compress spring and remove keepers. Remove spring and retainer. Check spring free length and pressure and replace as required. Install springs with tight winding (painted mark) facing cylinder head. Install retainers and keepers.

VALVE GUIDE SERVICE

1) Check valve guide for wear. If replacement is necessary, press out guide toward combustion chamber. Measure guide bore in cylinder head. If bore exceeds .5512″ (14 mm), ream head and install oversize guide.

2) Heat cylinder head to 428-482°F (220-250°C) and press in new guide from top side until tapered groove end protrudes .591″ (15 mm) for standard guide, or .531″ (13.5 mm) for modified guide. Ream guide to obtain specified clearance. Valve guides are available in the following sizes:

Valve Guide Sizes	
Application	**Guide O.D. In. (mm)**
Standard	.5532 (14.05)
1st Oversize	.5551 (14.10)
2nd Oversize	.5590 (14.20)
3rd Oversize	.5630 (14.30)
Standard Length	2.047 (52.0)
Modified Length	1.988 (50.5)

VALVE SEAT SERVICE

Refer to illustration and note minimum valve seat and valve head thicknesses. If either specification is not met, replace necessary component. When replacing valve seat, remove old seat by turning out with suitable cutting tool. Drill out bore to appropriate oversize: note valve seat oversize to be used and rebore head allowing for shrink-fit of replacement seat. When installing new seat, heat head to approximately 392°F (200°C) and chill valve seat to approximately −94°F (−70°C). Replacement seats are available in the following oversizes:

Replacement Valve Seat Rings	
Application	**Measurement In. (mm)**
Intake	
1st Oversize	1.864 (47.35)
2nd Oversize	1.872 (47.55)
Exhaust	
1st Oversize	1.589 (40.35)
2nd Oversize	1.596 (40.55)

320i 4-CYLINDER (Cont.)

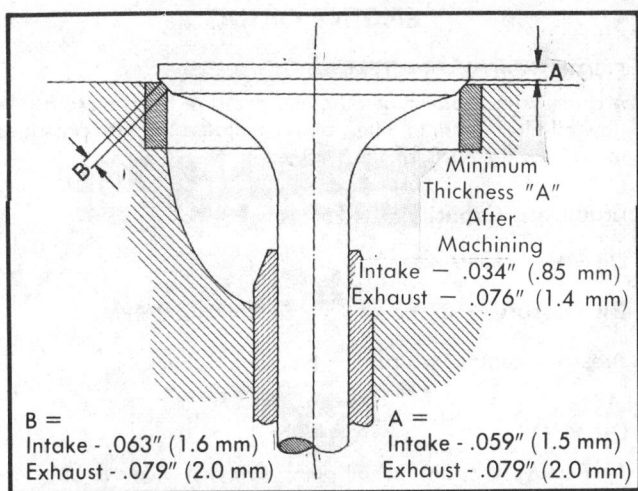

B =
Intake - .063" (1.6 mm)
Exhaust - .079" (2.0 mm)

A =
Intake - .059" (1.5 mm)
Exhaust - .079" (2.0 mm)

Fig. 7   Checking Valve Head and Seat Thickness

VALVE CLEARANCE ADJUSTMENT

Adjust valves in firing order sequence (1-3-4-2) with specific cylinder at TDC of compression stroke. Using a feeler gauge between rocker eccentric and valve stem, set clearance to .008-.010" (20-25 mm) with engine hot, or to .006-.008" (.15-.20 mm) with engine cold. Loosen nut of rocker exxentric, insert a rod in eccentric hole and rotate until proper clearance is obtained. *See Fig. 8.*

NOTE — *Never measure or adjust valve clearance between camshaft and rocker arm pad.*

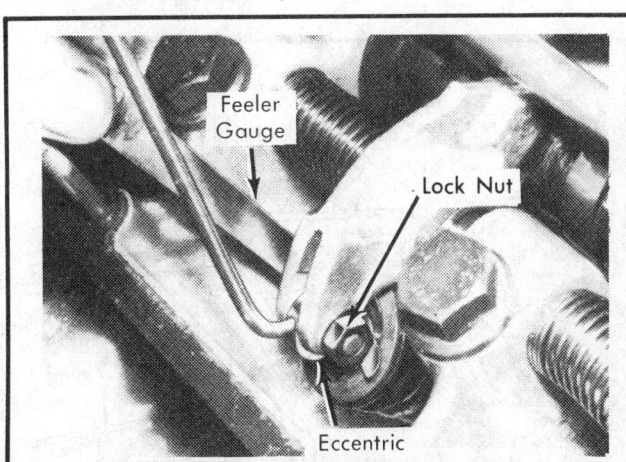

Fig. 8   Valve Clearance Adjustment

PISTONS, PINS & RINGS

OIL PAN

With engine installed, remove bolts securing steering to front axle carrier, move steering out of way. Drain oil, remove bolts securing oil pan, swing pan down. Turn crankshaft and remove oil pan. Coat crankcase ends where timing cover and rear main bearing cover join crankcase with sealing compound before reassembly.

PISTON & ROD ASSEMBLY

Removal — After removing oil pan and cylinder head, rotate crankshaft to BDC of piston and rod assembly to be removed. Unscrew connecting rod cap nuts and push assembly out top of engine. Replace worn or damaged parts as necessary, according to appropriate service procedure indicated in this article.

Installation — Place rings on piston with marking "TOP" facing upward and ring end gaps 120° apart. Install piston with arrow facing forward and oil hole in wrist pin end of connecting rod facing timing chain. Ensure connecting rod and bearing cap numbers match, with No. 1 rod nearest the timing chain.

CONNECTING ROD BUSHING

Wrist pins and pistons are matched to each other and must be replaced together. To remove piston pin from assembly, remove circlip and push out wrist pin. In event of excess clearance, new wrist pin bushing may be pressed in rod. Bushing seam should be at 90° to oil bore. Drill and deburr oil holes, then ream bushing so that pin is a light push fit through connecting rod.

FITTING PISTONS

Piston crowns are marked with arrow for direction of installation and a "+", "–" or no sign to show weight classification. All pistons should have same weight mark. Measure piston and cylinder diameter to determine clearance (see specifications). Measure piston diameter at 90° to wrist pin bore near bottom of piston skirt, see following table for distance from bottom of piston.

Piston Measuring Location	
Piston	①In. (mm)
Mahle	.630 (16.0)
KS	.959 (24.35)
① — Distance from bottom of piston.	

Piston Sizes	
Application (Grade)	**Diameter In. (mm)**
Standard	3.5027 (88.97)
Intermediate	3.5059 (89.05)
No. 1 Oversize	3.5126 (89.22)
No. 2 Oversize	3.5224 (89.47)

CRANKSHAFT MAIN & CONNECTING ROD BEARINGS

MAIN BEARING SERVICE

Plastigage method is used to determine connecting rod and main bearing journal clearances. Standard or undersize crankshafts are marked red or blue. Color coded inserts must agree with crankshaft color code as illustrated. The following tables show color code and undersizes available:

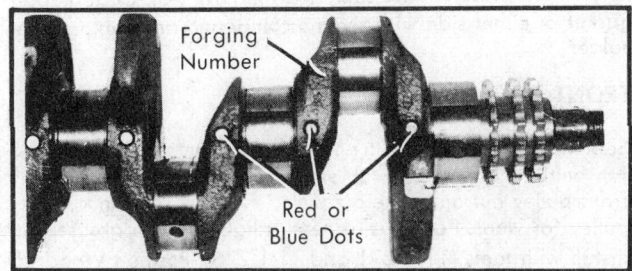

Fig. 9   View Showing Original Crankshaft Marks

320i 4-CYLINDER (Cont.)

Main Bearing Journal	
Application	**In. (mm)**
Original	2.165 (55.0)
1st Stage	2.156 (54.75)
2nd Stage	2.146 (54.50)
3rd Stage	2.136 (54.25)

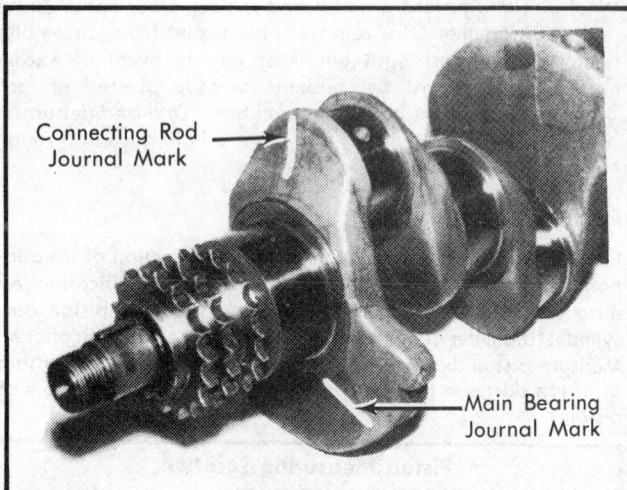

Fig. 10   View Showing Undersize Crankshaft Marking

Connecting Rod Journal	
Application	**In. (mm)**
Original	1.889 (48.0)
1st Stage	1.879 (47.75)
2nd Stage	1.870 (47.50)
3rd Stage	1.860 (47.25)

CAUTION — *Crankshaft should only be factory ground*

THRUST BEARING ALIGNMENT

Attach a dial indicator to crankcase with shaft touching flywheel. Move flywheel in and out to determine endplay of crankshaft. If endplay is excessive, replace center main bearing inserts.

REAR MAIN BEARING OIL SEAL SERVICE

With flywheel removed, unscrew six attaching bolts from rear crankshaft seal holder. Carefully run a knife blade between seal holder and oil pan gasket to break seal. Remove seal holder and press out old seal, press in new seal. Coat oil pan gasket at either side with sealing compound and replace seal holder.

FRONT COVER OIL SEAL

Seal may be replaced with engine in car. Remove radiator and fan belt. Lock flywheel with suitable tool (11 2 100), remove front pulley nut and take off pulley. Remove seal and inspect pulley for wear. Pack lips of new radial seal with grease and install with tools (11 1 271 and 11 1 273). Position Woodruff key correctly and install pulley.

ENGINE OILING

ENGINE OILING SYSTEM

A chain driven rotor type oil pump pressure feeds oil to a full-flow oil filter. From oil filter, oil is circulated through passages to all moving parts of the engine.

Crankcase Capacity — 4.25 qts.

Oil Filter — Full-Flow

Oil Pressure — 57 psi (4.0 kg/cm²) at 4000 RPM.

Pressure Regulator Valve — Non-adjustable

OIL PUMP

1) Remove oil pan and oil pump sprocket. Remove bolts attaching pump pick-up. Remove two bolts mounting pump to crankcase and lift out pump.

2) Unscrew union and remove spring and plunger from pump body. Remove pick-up tube and cover from pump body.

3) Measure clearance between outer rotor-to-pump body, rotor-to-rotor and rotor face-to-pump body flange (see specifications).

4) Using suitable puller, remove drive flange from rotor shaft. Press drive flange on new rotor shaft to a distance of 1.68″ (42.7 mm) between flange and rotor face. *See Fig. 11.*

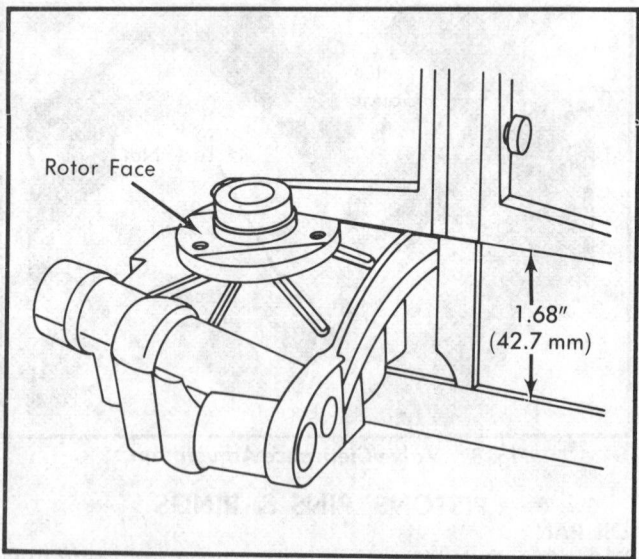

Fig. 11   Measuring Distance Between Flange and Rotor Face

Oil Pump Specifications	
Application	**Measurement In. (mm)**
Rotor-to-Pump Body	.006-.011 (.150-.275)
Inner-to-Outer Rotor	.0047-.0079 (.12-.20)
Cover-to-Rotor	.0014-.0037 (.035-.095)
Pressure Relief Spring	
Free Length	2.677 (68.0)
Installed Length	2.618 (66.5)

320i 4-CYLINDER (Cont.)

5) To install, reverse removal procedure noting that normal length (colored red) and extra long (colored green) chains are available. Further adjustment is possible by using shims between pump body and block. Oil hole in shims must line up with oil hole in pump. Chain tension is correct if chain gives under slight thumb pressure.

ENGINE COOLING

Thermostat — Opens at 176°F (80°C).
Cooling System Capacity — 7.4 qts.

WATER PUMP

1) Loosen alternator bracket. Remove fan and drive belt. Loosen hose clamps and remove water pump.

2) Using a suitable puller, remove fan hub from impeller shaft. Extract circlip and spacer ring from front of pump.

3) Press impeller off shaft and pump bearing out of housing. Drive friction seal out of housing and lift out cover ring.

4) Replace any worn or damaged parts. Using suitable tool, press impeller onto shaft until there is clearance of .039-.047" (1.0-1.2 mm) between impeller and pump face.

5) Press fan hub onto shaft until shaft extends .118-.138" (3.0-3.5 mm) beyond hub face. Install pump and fan, assuring that lockplates are crimped fan bolts.

ENGINE SPECIFICATIONS

GENERAL SPECIFICATIONS

| Year | Displ. | | Carburetor | HP at RPM | Torque (Ft. Lbs. at RPM) | Compr. Ratio | Bore | | Stroke | |
	cu. ins.	cc					in.	mm	in.	mm
1981	107.7	1766	Fuel Inj.	102@5800	100@4500	8.8:1	3.504	89	2.795	71

VALVES

Engine & Valve	Head Diam. In. (mm)	Face Angle	Seat Angle	Seat Width In. (mm)	Stem Diameter In. (mm)	Stem Clearance In. (mm)	Valve Lift In. (mm)
1766 cc Intake	1.805 (45.84)	45.5°	45°	.059-.083 (1.50-2.10)	.3134-.3139 (7.960-7.975)	.0010-.0020 (.025-.055)	.....
Exhaust	1.490 (37.84)	45.5°	45°	.061-.081 (1.55-2.05)	.3129-.3134 (7.945-7.960)	.0015-.0030 (.040-.070)	.....

VALVE SPRINGS

| Engine | Free Length In. (mm) ① | PRESSURE Lbs. @ In. (kg @ mm) | |
		Valve Closed	Valve Open
1766 cc	1.712 (43.5)	64@1.48 (29@37.6)	154@1.12 (70@28.5)

VALVE TIMING

| Engine | INTAKE | | EXHAUST | |
	Open (BTDC)	Close (ABDC)	Open (BBDC)	Close (ATDC)
1766 cc	4°	52°	52°	4°

① — May be 1.811" (46.0 mm) for some springs.

BMW Engines

320i 4-CYLINDER (Cont.)
ENGINE SPECIFICATIONS (Cont.)

PISTONS, PINS, RINGS						
	PISTONS	PINS		RINGS		
Engine	Clearance In. (mm)	Piston Fit In. (mm)	Rod Fit In. (mm)	Rings	End Gap In. (mm)	Side Clearance In. (mm)
1766 cc	.0018 (.045)	①.00008-.00024 (.002-.006)	.0001-.0004 (.003-.010)	No.1	.012-.020 (.30-.50)	②.0024-.0036 (.06-.092)
				No.2	.008-.016 (.20-.40)	②.0016-.0028 (.040-.072)
				No.3	.010-.016 (.25-.40)	②.0012-.0024 (.030-.062)

① — Mahle Pistons — .0004-.0020" (.001-.005 mm)
② — KS Pistons Shown. Mahle Piston Ring No. 1 — same as KS. Mahle Piston Ring No. 2 — .0012-.0024" (.030-.062 mm). Mahle Piston Ring No. 3 — .0008-.0020" (.020-.052 mm).

CRANKSHAFT MAIN & CONNECTING ROD BEARINGS						
	MAIN BEARINGS				CONNECTING ROD BEARINGS	
Engine	Journal Diam. In. (mm)	Clearance In. (mm)	Thrust Bearing	Crankshaft End Play In. (mm)	Journal Diam. In. (mm)	Clearance In. (mm)	Side Play In. (mm)
1766 cc Red	2.165 (55.0)	.0012-.0027 (.030-.070)	Center	.0033-.0068 (.085-.174)	1.8898 (48.0)	.0012-.0027 (.030-.070)	.....
Blue	2.165 (55.0)	.0012-.0026 (.030-.068)	Center		1.8898 (48.0)	.0012-.0026 (.030-.068)	.....

CAMSHAFT			
Engine	Journal Diam. In. (mm)	Clearance ①In. (mm)	Lobe Lift In. (mm)
1766 cc No. 1	1.3769-1.3795 (34.975-35.041)	.0013-.0029 (.034-.074)	.274-.280 (6.95-7.11)
No. 2	1.6525-1.6551 (41.975-42.041)	.0013-.0029 (.034-.074)	.274-.280 (6.95-7.11)
No. 3	1.6919-1.6945 (42.975-43.041)	.0013-.0029 (.034-.074)	.274-.280 (6.95-7.11)

① — End play is .0008-.005" (.020-.127 mm).

TIGHTENING SPECIFICATIONS

Application	Ft. Lbs. (N·m)
Cylinder Head Studs①	
Step 1	25-32 (33-44)
Step 2	49-52 (67-71)
Step 3	56-59 (77-81)
Main Bearing Caps	42-45 (57-62)
Connecting Rod Bolts	38-41 (51-56)
Flywheel-to-Crankshaft②	72-83 (98-113)
Crankshaft Pulley	101-108 (140-150)

	INCH Lbs. (N·m)
Rocker Arm Lock Bolts	84-96 (10-11)
Camshaft Oiler (Hollow Bolt)	96-108 (11-13)
Timing Cover	84-96 (10-11)

① — With engine at maximum of 95°F (35°C).
② — Coat bolts with Loctite.

528i, 633CSi & 733i 6-CYLINDER

ENGINE CODING

ENGINE IDENTIFICATION

Engine serial number is same as chassis serial number. Engine serial number is stamped in crankcase above starter.

ENGINE, CYLINDER HEAD & MANIFOLDS

NOTE − Transmission (manual or automatic) must be removed prior to removing engine.

MANUAL TRANSMISSION

Removal − 1) Remove exhaust system and support brackets from vehicle. Pull up boot from shift lever, remove circlip and pull shift lever up and out. Disconnect propeller shaft at output flange after compressing rubber coupling with compressing strap (261012).

2) Remove center support bearing and pull propeller shaft from transmission. Remove heat shield and clutch slave cylinder. Remove speedometer cable and disconnect backup light switch connection. Disconnect transmission from clutch housing. Support engine at front, remove transmission crossmember and transmission.

Installation − To install, reverse removal procedure. When installing drive shaft, push center support bearing forward .08" (2 mm) to preload bracket and tighten nuts.

AUTOMATIC TRANSMISSION

Removal − 1) Disconnect exhaust system and remove support brackets. Disconnect accelerator cable at transmission and take off of counterholder. Drain transmission and remove filler tube. Plug filler tube opening and disconnect oil cooler lines at transmission. Remove web from bottom of drive shaft tunnel and disconnect wire harness to transmission.

2) Rotate torque converter and remove 4 bolts securing converter to drive plate. Disconnect shift rod from lever. Disconnect drive shaft coupling at rear of transmission and loosen threaded coupling at rear of center support bearing.

3) Remove center support bearing and pull drive shaft down and out to remove. Disconnect speedometer cable and backup light connection. Remove transmission crossmember, allowing engine oil pan to rest on front axle crossmember.

4) Place a jack under transmission and remove ground strap. Separate transmission from engine, making sure torque converter stays in housing in transmission. Remove transmission.

Installation − Reverse removal procedures and note that center support of torque converter is below edge of transmission. Push center support forward .08" (2 mm) to preload center bearing and tighten nuts. Adjust accelerator cable lever.

ENGINE

Removal − 1) Drain cooling system and disconnect battery ground cable. Remove hood and radiator. Remove air cleaner with fuel injection air volume control unit. Remove distributor cap and secondary wiring. Disconnect vacuum line from distributor and primary wires from ignition coil.

2) Disconnect fuel feed hose at fuel filter, vapor hose at charcoal filter, and vacuum hoses from brake booster. Disconnect all remaining coolant and fuel hoses from engine. Remove engine ground cable and disconnect plug from fuel injection control unit. Pull control harness into engine compartment from glove box.

3) Mark for identification and disconnect all remaining electrical connections to engine. Detach air conditioner compressor (if equipped) and suspend from wire. Do NOT disconnect hoses. Disconnect wires from starter and alternator. Detach power steering pump from engine, leaving hoses connected.

4) Disconnect accelerator linkage from engine and remove nuts from engine mounts. Remove protective cover from under engine. Attach a hoist to lifting holes at front and rear of engine. On manual transmission models, push back rubber boot on slave cylinder, remove circlip and pull slave cylinder out toward front. Remove throw-out bearing lever and bearing from clutch housing.

5) On all models, gradually lift engine and turn as necessary to clear vehicle. If disassembling engine, mount on engine support tool and adapter (00 1 500 and 11 0 130).

Installation − On manual transmission models, lubricate contact surfaces of throw-out-bearing lever with suitable lubricant. To install engine on all models, reverse removal procedures. Ensure that all hoses, lines and electrical connections are restored to original position.

INTAKE MANIFOLD

NOTE − Throttle housing, air collector and intake pipes may be separated individually.

Removal − 1) Disconnect battery ground cable and remove cylinder head cover. Disconnect throttle linkage and detach throttle housing from collector, leaving water hose connected.

2) Mark for identification and remove hoses, lines and wires from intake system. Detach support bracket and press away from collector. Detach collector from intake pipes and remove collector.

Installation − Use all new gaskets and reverse removal procedure. Ensure that all hoses, lines and electrical connections are installed in correct locations.

CYLINDER HEAD

Removal − 1) Disconnect battery ground cable and drain cooling system. Remove air cleaner, spark plug wire tube and valve cover. Disconnect fuel line at fuel pump.

2) Disconnect all fuel and vacuum lines, along with all wiring from injection system and cylinder head. Disconnect accelerator linkage.

3) Remove upper front cover. See *Engine Front Cover & Oil Seal.* Bend back lock tabs and remove camshaft sprocket bolts and sprocket. Remove timing chain tensioner plug, spring and piston. Disconnect water hoses at base of intake manifolds.

528i, 633CSi & 733i 6-CYLINDER (Cont.)

4) Disconnect exhaust pipes. Remove cylinder head bolts and install aligning pins to keep rocker arm shafts from moving. Remove cylinder head.

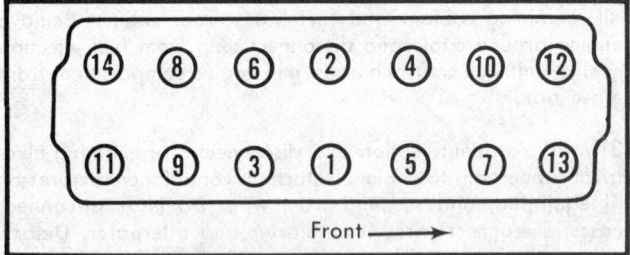

Fig. 1   Cylinder Head Tightening Sequence

Installation — 1) Ensure that there is no oil or fluid in recesses of block and insure that all mating surfaces are clean. Install new head gasket ensuring that openings for coolant flow are aligned. Install head and tighten head bolts in 3 steps in sequence illustrated. *See Tightening Specifications.*

NOTE — *Never loosen bolts during tightening sequence; turn only in tightening direction.*

2) Install camshaft sprocket and timing chain. *See Timing Chain Replacement.* Install valve cover and complete installation in reverse order of removal. Retighten cylinder head bolts after engine has been run and allowed to cool to approximately 100°F (38°C).

CAMSHAFT

ENGINE FRONT COVER AND OIL SEAL

Upper Front Engine Cover — 1) Remove distributor cap and valve cover. Remove thermostat housing and thermostat. Rotate crankshaft untill number one cylinder is at TDC of compression stroke. Distributor rotor should point at notch in distributor.

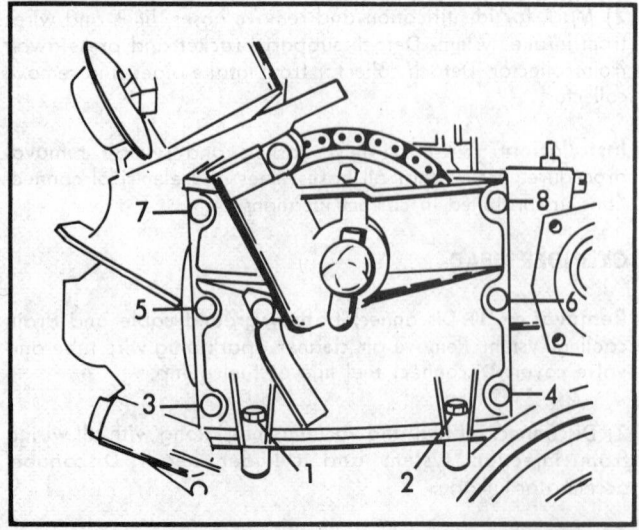

Fig. 2   Upper Front Cover Tightening Sequence

2) Disconnect vacuum lines to distributor. Loosen pinch bolt on distributor mounting and pull out distributor. Remove guard

and upper timing cover bolts. Take off cover with distributor drive gear.

3) To install, thoroughly clean all mating surfaces, fill bores of timing cover with Dirco (or equivalent) sealer, replace cord seal around distributor drive gear, and replace cover with new gasket and sealer. Turn distributor rotor counterclockwise so that rotor tip is about 1½" (38 mm) from notch in distributor housing and guide distributor into position. Note that vacuum advance unit is aligned approximately 90° to valve cover when installed properly.

4) Lightly tighten bolts one and two (see illustration), then tighten remaining bolts to specification in sequence shown in illustration. Tighten bolts one and two to specification. To install remaining components, reverse removal procedure.

Lower Front Engine Cover — 1) Remove upper front engine cover as previously outlined. Remove timing chain tensioner piston, fan clutch and crankshaft pulley. Remove lower front engine cover.

2) Replace oil seal. To install cover, reverse removal procedure. Thoroughly clean mating surfaces and use new gasket with sealer. Tighten bolts to specification.

NOTE — *Oil seal can be replaced without removing lower front engine cover.*

Timing Case Cover Oil Seal — 1) Remove lower flywheel cover and install suitable ring gear lock. Remove fan housing and all drive belts. Unscrew crankshaft nut and remove vibration damper with hub. Pry out radial seal.

2) Pack lips of new radial seal with grease. Press seal in with installing tool (11 1 280). Install components in reverse order of removal and remove lock on flywheel.

CAMSHAFT

Removal — 1) Cylinder head must be removed from engine. Remove coolant hose. Loosen bolts holding oil distribution line to rocker arm supports and remove line. Loosen all valve adjustments to maximum clearance position.

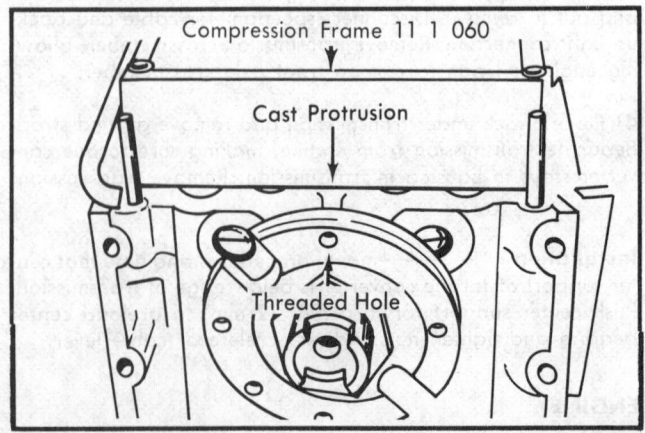

Fig. 3   Position of Camshaft with No. 6 Valves in Overlap Position

528i, 633CSi & 733i 6-CYLINDER (Cont.)

2) Rotate camshaft from TDC position of No. 1 cylinder toward intake approximately .59" (15 mm) and install compression tool (11 1 060). Tighten exhaust side nuts on tool to stop, then intake side nuts. Remove camshaft retaining bolts and pull out camshaft.

Installation — 1) Install camshaft in head and tighten thrust plate bolts. Cam must turn easily without excess end play. Turn camshaft to No. 6 overlap position as illustrated and remove compression tool.

2) Install oil line so that oil bores will give off spray between rocker arms and cams of intake and exhaust valves. Ensure that seals are used between line and rocker supports as well as under head of attaching bolts. Continue assembly in reverse order of removal.

CAMSHAFT END PLAY

Check camshaft end play with a feeler gauge. If end play exceeds .001-.007" (.03-.18 mm), replace camshaft thrust plate.

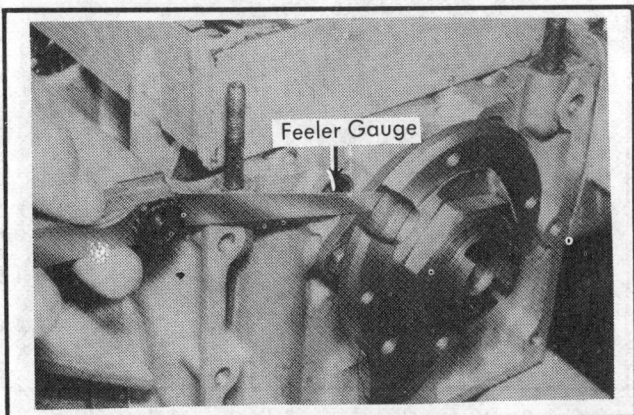

Fig. 4   Checking Camshaft End Play with Feeler Gauge

TIMING CHAIN REPLACEMENT

1) Rotate crankshaft until number one cylinder is at TDC of compression stroke. Rotor should point to notch in distributor. Remove front engine covers as previously outlined. Mark front side of timing chain for installation.

2) Bend over lock tabs and remove camshaft sprocket with timing chain. If mileage of vehicle exceeds 30,000 miles, replace timing chain. Replace sprockets if worn or damaged.

3) To replace crankshaft sprocket, remove oil pan, oil pump chain and sprocket, and crankshaft Woodruff key. Pull off sprocket with puller (11 2 000). To install, reverse removal procedure and adjust oil pump chain tension.

4) To install timing chain, reverse removal procedure, making sure number one cylinder is at TDC of compression stroke. Line up tapped hole in sprocket hub with cast protrusion in cylinder head and install timing chain and sprocket.

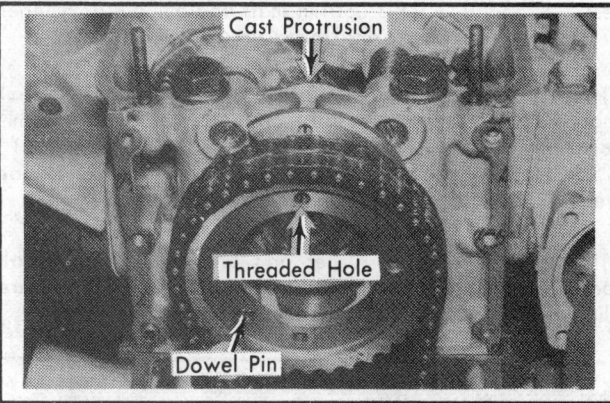

Fig. 5   Camshaft, Sprocket and Timing Chain Alignment for Installation

TIMING CHAIN TENSIONER

1) Remove tensioner plug, spring and piston. Check length of spring and piston assembly. Length of spring should be 6.122" (155.5 mm). Piston assembly length should be 2.441" (62.0 mm)

2) Check piston with compressed air to see if air vent slots (see illustration) are plugged. Clean slots if air does not pass through. When assembling piston, do not block air vents with disc.

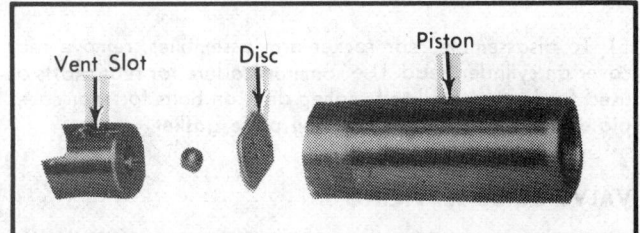

Fig. 6   Timing Chain Tensioner Components

3) Install piston, spring with conical end toward plug and slightly tighten plug. Fill oil well full of oil and remove valve cover to vent air from piston. Move tensioning rail back and forth until oil comes out at plug. Tighten plug and reverse removal procedure to install remaining components.

VALVES

VALVE ARRANGEMENT

Left Side — Intake valves.
Right Side — Exhaust valves.

ROCKER ARM ASSEMBLY

1) Remove camshaft. *See Camshaft Removal.* Push rocker arms and thrust rings against springs and remove circlips from front rocker arm shafts.

2) Remove two countersunk rocker arm shaft locking bolts next to number one bearing bore of camshaft. Install a suitable

528i, 633CSi & 733i 6-CYLINDER (Cont.)

removing tool (No. 11 3 060) in shaft and pull out of cylinder head. Remove rocker arms, thrust rings, springs and disc.

3) Check rocker arms and shaft for excessive play. Normal shaft diameter should be at least .609" (15.466 mm) and maximum bushing bore in rocker arms should not exceed .611" (15.518 mm). Check cam follower pads on rocker arms for wear and security. If loose, replace rocker arms.

4) Install spring, disc, rocker arm and thrust ring. Install rocker arm shafts and adjust so that recesses in shafts are aligned with cylinder head bolt holes in cylinder head.

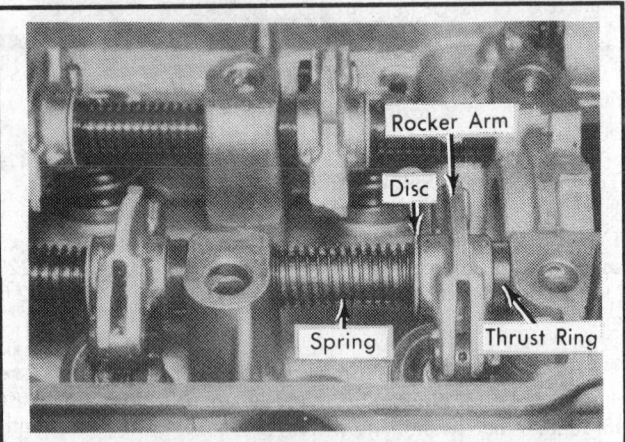

Fig. 7   Installed View of Rocker Arm Assembly

5) To disassemble rear rocker arm assemblies, remove rear cover on cylinder head. Use same procedure for rear shafts as used for front. Install self sealing discs on bolts for rear cover plate and use Cabritol sealer on plate gasket.

VALVE GUIDE SERVICING

1) With valve removed, check inside diameter of valve guide. If size exceeds specifications, drive guide out through combustion chamber with a suitable driver (No. 11 1 100).

2) Check size of valve guide bore in cylinder head. If size exceeds .5519" (14.018 mm), an oversize guide must be installed. If guide or bore condition warrant, the following sizes of guides are available for service replacement: .5551" (14.10 mm), .5591" (14.20 mm), and .5630" (14.30 mm).

3) Guides require a .0006-.0019" (.015-.044 mm) press fit in cylinder head with head heated to 430-480°F (220-250°C). Ream head bores according to guide size being installed.

4) Using suitable driver (No. 11 1 120), drive guide into cylinder head from top until top of guide protrudes .591" (15.0 mm) for standard guide, or .531" (13.5 mm) for modified guide. Ream valve guide until correct clearance with valve is obtained.

VALVE SPRING

With rocker arms and shafts removed, compress valve spring with suitable tool (11 1 060) and remove keepers. Remove valve spring and retainer and check spring free length. Check

compressed length and pressure in a suitable tester. Replace defective springs and assemble with paint stripe (tight coil end) against head. Install retainer and keepers.

VALVE STEM OIL SEALS

To replace valve stem oil seals, use guide or tape over stem grooves to prevent damage to new seals. Lubricate seal and press into position with suitable tool (11 1 130).

VALVE CLEARANCE ADJUSTMENT

Remove valve cover and turn crankshaft so that No. 1 cylinder is at TDC on firing stroke. Assure that engine temperature is cool (max. 95°F, 35°C) and use feeler gauge to check clearance between valve and adjusting eccentric. Clearance for both intake and exhaust valves should be .010-.012" (.25-.30 mm). To adjust clearance, loosen nut on rocker arm and rotate eccentric.

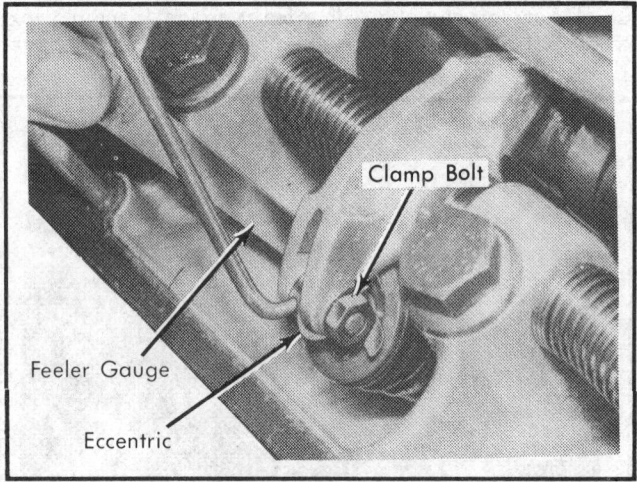

Fig. 8   Valve Clearance Adjustment Procedure

PISTONS, PINS & RINGS

OIL PAN

Removal — Drain engine oil and remove wires from oil level switch (if equipped). Remove power steering pump but do NOT disconnect hoses. Remove alternator and loosen mounting pad bolts enough to allow access to pan bolts. Remove bottom rear bolt of mounting pad and unscrew pan bolts. Turn crankshaft so that No. 6 connecting rod is above crankcase sealing surface and remove pan. On 733i, it may be necessary to detach engine mounts and lift engine slightly.

Installation — To install, use new gaskets and apply sealer to all junctions of block, pan and end covers. To complete installation, reverse removal procedure.

PISTON & ROD ASSEMBLY

With cylinder head, oil pan and oil pump removed, remove connecting rod cap. Push piston and rod assembly up and out through top of block. To install, ensure that ring gaps are offset 120° to each other. Apply ring compressor and insert bearing halves in rod and cap. Install with arrow on piston top facing timing chain. Assemble cap to rod with numbers matching and tighten cap.

528i, 633CSi & 733i 6-CYLINDER (Cont.)

PISTON PIN REPLACEMENT

1) With piston and rod assembly removed, remove circlips from piston pin hole in piston. Drive out piston pin and separate piston from connecting rod. Thoroughly clean and inspect rod and piston.

Piston Pin Class Designation	
Application	**Pin Diameter In. (mm)**
White	.8660-.8661 (21.997-22.000)
Black	.8659-.8660 (21.994-21.997)
Blue	.8661-.8663 (22.000-22.005)

2) Pistons and pins are installed as a matched set only. Pin class may be coded by white or black marking for standard or blue for oversize pins.

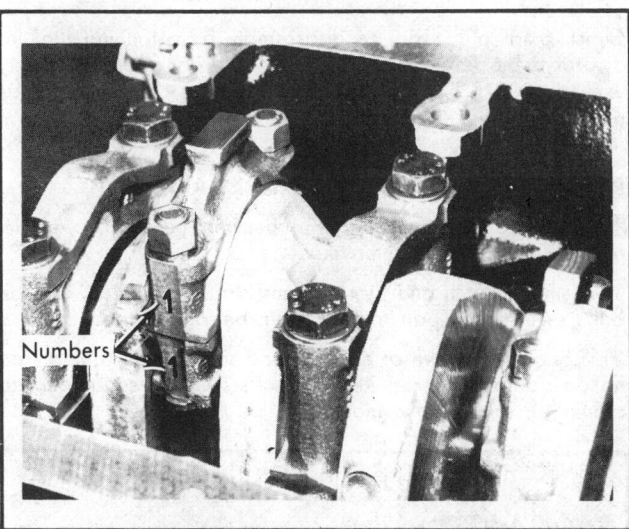

Fig. 9   View Showing Connecting Rod Cap Installation

3) Classes of pins and pistons must not be interchanged. If piston or pin is replaced, it must be replaced with one of a corresponding class and weight. Weight classification is designated by a "+" or "−" stamped in top of piston.

4) Check pin-to-piston clearance, if clearance exceeds that specified and pin is not worn, replace piston. Check pin-to-rod clearance, if clearance exceeds that specified, depending on pin class, new bushing must be installed.

5) Press out old bushing and install new one with split in bushing rotated 90° from oil hole in connecting rod. Drill through oil hole in connecting rod. Ream bushing to specified clearance with piston pin.

6) If connecting rod is replaced, replace with rod which is within 4 grams of rod being replaced. Position piston on connecting rod with arrow on piston facing in same direction as oil hole in connecting rod. Lubricate and install piston pin and circlips.

FITTING PISTONS

1) With piston removed and disassembled from connecting rod, measure diameter of piston. Measure with micrometer positioned 90° from pin hole and at a point measured from bottom of piston skirt. (Distance "A" in *Fig. 10*.)

NOTE – *Distance depends on engine and manufacturer of pistons.*

Application	Manufacturer	Distance "A"
528i	Mahle	.630" (16.0 mm)
528i	KS	.947" (24.05 mm)
633CSi, 733i	Mahle	1.024" (26.0 mm)
633CSi, 733i	KS	1.340" (34.05 mm)

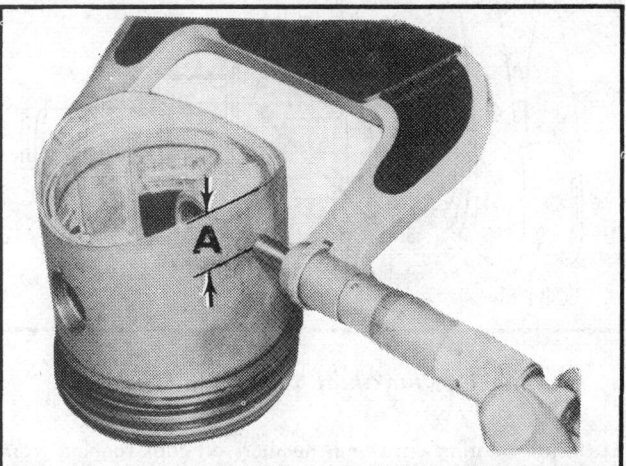

Fig. 10   Measuring Piston Diameter

2) Measure inside diameter of bore in crankcase. If clearance exceeds specification, crankcase must be bored for next oversize piston. Pistons are available in .010" (.25 mm) and .020" (.50 mm) oversize.

3) Check piston ring side clearance and end gap. If new rings are installed, install with word "TOP" stamped in ring toward top of piston.

CRANKSHAFT MAIN & CONNECTING ROD BEARINGS

MAIN & CONNECTING ROD BEARING SERVICE

1) With engine removed, remove clutch, flywheel, cylinder head, oil pan and timing chain. See *Timing Chain Replacement*. Remove rear main bearing oil seal mount.

2) Remove pistons and connecting rods. Remove main bearing caps and lift out crankshaft. Thoroughly clean and inspect crankshaft. Blow out oil passages with compressed air.

3) Main bearing journals are manufactured in 2 standard sizes. Sizes are designated by a colored dot on crankshaft balance weight next to individual journal. See *Fig. 11*.

528i, 633CSi & 733i 6-CYLINDER (Cont.)

4) Check main and connecting rod bearing clearance using Plastigage method. If clearance will not meet specifications when installing new bearings, it will be necessary to exchange crankshaft. Crankshaft is tenifer treated and may only be reground at the factory.

5) Install bearing halves in crankcase and bearing caps. Lubricate crankshaft bearing journals and install crankshaft in crankcase.

NOTE – *In the event of a crankshaft of a different color code than the crankcase, use one blue and one red bearing shell for each journal. Make sure that all red or all blue shells are installed facing up and the remaining color facing down.*

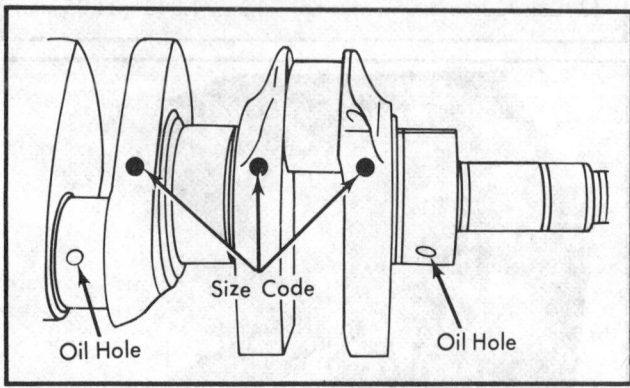

Fig. 11 Crankshaft Color Code Markings

6) Install bearing caps with numbers on caps running from one through six in order from front to rear. Install caps with bearing locks on same side as bearing locks in crankcase.

7) Tighten caps to specifications. Check crankshaft end play. *See Thrust Bearing Alignment.* To install remaining components, reverse removal procedure.

NOTE – *Crankshafts which have been ground undersize are marked with painted stripes. See Fig. 12.*

Fig. 12 View Showing Crankshaft Undersize Markings

Crankshaft Journal Sizes	
Application	**In. (mm)**
Connecting Rod	
Standard	1.888-1.889 (47.97-47.99)
1 paint stripe	1.852-1.853 (47.72-47.74)
2 paint stripes	1.851-1.852 (47.48-47.49)
3 paint stripes	1.850-1.851 (47.22-47.24)
Main Bearings (Red Code)	
Standard	2.361-2.362 (59.98-59.99)
1 paint stripe	2.324-2.325 (59.73-59.74)
2 paint stripes	2.323-2.324 (59.48-59.49)
3 paint stripes	2.322-2.323 (59.23-59.24)
Main Bearings (Blue Code)	
Standard	2.361-2.362 (59.98-59.99)
1 paint stripe	2.324-2.325 (59.72-59.73)
2 paint stripes	2.323-2.324 (59.47-59.48)
3 paint stripes	2.322-2.323 (59.22-59.23)

THRUST BEARING ALIGNMENT

Check axial play prior to disassembly by attaching dial indicator to block and moving flywheel to front and rear. If play exceeds .007" (.174 mm), check and replace main bearings as required.

REAR MAIN BEARING OIL SEAL REPLACEMENT

NOTE – *To replace rear main bearing oil seal in vehicle, transmission must be removed.*

1) Remove clutch and flywheel and drain engine oil. Remove bolts securing oil pan to rear main bearing oil seal mount.

2) Pry oil pan down at area around seal mount, taking care not to damage gasket. Remove bolts securing seal mount to crankcase and remove mount.

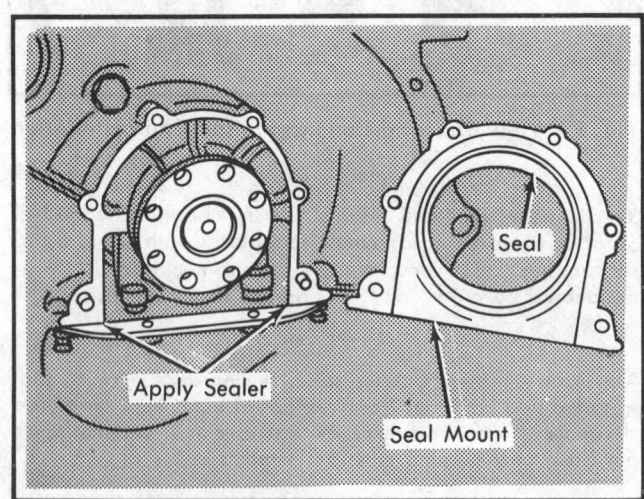

Fig. 13 Installing Crankshaft Rear Oil Seal

3) Pry old seal from mount and install new one using driver and adapter (00 5 500 and 11 1 260). Use guide (11 2 213) when replacing mount to prevent damage to seal. Pack seal lips with grease and apply Atmosit (or equivalent) sealer to junction of oil pan and seal mount. Reverse removal procedure to complete installation.

528i, 633CSi & 733i 6-CYLINDER (Cont.)

ENGINE OILING

ENGINE OILING SYSTEM

Full pressure oil system, utilizing a chain driven Eaton type oil pump, a full flow filter and a pressure regulator valve.

Crankcase Capacity — 6 quarts including filter.

Oil Filter — Full-flow, paper element type.

Normal Oil Pressure — 7-28 psi (.5-2.0 kg/cm²) at idle and 71 psi (5.0 kg/cm²) at max. RPM.

Pressure Regulator Valve — Mounted in oil pump. See *Oil Pump Removal.*

OIL PUMP

1) Remove oil pan, front engine covers and timing chain as previously outlined. Remove oil pump drive sprocket and chain. Remove oil pump.

2) Remove pressure regulator plug, spring and piston. Remove pump cover and thoroughly clean and inspect all components. Check clearance between inner and outer rotors. If clearance exceeds maximum specified, replace rotors.

3) Check clearance between outer rotor and pump body and clearance between rotor sealing face and mating surface of pump body and pump cover. If either clearance exceeds maximum specified, replace pump body.

4) Remove sprocket flange using puller (00 8500). Install flange so that distance between sprocket side of flange and sealing side of inner rotor is 1.744±.004" (44.3±.10 mm).

5) Check free length of regulator spring, if less than specified, replace spring. To assemble pump, reverse removal procedure. Attach oil pump to crankcase and install sprocket and chain. Chain should slightly depress when pushed in with thumb.

6) If chain depresses more than recommended, remove pump and install shims between pump and crankcase mounting points. Make sure oil holes line up on front shim. Rear shim must be same thickness as front. To install remaining components, reverse removal procedure.

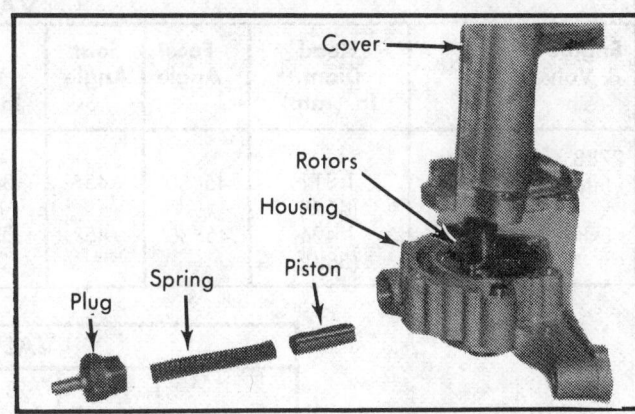

Fig. 14   View of Oil Pump Assembly

Oil Pump Specifications	
Application	**Measurement In. (mm)**
Rotor-to-Rotor Clearance	.005-.008 (.12-.20)
Rotor-to-Housing Clearance	
Radial	.006-.011 (.150-.275)
Axial	.0014-.0037 (.035-.095)
Regulator Spring Free Length	2.677 (67.99)

ENGINE COOLING

WATER PUMP

Remove clutch fan, pulley, side bar and connecting hose. Remove water pump. To install, reverse removal procedure. Use new gaskets and sealer.

Thermostat — Opens at 176°F (80°C).

Cooling System Capacity — 12.7 qts.

ENGINE SPECIFICATIONS

GENERAL SPECIFICATIONS										
Year	Displ.		Carburetor	HP at RPM	Torque (Ft. Lbs. at RPM)	Compr. Ratio	Bore		Stroke	
	cu. ins.	cc					in.	mm	in.	mm
1981										
528i	170	2788	Fuel Inj.	169 @ 5500	166 @ 4500	8.2:1	3.386	86	3.150	80
633CSi	196	3210	Fuel Inj.	177 @ 5500	192 @ 4000	8.4:1	3.504	89	3.386	86
733i	196	3210	Fuel Inj.	177 @ 5500	195 @ 4000	8.4:1	3.504	89	3.386	86

BMW Engines

528i, 633CSi & 733i 6-CYLINDER (Cont.)

ENGINE SPECIFICATIONS (Cont.)

VALVES							
Engine & Valve	Head Diam. In. (mm)	Face Angle	Seat Angle	Seat Width In. (mm)	Stem Diameter In. (mm)	Stem Clearance In. (mm)	Valve Lift In. (mm)
2788 cc & 3210cc Intake	1.811 (46.0)	45°30'	45°	.063-.079 (1.6-2.0)	.3134-.3140 (7.960-7.975)	.0010-.0022 (.025-.055)	.....
Exhaust	1.496 (38.0)	45°30'	45°	.079-.095 (2.0-2.4)	.3128-.3134 (7.945-7.960)	.0016-.0027 (.040-.070)	.....

VALVE SPRINGS			
Engine	Free Length In. (mm)	PRESSURE Lbs. @ In. (kg @ mm)	
		Valve Closed	Valve Open
2788 cc & 3210 cc	①1.712 (43.5)	64±2.5@1.480 (29±1.2@37.6)	154±6@1.122 (70±2.8@28.5)

① — Some springs are 1.811" (46.0 mm), depending on manufacturer.

PISTONS, PINS, RINGS						
	PISTONS	PINS		RINGS		
Engine	Clearance In. (mm)	Piston Fit In. (mm)	Rod Fit In. (mm)	Rings	End Gap In. (mm)	Side Clearance In. (mm)
2788 cc & 3210 cc	.0018 (.045)	0-.0002 (0-.005)	①.0002-.0005 (.005-.013) ②.0003-.0006 (.008-.016)	No. 1 No. 2 Oil	.012-.020 (.30-.50) .008-.016 (.20-.40) .010-.016 (.25-.40)	③.002-.004 (.06-.09) ③.001-.002 (.03-.06) ③.0008-.002 (.02-.06)

① — White color code.   ② — Black color code.   ③ — Mahle specifications shown; For KS, No. 1 .002-.004" (.06-.09 mm), No. 2 .002-.003" (.04-.07 mm), Oil .001-.002 (.03-.06 mm).

CRANKSHAFT MAIN & CONNECTING ROD BEARINGS						
	MAIN BEARINGS				CONNECTING ROD BEARINGS	
Engine	Journal Diam. In. (mm)	Clearance In. (mm)	Thrust Bearing	Crankshaft End Play In. (mm)	Journal Diam. In. (mm)	Clearance In. (mm)	Side Play In. (mm)
2788 cc & 3210 cc Red Code	2.3614-2.3618 (59.98-59.99)	.0012-.0028 (.030-.070)	No. 4	.0033-.0069 (.085-.174)	1.8888-1.8894 (47.975-47.991)	.0009-.0027 (.023-.069)	.....
Blue Code	2.3610-2.3614 (59.97-59.98)	.0012-.0027 (.030-.068)					

BMW Engines

528i, 633CSi & 733i 6-CYLINDER (Cont.)

ENGINE SPECIFICATIONS (Cont.)

CAMSHAFT			
Engine	Journal Diam. In. (mm)	Clearance In. (mm)	Lobe Lift In. (mm)
2788 cc & 3210 cc		.0013-.0029 (.034-.075)	.2802 (7.12)
No. 1	1.3764-1.3770 (34.96-34.98)		
No. 2	1.7304-1.7310 (43.95-43.97)		
No. 3	1.7704-1.7710 (44.97-44.98)		
No. 4	1.8094-1.8100 (45.96-45.97)		

VALVE TIMING				
	INTAKE		EXHAUST	
Engine	Open (BTDC)	Close (ABDC)	Open (BBDC)	Close (ATDC)
2788 cc				
①	7°	51°	51°	7°
②	18°	62°	62°	18°
3210 cc				
①	14°	54°	54°	14°
②	26°	66°	66°	26°

① — With .020″ (.51 mm) clearance between heel of camshaft and rocker pad.

② — With .014″ (.37 mm) clearance between heel of camshaft and rocker pad.

TIGHTENING SPECIFICATIONS

Application	Ft. Lbs. (N·m)
Cylinder Head Bolts ①	
1st Stage	26-32 (34-44)
2nd Stage	49-52 (67-71)
3rd Stage	56-59 (77-81)
Main Bearing Bolts	42-45 (57-62)
Rod Cap Nuts	38-41 (51-56)
Camshaft Thrust Plate	101-108 (137-147)
Upper Front Engine Cover	7-8 (9-11)
Lower Front Engine Cover	7-8 (9-11)
Timing Chain Tensioner Plug	22-29 (30-40)
Rocker Arm Clamp Bolt	7-8 (9-11)
Flywheel Bolts ②	72-83 (98-113)
Crankshaft Pulley Nut	318-333 (432-451)
Oil Pump Regulator Plug	26-30 (35-40)
Camshaft Oil Line Hollow Bolt	8-9 (11-13)

① — With engine cool — Max. 95°F (33°C).

② — Coat threads with Loctite.

Chrysler Corp. Import Engines

1400, 1600, 2000 & 2600 cc 4-CYLINDER

ENGINE CODING

ENGINE IDENTIFICATION

Engine model code and serial number are stamped on engine block just below No. 1 spark plug on right side of block. Model codes are listed in table.

Engine Identification		
Application In. (cc)	Engine Model	Model Code
86.0 (1400)	J	G12B
97.5 (1600)	K	G32B
121.7 (2000)	U	G52B
155.9 (2600)	①F	G54B

① — Code "W" for Pickup models.

ENGINE & CYLINDER HEAD

ENGINE

Removal (Rear Wheel Drive Models)— 1) Drain cooling system and remove engine undercover and hood. Remove battery and disconnect ground strap, wiring from ignition coil, vacuum control solenoid valve, fuel cut-off solenoid valve, alternator, starter, transmission switch, back-up light switch, water temperature gauge and oil pressure switch.

2) Remove air cleaner and disconnect attaching hoses. Disconnect accelerator linkage and heater hoses. Unbolt and separate exhaust pipe from manifold. Disconnect pipe mounting bracket at transmission.

3) Disconnect hose between fuel filter and fuel pump return pipe. Remove radiator and radiator shroud. If equipped with automatic transmission, remove oil cooler pipe and tie rod when removing radiator. If equipped with power steering, remove and suspend oil pump.

4) Remove console box, then detach control lever assembly from transmission. Remove hood. Disconnect speedometer cable and back-up light switch wiring from transmission. Disconnect clutch cable from shift lever and then disconnect cable from its bracket (if equipped with manual transmission).

5) Drain transmission. If equipped with a transmission dynamic damper, remove damper. Remove locking bolts for attaching flange yoke at rear of propeller shaft and draw shaft out of transmission.

6) Support transmission on a jack and remove front and rear mount bolts. Remove rear engine support bracket. Attach lifting device to front and rear engine hangers. Lift engine and transmission assembly at an angle, upwards and out of engine compartment.

NOTE — *Keep transmission lower than engine when removing. If lower part of bell housing interferes with relay rod, raise*

rear of transmission to clear rod, then remove engine-transmission assembly.

Removal (Front Wheel Drive Models) — 1) Drain cooling system and remove battery and tray. Remove air cleaner assembly. Remove purge control valve bracket from battery support and disconnect vacuum hose from valve. Remove windshield washer tank, radiator reservoir and damping canister.

2) Remove radiator assembly and cooling fan. Disconnect the following from the engine/transaxle: clutch, accelerator and speedometer cables, heater hose, fuel hoses, PCV vacuum hose, high altitude compensator vacuum hose (California models), wires from starter, engine ground, alternator, coolant temperature, ignition coil, high temperature sensor, back-up light and oil pressure switch.

3) Remove ignition coil. From under vehicle, remove undercover and drain transaxle. Remove right and left drive shafts from transaxle case and suspend with wire to prevent damaging joints. Cover holes in transaxle case to prevent entry of foreign matter.

NOTE — *Drive shaft retainer rings should be replaced whenever drive shafts are removed from transaxle.*

4) Remove assist rod, control rod and range selector cable from transaxle. Disconnect and suspend exhaust pipe. Remove front roll rod bolts and loosen transaxle mounting bracket attaching nuts. Remove bolts and nuts from front and rear engine insulators and disconnect rear roll rod.

5) Suspend engine from chains attached to hoisting brackets and remove mounting bracket nuts loosened previously. Lift engine-transaxle assembly from vehicle using care that assembly does not hit battery bracket during removal.

Installation (All Models) — Reverse removal procedures and tighten mounting bolts and nuts to specifications with weight of engine on insulators. Replace all fluids and adjust all cables and linkages.

CYLINDER HEAD & INTAKE MANIFOLD

Removal — 1) Drain cooling system. Disconnect water hoses at cylinder head, manifold and carburetor. Remove breather and purge hose, vacuum hose at distributor and purge control valve.

2) Disconnect accelerator linkage, spark plug wires, water temperature gauge unit and exhaust manifold flange. Remove air cleaner, fuel line, distributor and fuel pump. Remove exhaust manifold, then intake manifold and carburetor assembly.

3) Remove rocker cover and breather. On 1400 and 1600 cc engine, remove timing belt upper front cover. Turn crankshaft so number 1 piston is at TDC on compression stroke. Mark belt (1400 or 1600 cc) or chain (2000 and 2600 cc) with suitable marker in line with sprocket mark. On 1400 cc engine, move timing belt tensioner fully toward water pump and slide belt off camshaft sprocket.

4) Except on 1400 cc engine, remove camshaft sprocket from camshaft. Hang sprocket on holder provided on timing belt chain or belt lower front cover. On 1600 cc engine, remove timing belt upper inner cover.

1400, 1600, 2000 & 2600 cc 4-CYLINDER (Cont.)

NOTE — *If there is a large gap between camshaft sprocket and sprocket holder, insert a 2" (50 mm) piece of timing belt or similar material into the gap to prevent belt from disengaging from crankshaft or oil pump sprockets.*

5) Remove rocker cover and remove cylinder head bolts in the reverse of the sequence shown in *Fig. 2*. Lift off cylinder head being careful not to twist sprocket and chain (or belt).

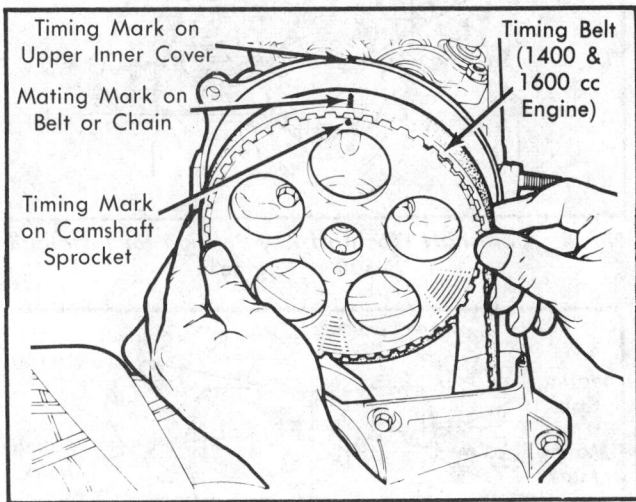

**Fig. 1   Aligning Timing Marks at TDC
(1400 & 1600 cc Engine Shown)**

Installation — 1) To install, reverse removal procedure. Gasket surfaces must be clean and NEW gaskets must be used. Use sealer ONLY at points where cylinder head joins front cover case (2000 and 2600 cc engines) and to intake manifold gasket around water passages (all models). On 1400 cc engine, ensure that timing belt tensioner is properly adjusted.

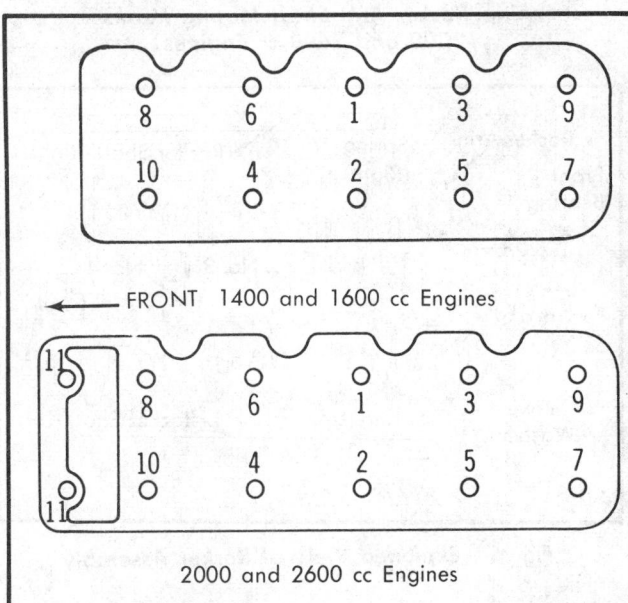

**Fig. 2   Cylinder Head Bolt Tightening Sequence
(Remove in Reverse Order)**

NOTE — *Avoid sliding cylinder head when installing in order to prevent damage to gasket and aligning dowels (when in-*

stalled). Engine should not be run with rocker cover off due to oil spray from rocker arms.

2) Tighten cylinder head bolts to initial torque of 25 ft. lbs. (34 N·m) for 1400 and 1600 cc engines. Tighten 2000 and 2600 cc cylinder head bolts to initial torque of 35 ft. lbs. (48 N·m). Follow sequence in *Fig. 2*. Repeat procedure, tightening bolts to final torque.

3) Temporarily set valve clearance to cold engine settings, then readjust to hot engine settings after engine is at normal operating temperature. Install rocker cover, air cleaner and breather hoses.

CAMSHAFT

ROCKER ARMS & SHAFTS (1400 cc)

Removal & Installation — Remove air cleaner, breather hose to rocker cover and rocker cover. Remove rocker shaft mounting bolts and lift off rocker shaft, rocker arms and rocker arm springs as an assembly. Remove bolts from shafts and slide off springs and rocker arms. To install, ensure that short springs are used on right hand rocker arm and reverse removal procedure.

CAMSHAFT (1400 cc)

Removal — 1) Remove rocker arms and shafts as previously described. Remove timing belt cover and move belt tensioner fully toward water pump, ensuring that camshaft sprocket mark is aligned with head timing mark. Remove timing belt and camshaft sprocket from camshaft.

2) Remove distributor and fuel pump. Remove camshaft rear cover from rear of head and thrust case tightening bolt from top of head. Remove camshaft from rear of head.

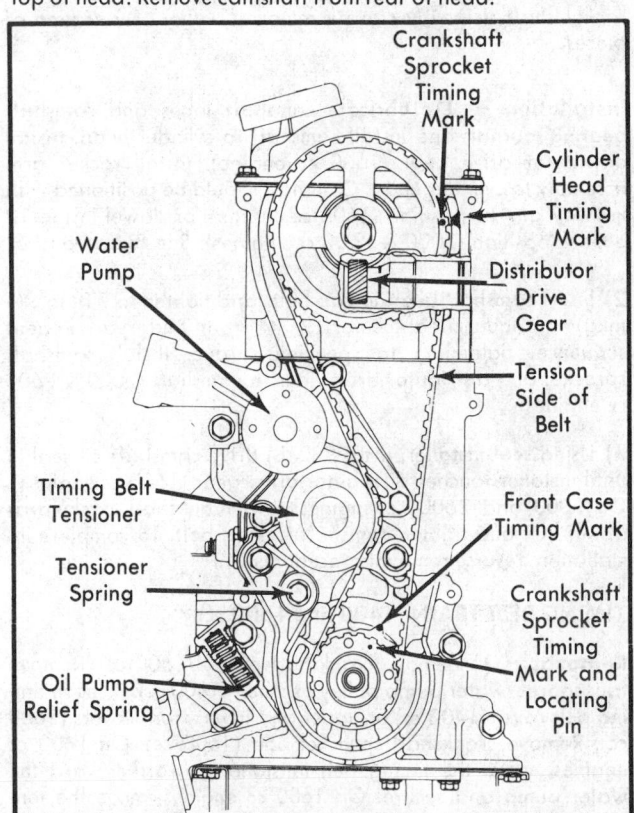

Fig. 3   View of 1400 cc Timing Belt Installation

1400, 1600, 2000 & 2600 cc 4-CYLINDER (Cont.)

3) Check thrust case for camshaft end play. If excessive, replace thrust case and recheck. If rear of camshaft journal is badly worn, replace camshaft.

Installation — To install, thoroughly lubricate camshaft and seal lips and reverse removal procedure.

ROCKER ASSEMBLY & CAMSHAFT (1600, 2000 & 2600 cc)

Removal — 1) Remove air cleaner, breather hoses and purge line. Remove fuel pump and line (2000 and 2600 cc engines). Disconnect spark plug wires and remove rocker cover. On 1600 cc engines, remove upper front cover. Remove breather and semi-circular seal (2000 and 2600 cc engines). Slightly loosen camshaft sprocket bolt and turn engine to TDC of compression stroke on No. 1 cylinder.

2) Make mating mark on timing belt or chain and camshaft sprocket. Remove camshaft sprocket and hang sprocket on sprocket holder provided on timing belt or chain lower front cover. Remove distributor drive gear (2000 and 2600 cc engines). Remove camshaft spacer and upper under cover (1600 cc engines).

NOTE — *If there is a large gap between camshaft sprocket and sprocket holder, insert a 2" (50 mm) piece of timing belt or similar material into the gap to prevent belt from disengaging from crankshaft sprocket or oil pump sprocket.*

3) Remove camshaft bearing caps, rocker arms and rocker shafts as an assembly. Remove oil seal and distributor drive gear from camshaft (1600 cc engine). Remove camshaft.

NOTE — *If front and rear bearing caps are left inserted, rocker shaft assembly can be removed without separation of pieces.*

Installation — 1) Lubricate camshaft lobes and camshaft bearing journals and install camshaft to cylinder head. Install distributor drive gear (1600 cc engine). Install rocker arm assembly to cylinder head. Camshaft should be positioned with keyway at 41° position (1600 cc engine), or dowel in the 12 o'clock position (2000 & 2600 cc engines). See Figs. 4 and 5.

2) Insert camshaft bearing cap bolts and tighten to 7 ft. lbs. (1 mkg) in sequence of center, 2, 4, front and rear. Repeat sequence, tightening to specified torque. Install camshaft sprocket and distributor drive gear to camshaft (2000 & 2600 cc engines).

3) Using seal installer, (MD998248) drive camshaft oil seal in until installer touches distributor drive gear (1600 cc engines). On 2000 and 2600 cc engines, turn crankshaft backwards about 90° and tighten camshaft locking bolt. To complete installation, reverse removal procedures.

TIMING BELT TRAIN (1400 and 1600 cc)

Removal — 1) Remove crankshaft pulley (1600 cc). Remove fan, spacer, water pump pulley and belt (1400 cc). Remove timing belt cover (1400 cc) or upper and lower front covers (1600 cc). Remove crankshaft sprocket bolt (1600 cc). On 1400 cc engines, move the timing belt tensioner upward toward the water pump and secure. On 1600 cc engines, move the tensioner fully to the far right side of the upper mounting slot and secure.

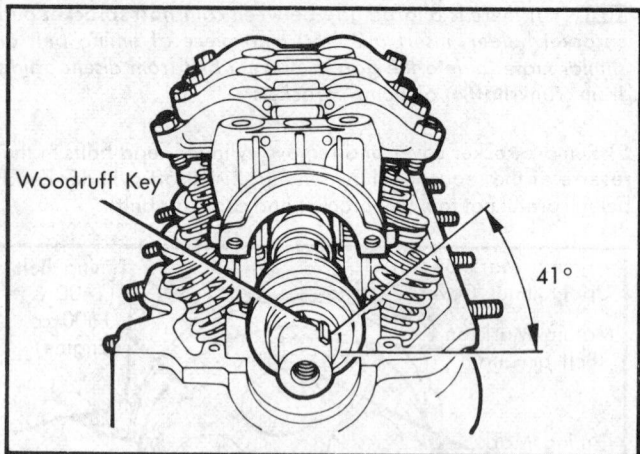

Fig. 4   Camshaft Woodruff Key Position for Installation (1600 cc Engine)

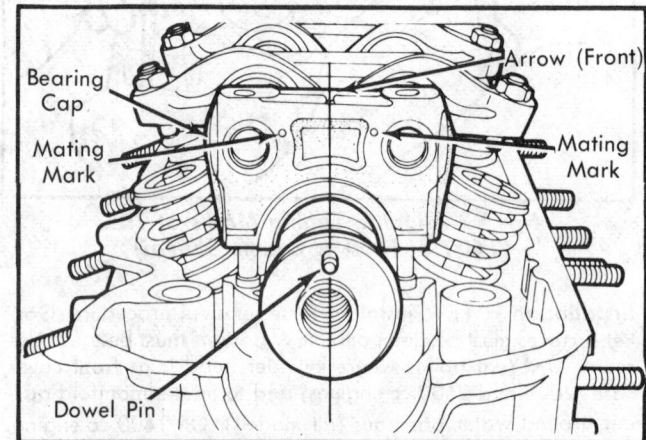

Fig. 5   Camshaft Installation Position and Bearing Cap/Rocker Arm Shaft Mating Marks (2000 and 2600 cc Engines)

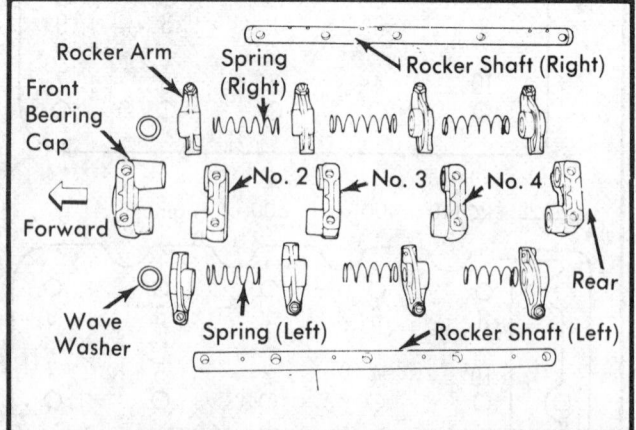

Fig. 6   Exploded View of Rocker Assembly

2) On 1400 cc engines, remove the timing belt from the camshaft sprocket. Remove the camshaft sprocket, crankshaft pulley and timing belt (1400 cc). On 1600 cc engines, remove timing belt completely and remove camshaft sprocket. Remove timing belt tensioner. On 1600 cc engines, remove upper and lower under timing belt covers.

1400, 1600, 2000 & 2600 cc 4-CYLINDER (Cont.)

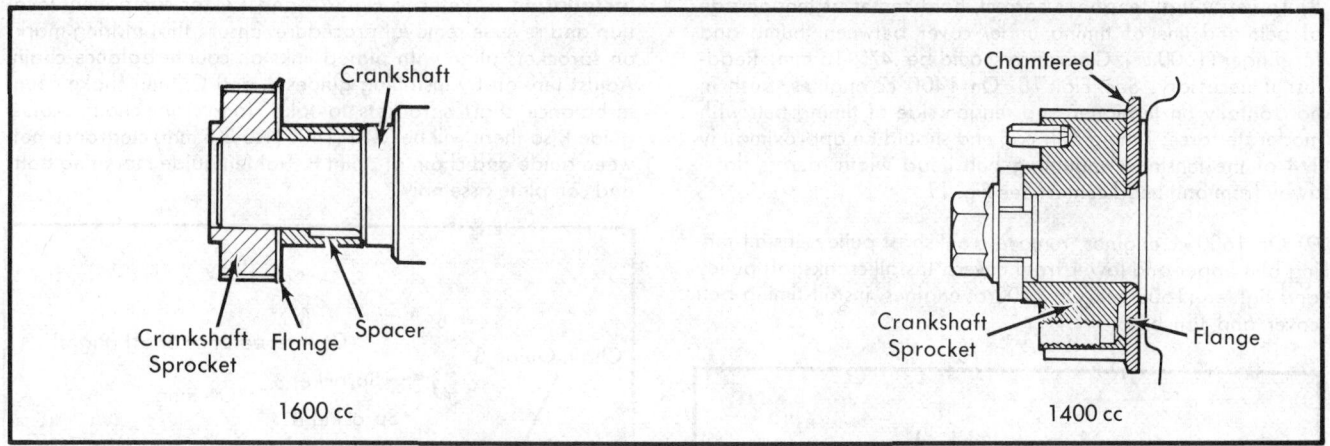

Fig. 7   Flange and Sprocket Mounting Directions

Installation — 1) Install crankshaft sprocket, flange and spacer (if equipped). *See Fig. 7.* Apply a light coat of engine oil to camshaft spacer and insert to camshaft (1600 cc). Install camshaft sprocket and tighten. Align the timing marks of the camshaft and crankshaft sprockets with No. 1 piston at TDC on compression stroke.

2) Install the timing belt tensioner, first installing the spring, and tighten the nut (1600 cc) or slotted hole side bolt (1400 cc). On 1400 cc engines, install the bottom end of the spring in the position of the case shown in *Fig. 8.*

3) On 1600 cc engines, push the flange located under the tensioner in the direction of the arrow, align the holes "A" and "B", and thread the bolts into the holes. Install the front end of the spring on the projections of the tensioner and the other (straight) end of the spring on the water pump body (1600 cc). *See Fig. 9.*

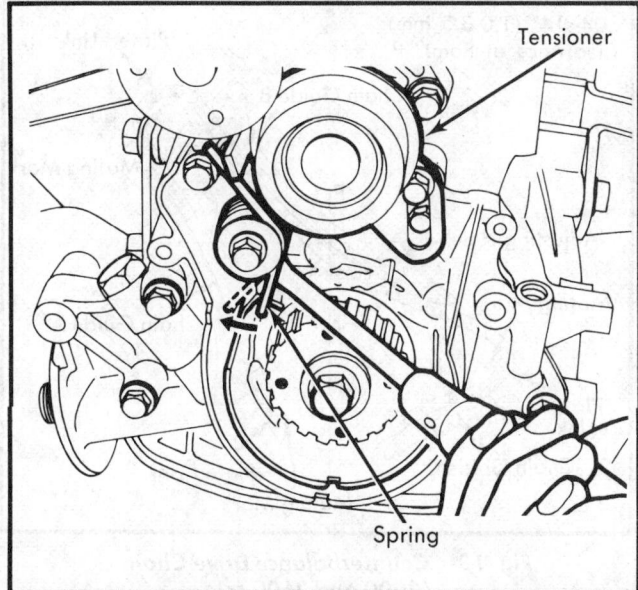

Fig. 8   Installing Tensioner on 1400 cc Engine

4) Secure the tensioner to the position nearest the water pump. Install the timing belt to crankshaft sprocket and then to camshaft sprocket (1400 cc). On 1600 cc engines, install belt first to crankshaft sprocket, then to oil pump sprocket and then

to camshaft sprocket. Check to ensure all individual timing marks are aligned and that tension side of belt is tight.

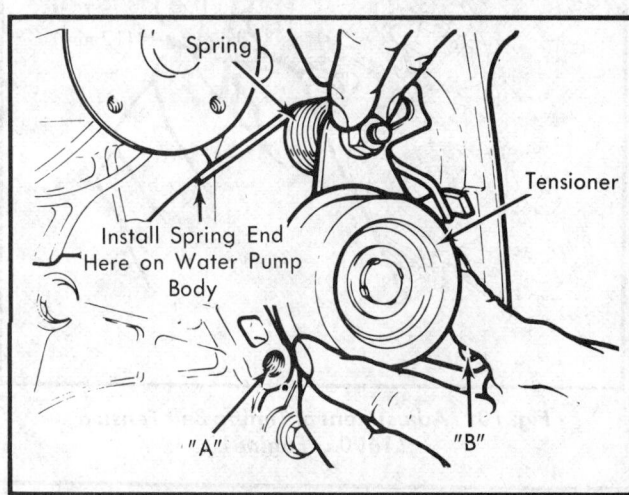

Fig. 9   Installing Tensioner on 1600 cc Engine

NOTE — *On 1400 cc engine, check to ensure that when the tension side of belt is tightened by turning the camshaft sprocket in a reverse direction, all timing marks are aligned.*

5) Temporarily install crankshaft pulley. Ensure that sprocket pin fits small hole in pulley (1400 cc). Loosen left and right tensioner bolts in that order (1400 cc) to give timing belt only spring tension. On 1600 cc engines, loosen tensioner bolt and nut and push tensioner up by hand to ensure proper mesh of belt and sprocket.

6) On 1400 cc engines, check for proper belt to sprocket mesh. Tighten right and left tensioner bolts in that order (1400 cc). On 1600 cc engines, tighten tensioner nut and then bolt. Check to ensure all timing marks are in alignment. Turn the crankshaft one revolution in the normal direction and realign crankshaft timing mark with TDC position.

NOTE — *Ensure that crankshaft is turned smoothly clockwise. Do not push or shake belt while turning.*

7) Loosen left and right bolts in that order and retighten tensioner bolts to specified torque (1400 cc). On 1600 cc engines, loosen tensioner bolt and then nut, then tighten nut followed by bolt to specified torque.

1400, 1600, 2000 & 2600 cc 4-CYLINDER (Cont.)

8) To verify that tension is correct, hold center of tension side of belt and line of timing under cover between thumb and forefinger (1600 cc). Clearance should be .47" (13 mm). Readjust if necessary. See *Fig. 10*. On 1400 cc engines, push in horizontally on tensioner and tension side of timing belt with moderate force. Timing belt cog end should be approximately 1/4 of the tensioner mounting bolt head width (across flats) away from bolt head center. See *Fig. 11*.

9) On 1600 cc engines, remove crankshaft pulley. Install timing belt upper and lower front covers. Install crankshaft pulley and tighten (1600 cc). On 1400 cc engines, install timing belt cover and fan belt.

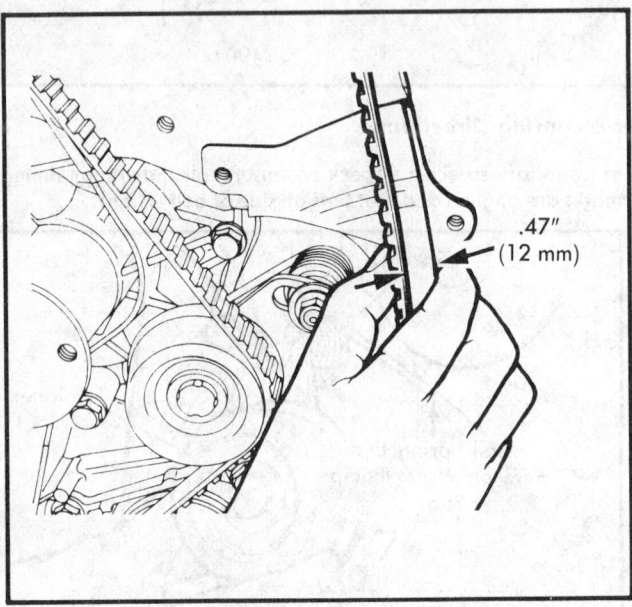

**Fig. 10   Adjustment of Timing Belt Tension
(1600 cc Engine)**

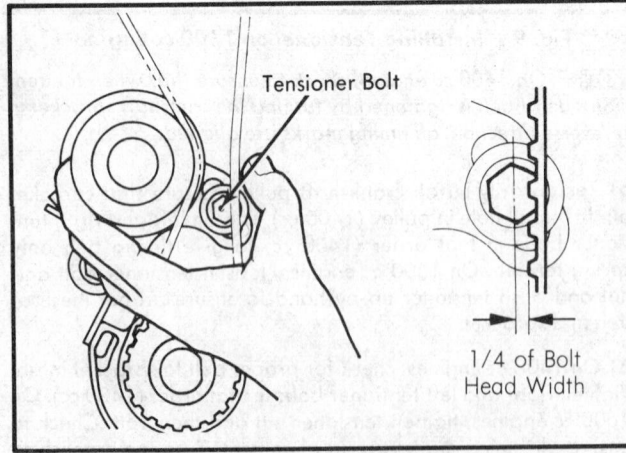

**Fig. 11   Confirming Timing Belt Tension
(1400 cc Engine)**

COUNTERBALANCE DRIVE CHAIN (2000 & 2600 cc)

Removal—Remove crankshaft pulley and timing chain case. Remove chain guides A, B, and C, sprocket B locking bolts and crankshaft sprocket (B). Remove both countershaft sprockets (B) and drive chain. See *Figs. 12 and 13.*

Installation — Refer to *Figs. 12 and 13* for component location and reverse removal procedure. Ensure that mating marks on sprockets align with plated links on counterbalance chain. Adjust tension by installing guides A and C, then shake counterbalance shaft sprockets to take slack from chain. Adjust guide B so there will be .040-.140" (1.0-3.5 mm) clearance between guide and chain at point P. Tighten guide mounting bolts and complete assembly.

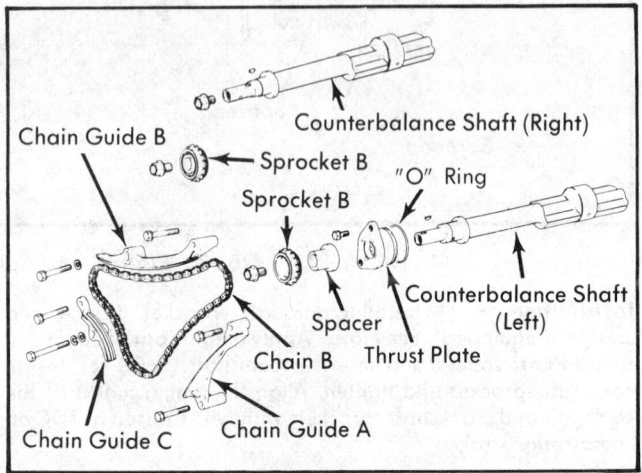

**Fig. 12   Exploded View of Counterbalance Shafts and
Drive Chain (2000 and 2600 cc)**

COUNTERBALANCE SHAFTS (2000 & 2600 cc)

Removal & Installation — 1) With counterbalance drive chain removed, remove oil pump mounting bolts. Remove bolt holding oil pump driven gear and counterbalance shaft together, then remove oil pump mounting bolts. Remove oil pump, then withdraw counterbalance shaft.

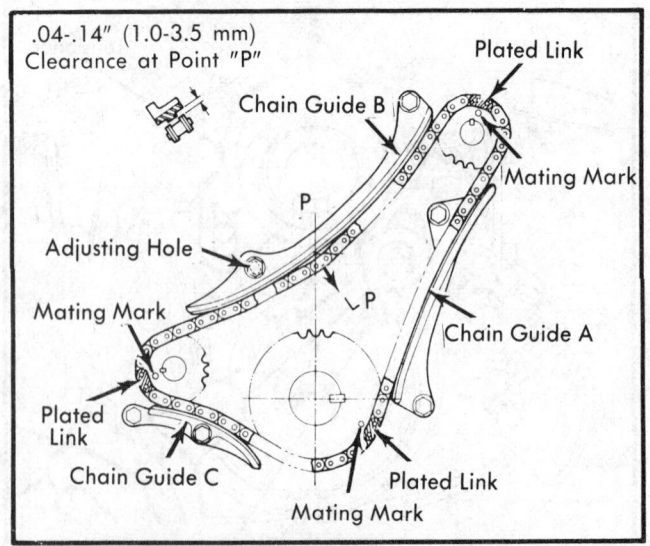

**Fig. 13   Counterbalance Drive Chain
(2000 and 2600 cc)**

NOTE — *If bolt locking oil pump driven gear and counterbalance shaft is hard to loosen, remove oil pump and counterbalance shaft as an assembly. Then remove lock bolt to disassemble.*

1400, 1600, 2000 & 2600 cc 4-CYLINDER (Cont.)

2) Remove thrust plate supporting front of left counterbalance shaft. (Thrust plate is removed by threading bolts into plate holes at same time). Withdraw counterbalance shaft from cylinder block. To install, reverse removal procedure.

TIMING CHAIN (2000 & 2600 cc)

Removal & Installation — With counterbalance drive chain removed, take off chain tensioner and right and left chain guides. Remove camshaft sprocket and timing chain. To install, rotate crankshaft until number 1 piston is at TDC on compression stroke, align mating marks on sprockets and chain, then install chain on camshaft and crankshaft with keys and keyways aligned. Inspect chain tensioner and complete installation in reverse order of removal.

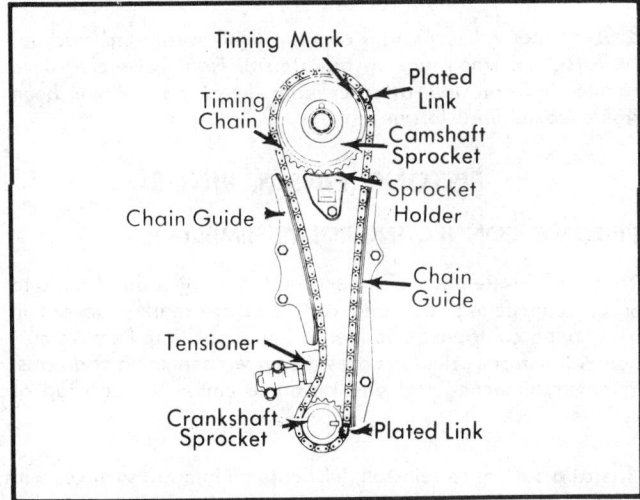

Fig. 14   Camshaft Sprocket Alignment and Installation (2000 and 2600 cc)

VALVES

VALVE ARRANGEMENT

Intake — Left side.
Exhaust — Right side.
Jet Valve — Left side.

JET VALVES

Using special Jet Valve Socket Wrench (MD998310), remove jet valves. Disassemble valve using spring pliers (MD998309) to compress spring and remove retainer lock. Check valve head and seat for damage and make sure jet valve slides smooth in body without play.

CAUTION — *Make certain that jet valve socket wrench is not tilted with respect to center of valve when used. If tool is tilted, stem may be bent resulting in defective valve operation and a broken wrench. Do not disturb jet valve and body combination. If defective, jet valve and body should be replaced as an assembly.*

VALVE SPRINGS

With camshaft and rocker arm assembly removed, use valve lifter and remove retainer locks (keepers). Remove all retainers, springs, spring seats and valves, keeping in proper order for

reassembly. Check valve spring free length and pressure. Standard spring squareness should be 1.5° or less. If beyond 3° replace spring.

VALVE GUIDE SERVICING

1) Check valve stem-to-guide clearance, and if clearance exceeds service limits as listed in table, replace valve guide with next oversize component. Guides are available in the following oversizes:

Valve Guide Oversizes		
Size Mark	Guide Size In. (mm)	Cyl. Head Bore In. (mm)
1400 cc		
5	.002 (.05)	.4766-.4770 (12.105-12.115)
25	.010 (.25)	.4844-.4848 (12.304-12.314)
50	.020 (.50)	.4943-.4947 (12.555-12.565)
1600, 2000 & 2600 cc		
5	.002 (.05)	.5138-.5145 (13.05-13.07)
25	.010 (.25)	.5216-.5224 (13.25-13.27)
50	.020 (.50)	.5315-.5323 (13.50-13.52)

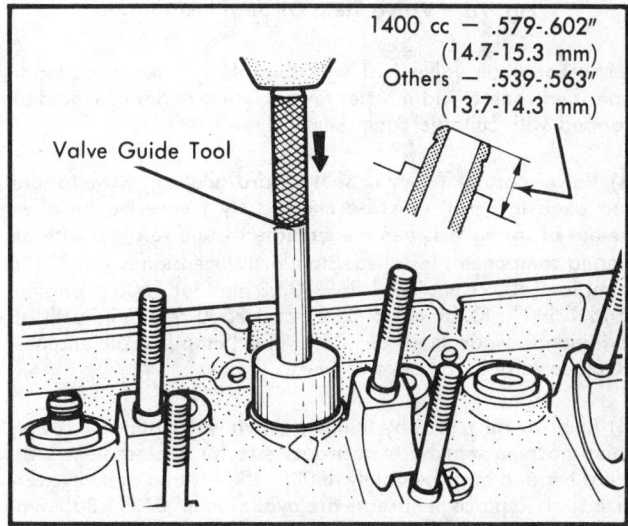

Fig. 15   Valve Guide Installation and Height

2) Heat cylinder head to approximately 480°F (249°C), and then use a suitable valve guide tool to drive out each guide toward the combustion chamber. Ream guide bore in cylinder head to specified size (after head has cooled to room temperature).

3) To install new guides, reheat head to same temperature, quickly insert and drive guides into head. Guide should protrude .579-.602" (14.7-15.3 mm) for 1400 cc or .539-.563" (13.7-14.3 mm) for other engines above head surface when properly installed. Check guide I.D. and ream as necessary.

1400, 1600, 2000 & 2600 cc 4-CYLINDER (Cont.)

VALVE STEM OIL SEALS

After installing valve spring seat, place stem seal on guide. Use installer to lightly hammer seal into correct position as tool bottoms on head. Do NOT use old seals and do NOT twist seals when installing.

VALVE SEAT SERVICING

1) Check valve seat for damage or wear. Replace or rework seat, as necessary. If reworking seat, check valve guide first. Make proper replacement, if required, then check seat for necessary corrections.

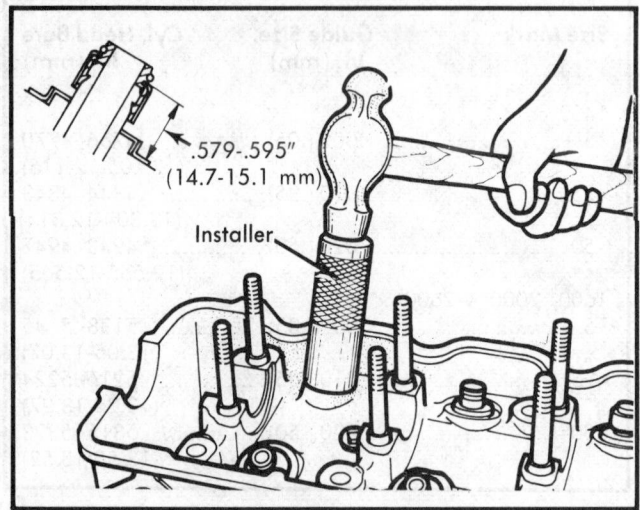

.579-.595"
(14.7-15.1 mm)

Installer

Fig. 16 Valve Stem Oil Seal Installation

2) Recondition valve seat with suitable grinder or cutter to specified contact width. After rework, valve and seat should be lapped with suitable compound.

3) Valve seat sink (wear of seat inward allowing valve to seat too deep in head) must be checked by measuring installed height of spring between the spring seat and retainer with all spring components installed. Standard dimension is 1.417" (36 mm) for 1400 cc engine, 1.469" (37.3 mm) for 1600 cc engine, and 1.590" (40.4 mm) for 2000 and 2600 cc engine with an additional wear limit of .039" (1.0 mm) for all engines. Replace valve seat if beyond limit.

4) Remove valve seat by thinning down with a suitable cutter, then machine seat bore to proper size for replacement seat. Heat head to approximately 480°F (250°C) and press in oversize seat. Replacement seats are available in .012" (.305 mm) and .024" (.610 mm) oversizes, marked "30" and "60" respectively.

VALVE CLEARANCE ADJUSTMENT

1) Ensure timing marks on camshaft sprocket and chain are aligned. With head assembly installed, temporarily adjust valves (sequence for adjustment; 1-3-4-2), according to following procedure: At compression stroke TDC, for cylinder being adjusted, loosen rocker arm nuts; then, turning adjusting screw, adjust valve clearance to specifications.

2) Complete engine assembly and temporarily install rocker cover. Warm engine until coolant temperature is 170 to 180°F. With piston at TDC on compression stroke, back intake valve adjusting screw off 2 or more turns. Adjust jet valve clearance,

then adjust intake valve clearance. Adjust exhaust valve clearance and assure that all adjusting screw lock nuts are tightened securely.

Valve Clearance		
Application	**Cold** In. (mm)	**Hot** In. (mm)
Intake	.003 (.07)	.006 (.15)
Exhaust	.007 (.17)	.010 (.25)
Jet Valve	.003 (.07)	.006 (.15)

NOTE — *Jet valve spring is comparatively weak and must not be forced in when making adjustment. Final valve clearance should be adjusted after cylinder head bolts have been tightened to final torque.*

PISTONS, PINS & RINGS

PISTON & CONNECTING ROD ASSEMBLY

Removal — Remove cylinder head and oil pan. Check to ensure connecting rods and rod caps are marked to aid in assembling components to their original position. Remove carbon ridge from cylinder bores. Remove connecting rod caps. Remove connecting rod and piston assembly through top of cylinder block.

Installation — To reinstall, lubricate all internal surfaces with engine oil before installation. Make sure front mark on piston head faces front of engine. Use a ring compressor to compress rings (without changing their position) and install piston and connecting rod assembly into cylinder block in their original position. Tap lightly on piston dome with wooden handle tool while guiding connecting rod onto crankshaft. Install rod cap onto proper piston and connecting rod assembly. Tighten attaching bolts. Install cylinder head and oil pan.

FITTING PISTONS

1) After checking block for distortion, cracks, scratches or other abnormalities, measure bores at 3 levels. If any distortion exceeds .001" (.02 mm) from standard bore size, block must be rebored and oversize pistons installed.

NOTE — *Pistons for all 4 engine sizes are available in standard, .010" (.25 mm), .020" (.50 mm), .030" (.75 mm) and .039" (1.0 mm) oversizes. Oversize pistons are stamped on crown to indicate oversize amount.*

2) Check outside diameter of piston by measuring at a point .079" (2 mm) from bottom of skirt and at 90° to pin bore. Determine amount of cylinder reboring required to meet specified clearance.

NOTE — *Pin-to-Rod fit at normal temperature for 1400 and 1600 cc engines will press in at 1,100-3,300 lbs.; for 2000 and 2600 cc engines, 1,654-3,859 lbs.*

PISTON PINS

Check piston pin-to-bore fit; pin should press in smoothly by hand (at room temperature). When assembling, apply engine

1400, 1600, 2000 & 2600 cc 4-CYLINDER (Cont.)

oil to outside of pin and to piston pin bore, position rod to piston ("FRONT" mark upward), align pin with pressing tool, and press pin into piston and rod.

PISTON RINGS

Measure piston ring side and end clearance for all pistons and replace rings as necessary. When replacing a ring without correcting the cylinder bore, check ring end gap at lower part of cylinder that is less worn. When replacing a ring, be sure to use one of the same size. Install rings on piston with end gaps staggered at 120° intervals, but make sure no ring gap is in line with thrust face of pin bore. Also be sure the manufacturer's marks are facing upward when rings are installed.

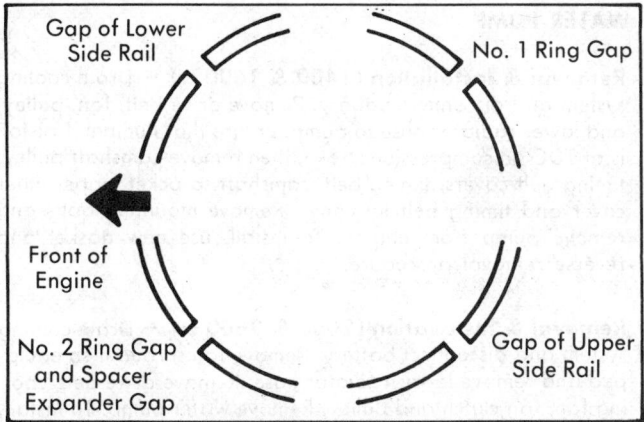

Fig. 17 Piston Ring Gap Positions

CAUTION — *Install oil ring first WITHOUT using a ring expander. Spacer expander gap should be installed more than 45° from side rail gaps, and rails should turn smoothly when installed.*

Piston Ring Sizes	
Ring Size	**Size Mark**
1400, 1600, 2000 & 2600 cc	
Standard	No Mark
.010" (.25 mm) OS	25
.020" (.50 mm) OS	50
.030" (.75 mm) OS	75
.039" (1.00 mm) OS	100

CRANKSHAFT MAIN & CONNECTING ROD BEARINGS

MAIN & CONNECTING ROD BEARINGS

1) Inspect each bearing for peeling, melting, seizure or improper contact. Replace defective bearings. Measure outside diameter of crankshaft and connecting rod journals to determine if out-of-round or tapered.

2) Cut Plastigage to same length as width of bearing. Place it parallel with journal (not over oil holes). Install crankshaft bearings and caps, tightening to specifications. Always install caps with arrow facing forward.

NOTE — *Do not turn crankshaft with Plastigage installed.*

3) Remove main bearing cap from crankshaft and measure Plastigage at widest part (using scale on Plastigage package). Repeat procedure for connecting rod bearings. If clearance exceeds limits, bearing should be replaced or undersize bearing installed. Undersize bearings are available in .010" (.25 mm), .020" (.50 mm), and .030" (.75 mm) undersizes.

THRUST BEARING

With crankshaft bearing caps installed, check thrust clearance (end play) by inserting feeler gauge between center main bearing and crankshaft thrust face. If clearance exceeds specified limits, replace center main bearing.

ENGINE OILING

ENGINE OILING SYSTEM

All engines use force-feed type lubrication system. 1400 cc engines uses gear-crescent type pump, 1600 cc engine uses a trochoid type pump, and all others use gear type pump. Driven gear of pump also drives counterbalance shaft on silent-shaft engines.

Crankcase Capacity (Includes Filter)	
Application	**Approximate Quantity**
1400 cc	3.7 quarts
1600 cc	4.2 quarts
2000 cc	4.5 quarts
2600 cc	4.5 quarts

Oil Pressure — 50-64 psi @2000 RPM.

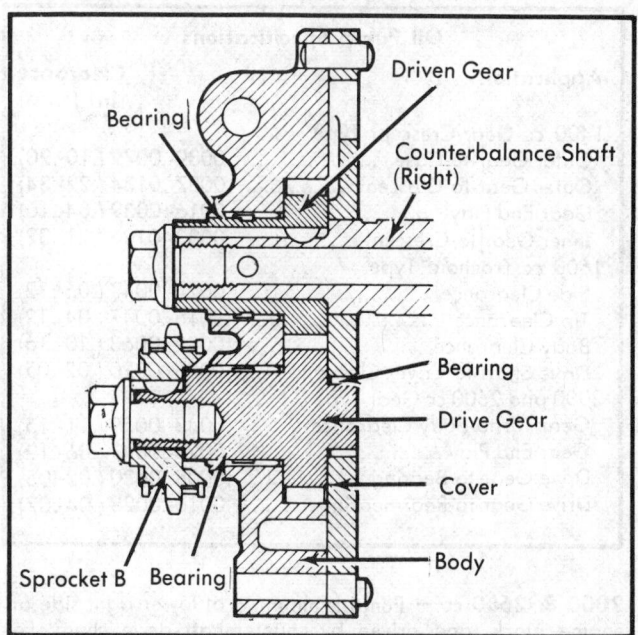

Fig. 18 Cutaway View of Gear Type Oil Pump

OIL PUMP

1400 cc — Gear-crescent type pump is mounted on front of engine assembly and driven directly by the crankshaft. Oil pan, oil screen and timing belt must be removed prior to

1400, 1600, 2000 & 2600 cc 4-CYLINDER (Cont.)

removing front cover-oil pump assembly. Remove 7 mounting bolts and remove pump assembly. Inspect gears, case and seal for wear or damage. Ensure that gears are assembled in same direction as originally installed. Use new gaskets and install pump and pan. Use suitable sealer at joint faces and seams.

1600 cc — Mounted at lower left of engine, driven by camshaft drive belt. Cover and rotor assembly may be removed after removing drive sprocket by taking out cover bolts and lifting assembly out. May also be removed with engine front cover as an assembly.

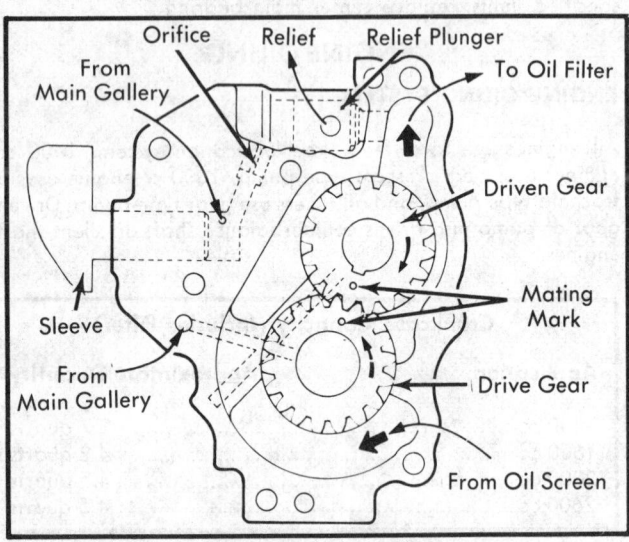

Fig. 19 Mating Marks of Oil Pump Gears

Oil Pump Specifications

Application	Clearance In. (mm)
1400 cc Gear-Crescent Type	
Outer Gear-to-Case	.0039-.0079 (.10-.20)
Outer Gear-to-Crescent	.0087-.0134 (.22-.34)
Gear End Play	.0016-.0039 (.04-.10)
Inner Gear-to-Crescent	.0083-.0126 (.21-.32)
1600 cc Trochoid Type	
Side Clearance	.0024-.0047 (.06-.12)
Tip Clearance	.0016-.0047 (.04-.12)
Body Clearance	.0039-.0063 (.10-.16)
Drive Shaft-to-Cover Clearance	.0008-.0020 (.02-.05)
2000 and 2600 cc Gear Type	
Gear Tip-to-Body Clearance	.0043-.0059 (.11-.15)
Gear End Play	.0024-.0047 (.06-.12)
Drive Gear-to-Bearing	.0008-.0020 (.02-.05)
Drive Gear-to-Rear Bearing	.0016-.0028 (.04-.07)

2000 & 2600 cc — Pump is mounted at lower right side of engine block, and driven by countershaft drive chain. For removal, see *COUNTERBALANCE SHAFTS, 2000 & 2600 cc.* To install, reverse removal procedure, assuring that oil pump gear mating marks are aligned and that woodruff key on counterbalance shaft fits in keyway of driven gear.

CAUTION — *Prior to installing oil pump (all models), fill with sufficient amount of engine oil to prime pump.*

ENGINE COOLING

Thermostat — 190°F (88°C).

Radiator Cap — 12.8 psi (0.9 kg/cm^2).

Cooling System

Application	Approximate Capacity
1400 cc	4.7 quarts
1600 cc	4.7 quarts
2000 cc	9.5 quarts
2600 cc	9.7 quarts

WATER PUMP

Removal & Installation (1400 & 1600 cc) — Drain cooling system and disconnect battery. Remove drive belt, fan, pulley, and lower radiator hose to pump. Ensure that number 1 piston is at TDC on compression stroke, then remove camshaft pulley, timing belt covers, timing belt, camshaft sprocket, upper inner cover and timing belt tensioner. Remove mounting bolts and remove pump from engine. To install, use new gasket and reverse removal procedure.

Removal & Installation (2000 & 2600 cc) — Drain cooling system and disconnect battery. Remove fan shroud if so equipped and remove lower radiator hose. Remove drive belt, cooling fan, fan clutch and pulley. Remove water pump. To install, reverse removal procedure using new gasket.

TIGHTENING SPECIFICATIONS

Application	Ft. Lbs. (N·m)
Camshaft Bearing Caps	
1600 cc	14-15 (19-20)
2000 & 2600 cc	13-14 (18-19)
Camshaft Sprocket	
1400 cc	47-54 (64-73)
1600 cc	44-57 (60-78)
2000 & 2600 cc	37-43 (50-58)
Main Bearing Caps	
1400 & 1600 cc	37-39 (50-53)
2000 & 2600 cc	55-61 (75-83)
Connecting Rod Caps	
1400 cc & 1600 cc	24-25 (33-34)
Crankshaft Pulley	
2000 & 2600 cc	80-94 (109-128)
Crankshaft Sprocket Bolt	
1400 cc	37-43 (50-58)
1600 cc	44-50 (60-68)
Flywheel-to-Crankshaft	94-101 (128-137)
Drive Plate-to-Crankshaft	
(Auto. Trans.)	94-101 (128-137)
Jet Valve	13-15 (18-20)
	INCH Lbs. (N·m)
Oil Pump/Cover	
1400, 2000 & 2600 cc	72-74 (8-10)
Crankshaft Pulley Bolt	
1400 & 1600 cc	90-102 (10-20)

Chrysler Corp. Import Engines

E N G I N E S

1400, 1600, 2000 & 2600 cc 4-CYLINDER (Cont.)
ENGINE SPECIFICATIONS

Year	Displ. cu. ins.	cc	Carburetor	HP at RPM	Torque (Ft. Lbs. at RPM)	Compr. Ratio	Bore in.	mm	Stroke in.	mm
1981	86.0	1400	2-Bbl.	.....	.....	8.8:1	2.91	74.0	3.23	82.0
	97.5	1600	2-Bbl.	.....	.....	8.5:1	3.03	76.9	3.39	86.0
	121.7	2000	2-Bbl.	93@5200	108@3000	8.5:1	3.31	84.0	3.54	90.0
	155.9	2600	2-Bbl.	105@5000	139@2500	8.2:1	3.59	91.1	3.86	98.0

VALVES

Engine & Valve	Head Diam.① In. (mm)	Face Angle	Seat Angle	Seat Width In. (mm)	Stem Diameter In. (mm)	Stem Clearance In. (mm)	Valve Lift In. (mm)
1400cc Intake	1.34 (34)	45°	45°	.035-.051 (.9-1.3)	.315 (8.0)	.0012-.0024 (.03-.06)	.346 (8.8)
Exhaust	1.18 (30)	45°	45°	.035-.051 (.9-1.3)	.315 (8.0)	.0020-.0035 (.05-.09)	.346 (8.8)
1600cc Intake	1.50 (38)	45°	45°	.035-.051 (.9-1.3)	.315 (8.0)	.0012-.0024 (.03-.06)	.362 (9.2)
Exhaust	1.22 (31)	45°	45°	.035-.051 (.9-1.3)	.315 (8.0)	.0020-.0035 (.05-.09)	.362 (9.2)
2000 & 2600cc Intake	1.7 (43)	45°	45°	.035-.051 (.9-1.3)	.315 (8.0)	.0012-.0024 (.03-.06)	.393② (10.0)
Exhaust	1.38 (35)	45°	45°	.035-.051 (.9-1.3)	.315 (8.0)	.0020-.0035 (.05-.09)	.393 (10.0)

① — Jet valve and body not individually serviceable. Replace as an assembly when defective.
② — 2600cc valve lift: .413" (10.5 mm).

PISTONS, PINS, RINGS

Engine	PISTONS Clearance In. (mm)	Piston Fit In. (mm)	Rod Fit In. (mm)	Rings	End Gap In. (mm)	Side Clearance In. (mm)
1400 & 1600 cc	.0008-.0016 (.02-.04)	①	Locked in Rod ②	No. 1	.008-.016 (.2-.4)	.0012-.0028 (.03-.07)
				No. 2	.008-.016 (.2-.4)	.0008-.0024 (.02-.06)
				Oil	.008-.020 (.2-.5)	....
2000 & 2600 cc	.0008-.0016 (.02-.04)	①	Locked in Rod ③	No. 1	.010-.018 (.25-.45)	.0024-.0039 (.06-.10)
				No. 2	.010-.018 (.25-.45)	.0008-.0024 (.02-.06)
				Oil	.008-.035 (.2-.9)	....

① — Thumb press fit without rod installed
② — Press in at 1100-3300 lbs. at room temp.
③ — Press in at 1654-3854 lbs. at room temp.

Chrysler Corp. Import Engines

1400, 1600, 2000 & 2600 cc 4-CYLINDER (Cont.)

ENGINE SPECIFICATIONS (Cont.)

CRANKSHAFT MAIN & CONNECTING ROD BEARINGS							
	MAIN BEARINGS				CONNECTING ROD BEARINGS		
Engine	Journal Diam. In. (mm)	Clearance In. (mm)	Thrust Bearing	Crankshaft End Play In. (mm)	Journal Diam. In. (mm)	Clearance In. (mm)	Side Play In. (mm)
1400 cc	1.890 (48)	.0008-.0028 (.02-07)	No. 3	.002-007 (.05-.18)	1.653 (42)	.0004-.0024 (.01-.06)	.004-.01 (.10-.25)
1600 cc	2.244 (57)	.0008-.0028 (.02-07)	No. 3	.002-.007 (.05-.18)	1.772 (45)	.0004-.0024 (.01-.06)	.004-.01 (.10-.25)
2000 & 2600 cc	2.362 (60)	.0008-.0028 (.02-.07)	No. 3	.002-.007 (.05-.18)	2.087 (53)	.0008-.0028 (.02-.07)	.004-.01 (.10-.25)

CAMSHAFT			
Engine	Cam Lobe Height In. (mm)	End Play In. (mm)	Lobe Lift In. (mm)
1400cc Intake	1.500 (38.1)	.002-.008 (.05-.20)	.....
Exhaust	1.504 (38.2)	.002-.008 (.05-.20)	.....
1600cc Int. & Exh	1.433 (36.4)	.002-.006 (.05-.15)	.359 (9.2)
2000 & 2600cc Int. & Exh	1.661 (42.2)	.004-.008 (.10-.20)	.393 (10.0)

VALVE SPRINGS			
Engine	Free Length In. (mm)	PRESSURE Lbs. @ In. (kg @ mm)	
		Valve Closed	Valve Open
1400 cc	1.697 (43.1)	69@1.417 (31.1@36)	.....
1600 cc	1.823 (46.3)	61.7@1.469 (27.9@37.3)	.....
2000 & 2600 cc	1.869 (47.5)	61@1.59 (27.6@40.4)	.....

① — Maximum wear limit is .020" (.5 mm)

2000 cc 4-CYLINDER

ENGINE CODING

ENGINE IDENTIFICATION

Vehicle identification and engine information is stamped on model plate at the right rear of the engine compartment. The last digit of the vehicle identification number indicates engine model. Engine displacement is listed below vehicle identification number.

Engine Identification	
Application	Code
2000 cc	1

ENGINE, CYLINDER HEAD & MANIFOLDS

ENGINE

Removal & Installation — **1)** Remove hood and disconnect battery. Drain cooling system and engine oil. Disconnect hoses from air cleaner body and remove air cleaner assembly. Disconnect wiring from distributor, alternator and ignition coil. Disconnect engine ground wire from right side of engine.

2) Disconnect connectors from oil pressure switch, water temperature gauge unit, slow fuel cut valve solenoid and water thermo switch. Disconnect wiring and battery positive cable from starter. Disconnect throttle linkage, choke cable and fuel pipes from carburetor.

3) Disconnect vacuum tube of power brake unit from intake manifold. Disconnect all other vacuum lines running between engine and engine compartment components. Disconnect heater hoses from intake manifold, and disconnect air hose from air control valve (if equipped).

4) Disconnect radiator hoses from radiator and remove radiator. Raise vehicle and remove exhaust pipe hanger from transmission. Disconnect exhaust pipe from exhaust manifold. Remove starter and bolts securing transmission to engine.

5) Lower vehicle and support transmission with a jack. Connect a lifting sling to engine hanger brackets. Disconnect engine mounts and pull engine forward until clear of transmission shaft. Lift engine from vehicle. To install, reverse removal procedure.

INTAKE MANIFOLD

Removal — **1)** Disconnect and drain cooling system. Remove air cleaner assembly and accelerator linkage. Disconnect choke cable and fuel line at carburetor. Index mark and remove all vacuum lines and electrical leads from intake manifold. Disconnect heater return and by-pass hose.

2) Disconnect air hoses and vacuum lines at air by-pass valve and remove valve. Disconnect EGR pipe from control valve. Remove valve and servo diaphragm of throttle position system. Remove EGR valve and pipe, remove manifold attaching nuts and lift manifold and carburetor off studs.

Installation — To install, reverse removal procedure while noting the following: Clean all gasket surfaces and install a new gasket. Install intake manifold and tighten attaching bolts working from the center of manifold towards each end. Fill cooling system when all components are installed.

EXHAUST MANIFOLD

Removal — **1)** Remove hot air ducting. Remove spark plug wires. Remove air injection from exhaust manifold. Remove upper and lower heat insulators.

2) Disconnect EGR line. Raise vehicle. Remove exhaust pipe hanger from bracket on transmission. Disconnect exhaust pipe at manifold. Remove manifold nuts and manifold.

Installation — To install, reverse removal procedure using a new gasket. Apply a light coat of graphite grease to exhaust manifold mating surfaces.

CYLINDER HEAD

Removal — **1)** Drain cooling system. Remove air cleaner assembly. Remove exhaust manifold. Disconnect throttle and choke. Disconnect fuel lines.

2) From cylinder head, disconnect EGR pipe at valve, slow fuel cut solenoid valve, all electrical wires, vacuum lines and heater hoses.

3) Remove water pump. Disconnect lead wire and vacuum line from distributor. Rotate crankshaft until No. 1 piston is TDC.

4) Remove valve cover. Remove distributor with plug wires. Remove timing chain tensioner cover and release chain tension. See *Fig. 3. Refer to Timing Chain Tension in this article.*

5) Remove nut, washer and distributor gear from camshaft. Remove nut and washer from camshaft sprocket. Remove lower front head bolt below camshaft sprocket on boss.

6) Remove cylinder head bolts. Remove rocker arm assembly. Separate camshaft and sprocket. Place camshaft sprocket and chain on top of chain guide strip and vibration damper. Make sure sprocket and chain are not moved. Remove cylinder head.

NOTE — *After removing cylinder head, release all tension from timing chain.*

Installation — To install, reverse removal procedure while noting the following: Clean all gasket surfaces and use new gaskets upon installation. Install cylinder head and tighten bolts to specifications in sequence as shown in illustration.

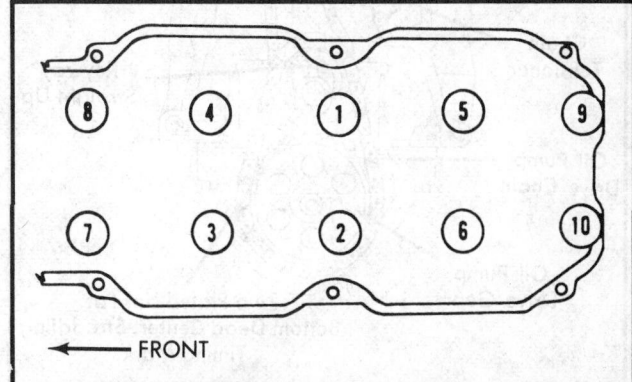

Fig. 1 Cylinder Head Tightening Sequence

ENGINE FRONT COVER

Removal — **1)** Remove hood and drain cooling system. Disconnect upper radiator hose at engine and lower hose at radiator.

2000 cc 4-CYLINDER (Cont.)

Remove fan. Remove radiator, drive belts, crankshaft pulley and water pump. Remove cylinder head-to-front cover bolts. Raise vehicle and remove splash shield.

2) Disconnect emission line from oil pan. Remove oil pan. Lower vehicle, remove alternator bracket to block bolts and position alternator to one side. Remove thermactor pump to block bolts and position to one side. Remove steel tube bolts and tube from front of engine. Remove attaching bolts for front cover and remove front cover.

Installation — To install, reverse removal procedure, using sealer on front cover gasket.

CAMSHAFT

TIMING CHAIN

Removal — **1)** Remove cylinder head and front cover. Remove timing chain tensioner. Loosen timing chain guide strip screws. Remove oil slinger. Straighten lock tab on washer and remove oil pump sprocket attaching nut.

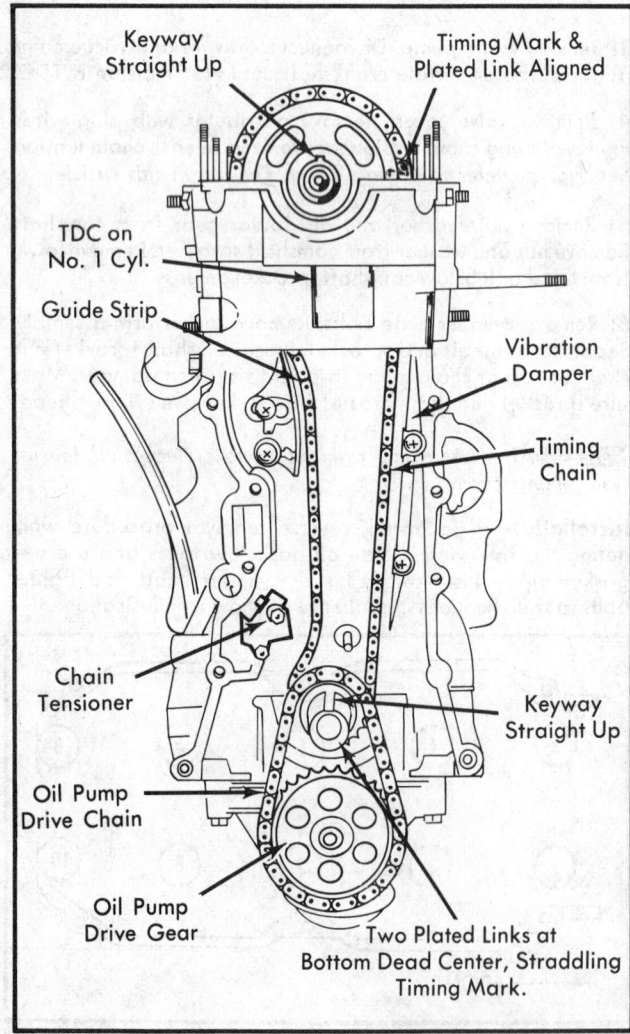

2) Remove oil pump, gear and chain as an assembly. Remove timing chain, crankshaft gear and camshaft gear from engine. Remove gears from the chain.

Installation — **1)** Position crankshaft gear to timing chain and install gear and chain to crankshaft. Position oil pump chain and gear to crankshaft and oil pump. Install the oil slinger. Install oil pump washer and nut, bending lock tab over nut. Install timing chain tensioner. See *Timing Chain Tension*. Do not release snubber spring tension. Install cylinder head and camshaft to cylinder block.

NOTE — *Do not install rocker arm assembly at this time.*

2) Obtain correct timing chain alignment referring to *Timing Chain Alignment* illustration and using the following procedure: Rotate crankshaft to TDC of compression stroke on number one cylinder. This will place crankshaft with keyway facing straight up. Position camshaft with keyway facing straight up. Timing chain must now be positioned on camshaft sprocket so single plated link is aligned with timing mark on right-hand side of camshaft sprocket at rocker arm cover joint face, while facing engine. The two plate links on timing chain must straddle timing mark on BDC of crankshaft sprocket.

3) Install rocker arm shaft assembly, cylinder head bolts, and tighten all bolts to specifications. Adjust timing chain tension. *See Timing Chain Tension*. Release tensioner snubber and install front cover. Install remaining components in reverse of removal procedure and adjust valve clearance.

TIMING CHAIN TENSION

1) Remove crankshaft pulley and water pump. Remove cover from tensioner. Rotate crankshaft slightly in direction of engine rotation. Lift release on tensioner and compress snubber spring fully. Install wedge in tensioner so it will not release.

2) Remove two access plugs and aluminum washers from holes in timing chain cover and side of head. Loosen guide strip attaching screws. Press top of strip with lever inserted through access hole in head.

3) Tighten guide strip attaching screws with screwdriver inserted through hole in cover. Remove wedge from tensioner, allowing snubber to take up chain slack.

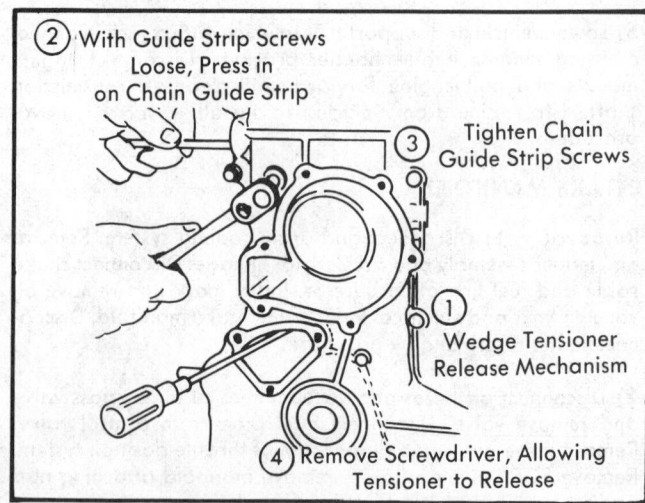

Fig. 3   Adjusting Timing Chain Tension

Fig. 2   Timing Chain & Sprocket Alignment

4) Install access plugs and aluminum washers to their respective holes. Replace chain tensioner cover and gasket. Install water pump and crankshaft pulley. Tighten bolts and adjust belt tension.

2000 cc 4-CYLINDER (Cont.)

OIL PUMP CHAIN

Check oil pump chain for excessive deflection as shown in illustration. If deflection is more than .157" (3.97 mm), install adjusting shims between cylinder block and oil pump body.

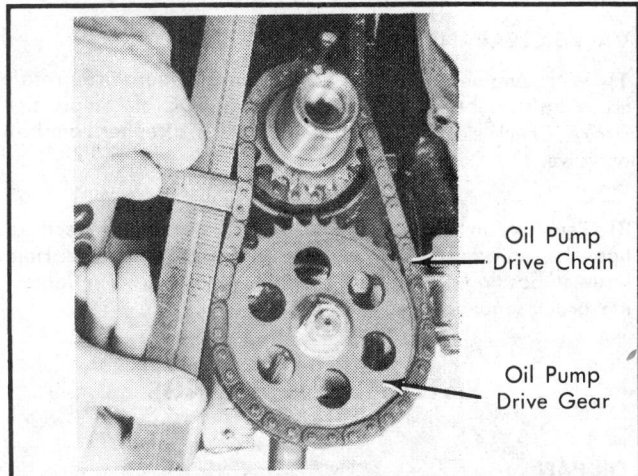

Oil Pump Drive Chain

Oil Pump Drive Gear

Fig. 4   Measuring Oil Pump Chain Deflection

CAMSHAFT

Removal — 1) Remove hood and water pump. Disconnect vacuum line and lead wire from distributor. Rotate crankshaft to position number one cylinder to TDC of compression stroke. Remove air cleaner and disconnect choke. Remove plug wires and distributor cap as an assembly.

2) Remove distributor from engine. Remove rocker arm cover. Remove crankshaft pulley, then remove cover from timing chain tensioner. Lift release on tensioner and compress snubber spring fully. Wedge a screwdriver in the tensioner to keep spring compressed.

3) Remove cylinder head bolts and rocker arm assembly. Remove nut, washer and distributor gear from camshaft. Remove camshaft gear from attaching nut and washer. Carefully remove camshaft from gear and cylinder head.

NOTE — *Do not remove camshaft gear from timing chain. Ensure that gear teeth-to-chain relationship is not disturbed.*

Installation — To install, reverse removal procedure while noting the following: When installing camshaft to gear take care not to disturb gear-to-chain relationship. Adjust timing chain tension. Check camshaft end play. Adjust valve clearance.

CAMSHAFT BEARINGS

Remove camshaft and inspect bearings for wear or damage. Use Plastigage method to determine clearance. Replace bearings which do not meet specifications.

CAMSHAFT END THRUST

Check camshaft end play with a feeler gauge inserted between thrust plate and camshaft flange. End play should be checked after gear is installed.

CAM LOBE LIFT

Remove rocker arm cover. Measure distance between major and minor diameters (see illustration) of each lobe with a Vernier caliper. Difference between diameters of each cam is lobe lift. If lobe lift loss exceeds .008" (.20 mm), replace camshaft. Check lift of each lobe in consecutive order and note each reading.

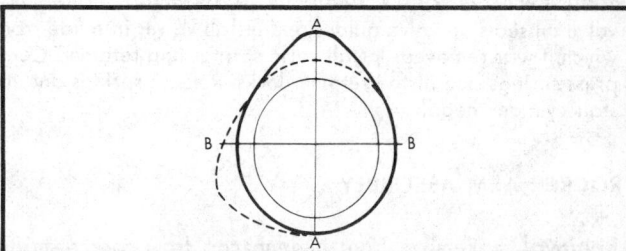

Fig. 5   Measuring Camshaft Base Circle and Lobe Lift

VALVE TIMING

Rotate crankshaft and camshaft until keyways are straight up. Place timing chain on camshaft sprocket so single plated link is aligned with timing mark on right-hand side of camshaft sprocket at rocker arm cover joint face, while facing engine. The two plate links on timing chain must straddle timing mark on BDC of crankshaft sprocket. Crankshaft in this position will be TDC of number one cylinder.

VALVES

VALVE ARRANGEMENT

Intake — Left side.
Exhaust — Right side.

VALVE GUIDE SERVICING

Check guides for wear or damage, replace as necessary. With valves removed, using suitable tool (T72J-6510), drive valve guides out top of cylinder head. Install new guides, making sure exhaust and intake guides are in proper locations. Drive guide in until ring around guide touches head.

VALVE STEM OIL SEALS

With valves and springs removed, pull oil seals off valve guides using suitable tools (T72J-6571 and T59L-100-B). Install new seals on valve guides with large diameter hole facing cylinder head.

VALVE SPRINGS

Removal — With cylinder head removed from engine proceed as follows: Compress valve springs and remove retainer locks. Release springs and remove spring retainers, springs, and valves.

NOTE — *Identify all valve components for installation in original positions. Exhaust and intake retainers must be installed in original positions to prevent premature valve failure.*

Courier Engines

2000 cc 4-CYLINDER (Cont.)

Inspection — Check valve spring pressure at specified height, replace if not within specifications. Measure free length of spring, if not within 3% of specified value, replace spring. Using a square, check that springs are not more than 1/16" (1.58 mm) out-of-square.

Installation — Lubricate valves, valve stems and valve guide with engine oil. Apply Lubriplate to valve tips. Install new valve oil seals on valve guides and install valves in guide from which it was removed. Install valve springs and retainer. Compress springs and install retainer locks. Release springs and install cylinder head.

ROCKER ARM ASSEMBLY

Removal — Remove front bearing cap from rocker shafts. Slide rocker arms, springs, supports and bearing caps (with oil pipe) off both shafts, keeping parts in order for reassembly. Remove oil pipe from bearing caps. Remove camshaft thrust plate from front bearing cap, if necessary.

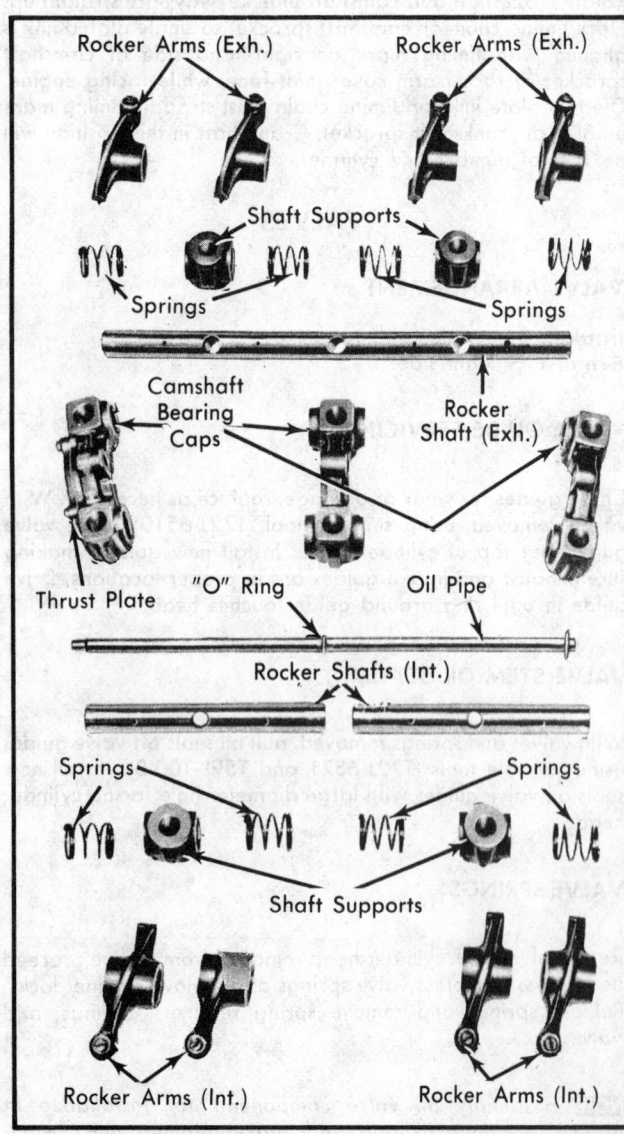

Fig. 6 Exploded View of Rocker Arm & Shaft Assembly

Installation — Lubricate arms and shafts with heavy (MS) motor oil. When installing shafts in intake side, ensure ends with longer length between oil hole and tip are turned inward, toward each other. Make sure "O" ring on oil pipe is centered in middle bearing cap passage. To complete installation, reverse removal procedure.

VALVE CLEARANCE ADJUSTMENT

1) With engine at normal operating temperature, rotate crankshaft until number one piston is at TDC of compression stroke. Check clearance with feeler gauge at either camshaft or valve.

2) Clearance must be .012" (.30 mm). If not within specifications, loosen adjusting screw with feeler gauge in place. Hold screw in position and tighten lock nut. Adjust valves in tightening order sequence; 1-3-4-2.

PISTONS, PINS & RINGS

OIL PAN

Removal — Raise vehicle on hoist and remove front splash shield. Drain crankcase, remove clutch release cylinder attaching nuts and position cylinder to one side. Remove the engine rear brace attaching bolts and loosen bolts on left side. Remove oil pan attaching nuts and bolts, and lower oil pan onto crossmember. Remove oil pump pick-up tube. Remove oil pan from vehicle.

Installation — To install, reverse removal procedure while noting the following: Clean all gasket surfaces and use new gaskets upon installation. Ensure that oil pump pick-up tube and screen are clean before installing.

PISTON & ROD ASSEMBLY

Removal — 1) With cylinder head and oil pan removed, remove oil pump. Rotate crankshaft until piston to be removed is at bottom of travel. Place a cloth on piston to collect cuttings, then using a ridge reamer, remove any ridge or deposits from upper end of cylinder.

NOTE — Do not cut into ring travel area in excess of 1/32" (.79 mm).

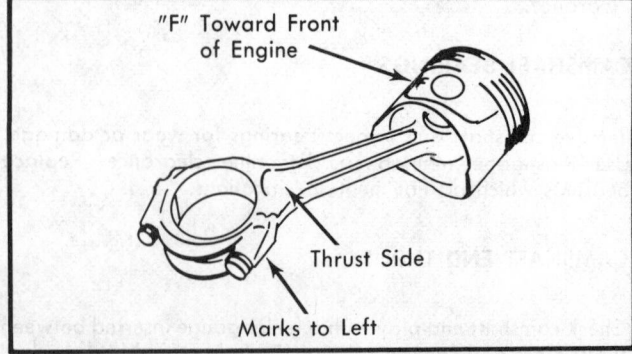

Fig. 7 Piston & Rod Assembly Installation Features

2000 cc 4-CYLINDER (Cont.)

2) Make sure connecting rod caps are marked so they may be replaced in their original positions, then remove rod caps. Push piston and rod assembly out top of cylinder. Take care not to damage bearing journal.

Installation — Oil piston rings, pistons and cylinder walls with engine oil. With rings properly spaced, install ring compressor onto piston. Install piston and rod assembly into its original bore. Make sure connecting rod marks are facing left side of engine and "F" mark on piston is facing forward (see illustration). Install rod caps and tighten rod bolts.

FITTING PISTONS

1) Determine piston-to-cylinder bore clearance. Check cylinder for out-of-round or taper. Fit new pistons if necessary. Pistons are available in .010", .020", .030" and .040" oversizes.

2) Place rings in cylinder near bottom of bore and measure end gaps. Place rings on piston and measure side clearance. If high steps have developed on lower back side of ring lands, replace piston. *See Fig. 8.*

3) Place rings on piston with end gaps 120° apart so that no gap is located on thrust face or piston pin bore. Using suitable ring compressor, install piston in proper bore with "F" marking facing forward.

PISTON PINS

Piston pins are removed using an arbor press, pilots and driver. Measure pin and connecting rod diameters to ensure proper fit.

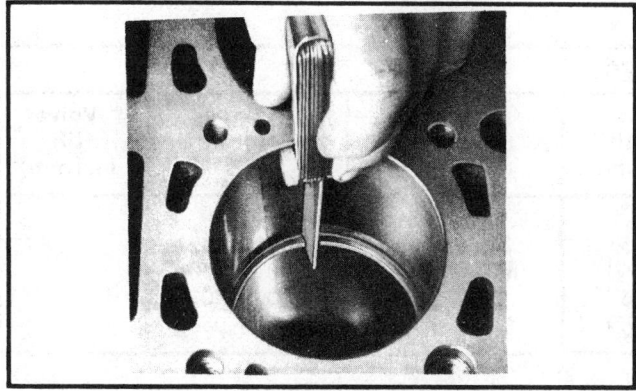

Fig. 8   Measuring Piston Ring Gap

CRANKSHAFT MAIN & CONNECTING ROD BEARINGS

MAIN & CONNECTING ROD BEARINGS

1) Inspect each bearing for scored, chipped or worn surface and replace if condition exists. If copper base is visible through bearing overlay, replacement is not necessary, if within specifications.

2) When installing new bearings, fit bearings to minimum specified clearance. Use Plastigage method to determine bearing clearances. Inserts are available in .010", .020" and .030" undersizes.

THRUST BEARING ALIGNMENT

Push crankshaft to one side to take up end play. Insert a feeler gauge between thrust washers and crankshaft. Replace thrust washers if measurement is not within specifications. Install new thrust washers with oil groove facing crankshaft thrust side.

REAR MAIN BEARING OIL SEAL

NOTE — *If rear main bearing seal replacement is only operation being performed, it can be done in vehicle; however if it is being replaced in conjunction with rear main bearing, engine must be removed.*

Remove transmission and clutch assembly. Using an awl, punch two holes in seal and install sheet metal screws. Using a pair of levers, pry out old seal. Coat seal to cylinder block surface with engine oil, and seal to crankshaft surface with Lubriplate. Press in new seal. Reinstall clutch and transmission.

FRONT COVER OIL SEAL

Drain cooling system, disconnect radiator hoses and remove radiator. Loosen alternator and Thermactor attaching bolts (if equipped). Remove drive belts. Remove crankshaft pulley, then pull seal from shaft, using suitable tool (T72J-6700). Install new seal using suitable tool (T72J-6700-A). Reverse removal procedures for remaining components.

ENGINE OILING

Crankcase Capacity — 4.1 qts. (Add 1 qt. with filter change).

Oil Filter — Disposable type.

Oil Pressure — 50-64 psi (3.5-4.5 kg/cm^2) at 3000 RPM; minimum 4.3 psi (.30 kg/cm^2) at idle.

ENGINE OIL SYSTEM

Rotor type oil pump is chain driven by crankshaft. Timing chain is lubricated by oil jet in cylinder block and oil holes in slipper head of adjuster. Oil holes in large end of connecting rods align with oil holes in crankshaft to lubricate pistons and components.

OIL PUMP

1) Remove oil inlet tube from pump. Remove and discard gaskets. Remove cover, withdraw inner rotor and shaft assembly. Remove outer race. Remove cotter pin from body, pull cap out of chamber, and take out spring and plunger.

2) Assemble in reverse order. Rotor, shaft and outer race are serviced as an assembly. If one component is damaged, replace all three. Install new cotter pin and gasket. Prime pump with oil before installing unit in block.

Courier Engines

2000 cc 4-CYLINDER (Cont.)

Oil Pump Specifications	
Application	**Clearance In. (mm)**
Lobe-to-Lobe	.002-.006 (.051-.152)
Rotor End Clearance.....................	.002-.004 (.051-.102)
Outer Rotor-to-Housing	.006-.010 (.152-.254)

ENGINE COOLING

Thermostat — Begins to open at 180°F (82°C); fully open at 203°F (95°C).

Cooling System Capacity — 7.6 qts.

Radiator Cap — 13 psi (.90 kg/cm²).

WATER PUMP

Removal & Installation — Remove hood and drain cooling system. Remove lower hose from water pump, disconnect upper radiator hose at engine and lower hose at radiator. Remove radiator from vehicle. Loosen alternator and Thermactor pump (if equipped). Remove drive belt(s), fan, and pulley. Remove crankshaft pulley. Remove water pump. To install, reverse removal procedure.

ENGINE SPECIFICATIONS

GENERAL SPECIFICATIONS

Year	Displ.		Carburetor	HP at RPM	Torque (Ft. Lbs. at RPM)	Compr. Ratio	Bore		Stroke	
	cu. ins.	cc					in.	mm	in.	mm
1981	120.2	1970	2-Bbl.	.....	.....	8.6:1	3.15	80	3.86	96.5

VALVES

Engine & Valve	Head Diam. In. (mm)	Face Angle	Seat Angle	Seat Width In. (mm)	Stem Diameter In. (mm)	Stem Clearance In. (mm)	Valve Lift In. (mm)
1970 cc Intake	1.6497-1.6575 (41.90-42.10)	45°	45°	.055 (1.397)	.3162-.3168 (8.031-8.047)	.0007-.0021 (.017-.053)	.....
Exhaust	1.2953-1.3031 (32.90-33.09)	45°	45°	.055 (1.397)	.3160-.3168 (8.026-8.047)	.0007-.0023 (.017-.058)	.....

VALVE SPRINGS

Engine	Free Length In. (mm)	PRESSURE Lbs. @ In. (kg @ mm)	
		Valve Closed	Valve Open
1970 cc Inner	1.438 (36.52)	20.9@1.260 (9.5@32)	.....
Outer	1.469 (37.31)	31.4@1.339 (14.3@34)	.....

VALVE TIMING

Engine	INTAKE		EXHAUST	
	Open (BTDC)	Close (ABDC)	Open (BBDC)	Close (ATDC)
1970 cc	14°	53°	58°	9°

Courier Engines

2000 cc 4-CYLINDER (Cont.)

ENGINE SPECIFICATIONS (Cont.)

PISTONS, PINS, RINGS

| Engine | PISTONS | PINS | | RINGS | | |
	Clearance In. (mm)	Piston Fit In. (mm)	Rod Fit In. (mm)	Rings	End Gap In. (mm)	Side Clearance In. (mm)
1970 cc	.0014-.0030 (.036-.076)	.0003-.0009 (.008-.023)	.....	1 & 2 Oil	.008-.016 (.20-.40) .012-.035 (.30-.89)	.0011-.0027 ① (.028-.069) .....

① — No. 2 ring side clearance .0011-.0025" (.028-.065 mm).

CRANKSHAFT MAIN & CONNECTING ROD BEARINGS

| Engine | MAIN BEARINGS | | | | CONNECTING ROD BEARINGS | | |
	Journal Diam. In. (mm)	Clearance In. (mm)	Thrust Bearing	Crankshaft End Play In. (mm)	Journal Diam. In. (mm)	Clearance In. (mm)	Side Play In. (mm)
1970 cc	2.4780-2.4786 (62.94-62.95)	.0005-.0024 (.013-.061)	5	.003-.009 (.076-.228)	2.0842-2.0848 (52.938-52.954)	.001-.003 (.025-.076)	.004-.008 (.102-.203)

CAMSHAFT

Engine	Journal Diam. In. (mm)	Clearance In. (mm) ①	Lobe Lift In. (mm)
1970 cc Front	1.7695-1.7701 (44.945-44.960)	.0007-.0027 (.018-.069)	②
Center	1.7691-1.7697 (44.935-44.950)	.0011-.0031 (.028-.079)	②
Rear	1.7695-1.7701 (44.945-44.960)	.0007-.0027 (.018-.069)	②

① — End play is .001-.007" (.025-.178 mm).
② — See Cam Lobe Lift procedure.

TIGHTENING SPECIFICATIONS

Application	Ft. Lbs. (N·m)
Main Bearing Caps	61-65 (83-88)
Connecting Rod Caps	36-40 (49-54)
Cylinder Head	
Cold	59-64 (80-87)
Hot	69-72 (94-98)
Flywheel	112-118 (152-160)
Distributor Drive Gear	51-58 (69-79)
Oil Pump-to-Block	13-20 (18-27)
Camshaft Sprocket	51-58 (69-79)
Oil Pump Sprocket	22-26 (30-35)
Intake Manifold	14-20 (19-27)
Exhaust Manifold	16-21 (22-29)

	INCH Lbs. (N·m)
Oil Pan	60-108 (7-12)
Rocker Arm Cover	12-24 (1-3)

2300 cc 4-CYLINDER

ENGINE CODING

ENGINE IDENTIFICATION

Vehicle identification and engine information is stamped on model plate at the right rear of the engine compartment. The last digit of the vehicle identification number indicates engine model. Engine displacement is listed below vehicle identification number.

Engine Identification	
Application	Code
2300 cc	2

ENGINE, CYLINDER HEAD & MANIFOLDS

ENGINE

Removal & Installation — 1) Mark location of hinges and remove hood. Disconnect battery and drain cooling system. Remove air cleaner and heat stove assembly. Disconnect radiator hoses and remove radiator and shroud. Disconnect thermactor hoses at pump. Disconnect heater hoses, choke cable and accelerator linkage. Disconnect brake vacuum booster hose and vacuum amplifier.

2) Disconnect all primary and secondary ignition wiring connections as well as sensor, emission control and electrical power connections between chassis and engine. Disconnect fuel line from carburetor and vacuum hoses from engine-chassis connections. Raise vehicle and drain engine oil. Disconnect exhaust pipe from manifold and hanger on transmission.

3) Remove starting motor and bolts holding transmission to engine. Lower vehicle and support transmission with a suitable jack. Attach engine hoisting sling and remove motor mount nuts and bolts. Pull engine forward until it clears transmission shaft and lift engine from vehicle. To install, reverse removal procedure.

INTAKE MANIFOLD

Removal & Installation — Remove air cleaner and disconnect fuel line from carburetor. Disconnect distributor and crankcase ventilation hoses at intake manifold. Disconnect carburetor linkage from carburetor. Remove nuts and bolts, then remove intake manifold and carburetor as an assembly from engine. To install, reverse removal procedure while noting the following: Use a new gasket upon installation. Tighten manifold nuts and bolts, in 2 steps, using sequence shown in *Fig. 1*.

EXHAUST MANIFOLD

Removal & Installation — Remove air cleaner and two attaching nuts from top of exhaust manifold shroud. Remove attaching nuts from muffler inlet pipe and manifold, then remove exhaust manifold. To install, apply a light film of graphite grease on exhaust manifold and install manifold. Tighten manifold bolts to specifications in 2 progressive steps in the sequence shown in *Fig. 1*.

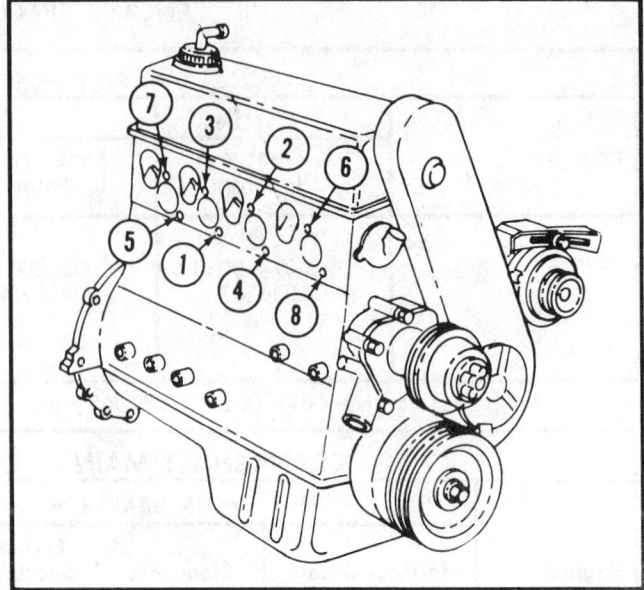

Fig. 1   Intake and Exhaust Manifold Tightening Sequence

CYLINDER HEAD

Removal — Drain cooling system, remove air cleaner and rocker arm cover. Remove exhaust manifold. Remove intake manifold and carburetor as an assembly. Disconnect spark plug wires from plugs. Remove all drive belts, fan, and pulley. Remove crankshaft pulley attaching bolt and crankshaft pulley. Remove camshaft drive belt cover, loosen drive belt tensioner and remove belt. Remove water outlet elbow from cylinder head. Remove timing belt inner cover-to-cylinder head attaching bolt. Remove cylinder head bolts in reverse of the sequence shown in *Fig. 2*. Remove cylinder head and camshaft as an assembly.

Installation — Clean gasket material from cylinder head and block. Install a new gasket on block. Place cylinder head assembly on block and install head bolts. Tighten bolts in 2 steps, using sequence shown in *Fig. 2*. Reverse removal procedure for remaining components and adjust timing belt tension.

NOTE — *When installing cylinder head, ensure that locating pin at the front of the camshaft is in the 5:30 position. Valves may protrude and cause damage in any other position.*

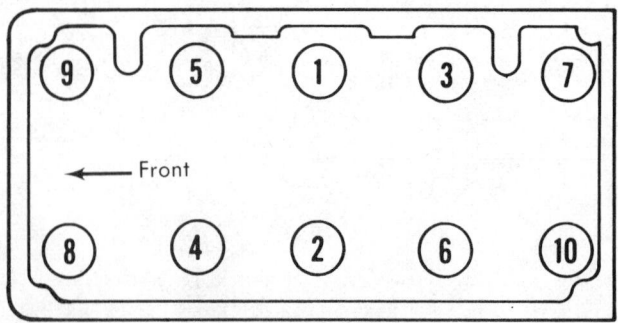

Fig. 2   Cylinder Head Tightening Sequence (Loosen in Reverse Order)

2300 cc 4-CYLINDER (Cont.)

CAMSHAFT

CAMSHAFT DRIVE BELT

Removal & Installation — *See Camshaft Timing.*

CAMSHAFT

Removal — With cylinder head removed from engine, remove rocker arms, keeping them in order for installation in original positions. Remove camshaft sprocket attaching bolt. Slide sprocket and belt guide plate from camshaft. Remove camshaft thrust plate from rear of cylinder head and carefully slide camshaft out rear of cylinder block.

Installation — Oil camshaft with engine oil and apply Lubriplate to valve stem tips. Oil rocker arms and carefully install camshaft in cylinder head. Install thrust plate, bolts and tighten. Check camshaft endplay and replace thrust plate if endplay is not within specifications.

NOTE — *Use new camshaft attaching bolt or use Teflon tape on threads of old bolt.*

CAMSHAFT BEARINGS

Removal & Installation — Use suitable tool (71P-6250A) to remove and install bearings.

NOTE — *Oil hole in bearing must be aligned with oil hole in journal.*

CAMSHAFT LOBE LIFT

Measure distance between major and minor diameters of each cam lobe with a micrometer. Difference in readings is lobe lift. If readings vary or do not meet specifications, replace camshaft.

CAMSHAFT END PLAY

With camshaft drive belt cover removed, push camshaft toward rear of engine. Install dial indicator so indicator point is on camshaft sprocket attaching screw or gear hub and zero dial indicator. Using a large screwdriver between camshaft sprocket or gear and cylinder head, pull the camshaft forward and release it. Read dial indicator and if endplay is not within specifications, replace thrust plate at rear of cylinder head.

CAMSHAFT TIMING

Checking Timing — 1) Remove access plug from belt cover and position crankshaft to TDC by aligning pointer on cover with "O" mark on crankshaft damper.

CAUTION — *Turn engine in normal rotation direction only.*

2) Look through access hole and check that timing mark on camshaft drive sprocket is aligned with pointer on inner belt cover. Remove distributor cap and check that rotor is facing number 1 position on cap.

Adjusting Timing — 1) If timing is incorrect or it is necessary to remove belt, remove timing belt outer cover and loosen belt tensioner adjustment screw. Position tension adjusting tool on tension spring roll pin and release belt tensioner. Tighten adjustment screw to hold tensioner in released position. Remove crankshaft damper, belt guide and drive belt.

2) Position crankshaft sprocket and camshaft sprocket as shown in *Fig. 3.* Remove distributor cap and set rotor to No. 1 firing position by turning auxiliary shaft. Install drive belt over crankshaft sprocket and then counterclockwise over auxiliary and camshaft sprocket. Align belt fore and aft on sprockets.

3) Loosen tensioner adjustment screw and allow tensioner to move against drive belt. Remove spark plugs and rotate crankshaft two complete turns in direction of normal rotation to remove slack from belt.

4) Tighten tensioner adjustment and pivot bolts. Recheck timing mark alignment. Install crankshaft damper, belt guide, timing belt cover and spark plugs. Check ignition timing.

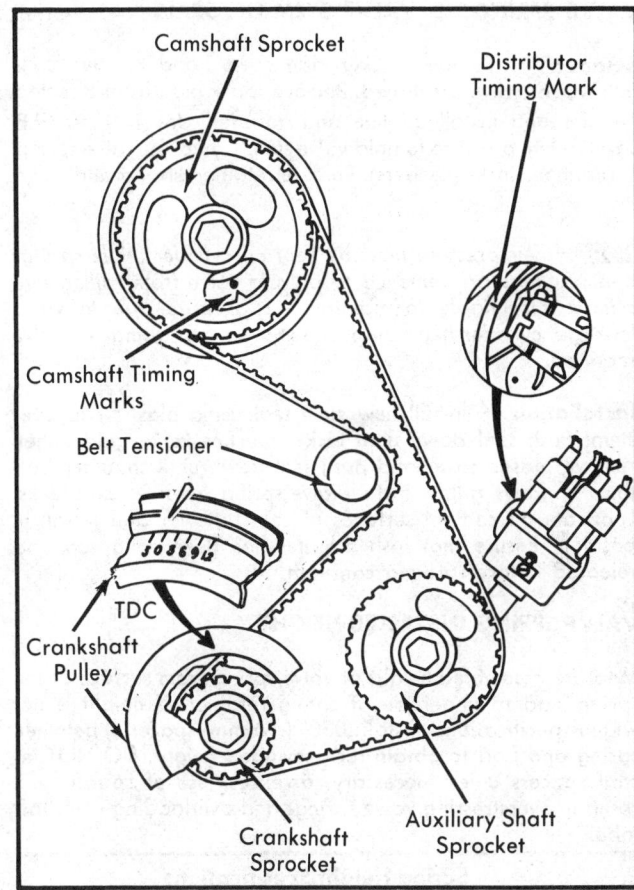

Fig. 3   Location of Timing Marks

AUXILIARY SHAFT

Removal — Remove drive belt cover, drive belt and auxiliary sprocket retaining bolt and washer. Slide sprocket from auxiliary shaft. Remove distributor and auxiliary shaft cover. Remove thrust plate and carefully remove shaft from cylinder block. Remove shaft bearing if worn or damaged.

Installation — 1) If bearing was removed, align oil holes in bearing with those in block and drive bearing into place. Oil shaft and slide into cylinder block.

CAUTION — *Do not allow shaft gear and eccentric to touch bearing surfaces during installation.*

2) Install thrust plate, gasket and shaft cover, distributor and sprocket. Install and adjust drive belt. Install drive belt cover.

2300 cc 4-CYLINDER (Cont.)

VALVES

VALVE ARRANGEMENT

E-I-E-I-E-I-E-I (front to rear).

VALVE GUIDES

If valve guides become worn they may be reamed to install a new valve with oversize stem. When going from a standard size stem to oversize, always use reamers in sequence to obtain final desired bore. The valve seat must be refaced after a guide has been reamed, and a suitable tool used to break sharp corner (ID) of guide.

VALVE SPRINGS & VALVE STEM OIL SEALS

Removal — Remove rocker arm cover, and remove cam follower of valve concerned. Remove spark plug from affected cylinder and install air line and adapter. Use 140 psi (9.8 kg/cm²) line pressure to hold valve shut. Compress valve spring and remove locks (keepers). Remove retainer, spring and valve stem seals.

NOTE — *Air pressure must be kept on cylinder while springs and retainers are removed to prevent valve from falling into cylinder. If unable to maintain air pressure due to valve leakage, cylinder head must be removed and damaged valve repaired.*

Installation — Install new stem seal using plastic cap over stem. Push seal down until jacket touches valve guide, then remove plastic cover and push seal down until shoulder bottoms on valve guide. Install valve spring, retainer and locks. Lubricate all contact surfaces of cam follower and install in position. Ensure that lash adjuster has been collapsed and released before rotating camshaft.

VALVE SPRING INSTALLED HEIGHT

Measure assembled height of valve spring from surface of the spring pad to underside of spring retainer. If height is not within specifications, install .030" (.76 mm) spacer(s) between spring and pad to obtain recommended height. DO NOT install spacers unless necessary, as excess use of spacers will result in overstressing valve springs and overloading camshaft lobe.

Spring Height Specifications	
Engine	**Installed Height**
2300 cc	1.531-1.594" (39.0-40.5 mm)

HYDRAULIC LASH ADJUSTER ASSEMBLY

Removal & Installation — With rocker arm cover removed, rotate camshaft so that cam lobe of applicable valve faces away from follower. Using suitable tool (T74P-6565-B), collapse adjuster or depress valve and slide follower out over adjuster. Lift adjuster out and inspect or clean as necessary. Replace entire assembly if plunger is not free in body. To install, reverse removal procedures.

CAUTION — *For any operation that requires removal of the rocker arm (follower), each affected lash adjuster must be collapsed after re-installation and released prior to rotating camshaft.*

HYDRAULIC LASH ADJUSTMENT

Position camshaft with lobe of valve to be checked pointing away from follower. Slowly apply pressure to follower with tool (T74P-6565-B) until adjuster is completely collapsed. Hold in this position and check clearance between follower and cam with feeler gauge. If not within specifications, check cam follower, cam, valve for sticking, and valve spring installed height.

Hydraulic Lash Adjustment	
Application	①**Clearance**
Base of Lobe-to-Rocker Arm	
Desired	.040-.050" (1.0-1.3 mm)
Allowable	.035-.055" (.9-1.4 mm)

① — Leak down rate is 2-8 seconds.

PISTONS, PINS & RINGS

OIL PAN

Removal & Installation — Raise vehicle on hoist and remove front lower engine shield. Drain oil and remove clutch release cylinder, leaving the cylinder hanging. Remove engine rear brace attaching bolts and loosen bolts on left side. Remove oil pan bolts and lower pan from vehicle. To install, first apply sealer to oil pan flange, pan side of gasket and joint of cylinder block and front cover. Use guide pins to align pan, and install the 4 larger (8 mm) bolts. Remove guide pins and install the remaining (6 mm) bolts. Tighten bolts to specifications starting with right rear bolt and proceeding in a clockwise direction. To complete installation, reverse removal procedure.

PISTON & ROD ASSEMBLY

Removal — Remove cylinder head, oil pan and oil pump. Remove ridge at top of cylinder bores prior to removing pistons. Ensure that connecting rods and caps are marked for position and remove bearing caps. Push piston-rod assembly out of block from bottom, using caution not to nick crankshaft journals. Install rod caps on mating rods.

Installation — Oil piston rings and cylinder walls with engine oil. Install ring compressor and insert piston-rod assembly into corresponding cylinder. Notch on piston head must be toward front of engine. Tap piston into position using a wooden handle and carefully guide rod over crankshaft journal. Install rod bearing cap and tighten to specifications.

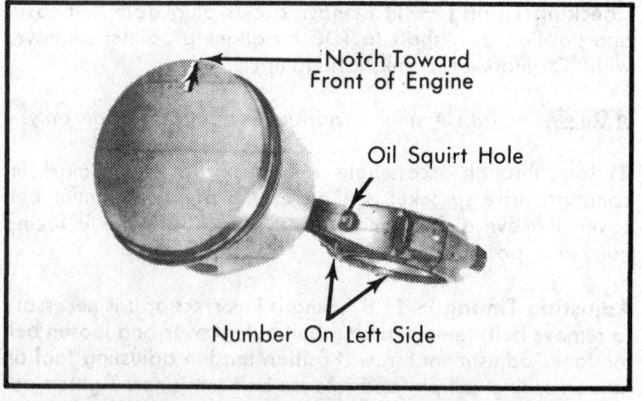

Notch Toward
Front of Engine

Oil Squirt Hole

Number On Left Side

Fig. 4 Piston & Rod Assembly Identification

2300 cc 4-CYLINDER (Cont.)

FITTING PISTONS

1) Check piston to cylinder bore clearance by measuring the piston and cylinder bore diameters. Measure outer diameter of piston at centerline of piston pin bore and at 90° to pin bore axis. Measure the diameter of each cylinder bore at the top, middle and bottom, with the gauge placed at right angles and parallel to the centerline of the engine.

2) Standard size pistons are color coded; red, blue or have .003" OS stamped on the dome. Select the piston to assure the proper clearance. When the bore diameter is in the lower one third of specified range, a red piston should be used. When the bore diameter is in the middle one third a blue piston should be used. When the bore diameter is in the upper one third, the .003" OS piston should be used.

3) If no piston can be fitted, refinish the cylinder to provide proper clearance. When a piston has been fitted, mark it for assembly in the cylinder to which it has been fitted.

Piston Clearance	
Piston Code	**Diameter In. (mm)**
Red	3.7780-3.7786 (95.961-95.976)
Blue	3.7792-3.7798 (95.991-96.006)
.003" O.S.	3.7804-3.7810 (96.022-96.037)

PISTON PINS

Removal — Remove bearing inserts from connecting rod and cap. Mark pistons and pins to assure assembly with same rod. Press piston pin from piston and connecting rod.

Installation — Apply light coat of engine oil to all parts. Assemble piston to connecting rod with oil squirt hole (in connecting rod) and notch (on piston head) positioned as shown in *Fig. 4*. Start piston pin in piston and connecting rod, then press pin through piston and connecting rod until pin is centered in piston.

CRANKSHAFT MAIN & CONNECTING ROD BEARINGS

MAIN & CONNECTING ROD BEARINGS

NOTE — *Following procedures are with oil pan and oil pump removed. If bearing replacement is required, both halves must be replaced. Do not use a new bearing in combination with a used bearing.*

Connecting Rod Bearings — After ensuring rod caps are marked for cylinder identification, remove rod caps. Use Plastigage method to check for proper bearing clearance. If not within specifications, new bearings must be installed. New bearings are available in .001" (.025 mm) and .002" (.051 mm) undersizes. Selective fitting is required on each connecting rod. A standard bearing may be used in combination with either undersize bearing. Coat bearing surfaces with oil, install bearing and cap and tighten nuts to specifications.

Main Bearings — **1)** Position jack under counterweight adjoining bearing being checked so weight of crankshaft will not compress Plastigage and provide an erroneous reading. With all bearing caps (other than one being checked) tight, check clearances using Plastigage method.

2) If clearances are excessive, a .001" (.025 mm) or .002" (.051 mm) undersize bearing may be used in combination with a standard bearing. If .002" (.051 mm) undersize bearings are used on more than one journal, they must be positioned in cylinder block rather than bearing cap. If standard and undersize bearings do not bring clearance within specified limits, crankshaft will have to be refinished and fitted with undersize bearings.

3) Remove all upper main bearings by inserting suitable tool in oil hole of crankshaft journal and rotating crankshaft clockwise to roll bearing from engine. Oil new upper bearing and insert plain (unnotched) end between crankshaft and indented (or notched) side of block. Rotate bearing into place. Install all main bearing caps with arrows pointing to front of engine.

REAR MAIN BEARING OIL SEAL

Removal & Installation — **1)** Split lip type seal is provided for service replacement. Remove oil pan and oil pump. Loosen all main bearing cap bolts, allowing crankshaft to drop (not more than 1/32") and remove rear main bearing cap. Remove oil seal from cap and clean oil seal groove. Remove upper seal half from block using seal removal tool or small metal screw in end of seal.

CAUTION — *Extreme care should be taken not to scratch or mar crankshaft seal surface.*

2) Dip new split lip type seal halves in clean engine oil. Carefully install upper seal into its groove with undercut side of seal toward front of engine, by rotating it on seal journal of crankshaft until ends of seal are flush with block. Ensure that no rubber has been shaved from outside of seal.

3) Install lower seal in rear bearing cap with locating tab to rear. Seal ends should be flush with bearing cap. Apply 1/16" bead of suitable sealer to bearing cap mating surfaces, using care that sealer does NOT contact seals. Install bearing cap and tighten bolts to specifications.

CRANKSHAFT FRONT OIL SEAL REPLACEMENT

Removal and Installation — Remove alternator drive belt and crankshaft pulley. Remove camshaft drive belt. See Camshaft Timing. Slide camshaft drive belt sprocket and belt off

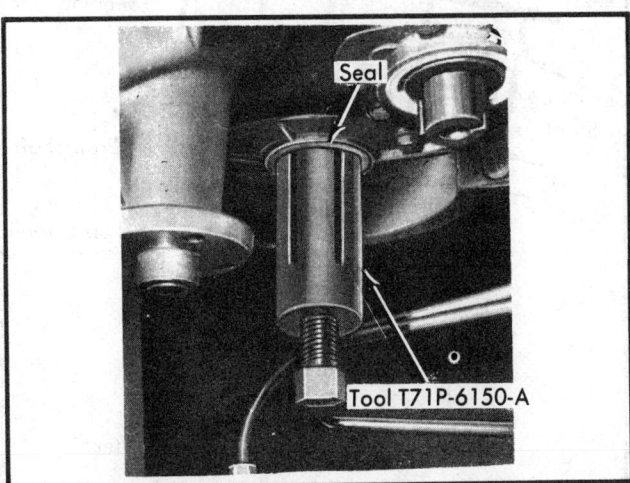

Fig. 5   Replacing Front Crankshaft Oil Seal

Courier Engines

2300 cc 4-CYLINDER (Cont.)

crankshaft, using puller if necessary. Fit a puller (T74P-6700-B) over end of crankshaft and remove seal. To install, use tool (T74P-6150-A) and reverse removal procedure. *See Fig. 5.*

NOTE — *Cylinder front cover and auxiliary shaft seals are replaced using procedure outlined above.*

ENGINE OILING

ENGINE OILING SYSTEM

Oiling system is force feed type using a full flow oil filter. Oil enters main oil gallery from oil filter and flows to main bearings and camshaft bearings. Connecting rod bearings are supplied from front and rear main bearings via inclined passages. A squirt hole in each main bearing supplies oil to piston thrust side of cylinder. Auxiliary shaft is connected with main oil gallery. Distributor shaft receives oil from passage drilled in auxiliary shaft. Cams and cam follower arms are supplied from camshaft. Valve lash adjusters receive oil from drilled oil passages in cylinder head.

Crankcase Capacity — 4 qts. (5 qts. including filter.)

Oil Filter — Full flow, spin-on type.

Normal Oil Pressure (Hot) — 40-60 psi (2.8-4.2 kg/cm²) at 2000 RPM.

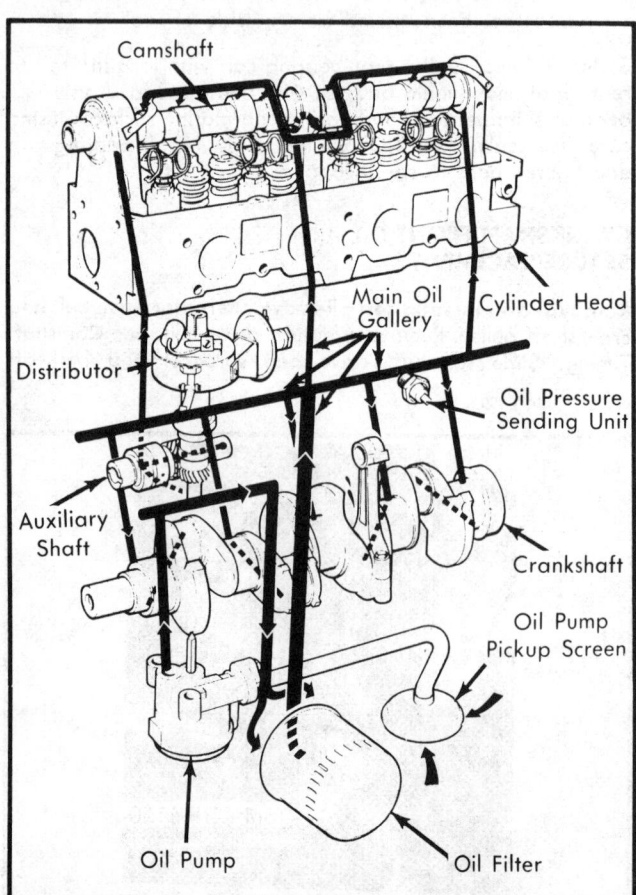

Fig. 6 Engine Oiling System

Pressure Relief Valve — Internal, non-adjustable.

OIL PUMP

Removal & Installation — With oil pan removed, remove oil pump mounting screws. Remove pump and take out oil inlet tube screws. Remove tube and gasket. Remove cover attaching screws and cover, inner rotor and shaft assembly, and pump outer race. If pump clearances are beyond limits, replace race, rotor and shaft as an assembly. To install, reverse removal procedures. Use new gaskets, prime pump with engine oil.

Oil Pump Specifications

Application	Clearance In. (mm)
Drive Shaft-to-Housing	.0015-.0030 (.04-.08)
Rotor Assembly End Clearance	.001-.004 (.03-.10)
Outer Rotor-to-Housing	.001-.013 (.02-.33)
Relief Valve Spring Tension	15.2-17.2 lbs. @ 1.20" (6.9-7.8 kg @ 30.4 mm)

ENGINE COOLING

Thermostat — Begins to open at 188-195° F (87-90° C). Opens fully at 212-215° F (100-102° C).

Cooling System Capacity — 8.8 quarts.

Radiator Cap — 13 psi (.90 kg/cm²).

TIGHTENING SPECIFICATIONS

Application	Ft·Lbs. (N·m)
Auxiliary Shaft Gear	28-40 (38-54)
Belt Tensioner Pivot	28-40 (38-54)
Belt Tensioner Adjuster	14-21 (19-29)
Camshaft Sprocket	80-90 (109-122)
Connecting Rod	
Step 1	25-30 (34-41)
Step 2	30-36 (41-49)
Crankshaft Pulley	100-120 (136-163)
Cylinder Head	
Step 1	60 (82)
Step 2	80-90 (109-122)
Exhaust Manifold-to-Cylinder Head	
Step 1	16-23 (22-30)
Step 2	27-34 (37-46)
Flywheel-to-Crankshaft	54-64 (73-87)
Intake Manifold-to-Cylinder Head	14-21 (19-29)
Main Bearing Cap	
Step 1	60 (82)
Step 2	80-90 (109-122)
Water Pump-to-Cylinder Block	14-21 (19-29)

	INCH Lbs. (N·m)
Auxiliary Shaft Thrust Plate	70-108 (8-13)
Camshaft Thrust Plate	70-108 (8-13)
Front Cover	70-108 (8-13)

2300 cc 4-CYLINDER (Cont.)

ENGINE SPECIFICATIONS

GENERAL SPECIFICATIONS										
Year	Displ.		Carburetor	HP at RPM	Torque (Ft. Lbs. at RPM)	Compr. Ratio	Bore		Stroke	
	cu. ins.	cc					in.	mm	in.	mm
1981	140	2300	2-Bbl.	.....	.....	8.4:1	3.78	96.01	3.126	79.40

VALVE SPRINGS			
Engine	Free Length In. (mm)	PRESSURE Lbs. @ In. (kg @ mm)	
		Valve Closed	Valve Open
2300 cc	1.824 (46.3)	71-79@1.56 (32-35.8@39.6)	180@1.116 (81.6-89.8@29.6)

CAMSHAFT			
Engine	Journal Diam. In. (mm)	Clearance In. (mm)	Lobe Lift In. (mm)
2300 cc	1.7713-1.7720 (44.991-45.009)	① .001-.003 (.025-.076)	.2437 (6.19)

① — End play is .001-.007" (.025-.178 mm).

VALVES							
Engine & Valve	Head Diam. In. (mm)	Face Angle	Seat Angle	Seat Width In. (mm)	Stem Diameter In. (mm)	Stem Clearance In. (mm)	Valve Lift In. (mm)
2300 cc Intake	1.73-1.74 (43.9-44.2)	44°	45°	.060-.080 (1.52-2.03)	.3416-.3423 (8.68-8.69)	.0010-.0027 (.025-.069)	.3997 (10.15)
Exhaust	1.49-1.51 (37.8-38.4)	44°	45°	.070-.090 (1.78-2.29)	.3411-.3418 (8.66-8.68)	.0015-.0032 (.038-.081)	.3997 (10.15)

PISTONS, PINS, RINGS						
Engine	PISTONS	PINS		RINGS		
	Clearance In. (mm)	Piston Fit In. (mm)	Rod Fit In. (mm)	Rings	End Gap In. (mm)	Side Clearance In. (mm)
2300 cc	.0014-.0022 (.035-.056)	.0002-.0004 (.005-.010)	①	Comp.	.010-.020 (.25-.51)	.002-.004 (.051-.102)
				Oil	.015-.055 (.38-1.40)	Snug

① — Interference Fit.

CRANKSHAFT MAIN & CONNECTING ROD BEARINGS						
Engine	MAIN BEARINGS				CONNECTING ROD BEARINGS	
	Journal Diam. In. (mm)	Clearance In. (mm)	Thrust Bearing	Crankshaft End Play In. (mm)	Journal Diam. In. (mm)	Clearance In. (mm)	Side Play In. (mm)
2300 cc	2.3982-2.3990 (60.91-60.93)	.0008-.0015 (.020-.038)	No. 3	.004-.008 (.10-.20)	2.0464-2.0472 (51.979-51.999)	.0008-.0015 (.020-.038)	.0035-.0105 (.089-.267)

Datsun Engines

210 & 310 4-CYLINDER

ENGINE CODING

ENGINE IDENTIFICATION

Engine serial and code number is stamped on right rear side of cylinder block, below mating surface of cylinder head and cylinder block. First 3 or 4 digits are engine code.

Engine Identification	
Application	**Code**
210 (1237 cc)	A12A
210 (1397 cc)	A14
210 & 310 (1488 cc)	A15

ENGINE, CYLINDER HEAD & MANIFOLDS

ENGINE

NOTE — *Manufacturer recommends that engine and transmission be removed as an assembly.*

Removal (210) — 1) Disconnect battery ground and fusible links. Mark hood location and remove hood. Remove engine protective undercover. Drain coolant and engine oil. Disconnect transmission cooler hoses (Auto. Trans. only).

2) Remove radiator. Disconnect electrical wires and other lines attached to air cleaner, then remove air cleaner assembly. Disconnect accelerator cable from carburetor. Disconnect the following components:
- Automatic choke wire.
- Throttle solenoid or throttle switch.
- Fuel cut solenoid.
- Vacuum switching valve.
- Coil and distributor.
- Thermal transmitter.
- Alternator and oil pressure switch.
- Engine ground and engine harness No. 2.
- Fuel pump and carbon canister hoses.
- Water temperature switch.
- Vacuum switch.
- Battery cable to starter.
- Brake power booster hose.

3) On models equipped with air conditioning, loosen compressor and lay out of the way without disconnecting any hoses. On models with manual transmissions, remove clutch slave cylinder. On all models, disconnect speedometer cable from extension housing. Remove shift linkage.

4) On manual transmission models, remove gear shift lever. On models with automatic transmissions, disconnect selector lever. On all models, disconnect exhaust at manifold and exhaust mounting bracket from transmission and hang up with wire.

5) Index mark and remove propeller shaft. Plug opening in rear of extension housing. Support transmission with a jack. Remove rear crossmember mounting bolts. Attach hoist to engine and raise slightly to support engine weight. Remove front engine mounts and remove engine and transmission as a unit.

Installation — To install, reverse removal procedure.

Removal (310) — 1) Remove hood and battery and drain coolant. Disconnect ducting and tubes to air cleaner and remove air cleaner assembly. Disconnect accelerator wire and speedometer cable.

2) Remove auxiliary fan, upper buffer (damper) rod, radiator grill and washer tank (air conditioning). Remove radiator and fan motor as a unit. Disconnect the following components:
- Battery cables.
- Coil and distributor wires.
- Engine and coil wiring harness connectors.
- Fuel lines and carbon canister hoses.
- Brake power booster hose.
- Ground strap (near hood edge).

3) On models equipped with air conditioning, loosen air conditioning equipment and lay components out of way. Do not discharge system. If equipped with power steering, remove belt and pulley and wire assembly out of way. Do not drain fluid or disconnect hoses.

4) Remove clutch slave cylinder, disconnect shift linkage and remove lower buffer (damper) rod. Attach hoist to engine.

5) Disconnect exhaust system at manifold, rear engine mount and "U" clamp. Disconnect both axle drive shafts at transaxle case. Lower out shift linkage. Disconnect engine mounts and lift out engine.

Installation — Install in reverse order of removal, ensuring that buffer (damper) rods are adjusted so that rubber will not be deformed.

INTAKE & EXHAUST MANIFOLDS

Removal & Installation — 1) Remove air cleaner and disconnect accelerator cable and choke cable. Disconnect and plug fuel line at carburetor. Disconnect exhaust pipe at exhaust manifold.

2) Remove nuts retaining intake and exhaust manifold to cylinder head and remove intake and exhaust manifold as an assembly. Remove gasket and thoroughly clean mating surfaces. Remove bolts and separate intake and exhaust manifold. To install, reverse removal procedure and use new gasket. Tighten nuts and bolts to specifications.

CYLINDER HEAD

Removal — Remove manifold assembly and take off rocker arm cover. Loosen valve adjusting screws to take tension off push rods. Remove rocker shaft assembly and withdraw push rods, keeping them in order for installation. Loosen head bolts gradually in reverse of tightening sequence and remove cylinder head. See *Fig. 1.*

Installation — Thoroughly clean mating surfaces. Use new gasket with no sealer and install cylinder head. Install cylinder head retaining bolts and tighten in 2 or 3 steps to specifications. *Follow sequence shown in Fig. 1.* Reverse removal procedure to install remaining components. Adjust valve clearance.

NOTE — *One cylinder head bolt is smaller diameter and has a hollow head. Install this bolt on right side center of cylinder head.*

210 & 310 4-CYLINDER (Cont.)

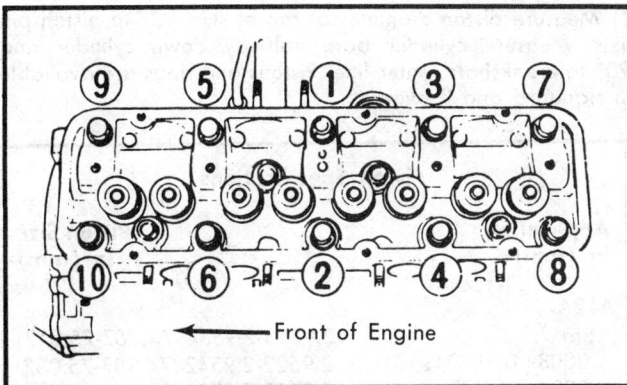

Fig. 1   Tightening Sequence for Cylinder Head (Loosen in Reverse Sequence)

VALVES

VALVE ARRANGEMENT

E-I-I-E-E-I-I-E (front to rear).

VALVE GUIDE SERVICING

1) Measure clearance between valve stem and valve guide with micrometer and hole gauge. Check diameter of valve stem in three places: top, center and bottom.

2) Insert hole gauge in valve guide bore and measure at center. Subtract highest reading of valve stem diameter from valve guide bore to determine clearance.

NOTE — *As a quick check, a valve may be inserted into valve guide and moved either left or right, (parallel with rocker arm). If tip moves .008" (.2 mm) or more, clearance is beyond maximum limit of .004" (.1 mm).*

3) If clearance is beyond acceptable limits and valve stem is not worn, the valve guide must be replaced. To replace guide, heat cylinder head to 300-400°F (150-200°C) and use suitable drift (ST110330000) to drive old guides out from combustion chamber side toward rocker arm cover.

4) With head at room temperature, ream valve guide hole to .480" (12.2 mm). Re-heat cylinder head and install new guide. Use suitable reamer (ST110320000) to finish stem bore to .31" (8.0 mm) and reface valve seat surface.

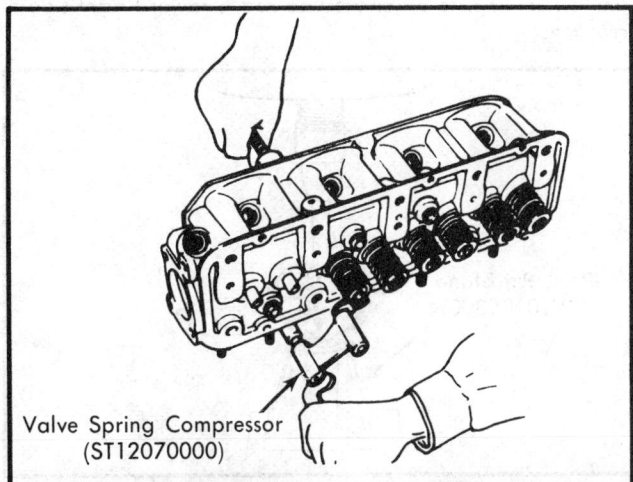

Valve Spring Compressor
(ST12070000)

Fig. 2   Valve Spring Removal & Replacement

VALVE STEM OIL SEALS

Valve stem lip seals are used on all guides. Valve spring seat must be in position, then place seal on guide. Tap installer tool (KV10104800) with plastic hammer to ensure proper position of seal on guide.

VALVE SPRINGS

Removal — With cylinder head removed, compress valve spring using a suitable valve spring compressor (ST12070000) and remove valve keepers. Release spring compressor and remove spring retainer and spring.

Installation — Install spring seat and oil seal, then insert valve in guide carefully to avoid damaging lip seal. Install spring with close coiled end (painted white) toward head. Install retainer and keepers.

VALVE SPRING INSTALLED HEIGHT

Valve spring must be square within $1/16$". Valve spring compressed height is 1.189" (30.2 mm). Check valve spring by applying specified load and measuring spring height. If spring height, pressure or squareness do not meet specifications, replace spring.

ROCKER ARM & SHAFT ASSEMBLY

1) Remove valve cover and loosen valve adjusting screws to remove tension. Loosen rocker arm assembly mounting bolts evenly and remove rocker arm and shaft assembly.

2) Slide off support stands, rocker arms and springs. Thoroughly clean and inspect all components for signs of wear or seizure. Measure rocker arm-to-shaft clearance by measuring diameter of rocker arm bore and shaft. Standard clearance is .0008-.0021" (.020-.054 mm). Replace as necessary.

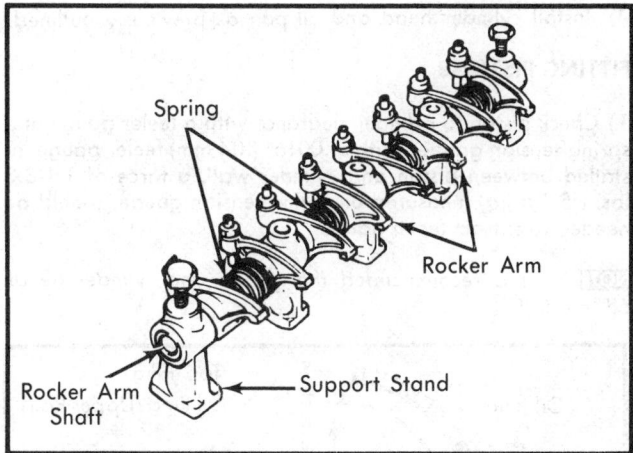

Spring

Rocker Arm

Rocker Arm Shaft

Support Stand

Fig. 3   Rocker Arm and Shaft Assembly

3) If valve contact surface of rocker arm is worn, resurface using a suitable grinder.

4) Reverse disassembly and removal procedures to assemble and install rocker arm assembly. Adjust valve clearance.

Datsun Engines

210 & 310 4-CYLINDER (Cont.)

VALVE CLEARANCE

Set valves to .010" (.25 mm) cold for assembly purposes. Rotate crankshaft until No. 1 cylinder is at TDC on compression stroke and adjust as follows:

- No. 1 Exhaust and Intake.
- No. 2 Intake.
- No. 3 Exhaust.

Rotate crankshaft and bring No. 4 cylinder to TDC on compression stroke and adjust remaining valves.

- No. 2 Exhaust.
- No. 3 Intake.
- No. 4 Intake and Exhuast.

Warm engine to normal operating temperature and repeat adjustment procedure. Set clearance to .014" (.35 mm).

PISTONS, PINS & RINGS

PISTON & ROD ASSEMBLY

1) Remove cylinder head and oil pan. Remove nuts from connecting rod and remove connecting rod cap with bearing half. Push piston and connecting rod assembly with bearing half up and out through top of cylinder block.

2) To install piston and connecting rod assembly, thoroughly oil rings, piston and cylinder wall. Make sure ring gaps are situated approximately 180° apart and not on thrust side of piston. See Fig. 4. Make sure bearing halves are properly seated in connecting rod and cap.

3) Install a ring compressor and compress rings. Install piston in cylinder with notch on top of piston toward front of engine. With piston installed in cylinder, and connecting rod and bearings seated against crankshaft journal, install rod cap with numbers on the same side as connecting rod. Tighten nuts to specification.

4) Install cylinder head and oil pan as previously outlined.

FITTING PISTONS

1) Check piston-to-cylinder clearance with a feeler gauge and spring tension gauge. With a .0016" (.04 mm) feeler gauge installed between piston and cylinder wall, a force of 1.1-3.3 lbs. (.5-1.5 kg) measured on spring tension gauge, should be needed to extract feeler gauge.

NOTE — It is recommended that piston and cylinder be at 68°F (20°C).

2) Measure piston diameter at top of skirt 90° to piston pin axis. Measure cylinder bore halfway down cylinder and 90° to crankshaft center line. Pistons and rings are available in standard and 3 oversizes.

Piston Specifications	
Application In. (mm)	Piston Size In. (mm)
A12A	
Std.	2.9515-2.9534 (74.967-75.017)
.0008 (.020) O/S	2.9522-2.9542 (74.987-75.037)
.020 (.50) O/S	2.9715-2.9734 (75.467-75.517)
.040 (1.0) O/S	2.9909-2.9928 (75.967-76.017)
A14 & A15	
Std.	2.9908-2.9928 (75.967-76.017)
.0008 (.020) O/S	2.9916-2.9936 (75.987-76.037)
.020 (.50) O/S	3.0105-3.0125 (76.467-76.517)
.040 (1.0) O/S	3.0302-3.0322 (76.967-77.017)

NOTE — If cylinder bore has exceeded wear limit, undersize cylinder liners are available. Liners are installed with an interference fit .0031-.0035" (.08-.09 mm).

PISTON PIN REPLACEMENT

1) Remove piston and connecting rod assembly as previously outlined. Use a press and suitable pin press stand to remove and install pin in piston/rod assembly.

2) Check piston-to-pin clearance by measuring pin and hole diameters. If clearance is not within specifications, replace both piston and piston pin. Piston pin should push fit by hand through piston with both piston and pin at room temperature.

3) Piston pin should be press fit into connecting rod. If interference fit is not within specifications, replace connecting rod or piston pin as necessary. If connecting rod is replaced, ensure weight difference between rods is within .2 ounces.

4) To assemble piston and connecting rod assembly, use same mandrel and driver used for disassembly. Thoroughly oil pin, piston and connecting rod. Install piston on connecting rod so that number on top of piston is pointing toward front of engine and oil squirt hole on connecting rod is toward right side of crankcase.

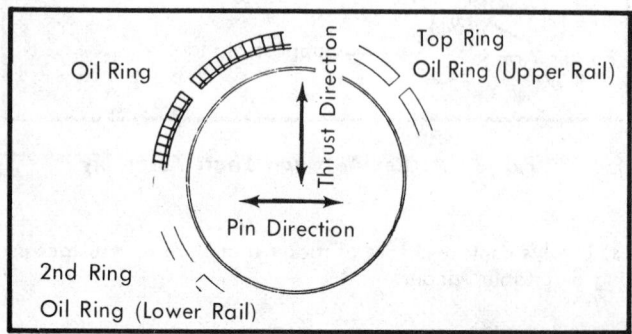

Fig. 4 Piston Ring Gap Positioning

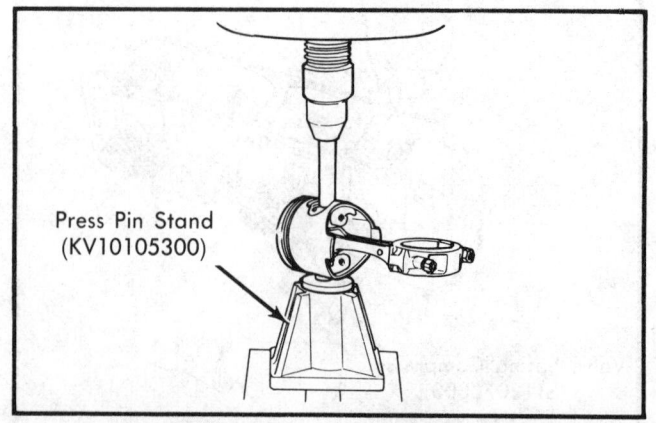

Fig. 5 Removing and Installing Piston Pin

210 & 310 4-CYLINDER (Cont.)

CRANKSHAFT MAIN & CONNECTING ROD BEARINGS

MAIN & CONNECTING ROD BEARINGS

Removal — With engine removed from vehicle, remove cylinder head, oil pan, and piston and connecting rod assemblies. Remove alternator and engine mounting bracket from left side. Remove water pump, crankshaft pulley, and timing chain cover. Remove oil thrower and chain tensioner. Remove camshaft sprocket bolt, and remove both sprockets and timing chain as an assembly. Remove clutch and flywheel. Loosen main bearing cap bolts in two or three steps, then remove caps. Remove rear oil seal and carefully lift out crankshaft.

Inspection — 1) Thoroughly clean and inspect crankshaft. Blow out oil passages with compressed air. Check crankshaft for runout on center main bearing journal. If runout is more than .004" (.10 mm), crankshaft is bent and must be replaced.

2) Check all main and connecting rod bearings using Plastigage method. Check main and connecting rod journals for out-of-round or taper. If more than .002" (.05 mm), crankshaft must be ground to next undersize. Main and connecting rod journals may be ground to the undersizes indicated in tables.

Main Bearing Journals	
Application In. (mm)	**Diameter In. (mm)**
Std.	1.9663-1.9671 (49.943-49.964)
.01 (.25) U/S	1.9567-1.9572 (49.701-49.714)
.02 (.50) U/S	1.9469-1.9474 (49.451-49.464)
.03 (.75) U/S	1.9370-1.9376 (49.201-49.214)

Installation — 1) Install main bearing halves to engine block ensuring that all bearings are on correct journal. Bearings for journal No. 1 and No. 5 are the same. Bearings for journals No. 2 and No. 4 are the same. Journal No. 3 requires the thrust bearing. Upper and lower bearings are not interchangeable except for journals No. 2 and No. 4.

Connecting Rod Journals	
Application In. (mm)	**Diameter In. (mm)**
Std	1.7698-1.7706 (44.954-44.974)
.003 (.08) U/S	1.7670-1.7675 (44.881-44.894)
.01 (.25) U/S	1.7603-1.7608 (44.711-44.724)
.02 (.50) U/S	1.7504-1.7509 (44.461-44.474)
.03 (.75) U/S	1.7406-1.7411 (44.211-44.224)

2) Apply oil to main bearing surface and install crankshaft. Install main bearing caps with arrow pointing toward front of engine. Tighten main bearing caps in 2 or 3 steps, starting at center bearing and working outward. Ensure crankshaft rotates smoothly.

NOTE — *Apply sealer to rear main bearing cap at point where cap contacts cylinder block.*

3) Check crankshaft end play. See *Thrust Bearing Alignment.* Install timing chain in correct position with crankshaft and camshaft sprockets. Install rear oil seal. Install clutch and flywheel. Install oil thrower and chain tensioner. Install timing chain cover, crankshaft pulley, and water pump. Install alternator and engine mounting bracket. Install piston and connecting rod assemblies, oil pan, and cylinder head.

THRUST BEARING ALIGNMENT

Thrust bearing is installed on No. 3 main bearing journal. Check crankshaft end play by inserting a feeler gauge between flange of thrust bearing and crankshaft. End play should be .002-.006" (.05-.15 mm). Service limit is .012" (.30 mm).

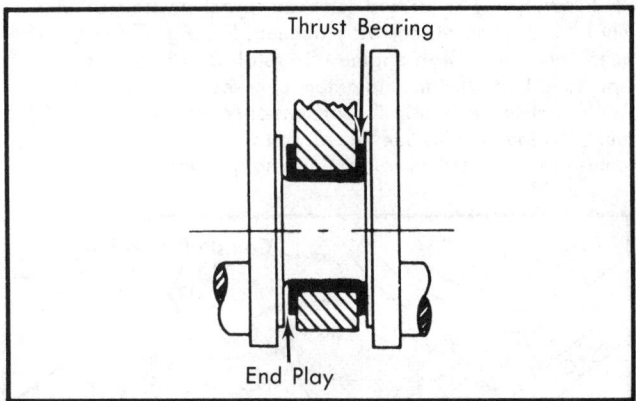

Fig. 6   Checking Crankshaft End Play

REAR MAIN BEARING OIL SEAL

Apply sealer to corners of crankcase at rear main bearing cap contact points and install cap. Lubricate seal lips and drive seal into position with suitable installer.

ENGINE FRONT COVER & OIL SEAL

Removal & Installation — Remove drive belt, fan, and water pump pulley. Remove water pump and crankshaft pulley. Remove oil pan and front cover. Replace seal in front cover whenever cover is removed. Thoroughly clean mating surfaces and apply sealer to both sides of gasket. Install gasket and cover. Tighten bolts and nuts to specifications. Reverse removal procedure to install remaining components.

CAMSHAFT

TIMING CHAIN

Removal — Remove engine front cover as previously outlined. Remove timing chain tensioner and bolt securing camshaft sprocket to camshaft. Pull off sprocket with timing chain.

Installation — 1) Insert crank sprocket keys in keyways of crankshaft. Install camshaft and crankshaft sprockets temporarily for adjustment of tooth height by using adjusting washers. Adjust height difference so it is less than .020" (0.5 mm).

Datsun Engines

210 & 310 4-CYLINDER (Cont.)

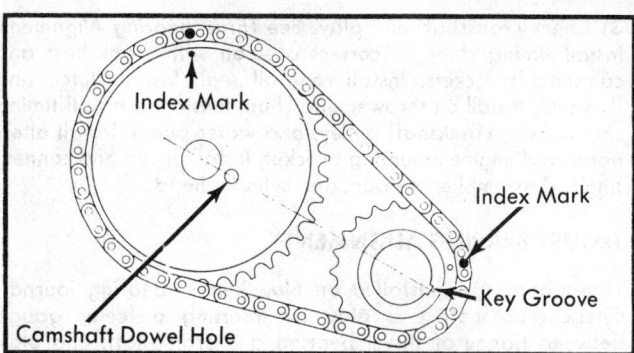

Fig. 7   Timing Chain Alignment Marks for Installation

2) Install timing chain and camshaft sprocket with markings on chain and sprockets correctly aligned. *See Fig. 7.* Oil sprocket teeth and chain with engine oil. Install and tighten camshaft sprocket bolt. Install chain tensioner and tighten attaching bolts. Check dimension "L" of tensioner and if over .59" (15 mm), replace chain. *See Fig. 8.* Install oil thrower in front of camshaft sprocket. Install timing chain cover.

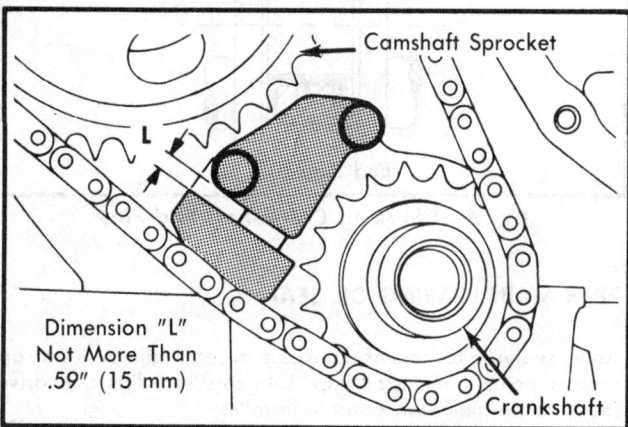

Fig. 8   Checking Timing Chain Tensioner Projection

CAMSHAFT

Removal — Remove engine front cover, and valve train components as previously outlined. Remove fuel pump and oil pump with filter. Remove timing chain tensioner and remove timing chain with sprockets. Remove two bolts from camshaft lock plate and carefully pull camshaft from engine block.

Inspection — Thoroughly clean and inspect camshaft for wear or scoring. Check runout of camshaft using a dial indicator on center bearing journal. If runout exceeds .004" (.10 mm), replace camshaft. Check journal diameter, and if diameter is more than .0059" (.15 mm) from standard, camshaft journals must be ground to next undersize. Bearings are available in standard and three undersizes.

Installation — Coat camshaft with light coat of engine oil and carefully install camshaft into engine. Install camshaft lock plate with word "LOWER" at bottom. Install valve train components. Install timing chain with sprockets and timing chain tensioner. Install engine front cover. Install fuel pump and oil pump.

CAMSHAFT END THRUST

Check camshaft end thrust with camshaft, lock plate, and camshaft sprocket in position by using a dial indicator on

camshaft sprocket bolt. If end play exceeds .0039" (.10 mm), replace lock plate.

CAMSHAFT BEARING REPLACEMENT

1) With camshaft removed, check journal diameter and bearing inside diameter. If journal measurement is within tolerance and clearance between camshaft journals and bearings exceeds .0059" (.15 mm), bearings must be replaced.

2) Remove and install appropriate bearings in crankcase using a suitable driver (ST16110000). Make sure oil holes in bearings align with oil holes in crankcase. Bearings must be line bored after installation. Install taper plug in crankcase using sealer. Install camshaft as previously outlined.

ENGINE OILING

Crankcase Capacity (With Filter)	
Application	**Quantity**
All Models	3.5 quarts

Oil Filter — Full-flow, replaceable element.

Oil Pressure — More than 11 psi (.8 kg/cm²) at idle; 54-74 psi (3.8-5.2 kg/cm²) at 3000 RPM.

Pressure Relief Valve — Nonadjustable, located in oil pump cover.

ENGINE OILING SYSTEM

Pressure is provided to oiling system by a trochoid rotor type pump. Oil pump is mounted on side of crankcase and driven

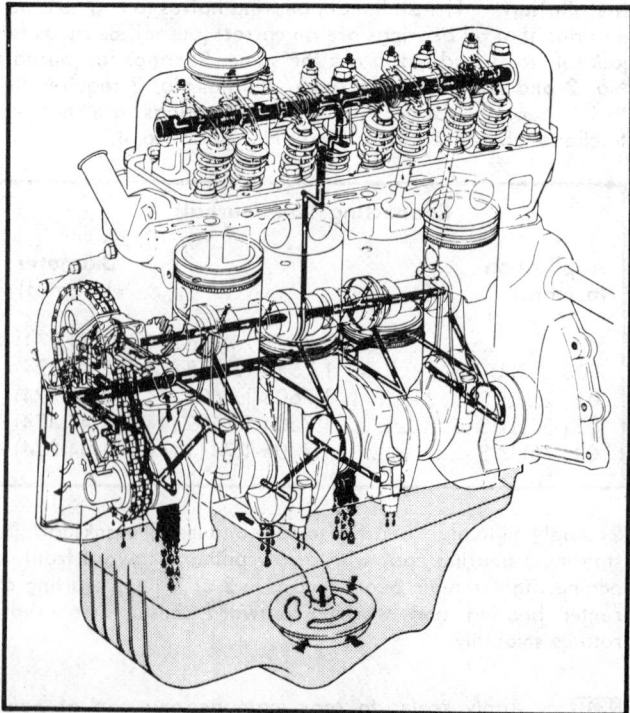

Fig. 9   Engine Oiling System

210 & 310 4-CYLINDER (Cont.)

by camshaft. Oil pump feeds oil from pan to full flow oil filter. Oil is then pumped into main oil gallery of crankcase where it is distributed to crankshaft journals, timing chain tensioner and squirter that lubricates timing chain.

Oil is circulated from crankshaft main bearing journals to camshaft journals and from center camshaft journal to rocker arm shaft to lubricate rocker arms and valves. Cylinder walls and piston pins are lubricated by oil squirted from squirt hole in connecting rod.

OIL PUMP

Removal & Installation — Place suitable drain pan under oil pump/filter assembly and remove oil filter with oil filter wrench. Remove 3 pump mounting bolts. Take out bolt securing cover to body and check all clearances with a feeler gauge. If beyond wear limit replace entire pump assembly. To install, reverse removal procedure.

Oil Pump Specifications	
Application	Wear Limit In. (mm)
Rotor-to-Rotor Side Clearance	.0024 (.06)
Rotor-to-Tip Clearance	.0079 (.20)
Rotor-to-Pump Body	.0197 (.50)
Regulator Valve Spring	
Free Length	1.71 (43.49)
Length at 8.09 lbs. (3.67 kg)	1.19 (30.3)

ENGINE COOLING

WATER PUMP

Removal & Installation — Drain coolant. On 310, loosen belt and remove fan and pulley. On 210, loosen bolts retaining shroud to radiator and remove shroud. On air conditioned 210 models, remove fan blade from torque coupling and remove torque coupling and pulley from hub. On all models, remove water pump and gasket from front cover. To install, use new gasket and reverse removal procedure. Be sure to clean gasket contact surfaces.

Thermostat — Opens at 180°F (82°C).

Cooling System Capacity	
Application	Quantity
210	
With Recovery Tank	6.0 quarts
Without Recovery Tank	5.5 quarts
310	6.0 quarts

ENGINE SPECIFICATIONS

GENERAL SPECIFICATIONS

Year	Displ.		Carburetor	HP at RPM	Torque (Ft. Lbs. at RPM)	Compr. Ratio	Bore		Stroke	
	cu. ins.	cc					in.	mm	in.	mm
1981										
A12A	75.5	1237	1 x 2-Bbl.	.....	.....	8.5:1	2.95	75	2.76	70
A14	85.2	1397	1 x 2-Bbl.	.....	.....	8.9:1	2.99	76	3.03	77
A15	90.9	1488	1 x 2-Bbl.	.....	.....	8.9:1	2.99	76	3.23	82

VALVES

Engine & Valve	Head Diam. In. (mm)	Face Angle	Seat Angle	Seat Width In. (mm)	Stem Diameter In. (mm)	Stem Clearance In. (mm)	Valve Lift In. (mm)
All							
Int.	1.38 (35)	45.5°	45.5°	.059 (1.5)	.3134-.3140 (7.960-7.975)	.0006-.0018 (.015-.045)	.....
Exh.	1.18 (30)	45.5°	45.5°	.075 (1.9)	.3128-.3134 (7.945-7.960)	.0016-.0028 (.040-.070)	.....

Datsun Engines

210 & 310 4-CYLINDER (Cont.)
ENGINE SPECIFICATIONS (Cont.)

VALVE SPRINGS

Engine	Free Length In. (mm)	PRESSURE Lbs. @ In. (kg @ mm)	
		Valve Closed	Valve Open
All	1.831 (46.5)	....	56.4@1.189 25.6@30.2

VALVE TIMING

Engine	INTAKE		EXHAUST	
	Open (BTDC)	Close (ABDC)	Open (BBDC)	Close (ATDC)
All	14°	50°	56°	12°

PISTONS, PINS, RINGS

Engine	PISTONS Clearance In. (mm)	PINS Piston Fit In. (mm)	Rod Fit In. (mm)	Rings	RINGS End Gap In. (mm)	Side Clearance In. (mm)
All	.0010-.0018 (.025-.045)	.0003-.0005 (.008-.012)	.0007-.0014① (.017-.035)	1	.0079-.0138 (.20-.35)	.0016-.0028 (.04-.07)
				2	.0059-.0118 (.15-.30)	.0012-.0024 (.03-.06)
				Oil	.0118-.0354 (.30-.90)	snug

① — Interference fit.

CRANKSHAFT MAIN & CONNECTING ROD BEARINGS

Engine	MAIN BEARINGS Journal Diam. In. (mm)	Clearance In. (mm)	Thrust Bearing	Crankshaft End Play In. (mm)	CONNECTING ROD BEARINGS Journal Diam. In. (mm)	Clearance In. (mm)	Side Play In. (mm)
A15 w/Man. Trans.	1.9663-1.9671 (49.94-49.96)	.0022-.0029 (.055-.073)	No. 3	.0020-.0059 (.050-.150)	1.7698-1.7706 (44.95-44.97)	.0015-.0031 (.038-.079)	.004-.008 (.1-.2)
All Others	1.9663-1.9671 (49.94-49.96)	.0010-.0035 (.026-.090)	No. 3	.0020-.0059 (.050-.150)	1.7698-1.7706 (44.95-44.97)	.0012-.0031 (.030-.079)	.004-.008 (.1-.2)

CAMSHAFT

Engine	Journal Diam. In. (mm)	Clearance In. (mm)	Lobe Lift In. (mm)
All No. 1	1.7237-1.7242 (43.78-43.80)	.0015-.0024 (.037-.060)	.....
2	1.7041-1.7046 (43.28-43.30)	.0011-.0020 (.027-.050)	.....
3	1.6844-1.6849 (42.78-42.80)	.0016-.0025 (.040-.063)	.....
4	1.6647-1.6652 (42.28-42.30)	.0011-.0020 (.027-.050)	.....
5	1.6224-1.6229 (41.21-41.22)	.0015-.0024 (.037-.060)	.....

TIGHTENING SPECIFICATIONS

Application	Ft. Lbs. (N·m)
Cylinder Head	51-54 (69-73)
Connecting Rod	23-27 (31-37)
Main Bearing Caps	36-43 (49-59)
Camshaft Sprocket	29-35 (39-48)
Rocker Arm Shaft	14-18 (19-25)
Manifolds	11-14 (15-19)
Crankshaft Pulley	108-145 (147-197)
Flywheel	58-65 (79-88)
Engine Mounts	14-18 (19-25)

	INCH Lbs. (N·m)
Camshaft Lock Plate	35-43 (4-5)
Timing Chain Tensioner	52-70 (6-8)
Front Cover	43-61 (5-7)
Oil Pump	78-121 (9-14)
Water Pump	78-120 (9-14)

200SX, 510 & PICKUP 4-CYLINDER

ENGINE CODING

ENGINE IDENTIFICATION

Engine number is stamped on left side of cylinder block on 200SX and Pickup models and right side of block on 510 models.

Engine Identification	
Application	**Code**
200SX	Z20E
510	Z20S
Pickup	Z22

ENGINE & CYLINDER HEAD

ENGINE

NOTE — *It is recommended that engine and transmission be removed as a unit. Engine can then be separated from transmission.*

Removal (200SX) — **1)** Reduce fuel pressure by disconnecting harness connector at upper-right fuel pump relay while engine is running. After stalling occurs, crank engine 2 or 3 times. Turn ignition to "OFF" and reconnect harness connector.

2) Mark hood and hinges for alignment on reassembly, then remove hood. Disconnect battery ground cable. Drain cooling system, transmission and crankcase. Disconnect all engine-to-chassis cables, hoses and wires.

3) On models with air conditioning, dismount compressor by removing mounting bolts and moving compressor aside toward fender. DO NOT discharge gas from compressor or system or separate refrigerant lines. Hold compressor out of way with wire to prevent interference with engine removal.

4) On models with power steering, dismount steering pump by removing belt and mounting bolts. Move aside toward fender and secure with wire to prevent interference with engine removal. DO NOT allow oil to drain from pump.

5) On manual transmission models, detach rubber boot, remove nut from shift lever and remove shift lever. On automatic transmission models, disconnect joint between control lever and selector rod. Remove oil cooler lines. On all models, remove radiator hoses, shroud and radiator.

6) Disconnect speedometer cable, downshift solenoid and inhibitor switch wires. On manual transmission models, remove clutch operating cylinder. On automatic transmission models, disconnect vacuum hose. On all models, mark for reassembly and remove propeller shaft. Remove front exhaust pipe.

7) Plug end of transmission. Attach a lifting hoist to engine and raise enough to take weight off engine mounts. Remove front and rear engine mounting bolts. Pull engine forward and carefully remove engine and transmission as an assembly.

Removal (510) — **1)** Disconnect battery ground cable. Drain cooling system, transmission and crankcase. Mark hood and hinges for alignment on reassembly, then remove hood. Remove grille.

2) Remove radiator hoses. Disconnect oil cooler lines and remove splash board on models with automatic transmission.

Disconnect inhibitor switch, downshift solenoid and engine ground cable wire connections.

3) Remove radiator and shroud. Remove all hoses and tubes to air cleaner, then remove air cleaner. Disconnect all engine-to-chassis cables, hoses and wires. Remove EGR vacuum reservoir tank and EGR valve.

4) On models with air conditioning, dismount compressor by removing mounting bolts and moving compressor aside toward fender. DO NOT discharge gas from compressor or system or separate refrigerant lines. Hold compressor out of way with wire to prevent interference with engine removal.

5) Disconnect speedometer cable. On manual transmission models, detach rubber boot, remove nut from shift lever and remove shift lever. Remove clutch operating cylinder. On automatic transmission models, disconnect joint between control lever and selector rod.

6) Remove front exhaust pipe. Mark for reassembly and remove propeller shaft. Plug end of transmission. Attach a lifting hoist to engine and raise enough to take weight off engine mounts. Remove front and rear engine mounting bolts. Pull engine forward and carefully remove engine and transmission as an assembly.

Removal (Pickup) — **1)** Disconnect battery ground cable. Drain cooling system, transmission and crankcase. Mark hood and hinges for reassembly, then remove hood. Remove all hoses and tubes to air cleaner, then remove air cleaner. Disconnect all engine-to-chassis cables, hoses and wires.

2) On models with air conditioning, dismount compressor by removing mounting bolts and moving compressor aside toward fender. DO NOT discharge gas from compressor or system or separate refrigerant lines. Hold compressor out of way with wire to prevent interference with engine removal.

3) On manual transmission models, detach rubber boot, remove nut from shift lever and remove shift lever. Remove clutch operating cylinder. On automatic transmission models, disconnect joint between control lever and selector rod. Remove oil cooler lines.

4) Remove radiator hoses, shroud and radiator. Disconnect speedometer cable and all switch wires on transmission case. Remove parking brake cable. Disconnect vacuum hose and oil pipes on automatic transmission models.

5) On 2WD models, mark for reassembly and remove propeller shaft. On 4WD models, remove front propeller shaft and pre-propeller shaft from transfer case. Remove front differential mounting bolts. On all models, remove front exhaust pipe and plug end of transmission.

6) Attach a lifting hoist to engine and raise enough to take weight off engine mounts. Remove front and rear engine mounting bolts. Remove differential mounting crossmember (4WD). Pull engine forward and carefully remove engine and transmission as an assembly.

Installation (All Models) — Replace any rubber engine mounts showing signs of deterioration or separation. Ensure proper placement of all engine mountings. Reverse removal procedures to complete installation.

CYLINDER HEAD

Removal — **1)** Reduce fuel pump pressure (200SX). Disconnect battery ground cable. Drain cooling system. Disconnect spark plug wires from spark plugs. Remove radiator and heater hoses. Disconnect drive belts, alternator bracket and adjusting bar. Move alternator aside.

200SX, 510 & PICKUP 4-CYLINDER (Cont.)

2) Remove fan, pulley and water pump. If equipped with air conditioning and/or power steering, remove as outlined in engine removal procedure. Disconnect throttle linkage. Remove air cleaner. Disconnect all cables, hoses and wires running from cylinder head to chassis or engine. Disconnect all hoses and vacuum lines from intake manifold to cylinder head or engine block.

3) Remove fuel pump, carburetor (510 and Pickup), and intake manifold. Remove EGR tube on all models. Remove air induction tubes on 510 and Pickup. Remove front exhaust pipe, exhaust manifold and rocker cover.

4) Turn crankshaft so No. 1 piston is at TDC on compression stroke. Paint aligning marks on timing chain and camshaft sprocket to aid in installation.

5) Remove camshaft sprocket and use retainer tool (KV10105800) to support timing chain as shown in Fig. 1. Remove cylinder head attaching bolts in reverse of sequence shown in Fig. 2. Remove cylinder head.

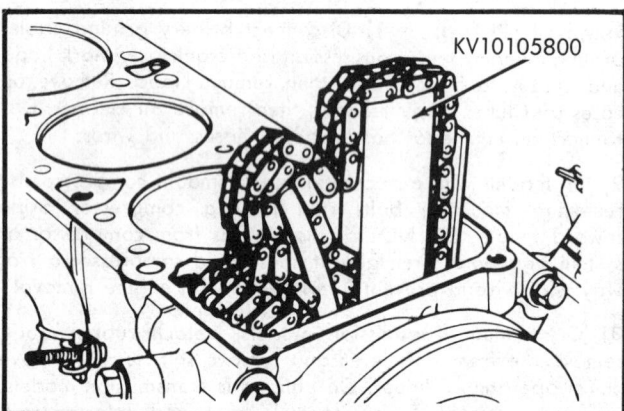

Fig. 1 Holding Timing Chain with Special Support Tool

Installation — 1) Ensure that mating surfaces of cylinder head and block are clean, then install cylinder head and gasket without sealer. Number 1 piston should be at TDC on compression stroke and camshaft sprocket location notch and plate oblong groove aligned.

2) Insert head bolts and tighten No. 1 and No. 2 to 14 ft. lbs. (19 N·m). Install and align sprockets and timing chain. Install remaining components in reverse order of removal, using new seals, gaskets and sealant where required.

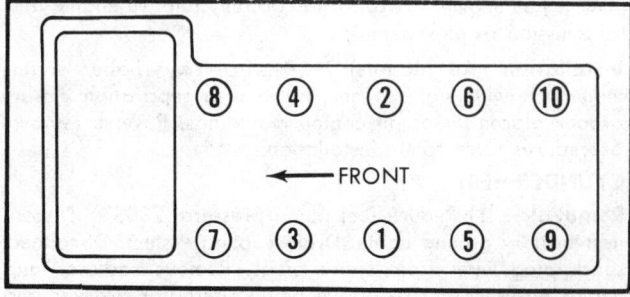

Fig. 2 Cylinder Head Tightening Sequence

3) Tighten head bolts in several steps in the sequence illustrated in Fig. 2 to final specified torque. Recheck torque after engine has been running for several minutes.

CAMSHAFT

CAMSHAFT

Removal — With cylinder head removed, evenly loosen rocker arm bolts from outside in sequence. DO NOT remove bolts from each end of rocker arm shaft or assembly will spring apart. Remove rocker arm assembly. Carefully remove camshaft.

Installation — Install camshaft on cylinder head with front camshaft dowel pin facing up. Install rocker arm assembly aligning to dowel pin on cylinder head. Place cylinder head on wooden blocks to allow for valve space. Tighten rocker arm bolts in 2 or 3 steps in outward sequence from center bracket.

CAMSHAFT BEARINGS

Measure inner diameter of camshaft bearing and outer diameter of camshaft journal. If wear or damage is excessive, replace cylinder head assembly.

ENGINE FRONT COVER

Removal — With engine removed from vehicle and mounted on engine stand, remove oil pump and drive spindle. Remove front cover attaching bolts and front cover.

Installation — Apply sealant at mating corners of oil pan, cylinder head and front cover. Oil seal should be coated with engine oil before installation in cover and before cover is installed. Use new gasket and install cover.

NOTE — *Check height difference between cylinder block and front cover upper face. Difference must not exceed .006" (.15 mm).*

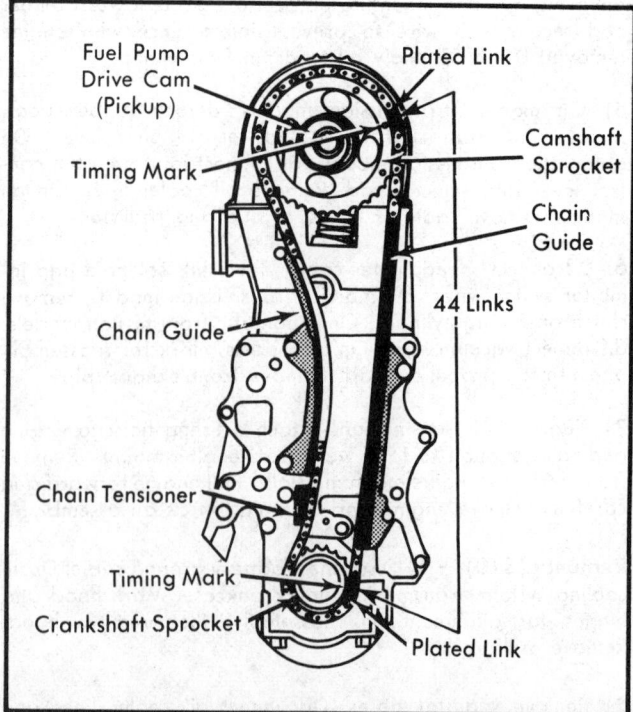

Fig. 3 Timing Chain and Sprocket Alignment

Datsun Engines

200SX, 510 & PICKUP 4-CYLINDER (Cont.)

TIMING CHAIN & GEARS

Removal — Remove valve cover. On Pickup and 510, remove fuel pump and fuel pump drive cam. Remove camshaft drive sprocket and engine front cover. Remove timing chain tensioner and guides. Remove timing chain, oil thrower, crankshaft worm gear and chain drive sprocket.

Installation — Ensure that crankshaft and camshaft keys point upward. Set timing chain so that mating marks align with crankshaft and camshaft sprockets. There are 44 chain links between the 2 timing marks. Complete installation in reverse order of removal.

VALVES

VALVE ARRANGEMENT

Right Side — All Intake
Left Side — All Exhaust

NOTE — *Camshaft MUST be removed to take out valves. See Camshaft Removal & Installation in this Section.*

VALVES

Removal — With camshaft removed, remove valves using valve spring compressor (ST12070000). Keep disassembled parts in order. Check each valve for worn, damaged or deformed heads or stems.

Installation — Install valve spring seat and oil seal on valve guide. Place springs in position with close-coiled (painted) end toward cylinder head. Use compressor and install valve collets and keepers.

VALVE GUIDE SERVICE

1) Measure clearance between valve stem and valve guide, with aid of micrometer and hole gauge. Check diameter of valve stem in three places: top, center, and bottom.

2) Insert hole gauge in valve guide bore and measure at center. Subtract highest reading of valve stem diameter from valve guide bore to obtain clearance.

NOTE — *As a quick check, a valve may be inserted into valve guide and moved either left or right, (parallel with rocker arm). If tip moves .008" (.2 mm) or more, clearance is beyond maximum limit of .004" (.1 mm).*

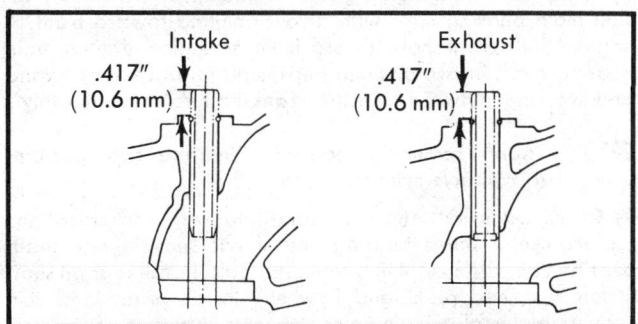

Fig. 4   Intake and Exhaust Valve Guides

VALVE SEAT INSERTS

1) Check valve seats for pitting at valve contact surface. Valve seat inserts of .02" (.5 mm) oversize are available if necessary. To remove old inserts, machine should be set so that boring cannot continue beyond bottom face of insert recess in cylinder head.

2) Machine cylinder head recess diameter in concentric circles to valve guide center so that insert will have correct fit. Heat cylinder head to 300-400°F (150-200°C) and install insert, making sure that it seats on bottom face of recess.

3) Valve seats should be cut or ground to correct face angle and seat width and to head diameter of valve to be installed.

VALVE SPRING INSTALLED HEIGHT

With valves closed, inner spring should have a height of 1.378" (35.0 mm) and outer spring should have a height of 1.575" (40.0 mm). See specification for pressure with valves opened or closed.

VALVE ADJUSTMENT

NOTE — *Valves should be adjusted with engine at normal operating temperature. Cold specifications are provided for initial settings after assembly.*

All Models — Turn engine until high point on No. 1 cam lobe points down. Adjust intake valve of No. 1 and No. 2 cylinder; exhaust valve of No. 3 and No. 4. Turn engine until high point on No. 1 cam lobe points up and adjust remaining valves.

Valve Adjustment Specifications		
Valve	**Hot**	**①Cold**
Intake	.012" (.30 mm)	.008" (.21 mm)
Exhaust	.012" (.30 mm)	.009" (.23 mm)
① — Use for initial settings only.		

PISTONS, PINS & RINGS

PISTON & ROD ASSEMBLY

Removal — Remove connecting rod nuts and bearing caps. Push piston and rod assembly out top of cylinder, using care not to damage any bearing surface. Retain all components in proper order for reassembly.

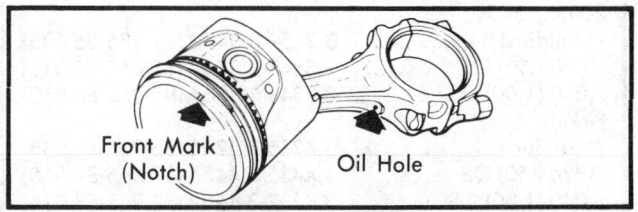

Fig. 5   Piston and Rod Assembly Installation Features

Datsun Engines

200SX, 510 & PICKUP 4-CYLINDER (Cont.)

Installation — Reassemble piston and rod so that oil hole in connecting rod is facing right side of engine and notch on top of piston is facing forward. Install connecting rod on original journal with rod and cap marks on same side. Tighten connecting rod nuts and check rod side play.

FITTING PISTONS

1) Measure cylinder bores for wear or taper at top, bottom and middle on thrust face and at 90° to thrust face. If excessive wear is found rebore cylinder and install oversize pistons. Oversize pistons are available as shown in table.

2) When boring cylinders, use cylinder order of 2-4-1-3 to prevent heat distortion. After honing cylinder to final fit, check piston fit using spring tension pull scale. A force of .4-3.3 lbs. (.2-1.5 kg) should be obtained extracting a .0016" (.04 mm) feeler gauge.

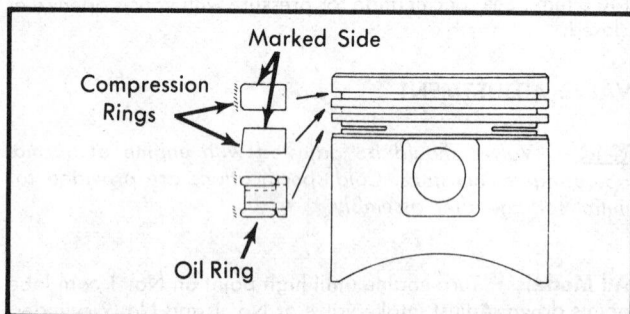

Fig. 6   Installation Order of Piston Rings

3) Measure piston ring end gap and side clearance and replace as necessary. Install rings on pistons with end gaps 180° apart and so no end gap is in line with thrust face. Install rings with top mark facing upward.

NOTE — *If only piston ring is to be replaced, measure gap at bottom of bore. Oversize rings are available in .020" (.50 mm) and .040" (1.00 mm).*

PISTON PINS

Pin must be a tight press fit in connecting rod, pressing force is from ½ to 1½ tons. When pressing pin into connecting rod, oil pin and press in so oil jet of connecting rod large end is directed toward right side of cylinder block.

Piston Specifications	
Application In. (mm)	**Piston Size In. (mm)**
200SX, 510	
Standard	3.3459-3.3478 (84-985-85.035)
.020 (.50) OS	3.3648-3.3667 (85.465-85.515)
.040 (1.00) OS	3.3844-3.3864 (85-965-86.015)
Pickup	
Standard	3.4246-3.4266 (86.985-87.035)
.020 (.50) OS	3.4435-3.4455 (87.465-87.515)
.040 (1.00) OS	3.4632-3.4652 (87.965-88.015)

CRANKSHAFT MAIN & CONNECTING ROD BEARINGS

CRANKSHAFT

Removal — With engine removed from vehicle, remove cylinder head and oil pan. Remove flywheel and rear plate. Remove oil strainer, oil pump and drive spindle. Remove front cover, chain tensioner, chain slack side guide, and timing chain. Remove oil thrower, crankcase worm gear, and timing drive sprocket. Remove piston and rod assemblies. Remove main bearing caps using suitable puller (KV101041SO) to remove center and rear main bearing caps.

NOTE — *Keep all main bearing caps in order to aid in reassembly. Remove rear oil seal, remove crankshaft.*

Inspection — Check all crankshaft journals for scoring, wear or cracks. Taper and out-of-round on all journals must not exceed .001" (.025 mm). Check crankshaft for bend using dial indicator at center journal of crankshaft. If bend exceeds .002" (.05 mm), which is ½ of indicator reading, replace crankshaft. Check main driveshaft pilot bearing at rear of crankshaft for wear or damage and replace if necessary.

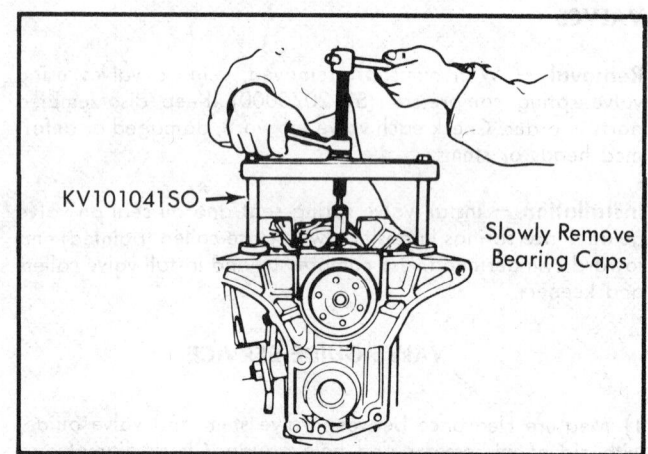

Fig. 7   Rear Main Bearing Cap Removal

Installation — 1) Install main bearing halves to engine block ensuring that all bearings are on correct journal. Journal No. 3 requires a thrust bearing. Bearing for No. 1 is the same as for No. 5 and bearing for No. 2 is the same as for No. 4. Upper and lower bearings are not interchangeable. Upper bearings have an oil groove.

2) Apply oil to main bearing surface and install crankshaft. Install main bearing caps with arrow pointing toward front of engine. Shift crankshaft toward front of engine, tighten main bearing caps, in two or three steps, starting at center bearing and working outwards. Ensure crankshaft rotates smoothly.

NOTE — *Apply sealer to rear main bearing cap at point where cap contacts cylinder block.*

3) Check crankshaft end play, and if not within specifications replace center thrust bearing. Install side seals in rear main bearing cap, after applying sealer to seals. Install oil seal. Install rear end plate and flywheel. Install piston and rod assemblies. Install remaining components in reverse of removal procedure

200SX, 510 & PICKUP 4-CYLINDER (Cont.)

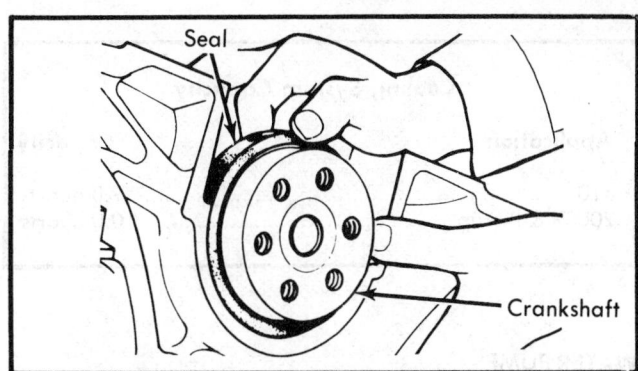

Fig. 8 Rear Oil Seal Removal

MAIN BEARINGS

1) Check all bearings for scoring or wear and replace if damage is found. Clean oil from crankshaft and place a strip of Plastigage on crankshaft journal. Install main bearing cap, with bearing installed, and tighten to 33-40 ft.lbs. (4.5-5.5 mkg).

NOTE — *Plastigage should run parallel with crankshaft and not block oil hole. Do not turn crankshaft while Plastigage is inserted.*

2) Remove cap and measure width of Plastigage at widest point using gauge provided. If clearance is not to specifications, replace bearings. Bearings are available in undersizes of .01" (.25 mm), .02" (.50 mm), .03" (.75 mm) and .04" (1.00 mm).

CONNECTING ROD BEARINGS

Check connecting rod bearings in same manner as main bearings using Plastigage. Tighten connecting rod caps to 33-40 ft. lbs. (4.5-5.5 mkg). Bearings are available in undersizes of .01" (.25 mm), .02" (.50 mm) and .03" (.75 mm). Check for clearance of .001-.002" (.025-.055 mm) when installing new bearings. Maximum wear limit for old bearings is .005" (.12 mm).

ENGINE OILING

Crankcase Capacity (With Filter)	
Application	**Capacity**
All Models	4.5 quarts

Oil Filter — Full-flow, disposable cartridge.

Oil Pressure — 50-60 psi. (3.5-4.2 kg/cm²) at 3000 rpm.

ENGINE OILING SYSTEM

Oil drawn from pan passes through screen to oil pump and is delivered to oil filter and to main oil gallery. Main oil gallery supplies oil to crankshaft main bearings and drilled passages in crankshaft. Oil sprayed from jet holes on connecting rods lubricates cylinders and piston pins. Oil from main gallery lubricates chain tensioner and timing chain. Center hole in crankshaft, center bearing feeds camshaft bearings on cylin-der head. Valve rocker mechanism is lubricated through oil gallery in camshaft and through a small channel at base circle portion of each cam. Rocker arms and valves are lubricated through small holes in oil pipe.

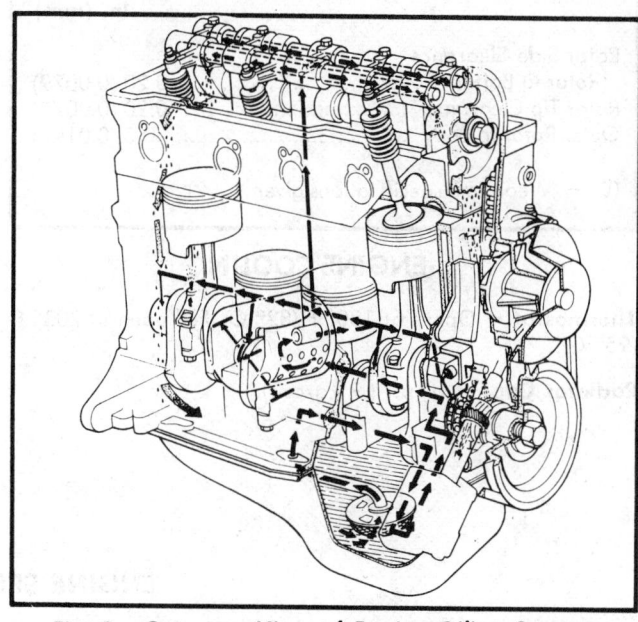

Fig. 9 Cutaway View of Engine Oiling System

OIL PUMP

Removal — Pump assembly is installed at bottom right of front cover and held in place by four bolts. Pump is driven by helical gear on crankshaft and in turn drives distributor shaft. With No. 1 cylinder at TDC on the compression stroke, remove retaining bolts and then remove oil pump and drive spindle assembly.

Inspection — Remove cover from oil pump body, remove gears. Wash parts with cleaning solvent, inspect for wear or damage. Make sure clearances are to specification. Pump is serviced as an assembly only. Replace pump if any part is worn or damaged.

Installation — Make sure that distributor rotor is in same position as it was before removal. Fill pump housing with oil and align punch mark on drive spindle with hole in pump. See *Fig. 10*. Using a new gasket, install oil pump and drive spindle assembly. Make sure that drive spindle tip securely fits distributor fitting hole. Tighten all bolts.

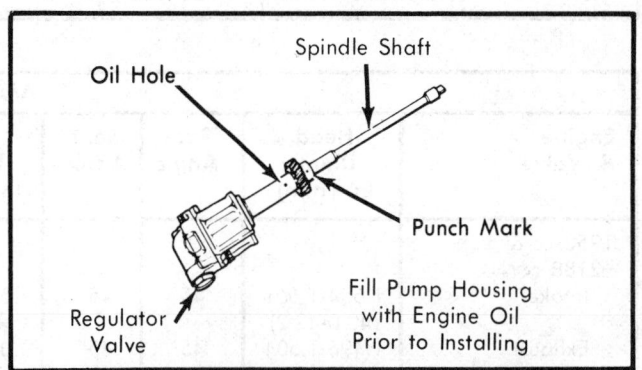

Fig. 10 Aligning Oil Pump Timing Marks

Datsun Engines

200SX, 510 & PICKUP 4-CYLINDER (Cont.)

Oil Pump Specifications

Application	①Clearance In. (mm)
Rotor Side Clearance (Rotor to Bottom Cover)	0.20 (0.0079)
Rotor Tip Clearance	0.20 (0.0079)
Outer Rotor to Body	0.5 (0.0197)

① — Wear limit specifications given.

ENGINE COOLING

Thermostat — Opens at 180° F (82° C). Full open at 203° F (95° C).

Radiator Cap — 13 psi (.9 kg/cm²).

Cooling System Capacity

Application	Capacity
510	9.0 quarts
200SX & Pickup	10.0 quarts

WATER PUMP

Centrifugal type pump with aluminum body. To remove drain cooling system and remove upper and lower radiator hoses, shroud, fan, belts and pulley. Remove pump attaching bolts and remove water pump.

ENGINE SPECIFICATIONS

GENERAL SPECIFICATIONS

Year	Displ. cu. ins.	Displ. cc	Carburetor	HP at RPM	Torque (Ft. Lbs. at RPM)	Compr. Ratio	Bore in.	Bore mm	Stroke in.	Stroke mm
1981										
Pickup	133.5	2188	2-Bbl.	.....	.....	8.5-1	3.43	87	3.62	92
200SX	119.1	1952	Fuel Inj.①	.....	.....	8.5-1	3.35	85	3.39	86
510	119.1	1952	2-Bbl.	.....	.....	8.5-1	3.35	85	3.39	86

① — Electronic Fuel Injection

CRANKSHAFT MAIN & CONNECTING ROD BEARINGS

Engine	MAIN BEARINGS Journal Diam. In. (mm)	Clearance In. (mm)	Thrust Bearing	Crankshaft End Play In. (mm)	CONNECTING ROD BEARINGS Journal Diam. In. (mm)	Clearance In. (mm)	Side Play In. (mm)
1952 cc & 2188 cc	2.1631-2.1636 (54.942-54.955)	.0008-.0024 (.020-.062)	No. 3	.002-.007 (.05-.18)	1.9670-1.9675 (49.961-49.974)	.001-.002 (.025-.055)	.0079-.0118 (.20-.30)

VALVES

Engine & Valve	Head Diam. In. (mm)	Face Angle	Seat Angle	Seat Width In. (mm)	Stem Diameter In. (mm)	Stem Clearance In. (mm)	Valve Lift In. (mm)
1952 cc & 2188 cc							
Intake	1.654-1.661 (42.0-42.2)	45°	45°	.071-.094 (1.8-2.4)	.3136-.3142 (7.965-7.980)	.0008-.0021 (.020-.053)	.....
Exhaust	1.496-1.504 (38.0-38.2)	45°	45°	.059-.075 (1.5-1.9)	.3128-.3134 (7.945-7.960)	.0016-.0029 (.040-.073)	.....

Datsun Engines

200SX, 510 & PICKUP 4-CYLINDER (Cont.)

ENGINE SPECIFICATIONS (Cont.)

	PISTONS, PINS, RINGS						
	PISTONS	PINS			RINGS		
Engine	Clearance In. (mm)	Piston Fit In. (mm)	①Rod Fit In. (mm)	Rings	End Gap In. (mm)	Side Clearance In. (mm)
1952 cc & 2188 cc	.0010-.0018 (.025-.045)	.0002-.0005 (.006-.013)	.0006-.0014 (.015-.035)	No. 1	.010-.016 (.25-.40)	.0016-.0029 (.040-.073)
				No. 2	.006-.012 (.15-.30)	.0012-.0025 (.030-.063)
				Oil	.012-.035 (.30-.90)	.....

① — Interference fit.

VALVE SPRINGS			
Engine	Free Length In. (mm)	PRESSURE Lbs. @ In. (kg @ mm)	
		Valve Closed	Valve Open
1952 cc & 2188 cc Inner	1.736 (44.10)	24.3@1.378 (11.0@35.0)	.....
Outer	1.959 (49.77)	50.7@1.575 (23@40.0)	.....

CAMSHAFT			
Engine	Journal Diam. In. (mm)	Clearance In. (mm)	Lobe Lift In. (mm)
1952 cc & 2188 cc	1.2967-1.2974 (32.935-32.955)	.0018-.0035 (.045-.090)	.008" (0.2)

TIGHTENING SPECIFICATIONS

Application	Ft. Lbs. (N·m)
Cylinder Head	51-58 (69-79)
Connecting Rods	33-40 (45-54)
Flywheel	101-116 (137-158)
Main Bearings	33-40 (45-54)
Camshaft Sprocket	87-116 (118-158)
Crankshaft Pulley	87-116 (118-158)
Manifolds	12-15 (16-20)
Rocker Arm Nuts	12-16 (16-22)

Application	INCH Lbs. (N·m)
Front Cover 6 mm Bolts	35-86 (4-10)
8 mm Bolts	84-144 (10-16)

PICKUP 4-CYLINDER DIESEL

ENGINE CODING

ENGINE IDENTIFICATION

Engine serial number is located on the front right side of the cylinder block below mating surface with head. Diesel engines are identified by the code number SD22.

ENGINE & CYLINDER HEAD

ENGINE

NOTE — *It is recommended that engine and transmission be removed as a unit. Engine can then be separated from transmission assembly.*

Removal — 1) Disconnect battery ground cable, drain engine coolant, transmission and crankcase. Mark hood and hinges for reassembly, then remove hood. Remove all hoses and tubes to air cleaner, then remove air cleaner. Disconnect all engine-to-chassis cables, hoses and wires.

2) Remove transmission shift linkage. Detach rubber boot, remove nut from shift lever and remove shift lever. Remove clutch operating cylinder. Remove radiator hoses, shroud and radiator. Disconnect speedometer cable and all switch wires on transmission case. Remove parking brake cable.

3) Mark for reassembly and remove propeller shaft. Remove front exhaust pipe. Plug end of transmission. Attach a lifting hoist to engine and raise enough to take weight off engine mounts. Remove front and rear engine mounting bolts.

4) Turn steering all the way left or right so that suspension center link clears oil pan. Pull engine forward and carefully remove engine and transmission as an assembly.

Installation — Replace any rubber engine mounts showing signs of deterioration or separation. Ensure proper placement of all engine mountings. Reverse removal procedures to complete installation.

CYLINDER HEAD

Removal — 1) Disconnect battery ground cable. Drain cooling system. Remove all hoses and ducts from air cleaner, then remove air cleaner. Remove injection pump timer cover and injection pump timer. Remove fuel injection pump, injection tubes and nozzle assemblies. Remove rocker cover and alternator.

2) Remove drive belts, fan and water pump. Disconnect all hoses and vacuum lines from intake manifold to cylinder head or block. Remove intake and exhaust manifolds. Remove thermostat housing, oil filter and oil cooler assembly.

3) Remove rocker shaft assembly. Remove push rods and keep in correct order for installation. Remove cylinder head bolts, loosening in several steps in reverse order of tightening sequence. See *Fig. 1.* Remove cylinder head.

Installation — 1) Ensure that mating surfaces of cylinder block and head are clean. Install cylinder head and new gasket with new rubber "O" rings in water and oil passages. Use no sealer.

2) Insert head bolts and tighten (in sequence shown) in at least 2 steps. Install push rods in same position as before, twisting the rod to ensure proper seating in lifter. Install rocker shaft.

Tighten shaft bolts in 2 or 3 steps starting from the center and working out. Fully loosen rocker arm adjusting screws.

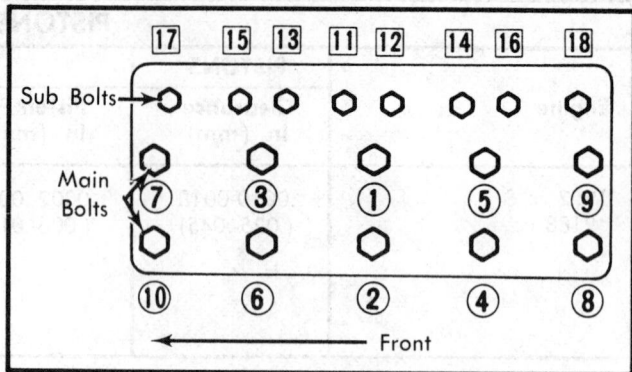

Fig. 1   Cylinder Head Tightening Sequence (Remove in Reverse Order)

3) Reverse removal procedure to complete installation. Adjust valves. After engine is warmed up, recheck head bolt torque.

CAMSHAFT

CAMSHAFT

NOTE — *Procedure must be performed with engine removed from vehicle.*

Removal — Remove cylinder head as outlined in previous section. Remove crank pulley and engine front cover. Remove oil pan and oil pump. Remove camshaft locating plate and, with engine inverted on stand, carefully remove camshaft.

Installation — Install camshaft carefully to avoid damaging cam bearings. Install remaining components in reverse of removal procedure and tighten all nuts and bolts.

CAMSHAFT BEARINGS

Measure inner diameter of camshaft bearing and outer diameter of camshaft journal. If wear or damage is excessive, replace bearings.

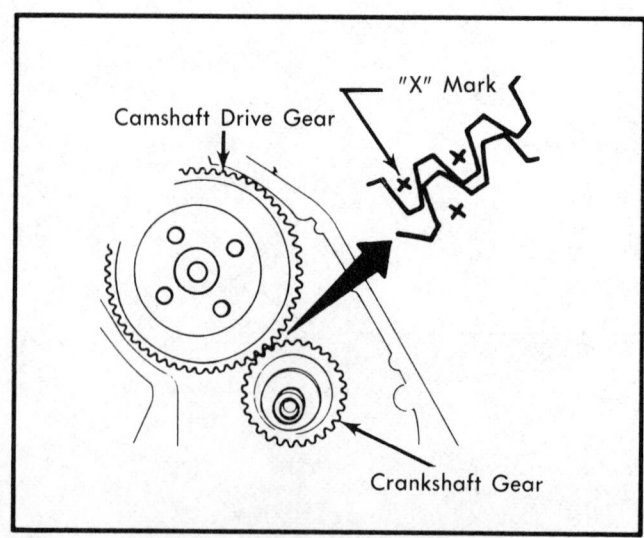

Fig. 2   Crankshaft Gear Installation

PICKUP 4-CYLINDER DIESEL (Cont.)

ENGINE FRONT COVER

Removal — To remove cover, follow camshaft removal procedures and then remove crankshaft gear. Remove 3 front cover retaining bolts and remove front cover.

Installation — Always use new gasket and oil seal when replacing front cover. Apply sealer to gasket and reverse removal procedures to install.

NOTE — *When replacing crankshaft gear, be sure to align the "X" mark on the gear between the 2 "X" marks on the camshaft gear.*

VALVES

VALVE ARRANGEMENT

E-I-I-E-E-I-I-E (Front to Rear)

VALVES

Removal — Remove cylinder head from engine block. Remove glow plugs. Remove valves using valve spring compressor (ST12070000). Remove valve stem oil seals. Keep disassembled parts in order. Check for worn or damaged valves. Replace as needed.

Installation — Always use new valve stem oil seals when valves are removed. Install valves and valve components using valve spring compressor. Make sure that the valve spring is installed with close coiled end (painted yellow) against cylinder head.

VALVE GUIDE SERVICE

1) Replaceable valve guides are not used in this engine. Measure clearance between valve stem and valve stem hole in head with micrometer and hole gauge. Check diameter of valve stem in three places: top, bottom and center.

2) Insert hole gauge in valve stem hole and measure at center. Subtract highest reading of valve stem diameter from valve stem hole to obtain clearance. If clearance exceeds maximum limits of .006" (.15 mm) for the intake valves or .008" (.20 mm) for the exhaust valves, oversize valves should be used and the valve stem holes reamed out to correct specifications.

Valve Stem Specifications

Stem Size In. (mm)	①Stem Diameter In. (mm)
Intake	
Standard	.3138-.3134 (7.970-7.985)
.008 (.2) O/S	.3217-.3222 (8.170-8.185)
.016 (.4) O/S	.3295-.3301 (8.370-8.385)
Exhaust	
Standard	.3128-.3134 (7.945-7.960)
.008 (.2) O/S	.3207-.3213 (8.145-8.160)
.016 (.4) O/S	.3285-.3291 (8.345-8.360)

① — Valve guide hole dimension should be between the stem diameter and .006" (.015 mm) greater.

VALVE SEAT INSERTS

1) Check valve seats for pitting or uneven wear at valve contact area. Reface seat if needed. Oversize exhaust valve seats of .008" (.2 mm) and .016" (.4 mm) are available.

2) To remove old inserts, use special seat removing tool (ST10830000). Place new valve seats on dry ice for about 5 minutes to cool. Heat cylinder head to about 175°F (80°C) and install valve seats on head with suitable tool (ST10820000). DO NOT touch valve seats with bare hands while cold.

3) Using a punch and hammer, secure new seat to head in at least 5 places. Make sure seat is punched in a new part of the head, not over previous marks.

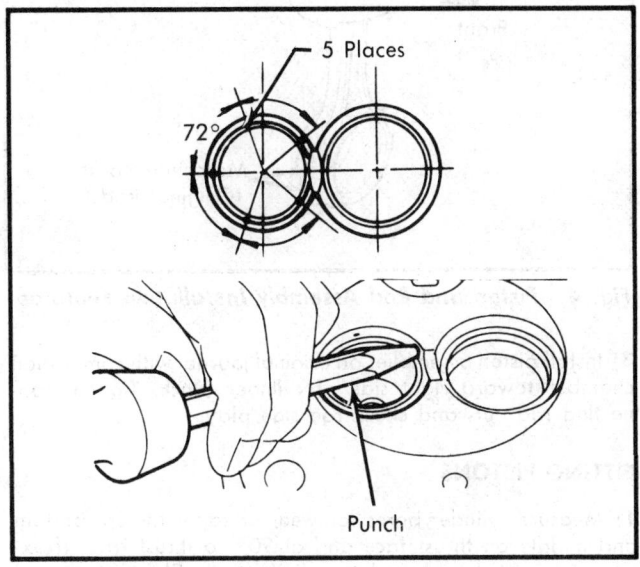

Fig. 3   Installing Valve Seat

VALVE SPRING INSTALLED HEIGHT

With valves closed, spring height should be 1.525" (39 mm). See specification chart for pressure with valves open or closed.

VALVE ADJUSTMENT

NOTE — *Valves should be adjusted with engine at normal operating temperature.*

With No. 1 cylinder at TDC on compression stroke, set clearances on No. 1 and No. 3 exhaust valves and No. 1 and No. 2 intake valves. Bring No. 4 cylinder to TDC on compression stroke and adjust remaining valves. Clearance should be .014" (.35 mm) on all valves, intake and exhaust.

PISTONS, PINS & RINGS

PISTON & ROD ASSEMBLY

Removal — Remove connecting rod nuts and bearing caps. Push piston and rod assembly out top of cylinder, using care not to damage any bearing surface. Retain all components in proper order for reassembly.

Installation — 1) Check connecting rods for cracking, bending or twisting. Replace as needed. Reassemble piston

PICKUP 4-CYLINDER DIESEL (Cont.)

and rod assembly so that the combustion chamber on the piston is opposite the matching marks on the connecting rod big end.

2) If replacement rods are used, which have no matching marks, install so that the slight offset of the rod, .06" (.15 mm), is toward the rear of the engine on cylinders No. 1 and 3, and toward the front of the engine on cylinders No. 2 and 4.

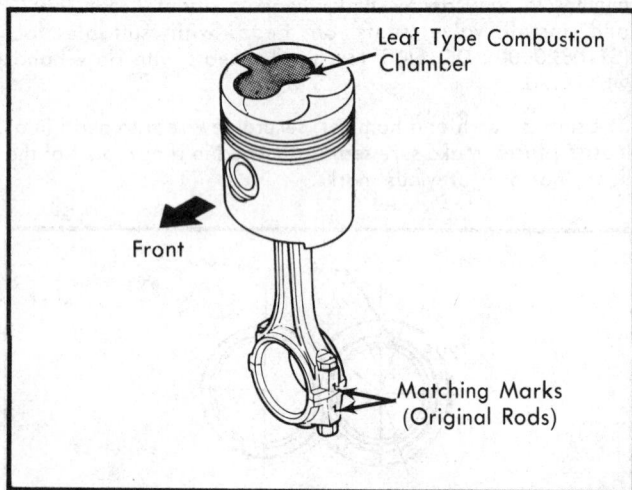

Fig. 4   Piston and Rod Assembly Installation Features

3) Install piston assemblies on original journal with combustion chamber toward right side of cylinder block. Tighten connecting rod nuts and check rod side play.

FITTING PISTONS

1) Measure cylinder bores for wear or taper at top, bottom and middle on thrust face and at 90° to thrust face. If excessive wear is found, replace cylinder liner. Check amount of liner projection from each cylinder. There should be less than .0020" (.05 mm) variation between cylinders.

2) Measure piston diameter 2.76" (70 mm) from top of piston. If diameter exceeds 3.264-3.266 (82.915-82.955 mm) by more than .006" (.15 mm), replace piston. After honing cylinder to final fit, install piston.

3) Check rod side clearance. If beyond .004-.008" (.1-.2 mm), replace connecting rod. Measure piston ring end gap and side clearance and replace as necessary. Install rings on pistons with end gaps 180° apart and so no end gap is in line with thrust face. Install rings with top mark facing upward.

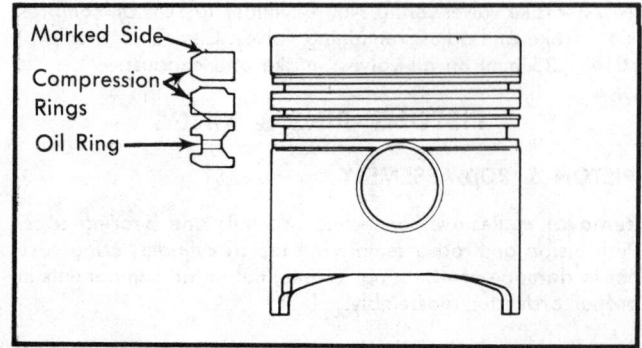

Fig. 5   Installation Order of Piston Rings

PISTON PINS

Piston pin is a full floating type. Clearance between piston and pin should be less than .0001" (.003 mm). If beyond this limit, replace piston and pin. To assemble piston, pin and connecting rod, immerse in oil bath at 175°F (80°C) and push in pin. Remove from oil and install snap rings.

CRANKSHAFT MAIN & CONNECTING ROD BEARINGS

CRANKSHAFT

Removal — With engine removed from vehicle, remove cylinder head and camshaft as previously outlined. Remove valve lifters and keep in correct order. Remove camshaft gear and engine front plate. Remove 2 oil jet bolts located on bottom right side of engine between 1st and 2nd main caps. Remove oil jet. Remove piston/rod assemblies and main bearing caps. Lift out crankshaft. Use special tool (ST16660000) to remove rear main bearing cap.

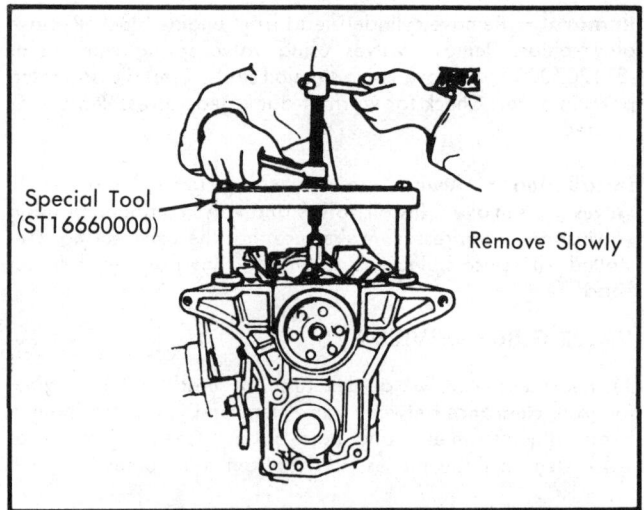

Fig. 6   Rear Main Bearing Cap Removal

Inspection — Check all bearing journals for scoring, excessive wear, cracks or plugged oil passages. Taper and out-of-round on all journals must not exceed .0004" (.01 mm). Check crankshaft for bend using dial indicator at center journal of crankshaft. If bend exceeds .004" (.1 mm) on dial, replace crankshaft. Check main driveshaft pilot bearing at rear of crankshaft for wear or damage and replace if necessary.

Installation — 1) Install main bearing halves to engine block ensuring that all bearings are on correct journal. All upper bearings have oil grooves and are not interchangeable with the lower bearing halves.

2) Install rear oil seals on main bearing cap and cylinder block so that they extend .020" (.5 mm) beyond block and bearing cap. Coat seal with grease where crankshaft will make contact. Apply oil to main bearing surfaces and install crankshaft. Install main bearing caps with "F" mark towards front of engine.

3) Apply sealer to rear main bearing cap at point where cap contacts cylinder block. Install cap by aligning the marks on cylinder block and main cap. Tighten main caps in several

PICKUP 4-CYLINDER DIESEL (Cont.)

steps, starting from center and working out. Ensure smooth crank rotation. Install crankshaft thrust washer at center journal with oil groove facing away from cap.

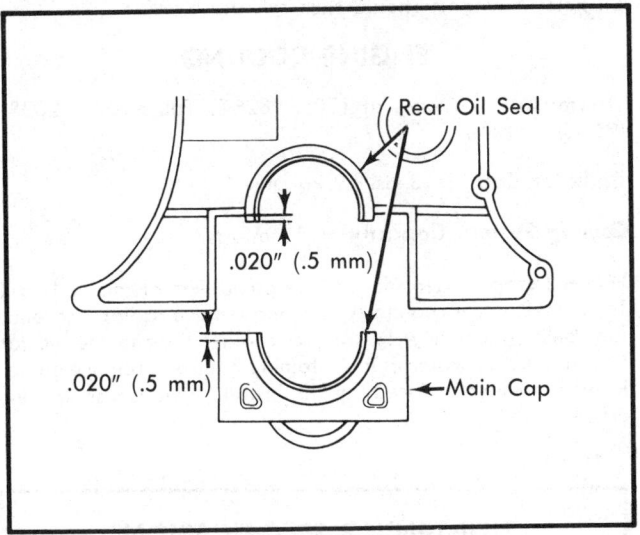

Fig. 7   Rear Oil Seal Installation

4) Install rear main cap side oil seal after coating with sealant. Install with groove in seal toward center, and leave seal protruding from block .020" (.5 mm). Measure crankshaft end play. If not to specification, replace thrust washer. Thrust washers are available in .008" (.2 mm) and .016" (.4 mm) oversize. Install remaining components in reverse of removal procedure.

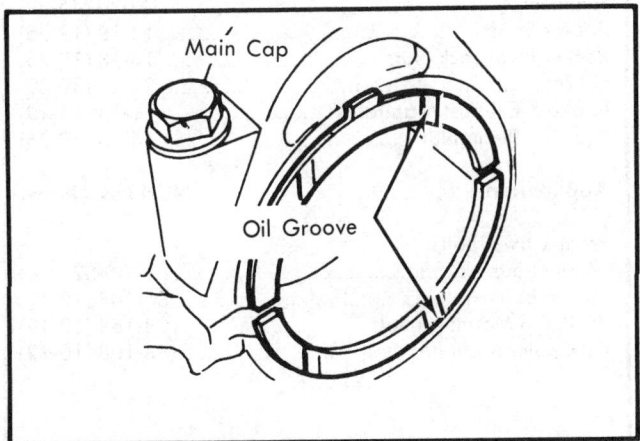

Fig. 8   Thrust Washer Installation

NOTE — *Make sure oil holes in oil jet are properly aligned.*

MAIN BEARINGS

1) Check all bearings for scoring or wear and replace if damage is found. Clean oil from crankshaft and place a strip of Plastigage on crankshaft journal. Install main bearing cap with bearing installed, and tighten to specifications.

NOTE — *Plastigage should run parallel with crankshaft and not block oil hole. Do not turn crankshaft while Plastigage is inserted.*

2) Remove cap and measure width of Plastigage at widest point using gauge provided. If clearance is not to specifica-

tions, replace bearings. Bearings are available in undersizes of .01" (.25 mm), .02" (.50 mm), .03" (.75 mm) and .04" (1.00 mm).

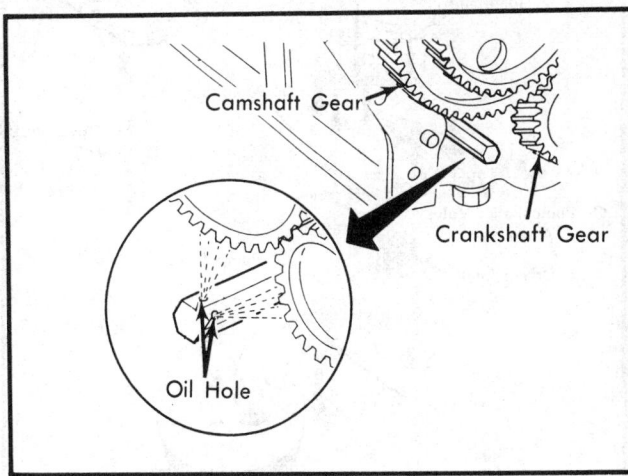

Fig. 9   Oil Jet Installation

CONNECTING ROD BEARINGS

Check connecting rod bearings in same manner as main bearings using Plastigage. Tighten connecting rod caps to specifications. Bearings are available in undersizes of .01" (.25 mm), .02" (.50 mm), .03" (.75 mm) and .04" (1.00 mm). Check for clearance of .001-.004" (.035-.093 mm) when installing new bearings. Maximum wear limit for old bearings is .006" (.15 mm).

ENGINE OILING

Crankshaft Capacity (with filter) — 6.5 quarts.

Oil Filter — Full-flow, disposable cartridge.

Oil Pressure — 45-55 psi. (3.1-3.7 kg/cm^2).

ENGINE OILING SYSTEM

Oil drawn from pan passes through screen to oil pump and is delivered to oil filter, oil cooler and main oil gallery. Main oil gallery supplies oil to crankshaft main bearings and drilled passages in crankshaft. Oil sprayed from oil jets lubricates drive gear assembly and cylinders and piston pins. Oil from main gallery lubricates injection pump, vacuum pump, camshaft and camshaft bearings. Valve rocker mechanism is lubricated through rocker shaft to rocker arms, down push rods to lifters.

OIL PUMP

Removal — Oil pump is located at bottom rear of engine, enclosed by oil pan. Pump is driven by helical gear on camshaft. Remove oil filter, oil pipe and oil cooler assembly. Remove cooler support and oil pump drive spindle. Drain crankcase,

Datsun Engines

PICKUP 4-CYLINDER DIESEL (Cont.)

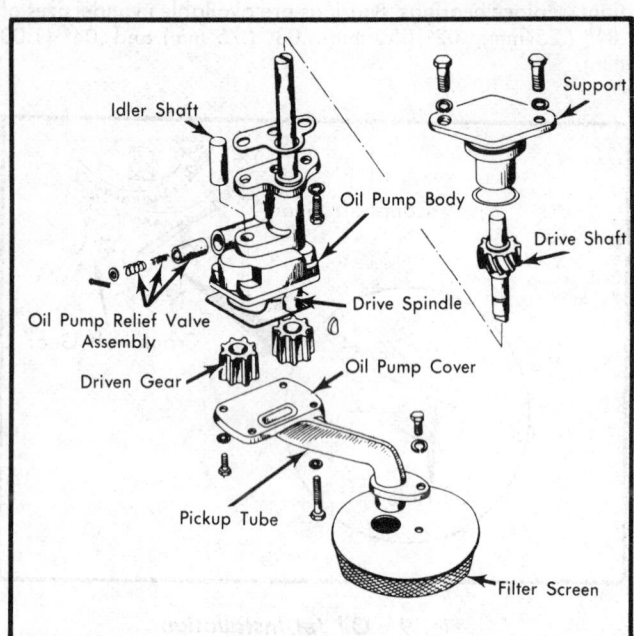

Fig. 10 Exploded View of Oil Pump & Pickup Tube

remove engine undercover and front suspension crossmember. Remove oil pan bolts and, with steering wheel all the way right or left, remove pan. Remove oil pump assembly.

Inspection — Disassemble oil pump and clean all parts thoroughly in clean solvent. Inspect for signs of unusual wear or damage. Check all clearances to specifications. Pump is serviced as an assembly only. Replace pump if any part is worn or damaged.

Oil Pump Specifications

Application	①Clearance In. (mm)
Gear Side Clearance (Gear to Bottom Cover)	.006 (.15)
Gear Tooth Clearance (Tooth to Body)	.01 (.25)
Gear Backlash	.02 (.50)
Shaft Ends to Bottom Cover	.020 (.50)

① — Wear limit specifications given.

Installation — Reverse removal procedure to install, ensuring that the drive spindle aligns properly with the camshaft drive gear and drive shaft groove. Install support with new oil seal. Oil hole in support should face cylinder block.

ENGINE COOLING

Thermostat — Opens at 180°F (82°C). Full open at 203°F (95°C).

Radiator Cap — 13 psi (.9 kg/cm²).

Cooling System Capacity — 10 quarts.

Water Pump — Centrifugal type pump with aluminum body. To remove, drain cooling system and remove radiator shroud, fan, belts and pulley. Disconnect coolant hose to thermostat housing, loosen water pump retaining bolts and remove pump. Reverse removal procedures to install. Always use a new gasket.

TIGHTENING SPECIFICATIONS

Application	Ft. Lbs. (N·m)
Cylinder Head	
Sub Bolt	36-47 (49-64)
Main Bolt	87-108 (118-147)
Connecting Rod	38-41 (52-56)
Camshaft Gear	33-36 (45-49)
Crankshaft Pulley	217-239 (295-325)
Flywheel	33-36 (45-49)
Rocker Shaft	14-18 (19-25)
Rocker Pivot Lock Nuts	14-18 (19-25)
Oil Jet	22-29 (30-39)
Intake & Exhaust Manifolds	11-13 (15-18)
Injection Pump Nut	14-18 (19-25)

Application	INCH Lbs. (N·m)
Front Cover Bolts	
6 mm Bolts	35-52 (4-6)
8 mm Bolts	84-108 (10-12)
Oil Pump Mounting Bolt	108-168 (12-19)
Oil Cooler Mounting Bolt	84-108 (10-12)

ENGINE SPECIFICATIONS

GENERAL SPECIFICATIONS

Year	Displ. cu. ins.	Displ. cc	Carburetor	HP at RPM	Torque (Ft. Lbs. at RPM)	Compr. Ratio	Bore in.	Bore mm	Stroke in.	Stroke mm
1981 Pickup	132	2164	Fuel Inj.	.....	.....	21.6-1	3.27	83	3.94	100

PICKUP 4-CYLINDER DIESEL (Cont.)

ENGINE SPECIFICATIONS (Cont.)

CRANKSHAFT MAIN & CONNECTING ROD BEARINGS

| Engine | MAIN BEARINGS | | | | CONNECTING ROD BEARINGS | | |
	Journal Diam. In. (mm)	Clearance In. (mm)	Thrust Bearing	Crankshaft End Play In. (mm)	Journal Diam. In. (mm)	Clearance In. (mm)	Side Play In. (mm)
2164 cc	2.7916-2.7921 (70.907-70.920)	.0014-.0037 (.035-.093)	①	.002-.006 (.06-.14)	2.0832-2.0837 (52.913-52.926)	.0014-.0037 (.035-.087)	.004-.008 (.10-.20)

① — Utilizes thrust washer on No. 3 crank journal.

VALVES

Engine & Valve	Head Diam. In. (mm)	Face Angle	Seat Angle	Seat Width In. (mm)	Stem Diameter In. (mm)	Stem Clearance In. (mm)	Valve Lift In. (mm)
2164 cc Intake	1.492-1.500 (37.9-38.1)	45°	89°	.....	.3138-.3144 (7.970-7.985)	.0006-.0018 (.015-.045)	.....
Exhaust	1.256-1.264 (31.9-32.1)	45°	89°	.....	.3128-.3134 (7.945-7.960)	.0016-.0028 (.04-.07)	.....

PISTONS, PINS, RINGS

| Engine | PISTONS | PINS | | RINGS | | |
	Clearance In. (mm)	Piston Fit In. (mm)	①Rod Fit In. (mm)	Rings	End Gap In. (mm)	Side Clearance In. (mm)
2164 cc	.0016-.0043 (.04-.11)	0-.0001 (0-.003)	.0010-.0018 (.025-.045)	No. 1	.0118-.0177 (.030-.045)	.0024-.0039 (.06-.10)
				No. 2	.0079-.0138 (.20-.35)	.0016-.0031 (.04-.08)
				Oil	.005-.0118 (.15-.30)	.0008-.0024 (.02-.06)

① — Interference fit.

VALVE TIMING

| Engine | INTAKE | | EXHAUST | |
	Open (BTDC)	Close (ABDC)	Open (BBDC)	Close (ATDC)
2164 cc	28°	67°	67°	28°

VALVE SPRINGS

| Engine | Free Length In. (mm) | PRESSURE Lbs. @ In. (kg @ mm) | |
		Valve Closed	Valve Open
2164 cc	1.976 (50.20)	1.535@66 (39@30)	1.197@134.7 (30.4@61.1)

CAMSHAFT

Engine	Journal Diam. In. (mm)	Clearance In. (mm)	Lobe Lift In. (mm)
2164 cc Front	1.7887-1.7892 (45.434-45.447)	.0009-.0040 (.024-.102)	.....
Middle	1.7282-1.7287 (43.897-43.910)	.0015-.0045 (.037-.115)	.....
Rear	1.6228-1.6233 (41.218-41.231)	.0009-.0040 (.024-.102)	.....

280ZX, 280ZX TURBO & 810 6-CYLINDER

ENGINE CODING

ENGINE IDENTIFICATION

Engine serial number is stamped on right rear side of cylinder block below mating surface with head.

Engine Identification		
Application	Engine Size	Code
810	2393 cc	L24E
280ZX	2753 cc	L28E
280ZX Turbo	2753 cc	L28ET

ENGINE, CYLINDER HEAD & MANIFOLDS

ENGINE

NOTE — *It is recommended that engine and transmission be removed as a unit. Engine can then be separated from transmission assembly.*

Removal — 1) Remove hood. Bleed off fuel pressure as follows: Start engine. Disconnect fuel pump relay harness connector with engine running. After engine stalls crank engine 2 or 3 times. Turn ignition switch off. Disconnect battery ground cable.

NOTE — *On models equipped with power steering and/or air conditioner, remove power steering pump and/or air conditioner compressor from engine but DO NOT disconnect lines. Suspend pump and/or compressor with wire to prevent damage to hoses.*

2) Drain cooling system and engine crankcase. Remove radiator hoses. Remove air cleaner and disconnect hoses from canister, then remove canister. Disconnect transmission oil cooler lines (automatic transmission models), and remove radiator and shroud. Remove lower engine splash guard (if equipped).

3) Disconnect accelerator linkage. Disconnect wiring to starter, alternator, oil pressure switch, neutral switch, back-up light switch, EGR solenoid valve, electronic fuel injection harness and connector, throttle valve switch, cold start valve, air regulator, vacuum cutting solenoid (manual transmission models), auxiliary cooling fan (if equipped), distributor and all wiring to thermostat housing. Remove canister hoses.

4) Disconnect wiring to boost controlled deceleration solenoid valve. Disconnect engine ground cable to engine, and high tension cable between coil and distributor. Disconnect wire for block terminal. Disconnect fuel return hose and fuel charge hose, heater hoses, and all vacuum hoses. On models with automatic transmission, disconnect wire to inhibitor switch and downshift solenoid.

5) Remove clutch operating cylinder on models with manual transmission. Disconnect speedometer cable from rear extension housing. Remove center console, "C" ring, and control lever pin from transmission striking rod guide, then remove control lever on models with manual transmission. On models with automatic transmission, disconnect shift control lever.

6) Disconnect exhaust pipe from exhaust manifold. Disconnect exhaust pipe bracket from rear extension housing and tie exhaust pipe out of the way. Mark propeller shaft and pinion flange to aid in reassembly, then remove propeller shaft from vehicle. Plug rear of extension housing to prevent oil leakage. Support transmission with a jack and remove rear engine mount. Use a hoist to raise engine and remove front engine mount attaching bolts. Raise engine and transmission and remove from vehicle as a unit.

Installation — To install, reverse removal procedures noting that rear engine mount is attached to car first. Ensure proper routing and attachment of all electrical harnesses, vacuum and liquid tubes. Refill all fluids to specified level before starting engine.

MANIFOLDS

Removal & Installation — 1) Disconnect battery ground cable and drain cooling system. Disconnect hose connecting rocker cover to throttle chamber at rocker cover. Disconnect tube connecting heater housing to water inlet at water inlet. Remove bolt securing water and fuel tubes to cylinder head.

2) Bleed off fuel pressure as described in engine removal procedure. Remove tube connecting heater housing to thermostat housing. Disconnect fuel line and remove intake manifold mounting bolts. Remove intake manifold and attached components.

3) Disconnect exhaust pipe from exhaust manifold (outlet). Remove PCV valve hose, sub-heat shield plate and EGR tube. On turbocharged models, disconnect oil passage tube from turbocharger, and remove turbocharger and exhaust outlet as a unit. Remove exhaust manifold mounting bolts and take off manifold. To install, use new gasket and reverse removal procedure.

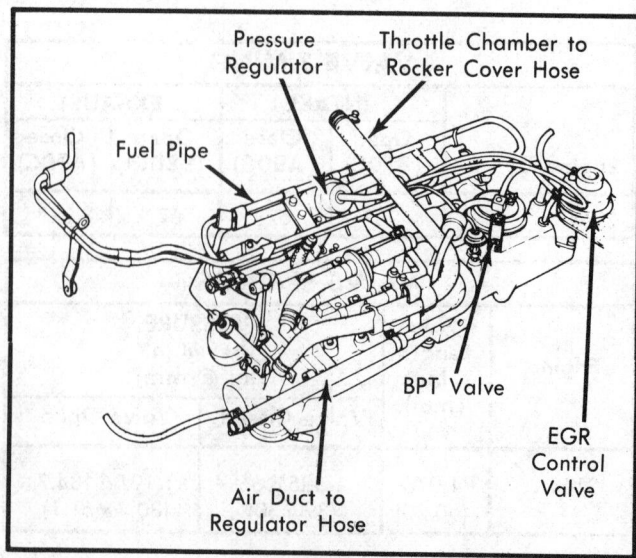

Fig. 1 Intake Manifold Assembly (Non-Turbo Shown, Turbo Models Similar)

280ZX, 280ZX TURBO & 810 6-CYLINDER (Cont.)

CYLINDER HEAD

Removal – 1) Drain cooling system and disconnect upper radiator hose and heater hoses. Release fuel hose pressure as described in engine removal procedure. Remove air regulator and all connecting hoses as an assembly. Remove spark plug wires at plug end. Remove EGR control valve, vacuum switching valve and hoses as an assembly. Remove throttle chamber with dash pot and boost controlled deceleration device.

2) Remove fuel lines, vacuum hoses, and canister purge hose pressure regulator. Remove thermostat housing and all attached switches as an assembly. Remove PCV valve hose, sub-heat shield plate, and EGR tube.

NOTE – *Remove clip attaching fuel inlet hose to injector and take care not to twist or bend hose during removal.*

3) Remove intake manifold and heat shield plate. Remove turbocharger with exhaust outlet (if equipped). Remove exhaust manifold. Remove all drive belts. Remove camshaft sprocket attaching bolt and remove sprocket from timing chain. Remove oil pipe. Remove cylinder head attaching bolts in reverse of tightening sequence. See *Fig. 2*. Remove bolts securing cylinder head to timing cover. Remove cylinder head from engine block.

NOTE – *Use special tool (KV10105800) to support timing chain so timing marks on crankshaft sprocket and timing chain will remain unchanged. This will simplify timing mark alignment during reassembly.*

Installation – 1) Ensure that mating surfaces of cylinder head and block are clean, then install cylinder head and gasket without sealer. Number 1 piston should be at TDC on compression stroke.

CAUTION – *Do not rotate crankshaft and camshaft separately or valves may hit head of pistons.*

2) Insert head bolts and tighten first 2 in tightening sequence to 14 ft. lbs. (19 N·m). Install and align sprockets and timing chain. Install remaining components in reverse order of removal, using new seals, gaskets and sealant where required.

3) Tighten head bolts in several steps in the sequence illustrated in *Fig. 2* to final specified torque. Recheck torque after engine has been running for several minutes.

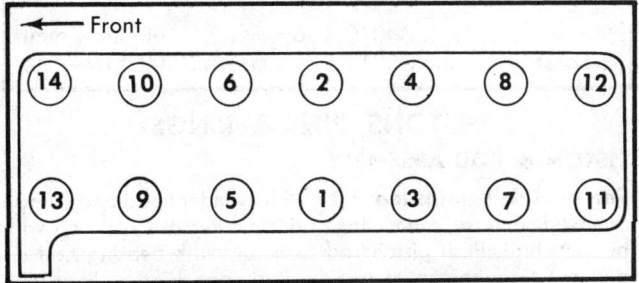

Fig. 2 Cylinder Head Tightening Sequence (Loosen in Reverse Sequence)

CAMSHAFT

CAMSHAFT

Removal – Remove cylinder head. Remove valve rocker springs. Loosen valve rocker pivot lock nuts and remove rocker arms by pressing down on spring. Use care not to lose valve rocker guide. Carefully remove camshaft from front of cylinder head.

Installation – Carefully install camshaft into cylinder head taking care not to damage bearings. Install camshaft locating plate with oblong groove of plate facing front of cylinder head. Install camshaft sprocket and tighten attaching bolt. Install remaining components in reverse of removal procedure, and tighten all nuts and bolts.

CAMSHAFT BEARINGS

NOTE – *Do not remove camshaft bearings. If bearings are removed, bearing centers will be out of alignment and proper reassembly will be difficult without center boring.*

Measure inner diameter of camshaft bearings and outer diameter of camshaft journals. If excessively worn or damaged, replace camshaft and/or cylinder head assembly. In event of excess end play, replace locating plate.

ENGINE FRONT COVER

Removal – Drain cooling system, disconnect hoses and remove radiator. Remove all drive belts, fan blade and pulley. Disconnect all wiring and connections to thermostat housing and remove housing. Remove crankshaft pulley and water pump. Remove spark plug wires from plugs, mark position of distributor base to engine and position of rotor to distributor. Disconnect distributor wires from coil and remove distributor. Remove oil pump with its drive spindle. Remove front cover attaching bolts and front cover.

Installation – Apply sealant to front cover gasket, front of cylinder block, and top of front cover. Install front cover on cylinder block. Tighten front cover-to-cylinder block bolts and cylinder head-to-front cover bolts. Install oil pump with drive spindle. Install distributor while aligning index marks. Reconnect spark plug wires and all distributor connections. Install thermostat housing and reconnect all wiring. Install fan and pulley. Install drive belts, radiator, hoses, and fill cooling system and oil pan.

TIMING CHAIN

Removal – Remove engine front cover. Remove camshaft drive sprocket, timing chain, tensioner and chain guide. Remove oil thrower, crankshaft worm gear and crankshaft sprocket.

Installation – Install components in reverse of removal procedure while noting the following: When installing timing chain, camshaft sprocket or crankshaft sprocket, make sure camshaft and crankshaft keys point upward. Set timing chain so that its mating marks match marks on crankshaft and camshaft sprockets on right-hand side. Locate camshaft dowel pin in No. 1 hole in camshaft sprocket.

280ZX, 280ZX TURBO & 810 6-CYLINDER (Cont.)

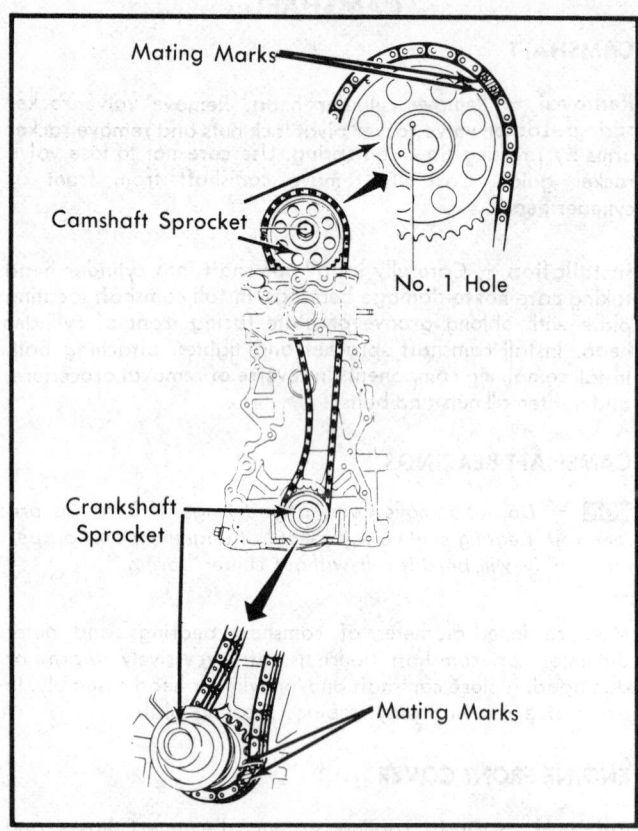

Fig. 3 Timing Chain and Sprocket Installation

VALVES

VALVE ARRANGEMENT

E-I-I-E-I-E-E-I-E-I-I-E (front to rear).

VALVE GUIDES CHECKING

1) Measure clearance between valve stem and valve guide with aid of micrometer and hole gauge. Check diameter of valve stem in three places: top, center and bottom.

2) Insert hole gauge in valve guide bore and measure at center. Subtract highest reading of valve stem diameter from valve guide bore to obtain clearance.

NOTE — *As a quick check, a valve may be inserted into valve guide and moved either left or right (parallel with rocker arm). If tip moves .008" (.2 mm) or more, clearance is beyond maximum limit of .004" (.1 mm).*

VALVE GUIDE REPLACEMENT

1) Using a press and drift pin, force worn guide from cylinder head working from combustion chamber side. Although this procedure may be carried out at room temperature, higher temperatures will aid removal.

2) With head at room temperature, ream valve guide hole to .4815" (12.23 mm). Heat head to 300-400°F (150-200°C) and install new guide.

3) Ream bore of valve guides to .3150-.3157" (8.000-8.018 mm). Correct valve seat surface using new valve guide as axis.

VALVE SEAT INSERTS

Check valve seats for pitting at valve contact surface. Valve seat inserts of .020" (.5 mm) oversize are available if necessary.

VALVE STEM OIL SEALS

An oil seal is installed on all intake and exhaust valve stems inside of valve spring.

VALVE SPRINGS

Removal — With cylinder head removed, loosen pivot lock nut and remove rocker arm by pressing valve spring down, taking care not to lose valve rocker guide. Remove camshaft taking care not to damage camshaft bearings and cam lobes. Compress valves and remove valve keepers. Remove compressing tool, then remove spring retainer, inner and outer springs, oil seal and valve spring seat.

Installation — Install spring seat and fit oil seal onto valve guide. Install valve springs, ensuring that close coiled end (painted white) of outer spring is against head. Install retainers, keepers and rocker guides. Install camshaft. Press valve springs down using a screwdriver and install rocker arms. Install valve rocker springs.

VALVE SPRING INSTALLED HEIGHT

Outer valve spring must be less than .087" (2.2 mm) and inner spring must be less than .047" (1.2 mm) out of square. Valve spring installed height is 1.38" (35 mm) for inner spring and 1.57" (40 mm) for outer spring. If spring height, pressure or squareness do not meet specifications, replace spring.

VALVE ADJUSTMENT

Valves can not be adjusted while engine is in operation. Cold settings are shown to provide initial clearance after assembly. Warm engine to operating temperature and remove valve cover. Rotate crankshaft so No. 1 cam lobe points up and adjust exhaust valve clearance on No. 1, 4 and 5 cylinder. Adjust intake valves on No. 2, 4 and 6 cylinder. Rotate crankshaft 360° so that lobe of No. 1 exhaust valve points down. Adjust exhaust valve clearance on No. 2, 3 and 6, and intake clearance on No. 1, 3 and 5 cylinder.

Valve Adjustment Clearances		
Valve	Hot	Cold
Intake	.010" (.25 mm)	.007" (.17 mm)
Exhaust	.012" (.30 mm)	.009" (.24 mm)

PISTONS, PINS & RINGS

PISTON & ROD ASSEMBLY

Removal & Installation — 1) With cylinder head and oil pan removed, remove connecting rod nuts. Remove rod cap with bearing half. Push piston/rod assembly with bearing half up and out through top of engine. Rod caps must be kept with their respective piston and rod assembly as caps are not interchangeable.

280ZX, 280ZX TURBO & 810 6-CYLINDER (Cont.)

2) To install piston and connecting rod assembly, thoroughly oil rings, piston and cylinder wall. Make sure ring gaps are situated approximately 180° apart and not on thrust side of piston or in line with piston pin. Make sure bearing halves are properly seated in connecting rod and cap.

3) Install a ring compressor and compress rings. Install piston in cylinder with notch mark on piston head toward front of engine. With piston installed in cylinder, and connecting rod and bearings seated against crankshaft journal, install rod caps to their respective piston and rod assembly. Oil jet of connecting rod should face right side of cylinder block. Install cylinder head and oil pan.

FITTING PISTONS

1) Visually inspect cylinder block for cracks or flaws. Using a bore gauge, measure cylinder for out-of-round or excessive taper. If cylinder bore out-of-round or taper exceeds .0008" (.02 mm), refinish cylinder bore. When any one cylinder is bored, all cylinders must be bored.

2) Determine piston oversize according to amount of wear in cylinder (see specifications). By measuring piston at thrust face and adding mean of piston-to-cylinder clearance, finish hone of cylinder may be determined.

3) After honing cylinder to final fit, measure piston-to-cylinder clearance using pull scale and feeler gauge. Extracting force to pull scale should be .44-3.31 lbs. (.2-1.5 kg) using a .0016" (.04 mm) feeler gauge. If cylinder bores are worn beyond limits, undersize cylinder liners are available. Liners should have an interference fit of .0031-.0035" (.08-.09 mm) in cylinder block.

Piston Specifications	
Piston Size In. (mm)	**Piston Diameter In. (mm)**
280ZX (includes Turbo)	
Standard	3.3844-3.3864 (85.965-86.015)
.020 (.50) O/S	3.4041-3.4061 (86.465-86.515)
.040 (1.0) O/S	3.4238-3.4258 (86.965-87.015)
810	
Standard	3.2663-3.2683 (82.965-83.015)
.020 (.50) O/S	3.2860-3.2880 (83.465-83.515)
.040 (1.0) O/S	3.3057-3.3077 (83.965-84.015)

PISTON PINS

Using suitable press and related adaptors, remove piston pin from piston and connecting rod. Measure pin bore diameter in piston and connecting rod. If wear exceeds specifications,

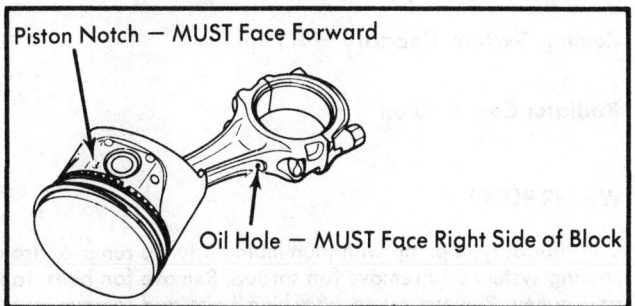

Fig. 4   Piston and Connecting Rod Alignment

replace both piston and pin. Pin must fit piston with light thumb pressure at room temperature. Piston pin is a press fit (interference) in connecting rod. If connecting rod is replaced, insure that new rod is within .247 ounce (7 grams) of the defective connecting rod. Install piston pin to piston and connecting rod so oil hole on connecting rod will face right side of engine and notch on piston head will face forward when assembly is installed.

CRANKSHAFT MAIN & CONNECTING ROD BEARINGS

CRANKSHAFT

Removal — With engine removed from vehicle, remove cylinder head and oil pan. Remove flywheel and end plate. Remove oil pump, front cover, chain tensioner and chain guides. Remove timing chain, oil thrower, crankshaft worm gear, and chain drive sprocket. Remove piston and rod assemblies. Remove main bearing caps using a special puller (KV101041S0) to remove center and rear main bearing caps. Remove rear oil seal, then remove crankshaft.

NOTE — *Keep all main bearing caps in order to aid in reassembly.*

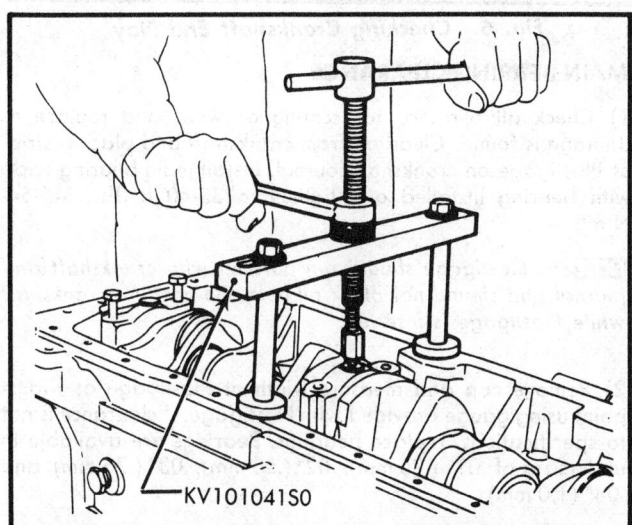

KV101041S0

Fig. 5   Removing Center Main Bearing Cap

Inspection — Check shaft journals and crankpins for scoring, wear, or cracks. Taper and out-of-round of journals and crankpins must not exceed .0012" (.03 mm). Check crankshaft for bend using a dial indicator at center journal of crankshaft. If bend exceeds .004" (.10 mm), which is one-half of indicator reading, replace crankshaft. Check main drive shaft pilot bearing at rear of crankshaft for wear or damage and replace if necessary.

Installation — **1)** Install main bearing halves to engine block ensuring that all bearings are on correct journal. Journal No. 4 requires a thrust bearing. Bearing for journal No. 1 is the same as for journal No. 7. Upper bearing halves have an oil groove and are not interchangeable with lower bearing halves.

2) Apply oil to main bearing surface and install crankshaft. Apply sealant to each side of rear main bearing cap and corners of cylinder block contact point. Install bearing caps so arrow faces front of engine. Shift crankshaft toward front of engine, then tighten main bearing caps in 2 or 3 steps, starting at center bearing and working outward. Ensure crankshaft rotates smoothly.

Datsun Engines

280ZX, 280ZX TURBO & 810 6-CYLINDER (Cont.)

3) Check crankshaft end play, and if not within specifications, replace center thrust bearing. Install side seals in rear main bearing cap after applying sealer to seals. Install rear oil seal. Install rear end plate and flywheel. Install piston and rod assemblies. Install cylinder head, crankshaft sprocket, worm gear, chain drive sprocket, oil thrower, and timing chain. Install chain guides and tensioner, front cover, oil pump and oil pan. Install remaining components in reverse of removal procedure.

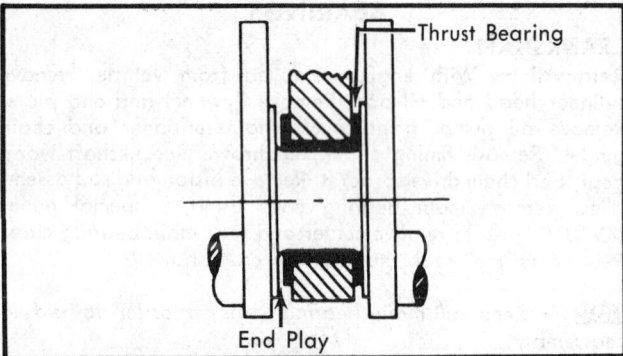

Fig. 6   Checking Crankshaft End Play

MAIN BEARING CLEARANCE

1) Check all bearings for scoring or wear and replace if damage is found. Clean oil from crankshaft and place a strip of Plastigage on crankshaft journal. Install main bearing cap, with bearing installed and tighten to 33-40 ft. lbs. (45-54 N·m).

NOTE — *Plastigage should run parallel with crankshaft and journal and should not block oil hole. Do not turn crankshaft while Plastigage is inserted.*

2) Remove cap and measure width of Plastigage at widest point using gauge provided with Plastigage. If clearance is not to specifications, replace bearings. Bearings are available in undersizes of .01" (.25 mm), .02" (.50 mm), .03" (.75 mm), and .04" (1.0 mm).

CONNECTING ROD BEARING CLEARANCE

Check connectng rod bearing clearance in same manner as main bearing clearance using Plastigage. Tighten connecting rod caps to 33-40 ft. lbs. (45-54 N·m). Bearings are available in undersizes of .0024" (.06 mm), .005" (.12 mm), .01" (.25 mm), .02" (.50 mm), .03" (.75 mm) and .04" (1.0 mm).

ENGINE OILING

ENGINE OILING SYSTEM

Oil drawn from oil pan passes through a screen to oil pump. Oil is delivered to full-flow filter and main oil gallery. Main oil gallery supplies oil to crankshaft main bearings and drilled passages in crankshaft. Oil sprayed from jet holes on connecting rods lubricates chain tensioner and timing chain. A center oil hole in the crankshaft center bearing feeds camshaft bearings on cylinder head. Valve rocker mechanism is lubricated through oil gallery in camshaft and through a channel at base circle portion of each cam. Rocker arms and valves are lubricated through holes in oil pipe.

NOTE — *On turbocharged models an oil cooler, oil passage tube to turbo housing, and special oil filter mounting bracket (for oil cooler supply and return lines) are added. Oil passage tube taps into main oil gallery in cylinder block. Lubricant drains from housing through oil tube to oil pan.*

Crankcase Capacity (with Filter)	
Application	**Quantity**
810	5.3 quarts
280ZX	4.8 quarts
280ZX Turbo	5.5 quarts

Oil Filter — Full-flow, with disposable cartridge.

Oil Pressure — 50-57 psi (3.5-4.0 kg/cm²) @ 2000 RPM.

OIL PUMP

Oil pump assembly is installed to bottom of front cover by four bolts. Pump is driven by oil pump drive spindle assembly which is in turn driven by gear on crankshaft. To remove oil pump, first remove distributor. Drain engine oil and remove oil pump body together with drive spindle. To disassemble, proceed as follows:

1) Remove pump cover and gasket. Slide pump rotors from pump body. Remove regulator cap, valve and spring. Clean all components with cleaning solvent, and inspect for wear or damage. Check the clearances indicated in the following table and ensure clearances are to specifications. If components are not to specifications, replace entire pump assembly.

2) Assemble pump in reverse order of disassembly while aligning hole in oil pump with punch mark on drive spindle. Fill pump housing with oil before installing to front cover.

Oil Pump Specifications	
Application	**Clearance In. (mm)**
Rotor Tip Clearance	Less Than .0079 (.20)
Outer Rotor-to-Body	Less Than .0197 (.50)
Rotor-to-Cover	Less Than .0024 (.06)
Rotor Side Clearance	Less Than .0012 (.03)

ENGINE COOLING

Thermostat — Opens at 180°F (82°C).

Cooling System Capacity — 11 qts.

Radiator Cap — 13 psi.

WATER PUMP

Centrifugal type pump with aluminum body. To remove, drain cooling system and remove fan shroud. Remove fan belts, fan, and pulley. Remove pump attaching bolts and remove water pump from front cover.

280ZX, 280ZX TURBO & 810 6-CYLINDER (Cont.)
ENGINE SPECIFICATIONS

GENERAL SPECIFICATIONS											
Year	Displ.		Carburetor	HP at RPM	Torque (Ft. Lbs. at RPM)	Compr. Ratio	Bore		Stroke		
	cu. ins.	cc					in.	mm	in.	mm	
1981											
L24E	146.0	2393	Fuel Inj.	.....	.....	8.9:1	3.27	83	2.90	73.7	
L28E	168.0	2753	Fuel Inj.	.....	.....	8.8:1	3.39	86	3.11	79	
L28ET	168.0	2753	Fuel Inj.	.....	.....	7.4:1	3.39	86	3.11	79	

VALVES							
Engine & Valve	Head Diam. In. (mm)	Face Angle	Seat Angle	Seat Width In. (mm)	Stem Diameter In. (mm)	Stem Clearance In. (mm)	Valve Lift In. (mm)
2753 cc							
Int.	1.73 (44.0)	45.5°	45°	.061 (1.55)	.3136-.3142 (7.965-7.980)	.0008-.0021 (.020-.053)	.....
Exh.	1.38 (35.0)	45.5°	45°	.061 (1.55)	.3128-.3134 (7.945-7.960)	.0016-.0029 (.040-.073)	.....
2393 cc							
Int.	1.65 (42.0)	45.5°	45°	.061 (1.55)	.3136-.3142 (7.965-7.980)	.0008-.0021 (.020-.053)	.....
Exh.	1.38 (35.0)	45.5°	45°	.055 (1.4)	.3128-.3134 (7.945-7.960)	.0016-.0029 (.040-.073)	.....

PISTONS, PINS, RINGS						
	PISTONS	PINS		RINGS		
Engine	Clearance In. (mm)	Piston Fit In. (mm)	Rod Fit In. (mm)	Rings	End Gap In. (mm)	Side Clearance In. (mm)
2753 cc	.0010-.0018 (.025-.045)	.0002-.0005 (.006-.013)	①.0006-.0013 (.015-.033)	No. 1	②.0098-.0157 (.25-.40)	.0016-.0029 (.040-.073)
				No. 2	.0059-.0118 (.15-.30)	.0012-.0025 (.030-.066)
				Oil	.012-.035 (.3-.9)	.0009-.0028 (.023-.070)
2393 cc	.0010-.0018 (.025-.045)	.0002-.0005 (.006-.013)	①.0006-.0013 (.015-.033)	No. 1	.0098-.0157 (.25-.40)	.0016-.0029 (.040-.073)
				No. 2	.0059-.0118 (.15-.30)	.0012-.0025 (.030-.066)
				Oil	.012-.035 (.30-.90)	.0009-.0028 (.023-.070)

① — Interference fit.
② — Turbo engines .0075-.0130″ (.19-.33 mm).

CRANKSHAFT MAIN & CONNECTING ROD BEARINGS						
	MAIN BEARINGS				CONNECTING ROD BEARINGS	
Engine	Journal Diam. In. (mm)	Clearance In. (mm)	Thrust Bearing	Crankshaft End Play In. (mm)	Journal Diam. In. (mm)	Clearance In. (mm)	Side Play In. (mm)
2753cc & 2393 cc	2.1631-2.1636 (54.942-54.955)	.0008-.0026 (.020-.066)	Center	.002-.007 (.05-.18)	1.9670-1.9675 (49.961-49.974)	.0009-.0026 (.024-.066)	.0079-.0118 (.20-.30)

Datsun Engines

280ZX, 280ZX TURBO & 810 6-CYLINDER (Cont.)

ENGINE SPECIFICATIONS (Cont.)

VALVE SPRINGS			
Engine	Free Length In. (mm)	PRESSURE Lbs. @ In. (kg @ mm)	
		Valve Closed	Valve Open
2753 cc Inner	1.766 (44.85)	27.1@1.378 (12.3@35)	56.2@.965 (25.5@24.5)
Outer	1.968 (49.98)	47@1.575 (21.3@40)	108@1.161 (49@29.5)
2393 cc Inner	1.766 (44.85)	27@1.378 (12.3@35)	56.2@.965 (25.5@24.5)
Outer	1.968 (49.98)	47@1.575 (21.3@40)	108@1.161 (49@29.5)

CAMSHAFT			
Engine	Journal Diam. In. (mm)	Clearance In. (mm)	Lobe Lift In. (mm)
2753 cc	1.8878-1.8883 (47.949-47.962)	.0015-.0026 (.038-.067)	.....
2393 cc	1.8878-1.8883 (47.949-47.962)	.0015-.0026 (.038-.067)	.....

VALVE TIMING				
	INTAKE		EXHAUST	
Engine	Open (BTDC)	Close (ABDC)	Open (BBDC)	Close (ATDC)
2393 cc	22°	38°	54°	6°
2753 cc	16°	44°	58°	10°

TIGHTENING SPECIFICATIONS

Application	Ft. Lbs. (N·m)
Cylinder Head	51-61 (69-83)
Connecting Rod	33-40 (45-54)
Flywheel	94-108 (128-147)
Camshaft Gear	94-108 (128-147)
Crankshaft Pulley	101-116 (137-158)
Main Bearing Cap	33-40 (45-54)
Rocker Pivot Lock Nuts	36-43 (49-58)
Intake & Exhaust Manifolds	
8 mm Bolts	11-18 (15-24)
8 mm Nuts	9-12 (12-16)
10 mm Bolts	25-33 (34-45)

Application	INCH Lbs. (N·m)
Oil Pan	52-86 (6-10)
Oil Pump-to-Front Cover	96-132 (11-15)
Oil Pump Cover	52-86 (6-10)
Camshaft Lock Plate	52-86 (6-10)
Front Cover	
6 mm Bolts	35-86 (4-10)
8 mm Bolts	84-144 (10-16)

Datsun Engines

810 6-CYLINDER DIESEL

ENGINE CODING

ENGINE IDENTIFICATION

Engine serial number is stamped on right rear side of cylinder block below mating surface with head. 810 diesel engines are identified by the number LD28.

ENGINE & CYLINDER HEAD

ENGINE

NOTE — *Engine and transmission should be removed as a unit. Engine can be separated from transmission assembly after removal.*

Removal — **1)** Remove hood. Bleed off fuel pressure as follows: Start engine. Disconnect fuel pump relay No. 2 harness connector with engine running. After engine stalls, crank engine 2 or 3 times. Turn ignition switch off. Disconnect battery ground cable.

NOTE — *Relay bracket is located on right side wheel well between battery and shock tower. Fuel pump relay No. 2 can be identified by the color of the wires used. The relay connector is the one with Light Green, Blue, Yellow/Red and Black/White wires.*

2) Remove power steering pump and air conditioning compressor from engine, but DO NOT disconnect lines or hoses. Suspend pump and compressor with wire to prevent damage to hoses.

3) Drain cooling system and engine crankcase. Remove radiator hoses. Remove air cleaner. Disconnect transmission oil cooler lines and remove radiator and shroud. Remove lower engine splash guard.

4) Disconnect accelerator linkage. Disconnect wiring to starter, alternator, oil pressure switch, neutral switch, back-up light switch, EGR solenoid valve, electronic fuel injection harness and connector, auxiliary cooling fan, distributor and all wiring to thermostat housing.

5) Disconnect wiring to boost controlled deceleration solenoid valve. Disconnect engine ground cable to engine. Disconnect wire for block terminal. Disconnect fuel return hose and fuel charge hose, heater hoses, and all vacuum hoses. Disconnect wire to inhibitor switch and downshift solenoid.

6) Disconnect speedometer cable from rear extension housing. Remove center console, "C" ring, and control lever pin from transmission striking rod guide. Disconnect shift control lever.

7) Disconnect exhaust pipe from exhaust manifold. Disconnect exhaust pipe bracket from rear extension housing and tie exhaust pipe out of the way. Mark propeller shaft and pinion flange to aid in reassembly, then remove propeller shaft from vehicle. Plug rear of extension housing to prevent oil leakage.

8) Support transmission with a jack and remove rear engine mount. Use a hoist to raise engine and remove front engine mount attaching bolts. Raise engine and transmission and remove from vehicle as a unit.

Installation — To install, reverse removal procedures noting that the rear engine mount is attached first. Ensure proper routing and attachment of all electrical harnesses, vacuum and liquid tubes. Refill all fluids to specified level before starting engine.

CYLINDER HEAD

Removal — **1)** Disconnect battery ground cable. Drain cooling system and disconnect upper radiator hose and heater hoses. Release fuel pressure as described in engine removal section. Remove EGR valve and tube. Remove thermostat housing and bottom bypass inlet with hose. Remove intake and exhaust manifolds. Do not separate intake manifold.

2) Disconnect oil feed pipe to head and return line to oil pan. Remove injection tube and nozzle assemblies, including return hose and spill tube. Disconnect injection pump hoses. Remove oil cooler, oil lines and oil filter as an assembly. Remove front engine hoist bracket and power steering oil pump bracket.

3) Remove rocker arm cover, camshaft sprocket retaining bolt and camshaft sprocket. Remove cylinder head attaching bolts working outward from center of cylinder head. Remove bolts securing cylinder head to front cover. Remove head from block.

NOTE — *Use special tool (ST1740001) to support timing chain so timing marks on crankshaft sprocket and timing chain will remain unchanged. This will simplify timing mark alignment during reassembly.*

Installation — **1)** Ensure that mating surfaces of cylinder head and block are clean, then install cylinder head and gasket without sealer. Number 1 piston should be at TDC on compression stroke.

CAUTION — *Do not rotate crankshaft and camshaft separately or valves may hit heads of pistons.*

2) Insert head bolts and tighten first 2 in tightening sequence to 14 ft. lbs. (19 N·m). Install and align sprockets and timing chain. Install remaining components in reverse order of removal, using new seals, gaskets and sealant where required.

3) Tighten head bolts in several steps in the sequence illustrated in *Fig. 1* to final specified torque. Recheck torque after engine has been running for several minutes.

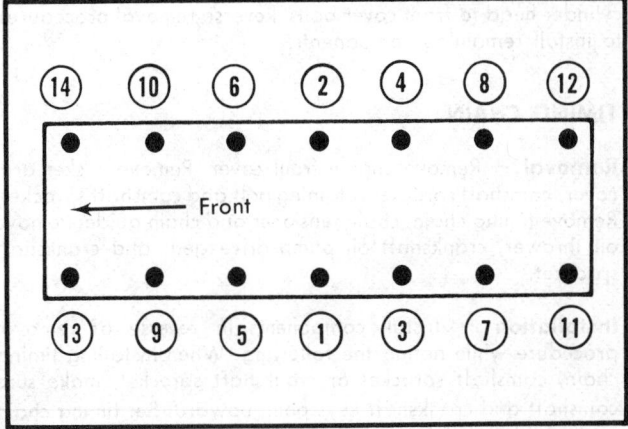

Fig. 1 Cylinder Head Tightening Sequence

Datsun Engines

810 6-CYLINDER DIESEL (Cont.)

CAMSHAFT

CAMSHAFT

Removal — Remove cylinder head. Remove glow plug connecting plate and glow plugs. Remove valve rocker springs. Loosen valve rocker pivot lock nuts and remove rocker arms by pressing down on spring. Use care not to lose valve rocker guide. Carefully remove camshaft from front of cylinder head.

Installation — Carefully install camshaft into cylinder head taking care not to damage bearings. Install camshaft locating plate with oblong groove of plate facing front of cylinder head. Install camshaft sprocket and tighten attaching bolt. Install remaining components in reverse of removal procedure, and tighten all nuts and bolts.

CAMSHAFT BEARINGS

NOTE — *Do not remove camshaft bearings. If bearings are removed, bearing centers will be out of alignment and proper reassembly will be difficult without center boring.*

Measure inner diameter of camshaft bearings and outer diameter of camshaft journals. If excessively worn or damaged, replace camshaft and/or cylinder head assembly. In event of excess end play, replace thrust plate.

ENGINE FRONT COVER

Removal — 1) Drain cooling system, disconnect hoses and remove radiator. Remove all drive belts, fan blade and pulley. Remove crankshaft pulley and water pump. Remove front dust cover, thermostat housing and bottom bypass inlet with hose. Disconnect injection tubes from injection nozzles and hoses to injection pump.

2) Remove front engine hoist bracket and power steering oil pump bracket. Remove injection pump and injection tubes as an assembly. Pull off injection pump drive crank pulley. Remove oil pump with drive spindle. Remove front cover attaching bolts and front cover.

Installation — Apply sealant to front cover gasket, front of cylinder block, and top of front cover. Install front cover on cylinder block. Tighten front cover-to-cylinder block bolts and cylinder head-to-front cover bolts. Reverse removal procedures to install remaining components.

TIMING CHAIN

Removal — Remove engine front cover. Remove rocker arm cover, camshaft sprocket retaining bolt and camshaft sprocket. Remove timing chain, chain tensioner and chain guide. Remove oil thrower, crankshaft oil pump drive gear and crankshaft sprocket.

Installation — Install components in reverse of removal procedure while noting the following: When installing timing chain, camshaft sprocket or crankshaft sprocket, make sure camshaft and crankshaft keys point upward. Set timing chain so that plated links on chain line up with match marks on camshaft and crankshaft sprockets on right-hand side. Locate camshaft dowel pin in No. 1 hole in camshaft sprocket.

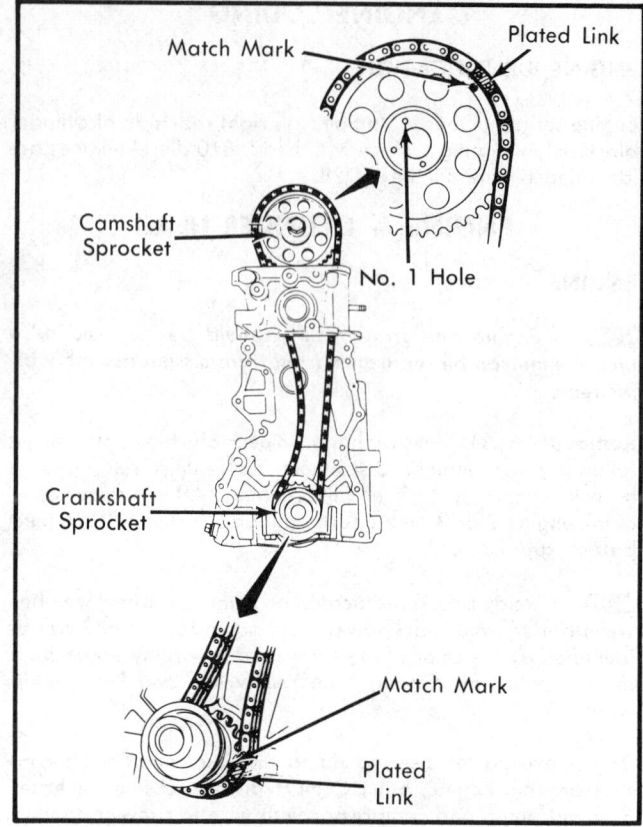

Fig. 2 Timing Chain and Sprocket Installation

VALVES

VALVE ARRANGEMENT

E-I-I-E-I-E-E-I-E-I-I-E (front to rear).

VALVE GUIDE CHECKING

1) Measure clearance between valve stem and valve guide with the aid of a micrometer and hole gauge. Check diameter of valve stem in three places: top, center and bottom.

2) Insert hole gauge in valve guide bore and measure at center. Subtract highest reading of valve stem diameter from valve guide bore to obtain clearance.

NOTE — *As a quick check, a valve may be inserted into valve guide and moved either left or right (parallel with rocker arm). If its tip moves .008" (.2 mm) or more, clearance is beyond maximum limit of .004" (.1 mm).*

VALVE GUIDE REPLACEMENT

1) If clearance is beyond acceptable limits and valve stem is not worn, the valve guide must be replaced. To replace guide, heat cylinder head to 300-400°F (150-200°C) and use suitable drift (ST110330000) to drive old guides out from combustion chamber side toward rocker arm cover.

2) With head at room temperature, ream valve guide hole to .481" (12.2 mm). Reheat cylinder head and install new guide. Use suitable reamer (ST110320000) to finish stem bore to .315" (8.0 mm) and reface valve seat surface.

810 6-CYLINDER DIESEL (Cont.)

VALVE SEAT INSERTS

Check valve seats for pitting at valve contact surface. Valve seat inserts of .020″ (.5 mm) oversize are available if necessary.

VALVE STEM OIL SEALS

An oil seal is installed on all intake and exhaust valve stems inside of valve spring.

VALVE SPRINGS

Removal — With cylinder head removed, remove glow plug connecting plate and glow plugs. Remove camshaft as previously outlined. Compress valves and remove valve keepers. Remove compressing tool, then remove spring retainer, valve spring, oil seal and valve spring seat. Keep components in correct order for installation.

Installation — Install spring seat and fit oil seal onto valve guide. Install valve springs, spring retainers, keepers and rocker guides. Install camshaft. Press valve springs down using a screwdriver and install rocker arms. Install valve rocker springs.

VALVE SPRING INSTALLED HEIGHT

Valve spring must be less than .087″ (2.2 mm) out of square. Valve spring installed height is 1.575″ (40.0 mm) with valve closed and 1.181″ (30.0 mm) with valve open. If spring height, pressure or squareness do not meet specifications, replace spring.

VALVE ADJUSTMENT

Valves can not be adjusted while engine is in operation. Cold settings are shown to provide initial clearance after assembly. Warm engine to operating temperature and remove valve rocker arm cover. Rotate crankshaft so No. 1 exhaust cam lobe points up and adjust exhaust valve clearance on No. 1, 4 and 5 cylinders. Adjust intake valves on No. 2, 4 and 6 cylinders. Rotate crankshaft 360° so that lobe of No. 1 exhaust valve points down. Adjust exhaust valve clearance on No. 2, 3 and 6, and intake clearance on No. 1, 3 and 5 cylinders.

Valve Adjustment Clearances		
Valve	**Hot**	**Cold**
Intake	.010″ (.25 mm)	.007″ (.18 mm)
Exhaust	.012″ (.30 mm)	.010″ (.25 mm)

PISTONS, PINS & RINGS

PISTON & ROD ASSEMBLY

Removal & Installation — 1) With cylinder head, front cover and oil pan removed, remove connecting rod nuts. Remove rod cap with bearing half. Push piston/rod assembly with bearing half up and out through top of engine. Rod caps must be kept with their respective piston and rod assemblies as caps are not interchangeable.

2) To install piston and connecting rod assembly, thoroughly oil rings, piston and cylinder wall. Make sure ring gaps are situated approximately 180° apart and not on thrust side of piston or in line with piston pin. Make sure bearing halves are properly seated in connecting rod and cap.

3) Install a ring compressor and compress rings. Install piston in cylinder. There is a grade mark stamped in the top of each piston. Be sure to install piston with this mark toward the front of the engine.

4) With piston installed in cylinder, and connecting rod and bearings seated against crankshaft journal, install rod caps to their respective piston and rod assembly. Oil jet of connecting rod should face right side of cylinder block. Install cylinder head, front cover and oil pan.

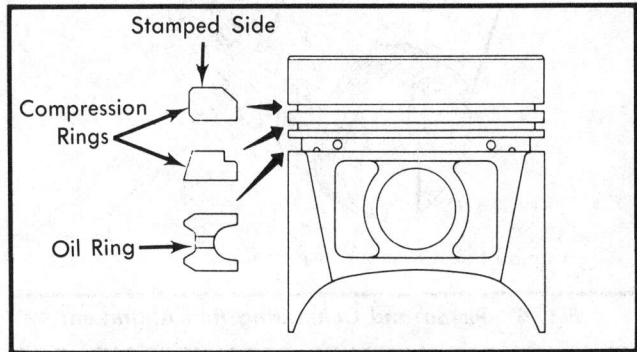

Fig. 3   Installation Order of Piston Rings

FITTING PISTONS

1) Visually inspect cylinder block for cracks or flaws. Measure block deck for warpage. If warpage exceeds .004″ (.10 mm), grind deck to correct. Using a bore gauge, measure cylinder for out-of-round or excessive taper. If cylinder bore out-of-round or taper exceeds .0008″ (.02 mm), refinish cylinder bore. When any one cylinder is bored, all cylinders must be bored.

2) Determine piston oversize according to amount of wear in cylinder (see specifications). By measuring piston at thrust face and adding mean of piston-to-cylinder clearance, finish hone of cylinder may be determined.

3) After honing cylinder to final fit, measure piston-to-cylinder clearance using pull scale and feeler gauge. With piston and cylinder at room temperature (70°F, 20°C), extracting force to pull scale should be 1.3-2.6 lbs. (.6-1.2 kg) using a .0024″ (.06 mm) feeler gauge.

Piston Specifications	
Piston Size **In. (mm)**	**Piston Diameter** **In. (mm)**
Standard	3.3244-2.3264 (84.44-84.49)
.020 (.50) O/S	3.3441-3.3461 (84.94-84.99)
.040 (1.00) O/S	3.3638-3.3657 (85.44-85.49)

PISTON PINS

1) With piston and rod assembly heated to about 150°F (65°C), drive out piston pin with suitable drift. Be sure to

810 6-CYLINDER DIESEL (Cont.)

remove piston pin snap rings before driving out pin. Using micrometer and hole gauge, measure diameter of piston pin and piston pin hole in piston. Use these measurements to determine pin to piston clearance. If wear exceeds .0002" (.004 mm), replace piston and pin.

2) To assemble piston and connecting rod, heat piston with a heater or hot water to about 150°F (65°C) and insert piston pin into piston while holding piston and connecting rod in proper alignment. Assemble so that the oil hole in the connecting rod is on the same side as the combustion chamber in the top of the piston.

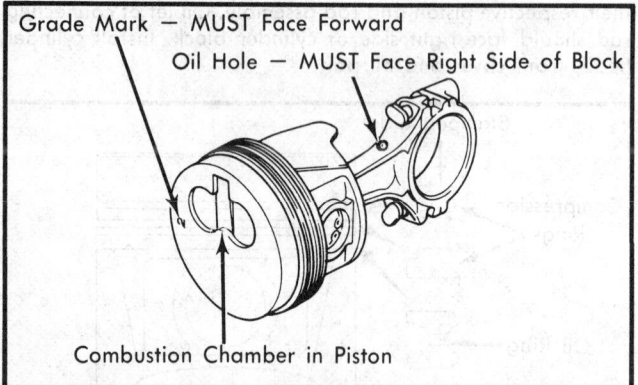

Grade Mark — MUST Face Forward
Oil Hole — MUST Face Right Side of Block
Combustion Chamber in Piston

Fig. 4   Piston and Connecting Rod Alignment

CRANKSHAFT MAIN & CONNECTING ROD BEARINGS

CRANKSHAFT

Removal — 1) With engine removed from vehicle, remove cylinder head, front cover and oil pan. Remove flywheel and end plate. Remove oil pump, chain tensioner and chain guides. Remove timing chain, oil thrower, crankshaft oil pump drive gear and crankshaft sprocket.

2) Remove piston and rod assemblies. Remove main bearing caps using a special tool (KV101041S0) to remove center and rear caps. Remove rear oil seal, then remove crankshaft. Remove upper main bearing halves.

NOTE — *Keep all main bearing caps in order to aid in reassembly.*

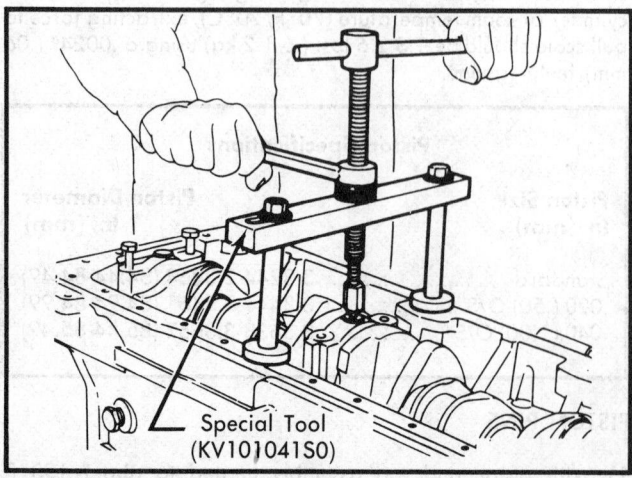

Special Tool
(KV101041S0)

Fig. 5   Removing Center Main Bearing Cap

Inspection — Check shaft journals and crankpins for scoring, wear, or cracks. Taper and out-of-round of journals and crankpins must not exceed .0012" (.03 mm). Check crankshaft for bend using a dial indicator at center journal of crankshaft. If bend exceeds .002" (.05 mm), which is half of indicator reading, replace crankshaft. Check main drive shaft pilot bearing at rear of crankshaft for wear or damage and replace if necessary.

Installation — 1) Install main bearing halves to engine block ensuring that all bearings are on correct journal. Journal No. 4 requires a thrust bearing. Bearing for journal No. 1 is the same as for journal No. 7. Upper bearing halves have an oil hole and groove and are not interchangeable with lower bearing halves.

2) Apply oil to main bearing surface and install crankshaft. Apply sealant to each side of rear main bearing cap and corners of cylinder block contact point. Install bearing caps so arrow faces front of engine. Shift crankshaft toward front of engine, then tighten main bearing caps in 2 or 3 steps, starting at center bearing and working out. Ensure crankshaft rotates smoothly.

3) Check crankshaft end play. If not within specifications, replace center thrust bearing. Install side seals in rear main bearing cap after applying sealer to seals. Install rear oil seal. Install rear end plate and flywheel. Install piston and rod assemblies.

4) Install cylinder head, crankshaft sprocket, crankshaft oil pump drive gear, chain drive sprocket, oil thrower, and timing chain. Install chain guides and tensioner, front cover, oil pump and oil pan. Install remaining components in reverse of removal procedure.

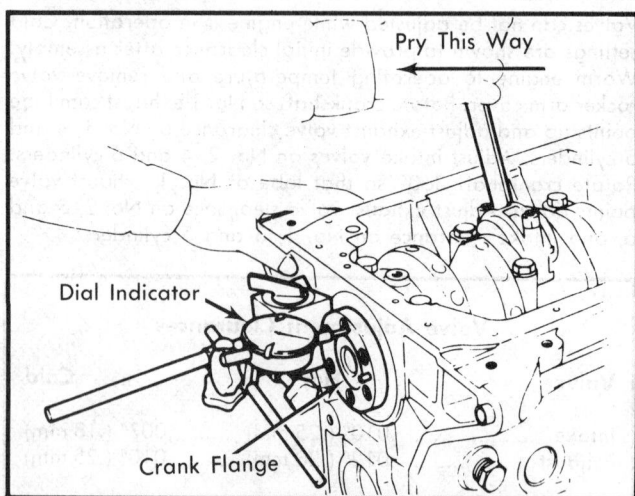

Pry This Way
Dial Indicator
Crank Flange

Fig. 6   Checking Crankshaft End Play

MAIN BEARINGS

Check all bearings for scoring or wear and replace if damage is found. Clean oil from crankshaft and place a strip of Plastigage on crankshaft journal. Install main bearing cap with bearing installed, and tighten to 51-61 ft. lbs. (69-83 N·m).

NOTE — *Plastigage should run parallel with crankshaft and journal and should not block oil hole. Do not turn crankshaft while Plastigage is inserted.*

Datsun Engines

810 6-CYLINDER DIESEL (Cont.)

2) Remove cap and measure width of Plastigage at widest point using gauge provided with Plastigage. If clearance is not to specifications, replace bearings. Bearings are available in undersizes of .01" (.25 mm), .02" (.50 mm), .03" (.75 mm) and .04" (1.00 mm).

CONNECTING ROD BEARINGS

Check connecting rod bearing clearance. Use Plastigage as in checking main bearing clearance. Tighten connecting rod caps to 33-40 ft. lbs. (45-54 N·m). Bearings are available in undersizes of .0024" (.06 mm), .0047" (.12 mm), .01" (.25 mm), .02" (.50 mm), .03" (.75 mm) and .04" (1.00 mm).

ENGINE OILING

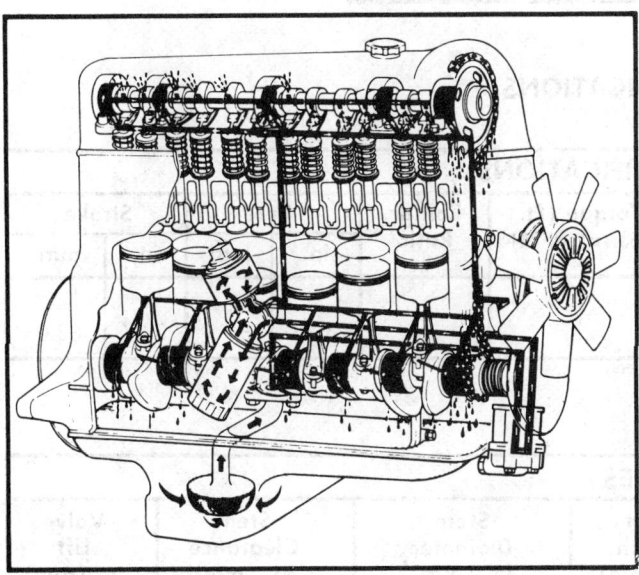

Fig. 7   Cutaway View of Engine Oiling System

ENGINE OILING SYSTEM

Oil drawn from oil pan passes through a screen to oil pump. Oil is delivered to full flow oil filter, oil cooler, and main oil gallery. Main oil gallery supplies oil to crankshaft main bearings and drilled passages in crankshaft. Oil sprayed from jet holes on connecting rods lubricates cylinders and piston pins.

Oil from main gallery lubricates chain tensioner and timing chain. A center oil hole in the crankshaft center bearing feeds camshaft bearings on cylinder head. Valve rocker mechanism is lubricated through oil gallery in camshaft and through a small channel at base circle portion of each cam. Rocker arms and valves are lubricated intermittently through small holes or oil pipe.

Crankcase Capacity — 6.5 quarts (includes filter).

Oil Filter — Full-flow, with disposable cartridge.

Oil Pressure — 45-55 psi (3.1-3.7 kg/cm²).

OIL PUMP

Removal — Oil pump assembly is installed to bottom of front cover by four bolts. Pump is driven by oil pump drive spindle assembly which is in turn driven by gear on crankshaft. To remove pump, drain engine oil, remove 4 retaining bolts and remove oil pump body together with drive spindle.

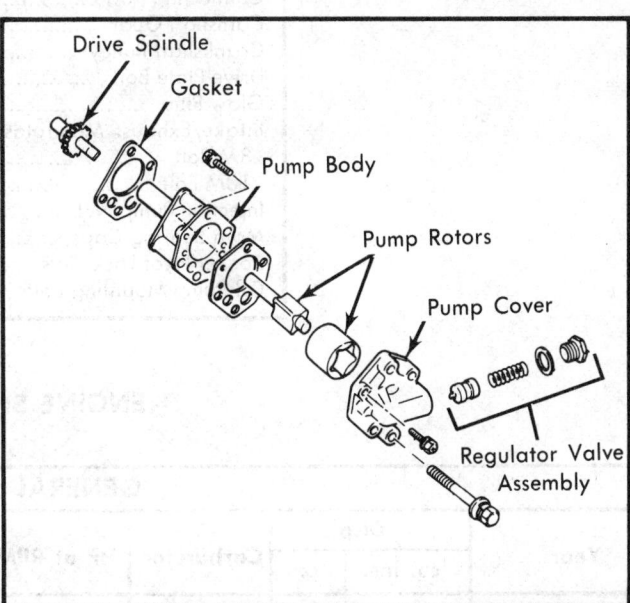

Fig. 8   Exploded View of Oil Pump Assembly

Inspection — Disassemble oil pump and wash all parts thoroughly in clean solvent. Inspect for signs of unusual wear or damage. Check all clearances to specifications. Pump is serviced as a complete assembly only. If components are not to specifications, replace entire pump assembly.

Installation — Fill pump with oil and reverse removal procedure to install.

Oil Pump Specifications	
Application	**Clearance In. (mm)**
Rotor Tip Clearance	Less Than .008 (.20)
Outer Rotor-to-Body	Less Than .020 (.50)
Rotor-to-Cover	Less Than .002 (.06)
Rotor Side Clearance	Less Than .001 (.03)

ENGINE COOLING

WATER PUMP

Centifugal type pump with aluminum body. To remove, drain cooling system and remove fan shroud. Remove fan belts, fan, and pulley. Remove pump attaching bolts and remove water pump from front cover.

Thermostat — 180°F (82°C).

Cooling System Capacity — 11.6 quarts.

Radiator Cap — 13 psi (.9 kg/cm²).

Datsun Engines

810 6-CYLINDER DIESEL (Cont.)

TIGHTENING SPECIFICATIONS

Application	Ft. Lbs. (N·m)
Cylinder Head	87-94 (118-128)
Connecting Rod	33-40 (45-54)
Camshaft Gear	87-116 (118-158)
Crankshaft Pulley	101-116 (137-158)
Drive Plate Bolt	101-116 (137-158)
Glow Plug	14-18 (19-25)
Intake/Exhaust Manifolds	
8M Bolt	12-15 (16-20)
10M Bolt	24-27 (33-37)
Injection Pump Nut	12-15 (16-20)
Main Bearing Caps	51-61 (69-83)
Rocker Pivot Lock Nuts	36-43 (49-59)
Oil Pump Mounting Bolts	96-132 INCH Lbs. (11-15)

ENGINE SPECIFICATIONS

GENERAL SPECIFICATIONS

Year	Displ. cu. ins.	Displ. cc	Carburetor	HP at RPM	Torque (Ft. Lbs. at RPM)	Compr. Ratio	Bore in.	Bore mm	Stroke in.	Stroke mm
1981 LD28	170.9	2793	Fuel Inj.	.....	.....	.....	3.33	84.5	3.27	83.0

VALVES

Engine & Valve	Head Diam. In. (mm)	Face Angle	Seat Angle	Seat Width In. (mm)	Stem Diameter In. (mm)	Stem Clearance In. (mm)	Valve Lift In. (mm)
2793 cc Int.	1.54 (39.0)	45.5°	45°	.075 (1.91)	.3136-.3142 (7.965-7.980)	.0008-.0021 (.020-.053)	.....
Exh.	1.26 (32.0)	45.5°	45°	.061 (1.56)	.3128-.3134 (7.945-7.960)	.0016-.0029 (.040-.073)	.....

PISTONS, PINS, RINGS

Engine	PISTONS Clearance In. (mm)	PINS Piston Fit In. (mm)	PINS ①Rod Fit In. (mm)	RINGS Rings	RINGS End Gap In. (mm)	RINGS Side Clearance In. (mm)
2793 cc	.0020-.0028 (.05-.07)	0-.0002 (0-.004)	.0010-.0017 (.025-.044)	No. 1	.0067-.0100 (.17-.26)	.0024-.0039 (.060-.100)
				No. 2	.0079-.0138 (.20-.35)	.0016-.0013 (.040-.080)
				Oil	.0118-.0177 (.30-.45)	.0012-.0028 (.030-.070)

① — Interference Fit.

Datsun Engines

810 6-CYLINDER DIESEL (Cont.)

ENGINE SPECIFICATIONS (Cont.)

CRANKSHAFT MAIN & CONNECTING ROD BEARINGS

Engine	MAIN BEARINGS				CONNECTING ROD BEARINGS		
	Journal Diam. In. (mm)	Clearance In. (mm)	Thrust Bearing	Crankshaft End Play In. (mm)	Journal Diam. In. (mm)	Clearance In. (mm)	Side Play In. (mm)
2793 cc	2.1631-2.1636 (54.942-54.955)	.0008-.0024 (.020-.062)	No. 4	.002-.007 (.05-.18)	1.9670-1.9675 (49.961-49.974)	.0008-.0024 (.020-.062)	.008-.012 (.2-.3)

VALVE SPRINGS

Engine	Free Length In. (mm)	PRESSURE Lbs. @ In. (kg @ mm)	
		Valve Closed	Valve Open
2793 cc	1.9594 (49.77)	51@1.575 (23@40.0)	115@1.181 (52@30.0)

VALVE TIMING

Engine	INTAKE		EXHAUST	
	Open (BTDC)	Close (ABDC)	Open (BBDC)	Close (ATDC)
2793 cc	14°	38°	60°	8°

CAMSHAFT

Engine	Journal Diam. In. (mm)	Clearance In. (mm)	Lobe Lift In. (mm)
2793 cc	1.8878-1.8883 (47.949-47.962)	.0015-.0026 (.038-.067)	.....

Fiat Engines

BRAVA & SPIDER 2000 4-CYLINDER (Cont.)

ENGINE CODING

ENGINE IDENTIFICATION

Engine identification number is stamped in pad above oil filter mount on left side of engine.

Engine Identification	
Application	**Code**
1995 cc	132 C3.031

ENGINE & CYLINDER HEAD

ENGINE

NOTE — *Specific removal and installation procedures were not available for turbo models. Remove additional components as necessary before removing engine.*

Removal — 1) Remove hood and air cleaner. Loosen fuel tank cap to relieve pressure. Disconnect battery. Mark for identification and disconnect vacuum and fuel lines and electrical leads. Disconnect accelerator and remove linkage.

NOTE — *On A/C equipped cars, it will be necessary to discharge system and remove condenser and fan assembly prior to removal of engine. When installing, system will require evacuation and charging.*

2) Drain cooling system and disconnect hoses. Disconnect automatic transmission cooling lines (if equipped). Remove radiator and cooling fan assembly.

3) Disconnect remaining hoses and wires from chassis-to-engine at engine. Disconnect exhaust pipe at manifold. Remove automatic transmission dipstick from support bracket (if so equipped).

4) From underneath vehicle, remove oil filter, engine splash pans and any remaining electrical connections. Remove starter by passing through oil filter opening. (On A/C equipped vehicles, pull starter from mounted position and tie to engine until engine is removed.) Remove speedometer cable support bracket from engine mount.

5) Remove nuts and washers holding engine mount isolators to crossmembers. Remove ground strap to engine mount. Install transmission support and remove bolts securing transmission to engine. On automatic transmission models, remove bolts attaching flywheel to torque converter.

6) Attach engine sling and hoist engine until mount clears cross members. Move engine forward until clear and lift from engine compartment.

Installation — To install, reverse removal procedure. Ensure that pilot shaft engages clutch properly (manual transmission).

CYLINDER HEAD

Removal — 1) Drain cooling system. Remove air cleaner and heated air tube. Disconnect battery ground cable. Loosen and remove top radiator hose from thermostat housing. Remove union with hoses from attachment point at cylinder head. Remove timing belt cover.

2) Manually turn crankshaft so that holes in camshaft sprocket align with timing pointers. Block flywheel to prevent further

turning and remove crankshaft pulley. Remove lower timing cover and take off oil dipstick tube. Loosen belt tensioner and remove timing belt.

NOTE — *Mark belt as "NOT USABLE". A new belt must be installed any time tension is removed from timing belt. See Timing Belt Replacement.*

3) Remove rear timing belt covers. From left side of engine, mark for identification and remove all fuel, vacuum, air and water hoses. Disconnect accelerator and remove linkage. At engine right side, remove coil wires from distributor and white lead wire from electronic control module.

4) Mark for identification and remove all remaining wires, hoses and tubes. Disconnect exhaust pipe from manifold and automatic transmission fluid dipstick (if equipped) from support bracket. Remove cylinder head bolts and lift off head assembly with gasket.

Installation — 1) Position camshafts so that reference marks on sprockets are aligned with fixed pointers on front of head. Ensure that crankshaft is positioned so that No. 1 and No. 4 pistons are at TDC. Install guide stud at front and rear of block.

2) Place new head gasket in position and guide head over studs, ensuring that camshafts are not moved from reference position. Install a few head bolts finger tight, then remove guide studs. Install remaining bolts and tighten in sequence shown to 29 ft. lbs. (39 N.m), then to a final torque of 69 ft. lbs. (94 N.m) To complete installation, reverse removal procedure.

NOTE — *Use Kent Moore Tool No. 28036 (Fiat No. 50149) to torque bolts.*

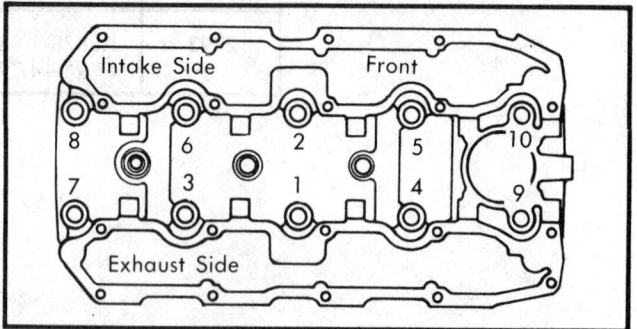

Fig. 1 Cylinder Head Tightening Sequence

CAMSHAFTS

CAMSHAFTS

Removal — 1) With cylinder head removed from engine, remove distributor and manifolds. Install pulley holder (A.60446) at front of cam housing and remove bolt, washer and pulley from camshaft.

2) Remove attaching bolts and lift off cam housing with camshaft. Remove cap from rear of housing and pull out camshaft. Repeat for other camshaft.

Installation — To install, reverse removal procedure, noting that distributor drive gear is on exhaust camshaft.

BRAVA & SPIDER 2000 4-CYLINDER (Cont.)

AUXILIARY SHAFT

Auxiliary shaft is driven by timing belt and drives oil pump and fuel pump. With engine out of vehicle and front crankshaft pulley removed, take off auxiliary drive pulley. Remove auxiliary shaft cover and gasket. Remove spacer and gasket. Rotate auxiliary shaft to raise oil pump gear and lift gear out with long nose pliers. Remove bolts holding retainer at front of block and pull out shaft along with retainer. To install, reverse removal procedure.

TIMING BELT REPLACEMENT

NOTE – *Timing belts must not be reused once tension is relieved. Crankshaft and/or camshafts must not be turned with belt removed due to resultant valve and/or piston damage.*

Removal – **1)** Disconnect battery ground cable and drain cooling system. Remove spark plugs and set engine to fire (TDC) on No. 4 cylinder. Crankshaft and camshaft timing marks must be aligned with indicators. Remove upper radiator hose from "T" union, then unbolt and remove union from cylinder head.

2) Remove hot air hose from exhaust manifold to air intake. Remove all drive belts from crankshaft pulley. Remove water pump pulley bolts and take off pulley. Remove outer timing belt cover.

3) Lock crankshaft to prevent turning and remove crankshaft pulley. Remove lower timing cover. Loosen belt tensioner and lock in belt-slack position. Remove and discard timing belt.

Installation – Turn auxiliary sprocket to align hole in sprocket with sprocket bolt and spring retaining bolt. Install belt and adjust tensioner, then turn crankshaft 2 full turns and recheck tension and timing. To complete installation, reverse removal procedures.

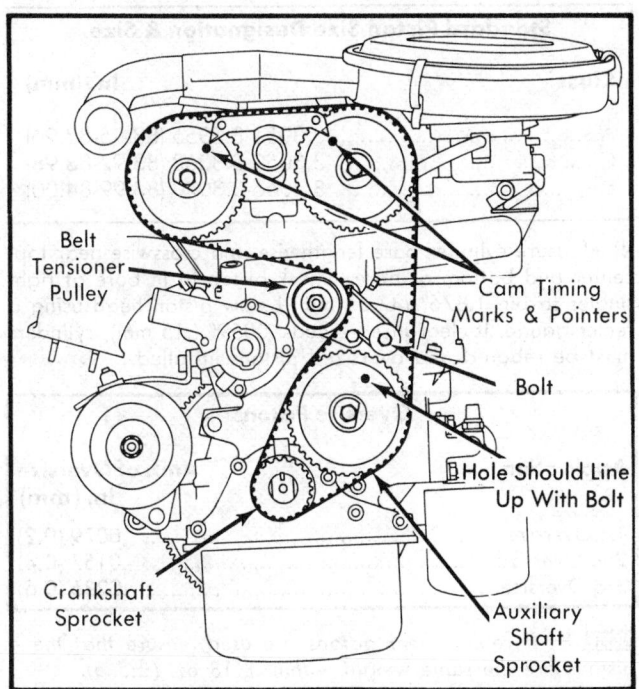

Belt Tensioner Pulley

Cam Timing Marks & Pointers

Bolt

Hole Should Line Up With Bolt

Crankshaft Sprocket

Auxiliary Shaft Sprocket

Fig. 2 Sprocket Alignment for Timing Belt Installation

VALVES

VALVE ARRANGEMENT

Left Side – All Intake
Right Side – All Exhaust

VALVE GUIDE SERVICING

1) Measure clearance of valve stem in guide with a dial indicator. If clearance exceeds specifications, valve guide must be replaced.

2) With driver (A.60153/60395), remove defective guides from head, driving from combustion chamber side. Press new guide in place from camshaft side with drift (A.60462). Guides are prefinished to size, however minor faults caused during replacement may be hand reamed if necessary.

VALVE STEM OIL SEALS

Removal – **1)** Remove spark plug from cylinder No. 1. Piston should be approximately ⅔ of the way up the cylinder. Screw in compressor gauge hose/adapter into spark plug hole and connect an air hose, pressurizing cylinder to approximately 120-150 psi (8.4-10.5 kg/cm²).

2) Using valve spring compressor (Kent-Moore J28067), compress valve springs. Remove valve keepers. Slowly release tension from spring. Remove tool, spring retainer, inner and outer springs and lower spring seat from valve stem. Remove valve stem seal. Ensure that all portions of seal have been removed from valve guide.

Installation – **1)** Using a light grease, lubricate the seal protector pin (60313/1) of valve guide seal installer and protector (Kent-Moore J28069). Place protector pin on end of valve stem. Slide new oil seal down pin and valve stem onto guide. Remove protector pin.

2) Place installer (60313/2) over valve stem seal. Lightly tap end of installer until oil seal is properly seated on valve guide. Remove installer. Reinstall lower spring seat, inner and outer springs and spring retainer. Using valve spring compressor, (J28067) compress valve springs and install valve keepers.

3) Repeat procedure for other valve of cylinder No. 1. After seal replacement, remove air hose, reinstall spark plug and repeat procedure on remaining cylinders. Reinstall camshaft housing and related parts onto cylinder head. See Camshaft Removal and Installation. Use a new timing belt.

VALVE SPRINGS

Removal & Installation – With cylinder head removed, remove camshaft carriers and camshafts. Compress valve spring with a suitable compressor and remove keepers. Release spring compressor and remove upper spring retainer, inner and outer springs and lower spring retainer. To install, reverse removal procedure.

VALVE CLEARANCE ADJUSTMENT

1) Valve clearance is checked and/or adjusted with engine cold. Remove camshaft covers from head and rotate crankshaft until camshaft lobe of valve being checked is

BRAVA & SPIDER 2000 4-CYLINDER (Cont.)

pointing up and at right angle to valve. Using a feeler gauge, check clearance between camshaft lobe and valve tappet plate.

Valve Clearance Specifications	
Application	**In. (mm)**
Intake	.016-.019 (.41-.49)
Exhaust	.018-.021 (.46-.54)

2) Tappet plates are available in service thicknesses of .128" (3.25 mm) and increments of .004" (.10 mm) from .130" to .185" (3.30 mm to 4.70 mm). To replace tappet plate, rotate camshaft down to depress tappet. Install clamping tool (A.60594) over cam lobe of valve being adjusted.

3) Rotate crankshaft/camshaft and remove tappet plate by means of a scribe through notch in tappet. As an alternate method, tappet may be pried down using tool (A 60443) and tappet plate removed with a scribe. Insert proper thickness tappet plate and remove tool.

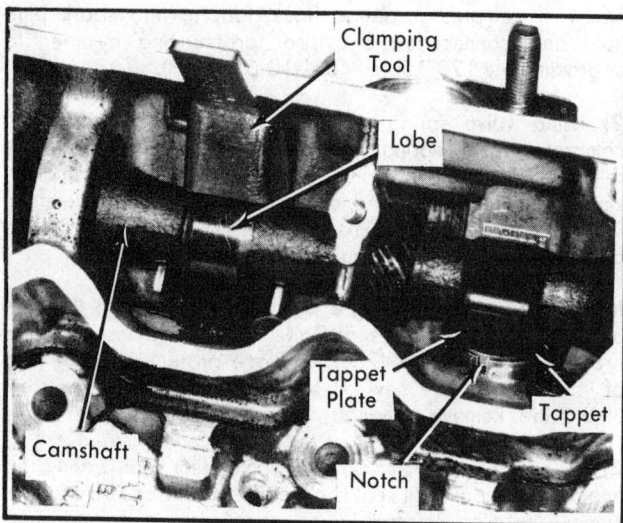

Fig. 3   Checking and Adjusting Valve Clearance

PISTONS, PINS & RINGS

OIL PAN

Removal — 1) Drain crankcase. Remove engine splash shields. Remove nuts from engine mounts at crossrails. Raise engine about 6" (152 mm).

2) Remove flywheel cover and oil pan bolts. Strike pan firmly with rubber mallet to free from block assembly.

Installation — To install, clean all mating surfaces and install gasket with sealer applied to BOTH sides. Reverse removal procedure and tighten bolts evenly.

PISTON & ROD ASSEMBLY

Lubricate cylinder bores, wrist pins and bearing journals with light engine oil. Ensure that piston ring gaps are staggered approximately 120° apart and that pistons and rings are coated lightly with engine oil. Use suitable compressor and install

assembly so that numbers on connecting rod and cap are facing away from auxiliary shaft.

FITTING PISTONS

1) Standard pistons are manufactured in 3 size classes, and cylinder bores are machined according to piston class. Class of piston and bore is designated by a letter code.

2) Class code of piston is stamped on bottom of piston pin boss. Class of cylinder bore is stamped next to appropriate cylinder on oil pan flange at bottom of cylinder block.

3) Measure Piston size at right angles to piston pin and 1.181" (30 mm) from piston skirt. If piston is replaced for any reason, one of the same class must be installed.

NOTE — *Refer to class designation letter on bottom of piston pin boss and mating surface of crankcase. See Fig. 4 and 5.*

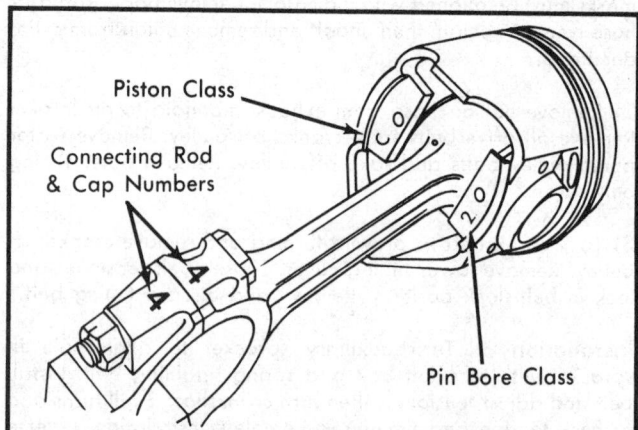

Fig. 4   Piston and Rod Assembly Markings

Standard Piston Size Designation & Size	
Class	**In. (mm)**
A	3.3051-3.3055 (83.95-83.96)
C	3.3059-3.3063 (83.97-83.98)
E	3.3066-3.3070 (83.99-84.00)

4) Measure cylinder bore lengthwise and crosswise near top, center and bottom of bore. Check piston fit in bore at right angles to pin 1.876" (47.65 mm) below piston head using a feeler gauge. If clearance exceeds .0059" (.15 mm), cylinders must be rebored and oversized pistons installed.

Oversize Pistons	
Application	**Amt. of Oversize In. (mm)**
1st Oversize	.0079 (0.2)
2nd Oversize	.0157 (0.4)
3rd Oversize	.0236 (0.6)

NOTE — *If replacement pistons are used, ensure that the 4 pistons are the same weight within ±.18 oz. (±5 g).*

5) Check ring side clearance in piston grooves prior to intallation on piston. Push rings squarely into cylinder bores and

Fiat Engines

BRAVA & SPIDER 2000 4-CYLINDER (Cont.)

check ring gaps with feeler gauge. Install rings on pistons with gaps 120° apart.

PISTON PIN REPLACEMENT

1) Remove circlips from piston and push piston pin out of piston and connecting rod. Separate piston from connecting rod and check pin clearance in piston and rod. If clearance is excessive, piston and connecting rod must be rebored for a .0079" (.2 mm) oversize pin.

2) Bushing in small end of rod is replaceable and requires a .0017-.0040" (.043-.102 mm) interference fit. To assemble piston and rod, piston side with offset portion of pin bore must be on same side as numbers on connecting rod and cap. Oil piston pin and insert in piston and rod. Install circlips and check alignment and freedom of movement.

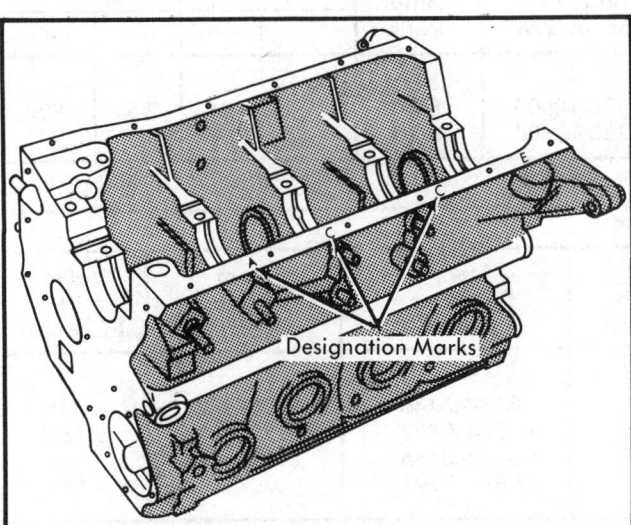

Fig. 5 Piston Bore Class Designation Marks

CRANKSHAFT MAIN & CONNECTING ROD BEARINGS

MAIN & CONNECTING ROD BEARINGS

1) With crankshaft removed, thoroughly clean and inspect for cracks or scoring on journals. Check all journals for out-of-round condition, using a micrometer. If journal is out-of-round or tapers more than .0002" (.005 mm), crankshaft must be reground for undersize bearings.

2) Bearing-to-journal clearance is checked using the Plastigage method. If clearance exceeds specifications, crankshaft must be ground for undersize bearings. Main and connecting rod bearings are available in .010" (.25 mm), .020" (.51 mm), .030" (.76 mm), and .040 (1.02 mm) undersizes.

NOTE — *Main bearing caps are stamped with a number that must correspond to the number stamped on crankcase near flywheel. Notches on caps face auxiliary shaft side and coincide with position. Front main bearing cap has no notch, however 2nd, center 4th and rear caps have 1, 2, 3, and 4 notches respectively.*

CRANKSHAFT END PLAY

Check crankshaft end play using a dial indicator mounted at front of engine. Pry crankshaft back and forth to read clearance. If beyond specifications, install new thrust washers to bring end play within limits.

ENGINE FRONT COVER & OIL SEAL

Engine front cover oil seal should be replaced whenever front cover is removed. Make sure new seal is squarely seated in cover. Lubricate seal contact lip before installing cover.

ENGINE OILING

Crankcase Capacity — Normal drain and refill capacity of system is 4.3 quarts.

Oil Filter — Full-flow, cartridge type.

Normal Oil Pressure — 50-71 psi (3.5-5.0 kg/cm^2) at 212° F (100° C) and 4000 RPM.

Pressure Regulator Valve — Installed in pump cover.

NOTE — *On air conditioned models, oil filter support mounts A/C compressor. Filter screws on from side rather than from bottom.*

ENGINE OILING SYSTEM

Engine oiling system is full pressure lubrication utilizing a gear type oil pump driven by the auxiliary shaft. A full-flow filter and a pressure regulator valve is also used.

OIL PUMP

Removal — 1) Drain crankcase and remove oil pan. *See Oil Pan.* Remove 2 bolts and washers holding oil pump to engine and remove pump and gasket. Visually inspect all parts for wear or damage.

2) Check gears for tooth-to-housing clearance. Clearance should be .004-.007" (.11-.18 mm). Place straightedge across pump body and measure gear end play. End play should be .0010-.0051" (.026-.131 mm). Check relief valve spring for pressure of at least 12.7 lbs. (5.8 kg) at .886" (22.5 mm).

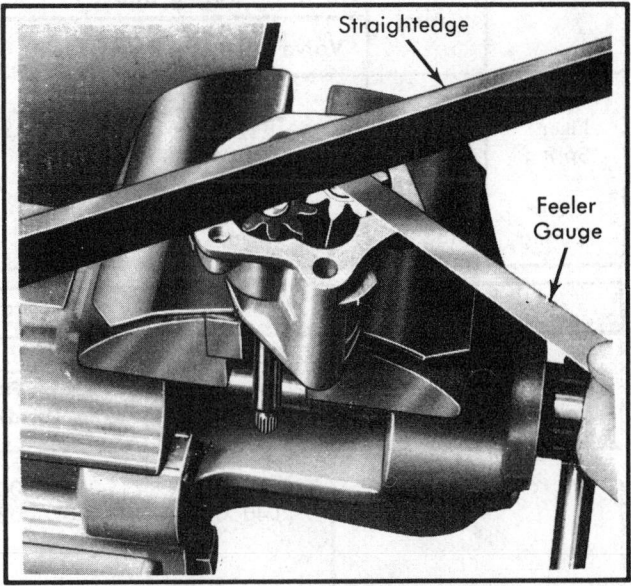

Fig. 6 Checking Oil Pump Gear End Play

Fiat Engines

BRAVA & SPIDER 2000 4-CYLINDER (Cont.)

Installation — To install, reverse removal procedure and mount pump using a new gasket. Make sure pump is seated before tightening mounting bolts.

ENGINE COOLING

Thermostat — Opens at 172-180°F (78-82°C).

Thermoswitch — Operates at 194° F (90° C).

Cooling System Capacity — 8.5 quarts.

Radiator Cap — 11 psi (.8 kg/cm²).

WATER PUMP

Removal — Drain cooling system. Remove 3 water pump pulley bolts. Remove drive belt and water pump pulley. Remove radiator hose from water pump. Remove 4 mounting bolts, then remove pump.

Installation — To install, ensure that mating surfaces are clean. Install new gasket and reverse removal procedure.

ENGINE SPECIFICATIONS

GENERAL SPECIFICATIONS

Year & Model	Displ. cu. ins.	Displ. cc	Carburetor	HP at RPM	Torque (Ft. Lbs. at RPM)	Compr. Ratio	Bore in.	Bore mm	Stroke in.	Stroke mm
1981 Fuel Inj.	121.7	1995	Fuel Inj.	102@5500	110@3000	8.2:1	3.31	84	3.54	90
Turbo	121.7	1995	Fuel Inj.	120@6000	130@3600	8.2:1	3.31	84	3.54	90

VALVES

Engine & Valve	Head Diam. In. (mm)	Face Angle	Seat Angle	Seat Width In. (mm)	Stem Diameter In. (mm)	Stem Clearance In. (mm)	Valve Lift In. (mm)
1995 cc Intake	1.638-1.654 (41.6-42.0)	45.5°	45°	.079 (2.0)	.3139-.3146 (7.974-7.992)	.0012-.0026 (.030-.066)	.3765 (9.564)
Exhaust	1.412-1.435 (35.85-36.45)	45.5°	45°	.079 (2.0)	.3139-.3146 (7.974-7.992)	.0012-.0026 (.030-.066)	.3765 (9.564)

VALVE SPRINGS

Engine	Free Length In. (mm)	Pressure Lbs. @ In. (kg @ mm) Valve Closed	Pressure Lbs. @ In. (kg @ mm) Valve Open
1995 cc Inner Spring	1.646 (41.8)	33@1.220 (14.9@31)	62@.846 (28.1@21.5)
Outer Spring	2.122 (53.9)	86@1.417 (38.9@36)	141@1.043 (63.9@26.5)

VALVE TIMING

Engine	INTAKE Open (BTDC)	INTAKE Close (ABDC)	EXHAUST Open (BBDC)	EXHAUST Close (ATDC)
1995 cc	5°	53°	53°	5°

PISTONS, PINS, RINGS

Engine	PISTONS Clearance In. (mm)	PINS Piston Fit In. (mm)	PINS Rod Fit In. (mm)	RINGS Rings	RINGS End Gap In. (mm)	RINGS Side Clearance In. (mm)
1995 cc	.0016-.0024 (.040-.060)	.0001-.0003 (.002-.008)	.0004-.0006 (.010-.016)	No. 1	.0118-.0177 (.30-.45)	.0018-.0030 (.045-.077)
				No. 2	.0118-.0177 (.30-.45)	.0011-.0027 (.030-.070)
				Oil	.0098-.0157 (.25-.40)	.0011-.0024 (.030-.062)

Fiat Engines

BRAVA & SPIDER 2000 4-CYLINDER (Cont.)
ENGINE SPECIFICATIONS (Cont.)

CRANKSHAFT MAIN & CONNECTING ROD BEARINGS							
	MAIN BEARINGS				CONNECTING ROD BEARINGS		
Engine	Journal Diam. In. (mm)	Clearance In. (mm)	Thrust Bearing	Crankshaft End Play In. (mm)	Journal Diam. In. (mm) ①	Clearance In. (mm) ②	Side Play In. (mm)
1995 cc	2.086-2.087 (52.99-53.00)	.001-.003 (.03-.07)	No. 5	.002-.012 (.05-.30)	1.9997-2.0001 (50.79-50.80)	.001-.003 (.03-.07)	.....

① — Journal diameter is machined in two sizes designated by class codes. Specification given is class "A". Class "B" is smaller by .0004" (.010 mm).

② — Clearance varies according to class of connecting rod journal. Specification given is class "A". Class "B" clearance is larger by .0001" (.002 mm).

CAMSHAFT			
Engine	Journal Diam. In. (mm)	Clearance In. (mm)	Lobe Lift In. (mm)
1995 cc Front	1.1788-1.1795 (29.94-29.96)	.0019-.0035 (.049-.090)	.3765 (9.56)
Middle	1.8013-1.8020 (45.75-45.77)	.0011-.0027 (.029-.070)	.3765 (9.56)
Rear	1.8171-1.8178 (46.15-46.17)	.0011-.0027 (.029-.070)	.3765 (9.56)

TIGHTENING SPECIFICATIONS

Application	Ft. Lbs. (N.m)
Cylinder Head Bolts ①	69 (94)
Main Bearing Cap Bolts	
Front	59 (80)
Center & Rear	83 (113)
Intake & Exhaust Manifold Nuts	18 (24)
Intake Manifold Bolts	18 (24)
Connecting Rod Nuts	54 (73)
Flywheel-to-Crankshaft Bolt	105 (143)
Camshaft Sprocket Bolt	87 (118)
Oil Pump Mounting Bolt	14 (19)
Timing Belt Tensioner Nut	33 (45)

① — Tighten when cold only. Recheck after 700-1000 miles.

STRADA & X1/9 4-CYLINDER

ENGINE CODING

ENGINE IDENTIFICATION

Engine identification and serial numbers are stamped on crankcase on flywheel side of engine next to union for radiator hoses. Engine code is stamped above serial number.

Engine Identification	
Application	**Code**
Strada	138 B2.031
X1/9	138 BS.031

ENGINE, CYLINDER HEAD & MANIFOLDS

ENGINE

NOTE — *Engine and transmission are removed as an assembly.*

Removal (Strada) — 1) Raise hood, mark hood hinge position, and remove hinge retaining bolts and hood. Remove spare tire and tools. Disconnect both battery cables. Drain cooling system. Remove radiator and heater hoses. On air conditioned models, slowly drain freon and remove compressor hoses.

2) Remove hose from air flow sensor to intake manifold. Remove from engine all fuel lines, throttle control cables, vacuum hoses, wiring harness and electrical connector.

3) Raise vehicle on lift. Remove front wheels and lower protective shields. Remove left side reaction rod bracket, reaction rod and hub support brackets. Remove left and right strut assemblies. Using suitable tool (A.47038), disconnect tie rod ball joints from hub carriers.

4) Remove axle shafts and control arms. Remove front section of exhaust system. Disconnect speedometer cable from transmission. On manual transmission models, mark gear control rod in relation to bracket and remove. On automatic transmission models, move gear selector to position "1". Disconnect shift cable from transmission lever and lay aside.

5) Attach a lifting fixture (A.60592) to engine and engine hoist. Lift engine slightly to remove weight from engine mounting points. Place a jack under center engine mount. Remove engine-to-body mounting bolts and engine support crossmember.

6) Remove mounting brackets and on automatic transmission models, the stabilizer bar. Remove engine and transmission from beneath vehicle. Separate transmission from engine once assembly is removed.

Removal (X1/9) — 1) Disconnect battery cables. Drain cooling system. Remove radiator and heater hoses. Remove cooling system expansion tank and disconnect hoses from thermostat.

2) Remove hose from air flow sensor to intake manifold. Remove from engine all fuel lines, throttle control cables, vacuum hoses, wiring harness and electrical connector.

3) Remove bolts holding louvered protection panel below carbon trap in rear firewall. Raise and support vehicle with safety stands. Remove remaining bolt attaching louvered panel in rear firewall, then remove panel. Remove alternator heat shield, engine panels and wheel panels.

4) Drain transmission and differential assembly. Disconnect back-up light and seat belt interlock connectors, then remove clamps to allow wires to come with engine. Disconnect speedometer cable and gearshift linkage from transmission.

5) Disconnect ground strap at engine, then remove muffler and muffler upper bracket. Remove axle boot retaining bolts and slide boots away from differential.

6) Remove nuts securing hand brake cable brackets to control arms. Remove bolts attaching control arms to body and swing arms down out of brackets. Move control arms away from differential until axles are free of differential.

7) Remove lower crossmember attaching bolts and remove crossmember. From above engine, disconnect reaction arm beneath vehicle. Separate transmission and differential from engine.

NOTE — *Record number of shims at control arm mounting points for installation purposes. Also note sizes of shims. If shims are worn or damaged, rear end alignment should be checked and adjusted, if necessary, after engine and transmission are reinstalled.*

Installation (All Models) — To install, reverse removal procedure. Upon completion of installation, refill cooling system and inspect all lines and hoses for tightness.

INTAKE & EXHAUST MANIFOLDS

NOTE — *The following procedure refers to carbureted models only. Information is not available from manufacturer on fuel injected models.*

Removal — 1) Drain cooling system. Remove spare tire from engine compartment. Remove air cleaner and cartridge from carburetor. Remove carburetor pre-heating water hoses.

2) Remove carburetor with guard and gaskets. Remove shroud from intake and exhaust manifold. Remove intake and exhaust manifold from engine.

Installation — To install, reverse removal procedure and use new gaskets.

CYLINDER HEAD

NOTE — *The following procedure refers to carbureted models only. Information is not available from manufacturer on fuel injected models.*

Removal — 1) Disconnect positive battery cable. Drain engine cooling system. Remove spare tire from engine compartment. Remove air cleaner housing and cartridge. Disconnect spark plug wires at spark plugs.

2) Disconnect accelerator linkage and choke cable at carburetor. Disconnect fuel line at carburetor. Disconnect wire from temperature sending unit.

STRADA & X1/9 4-CYLINDER (Cont.)

3) Disconnect heater hose at cylinder head. Disconnect all water hoses at union on left side of engine. Disconnect exhaust pipe from exhaust manifold.

4) Disconnect reaction rod from engine bracket and hose from exhaust shroud. Remove timing cover, then remove alternator and water pump drive belt. Remove air pump drive belt, then loosen nut on tensioner pulley and remove timing belt. Remove cylinder head nuts and bolts, then remove head and manifolds as an assembly.

Installation — 1) Thoroughly clean all gasket surfaces on cylinder head and block. Use new head gasket with word "ALTO" facing up wen installing cylinder head.

2) For vehicles with .75" (19 mm) head bolts, tighten bolts in sequence shown in *Fig. 1* in 3 stages. If necessary, modify tool J28032 (Fiat A50131/1) by removing ¼" (6 mm) of material from bottom of tool. Tighten bolts first to 29 ft. lbs. (93 N.m), then to 69 ft. lbs. (94 N.m) following sequence in *Fig. 1*. Loosen bolts ½ turn and retighten in sequence.

3) For vehicles with .67" (17 mm) head bolts, lubricate all bolts and washers with SAE engine oil and let excess oil drip for 30 minutes. Tighten bolts in 4 stages using special tool (Fiat A50172) in sequence shown. *See Fig. 1*. First tighten bolts to 15 ft. lbs. (20 N.m), then retighten to 29 ft. lbs. (39 N.m).

4) Apply paint marks to 1 corner of all the head bolts and a corresponding mark to the cylinder head. Tighten all bolts to a 90° angle. Retighten bolts another 90°. Bolts must now have been tightened a total of 180° in 2 stages.

5) For all vehicles complete installation in reverse order of removal. See Timing Belt Replacement in this article.

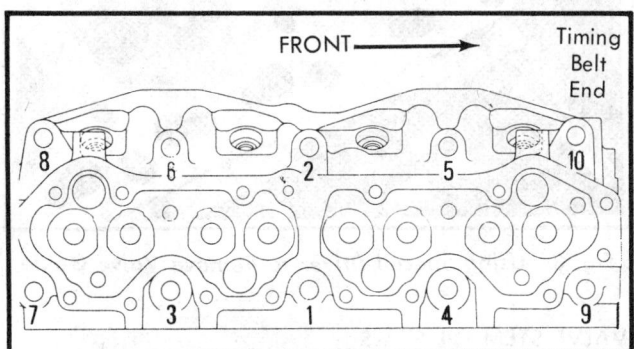

Fig. 1   Cylinder Head Tightening Sequence

CAMSHAFT

TIMING BELT REPLACEMENT

NOTE — *If timing belt is loosened or removed to perform repair work, install new belt.*

Removal (Strada) — 1) Disconnect battery cable. Remove timing belt covers (lower cover bolt must be removed from under vehicle). Turn engine with tool (A.60459) until crankshaft pulley mark is aligned with TDC indicator and camshaft sprocket index mark is aligned with mark on belt guard.

2) Loosen alternator and A/C compressor (if equipped) mounting bolts and remove pulley drive belt. Loosen idler pulley nut and move pulley left as far as possible. Secure with nut and remove belt.

Installation — Install new timing belt with slack on tensioner side. Ensure timing belt teeth are perfectly coupled with sprockets. Loosen idler pulley nut to allow tensioner to tighten belt. Tighten idler pulley nut. Check that timing marks are correctly aligned. To complete installation, reverse removal procedure.

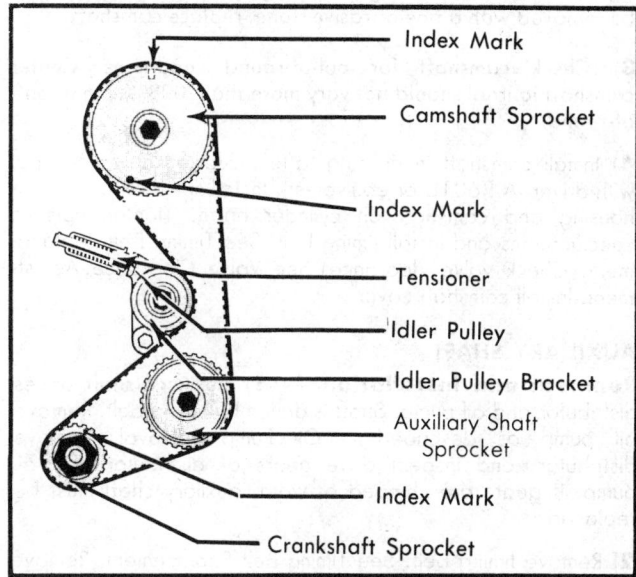

Fig. 2   Timing Belt Correctly Installed on Camshaft, Auxiliary Shaft and Crankshaft Sprockets

Removal (X1/9) — 1) Rotate crankshaft to position No. 4 piston at TDC of compression stroke. Place gear selector in 4th gear position and set parking brake.

CAUTION — *DO NOT turn camshaft independently of crankshaft. This could cause valve to come in contact with pistons and damage engine.*

2) Remove right guard from under engine. Remove timing bolts and cover. Loosen alternator and remove alternator/water pump drive belt. Loosen air pump and remove drive belt.

3) Remove valve cover and check that camshaft lobes of No. 4 cylinder are pointing up. Remove distributor. Loosen idler pulley lock nut. Remove timing belt starting at idler pulley.

Installation — 1) Install timing belt making sure that teeth are properly engaged in sprockets. Start installation of timing belt at crankshaft pulley. Release idler pulley lock nut and retighten after tension is on belt.

CAUTION — *Never allow crankshaft to rotate counterclockwise. This could slacken belt, causing it to jump timing.*

2) Rotate engine one-half turn. Loosen idler pulley lock nut to ensure all slack is removed. Retighten lock nut. Rotate engine until No. 4 cylinder is in firing position (cam lobe up). Install remaining components in reverse of removal order.

STRADA & X1/9 4-CYLINDER (Cont.)

CAMSHAFT

Removal & Installation — 1) Remove timing belt protective cover and loosen belt tensioner. Remove timing belt from camshaft sprocket and remove sprocket from camshaft. Remove camshaft cover, camshaft and housing. Remove camshaft from housing and thoroughly clean and inspect both camshaft and housing.

2) If camshaft housing bores show signs of wear or scoring and are out of round, replace housing. Check camshaft for signs of seizure or scoring. If scoring or seizure marks cannot be removed with a fine abrasive stone, replace camshaft.

3) Check camshaft for out-of-round conditions. Center camshaft journal should not vary more than .008" (.2 mm) out-of-round.

4) Install camshaft in housing, after installing new end seal with driver (A.86018 or equivalent). Install sprocket and place housing and camshaft on cylinder head. Tighten nuts to specifications and install timing belt. See Timing Belt Replacement. Check valve clearance. See Valve Clearance Adjustment. Install camshaft cover.

AUXILIARY SHAFT

Removal and Installation — 1) Auxiliary shaft drives distributor and oil pump. Shaft is driven by timing belt. Remove oil pump as described in Oil Pump Removal. Remove distributor, and inspect drive gears of distributor and oil pump. If gears are chipped or worn, auxilary shaft must be replaced.

2) Remove timing belt. See Timing Belt Replacement. Remove auxiliary shaft sprocket. Remove lock plate and auxiliary shaft. Thoroughly clean and inspect shaft.

3) Check inner and outer journals of shaft. If journal size is less than specified, replace shaft. Check inside diameter of inner and outer bushings, if more than specified, replace bushings.

4) To replace bushings, drive out of crankcase using a suitable driver (A.60372/1/2 outer journal and A.660372/1 inner journal). Install new bushings using same drivers as used for removal. Make sure oil holes in bushings align with oil holes in crankcase. Ream bushings to specified clearance with shaft using a suitable reamer (A.90365).

5) Install auxiliary shaft and lock plate. Install sprocket and secure with lock plate and screw. Install remaining components as previously outlined or in reverse of removal order.

Auxiliary Shaft Specifications	
Application	**Size**
Auxiliary Shaft	
Outer Journal	1.4013-1.4023" (35.59-35.62mm)
Inner Journal	1.2575-1.2583" (31.94-31.96mm)
Bushings (Reamed)	
Outer Journal	1.4041-1.4049" (35.66-35.68mm)
Inner Journal	1.2598-1.2606" (32.00-32.02mm)
Clearance	
Outer Journal	.0018-.0036" (.046-.091mm)
Inner Journal	.0016-.0031" (.04-.08mm)

VALVE TIMING

1) With timing belt removed, rotate camshaft sprocket until marks on sprocket are in alignment with index marks on belt guard.

2) Rotate crankshaft sprocket until mark on sprocket aligns with index on end plate. Install timing belt as previously outlined, making sure camshaft or crankshaft are not rotated.

VALVES

VALVE ARRANGEMENT
E-I-I-E-E-I-I-E

VALVE GUIDE SERVICING

With cylinder head removed and disassembled, check clearance between valve stem and valve guide. If clearance is more than .006" (.15 mm), and valve stem is not worn, valve guide must be replaced. Use driver A 60395 to remove guides, and A 60462 to install guides. If guides are damaged during installation, finish ream with reamer (A.90310).

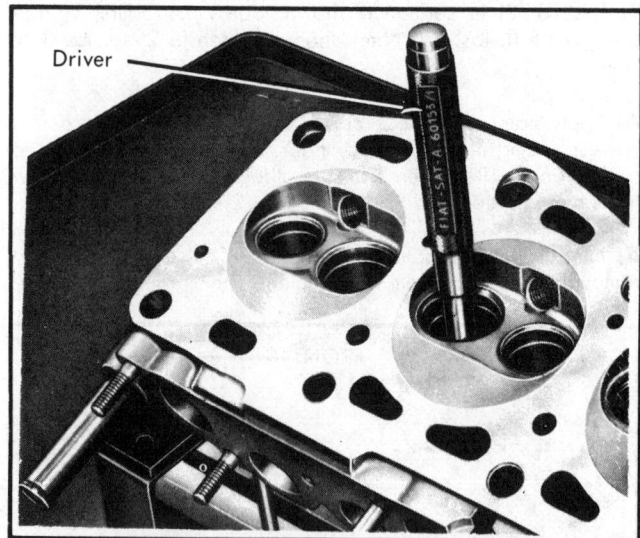

Fig. 3   Using Special Driver to Remove Valve Guide

VALVE STEM OIL SEALS

Removal — 1) Remove spark plug from cylinder No. 1. Piston should be approximately ⅔ of the way up the cylinder. Screw in compressor gauge hose/adapter into spark plug hole and connect an air hose, pressurizing cylinder to approximately 120-150 psi (8.4-10.5 kg/cm²).

2) Using valve spring compressor (Kent-Moore J28067), compress valve springs. Remove valve keepers. Slowly release tension from spring. Remove tool, spring retainer, inner and outer springs and lower spring seat from valve stem. Remove valve stem seal. Ensure that all portions of seal have been removed from valve guide.

Installation — 1) Using a light grease, lubricate the seal protector pin (60313/1) of valve guide seal installer and protector (Kent-Moore J28069). Place protector pin on end

STRADA & X1/9 4-CYLINDER (Cont.)

of valve stem. Slide new oil seal down pin and valve stem onto guide. Remove protector pin.

2) Place installer (60313/2) over valve stem seal. Lightly tap end of installer until oil seal is properly seated on valve guide. Remove installer. Reinstall lower spring seat, inner and outer springs and spring retainer. Using valve spring compressor, (J28067) compress valve springs and install valve keepers.

3) Repeat procedure for other valve of cylinder No. 1. After seal replacement, remove air hose, reinstall spark plug and repeat procedure on remaining cylinders. Reinstall camshaft housing and related parts onto cylinder head. See Camshaft Removal and Installation. Use a new timing belt.

VALVE SPRINGS

Removal — 1) With cylinder head removed, remove camshaft housing cover, intake and exhaust manifolds and camshaft with camshaft housing.

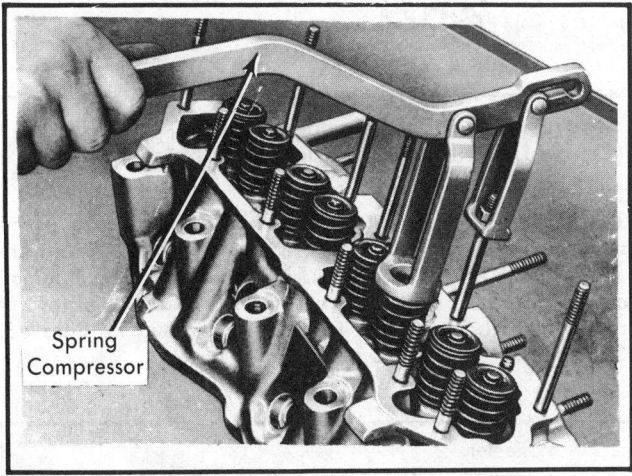

Fig. 4   Using Special Valve Spring Compressor to Remove Valve Springs

Valve Spring Tension	
Height in Inches (mm)	**Load in Lbs. (kg)**
Inner Spring	
1.220 (31)	33 ± 1.1 (14.9 ± 0.5)
.846 (21.5)	64 ± 2.6 (28.1 ± 1.2)
Outer Spring	
1.417 (36)	85 ± 3.3 (38.9 ± 1.5)
1.043 (26.5)	14 ± 5.5 (59.5 ± 2.5)

2) Using a suitable valve spring compressor (A.60311) compress valve spring. Remove valve keepers and release compressor. Remove spring retainer, inner spring, outer spring, lower spring seat and washer.

3) Inspect valve springs for wear or cracking. Using a suitable spring tester (AP.5049) check inner and outer springs against specifications with specified load applied.

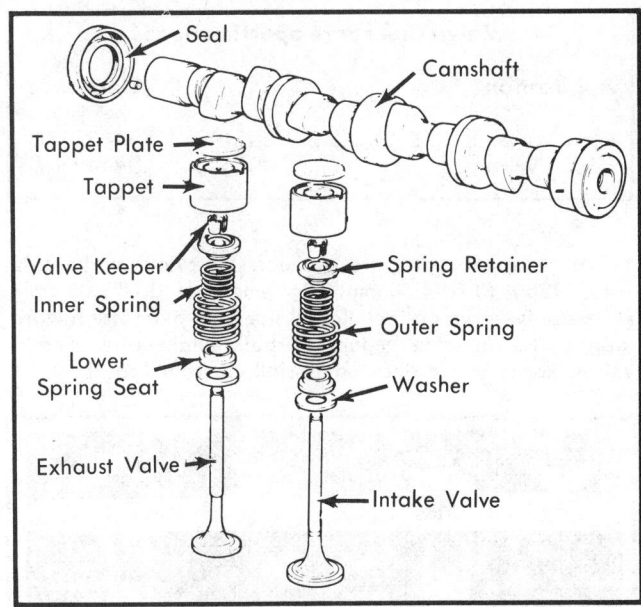

Fig. 5   Exploded View of Valve Train Components

VALVE CLEARANCE ADJUSTMENT

NOTE — *Check and adjust valve clearance with engine cold.*

1) Remove camshaft cover. Rotate engine until lobe on camshaft of valve being checked is pointing straight up. Using a feeler gauge, check clearance between camshaft lobe and valve tappet plate.

2) If clearance is not as specified, insert a suitable spring compressor (A.60421) under camshaft to release spring tension against camshaft lobe. Remove tappet plate with a suitable removing tool (A.87001). With plate removed, measure thickness to determine size of plate to be installed.

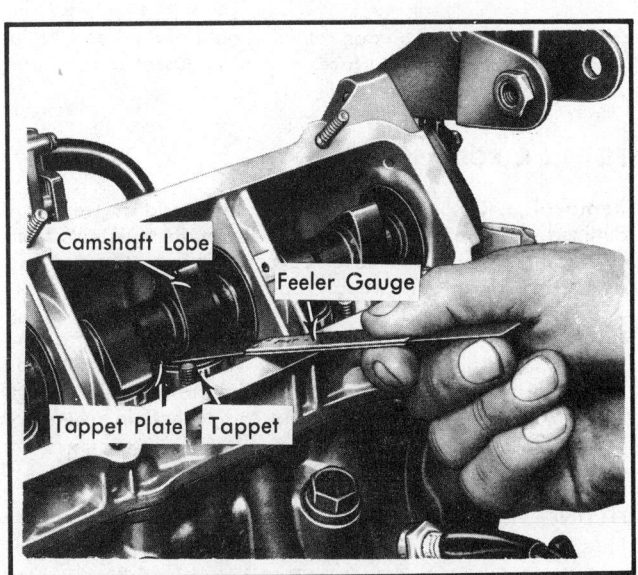

Fig. 6   Checking Valve Clearance

STRADA & X1/9 4-CYLINDER (Cont.)

Valve Clearance Specifications	
Application	**Clearance**
Intake Valve	.011-.014" (.24-.32 mm)
Exhaust Valve	.015-.018" (.34-.42 mm)

side clearance, side clearance should be no more than .006" (.15mm). Check ring end gap in cylinder against specifications.

3) Valve tappet plates are available in various thicknesses: .1457-.1850" (3.70-4.70 mm) in increments of .002" (.05 mm). Plate size is shown on face. Install side with plate size toward tappet. Use same procedure on both intake and exhaust valves. Recheck clearance and install camshaft cover.

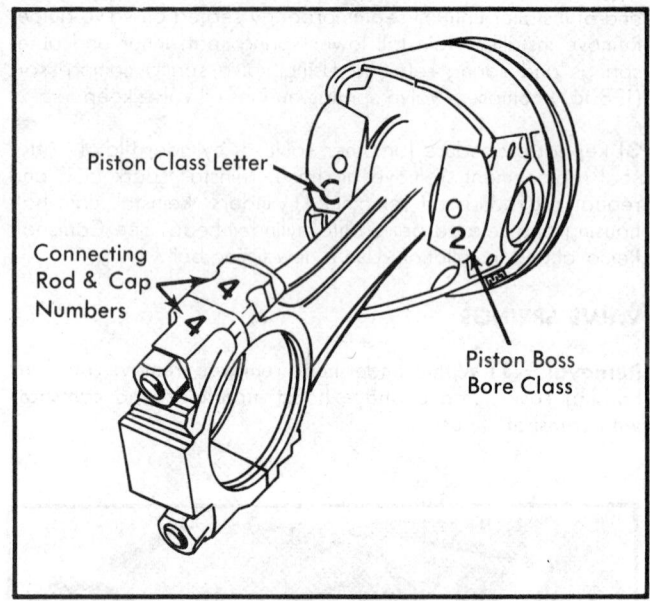

Fig. 8 Piston & Connecting Rod Assembly Showing Identification Class Numbers

2) Check fit of piston in cylinders with rings removed. There should be no more than .006" (.15mm) clearance. Pistons are available in .0079" (.2mm), .0157" (.4mm) and .0236" (.6mm) oversizes. There are three classes of standard size pistons. If piston is replaced, one of the same class must be installed. Class of piston is stamped on bottom of piston.

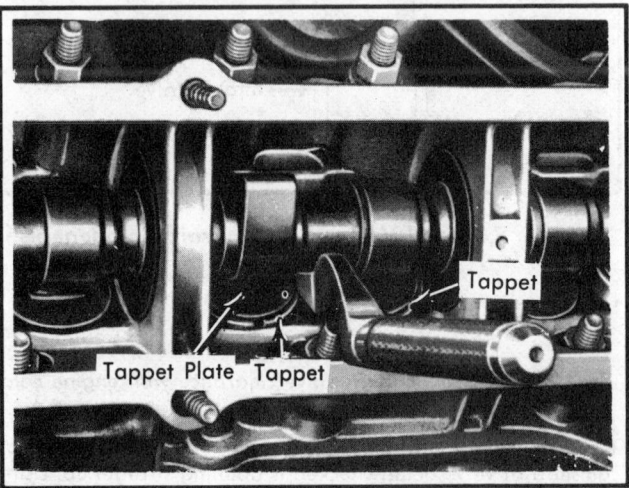

Fig. 7 Using Special Tool to Remove Valve Tappet Plate

PISTONS, PINS & RINGS

OIL PAN

1) Attach a suitable engine support to top of engine. Remove protective shields and engine crossmember.

2) Drain oil. Remove oil pan retaining bolts and oil pan. To install, clean all gasket surfaces, use new gasket and reverse removal procedure.

PISTON & ROD ASSEMBLY

Removal — Remove oil pan and cylinder head as previously outlined. Remove oil pump. See *Oil Pump*. Remove nuts from connecting rods and remove rod caps. Push piston and rod assembly up and out through top.

Installation — To install, compress piston rings with a ring compressor. Pistons must be installed with number stamped on connecting rod and rod cap facing away from auxiliary shaft. Tighten rod nuts. Install remaining components in reverse of removal procedure.

FITTING PISTONS

1) With piston and rod assembly removed and disassembled as previously outlined, thoroughly clean piston. Check ring

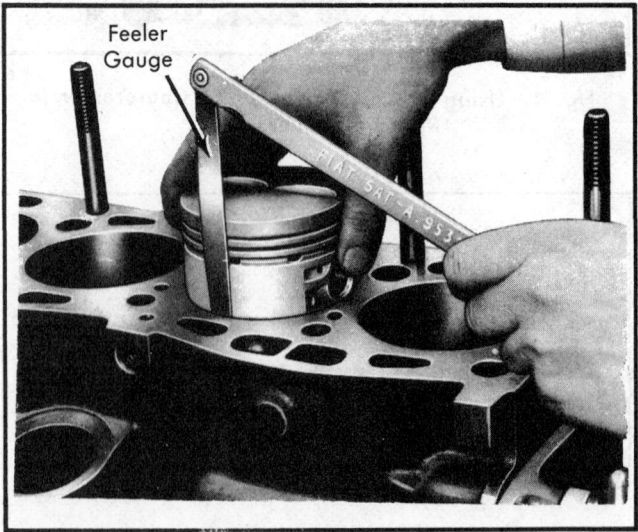

Fig. 9 Using a Feeler Gauge to Check Piston-to-Cylinder Wall Clearance

3) When installing rings, make sure gaps are spaced approximately 120° apart. Assemble piston and connecting rod and install in vehicle as previously outlined.

STRADA & X1/9 4-CYLINDER (Cont.)

Piston Class Specification	
Application	①**Size**
Strada & 1/9	
Class A	3.3999-3.4003" (86.360-86.370 mm)
Class B	3.4007-3.4011" (86.380-86.390 mm)
Class C	3.4015-3.4019" (86.400-86.410 mm)
① — Measured at 1.08" (27.5 mm) from piston skirt edge.	

PISTON PIN REPLACEMENT

1) Remove piston and rod assembly as previously outlined. Remove circlips and drive out piston pin using a suitable driver (A.60251).

2) Check fit of pin in piston. Pin should be push fit in piston and not fall through under its own weight. There are 2 classes of piston pin and piston bore sizes. If piston pin is to be replaced, it must be replaced with a pin of the same class. Class of piston is stamped on bottom of piston and class of pin is stamped on face of pin and bottom of piston. *See Fig. 8.*

Piston Pin & Bore Class Specifications	
Application	**Size**
Piston Pin	
Class 1	.8658-.8659" (21.991-21.994mm)
Class 2	.8659-.8660" (21.994-21.996mm)
Piston Pin Bore	
Class 1	.8660-.8661" (21.996-21.999mm)
Class 2	.8661-.8662" (21.999-22.002mm)

3) Check piston pin clearance in connecting rod. If clearance is more than specified, drive bushing from connecting rod using a suitable driver (A.60054). Install a new bushing with same driver and ream to size with a new piston pin.

4) Piston pin bore in piston is offset .08" (2 mm). Install connecting rod with numbered side on same side as pin offset.

5) Lubricate piston and secure connecting rod big end in a vise. Place piston in proper position on connecting rod and push in piston pin with driver (A.60251). Install circlips using special tool (A.60301).

6) After installation, ensure circlips end gap is not in line with slot provided in piston. Install piston and connecting rod assembly as previously outlined.

CRANKSHAFT MAIN & CONNECTING ROD BEARINGS

MAIN & CONNECTING ROD BEARING SERVICE

1) Remove engine as previously outlined. Remove cylinder head, oil pan, clutch and flywheel as previously outlined.

Remove oil pump. See *Oil Pump.* Remove all sprockets and timing belt. See *Timing Belt Replacement.*

2) Remove cover plates and seals from both ends of engine. Remove all piston and connecting rod assemblies. Remove main bearing caps with lower bearing halves.

3) Remove crankshaft and upper bearing halves. Remove thrust bearings from flywheel end main bearing saddle. Thoroughly clean and inspect crankshaft and crankcase.

4) Check crankshaft journals for out-of-round. If more than .0002" (.005 mm) out-of-round, crankshaft must be ground to next undersize. Bearings for undersize crankshafts are available in .010" (.25 mm), .020" (.50 mm), .030" (.76 mm) and .040" (1 mm) undersizes.

5) Use the Plastigage method to check main bearing clearances. Install upper bearing halves in crankcase and install crankshaft. Place a piece of Plastigage on journal and install main bearing cap with bearing. Tighten bolts to specifications and then remove main bearing cap.

6) With cap removed, check flattened Plastigage against scale on back of package to determine if clearance is as specified. Check connecting rod bearing clearance using same procedure. If clearance is incorrect, crankshaft must be ground to next undersize and bearings of corresponding undersize installed.

7) With correct clearance obtained, install upper bearing halves in crankcase. Lubricate bearings and install crankshaft. Install main bearing caps with bearings and tighten bolts to specifications. Rotate crankshaft to check for freedom of movement.

8) Check crankshaft endplay. See *Thrust Bearing Alignment.* Install remaining components in reverse of removal order or as previously outlined. Install engine as previously outlined.

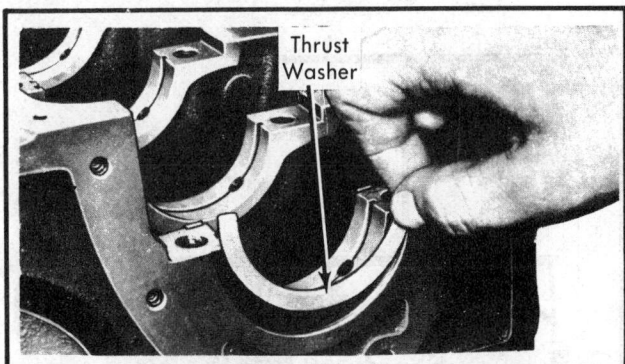

Fig. 10 Fitting Crankshaft Thrust Washer to Block

THRUST BEARING ALIGNMENT

1) With crankshaft installed and main bearing caps tightened, attach a dial indicator to crankcase with arm against flywheel end of crankshaft. Pry crankshaft back and forth to measure end play.

2) If end play is more than .0137" (.35 mm), remove flywheel end main bearing cap and install oversize thrust rings. Thrust rings are available in .005" (.13 mm) oversize. Install thrust rings with grooves facing crankshaft shoulder.

Fiat Engines

STRADA & X1/9 4-CYLINDER (Cont.)

FRONT & REAR MAIN BEARING OIL SEAL SERVICE

1) Front and rear main bearing oil seals are secured in end plates mounted to both ends of crankcase. Both seals should be replaced when crankshaft has been removed.

2) Drive seals from end plates and install new ones. Lubricate sealing lip of seal and use new gaskets when installing end plates.

ENGINE OILING

Crankcase Capacity — Normal drain and refill capacity for both models is 4½ quarts.

Oil Filter — Full flow, mounted on front side of engine.

Normal Oil Pressure — 50-71 psi (3.5-5.0 kg/cm²) with engine at 212°F (100°C).

Pressure Relief Valve — Mounted in oil pump. *See Oil Pump.*

ENGINE OILING SYSTEM

Oil is circulated through engine by pressure provided by a gear type oil pump. Pump is mounted on bottom of crankcase and driven by the auxiliary shaft. Oil is drawn from oil pan by oil pump and circulated through a full flow oil filter. Oil is then pumped into main oil gallery of crankcase where it is distributed to crankshaft and camshaft. Oil flows through crankshaft to lubricate main and connecting rod bearings. Cylinders, pistons and piston pins are lubricated by oil squirted from hole in connecting rod. Oil flows through camshaft to journals. Oil is squirted from number two and four journal to lubricate valve tappets and valves. Auxiliary shaft is lubricated by oil from main oil gallery. Excess oil flows back into oil pan.

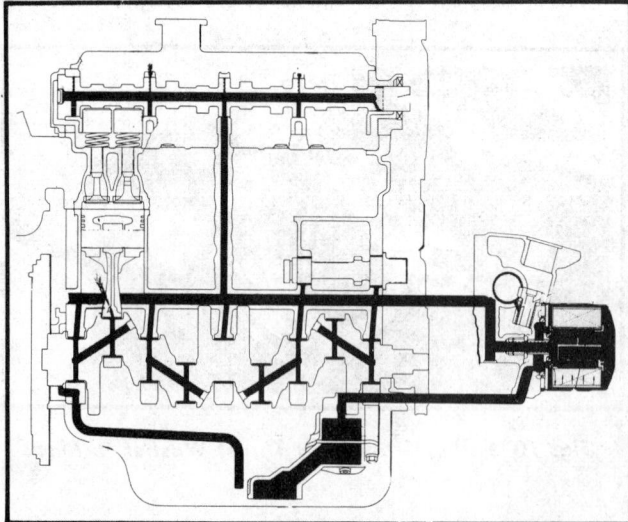

Fig. 11 Diagram Showing Engine Lubrication Flow

OIL PUMP

Removal & Installation — 1) Remove oil pan as previously outlined. Remove retaining screws and slide out oil pump with suction tube.

2) Clamp pump housing in a vise and remove suction pipe with filter screen and relief valve. Remove pump cover and gears. Thoroughly clean all components.

3) Check both gears for excessive wear and replace as necessary. Check clearance between gears. If more than .010" (.25 mm), replace both gears. Check gear-to-pump housing clearance. If more than .010" (.25 mm), replace gears or housing as necessary.

4) Check gear end play by placing a straightedge on mating surface of pump and inserting a feeler gauge between straightedge and gears. If clearance is more than .006" (.15 mm), replace gears or housing as necessary. Check clearance between drive gear shaft and housing. If more than .004" (.10 mm), replace gear or housing as necessary.

5) Inspect pressure relief spring for cracking or wear. Inspect valve for wear or scoring.

6) Assemble oil pump in reverse order of disassembly. To install, reverse removal procedure.

Oil Pump Specifications	
Application	**Clearance**
Gear-to-Gear	.006" (.15mm)
Gear-to-Housing	.004-.007" (.11-.18mm)
Gear Endplay	.0008-.0041" (.02-.11mm)

ENGINE COOLING

Radiator Cap — Opens at 11 psi (0.8 kg/cm²).

Thermostat — Temperature range was not available from manufacturer.

Thermoswitch — Operates at 185° F (85° C).

Cooling System Capacity	
Application	**Capacity**
Strada	7.5 quarts
X1/9	12.2 quarts

WATER PUMP

Removal — 1) Remove protective panels from bottom of engine and drain cooling system. Remove alternator and drive belt. On models with air conditioning, remove compressor and mount. On models with air pump, remove top half of timing belt cover, air pump and drive belt.

2) Disconnect hoses from water pump, then remove nuts attaching water pipe to pump and disconnect pipe. Remove bolts holding water pump to engine and remove pump.

Installation — Clean all gasket surfaces and install new gasket. Reverse removal procedure and refill cooling system. Run engine and check for leaks.

Fiat Engines

STRADA & X1/9 4-CYLINDER (Cont.)

ENGINE SPECIFICATIONS

GENERAL SPECIFICATIONS

Year	Displ. cu. ins.	Displ. cc	Carburetor	HP at RPM	Torque (Ft. Lbs. at RPM)	Compr. Ratio	Bore in.	Bore mm	Stroke in.	Stroke mm
1981	91.4	1498	Fuel Inj.	75@5500	.....	8.5:1	3.40	86.4	2.52	63.9

VALVES

Engine & Valve	Head Diam. In. (mm)	Face Angle	Seat Angle	Seat Width In. (mm)	Stem Diameter In. (mm)	Stem Clearance In. (mm)	Valve Lift In. (mm)
1498cc Intake	1.4173 (36)	45.5°	45°	.0787 (2)	.3139-.3146 (7.974-7.992)	.0012-.0026 (.030-.066)	.3622 (9.20)
Exhaust	1.3031 (33.1)	45.5°	45°	.0787 (2)	.3139-.3146 (7.974-7.992)	.0012-.0026 (.030-.066)	.3641 (9.25)

VALVE SPRINGS

Engine	Free Length In. (mm)	PRESSURE Lbs. @ In. (kg @ mm) Valve Closed	PRESSURE Lbs. @ In. (kg @ mm) Valve Open
1498 cc Inner	1.646 (41.8)	62@.846 (28@21.5)	32.8@1.220 (14.9@31)
Outer	2.122 (53.9)	131@1.043 (59.4@26.5)	85.7@1.417 (38.8@36)

VALVE TIMING

Engine	INTAKE Open (BTDC)	INTAKE Close (ABDC)	EXHAUST Open (BBDC)	EXHAUST Close (ATDC)
1498 cc	10°	54°	54°	12°

PISTONS, PINS, RINGS

Engine	PISTONS Clearance In. (mm)	PINS Piston Fit In. (mm)	PINS Rod Fit In. (mm)	Rings	End Gap In. (mm)	Side Clearance In. (mm)
1498cc	.0011-.0019 (.03-.05)	.0001-.0003 (.002-.008)	.0004-.0006 (.010-.016)	No. 1	.0118-.0177 (.30-.45)	.0018-.0030 (.045-.077)
				No. 2	.0118-.0177 (.30-.45)	.0016-.0028 (.040-.072)
				No. 3	.0098-.0157 (.25-.40)	.0012-.0024 (.030-.062)

CRANKSHAFT MAIN & CONNECTING ROD BEARINGS

Engine	MAIN BEARINGS Journal Diam. In. (mm)	MAIN BEARINGS Clearance In. (mm)	Thrust Bearing	Crankshaft End Play In. (mm)	CONNECTING ROD BEARINGS Journal Diam. In. (mm)	Clearance In. (mm)	Side Play In. (mm)
1498cc	1.9990-1.9997 (50.775-50.795)	.0019-.0037 (.050-.095)	①	.0021-.0104 (.055-.265)	1.7913-1.7920 (45.498-45.518)	.0014-.0034 (.036-.086)	.....

① — Thrust ring is installed at flywheel end main bearing cap.

Fiat Engines

STRADA & X1/9 4-CYLINDER (Cont.)
ENGINE SPECIFICATIONS (Cont.)

CAMSHAFT			
Engine	Journal Diam. In. (mm)	Clearance In. (mm)	Lobe Lift In. (mm)
1498 cc			
No. 1	1.1789-1.1795 (29.944-29.960)	.0011-.0028 (.029-.070)	....
No. 2	1.8872-1.8878 (47.935-47.950)	.0012-.0028 (.030-.070)	....
No. 3	1.8951-1.8957 (48.135-48.150)	.0012-.0028 (.030-.070)	....
No. 4	1.9030-1.9035 (48.335-48.350)	.0012-.0028 (.030-.070)	....
No. 5	1.9108-1.9114 (48.535-48.550)	.0012-.0028 (.030-.070)	....

TIGHTENING SPECIFICATION

Application	Ft. Lbs. (N.m)
Cylinder Head Bolt	See Text
Main Bearing Cap Bolts	59 (80)
Connecting Rod Cap Bolts	38 (51)
Intake and Exhaust Manifold	20 (27)
Camshaft Sprocket Bolt	61 (83)
Timing Belt Tensioner Pulley Nut	33 (44)
Crankshaft Pulley and Sprocket Nut	101 (137)
Flywheel-to-Crankshaft Bolts	61 (83)

ACCORD, CIVIC & PRELUDE 4-CYLINDER

ENGINE CODING

ENGINE IDENTIFICATION

Engine serial number is stamped on firewall side of engine block, near the transaxle. Serial number is proceeded by engine model number.

Engine Identification	
Application	**Code**
Civic	
1335 cc	EJ1
1487 cc	EM1
Accord (1751 cc)	EK1
Prelude (1751 cc)	EK1

ENGINE, CYLINDER HEAD, & MANIFOLDS

ENGINE

Removal — 1) Remove battery cables, battery, and mounting tray. Remove headlight trim, front bumper apron, and grille to gain access to hood brackets. Remove hood. Drain coolant, engine oil, and transmission fluid. Remove air cleaner and attached ducting. Disconnect brake booster hose at elbow and all electrical connections and wires to engine. Disconnect fuel lines and throttle cable. Remove radiator hoses and heater hoses. If equipped, detach EGR control box and let hang next to engine. Remove alternator.

2) If equipped, remove air conditioner hoses and compressor (Accord). On other models, remove compressor with hoses attached and wire out of way. On manual transmission models, remove clutch slave cylinder with hydraulic line attached. On automatic transmission models, remove oil cooling lines. On all models, disconnect speedometer cable. If equipped, remove power steering pump and bracket.

3) Place front of vehicle on jack stands and remove front wheels. On Prelude, remove engine guards and stabilizer bars. On all models, disconnect right and left lower arm ball joints and tie rod ends. Remove right and left axles. On vehicles with automatic transmissions, remove shift console, indicator, shift cables, and housing. On manual transmission models, disconnect shift rod clevis and torque rod. On all models, disconnect exhaust pipes.

4) Attach suitable lifting device, and raise engine enough to off-load engine mounts. Remove engine support bolts, and push left engine support into shock mount bracket. Remove front and rear engine mounts and torque rods. Carefully lift engine/transaxle assembly out of vehicle, ensuring all wires and hoses are detached.

Installation — Install engine in reverse order of removal. When replacing axles, insert shaft until spring clip "clicks" into groove in differential side gear. Make sure all control cables are adjusted properly.

CYLINDER HEAD

NOTE — *To avoid damage, do not remove cylinder head until engine has been allowed to cool.*

Removal — 1) Disconnect battery, drain cooling system, and remove air cleaner and related hoses. Disconnect all electrical wires and connections to cylinder head. Disconnect fuel line, throttle cable, and emission hoses from carburetor, and remove carburetor.

2) Remove radiator and heater hoses. Disconnect hot air ducts and remove header pipe from exhaust manifold. On vehicles with air conditioning, remove alternator and bracket. On vehicles without air conditioning, remove bolt securing alternator bracket to cylinder head, and loosen alternator adjusting bolt. Remove valve cover and timing belt upper cover.

3) Bring No. 1 piston to TDC. Loosen timing belt pivot and adjusting bolts, and slip timing belt off camshaft pulley. Remove oil pump gear cover and pull oil pump shaft out of cylinder head. Remove cylinder head bolts in reverse of tightening sequence by turning 30° at a time until loose. Remove cylinder head.

NOTE — *Do not crimp or bend timing belt more than 90°, or less than 1" (25 mm) in diameter.*

4) Measure cylinder head warpage along the edge and 3 ways across center. If under .002" (.05 mm), resurfacing is not required. If clearance is .002-.008" (.05-.20 mm), resurfacing is necessary.

Installation — 1) Ensure that all mating surfaces are clean and free of cracks. Place new gasket on cylinder block engaging dowel pins.

2) Position cylinder head on block making sure holes in head line up with dowel pins in block. On 1751 cc engines, "UP" mark on camshsft gear should be toward top. See *Fig. 3*.

3) On 1335 and 1487 cc engines, cutout on camshaft gear should be at top. See *Fig. 4*. On all models, tighten head bolts in 2 steps in sequence shown in *Fig. 1*.

4) To complete installation, reverse removal procedure.

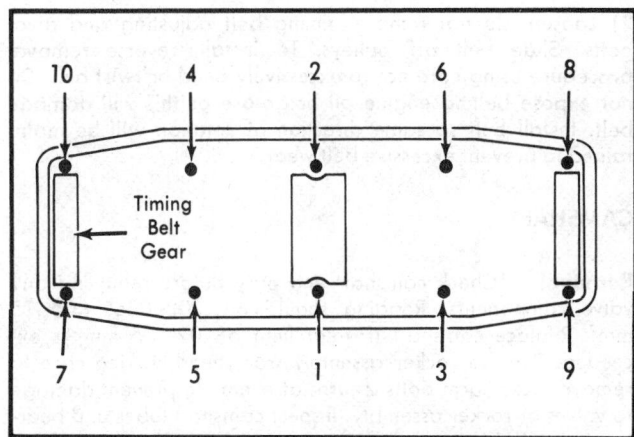

**Fig. 1 Cylinder Head Tightening Sequence
(Loosen in Reverse Sequence)**

MANIFOLDS

Removal — Loosen 4 intake-to-exhaust manifold bolts. Remove manifold-to-head mounting nuts in reverse order of tightening sequence. See *Fig. 2*. Remove and disassemble manifolds.

ACCORD, CIVIC & PRELUDE 4-CYLINDER (Cont.)

Installation — 1) Use new gaskets between manifolds and heat shield. Tighten 4 bolts holding manifolds together FINGER TIGHT.

2) Place manifolds and new gasket in position on cylinder head. Tighten mounting bolts in sequence shown in *Fig. 2*. Tighten exhaust-to-intake manifold bolts.

NOTE — *Spring washers under special nuts must be mounted with dished surface facing in.*

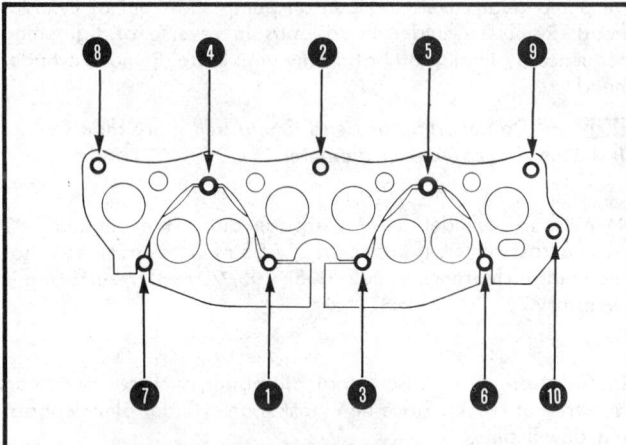

Fig. 2   Manifold Tightening Sequence (Loosen in Reverse Sequence)

TIMING BELT

1) Remove water pump drive belt, water pump pulley and crankshaft pulley. Remove upper timing belt cover from cylinder head and remove lower timing belt cover from engine block.

2) Loosen, do not remove, timing belt adjusting and pivot bolts. Slide belt off pulleys. To install, reverse removal procedure using care not to excessively bend or twist belt. Do not expose belt to engine oil or grease as this will damage belt. Install belt so same direction of rotation will be maintained to prevent excessive belt wear.

CAMSHAFT

Removal — Check camshaft end play before removing any valve components. Reading should be .002-.006" (.05-.15 mm). Replace camshaft if wear limit of .02" (.5 mm) is exceeded. Remove rocker assembly from head, taking care to remove rocker arm bolts 2 turns at a time to prevent damage to valves or rocker assembly. Inspect camshaft lobes and bearing journals for wear or damage. Using Plastigage method, check camshaft journal clearance. Check camshaft for runout. If it exceeds .002" (.06 mm), replace camshaft.

Installation — Oil camshaft bearing journals and install camshaft with keyway pointing up (No. 1 piston at TDC). Apply a non-hardening sealer to mating surfaces on end camshaft supports and cylinder head. Set rocker assembly in place and tighten bolts from the center out, two turns at a time until proper torque is reached.

CAMSHAFT	
Camshaft Lobe Height	
Application	**In. (mm)**
1335 cc	
Intake	1.4930-1.5025 (37.92-38.16)
Exhaust	1.4942-1.5037 (37.95-38.19)
Auxiliary	1.3223-1.3381 (33.58-33.98)
1487 cc	
Intake	1.4807-1.4901 (37.61-37.85)
Exhaust	1.4819-1.4913 (37.65-37.88)
Auxiliary	1.3223-1.3381 (33.58-33.98)
1751 cc	
Intake	1.4930-1.5025 (37.92-38.16)
Exhaust	1.4962-1.5057 (38.01-38.24)
Auxiliary	1.3121-1.3247 (33.33-33.65)

VALVE TIMING

1) Rotate crankshaft until TDC mark on flywheel or driveplate is aligned with index mark. On 1751 cc engines, "UP" mark on camshaft gear should be at 11 o'clock position and timing mark aligned with arrow on cylinder head. *See Fig. 4.*

2) On 1335 cc engines, cutaway in camshaft gear should be at top, and timing marks aligned with valve cover surface. On 1487 cc engines, cutaway should be at top and timing mark aligned with arrow on cylinder head. *See Fig. 5.* Slide timing belt on without disturbing pulley positions and adjust belt tension.

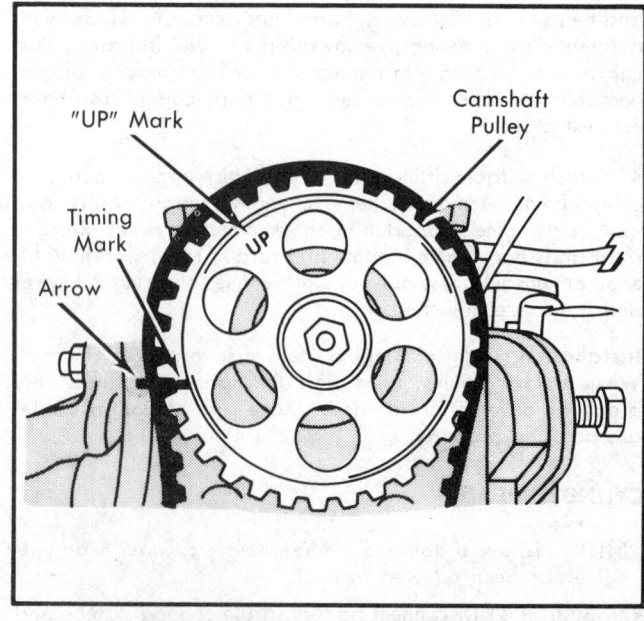

Fig. 3   Camshaft Alignment Marks in Position for Installing Camshaft Belt (1751 cc Engine)

ACCORD, CIVIC & PRELUDE 4-CYLINDER (Cont.)

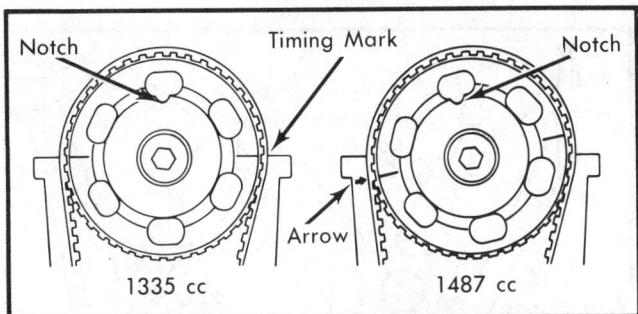

Fig. 4 Camshaft Alignment Marks (1335 & 1487 cc Engines)

TIMING BELT TENSION

Tension is spring loaded to apply proper tension to timing belt automatically. First make the following adjustment: Loosen timing belt pivot bolt (upper) and adjusting bolt (lower). Rotate crankshaft about ¼ turn COUNTERCLOCKWISE to create tension on timing belt. Tighten adjusting bolt, then tighten pivot bolt.

VALVES

VALVE ARRANGEMENT

Rear Side — I-E-E-I-I-E-E-I (left to right).
Front Side — All Auxiliary.

ROCKER ARM ASSEMBLY

Removal — Loosen rocker arm shaft support bolts in crisscross pattern starting with end supports. Pull out roll pins from both end shaft supports and remove supports, rocker collars, rocker arms and springs. Retain components in proper order for reassembly.

Installation — Measure all rocker arms for arm-to-shaft clearance. If clearance exceeds .0035" (.08 mm), replace rocker shaft and/or arms. Assemble in reverse of disassembly and install rocker arm assembly on engine. Tighten support bolts in a criss-cross pattern starting with center support.

VALVE SPRINGS

Intake & Exhaust Valves — Using valve spring compressor, remove valve keepers, collars and springs. Check valve springs for squareness, free length and tension. Install in reverse of removal procedure, making sure closely wound coils are nearest cylinder head.

AUXILIARY VALVES

1) Remove auxiliary valve holder nut using special "T" wrench (07907-657001) and pull valve holder assembly out of head. Auxiliary chamber collar may be removed with a slide hammer type puller.

2) Compress spring and remove keepers. Disassemble and inspect valve assembly. Valve seat may be reconditioned, however entire assembly should be replaced if any component exceeds service limit.

3) Install chamber collar in each auxiliary valve hole with 2 new gaskets. Use alignment tool (07944-6590000) inserted in

round hole toward spark plug opening with oval hole of collar towards combustion chamber. Leave alignment tool in place and insert auxiliary valve with new "O" ring, torquing to final specification with same tool used for removal.

VALVE GUIDE SERVICING

NOTE — *For best results, heat cylinder head to 300°F (150°C) to remove or replace valve guides.*

Using suitable driver, drive valve guides out of cylinder head from port side. Install new guides from top of head with driver and attachment. Drive guide in until attachment bottoms on head. Ream valve guides to provide proper clearance.

VALVE CLEARANCE ADJUSTMENT

Remove rocker arm cover. Rotate crankshaft so that No. 1 piston is at TDC on firing stroke. Adjust valve clearance on No. 1 cylinder. Rotate 180° COUNTERCLOCKWISE so that No. 3 piston is at TDC on firing stroke. Adjust valve clearance on No. 3 cylinder. Rotate crankshaft 180° and adjust valve clearance on No. 4 cylinder. Rotate crankshaft 180° and adjust valve clearance on No. 2 cylinder.

Valve Clearance Specifications	
Application	**In. (mm)**
1335 cc and 1487 cc	
Intake and Aux.	.005-.007 (.12-.17)
Exhaust	.007-.009 (.17-.22)
1751 cc	
Intake and Aux.	.005-.007 (.12-.17)
Exhaust	.010-.012 (.25-.30)

PISTONS, PINS & RINGS

PISTON & ROD ASSEMBLY

1) With oil pan and cylinder head removed, ream any ridge from top of cylinders. Mark piston and rod assemblies for proper reinstallation. Remove rod caps and push piston and rod assemblies out top of cylinder with a hammer handle.

2) Assemble piston and connecting rod with piston front mark and connecting rod oil jet hole on same side and facing intake manifold. Using a ring compressor, install piston and rod assemblies in proper cylinder.

NOTE — *Do NOT confuse reference number stamped across bearing cap and connecting rod with number indicating position of assembly in engine. This number indicates rod bore diameter only.*

FITTING PISTONS

1) Measure cylinder bore for taper and out-of-round. If taper exceeds .004" (.1 mm) or out-of-round exceeds .002" (.05 mm), rebore cylinder for oversize pistons. Determine piston-to-cylinder clearance. If not within specifications, reboring is necessary. Oversize pistons are available in diameters of 2.843" (72.21 mm) for 1335 cc engines, 2.927" (74.35 mm) for 1487 cc engines and 3.040" (77.22 mm) for 1751 cc engines.

2) Install 3 piece oil ring on piston with end gaps of rails and spacer staggered about 15°. Install top ring gap approx-

ACCORD, CIVIC & PRELUDE 4-CYLINDER (Cont.)

imately 90° from oil spacer and second ring gap 180° from spacer. Make sure no end gaps are in line with piston pin or thrust face of piston. Install all rings with markings facing upward.

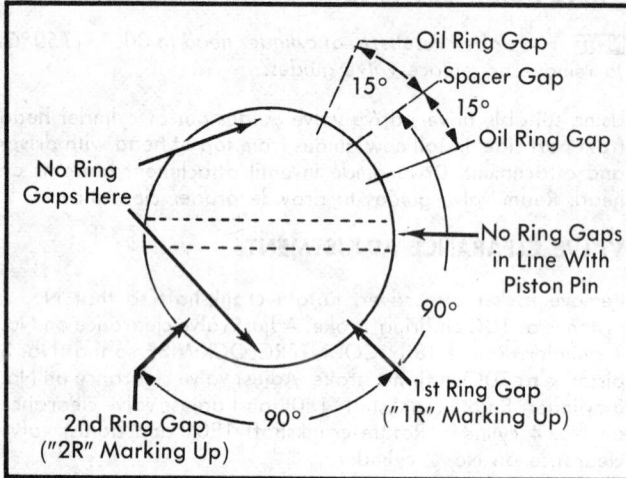

Fig. 5 Piston Ring Installation

PISTON PINS

Using a hydraulic press, remove piston pin from piston and connecting rod. Be sure recessed flat portion aligns with lips on collar. Install new pin by lightly oiling pin and pressing it into connecting rod until centered. Make sure piston is installed with mark on crown on same side as oil hole in connecting rod.

CRANKSHAFT MAIN & CONNECTING ROD BEARINGS

MAIN & CONNECTING ROD BEARINGS

1) Prior to disassembly, mark main and connecting rod bearings caps for reassembly in their original positions and check crankshaft endplay and connecting rod side play. Remove piston and connecting rod assemblies, remove main bearing caps and remove crankshaft.

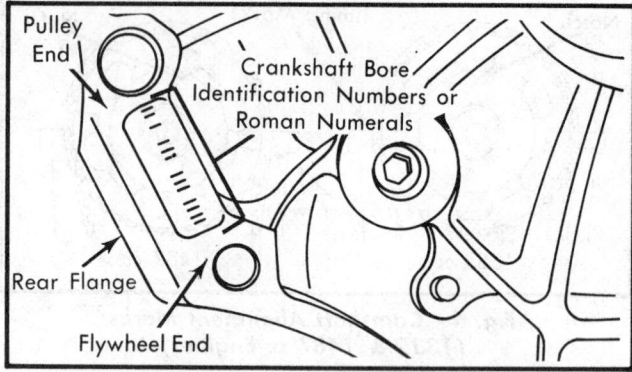

Fig. 6 Crankshaft Identification Locations (1751 cc and 1487 Engines)

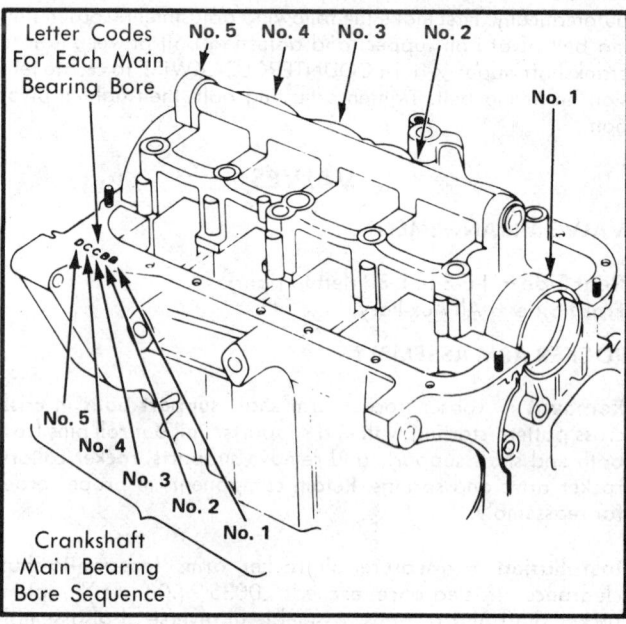

Fig. 7 Crankshaft Identification Locations (1335 cc Engine)

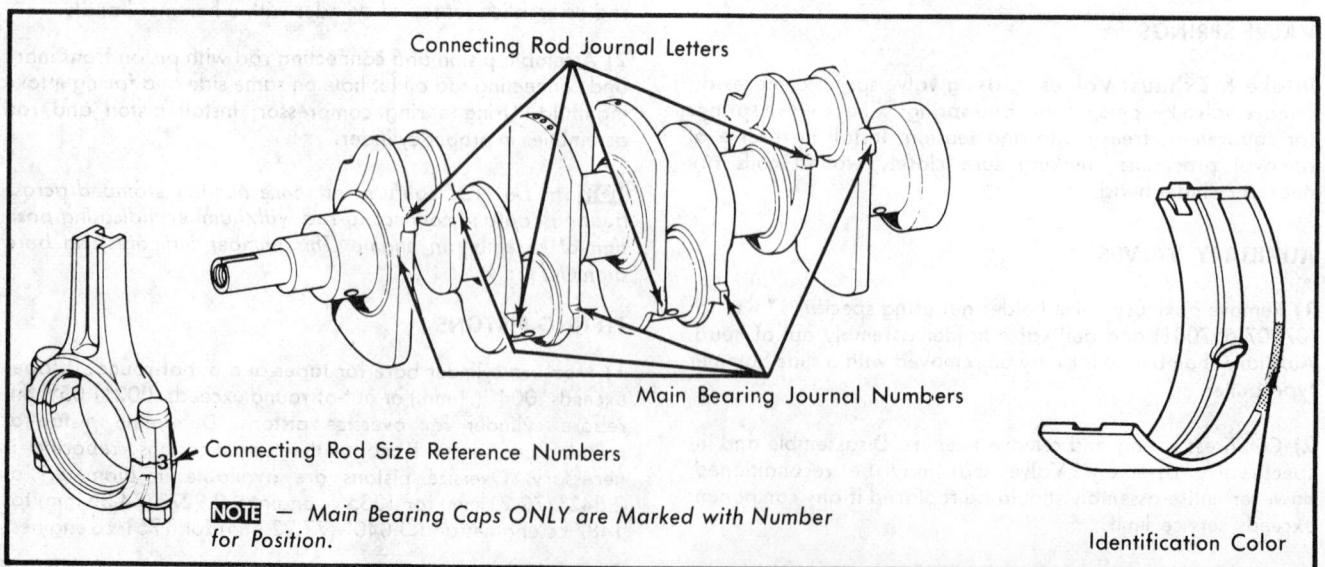

NOTE — Main Bearing Caps ONLY are Marked with Number for Position.

Fig. 8 Connecting Rod Bearing & Cylinder Block Identification Locations

ACCORD, CIVIC & PRELUDE 4-CYLINDER (Cont.)

2) Measure crankshaft for bend, out-of-round and taper (*See Specifications*). If any measurement exceeds specifications, crankshaft must be replaced. Do not attempt to regrind crankshaft as bearing journals are specifically heat-treated.

3) Using Plastigage method, determine bearing clearances. If bearing replacement is necessary, use following procedure to determine bearing size to use.

4) Referring to *Figs.* 7 and 9, note that all letters stamped on crankshaft counterweight pads apply to nearest connecting rod journal. All numbers stamped on crankshaft counterweight apply to nearest main bearing journal. Connecting rod caps have numbers stamped on cap.

5) The 1751 cc engine has Roman numerals stamped on a pad at flywheel end of engine block indicating each crankshaft bore dimension. The 1487 cc engine has the letters "A", "B", "C", or "D" stamped on a pad at flywheel end of engine block, also indicating each crankshaft bore dimension. The 1335 cc engine block has letters stamped on pads near contact surfaces of block, indicating each main bearing bore dimension. See *Fig.* 8.

6) To determine proper size (color) bearing insert, match crankshaft bore identification numerals or letters with main

Crankshaft Wear Specifications		
Application	Standard In. (mm)	Service Limit In. (mm)
Runout	.0012 (.03)	.0024 (.06)
Taper	.0002 (.005)	.0004 (.010)
Out-of-Round	.0002 (.005)	.0004 (.010)

CIVIC (1335 cc) MAIN BEARING JOURNALS In. (mm)

Journal Dia. 1.97 (50) / Crankcase Bore Dia. 2.13 (54)	A	B	C	D
	①0 to +.0002 (0 to +.006) ②-.0004 to -.0002 (-.010 to -.004)	①+.0002 to +.0005 (+.006 to +.012) ②-.0002 to +.0001 (-.004 to +.002)	①+.0005 to +.0007 (+.012 to +.018) ②+.0001 to +.0003 (+.002 to +.008)	①+.0007 to +.0009 (+.018 to +.024) ②+.0003 to +.0006 (+.008 to +.014)
1 -.0002 to 0 (-.006 to 0)	Red -.0001 to -.0002 (-.002 to -.005)	Pink -.0001 to +.00004 (-.002 to +.001)	Yellow +.00004 to +.0002 (+.001 to +.005)	Green +0002 to +.0003 (+.004 to +.007)
2 -.0005 to -.0002 (-.012 to -.006)	Pink -.0001 to +.00004 (-.002 to +.001)	Yellow +.00004 to +.0002 (+.001 to +.004)	Green +.0002 to +.0003 (+.005 to +.007)	Brown +.00004 to +.0003 (+.001 to +.007)
3 -.0007 to -.0005 (-.018 to -.012)	Yellow +.00004 to +.0002 (+.001 to +.005)	Green +.0002 to +.0003 (+.005 to +.007)	Brown +.00004 to +.0003 (+.001 to +.007)	Black +.0004 to +.0005 (+.010 to +.013)
4 -.0009 to -.0007 (-.024 to -.018)	Green +.0002 to +.0003 (+.005 to +.007)	Brown +.00004 to +.0003 (+.001 to +.007)	Black +.0004 to +.0005 (+.010 to +.013)	Blue +.0005 to +.0006 (+.013 to +.016)

① — Bore dia. tolerance for No. 1, 2, 4 or 5.
② — Bore dia. tolerance for No. 3 only.

CIVIC (1476 cc) MAIN BEARING JOURNALS In. (mm)

Journal Dia. 1.97 (50) / Crankcase Bore Dia. 2.13 (54)	A	B	C	D
	+.0016 to +.0018 (+.040 to +.046)	+.0018 to +.0020 (+.046 to +.052)	+.0020 to +.0023 (+.052 to +.058)	+.0023 to +.0025 (+.058 to +.064)
1 +.0009 to +.0012 (+.024 to +.030)	Red -.0001 to -.0002 (-.002 to -.005)	Pink -.0001 to +.00004 (-.002 to +.001)	Yellow +.00004 to +.0002 (+.001 to +.005)	Green +0002 to +.0003 (+.004 to +.007)
2 +.0007 to +.0009 (+.018 to +.024)	Pink -.0001 to +.00004 (-.002 to +.001)	Yellow +.00004 to +.0002 (+.001 to +.004)	Green +.0002 to +.0003 (+.005 to +.007)	Brown +.00004 to +.0003 (+.001 to +.007)
3 +.0005 to +.0007 (+.012 to +.018)	Yellow +.00004 to +.0002 (+.001 to +.005)	Green +.0002 to +.0003 (+.005 to +.007)	Brown +.00004 to +.0003 (+.001 to +.007)	Black +.0004 to +.0005 (+.010 to +.013)
4 +.0002 to +.0005 (+.006 to +.012)	Green +.0002 to +.0003 (+.005 to +.007)	Brown +.00004 to +.0003 (+.001 to +.007)	Black +.0004 to +.0005 (+.010 to +.013)	Blue +.0005 to +.0006 (+.013 to +.016)

Honda Engines

ACCORD, CIVIC & PRELUDE 4-CYLINDER (Cont.)

journal identification numbers in the following tables. Where the column and row intersect, find proper bearing insert. Example: For a main bearing, use "Main Bearing Journals" table. If number stamped on crankshaft is "2", and Roman numeral or letter stamped on block for corresponding journal is "III" or "C" respectively, use a "green" insert.

THRUST BEARINGS

Measure crankshaft end play. If found to be excessive, inspect thrust washers and thrust surface of crankshaft. Replace parts if necessary. Do not change thrust washer thickness by either grinding or shimming.

ACCORD & PRELUDE (1751 cc) MAIN BEARING JOURNALS In. (mm)

Journal Dia. 1.97 (50) / Crankcase Bore Dia. 2.13 (54)	I +.0016 to +.0018 (+.041 to +.046)	II +.0018 to +.0020 (+.046 to +.051)	III +.0020 to +.0023 (+.051 to +.058)	IIII +.0023 to +.0025 (+.058 to +.064)
1 +.0009 to +.0012 (+.023 to +.030)	Red −.0001 to −.0002 (−.002 to −.005)	Pink −.0001 to +.00004 (−.002 to +.001)	Yellow +.0002 to +.00004 (+.005 to +.001)	Green +.0002 to +.0003 (+.005 to +.007)
2 +.0007 to +.0009 (+.018 to +.023)	Pink −.0001 to +.00004 (−.002 to +.001)	Yellow +.0002 to +.00004 (+.005 to +.001)	Green +.0002 to +.0003 (+.005 to +.007)	Brown +.00004 to +.0003 (+.001 to +.007)
3 +.0005 to +.0007 (+.013 to +.018)	Yellow +.0002 to +.00004 (+.005 to +.001)	Green +.0002 to +.0003 (+.005 to +.007)	Brown +.00004 to +.0003 (+.001 to +.007)	Black +.0004 to +.0005 (+.010 to +.013)
4 +.0002 to +.0005 (+.005 to +.013)	Green +.0002 to +.0003 (+.005 to +.007)	Brown +.00004 to +.0003 (+.001 to +.007)	Black +.0004 to +.0005 (+.010 to +.013)	Blue +.0005 to +.0006 (+.013 to +.015)

CONNECTING ROD BEARING JOURNALS In. (mm)

Journal Dia. 1.654 (42) 1.57 (40)① / Connecting Rod Dia. 1.77 (45) ①1.69 (43)	1 0 to +.0002 (0 to +.006)	2 +.0002 to +.0005 (+.006 to +.012)	3 +.0005 to +.0007 (+.012 to +.018)	4 +.0007 to +.0009 (+.018 to +.024)
A 0 to −.0002 (0 to −.006)	Red −.0002 to −.0003 (−.005 to −.008)	Pink −.0001 to −.0002 (−.002 to −.005)	Yellow −.0001 to +.00004 (−.002 to +.001)	Green +.00004 to +.0002 (+.001 to +.004)
B −.0002 to −.0005 (−.006 to −.012)	Pink −.0001 to −.0002 (−.002 to −.005)	Yellow −.0001 to +.00004 (−.002 to +.001)	Green +.00004 to +.0002 (+.001 to +.004)	Brown +.0002 to +.0003 (+.004 to +.007)
C −.0005 to −.0007 (−.012 to −.018)	Yellow −.0001 to +.00004 (−.002 to +.001)	Green +.00004 to +.0002 (+.001 to +.004)	Brown +.0002 to +.0003 (+.004 to +.007)	Black +.0003 to +.0004 (+.007 to +.010)
D −.0007 to −.0009 (−.018 to −.024)	Green +.00004 to +.0002 (+.001 to +.004)	Brown +.0002 to +.0003 (+.004 to +.007)	Black +.0003 to +.0004 (+.007 to +.010)	Blue +.0004 to +.0005 (+.010 to +.013)

① — 1335 cc Engine.

Honda Engines

ACCORD, CIVIC & PRELUDE 4-CYLINDER (Cont.)

ENGINE OILING

ENGINE OILING SYSTEM

A rotor type oil pump draws oil from oil pan and delivers it under pressure through main bearing cradle to main and connecting rod bearings. Oil passes through rods to an oil jet which lubricates pistons and cylinder walls. An oil passage carries oil to camshaft bearings and rocker arms. Oil mist lubricates valve stems.

OIL PUMP

1) Remove oil pan, then oil pump assembly may be removed by removing four long bolts (one bolt under strainer). Pull out relief valve cotter pin and remove seat, spring and valve.

2) Remove two pump body bolts and disassemble pump. Inspect pump for wear or damage. Measure pump operating clearances and relief valve spring free length. Reassemble pump making sure marks on rotors face outward and are adjacent to each other. Place oil pickup in container of oil and operate pump with screwdriver to ensure that it is operating. Place finger over outlet hole and check the pressure is created as pump is turned.

Oil Pump Specifications

Application	Standard In. (mm)	Service Limit In. (mm)
Inner-to-Outer Rotor	.002-.006 (.04-.14)	.008 (.20)
Rotor-to-Body	.0039-.0071 (.10-.18)	.008 (.20)
Rotor End Clearance	.0012-.0039 (.03-.10)	.006 (.15)

Crankcase Capacity (with Filter)

Application	Capacity
Civic (1335 & 1487 cc)	3.8 quarts
Accord & Prelude (1751 cc)	3.7 quarts

NOTE – If oil pump driven gear is to be replaced, camshaft must also be replaced.

Oil Filter – Disposable with built-in by-pass valve

Pressure Regulator Valve – Non-adjustable

Normal Oil Pressure – 1335 cc & 1487 cc engines, at operating temperature, minimum of 20 psi (1.41 kg/cm²) at idle and 48-60 psi (3.37-4.22 kg/cm²) at 3000 RPM. For 1751 cc engine, at operating temperature, minimum of 21 psi (1.48 kg/cm²) at idle and 54-60 (3.80-4.22 kg/cm²) at 3000 RPM.

ENGINE COOLING

Thermostat – Starts to open at 176-183°F (80-84°C) and is fully open at 203°F (95°C).

Thermoswitch – Operates at 191-197°F (88.5-91.5°C).

Cooling System Capacity

Application	Capacity (Qts.)
Civic	
1335 cc	5.2
1487 cc	6.4
Accord & Prelude (1751 cc)	6.4

WATER PUMP

Removal – Drain radiator and loosen alternator adjusting bolts. Push alternator toward engine and remove drive belt. Remove water pump and "O" ring seal.

Installation – 1) Reinstall water pump. Loosen cooling system bleed valve located on thermostat housing. Fill radiator with coolant. When air bubbles no longer appear in coolant draining from bleed valve, close valve.

2) Start engine and place heater temperature control lever in high position. Run engine about ten minutes. Again open bleed valve and bleed system until there are no air bubbles in coolant draining from bleed valve. Refill radiator.

TIGHTENING SPECIFICATIONS

Application	Ft. Lbs. (N·m)
Camshaft Sprocket Bolt	22 (30)
Connecting Rod Bolts	23 (31)
Cylinder Head Bolts	43 (58)
Intake-to-Exhaust Manifold Bolts	18 (24)
Main Bearing Bolts	48 (65)
Manifold Nuts	16 (22)
Rocker Arm Support	
6 mm Bolts	9 (12)
8 mm Bolts	16 (22)
Timing Belt Adjustment Bolt	32 (44)
Timing Belt Pivot Bolt	32 (44)

ENGINE SPECIFICATIONS

GENERAL SPECIFICATIONS

Year	Displ. cu. ins.	cc	Carburetor	HP at RPM	Torque (Ft. Lbs. at RPM)	Compr. Ratio	Bore in.	mm	Stroke in.	mm
1981 Civic	81	1335	1 x 3-Bbl.	.....	.....	8.8:1	2.83	72.0	3.23	82.0
	91	1487	1 x 3-Bbl.	.....	.....	8.8:1	2.91	74.0	3.41	86.5
Accord & Prelude	107	1751	1 x 3-Bbl.	.....	.....	8.8:1	3.03	77.0	3.70	94.0

Honda Engines

ACCORD, CIVIC & PRELUDE 4-CYLINDER (Cont.)

ENGINE SPECIFICATIONS (Cont.)

VALVES							
Engine & Valve	Head Diam. In. (mm)	Face Angle	Seat Angle	Seat Width In. (mm)	Stem Diameter In. (mm)	Stem Clearance In. (mm)	Valve Lift In. (mm)
1335 cc							
Intake	1.374-1.382 (34.9-35.1)	45°	45°	.055-.061 (1.4-1.55)	.2591-.2594 (6.58-6.59)	.0008-.0020 (.02-.05)	.....
Exhaust	1.098-1.106 (27.9-28.1)	45°	45°	.055-.061 (1.4-1.55)	.2574-.2578 (6.537-6.547)	.0025-.0037 (.063-.093)	.....
Auxiliary	.469-.476 (11.9-12.1)	45°	45°	.0139-.0194 (.353-.494)	.215-.216 (5.472-5.487)	.0009-.0023 (.023-.058)	.....
1487 cc							
Intake	1.374-1.382 (34.9-35.1)	45°	45°	.055-.061 (1.4-1.55)	.2591-.2594 (6.58-6.59)	.0008-.0020 (.02-.05)	.....
Exhaust	1.098-1.106 (27.9-28.1)	45°	45°	.055-.061 (1.4-1.55)	.2574-2578 (6.537-6.547)	.0025-.0037 (.063-.093)	.....
Auxiliary	.469-.476 (11.9-12.1)	45°	45°	.0139-.0194 (.353-.494)	.2580-.2593 (6.572-6.587)	.0009-.0023 (.023-.058)	.....
1751 cc							
Intake	1.37-1.38 ① (34.9-35.1)	45°	45°	.049-.061 (1.25-1.55)	.2748-.2751 (6.98-6.99)	.0008-.0020 (.02-.05)	.....
Exhaust	1.098-1.106 (27.9-28.1)	45°	45°	.049-.061 (1.25-1.55)	.273-.274 (6.94-6.95)	.0024-.0035 (.06-.09)	.....
Auxiliary	.469-.476 (11.9-12.1)	45°	45°	.008-.020 (.20-.50)	.2580-.2593 6.572-6.587	.0009-.0023 (.023-.058)	.....

① — Calif. automatic.

PISTONS, PINS, RINGS						
	PISTONS	PINS		RINGS		
Engine	Clearance In. (mm)	Piston Fit In. (mm)	Rod Fit In. (mm)	Rings	End Gap In. (mm)	Side Clearance In. (mm)
1335 cc	.0004-.0020 (.01-.05)	.0004-.0009 (.010-.022)	.0006-.0015 (.016-.039)	No. 1	.006-.014 (.15-.35)	.0008-.0018 (.020-.045)
				No. 2	.006-.014 (.15-.35)	.0008-.0018 (.020-.045)
				Oil	.012-.035 (.3-.9)	.....
1487 cc	.0004-.0024 (.01-.06)	.0004-.0009 (.010-.022)	.0006-.0016 (.014-.040)	No 1	.006-.014 (.15-.35)	.0008-.0018 (.020-.045)
				No. 2	.006-.014 (.15-.35)	.0008-.0018 (.020-.045)
				Oil	.012-.035 (.3-.9)	.....
1751 cc	.0008-.0028 (.02-.07)	.0004-.0009 (.010-.022)	.0006-.0016 (.014-.040)	No. 1 & 2	.006-.014 (.15-.35)	.0008-.0018 (.020-.045)
				Oil	.012-.035 (.3-.9)	.....

Honda Engines

ACCORD, CIVIC & PRELUDE 4-CYLINDER (Cont.)
ENGINE SPECIFICATIONS (Cont.)

CRANKSHAFT MAIN & CONNECTING ROD BEARINGS

| Engine | MAIN BEARINGS | | | | CONNECTING ROD BEARINGS | | |
	Journal Diam. In. (mm)	Clearance In. (mm)	Thrust Bearing	Crankshaft End Play In. (mm)	Journal Diam. In. (mm)	Clearance In. (mm)	Side Play In. (mm)
1335 cc	1.9676-1.9685 (49.977-49.999)	.0009-.0017 (.024-.042)	No. 4	.004-.014 (.10-.35)	1.6526-1.6535 (41.976-41.998)	.0008-0015 (.020-.038)	.006-.012 (.15-.30)
1487 cc	1.9676-1.9685 (49.977-49.999)	.0010-.0022 (.026-.055)	No. 4	.004-.014 (.10-.35)	1.6526-1.6535 (41.976-41.998)	.0008-.0015 (.020-.038)	.006-.012 (.15-.30)
1751 cc	1.9687-1.9697 (50.006-50.030)	.0010-.0017 (.026-.044)	No. 4	.004-.014 (.10-.35)	1.6526-1.6535 (41.976-41.998)	.0008-.0015 (.020-.038)	.006-.012 (.15-.30)

VALVE SPRINGS

| Engine | Free Length In. (mm) | PRESSURE Lbs. @ In. (kg @ mm) | |
		Valve Closed	Valve Open
1335 cc & 1487 cc Intake			
Inner	1.665 (42.3)	.....	27-33@1.028 (12-15@26)
Outer	1.665 (42.3)	.....	94-114@1.114 (43-52@28)
Exhaust			
Inner	1.665 (42.3)	.....	27-33@1.028 (12-15@26)
Outer	1.665 (42.3)	.....	94-115@1.114 (43-52@28)
Auxiliary	1.169 (29.7)	.....	26-32@.866 (12-14@22)
1751 cc Intake			
Inner	1.67 (42.4)	.....	28-34@1.008 (13-15@26)
Outer	1.67 (42.4)	.....	99-117@1.094 (45-53@28)
Exhaust			
Inner	1.67 (42.4)	.....	28-34@1.008 (13-15@26)
Outer	1.67 (42.4)	.....	99-117@1.094 (45-53@28)
Auxiliary	1.17 (29.7)	.....	30-36@.866 (14-17@22)

CAMSHAFT

Engine	Journal Diam. In. (mm)	Clearance In. (mm)	Lobe Lift In. (mm)
1335 cc, 1487 cc & 1751 cc	.....	.002-.004 (.05-.098)	.002-.006 (.05-.15)

Isuzu & LUV Engines

ISUZU & LUV 4-CYLINDER

ENGINE CODING

ENGINE IDENTIFICATION

Engine may be identified by the Vehicle Identification Number (VIN) stamped on a metal tab located on top of instrument panel at lower left of windshield. The Engine Code is the 8th digit of the Vehicle Identification Number. The Engine Serial Number is stamped on the top right front corner of engine block.

Engine Identification	
Application	**Code**
Isuzu	
I-Mark & Pickup (1816 cc)	B
LUV	
Pickup (1816 cc)	N

ENGINE, CYLINDER HEAD & MANIFOLDS

ENGINE

Removal — 1) Disconnect battery cables, drain crankcase and cooling system. Disconnect carburetor linkage, all necessary water and fuel hoses. Disconnect all necessary vacuum lines and electrical leads. Disconnect exhaust pipe at manifold flange. Remove radiator and cooling fan.

2) Disconnect drive shaft, slave cylinder and speedometer-cable. Remove starter. Remove flywheel inspection cover and bell housing bolts. Support transmission. Attach hoist and take up vehicle weight. Remove front and rear engine mount nuts. Pull engine forward and lift out of vehicle.

Installation — To install engine, reverse removal procedure.

INTAKE MANIFOLD

Removal & Installation — 1) Disconnect battery ground cable and drain cooling system. Remove air cleaner assembly. Remove EGR pipe clamp bolt at rear of cylinder head. From underneath vehicle, remove EGR pipe from manifolds, and remove EGR valve and bracket assembly from bottom of intake manifold.

2) Disconnect upper radiator hose at water outlet and heater hose at top of manifold. Disconnect fuel line, accelerator linkage, vacuum lines and electrical connections at carburetor. Remove manifold mounting nuts and pull assembly off studs. To install, reverse removal procedure and tighten nuts in several steps, beginning with inner nuts and working outward.

NOTE — *PCV hose must be on upper left side, hot idle compensator hose on upper right, and air vacuum hose on lower side. Incorrect installation could cause poor engine operation.*

EXHAUST MANIFOLD

Removal & Installation — 1) Disconnect battery ground cable and remove EGR pipe clamp bolt at rear of cylinder head. Working under vehicle, remove EGR pipe from manifolds and attachments from exhaust pipe to bell housing and manifold. Separate exhaust pipe from manifold.

2) Remove manifold shield bolts and shield. Disconnect heat stove hose at air cleaner and remove heat stove. Remove mounting nuts and take off manifold. To install, reverse removal procedure, ensuring that mounting nuts are tightened in steps from center outward.

CYLINDER HEAD

Removal & Installation — 1) Drain cooling system and remove EGR pipe clamp bolt at rear of cylinder head. Disconnect exhaust pipe from manifold. Disconnect all necessary water hoses, vacuum lines, carburetor linkage and electrical leads. Remove air cleaner assembly and valve cover. Rotate crankshaft so number 4 cylinder is in firing position.

2) Mark rotor-to-housing relationship. Lock timing chain adjuster by depressing and turning automatic adjuster slide 90° clockwise. Remove timing chain sprocket from camshaft. Disconnect A.I.R. hose and check valve at exhaust manifold. Remove cylinder head-to-timing cover bolts and remove front cover.

3) Using special tool (J-24239), remove cylinder head bolts in sequence starting with outer bolts. Remove cylinder head, intake and exhaust manifold as an assembly. To install, reverse removal procedure.

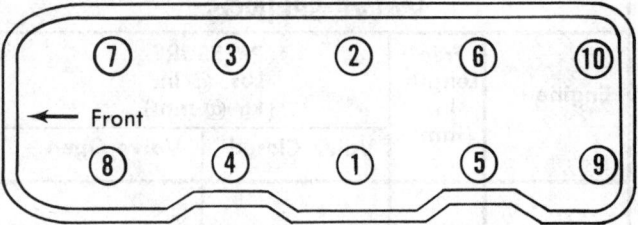

Fig. 1   Cylinder Head Tightening Sequence

CAMSHAFT

CAMSHAFT

Removal & Installation — 1) Remove valve cover and position No. 4 cylinder in firing position. Remove distributor cap and mark rotor position. Lock timing chain adjuster by depressing and turning automatic adjuster slide pin 90° in a clockwise direction. Ensure that chain is slack after locking adjuster.

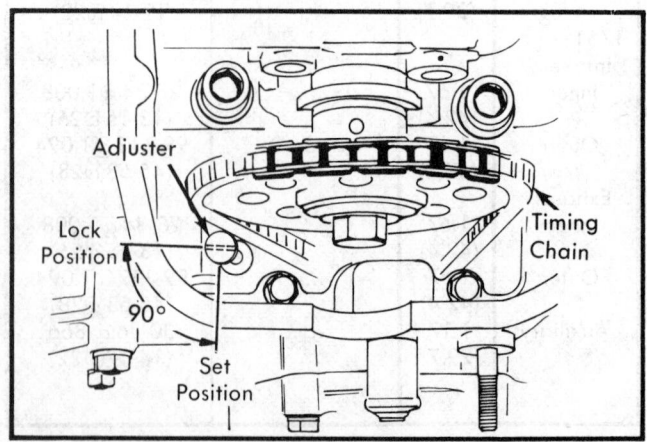

Fig. 2   Locking Timing Chain Adjuster

2) Remove timing sprocket from camshaft, keeping sprocket on chain damper and tensioner without removing sprocket from chain. Remove rocker arm shaft and bracket assembly. Remove camshaft.

3) Check camshaft journals and cams for wear or damage. Measure height of cams with a micrometer and replace

ISUZU & LUV 4-CYLINDER (Cont.)

camshaft if height is less than 1.4311" (36.3 mm). If working faces of cams have slight scores or steps, eliminate them by honing.

4) Measure outside diameter of camshaft journals, replace camshaft if diameter is less than 1.3307" (33.8 mm). Check camshaft runout by placing camshaft in v-blocks and using a suitable dial indicator, measure runout. If runout exceeds .0038" (.096 mm) replace camshaft.

CAMSHAFT END PLAY

Measure camshaft end play with thrust plate installed in thrust groove. Replace thrust plate if end play is found to exceed .0078" (.198 mm). Standard end play is .002-.006" (.05-.15 mm).

CAMSHAFT BEARING REPLACEMENT

Camshaft bearings are not replaceable. Camshaft rides in a carrier. If clearance is beyond limits, replace camshaft carrier.

OIL SEAL

Removal & Installation — 1) Disconnect negative battery terminal and drain cooling system. Disconnect radiator hoses and remove radiator. Remove fan and air conditioning belts and remove fan assembly. Remove crankshaft pulley bolt. Using a suitable puller, remove pulley and assembly.

2) Using a large screwdriver, pry seal out of cover. Using special tool (J-26587), install new seal in cover. Reverse removal procedure to complete installation. Replenish fluid levels previously drained.

FRONT COVER

Removal — Remove cylinder head and oil pan as previously outlined. Remove oil pump pickup tube. Remove harmonic balancer and AIR belt. If equipped with air conditioning, remove compressor and mounting brackets. Remove distributor cap (wires attached), then remove distributor. Remove front cover.

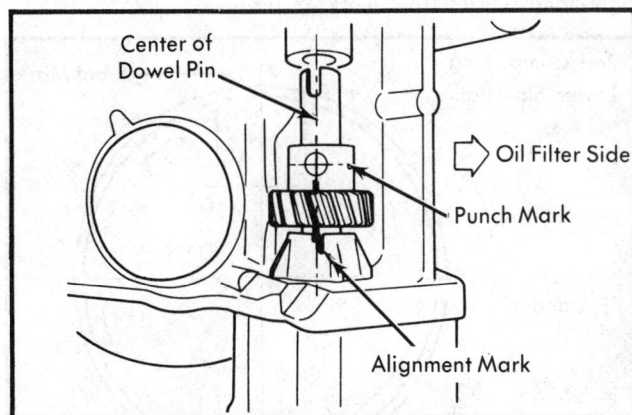

Fig. 3   Oil Pump Alignment

Installation — Align oil pump drive gear punch mark with oil filter side of cover. Align center of dowel pin with alignment mark on oil pump case. Rotate No. 1 and 4 cylinders to top dead center. Install front cover by engaging pinion gear with oil pump drive gear on crankshaft. Ensure that punch mark on oil pump drive gear is turned to rear side as viewed between front cover and cylinder block. Slit at end of oil pump shaft must be offset forward and parallel with front face of cylinder block. Install front cover and reverse removal procedure.

TIMING CHAIN

Removal — Remove front cover as outlined previously. Remove camshaft gear attaching bolt and remove timing chain from camshaft and crankshaft sprockets.

Inspection — 1) Check camshaft and crankshaft sprockets for wear or damage. Check timing chain for wear by pulling chain straight with proper tension measuring gauge. Pull chain at 22 lbs. (10 kg) and measure distance of 40 links from front of link as shown in *Fig. 4.*

2) If distance exceeds 15.16" (385 mm), replace chain. Check automatic adjuster, chain tensioner, and tensioner pins for wear or damage. Make sure that tensioner and adjuster have free rotation movement on pins. Ensure that oil jet in chain guide mounting is not plugged.

Installation — 1) Install timing sprocket and pinion gear with groove side toward front cover. Align keyway on crankshaft sprocket with key on crankshaft and drive sprocket onto crankshaft using suitable installing tool. Turn crankshaft so that key is facing straight upward, thus ensuring that No. 1 or No.4 piston is at TDC.

2) Align mark plate on chain with mark on crankshaft sprocket, install camshaft sprocket in upper portion of chain with marked side of sprocket facing forward and triangular marks align with chain mark plate. Reverse removal procedure to complete installation.

NOTE — *The side of chain with mark plate is on front side and side of chain with most links between mark plates is on chain guide side. See Fig. 5.*

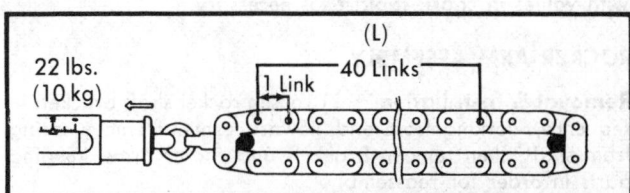

Fig 4   Timing Chain Stretch Test

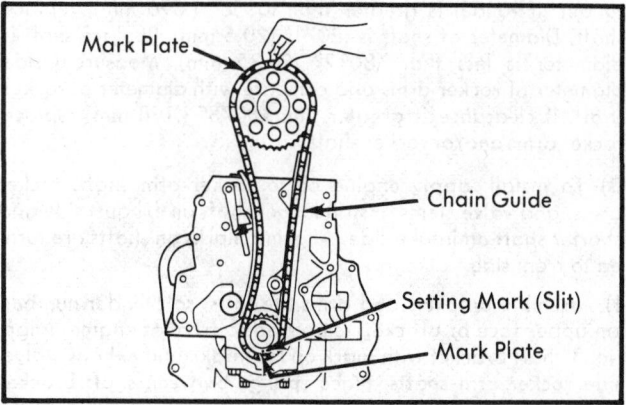

Fig. 5   Timing Chain Alignment

VALVES

VALVE ARRANGEMENT

Right Side — Intake.

Left Side — Exhaust.

ISUZU & LUV 4-CYLINDER (Cont.)

VALVE GUIDES

Removal & Installation — **1)** Inspect inside diameter of valve guide for grooves or uneven wear. Measure inside diameter of valve guides with caliper gauge. Measure diameter of valve stem and compare measured values to determine clearance. If clearance is excessive, replace both valve and valve guide.

2) Use valve guide removal tool (J-26512) and drive old guide out from combustion chamber side. Remove lower spring seat. To install, oil outside of new guide and place in position in cylinder head. Use installer (J-26512-1&2) and drive guide in until tool bottoms on cylinder head.

VALVE SPRINGS & VALVE STEM OIL SEALS

Removal — With rocker arm shaft assembly removed, use compressed air method to hold valve in closed position. Use suitable spring compressor (J-26513) and remove valve spring retainers (keepers). Remove spring and cap. Remove valve stem oil seal and spring lower seat.

Installation — Lubricate valve stem and spring lower seat. Place seat in position, then slide new seal over valve stem and onto guide, ensuring that ridge in oil seal fits in groove in valve guide. Install springs and retainers.

VALVE SPRING INSTALLED HEIGHT

Visually check valve springs for damage and replace as necessary. Measure free length of valve springs using suitable calipers and replace if measured value is beyond limit. With a valve spring tester check valve spring tension and compare it with values in chart, replace as necessary.

ROCKER ARM ASSEMBLY

Removal & Installation — **1)** Loosen rocker shaft brackets in sequence, working from ends toward center. Remove spring from shaft, then remove brackets and rocker arms, keeping parts in order for reassembly.

2) Inspect rocker arm shaft for wear damage or excessive runout. If runout is greater than .0156″ (.396 mm), replace shaft. Diameter of shaft is .8071″ (20.5 mm). Replace shaft if diameter is less than .8012″ (20.35 mm). Measure inside diameter of rocker arms and compare with diameter of rocker shaft. If clearance is greater than .0078″ (.198 mm) replace rocker arms and/or rocker shaft.

3) To install, apply engine oil to rocker arm shaft, rocker arms, and valve stems. Install longer shaft on exhaust side and shorter shaft on intake side. Aligning marks on shafts are turned to front side.

4) Assemble brackets and arms to shafts, so cylinder number (on upper face of bracket) is pointed to front of engine. Align No. 1 shaft bracket with mark on the intake and exhaust valve side rocker arm shafts. Place springs between shaft bracket and rocker arm. Punch mark on rocker arm shafts must be turned upward. Tighten shaft bracket nuts.

NOTE — *Hold rocker arm springs with a wrench while tightening nuts to prevent damaging springs.*

VALVE CLEARANCE

With No. 1 or No. 4 cylinder piston at top dead center, loosen lock nut and adjust intake valves to .006″ (.15 mm), and ex- haust valves to .010″ (.25 mm). When valves are correctly adjusted reset lock nut.

Valve Adjustment Sequence		
Application	**Intake/Cylinder**	**Exhaust/Cylinder**
No. 1 @ TDC	1,2	1,3
No. 4 @ TDC	3,4	2,4

PISTONS, PINS & RINGS

OIL PAN

Removal & Installation — Disconnect battery ground cable and drain engine oil. Remove front splash shield and front crossmember. Disconnect and lower relay rod at idler arm. Remove left hand bell-housing brace and disconnect vacuum line at oil pan. Remove oil pan bolts and lower pan from engine. To install, reverse removal procedure.

NOTE — *To remove pan on 4-wheel drive models, engine must be removed from vehicle.*

PISTON & ROD ASSEMBLY

Removal & Installation — **1)** With cylinder head and pan removed, mark piston, connecting rods and bearing caps on starter side for assembly order. Scrape carbon deposits from upper part of cylinder wall.

2) Remove connecting rod bearing cap nuts and bearing cap. Using a wood rod, push piston, together with connecting rod, upward. Removal sequence is 1, 4, 2, & 3.

NOTE — *Ensure piston and connecting rod are pulled parallel to cylinder wall.*

3) To install piston and rod assembly, position piston so notch mark on crown of piston is facing front of engine. Align cylinder number marks on connecting rods so they will be on right-hand side of front mark on piston.

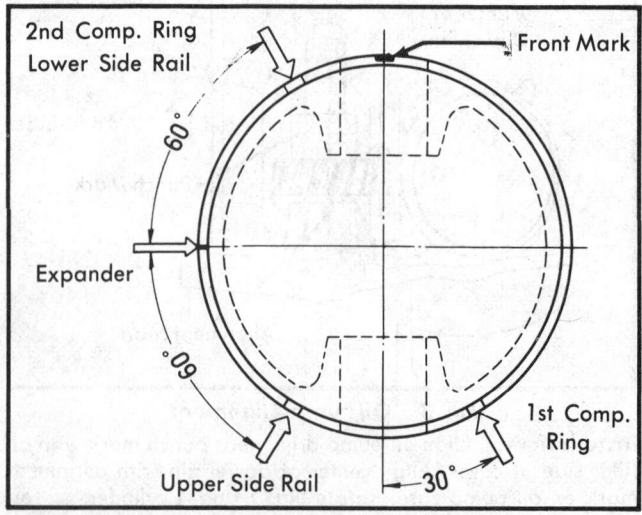

Fig. 6   Piston Ring Gap Arrangement

PISTON PIN

Removal — Using a press and piston pin removal tool set (J-25270), press piston pin out of piston and connecting rod assembly.

ISUZU & LUV 4-CYLINDER (Cont.)

Installation — Install new pin by placing pilot through piston and connecting rod. Lightly oil piston pin and place piston, rod, pin, and ram on press base. Press in pin until its centered in connecting rod.

PISTON RINGS

1) Assemble piston rings to piston with a piston ring expander. When replacing piston rings, position compression rings so that "NPR" or "TOP" mark is turned up. The expander ring and side rail is not marked.

2) Install oil control ring in this order; expander ring, lower side rail, and upper side rail. After installing all rings, apply clean engine oil to the entire rings. Check that rings turn smoothly in their ring grooves.

FITTING PISTONS

1) Measure piston at right angles to piston pin, 1.575" (40 mm) below piston head. Measure bore diameter at lower section, where least wear occurs. If clearance exceeds specifications, pistons must be replaced.

2) Measure weight of assembled piston-rod assembly. Variance between assemblies must not exceed .42 oz. (.01 kg). If correction is necessary, arched portions of connecting rod bearing caps may be ground to reduce weight.

Piston Class		
Piston Size	Piston Grade	Piston Diameter
Standard	A	3.3049-3.3053 (83.944-83.955)
Standard	B	3.3053-3.3057 (83.955-83.965)
Standard	C	3.3057-3.3061 (83.965-83.975)
Standard	D	3.3061-3.3065 (83.975-83.985)

NOTE — *Pistons are available in .020" (0.5 mm) and .040" (1.0 mm) oversize.*

CRANKSHAFT MAIN & CONNECTING ROD BEARINGS

MAIN & CONNECTING ROD BEARING SERVICE

NOTE — *The following procedure is with engine, cylinder head, timing cover, oil pan, and timing chain removed.*

Connecting Rod Bearings — After ensuring rod caps are marked for cylinder identification, remove rod caps. Use Plastigage method to check for proper clearance. If not within specifications, new bearings must be installed. New bearings are available in standard, .010", and .020".

NOTE — *Always replace bearings in pairs. Never use a new bearing in combination with a used bearing.*

Main Bearings — 1) With all bearing caps (except one being checked) tight, check clearances using Plastigage method. If clearances are excessive, undersized bearings will have to be installed. Remove upper bearings by inserting tool into oil hole of crankshaft and rotating crankshaft clockwise to roll bearing from engine.

2) To check crankshaft out of round place crankshaft on two "V" shaped blocks at No. 1 and No. 5 journals. Hold dial indicator in contact with No. 3 journal and slowly turn crankshaft, recording highest point on journal. Replace crankshaft if bend exceeds .0038" (.097 mm). Standard assembly value is .0012" (.030 mm) or less.

3) To check crankshaft end play, place bearings and crankshaft in crankcase. Install thrust bearing on both sides of No. 3 crankshaft journal. Shift crankshaft endwise and measure clearance between thrust bearing and journal side face. If clearance is greater than .0117" (.297 mm), install oversize thrust bearings. Standard value is .0024-.0094" (.061-.239 mm).

4) Install bearing caps so that arrow mark on rear face of each bearing cap is turned to front of engine. Bearings should be well lubricated prior to installation. Tighten in 2 steps in sequence of 3, 4, 2, 5 and 1.

REAR MAIN OIL SEAL

Removal — Remove oil pan and transmission. Remove clutch (if equipped). Remove starter and flywheel assembly. Remove seal retainer bolts and pry seal out of retainer.

Installation — To install, reverse removal procedure noting the following: Fill clearance between lips of seal with grease, and coat lips of seal with engine oil. Place retainer on flat surface and drive seal into place using suitable seal installer tool (J-22354).

ENGINE OILING

ENGINE OILING SYSTEM

Trochoid type oil pump is designed to deliver 3.7 gallons of oil per minute through the engine at a pump speed of 1400 RPM. Lubricating system is designed to deliver oil at a rate of 57 psi.

Crankcase Capacity — 4.2 qts. with filter.

Oil Filter — Full-flow disposable canister type.

Normal Oil Pressure — 57-71 psi (4-5 kg/cm²) at 2800 RPM.

Relief Valve — Located on side of cylinder block near oil filter. Opening pressure is 57-71 psi (4-5 kg/cm²).

OIL PUMP

NOTE — *Oil pump can be serviced with engine in or out of vehicle. Procedure given is with engine in vehicle.*

Removal — Remove front cover, distributor, and oil pan as outlined previously. Remove oil pickup tube. Remove oil pump mounting bolts and remove pump assembly.

Inspection — 1) Measure tip clearance with a feeler gauge, between drive rotor and driven rotor. Replace entire pump assembly if clearance is greater than .0079" (.2 mm).

2) Measure clearance between driven rotor and inner wall of pump body. Replace entire pump assembly if clearance is greater than .0098" (.249 mm).

3) Using a square and a feeler gauge, measure clearance between drive rotor, driven rotor, and oil pump cover. Replace entire pump assembly if clearance is greater than .0079" (.2 mm). Inspect all parts wear or damage.

Isuzu & LUV Engines

ISUZU & LUV 4-CYLINDER (Cont.)

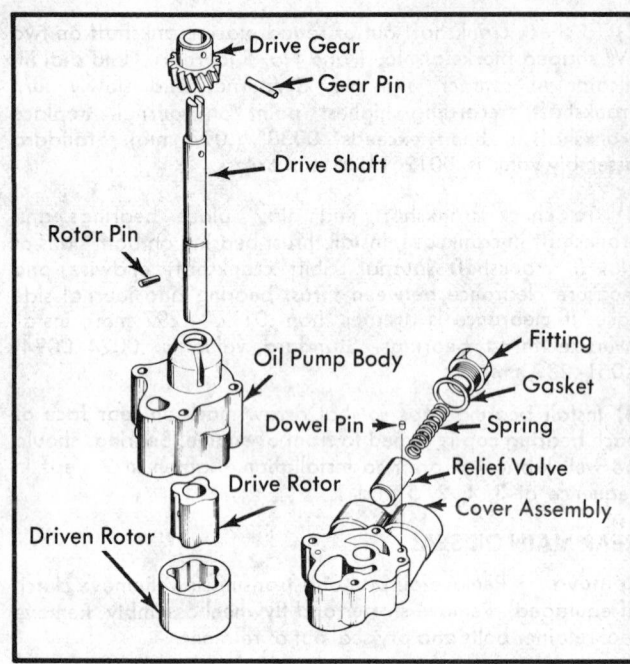

Fig. 7 Exploded View of Oil Pump Assembly

Installation — 1) Align mark on camshaft with mark on No. 1 rocker arm shaft bracket. Align notch on crankshaft pulley with "O" mark on front cover. When the two sets of marks are aligned, No. 4 cylinder is at top dead center on compression stroke.

2) Install driven rotor so that alignment mark aligns with mark on the drive rotor. Engage drive gear with pinion gear on crankshaft so alignment mark is turned rearward and is away from crankshaft by approximately 20° in clockwise rotation.

3) When oil pump is installed, make sure mark on drive gear is turned to rear side as viewed from the clearance between front cover and cylinder block. Slit at end of shaft must be parallel with front face of cylinder block, and is offset as viewed through distributor fitting hole.

4) Install pump cover by fitting it to the dowel pins, then install mounting bolts. Install relief valve assembly and rubber hose on cover. Reverse removal procedure.

ENGINE COOLING

WATER PUMP

Disconnect negative battery cable. Remove lower cover. Drain cooling system. If equipped with air conditioning, remove fan and air pump drive belt. Remove fan, fan pulley, and air pump drive pulley. Remove set plate and pulley. On all other models remove fan nuts and fan. On all models, remove attaching bolts and water pump from vehicle.

Thermostat — Opens at about 180°F (82°C).

Cooling Capacity — 6.4 quarts with automatic transmission; 6.8 quarts with manual transmission.

Pressure Cap — 15 psi (1.1 kg/cm²).

ENGINE SPECIFICATIONS

GENERAL SPECIFICATIONS

Year	Displ.		Carburetor	HP at RPM	Torque (Ft. Lbs. at RPM)	Compr. Ratio	Bore		Stroke	
	cu. ins.	cc					in.	mm	in.	mm
1981	110.8	1816	1x2-Bbl.	80 @4800	95 @3000	8.5:1	3.31	84	3.23	82

VALVES

Engine & Valve	Head Diam. In. (mm)	Face Angle	Seat Angle	Seat Width In. (mm)	Min. Stem Diameter In. (mm)	Stem Clearance In. (mm)	Valve Lift In. (mm)
1816 cc Int.	1.59 (40.3)	45°	45°	.047-.063 (1.19-1.60)	.3102 (7.88)	.0009-.0022 (.023-.056)	.....
Exh.	1.34 (34.0)	45°	45°	.047-.063 (1.19-1.60)	.3091 (7.85)	.0015-.0031 (.038-.079)	.....

Isuzu & LUV Engines

ISUZU & LUV 4-CYLINDER (Cont.)

ENGINE SPECIFICATIONS (Cont.)

PISTONS, PINS, RINGS

Engine	PISTONS Clearance In. (mm)	PINS Piston Fit In. (mm)	PINS Rod Fit In. (mm)	RINGS Rings	RINGS End Gap In. (mm)	RINGS Side Clearance In. (mm)
1816 cc	.0018-.0026 (.046-.066)	Press Fit	.0024 (.061)	1	.008-.016 (.20-.41)	.....
				2	.008-.016 (.20-.41)	.....
				Oil	.008-.035 (.20-.89)	.....

CRANKSHAFT MAIN & CONNECTING ROD BEARINGS

Engine	MAIN BEARINGS Journal Diam. In. (mm)	Clearance In. (mm)	Thrust Bearing	Crankshaft End Play In. (mm)	CONNECTING ROD BEARINGS Journal Diam. In. (mm)	Clearance In. (mm)	Side Play In. (mm)
1816 cc	2.205 (56.01)	.0008-.0025 (.020-.063)	No. 3	.012 (.30)	1.929 (48.99)	.0007-.0030 (.017-.076)	.011 (.28)

CAMSHAFT

Engine	Journal Diam. In. (mm)	Clearance In. (mm)	Lobe Lift In. (mm)
1816 cc	1.3362-1.3368 (33.94-33.95)	.0024 ① (.061)	.....

① — End Play .002-.006" (.05-.15 mm)

VALVE TIMING

Engine	INTAKE Open (BTDC)	INTAKE Close (ABDC)	EXHAUST Open (BBDC)	EXHAUST Close (ATDC)
1816 cc	21°	65°	55°	20°

VALVE SPRINGS

Engine	Free Length In. (mm)	PRESSURE Lbs. @ In. (kg @ mm) Valve Closed	Valve Open
1816 cc Inner	1.78 (45.2)	21.5 @1.52 (9.7 @38.6)	.....
Outer	1.85 (47.0)	37.0 @1.61 (16.8 @40.9)	.....

TIGHTENING SPECIFICATIONS

Application	Ft. Lbs. (N·m)
Camshaft Sprocket	58 (79)
Connecting Rod Bearings	43 (58)
Cylinder Head Step 1	61 (83)
Step 2	72 (98)
Flywheel	69 (94)
Main Bearings	72 (98)
Rocker Arm Shaft Bracket Nuts	16 (22)

LUV & P'UP 4-CYLINDER DIESEL

ENGINE CODING

ENGINE IDENTIFICATION

Engine number is stamped on the right side of the cylinder block next to the intake manifold. Diesel engine is identified by the number C223.

ENGINE & CYLINDER HEAD

ENGINE

Removal — 1) Mark hood hinges for reassembly and remove hood. Disconnect battery cables. Remove cables, battery hold-down and battery. Drain engine cooling system, crankcase and transmission. Remove engine under cover.

2) Remove air cleaner assembly. Disconnect radiator hoses and loosen compressor drive belts. Remove fan, fan shroud, radiator grill and radiator. Disconnect accelerator control cable. Disconnect air conditioner compressor control cable (if equipped).

3) Disconnect fuel lines, all transmission and transaxle wiring, vacuum hose at fast idle actuator and connector at fuel cut solenoid. Disconnect heater hoses at heater unit inside of cab. Disconnect sensing resistor, thermoswitch and air conditioner compressor switch connectors.

4) Disconnect vacuum hoses from vacuum pump. Disconnect alternator wiring. Disconnect exhaust pipe from manifold and remove mounting bracket from engine backing plate. Remove all starter wiring and battery cable from starter.

5) Working from passenger compartment, slide shift lever boot(s) up and remove gearshift and transfer lever retaining bolts. On 4WD models, remove return spring from transfer shift lever. Remove shift lever(s). Disconnect speedometer and ground cables from transmission.

6) Mark for installation and remove propeller shaft(s). On long wheel base 4WD models, 1st and 2nd rear propeller shafts must be removed separately and center support bearing must be removed with 1st shaft as a unit. Remove clutch fork return spring and clutch cable from hooked portion of fork. Remove cable through stiffener bracket.

7) Remove rear bracket to transmission mount bolts, attach engine hoist and raise engine and transmission for clearance to remove crossmember to frame bracket bolts. On 4WD models remove rear mounting nuts from transfer case, then lower assembly and support rear of engine.

8) On 2WD models, remove transmission rear extension mounting nuts. Remove engine mounting bolt and nuts. Disconnect any remaining engine or transmission to chassis wiring, pull engine forward and carefully remove engine and transmission as an assembly.

9) On 4WD models, remove transfer side case. Remove shifter cover and gasket from top of transfer case. Remove transmission-to-engine attaching bolts and remove transmission. When removing transmission, turn side case surface downward and pull the case straight back until disengaged from clutch. Lift engine slightly and remove engine mounting bolts and nuts. Disconnect any remaining engine or transmission to chassis wiring, pull engine forward and carefully remove engine and transmission as an assembly.

Installation — Replace any rubber engine mounts showing signs of deterioration, separation or unusual wear. Reverse removal procedures to complete installation. Check all fluid levels.

CYLINDER HEAD

Removal — 1) Drain cooling system. Remove air cleaner, remove intake manifold retaining bolts (2) and nuts (4) and remove intake manifold. Disconnect exhaust pipe from exhaust manifold, remove nuts holding manifold in place and remove manifold.

2) Disconnect upper radiator hose and remove fan and fan shroud. Disconnect injection pipes, remove nozzle holder retaining nuts and remove nozzle holder assembly. Loosen rocker shaft retaining bolts in several steps starting from the ends and working towards the middle. Remove rocker shaft with rocker arms and mounting brackets.

3) Remove push rods. Disconnect fuel over-flow line and loosen head bolts in reverse of tightening sequence. Remove cylinder head and gasket.

Installation — Install new head gasket with "TOP" mark facing up and install cylinder head. Replace push rods and install rocker shaft. Reverse removal procedure to complete installation.

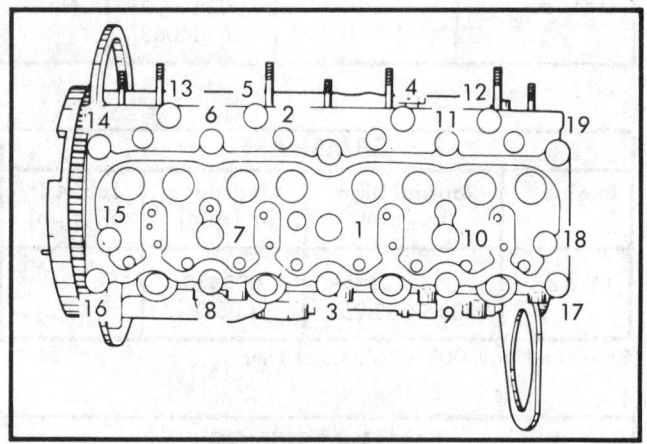

Fig. 1 Cylinder Head Tightening Sequence
(Loosen in Reverse Sequence)

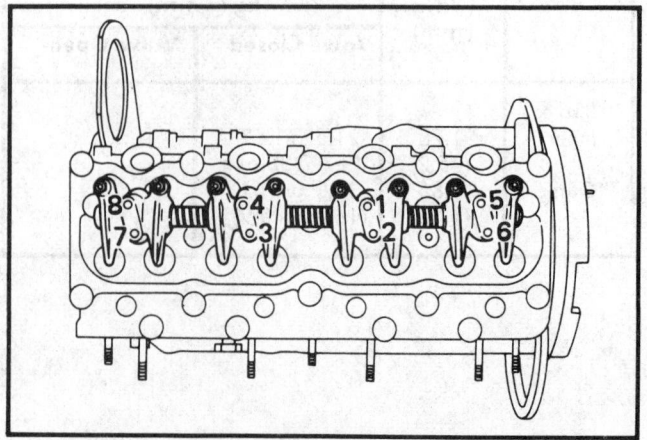

Fig. 2 Rocker Shaft Tightening Sequence
(Loosen in Reverse Sequence)

LUV & P'UP 4-CYLINDER DIESEL (Cont.)

CAMSHAFT

ENGINE FRONT COVER

Removal — Drain cooling system. Remove battery, fan and fan shroud. Disconnect radiator hoses at engine, remove radiator grill and radiator. Remove all belts. Remove crankshaft pulley retaining bolts and remove crankshaft pulley. Remove front cover retaining bolts and remove front cover (2 pieces).

Installation — Reverse removal procedure to install.

TIMING BELT

Removal — Remove engine front cover. Remove injection pump timing pulley flange bolts and remove flange. Remove tension pulley retaining nut. Remove tension pulley and center. Remove timing belt.

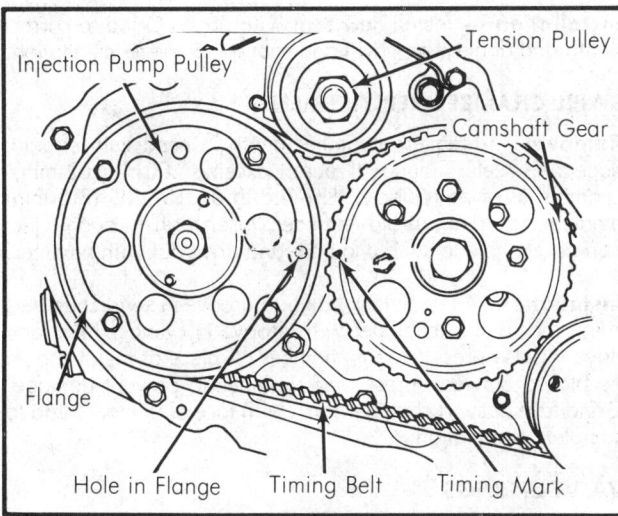

Fig. 3 Timing Belt Installation

Installation — 1) Before installing timing belt, check that the timing marks on the injection pump, camshaft and crankshaft pulleys are properly aligned. *See Fig. 4*. Install timing belt over crankshaft pulley first, then camshaft pulley and injection pump pulley.

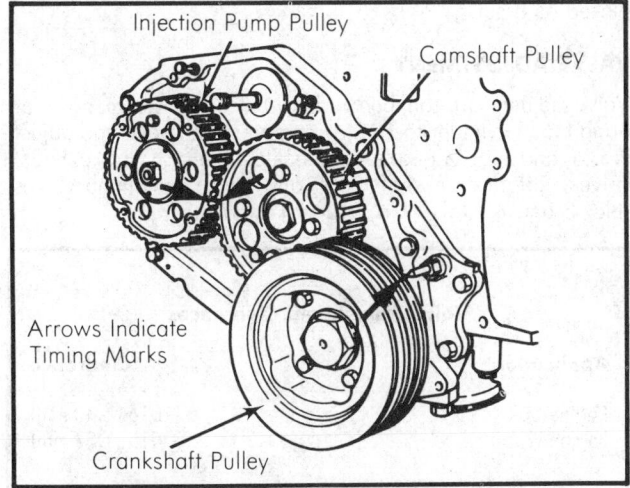

Fig. 4 Timing Mark Alignment

2) Install tension pulley center and tension pulley. The end of the tension center must be in contact with 2 pins on the timing pulley housing. *See Fig. 5*. Hand tighten nut, install tension spring and tighten nut to 22-36 ft. lbs. (30-50 N•m).

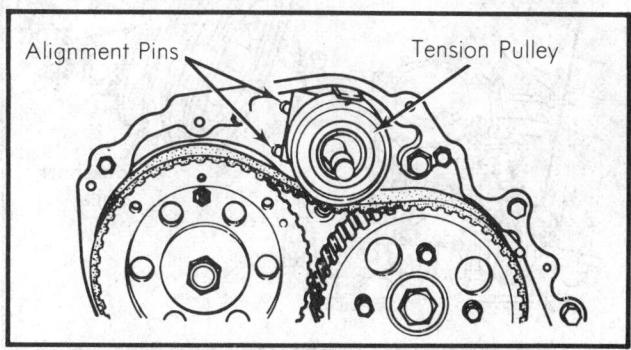

Fig. 5 Tension Pulley Installation

3) Turn crankshaft 2 turns plus 90 degrees in direction of normal rotation. Loosen tension pulley nut completely and allow pulley to take up slack. Tighten nut to proper specification. Install injection pump pulley flange and check that hole in flange lines up with timing mark on camshaft gear.

4) Turn crankshaft 2 turns more, bringing No. 1 cylinder to TDC on the compression stroke. Check timing mark alignment. Check belt tension with gauge (J-29771). Tension should be 33-55 lbs. (147-245 N). Adjust valves. Reverse removal procedure to complete installation.

INJECTION PUMP TIMING

1) Check that notched lines on injection pump flange and injecton pump front bracket are aligned. With No. 1 cylinder at TDC on compression stroke and timing pulley housing cover removed, check timing belt tension and timing mark alignment.

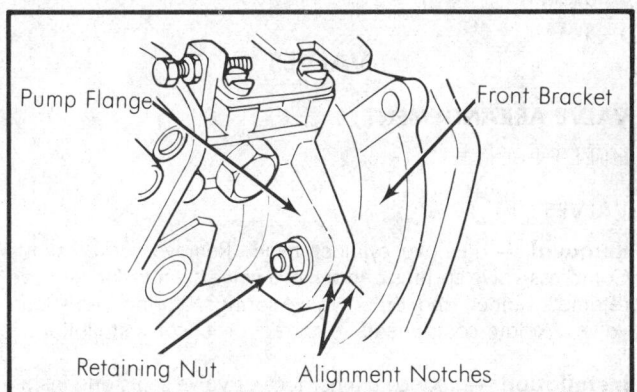

Fig. 6 Injection Pump Alignment Marks

2) Disconnect injection pipe from pump and remove distributor head screw. Install static timing gauge (dial indicator) and set lift approximately .04" (1 mm) from the plunger.

3) Turn engine until No. 1 cylinder is 45-60° BTDC, then calibrate dial indicator to zero. Turn crankshaft pulley slightly in both directions and check that gauge indication is stable. Turn crankshaft in normal direction of rotation until timing mark (15° BTDC) is aligned with indicator. Dial indicator should read .020" (.5 mm).

LUV & P'UP 4-CYLINDER DIESEL (Cont.)

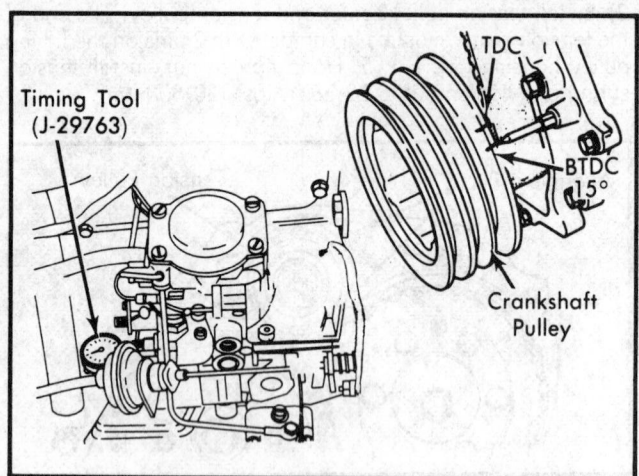

Fig. 7 Injection Pump Timing Adjustment

4) If indicator reading is not correct, loosen the 2 injection pump flange retaining nuts and rotate housing until a correct reading is obtained. Tighten nuts and recheck reading.

CAMSHAFT

Removal — 1) Remove engine front cover and timing belt as described. Remove rocker shaft assembly as described in *Cylinder Head* removal section. Remove push rods.

2) Install a 6 mm bolt through hole in camshaft pulley and into threaded hole in housing to prevent turning of pulley. Remove timing pulley bolts and remove pulley with puller (J-22888). Remove camshaft carefully so as not to damage camshaft bearings.

Installation — Coat camshaft lobes, bearing surfaces and camshaft bearings with oil. Carefully install camshaft to avoid damage to bearings. Reverse removal procedure to complete installation.

VALVES

VALVE ARRANGEMENT

E-I-I-E-E-I-I-E

VALVES

Removal — Remove cylinder head. Remove rocker shaft. Compress valve springs and remove valve stem locks. Remove retainers, inner and outer valve springs, spring seats and valves. Retain components in correct order for installation.

Installation — Lubricate inner face of valve seals and install on valve guide. Reverse removal procedure to complete installation. Valve springs are of a varied pitch design. Be sure that they are installed with the close coiled end (painted green) against the cylinder head.

VALVE GUIDE SERVICE

Check valve stem clearance in valve guide with a dial indicator. Insert valve in valve guide and move left or right (parallel with rocker arm). Measure stem movement .4" (10 mm) above guide edge. If movement exceeds .008" (.2 mm) and valve stem is not worn, the valve guide must be replaced.

Removal — Drive out old guide with tool (J-26512) from combustion chamber side.

Installation — To install new guide, coat outer surface of guide with engine oil and drive into head from opposite side with tool (J-26512). Guide should project from cylinder head .472" (12 mm). Whenever a valve is replaced, a new guide should be used.

VALVE SEAT INSERTS

Check condition of valve seat contact area. If pitted, worn or otherwise damaged, replace seat.

Removal — With valve in place, measure depth of valve face below surface of head with depth gauge. If valve is more than .08" (2.0 mm) below head surface, seat must be replaced. To remove, arc-weld a bead of metal around contact surface of seat. Allow to cool a few minutes. Pry out valve seat.

Installation — Install new seat with press. Grind to correct width and angle. Lap valve and seat to complete installation.

SWIRL CHAMBER REPLACEMENT

Removal — Measure chamber depth in head with straight edge and feeler gauge. If depth exceeds .001" (.02 mm), chamber must be replaced. Use a drift of .15-.20" (3-5 mm) diameter to drive out old chamber. Insert drift through injection nozzle hole to swirl chamber and drive out with hammer.

Installation — Install lock ball into groove in swirl chamber. Align lock ball in chamber with groove in cylinder head and drive in. Use press to seat chamber. A piece of metal should be placed between press and chamber to prevent damage. Grind face of swirl chamber flush with face of cylinder head to complete installation.

VALVE SPRINGS

Valve springs must be less than .04" (1.0 mm) out of square. Inner valve spring should have a free length of 1.89" (47.9 mm) and a compressed length of 1.46" (37 mm) at 12.2-13.8 lbs. (54.3-61.4 N). Outer valve spring should have a free length of 1.86" (47.3 mm) and a compressed length of 1.54" (39 mm) at 43.2-48.7 lbs. (192-216 N). If tension required is less than 11.0 lbs. (49.1 N) for the inner spring or 39.8 lbs. (177.1 N) for the outer, the spring should be replaced. Inner and outer springs should always be replaced as a set.

VALVE ADJUSTMENT

Valve adjustment can be made with engine warm or cold. Bring No. 1 cylinder to TDC on compression stroke and adjust No. 1 and No. 2 intake valves, No. 1 and No. 3 exhaust valves. Rotate crankshaft 180° and adjust remaining valves (No. 3 and 4 intake, No. 2 and 4 exhaust).

Valve Adjustment Clearances	
Application	Clearance
Engine Cold	.016" (.40 mm)
Engine Warm	.015" (.37 mm)

LUV & P'UP 4-CYLINDER DIESEL (Cont.)

PISTONS, PINS & RINGS

PISTON AND ROD ASSEMBLY

Removal — Remove engine from vehicle. Remove cylinder head. Remove crankcase and oil pan as an assembly. Remove oil pipe sleeve nut, oil pump bolts and oil pump with oil pipe. Remove rod cap with bearing half. Push piston/rod assembly with bearing half up and out through top of engine. Rod caps must be kept with their respective piston and rod assembly as caps are not interchangeable.

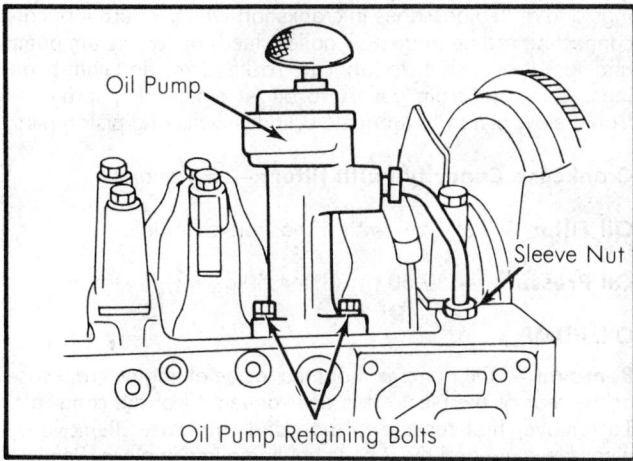

Fig. 8   Oil Pump Removal and Installation

Installation — **1)** Lightly oil rings, piston and cylinder wall. Make sure ring gaps are located 180° apart and not on thrust side of piston or in line with piston pin. Make sure bearing halves are properly seated in connecting rod and cap.

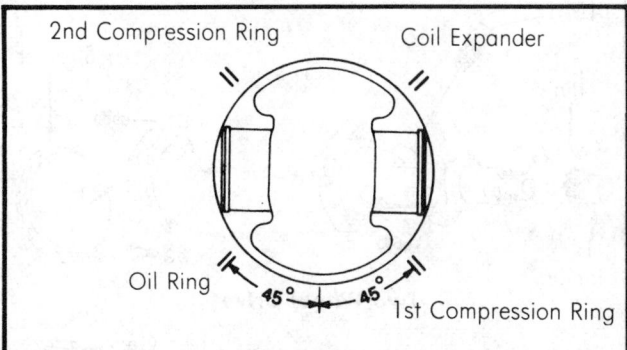

Fig. 9   Piston Ring Gap Locations

2) Install a ring compressor and compress rings. Install piston in cylinder. Ensure mark in piston top points towards front of engine. With piston installed in cylinder, and connecting rod and bearings seated against crankshaft journal, install rod caps to their respective piston and rod assembly. Make sure that marks in cap and rod end match and are installed on the same side.

3) Lubricate threads of rod bolts and seating face of nuts with engine oil. Reverse removal procedure to complete installation.

FITTING PISTONS

1) Measure cylinder bores for wear at depths of .6" and 4.5" (16 and 114 mm). Measurements should be made in line with and at right angles to the crankshaft centerline. If excessive wear is found, cylinder should be bored to accommodate next oversize piston. Whenever one cylinder is bored, all cylinders must be bored.

2) Measure piston diameter at right angle to piston pin. Subtract this figure from cylinder diameter to obtain piston to wall clearance. Final hone of cylinder wall should provide .006-.007" (.16-.18 mm) clearance.

Piston Specifications	
Piston Size In. (mm)	**Piston Diameter** In. (mm)
Standard	3.454-3.455 (87.73-87.75)
.020 (.50) O/S	3.477-3.478 (88.33-88.35)
.040 (1.0) O/S	3.497-3.498 (88.83-88.85)

PISTON PINS

Removal — To remove pin, use snap ring pliers and remove snap rings from piston. Use a brass rod to drive out pin.

Inspection — Visually inspect pin for signs of damage or excessive wear. Replace if needed. With hole gauge and micrometer, measure piston pin diameter and diameter of pin hole in piston. Subtract pin diameter from hole diameter to get pin to piston clearance figure. Clearance should be .0002-.0014" (.004-.034 mm). If clearance exceeds this limit, pin and piston should be replaced.

Installation — Heat piston to about 175° F (80° C). Coat pin with oil and install in piston and rod. Make sure that piston and rod are joined so that the combustion chamber on the piston is on the same side as the match marks on the connecting rod. Install snap rings.

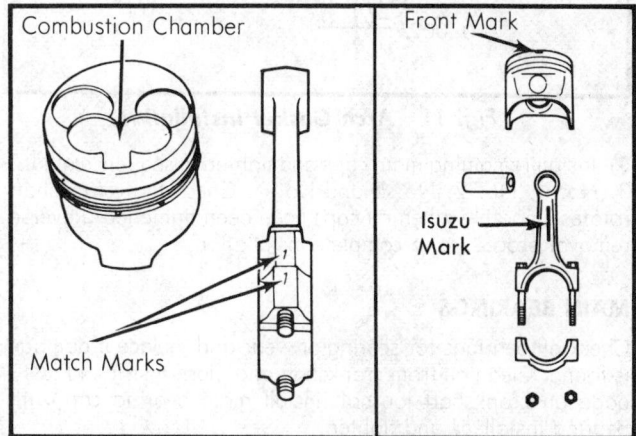

Fig. 10   Piston to Rod Positioning

CRANKSHAFT MAIN & CONNECTING ROD BEARINGS

MAIN & CONNECTING ROD BEARINGS

Removal — With engine removed from vehicle, remove cylinder head and timing belt as outlined. Remove flywheel and rear plate. Remove piston and rod assemblies, camshaft

LUV & P'UP 4-CYLINDER DIESEL (Cont.)

and front timing pulley housing. Loosen crankshaft main bearing caps starting with outside caps and working toward the middle. Remove caps and lift out crankshaft.

Inspection — Check all shaft journals and crankpins for scoring, wear, or cracks. Taper and out-of-round on all journals must not exceed .001" (.015 mm). Check crankshaft for bend using dial indicator at center journal. If bend exceeds limit of .0024" (.06 mm), the crankshaft must be replaced.

NOTE — *Crankshafts have been specially hardened and should never be ground to obtain correct clearances. If journals are worn beyond acceptable limits, the crankshaft must be replaced.*

Installation — **1)** Install main bearing halves to engine block ensuring that all bearings are on their respective journal. Fit tab on bearing into corresponding slot in bearing seat. All main bearing halves are grooved. Install thrust bearing with the oil groove turned outward.

2) Coat all bearing surfaces liberally with clean engine oil. Carefully install crankshaft. Install arch gasket on No. 1 and No. 5 main bearing caps. Use liquid gasket sealer to hold gasket in place while installing caps. Apply a thin film of gasket sealer to contact surfaces of No. 1 and 5 caps before installing. Make sure that projecting part of arch gasket (.002" max.) fits into the proper position on cylinder block.

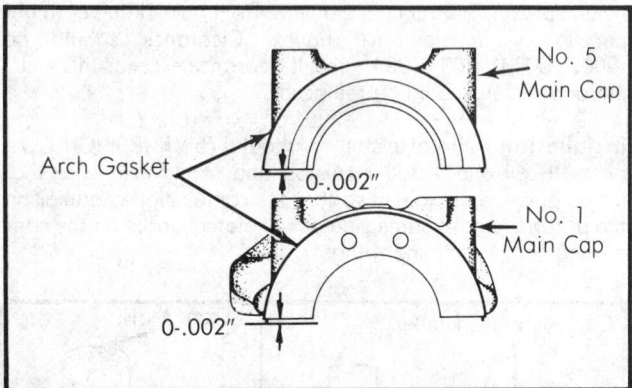

Fig. 11   Arch Gasket Installation

3) Install remaining main caps and tighten in sequence of No. 3, No. 4, No. 2, No. 5 and No. 1. Check that crankshaft rotates smoothly when all caps have been tightened. Reverse removal procedure to complete installation.

MAIN BEARINGS

Check all bearings for scoring or wear and replace if damage is found. Clean oil from crankshaft and place a strip of Plastigage on crankshaft journal. Install main bearing cap with bearing installed, and tighten.

NOTE — *Plastigage should run parallel with crankshaft and not block oil hole. Do not turn crankshaft while Plastigage is inserted.*

Remove cap and measure width of Plastigage at widest point using gauge provided. If clearance is not to specifications, replace bearings.

CONNECTING ROD BEARINGS

Check all bearings for scoring or signs of excessive wear and replace if damage is found. Measure inside diameter of bear-

ings and outside diameter of crankshaft connecting rod journals. Use these figures to determine rod bearing clearance. If not to specifications, replace rod bearings. Assemble rod caps to rods with bearings in place and tighten rod bolts.

ENGINE OILING

ENGINE OILING SYSTEM

Oil drawn from pan passes through a screen to oil pump. Oil is delivered to full flow oil filter, oil cooler, and main oil gallery. Main oil gallery supplies oil to crankshaft main bearings and drilled passages in crankshaft which in turn lubricate connecting rod bearings. Oil gallery feeds oil to vacuum pump and rocker arm shaft to lubricate rocker arms and cam bearings. Oil is fed from gallery to oil jet pipe which sprays oil from below piston to lubricate cylinder walls and piston pins.

Crankcase Capacity (with filter) — 6.4 quarts.

Oil Filter — Full-flow with disposable cartridge.

Oil Pressure — 50-60 psi (3.5-4.5 kg/cm^2).

OIL PUMP

Removal — Oil pump is mounted inside of engine crankcase at the rear of the block. It is gear driven off of the camshaft. To remove, first remove oil pan and crankcase. Remove oil pipe sleeve nut and the 2 bolts holding pump in place. Remove oil pump.

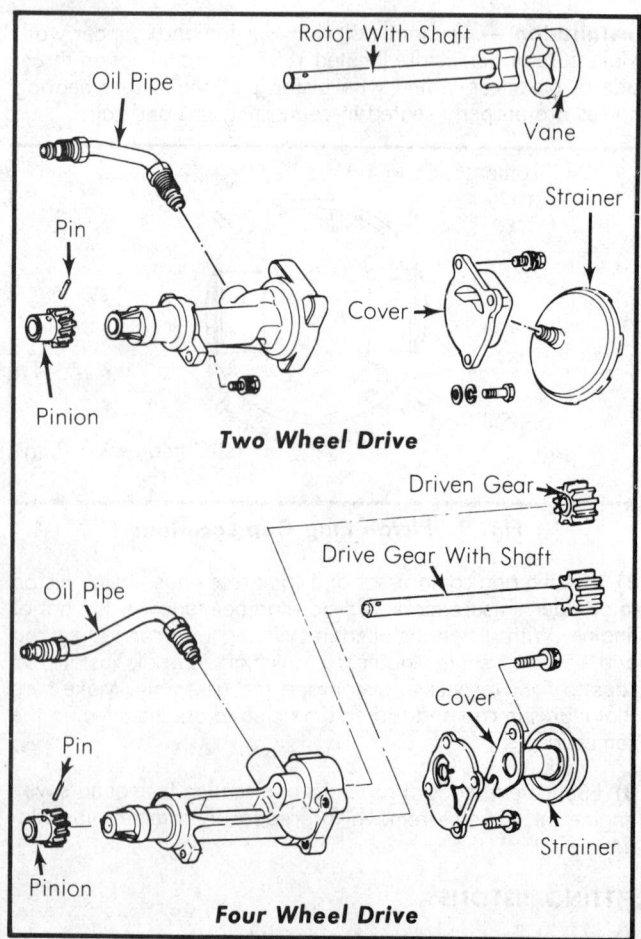

Fig. 12   Oil Pump Assemblies

LUV & P'UP 4-CYLINDER DIESEL (Cont.)

Inspection — Disassemble oil pump and wash all parts thoroughly in clean solvent. Inspect for signs of unusual wear or damage. Replace as needed. Check all clearances to specifications. If vane to pump body clearance or rotor shaft to pump body clearance is beyond specificaton, entire pump assembly must be replaced.

Installation — Reverse removal procedure to install.

Make sure mating surfaces of pump and block are clean and always use a new gasket.

Thermostat — Opens at 180°F (82°C). Full open at 203°F (95°C).

Cooling System Capacity — 7 quarts.

Oil Pump Specifications

Application	①Clearance In. (mm)
2WD	
Vane Depth in Housing	.006 (.15)
Rotor-to-Vane Side Clearance	.006 (.15)
Vane-to-Pump Body Side Clearance	.011 (.27)
Rotor Shaft-to-Pump Body	.008 (.20)
4WD	
Gear Depth in Housing	.004 (.09)
Gear Tip Side Clearance	.006 (.14)

① — Clearances given are wear limits.

ENGINE COOLING

WATER PUMP

Removal & Installation — Drain cooling system and remove battery, fan, fan shroud and upper radiator hose. Remove drive belts and fan pulley. Remove water pump retaining bolts (5) and remove pump. Reverse removal procedure to install.

TIGHTENING SPECIFICATIONS

Application	Ft. Lbs. (N·m)
Cylinder Head	
New Bolt	54-61 (76-85)
Used Bolt	61-69 (85-97)
Camshaft	
Hub	72-87 (101-122)
Pulley	78-95 (109-133)
Connecting Rod	58-65 (81-91)
Crankshaft Gear Bolt	124-151 (174-211)
Crankshaft Pulley Bolts	10-17 (14-24)
Crankcase Pan	10-17 (14-24)
Engine Plate – Rear	55-67 (77-94)
Flywheel	65-72 (91-101)
Main Bearing Caps	116-130 (162-182)
Manifolds (Intake & Exhaust)	10-17 (14-24)
Injection Pump Timing Pulley	42-52 (59-73)
Oil Jet Pipe (1)	24-27 (34-38)
Oil Jets (4)	22 (31)
Oil Cooler	54-61 (76-85)
Rocker Shaft	10-17 (14-24)
Tension Pulley	78-95 (109-133)
Timing Pulley Housing	10-17 (14-24)
Water Pump	24-31 (34-43)

ENGINE SPECIFICATIONS

GENERAL SPECIFICATIONS

Year	Displ. cu. ins.	cc	Carburetor	HP at RPM	Torque (Ft. Lbs. at RPM)	Compr. Ratio	Bore in.	mm	Stroke in.	mm
1981	136.6	2238	Fuel Inj.	.....	.....	21:1	3.46	88	3.62	92

VALVES

Engine & Valve	Head Diam. In. (mm)	Face Angle	Seat Angle	Seat Width In. (mm)	Stem Diameter In. (mm)	Stem Clearance In. (mm)	Valve Lift In. (mm)
2238 Int.	.....	45°	45°°	.051 (1.3)	.315 (8.0)	.0015-.0027)	.....
Exh.	.....	45°	45°	.051 (1.3)	.315 (8.0)	.0025-.0037 (.064-.093)	.....

CRANKSHAFT MAIN & CONNECTING ROD BEARINGS

Engine	MAIN BEARINGS Journal Diam. In. (mm)	Clearance In. (mm)	Thrust Bearing	Crankshaft End Play In. (mm)	CONNECTING ROD BEARINGS Journal Diam. In. (mm)	Clearance In. (mm)	Side Play In. (mm)
2238	2.3591-2.3594 (59-92-59-93)	.0011-.0033 (.029-.085)	①	.0039-.0100 (0.10-0.250)	2.0835-2.039 (52.92-52.93)	.0016-.0040 (.040-.014)	.....

① — Utilizes thrust washer on No. 3 main journal.

Isuzu & LUV Engines

LUV & P'UP 4-CYLINDER DIESEL (Cont.)

ENGINE SPECIFICATIONS (Cont.)

PISTONS, PINS, RINGS

Engine	PISTONS	PINS		RINGS		
	Clearance In. (mm)	Piston Fit In. (mm)	Rod Fit In. (mm)	Rings	End Gap In. (mm)	Side Clearance In. (mm)
2238	.0062-.0070 (.157-.177)	.0002 (.004)	①.003-.0008 (.008-.020)	No. 1	.0079-.0158 (.20-.40)	.0018-.0028 (.045-.070)
				No. 2	..0079-.0158 (.20-.40)	.0012-.0021 (.030-.055)
				Oil	.0079-.0158 (.20-.40)	.0008-.0021 (.020-.054)

① — Floating pin. Clearance shown is between bushing and pin.

VALVE SPRINGS

Engine	Free Length In. (mm)	PRESSURE Lbs. @ In. (kg @ mm)	
		Valve Closed	Valve Open
2238 Inner	1.89 (47-9)	①13.0@1.46 (5.9@37)	.....
Outer	1.86 (47.3)	46.0@1.54 (20.9@39)	.....

① — Compressed height as measured in tester.

VALVE TIMING

Engine	INTAKE		EXHAUST	
	Open (BTDC)	Close (ABDC)	Open (BBDC)	Close (ATDC)
2238	16°	54°	56°	14°

CAMSHAFT

Engine	Journal Diam. In. (mm)	Clearance In. (mm)	Lobe Lift In. (mm)
2238	1.89 (48.0)	.002 (.05)	.....

I-MARK 4-CYLINDER DIESEL

ENGINE CODING

ENGINE IDENTIFICATION

Engine number is stamped on the left rear corner of the cylinder block. Diesel engines are identified by the number 4FB1.

ENGINE & CYLINDER HEAD

ENGINE

NOTE — *Engine and transmission should be removed as a unit. Engine can then be separated from transmission.*

Removal — **1)** Mark hood hinges for reassembly and remove hood. Disconnect battery cables. Remove cables, battery hold-down and battery. Drain engine cooling system, crankcase and transmission. Remove lower engine splash guard.

2) Remove fan shroud, disconnect radiator hoses, remove radiator attaching bolts and lift out radiator. Disconnect heater hoses. Remove heat riser tube. Disconnect thermo switch wiring at connector on thermostat housing.

3) Disconnect alternator wiring at connector. Disconnect vacuum hose from rear of vacuum pump and fast idle actuator. Disconnect exhaust pipe from manifold and mounting bracket and remove front pipe. Disconnect accelerator cable from injection pump lever and fuel cut solenoid switch wiring at connector.

4) Disconnect tachometer wire (if equipped), starter, oil pressure switch and fuel hoses at injection pump. Disconnect any remaining engine/transmission to chassis wiring, tubes or hoses.

5) Mark for installation and remove propeller shaft. Plug transmission. Remove console, pry off shift lever dust boot, remove shift lever cover bolts and remove shift lever assembly. Remove rear engine mount bolts and attach hoist to engine.

6) Lift engine slightly to remove weight from engine mounts and remove front mount and engine damper. Pull engine forward and carefully remove engine and transmission as an assembly.

Installation — Replace any rubber engine mounts showing signs of deterioration or separation. Check engine damper for leakage, worn bushings or any other signs of wear or damage. Replace if needed. Reverse removal procedures to complete installation. Check all fluid levels and bleed fuel system.

CYLINDER HEAD

Removal — **1)** Drain cooling system and remove camshaft as outlined in camshaft removal section. Remove 6 injection pipe clip retaining screws and remove clip. Loosen 8 injection pipe nuts and separate injection pipe. Remove fuel return hose.

2) Disconnect exhaust pipe from manifold. Disconnect oil feed pipe from cylinder head and heater hose from thermostat housing. Loosen head bolts in reverse of tightening sequence shown in *Fig. 1* and remove cylinder head.

Installation — Make sure new head gasket is clean and free of any scratches or nicks. Do not use sealer. Install cylinder

head and tighten bolts in at least 2 steps in order shown. Install camshaft and rocker arm assembly. Install timing belt. Reverse removal procedures to complete installation.

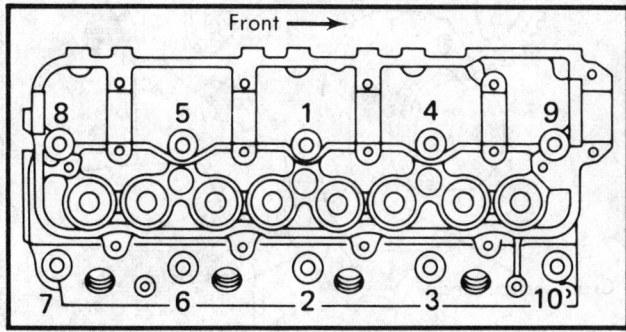

Fig. 1 *Cylinder Head Tightening Sequence (Loosen in Reverse Order)*

TIMING BELT & CAMSHAFT

TIMING BELT

Removal — **1)** Disconnect battery ground cable and drain engine coolant. Remove lower engine splash guard. Remove fan shroud, fan belt, fan and pulley. Remove upper front cover and bypass hose located in front of camshaft sprocket.

2) With No. 1 cylinder at TDC on compression stroke, check that timing marks on the injection pump and pump pulley are in alignment. Fix pulley position with lock bolt inserted through pulley into block.

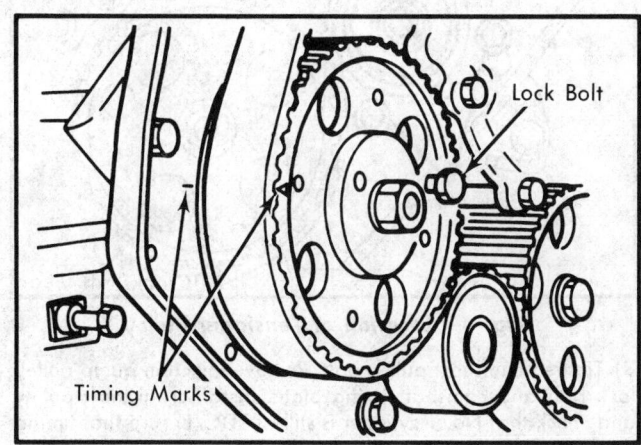

Fig. 2 *Injection Pump Timing Marks*

3) Remove air connecting hose, PCV hoses, and 3 cam cover retaining bolts. Remove cam cover. Loosen adjusting screws on rocker arms and fix camshaft in position using special fixing plate (J-29761) fitted through slot in rear of camshaft.

4) Remove crankshaft pulley. Remove lower dust cover, timing belt holder and tension spring. Loosen tension pulley and pivot plate bolts and remove timing chain.

I-MARK 4-CYLINDER DIESEL (Cont.)

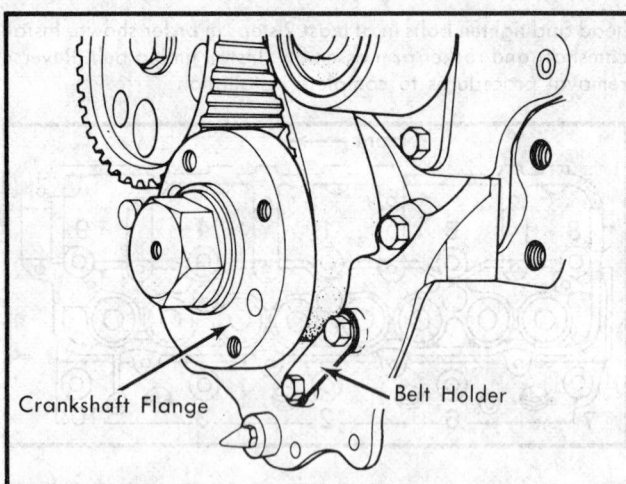

Fig. 3 Location of Timing Belt Holder

Installation — 1) Remove camshaft pulley retaining bolt and camshaft pulley. Install pulley and tighten bolt finger tight. Ensure that pulley can be turned smoothly by hand.

2) Install timing belt on pulleys one at a time starting at the crankshaft pulley and working in a counterclockwise direction. Check that belt is properly engaged on all pulleys. Take up belt slack at tension pulley and tighten pivot bolts just enough to prevent pulley movement.

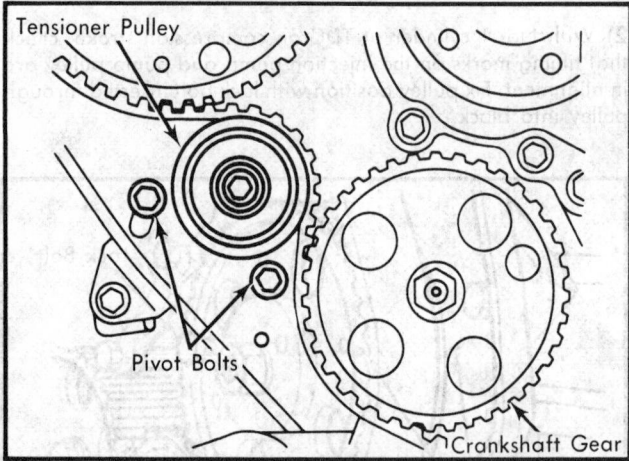

Fig. 4 Location of Tensioner Pulley

3) Tighten camshaft pulley bolt. Remove injection pump pulley lock bolt and camshaft fixing plate. Install crankshaft pulley and check that No. 1 cylinder is still at TDC. Ensure that timing marks on injection pump and pulley are still aligned.

4) Loosen tensioner pulley bolts and take up belt slack. Tighten pivot and pivot pulley bolts (in that order). Check that belt tension between camshaft pulley and injection pump is 47-64 lbs. (21-29 kg). Adjust valves and install cam cover. Reverse removal procedures to complete installation.

CAMSHAFT

Removal — Remove timing belt. Remove camshaft pulley bolt and camshaft pulley. Remove 4 head plate retaining bolts and remove front head plate. Remove cam bearing caps with bearing halves. Remove camshaft oil seal and camshaft.

Installation — Install camshaft with new oil seal. Apply sealant to contact surface of No. 1 cam bearing cap. Reverse removal procedures to complete installation.

VALVES

VALVE ARRANGEMENT

Right Side — All intake.
Left Side — All exhaust.

VALVES

Removal — 1) Remove cylinder head. Remove intake and exhaust manifolds from head. Loosen rocker shaft bolts in several steps starting with end bolts and working to the middle. Remove rocker shaft.

2) Remove valve caps. Compress valve springs with spring compressor (J-29760), and remove valve locks, retainers, inner and outer spring seats and valves. Retain components in correct order for installation.

Installation — Reverse removal procedures to install. Valve springs are of a varied pitch design. Be sure that they are installed with the close coiled end (painted green) against the cylinder head.

VALVE GUIDE SERVICE

Check valve stem clearance in valve guide with a dial indicator. Insert valve in valve guide and move left or right (parallel with rocker arm). Measure stem movement .4" (10 mm) above guide edge. If movement exceeds .008" (.2 mm) and valve stem is not worn, the valve guide must be replaced.

Removal — Drive out old guide with tool (J-26512) from combustion chamber side.

Installation — To install new guide, coat outer surface of guide with engine oil and drive into head from opposite side with tool (J-26512). Guide should project from cylinder head .583" (14.8 mm). Whenever a valve is replaced, a new guide should be used.

VALVE SEAT INSERTS

Check condition of valve seat contact area. If pitted, worn or otherwise damaged, replace seat. To remove, arc-weld a bead of metal around contact surface of seat. Allow to cool a few minutes. Pry out valve seat. Install new seat with press. Grind to correct width and angle. Lap valve and seat to complete installation.

SWIRL CHAMBER REPLACEMENT

Removal — Measure chamber depth in head with straight edge and feeler gauge. If depth exceeds .001" (.2 mm), chamber must be replaced. Use a drift of .15-.20" (3-5 mm) diameter to drive out old chamber. Insert drift through injection nozzle hole to swirl chamber and drive out with hammer.

Installation — Install lock ball into groove in swirl chamber. Align lock ball in chamber with groove in cylinder head and

Isuzu Engines

I-MARK 4-CYLINDER DIESEL (Cont.)

drive in. To seat chamber, use press to apply 1000-1100 lbs. (450-500 kg.) pressure. A piece of metal should be placed between press and chamber to prevent damage.

VALVE SPRING TENSION

Valve springs must be less than .004" (1.0 mm) out of square. Inner valve springs should require 20 lbs. (9.1 kg) of pressure at a height of 1.52" (38.5 mm). Outer spring should require 34.6 lbs. (15.7 kg) at 1.61" (41.0 mm). If tension required is less than 16.5 lbs. (7.5 kg) for the inner spring or 30.8 lbs. (14.0 kg) for the outer, the spring should be replaced. Inner and outer springs should always be replaced as a set.

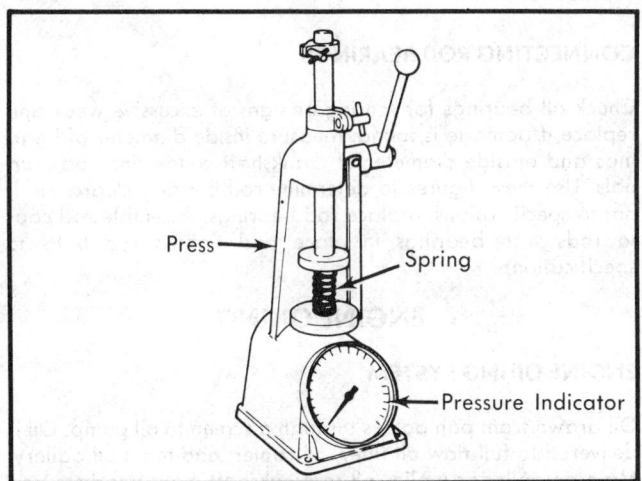

Fig. 5   Checking Valve Spring Tension

VALVE ADJUSTMENT

Valve adjustment can be made with engine warm or cold. Bring No. 1 cylinder to TDC on compression stroke and adjust No. 1 and No. 2 intake valves, No. 1 and No. 3 exhaust valves. Rotate crankshaft 180° and adjust remaining valves (No. 3 and 4 intake, No. 2 and 4 exhaust).

Valve Adjustment Clearances	
Valve	**Clearance**
Intake	.010" (.25 mm)
Exhaust	.014" (.35 mm)

PISTONS, PINS & RINGS

PISTON & ROD ASSEMBLY

Removal — With cylinder head and oil pan removed, remove connecting rod cap nuts. Remove rod cap with bearing half. Push piston/rod assembly with bearing half up and out through top of engine. Rod caps must be kept with their respective piston and rod assembly as caps are not interchangeable.

Installation — **1)** Thoroughly oil rings, piston and cylinder wall. Make sure ring gaps are located 180° apart and not on thrust side of piston or in line with piston pin. Make sure bearing halves are properly seated in connecting rod and cap.

2) Install a ring compressor and compress rings. Install piston in cylinder. Ensure mark in piston top points towards front of the engine. With piston installed in cylinder, and connecting rod and bearings seated against crankshaft journal, install rod caps to their respective piston and rod assembly. Make sure that marks in cap and rod end match and are installed on the same side.

3) With threads of rod bolts and seating face of nuts oiled, install and tighten nuts to specifications. Reverse removal procedures to complete installation.

FITTING PISTONS

1) Measure cylinder bores for wear at depths of .5" and 3.0" (10 and 80 mm). Measurements should be made in line with and at right angles to the crankshaft centerline. If excessive wear is found, cylinder should be bored to accomodate next oversize piston. Whenever one cylinder is bored, all cylinders must be bored.

2) Measure piston diameter at right angle to piston pin. Subtract this figure from cylinder diameter to obtain piston to wall clearance. Final hone of cylinder wall should provide .0002-.0020" (.005-.045 mm) clearance.

Piston Specifications	
Piston Size In. (mm)	**Piston Diameter** In. (mm)
Standard	3.307-3.309 (84.00-84.05)
.020 (.50) O/S	3.326-3.328 (84.50-84.54)
.040 (1.0) O/S	3.346-3.348 (85.00-85.04)

PISTON PINS

Removal — Piston pin is a full floating type. To remove pin, use snap ring pliers and remove snap ring from piston. Push out pin.

Inspection — Visually inspect pin for signs of damage or excessive wear. Replace if needed. With hole gauge and micrometer, measure piston pin diameter and diameter of pin hole in piston. Subtract pin diameter from hole diameter to get pin to piston clearance figure. Clearance should be between .0001 and .0005" (.002-.012 mm). If clearance exceeds limit of .0019" (.05 mm), pin and piston should be replaced.

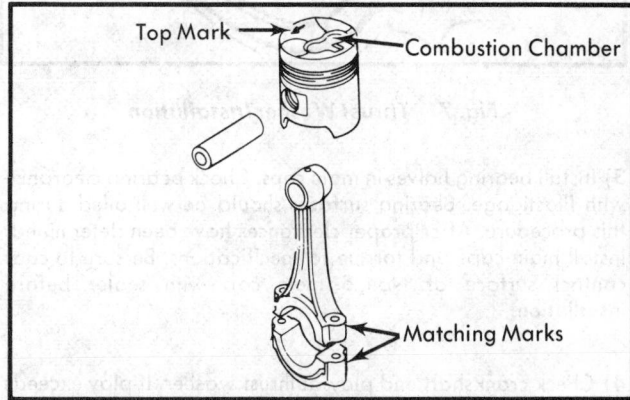

Fig. 6   Relationship of Piston to Connecting Rod

I-MARK 4-CYLINDER DIESEL (Cont.)

Installation — Reverse removal procedures to install. Make sure that piston and rod are joined so that the combustion chamber on the piston is on the same side as the match marks on the connecting rod.

CRANKSHAFT MAIN & CONNECTING ROD BEARINGS

CRANKSHAFT

Removal — With engine removed from vehicle, remove cylinder head and timing belt as outlined. Remove front crank pulley, front oil seal, oil pan and pump, and crankshaft rear oil seal. Remove piston and rod assemblies. Remove flywheel and crankshaft rear mounting hub. Loosen crankshaft main bearing caps starting with outside caps and working toward the middle. Remove caps and lift out crankshaft.

Inspection — Check all shaft journals and crankpins for scoring, wear, or cracks. Taper and out-of-round on all journals must not exceed .001" (.015 mm). Check crankshaft for bend using dial indicator at center journal. If bend exceeds limit of .0023" (.06 mm), the crankshaft must be replaced.

NOTE — *Crankshafts have been tufftrided and should never be ground to obtain correct clearances. If journals are worn beyond acceptable limits, the crankshaft must be replaced.*

Installation — **1)** Install main bearing halves to engine block ensuring that all bearings are on their respective journal. All main bearings are grooved on both halves except for the No. 3 lower (cap side) bearing half. All grooved bearings have an oil hole as well.

2) Coat all bearing surfaces liberally with clean engine oil. Carefully install crankshaft. Insert thrust washer on No. 3 crankshaft journal with oil grooves facing outwards.

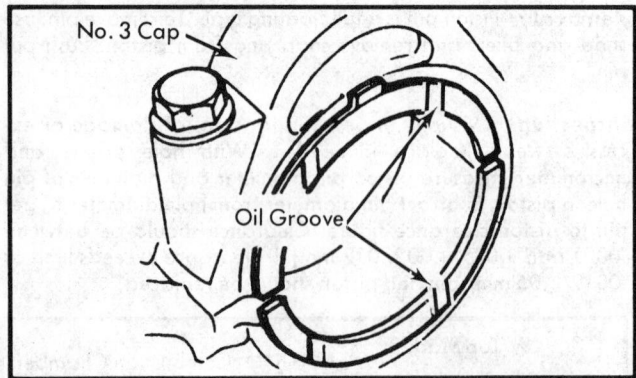

Fig. 7   Thrust Washer Installation

3) Install bearing halves in main caps. Check bearing clearance with Plastigage. Bearing surfaces should be well oiled during this procedure. After proper clearances have been determined, install main caps and torque to specifications. Be sure to coat contact surface of No. 5 main cap with sealer before installation.

4) Check crankshaft end play at thrust washer. If play exceeds .012" (.30 mm) replace the thrust washer. Reverse removal procedures to complete installation.

MAIN BEARINGS

Check all bearings for scoring or wear and replace if damage is found. Clean oil from crankshaft and place a strip of Plastigage on crankshaft journal. Install main bearing cap with bearing installed, and tighten to specifications.

NOTE — *Plastigage should run parallel with crankshaft and not block oil hole. Do not turn crankshaft while Plastigage is inserted.*

Remove cap and measure width of Plastigage at widest point using gauge provided. If clearance is not to specifications, replace bearings.

CONNECTING ROD BEARINGS

Check all bearings for scoring or signs of excessive wear and replace if damage is found. Measure inside diameter of bearings and outside diameter of crankshaft connecting rod journals. Use these figures to determine rod bearing clearance. If not to specifications, replace rod bearings. Assemble rod caps to rods with bearings in place and tighten rod bolts to specifications.

ENGINE OILING

ENGINE OILING SYSTEM

Oil drawn from pan passes through a screen to oil pump. Oil is delivered to full flow oil filter, oil cooler, and main oil gallery. Main oil gallery supplies oil to crankshaft main bearings and drilled passages in crankshaft which in turn lubricate connecting rod bearings.

Oil gallery feeds oil to vacuum pump and rocker arm shaft to lubricate rocker arms and cam bearings. Oil is fed from gallery to oil jet pipe which sprays oil from below piston to lubricate cylinder walls and piston pins.

Crankcase Capacity (with filter) — 5.8 quarts.

Oil Filter — Full-flow with disposable cartridge.

Oil Pressure — 50-60 psi (3.5-4.5 kg/cm²).

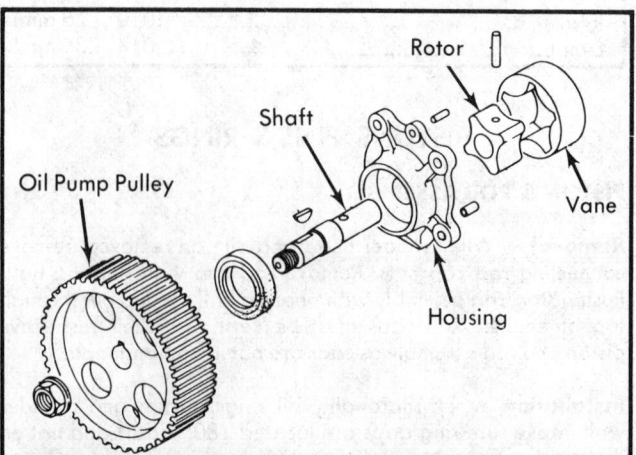

Fig. 8   Exploded View of Oil Pump

I-MARK 4-CYLINDER DIESEL (Cont.)

OIL PUMP

Removal — Oil pump is mounted to front of engine between water pump and crankshaft pulley. It is belt driven by the timing belt. To remove, first remove timing belt. Remove 4 allen head retaining bolts located behind oil pump pulley. Remove pump.

Inspection — Disassemble oil pump and clean all parts thoroughly in clean solvent. Inspect for signs of unusual wear or damage. Replace as needed. Check all clearances to specifications. Check outside diameter of pulley sleeve. If sleeve measures less than 1.1" (27.9 mm), the pulley should be replaced.

Installation — Reverse removal procedures to install.

Oil Pump Specifications	
Application	① **Clearance In. (mm)**
Vane Depth in Cylinder Block	.008 (.200)
Vane Side Clearance	.016 (.400)
Rotor Tip Clearance	.008 (.200)
① — Clearances given are wear limits.	

ENGINE COOLING

Thermostat — Opens at 180°F (82°C). Full open at 203°F (95°C).

Radiator Cap — 13 psi (.9 kg/cm²).

Cooling System Capacity — 7.4 quarts.

Water Pump — Centrifugal type pump with aluminum body.

Removal & Installation — To remove, drain cooling system and remove fan, pulley and fan belt. Remove crankshaft pulley and front covers. Remove by-pass hose, water pump retaining bolts (5) and water pump with gasket. Reverse removal procedures to install. Make sure mating surfaces of pump and block are clean, and always use a new gasket.

TIGHTENING SPECIFICATIONS	
Application	**Ft. Lbs. (N·m)**
Cylinder Head	
New Bolts	85-100 (116-136)
Used Bolts	90-105 (122-143)
Camshaft Bearing Cap	
Camshaft Gear	40-47 (54-64)
Connecting Rod	54-61 (73-83)
Crankshaft Gear Bolt (1)	100-120 (136-163)
Crankshaft Pulley Bolts (4)	10-20 (14-27)
Engine Plate — Rear	25-33 (34-45)
Flywheel	36-43 (49-59)
Head Plate	11-18 (15-25)
Main Bearing Caps	65-72 (88-98)
Manifolds	
Intake	25-32 (34-44)
Exhaust	11-18 (15-25)
Idler Pulley	47-61 (64-83)
Injection Pump Drive Gear	43-50 (58-68)
Oil Jet Pipe	40-54 (54-73)
Oil Pump	11-18 (15-25)
Oil Pump Drive Gear	47-61 (64-83)
Rocker Shaft	15-22 (20-30)
Tensioner Pulley	
Pulley Bolt (1)	47-61 (64-83)
Plate Bolts (4)	11-18 (15-25)

ENGINE SPECIFICATIONS

GENERAL SPECIFICATIONS										
Year	Displ.		Carburetor	HP at RPM	Torque (Ft. Lbs. at RPM)	Compr. Ratio	Bore		Stroke	
	cu. ins.	cc					in.	mm	in.	mm
1981 4FB1	110.8	1817	Fuel Inj.	. . . . .	. . . . .	22:1	3.3	84	3.2	82

CRANKSHAFT MAIN & CONNECTING ROD BEARINGS							
	MAIN BEARINGS				CONNECTING ROD BEARINGS		
Engine	Journal Diam. In. (mm)	Clearance In. (mm)	Thrust Bearing	Crankshaft End Play In. (mm)	Journal Diam. In. (mm)	Clearance In. (mm)	Side Play In. (mm)
1817	2.201-2.202 (55.92-55.93)	.0012-.0027 (.039-.080)	①	.0024-.0094 (.06-.24)	1.925-1.926 (48.92-48.94)	.0016-.0027 (.040-.080)	. . . . .

① — Utilizes thrust washer on No. 3 main journal.

Isuzu Engines

I-MARK 4-CYLINDER DIESEL (Cont.)
ENGINE SPECIFICATIONS (Cont.)

PISTONS, PINS, RINGS

	PISTONS	PINS		RINGS		
Engine	Clearance In. (mm)	Piston Fit In. (mm)	Rod Fit In. (mm)	Rings	End Gap In. (mm)	Side Clearance In. (mm)
1817	.0002-.0017 (.005-.045)	.0001-.0005 (.002-.012)	① .0003-.0078 (.008-.020)	No. 1	.0078-.0157 (.200-.400)	.0035-.0049 (.090-.125)
				No. 2	.0078-.0157 (.200-.400)	.0015-.0019 (.035-.050)
				Oil	.0078-.0157 (.200-.400)	.0012-.0027 (.030-.070)

① — Clearance between pin and bushing.

VALVES

Engine & Valve	Head Diam. In. (mm)	Face Angle	Seat Angle	Seat Width In. (mm)	Stem Diameter In. (mm)	Stem Clearance In. (mm)	Valve Lift In. (mm)
1817 Int.	....	45°	45°	.0472-.0590 (1.200-1.500)	.313 (7.95)	.0015-.0027 (.040-.070)	.....
Exh.	....	45°	45°	.0472-.0590 (1.200-1.500)	.313 (7.95)	.002-.003 (.05-.08)	.....

VALVE TIMING

	INTAKE		EXHAUST	
Engine	Open (BTDC)	Close (ABDC)	Open (BBDC)	Close (ATDC)
1817	32°	60°	65°	29°

CAMSHAFT

Engine	Journal Diam. In. (mm)	Clearance In. (mm)	Lobe Lift In. (mm)
1817	1.1004-1.1010 (27.95-27.97)	.0008-.0035 (.020-.090)	....

VALVE SPRINGS

Engine	Free Length In. (mm)	PRESSURE Lbs. @ In. (kg @ mm)	
		Valve Closed	Valve Open
1817 Inner	1.783 (45.3)	① 20 @ 1.515 (9.1 @ 38.5)	....
Outer	1.846 (46.9)	34.6 @ 1.614 (15.7 @ 41.0)	....

① — Compressed height as measured in tester.

XJ6 6-CYLINDER

ENGINE CODING

ENGINE IDENTIFICATION

Engine can be identified by the number stamped on top of cylinder block at rear of engine and on identification plate in engine compartment.

ENGINE & CYLINDER HEAD

ENGINE

NOTE − *Engine and transmission are removed as an assembly.*

Removal − **1)** Remove hood and disconnect battery. Discharge air conditioning system. Disconnect and cap refrigerant lines. Remove fuel lines from fuel cooler and plug fuel inlet line. Remove fuel cooler mounting screws and secure cooler, receiver-drier, refrigerant lines and fuel lines away from engine.

2) Remove fender brace rods. Remove air cleaner. Detach and remove radiator. Disconnect coolant hoses to expansion tank. Remove both engine mount-to-bracket nuts. Drain power steering fluid. Disconnect power steering lines. Slacken pump mounting bolts and push pump as close as possible to engine.

3) Pull connectors from alternator. Separate connector plug from engine harness. Disconnect brake vacuum pipe at manifold, and secure pipe out of way. Release pipe clip and pull heater-A/C operating vacuum pipe from non-return valves; secure away from engine. Remove exhaust manifolds.

4) Remove starter cable and solenoid cable. Disconnect heater hoses at firewall connectors. From fuel injection system, disconnect the following: Thermotime switch, cold start injector, throttle switch, oxygen sensor, auxiliary air valve, water temperature sensor and throttle linkage. Disconnect hoses from charcoal canister.

5) Position suitable lifting device and attach to rear lifting eye on engine. Remove nut at center of rear transmission mounting. Unscrew nuts securing bracket on transmission. Remove heat shield. Position jack to support mounting plate of transmission and unscrew mounting bolts. Lower jack and remove mounting plate along with spring washers and rubber rings.

6) Remove special nuts securing propeller shaft to output flange. From transmission unit selector lever, remove nut to release ball peg on inner selector cable. Remove setscrew and spring washer securing outer selector cable clamp. Disconnect speedometer cable from transmission.

7) From front of vehicle, position jack to support transmission assembly below oil sump. Support engine on lifting assembly. Lift front of engine while lowering rear and withdraw engine/transmission assembly forward and upward.

CAUTION − *Use extreme care when withdrawing engine to prevent damage to air conditioning expansion valve.*

Installation − Fit insulating material across transmission and reverse removal procedure to complete installation. Ensure that all fluid levels are to specifications. Evacuate and charge air conditioning system.

CYLINDER HEAD

Removal − **1)** Disconnect battery and drain cooling system. Remove both wing valance stays (firewall-to-fender support rods), removing pressure line from support rod. Remove air cleaner. Detach throttle linkage and disconnect thermotime switch, cold start injector, throttle switch, oxygen sensor, auxiliary air valve and water temperature sensor.

2) Disconnect and plug fuel lines at fuel cooler (heat exchanger) and move cooler to side of engine compartment. Remove heat shield from exhaust manifold. Remove steering pump drive belt and swing pump away from engine. Remove top radiator hose and pull remote header and radiator bleed lines from header tank. Disconnect coolant hose from water pump.

3) Disconnect any remaining lines or wires from intake manifold, noting position for assembly. Detach exhaust manifolds from head. Remove distributor cap, spark plugs and plug wires. Disconnect 2 camshaft oil lines from rear of head and remove camshaft covers. Detach breather housing from front of head.

4) Remove camshaft sprocket retaining bolts from both camshafts and slide sprockets up support brackets. Mark aligning holes in adjuster plates. Working from center outward, remove cylinder head bolts. Carefully lift cylinder head assembly from engine.

CAUTION − *Crankshaft must NOT be rotated after camshaft sprockets are disconnected and head is still in place. When head is removed, it must not rest on a flat surface. Support head with wooden blocks at each end to protect open valves which protrude.*

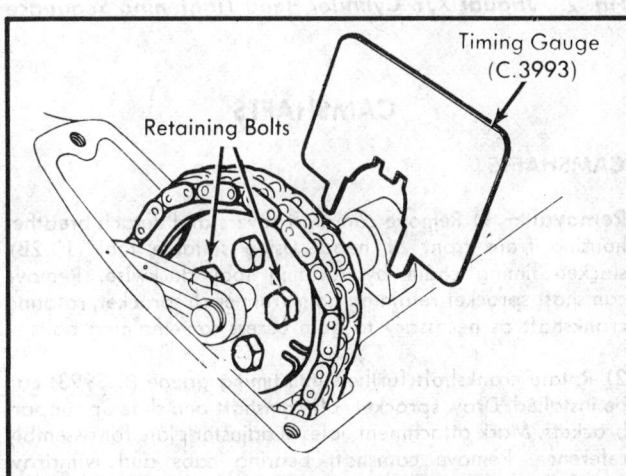

Fig. 1 Retaining Bolts Installed to Hold Camshaft During Cylinder Head Installation

Installation − **1)** Install new head gasket (ensuring "TOP" mark is upward). Rotate crankshaft until No. 6 cylinder (front) is at TDC, with rotor pointing approximately forward along engine.

2) Rotate camshafts until suitable timing gauge (C.3993) can be located in front flange slots. *See Fig. 1.* Lower cylinder head into position, attach spark plug wire brackets and lifting brackets to appropriate head studs, then place washers and

Jaguar Engines

XJ6 6-CYLINDER (Cont.)

14 large domed nuts on studs. Affix nuts and washers at forward end of head, then tighten all nuts. *See Fig. 2.*

3) Locate sprockets on camshaft flanges and ensure both holes in each flange are positioned with aligning holes marked during removal. If necessary, remove circlip and reposition adjuster plate. Make sure engine is not rotated until camshaft sprockets are fully seated and chain installed.

4) Secure each adjuster plate to camshaft, then rotate engine until remaining attachment holes are accessible. Install bolts and bend up lock plate tabs. Set timing chain tension using a suitable adjusting tool (JD2B). Tighten lock nut.

5) Ensure No. 6 (front) cylinder is at TDC and recheck position of camshafts using timing gauge (C.3993). Complete installation by reversing remainder of removal procedures. Recheck ignition timing and perform exhaust emission check.

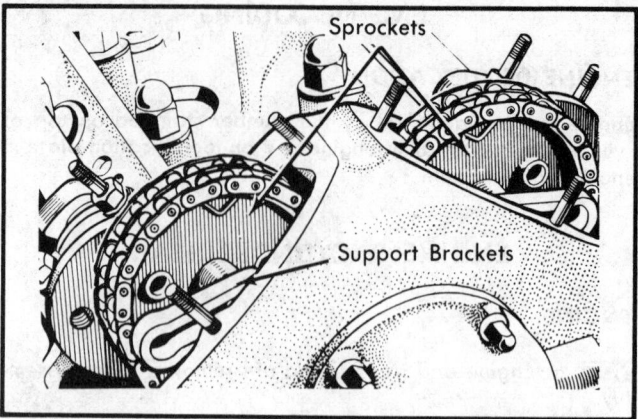

Fig. 3   Camshaft Sprockets in Disconnected Position

ENGINE FRONT COVER & OIL SEAL

Removal — 1) Remove radiator and fan belt. Mark position of vibration damper for reassembly. Remove pulley. Using a pair of levers, pry damper off of split cone. Remove split cone from crankshaft.

2) Remove oil pan and water pump. Unscrew screws attaching timing cover and slide timing cover and oil seal off of crankshaft.

Installation — 1) Place new seal in groove in timing cover. Using a new gasket and sealing compound, intall timing cover and seal. Reinstall oil pan with a new gasket. Install short screw in front right hand corner of oil pan.

2) Reinstall split cone on crankshaft. Position crankshaft damper to mark, install pulley and torque attaching bolts to specifications. Reinstall remaining components in reverse of removal procedures.

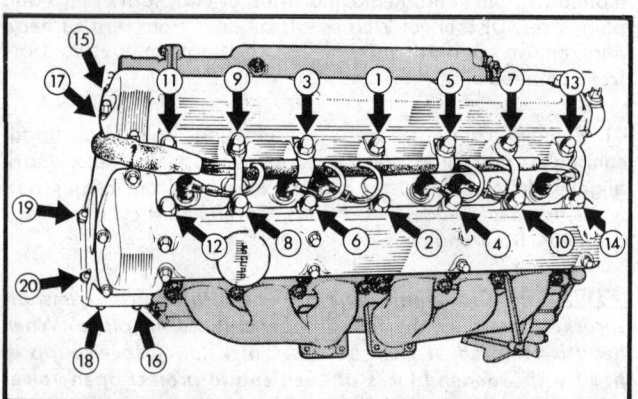

Fig. 2   Jaguar XJ6 Cylinder Head Tightening Sequence

CAMSHAFTS

CAMSHAFTS

Removal — 1) Remove camshaft covers and detach breather housing from front of head. Using suitable tool (JD.2B), slacken timing chain by rotating tool clockwise. Remove camshaft sprocket retaining bolts from each sprocket, rotating crankshaft as necessary to gain access to remaining bolts.

2) Rotate crankshaft further until timing gauge (C.3993) can be installed. Draw sprockets off camshaft and slide up support brackets. Mark attachment holes in adjuster plate for assembly reference. Remove camshaft bearing caps and withdraw camshaft.

CAUTION — *Crankshaft MUST NOT be rotated after camshaft sprockets are removed.*

Installation — To install, reverse removal procedure, ensuring that all components are replaced in original position.

NOTE — *If preceding instructions have not been followed, it will be necessary to ensure that valve timing is still correct. See Valve Timing.*

VALVE TIMING

1) Rotate engine so that No. 6 (front) piston is at TDC on compression stroke and distributor rotor arm points to No. 6 segment. Check that timing chains are properly adjusted. *See Timing Chain Replacement.*

2) Remove lock wire from camshaft sprocket screws. Rotate crankshaft until inaccessible screws can be removed. Return engine to TDC of No. 6 piston and remove retaining screws. Tap camshaft sprockets off camshaft flanges.

3) Position camshafts accurately with valve timing gauge, and check that TDC marks are in exact alignment. *See Fig. 1.* Withdraw clips from camshaft sprockets and press adjusting plates forward until serrations disengage. *See Fig. 4.*

4) Replace sprockets on flanges of camshaft and align two holes in adjuster plate with holes in flanges. Engage serrations of adjuster plates with serrations in sprocket.

NOTE — *Screw holes must be in exact alignment. If difficulty is experienced in aligning holes turn adjuster plates 180° and realign holes.*

5) Replace circlips in camshaft sprockets. Replace camshaft sprocket screws and lock wire. Recheck valve timing.

Jaguar Engines

XJ6 6-CYLINDER (Cont.)

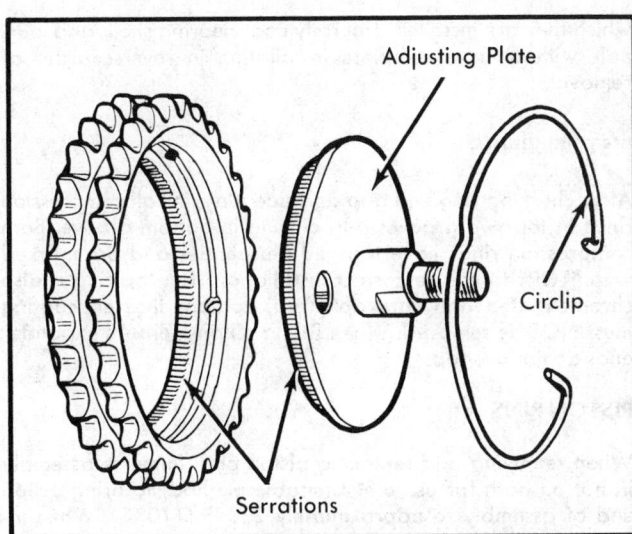

Fig. 4   Expanded View of Camshaft Sprocket Assembly

VALVES

VALVE ARRANGEMENT

Left Side — All exhaust.
Right Side — All intake.

VALVE GUIDE SERVICING

Check valve guide for wear and proper guide-to-valve stem clearance. If guide is worn beyond specifications, replace guide by heating head in boiling water for approximately 30 minutes (or by other suitable method), then drive guide(s) out of head from combustion chamber end. Coat new guide with graphite grease and refit circlip. Reheat head and drive new guide in from top until circlip is seated in groove.

NOTE — *When installing oversize replacement guides, check O.D. of guide to be used. If necessary, ream cylinder head bore to obtain proper interference fit.*

Replacement Valve Guides		
Application	**Size Mark**	**Dimension In. (mm)**
Standard	No Mark	.501-.502 (12.73-12.75)
1st Oversize	1 Groove	.503-.504 (12.78-12.80)
2nd Oversize	2 Grooves	.506-.507 (12.85-12.87)
3rd Oversize	3 Grooves	.511-.512 (12.98-13.00)

VALVE SPRING SERVICING

CAUTION — *Support ends of cylinder head with wooden blocks to prevent damage to valves. Opened valves protrude below face of cylinder head.*

1) Remove camshaft bearing caps, note markings for reassembly. Remove camshaft, tappets and adjusting pads. Retain tappets and pads in proper order for reassembly.

2) Install suitable spring compressor (Churchill No. JD.6118C) and a block of wood between valve and work table. Compress springs and remove valve keepers. Compare old spring with new spring or with specification table. Replace springs as necessary. To install, reverse procedure.

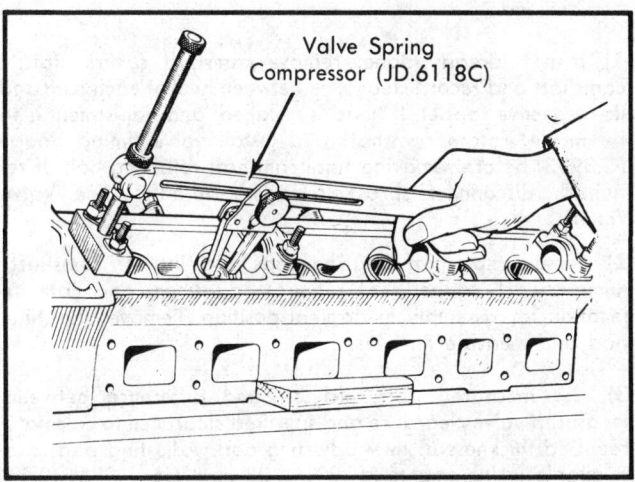

Fig. 5   Valve Spring Compressor Tool Installation

VALVE TAPPET SERVICE

NOTE — *Valves and operating mechanisms are numbered and must be kept in order when disassembled. No. 1 is at flywheel end of engine.*

1) Remove tappets and adjusting pads and inspect guides, tappets and pads for wear. If tappet guide is to be replaced, bore out old guide until it collapses, using care not to damage head bore. Ensure head is at room temperature and measure head bore of tappet guide.

2) Grind replacement guide to obtain a .003" (.076 mm) interference fit in head. Grind same amount from "lead-in" at bottom end of guide. Heat head and install tappet guide, ensuring that lip at top guide seats evenly in head recess. Allow to cool and ream guide bore to 1.375" (34.93 mm). Replace other parts as necessary.

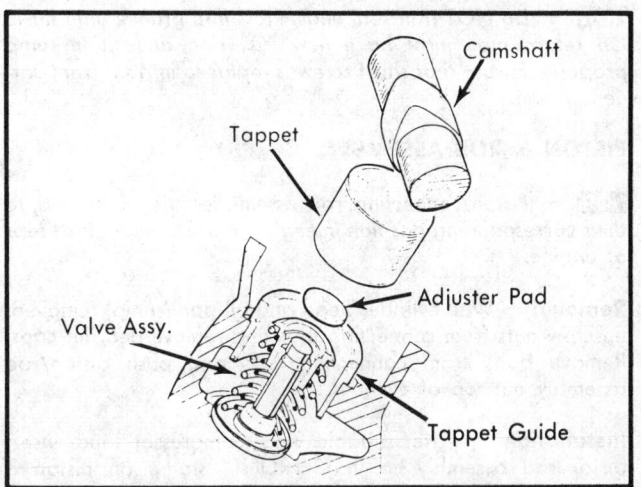

Fig. 6   Valve Tappet and Guide Assembly

6-148

Jaguar Engines

XJ6 6-CYLINDER (Cont.)

VALVE TAPPET CLEARANCE

NOTE — *If checking valve clearances with cylinder head removed, the camshafts must be installed and checked one at a time. It is imperative that this be followed, as position fouling is likely if camshafts are rotated independently while both are installed.*

1) If not already done, remove camshaft covers. Rotate camshaft and record clearance between heel of each cam and its respective tappet. If head is installed, and adjustment is to be made, rotate camshaft and install valve timing gauge (C.3993) before removing final camshaft retaining bolt. If required, disconnect sprockets from camshafts. See *Valve Timing.*

2) Remove camshaft bearing caps and lift off camshaft. Remove each tappet that requires adjustment and note its location for assembly in original position. Remove adjusting pad and measure thickness.

3) Use measured pad thickness and difference between measured valve clearance and specified clearance to calculate required thickness of new adjusting pad. Adjusting pads are available in increments of .001" (.03 mm) from .085" (2.16 mm) to .110" (2.79 mm) and are marked with letters from "A" to "Z" respectively.

4) Insert correct adjusting pads and install tappets. Attach camshafts (using timing gauge). Torque camshaft bearing cap nuts to 9 ft. lbs. (1.2 mkg), connect camshaft sprockets, and install camshaft covers.

PISTONS, PINS & RINGS

OIL PAN

NOTE — *Oil pan removal is best accomplished with engine out of vehicle. Following procedures may be used with engine installed.*

Removal & Installation — Remove front suspension components to gain access and suitable clearance. Drain engine oil. Remove oil return pipe nuts and transmission oil cooler line clips. Remove screws and nuts holding pan to engine and remove pan. To install, ensure that all mating surfaces are clean. Lightly grease seals and gaskets and install pan. Reverse removal procedure to complete installation.

NOTE — *Do NOT trim seal ends. Press into groove until flush. Oil return pipe must have new "O" ring and fit in sump properly. Ensure that short screw is replaced in right front corner of pan.*

PISTON & ROD ASSEMBLY

NOTE — *Piston/connecting rod assemblies are numbered to their corresponding position in engine. No. 1 cylinder is at rear of engine.*

Removal — With cylinder head and oil pan (sump) removed, unscrew nuts from connecting rods and remove bearing caps. Remove bolts from connecting rods and push piston/rod assembly out top of cylinder.

Installation — Use suitable ring compressor and insert piston/rod assembly so that "FRONT" stamp on piston is toward front of engine. If installing new parts, stamp-mark with numbers "1" through "6" corresponding to the bore in which they are installed. Liberally coat bearing shells and journals with oil and complete installation in reverse order of removal.

PISTON RINGS

After checking ring end gap and side play, install compression rings in top two grooves and oil ring in bottom groove. Both compression rings have tapered peripheries and are marked with "TOP" to ensure correct installation. The top ring is also chrome-plated and cargraph (red) coated; the red coating must NOT be removed. When fitting oil ring, ensure expander ends do not overlap.

PISTON PINS

When removing and replacing piston pins, immerse assembly in hot oil bath (or use other suitable method) to bring piston end of assembly to approximately 230°F (110°C). When installing pins, always use new pin circlips. Note that pins are color coded for grading purposes. Always select proper color pin for replacement.

FITTING PISTONS

Check piston and cylinder bore to determine if proper clearance exists. If necessary to rebore cylinder for installation of oversize piston, note that reboring is not to exceed .030" (.76 mm). Oversize pistons are available in .010", .020", and .030" (.25 mm, .51 mm, and .76 mm) oversizes. If replacing pistons with standard sizes (no reboring), note the following list of piston grades and select replacement piston of same grade. Piston grade is stamped in piston crown and on top face of block adjacent to cylinder.

Standard Piston Grading	
Stamp Mark	**Cylinder Diameter In. (mm)**
F	3.6250-3.6253 (92.075-92.083)
G	3.6254-3.6257 (92.085-92.093)
H	3.6258-3.6261 (92.095-92.103)
J	3.6262-3.6265 (92.106-92.113)
K	3.6266-3.6269 (92.116-92.123)

CYLINDER LINERS

1) Should piston-to-cylinder clearance be excessive and reboring requires more than .030" (.76 mm) to clean up cylinders, new cylinder liners must be installed.

2) Press out the worn liners from below, using a suitable block. Lightly coat outer top half of new liner with a jointing compound, then press in new liner until flush with top of block. Smear more jointing compound around area of liner-to-block mating surface.

3) Bore out liner to correspond with grade of piston to be installed. Following reboring process, the blanking plugs in the main oil gallery should be removed and cylinder block oilways

XJ6 6-CYLINDER (Cont.)

thoroughly cleaned. When dry, coat interior of crankcase with an oil and heat resistant paint.

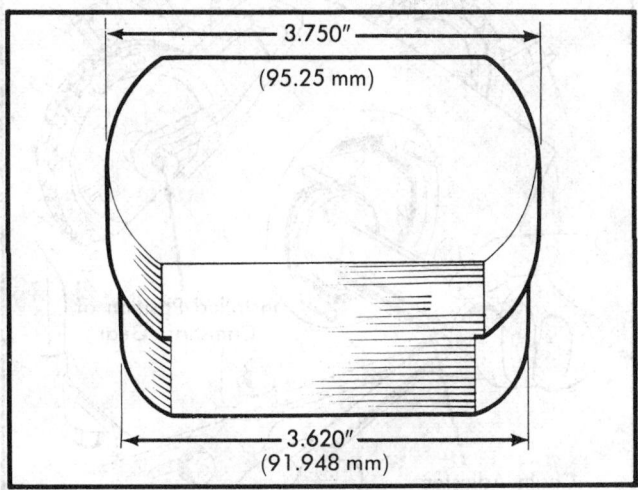

Fig. 7   Cylinder Liner Removing and Installing Block

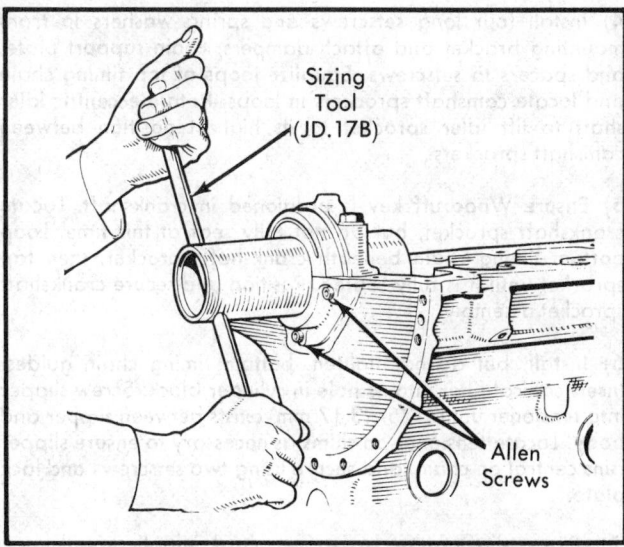

Fig. 8   Sizing Rear Oil Seal

CRANKSHAFT MAIN & CONNECTING ROD BEARINGS

THRUST BEARING ALIGNMENT

Thrust bearing washers are used on center main bearing caps to adjust endplay. If beyond specifications, bearings .004" (.10 mm) oversize as well as standard are available. Install with white metal side (with groove) outwards.

MAIN BEARING SERVICE

Remove connecting rod and main bearing caps, retaining all parts in exact order for reassembly. Note that all caps are numbered for reassembly reference. When wear or out-of-roundness exceeds .003" (.08 mm), regrind crankshaft and install undersize bearings. Bearings are available in .010", .020", .030", and .040" (.25 mm, .51 mm, .76 mm, and 1.02 mm) undersizes. If regrinding must exceed .040" (1.02 mm), replace crankshaft.

REAR MAIN BEARING OIL SEAL

NOTE — *The following procedure must be performed before crankshaft is reinstalled.*

1) Carefully tap new rear oil seal halves into position, then roll seal into housing (with a hammer handle) until ends do not protrude.

NOTE — *DO NOT cut seal ends. When both halves are properly in place, secure them with Allen screws.*

2) Attach rear main bearing cap without bearings and torque to 72 ft. lbs. (10 mkg). Assemble rear oil seal housing to cylinder block, using three Allen screws. Lightly coat inside surface of oil seal with graphite grease and insert a suitable sizing tool (JD.17B) as shown in illustration. Press tool inward and turn until it is fully seated; this should properly size the oil seal. Remove sizing tool by pulling and twisting in opposite direction. Remove oil seal housing and install crankshaft.

TIMING CHAIN

TIMING CHAIN REPLACEMENT

Removal — 1) Remove cylinder head, oil pan, water pump, crankcase breather, vibration damper (including cone and Woodruff key), and timing gear cover. Withdraw timing pointer, distance piece, and front oil seal.

2) Remove oil slinger from crankshaft. Unscrew two bottom timing chain tensioner and chain guides retaining screws. Withdraw conical filter behind tensioner. Slacken four setscrews securing top timing chain assembly (do not remove setscrews at this point).

3) Withdraw crankshaft timing sprocket and chain assembly. Be sure to remove spacers, top timing chain damper, and top timing chain retainer. Disengage camshaft sprockets from top chain. Remove nut and serrated washer from idler shaft and withdraw serrated plate, plunger, and spring.

4) Remove nuts retaining front mounting bracket to rear mounting bracket. Remove timing chains from intermediate and idler sprockets. Draw idler shaft, idler sprocket, and bushing from rear mounting bracket. Remove circlip and press intermediate shaft from rear mounting bracket. Note location of bushing and shim under intermediate sprocket.

Installation — 1) Position eccentric idler shaft to hole in front mounting bracket. Position spring and plunger in bracket and locate serrated plate on shaft. Loosely secure plate using washer and nut.

2) Attach idler sprocket (21 teeth) to idler shaft. Replace intermediate sprocket (large gear forward) onto intermediate shaft, placing shim in position. Install shaft assembly in rear mounting bracket, ensuring roll pin engages in slot; retain with circlip.

3) Locate top timing chain (longer) on small intermediate sprocket, and lower timing chain on large sprocket. Loop top chain beneath idler sprocket and secure top mounting bracket to rear bracket.

XJ6 6-CYLINDER (Cont.)

4) Install four long setscrews and spring washers to front mounting bracket and attach dampers, chain support plate, and spacers to setscrews. Equalize loops of top timing chain and locate camshaft sprockets in loops. Rotate eccentric idler shaft to lift idler sprocket to its highest position between camshaft sprockets.

5) Ensure Woodruff key is positioned in crankshaft. Locate crankshaft sprocket, but do not fully seat at this time. Loop bottom timing chain beneath crankshaft sprocket, then tap sprocket until it is fully seated. Position and secure crankshaft sprocket assembly.

6) Install, but do not tighten, bottom timing chain guides. Insert conical filter into its hole in cylinder block. Screw slipper into tensioner until .125" (3.17 mm) exists between slipper and body. Locate tensioner on shims as necessary to ensure slipper runs central on chain, and secure using two setscrews and lock plate.

7) Place slip gauge or spacer card supplied with new tensioner between slipper and body of tensioner to maintain dimension set earlier, then adjust intermediate damper to touch chain. Tighten setscrews and bend up tabs of lock plate. Remove slip gauge and top chain or tensioner slipper to release ratchet. Position oil slinger on crankshaft. Replace timing cover.

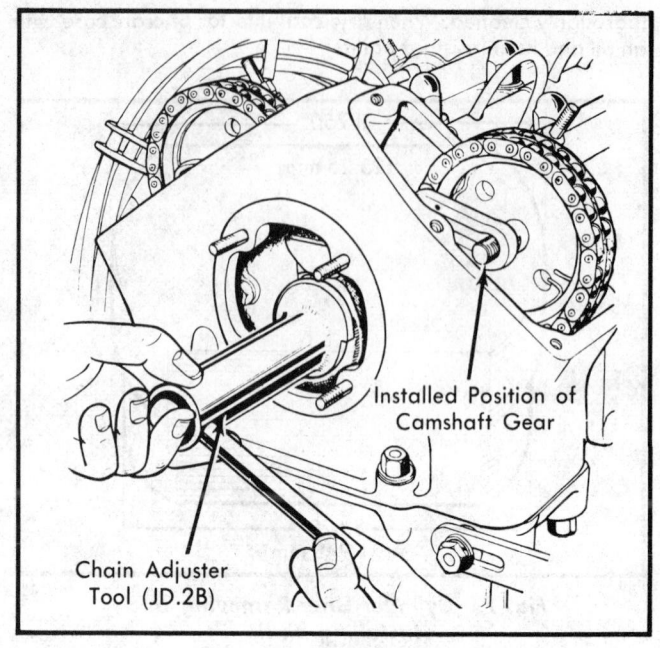

Installed Position of Camshaft Gear

Chain Adjuster Tool (JD.2B)

Fig. 10 Adjusting Upper Timing Chain

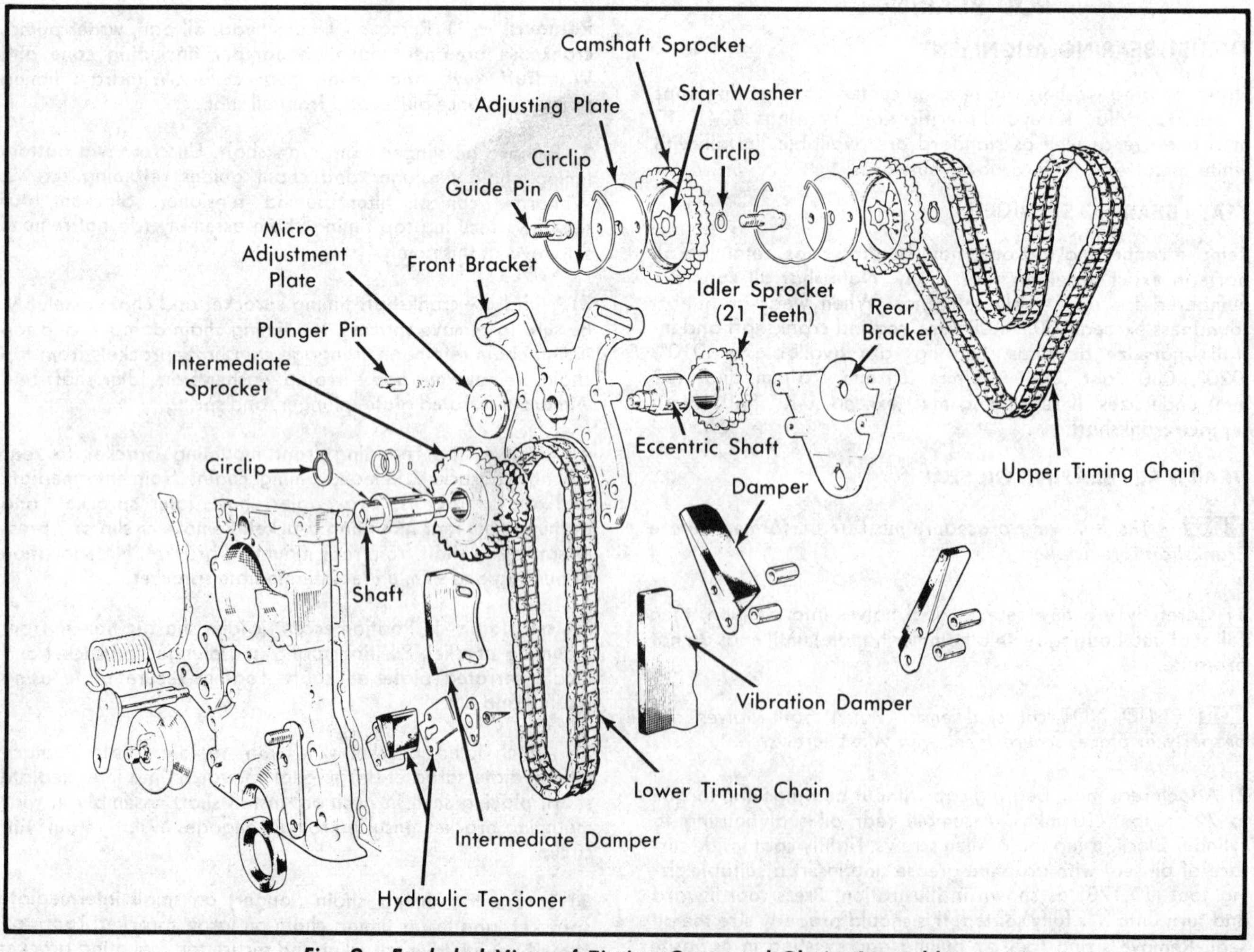

Fig. 9 Exploded View of Timing Gear and Chain Assembly

XJ6 6-CYLINDER (Cont.)

8) Adjust upper timing chain by loosening locknut on eccentric shaft, then use tool (JD.2B) to rotate eccentric counterclockwise until chain has proper tension. DO NOT use excessive force to tighten chain. Tighten locknut and install remaining components.

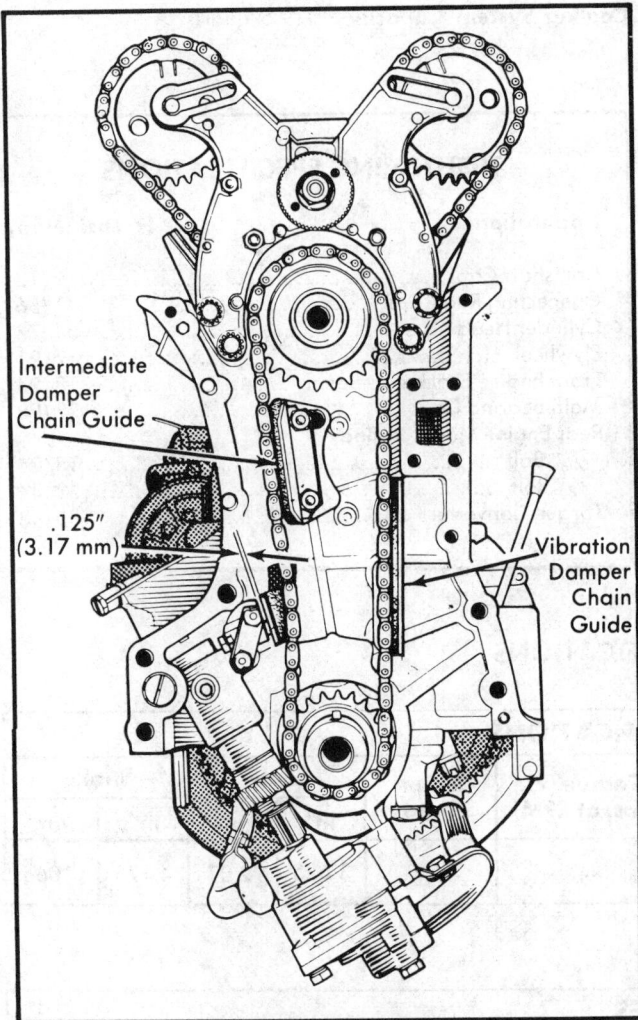

Fig. 11 Lower Timing Chain Adjustment Measuring Point

ENGINE OILING

ENGINE OILING SYSTEM

Lubrication is provided by a gear driven eccentric rotor type pump. Oil from pump goes through a full-flow oil filter to all moving engine components.

Crankcase Capacity — 8.7 quarts.

Oil Filter — Replace every 3,000 miles.

Normal Oil Pressure (Hot) — 40 psi @ 3,000 RPM.

OIL PUMP

Removal — Remove oil pan, suction and delivery pipes. Remove bolts attaching oil pump to front main bearing cap. Withdraw pump and coupling sleeve at top of drive shaft.

Disassembly — **1)** Remove bolts and take off bottom cover. Remove inner and outer rotors. Inner rotor is pinned to drive shaft and cannot be disassembled.

2) Check clearances of inner and outer rotor lobes, outer rotor-to-body and rotor-to-cover plate. Place drive shaft in a soft jawed vise and check that rotor is tight on pin.

Reassembly — Reassemble in reverse order of disassembly. Install outer rotor to pump body with chamfered end forward. Use new "O" rings on suction and delivery pipes.

Installation — To install, reverse removal procedures.

Oil Pump Specifications	
Application	**Clearance In. (mm)**
Inner-to-Outer Rotor	.006 (.15)
Outer Rotor-to-Body	.010 (.25)
Rotor-to-Cover (End Play)	.0025 (.06)

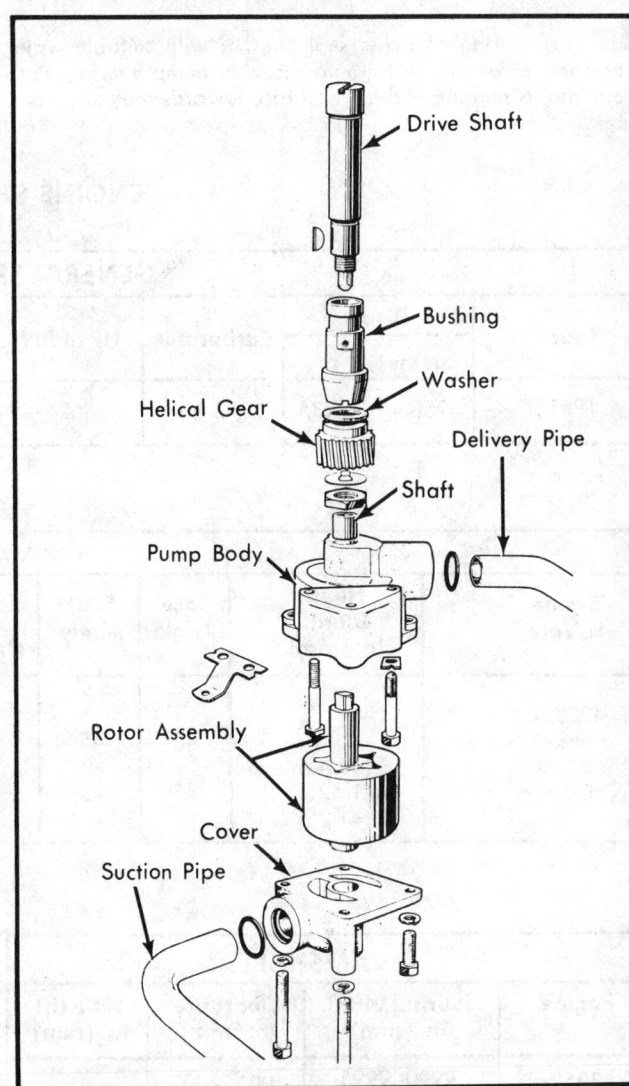

Fig. 12 Exploded View of Jaguar Oil Pump

Jaguar Engines

XJ6 6-CYLINDER (Cont.)

ENGINE COOLING

WATER PUMP

Disassembly — 1) Remove water pump and gasket from timing cover. Pull fan hub from shaft with a puller. Loosen lock nut and remove Allen locating screw.

2) Using an arbor press and a tube measuring 1.094" (27.79 mm) O.D. and .969" (24.60 mm) I.D., press shaft and impeller assembly out of pump body.

3) Press shaft from impeller and remove seal and rubber thrower. Spindle and bearing assembly cannot be further disassembled.

4) Clean and inspect all parts for wear or damage. Bearing is sealed and lubricated, therefore do not wash in solvents.

Reassembly — 1) Install shaft and bearing assembly into pump body from rear. Align and install locating screw and lock nut. Place rubber thrower in its groove on shaft in front of seal.

2) Coat outside of brass seal housing with suitable water resistant sealer and install into recess in pump housing. Push seal into its housing with carbon face towards rear of pump.

3) Press impeller onto shaft until rear face of impeller is flush with end of shaft. Press fan hub onto shaft until it is flush with end of shaft.

Cooling System Capacity — 19.5 quarts.

TIGHTENING SPECIFICATIONS

Application	Ft. Lbs. (N·m)
Camshaft Cap	9 (12)
Connecting Rod Caps	41 (56)
Cylinder Head Nuts	54 (73)
Flywheel	67 (91)
Front Engine Bracket-to-Beam	18 (24)
Main Bearing Caps	72 (98)
Rear Engine Mount-to-Body	
5/16" Bolt	18 (24)
3/8" Bolt	32 (44)
Torque Converter	35 (48)

ENGINE SPECIFICATIONS

GENERAL SPECIFICATIONS

Year	Displ. cu. ins.	Displ. cc	Carburetor	HP at RPM	Torque (Ft. Lbs. at RPM)	Compr. Ratio	Bore in.	Bore mm	Stroke in.	Stroke mm
1981	258.4	4235	Fuel Inj.	.....	.....	8.1:1	3.625	92.07	4.173	106

VALVES

Engine & Valve	Head Diam. In. (mm)	Face Angle	Seat Angle	Seat Width In. (mm)	Stem Diameter In. (mm)	Stem Clearance In. (mm)	Valve Lift In. (mm)
4235 cc Intake	1.75 (44.45)	45°	45°	.....	.310-.3125 (7.87-7.94)	.001-.004 (.025-.10)	.375 (9.525)
Exhaust	1.625 (41.28)	45°	45°	.....	.310-.3125 (7.87-7.94)	.001-.004 (.025-.10)	.375 (9.525)

CAMSHAFT

Engine	Journal Diam. In. (mm)	Clearance In. (mm)	Lobe Lift In. (mm)
4235 cc	.9990-.9995 (25.375-25.387)	.0005-.002 (.013-.05)	.....

VALVE TIMING

Engine	INTAKE Open (BTDC)	INTAKE Close (ABDC)	EXHAUST Open (BBDC)	EXHAUST Close (ATDC)
4235cc	15°	57°	57°	15°

XJ6 6-CYLINDER (Cont.)

ENGINE SPECIFICATIONS (Cont.)

PISTONS, PINS, RINGS						
	PISTONS	PINS		RINGS		
Engine	Clearance In. (mm)	Piston Fit In. (mm)	Rod Fit In. (mm)	Rings	End Gap In. (mm)	Side Clearance In. (mm)
4235 cc	.0007-.0013 (.018-.033)	① Press Fit	② Push Fit	No. 1	.015-.020 (.38-.51)	.0015-.0035 (.038-.089)
				No. 2	.009-.014 (.23-.35)	.0015-.0035 (.038-.089)
				Oil	.015-.045 (.38-1.14)	③

① — When heated to 230°F (110°C).   ② — At room temperature, without piston.   ③ — Self-expanding.

CRANKSHAFT MAIN & CONNECTING ROD BEARINGS						
	MAIN BEARINGS				CONNECTING ROD BEARINGS	
Engine	Journal Diam. In. (mm)	Clearance In. (mm)	Thrust Bearing	Crankshaft End Play In. (mm)	Journal Diam. In. (mm)	Clearance In. (mm)	Side Play In. (mm)
4235 cc	2.749-2.750 (69.85-69.86)	.0008-.0025 (.020-.063)	Center	.004-.006 (.10-.15)	2.086-2.0866 (52.98-53.00)	.001-.0027 (.025-.069)	.0058-.0087 (.147-.221)

VALVE SPRINGS			
	Free Length In. (mm)	PRESSURE Lbs. @ In. (kg @ mm)	
Engine		Valve Closed	Valve Open
4235 cc Inner	1.734 (44.04)	.....	.....
Outer	2.103 (53.42)	.....	.....

Mazda Engines

GLC, B2000 & 626 4-CYLINDER

ENGINE CODING

ENGINE IDENTIFICATION

Engine number is located on right front side of engine block.

ENGINE & CYLINDER HEAD

ENGINE

Removal (RWD Models) — 1) Remove hood after marking hinge location. Drain cooling system and crankcase. On GLC, remove cooling fan. On all models, remove battery and air cleaner. Disconnect accelerator cable and choke heater wire from carburetor. Disconnect fuel lines at fuel pump and carburetor. On automatic transmission models, disconnect and plug transmission cooler lines at radiator. On all models, remove radiator hoses and radiator. Disconnect all engine vacuum hoses.

2) Disconnect wires from temperature sending unit, oil pressure switch, alternator, distributor, back-up light switch and starter. Disconnect exhaust pipe from manifold. On manual transmission models, remove cover plate from clutch housing and clutch release cylinder. On automatic transmission models, remove torque converter and drive plate support bolts. On all models, support transmission with a jack and remove nuts and bolts attaching transmission to engine.

3) Remove starter. On manual transmission models, remove clutch slave cylinder. On all models, remove engine mount attaching nuts and bolts. Install a lifting sling to engine lifting brackets, attach a lifting hoist and raise slightly. Pull engine forward until clear of transmission. Lift engine from vehicle.

Removal (FWD Models) — 1) Remove hood and battery. Raise and support vehicle. Remove engine undercover. Drain engine oil, transaxle oil and coolant. Remove the crossmember. Lift engine slightly and remove front wheels.

2) Detach steering knuckles. Remove driveshafts from transaxle. Disconnect shifting rod and extension bar (if equipped) from transaxle. Remove lower hose from radiator. Remove transaxle mounting rubbers. Disconnect exhaust pipe from front catalytic converter.

3) Remove transaxle bracket and air cleaner. Disconnect all electrical wiring from engine. Disconect accelerator wire. Remove speedometer cable from transaxle. Disconnect clutch cable (if equipped), bracket and ground cable from transaxle.

4) Remove upper radiator hose and heater hose. Disconnect all remaining hoses from engine. Remove canister and disconnect engine mounting bracket. Lift engine and transaxle from vehicle at the same time.

Installation (All Models) — To install, reverse removal procedure.

CYLINDER HEAD

NOTE — Before removal, check timing chain for excessive stretch (RWD Models). To check, readjust the chain tension as outlined in TIMING CHAIN installation procedure. If the gap between slipper head and chain tensioner body exceeds .67" (17 mm), replace the chain.

Removal — 1) Remove engine lifting brackets from cylinder head. Remove exhaust manifold along with port liners and gaskets. Disconnect ignition wires and vacuum lines at distributor. Remove lock nut, then remove distributor from cylinder head.

2) Disconnect hoses and remove air pump with bracket. Remove water pump fan and pulley. Disconnect hose from PCV valve at intake manifold. On manual transmission models, disconnect anti-afterburn valve. On all models, remove attaching bolts, then remove intake manifold and carburetor as an assembly.

3) Remove rocker arm cover, gasket and oil seals. Install ring gear brake tool (49 0118 271A or equivalent) on flywheel to prevent flywheel from rotating. Remove lock nut and washer, then slide distributor drive gear from camshaft. Remove camshaft sprocket lock nut. Remove cylinder head-to-front cover attaching bolt.

NOTE — On FWD models, remove the timing chain tensioner from the timing chain cover.

4) Loosen cylinder head bolts gradually, in the reverse order of the tightening sequence, and remove bolts. Remove rocker arm assembly. Carefully pull camshaft to rear and remove from sprocket and cylinder head. Remove camshaft sprocket.

CAUTION — On RWD models, timing chain should be lifted upwards to prevent tensioner head from disengaging and dropping down inside front cover. Installation of chain adjuster guide (49-3953-260) through front cover inspection hole prior to sprocket removal will prevent disengagement.

5) Remove camshaft bearings from cylinder head, noting their respective locations. Remove the cylinder head and gasket.

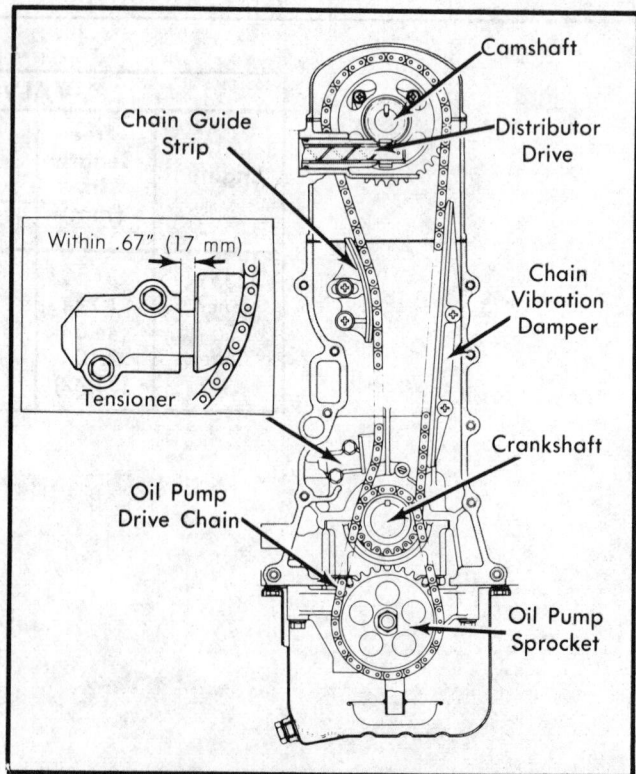

Fig. 1 Engine Cross-Section with Detail of Timing Chain Tensioner (RWD Models)

Installation — 1) Install camshaft sprocket in timing chain and position on top of chain guide strip and chain vibration damper, ensuring that matching marks on chain and sprocket are aligned. Install new head gasket. Place cylinder head on aligning dowels.

GLC, B2000 & 626 4-CYLINDER (Cont.)

2) Install camshaft bearings in cylinder head and bearing caps. Lubricate bearings with engine oil. Install camshaft in cylinder head. Install bearing caps. Carefully install camshaft on sprocket while aligning keyway. Position rocker arm assembly on cylinder head.

CAUTION — *Ensure that the flat surface of the ball on each rocker arm is facing down.*

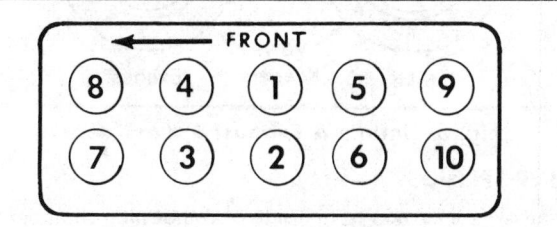

Fig. 2   Tightening Sequence for Cylinder Head

3) Install cylinder head bolts and tighten, in steps, according to sequence shown in *Fig. 2.* Install cylinder head-to-front cover bolt. Install distributor drive gear, tighten nut and bend lock washer.

4) Adjust timing chain tension as outlined in Timing Chain section of this article. Install remaining components in reverse order of removal.

CAMSHAFT

CAMSHAFT

NOTE — *On RWD models, lift timing chain upward to keep the slipper head of the tensioner from falling out. On FWD models, remove timing chain tensioner from the timing chain cover.*

Removal — 1) Remove valve cover. Install ring gear brake tool to flywheel. Remove lock nut and washer, slide distributor drive gear from camshaft. Remove lock nut from camshaft sprocket.

2) Remove the bolt that attaches timing chain cover to cylinder head. Remove cylinder head bolts in reverse order of tightening sequence. Lift out rocker arm assembly. Pull camshaft rearward and remove sprocket. Carefully remove camshaft. If necessary, camshaft bearings can be removed at this time.

Installation — To install, reverse removal procedure. Adjust timing chain tension as outlined in Timing Chain section of this article.

CAMSHAFT BEARING REPLACEMENT

1) Inspect cam face and journals, ensuring that they are not worn or scored. Using a micrometer, measure cam height. Standard cam height for 1490 cc engine is 1.737" (44.12 mm) for intake and exhaust. Standard cam height for the 1970 cc engine is 1.7718" (45.004 mm) for exhaust cam lobes and 1.7731" (45.037 mm) for intake lobes. Wear in excess of .008" (.2 mm) requires replacement of camshaft.

2) Measure diameter of camshaft bearing journals. If wear is more than .002" (.051 mm) below minimum standard diameter, camshaft must be ground to accept .010" (.25 mm), .020" (.50 mm) or .030" (.75 mm) undersize bearings.

3) Inspect camshaft bearing clearances using Plastigage method. If standard clearances are exceeded, replace bear-

ings. If new bearings are properly fitted, correct clearance can be obtained without filing, shimming or scraping.

4) Using a dial indicator, check camshaft out-of-round. Camshaft must not exceed .0012" (.030 mm) out-of-round.

5) Check camshaft end play using a feeler gauge. Standard clearance is .001-.007" (.025-.178 mm). If wear limit of .008" (.20 mm) is exceeded, replace the thrust plate.

TIMING CHAIN

Removal — 1) Remove cylinder head and oil pan with engine removed from vehicle. Remove front cover and gaskets, then remove oil thrower from crankshaft. Remove chain tensioner, guide strip and vibration damper.

2) Remove oil pump sprocket lock nut and washer. Remove crankshaft spacer, timing chain and crankshaft sprocket. Remove key and spacer from crankshaft.

Installation (RWD Models) — 1) Install timing chain guide strip, but do not tighten screws. Install timing chain vibration damper. Install spacer and key onto crankshaft. Place timing chain on crankshaft and camshaft sprockets with index marks properly aligned. *See Fig. 3.*

2) Align crankshaft and its sprocket keyway, then fit sprocket onto crankshaft. Install crankshaft spacer. Fit key on oil pump and shaft. Install oil pump drive chain onto oil pump and crankshaft sprockets, align keyway and install assembly onto crankshaft and oil pump shafts. Install chain adjuster guide (49-3953-260) on adjuster.

3) Install adjuster to cylinder block. Tighten oil pump sprocket nut and bend lock washer tab. Install oil baffle plate and spacer onto crankshaft. Check oil pump drive chain slack. Slack should not exceed .157" (4 mm). Excessive slack on 1970 cc engines can be reduced by installing shims between cylinder block and oil pump body. On 1490 cc engines, chain must be replaced.

4) Install oil pan and timing cover. Install cylinder head and camshaft as previously outlined. Install distributor drive gear to camshaft as previously outlined. Install distributor drive gear to camshaft. Tighten lock nut and bend tab of lock washer. Adjust timing chain tension by slightly rotating the crankshaft in the direction of engine rotation. Press the top of the guide strip with a lever through the top of the cylinder head (1490 cc engine) or through opening in timing cover (1970 cc engine).

5) Tighten guide strip screws with a screwdriver inserted through 2 holes in timing cover. Remove the timing chain adjuster guide which was installed to timing chain tensioner. Install blind plugs and aluminum washers to the 2 holes in timing cover.

Installation (FWD Models) — 1) Install oil pump sprocket and chain. Install timing chain and sprocket with timing marks aligned. Install guide strip (adjuster blade) and chain vibration damper. Install timing chain cover and oil pan. Install cylinder head and camshaft as previously outlined.

2) Install crankshaft pulley, applying sealer to inside of pulley bolt. Tighten camshaft pulley bolt. Push sleeve of timing chain adjuster back into adjuster body and lock with pin. *See Fig. 4.* Install timing chain adjuster to timing cover and tighten. Install distributor and turn engine over by hand to actuate tensioner.

NOTE — *Pin on adjuster is released by action of the timing chain. Sleeve projects automatically, completing adjustment.*

GLC, B2000 & 626 4-CYLINDER (Cont.)

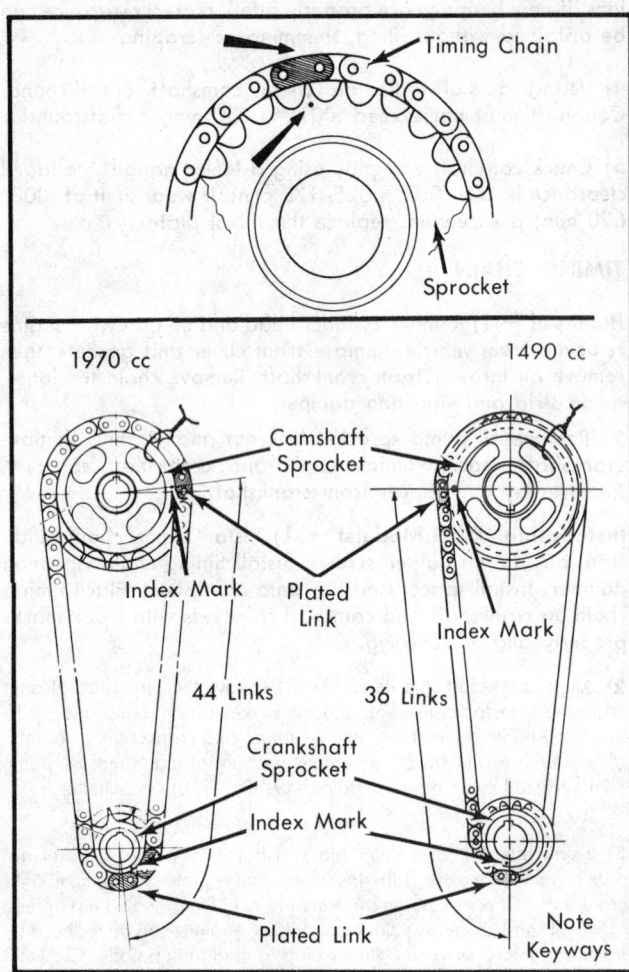

Fig. 3 Alignment Marks of Timing Chain & Sprockets

1970 cc

1490 cc

Camshaft Sprocket

Index Mark

Plated Link

Index Mark

44 Links

36 Links

Crankshaft Sprocket

Index Mark

Plated Link

Note Keyways

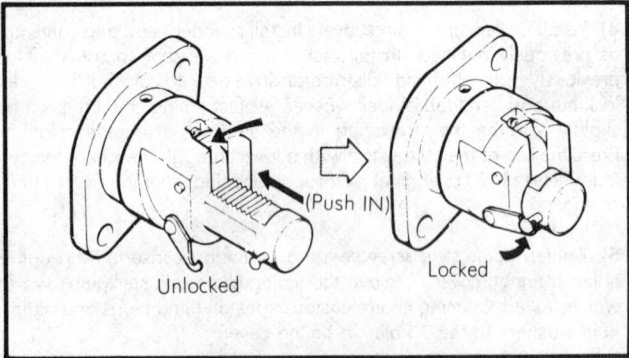

(Push IN)

Unlocked

Locked

Fig. 4 Timing Chain Adjuster (FWD Models)

VALVES

VALVE ARRANGEMENT

Right Side — All Intake
Left Side — All Exhaust

VALVE GUIDE SERVICING

Remove worn valve guide, using valve guide removal/installation tool (49-0221-251A) and hammer. Drive new guide until ring of guide just touches cylinder head. Install new valve seal on valve guide using a seal pusher tool (49-0223-160D or equivalent).

NOTE — *The valve keepers for intake and exhaust valves are not interchangeable. Care must be taken to keep them properly identified.*

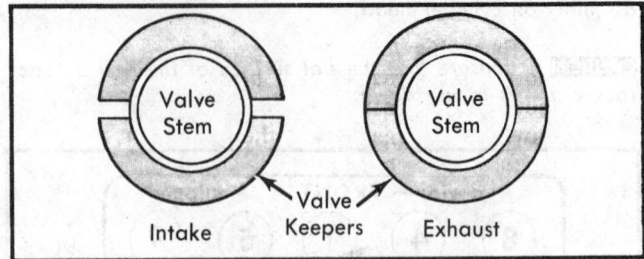

Valve Stem

Valve Stem

Intake

Valve Keepers

Exhaust

Fig. 5 Intake & Exhaust Valve Keepers

VALVE SPRINGS

1) Remove all carbon from inside of combustion chamber. Using a suitable valve spring compressor, collapse springs and remove stem keepers, retainers, valve springs and seats. Valves can now be removed.

2) With valve springs removed, inspect for corrosion or obvious damage. Use a valve spring tester to determine valve spring condition under a load. Measure valve spring free length and compare findings with specifications.

ROCKER ARM ASSEMBLY

1) With rocker arm assembly removed and disassembled, inspect all components for wear or damage. The standard clearance between rocker arm bore and shaft is .0008-.0029" (.020-.074 mm) on 1490 cc engines and .0011-.0032" (.027-.081 mm) for 1970 cc engines. If measured clearance is more than .004" (.10 mm) replace rocker arm or shaft.

2) Reassemble and install rocker shaft while noting the following: Intake and rocker arm supports are interchangeable. Intake side uses 2 rocker shafts. On intake side, end of shaft with longer distance between oil hole and shaft end face each other. Center bearing cap oil hole faces toward intake side.

3) When installing the oil distribution pipe, make sure the oil holes face camshaft. After pipe is installed, press "O" ring into hole for pipe on center bearing cap. When installing rocker arm assembly, make sure flat surface on ball of each rocker arm faces downward. Align dowels and install assembly on cylinder head. Before tightening cylinder head bolts, offset each of the rocker arms .040" (1 mm) from valve stem center by shifting the rocker shaft support stands slightly.

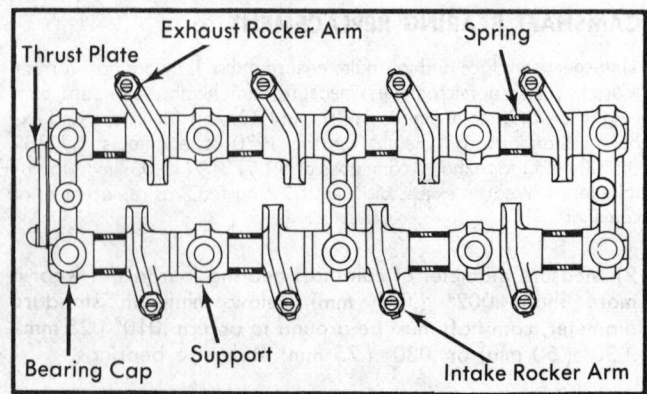

Thrust Plate

Exhaust Rocker Arm

Spring

Bearing Cap

Support

Intake Rocker Arm

Fig. 6 1490 cc Rocker Arm Assembly

Mazda Engines

GLC, B2000 & 626 4-CYLINDER (Cont.)

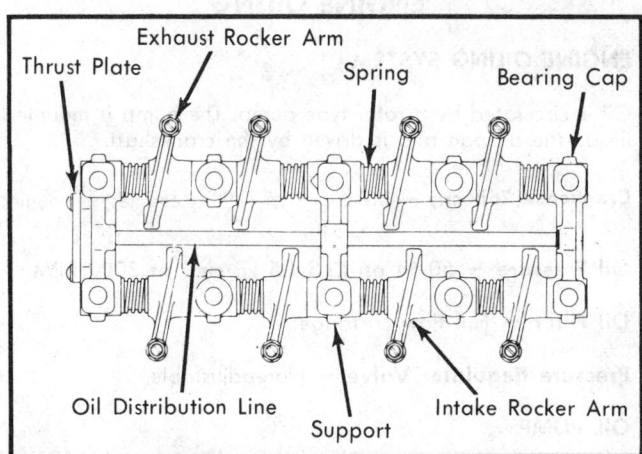

Fig. 7 1970 cc Rocker Arm Assembly

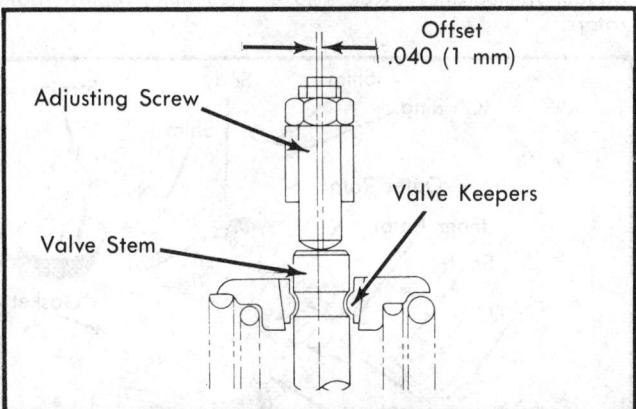

Fig. 8 Rocker Arm Offset

VALVE CLEARANCE

With engine warmed to operating temperature, having torqued the cylinder head bolts to specifications, adjust valves. Loosen lock nut and insert feeler gauge between rocker and valve stem. Turn adjusting screw until proper clearance is obtained.

NOTE — *Before adusting, ensure flat surface of ball on rocker arm is facing downward.*

Valve Clearance Specifications		
Application	Intake In. (mm)	Exhaust In. (mm)
1490 cc		
Valve Side	.010 (.25)	.012 (.30)
Cam Side	.007 (.18)	.009 (.22)
1970 cc		
Valve Side	.012 (.30)	.012 (.30)
Cam Side	.009 (.22)	.009 (.22)

PISTONS, PINS & RINGS

PISTON & ROD ASSEMBLY

Removal — Remove oil pan, cylinder head, and oil pump. Make sure connecting rods are marked so they are replaced in their original positions, then remove rod caps. Push piston and rod assembly out of top of cylinder. Take care not to damage bearing journal.

Installation — **1)** Lubricate piston rings, pistons, and cylinder walls with engine oil. Place piston rings with gaps approximately 120° apart. Be sure gap is not on thrust side or piston pin side. Install a ring compressor onto piston without disturbing position of rings.

2) Install piston and rod assembly into its original bore. Make sure "F" mark of piston is facing front of engine. Install rod caps and tighten rod bolts. Install oil pump, oil pan and cylinder head.

FITTING PISTONS

1) Cylinder bore can be measured using a cylinder gauge. Measurement must be taken at 3 depths and 2 angles as shown in *Fig. 9*. Difference between minimum and maximum value is actual wear. If cylinder bore wear is .006" (.15 mm) or more, all cylinders must be rebored. If cylinder is honed or rebored, oversized pistons and rings are available in .010" (.25 mm), .020" (.50 mm), .030" (.75 mm) and .040" (1.00 mm) oversizes.

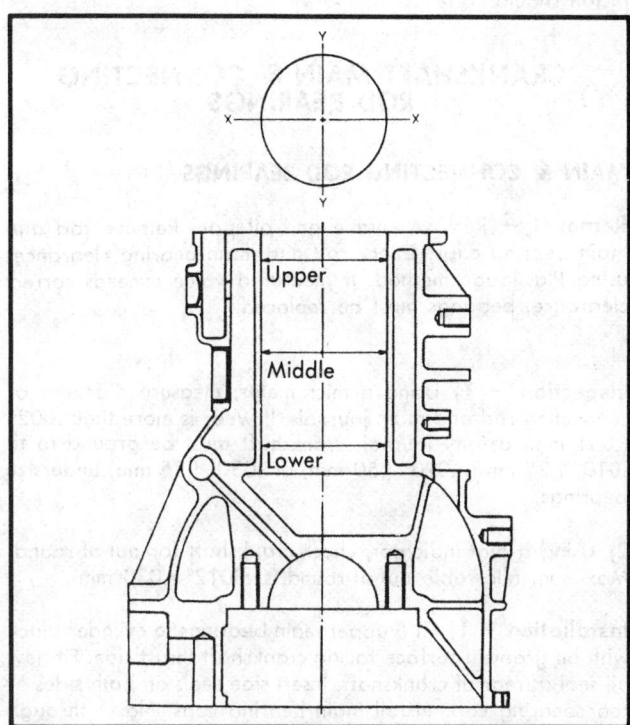

Fig. 9 Points for Measuring Cylinder Bore

2) Carefully inspect pistons and replace those severely damaged due to scoring, scratching or burning. Measure pistons at points A, B, and C as shown in *Fig. 10*, using a micrometer. If piston is not within specifications, replace piston and rebore cylinder.

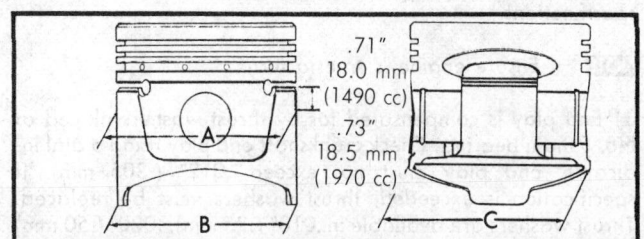

Fig. 10 Points for Measuring Piston

GLC, B2000 & 626 4-CYLINDER (Cont.)

Standard Piston Specifications	
Application	**Diameter In. (mm)**
1490 cc①	
A	3.0297-3.0305 (76.954-76.974)
1970 cc	
A	3.1474-3.1482 (79.944-79.964)
B	3.1489 (79.980)
C	3.1319 (79.550)
① — "B" and "C" diameters not available.	

PISTON PIN REPLACEMENT

Piston pin is press fit in connecting rod. Use special tool set (49 8134 040 or equivalent) for removal and installation. For installation, a press load of 1102-3307 lbs. (500-1500 kg) is required. If the press load is not within load range, replace the pin or connecting rod. Ensure that the piston pin offset is correct. The connecting rod big end hole and "F" mark on piston should correspond.

CRANKSHAFT MAIN & CONNECTING ROD BEARINGS

MAIN & CONNECTING ROD BEARINGS

Removal — Remove engine and oil pan. Remove rod and main bearing caps. Check rod and main bearing clearances using Plastigage method. If measured value exceeds correct clearance, bearings must be replaced.

Inspection — 1) Using a micrometer, measure diameter of connecting rod and main journals. If wear is more than .002" (.051 mm) at any journal, crankshaft must be ground to fit .010" (.25 mm), .020" (.50 mm) or .030" (.75 mm) undersize bearings.

2) Using a dial indicator, check crankshaft for out-of-round. Maximum allowable out-of-round is .0012" (.030 mm).

Installation — 1) Fit 5 upper main bearings to cylinder block with oil grooved surface facing crankshaft thrust side. Fit new oil seal at rear of crankshaft. Insert side seals on both sides of rear bearing cap. Install main bearing caps. No. 1 through No. 4 bearing caps are marked for correct installation. No. 5 may or may not be indexed.

2) Insert connecting rod assembly into cylinder as previously described. Fit upper bearing to rod and over crankshaft. Fit lower bearing to rod cap and install cap. Tighten all bolts to specifications.

NOTE — Ensure engine is free to turn.

3) End play is compensated for by thrust washers placed at No. 5 main bearing. Check crankshaft end play using a dial indicator. End play must not exceed .012" (.305 mm). If specification is exceeded, thrust washers must be replaced. Thrust washers are available in .010" (.25 mm), .020" (.50 mm) and .030" (.75 mm) oversizes.

ENGINE OILING

ENGINE OILING SYSTEM

Oil is circulated by a rotor-type pump. The pump is mounted inside the oil pan and is driven by the crankshaft.

Crankcase Capacity — 3.7 quarts for 1490 cc engines, 4.1 quarts for 1970 cc engines.

Oil Pressure — 50-64 psi (3.5-4.5 kg/cm²) at 3000 RPM.

Oil Filter — Full flow cartridge.

Pressure Regulator Valve — Non-adjustable

OIL PUMP

1) Check clearance between lobes of rotor with a feeler gauge. If clearance exceeds .010" (.25 mm), replace both rotors.

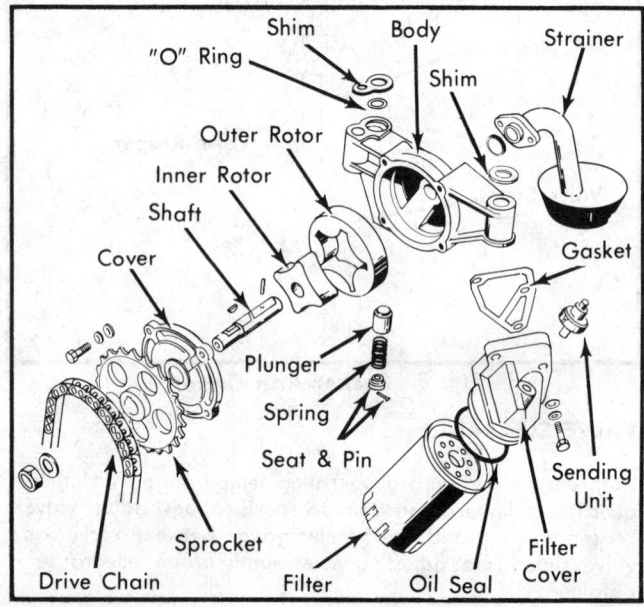

Fig. 11   1970 cc Oil Pump Assembly

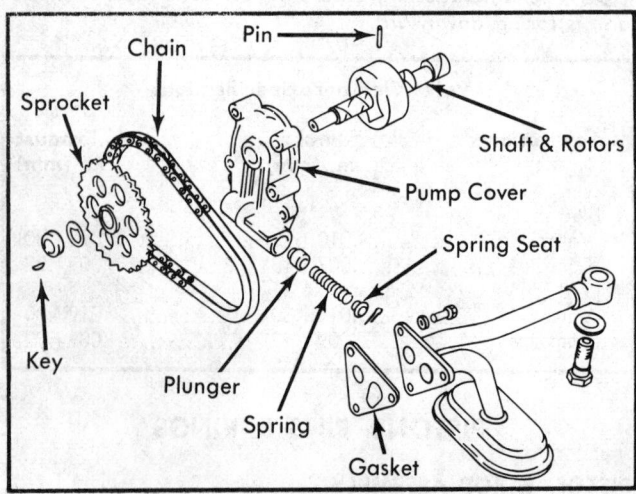

**Fig. 12   1490 cc Oil Pump Assembly
(RWD Model Shown, FWD Similar)**

GLC, B2000 & 626 4-CYLINDER (Cont.)

Oil Pump Specifications

Application	Clearance In. (mm)
Rotor-to-Rotor	
RWD	.002-.006 (.05-.15)
FWD	.001-.005 (.03-.12)
Rotor-to-Body	
RWD	.006-.010 (.14-.25)
FWD	.008-.012 (.20-.30)
End Play	.002-.004 (.05-.10)
Pump Shaft-to-Body	
RWD	.0013-.0034 (.032-.066)
FWD	.0008-.0022 (.020-.056)

2) Check clearance between outer rotor and body with feeler gauge. Maximum clearance is .012" (.30 mm) for rear wheel drive models, .0134" (.35 mm) for front wheel drive models.

3) To check rotor ends, place a straightedge across pump body and measure clearance rotor and straightedge, using a feeler gauge. Then place straightedge across cover and measure clearance between straightedge and cover.

ENGINE COOLING

WATER PUMP

NOTE — *It may be necessary to remove radiator to facilitate water pump removal.*

Removal (RWD Models) — Drain cooling system. Remove cooling fan and radiator shroud (if necessary). Remove drive belts and pulley from water pump. Detach water hoses from pump (if equipped). Remove nuts and bolts attaching water pump to timing cover and remove pump.

Removal (FWD Models) — Raise and support vehicle. Drain coolant. Remove engine undercover, pump drive belt, water hoses and "O" ring. Remove mounting bolts and water pump.

Installation (All Models) — Using a new gasket, install by reversing removal procedure.

Cooling System Capacity — 5.8 quarts for 1490 cc engine and 7.6 quarts for 1970 cc engine.

Thermostat — Begins to open at 190°F (88°C) and is fully open at 212°F (100°C) for 1490 cc (RWD) engine. Thermostat for 1970 cc and 1490 cc (FWD) engine begins to open at 180°F (82°C) and fully opens at 203°F (95°C).

Radiator Cap — 13 psi.

TIGHTENING SPECIFICATIONS

Application	Ft. Lbs. (N·m)
1490 cc	
Cylinder Head	
Cold	56-59 (76-79)
Hot	61-65 (83-88)
Main Bearing Cap	48-51 (65-69)
Connecting Rod Cap	22-25 (30-35)
Oil Pump Sprocket	22-25 (30-35)
Camshaft Sprocket	51-58 (70-80)
Crankshaft Pulley	80-87 (110-120)
Distributor Drive Gear	51-58 (70-80)
Intake Manifold	14-19 (19-26)
Exhaust Manifold	14-17 (19-23)
1970 cc	
Cylinder Head	
Cold	59-64 (82-88)
Hot	69-72 (95-100)
Main Bearing Cap	61-65 (84-90)
Connecting Rod Cap	30-33 (41-46)
Oil Pump Sprocket	22-25 (30-35)
Camshaft Sprocket	51-58 (70-80)
Crankshaft Pulley	101-108 (140-149)
Distributor Drive Gear	51-58 (70-80)
Intake Manifold	14-19 (19-26)
Exhaust Manifold	16-21 (22-29)

ENGINE SPECIFICATIONS

GENERAL SPECIFICATIONS

Year	Displ. cu. ins.	Displ. cc	Carburetor	HP at RPM	Torque (Ft. Lbs. at RPM)	Compr. Ratio	Bore in.	Bore mm	Stroke in.	Stroke mm
1981										
GLC	90.9	1490	1x2 Bbl.	.....	.....	9.0:1	3.03	77	3.15	80
B2000	120.2	1970	1x2 Bbl.	.....	.....	8.6:1	3.15	80	3.86	98
626	120.2	1970	1x2 Bbl.	.....	.....	8.6:1	3.15	80	3.86	98

CRANKSHAFT MAIN & CONNECTING ROD BEARINGS

Engine	MAIN BEARINGS Journal Diam. In. (mm)	Clearance In. (mm)	Thrust Bearing	Crankshaft End Play In. (mm)	CONNECTING ROD BEARINGS Journal Diam. In. (mm)	Clearance In. (mm)	Side Play In. (mm)
1490 cc	1.9661-1.9668 (49.938-49.956)	.0009-.0017 (.023-.042)	No. 5	.004-.006 (.10-.15)	1.5724-1.5731 (39.940-39.956)	.0009-.0026 (.024-.0066)	.004-.01 (.11-.26)
1970 cc	2.4780-2.4786 (62.940-62.955)	.0012-.0020 (.031-.050)	No. 5	.003-.009 (.08-.24)	2.0842-2.0848 (52.9440-52.955)	.0011-.0030 (.027-.077)	.004-.008 (.11-.21)

Mazda Engines

GLC, B2000 & 626 4 CYLINDER (Cont.)
ENGINE SPECIFICATIONS (Cont.)

VALVES

Engine & Valve	Head Diam.① In. (mm)	Face Angle	Seat Angle	Seat Width In. (mm)	Stem Diameter In. (mm)	Stem Clearance In. (mm)	Valve Lift In. (mm)
1490 cc Intake	1.4173 (36.00)	45°	45°	.055 (1.4)	.3162-.3168 (8.03-8.05)	.0007-.0021 (.018-.053)	.....
Exhaust	1.2205 (31.00)	45°	45°	.055 (1.4)	.3160-.3168 (8.025-8.05)	.0007-.0023 (.018-.058)	.....
1970 cc Intake	1.6536 (42.00)	45°	45°	.055 (1.4)	.3162-.3168 (8.03-8.05)	.0007-.0021 (.018-.053)	.....
Exhaust	1.2992 (33.00)	45°	45°	.055 (1.4)	.3160-.3168 (8.025-8.05)	.0007-.0023 (.018-.058)	.....

① — Specification is ±.0039" (.01 mm).

PISTONS, PINS, RINGS

Engine	PISTONS Clearance In. (mm)	PINS Piston Fit In. (mm)	PINS Rod Fit In. (mm)	RINGS Rings	RINGS End Gap In. (mm)	RINGS Side Clearance In. (mm)
1490 cc & 1970 cc	①.001-.0026 (.026-.065)	②0-.0009 (0-.024)	.....	No. 1	.008-.016 (.20-.41)	③.0012-.0025 (.030-.064)
				No. 2	.008-.016 (.20-.41)	④.0012-.0025 (.030-.064)
				Oil	.012-.035 (.31-.89)	.....

① — 1970 cc should be .0014-.0030" (.036-.075 mm).
② — Interference fit.

③ — 1970 cc should be .0012-.0028" (.030-.070 mm).
④ — 1970 cc should be .0012-.0025" (.030-.065 mm).

VALVE TIMING

Engine	INTAKE Open (BTDC)	INTAKE Close (ABDC)	EXHAUST Open (BBDC)	EXHAUST Close (ATDC)
1490 cc	15°	55°	58°	12°
1970 cc B2000	14°	53°	58°	9°
626	10°	57°	54°	13°

CAMSHAFT

Engine	Journal Diam. In. (mm)	Clearance In. (mm)	Lobe Lift In. (mm)
1490 cc Front	1.6515-1.6522 (41.949-41.965)	.0014-.0030 (.035-.076)	.....
Center	1.6504-1.6510 (41.919-41.935)	.0026-.0042 (.065-.106)	.....
Rear	1.6515-1.6522 (41.949-41.965)	.0014-.0030 (.035-.076)	.....
1970 cc Front	1.7695-1.7701 (44.945-44.960)	.0007-.0027 (.019-.069)	.....
Center	1.7691-1.7697 (44.935-44.950)	.0011-.0031 (.029-.079)	.....
Rear	1.7695-1.7701 (44.945-44.960)	.0007-.0027 (.019-.069)	.....

VALVE SPRINGS

Engine	Free Length In. (mm)	PRESSURE Lbs. @ In. (kg @ mm) Valve Closed	PRESSURE Lbs. @ In. (kg @ mm) Valve Open
1490 cc	1.705 (43.3)	63.3@1.319 (28.7@33.5)	.....
1970 cc Inner	1.449 (36.8)	20.9@1.26 (9.5@32)	.....
Outer	1.469 (37.3)	31.4@1.339 (14.3@34)	.....

RX7 ROTARY ENGINE

ENGINE CODING

ENGINE IDENTIFICATION

Engine identification number is stamped on front engine housing behind the distributor.

Engine Identification	
Application	Code
RX7	12A

ENGINE REMOVAL & INSTALLATION

Removal — 1) Remove hood and disconnect battery ground cable. Drain engine oil and coolant. Remove engine under cover. Disconnect following electrical wires: Primary and secondary ignition wires at coils, pick-up coil wiring connections, condensor lead, oil level sensor lead, temperature sensor and oil thermo sensor (except California vehicles).

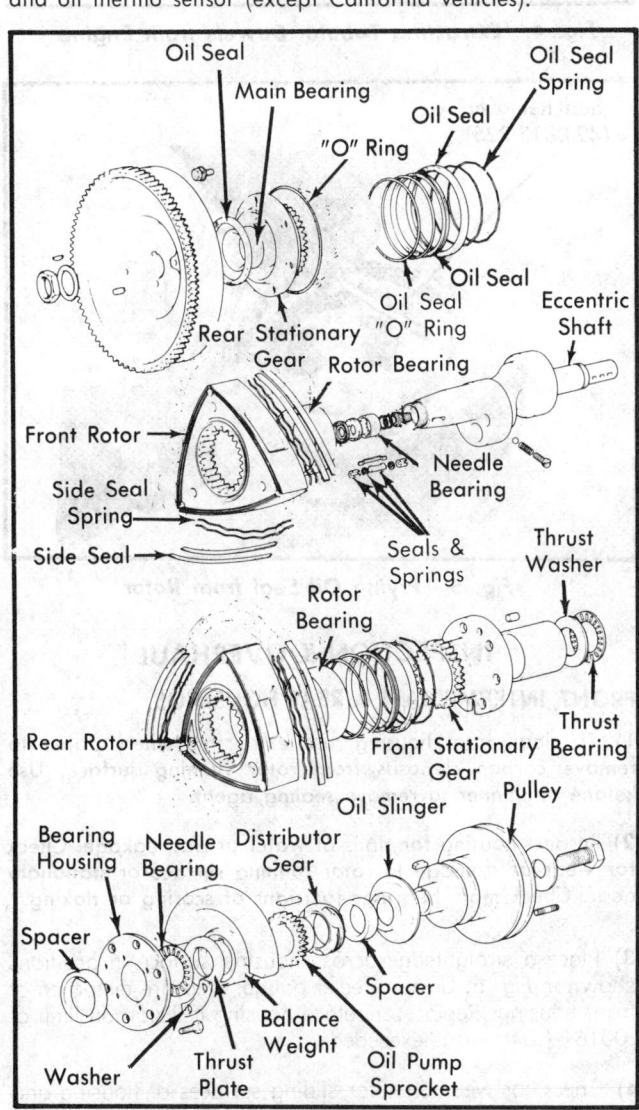

Fig. 1 Exploded View of Rotors & Eccentric Shaft Assembly

Oil Seal
Main Bearing
"O" Ring
Oil Seal
Oil Seal
Oil Seal
Spring
Oil Seal
"O" Ring
Eccentric Shaft
Rear Stationary Gear
Rotor Bearing
Front Rotor
Needle Bearing
Side Seal Spring
Side Seal
Seals & Springs
Thrust Washer
Rotor Bearing
Thrust Bearing
Rear Rotor
Front Stationary Gear
Oil Slinger
Pulley
Bearing Housing
Needle Bearing
Distributor Gear
Spacer
Spacer
Washer
Thrust Plate
Balance Weight
Oil Pump Sprocket

2) Remove air cleaner assembly. Disconnect the following tubes and hoses: Oil hoses at cooler, radiator hoses, automatic transmission cooler lines (if equipped), heater hoses, fuel supply and return lines, vacuum and evaporative hoses, and air pipe at rear of intake manifold.

3) Remove cooling fan and drive assembly, radiator, and radiator shroud assembly. Disconnect connector and "B" terminal from alternator. Disconnect connector from throttle sensor. Dismount compressor and condensor of air conditioner and tie out of the way without disconnecting refrigerant lines (if equipped).

4) Disconnect choke heater connector. Disconnect accelerator, choke and hot start assist cables. Disconnect any remaining wires, tubes or linkages between engine and chassis at top of engine. Remove upper engine-to-transmission bolts.

5) Raise and support vehicle. Remove starter. Remove lower engine-to-transmission bolts. Remove exhaust pipe front cover. Remove nuts and bolts and disconnect exhaust pipe from exhaust manifold. Support front catalytic converter.

6) Support front of transmission with suitable jack and remove left and right engine mount nuts. Attach sling to engine and take up slack. Pull engine forward to clear clutch shaft, then lift engine from vehicle.

Installation — To install engine, reverse removal procedure ensuring that linkages, tubes and electrical connections are restored in original position. Refill all fluids to specified levels, warm up engine and check for leaks.

ENGINE DISASSEMBLY

NOTE — *To ease engine disassembly, manufacturer recommends use of special engine stand (49 0107 680A) and hanger (49 1114 005).*

1) Loosen drive belts and hoses and disconnect air pump and alternator. Disconnect metering oil pump connecting rod and hoses at metering oil pump outlets. Remove exhaust manifold cover. Remove intake manifold and carburetor. Remove gasket and "O" ring.

2) Remove exhaust manifold and gasket. Remove engine mount and distributor lock nut. Remove distributor, oil filter and cover from front housing. Remove water pump and drive pulley from air conditioning compressor (if equipped). Turn engine over and remove oil pan and strainer. Install flywheel brake (49 1881 060) on manual transmission models or stopper (49 1881 055) on automatic transmission models.

3) Remove eccentric shaft pulley. Take off front cover with gasket and slide distributor gear off shaft. Remove "O" ring from oil passage. Remove oil pump sprocket nut and slide oil pump sprocket, eccentric shaft sprocket and drive chain off together. Remove oil pump.

4) Remove balance weight and following parts in order: Thrust washer, needle bearing, bearing housing, needle bearing, spacer and thrust plate. On manual transmission models, remove clutch assembly, then use puller to remove flywheel. On automatic transmission models, remove drive plate, then use puller to remove counterweight.

Mazda Engines

RX7 ROTARY ENGINE (Cont.)

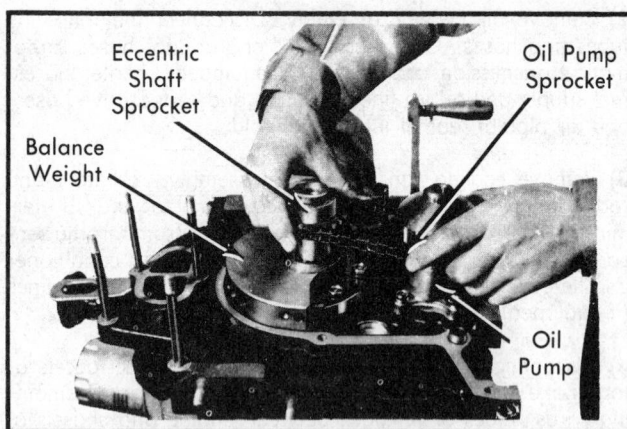

Fig. 2 Oil Pump Drive and Sprocket Removal

5) Remove tension bolts on rear housing in sequence shown in *Fig. 3* by loosening in 2 or 3 steps. Lift rear housing off shaft and remove any seals stuck to rotor sliding surface, placing them back in original positions. Remove seals and "O" rings from rear side of rear rotor housing.

6) Attach dowel puller (49 0813 215A) and pull tubular dowels off rear rotor housing. Hold rotor housing by hand to keep it from moving up and remove rear rotor housing. Use caution to avoid dropping apex seals and side pieces of rear rotor. Remove seals and "O" ring from front side of rear rotor housing.

Fig. 3 Loosening Sequence of Tension Bolts

7) Remove side pieces, apex seals and springs from rear rotor and store in order for reassembly. Remove all corner seals, corner seal springs, side seals and side seal springs and store in order for reassembly. Remove rear rotor and place on clean pad with internal gear side down.

8) Remove seals and springs on remaining side of rotor and store in order for reassembly. Place suitable protector on seal inner lip and remove outer seal with remover (49 0813 225), then remove inner seal. Remove seals and springs and store in order for reassembly. Mark rear rotor with felt tip pen for assembly identification.

9) Attach puller and pull tubular dowels off intermediate housing while holding housing down. Remove intermediate housing

by sliding beyond rear rotor journal on eccentric shaft. Lift out eccentric shaft carefully to avoid damage to rotor bearing and main bearing. Repeat steps **6)** through **8)** to remove front rotor housing and rotor assembly.

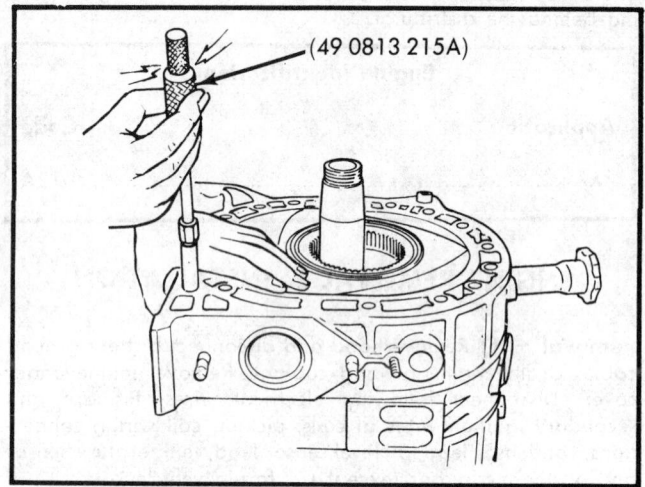

Fig. 4 Extracting Tubular Dowels from Engine

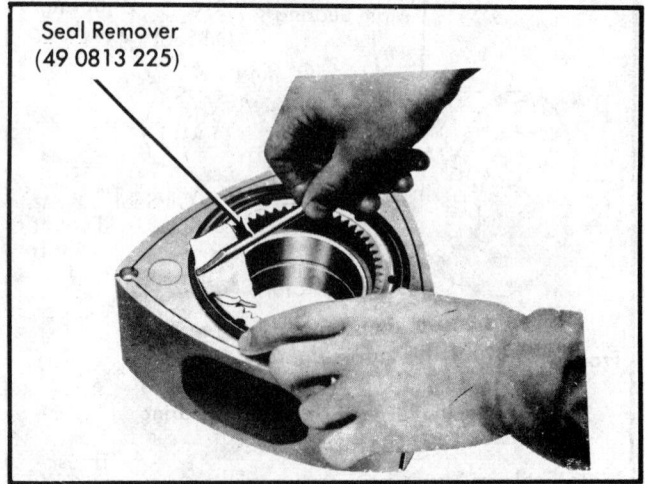

Fig. 5 Prying Oil Seal from Rotor

INSPECTION & OVERHAUL

FRONT, INTERMEDIATE & REAR HOUSINGS

1) To clean front housing, use extra fine emery paper to remove carbon deposits from rotor running surface. Use ketone or thinner to remove sealing agent.

2) Inspect housing for signs of water or gas leakage. Check for wear or damage to rotor running surface or stationary gear. Check main bearings for signs of scoring or flaking.

3) Place a straightedge across housing surface in positions shown in *Fig. 6*. Using a feeler gauge, measure distortion of front housing. Replace or reface housing if distortion limit of .0016" (.04 mm) is exceeded.

4) Check for wear on rotor sliding surfaces of housing and joint surfaces with rotor housing. Measurements are made using a dial indicator. If wear exceeds .0039" (.10 mm), reface or replace housing. See *Fig. 7*.

RX7 ROTARY ENGINE (Cont.)

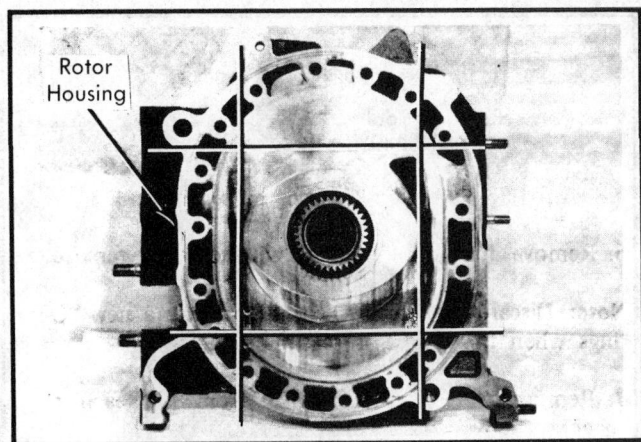

Fig. 6   Straightedge Positions for Checking Housing Distortions

NOTE – *Side housings (front, intermediate and rear housings) can be reused by grinding them, if the required finish can be maintained.*

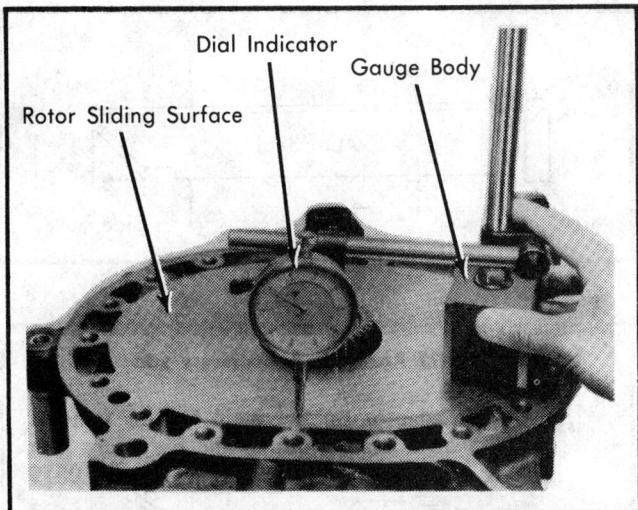

Fig. 7   Measuring Housing Wear with Dial Indicator

5) Measure inner diameter of main bearing and outer diameter of bearing journal on eccentric shaft. Standard clearance is .0016–.0028" (.04–.07 mm). If clearance exceeds .0039" (.10 mm), replace bearing.

6) To replace main bearing, remove stationary gear retaining bolts. Drive stationary gear, with bearing, out of housing using a suitable mandrel (49 0813 235).

7) Place stationary gear in a press, use same mandrel and press main bearing out of stationary gear. Install new bearings while aligning tang bearing with a slot of stationary gear. Press bearing into gear until adapter of mandrel just contacts stationary gear flange. Install the stationary gear into the housing, aligning the slot of the gear flange with the dowel pin on the housing.

NOTE – *When installing rear main bearing, check condition of "O" ring and replace if necessary. Apply sealing agent on*

stationary gear flange prior to installing it on rear housing. Align pin and slot.

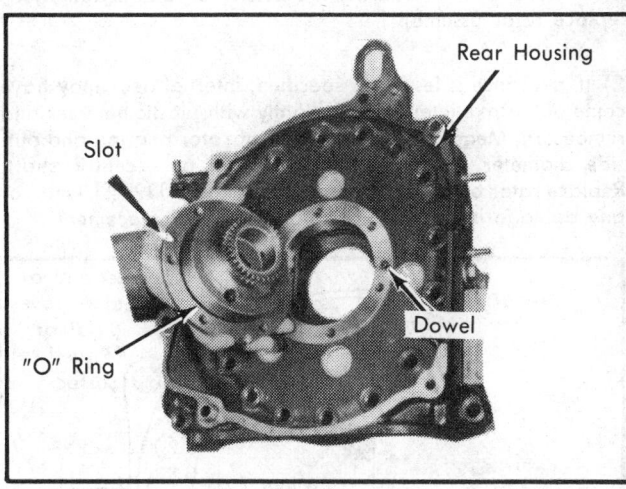

Fig. 8   Stationary Gear Slot & Dowel Alignment

ROTOR HOUSINGS

1) To clean housing, wipe off sealing agent or carbon in rotor running surface with a rag and ketone or thinner. Remove rust deposits in water cooling passages.

2) Inspect for cracks or damage to chromium plated surface. Check for signs of gas or water leakage. Housing must be replaced if any of these conditions exist.

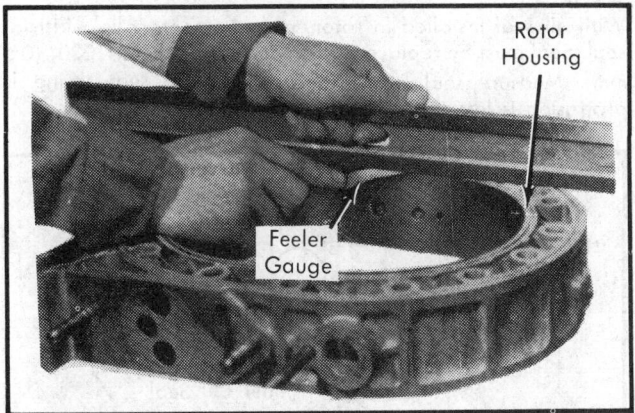

Fig. 9   Measuring Rotor Housing for Distortion

3) Place a straightedge across sealing surface of rotor housing and check for distortion, using a feeler gauge. If distortion exceeds .0016" (.04 mm), replace housing. *See Fig. 9.*

4) Check rotor housing thickness at points A, B, C, and D in *Fig. 10.* If micrometer readings vary between point A and minimum value for B, C, and D by more than .0024" (.06 mm), replace rotor housing.

NOTE – *This excessive clearance would indicate a possibility of gas or water leakage.*

ROTORS

1) Inspect rotor for wear or damage and check internal gear for chips, cracks or scoring. Measure rotor width at 3 points

RX7 ROTARY ENGINE (Cont.)

and subtract maximum width from width of rotor housing at point "A". Difference should be between .0047" (.12 mm) and .0071" (.18 mm). If clearance is excessive or rotor is damaged, replace rotor assembly.

2) If clearance is less than specified, internal gear may have come out. Strike internal gear lightly with plastic hammer and remeasure. Measure inner diameter of rotor bearing and outside diameter of rotor bearing journal on eccentric shaft. Replace rotor bearing if clearance exceeds .0039" (.10 mm) or any damage is shown. *See Rotor Bearing Replacement.*

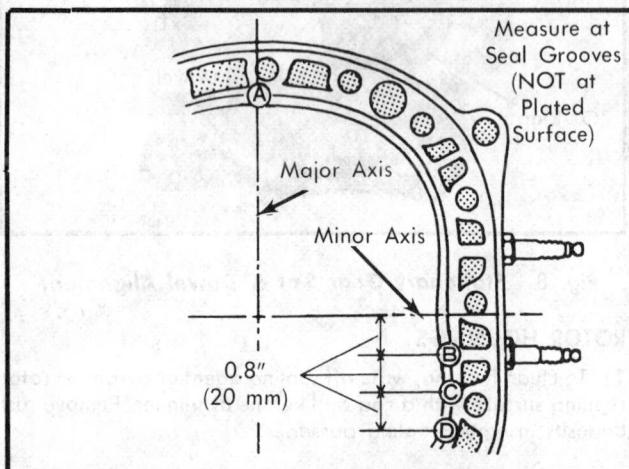

Fig. 10 Rotor Housing Thickness Check Points

ROTOR OIL SEAL

With oil seal installed in rotor, measure contact lip width of seal. Seal must be replaced if contact width exceeds .020" (0.5 mm). Measure seal protrusion and replace seal spring if protrusion is less than .020" (0.5 mm). *See Fig. 11.*

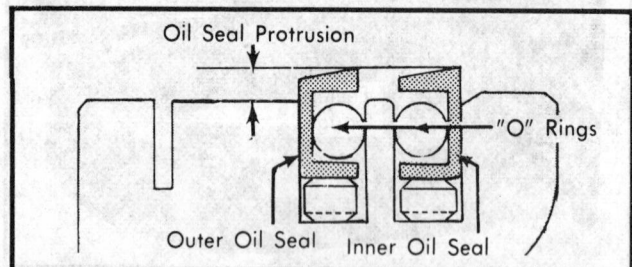

Fig. 11 Measuring Point of Oil Seal Protrusion

ROTOR BEARING REPLACEMENT

Place rotor bearing on support so internal gear is facing downward. Using rotor bearing replacer (49 0813 240), without adapter ring, press bearing out of rotor. Place rotor on support with internal gear facing upward. Place a new rotor bearing so slot in rotor bore is in line with bearing lug. Press new bearing (using tool with adapter) until bearing is flush with rotor boss. *See Fig. 12.*

APEX SEAL

1) Clean all carbon from apex seal and spring with a cleaning solution (not emery paper). Measure height of apex seal with a micrometer. *See Fig. 13.* Replace seal if height is less than

Fig. 12 Pressing Rotor Bearing from Rotor

.275" (7.0 mm). Check for warpage by measuring the clearance between the top surfaces of 2 apex seals with a feeler gauge. Replace all 3 seals if clearance exceeds .0024" (.06 mm). *See Fig. 14.*

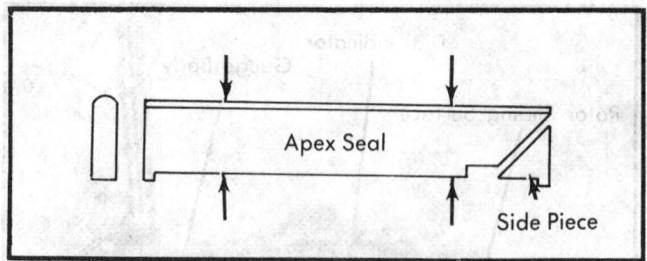

Fig. 13 Measuring Apex Seal Height

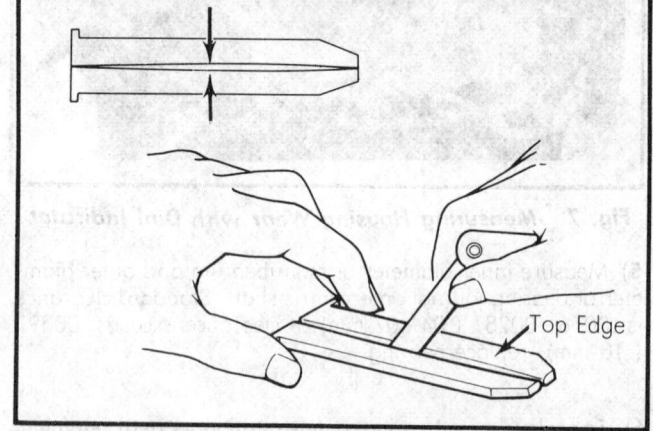

Fig. 14 Apex Seal Warpage

2) Check gap between apex seal and groove in rotor with a feeler gauge. Feeler gauge should be inserted until tip of feeler gauge reaches bottom of groove. Standard clearance is .0020–.0035" (.05–.09 mm). Replace apex seal if gap exceeds .0059" (.15 mm). Check seal spring height as shown in *Fig. 15.* Replace spring if free height is less than .2165" (5.5mm).

SIDE SEAL

1) Remove all carbon from side seal and spring. Check side seal protrusion from rotor surface, and confirm free movement

RX7 ROTARY ENGINE (Cont.)

by pressing with finger. Protrusion should be more than .02"
(.5 mm). Check gap between side seal and groove with a
feeler gauge. Standard gap is .0012-.0031" (.03-.08 mm). If
wear limit of .004" (.10 mm) is measured, replace side seal.

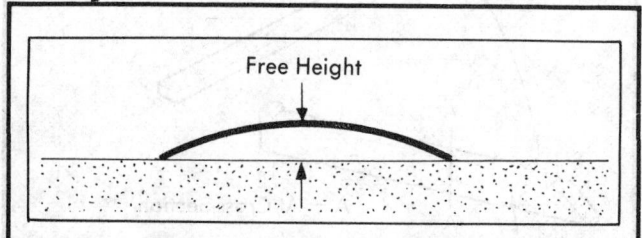

Fig. 15 Measuring Free Height of Apex Seal Spring

2) Check gap between side seal and corner seal with seals
installed on rotor. Insert feeler gauge between end of side seal
(against rotating direction of rotor) and the corner seal. If gap
exceeds .016" (.4 mm), replace side seal.

3) When side seal is replaced, adjust gap between side seal
and corner seal by grinding one end of side seal along round
shape of corner seal, using a fine file. Make gap .002-.006"
(.05-.15 mm).

CORNER SEAL

1) Clean carbon from corner seal. Check corner seal protrusion from rotor surface, and check free movement by pressing
with finger. Protrusion should be more than .02" (.5 mm).

2) Extent of corner seal groove wear is determined by using
special Bar Limit Gauge (490839165), and is classified according to the following:

Neither End of Gauge Goes Into Groove — Indicates that
gap conforms to specifications.

"Go" End of Gauge Goes Into Groove — Indicates that gap
is more than standard, but less than wear limit. In this case
replace corner seal, (Fig. 16).

Both Ends of Gauge ("Go" and "No Go") Fit in Groove —
Indicates that gap exceeds wear limit. Replace rotor.

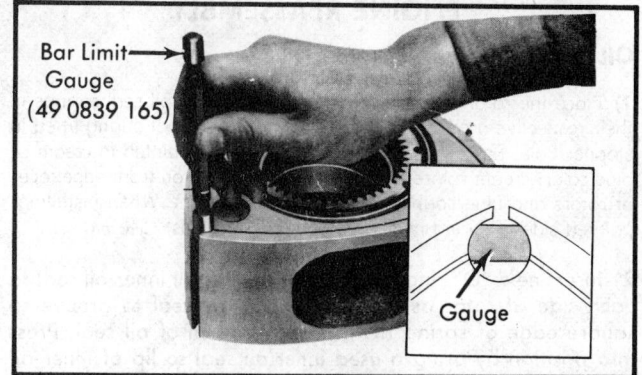

Fig. 17 Checking Corner Seal Groove Measurement

ECCENTRIC SHAFT

1) Thoroughly clean eccentric shaft in a suitable cleaning
solution and blow out oil passages with compressed air.
Inspect shaft for scratching or scoring of bearing journals and
possible blocked oil passages.

2) Check rotor bearing clearance by measuring inner
diameter of the rotor bearing and outer diameter of the
eccentric shaft rotor journal. Clearance should be .0016-
.0031" (.04-.08 mm). Replace the bearing if clearance exceeds
.0039" (.10 mm). Replace eccentric shaft if journal diameters
are under specified limits.

3) Place eccentric shaft in two "V" blocks. Mount a dial
indicator and check runout of both ends by rotating shaft
slowly. If runout exceeds .0024" (.06 mm), replace shaft.

4) Oil passages in eccentric shaft are sealed by a blind plug in
rear of shaft. Inspect plug for possible oil leakage. If leakage
is detected, remove plug with an Allen wrench and install new
"O" ring. Tighten plug.

5) Inspect needle bearings in end of shaft for wear or
damage. Check for spring weakness, stuck, or damaged steel
ball at the oil jets. Inspect front needle bearing, bearing housing, and thrust plate for wear or damage. Inspect front and
rear oil seals for leaks, replace as necessary.

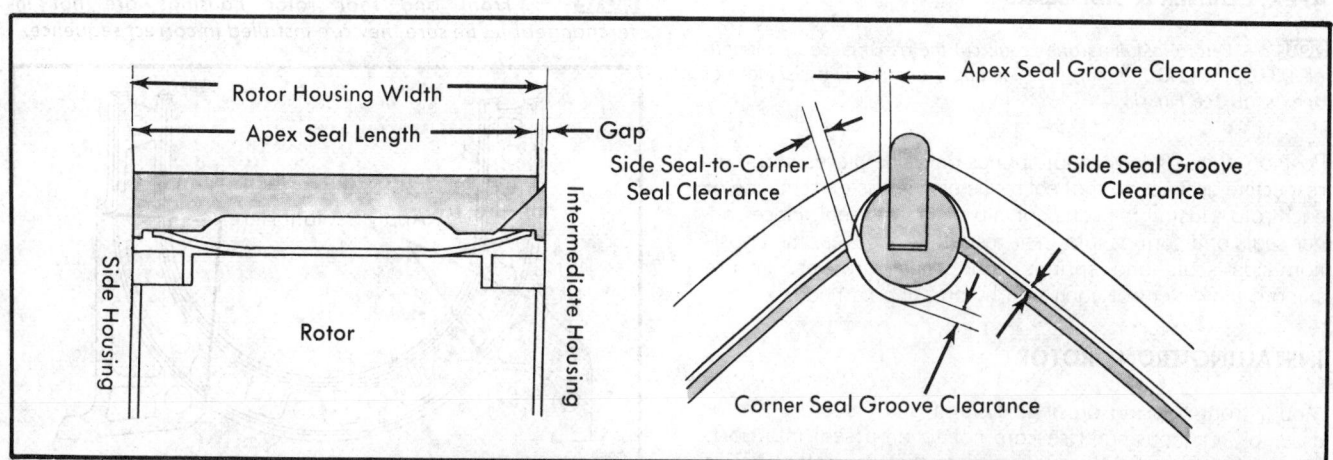

Fig. 16 Measuring Clearance of Apex, Side & Corner Seals

RX7 ROTARY ENGINE (Cont.)

ENGINE REASSEMBLY

OIL SEALS

1) Place the rotor on rubber pad or cloth. Install oil seal springs in their respective grooves on rotors, with each edge of spring fitted in stopper hole. Ensure oil seal springs have been painted in cream or blue color: cream colored springs must be placed on front edge faces of rotors and blue springs on rear faces of rotors. When installing, painted side of spring must face oil seal (upwards). *See Fig. 18.*

2) Insert new "O" ring in each oil seal. Install inner oil seal to each side of rotor as follows: Position oil seal to groove so square edge of spring fits in stopper notch of oil seal. Press into position by using a used inner oil seal so lip of inner oil seal sinks into position approximately .016" (.4 mm) below surface of rotor.

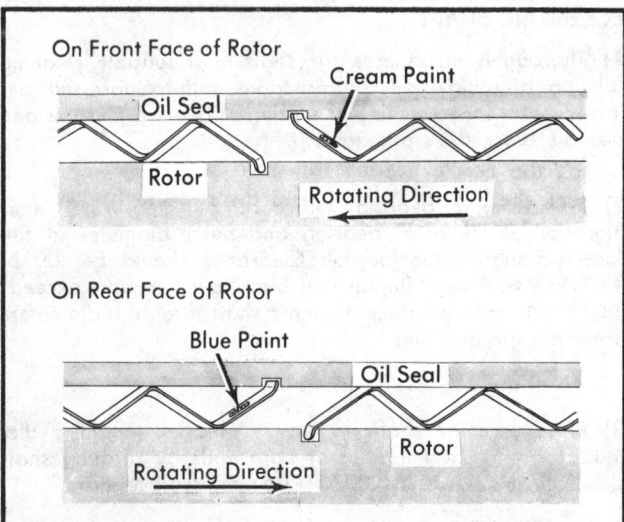

Fig. 18 Installing Oil Seal Spring on Rotor

3) Install outer oil seal so square edge of spring fits in stopper notch of oil seal. Push oil seal in position slowly with fingers. Confirm smooth movement of each oil seal by pressing oil seal. Check oil seal protrusion. Install oil seal springs and oil seals on the other side of rotor.

NOTE — *Take care not to deform lip of oil seal.*

APEX, CORNER & SIDE SEALS

NOTE — *Before installing apex seal, cut the assist piece to a length of .08-.011". (2.0-2.8 mm). Peel off paper and install assist piece of apex seal. See Fig. 19.*

Position apex seals without springs and side pieces into their respective grooves so that each side piece rests on rear side of each rotor. Install the soft seal into the corner seal. Place corner seals and springs into their respective grooves, then position side seals and springs into proper grooves. Ensure smooth movement of each seal by pressing its head.

INSTALLING FRONT ROTOR

Mount front housing on engine stand and place front rotor assembly on housing. Use care not to drop seal into port. Mesh internal and stationary gears so that one rotor apex is set to one of 4 positions shown in *Fig. 20.*

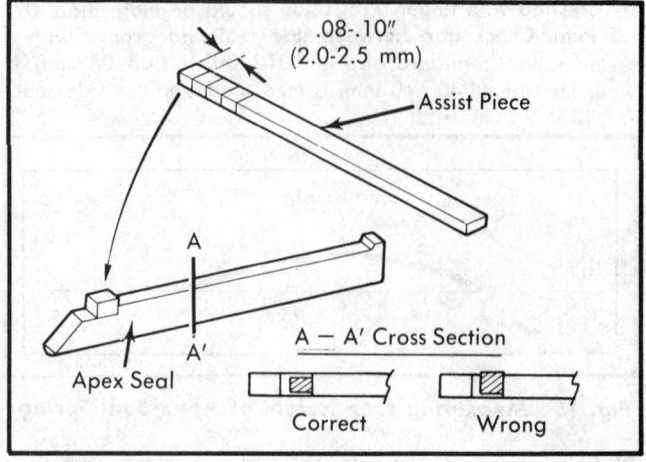

Fig. 19 Installing Assist Piece on Apex Seal

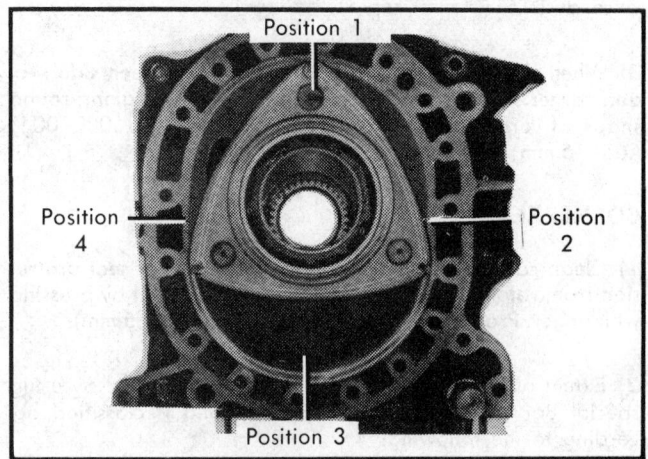

Fig. 20 Positioning Rotor Apex for Reassembly

INSTALLING ECCENTRIC SHAFT

Lubricate front rotor journal and main journal on shaft with engine lubricant. Insert eccentric shaft being careful not to damage rotor bearing and main bearing.

INSTALLING FRONT ROTOR HOUSING

NOTE — *Front and rear rotor housings are not interchangeable. Be sure they are installed in correct sequence.*

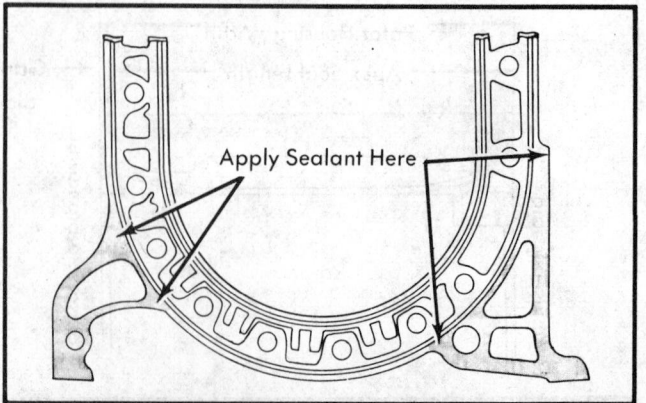

Fig. 21 Applying Sealing Agent to Rotor Assembly

RX7 ROTARY ENGINE (Cont.)

1) Apply sealing agent to front side of rotor housing as shown in *Fig. 21*. To provide greater durability to sealing rubbers, install a protector behind each inner sealing rubber. *See Fig. 22*. Install a new "O" ring, sealing rubbers and protector in front side of engine housing. Apply light coat of petroleum jelly to hold seals in place.

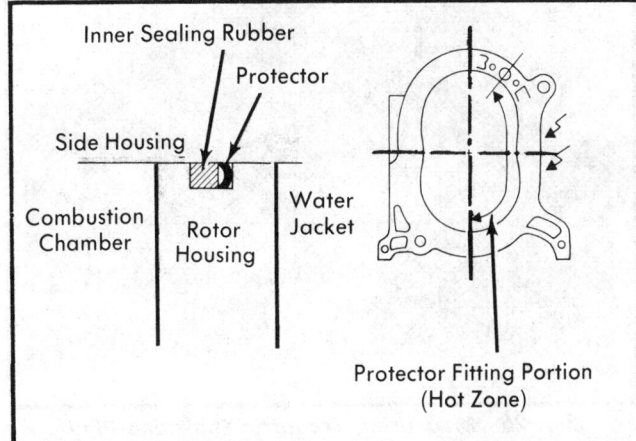

Fig. 22   Installing Protectors for Inner Sealing Rubbers

NOTE — *Inner sealing rubber is square type. The wider white line of sealing rubber should face toward combustion chamber and seam of rubber should be placed as shown in Fig. 23. Do not stretch sealing rubbers.*

2) Invert front rotor housing using care that seals remain in position, and install on front housing. Lubricate tubular dowels and insert through front rotor housing holes.

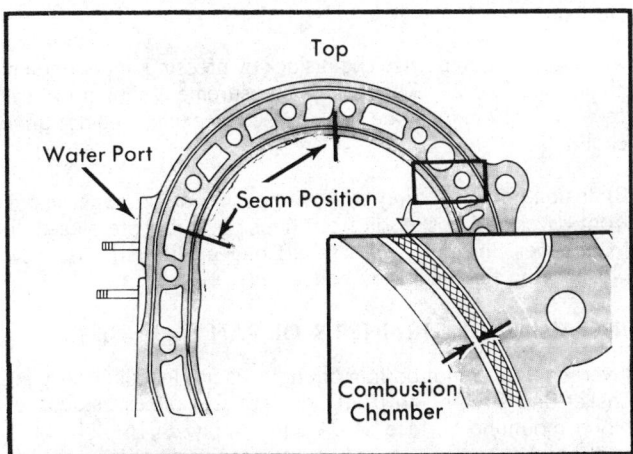

Fig. 23   Positioning Inner Sealing Rubber

3) Insert apex seal springs so that both ends of spring may support the back side of the apex seal. Install the soft seal into corner seal. Install corner seal springs and seals into their respective grooves. Fit side pieces to original positions and lubricate with engine oil.

4) Confirm that spring is set correctly on side piece. *See Fig. 24*. Confirm smooth movement of each seal by pressing on head. Apply sealing agent on the rear side of front housing in areas shown in *Fig. 21* and then place new "O" ring, sealing rubbers and protector on rear side of front housing. Apply engine oil to sliding surfaces of front rotor housing.

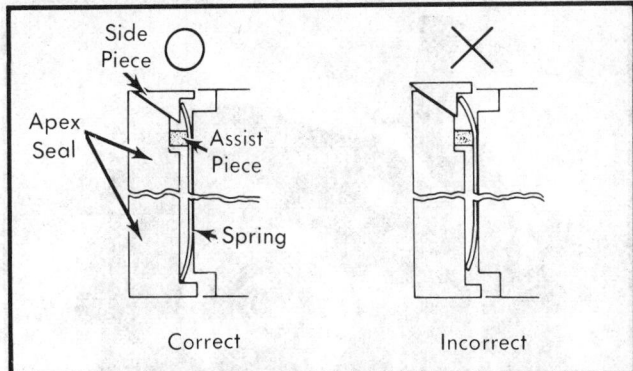

Fig. 24   Positioning of Apex Seal and Spring

INSTALLING INTERMEDIATE HOUSING

Turn front housing and rotor assembly so that top of housing is upward. Pull eccentric shaft outward approximately 1.0" (25 mm), but not more than 1.5" (38 mm). Rotate eccentric shaft until eccentric portion points to 2 o'clock position. Install intermediate housing over eccentric shaft and turn engine so that rear of engine is upward.

INSTALLING REAR ROTOR

Use same procedures up to *Intermediate Housing* when installing rear rotor and rotor housing.

INSTALLING REAR HOUSING

Position engine with rear end upward. Apply sufficient lubricant onto stationary gear and main bearing. Install rear housing onto rear rotor housing, and turn rear rotor slightly to engage rear housing stationary gear with rear rotor internal gear.

TIGHTENING TENSION BOLTS

Place a new sealing washer on each tension bolt and oil threads of each bolt. Tighten bolts in sequence shown in *Fig. 25* in stages until final torque is reached. After tightening, turn eccentric shaft to make sure rotation is light and smooth.

FLYWHEEL COUNTERWEIGHT INSTALLATION

Man. Trans. — 1) Apply engine oil to oil seal in the rear housing. Mount flywheel to rear end of eccentric shaft so that key fits into flywheel keyway. Apply sealing agent to lock nut surface that contacts flywheel and install lock nut. Hold flywheel with ring gear brake (49 1881 060) and tighten lock nut.

2) Hold clutch disc in position with clutch disc centering tool (49 0813 310). Mount clutch cover and pressure plate assembly on flywheel and align the "0" marks of clutch cover and flywheel. Install 4 standard and 2 reamer bolts finger tight. To avoid distortion of pressure plate cover, tighten bolts in steps, a few turns at a time, until all are tight.

Auto Trans. — 1) Apply engine oil to oil seal in rear housing. Fit key to eccentric shaft. Install counterweight to eccentric shaft. Apply sealing agent to lock nut surface that will

RX7 ROTARY ENGINE (Cont.)

Fig. 25 Tightening Sequence of Tension Bolts

**Fig. 26 Measuring Eccentric Shaft End Play
with Dial Indicator**

contact counterweight and install lock nut. Hold counterweight with stopper (49 1881 055) and tighten lock nut. Install drive plate to counterweight so hole in counterweight and drive plate line up.

ECCENTRIC SHAFT END-THRUST ADJUSTMENT

1) Turn engine so front is up. Install thrust plate with chamfer downward, and slide spacer and needle bearing on eccentric shaft. Lubricate shaft and bearings and install bearing housing.

NOTE — *If bearing housing has not been removed, use care that center of needle bearing in bearing housing comes to center of eccentric shaft and that spacer is seated to thrust plate.*

2) Lubricate and install needle bearing, thrust washer, and balance weight on shaft. Install keys in oil pump and eccentric shaft keyways. Place oil pump drive chain on oil pump sprocket and eccentric shaft sprocket, and install sprockets on shafts.

3) Install key in eccentric shaft. Install distributor drive gear with "F" mark on gear facing front of engine. Install eccentric shaft pulley on shaft. Use new washer and tighten pulley bolt.

4) Turn engine so top is upward. Attach a dial indicator on the flywheel or counterweight so it contacts rear housing. Move flywheel or counterweight back and forth. Standard end play is .0016-.0028" (.04-.07 mm). If end play is more than .0035" (.09 mm) grind spacer on surface plate with emery paper or install thinner spacer. If end play is less than .0016" (.04 mm), install thicker spacer.

5) Oversize spacers are available in 5 sizes from .3181" to .3150" (8.08 mm to 8.00 mm) and are identified by stamped letter "X", "K", "Y", "V", and "Z" respectively. When spacer has been installed, recheck end play.

NOTE — *If end play is below specified amount, spacer thickness is too small; if end play is beyond specifications, spacer is too thick.*

INSTALLING FRONT COVER & ECCENTRIC SHAFT PULLEY

1) Turn engine so front is upward. Remove eccentric shaft pulley. Tighten oil pump sprocket nut and bend tab of lock washer.

2) Check oil pump drive chain slack by pressing finger against chain. *See Fig. 28.* Chain slack measurement should not exceed .47" (12 mm). If the slack exceeds the limit, replace drive chain.

3) Install new "O" ring on front housing oil passage. Install front cover and gasket on front housing. Lubricate oil seal in front cover. Install eccentric shaft pulley on shaft. Use new washer and tighten pulley bolt.

INSTALLING OIL STRAINER & OIL PAN

Invert engine so that bottom of engine is up. Install oil strainer gasket and strainer on front housing. Cut off excess gasket along mounting surface of oil pan. Apply a .16-.24" (4-6 mm) bead of sealer on mounting surface of oil pan (to the inside of pan bolt holes) and install gasket. Apply a similar bead of sealant to gasket, install pan and tighten bolts.

INSTALLING WATER PUMP

Turn engine upright, position gasket and water pump on front housing and tighten attaching bolts. **NOTE** — *For further information on cooling system components, see Cooling System in this article.*

INSTALLING DISTRIBUTOR

Rotate eccentric shaft until yellow mark (leading timing mark) on pulley aligns with indicator pin on front cover. Align notch

RX7 ROTARY ENGINE (Cont.)

on distributor housing with punch mark on driven gear. Insert distributor and lock nut. Turn distributor housing until a trigger wheel blade aligns with pick-up coil. Tighten lock nut.

INSTALLING EXTERNAL COMPONENTS

Install exhaust manifold, engine mount, intake manifold with carburetor, and alternator and drive belt. Check clearance between alternator support and bracket. Limit is .0059" (.15 mm). Adjust with shim if necessary. Install air pump and drive belt, oil filter assembly and all other external components. Before removing engine from stand, install engine hanger bracket to front cover.

ENGINE OILING

Crankcase Capacity — 5.5 quarts.

Oil Filter — Full-flow, disposable cartridge-type filter mounted on rear housing.

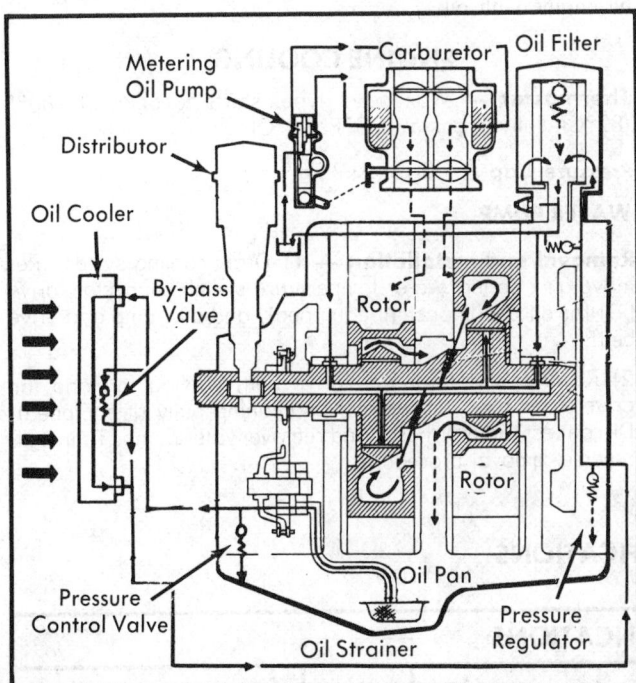

Fig. 27 Cutaway View of Engine Oiling System

Normal Oil Pressure — 10-26 psi (0.7-1.8 kg/cm^2) at idle speed, 64-78 psi (4.5-5.5 kg/cm^2) at 3000 RPM.

Pressure Regulator Valve — Mounted in rear housing, valve regulates oil pressure at high RPM. Valve opens to release oil pressure. If oil pressure is less than normal, check regulator valve piston for wear and ensure that spring free length is 1.827" (46.4 mm).

ENGINE OILING SYSTEM

Engine oiling system is forced circulation utilizing a two rotor type oil pump. Oil pump is mounted on front housing and is chain driven through eccentric shaft. A full-flow oil filter is mounted on rear housing. An oil metering pump, pressure regulator valve and an oil cooler in radiator are also employed.

OIL PUMP

NOTE — *Oil pump is mounted on front engine housing and must be checked or overhauled with front engine cover removed.*

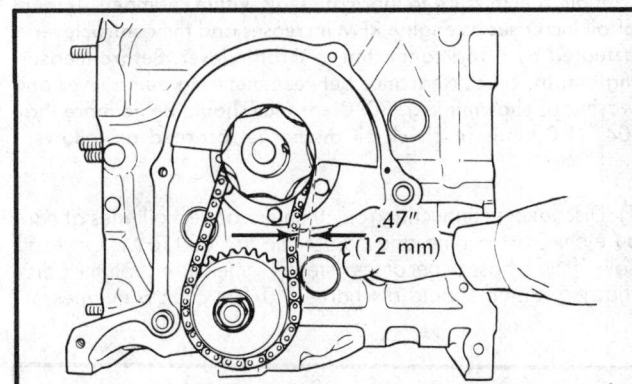

Fig. 28 Measuring Oil Pump Drive Chain Slack

1) With front engine cover removed, check oil pump drive chain slack by pressing finger against chain and measuring slack. If measurement exceeds .47" (12 mm), replace drive chain. *See Fig. 28.*

2) With oil pump removed, disassemble in following order: Remove snap ring, rear outer rotor, rear inner rotor, key and middle plate; remove front inner rotor, key, shaft, spring pin and front outer rotor.

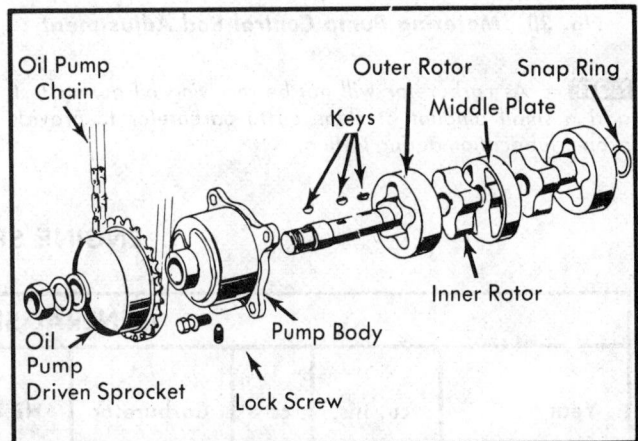

Fig. 29 Exploded View of Oil Pump Assembly

3) Insert a feeler gauge between lobes of inner and outer rotors and check clearance. If beyond .006"(.15 mm), replace both rotors.

4) Check clearance between outer rotor and pump housing with a feeler gauge. If clearance exceeds .012" (.30 mm), replace rotors or housing.

5) Place a straightedge across pump mounting surface and check rotor end play with a feeler gauge. If beyond .006" (.15 mm), replace pump body or rotors.

6) To assemble oil pump, reverse disassembly procedure. Install oil pump and tighten bolts. Install sprockets and chain as previously outlined. *See Eccentric Shaft Endthrust Adjustment.*

Mazda Engines

RX7 ROTARY ENGINE (Cont.)

METERING OIL PUMP

Metering oil pump regulates the amount of oil pumped to float chamber of carburetor. The oil enters combustion chamber with air/fuel mixture to lubricate seals within chamber. Amount of oil increases as engine RPM increases and the control lever is actuated by a rod connected to throttle lever. Before measuring output, check clearance between metering pump lever and washer as shown in *Fig. 30*. Clearance should be no more than .04" (1.0 mm). To check oil discharge, proceed as follows:

1) Disconnect connecting rod, then disconnect oil lines at carburetor. Start engine and adjust idle to 2000 RPM. Once oil flow from hoses becomes steady, measure volume discharged. Pump should discharge 2.0-2.4 cc in 6 minutes.

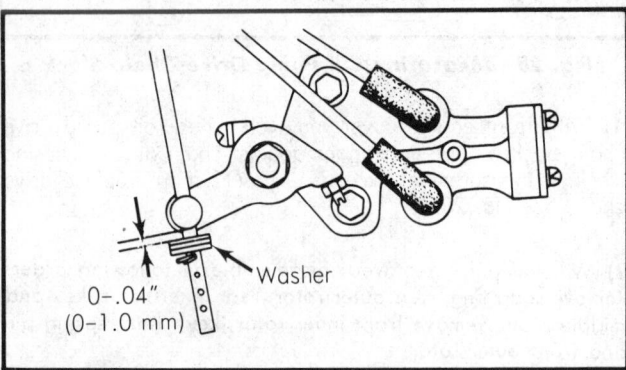

Fig. 30 Metering Pump Control Rod Adjustment

NOTE — *As carburetor will not be receiving oil during test, add a small amount of clean oil to carburetor to provide proper lubrication during testing.*

2) To adjust oil metering pump, turn the adjusting screw clockwise to increase flow or counterclockwise to decrease flow. One complete turn will change oil discharge flow by 0.2-0.3 cc for six minutes of operation. Make sure lock nut of adjustment screw is locked, then recheck metering oil pump discharge rate.

OIL COOLER

1) Inspect oil cooler for damage, cracks and leakage. Any defects found are repaired by aluminum welding or replacement.

2) Drain engine oil and remove engine under cover. Remove cap nut at bottom of oil cooler and pull out by-pass valve.

3) Check by-pass valve after removing it from bottom of oil cooler. Heat and soak by-pass valve in oil gradually to 158°F (70°C) and check if protrusion of valve exceeds 0.2" (5 mm). If less, replace by-pass valve.

4) Install by-pass valve in reverse of removal procedure and fill engine with oil.

ENGINE COOLING

Thermostat — Wax pellet type, starts to open at 180°F (82°C), fully opens at 203°F (95°C).

Pressure Cap — 13 psi (0.9 kg/cm²)

WATER PUMP

Removal and Installation — 1) Drain cooling system. Remove air cleaner, water temperature switch connector, drive belt for air conditioner (if equipped), and air pump and drive belt.

2) Remove alternator and drive belt, cooling fan and fan drive assembly. Remove air conditioning pully (if equipped). Disconnect radiator hoses and remove water pump. To install, reverse removal procedures.

ENGINE SPECIFICATIONS

GENERAL SPECIFICATIONS

Year	cu. ins.	cc	Carburetor	HP at RPM	Torque (Ft. Lbs. at RPM)	Compr. Ratio	Rotor Housing Width in.	mm
1981	70	1146	4-Bbl.	.....	.....	9.4:1	2.756	70

ROTOR HOUSING, INTERMEDIATE HOUSING & ROTOR

Engine	ROTOR HOUSING Width In. (mm)	Distortion Limit In. (mm)	INTERMEDIATE HOUSING Width In. (mm)	Distortion Limit In. (mm)	Inside Diameter In.(mm)	ROTOR Housing-to-Rotor Clearance In. mm)	Land Protrusion In. (mm)
1146 cc Rotary	2.756 (70)	.0024 (.06)	1.969 (50)	.0016 (.04)	.....	.0047-.0071 (.12-.18)	.....

RX7 ROTARY ENGINE (Cont.)
ENGINE SPECIFICATIONS (Cont.)

① APEX SEAL

Engine	Length	Seal Width	Height	Seal-to-Housing		Seal-to-Rotor	
				Clearance	Wear Limit	Groove Clearance	Wear Limit
1146 cc Rotary	2.750 (69.8)	.118 (3.0)	.335 (8.5)	.0051-.0075 (.13-.19)	.....	.0020-.0035 (.051-.089)	.006 (.15)

① — In. (mm)

SIDE SEAL

Engine	Thickness In. (mm)	Width In. (mm)	Seal-to-Groove		Side Seal-to-Corner Seal	
			Clearance In. (mm)	Limit In. (mm)	Clearance In. (mm)	Limit In. (mm)
1146 cc Rotary	.039 (1.0)	.138 (3.5)	.0012-.0031 (.03-.08)	.004 (.10)	.0020-.0059 (.05-.15)	.016 (.40)

CORNER SEAL

Engine	Diameter In. (mm)	Height In. (mm)	Seal-to-Groove		Side Seal-to-Corner Seal	
			Clearance In. (mm)	Limit In. (mm)	Clearance In. (mm)	Limit In. (mm)
1146 cc Rotary	.433 (11.0)	.276 (7.0)	.....	.....	.0020-.0059 (.05-.15)	.016 (.40)

ECCENTRIC SHAFT MAIN & ROTOR BEARINGS

Engine	MAIN BEARINGS			ROTOR BEARINGS	
	Journal Diameter In. (mm)	Clearance In. (mm)	Eccentric Shaft Endplay In. (mm)	Journal Diameter In. (mm)	Clearance In. (mm)
1146 cc Rotary	1.6929 (43)	.0016-.0031 (.04-.08)	.0016-.0028 (.04-.07)	2.9134 (74)	.0016-.0028 (.04-.07)

OIL SEAL

Height In. (mm)	Seal Lip Contact Width	
	Standard In. (mm)	Limit In. (mm)
.220 (5.6)	.020 (.5)	.....

PORT TIMING

Engine	INTAKE		EXHAUST	
	Open (ATDC)	Close (ABDC)	Open (BBDC)	Close (ATDC)
1146 cc Rotary	32°	40°	75°	38°

TIGHTENING SPECIFICATIONS

Application	Ft. Lbs. (N·m)
Oil Pump Sprocket	23-34 (32-47)
Eccentric Shaft Pulley	72-87 (98-118)
Intake Manifold	14-19 (19-26)
Flywheel Lock Nut	289-362 (393-492)
Water Pump	13-20 (18-27)
Clutch Cover	13-20 (18-27)

4-CYLINDER & 5-CYLINDER DIESEL

ENGINE CODING

ENGINE IDENTIFICATION

Engine identification number is stamped on left side of cylinder block. First six digits of this number are used for engine identification purposes.

Engine Identification		
Application	Chassis Type	Engine Code
240D (4-Cyl.)	123.123	616.912
300D (5-Cyl.)	123.130	617.912
300CD (5-Cyl.)	123.150	617.912
300SD (5-Cyl.)	126.120	617.951
300TD (5-Cyl. Turbo) ..	123.193	617.952

ENGINE & CYLINDER HEAD

ENGINE

Removal — 1) Drain cooling system from plug on side of crankcase. Remove engine hood, radiator and fan shroud. (On some models, hood may be raised 90° to allow engine removal.) Remove air filter with intake duct. Draw oil from power steering pump reservoir and disconnect hoses. If equipped with air conditioning, dismount and set compressor aside but DO NOT disconnect refrigerant hoses.

2) Remove control linkage with shaft and place aside. Disconnect all coolant, vacuum, oil, fuel and electrical lines which lead to engine. On turbocharged models, loosen oil filter cover and raise slightly, and disconnect exhaust system at turbocharger. On all other models, disconnect exhaust pipe at exhaust manifold. On all models, remove lateral support for exhaust pipe at transmission.

3) If equipped with level control, remove pump and set aside, leaving lines connected. Disconnect engine shock absorbers at chassis. Remove drive shaft shield and disconnect drive shaft at transmission. Disconnect shift lever and all connections at transmission. Unscrew front and rear engine mountings. Attach suitable sling to lifting eyes and hoist engine/transmission assembly out at an angle of approximately 45°.

Installation — Ensure that oil cooler, lines and filter housing have been flushed if installing new engine as a result of bearing failure. Lower engine/transmission assembly into position and complete installation in reverse order of removal.

NOTE — *DO NOT use oil or grease on engine stops or mounts.*

TURBOCHARGER (Turbo Diesel Only)

Removal — 1) Remove air filter assembly and all ducting. Disconnect wire from temperature switch and remove vacuum line and crankcase breather pipe. Disconnect engine oil supply line to turbocharger.

2) Remove air filter mounting bracket and disconnect exhaust flange. Remove exhaust bracket on automatic transmission and press exhaust pipe to rear. Remove intermediate flange mounting bracket. Remove 4 mounting nuts holding turbocharger to manifold and remove turbocharger. Cover oil return pipe.

Installation — Install new flange gasket so that reinforcing bead is towards exhaust manifold. Ensure that center housing is filled with approximately ¼ pint of oil. Install intermediate flange and oil return pipe and install turbocharger. Complete installation in reverse order of removal.

CYLINDER HEAD

NOTE — *Remove head only after engine has cooled down.*

Removal — 1) Drain cooling system and disconnect all water hoses attached to cylinder head. Remove air cleaner and ducting. If equipped with level control, remove pump and set aside, leaving lines connected. If equipped with power steering, remove pump with bracket and fuel filter and set aside. On turbocharged models, loosen and pull up oil filter cover slightly, and remove turbocharger.

2) Detach all remaining electrical connections, water, fuel and vacuum lines from cylinder head and intake manifold. Unbolt dipstick guide tube of automatic transmission from intake manifold. Disconnect exhaust pipe from manifold or turbocharger and at transmission support. Remove throttle control linkage and place aside. Remove injection lines and cover all connections.

3) Unbolt exhaust manifold support at manifold. Remove cylinder head cover and loosen, but do not remove camshaft sprocket bolt. Position camshaft to free rocker arms of tension and remove rocker arm assemblies. Rotate crankshaft by using socket tool on crankshaft pulley so that No. 1 cylinder is at TDC on firing stroke.

4) Mark camshaft sprocket and timing chain for proper assembly. Unscrew chain tensioner plug and remove compression spring. Remove guide rail from cylinder head and pull out guide rail bolt with an impact puller. Remove camshaft sprocket. Loosen and remove head bolts in reverse of tightening sequence. Injection nozzles must be removed prior to removing the 5 bolts next to nozzles.

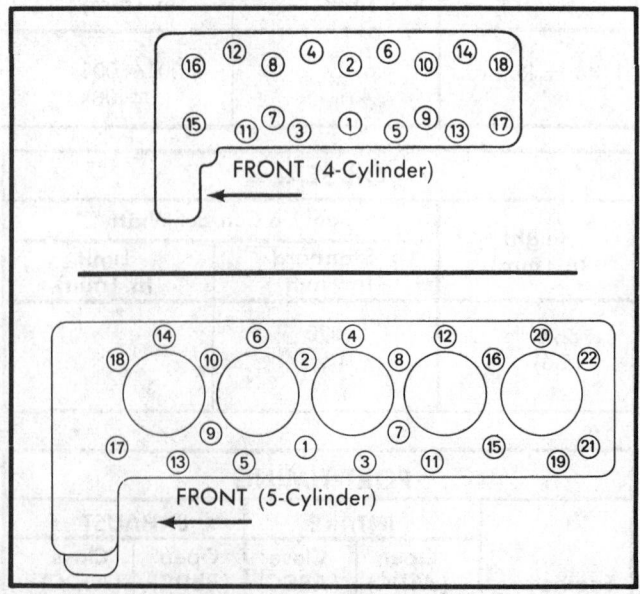

Fig. 1 Cylinder Head Tightening Sequence (Loosen in Reverse Order)

4-CYLINDER & 5-CYLINDER DIESEL (Cont.)

5) Attach sling to lifting eyes on head and lift head from engine. Thoroughly clean all mating surfaces of head and cylinder block.

Installation — 1) Ensure that No. 1 cylinder is still at TDC. Place new head gasket into position, ensuring that locating dowels are in correct position. Place head on block and insert oiled bolts of proper length. Tighten bolts to specifications.

2) Complete installation in reverse order of removal and adjust valve clearance. Use new seals and gaskets when installing all components. Run engine until warm, then loosen each head bolt ¼ turn and tighten in sequence shown.

CAMSHAFT

CAMSHAFT

Removal & Installation — Remove cylinder head cover and camshaft sprocket. (See *CYLINDER HEAD* in this article). Remove shim from camshaft together with bearings and oil pipe. To install apply engine oil to camshaft bearings, camshaft journals and cams. Place camshaft into bearings from rear. Reverse removal procedure ensuring that camshaft supports and dowel pins are aligned.

CAMSHAFT BEARING REPLACEMENT

1) Inspect camshaft bearings for wear. If worn, grind bearing journals and fit undersize bearings.

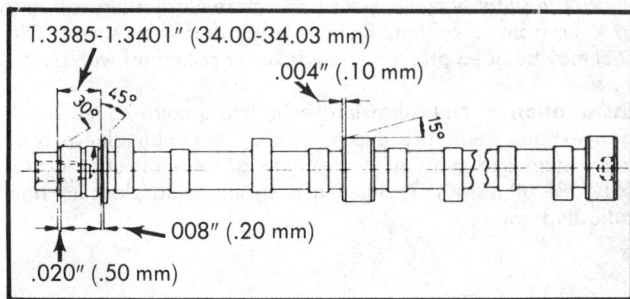

Fig. 2   Detailed View of Camshaft

2) Bearing on No. 1 journal controls camshaft end play. Width of journal is 1.3385-1.3401" (34.0-34.03 mm). Place bearing on camshaft and install retaining ring. Using a feeler gauge, measure clearance between camshaft flange and bearing. Lap bearing to proper fit. The following table lists camshaft bearing journal diameters for standard and undersize bearings:

Camshaft Journal Diameters

Application	Bearing No. 1 In. (mm)	No. 2 & 3 In. (mm)	①No. 4 In. (mm)
Standard	1.375 (34.94)	1.831 (46.51)	1.926 (48.94)
Intermediate (Grey)	1.371 (34.84)	1.824 (46.34)	1.923 (48.84)
1st Undersize (Red)	1.365 (34.69)	1.818 (46.19)	1.916 (48.69)

① — 5-Cyl. only.

TIMING CHAIN

Removal & Installation — 1) A split link timing chain is available for repairs without dismantling engine. Remove glow plugs and cylinder head cover. Remove air cleaner adapter. Cover chain guard with cloth and grind open both pins of a link in the timing chain.

2) Remove old link and insert new split link with new chain attached. Turn crankshaft slowly in normal direction while feeding new chain in and old chain out. Ensure that chain does not slip on sprockets and install master (split) link from rear so that retainer will be at front.

3) Install spring lock with closed end facing direction of rotation. Rotate crankshaft through one complete revolution and check that all timing marks still agree. To complete installation, reverse removal procedures.

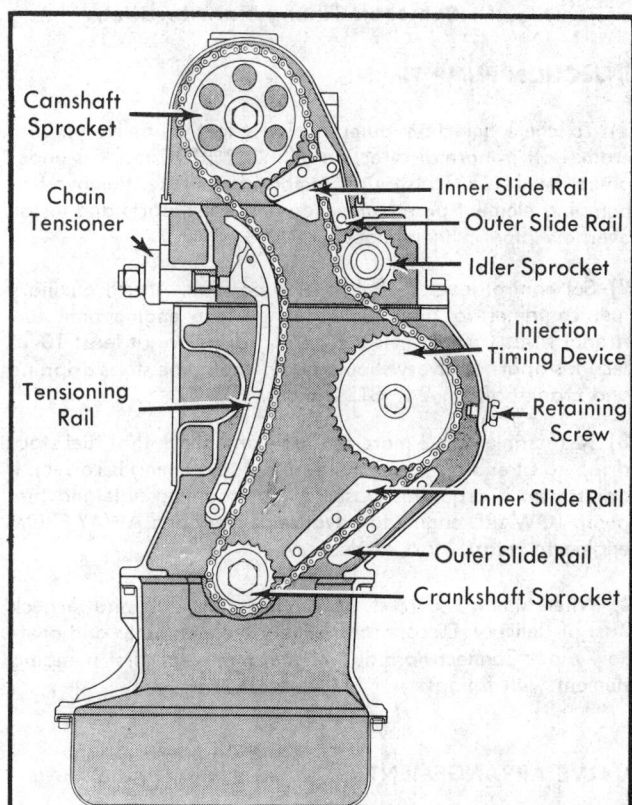

Fig. 3   Timing Chain and Related Components

VALVE TIMING

1) Rotate No. 1 piston to TDC of compression stroke. Align camshaft timing mark with mark on No. 1 camshaft bearing support bracket. Install camshaft sprocket.

2) If correct valve timing is not achieved when camshaft sprocket is installed, offset Woodruff keys are available to make timing corrections, see following table:

Offset Woodruff Keys

Offset	Crankshaft Correction
.0275" (.7 mm)	4°
.0354" (.9 mm)	6 1/2°
.0433" (1.1 mm)	8°
.0511" (1.3 mm)	10°

4-CYLINDER & 5-CYLINDER DIESEL (Cont.)

Fig. 4 Camshaft Timing Mark Locations

INJECTION PUMP TIMING

1) To check injection pump timing (start of delivery), turn crankshaft in normal direction until 24° BTDC mark is under pointer with No. 1 piston on compression stroke. Remove first pumping element pipe connection and valve ports and install overflow pipe in their place.

2) Set control lever to full throttle position. Attach auxiliary fuel container to pump inlet fitting. Turn engine until fuel stream stops from overflow pipe and drips are at least 10-15 seconds apart. Delivery should occur when pipe stops dripping and crankshaft on 24° BTDC mark.

3) Turn crankshaft 2 more full turns and check that fuel stops dripping at end of second full turn if pump timing is correct. If adjustment is required, loosen pump mounting nuts and turn pump TOWARD engine to advance delivery and AWAY FROM engine to retard start of delivery.

4) When timing is correct, tighten mounting nuts and recheck start of delivery. Disconnect auxiliary fuel container and overflow pipe. Connect normal fuel line and install first pumping element with fittings.

VALVES

VALVE ARRANGEMENT

4-Cylinder — E-I-I-E-E-I-I-E (Front-to-Rear)

5-Cylinder — E-I-I-E-E-I-I-E-E-I (Front-to-Rear)

VALVE GUIDE SERVICING

Checking Valve Guides — After removal of valve spring and valve stem seal, the wear on valve guide can be determined by moving valve stem crosswise in relation to engine. Maximum movement of approximately .004" (.12 mm) is allowed.

Removing & Inserting Guides — 1) Drive out valve guide with knock-out mandrel from direction of combustion chamber or press out. Insert valve guide into liquid oxygen for approximately 3-4 minutes. Insert immediately into respective bore while following-up with a hammer.

2) If no liquid oxygen is available, heat head in a water bath, or heat in an oven to a maximum of 176° F (80° C). Coat valve guide with tallow and drive in with knock-in mandrel until circlip or knock-in mandrel rests against cylinder head. Guides are pressed in from rocker side. Check guide bores and ream for proper clearance as required.

3) Valve guides are available in standard and 1 oversize (color red). An interference fit of .0004-.0015" (.010-.040 mm) is used. If guide does not meet specifications, replace. Note that intake guides are 2.362" (60 mm) long and exhaust guides are 1.909" (48.5 mm) long.

Valve Guides Specifications		
Application	**Guide O.D. In. (mm)**	**Cyl. Head Bore In. (mm)**
Standard	.5522-.5527 (14.03-14.04)	.5511-.5518 (14.00-14.02)
Oversize (Red)	.5601-.5605 (14.23-14.24)	.5590-.5597 (14.20-14.22)

VALVE STEM OIL SEALS

Removal — With rocker arms and brackets removed from head, use suitable compressor and unscrew adjusting cap and lock nut from valve stem. Remove collar and valve spring. Old seal may be pried off with screwdriver or pulled off with pliers.

Installation — Note that intake seals are color coded black and exhaust seals are green. Position assembly sleeve over valve stem and press new seal onto guide with suitable tool (617 589 00 43 00). Replace valve spring, collar, lock nut and adjusting cap.

ROCKER ARM ASSEMBLIES

Removal & Installation — Remove air cleaner and cylinder head cover. Loosen rocker arm bracket bolts and rotate camshaft so there is no load on rocker arms being removed. Remove front assembly (serving 2 front cylinders), then rotate camshaft so that rear assembly can be removed without tension. Disassemble and replace parts as required. To install, reverse removal procedures.

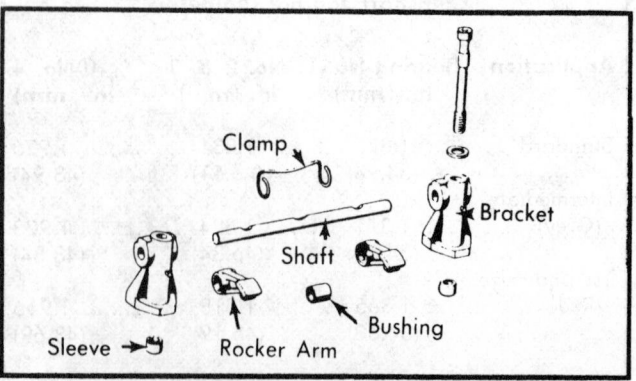

Fig. 5 Detail of Rocker Arm Assembly

4-CYLINDER & 5-CYLINDER DIESEL (Cont.)

VALVE CLEARANCE ADJUSTMENT

NOTE — *Valves should be adjusted with engine at normal operating temperature. Cold specifications are provided for initial settings after assembly.*

1) Adjust valves according to firing sequence (1-3-4-2 on 4 cylinder engine and 1-2-4-5-3 on 5 cylinder engine). Rotate crankshaft so piston of valves to be adjusted is at TDC on firing stroke. Measure clearance between slide surface of camshaft and rocker arm.

2) To adjust, fit holding wrench on valve retainer. Loosen cap nut while holding hex nut and adjust clearance by turning cap nut. After adjustment, lock cap nut by tightening hex nut and recheck valve clearance.

Valve Clearance Specifications	
Valve	**Inches (mm)**
Intake	
Cold	.004 (.10)
Warm	.006 (.15)
Exhaust	
Cold	①.012 (.30)
Warm	①.014 (.35)
① — Turbo Diesel — .04" (.35 mm) cold, .016" (.40 mm) hot.	

PISTONS, PINS & RINGS

OIL PAN

Removal — 1) Drain engine oil and remove or raise hood to 90° position. Disconnect air cleaner corrugated duct and remove throttle control shaft. Unbolt fan shroud and place over fan. Remove oil dipstick tube bracket at power steering pump bracket.

2) Remove air conditioner compressor and loosen clamp for air/oil cooler lines. Remove engine shock absorbers at frame crossmember. Loosen exhaust system lateral support at transmission. Remove engine mounting bolts from below. Unbolt oil cooler lines for automatic transmission at transmission, intermediate flange and upper section of pan.

3) Remove 4 lower bolts on intermediate flange and remove intermediate flange shield. Unbolt and remove LOWER oil pan. Use suitable drift and drive oil dipstick guide tube out as far as it will go. Remove strainer extension with strainer from oil pump. Remove upper oil pan bolts.

4) Attach engine sling and hoist to front of engine and raise enough to remove pan upper section. Pull out oil dipstick guide tube. Turn crankshaft until counterweights and connecting rods clear pan and lower pan from block.

Installation — 1) Install new radial seal in groove at rear of pan. Ensure that mating surfaces are clean and coat upper pan section with gasket compound. Place upper pan in position and insert dipstick guide tube. On turbocharged engine, insert oil return line from turbocharger.

2) Bolt upper section of pan to engine. Mount strainer extension and strainer to oil pump. Use new gasket and bolt lower pan to upper pan. To complete installation, reverse removal procedure.

PISTON & ROD ASSEMBLY

Removal — With cylinder head and oil pan removed, unscrew connecting rod nuts. Tap bolts with plastic mallet to loosen rod on crankshaft and push piston/rod assembly out top of cylinder block. To remove piston from rod, remove piston pin circlips. Push out piston pins.

NOTE — *On Turbo Diesel, oil spray nozzles in crankcase must be removed prior to removal and installation of pistons. Nozzles must be replaced in orginal location after piston/rod assemblies are installed.*

Installation — 1) Place piston on connecting rod with arrow on piston crown facing forward. Circlip grooves in connecting rods face to left side of engine (intake manifold). Coat piston pin with engine oil and press in by hand. Insert piston pin circlips in grooves.

2) Lubricate cleaned cylinder bores, rod bearing journals, rod bearing shells and pistons. Distribute gaps of piston rings around piston circumference evenly. Install piston ring compressor, and guide in piston with arrow facing forward.

3) Place connecting rod bearing caps on connecting rods, with cap code numbers aligning with connecting rod code numbers. Tighten to specifications. Check for normal crankshaft rotation. Measure piston protrusion above top of cylinder block with piston at TDC. Piston should project at least .020" (.50 mm), but not more than .035" (.90 mm) above block.

FITTING PISTONS

Measure piston and cylinder diameters to determine running clearance. Piston diameter is measured at 90° to piston pin bore near bottom of piston skirt. There are two compression rings and one oil ring. Install compression rings with markings "top" or "F" and oil ring with marking "GOE" or "F" facing upward.

CRANKSHAFT MAIN & CONNECTING ROD BEARINGS

MAIN BEARING SERVICE

Measure main bearing and connecting rod journals for out-of-round and taper. Out-of-round must not exceed .0002-.0004" (.005-.010 mm) and taper must not exceed .0004-.0006" (.010-.015 mm). Select proper undersize, if required, and grind crankshaft to following diameters:

Crankshaft Journal Diameters		
Application	**Main In. (mm)**	**Con. Rod In. (mm)**
Standard	2.7541-2.7545 (69.95-69.96)	2.0454-2.0458 (51.95-51.96)
1st Undersize	2.7442-2.7446 (69.70-69.71)	2.0356-2.0360 (51.70-51.71)
2nd Undersize	2.7344-2.7348 (69.45-69.46)	2.0257-2.0261 (51.45-51.46)
3rd Undersize	2.7246-2.7249 (69.20-69.21)	2.0159-2.0163 (51.20-51.21)
4th Undersize	2.7147-2.7151 (68.95-68.96)	2.0060-2.0064 (50.95-50.96)

4-CYLINDER & 5-CYLINDER DIESEL (Cont.)

THRUST BEARING ALIGNMENT

Third main bearing is equipped with separate shells and thrust washers in place of 2 one piece bearing inserts. Two identical thrust washers are inserted in crankcase and 2 remaining halves are fitted in bearing cap. Bottom halves have 2 tabs to prevent turning and avoid incorrect installation. Following size thrust washers are available to adjust crankshaft end play: .085" (2.15 mm), .087" (2.20 mm), .089" (2.25 mm), .092" (2.35 mm) and .094" (2.40 mm).

CRANKSHAFT REAR OIL SEAL

Removal & Installation — With oil pan and crankshaft removed, pull old seal from groove in crankcase and oil pan. Insert new radial seal in groove and press into place using an oiled hammer handle. To provide overlap, cut seal off .040" (1 mm) above separation surface. Coat seal halves with engine oil.

FRONT OIL SEAL

Removal — With radiator and shroud removed, take off front pulley and vibration dampener. Pry old oil seal from engine with screwdriver. If fitted with original seal, remove spacer washer with puller (616 589 00 33 00).

NOTE — *On some engines, chrome plated spacer ring will not be required. Replacement seals for Turbo Diesel are of green Viton inside and black acrylic outside. Other seals are black outside and white inside.*

Installation — Install new spacer ring (if required) and lubricate seal lips with engine oil. Ensure that seal cavity is clean and free of nicks and scratches. Place seal SQUARELY in recess and use installation sleeve to press seal into proper position.

ENGINE OILING

ENGINE OILING SYSTEM

Engine lubrication is provided by a gear type oil pump, which force feeds oil through an oil filter to oil gallery. From oil gallery, oil flows to main and connecting rod bearings. Pistons, wrist pins and connecting rod bushings are splash lubricated. A vertical oil passage from oil gallery has a transverse passage which supplies oil to intermediate sprocket shaft and bearings. Another oil passage supplies oil to oil pump drive shaft and helical gear. Vertical passage also supplies oil to No. 1 camshaft bearing. An external oil tube attached to No. 1 camshaft bearing support lubricates other camshaft bearings and rocker arms.

NOTE — *Turbo Diesel models also have an external line feeding oil to the turbocharger with a gravity feed back to the crankcase. Additionally, the main oil gallery feeds spray nozzles for cooling of the pistons.*

Crankcase Capacities (With Filter)	
Application	**Capacity**
4 & 5-Cylinder	7.0 qts.
5-Cylinder Turbo	7.9 qts.

Normal Oil Pressure — 7.1 psi. (.5 kg/cm^2) at 700-780 RPM idle speed; 42 psi. (3 kg/cm^2) at 3000 RPM.

Oil Filter — Oil filter is vertically mounted and contains a single cartridge composed of a main and by-pass section.

Pressure Regulator Valve — Non-adjustable.

OIL PUMP

Removal — With oil pan removed, pump may be removed by taking out mounting bolts except on turbocharged engine. On Turbo Diesel, pump is chain driven and must have sprocket and chain removed prior to pump removal. Remove 5 mounting bolts and take off pump. Remove connecting pipe from engine block.

Installation — On Turbo Diesel, use new "O" ring and insert connecting pipe. Ensure that sprocket is mounted in duplex chain properly and install oil pump. Mount sprocket on pump drive shaft and install tensioning rail and spring. On all other models, install pump and tighten mounting screw on crankcase and bearing cap.

ENGINE COOLING

Thermostat — Opens at 172-180°F (78-82°C).

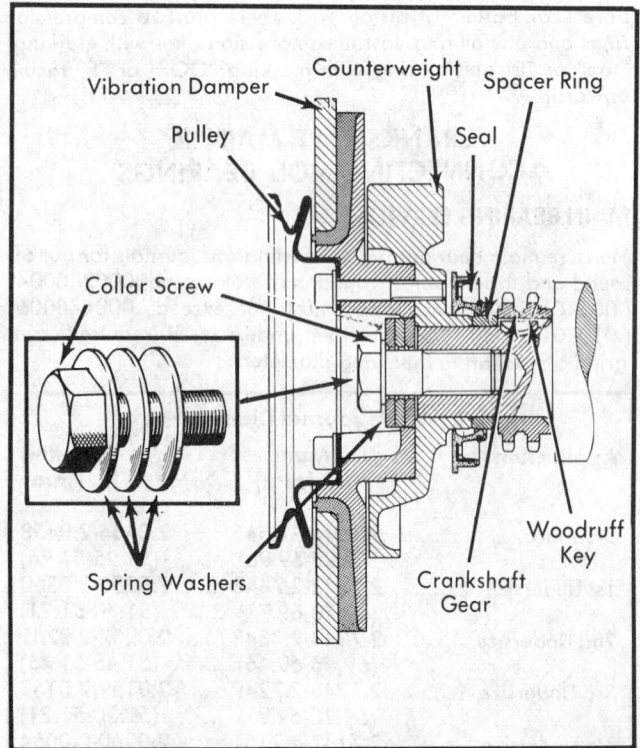

Fig. 6 Sectional View of Crankshaft Front Oil Seal

Labels: Vibration Damper, Pulley, Counterweight, Spacer Ring, Seal, Collar Screw, Spring Washers, Crankshaft Gear, Woodruff Key

Cooling System Capacity	
Application	**Capacity**
4-Cylinder	10.6 qts.
5-Cylinder	11.6 qts.
5-Cylinder Turbo	12.7 qts.

4-CYLINDER & 5-CYLINDER DIESEL (Cont.)

WATER PUMP

Removal — Drain cooling system and loosen "V" belts. Remove fan and drive pulley. Remove or loosen hoses from pump and take out mounting bolts. Remove pump.

Installation — Coat new gasket with suitable sealer and mount with pump on engine. Install fan and hub and adjust belts. Fill radiator and expansion tank to mark and run engine. After temperature reaches approximately 140°F (60°C), install radiator cap and check for leaks.

ENGINE SPECIFICATIONS

GENERAL SPECIFICATIONS

Year	Displ. cu. ins.	Displ. cc	Carburetor	HP at RPM	Torque (Ft. Lbs. at RPM)	Compr. Ratio	Bore in.	Bore mm	Stroke in.	Stroke mm
1981										
4-Cyl.	146.4	2399	Fuel Inj.	67@4000	97@2400	21.0:1	3.57	90.9	3.64	92.4
5-Cyl.	183.0	2998	Fuel Inj.	83@4200	120@2400	21.0:1	3.57	90.9	3.64	92.4
5-Cyl. Turbo	183.0	2998	Fuel Inj.	120@4350	170@2400	21.5:1	3.57	90.9	3.64	92.4

VALVES

Engine & Valve	Head Diam. In. (mm)	Face Angle	Seat Angle	Seat Width In. (mm)	Stem Diameter In. (mm)	Stem Clearance In. (mm)	Valve Lift In. (mm)
All							
Intake	1.563-1.571 (39.70-39.90)	30°	30°	.051-.063 (1.3-1.6)	.3906-.3913 (9.92-9.94)	.0030 (.075)	.....
Exhaust	1.343-1.350 (34.10-34.30)	30°	30°	.098-.114 (2.5-2.9)	.3906-.3913 (9.92-9.94)	.0030 (.075)	.....

PISTONS, PINS, RINGS

Engine	PISTONS Clearance In. (mm)	PINS Piston Fit In. (mm)	PINS Rod Fit In. (mm)	RINGS Rings	RINGS End Gap In. (mm)	RINGS Side Clearance In. (mm)
All	.0007-.0015 (.018-.038)	①	Push Fit	No. 1	.0079-.0138 (.20-.35)	.004-.005 (.100-.132)
				No. 2	.0079-.0138 (.20-.35)	.003-.004 (.070-.102)
				No. 3	.0098-.0157 (.25-.40)	.001-.002 (.030-.062)

① — Interference fit. See *Piston & Rod Assembly* in this article.

CRANKSHAFT MAIN & CONNECTING ROD BEARINGS

Engine	MAIN BEARINGS Journal Diam. In. (mm)	MAIN BEARINGS Clearance In. (mm)	MAIN BEARINGS Thrust Bearing	MAIN BEARINGS Crankshaft End Play In. (mm)	CONNECTING ROD BEARINGS Journal Diam. In. (mm)	CONNECTING ROD BEARINGS Clearance In. (mm)	CONNECTING ROD BEARINGS Side Play In. (mm)
All	2.7541-2.7545 (69.95-69.96)	.0012-.0027 (.031-.068)	Center	.0039-.0090 (.10-.22)	2.0454-2.0458 (51.95-51.96)	.0012-.0027 (.031-.068)	.005-.010 (.12-.26)

Mercedes-Benz Engines

4-CYLINDER & 5-CYLINDER DIESEL (Cont.)
ENGINE SPECIFICATIONS (Cont.)

VALVE SPRINGS

Engine	Free Length In. (mm)	PRESSURE Lbs. @ In. (kg @ mm)	
		Valve Closed	Valve Open
All	2.015 (51.2)	.....	130.1@1.102 (59.0@28.0)

CAMSHAFT

Engine	Journal Diam. In. (mm)	Clearance In. (mm)	Lobe Lift In. (mm)
All No. 1	1.375 (34.94)	.0010-.0026 (.025-.066)	.003-.006 (.070-.149)
No. 2, 3 & 4	1.926 (48.94)	.0010-.0026 (.025-.066)	.....

VALVE TIMING

Engine	INTAKE		EXHAUST	
	Open (ATDC)	Close (ABDC)	Open (BBDC)	Close (BTDC)
All	13.5°	15.5°	19°	17°

TIGHTENING SPECIFICATIONS

Application	Ft. Lbs. (N·m)
Cylinder Head (Hexagon Head Bolts)①	
Step 1	51 (70)
Step 2	66 (90)
Step 3	73 (100)
Cylinder Head (Twelve-Point Head Bolts)	
Step 1	30 (40)
Step 2	②51 (70)
Rocker Arm Support Bolts	29 (39)
Prechamber in Cyl. Head	108-130 (147-177)
Nozzle Holder in Prechamber	51-58 (69-79)
Glow Plugs	36 (49)
Connecting Rod Caps	36 (49)
Main Bearing Caps	65 (88)
Crankshaft Front Hex Bolt	195-239 (265-325)
Camshaft Sprocket Bolt	58 (79)

① — Setting time between step 2 & 3 is 10 minutes.
② — Loosen head bolts ¼ turn, and retighten in sequence to final torque after engine is warm.

280 6-CYLINDER

ENGINE CODING

ENGINE IDENTIFICATION

Engine number is stamped on front left side of cylinder block. Engine is a six cylinder double overhead cam type referred to as an M110.

Engine Identification		
Application	Chassis Type	Engine Coding
280E	123.033	110.984
280CE	123.053	110.984

ENGINE, CYLINDER HEAD & MANIFOLDS

ENGINE

NOTE — *Engine and transmission must be removed as a unit. On 123 series vehicles, engine hood does not have to be removed. The hood can be opened to a 90° position and held in place by a locking mechanism on the left hinge.*

Removal & Installation — 1) Disconnect battery. Drain coolant and disconnect lines for air/oil cooler and transmission oil cooler on radiator. Remove radiator with air/oil cooler. Remove fan. On vehicles with air conditioning, disconnect compressor and put aside with lines attached. When removing air conditioning unit, drain system. Disconnect lines at oil pump. (Only loosen bolts to detach oil pump).

2) Draw oil out of power steering pump. Disconnect hoses at power steering. Disconnect start and alternator. Disconnect all electrical connections on engine. Remove longitudinal control shaft. All coolant, vacuum, oil and electrical lines should be disconnected. Pull off TDC transmitter wires at test socket by unscrewing test socket at holder. Detach exhaust pipes at exhaust manifold and exhaust strut at transmission.

3) Remove left and right engine shock absorbers. From bottom of vehicle, remove engine mounting bolts from engine mount. Remove rear engine carrier with engine mount. Disconnect tachometer shaft on transmission. Disconnect propeller shaft on transmission. Loosen all connections and shift rods on transmission. Attach engine at rear and front to suspension eyes. Lift engine with transmission, in an approximately a 45° diagonal position. Prior to installing engine check all components for wear or damage and replace if necessary. To complete installation reverse removal procedure.

INTAKE MANIFOLD

Removal — Partially drain radiator and remove air cleaner. Disconnect electrical wires, water hoses and vacuum lines. Disconnect cold start valve and remove linkage. Remove attaching screws and remove intake manifold.

Installation — To install, reverse removal procedure, using a new gasket.

CYLINDER HEAD

NOTE — *Cylinder head may only be removed after engine has cooled down. Head is removed complete with manifolds and camshaft housing.*

Removal — 1) Drain cooling system. Remove A/C compressor (leave lines connected) and level control oil pump for models so equipped. Remove both camshaft housing front covers.

2) Remove cover and vacuum pump from front of camshaft housing. Disconnect all electrical leads, water hoses and vacuum lines from cylinder head and manifold.

3) Remove longitudinal regulating linkage and EGR line. Disconnect oil return line at cylinder head. Loosen hose between water pump and thermostat housing. Disconnect bypass line at water pump.

4) Loosen dipstick guide tube at cylinder head and bend slightly to the side. Disconnect exhaust pipes at manifold and transmission. Using a screwdriver, force out rocker arm tension springs. Using suitable tool (110 589 04 61 00), remove all rocker arms.

5) Rotate crankshaft until both camshaft timing marks are correctly aligned with crankshaft at TDC on firing stroke. Using suitable holding wrench (116 589 01 01 00), remove both camshaft sprocket bolts.

6) Remove upper slide rail and pull out bearing bolts with suitable extractor (116 589 20 33 00). Remove chain tensioner. Push both camshafts to rear and remove sprockets.

7) Using suitable extractor, pull out bearing pins and remove idler pulley. Extract guide rail bearing pins and remove guide rail.

8) Loosen head bolts in reverse of tightening order. Remove two 8mm bolts in chain box with a magnet, do not drop washers into timing cover. Pull up timing chain and force tension rail toward center of engine. Using two men, lift cylinder head vertically from cylinder block.

Installation — 1) Place head gasket on cylinder block. Lay two pieces of wood, ½"x1¾"x9½" long, upright between cylinders one and two and flat between cylinders five and six. Mount cylinder head at an inclined position, so that timing chain and tensioner rail can be installed.

2) Lift cylinder head and carefully remove wooden pieces. Lower head carefully, ensuring that front and rear dowels are properly engaged. Insert lubricated head bolts and tighten in 2 stages according to sequence shown in *Fig. 1.* Insert and tighten 8 mm bolts in chain box with Allen wrench.

NOTE — *After tightening all head bolts, camshaft should be free to turn by hand.*

3) Install lower slide rail and idler sprocket. Place spacer on intake camshaft journal. With engine at TDC, install camshaft sprockets with timing marks aligned.

NOTE — *TDC mark on vibration damper is next to dowel pin.*

4) Place spacers in front camshaft bearing of both camshafts. Install camshaft sprockets bolts, but do not tighten. Install upper slide rail and rigid chain tensioner. Using suitable holder tool (116 589 01 01 00), tighten expansion bolts.

5) Rotate engine two revolutions and recheck camshaft timing marks. Install swing lever and tensioner springs. Install chain tensioner and adjust valve clearances. Retighten head bolts after engine has been warmed to 176°F (water temperature).

280 6-CYLINDER (Cont.)

Tighten by first loosening head bolts a ¼ of a turn, one at a time and tighten in tightening order. Retighten 8mm bolts in chain box.

NOTE — *Further tightening of head bolts after 300-500 miles is no longer required. It is not necessary to recheck valve clearances after final tightening of head bolts.*

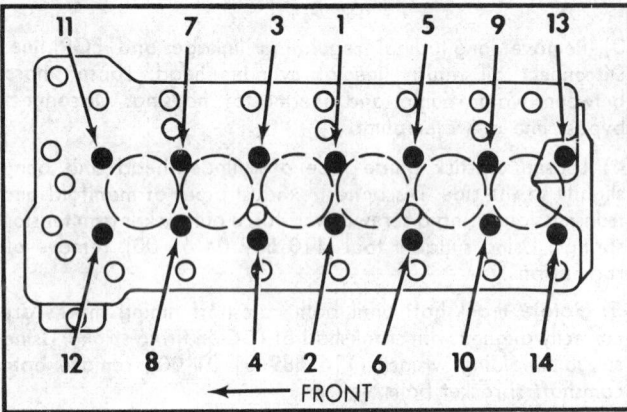

Fig. 1 Cylinder Head Tightening Sequence (Remove in Reverse Sequence)

CAMSHAFT

TIMING CHAIN

1) Remove spark plugs and cylinder head cover. Remove rocker arms of right hand (exhaust) camshaft. Remove chain tensioner and install rigid chain tensioner (110 589 03 31 00).

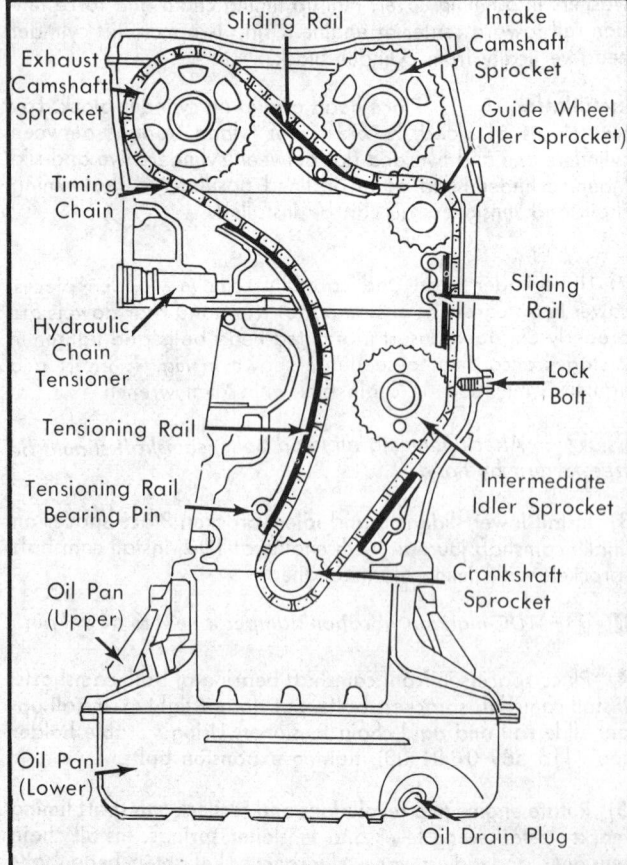

Fig. 2 Front View of Timing Chain and Sprockets

2) Cover chain box with a rag, using a chain breaker, separate chain. Join ends of new and old chains together with a master link. Rotate crankshaft in direction of rotation and pull old chain out of engine. Use care that chain does not jump a tooth on sprockets.

CAUTION — *Do not turn engine by camshaft bolts. Do not rotate crankshaft in reverse.*

3) Join ends of new chain. Rotate crankshaft and check timing marks. Replace rigid chain tensioner with normal chain tensioner. Install rocker arms and adjust exhaust valve clearance. Install camshaft cover and spark plugs.

CAMSHAFT & CAMSHAFT HOUSING

Removal — 1) Remove battery and A.I.R. pump. Disconnect air conditioning compressor and set aside with hoses connected. Drain radiator and remove hose between radiator and engine. Remove camshaft cover.

2) Remove camshaft sprocket covers from front of housing. Pry all rocker arm tension springs from rocker arms. Using a suitable tool (110 589 04 61 00), remove all rocker arms.

3) Using suitable holding tool (116 589 01 01 00), remove right-hand camshaft sprocket bolt. Set number one piston to TDC on firing stroke with both camshaft timing marks aligned. Remove chain tensioner.

4) Remove slide rail in camshaft housing, using suitable puller (115 589 19 33 00). Remove rear right-hand camshaft cover. Push camshaft to the rear, using suitable tool (110 589 03 33 00), while holding camshaft sprocket in place. Remove sprocket and slide camshaft back in place.

5) Remove head bolts, shown in illustration, in reverse of tightening sequence. Do not remove bolts marked with an "x" in illustration. Remove camshaft housing and camshafts.

NOTE — *Camshaft housing may only be removed after engine has cooled down.*

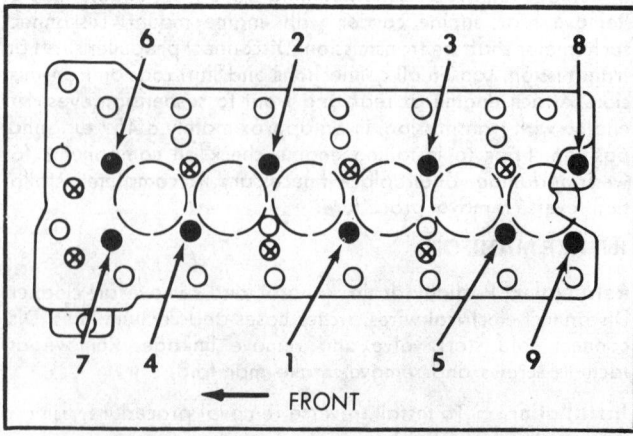

Fig. 3 Camshaft Housing Tightening Sequence (Remove ONLY Numbered Bolts in Reverse Sequence)

6) Remove left-hand camshaft sprocket in same manner as right-hand sprocket. Remove spacer ring at intake camshaft and slide both camshafts out rear of housing.

280 6-CYLINDER (Cont.)

Installation — Install steel gasket on cylinder head without sealing compound. Place camshaft housing on head. Oil head bolts and tighten to specifications. Loosen 5 deeper head bolts slightly, then tighten all head bolts to final torque in sequence shown in Fig. 1.

CAMSHAFT BEARINGS

If camshaft bearing journals are worn, damaged or have excessive clearance in camshaft housing bearings, camshaft journals may be ground undersize and a repair housing installed.

Front bearing journal is not ground and remains standard. See "a" in Fig. 4. Journal should be fitted with a spacer sleeve. Camshafts do not have to be ground or replaced because of rough surfaces or bearings.

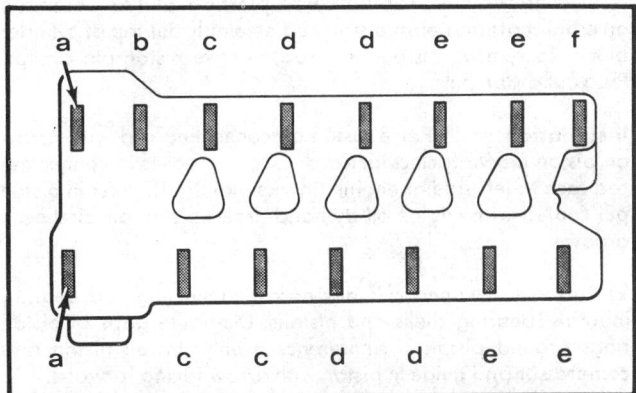

Fig. 4 Camshaft Housing Bearing Identification

VALVE TIMING

Rotate crankshaft until number one piston is at TDC on firing stroke. Both camshaft timing marks should be aligned with marks on camshaft housing. Offset woodruff keys are available to make corrections to timing. Remember that camshaft sprockets rotate in opposite directions, they rotate toward each other.

NOTE — *Some balance discs have two "O" degree marks. TDC is next to a dowel pin.*

Offset Woodruff Keys

Offset	Part No.	Correction
.0275" (.7 mm)	621 991 04 67	4°
.0354" (.9 mm)	621 991 02 67	6.5°
.0433" (1.1 mm)	621 991 01 67	8°
.0511" (1.3 mm)	621 991 00 67	10°

Fig. 5 Camshaft Timing Marks with No. 1 Piston at TDC on Firing Stroke

VALVES

VALVE ARRANGEMENT

Right Side — All exhaust.
Left Side — All intake.

VALVE GUIDE SERVICING

Checking Valve Guide — After removal of valve spring and valve stem seal, the wear on valve guide can be determined in installed condition by moving valve stem crosswise in relation to engine. Maximum wear of approximately .004" (.12 mm) is allowed.

Removing & Installing Guides — Press or drive out valve guide with mandrel from direction of combustion chamber. Insert valve guide for approximately 3-4 minutes into liquid oxygen, then insert immediately into respective bore while following-up with a hammer. If no liquid oxygen is available, heat cylinder head in a water bath, or heat in an oven to a maximum of 176° F (80° C). Coat valve guide with tallow and drive in with mandrel until circlip or mandrel rests against cylinder head. Guides are pressed in from rocker side. Check guide bores and ream for proper clearance as required.

Valve Guide Specifications

Application	Guide O.D. In. (mm)	Head I.D. In. (mm)
Intake		
Std.	.5523-.5331 (14.03-14.05)	.5519-.5527 (14.02-14.04)
1st O.S. (red)	.5594-.5602 (14.21-14.23)	.5590-.5598 (14.20-14.22)
2nd O.S. (white)	.5673-.5681 (14.41-14.43)	.5669-.5677 (14.40-14.42)
Exhaust		
Std.	.5917-.5925 (15.03-15.05)	.5913-.5921 (15.02-15.04)
1st O.S. (red)	.5988-.5996 (15.21-15.23)	.5984-.5992 (15.20-15.22)
2nd O.S. (white)	.6066-.6074 (15.41-15.43)	.6062-.6070 (15.40-15.42)

VALVE STEM OIL SEALS

With valve springs removed, pull off old seal. Place assembly sleeves over intake valve stems and slide new valve stem seal over valve stems. Remove assembly sleeve and force seal over end of valve guide with installation mandrel.

VALVE SPRINGS

1) With camshaft housing removed, place piston on TDC of cylinder from which springs are to be removed. Install a compressed air line to spark plug hole to pressurize valves.

2) Remove valve thrust pieces. Attach suitable holding rail (110 589 06 62 00) to cylinder head. Lightly tap valve collars to loosen keepers. Install suitable spring compressor and press down on springs. Remove valve keepers and release pressure on springs. Remove inner and outer springs and check for wear or fatigue. To install, reverse removal procedures with close wound coils (color coding) next to cylinder head.

ROCKER ARM & STUD ASSEMBLY

1) With a screwdriver, pry out rocker arm tensioner springs. Using crankshaft, rotate engine until heel of cam lobe is next to

Mercedes-Benz Engines

280 6-CYLINDER (Cont.)

rocker arm. Using suitable tool (110 589 04 61 00), remove rocker arm.

2) Unscrew threaded bushing with valve adjusting screw. Lubricate threads of adjusting screw with tallow and check that screw has at least 14.5 ft. lbs. of turning torque in bushing.

3) Install threaded bushing and adjusting screw in cylinder head. Lubricate rocker arm and pivot. Using suitable tool (110 589 04 61 00), install rocker arms and tensioner springs. Readjust valve clearances.

CAUTION — *Do not rotate engine by camshaft sprocket bolts. Do not rotate engine in reverse as camshaft sprocket may jump time.*

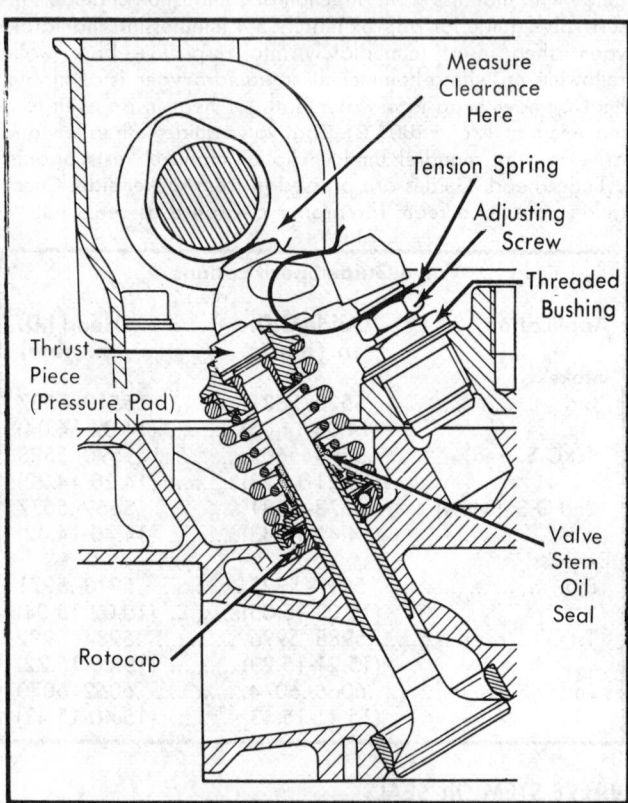

Measure Clearance Here
Tension Spring
Adjusting Screw
Threaded Bushing
Thrust Piece (Pressure Pad)
Valve Stem Oil Seal
Rotocap

Fig. 6 Sectional View of Rocker Arm and Valve Assembly

VALVE CLEARANCE ADJUSTMENT

Rotate crankshaft until heel of camshaft lobe is next to rocker arm. Insert a feeler gauge between camshaft and rocker arm. Turn adjusting screw until proper clearance is achieved.

NOTE — *Valves should be adjusted with engine at normal operating temperature. Cold specifications are provided for initial settings after assembly.*

Valve Clearance	
Application	**In. (mm)**
Intake	
Hot	①.006 (.15)
Cold	①.004 (.10)
Exhaust	
Hot	.012 (.30)
Cold	.010 (.25)
① — Winter Clearance, add .002" (.05mm).	

PISTONS, PINS & RINGS

OIL PAN

NOTE — *A 2 piece oil pan is used. Due to complexity of operation, engine assembly must be removed to remove complete oil pan.*

Removal & Installation — Remove engine. Remove oil filter complete with lines. Pull off oil return line. Loosen strut for alternator bracket on oil pan. Remove oil pan. To install, use sealant on clean surface, use new gasket and reverse removal procedure.

PISTON & ROD ASSEMBLY

Removal — With cylinder head and oil pan removed, unscrew connecting rod nuts. Tap bolts with plastic mallet to loosen rod on crankshaft and push piston/rod assembly out top of cylinder block. To remove piston from rod, remove piston pin circlips. Push out piston pins.

Installation — 1) Place piston on connecting rod with arrow on piston crown facing forward. Circlip grooves in connecting rod face to left side of engine (intake manifold). Press in piston pin coated with engine oil by hand. Insert piston pin circlips in grooves.

2) Lubricate cleaned cylinder bores, connecting rod bearing journals, bearing shells and pistons. Distribute gaps of piston rings around piston circumference evenly. Install piston ring compressor and guide in piston with arrow facing forward.

3) Place connecting rod bearing caps with code numbers facing each other on connecting rod and tighten to specifications. Check for normal crankshaft rotation. Measure piston protrusion above top of cylinder block with piston at TDC. Piston should project at least .020" (.50 mm), but not more than .035" (.90 mm) above block.

FITTING PISTONS

Measure cylinder bores near top, bottom, and center in at least 2 directions. If greater than .004" (.10 mm) from standard, cylinders must be bored and new pistons fitted.

Cylinder Bore Specifications	
Application	**In. (mm)**
Standard	3.3858-3.3866 (86.0-86.02)
1st Oversize	3.4055-3.4063 (86.50-86.52)
2nd Oversize	3.4252-3.4260 (87.0-87.02)

CRANKSHAFT MAIN & CONNECTING ROD BEARINGS

MAIN & CONNECTING ROD BEARINGS

1) Remove connecting rod and main bearing caps. Check all bearing journals for wear, taper or out-of-round. The following table gives maximum dimensions which are permissible without repair or new bearings.

2) Bearing inserts for both main and connecting rod journals are color coded. Main bearing inserts with no color are thicker than ones which are blue. Connecting rod inserts with red color are thicker than ones with blue color. Select inserts which will give the mean of clearance range.

280 6-CYLINDER (Cont.)

Crankshaft Specifications

Application	In. (mm)
Out-of-Round	.0002 (.005)
Journal Taper	.0004 (.010)
Journal Flatness	.0006 (.015)
Bearing Bore Out-of-Round	.0004 (.010)
Bearing Bore Taper	.0004 (.010)

Crankshaft Journal Diameters

Application	Main Bearings In. (mm)	Connecting Rod In. (mm)
Std.	2.3602-2.3606 (59.95-59.96)	1.8878-1.8882 (47.95-47.96)
1st U.S.	2.3504-2.3508 (59.70-59.71)	1.8779-1.8783 (47.70-47.71)
2nd U.S.	2.3405-2.3409 (59.45-59.46)	1.8681-1.8685 (47.45-47.46)
3rd U.S.	2.3307-2.3311 (59.20-59.21)	1.8583-1.8587 (47.20-47.21)
4th U.S.	2.3209-2.3213 (58.95-58.96)	1.8484-1.8488 (46.95-46.96)

Bearing Insert Wall Thickness

Application	Main Bearing In. (mm)	Connecting Rod In. (mm)
Std.	.1378 (3.50)	.0713 (1.81)
1st U.S.	.1429 (3.63)	.0764 (1.94)
2nd U.S.	.1476 (3.75)	.0811 (2.06)
3rd U.S.	.1528 (3.88)	.0858 (2.18)
4th U.S.	.1575 (4.00)	.0909 (2.31)

THRUST BEARING ALIGNMENT

Install number three main bearing and measure clearance between bearing and crankshaft sides. If clearance is excessive, install new bearing. New bearings are supplied in oversize widths and must be lapped on non-thrust side to achieve proper clearance. Lap only side away from flywheel.

REAR MAIN BEARING OIL SEAL

Press pieces of seal into block and oil pan with a wooden hammer handle. Cut ends of seal so they protrude .004" (.1 mm) above parting surfaces. Oil seal halves liberally and install crankshaft and oil pan. Check for easy rotation of crankshaft and reassemble engine.

FRONT COVER OIL SEAL

1) Remove radiator and fan, pulley and vibration damper. Mark balance disc and crankshaft with punch for assembly purposes. Use suitable puller and remove balance disc.

2) Pry old seal out with screwdriver, using caution not to damage seal bore or crankshaft journal. Clean and inspect seal bore and apply oil to new seal (do NOT use sealing compound). Press seal into position with installing tool (110 589 07 61 00).

3) Install new spacing ring or turn used ring around so that worn groove is at rear. Install remaining components in reverse order of assembly.

ENGINE OILING

Crankcase Capacity — 6.3 qts. (including filter).

Oil Filter — Full flow type.

Normal Oil Pressure — 7.1 psi (.5 kg/cm^2) at 800-900 RPM; 42 psi (3 kg/cm^2) at 3000 RPM.

Pressure Regulator Valve — Nonadjustable.

ENGINE OILING SYSTEM

Oil is drawn from the oil pan by a gear type oil pump and pressure fed through a full-flow oil filter to crankshaft main bearings. Passages drilled in crankshaft carry oil to connecting rod bearings. A passageway drilled longitudinally through the connecting rod carries oil from connecting rod bearing to wrist pin bushing. A further passageway carries oil to intermediate shaft, oil pump, and distributor drive gears. This passageway also lubricates camshaft bearings, cam lobes, rocker arms, idler sprocket, and chain tensioner.

OIL PUMP

Remove fuel pump and lower half of oil pan. Remove screws from crankcase and main bearing cap. Pull out oil pump. Disassemble, clean and inspect oil pump. To install, reverse removal procedure.

ENGINE COOLING

Cooling System Capacity —280E, 280CE — 10.6 qts.

Thermostat — Opens at 185-193°F (85-89°C).

WATER PUMP

Drain radiator and disconnect water hoses. Loosen radiator shell and remove radiator. Remove fan and fan clutch (store in upright position). Remove all drive belts. Remove six Allen screws attaching pulley and vibration damper. Withdraw pulley and damper. Remove water pump. To install, reverse removal procedure.

TIGHTENING SPECIFICATIONS

Application	Ft. Lbs. (N·m)
Main Bearings	58 (79)
Connecting Rods	①36 (49)
Crankshaft Bolt	289-325 (393-442)
Cylinder Head Bolts	
Step 1	51 (70)
Step 2	72 (98)
Step 3	②72 (98)
Camshaft Bolt	72 (98)
Oil Pump	21 (29)
Chain Tensioner Nut	36 (49)

① — Tighten bolts to 36 Ft. Lbs. (49 N·m) and then turn bolts an additional 100° of rotation.

② — With engine warm (176° F or 80° C), loosen all head bolts ¼ turn in tightening sequence, then tighten to final torque.

Mercedes-Benz Engines

280 6-CYLINDER (Cont.)
ENGINE SPECIFICATIONS

GENERAL SPECIFICATIONS

Year	Displ. cu. ins.	Displ. cc	Carburetor	HP at RPM	Torque (Ft. Lbs. at RPM)	Compr. Ratio	Bore in.	Bore mm	Stroke in.	Stroke mm
1981	167.6	2746	Fuel Inj.	140@5500	145@4500	8.0:1	3.39	86	3.10	78.8

VALVES

Engine & Valve	Head Diam. In. (mm)	Face Angle	Seat Angle	Seat Width In. (mm)	Stem Diameter In. (mm)	Stem Clearance In. (mm)	Valve Lift In. (mm)
2746 cc Intake	1.775-1.783 (45.1-45.3)	45°	45°	.071-.098 (1.8-2.5)	.3524-.3531 (8.95-8.97)	.0019 (.05)	.....
Exhaust	1.5315-1.5354 (38.9-39.0)	45°	45°	.059-.079 (1.5-2.0)	.3520-.3528 (8.94-8.96)	.0023 (.06)	.....

PISTONS, PINS, RINGS

Engine	PISTONS Clearance In. (mm)	PINS Piston Fit In. (mm)	PINS Rod Fit In. (mm)	Rings	RINGS End Gap In. (mm)	RINGS Side Clearance In. (mm)
2746 cc	.0010-.0014 (.025-.035)	.00008-.0004 (.002-.011)	.0003-.0007 (.007-.017)	No. 1	.012-.018 (.30-.45)	.0019-.0032 (.050-.082)
	Limit .003 (.08)			No. 2	.012-.018 (.30-.45)	.0011-.0024 (.030-.062)
				No. 3	.010-.016 (.25-.40)	.0004-.0016 (.010-.042)

CRANKSHAFT MAIN & CONNECTING ROD BEARINGS

Engine	MAIN BEARINGS Journal Diam. In. (mm)	MAIN BEARINGS Clearance In. (mm)	Thrust Bearing	Crankshaft End Play In. (mm)	CONNECTING ROD BEARINGS Journal Diam. In. (mm)	CONNECTING ROD BEARINGS Clearance In. (mm)	Side Play In. (mm)
2746 cc	2.3602-2.3606 (59.95-59.96)	.001-.002 (.03-.05)	No. 3	.004-.009 (.10-.24)	1.8878-1.8882 (47.95-47.96)	.0005-.0020 (.013-.050)	.004-.009 (.10-.24)

VALVE SPRINGS

Engine	Free Length In. (mm)	PRESSURE Lbs. @ In. (kg @ mm) Valve Closed	PRESSURE Lbs. @ In. (kg @ mm) Valve Open
2746 cc Inner	1.772 (45)	26.01@1.299 (11.8@33)	50.7@.846 (23@21.5)
Outer	1.949 (49.5)	67.24@1.6535 (30.5@42)	194@1.20 (88@30.5)

CAMSHAFT①

Engine	Journal Diam. In. (mm)	Clearance In. (mm)	Lobe Lift In. (mm)
2746 cc a	.9441-.9445 (23.98-23.99)	.002-.005 (.06-.12)	.....
b	1.9654-1.9661 (49.92-49.94)	.003-.006 (.10-.14)	.....
c	1.9657-1.9665 (49.93-49.95)	.002-.004 (.06-.09)	.....
d	2.0244-2.0252 (51.42-51.44)	.002-.004 (.06-.10)	.....
e	2.0835-2.0842 (52.92-52.94)	.002-.004 (.06-.10)	.....
f	2.1228-2.1236 (53.92-53.94)	.002-.004 (.06-.10)	.....

VALVE TIMING

Engine	INTAKE Open (ATDC)	INTAKE Close (ABDC)	EXHAUST Open (BBDC)	EXHAUST Close (BTDC)
2746 cc	7°	21°	30°	12°

① — Journal diameters vary, with steps from smaller to larger going from front to rear. See Fig. 4. End play is .002-.005" (.050-.128 mm).

3.8 LITER V8

ENGINE CODING

ENGINE IDENTIFICATION

Identification number is located on tag attached to engine crankcase. First six digits of code are used to identify engine, as follows:

Engine Identification		
Application	Chassis Type	Engine Code
380 SLC	107.025	116.960
380 SL	107.045	116.960
380 SEL	126.033	116.961

ENGINE, CYLINDER HEAD & MANIFOLD

ENGINE

Removal — 1) Remove hood and drain cooling system, using both left and right engine block drains. Disconnect and remove battery and remove battery frame. Remove air conditioning system and remove pipe set at compressor. Disconnect and remove all water, vacuum, oil, fuel and electrical lines leading to engine.

2) Completely remove exhaust system (except model 126), remove right drag link end from ball head. On all models, drain power steering reservoir and disconnect hoses. Unscrew TDC test socket and remove cable from TDC transmitter.

3) Remove left and right engine shock absorbers. Attach engine sling and hoist to engine and remove engine mount bolts. Remove rear engine carrier with engine mount. Loosen and disconnect driveshaft from transmission. Remove linkages connecting transmission to chassis and lift engine out (with transmission attached) at a 45° angle.

Installation — Ensure that oil cooler and all hoses have been flushed and are free from contamination. Renew engine mounts and components as required and reverse removal procedure. Clean and recharge air conditioning system and check entire installation for leaks.

INTAKE MANIFOLD

Removal and Installation — Disconnect battery and partially drain coolant. Unscrew injection lines and fuel lines. Pull off air lines. Force off bowden wire from automatic transmission. Unscrew bearing bracket from linkage regulation and bearing bracket from longitudinal regulating shaft. Pull off connecting cables and plug. Pull off vacuum lines from automatic transmission, unscrew from brake unit. Loosen and pull off cooling water hoses. Unscrew all fastening screws and remove intake manifold toward the rear. Clean intake manifold and check flange surfaces with straightedge. To install, reverse removal procedure.

CYLINDER HEAD

NOTE — *Cylinder head removal should not be attempted until engine has cooled down. Several specially shaped Allen wrenches are required for cylinder head bolt removal and replacement.*

Removal — 1) Remove left and right drain plugs and drain cooling system. Remove air cleaner and battery. Remove fuel line and injection valves. Disconnect fuel injection linkage.

2) Disconnect and remove intake pipe (manifold). Remove A/T fluid filler pipe from attachment to cylinder head. Remove alternator and mounting bracket. Remove distributor and power steering pump with mounting bracket.

3) Disconnect exhaust pipe from manifold and exhaust gas return line at 90° fitting. Remove chain tensioner and slide rails. Mark camshaft sprocket and timing chain position for assembly reference. Remove sprocket from camshaft. Using specially shaped Allen wrenches, remove head bolts and lift off head.

Installation — 1) Ensure that all mating surfaces are clean and install new cylinder head gasket. Tighten cylinder head bolts in sequence shown.

2) Complete assembly in reverse order of removal and run engine until normal operating temperature is reached. Slightly loosen head bolts individually, then retighten in sequence shown.

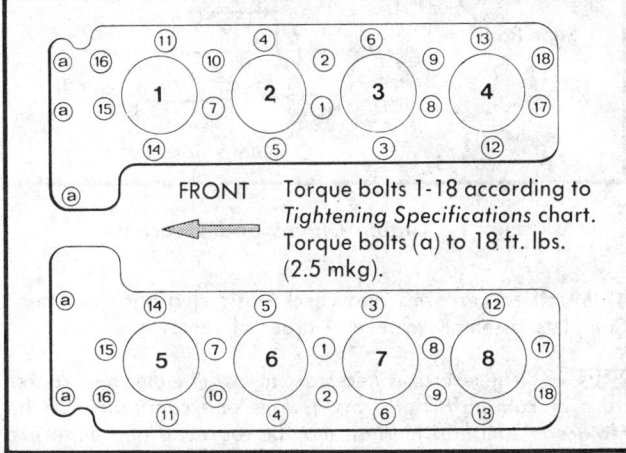

FRONT

Torque bolts 1-18 according to *Tightening Specifications* chart. Torque bolts (a) to 18 ft. lbs. (2.5 mkg).

Fig. 1 Cylinder Head Tightening Sequence (Loosen in Reverse Order)

CAMSHAFT

Removal — With cylinder head covers removed, set No. 1 piston at TDC firing position and remove rocker arms. Mark sprockets and timing chain for reassembly. Remove camshaft sprockets. Unbolt and remove camshaft bearings, oil tube and camshaft as an assembly.

Installation — 1) Assemble bearings on camshaft. Note that smooth bearing journals must fit in bearings with an oil groove, and camshaft journals with an oil groove fit only in bearings WITHOUT an oil groove.

2) Place camshaft and bearing assembly on head. Note that outer screw of left camshaft rear bearing must be inserted in bearing prior to mounting due to interference from brake unit.

Mercedes-Benz Engines

3.8 LITER V8 (Cont.)

Oil pipe connections on bearings must be renewed to ensure proper oil pressure.

3) Tighten camshaft bearing mounting screws and check that camshaft rotates freely. Mount compensating washer so that both inner and outer notches align with Woodruff key in camshaft. Assmble sprockets to camshaft so that white color faces camshaft and timing marks are aligned.

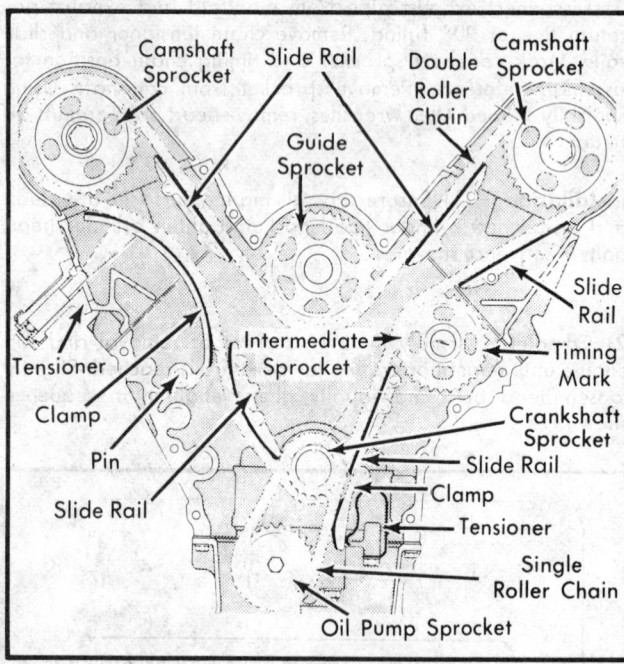

Fig. 2 Timing Chains and Sprockets

4) Install rocker arms and check basic clearance of lifters. Complete assembly in reverse order of removal.

NOTE — *Whenever it is necessary to install either new rocker arms or camshaft, both rocker arms and camshaft must be replaced. Camshaft journals may be reground and undersize bearings installed.*

DISTRIBUTOR DRIVE GEAR

1) With timing and crankshaft chains exposed, disconnect slide rails as needed and timing chain tensioners. Remove chain from intermediate sprocket and pull sprocket from engine.

2) Use suitable puller to extract bushing from crankcase and cover. Press new bushings in position so that lubricating groove is at bottom. Lubricate bushings and install intermediate sprocket. Note that mark on sprocket must align with mark on crankcase with engine at TDC position. Continue assembly in reverse order of removal.

CHAIN TENSIONER

NOTE — *In all instances chain tensioner is lubricated and connected to oiling circuit.*

1) Remove air injector pipe and 3 screws fastening tensioner. Remove chain tensioner.

2) To check tensioner, place in container of oil vertically so that oil covers flange. Actuate plunger to fill tensioner with oil. After filling and venting, plunger should allow compression very slowly and evenly, and with considerable force.

3) To install, use new gasket and tighten screws evenly. Pressure pin of tensioner must press against lug of tensioning rail.

VALVE TIMING

1) Measure timing periods on inlet valves of cylinder 1 and 6. Remove hydraulic valve lifters and replace with adjusting screws (116 050 11 20). Adjust each screw so rocker arm just touches the base circle of the cam.

2) Attach dial indicator so that pointer rests vertically on valve spring retainer. Pin should have .118" (3 mm) preload and dial should be set to zero.

3) Turn engine in direction of normal rotation until pointer moves .0787" (2 mm), leaving a preload of .039" (1 mm). Readings should be in accordance with valve timing chart. Repeat for No. 6 intake valve.

4) If timing requires correction, install an offset Woodruff Key or new chain. Keys are available in four offsets providing corrections of 4°, 6½°, 8°, and 10°.

5) After checking and adjusting valve timing, reinstall hydraulic lifters and adjust for proper base setting.

VALVES

VALVE ARRANGEMENT

Right Bank — E-I-E-I-E-I-I-E (front to rear).
Left Bank — E-I-I-E-I-E-I-E (front to rear).

HYDRAULIC VALVE LIFTERS

1) Hydraulic valve lifters eliminate the need to adjust valve clearance. Constant contact of rocker arms with camshaft, valves and lifters not only reduces noise, but also compensates for wear or temperature changes.

2) The ball valve closes when the cam lobe exerts pressure on rocker arm. Trapped oil in pressure chamber forms a solid hydraulic connection which prevents the plunger from moving fully downward. Leak-off vents permit air and excess oil to escape.

3) To check hydraulic lifter performance, press on rocker arm at lift end with valves in closed position. If pressure bleeds off to rapidly in comparison with other elements, replacement is required. If lifters are removed, they should be stored in an upright position and reinstalled in original location.

3.8 LITER V8 (Cont.)

VALVE GUIDE SERVICING

1) With cylinder head removed and suitably supported, clean bores of valve guides. Hard oil carbon deposits can be eliminated with a honing needle.

2) Using a suitable plug gauge, inspect valve guides. Inner diameter of new inlet and exhaust guides should be .354-355" (9.000-9.015 mm). If guide is beyond this tolerance, replace with new guide.

3) With mandrel, drive or press worn guide from combustion chamber side. Inspect valve guide bore in cylinder head and ream to accept next oversize guide.

NOTE — *Replacement valve guides are available in overlapping sizes, ranging from .552-.568" (14.014-14.431 mm) outside diameter.*

4) Heat cylinder head to approximately 194°F (90°C) or cool valve guide. Coat guide bore with oil and using mandrel, seat new guide in bore.

NOTE — *Be sure snap ring is properly installed. Recheck valve guide clearance and that valve moves freely in guide.*

VALVE STEM SEALS

Removal — Using spring compressor (123 589 03 61 00) remove rocker arms. Lift out thrust plate and, using special magnet (116 589 06 63 00), remove valve keepers. Remove spring retainer, inner and outer valve springs, valve stem seals and rotocaps.

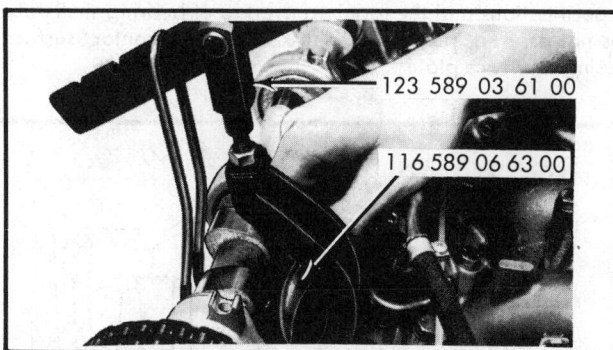

Fig. 3   Removing Valve Keepers

Installation — Replacement valve stem seals are supplied in a kit which includes assembly sleeves. Place sleeve over stem and install lubricated seal with installing tool. Install remaining components in reverse order of removal. *See Fig. 4.*

Fig. 4   Installing Valve Stem Seals

VALVE SEAT RING

1) Check valve guide prior to removing seat ring. *See Valve Guide Servicing.* If seat ring is worn, carefully remove it by machining with a valve seat ring turning tool.

2) Thoroughly clean the receiving bore and check its diameter. If diameter is within specifications, install a new valve seat ring of the same size. If diameter is not within specifications, 1.811-1.812" (46.0-46.02 mm) for intake or 1.575-1.576" (40.0-40.01 mm) for exhaust, machine bore to next oversize.

3) To install, heat cylinder head in water to approximately 140° F (60° C). Place pre-cooled seat ring into bore. To position seat ring, lightly tap ring, using a suitable mandrel and hammer. Machine valve seat to correct width and correct for runout. Do NOT machine rounded bead on lower part of valve seat. Valve seat runout should not exceed .0016" (.04 mm).

ROCKER ARMS

1) Rocker arms are individually-mounted on the 16 valves, without use of a shaft. They are in constant contact with the camshaft, thrust plates above the valve stems, and hydraulic valve lifters. To remove, compress spring on each valve using compressor (123 589 03 61 00). Mark each arm for installation in original position.

2) Rocker arms have a chamfer behind ball socket (lifter end). This prevents rocker arm from striking retaining cap of lifters in extreme cases. Do not use rocker arms unless they have this chamfer.

3) Whenever camshaft is replaced, new rocker arms must also be installed. Likewise, when new rocker arms are installed, replace the camshaft, as well. When making replacements, check base setting of hydraulic valve lifters using test gauge (100 589 04 23 00). Correct, as required, using new thrust piece. Thrust pieces are available in steps of .0014" (.35 mm) from .147" (3.7 mm) to .228" (5.8 mm). *See Adjusting Lifters to Base Setting.*

ADJUSTING LIFTERS TO BASE SETTING

NOTE — *Always keep hydraulic valve lifters in an upright position. Rocker arms and valve lifters should always be reinstalled in original locations. When checking and adjusting lifter settings, crank engine for 30 seconds with starter contact switch.*

1) When replacing compensating element (hydraulic lifters) or camshaft and rocker arms, basic position of compensating element must be checked. Rotate engine so that cam lobe of element to be checked is in the upright position and install test gauge (100 589 04 23 00).

2) Set measuring pin of gauge through rocker arm hole so that it rests on ball pin of lifter. Basic position is correct when red groove of pin is aligned with measuring edge of tool. If groove is below measuring edge, a plus (+) deviation is indicated, re-

3.8 LITER V8 (Cont.)

quiring a thinner thrust piece. Entire groove showing above measuring edge indicates a minus (−) deviation and requires a thicker thrust piece.

3) To correct setting, remove rocker arm and thrust piece. Install thinner or thicker thrust piece as required and reinstall rocker arm. Repeat measuring procedure. Position is correct when center of measuring groove aligns with edge of gauge.

PISTONS, PINS & RINGS

OIL PAN

Removal & Installation (Model 107) — 1) Remove radiator shell and shroud. Remove front axle assembly. Remove A/C compressor and mounting bracket. Remove supporting angle bracket between pan and transmission.

2) Remove oil pan bolts and lower oil pan along with dip stick guide tube from engine. To install, apply grease to clean mating surfaces and install new gasket. Place pan in position and reverse removal procedure.

Removal & Installation (Model 126) — 1) Remove A/C compressor and mounting bracket from engine. Remove drive belt tensioning pulley. Unbolt and remove oil pan lower half. Remove oil pump drive sprocket and mounting bolts. Remove oil pump.

2) Unscrew oil pan upper half. Unscrew both fastening screws for engine on engine mount. Loosen both engine shock absorbers. Remove radiator shell. Lift engine until oil pan can be removed.

3) To install, ensure that all mating surfaces are clean and apply thin layer of grease. Use new gasket and install oil pan upper half. Continue assembly in reverse order of removal.

PISTON & ROD ASSEMBLY

Removal — 1) With cylinder head and oil pan removed, remove connecting rod nuts and bearing caps. Push piston and rod assembly out top of cylinder. Use care not to damage any bearing surface.

2) Remove piston pin snap ring and push out piston pin. Retain all components in proper order for reassembly.

Installation — 1) Check rings for gap and end clearance. Replace if not within specifications. Lubricate piston pins and connecting rod bushings. Push in piston pin (do NOT heat piston) and insert snap rings.

2) Stagger ring gaps on piston and fit ring compressor. Install piston and rod assembly with arrow on piston facing toward front of engine.

3) Install rod caps, matching code numbers to and facing rod numbers. Tighten rod cap nuts and check all clearances.

FITTING PISTONS

Measure cylinder bores near top, bottom and center in at least 2 directions. If greater than .004" (.10 mm) from standard, cylinders must be bored and new pistons fitted.

Cylinder Bore Specifications	
Application	**In. (mm)**
Standard	3.6220-3.6228 (92.0-92.02)
1st Oversize	3.6417-3.6425 (92.50-92.52)
2nd Oversize	3.6614-3.6622 (93.0-93.02)

PISTON PINS

Piston pins are retained with circlips in pistons. To remove pins, remove circlips and push out pins. To install, ensure that arrow on piston crown faces front (timing chain end) and that bearing retaining notch in connecting rod faces toward outside of engine. Lubricate pin and push into piston and rod assembly by hand.

NOTE — *Do NOT heat piston to install piston pin.*

CRANKSHAFT MAIN & CONNECTING ROD BEARINGS

MAIN & CONNECTING ROD BEARINGS

1) Mount main bearing cap to cylinder block without bearings in place. Measure inside diameter at 3 locations as illustrated. Be sure cap is properly positioned when taking reading. Offset bearing caps can be moved into center position by lightly tapping them with a plastic hammer.

2) All three measurements should agree. If basic bores exceed specifications and the required overlap of bearing shell halves is not assured, remove .008" (.02 mm) from contact surfaces, using a surface plate.

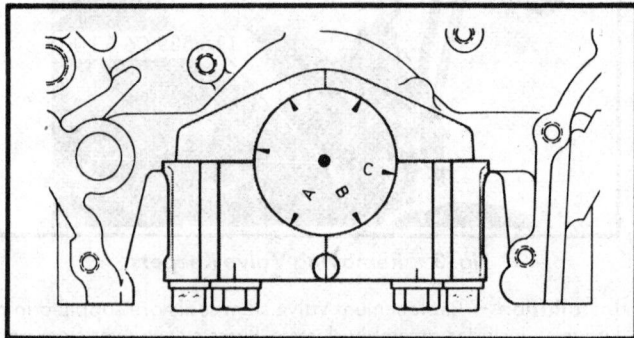

Fig. 5   Location for Measuring Main Bearing Bore Diameter

3) Measure main bearing and connecting rod bearings at front and rear to check for taper. If beyond .0006" (.015 mm), remove excess material from one side of bearing cap, using surface plate.

4 Use proper bearing shells to match measurements obtained. Several overlapping bearing sizes are available. Fit bearing halves into bearing bore and tighten bolts to proper torque. Measure inner diameter of bearings and outer diameter of journals. Difference in measurements should be within bearing clearance specifications. If not, change bearing shell halves.

3.8 LITER V8 (Cont.)

5) When proper clearance is calculated, clean and oil all parts and install crankshaft. Torque to specifications according to sequence. *See Fig. 6.*

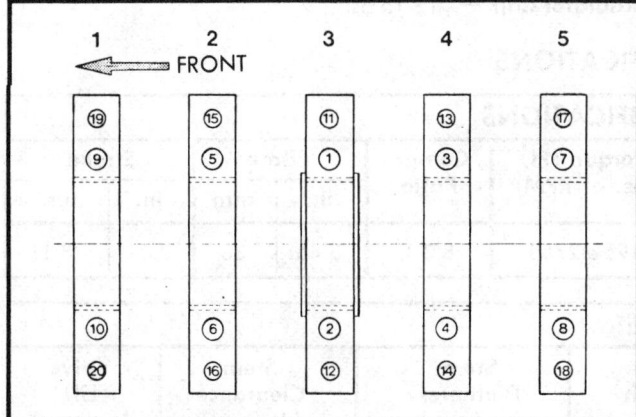

Fig. 6   Crankshaft Main Bearing Tightening Sequence

6) With crankshaft properly installed, check for free rotation and for proper end play. Install connecting rods.

REAR CRANKSHAFT SEALING RING

1) With engine removed from vehicle, unbolt and remove rear cover, (only if necessary). Force out old sealing ring. Clean sealing surfaces.

2) Check crankshaft running surface for scoring. Sealing ring with sealing lip offset inward is available in case of scored crankshaft. Press new seal into cover with suitable tool.

3) Lubricate lip of seal and coat cover with sealing compound. Place conical sleeve (116 589 03 43 00) over crankshaft end and place cover in position. Use care so that pan gasket is not damaged. Tighten cover bolts evenly and install drive plate.

NOTE — *Drive plate (flywheel) can only be mounted in one position due to offset of 1 of the 8 fastening bolts.*

Fig. 7   Installing Rear Cover and Seal

FRONT CRANKSHAFT SEALING RING

Removal — With engine removed from vehicle. Remove all V-belts, mark hub and crankshaft with paint or chalk. Remove

vibration damper, pulley and hub. Remove sealing ring, making sure that crankshaft and receiving bore are not damaged.

Installation — Deburr edge of receiving bore before installing new seal. Lubricate receiving bore and seal lip with oil. Install sealing ring with installation sleeve (110 589 07 61 00). Reassemble remaining components in reverse of removal procedure.

ENGINE OILING

ENGINE OILING SYSTEM

Lubrication is provided by a gear type oil pump directly driven by crankshaft. Oil is picked up through a strainer from lower portion of oil pan and forced to oil filter through a duct in timing casing. After passing through filter, oil flows to center main duct, to crankshaft and through rod bearings up rods to piston pin bushing. Oil galleries run to cylinder head, valve assemblies and to camshafts. Circuit also includes chain tensioner, ignition and, if applicable, air compressor.

Oil Filter — Disposable cartridge type. Located near front of engine. Some models use upright oil filters, (canister type).

Normal Oil Pressure — 7.1 psi@idle; 42.6 psi@3000 RPM.

Over Flow Valve — Valve is located in crankcase and enters into main oil gallery. When filter becomes severely contaminated valve will open and oil will enter in an unfiltered state.

Crankshaft Capacity — 8.5 quarts with filter.

ENGINE COOLING

WATER PUMP

Disconnect all necessary water hoses and any remaining components from water pump housing. Remove distributor and all mounting bolts. Remove pump from vehicle. To install, reverse removal procedure.

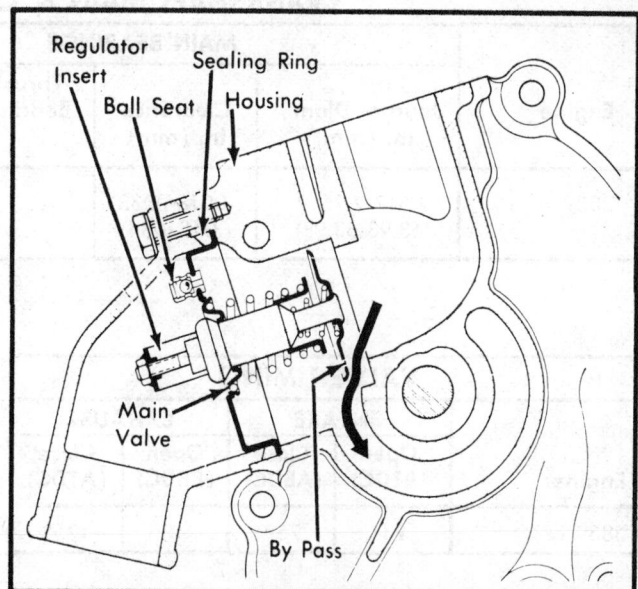

Fig. 8   Thermostat Installation

Mercedes-Benz Engines

3.8 LITER V8 (Cont.)

Thermostat — Located in water pump housing, as shown in illustration. To remove, drain cooling system, remove air cleaner, disconnect battery and alternator. Remove housing and thermostat. When installing ensure ball valve is mounted at highest point.

Cooling System Capacity — 15.8 U.S. quarts.

Thermostat — Opens at 162-169° F (72-76° C).

Radiator Cap — 13-15 psi.

ENGINE SPECIFICATIONS

GENERAL SPECIFICATIONS

| Year | Displ. | | Carburetor | HP at RPM | Torque (Ft. Lbs. at RPM) | Compr. Ratio | Bore | | Stroke | |
	cu. ins.	cc					in.	mm	in.	mm
1981	234.3	3839	Fuel Inj.	155@4750	196@2750	8.3:1	3.46	88	3.11	78.1

VALVES

Engine & Valve	Head Diam. In. (mm)	Face Angle	Seat Angle	Seat Width In. (mm)	Stem Diameter In. (mm)	Stem Clearance In. (mm)	Valve Lift In. (mm)
3839 cc Int.	1.5433 (39.2)	45°	45°	.051-.078 (1.3-2.0)	.3523-.3531 (8.95-8.97)	Limit .003 (.075)	.....
Exh.	1.4606 (37.1)	45°	45°	.059-.079 (1.5-2.0)	.3523-.3531 (8.95-8.97)		.....

PISTONS, PINS, RINGS

| Engine | PISTONS | PINS | | RINGS | | |
	Clearance In. (mm)	Piston Fit In. (mm)	Rod Fit In. (mm)	Rings	End Gap In. (mm)	Side Clearance In. (mm)
3839 cc	.0005-.0015 (.013-.023)	.....	.0002-.0007 (.005-.018)	No. 1	.014-.022 (.35-.55)	.002-.0036 (.050-.092)
				No. 2	.014-.022 (.35-.55)	.0016-.0030 (.040-.082)
				Oil	.010-.016 (.25-.40)	.0012-.0030 (.030-.072)

CRANKSHAFT MAIN & CONNECTING ROD BEARINGS

| Engine | MAIN BEARINGS | | | | CONNECTING ROD BEARINGS | | |
	Journal Diam. In. (mm)	Clearance In. (mm)	Thrust Bearing	Crankshaft End Play In. (mm)	Journal Diam. In. (mm)	Clearance In. (mm)	Side Play In. (mm)
3839 cc	2.517-2.2519 (63.93-63.98)	.0018-0033 (.045-.084)	.....	.004-.009 (.10-.23)	2.031 (51.6)	.0008-.0027 .021-.068)	.009-.015 (.233-.39)

VALVE TIMING

| Engine | INTAKE | | EXHAUST | |
	Open (BTDC)	Close (ABDC)	Open (BBDC)	Close (ATDC)
3839 cc	24°	75°	4°	125°

CAMSHAFT

Engine	Journal Diam. In. (mm)	Clearance In. (mm)	Lobe Lift In. (mm)
3839 cc No. 1	1.376-1.377 (34.96-34.98)	.0004-.0023 (.02-.06)	.....
Nos. 2&3	1.935-1.936 (49.16-49.18)	.0011-.0027 (.03-.07)	.....
Nos. 4&5	1.943-1.944 (49.36-49.38)	.0011-.0027 (.03-.07)	.....

3.8 LITER V8 (Cont.)
ENGINE SPECIFICATIONS (Cont.)

VALVE SPRINGS			
Engine	Free Length In. (mm)	PRESSURE Lbs. @ In. (kg @ mm)	
		Valve Closed	Valve Open
3839 cc Inner	1.77 (45)	24.7@1.3 (11.2@33)	50.7@846 (23@21.5)
Outer	1.95 (49.5)	67.24@1.65 (30.5@42)	194@1.2 (88@30.5)

TIGHTENING SPECIFICATIONS	
Application	Ft. Lbs. (N·m)
Cylinder Head Bolts	
Cold Step 1	22 (30)
Cold Step 2	43 (58)
Warm Step 3	43 (58)
Camshaft Bracket Bolts	36 (49)
Camshaft Srocket Bolts	72 (98)
Connecting Rod Bolts	33 (45)
Main Bearing Caps	
Large Bolts	72 (98)
Small Bolts	47 (64)
Crankshaft Bolts	195-239 (265-325)
Oil Pressure Relief Valve	29 (39)
Flywheel (Drive Plate)	①25 (35)
Hydraulic Valve Lifters	36 (49)
Chain Tensioner Nut	80 (109)

① — After torque valves are achieved, torque an additional 90-100°.

505 GASOLINE 4-CYLINDER

ENGINE CODING

ENGINE IDENTIFICATION

Engine serial number is stamped on left side engine mounting face and is also located on identification plate attached to top panel, above center of grille.

Engine identification number is stamped on camshaft tunnel on left side of block, near the starter. The letters at the beginning and end of the number are used for identification as follows:

Engine Identification Codes		
Application	**Transmission**	**Engine Codes**
XN6 Engine	Manual	BVM
XN6 Engine	Automatic	BVA

ENGINE & CYLINDER HEAD

ENGINE

Removal — 1) Remove hood, battery and fan shroud. Drain radiator and remove upper and lower hoses. Remove electrical lead from cooling fan switch, and remove radiator lower mounting bolts. Remove rubber duct hose at mixture regulator throttle plate housing.

2) Remove fuel supply and return hoses and hose from cold start injector. Remove PCV hose and electrical connectors from cold start injector and fuel distributor. Remove fuel hoses and electrical connector from control pressure regulator.

3) Remove fuel injectors, mixture regulator and air filter. If equipped, remove air conditioning compressor and freon hose clamp near alternator. Disconnect accelerator cable and electrical harness near brake master cylinder.

4) Remove diagnostic plug for TDC sensor, located near ignition coil. Separate 2 connectors. Remove high tension lead from coil. Remove vacuum hoses from charcoal canister.

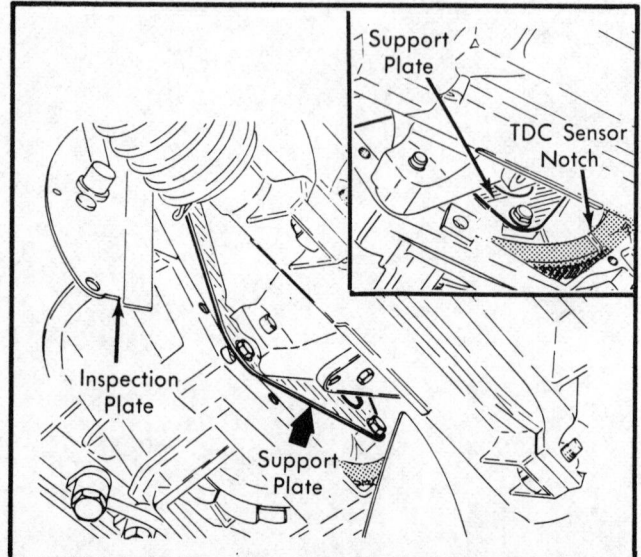

Fig. 1   Positioning Support Plate for Torque Converter During Engine Removal

5) Remove heater hose near charcoal canister and fan. Remove oxygen sensor (Lambda) wire near vacuum switches, and disconnect air injection hose to catalytic converter. Remove vacuum switches support and 3-wire electrical connector nearby. Install engine sling assembly (8.0102-X).

6) Remove starter, clutch housing bolts, and left engine mount. Remove right engine mount. Remove 3 power steering pump bolts and set pump aside. Remove exhaust header pipe.

7) Remove inspection plates and clutch housing. On vehicles with automatic transmission, remove inspection plate without altering TDC sensor adjustment. To do so, position torque converter support plate as shown in *Fig. 1*. Mark TDC sensor notch in reference to support plate. Support torque converter with special clamp (8.0315-A).

8) Remove air conditioning condenser and set to left side, keeping hoses connected. Remove and set receiver-drier to one side. Lift engine with 8.0102-X engine sling assembly until top of bell housing contacts lower firewall. See *Fig. 2*.

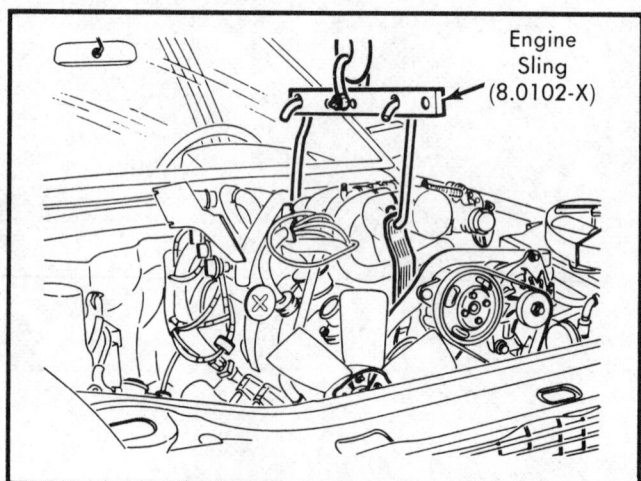

Fig. 2   Removing Engine from Vehicle

9) Install transmission supporting brace (8.0125). Disengage engine from transmission and lift engine carefully out of engine compartment. Check for electrical leads, cables, hoses or pipes which have not been detached from engine.

Installation — 1) To install engine, reverse removal procedures, noting the following precautions: On vehicles with automatic transmissions, lubricate torque converter centering nipple with Calysol grease (F 3015 or equivalent). Position TDC sensor notch, and align reference marks made during removal. Coat 4 torque converter bolts with Loctite and tighten. Use ring gear locking pawl (8.0110-J) when tightening bolts.

2) On vehicles with manual transmissions, lightly lubricate splines, front and mainshaft pilot bushings with Molykote 321 (or equivalent). Place gearshift lever in gear. Tighten engine mount-to-crossmember bolts and engine-to-clutch housing bolts to specifications.

3) Adjust TDC sensor, if new, by bringing 3 nipples in contact. If reusing TDC sensor, deburr 3 nipples so gap of .067" (1.7 mm) exists between sensor and ring gear.

4) Refill radiator, cooling system, engine crankcase and automatic transmission. Check power steering fluid reservoir level.

Peugeot Engines

505 GASOLINE 4-CYLINDER (Cont.)

5) To adjust accelerator cable, depress accelerator pedal against its stop, placing a .20" (5 mm) spacer between pedal and stop (full throttle position). Connect cable to throttle drum. Rotate drum to full throttle position. Exert slight pull on cable housing stop to place control under slight load. Install clip to obtain minimum gap between clip and common manifold.

6) To adjust kick-down cable, place throttle plate in idle position. Extend cable to obtain a maximum play of .02" (.5 mm) between cable housing stop and cable travel limiter. Tighten cable on drum.

CYLINDER HEAD

Removal — 1) Drain cooling system, including cylinder block. Disconnect battery. Remove exhaust header pipe and oxygen sensor. Remove mounting brackets for common manifold and intake manifold.

2) Pull common manifold off pipes. Remove distributor cap, injectors, and diagnostic plug bracket. Disconnect electrical connector near ignition coil and remove high tension lead from coil. Remove all clamps and wire ties from vicinity of ignition coil. Remove vacuum hoses from charcoal canister.

3) Remove air pump outlet hose at pump. Remove upper wire and lower connector from thermo-time switch. Remove sliding lug bolt from air pump-to-alternator bracket. Remove upper and lower radiator hoses. Remove heater hose and power steering reservoir.

4) Remove radiator, fan and fan shroud. Using a rag, remove water pump belt from pulley. Use crankshaft pulley bolt socket (8.0118-PZ) to turn crankshaft counterclockwise while removing belt.

5) Remove thermostatic air slide valve bracket. Remove vacuum hoses, coolant hoses, and thermostatic wire from valve. Remove two large hoses from diverter valve. Remove bracket from valve. Remove air injection assembly.

6) Remove heater hose near dipstick and remove auxiliary air device. Remove remaining electrical connectors from switches or sensors mounted in cylinder head. Remove rocker arm oil feed pipe. Disconnect all vacuum hoses remaining on common manifold side of engine, including hose at diverter valve.

7) Remove spark plug wire brackets and wires at spark plug. Remove valve cover. Remove cooling fan brush holder. Remove sealing rings from spark plug tubes. Remove rocker arm assembly and push rods.

8) Use pivoting handles (0.0149) to break cylinder head loose. Install cylinder liner retainers (8.0132) to prevent liners from moving.

Inspection — 1) Plug passages in cylinder block for valve lifters and oil return. Clean and scrape cylinder block gasket surface, and run a tap in cylinder block bolt holes.

2) Check liner protrusion above block (.0028-.0055" or .07-.14 mm) at engine centerline. No liner should protrude more than .0015" (.04 mm) above adjacent liner. If not to specifications, replace liner gaskets.

3) Using a plastic or wooden scraper, clean cylinder head gasket surface. Clean cylinder head bolts. Check for cylinder head warpage (maximum allowable is .004" or .10 mm). Check

cylinder head thickness. Original thickness is 3.636-3.648" (92.35-92.65 mm), with minimum permissable thickness being 3.616" (91.85 mm). If cylinder head must be planed, check thickness before and after planing to be sure thickness is within tolerances.

4) Clean and check valve lifters, using caution not to mix them. DO NOT scrape carbon off piston tops, as liner damage could result.

Installation — 1) Install cylinder head in reverse of removal sequence, noting the following. When installing cylinder head, use 2 locating guides (8.0115-BZ). Install new gasket with word, "DESSUS", "ALTO" or "TOP" facing up (toward cylinder head).

2) Install cylinder head and rocker arm assembly. Lightly tighten cylinder head bolts (with flat washers), using a drop of engine oil on threads. Lightly tighten rocker shaft nuts. Remove 2 head guides, using removal tools (8.0115-A). Install last 2 head bolts.

NOTE — *Do not get oil in cylinder head bolt holes, as this could cause hydraulic blockage and prevent proper tightening.*

3) Using tightening sequence shown in Fig. 3, tighten head bolts to 36 ft. lbs. (50 N•m) and rocker shaft nuts to 11 ft. lbs. (15 N•m). Place angular head torquing tool (8.0129) on 2 center bolts (1 and 2). Completely loosen No. 1 bolt and retighten to 14 ft. lbs. (20 N•m). Keep tool in place and maintain tension on torque wrench.

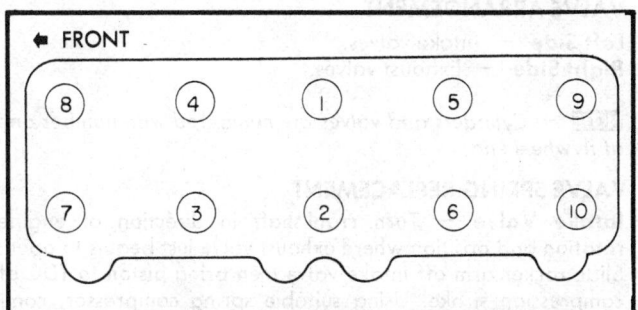

Fig. 3 Cylinder Head Bolt Tightening Sequence

4) Position pointer on tool at "0" notch by moving spring loop. Continue torquing until pointer lines up with "90" notch. Repeat entire procedure with No. 2 bolt. Then move tool and complete tightening procedure in proper sequence. If there is any doubt concerning torque of any one bolt, loosen it completely and repeat all tightening procedures for that one head bolt. Adjust valves, and complete installation. Refill cooling system.

NOTE — *After cylinder head removal, adjust intake valve clearance to .006" (.15 mm) and exhaust valves to .012" (.30 mm). After 1000-1500 miles, retorque cylinder head bolts (after 6 hours of engine cooling), and adjust valve clearances to standard specifications. See Valve Clearance Adjustment.*

5) Adjust air pump and alternator belt tension at idler pulley. Loosen both idler pulley mounting bolts. Apply 36 ft. lbs. (50 N•m) torque to nut directly above idler pulley. Tighten mounting bolts. Turn engine 1 full turn to align belt on idler pulley. Loosen mounting bolts. Tighten idler pulley nut to 58 ft. lbs. (79 N•m). Retighten mounting bolts.

Peugeot Engines

505 GASOLINE 4-CYLINDER (Cont.)

SPARK PLUG TUBE REPLACEMENT

Removal — With cylinder head supported, screw in plugs without springs to prevent dirt from falling into cylinder. Remove tubes using mallet or suitable extractor.

NOTE — *If tubes are removed, new tubes MUST be inserted.*

Installation — To install tubes, coat with suitable sealing compound and insert so plug caps are facing as shown in illustration. When tube is fully seated, it will protrude 2.835" (72 mm) upward from cylinder head.

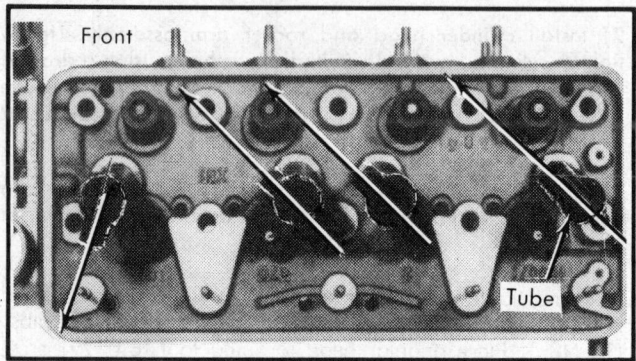

Fig. 4   Position of Spark Plug Tubes for Installation. Arrows Indicate Direction of Plug Caps.

VALVES

VALVE ARRANGEMENT

Left Side — Intake valves.
Right Side — Exhaust valves.

NOTE — *Cylinders and valves are numbered with number one at flywheel end.*

VALVE SPRING REPLACEMENT

Intake Valve — Turn crankshaft in direction of engine rotation and position where exhaust valve just begins to open. Slide rocker arm off intake valve then bring piston to TDC of compression stroke. Using suitable spring compressor, compress spring and remove keepers, spring retainer and spring.

Exhaust Valve — 1) Remove spark plug from cylinder requiring attention. Rotate crankshaft in direction of engine rotation and bring intake valve to fully closed position. Slide rocker arm off exhaust valve.

2) Insert suitable hinged tool (0 0136) into spark plug hole and bring piston to TDC without forcing as tool is between piston and valve. Using suitable spring compressor, compress spring and remove keepers, spring retainer and spring.

VALVE CLEARANCE ADJUSTMENT

NOTE — *Engine must be allowed to cool at least 6 hours before adjusting valves. Adjust valves in firing order sequence (1-3-4-2). No. 1 cylinder is on flywheel end.*

Rotate engine until exhaust valve number one is fully opened, then adjust intake valve number three and exhaust valve number four. Rotate engine one half turn until next number valve is fully opened and adjust corresponding valves. *See table.* Continue until all valves have been adjusted.

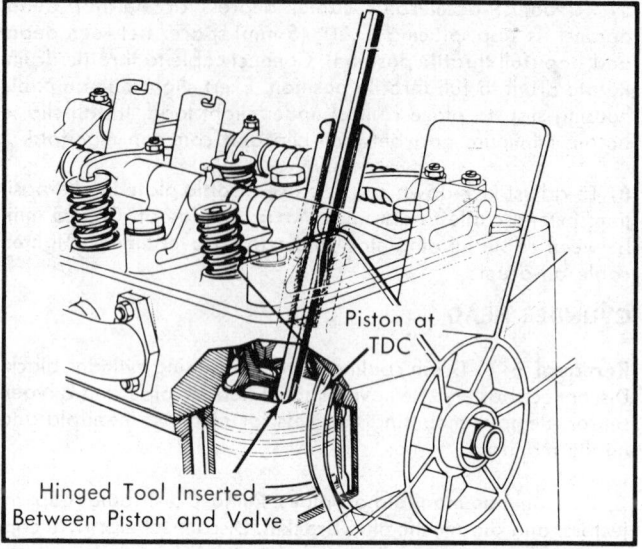

Fig. 5   Removing Valve Spring with Valve Held in Place

Valve Adjustment Sequence

Valve Open	Adjust Valves
E 1	I 3 & E 4
E 3	I 4 & E 2
E 4	I 2 & E 1
E 2	I 1 & E 3

Valve Clearance Adjustment①

Application	Intake② In. (mm)	Exhaust③ In. (mm)
All Models	.004 (.10)	.010 (.25)

① — Tolerance range of +0 to +.002" (+0 to +.05 mm).

② — Adjust to .006" (.15 mm) after installing cylinder head. Retorque to above specifications after 1000-1500 miles.

③ — Adjust to .012" (.30 mm) after installing cylinder head. Retorque to above specifications after 1000-1500 miles.

PISTONS, PINS & RINGS

PISTON & ROD ASSEMBLY

NOTE — *Engine must be removed to replace liners and pistons.*

Removal — 1) Drain crankcase. With engine mounted on suitable engine stand, remove intake and exhaust manifolds. Remove all auxiliary equipment, including alternator, air pump and fuel pump plunger. *See Fig. 6.*

2) Remove cylinder head. *See Cylinder Head Removal in this article.* Remove camshaft hydraulic lifters, keeping them in original order. Remove distributor support drive shaft.

505 GASOLINE 4-CYLINDER (Cont.)

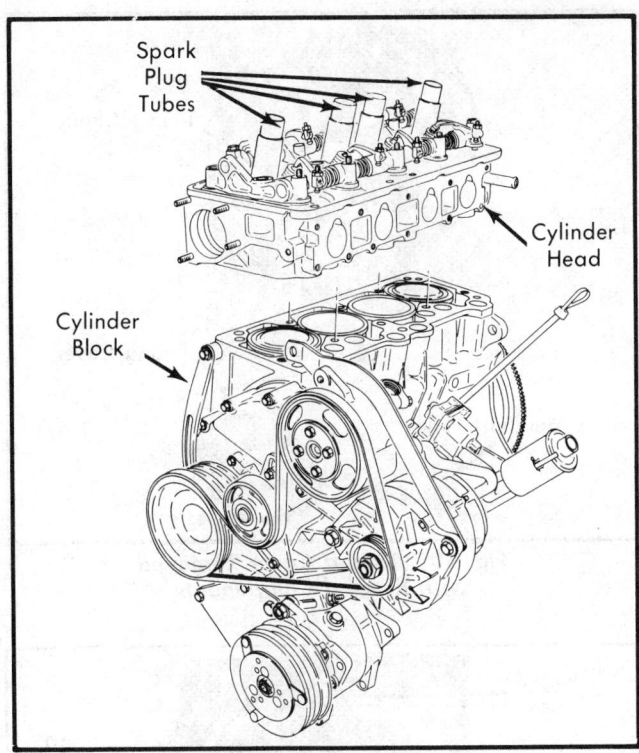

Fig. 6 Cylinder Block and Cylinder Head Assembly

Installation — 1) To install, fit piston ring clamp on piston. Insert piston and rod assembly, without twisting it. Index arrow must face front of engine.

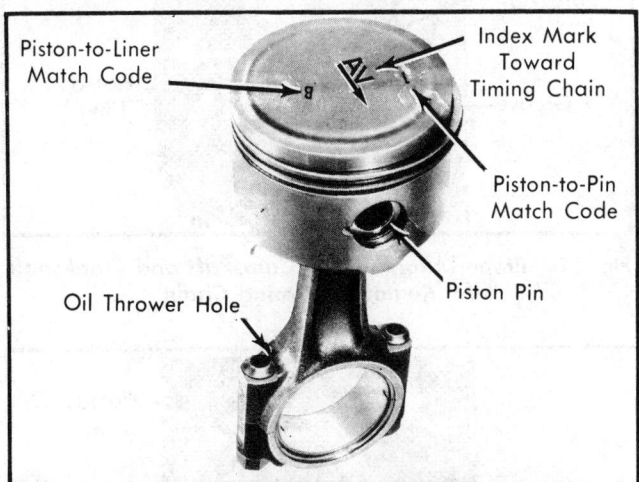

Fig. 7 Piston and Rod Assembly with Index Marks and Codes

2) Push piston down cylinder and guide connecting rod with bearing over crankshaft journal. Install bearing cap and tighten.

NOTE — *Marks on rods and caps must be on same side.*

PISTON PIN REPLACEMENT

Remove snap rings and piston pin. Fit piston to rod with index mark "AV" at right angle to oil thrower, so that it will face front of engine. If necessary heat piston in boiling water and insert pin. Install snap rings.

NOTE — *"AV" mark on piston top must face front of engine. Pistons and liners must be matched by letter code. Number on top of piston refers to piston pin code (1 — Blue, 2 — White, and 3 — Red).*

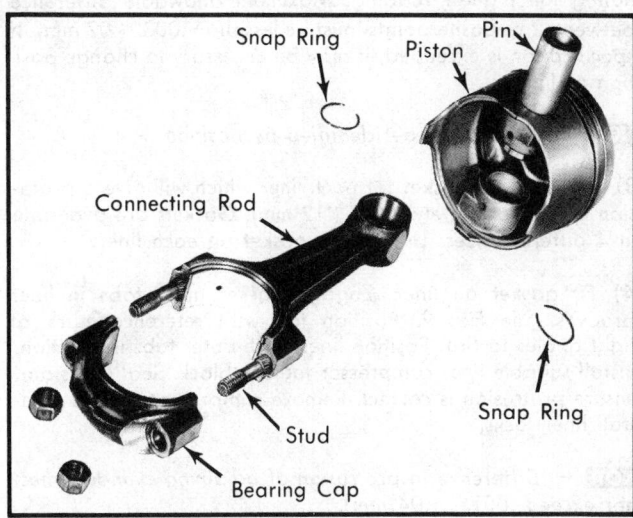

Fig. 8 Exploded View of Piston and Connecting Rod

CYLINDER LINER REPLACEMENT

1) Remove cylinder liners, using suitable extractor if required. Before installing liners, clean and inspect for burrs and dirt. Insert liners, without base gaskets, with flats on shoulder of liners 1-2 and 3-4 parallel.

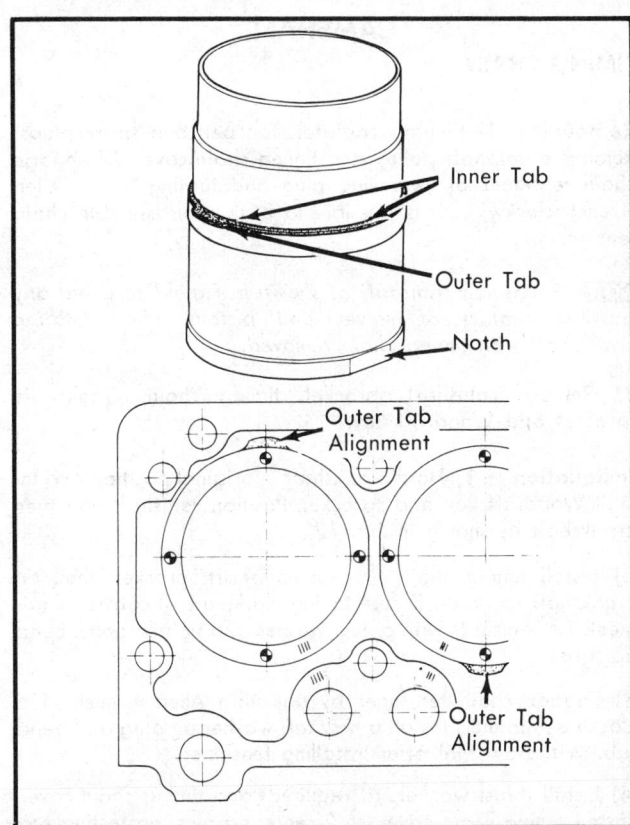

Fig. 9 Cylinder Liner Gasket Installation

505 GASOLINE 4-CYLINDER (Cont.)

NOTE — *Do not alter piston/liner pairings.*

2) Place a suitable dial gauge and support on block face. Synchronize dial at 0 and 5. Check each liner at 4 different points, noting the highest reading. Maximum allowable difference between 2 opposite points must be less than .003" (.07 mm). If specification is exceeded, it may be necessary to change position of liners.

NOTE — *Liners must be identified by position.*

3) Select a base gasket for each liner which will give a protrusion of approximately .005" (.12 mm). Gaskets are available in 4 different sizes. Use only 1 gasket on each liner.

4) Fit gasket on liner. Engage gasket inner tabs in liner grooves. *See Fig. 9.* Position tab with reference mark at right angles to flat. Position liners with outer tabs in position. Install suitable liner compressor tools to block. Seat liners and ensure protrusion is correct. Remove compressor tools and install liner locks.

NOTE — *Difference in protrusion of adjoining cylinders must not exceed .0015" (.04 mm).*

CRANKSHAFT MAIN & CONNECTING ROD BEARINGS

THRUST BEARING WASHERS

After installing crankshaft, check end play. Play must not exceed .008" (.20 mm). If specification is exceeded, oversize thrust washers are available in .094" (2.40 mm), .096" (2.45 mm), and .098" (2.50 mm) sizes.

CAMSHAFT

TIMING CHAIN

Removal — **1)** Remove radiator, fan belt and spark plugs. Remove crankshaft pulley and timing chain cover. Disengage chain tensioner by removing plug and turning 3 mm Allen wrench clockwise. It is possible to further disassemble chain tensioners.

NOTE — *Position camshaft as shown in Fig. 11 to avoid any possible contact of valves and pistons when rotating crankshaft with timing chain removed.*

2) Remove camshaft sprocket, timing chain, crankshaft sprocket and Woodruff key.

Installation — **1)** Hold crankshaft in original position and install Woodruff key and sprocket. Position camshaft and then crankshaft as shown in *Fig. 12.*

2) Install timing chain first on camshaft sprocket, then on crankshaft sprocket. Ensure timing marks are in correct alignment. Fit camshaft with a new washer and tighten bolts. Bend up tabs.

3) Engage chain tensioner by adjusting Allen wrench in a clockwise manner. Install a new tab washer on plug and bend tab. Withdraw tool after installing tensioner.

4) Install thrust washers (if required) and timing chain cover. Install timing chain cover on 2 centering pins, protecting seal with suitable tool. Install crankshaft pulley after cover bolts are tightened.

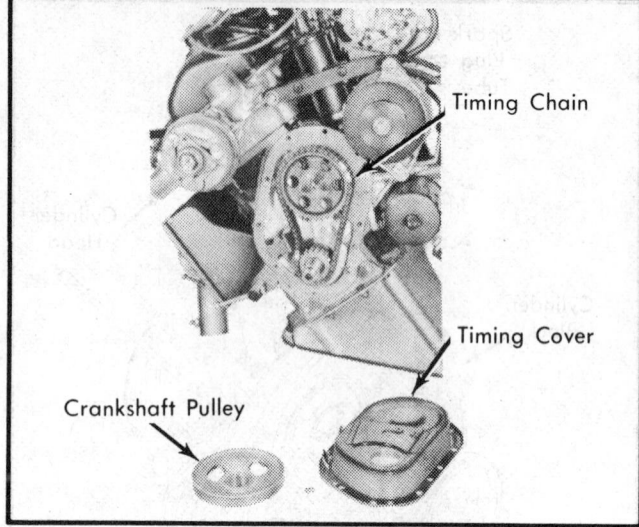

Fig. 10   Timing Cover Removed with Related Components

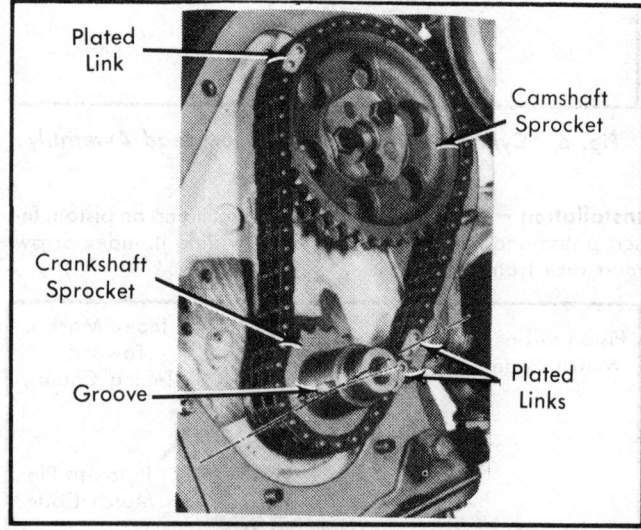

Fig. 11   Proper Alignment of Camshaft and Crankshaft for Removing Timing Chain

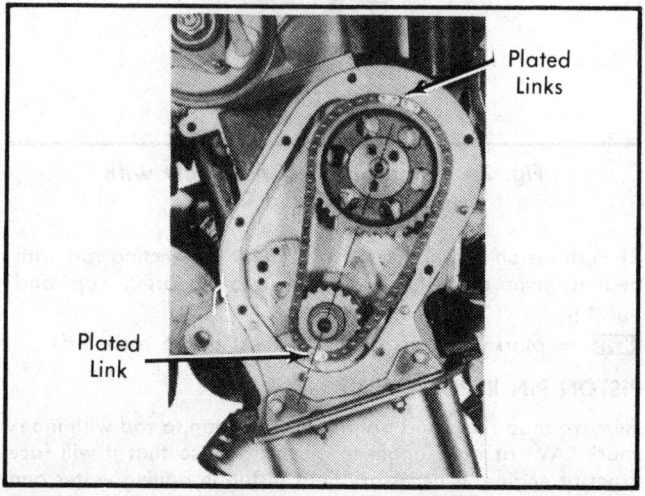

Fig. 12   Proper Alignment of Camshaft and Crankshaft

505 GASOLINE 4-CYLINDER (Cont.)

3) Remove oil pan and oil pump. Remove timing cover. Remove bearing caps, keeping them in original order. Remove pistons and connecting rods. Attach connecting rods to matching cap, mark rod assemblies 1-4.

ENGINE OILING

ENGINE OILING SYSTEM

A high output, gear type oil pump is mounted to engine block lower surface and is operated by camshaft.

Crankcase Capacity — Approximately 4.2 qts. for refill.

Oil Filter — Full-flow cartridge type.

Normal Oil Pressure — 28-51 psi (2-3.6 kg/cm²) at idle; 44-67 psi (3-4.7 kg/cm²) at 4000 RPM.

ENGINE COOLING

Thermostat — Opens at 180°F (82°C).

Cooling System Capacity — Auto. Trans. — 7.7 qts.
Man. Trans. — 7.5 qts.

Radiator Cap — 14.3 psi (1.0 kg/cm²).

WATER PUMP

Removal & Installation — Remove radiator, top hose and fan belt. Disconnect heater hose from pump and self-engaging fan brush holder. Remove water pump. To install, reverse removal procedure and ensure contact surfaces are clean before installing new gasket.

SELF-DISENGAGING FAN

Driven by water pump shaft and controlled by a thermal contact-breaker. Fan engages at approximately 190° F (88° C) and disengages at 174° F (79° C).

TIGHTENING SPECIFICATIONS

Application	Ft. Lbs. (N·m)
Cylinder Head	See Text
Crankshaft Main Bearing Bolts	54 (73)
Connecting Rod Nuts	29 (39)
Camshaft Retaining Plate Bolts	12 (16)
Camshaft Sprocket Bolts	16 (22)
Crankshaft Pulley Bolts	123 (167)
Flywheel-to-Crankshaft Bolts	49 (67)
Engine-to-Clutch Housing	40 (54)
Oil Pump Mounting Bolts	7 (10)
Engine-to-Converter Housing	22 (30)
Engine Mounts-to-Crossmember	22 (30)
Rocker Arm Support Nut	11 (15)
Belt Tension Nut	①58 (79)

① — First step, tighten to 36 ft. lbs. (50 N·m), turn engine one full turn, and retighten to 58 ft. lbs. (79 N·m).

ENGINE SPECIFICATIONS

GENERAL SPECIFICATIONS

Year	Displ. cu. ins.	Displ. cc	Fuel Inj.	HP at RPM	Torque (Ft. Lbs. at RPM)	Compr. Ratio	Bore in.	Bore mm	Stroke in.	Stroke mm
1981	120.3	1970	K-Jetronic	96@4900	116@3300	8.35:1	3.465	88	3.189	81

CRANKSHAFT MAIN & CONNECTING ROD BEARINGS

Engine	MAIN BEARINGS Journal Diam. In. (mm)	MAIN BEARINGS Clearance In. (mm)	Thrust Bearing	Crankshaft End Play In. (mm)	CONNECTING ROD BEARINGS Journal Diam. In. (mm)	CONNECTING ROD BEARINGS Clearance In. (mm)	Side Play In. (mm)
1970 cc No. 1 (Rear)	2.1616-2.1646 (54.905-54.980)	...	Rear	.003-.008 (.08-.20)	2.1123-2.1131 (53.652-53.673)	.0006-.003 (.016-.076)	.....
No. 2	2.2102-2.2112 (56.140-56.165)						
No. 3	2.2509-2.2515 (57.174-57.189)						
No. 4	2.3050-2.3060 (58.548-58.573)						
No. 5 (Front)	2.3386-2.3392 (59.401-59.416)						

Peugeot Engines

4-CYLINDER DIESEL & TURBO DIESEL

ENGINE CODING

ENGINE IDENTIFICATION

Engine identification number is stamped on front left side of engine block just below cylinder head. Engine identification number corresponds with Vehicle Identification Number, and runs from number 1340000 upward.

Engine Identification	
Application	**Code**
504 & 505 Diesel	XD2C
505 & 604 Turbo Diesel	XD2S

ENGINE & CYLINDER HEAD

ENGINE

NOTE — *Specific engine removal and installation procedures were not available for 504 diesel and 604 Turbo diesel engines. Procedures should be similar to normally aspirated engines for Turbo. Disconnect any additional components necessary for removal.*

Removal — 1) Drain cooling system. Remove battery, battery tray, radiator expansion tank, air filter and intake pipe on vacuum pump. Remove upper and lower radiator hoses and mountings. Disconnect power steering hoses from pump and transmission cooler lines at radiator and suspend high enough to prevent drainage.

2) Remove radiator. Remove starter and clutch housing sealing plates. Remove fan and belt tensioners. On air conditioned models, protect condenser with plywood. Remove air conditioner compressor and hang along inner fender with hoses attached. Route refrigerant hoses to back of engine.

3) On all models, remove sound proofing panel clips on the cowl panel and remove degassing tank bracket. Remove mounting bolts on front header pipe to manifold, intermediate exhaust muffler and lower the compressor cut-out switch (if equipped). Lower front crossmember after having removed mounting bolts. Suspend crossmember with two 12×150 bolts approximately 2¾-4" (70-100 mm) long (P.N. 6902.77).

4) On automatic transmission models, remove the torque converter bolts (accessible through starter motor opening). Move torque converter back from flywheel. Loosen 3 engine-to-clutch housing bolts slightly using a hex socket (8.0208). Remove the top converter bolt.

5) On all models, remove the 4 mounting bolts of the engine mounts on the main crossmember. Install lifting hooks (8.0102X) and lift until transmission touches tunnel. Install engine support bracket (8.0125). Disconnect the power steering line leading to the distribution valve.

6) Remove the 2 lower engine-to-transmission mounting bolts, clear engine and lift, being careful not to pull on refrigerant lines. On automatic transmission models, ensure torque converter is fully disengaged, and install torque converter retaining clamp.

Installation — On manual transmission models, coat mainshaft splines with Molykote 321. On automatic transmission models, coat converter nipple with Calysol F3015 grease. To complete installation, reverse removal procedures.

CYLINDER HEAD

CAUTION — *Cylinder head bolts must not be loosened while engine is warm.*

Removal — 1) Drain cooling system. Disconnect and remove battery. Disconnect exhaust pipe from manifold, vacuum pump, overflow reservoir, electrical connections and harness securing clips from engine. Disconnect heater hose, rocker oil feed pipe at cylinder head, and remove upper power steering pump bracket mounting bolt.

2) Remove water pump bolt, valve cover, rocker shaft assembly and push rods. Gradually loosen cylinder head bolts in sequence shown in *Fig. 1*. Remove cylinder head using levers (0.0149).

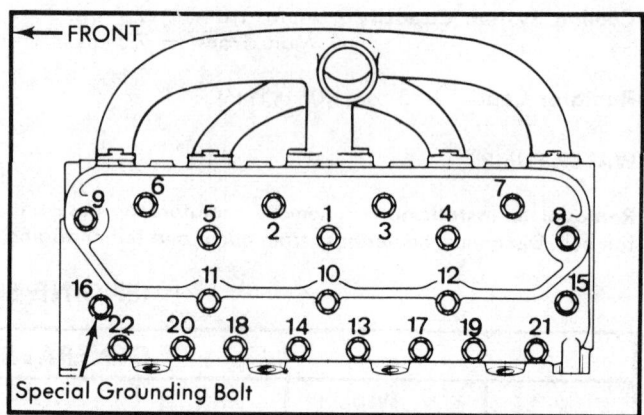

Fig. 1 Cylinder Head Bolt Tightening Sequence

Installation — 1) Run an 11 × 150 tap through bolt holes to clean threads and clean all foreign material and oil from threads. Brush clean bolt threads. Use new domed washers on non-Turbo engines with dome installed up (on Turbo engines, use flat washers). Carefully clean mating surfaces of cylinder head and block.

2) Check amount of piston protrusion to determine correct head gasket thickness. Measure the amount of piston protrusion with a dial indicator and tool (8.011 P). Select the maximum amount of protrusion (all 4 cylinders). If protrusion is greater to or equal to .030" (.79 mm) for Turbo, or more than .033" (.84 mm) for non-Turbo engines, gasket thickness needed is .067" (1.7 mm).

3) Reference mark for this gasket is 3 notches. If protrusion is less than .030" (.79 mm) for Turbo, or less than .033" (.84 mm) for non-Turbo engines, gasket thickness required is .067" (1.58 mm). Reference mark for this gasket is 2 notches.

4) Install cylinder head guides (8.0114) in bolt holes 15 and 16. See *Fig. 1*. Install the correct thickness gasket dry. Place cylinder head over guides and install remaining bolts, noting

4-CYLINDER DIESEL & TURBO DIESEL (Cont.)

that 8 short bolts are installed on injector side, 7 medium length bolts are installed on manifold side and 6 long bolts are installed in center.

5) Bolt threads and contact faces should be lightly lubricated with engine oil on non-Turbo engines, and coated with Molykote 6 Rapid (PN 9730.08) on Turbo engines. Remove guides and install remaining bolts. Special ground bolt is installed in No. 16 position.

6) Tighten cylinder head bolts in 1st step to 22 ft. lbs. (30 N•m) in sequence shown in *Fig. 1*. In 2nd step, tighten in sequence Turbo bolts to 51 ft. lbs. (69 N•m), non-Turbo to 47 ft. lbs. (64 N•m). Third and final step consists of loosening each bolt (1 at a time in sequence) 1/4 turn and retightening.

7) Install injector holders with new seals, injector shields and washers. Install push rods to original positions and install rocker arm assembly. See Rocker Arm Assembly in this article. Adjust valves as outlined in Valve Clearance Adjustment.

NOTE — *Cylinder head bolts must be retightened after 30-60 miles and again after 1000-1500 miles. Engine must be allowed to cool 6 hours before retightening bolts. To retighten, loosen bolt 1/4 turn (1 bolt at a time) and tighten to final torque following sequence shown in Fig. 1.*

VALVES

VALVE ARRANGEMENT

I-E-E-I-I-E-E-I (Front to Rear).

NOTE — *Cylinders and valves are numbered with number one at flywheel end.*

VALVE DEPTH

After cylinder head has been resurfaced or valve seats reground or replaced, depth of valve face beneath cylinder head must be checked. Measure depth with a dial indicator. If less than specification, replace valves and/or valve seats. If more than specification, regrind valve seats.

Valve Face Depth	
Application	Depth In. (mm)
Non-Turbo	.033-.047 (.85-1.20)
Turbo	
Intake	.041-.047 (2.05-1.40)
Exhaust	.033-.047 (.85-1.20)

ROCKER ARM ASSEMBLY

1) To remove rocker arm assembly, remove rocker arm cover and remove rocker shaft support bolts. Lift rocker arm assembly noting oil line union sealing washer.

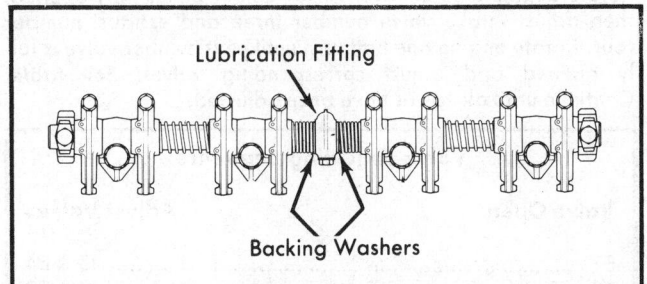

Fig. 2 Assembled View of Rocker Arm Assembly with Oil Holes Detailed

2) To disassemble rocker arm assembly, remove end shaft supports and remove rocker arms, supports, springs and washers. Remove locating screw on lubrication fitting, then remove shaft.

3) Check shaft diameter at areas where rocker arms contact shaft. Minimum diameter of shaft is .746" (18.95 mm). Replace shaft and/or rocker arms if excessive wear or scoring is evident.

4) To assemble rocker arm assembly, slide rocker shaft into lubrication fitting noting that oil holes in shaft are on same side as screw hole in fitting. Line up screw hole in shaft with threaded hole in fitting and install locating screw and copper washer.

Fig. 3 Installing Rocker Arm Assembly to Cylinder Head

5) Lubricate rocker shaft and install washers, springs, rocker arms and supports. Install push rods and install rocker shaft assembly to cylinder head. Install .004" (.10 mm) shims between each of the end rocker shaft bearing blocks and on Turbo, between No. 1 & 4 intake rockers.

6) Install new oil union seal washer. Tighten intermediate bearing blocks (nuts), then tighten end supports (bolts). Remove shims and check for free movement of the 2 end rockers. There should be .004" (.10 mm) play at the 2 end rocker arms.

VALVE CLEARANCE ADJUSTMENT

NOTE — *Engine must be allowed to cool at least six hours before adjusting valves.*

4-CYLINDER DIESEL & TURBO DIESEL (Cont.)

Rotate engine until exhaust valve number one is fully opened, then adjust intake valve number three and exhaust number four. Rotate engine one half turn until next number valve is fully opened and adjust corresponding valves. *See table.* Continue until all valves have been adjusted.

Valve Adjusting Sequence

Valve Open	Adjust Valves
E1	I3 & E4
E3	I4 & E2
E4	I2 & E1
E2	I1 & E3

Valve Clearance Adjustment

Application	Intake In. (mm)	Exhaust In. (mm)
Turbo	.006 (.15)	.010 (.25)
Non-Turbo	.010-.012 (.250-.255)	.010-.012 (.250-.255)

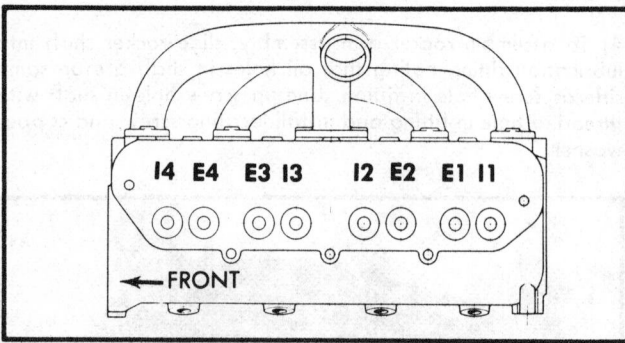

Fig. 4   View of Intake and Exhaust Valve Arrangement

COMBUSTION (SWIRL) CHAMBERS

Removal — Remove cylinder head from vehicle and remove injectors, injector studs, rocker arms, rocker arm mounting

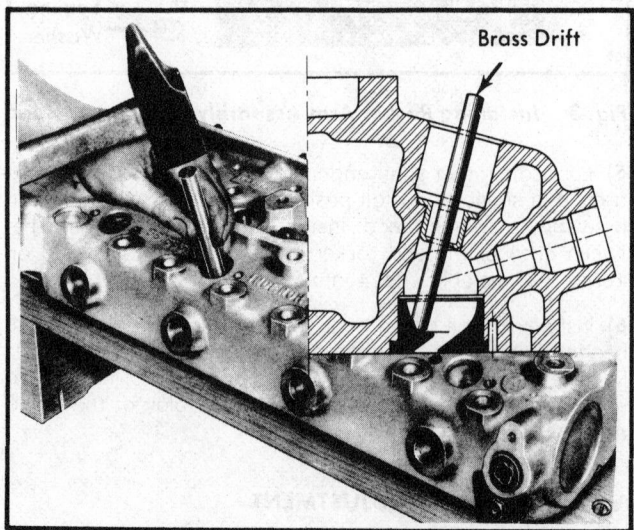

Fig. 5   Removing Combustion Chamber with Hammer and Drift

cylinder head. Tap drift LIGHTLY so as not to damage inner face of chamber.
studs, manifolds and glow plugs. Using suitable drift (see illustration) carefully drive swirl chambers down and out of

CAUTION — *If the swirl chamber twists and/or sticks in its bore, turn head over, tap chamber back into place with soft mallet, and start over again.*

Inspection — **1)** Inspect swirl chambers for distortion and cracks. Small cracks around the gas outlet are acceptable and do not effect engine operation. Replace all doubtful chambers. Measure thickness of shoulder and overall height of chamber.

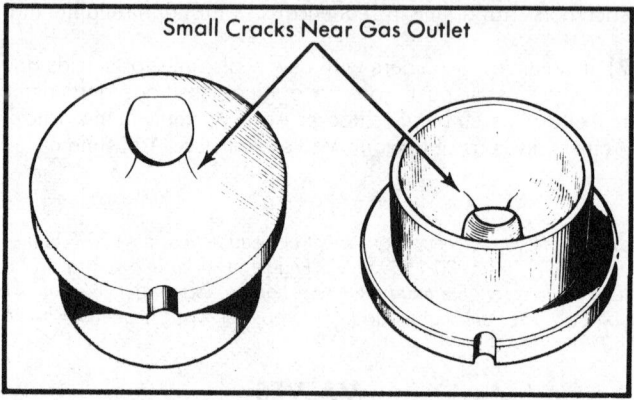

Fig. 6   View Showing Acceptable Cracks in Combustion Chamber

2) Place suitable truing punch (0.0139) over chamber bore in cylinder head, making sure dowel pin in punch is correctly located in head. Tap truing punch to make sure shoulder surface of bore is parallel with cylinder head. Slightly chamfer the edges of the chamber bore.

3) Measure depth of bore and depth to shoulder. Swirl chamber should protrude from cylinder head surface .000-.001" (.00-.03 mm) and clearance from swirl chamber to bottom of chamber bore should be .004-.020" (.10-.50 mm). To adjust clearances, chamber may be machined on shoulder surface and on bottom surface. Never machine face of chamber.

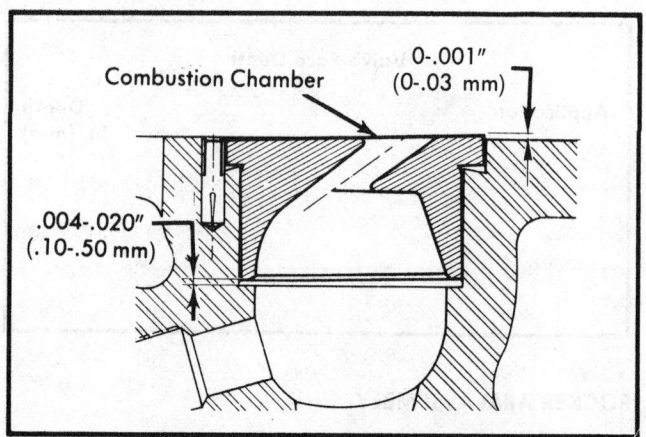

Fig. 7   Cross-Sectional View Showing Combustion Chamber Clearance and Protrusion

4-CYLINDER DIESEL & TURBO DIESEL (Cont.)

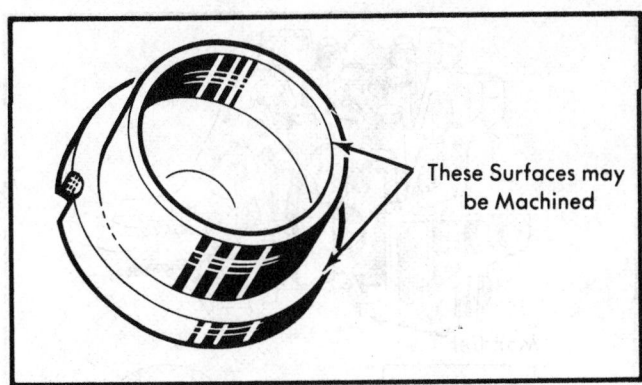

Fig. 8   Combustion (Swirl) Chamber with Detail of Machinable Surfaces

Installation — 1) Insert new wedge pins into the cylinder head and using chamfered drift, drive pins .028" (.7 mm) below cylinder head surface. Carefully insert the swirl chambers in the original bores and lightly tap into place with soft mallet.

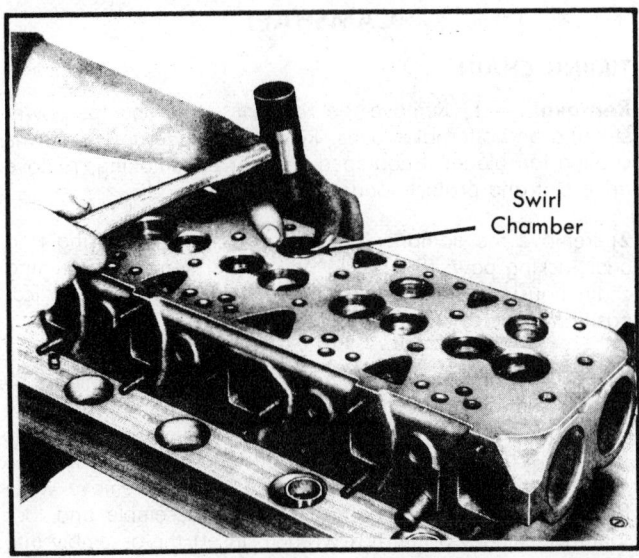

Fig. 9   Installing Combustion (Swirl) Chambers

2) Check for tight fit. If chamber is loose, chamber recess must be bored for oversize chamber. Using a dial gauge, check protrusion and parallelism with the cylinder head. Protrusion must be .000-.001" (.00-.03 mm) and difference between any two points must not exceed .001" (.03 mm).

PISTONS, PINS & RINGS

PISTON PIN & ROD ASSEMBLY

1) Remove engine from vehicle and drain oil. Remove oil pan, oil pump and cylinder head. Mark connecting rods for replacement in original location and remove connecting rod caps.

2) Push pistons up through top of cylinder block and replace connecting rod caps so they do not become mixed. Remove piston pin circlip and remove piston pin.

NOTE — *Pistons, pins and rings are matched at factory and must not be intermixed.*

3) Clean new piston assemblies with trichlorethylene. Do not remove piston rings to clean pistons. Make sure all protective coating has been removed from ring grooves. Blow with compressed air and check that piston rings move freely in grooves.

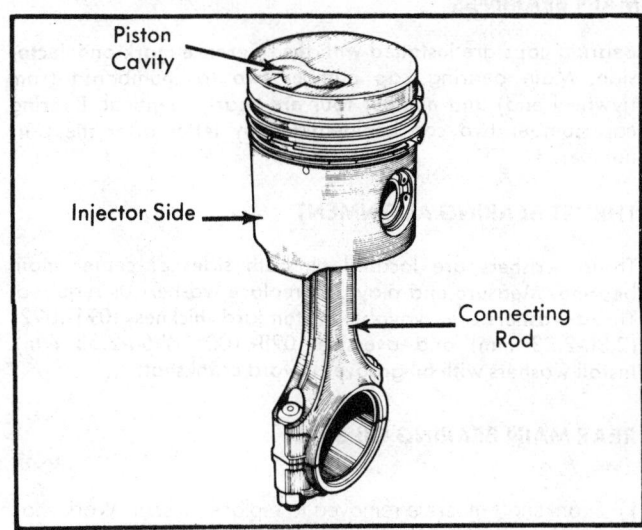

Fig. 10   Assembled View of Piston and Connecting Rod

4) Check fit of piston pin in connecting rod small end bushing. Ream bushing if too tight and replace bushing if too loose. Remove circlip from piston and partially remove piston pin. Position piston and rod so cavity on piston and reference marks on rod are on same side. Lubricate pin and install in piston. Replace circlip.

5) Do not remove connecting rod bolts. If any damage is evident, only 1 may be replaced. Lubricate pistons and bearings. Ensuring that compression rings are staggered 120° from slot of oil ring, use ring compressor and install each piston in its respective cylinder bore with cavity in piston facing injector side of engine.

NOTE — *Take into account the pairing of pistons to bores (reference marks A, B, C, D, E, F). If only 1 reference mark is evident, all 4 bores are identical. "A" and "B" are standard sizes, all others oversize. See Fig. 11.*

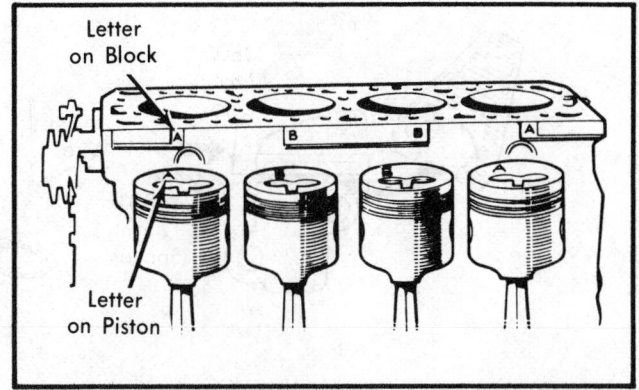

Fig. 11   Matching Pistons to Cylinder Bores

Peugeot Engines

4-CYLINDER DIESEL & TURBO DIESEL (Cont.)

NOTE — *On non-Turbo engines, turn engine over a few times by hand. Using a driving pawl (8.0110), check that moving parts torque does not exceed 44 ft. lbs. (59 N·m).*

CRANKSHAFT MAIN & CONNECTING ROD BEARINGS

MAIN BEARINGS

Bearing caps are installed with the reference mark on injector side. Main bearing cap number two (as numbered from flywheel end) and number four are nearly identical. Bearing cap number two can be identified by letter after the part number.

THRUST BEARING ALIGNMENT

Thrust washers are located on both sides of center main bearing. Measure end play and replace washers as required. Thrust washers are available in standard thickness .091-.092" (2.30-2.33 mm) and oversize .098-.100" (2.50-2.53 mm). Install washers with oil grooves toward crankshaft.

REAR MAIN BEARING OIL SEAL

1) Crankshaft must be removed to replace oil seal. Work seal packing manually into cylinder block and into bearing cap grooves. Place seal forming mandrel (8.0110 A) onto packing and form packing into groove by tapping mandrel with a hammer.

2) Make sure packing is correctly seated in its groove without being crushed (see illustration). Cut seal packing clean flush with mating surface and follow same procedure for bearing cap.

3) Place side seals in grooves of bearing cap and hold seals in place with suitable shim tool (8.0110 CZ and 8.0110 B). Lubricate shims and bring into place in cylinder block, tapping down with hammer handle. Install and tighten bearing cap bolts and check that bearing cap has seated properly. Trim side seals with knife so they protrude .020" (.50 mm) above lower crankcase mating surface. Gauge (8.0110 D) can be used for measurement.

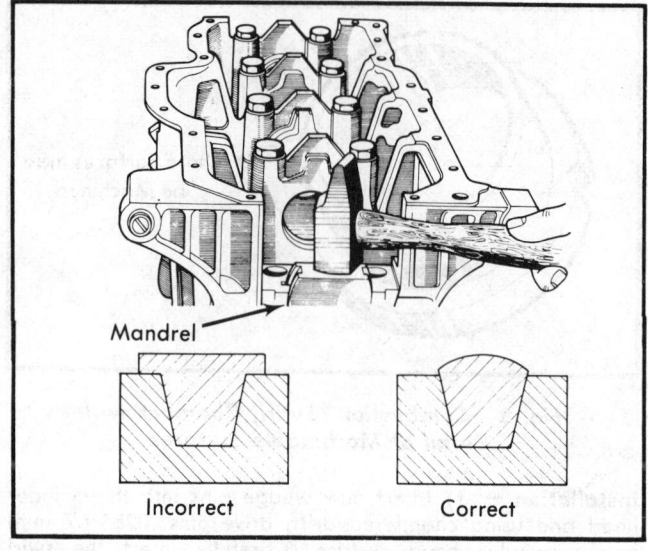

Mandrel

Incorrect   Correct

Fig. 12   Using a Mandrel and Mallet to Install Upper Rear Main Oil Seal

CAMSHAFT

TIMING CHAIN

Removal — 1) Remove the radiator, water pump, power steering and alternator belts. Remove the alternator and the cooling fan blade. If equipped with air conditioning, remove drive belt and protect condenser with plywood.

2) Remove the dampner pulley. Lock crankshaft using ring gear locking pawl (8.0110 L) on vehicle. Remove the timing chain housing. Turn crankshaft to bring keyway to vertical position. Unload chain tensioner as follows:

3) For non-automatic loading tensioner (Sedis) unload by placing the lock in position No. 1. Push pad in all the way. Place lock in position No. 2. DO NOT attempt to dismantle the lock. For automatic loading tensioner (Brampton) wrap with wire. Remove from vehicle. To unload, remove wire. Retrieve the pad, spring and piston. Reassemble and lock together using a 3 mm hex wrench. Insert the assembly into the housing leaving a gap of .080" (2 mm). See Fig. 13.

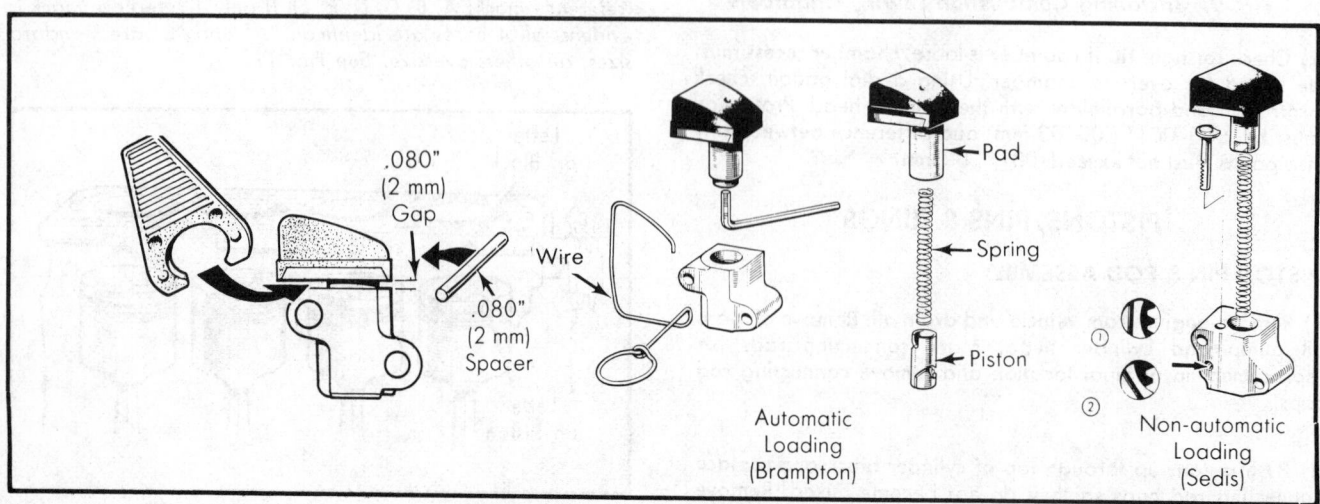

.080" (2 mm) Gap

Wire

.080" (2 mm) Spacer

Pad

Spring

Piston

Automatic Loading (Brampton)

Non-automatic Loading (Sedis)

Fig. 13   Hydraulic Chain Tensioners

4-CYLINDER DIESEL & TURBO DIESEL (Cont.)

Installation — 1) Install the chain ensuring that the reference links align with each of the pinion references. *See Fig. 14.* If it becomes necessary to turn the camshaft, bring the crankshaft keyway to the horizontal plane (1/2 stroke of the piston).

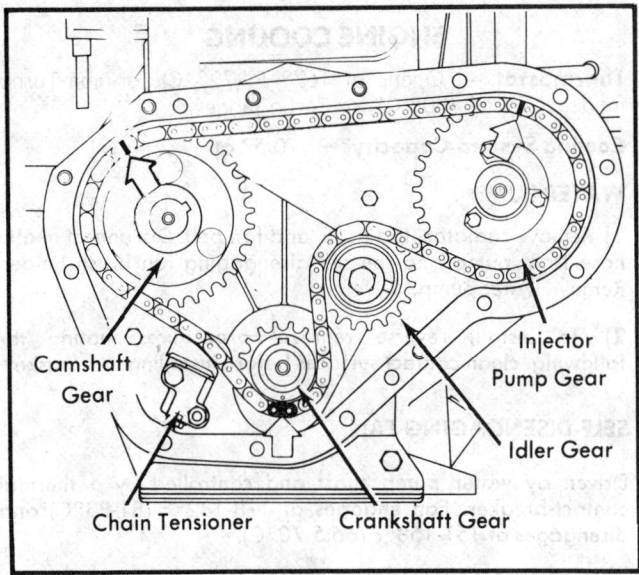

Camshaft Gear

Injector Pump Gear

Idler Gear

Chain Tensioner

Crankshaft Gear

Fig. 14   Timing Chain Installed to Illustrate Timing Mark Alignment

2) Reinstall the hydraulic tensioner and support plate. Install the eccentric idler pinion and turn it in the direction of chain rotation until a play between chain and tensioner of .020-.040" (.5-1 mm) is obtained for Turbo, .040-.080" (1-2 mm) for non-Turbo engines.

3) Mount the tensioner to the engine. For non-automatic loading tensioner, place lock in position No. 1 and let pad release pad freely. For automatic loading tensioner, remove the spacer, push the pad in all the way, and release freely. Allow the tensioner to freely tension the chain (both types of tensioners). Rotate the crankshaft 1 full turn to ensure there is no piston-to-valve contact.

4) Reinstall the timing chain housing with a new gasket. After carefully cleaning the crankshaft pulley bolt threads, crankshaft threads, pulley, spacer and bearing faces, install the pulley. Lock the crankshaft using ring gear locking pawl (8.0110 L). Put a few drops of Loctite on the crankshaft threads.

5) Tighten the bolt to 40 ft. lbs. (54 N•m). Mark one of the bolt flats and a corresponding point on the pulley. Tighten the bolt an additional 60° (one flat on the bolt). Remove ring gear pawl. To complete installation, reverse removal procedures.

CAMSHAFT

Removal — With timing chain removed, remove the support plate bolts and remove the camshaft and timing case support plate as an assembly.

Installation — Install the timing case support plate and camshaft to the block together, using a new gasket. Bolt the support plate to the block, using Loctite on threads.

FUEL INJECTION PUMP

Removal — Remove battery. On the pump, disconnect fuel supply and return lines. Disconnect control cables, fuel shut-off electrovalve wire, and load sensor harness (if equipped). Remove injector pipes. Remove 2 front mounting bolts and pump rear support. Remove the pump and cap and all fuel openings.

Installation — 1) Remove engine valve cover. Bring the valves of No. 1 cylinder back to approximately 90°. Using a valve spring compressor, compress No. 4 exhaust valve spring and move rocker arm over.

2) Rotate engine back to rocking position of No. 1 cylinder. Remove half cones, washers and springs from No. 4 exhaust valve. Install a dial indicator onto No. 4 exhaust valve stem, using suitable supports (8.0177 ZZ).

3) Bring the engine to TDC at No. 4 cylinder. Zero the dial indicator. Rotate the engine backwards to .27" (7 mm) before TDC. Clean the hydraulic head on the injection pump and remove the inspection plug. Turn the pump shaft to bring the double tooth of the injection pump in line with the double groove of the engine pump hub pinion.

4) Coat a new gasket with grease and install on pump flange. Install pump on engine and install mounting bolts without tightening. Adjust timing as outlined in Adjustments.

Adjustment — 1) With injection pump mounting bolts loose, dial indicator attached to No. 4 cylinder exhaust valve, and engine at .27" (7 mm) before TDC, rotate the injection pump body away from the engine. Install dial indicator to pump using adapters (8.0117T, P, and S).

2) Turn engine and locate BDC and TDC points on the dial indicator. At BDC the pump dial indicator should have some preload. Zero the pump dial indicator at BDC. Bring piston No. 4 to TDC of compression stroke. Check zero point of engine dial indicator.

3) Turn engine 90° in reverse, and recheck pump dial indicator. Turn engine in normal direction of rotation and bring No. 4 piston to .038" (.97 mm) BTDC for non-Turbo models, and to .016" (.40 mm) BTDC for Turbo models. Rotate the pump toward the engine until the dial indicator indicates a lift of .020" (.50 mm).

4) Tighten pump mounting bolts, front and rear. Check timing by rotating the engine the normal direction 2 turns. Turn the engine back approximately 90°. Rotate engine slowly in normal direction while watching the pump dial indicator. Stop turning the engine when the indicator shows a lift of .020" (.50 mm).

5) No. 4 piston should then be at .038" (.97 mm) BTDC for non-Turbo models, and .016" (.40 mm) for Turbo models. If readjustment is necessary rotate the pump. Remove the dial indicators and supports. Reinstall the inspection plug with a new gasket. Install springs, washer and half cones of No. 4 exhaust valve and adjust clearance. Reinstall pipes, hoses and controls. Adjust cables and bleed fuel circuit.

Peugeot Engines

4-CYLINDER DIESEL & TURBO DIESEL (Cont.)

ENGINE OILING

Crankcase Capacity — 5.29 qt.

Oil Filter — Full flow cartridge type.

Pressure Regulator Valve — Located in oil pump.

Normal Oil Pressure — Non-Turbo, 22 psi (1.6 kg/cm^2) at idle, 42-58 psi (3.0-4.1 kg/cm^2) at 4000 RPM. Turbo models, 37-55 psi (2.6-3.9 kg/cm^2) at 2000 RPM, 46-65 psi (3.2-4.5 kg/cm^2) at 4000 RPM.

ENGINE OILING SYSTEM

A high output, gear type oil pump, driven by camshaft, is mounted in oil pan.

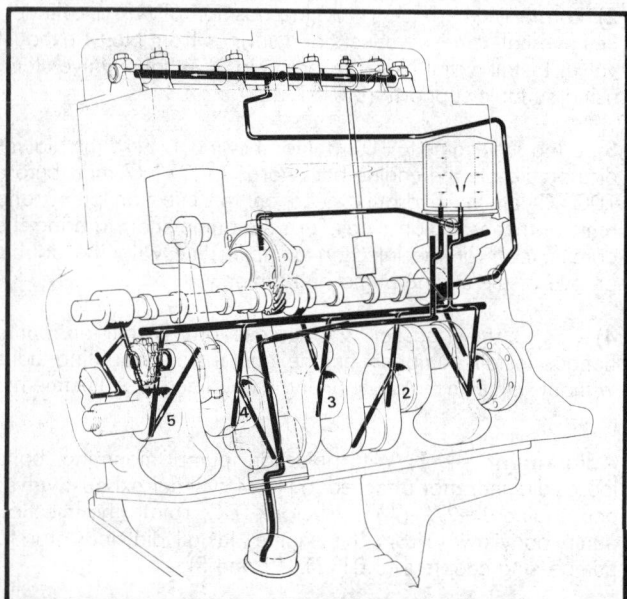

Fig. 15 Sectional View of Diesel Engine Oiling Circuit (Non-Turbo shown, Turbo Similar)

OIL PUMP

1) Insert the oil pump into its housing. Install the pump to its seat and position it with the positioning hole in the pump body aligned with the positioning screw hole in the block. Install the positioning screw and tighten. Install the acorn nut (cap nut) with a new gasket and tighten. Install the oil pump shaft endplay cap nut and tighten lightly without any shims.

2) Using a feeler gauge, measure the gap between the cap nut bearing face and the cylinder block through the slot provided. Remove the cap nut and install a shim to obtain correct end play. For Turbo, shim should be .020-.040" (.05-.1 mm) greater than feeler gauge reading, for non-Turbo models, shim should be .040" (1 mm) greater than feeler gauge reading. Reinstall cap nut and tighten.

ENGINE COOLING

Thermostat — Opens at 167° F (72° C) for non-Turbo models, 176° F (80° C) for Turbo models.

Cooling System Capacity — 10.57 qt.

WATER PUMP

1) Remove radiator, top hose, and fan belt. Disconnect heater hose from pump and the self-disengaging fan brush holder. Remove water pump.

2) To install, reverse removal procedures, noting the following: clean contact surfaces before installing new gasket.

SELF-DISENGAGING FAN

Driven by water pump shaft and controlled by a thermal contact-breaker. Fan engages at 178-182°F (81-83°C) and disengages at 151-158°F (66.5-70°C).

TIGHTENING SPECIFICATIONS

Application	Ft. Lbs. (N·m)
Cylinder Head	①
Clutch Housing-to-Block	43 (58)
Rocker Arm End Supports	
End Supports	14 (19)
Center Supports	34 (46)
Connecting Rod Caps	43 (58)
Main Bearing Caps	80 (109)
Eccentric Idler Gear	16 (22)
Crankshaft Pulley	① 40 (54) plus 60°
Flywheel Bolts	56 (76)
Glow Plugs	16 (22)
Injection Pump Mounting Bolts	14 (19)
Oil Pump Cap Nut	65 (88)

① — See text.

ENGINE SPECIFICATIONS

GENERAL SPECIFICATIONS

Year	Displ.		Carburetor	HP at RPM	Torque (Ft. Lbs. at RPM)	Compr. Ratio	Bore		Stroke	
	cu. ins.	cc					in.	mm	in.	mm
1981 Turbo	140.6	2304	Fuel Inj.	80 @ 4150	136 @ 2000	21:1	3.700	94	3.267	83
Others	140.6	2304	Fuel Inj.	71 @ 4500	99 @ 2500	23:1	3.700	94	3.267	83

4-CYLINDER DIESEL & TURBO DIESEL (Cont.)

ENGINE SPECIFICATIONS (Cont.)

VALVES							
Engine & Valve	Head Diam. In. (mm)	Face Angle	Seat Angle	Seat Width In. (mm)	Stem Diameter In. (mm)	Stem Clearance In. (mm)	Valve Lift In. (mm)
Turbo Intake	1.594 (40.5)	90°	90°	—	.3339-.3344 (8.480-8.495)	.0024 (.062)	—
Exhaust	1.319 (33.5)	90°	90°	—	.3330-.3337 (8.460-8.475)	.0032 (.082)	—
Others Intake	1.594 (40.5)	30°	30°	—	.3336-.3344 (8.473-8.495)	.0018 (.047)	.243 (6.173)
Exhaust	1.319 (33.5)	45°	45°	—	.3328-.3337 (8.453-8.475)	.0026 (.067)	.243 (6.173)

PISTONS, PINS, RINGS						
	PISTONS	PINS		RINGS		
Engine	Clearance In. (mm)	Piston Fit In. (mm)	Rod Fit In. (mm)	Rings	End Gap In. (mm)	Side Clearance In. (mm)
2304 cc ①	.005-.006 (.13-.16)	Press Fit	.....	No. 1	.014-.024 (.35-.60)	.....
				No. 2	.014-.024 (.35-.60)	.....
				Oil	.006-.012 (.16-.30)	.....

① — Turbo specifications not available.

CRANKSHAFT MAIN & CONNECTING ROD BEARINGS							
	MAIN BEARINGS				CONNECTING ROD BEARINGS		
Engine	Journal Diam. In. (mm)	Clearance In. (mm)	Thrust Bearing	Crankshaft End Play In. (mm)	Journal Diam. In. (mm) ①	Clearance In. (mm)	Side Play In. (mm)
2304 cc	2.1651-2.1661 (54.994-55.021)	.002-.004 (.05-.10)	Center	.003-.011 (.08-.29)	1.9678-1.9689 (49.984-50.011)	.002-.004 (.05-.10)	.....

① — Turbo journal diameter 2.1651-2.1661" (54.994-55.021 mm).

VALVE TIMING				
	INTAKE		EXHAUST	
Engine	Open (BTDC)	Close (ABDC)	Open (BBDC)	Close (ATDC)
Turbo	12°	16°	56°	12°
Others	12°	40°	56°	12°

924 4-CYLINDER

ENGINE CODING

ENGINE IDENTIFICATION

Engine number is located on left side of crankcase next to the clutch housing. Engine number is coded as follows:

Engine Identification	
Application	**Code**
924	V/C
924 Turbo	M31/02

ENGINE & CYLINDER HEAD

ENGINE

NOTE — *Manufacturer does not provide specific instructions for 924 Turbo.*

Removal — 1) Disconnect battery cable and remove engine protection plate. Scribe hood at hinges and remove hood. Drain cooling system, remove hoses and expansion tank. Remove fan motors with shroud and alternator cooling hose.

NOTE — *Remove A/C compressor without disconnecting hoses and lay aside.*

2) Disconnect all wiring, hoses, lines, linkage and brackets from engine. On 924 Turbo, disconnect necessary parts of turbocharger and oiling system. On all models, disconnect exhaust pipe at manifold. Support drive line at front brace with wooden block. See Fig. 1.

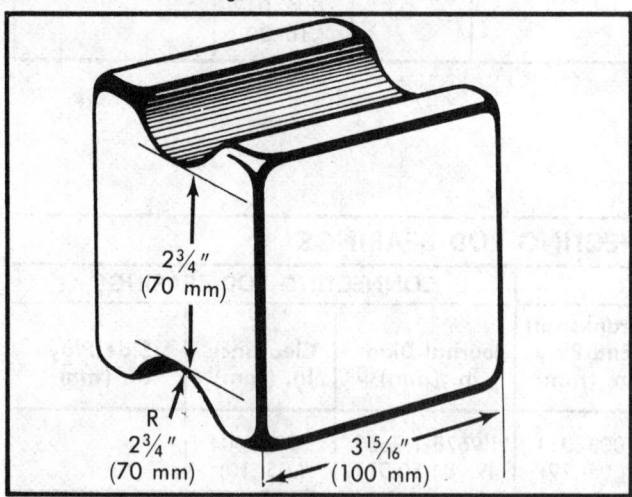

Fig. 1   Drive Line Support Block

3) Disconnect universal joint at steering rack. Disconnect stabilizer bar at frame on both sides and remove crossmember. Attach hoist and lift engine slightly. Remove bellhousing bolts and engine mounts. On vehicles equipped with automatic transmissions, remove bolts from metal/rubber damper. Lift engine carefully and turn at same time.

Installation — To install engine, reverse removal procedure.

CYLINDER HEAD

Removal & Installation — 1) Disconnect battery ground strap and drain cooling system. Remove hoses and wiring connected to cylinder head. Remove exhaust pipe at manifold and remove camshaft timing belt and "V" belt.

2) Remove cylinder head cover and head bolts in sequence. To install, coat threads of cylinder head bolts with a light coat of oil and tighten in sequence as described below.

3) On 924, insert head bolts Nos. 8 and 10 first to center head. With engine cold, tighten bolts in numerical sequence shown in Fig. 2. Mark position of bolt head and then turn each bolt an additional 1/2 turn (180°) in sequence.

4) On 924 Turbo, install bolts Nos. 8 and 10 to center head. Tighten bolts in sequence in steps to specifications. After 60 minutes, loosen bolts approximately 30° in reverse sequence, then tighten once again. Run engine to operating temperature of 176°F (80°C), let engine cool and repeat loosening and tightening procedure.

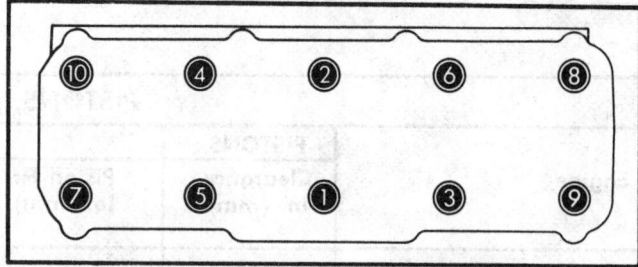

Fig. 2   Cylinder Head Tightening Sequence (Loosen in Reverse Order)

CAMSHAFT

FRONT MAIN BEARING OIL SEAL

Remove pulley bolt and using oil seal removing tool 10-221 (or equivalent), pry oil seal out of oil pump. Use installing tool 2033 to install new seal.

TIMING BELT

Remove belt cover and loosen drive belt tensioner. Remove crankshaft pulley and drive belt pulley. Remove drive belt. To install, reverse removal procedure.

NOTE — *Belt must be tightened until belt can be turned 90° with thumb and index finger at a point midway between crankshaft and camshaft.*

CAMSHAFT

1) Remove cylinder head cover and timing belt cover. Rotate crankshaft so marks on crankshaft pulley and camshaft sprocket are in No. 1 TDC position. Remove camshaft sprocket, distributor and distributor drive housing.

2) Remove camshaft lubrication tube, then replace nuts (hand tight) on bearing caps 2 and 4. Remove bearing caps 5, 1 and 3. Loosen bearing caps 2 and 4 evenly in a crosswise pattern and lift out camshaft.

NOTE — *Ensure that bearing caps are replaced in original position. Note the correct off-center position of bearing caps.*

924 4-CYLINDER (Cont.)

3) To install camshaft, reverse removal procedure and note the following: Place camshaft into position and install caps 2 and 4, tighten nuts in a crosswise pattern. Install caps 1, 3 and 5 and tighten all nuts to specifications. Loosen nuts 2 and 4 to install lubrication tube. Press in new camshaft oil seal.

VALVE TIMING

Using either TDC mark on flywheel and casting in bell housing, or crankshaft pulley TDC mark, rotate crankshaft to TDC position. Mark on rear of camshaft sprocket and indicator on cylinder head cover must be in line. Ensure that Woodruff key is installed and camshaft sprocket bolt is tightened properly. Install timing belt and adjust tension.

Fig. 3   Camshaft Sprocket Alignment

VALVES

VALVE ARRANGEMENT

I-E-I-E-I-E-I-E (Front to rear).

VALVE GUIDE SERVICING

1) With dial indicator, measure amount of clearance between valve and guide with end of stem flush with guide. If wear exceeds limits of .032" (0.8 mm) for intake, or .039" (1.0 mm) for exhaust, replace valve guides.

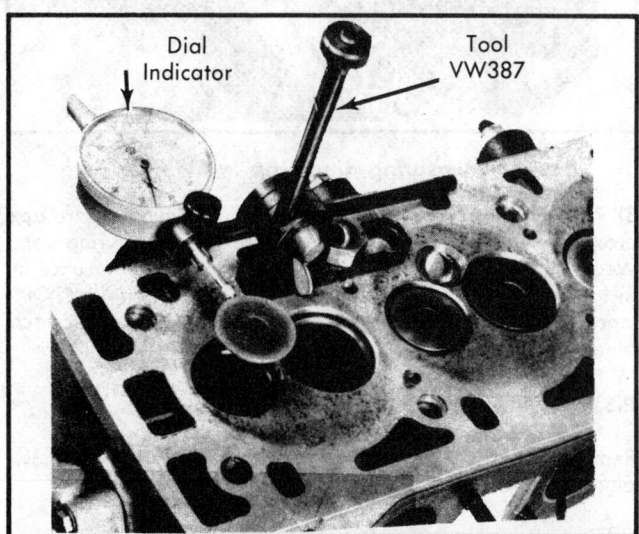

Fig. 4   Measuring Valve Guide Clearance

2) Press worn guide out from combustion chamber side. Place circlip into groove on replacement guide and press guide in from camshaft side. Replacement guides have a circlip in addition to 1 or 2 grooves.

3) Ream replacement guide by hand with dry reamer for proper clearance. Change valve spring retainer resting on head to replacement type with groove.

Valve Guide Identification		
Valve	**Marking**	**Outside Diameter In. (mm)**
Intake	No Groove	.5542 (14.079)
Exhaust	No Groove	.5538 (14.068)
Intake	1 Groove	.5622 (14.279)
Exhaust	1 Groove	.5617 (14.268)
Intake	2 Grooves	.5700 (14.479)
Exhaust	2 Grooves	.5695 (14.467)

NOTE — *During repairs, installed guides must have the same codes as those replaced.*

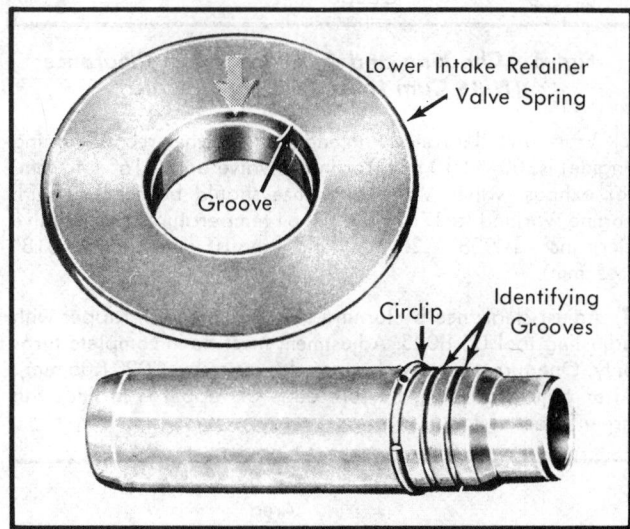

Fig. 5   Replacement Valve Guide and Intake Spring Retainer

VALVE STEM OIL SEALS

NOTE — *Valve stem oil seal may be replaced with cylinder head installed.*

Remove spark plug on cylinder being serviced, install air hose and adapter to maintain constant pressure in cylinder. Remove camshaft, tappets, valve stem keepers and valve spring. Remove oil seal and discard. To install, reverse removal procedures while noting the following; Be sure plastic sleeve is installed prior to seal installation. Place sleeve on valve stem, lubricate seal and install onto valve stem.

MECHANICAL VALVE LIFTERS

With camshaft removed, lift out tappet and inspect for wear or damage. Oil tappets lightly and replace in original position.

VALVE CLEARANCE ADJUSTMENT

1) Remove cylinder head cover and turn crankshaft until cam lobes of cylinder to be adjusted are pointing upward. Check valve clearance with feeler gauge between tappet and lobe.

Porsche Engines

924 4-CYLINDER (Cont.)

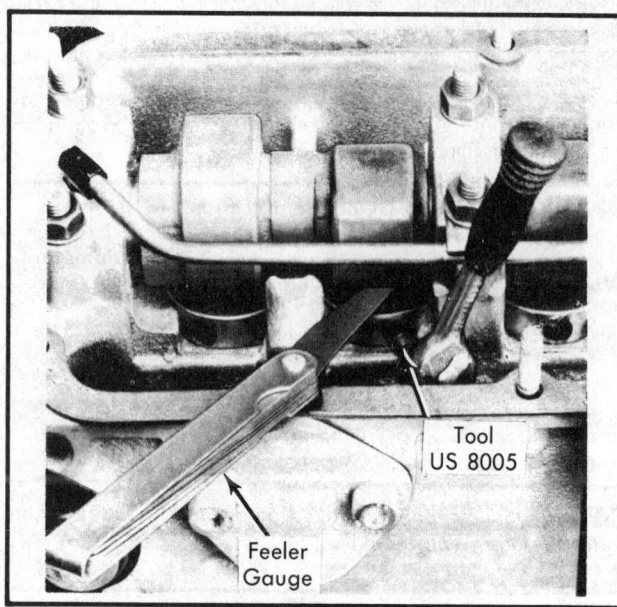

Fig. 6   Checking and Adjusting Valve Clearance (Note Cam Lobes Pointing Upward)

2) Basic valve clearance with engine cold (when reconditioning engine) is .004" (.10 mm) for intake valve and .016" (.40 mm) for exhaust valve. Valve clearance should be checked with engine warmed to 176°F (80°C) oil temperature. Intake valve clearance is .008" (.20 mm) and exhaust clearance is .018" (.45 mm).

3) Adjust clearance by turning screw mounted in tappet with adjusting tool US 8005. Adjustment must be in complete turns only. One turn of screw changes clearance by .002" (.05 mm). After adjusting valve, be sure edge of tappet is in line with green area of tool.

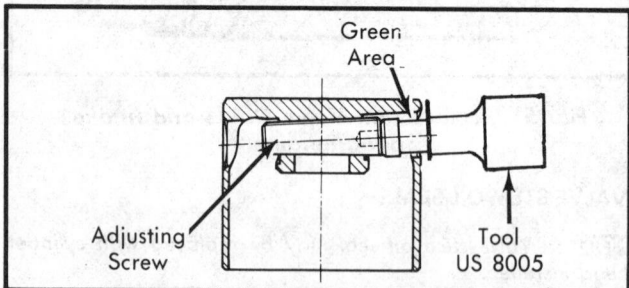

Fig. 7   Valve Lifter (Tappet) with Adjusting Screw and Tool

PISTONS, PINS & RINGS

OIL PAN

Drain engine oil and loosen left engine mount slightly. Disconnect steering at crossmember and remove crossmember. Remove oil pan bolts and lower oil pan. To install, reverse removal procedure and tighten pan bolts.

PISTONS & ROD ASSEMBLY

1) Before removing connecting rods, mark rod and cap for installation in original position. Remove rod caps and carefully push piston and rod assembly out top of block.

2) On reassembly of piston and rod assembly, cast bosses on rod and cap must face pulley end of engine. Code numbers must be on same side. Using a suitable ring compressor, install piston and rod assembly with arrow on crown of piston facing front of engine.

FITTING PISTONS

1) Measure cylinder bore .39" (9.9 mm) down from top and up same distance from bottom, also in the center. Take two measurements, one in line with crankshaft and again 90° to crankshaft.

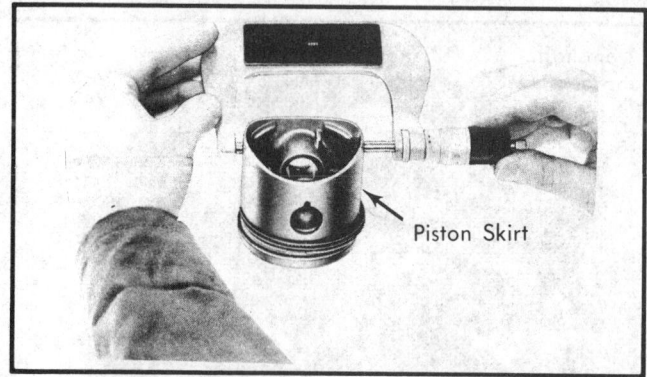

Fig. 8   Measuring Piston Diameter at Skirt

2) Measure piston .63" (16 mm) from bottom of skirt, 90° to pin bore. Combine measurements with those taken from cylinder bore. If piston-to-cylinder measurement exceeds .0016" (.04 mm), oversized pistons must be installed.

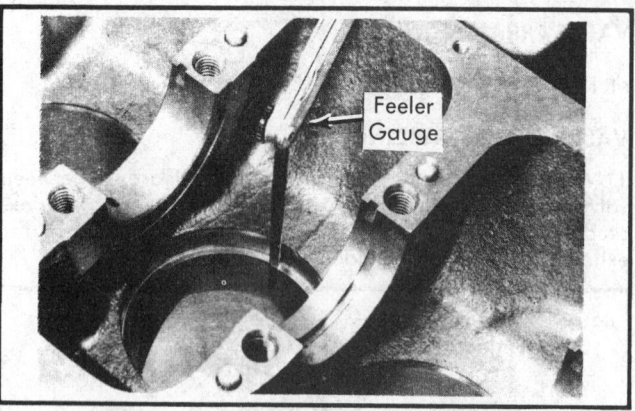

Fig. 9   Measuring Ring Gap in Cylinder Bore

3) Place piston rings squarely in bottom of cylinder bore approximately .59" (15 mm) from surface and measure ring gap. Wear limit is .039" (1.0 mm). Measure ring side clearance in piston. Wear limit is .004" (0.1 mm). Install rings with "TOP" mark facing piston crown and gaps offset 120° from each other.

PISTON PINS

Remove circlip and using piston pin remover VW 207c, remove pins. To install, reverse removal procedure.

NOTE — If pin is hard to install, heat piston to approximately 140°F (60°C).

924 4-CYLINDER (Cont.)

Fig. 10   Piston Pin Removal and Installation

CRANKSHAFT MAIN & CONNECTING ROD BEARINGS

MAIN & CONNECTING ROD BEARINGS

1) Push crankshaft toward one end and measure end play at No. 3 thrust bearing. Be sure main bearing caps are marked for reinstallation. Measure connecting rod side play. Remove rod and main bearing caps and check bearing clearance using Plastigage method.

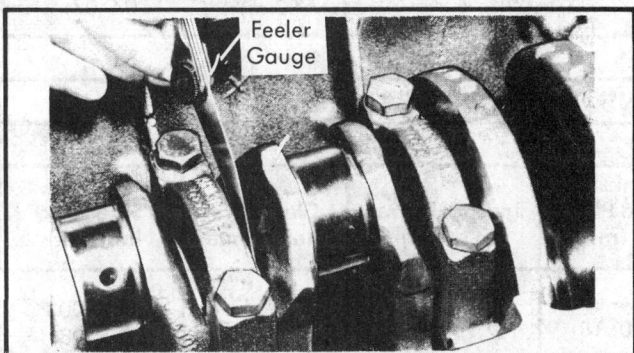

Fig. 11   Measure Crankshaft End Play as Shown (Check Connecting Rod Side Clearance Using Same Method)

2) Install plain bearing shell into bearing cap. Place grooved shell in block. Do not mix shells. Lubricate bearings and install caps.

NOTE — *On No. 5. bearing, coat mating surface of bearing with sealing compound.*

ENGINE OILING

Crankcase Capacity (Includes Filter) — 5.3 quarts for 924, 5.8 quarts for 924 Turbo.

Oil Filter — Spin-on type. Change at first oil change and every other one thereafter.

Oil Pressure — 73-101 psi (5.1-7.1 kg/cm^2) at 5000 RPM.

ENGINE OILING SYSTEM

The engine oiling system is full pressure with rotary (sickle) type pump. Oil is picked up by pump through strainer and suction tube. Oil passes through pump and pressure control valve to oil filter and main oil channels. It is then distributed to main bearings, connecting rods and crankshaft. Camshaft lubrication is provided by spray tube at No. 1 cam bearing. Oil pressure switch is located at end of camshaft lubrication passage. A temperature sensor is located in oil pan. Lubrication system for 924 Turbo includes the following additional componets: an oil cooler in front of engine, oil filter flange with thermostat for the oil cooler, and delivery and return lines for the turbocharger.

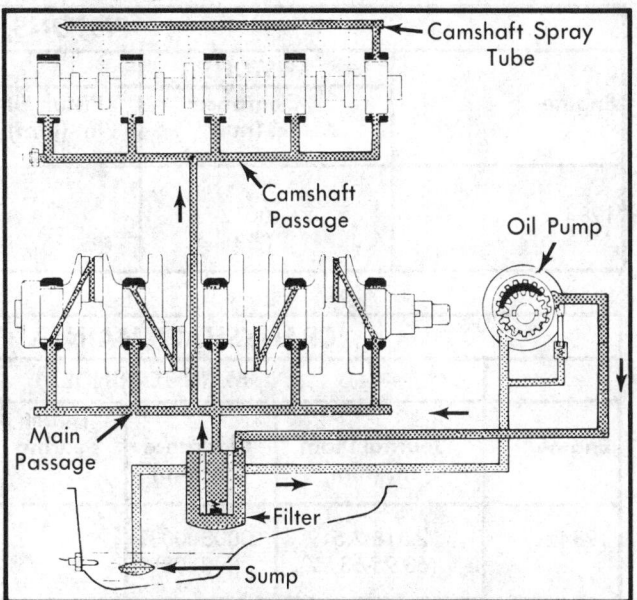

Fig. 12   Engine Oiling System (924 Shown, 924 Turbo Similar)

OIL PUMP

Oil pump is gear driven sickle type. Pump is mounted at front of engine and driven directly by crankshaft. Gear replacement is in pairs only.

ENGINE COOLING

Cooling System Capacity — 8.4 quarts with heater.
Thermostat — Opens at approximately 180°F.
Radiator Cap — 12-8-16-4 psi (.90-1.15 kg/cm^2).
Cooling Fan — Comes on at 198°F, goes off at 189°F.

ENGINE SPECIFICATIONS

GENERAL SPECIFICATIONS										
Year	Displ.		Carburetor	HP at RPM	Torque (Ft. Lbs. at RPM)	Compr. Ratio	Bore		Stroke	
	cu. ins.	cc					in.	mm	in.	mm
1981										
924	121	1984	Fuel Inj.	115 @ 5700	114 @ 3500	8.5:1	3.41	86.5	3.32	84.4
924 Turbo	121	1984	Fuel Inj.	156 @ 5700	154 @ 3500	8.0:1	3.41	86.5	3.32	84.4

Porsche Engines

924 4-CYLINDER (Cont.)
ENGINE SPECIFICATIONS (Cont.)

VALVES

Engine & Valve	Head Diam. In. (mm)	Face Angle	Seat Angle	Seat ① Width In. (mm)	Stem Diameter In. (mm)	Stem Clearance In. (mm)	Valve Lift In. (mm)
1984 cc Int.	1.575 (40)	45°	45°	.087-.118 (2.2-3.0)	.3532 (8.97)	.0157 (0.4)	.....
Exh.	1.299② (33)	45°	45°	.087-.118 (2.2-3.0)	.3524 (8.95)	.020 (0.5)	.....

① — Maximum seat width .138" (3.5 mm).   ② — 924 Turbo 1.417" (36 mm) diameter.

PISTONS, PINS, RINGS

Engine	PISTONS Clearance In. (mm)	PINS Piston Fit In. (mm)	PINS Rod Fit In. (mm)	Rings	RINGS End Gap In. (mm)	RINGS Side Clearance In. (mm)
1984 cc	.0012 (.03)	.....	.0004-.0008 (.01-.02)	.....	.012-.020 (.3-.5)	.0016-.0028 (.04-.07)

CRANKSHAFT MAIN & CONNECTING ROD BEARINGS

Engine	MAIN BEARINGS Journal Diam. In. (mm)	Clearance In. (mm)	Thrust Bearing	Crankshaft End Play In. (mm)	CONNECTING ROD BEARINGS Journal Diam. In. (mm)	Clearance In. (mm)	Side Play In. (mm)
1984 cc	2.518-2.519 (63.95-63.97)	.0008-.0031 (.02-.08)	3	.004-.007 (.10-.18)	1.888-1.889 (47.95-47.97)	.0008-.0027 (.02-.07)	.002-.003 (.05-.08)

VALVE TIMING

Engine	INTAKE Open (BTDC)	INTAKE Close (ABDC)	EXHAUST Open (BBDC)	EXHAUST Close (ATDC)
1984 cc①	6°	42°	47°	2°

① — With .039" (1 mm) valve clearance.

CAMSHAFT

Engine	Journal Diam. In. (mm)	Clearance In. (mm)	Lobe Lift In. (mm)
1984 cc	1.0213-1.0220 (25.94-25.96)	.0015-.0032 (.040-.081)	.....

TIGHTENING SPECIFICATIONS

Application	Ft. Lbs. (N·m)
Cylinder Head Bolts	
924	47 (64)
924 Turbo	
Step 1	29 (40)
Step 2	58 (79)
Step 3	①80 (110)
Main Bearing Caps	58 (79)
No. 5 Allen Head Bolt	47 (64)
Connecting Rod Nuts	43 (58)
Flywheel	②65 (88)
Crankshaft Pulley	180 (245)
Exhaust Manifold	18 (24)
Intake Manifold	17 (23)
Camshaft Bearing Cap Bolts	7 (10)
Camshaft Bearing Cap Nuts	12-15 (16-20)
Camshaft Sprocket Bolt	58 (79)

① — Retighten after 1 hour and after warming engine. See Text.
② — On Turbo, flywheel is a press fit and must be heated to install.

911SC 6-CYLINDER

ENGINE CODING

ENGINE IDENTIFICATION

Engine identification number is die stamped on blower fan support near oil temperature sensor. Second digit of number identifies engines as follows:

Engine Identification	
Application	**Code**
911SC (2994 cc)	4

ENGINE & CYLINDER HEADS

ENGINE

Removal — 1) Place vehicle on jack stands. Disconnect negative battery cable. Remove air cleaner. Detach air conditioning compressor from brackets, but leave hoses attached.

2) Disconnect all electrical wires running between engine and engine compartment. Remove fuel lines at filter and return line. Disconnect accelerator linkage.

3) Remove rear center tunnel cover in passenger compartment. Remove rubber boot in tunnel by pulling forward over the selector rod. Loosen shift rod coupling and pull coupling off of transmission inner shift rod.

4) Disconnect speedometer sensor wires in tunnel. Remove rubber plug with wire plug. Drain crankcase and plug hoses on engine and oil tank. Remove heater hoses at exchangers. Remove rear stabilizer.

5) Disconnect ground strap at body and battery wires at starter. Disconnect accelerator linkage from pedal and clutch cable from transmission. Loosen drive shaft flange socket head screws at transmission.

6) Place a suitable jack under engine/transmission assembly and apply a little upward pressure to relieve tension on motor mounts. Remove transmission and engine mount bolts. Lower engine/transmission assembly out of vehicle.

CAUTION — *Do not move vehicle unless drive shafts are suspended horizontally.*

Installation — Reverse removal procedure and note the following: Do not clamp heater hoses, slide them onto the exchangers just before the engine/transmission assembly is in final installation position.

CYLINDER HEADS

Removal — 1) With fuel injection system removed, take off distributor cap and spark plug wires. Remove cooling air ducts, cover shrouds, ducts connecting air blower outlets and heat exchanger inlets with cover shrouds.

2) Remove rear engine mount from holder. Remove exhaust system, engine mounting bracket, blower pulley and drive belt. Loosen both screws of band strap which attaches alternator to blower housing and pull housing rearward. Disconnect alternator cables and remove blower housing along with alternator.

3) Remove heat exchanger using suitable wrenches (P 205 & P 217). Disconnect camshaft oil lines between crankcase and chain housing covers. Remove covers. Remove chain tensioner, pivot lever and chain sprocket as an assembly.

4) Remove camshaft sprocket nuts using suitable tools (P 202 & P 203). Withdraw sprocket dowel pin with tool (P 212). Use a screwdriver to lift spring retainers from groove and remove chain guides. Remove camshaft sprockets and flanges. Pry Woodruff keys from camshafts.

NOTE — *Each cylinder has a separate head. If camshaft housing is removed, any single head may be removed. If camshaft housing is left attached to cylinder heads, cylinder heads and camshaft housing may be removed as an assembly.*

5) To remove a single head, rotate camshaft to take load off of rocker arm shaft to be removed. Loosen and remove rocker arm shafts and remove camshaft housing. With suitable tool (P 119), remove cylinder head nuts and lift off cylinder head.

NOTE — *Mark cylinder heads, cylinders and camshaft housings for reassembly in original positions.*

6) To remove all 3 cylinder heads and camshaft housing as an assembly, evenly loosen and unscrew cylinder head nuts with suitable tool (P 119).

Installation — 1) Place cylinder head gaskets on cylinders with perforated side of steel insert facing cylinder. Install cylinder heads and oil return tubes at same time. Coat oil return tubes with engine oil for easier installation. Lightly tighten cylinder head nuts.

NOTE — *Split (2 piece) oil return pipes may be installed without removing and disassembling the engine. If using this type, all "O" rings and seals must be lightly oiled and pipe telescoped. Extend pipe until end seals are seated and place retaining ring in its groove. Short pipe must be installed in crankshaft housing.*

2) Install cool air shrouds and attach with clamps. Thinly coat camshaft housing gasket with gasket compound. Slide camshaft housing onto mounting studs. Tighten camshaft housing nuts down a few turns to ensure gasket seal. Install Allen screws in proper location and tighten camshaft housing in a crosswise pattern.

NOTE — *Camshaft housings are interchangeable, but camshafts are not. Camshafts must be positioned on their proper side. See Fig. 4.*

3) Tighten cylinder head nuts in a crosswise pattern, checking that camshaft does not bind in housing. If camshaft binds, loosen cylinder head nuts and tighten in a different sequence. With cylinder head nuts tight, camshaft must be free to rotate.

4) Install rocker shafts and arms so grooves in shafts are recessed approximately .060" (1.52 mm) into bores. *See Fig. 1.* Tighten Allen bolts using suitable tools (P 210 & P 211).

911SC 6-CYLINDER (Cont.)

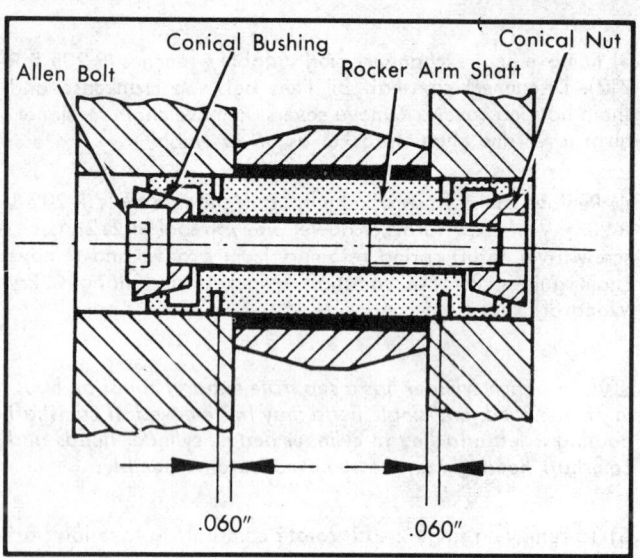

Fig. 1   Cross Section of Rocker Arm Shaft Assembly

5) Install gasket, "O" ring, sealing flange, thrust plate, spacer, Woodruff key and camshaft sprocket flange as shown in *Fig. 2*. No provision is made to adjust camshaft end play. If sealing flange is worn, replace it.

6) Install camshaft sprockets and check chain alignment. See *Fig. 5*. Install heat exchanger, then chain tensioner. Slide chain guides on mounting studs. Lift retaining spring with screwdriver and slide chain guide into place. Install chain tension pivot lever and sprocket. Ensure that oil holes in pivot stud face upward.

7) Fill and bleed chain tensioners. Depress and install tensioners. Left tensioner may be positioned in only far enough to let camshaft nut be installed after valve timing. See *Valve Timing*. Install chain housing covers and camshaft oil lines. To complete installation, reverse removal procedures.

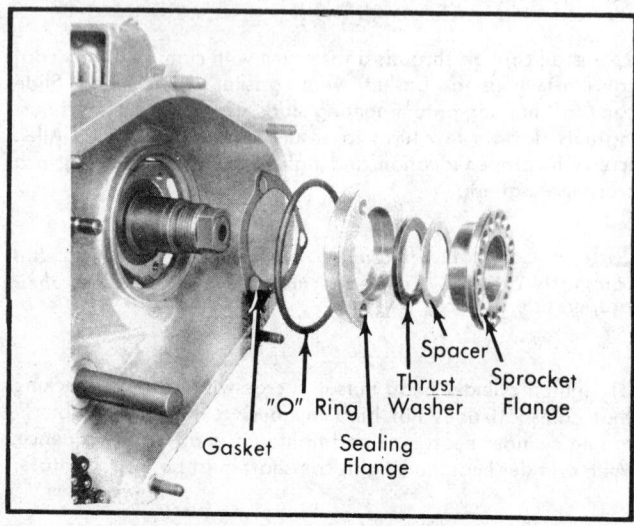

Fig. 2   Assembling Components to Install Camshaft Sprocket Flange and Sprocket

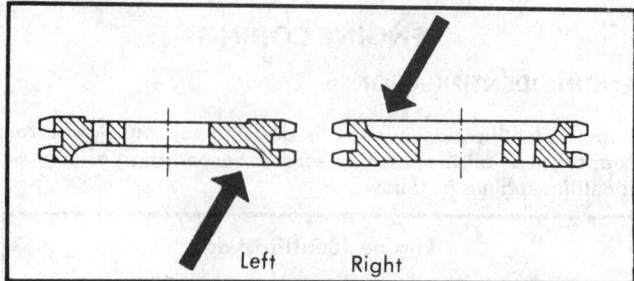

Fig. 3   Camshaft Sprocket Position (Viewed from Blower End of Engine)

CAMSHAFTS

CAMSHAFTS

Removal — 1) With engine out of vehicle, remove rocker covers and rocker arm assemblies. Remove muffler, oil hose from crankcase to chain housing cover, chain tensioner and chain tensioner sprocket.

2) Remove belt pulley from left camshaft. Remove bearing and chain housing covers. Remove ball bearing from camshaft with a puller.

3) Unscrew nuts attaching camshaft sprocket with suitable tools (P 202 & P 203). Remove dowel pin from camshaft sprocket with tool (P 212). Pull sprocket and sprocket flange from camshaft. Remove 3 attaching screws and sealing flange with "O" ring, and withdraw camshaft rearward. See *Fig. 2*.

NOTE — *Camshafts are not symetrical and must be replaced on side they were removed from during disassembly.*

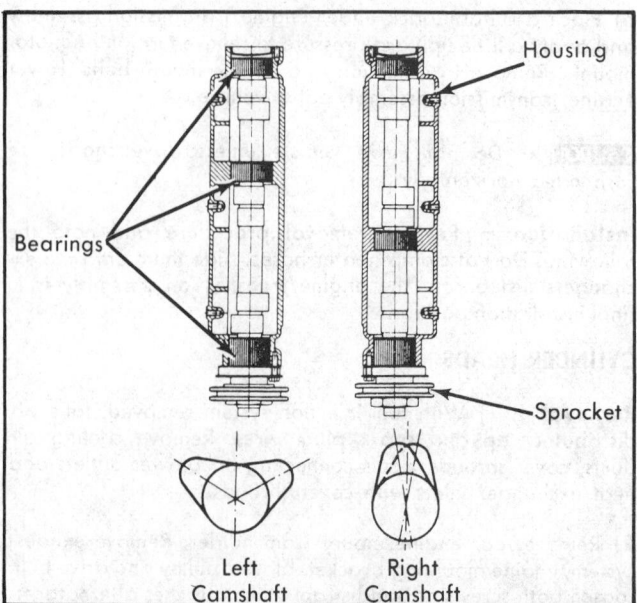

Fig. 4   Camshaft and Housing Viewed from Blower End of Engine

911SC 6-CYLINDER (Cont.)

CAMSHAFT END THRUST

Measure camshaft end play with a dial indicator. If play is excessive, replace aluminum thrust washer located behind camshaft sprocket flange.

TIMING CHAIN

Remove timing chain housing covers. Remove chain tensioner and chain tensioner sprocket. Remove timing chains. Install in reverse order of removal, ensuring that valve timing and chain alignment are as specified. *See Figs. 5 and 7.*

VALVE TIMING

1) Rotate crankshaft until mark "Z 1" on crankshaft pulley aligns with mark on crankcase. Use suitable tool (P 202) to rotate camshaft until dot on end of shaft is on top of camshaft vertical centerline. *See Fig. 7.* Find hole in camshaft sprocket which exactly lines up with camshaft flange and insert dowel pin. Install lock washer and nut.

CAUTION — *Use care when rotating crankshaft or camshafts so that valve and piston do not collide. If resistance is felt, back off a little and rotate camshaft until you are free to continue.*

2) Adjust cylinder No. 1 intake valve clearance to .004" (.10 mm). Install a dial indicator with pressure foot resting squarely on valve spring collar. Preload indicator to .4" (10 mm) to provide for valve movement. Depress chain tensioner with screwdriver on side to be measured and block it with a piece of metal.

3) Rotate crankshaft 360° until "Z 1" (TDC) mark is aligned with mark on crankcase. Read dial indicator and compare with measurement given in *Intake Valve Lift Table.*

4) If correct valve opening measurement is not achieved, loosen camshaft nut, remove dowel pin and rotate camshaft

Intake Valve Lift	
Application	**In. (mm)**
911SC	.055-.067 (1.4-1.7)

until valve is open correct amount. Locate holes which align exactly and install dowel pin. Make sure crankshaft remains on TDC. Rotate crankshaft 2 complete revolutions and recheck valve lift. Repeat timing procedure if necessary. Repeat procedure on No. 4 cylinder for other side of engine.

VALVES

VALVE ARRANGEMENT

All upper valves are intake.

All lower valves are exhaust.

VALVE GUIDE SERVICING

1) In order to avoid spreading the end of the valve guide when removing it, mill the guide down to the head on the camshaft side. A .433" (11 mm) drill bit may be used if milling tool not available. Drive valve guide out into combustion chamber.

2) Using a hole gauge, measure bore in cylinder head. Turn oversize guide down in a lathe so that O.D. gives an interference fit of .0024-.0035" (.060-.090 mm).

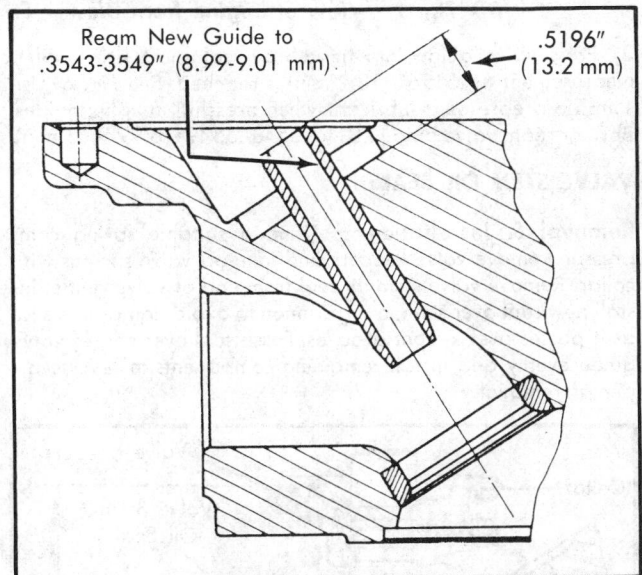

Ream New Guide to .3543-3549" (8.99-9.01 mm)

.5196" (13.2 mm)

Fig. 6   Cross Section of Valve Guide Installed in Head

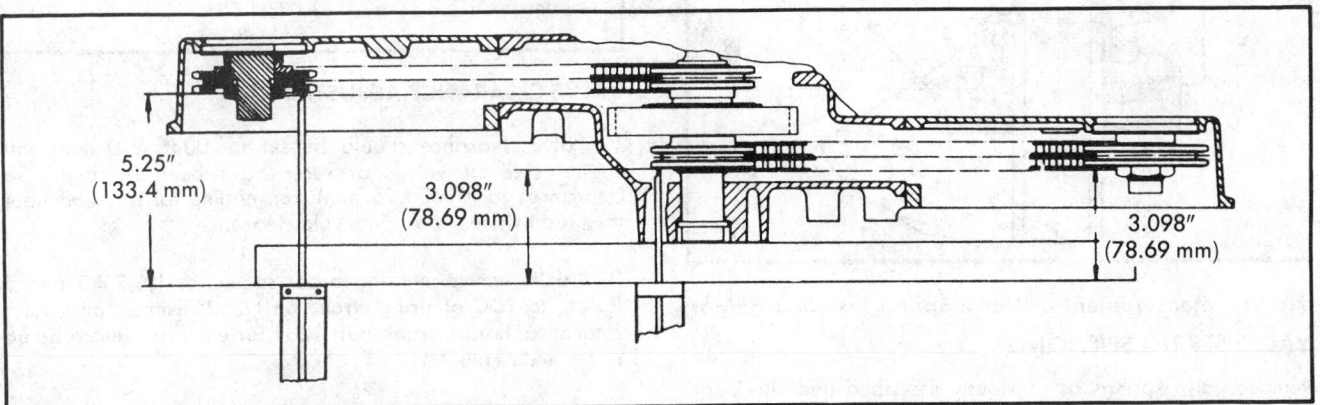

5.25" (133.4 mm)

3.098" (78.69 mm)

3.098" (78.69 mm)

Fig. 5   Top View Showing Timing Chain Alignment

Porsche Engines

911SC 6-CYLINDER (Cont.)

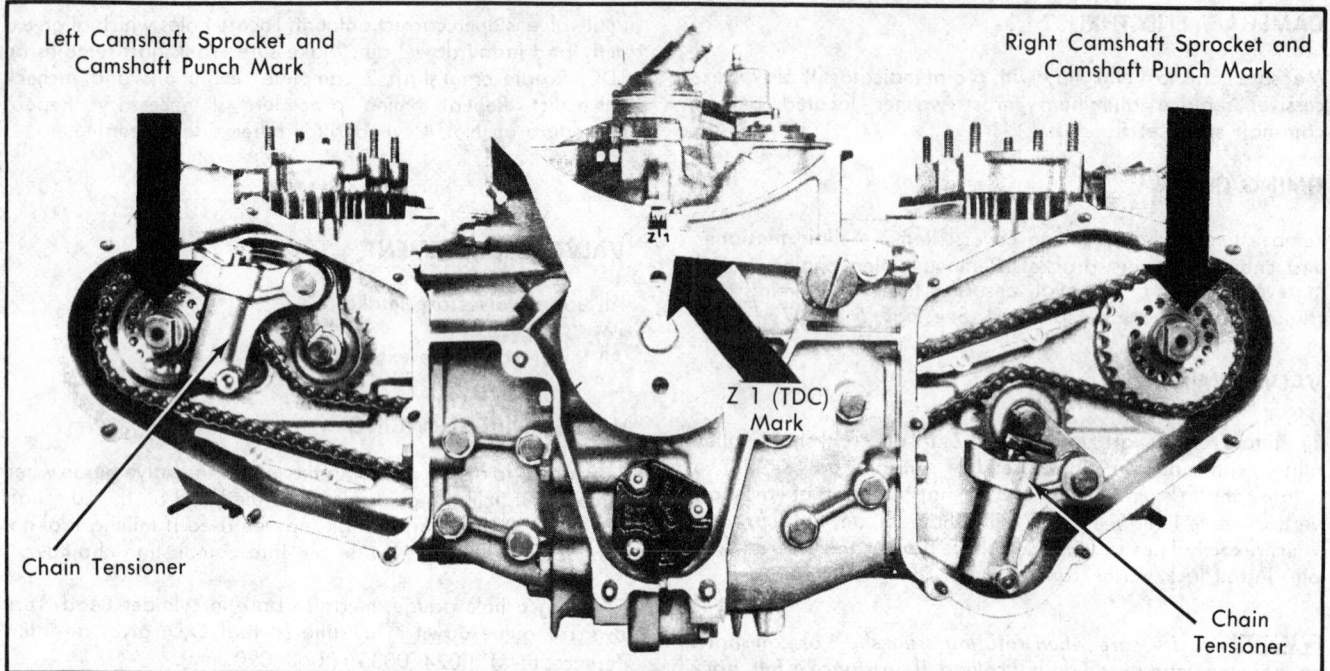

Left Camshaft Sprocket and Camshaft Punch Mark

Right Camshaft Sprocket and Camshaft Punch Mark

Z 1 (TDC) Mark

Chain Tensioner

Chain Tensioner

Fig. 7   View of Engine from Blower End (Rear of Car) Showing Valve Timing Marks

3) Press valve guide into head from camshaft side until a measurement of .5196" (13.2 mm) is reached. See Fig. 6. Use suitable grease as a lubricant when pressing in valve guides. Bore or ream valve guide I.D. to .3543-.3549" (8.99-9.01 mm).

VALVE STEM OIL SEALS

Removal & Installation — Using a suitable spring compressor, remove valve keepers and take off valve springs with collar. Remove valve stem oil seal from end of valve guide. Install new seal over stem, using caution to avoid damage to seal as it passes over keeper grooves. Force seal over end of valve guide evenly and install remaining components in reverse order of removal.

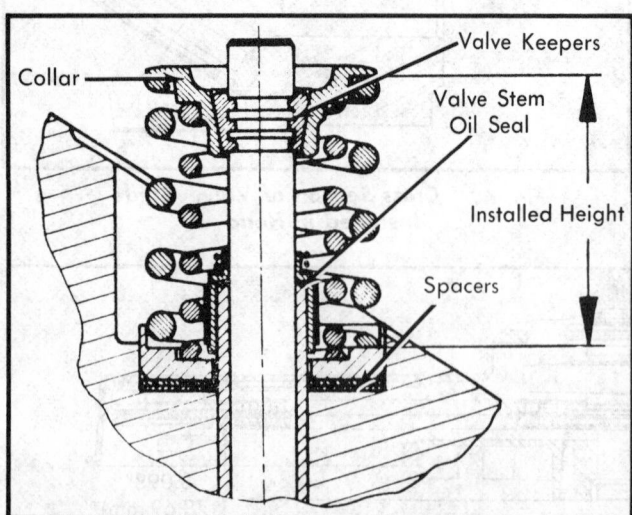

Valve Keepers

Collar

Valve Stem Oil Seal

Installed Height

Spacers

Fig. 8   Measurement of Valve Spring Installed Height

VALVE SPRING SERVICING

Remove valve springs as previously described and check for wear or fatigue. Replace as necessary and install with closely wound coils next to cylinder head. Check installed height with special tool (P 10) and add or remove spacers under the valve spring to attain specified installed height.

ROCKER ARMS

Using an Allen wrench, loosen rocker arm shaft bolt. Slide rocker shaft out of cylinder head and remove arm. Check rocker arm shaft and bushing for wear and replace as required. Install rocker arm shaft with Allen bolt facing either No. 2 or No. 5 cylinder. Center shaft in housing and tighten Allen bolt. See Fig. 1.

Rocker Arm Specifications		
Application	Diameter In. (mm)	Wear Limit In. (mm)
Rocker Arm Bushing	.7090-.7094 (18.009-18.019)	.............7106 (18.049)
Rocker Arm Shaft	.7080-.7084 (17.983-17.993)	.............7074 (17.968)
Rocker Arm Width........	1.015-1.019 (25.78-25.88)	,............1.011 (25.68)
Housing Width	1.023-1.029 (25.98-23.14)	.... 1.033 (26.24)

VALVE CLEARANCE ADJUSTMENT

1) Valve clearance should be set to .004" (.10 mm) with engine cold. If valves or seats have been reground, set clearances to .010" (.25 mm), run engine for one-half hour, then reset valves to original cold clearance.

2) Adjust valves in firing order sequence: 1,6,2,4,3 and 5. Rotate to TDC of firing stroke on No. 1 cylinder and adjust clearance. Rotate crankshaft 120° for each cylinder to be adjusted until complete.

NOTE — *Cylinders are numbered from pulley end on left side, 1, 2, and 3, with 4, 5 and 6 on right side, 6 at flywheel end.*

Porsche Engines

911SC 6-CYLINDER (Cont.)

PISTONS, PINS & RINGS

OIL PAN

Remove nuts attaching oil pan (strainer cover plate) and remove strainer plate gaskets and strainer. Clean and inspect strainer and cover plate. Using new gaskets, replace strainer and cover plate. Ensure that oil strainer hole slides over pickup tube.

PISTON ASSEMBLY

Mark piston and cylinder for proper assembly location. Remove cylinders and take out piston pin circlip. Heat piston to approximately 176°F (80°C) and press out pin. Clean and inspect piston, rings and pin for each cylinder. Replace parts as necessary.

NOTE — See measurement procedures in Fitting Pistons.

FITTING PISTONS

The 911SC piston has a depressed dome shape, and this depression must face the exhaust valve when installed. Pistons must be of same weight class and cylinders of same size in order to prevent unbalance of the engine.

1) Measure cylinder for wear and out-of-round. Cylinders and pistons are marked according to size. "0" indicates standard, while "1" or "2" indicates first or second oversize. Measure cylinder diameter 1.18" (30 mm) below top edge of cylinder.

2) Take one measurement in line with thrust face and another at 90° to this measurement. Cylinder is worn if diameter measurement is more than .004" (0.1 mm) beyond diameter specification. If difference in the two measurements is more than .0016" (.04 mm), then cylinder has exceeded its ovality limit.

3) Position piston rings in bottom of cylinder and measure ring gap. Check side clearance in piston ring grooves. Install rings on piston with marking "TOP" facing upward.

CRANKSHAFT MAIN & CONNECTING ROD BEARINGS

MAIN BEARING SERVICE

1) Separate crankcase halves. Lift out crankshaft and connecting rods. Place crankshaft on a suitable stand and remove connecting rods. Inspect crankshaft and connecting rods for wear, damage or out-of-true. Crankshaft main journals 1 through 7 and all connecting rod journals have the same diameter. Replace bearings or fit undersize bearings as required.

NOTE — Connecting rod bolts are stretch bolts and should never be reused. Replace connecting rod bolts whenever rods are disassembled.

2) Main bearing No. 8 is a special bearing with an external "O" ring and an internal oil seal. A steel dowel pressed in the crankcase is used to locate No. 8 bearing and prevent it from turning. Use care when installing bearing so that dowel engages hole and not groove in bearing.

THRUST BEARING ALIGNMENT

Check end play at No. 1 main bearing. Width of No. 1 bearing is 1.1024-1.1044" (28.0-28.05 mm). Maximum wear limit is .011" (.28 mm) beyond specifications. Replace main bearing or crankshaft if excessive wear is present.

MAIN BEARING OIL SEALS (BLOWER END)

Remove belt pulley. Using a screwdriver, pry out old seal. Coat new seal with oil and press in place with suitable tool (P 216).

MAIN BEARING OIL SEAL SERVICE (FLYWHEEL END)

Remove flywheel. Displace oil seal with a chisel or drift and pry out with screwdriver. Coat outer seal edges with sealing compound and press into crankcase with driver (P 215) until seal is flush with face of crankcase.

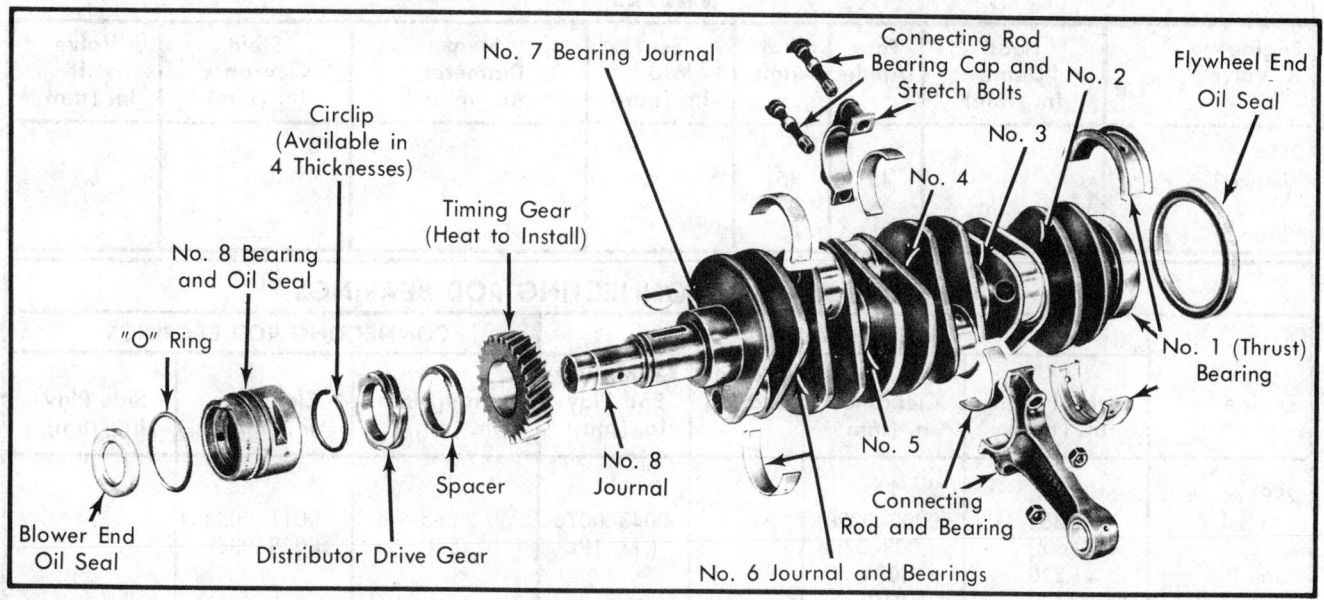

Fig. 9 Crankshaft Assembly with Component Locations

Porsche Engines

911SC 6-CYLINDER (Cont.)

INTERMEDIATE SHAFT BEARING SERVICE

With crankcase halves separated, lift out intermediate shaft and bearings. Inspect shaft and bearings for wear or damage and replace as necessary. Undersize bearings are NOT available.

ENGINE OILING

Oil Capacity — 13.7 qts. total; 10.6 qts for oil change.

Oil Filter — Disposable spin-on type.

Normal Oil Pressure — 65 psi (4.6 kg/cm) at 5000 RPM with an oil temperature of 194°F (90°C).

Pressure Relief and Safety Valves — Identically constructed coil spring operated valves. Safety valve is set to operate at a higher pressure than relief valve.

ENGINE OILING SYSTEM

Lubrication is dry sump type. Two independent oil pumps provide for pressure and suction in system. Pressure pump takes oil from externally mounted oil tank, and forces oil through passages to main, connecting rod and intermediate shaft bearings. Camshaft bearings are oiled by external oil lines leading to camshaft housing. Oil splashes against valve cover to drip on rocker arms and valve stems.

Suction pump takes oil from sump through strainer and forces it through oil filter to oil tank. Oil from lower part of camshaft housing is returned to crankcase by oil return pipes. Pressure is controlled by 4 separate valves. At low temperatures, a thermostatically controlled valve directs oil to engine. At higher temperatures, oil first flows through cooler and then to bearings.

A pressure and relief valve directs oil into crankcase if pressure rises above 76.9-99.6 psi (5.4-7.0 kg/cm^2). Additional saftey and by-pass valves are built into the system to prevent damage from excess pressure.

OIL PUMP

Oil pump may be removed when crankcase halves are separated. No repair of pump is possible, replace if defective.

ENGINE COOLING

Cooling is accomplished by means of a blower, consisting of an impeller and blower housing. Center of blower housing holds support for alternator. Impeller and belt pulley are attached to alternator shaft. Blower delivers air required for cooling engine, oil cooler, alternator as well as fresh air for heating system. Cooling air flows through upper molded plastic air guides to cylinders and heads. Baffle plates provide uniform distribution of air. A duct incorporated into upper air guide leads air flow directly to oil cooler. Ducting for air delivery to heat exchangers is on both sides of blower housing. Adjustment of blower drive belt is done by adding or removing spacers between impeller housing and pulley half. This will cause belt to ride higher of lower on pulley, thereby loosening or tightening drive belt.

ENGINE SPECIFICATIONS

GENERAL SPECIFICATIONS

Year	Displ.		Carburetor	HP at RPM	Torque (Ft. Lbs. at RPM)	Compr. Ratio	Bore		Stroke	
	cu. ins.	cc					in.	mm	in.	mm
1981	182.7	2994	Fuel Inj.	172@5500	175@4200	9.3:1	3.74	95	2.77	70.4

VALVES

Engine & Valve	Head Diam. In. (mm)	Face Angle	Seat Angle	Seat Width In. (mm)	Stem Diameter In. (mm)	Stem Clearance In. (mm)	Valve Lift In. (mm)
2994 cc Intake	.....	45°	45°	.....	.....	.....	.....
Exhaust	.....	45°	45°	.....	.....	.....	.....

CRANKSHAFT MAIN & CONNECTING ROD BEARINGS

Engine	MAIN BEARINGS				CONNECTING ROD BEARINGS		
	Journal Diam. In. (mm)	Clearance In. (mm)	Thrust Bearing	Crankshaft End Play In. (mm)	Journal Diam. In. (mm)	Clearance In. (mm)	Side Play In. (mm)
2994 cc Jrnls 1-7	2.362 (60)	.0003-.0028 (.008-.07)	No. 1	.0043-.0076 (.11-.19)	2.085 (53)	.0011-.0034 (.028-.086)	.....
Jrnl 8	1.220 (31)	.004 (.10)					

911SC 6-CYLINDER (Cont.)
ENGINE SPECIFICATIONS (Cont.)

PISTONS, PINS, RINGS

Engine	PISTONS	PINS		RINGS		
	Clearance In. (mm)	Piston Fit In. (mm)	Rod Fit In. (mm)	Rings	End Gap In. (mm)	Side Clearance In. (mm)
2994 cc	.001-.002 (.023-.044)	Press Fit	.0007-.0015 (.018-.038)	No. 1	.004-.008 (.10-.20)	.003-.004 (.07-.10)
				No. 2	.004-.008 (.10-.20)	.001-.003 (.04-.07)
				Oil	.006-.012 (.15-.30)	.0008-.002 (.02-.05)

VALVE SPRINGS

Engine	Free Length In. (mm)	INSTALLED VALVE HEIGHT①	
		Valve Closed	Valve Open
2994 cc Intake	.....	1.346-1.358 (34.2-34.5)	.....
Exhaust	.....	1.346-1.358 (34.2-34.5)	.....

① — Upper value must not be exceeded.

VALVE TIMING

Engine	INTAKE		EXHAUST	
	Open (BTDC)	Close (ABDC)	Open (BBDC)	Close (ATDC)
2994 cc	1°	53°	43°	3°

TIGHTENING SPECIFICATIONS

Application	Ft.Lbs. (N.m)
Crankcase Joining Bolts	25 (34)
Camshaft Housing	18 (24)
Main Bearing Caps	25 (34)
Flywheel (9 Bolt)	65 (88)
Connecting Rod Caps	36 (49)
Cylinder Head	22 (30)
Crankshaft Pulley	58 (79)
Camshaft Nut	101 (137)
Rocker Arm Shafts	13 (18)

Porsche Engines

928 V8

ENGINE CODING

ENGINE IDENTIFICATION

Engine code and identification number is stamped on the front reinforcing rib in the top half of the crankcase.

Engine Identification	
Application	**Code**
928 (4474 cc)	M 28

ENGINE & CYLINDER HEADS

ENGINE

Removal — 1) With car standing on all 4 wheels, loosen engine compartment cross braces. Disconnect battery ground cable at spare wheel well. Detach windshield washer hoses and engine compartment light wires. Remove engine hood. Remove cap from coolant expansion tank. Remove air intake hoses and entire air cleaner assembly.

2) Raise car on hoist at specified pick up points. Place wooden block between central tube and rear tunnel brace. Detach splash shield at bottom and drain radiator. Remove left and right water drain plugs from crankcase. Drain engine oil and remove lower body brace. Disconnect exhaust pipes at manifolds and remove left and right heat shields. Detach ground cable at body. Install and tighten drain plugs.

3) Unscrew clutch slave cylinder at clutch housing and remove with line connected. Remove mounting strap for pressure line to slave cylinder. Disconnect wires at starter and remove clutch housing with starter.

4) Disconnect clutch lever by pressing down in direction of clutch. Release starter wire from clamps on steering cross member. Remove socket head bolts and push drive shaft coupling back on drive shaft. Unscrew throwout bearing sleeve mounting bolts and push sleeve toward flywheel.

5) Detach left and right engine shock absorbers at control arms, then at upper mountings. Disconnect air conditioner temperature switch wires on radiator and compressor clutch at connector plug. Loosen compressor and remove from console but do not disconnect hoses. Suspend compressor with wire.

6) Remove air pump filter housing and alternator cooling hose. Remove lower fan shroud. Disconnect all coolant hoses and bottom oil hose at radiator. Remove engine mounts separately by lifting with hydraulic jack and wooden block on oil pan. Lower engine to front cross member carefully. Move jack and pad to second side and remove mount in same manner.

7) Remove clutch/engine mounting bolts and lower car. Remove remaining coolant/heater hoses between engine and radiator/chassis. Disconnect upper oil hose at radiator. Remove radiator mounting bolts and lift out radiator. Disconnect engine wire harness and distributor wire transmitter plugs. Disconnect B+ wire and remove control unit. Detach and place ignition coil aside.

8) Disconnect fuel feed and return lines. Detach power steering pump lines at pump and supply tank. Drain oil and remove tank. Disconnect brake booster vacuum hose at manifold. Disconnect accelerator and cruise control cable, remove holder and clamp and place cables outside. Cover A/C condenser with a thin board to prevent damage when removing engine.

9) With engine adapter (9137) in eyelets provided, lift until snug with car resting on its wheels. Remove upper engine block/clutch housing mounting bolts. Pull engine forward carefully and remove short drive shaft with guide tube. Lift engine out of car.

Installation — To install, reverse removal procedures noting that heater lever should be in "warm" position when filling cooling system. Coolant level must reach center of expansion tank with engine warm.

CYLINDER HEADS

NOTE — *Manufacturer does not furnish removal and replacement procedures for cylinder heads. Heads may be removed with engine in vehicle. Following items must be noted when performing cylinder head operations:*

1) Allow engine to cool prior to draining coolant. Heads must not be removed while engine is still hot. Remove camshaft housing, then loosen cylinder head nuts in reverse of tightening sequence.

2) Left and right cylinder head gaskets are different. Arrow must face forward and word "TOP/OBEN" must face up. Tighten head in 3 steps according to the sequence shown in Fig. 1. Tighten to final torque and allow to stand at least 30 minutes. Loosen nuts by 1/4 turn, then tighten to final torque.

NOTE — *Washers must not turn while tightening cylinder head nuts. Control by making paint marks if necessary.*

3) Flat gasket between cylinder head and camshaft housing must be placed properly to ensure that oil supply bore to camshaft is not blocked. Camshaft housing must be completely assembled prior to installation. Housing is located on heads with 2 dowel pins and mounted with Allen head bolts.

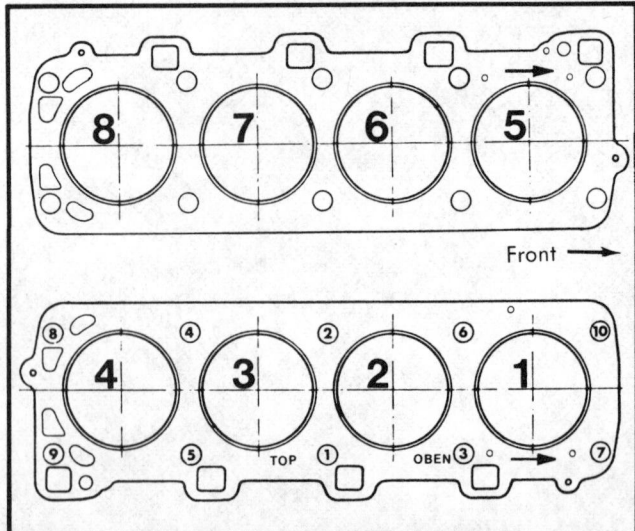

Fig. 1 Cylinder Head Tightening Sequence (Loosen in Reverse Order)

CAMSHAFT

TIMING BELT

Toothed timing belt drives camshafts, distributor, oil pump and water pump. As the engine assembly heats and cools,

928 V8 (Cont.)

belt tension varies, so a multiple disc belt tensioner is installed to compensate for these changes. To adjust tension, remove right hand camshaft drive belt upper cover. Turn engine in direction of rotation to TDC of cylinder No. 1. Turn engine over 2 more times until TDC is reached again. Check drive belt for damage and wear. Using tester (9131) check belt tightness between tension roller and camshaft sprocket. Set adjustment screw on tensioner as required and recheck tension.

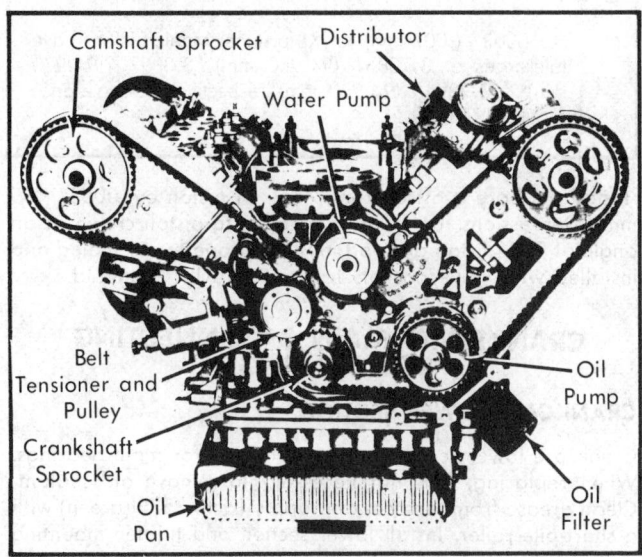

Fig. 2 Front View of Engine with Belt Covers Removed

Fig. 3 View of Left Camshaft Sprocket and Front Pulley with Timing Marks Aligned

CAMSHAFT TIMING ADJUSTMENT

With timing belt and tensioner removed, turn both camshafts until notches in drive sprockets align with marks on camshaft housings. Rotate crankshaft so that TDC mark on vibration damper aligns with indicator. Install belt and tensioner. Rotate crankshaft and recheck tension as in previous step.

DRIVE BELT TENSIONER

Tensioner consists of 7 packets of 5 bimetal discs stacked alternately. If service is required, remove housing from engine and disassemble, noting that housing contains transmission fluid. Clean and reassemble, ensuring that packets of discs are installed alternately. Fill housing 1/3 full of SAE 90 transmission oil. Slide piston assembly in and install circlip. Add transmission oil, if necessary, until oil level reaches circlip. Replace dust cover, clamp and pressure rod. Install on engine.

CAMSHAFTS

Camshafts run in 5 bearings without shells in camshaft housing. Housing cover plates must be removed in order to remove rubber plugs covering top row of bolts. Camshaft housing assembly must be completely assembled before installation. Housing is located on heads with 2 dowel pins and mounted with Allen head bolts.

VALVES

VALVE ARRANGEMENT

Valves are arranged in-line with the larger, intake valve at the front of each cylinder.

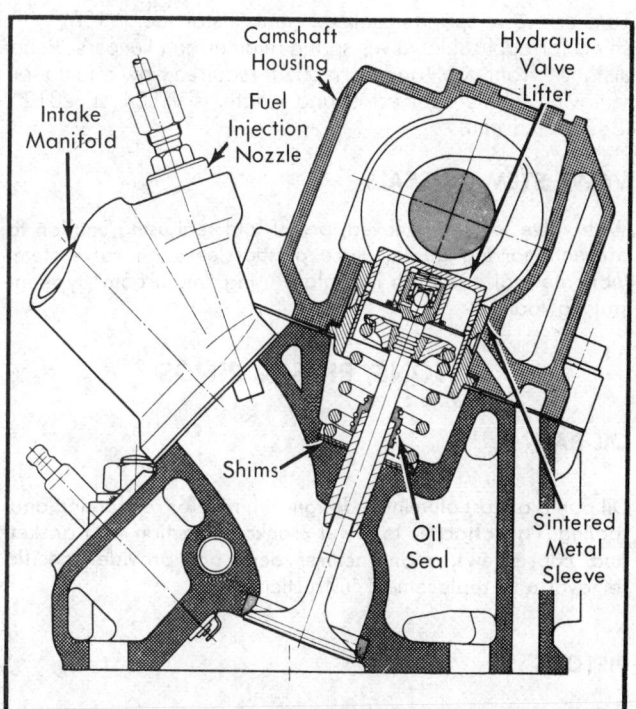

Fig. 4 Cross Sectional View of Cylinder Head with Valve Lifter and Camshaft

Porsche Engines

928 V8 (Cont.)

HYDRAULIC VALVE LIFTERS

Bucket type hydraulic lifters operate in sintered metal sleeves. Cam lobes depress the lifters which are filled with engine oil under pressure through internal passages. With hydraulic lifters, no further valve clearance adjustment is necessary.

NOTE — *Use caution that lifters and sleeves are installed in original positions. Do NOT mix up lifters and sleeves.*

VALVE SPRINGS

Valve springs may be removed using conventional overhead valve type compressor. Remove keepers and lift off retainer and spring. To install, reverse removal procedures.

CAUTION — *Note number of shims between valve spring and cylinder head and replace in same position.*

Fig. 5 Measuring Installed Valve Spring Length

VALVE SPRING INSTALLED LENGTH

To check valve spring installed height, install tool (9138) with shims for applicable valve, spring retainer and keepers. Read distance from tool and correct, if required, by adding or removing shims. Correct spring length is 1.504 ± .012" (38.2 ± .3 mm).

VALVE STEM OIL SEALS

With valve springs removed, pry off old seal using caution to prevent marring guide. Place plastic sleeve on valve stem, lubricate seal and push into place using "mushroom" type installing tool.

PISTONS, PINS & RINGS

OIL PAN

Oil pan is of cast aluminum design with ribs for reinforcing and cooling. Pan attaches to lower crankcase section with gasket and cap screws. Manufacturer does not provide specific removal and replacement instructions.

PISTONS

Pistons and bore diameters come in 3 tolerance groups. Piston crown is stamped "0", "1" or "2" to correspond with similar marking stamped on cylinder block.

Piston-Bore Tolerance Groups		
Tolerance Group	Cylinder Bore [1] In. (mm)	Piston Diameter [2] In. (mm)
0	3.7050 (95.000)	3.7036 (94.964)
1	3.7054 (95.010)	3.7040 (94.974)
2	3.7058 (95.020)	3.7044 (94.984)

[1] — ± .0002" (.005 mm).

[2] — ± .0003" (.007 mm) for KS pistons. Mahle pistons have tolerances of 3.7386" (94.960 mm), 3.3897" (94.970 mm) & 3.7394" (94.980 mm) respectively for tolerance groups 0, 1 & 2.

Piston pin bore is offset from center of piston by .0058" (1.5 mm). Depressions for valves are cast into piston crown at an angle of 20°. Piston and rod must be properly assembled and installed with valve pockets facing EXHAUST manifold.

CRANKSHAFT MAIN & CONNECTING ROD BEARINGS

CRANKCASE LOWER SECTION

Crankcase lower section provides saddles for main bearings. When replacing, it is not necessary to remove old sealant. Clean grease from surfaces and apply Loctite 573 (green) with a short-pile roller. Install lower section and tighten mounting bolts by hand. Install oil pump, then tighten lower section mounting nuts to final torque in sequence illustrated.

MAIN & CONNECTING ROD BEARINGS

Use Plastigage method for determining main and connecting rod clearances. Check crankshaft end play using dial indicator. Ensure that connecting rods are installed to piston correctly. With piston indentations facing away from centerline (down), small chamfer on rod faces rod on same journal. Larger chamfer faces web of crankshaft.

Fig. 6 Crankcase Lower Section Tightening Sequence

CRANKSHAFT OIL SEALS

Crankshaft oil seals are installed with crankcase lower half removed. Use tool (9126) to align flywheel end seal, and tool (9125) to install pulley end oil seal.

Porsche Engines

928 V8 (Cont.)

ENGINE OILING

ENGINE OILING SYSTEM

Engine utilizes a wet sump with an oil cooler integrated in the car radiator as a heat exchanger. Sickle type oil pump is located in a separate cast iron housing bolted to the left front of the engine. Pump is driven by toothed belt. Full pressure system pumps oil to pressure relief valve, thermostat, main oil passage, filter, crankcase upper section, cylinder heads and camshaft housings. All main oil passages are cast into the mating surface of the crankcase lower section.

Oil Filter — Full-flow spin-on type oil filter is easily changed from beneath left side of car.

Normal Oil Pressure — 72 psi (5.06 kg/cm²) at 5000 RPM, 178°F (80°C).

Crankcase Capacity — Approximately 8.5 quarts, with filter change.

OIL PUMP

Removal and Installation — Hold oil pump drive gear with locking tool (9157) and loosen mounting nuts. Remove nuts and gear. Remove oil pump mounting bolts and remove pump. To install, reverse removal procedures.

Inspection — Check end play with dial indicator (387). Permissible end play is .003–.005" (.08–.12 mm).

ENGINE COOLING

928 utilizes an aluminum radiator and a mechanically driven visco-fan. Water pump is driven by the back side of the toothed timing belt. An expansion tank with filler opening and water level sending unit is mounted at the right rear of the engine compartment. Water level is indicated on the instrument cluster.

Cooling System Capacity — 17 quarts.

Thermostat — Opens at 178–185° F (81–85° C).

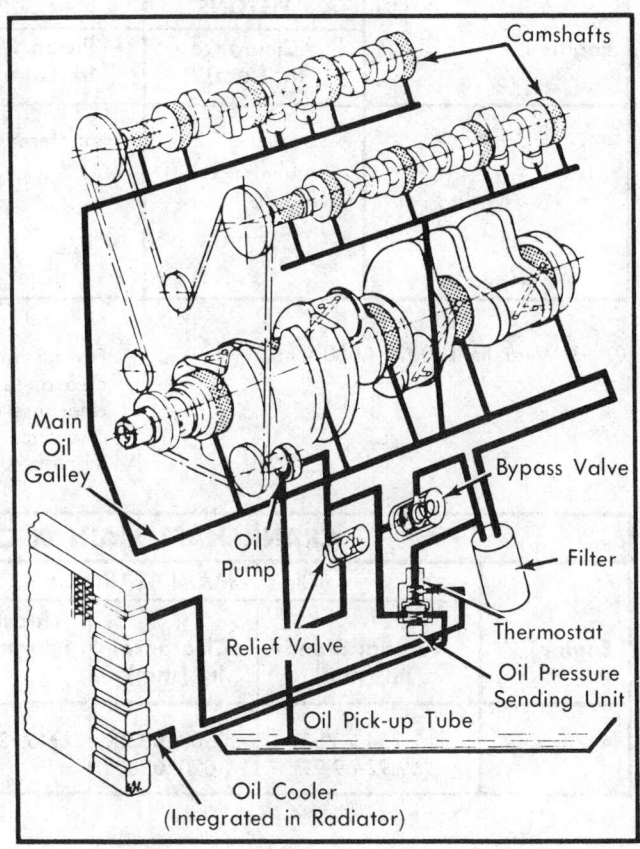

Fig. 7   Porsche 928 Engine Lubrication System

ENGINE SPECIFICATIONS

GENERAL SPECIFICATIONS

| Year | Displ. | | Carburetor | HP at RPM | Torque (Ft. Lbs. at RPM) | Compr. Ratio | Bore | | Stroke | |
	cu. ins.	cc					in.	mm	in.	mm
1981	273	4474	Fuel Inj.	220@5500	265@4000	9:1	3.74	95.0	3.11	78.9

VALVES

Engine & Valve	Head Diam. In. (mm)	Face Angle	Seat Angle	Seat Width In. (mm)	Stem Diameter In. (mm)	Stem Clearance In. (mm)	Valve Lift In. (mm)
4474 cc Intake	1.692 (43)	45°	45°	.067 (1.7)	.3498 (8.97)	.0010–.0020 (.030–.057)	.....
Exhaust	1.496 (38)	45°	45°	.078 (2.0)	.3490 (8.95)	.0200–.0028 (.050–.077)	....

1 — Limit .020" (.5 mm).

Porsche Engines

928 V8 (Cont.)
ENGINE SPECIFICATIONS (Cont.)

PISTONS, PINS, RINGS

| Engine | PISTONS | PINS | | RINGS | | |
	Clearance In. (mm)①	Piston Fit In. (mm)	Rod Fit In. (mm)	Rings	End Gap In. (mm)	Side Clearance In. (mm)②
4474 cc	.001-.002 (.024-.050)	Interference	.0007-.0012 (.019-.032)	1	.008-.015 (.20-.40)	.002-.003 (.050-.082)
				2	.008-.015 (.20-.40)	.002-.003 (.050-.082)
				3	.015-.055 (.40-1.4)	.0009-.0050 (.023-.137)

① — Wear limit .003" (.080 mm).

② — For KS piston rings. For Mahle piston rings, No. 1 clearance is .002-.004" (.060-.102 mm), No. 2 clearance is .0015-.0026" (.040-.072 mm), and No. 3 clearance is .0005-.0049" (.013-.127 mm). Piston manufacturer must match ring manufacturer.

CRANKSHAFT MAIN & CONNECTING ROD BEARINGS

| Engine | MAIN BEARINGS | | | | CONNECTING ROD BEARINGS | | |
	Journal Diam. In. (mm)	Clearance In. (mm)	Thrust Bearing	Crankshaft End Play In. (mm)	Journal Diam. In. (mm)	Clearance In. (mm)	Side Play In. (mm)
4474 cc	2.754-2.755 (69.97-69.99)	.0008-.0038 (.020-.098)	No. 3	.0039-.0157 (.100-.400)	2.046-2.047 (51.97-51.99)	.001-.004 (.034-.092)	.004-.016 (.10-.40)

VALVE TIMING

| Engine | INTAKE | | EXHAUST | |
	Open (ATDC)	Close (ABDC)	Open (BBDC)	Close (BTDC)
4474 cc	12°	48°	32°	6°

TIGHTENING SPECIFICATIONS

Application	Ft. Lbs. (N·m)
Cylinder Head Bolts	
Step 1	14 (20)
Step 2	36 (50)
Step 3①	61 (85)
Main Bearing Carrier	
10 mm Bolt	
Step 1	14 (20)
Step 2	29-33 (40-45)
12 mm Bolt	
Step 1	14 (20)
Step 2	29 (40)
Step 3	44-47 (60-65)
Connecting Rod Nuts	42-46 (58-63)
Camshaft Housing	33 (45)
Flywheel	69-73 (95-100)
Front Pulley	181-188 (250-260)
Camshaft Pulley	33 (45)
Oil Pump	
Step 1	11 (15)
Step 2	14-16 (20-22)
Spark Plugs	18-22 (25-30)
Oil Drain Plug	44 (60)

① — Allow to stand for 30 minutes after setting Step 3 torque, then loosen 1/4 turn each. Retighten to 61 ft. lbs. (85 N·m).

LE CAR 4-CYLINDER

ENGINE CODING

ENGINE IDENTIFICATION

Type of vehicle and engine number is marked on a number plate riveted to the left rear side of the engine block. Plate is located just below cylinder head mating surface. First five digits indicate engine type.

Engine Identification	
Application	Code
Le Car (1397 cc)	847-25

ENGINE, CYLINDER HEAD & MANIFOLDS

ENGINE

NOTE — *Engine and transaxle are removed as an assembly.*

Removal — 1) Remove battery. Drain coolant from engine and radiator. Drain oil. Take out grille. Remove hood and inner fender support. Remove air cleaner.

2) Disconnect all electrical leads, control cables, vacuum lines and coolant hoses that might interfere with engine removal. Mark each item as it is disconnected. Remove transaxle cover.

3) Remove exhaust pipe flange. Remove radiator mounting nuts. Lift out radiator, cooling fan, and expansion tank. Disconnect steering shaft at flexible coupling. Do not lose rubber bushing.

4) Remove front wheels. Remove brake calipers without disconnecting hoses and support out of way. Disconnect tie rods at rack. Use suitable tool and separate upper ball joints. Remove steering gear box. Be sure to index steering box shims.

5) Remove air pump complete with bracket. Remove top transaxle bolts on bell housing. Attach hydraulic hoist to engine. Remove nuts from engine mounts. Remove shift rod support bolts.

6) Disconnect clutch cable. Remove front transaxle mounting bracket. Slide transaxle to left, then to right to free axle drive shafts. Remove engine assembly from vehicle.

Installation — To install, reverse removal procedure and note: Grease transaxle input shaft and axle drive shafts. Do not damage oil seals on axle drive shafts. Make sure axle drive shafts fully seat. Adjust clutch. Refit steering rubber bushing. Bleed cooling system.

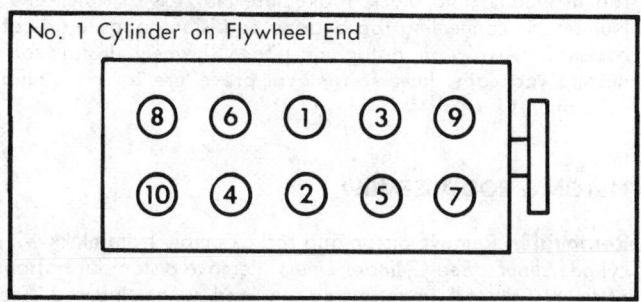

Fig. 1   Cylinder Head Tightening Sequence

INTAKE/EXHAUST MANIFOLD

Removal — Disconnect battery. Remove air filter hose. Disconnect and plug carburetor heating hose. Disconnect choke, accelerator, fuel lines and vacuum lines. Take off carburetor. Separate exhaust pipe. Remove manifold nuts and starter heat shield. Pull manifold from engine.

NOTE — *It may be necessary to remove nut on left engine mount and tilt engine to right to gain enough clearance for removal.*

Installation — To install, reverse removal procedure and replace all gaskets.

CYLINDER HEAD

Removal — 1) Disconnect battery. Drain cooling system. Remove air cleaner. Disconnect all hoses, vacuum lines, wires, and cables from cylinder head. Loosen air pump and take off belt. Disconnect exhaust pipe at manifold.

2) Disconnect hood lock control cable, place out of way. Take off valve cover. Remove cylinder head bolts; only loosen bolt next to distributor ½ turn. Tap head until free. Remove bolt and head.

Installation — To install cylinder head, reverse removal procedure and note: Make sure new head gasket is installed with "HAUT-TOP" facing up.

VALVES

VALVE ARRANGEMENT

E-I-I-E-E-I-I-E

VALVE GUIDE SERVICING

1) Measure O.D. of worn guide and replace with nearest oversize. Standard valve guide O.D. is .433" (11 mm). First oversize is .437" (11.10 mm) and is identified by 1 groove mark. Second oversize is .443" (11.25 mm) and is identified by 2 groove marks.

2) Ream valve guide hole in head to accept new guide. Size of reamer must be equal to outside diameter of new valve guide. To install new guide, lightly lubricate with oil. Fit guide to press with chamfer facing out. Seat guide completely in head. Finish ream valve guide bore to accept valve.

VALVE SPRINGS

Removal, Cylinder Head Installed — Remove valve cover. Remove spark plug of cylinder requiring work. Loosen rocker arm as far as possible and remove push rod. Fit valve retaining tool in spark plug hole. Compress valve spring. Remove keepers, top cup, spring, and base washer. Check spring at free length and under a load.

Installation — Reverse removal procedure and note: Make sure valve spring is installed with closest coil spacing toward cylinder head.

LE CAR 4-CYLINDER (Cont.)

ROCKER SHAFT

After cleaning rocker shaft components, remove clips and take off springs, rocker arms, and support bearings. End plugs are press fit and cannot be removed. For correct reassembly sequence refer to *Fig. 2*.

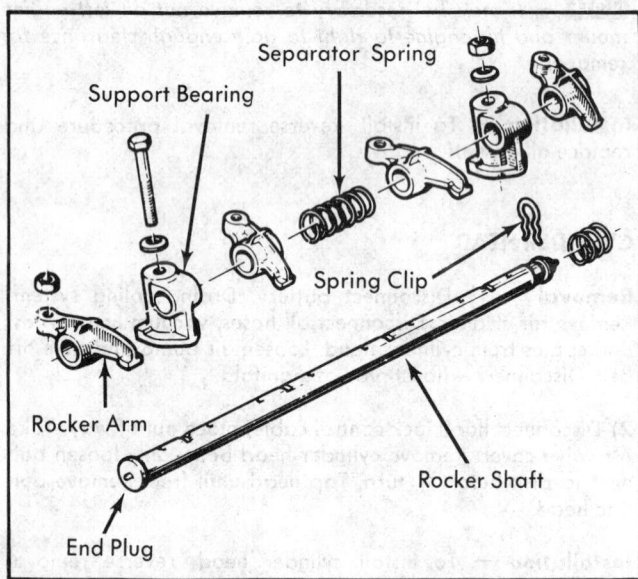

Fig. 2   Exploded View of Rocker Arm & Shaft Assembly

VALVE CLEARANCE

Set intake valve clearance to .006″ (.15 mm) cold or .007″ (.18 mm) hot. Set exhaust valve clearance to .008″ (.20 mm) cold or .010″ (.25 mm) hot. Hot refers to an engine that has been operated at normal engine temperature and allowed to cool for 50 minutes.

Valve Adjusting Sequence	
Valve Open	**Valve to Adjust**
No. 1 Exhaust	No. 3 Int. & No. 4 Exh.
No. 3 Exhaust	No. 4 Int. & No. 2 Exh.
No. 4 Exhaust	No. 2 Int. & No. 1 Exh.
No. 2 Exhaust	No. 1 Int. & No. 3 Exh.

PISTONS, PINS & RINGS

OIL PAN

Removal — 1) Drain oil. Remove sway bar "U" brackets and pull bar down. Remove lower transaxle metal cover. Remove transaxle bolts that mount through gear shift bracket. Clutch protective cover must be removed.

2) Place a jack under front of transaxle to support it. Remove front pad. Raise transaxle front. Remove mounting bolts and tilt pan toward back of vehicle. Rotate crankshaft to provide clearance. Clean gasket surfaces.

Installation — To install, reverse removal procedure and note: Apply gasket sealer to rubber gaskets. Make sure pan side gaskets overlap bearing gaskets.

CYLINDER LINERS

Removal — 1) Disconnect battery. Drain cooling system and oil pan. Remove air cleaner, cylinder head, oil pan, and oil pump. Fit liner clamp on head.

2) Index connecting rods and bearing caps. Remove connecting rod caps and bearings. Remove liner clamp and liner-piston-rod assembly.

Installation — 1) Check cylinder liner protrusion WITHOUT sealing "O" ring installed on liner base. Install dial indicator (Mot. 251) and measuring block (Mot. 252) as shown in *Fig. 3*. Protrusion must be .001-.004″ (.02-.09 mm). If protrusion is incorrect, substitute a new set of liners to determine if defect is in liners or cylinder block.

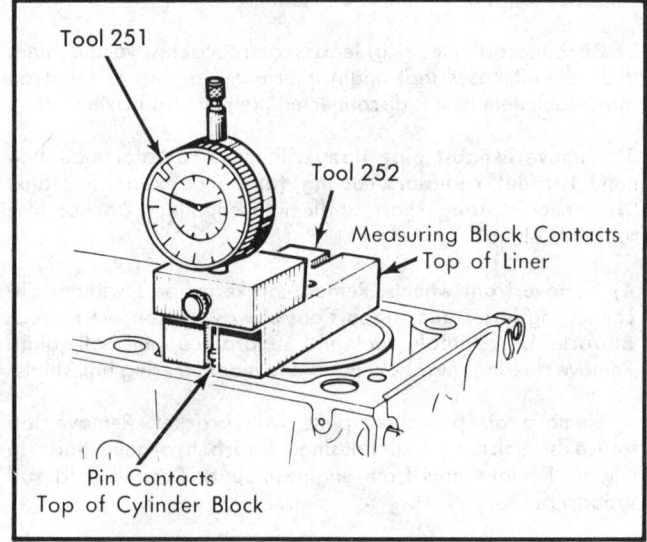

Fig. 3   Checking Cylinder Liner Protrusion

2) Remove liners from cylinder block and install "O" rings on base of liners. Install piston assemblies in liners.

3) Lubricate rod bearings and install liner-piston-connecting rod assemblies into block. Make sure No. 1 is at clutch end. Number on connecting rod bearing end is on opposite side of camshaft. Arrow on piston must face flywheel. Install connecting rod caps. Reverse removal procedure for remaining components.

PISTON & ROD ASSEMBLY

Removal — Remove piston and rod assembly from block with cylinder liners. *See Cylinder Liners.* Remove piston out bottom of liner. Take off rings, piston pin, and connecting rod. *See Piston Pins.*

LE CAR 4-CYLINDER (Cont.)

Installation — Fit piston pin. Fit rings. Piston rings are pregapped. Assemble with "O" mark or "TOP" facing up. Lubricate connecting rod assemblies with oil and fit to liner. Make sure machined side of connecting rod bearing is parallel with flat edge on liner top.

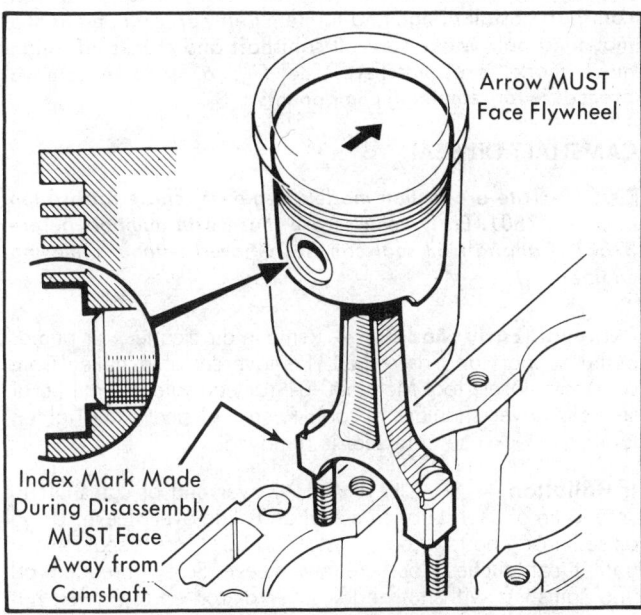

Fig. 4 *Piston Mounting and Identification Marks. Reassemble Piston and Connecting Rod Assemblies According to Illustration*

PISTON PIN

Removal — Remove piston assembly from liner. Remove rings. Using suitable tool (Mot. 574), extract piston pin.

Installation — 1) Position piston with arrow facing flywheel. Index mark made during removal on connecting rod must face away from camshaft.

2) Heat connecting rod to 482° F (250° C). Slide new piston over installing mandrel and screw in locating plug (part of tool kit Mot. 574). Lightly oil piston pin. Push mandrel, pin guide, and pin assembly through piston by hand, until piston pin makes contact with rod. This procedure will automatically center and correctly space pin.

CRANKSHAFT MAIN & CONNECTING ROD BEARINGS

MAIN BEARING SERVICE

1) Remove cylinder head and oil pan. Invert engine. Remove connecting rod bearing caps. Mark position of main bearing to block. Remove main bearing caps. Remove crankshaft, upper main bearings, and thrust washers.

2) Use a micrometer and measure crankshaft journals. If any main bearing journal is worn beyond 2.147" (54.55 mm) or any connecting rod journal is worn beyond 1.722" (43.73 mm), crankshaft must be reground and fitted with new bearings.

NOTE — *Connecting rod journals are roll hardened. Make sure roll hardening remains intact over a 140° section facing rotational centerline of crankshaft.*

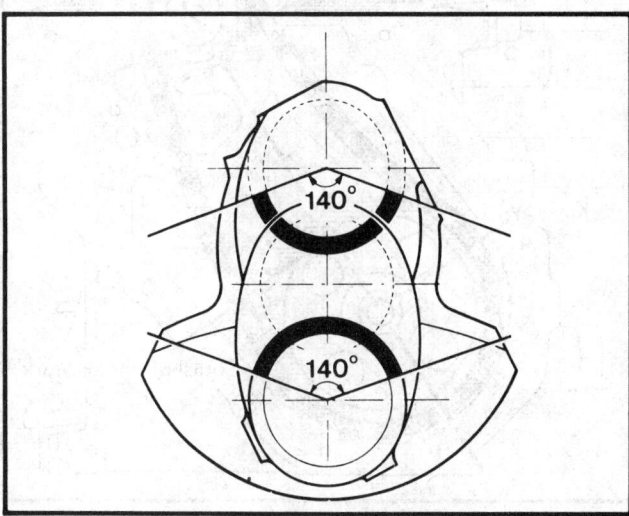

Fig. 5 *Crankshaft MUST Maintain Roll Hardened Surfaces as Shown in Illustration*

3) Fit upper main bearings. Nos. 1 and 3 are same. Nos. 2, 4, and 5 have two oil holes. Lubricate main bearing journals and fit crankshaft into position. Fit thrust washers, white metal toward crankshaft. Fit bearing to main bearing caps (those with no oil holes). Fit caps being sure to align with previously made reference marks.

4) Fit upper connecting rod bearings and slide over crankshaft. Fit lower half of bearing in cap, then tighten cap. Make sure crankshaft is free to turn.

5) Use a dial indicator and check crankshaft end play. Crankshaft should not have more than .002-.009" (.05-.23 mm) end play. Replace thrust washers if end play is beyond specification.

REAR MAIN BEARING OIL SEAL

With New Crankshaft — Fit new seal to tool Mot. 259-01 (or equivalent). Lubricate outer seal lip. Install seal in original position, seating it until tool lip just contacts cylinder block.

With Original Crankshaft — Offset new seal approximately ⅛" (3 mm) to position seal so it does not rest in same place original seal did. Drive seal into place with tool Mot 259-01 (or equivalent). Seal is seated when tool edge just touches block. Remove tool, insert ⅛" thick spacer, and repeat seating process. This will correctly seat seal into position.

CAMSHAFT

TIMING CHAIN

Removal — With engine removed and suitably supported, remove timing cover. Wire tensioner shoe away from chain. *See Fig. 7.* Remove camshaft sprocket lock bolt. Use a puller to remove camshaft sprocket with timing chain. Chain will come off without disturbing crankshaft sprocket.

Renault Engines

LE CAR 4-CYLINDER (Cont.)

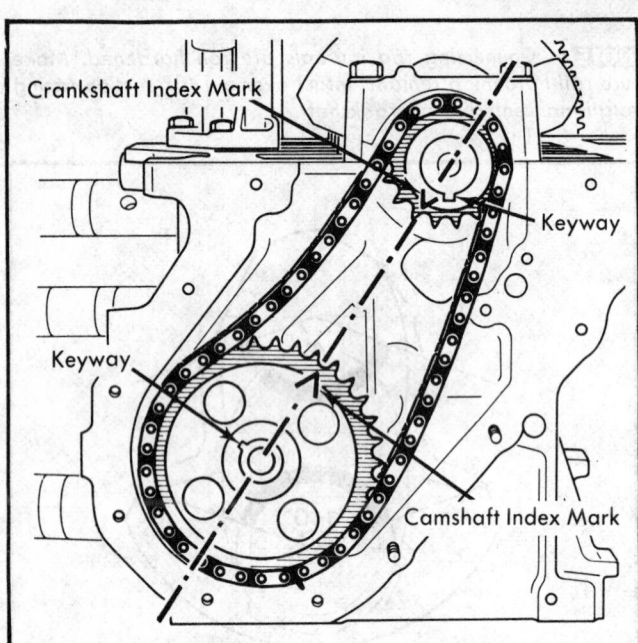

Fig. 6 Index Mark and Keyway Positions for Timing Chain Installation (Engine Inverted)

Installation — 1) Position chain on camshaft sprocket. Align camshaft reference mark with one on crankshaft. Note position of of camshaft and crankshaft keyway shown in *Fig. 6.* Using a small Allen wrench, activate tensioner mechanism.

2) Refit chain tensioner with thrust plate. Tighten mounting bolts and release load on automatic wear compensator tensioner. Release load by pressing down on bottom of tensioner body. Install new timing chain tensioner.

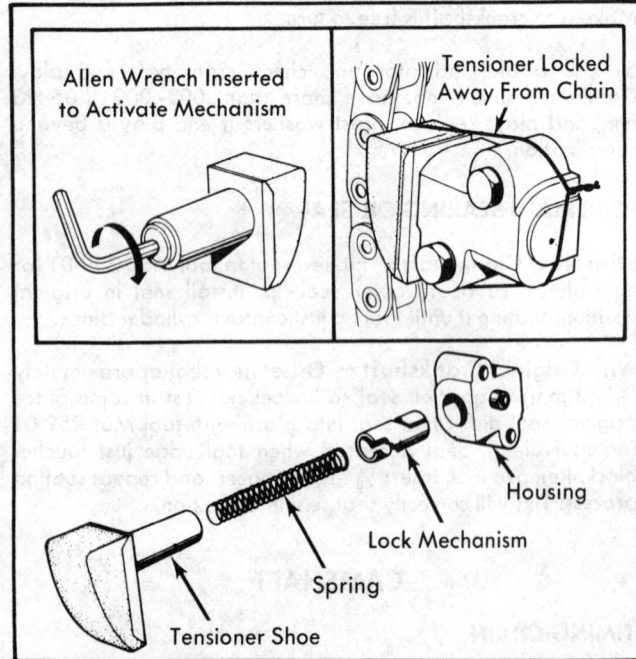

Fig. 7 Views of Timing Chain Tensioner

CAMSHAFT

Removal — Remove engine and suitably support on stand. Remove cylinder head, distributor drive gear, oil pan, timing

chain cover, and timing chain. Work through access slots in camshaft sprocket and remove two flange bolts. Carefully slide camshaft from engine.

Installation — Check clearance between camshaft sprocket and flange. Clearance must not exceed .002-.005" (.05-.12 mm). Lubricate camshaft journals and lobes, then refit camshaft. Install flange and tighten. Refit sprocket and tighten mounting bolt. Make sure all camshaft and crankshaft alignment marks are matched. *See Fig. 6.* Reverse removal procedure for remaining components.

CAMSHAFT OIL SEAL

NOTE — *Late production models begin at vehicle fabrication number 37801. Early vehicles are those with numbers before 37801. Camshaft oil seal can be removed without removing engine.*

Removal (Early Models) — Remove air cleaner, air pump, pump support and drive belt. Remove serrated pulley from camshaft. Insert tool Mot. 500-01 (or equivalent) until lip of seal slips over shoulder of tool. Push tool sleeve in. Tighten tool bolt clockwise until seal is removed.

Installation — Slip sleeve of tool over end of camshaft to spread lip of seal. Lubricate seal and slide over sleeve. Using oil seal inserting tool (part of Mot. 500-01), press seal inward until it just touches block. Remove sleeve. Screw threaded rod into camshaft with nut and washer at rod end. Tighten nut until tool just meets clutch housing. Replace remaining components in reverse order of removal procedure.

Removal (Late Models) — Remove air cleaner, air pump, pump support and drive belt. Remove serrated pulley from camshaft. Remove camshaft bearing using puller (Mot. 876). Install a spacer of 1.0" (25 mm) diameter and 1.75" (45 mm) length between camshaft and bolt of tool Mot. 500.02. Install tool with spacer and push past the seal. Expand the tool ends by moving ring expander as far in as possible. Screw in bolt and remove seal.

Installation — Place the new seal on tool Mot. 500.02. Install the seal on the camshaft and tap gently into place all the way to the centering spacer. Install the bearing using tool Mot. 876 with the tool grip facing outward. Install the remaining components in reverse order of removal.

ENGINE OILING

Crankcase Capacity — 3.4 quarts with filter change.

Oil Filter — Disposable canister type.

Normal Oil Pressure — 10 psi (.7 kg/cm^2) at idle speed. 50 psi (3.5 kg/cm^2) at 4000 RPM.

OIL PUMP

Removal — Drain oil. Remove oil pan. Take out three bolts mounting oil pump and remove pump.

Disassembly — Remove four pump cover bolts. Remove cover slowly; relief valve is under spring tension. Remove driven gear, drive gear, and drive gear shaft.

Inspection — Examine splines on drive shaft. Check ball seat for damage. Check pressure relief spring for fatigue. Check clearance between gears and body. Replace gears if clearance exceeds .008" (.2 mm).

LE CAR 4-CYLINDER (Cont.)

Reassembly — Reverse disassembly procedure.

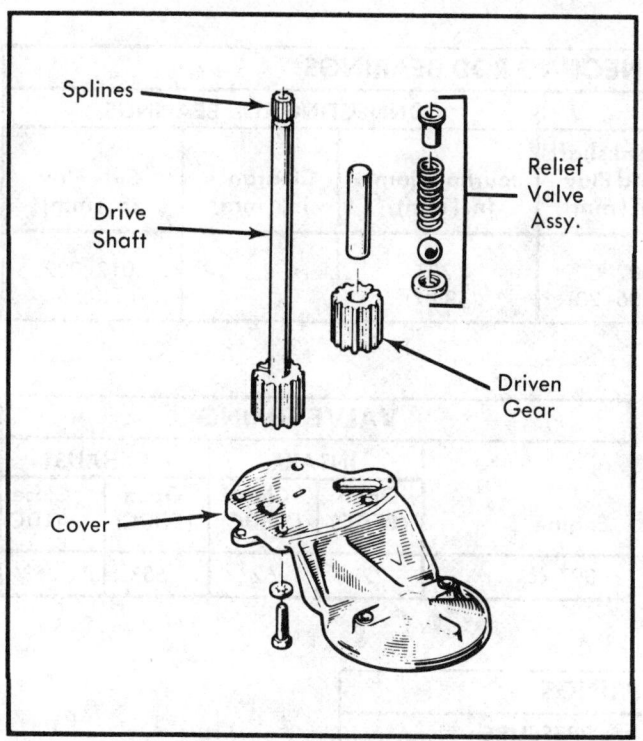

Fig. 8   Exploded View of Oil Pump Assembly

Splines

Drive Shaft

Relief Valve Assy.

Driven Gear

Cover

Installation — Install pump, do not use gasket between oil pump and block. Tighten mounting bolts.

ENGINE COOLING

WATER PUMP

Removal — Disconnect battery. Disconnect hoses. Drain block at plug near timing cover. Loosen alternator. Remove water pump drive belt. Remove A.I.R. pump, water pump pulley, grooved belt, and temperature sending unit. Remove mounting bolts and tap pump free.

Installation — To install, reverse removal procedure and be sure to bleed air from cooling system.

Cooling System Capacity — Approximately 6.5 quarts, including heater.

TIGHTENING SPECIFICATIONS

Application	Ft. Lbs. (N·m)
Cylinder Head Bolts	
Cold	40 (54)
Hot	45 (61)
Connecting Rod Nuts	35 (48)
Main Bearings	40-50 (54-68)
Manifolds	10 (14)
Rocker Arm Shaft	10-15 (14-20)
Timing Sprocket-to-Camshaft	20 (27)

ENGINE SPECIFICATIONS

GENERAL SPECIFICATIONS

Year	Displ. cu. ins.	Displ. cc	Carburetor	HP at RPM	Torque (Ft. Lbs. at RPM)	Compr. Ratio	Bore in.	Bore mm	Stroke in.	Stroke mm
1981	85.4	1397	1x2-Bbl.	.....	.....	8.8:1	2.99	76	3.03	77

VALVES

Engine & Valve	Head Diam. In. (mm)	Face Angle	Seat Angle	Seat Width In. (mm)	Stem Diameter In. (mm)	Stem Clearance In. (mm)	Valve Lift In. (mm)
1397 cc							
Int.	1.346 (34.2)	60°	60°	.043-.055 (1.1-1.4)	.276 (7)	.....	.....
Exh.	1.141 (29.0)	45°	45°	.055-.067 (1.4-1.7)	.276 (7)	.....	.....

PISTONS, PINS, RINGS

Engine	PISTONS Clearance In. (mm)	PINS Piston Fit In. (mm)	PINS Rod Fit In. (mm)	RINGS Rings	RINGS End Gap In. (mm)	RINGS Side Clearance In. (mm)
1397 cc	.....	Free Fit	Press Fit	.....	①	.....

① — Pre-set gap; do not alter.

Renault Engines

LE CAR 4-CYLINDER (Cont.)

ENGINE SPECIFICATIONS (Cont.)

CRANKSHAFT MAIN & CONNECTING ROD BEARINGS							
	MAIN BEARINGS				CONNECTING ROD BEARINGS		
Engine	Journal Diam. In. (mm)	Clearance In. (mm)	Thrust Bearing	Crankshaft End Play In. (mm)	Journal Diam. In. (mm)	Clearance In. (mm)	Side Play In. (mm)
1397 cc	2.157 (54.80)	.....	No. 3	.002-.009 (.05-.23)	1.731 (43.97)	.....	.012-.022 (.30-.56)

CAMSHAFT			
Engine	Journal Diam. In. (mm)	Clearance In. (mm)	Lobe Lift In. (mm)
1397 cc	.....	①	.....

① — End play .002-.005″ (.05-.12 mm).

VALVE TIMING				
	INTAKE		EXHAUST	
Engine	Open (BTDC)	Close (ABDC)	Open (BBDC)	Close (ATDC)
1397 cc	22°	62°	65°	25°

VALVE SPRINGS			
Engine	Free Length In. (mm)	PRESSURE Lbs. @ In. (kg @ mm)	
		Valve Closed	Valve Open
1397 cc	1.65 (42)	.....	80@1.0 (36@25)

18i 4-CYLINDER

ENGINE CODING

ENGINE IDENTIFICATION

Engine identification plate is located on left side of engine block above starter. First 3 characters show engine type, and last 2 identify engine equipment.

Engine Identification	
Application	**Code**
18i (1647 cc)	
Man. Trans.	843-7-18
Auto. Trans.	843-7-19

ENGINE & CYLINDER HEAD

ENGINE

Removal — 1) Remove battery and engine undercover. Drain cooling system at engine and radiator. Drain engine oil. Remove radiator grill (remove parking light bulbs first), grill upper crossmember, radiator and cooling fan.

2) If equipped with air conditioning, remove cooling fans, disconnect condensor from radiator and place on bumper. Remove starter and exhaust heat shields, catalytic converter and air intake hose. Remove clutch cable, bracket and alternator.

3) If equipped with power steering, remove pump and place it with lines attached on frame rail. If equipped with air conditioning, disconnect compressor and place on frame rail with lines. Disconnect all electrical leads, control cables, vacuum lines and coolant hoses that might interfere with engine removal.

4) Disconnect fuel lines and clamp to prevent tank drainage. Remove sending units from cylinder head. Remove upper engine-to-transaxle bolts. Remove flywheel shield, lower engine-transaxle bolts, and side engine bolts. If equipped with auto transmission, remove converter shield and converter fixing bolts on drive plate. Clamp plate with converter locking tool (Mot. 582).

5) Attach lifting sling (Mot. 597) and raise engine until transaxle touches steering crossmember. Secure transaxle. Pull engine forward to disengage from transaxle. Remove engine from vehicle. If equipped with automatic transmission, attach retaining plate (B. Vi. 465) to prevent converter movement.

Installation — To install, reverse removal procedure noting the following: on manual transmission models, lightly grease the clutch shaft splines and the surface of the clutch thrust plate with Molykote BR 2 grease. Adjust clutch cable clearance. On automatic transmission models, lubricate the converter centering housing in crankshaft with Molykote BR 2 grease (or equivalent). Line up paint mark on converter facing part of driving plate blade sharp edges. Replace driving plate to converter bolts.

CYLINDER HEAD

Removal — 1) Disconnect battery. Remove radiator grill and upper crossmember. Drain cooling system at cylinder block and radiator. Disconnect wiring, cables, and the heater hoses at water pump. Remove catalytic converter.

2) Remove water pump belt and air intake hose. Remove distributor, valve cover, and diagnostic socket. Disconnect fuel lines and clamp to prevent tank drainage. Unscrew rocker arm adjusting screws and remove pushrods, arranging in proper sequence.

3) Loosen cylinder head bolts and remove inner 6. Remove rubber washers and cups in spark plug recesses. Clamp rocker arm assembly with a rubber band or string around the 4 end bolts and remove rocker arm assemblies.

4) Unstick cylinder head from block by rotating cylinder head around centering dowel on distributor side. Tap each end of cylinder head with a plastic mallet on each side. See Fig. 1. DO NOT merely lift off cylinder head.

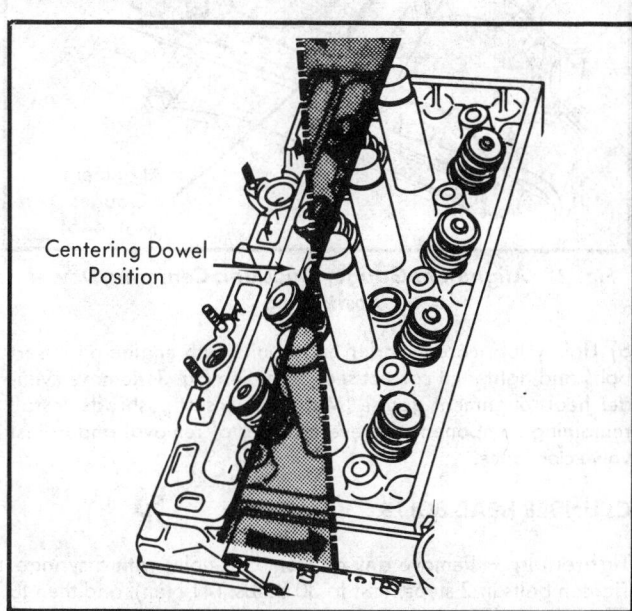

Fig. 1   Rotating Cylinder Head Around Centering Dowel

5) Raise cylinder head slightly and remove lifters, arranging them in sequence. Remove cylinder head and lifter chamber seal. Place liner clamp (Mot. 521-01) in position on cylinder block.

Installation — 1) Remove old gasket pieces with Magnus ''Magstrip'' or Decaplock ''88'' liquid. Remove any oil from cylinder head bolt holes with a syringe. Check cylinder liner protrusion as outlined under Pistons, Pins & Rings in this article.

2) Remove liner clamp. Ensure centering dowel and distributor drive gear are properly positioned in cylinder block. See Camshaft and Timing Chain in this Article. Position cylinder head gasket. See Fig. 2.

3) Screw alignment studs (Mot. 451) into indicated positions until ball makes contact with cylinder head gasket. Install lifter chamber gasket, ensuring ends do not overlap with cylinder head gasket. Place alignment gauge (Mot. 446) in cylinder block hole. See Fig. 2.

4) Place lifters in cylinder head in correct order. Tap lightly to seat in their housings. Install rocker arm assemblies to cylinder

Renault Engines

18i 4-CYLINDER (Cont.)

head. Ensure that 2 rocker arm supports with holes fit properly over their centering dowels. Place cylinder head on block. Be careful not to move lifter chamber gasket. Remove studs using "T" handle of tool set Mot. 451.

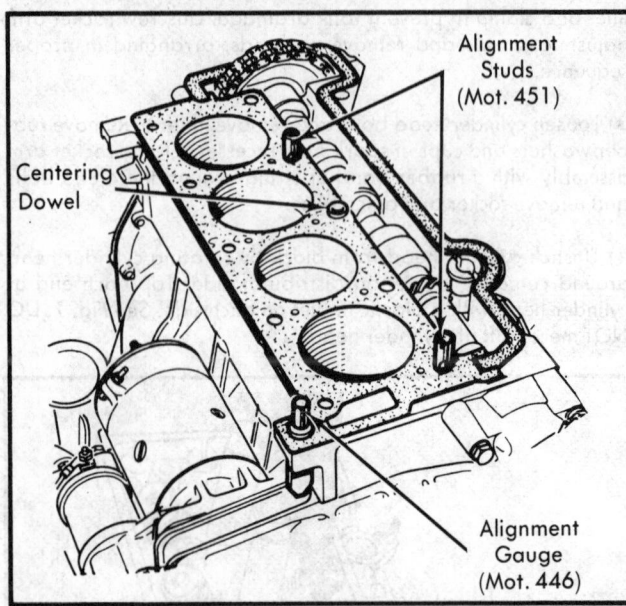

Fig. 2   Alignment Gauge, Studs and Centering Dowel Positioning

5) Lightly lubricate cylinder head bolts with engine oil. Insert bolts and tighten in correct sequence. See Fig. 3. Remove cylinder head alignment gauge (Mot. 446). Insert pushrods. Install remaining components in reverse order of removal and adjust valve clearance.

CYLINDER HEAD BOLTS

Tightening — Remove any oil from bolt holes with a syringe. Tighten bolts in 2 steps, first to 30 ft. lbs. (41 N·m), and then to 57-61 ft. lbs. (78-83 N·m). Run engine till thermostat opens and allow to cool 2½ hours. Loosen bolt No. 1 a half turn and retighten to 57-61 ft. lbs. (78-83 N·m). Repeat for remaining bolts in correct sequence.

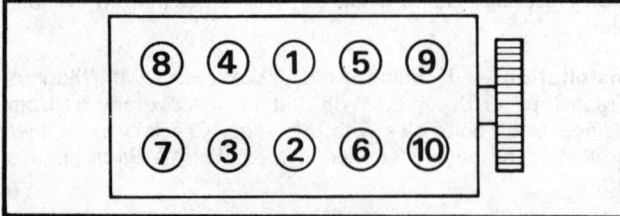

Fig. 3   Cylinder Head Bolt Tightening Sequence

VALVES

VALVE ARRANGEMENT

Right side — All intake.

Left side — All exhaust.

VALVE GUIDE SERVICING

1) With cylinder head removed, lay cylinder head on wedge shaped block so guide is vertical. Valve guide angles are 23°

for intake valves, 26° for exhaust valves. Push the guide out in a press, using mandrel from Mot. 356 tool set.

2) Examine the valve guide and determine whether it is original or a replacement. Replace with the next oversize. First oversize has 1 groove mark, 2nd oversize has 2 groove marks. Turn the cylinder head over on the block and ream the guide bore for valve guide. Ream to .516" (13.19 mm) for 1st oversize, .522" (13.25 mm) for 2nd oversize.

3) Fit the valve guide on the end of the mandrel with chamfer facing outward. Lubricate the guide and press in until positioned correctly. Distance between valve seat and end of valve guide should be 1.575" (40 mm) for intake valves, 1.220" (31 mm) for exhaust valves.

4) Ream the valve guide bore to accept valve stem using Mot. 357. Recut valve seat.

VALVE SPRINGS

Removal — Disconnect battery. Remove valve cover. Remove distributor (if necessary). Position piston corresponding to spring to be removed at TDC. Unscrew appropriate rocker arm screw and remove pushrod. Compress valve spring with spring compresser (Mot. 382). Hold valve stem with pliers and remove split keepers, cap and springs.

Installation — Reverse removal procedure and note: Ensure valve spring is installed with closest coil spring spacing toward cylinder head.

ROCKER SHAFT

Disassembly — Remove the retaining roll pin from the rocker shafts. Note relative positions of parts and remove and clean them.

NOTE — *Cup plugs at ends of shafts must not be removed.*

Reassembly — Install the 2 shafts into supports at clutch end of head. Install intake shaft retaining pin. Install the remaining parts and install the exhaust shaft retaining pin.

NOTE — *Supports 1 and 4 are identical, with lubrication holes and locating dowel. Supports 2, 3 and 5 are identical, with no lubrication hole. The 2 shafts are also identical.*

VALVE CLEARANCE ADJUSTMENT

Set valves cold. To adjust, rotate crankshaft until valve listed in column 1 of table is fully open, then adjust valves specified in second column of table. Note that valves and cylinders are numbered from rear to front.

Valve Adjustment	
Valve Open	**Adjust**
No. 1 Exhaust	No. 3 Intake & No. 4 Exhaust
No. 3 Exhaust	No. 4 Intake & No. 2 Exhaust
No. 4 Exhaust	No. 2 Intake & No. 1 Exhaust
No. 2 Exhaust	No. 1 Intake & No. 3 Exhaust

18i 4-CYLINDER (Cont.)

PISTONS, PINS & RINGS

CYLINDER LINERS & PISTON ASSEMBLY

Removal — Remove cylinder head, oil pan, and oil pump. Mark the connecting rods and caps on camshaft side. Remove caps and bearings. Remove liner clamp and remove piston and rod assembly from block with liner.

Installation — **1)** Check cylinder liner protrusion WITHOUT sealing "O" ring installed on liner base. Install dial indicator (Mot. 251-01) and measuring block (Mot. 252-01) and measure protrusion. It should be .004-.007" (.10-.17 mm). See Fig. 4. If protrusion is incorrect, check with a new set of liners to determine if the problem is the block or the liners.

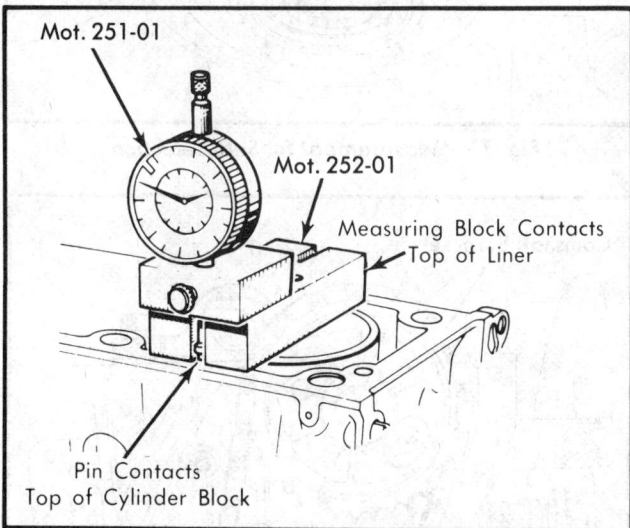

Fig. 4 Checking Cylinder Liner Protrusion

2) Position the liners with "O" rings installed so that difference in protrusion is not greater than .002" (.04 mm) on any 2 adjacent cylinders. Liners should also be stepped down from front to rear or vice-versa. Oil the piston and connecting rod assembly and insert to liner using ring compressor (Mot. 851).

3) Flat surface of big end of connecting rod must be parallel to flat surface at top of liner. Connecting rod markings face camshaft. Install liner clamp (Mot. 521-01). Place connecting rods with bearings on lubricated rod bearing journals and install matching rod caps and bearings. Install remaining components in reverse order of removal.

PISTON PIN

Removal — Remove piston from liner and rings from piston. Using pin press (Mot. 574-04), press out piston pin.

Installation — **1)** Position piston with arrow facing flywheel. Index mark on connecting rod must face camshaft. Heat connecting rod to 482°F (250°C).

2) Insert centering guide (of tool kit Mot. 574) into piston. Place the connecting rod in the piston. Lightly oil the piston pin with Molykote M55 (or equivalent) and press in piston pin until the guide butts up against support block.

NOTE — *Check to ensure that pin is recessed from piston diameter. See Fig. 5.*

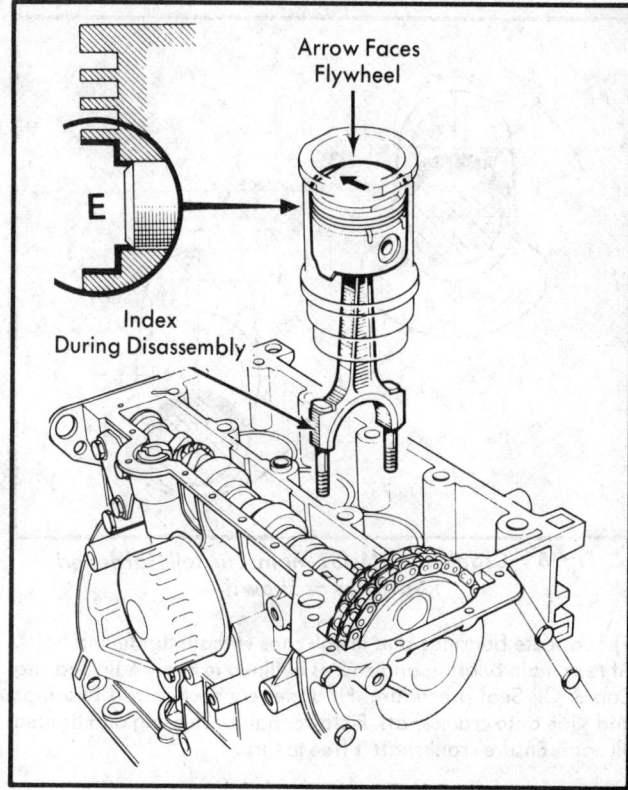

Fig. 5 Piston Mounting & Identification Marks

PISTON RINGS

Fit rings to pistons with "O" mark or "TOP" facing up. Oil pistons before inserting to liners. Rings are pre-gapped. Ensure that flat surface of connecting rod is parallel to flat surface on liner.

CRANKSHAFT MAIN & CONNECTING ROD BEARINGS

MAIN & CONNECTING ROD BEARING SERVICE

1) Remove cylinder head and oil pan. Invert engine and mark bearing caps. Remove connecting rod bearing caps and all main bearing caps except No. 1. Remove all bearing shells.

2) Remove No. 1 main bearing cap by tapping underneath with a hammer at each end. Remove oil seals, crankshaft, main bearings and thrust washers.

3) Use a micrometer and measure crankshaft journals. If any main bearing journal is worn beyond 2.148" (54.55 mm) or any connecting rod journal is worn beyond 1.880" (47.75 mm), crankshaft must be reground and fitted with new bearings.

NOTE — *Journals are roll hardened. Make sure roll hardening remains intact over a 140° section facing rotational centerline of crankshaft. See Fig. 6.*

4) Install upper main bearings (they have lubrication holes). Lubricate bearings and crankshaft journals. Fit crankshaft to block. Insert thrust washers with white metal face toward the crankshaft. Fit main bearings No. 2, 3, 4, and 5 to caps (they have no lubrication holes).

Renault Engines

18i 4-CYLINDER (Cont.)

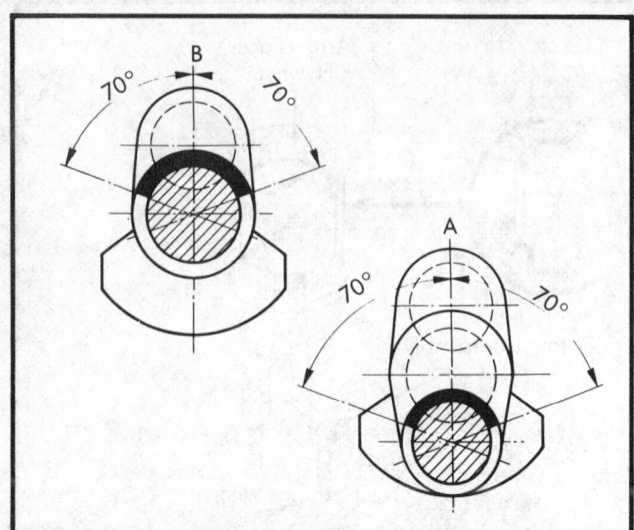

Fig. 6 Crankshaft MUST Maintain Roll Hardened Surfaces as Shown

5) Lubricate bearings and install caps without tightening bolts. Fit rear main bearing and cap as outlined in Rear Main Bearing Cap & Oil Seal procedure. Fit upper connecting rod bearings and slide onto crank shaft. Fit lower half of bearing and tighten all caps. Ensure crankshaft is free to turn.

6) Use a dial indicator and check crankshaft end play. If end play exceeds .009″ (.23 mm) replace thrust washers to obtain correct specification.

REAR MAIN BEARING CAP AND OIL SEAL

Insert bearing to cap. Temporarily install cap and tighten bolts. Measure dimension "C" between cylinder block and main bearing seal housing. See Fig. 7. If less than .20″ (5 mm) select seals .201″ (5.1 mm) thick. If greater than .20″ (5 mm), select seals .213″ (5.40 mm) thick (white marking).

2) Remove cap. Place 2 side seals on cap with seal groove facing outward. Seal protrusionon cylinder block side should be .031″ (.2 mm) Lubricate seals and bearing and install cap over 2 centering studs, placing foil shims between block and seals to protect seals. When cap is almost in place, use a ruler to ensure seals still protrude slightly.

3) Remove shims and studs and tighten bolts. After checking end play, install oil seal with Mot. 259-01. Be careful of oil seal lip.

CAMSHAFT

CAMSHAFT & TIMING CHAIN

Removal — Remove the cylinder head, distributor, and camshaft end bearing cover plate. Remove oil pan and crankshaft pulley. Remove timing cover, and timing chain tensioner with thrust plate and filter. Remove 2 chain guides. Remove crankshaft pulley key, and remove crankshaft sprocket and chain together using puller (Mot. 49). Screw bolt (Mot. 525) into crankshaft and then remove camshaft.

Installation — **1)** Lubricate the camshaft bearings and slide the camshaft in, but not all the way. Place the chain over the camshaft sprocket. Line up the mark on the sprocket with center of the crankshaft and camshaft. See Fig. 8.

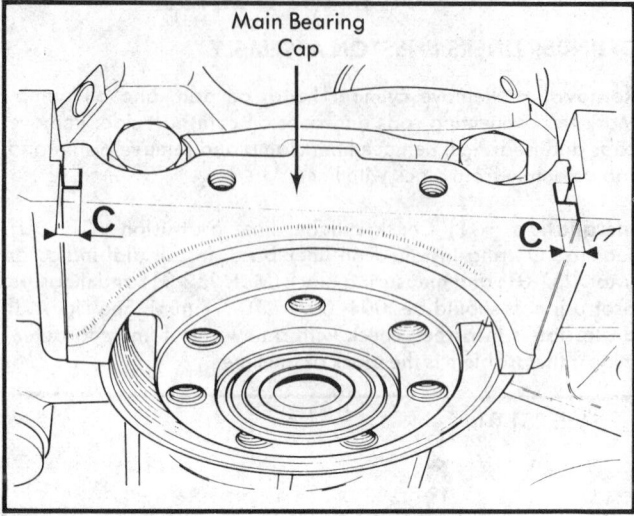

Fig. 7 Measurement for Seal Selection

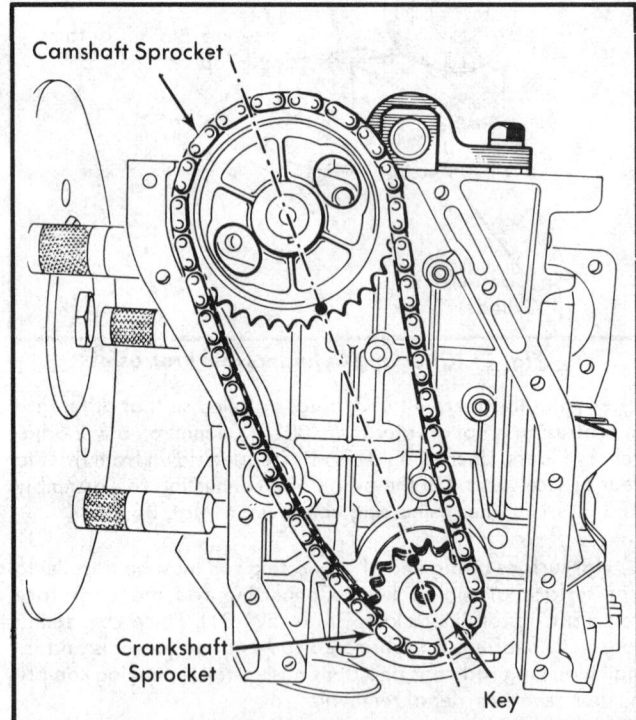

Fig. 8 Alignment of Camshaft and Crankshaft Sprockets

2) Place the key on the crankshaft. Rotate the crankshaft to bring the key to the top. Place the crankshaft sprocket on the chain. The timing mark must line up with the camshaft sprocket mark as well as the center of the camshaft and crankshaft. See Fig. 8.

3) Place the sprocket on the crankshaft. Use tool Mot. 525 to install sprocket, while gradually pushing camshaft into position. Insert and tighten 2 camshaft clamp bolts. Install chain tensioner with oil filter and thrust plate. Tighten bolts.

4) Install chain guides. If chain gauge (Mot. 420) is available, place on the chain. Push the 2 guides against the gauge, tighten bolts and remove the gauge. See Fig. 9. If gauge is not available, stretch the chain and position the guides so there is

18i 4-CYLINDER (Cont.)

.012–.020" (.30–.50 mm) between chain and the guides. Tighten the bolts.

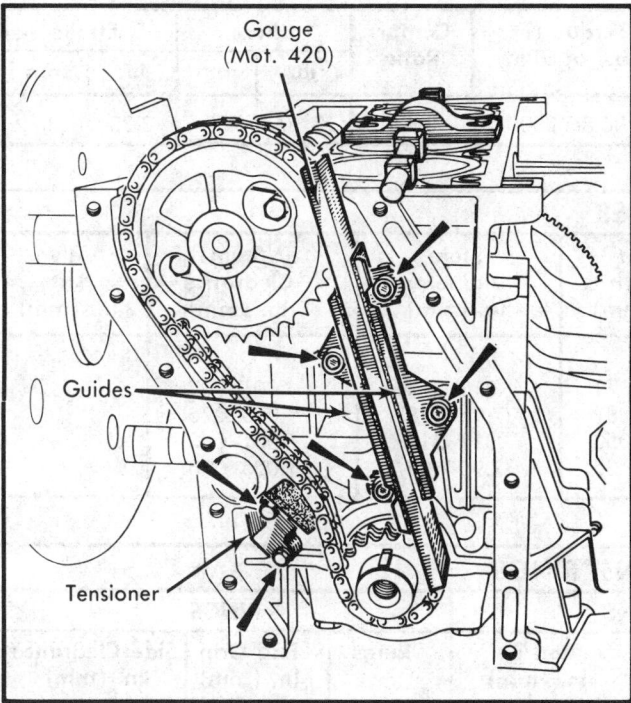

Fig. 9   Adjusting Timing Chain Tension Using Gauge. Broad Arrows Indicate Tensioner & Guide Bolts.

5) Install crankshaft pulley key. Install timing cover centering dowels and install timing cover to block. Install new oil seal as follows: Place oil seal over assembly sleeve of installation tool (Mot. 525). Place assembly against timing cover and screw bolt into crankshaft until seal contacts timing cover. Install remaining components in reverse order of removal.

DISTRIBUTOR DRIVE GEAR

Rotate engine to bring No. 1 cylinder to TDC. Install distributor drive gear with smaller offset toward camshaft. Angle formed by drive gear slot and a line perpendicular to camshaft should equal 53°. Fill camshaft oil galley with oil and install rear camshaft bearing cover plate and gasket.

ENGINE OILING

Crankcase Capacity — 4.5 quarts with filter change.

Oil Filter — Disposable canister type.

Normal Oil Pressure — 29 psi (2.1 kg/cm²) at idle, 58 psi (4.0 kg/cm²) at 4000 RPM.

OIL PUMP

Removal — Drain oil pan and remove flywheel protective cover (if necessary). Remove oil pan, oil pump and 2 rotors.

Disassembly — Unscrew suction pipe bolts. Remove cotter pin from pressure relief valve and remove spring cup, spring and piston.

Inspection — Check clearance of 2 rotors in positions shown in *Fig. 11*. Dimension "A" should be .002–.011" (.04–.09 mm).

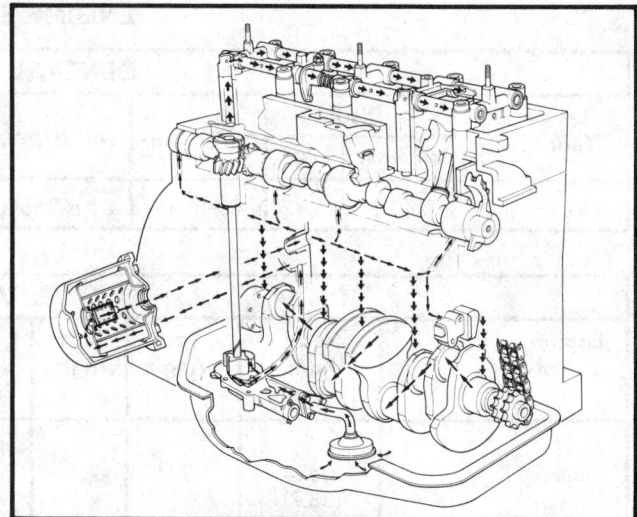

Fig. 10   Engine Oiling System

Dimension "B" should be .001–.006" (.02–.14 mm). If clearance exceeds specifications, replace rotors.

Reassembly — Place piston, spring, and spring cup in pump body. Install cotter pin, suction pipe and gasket. Tighten bolts and bend lock plate over.

Installation — Install assembly with rotors to block. Install oil pan and new gasket.

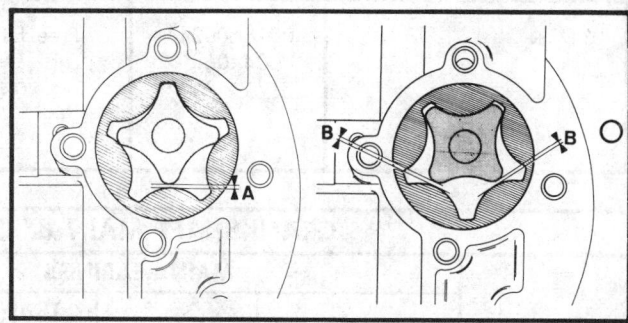

Fig. 11   Oil Pump Rotor Clearances

ENGINE COOLING

Cooling System Capacity — 7.5 quarts (fill at reservoir tank).

WATER PUMP

Removal and Installation — Disconnect battery. Drain cooling system and remove upper grill crossmember, grill, radiator and cooling fan. Remove water pump drive belt and pump fixing bolts. Free pump by tapping with a mallet. To install, reverse removal procedures noting that seal is dry mounted.

TIGHTENING SPECIFICATIONS

Application	Ft. Lbs. (N•m)
Connecting Rod Cap Nuts	33 (45)
Crankshaft Pulley Bolt	67 (91)
Cylinder Head Bolts①	57-61 (78-83)
Flywheel Bolt	37 (50)
Main Bearing Caps	48 (65)

① — See text.

Renault Engines

18i 4-CYLINDER (Cont.)

ENGINE SPECIFICATIONS

GENERAL SPECIFICATIONS

Year	Displ. cu. ins.	Displ. cc	Carburetor	HP at RPM	Torque (Ft. Lbs. at RPM)	Compr. Ratio	Bore in.	Bore mm	Stroke in.	Stroke mm
1981	100.5	1647	Fuel Inj.	81.5@5500	86.3@2500	8.6:1	3.10	79	3.30	84

VALVES

Engine & Valve	Head Diam. In. (mm)	Face Angle	Seat Angle	Seat Width In. (mm)	Stem Diameter In. (mm)	Stem Clearance In. (mm)	Valve Lift In. (mm)
1647 cc Intake	1.524 (38.7)	90°	90°	.059-.071 (1.5-1.8)	.313-.314 (7.95-7.98)	.001-.003 (.025-.076)	.....
Exhaust	1.358 (34.5)	90°	90°	.039-.053 (1.00-1.35)	.313-.314 (7.95-7.98)	.001-.003 (.025-.076)	.....

PISTONS, PINS, RINGS

Engine	PISTONS Clearance In. (mm)	PINS Piston Fit In. (mm)	PINS Rod Fit In. (mm)	RINGS Rings	RINGS End Gap In. (mm)	RINGS Side Clearance In. (mm)
1647 cc	.0016-.0024 (.04-.06)	Free Fit	Press Fit	#1	.012-.018 (.30-.45)	.....
				#2	.012-.018 (.30-.45)	.....
				#3	.....	.....

CRANKSHAFT MAIN & CONNECTING ROD BEARINGS

Engine	MAIN BEARINGS Journal Diam. In. (mm)	MAIN BEARINGS Clearance In. (mm)	MAIN BEARINGS Thrust Bearing	MAIN BEARINGS Crankshaft End Play In. (mm)	CONNECTING ROD BEARINGS Journal Diam. In. (mm)	CONNECTING ROD BEARINGS Clearance In. (mm)	CONNECTING ROD BEARINGS Side Play In. (mm)
1647 cc	2.157 (54.80)	.....	#3	.002-.009 (.05-.23)	1.890 (48.00)	.....	.012-.022 (.31-.57)

CAMSHAFT

Engine	Journal Diam. In. (mm)	Clearance In. (mm)	Lobe Lift In. (mm)
1647 cc	.....	①	.....

① — End play .002-.005" (.05-.12 mm).

VALVE SPRINGS

Engine	Free Length In. (mm)	PRESSURE Lbs. @ In. (kg @ mm) Valve Closed	PRESSURE Lbs. @ In. (kg @ mm) Valve Open
1647 cc Outer	2.138 (54.3)	.....	117@1.201 (53@20.5)
Inner	1.843 (46.8)	36@.95 (16.3@24.5)	.....

VALVE TIMING

Engine	INTAKE Open (BTDC)	INTAKE Close (ABDC)	EXHAUST Open (BBDC)	EXHAUST Close (ATDC)
1647 cc	21°	59°	59°	21°

Saab Engines

900 4-CYLINDER

ENGINE CODING

ENGINE IDENTIFICATION

Engine number is stamped on engine block and is located in the left front corner of the engine compartment. The 4th character of the number indicates whether the engine is turbo-charged or normally aspirated, the 5th character indicates automatic or manual transmission.

Engine Identification	
Application	**Code**
900	
Manual Trans.	B20IMUC
Auto. Trans.	B20IAUC
Turbo	
Man. Trans.	B20SMUC
Auto. Trans.	B20SAUC

ENGINE & CYLINDER HEAD

ENGINE

NOTE — *Engine and transaxle assembly are removed as a unit. Transaxle housing is engine lower crankcase (pan).*

Removal — 1) Disconnect and remove battery. Disconnect windshield washer hose. Remove hood and drain cooling system. Disconnect ground strap between engine and chassis and disconnect positive cable from starter motor. Disconnect servo vacuum hose at manifold and remove bellows between air flow sensor and intake manifold.

2) Clean area around fuel distributor lines and detach at connectors. Cover openings and plug fuel line ends. Remove air cleaner assembly along with mixture control unit. Disconnect EGR system (if equipped). Disconnect upper and lower radiator hoses and heater hoses.

3) Disconnect all ignition wiring connectors as well as sensors, emission control and electrical power connections between chassis and engine. Disconnect heating system and vacuum hoses. Disconnect throttle control wire. Disconnect 2 hydraulic lines at power steering pump (if equipped).

4) On manual transmission models, disconnect clutch line from slave cylinder. Cap hose and slave cylinder opening, put gear lever in neutral, and drive front taper pin from shift rod joint. Separate joint from gear shift rod.

5) On automatic transmission models, remove protective cover from exhaust manifold (if equipped), and place gear selector in "P" position. Remove selector cable retaining screw, push back spring loaded sleeve on shift rod, and disconnect cable.

6) On all models, disconnect exhaust pipe at manifold. Disconnect speedometer cable at transmission. Loosen clamps and remove bellows from inner universal joints at transaxle. Place spacer tool (83 93 209) between upper control arm and body so front suspension will be unloaded when car is raised.

7) Raise and support vehicle, then remove lower end piece from right side control arm. Remove rear engine mounting bolts and loosen the front engine mounting nut so mount can be lifted from the bracket. Attach lifting sling and slightly raise engine.

8) Move engine to the right and remove left universal joint, then move engine to left and remove right universal joint. Ensure that all cables and lines are free from engine and remove entire power unit from vehicle.

Installation — 1) Ensure that universal joints are packed with grease. Fit new gaskets to the exhaust pipe flanges. Suspend engine and balance it so the front engine mount will locate in its bracket before the rear. Lower the assembly, guiding the front mount into its bracket and continue to lower engine until rear of engine is 2" (50-60 mm) above mountings.

2) Move the engine to the right and guide in the left universal joint. Lower the engine carefully, guiding it into the mountings, and at the same time aligning the right universal joint. Ensure that exhaust pipe flanges line up. Refit the right end piece to the control arm. Tighten universal joints and install rear engine mounting bolts. Tighten all engine mountings. To complete installation, reverse removal procedures.

CYLINDER HEAD

Removal — 1) Remove battery leads. Drain cooling system. Remove upper radiator hose. Remove PCV hose from valve cover. Remove wiring from distributor and temperature sending unit. Remove warm-up regulator and auxilliary air valve from cylinder head.

2) Rotate crankshaft to TDC position on firing stroke of No. 1 cylinder. Remove valve cover. Place a jack under the transmission case. Detach the stay between right engine mount and cylinder head and rotate it to one side.

3) Jack up engine slightly and support it with a piece of wood between cross member and transmission case. Detach and support the intake and exhaust manifolds. Detach the chainwheel from the camshaft but keep the chain hanging on the chainwheel.

4) Place the chainwheel between the chain guide and tensioner. Remove 2 timing cover-to-cylinder head bolts. Remove cylinder head bolts in the reverse of sequence shown in *Fig. 1*. Lift the cylinder head off block and remove from vehicle.

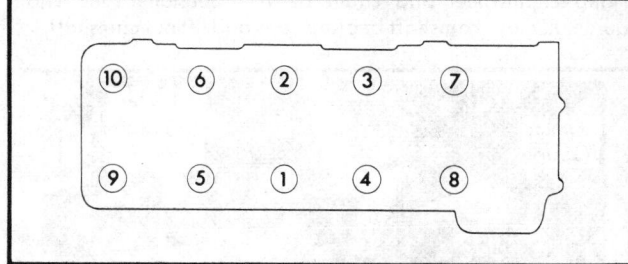

Fig. 1   Cylinder Head Tightening Sequence (Loosen in Reverse Order)

Installation — 1) Place a new gasket on engine block. With crankshaft at "0" position, temporarily install the camshaft chainwheel and place camshaft at TDC position on No. 1 cylinder firing stroke. Position the chain on the chainwheel and place chain between chain guide and tensioner.

2) Install the cylinder head and tighten the bolts in 2 stages in the sequence shown in *Fig. 1*. Install the cylinder head-to-timing cover bolts. Take tension off of timing chain tensioner by in-

900 4-CYLINDER (Cont.)

serting tool (83 93 357) into tensioner catch and pulling up-ward. See. *Fig. 2*.

3) Place the chainwheel on the camshaft so that the marks on bearing cap, chainwheel, and screw holes align. If necessary, alter position of chain. Install the camshaft chainwheel retaining bolts using flat washers. Using tool (83 93 357), push tensioner catch down to tension chain. To complete installation, reverse removal procedures.

NOTE — *Cylinder head bolts should be retightened in the following manner. Run engine till warm and allow to cool 30 minutes. Slightly loosen each head bolt following sequence and retighten. Then tighten each bolt and additional ¼ turn (90°), following the proper sequence.*

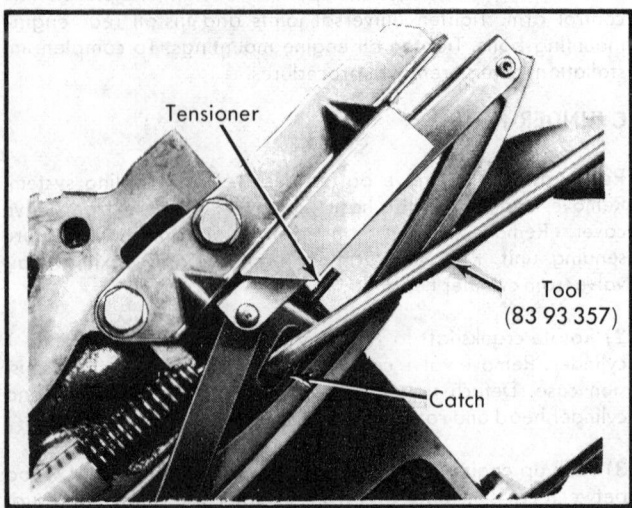

**Fig. 2   Chain Tensioner and Tensioner Tool
(Tension Release Position)**

CAMSHAFT

CAMSHAFT

Removal — Remove valve cover and camshaft chainwheel. Hang chainwheel and chain between tensioner and chain guide. Remove camshaft bearing caps and lift out camshaft.

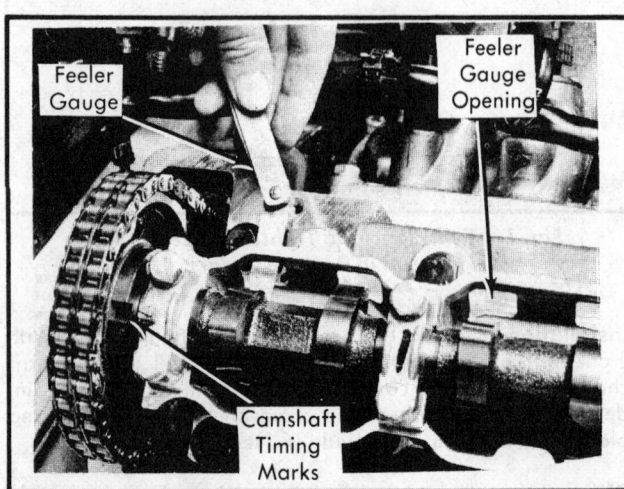

Fig. 3   Camshaft Timing Marks

Installation — Install camshaft and bearing assembly so that feeler gauge openings are at top. Ensure that crankshaft is still at TDC for No. 1 cylinder and reverse removal procedure.

TIMING CHAIN ASSEMBLY

Removal — 1) With engine removed from vehicle, place cylinder No. 1 at TDC of compression stroke. Remove valve cover. Remove chainwheel from camshaft and hang between tensioner and chain guide.

2) Remove crankshaft pulley and oil pump. Remove water pump. See Oil Pump and Water Pump Removal procedures. Remove 2 cylinder head-to-timing cover bolts.

3) Remove timing cover bolts and remove timing cover. Remove timing chain, camshaft chainwheel, tensioner and chain guide.

Installation — 1) Ensure that both crankshaft and camshaft are in TDC position for No. 1 cylinder compression stroke. Install chain tensioner and chain guide. Temporarily install camshaft chainwheel. Position the chain on the camshaft and crankshaft chainwheels and between the tensioner and chain guide.

2) Install the timing cover, oil pump and water pump. Take the tension off of the timing chain by inserting tool (83 93 357) into tensioner catch and pressing down. Place the chainwheel on the camshaft sprocket so that marks on the camshaft bearing cap, chainwheel and screw holes align. Install the camshaft chainwheel using flat washers.

3) Tension chain by inserting tool (83 93 357) into tensioner catch and pushing down to turn catch over latch arm. See Fig. 2. To complete installation, reverse removal procedures.

VALVES

VALVE ARRANGEMENT

E-I-I-E-E-I-I-E

VALVE SPRINGS

NOTE — *Valve spring replacement is possible without removing cylinder head from engine.*

Removal & Installation — Remove camshaft as previously described. Remove camshaft bearing support assembly. With cylinder head installed, take spark plug out of cylinder and fit air hose connector. Supply air pressure to keep valve from dropping into cylinder. Remove valve depressors and adjusting pallets. Use a valve compressor and remove retainers (keepers) with a magnet. To install, reverse removal procedures.

VALVE GUIDE SERVICING

To check for wear, pull valve about .12" (3 mm) from its seat and check radial play at valve head. If play exceeds .020" (.5 mm), replace valve and/or guide. To replace guide, run hot water through head and pull guide from head using suitable puller (8392631). To install, ensure that head is warm as in removal. Use guide tool (8392631) and press in new guide from the top.

900 4-CYLINDER (Cont.)

VALVE CLEARANCE ADJUSTMENT

1) Check clearance with valve cover removed by rotating crankshaft so that cam lobe of valve to be measured points away from valve. Measure clearance with feeler gauge between heel of cam and follower. Clearance should be between .006-.012" (.15-.30 mm) for intake and .014-.020" (.35-.50 mm) for exhaust. Turbo exhaust valve clearance is .016-.020" (.40-.50 mm).

2) If any valve clearance is beyond limits, direct measurement of all valve clearance is required. Use tool (8391450) and a dial indicator to measure actual clearance. Record clearance readings on all valves. Adjust intake clearances if beyond .008-.010" (.20-.25 mm) and exhaust clearances if beyond .016-.018" (.40-.45 mm). Turbo exhaust clearance should be adjusted if beyond .018-.020" (.45-.50 mm).

3) Remove camshaft, followers and adjusting pallets of any valve requiring adjustment. Measure pallet thickness and add noted valve clearance to determine total clearance. Subtract proper valve clearance to find needed pallet thickness. Install new pallets. Install followers and camshaft and recheck valve clearance.

PISTONS, PINS & RINGS

PISTON & ROD ASSEMBLY

Removal — With cylinder head and pan removed, note that rods and rod caps are numbered. Remove carbon or wear ridge from top of cylinders. Remove bearing caps and place plastic sleeves over rod bolts. Push piston/rod assembly out of cylinder.

Installation — Ensure that ring gaps are staggered and install ring compressor. Compression ring gaps should be equally spaced from each other. Notch on piston top must face timing cover and connecting rod numbers face exhaust side.

PISTON PIN REPLACEMENT

Pistons are retained by circlips. Remove circlips and press out piston pins. Check pins and bearings for wear or damage and replace as required.

FITTING PISTONS

1) To fit pistons to cylinder bores, use a feeler gauge .500" (12.7 mm) wide and .0005-.0016" (.014-.040 mm) thick. Oil cylinder lightly and insert piston without rings.

2) Attach feeler gauge to a spring scale. Insert feeler gauge between piston and cylinder wall at right angles to piston pin. When feeler gauge can be pulled out of cylinder with a force of 1.8-2.6 lbs. (.816-1.18 kg), piston clearance has been determined.

3) Repeat test at several different depths in cylinder bore. Graded standard and non-graded oversize pistons are available.

Piston Specifications

Application	Diameter In. (mm)
Std. (AB)	3.5425-3.5427 (89.980-89.986)
Std. (C)	3.5433-3.5437 (89.999-90.010)
1st Oversize	3.5619-3.5625 (90.472-90.487)
2nd Oversize	3.5816-3.5822 (90.972-90.987)

4) Check piston rings for end gap and side clearance, using an inverted piston to position ring in bore. On worn bores, measure at lower end of bore.

5) Install rings on pistons, staggering ring gaps. Compression ring gaps should be located above piston pin (180° from each other). Oil ring gaps should be equally spaced from each other.

CRANKSHAFT MAIN & CONNECTING ROD BEARINGS

BEARING SERVICE

1) Remove connecting rods and main bearing caps. Measure journals with a micrometer. Out-of-round should not exceed .002" (.051 mm). If crankshaft is near or over stated limit of wear, regrind journals and fit undersize bearings.

2) Using "V" blocks and a dial indicator check crankshaft for bend. If bend exceeds .002" (.051 mm), replace or repair crankshaft.

3) Using Plastigage method, check main bearing and connecting rod bearing journals. If clearance is found excessive, combine suitable undersize bearings to correct clearance. Undersize bearings are available in various thicknesses.

THRUST BEARING ALIGNMENT

Center main bearing is thrust bearing. Check crankshaft endplay. If beyond specifications, replace thrust washers with oil grooves facing crankshaft.

ENGINE OILING

Crankcase Capacity — 3.7 quarts with filter (4.5 quarts for turbocharged engine).

Oil Filter — Full-flow type.

Normal Oil Pressure — 43 psi (3.0 kg/cm²) @2000 RPM.

Pressure Regulator Valve — Non-adjustable; opens at 51-74 psi (3.6-5.2 kg/cm²).

ENGINE OILING SYSTEM

Oil pressure is generated by a gear type oil pump with one gear wheel and an eccentric ring gear. The pump is mounted on the timing cover and is driven by a crankshaft mounted driving plate. Oil is forced through a full flow filter and oil channels to crankshaft main and connecting rod bearings and valve train.

OIL PUMP

Removal — Clean area around pump. Immobilize crankshaft by attaching locking device (83 92 987) to flywheel ring gear.

Saab Engines

900 4-CYLINDER (Cont.)

Remove crankshaft pulley retaining bolt and remove pulley from crankshaft. Remove oil pump retaining bolts and extract the pump.

Inspection — Using a straight edge and feeler gauge, check end float between pump body and gear wheel.

Installation — Oil the gear wheels. Install the ring gear so that the mark on its face is visible. Fit a new sealing ring in groove in pump body. Prime pump with oil and install to engine. Remove oil filter adapter casting and fill passage with oil. Reinstall casting.

NOTE — It may be necessary to extract the pump gear slightly to locate it on driving plate.

ENGINE COOLING

Cooling System Capacity — 10.8 quarts.

Thermostat — Thermostat begins to open at approximately 190°F (88°C).

Radiator Cap — Opens at 12.9–17.1 psi (.907–1.2 kg/cm^2).

WATER PUMP

Removal — Drain coolant. Remove driving belt. Remove water pump attaching screws and remove water pump.

Installation — Clean gasket mating surfaces and install a new gasket. Install pump to timing cover. Install pulley and driving belt.

TIGHTENING SPECIFICATIONS

Application	Ft. Lbs. (N·m)
Main Bearings	79 (108)
Rod Bearings	40 (54)
Camshaft Bearing Caps	13 (18)
Crankshaft Pulley	137 (190)
Cylinder Head ①	
Step 1	45 (60)
Step 2	65 (90)
Flywheel	43 (59)
Oil Pump	13 (18)
Camshaft Sprocket	14 (20)
Intake Manifold	13 (18)
Exhaust Manifold	18 (25)

① Retighten as described in Installation procedures.

ENGINE SPECIFICATIONS

GENERAL SPECIFICATIONS

Year	Displ. cu. ins.	Displ. cc	Carburetor	HP at RPM	Torque (Ft. Lbs. at RPM)	Compr. Ratio	Bore in.	Bore mm	Stroke in.	Stroke mm
1981										
900	121	1985	Fuel Inj.	110 @ 5200	119 @ 3500	9.25:1	3.54	90	3.07	78
Turbo	121	1985	Fuel Inj.	135 @ 5000	160 @ 3500	7.20:1	3.54	90	3.07	78

CAMSHAFT

Engine	Journal Diam. In. (mm)	Clearance In. (mm)①	Lobe Lift In. (mm)②
1985 cc	1.139 (28.94)	.....	Int. .421 (10.8) Exh. .433 (11.0)

① — End play is .003–.010" (.08–.25 mm).

② — Turbo lobe lift is .358" (9.1 mm) for intake, .413" (10.5 mm) for exhaust.

VALVE TIMING

Engine	INTAKE① Open (BTDC)	INTAKE① Close (ABDC)	EXHAUST② Open (BBDC)	EXHAUST② Close (ATDC)
1985 cc				
99 & 900	10°	54°	46°	18°
Turbo	12°	40°	62°	2°

① — With .014" (.35 mm) valve clearance.

② — With .022 (.55 mm) valve clearance.

VALVE SPRINGS

Engine	Free Length In. (mm)	PRESSURE Lbs. @ In. (kg @ mm) Valve Closed	PRESSURE Lbs. @ In. (kg @ mm) Valve Open
1985 cc	1.700 (43.1)	.....	170-183@1.161 (77-83@29.5)

900 4-CYLINDER (Cont.)
ENGINE SPECIFICATIONS (Cont.)

VALVES							
Engine & Valve	Head Diam. In. (mm)	Face Angle	Seat Angle	Seat Width In. (mm)	Stem Diameter In. (mm)	Stem Clearance In. (mm)	Valve Lift In. (mm)
1985 cc							
Int.	1.654 (42.0)	44.5°	45°	.004-.008 (1-2)	.313-.314 (7.960-7.975)	0.02 (0.5)	.....
Exh.	1.398 (35.5)	44.5°	45°	.004-.008 (1-2)	.313-.314 (7.955-7.980)	0.02 (0.5)	.....

PISTONS, PINS, RINGS						
	PISTONS	PINS		RINGS		
Engine	Clearance In. (mm)	Piston Fit In. (mm)	Rod Fit In. (mm)	Rings	End Gap In. (mm)	Side Clearance In. (mm)
1985 cc	.0006-.0016 ② (.014-.040)	.0002-.0006 (.005-.014)	①	No. 1	.014-.021 (.35-.55)	.002-.003 (.050-.082)
				No. 2	.012-.018 (.30-.45)	.0016-.003 (.040-.072)
				Oil	.015-.055 (.38-1.40)	.....

① — Interference fit.
② — Turbo clearance .024-.050″ (.61-1.27 mm).

CRANKSHAFT MAIN & CONNECTING ROD BEARINGS						
	MAIN BEARINGS				CONNECTING ROD BEARINGS	
Engine	Journal Diam. In. (mm)	Clearance In. (mm)	Thrust Bearing	Crankshaft End Play In. (mm)	Journal Diam. In. (mm)	Clearance In. (mm)	Side Play In. (mm)
1985 cc	2.283-2.284 (57.981-58.000)	.001-.002 (.020-.062)	Center	.003-.011 (.08-.28)	2.046-2.047 (51.981-52.000)	.001-.002 (.026-.062)	.....

Subaru Engines

1600 & 1800 4-CYLINDER

ENGINE CODING

ENGINE IDENTIFICATION

Engine number is stamped on a machined pad near distributor. See table below for engine codes.

Engine Identification	
Application	Code
2-WD	
Federal	
Man. Trans.	E71AA3, E71GA3A
Auto. Trans.	E81TA
Calif.	
Man. Trans.	E71AC3
Auto. Trans	E81TC
4-WD	
Federal	E71WA3, E71WA4
Calif.	E71WC3, E71WC4

ENGINE

ENGINE

NOTE – *It is possible to remove engine with transmission fitted. Removal procedure given is with transmission remaining in vehicle.*

REMOVAL & INSTALLATION

Removal – 1) Disconnect battery cable. Remove spare wheel from engine compartment. Remove air cleaner assembly.

2) Disconnect fuel line from fuel pump intake, allow fuel to drain into a suitable container. Drain radiator and engine block. Disconnect radiator hoses at engine.

3) Disconnect all wiring to engine and accessories. On 4-WD models remove engine fan from pulley. On Automatic Transmission models disconnect oil cooler pipes.

4) Remove 2 upper radiator bolts and lift out radiator. Remove nuts on each of engine-to-firewall struts and remove strut by moving to rear to clear engine hanger.

5) Remove all control cables and vacuum hoses from engine. On automatic transmission models, disconnect torque converter from engine by rotating crankshaft to allow removal of 4 bolts through timing hole. Use care that bolts do not fall into housing. On manual transmission models, remove clutch return spring. Remove nuts from brackets on engine and firewall, and remove engine stabilizer.

6) Remove engine-to-transmission bolts and nuts and disconnect exhaust pipe. Remove bolts securing front engine mounts-to-engine. Slightly hoist engine with chain hoist attached to front to rear hangers and separate engine from transmission.

7) When separating engine from transmission, ensure that torque converter remains with transmission (Automatic Transmission only). Also, it may be helpful to slightly jack up transmission during removal procedure. Remove engine completely and place on engine stand.

Installation – To install, reverse removal procedure and tighten all bolts and nuts. Adjust all controls and fill engine with suitable coolant.

ENGINE DISASSEMBLY & REASSEMBLY

NOTE – *Remove engine, place on engine stand (399814300X2 or equivalent). Remove starter and proceed as follows:*

Disassembly – 1) Separate engine from transmission if necessary. Ensure that converter remains attached to automatic transmission (if equipped). Drain oil and coolant. Make sure that liquid does not run over clutch cover. On manual transmission models, remove clutch cover and disc.

2) Disconnect ignition wiring from engine. Remove distributor and distributor plate. Remove bolts securing alternator to alternator bracket and remove alternator. Remove EGR pipe and cover. Disconnect wiring harness leads for oil pressure gauge or switch. Remove clamp securing air suction manifold. Remove connecting hoses from valve covers. Unclamp heater hoses. Disconnect 2 water by-pass hoses from intake manifold. Remove intake manifold assembly. Remove alternator brackets and air suction system.

3) Remove oil filter duct. 4WD models have a bracket. Use a puller to remove crankshaft pulley. Remove oil pump and filter as an assembly. Remove water pump with hoses and tubes attached. Remove pressure plate and clutch disc.

NOTE – *Insert rod through timing hole to prevent flywheel from turning.*

4) Turn engine over on stand and remove oil pan, crankcase, gasket and transmission cover (if necessary). Remove oil strainer and brackets. Remove either flywheel or converter drive plate. Take off flywheel housing.

5) Remove spark plugs and valve cover. Remove rocker assembly and push rods. Remove cylinder head bolts in sequence *See Fig. 1.* Remove cylinder head and gasket. Use Allen wrench and remove crankcase plug.

NOTE – *Keep push rods in proper order for proper reassembly.*

6) Position pistons at bottom dead center and remove circlip with long nosed pliers. Access to No. 1 and No. 2 pins is through front crankcase plug holes. Access to No. 3 and No. 4 pins is through rear service holes. Remove pins and pistons, marking for reassembly.

7) Work through hole in camshaft gear and straighten lockwasher, then remove nut. Remove nuts and washers and separate cases. Use valve lifter clips (899804100 or equivalent), to prevent upper crankcase lifters from falling off.

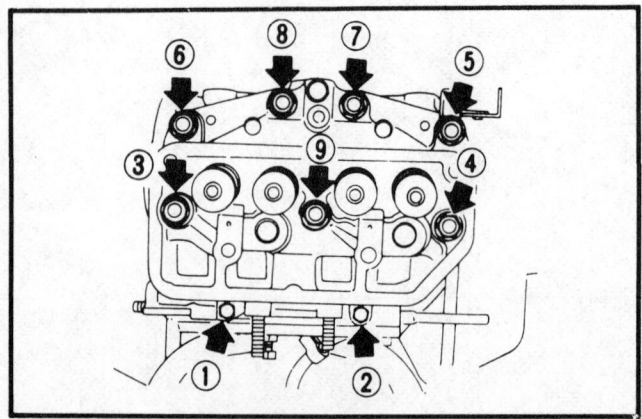

Fig. 1 Cylinder Head Nut Loosening Sequence

1600 & 1800 4-CYLINDER (Cont.)

NOTE – *Pull camshaft to rear for crankcase clearance.*

8) Remove oil seal. Lift out crankshaft, distributor gear, and connecting rods. Keep crankshaft bearings in order for reassembly. Remove camshaft and gear. Remove oil pressure switch and valve lifters.

Reassembly – Lubricate all friction surfaces with engine oil prior to reassembly. Install crankshaft and camshaft with bearings in left half (No. 2 & 4 Cyl.) of crankcase. Apply gasket sealer to mating surfaces of crankcase and continue to reverse order of disassembly. Tighten crankcase halves and cylinder heads in sequence shown in *Fig. 3*.

NOTE – *Use spacers (899848600) in place of rocker arm supports when tightening head nuts.*

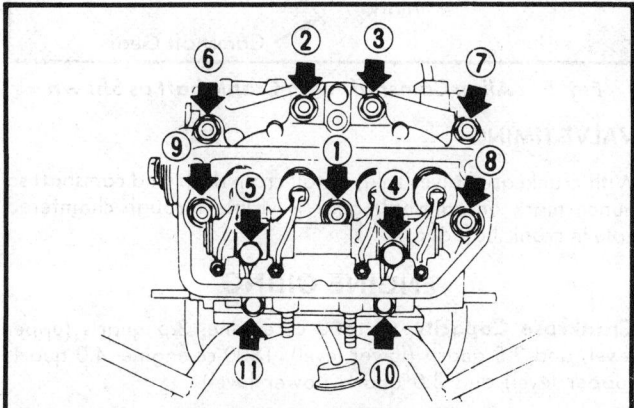

Fig. 2   Cylinder Head Tightening Sequence

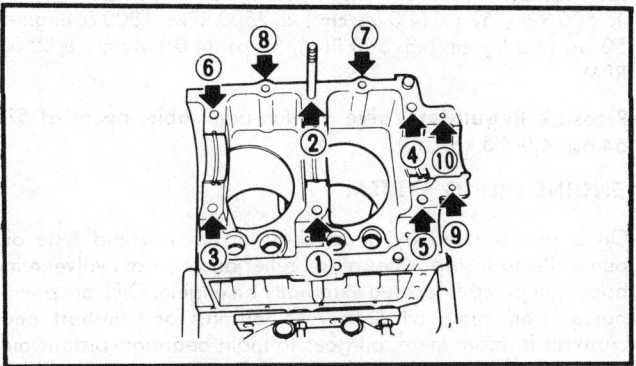

Fig. 3   Tightening Sequence for Crankcase

VALVES

VALVE ARRANGEMENT

I-E-E-I (both banks, front to rear).

VALVE GUIDE SERVICING

1) Check valve guide for wear or damage. Replace defective guides by using a drift punch and driving out guide through top of head. Press in new guide from top of head until it projects .689-.709" (17.50-18.00 mm) for intake valve guide and .886-.906" (22.50-23.01 mm) for exhaust valve guide.

2) Ream valve guide to provide correct clearance. Inspect valve seat to make sure it is true with guide. Reface valve seat if necessary.

VALVE STEM OIL SEALS

Valve stem oil seals are used only on intake valves. Slide seal off of valve guide and replace with a new seal. Use care when inserting stem not to damage seal.

VALVE SPRING

Using a spring compressor, remove "O" ring, valve keepers and spring retainer. Check spring under pressure and at free length. Spring squareness must be within .083" (2.10 mm). Replace if necessary. Install spring with wide spaced coil (paint marks) facing valve spring retainer.

ROCKER ARM ASSEMBLY

Check rocker shaft, rocker arm and bushing for wear or damage. Replace any worn parts. Press in new bushing and ream until a clearance of .0006-.002" (.016-.052 mm) is achieved between bushing and shaft.

VALVE TAPPET SERVICE

Remove lifters from crankcase. Inspect tappet for wear or clogged oil hole. Replace lifter if lifter-to-crankcase clearance exceeds .004" (.10 mm). Standard lifter clearance is .0012-.0028" (.030-.07 mm).

VALVE CLEARANCE ADJUSTMENT

With engine cold, rotate engine to TDC of firing stroke. Insert feeler gauge between rocker arm and valve stem. Clearances should be as follows:

Valve Clearance		
Application	**Intake** In. (mm)	**Exhaust** In. (mm)
1600 cc & 1800 cc	.010 (.25)	.014 (.35)

PISTONS, PINS & RINGS

FITTING PISTONS

1) Measure piston bore .028" (.7 mm) from top of cylinder in line with crankshaft and again 90° from centerline of crankshaft. Make same measurements 1.48" (37 mm) and then 2.65" (67 mm) from top of cylinder bore. If inner cylinder diameter exceeds .0197" (.50 mm) more than standard bore of 3.6205-3.6216" (91.960-91.990 mm) after boring and honing, replace crankcase.

2) Measure piston 1.04" (26.3 mm) from bottom of skirt, 90° from piston pin hole.

NOTE – *Measurement of both pistons and cylinder bores should be performed at 68° F (20° C). All cylinders must be bored at same size and use same size pistons.*

3) Check piston ring end gap and side clearance. Check gap at bottom of cylinder bore. Fit piston rings with "R" or "N" facing up.

PISTON PIN

Check piston pin for damage, cracks, wear or distortion. Check connecting rod bushing for wear. If pin or bushing are worn beyond specification, replace bushing in connecting rod

1600 & 1800 4-CYLINDER (Cont.)

and ream to fit standard pin. Piston pin is a thumb push fit at 68° F (20° C).

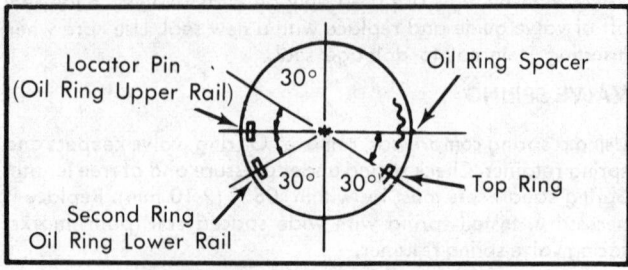

Fig. 4   Piston Ring Gap Position

CRANKSHAFT MAIN & CONNECTING ROD BEARINGS

MAIN & CONNECTING ROD BEARINGS

1) Check connecting rod side play with a feeler gauge. If side play exceeds specifications, replace connecting rod.

2) Use Plastigage method to measure both main and connecting rod bearing clearances. Main bearing inserts are available in standard, .001" (.03 mm), .002" (.05 mm) and .010" (.25 mm) undersize. Connecting rod bearing inserts are available in standard, .002" (.05 mm) and .010" (.25 mm) undersize.

3) Check crankshaft for bend by placing front and rear main journals on "V" blocks and fitting a dial indicator on center journal. Correct or replace crankshaft if bend exceeds .0014" (.035 mm).

REAR MAIN BEARING OIL SEAL SERVICE

Seal is replaced when crankcase halves are split. After crankcase halves have been reassembled, install new seal.

CAMSHAFT

ENGINE FRONT COVER OIL SEAL

With front cover removed, drive out old seal. Install new seal using installer tool (499067000), with or without front cover on engine.

CAMSHAFT

1) Camshaft may be removed when crankcase has been split. Check for wear or damage, replace camshaft if necessary. Using a dial indicator, check that bend does not exceed .002" (.051 mm).

2) Measure thrust clearance between camshaft and camshaft plate. Standard clearance is .0008-.0035" (.02-.09 mm). If clearance exceeds limit of .008" (.20 mm), replace camshaft plate. Measure camshaft lobe height. If less than 1.269-1.273" (32.23-32.33 mm) overall, replace camshaft.

NOTE — If camshaft is replaced, all valve lifters should also be replaced. Check identification marks. 1600 cc engine uses camshaft marked "51", while 1800 cc engine uses camshaft "72".

3) Measure camshaft gear runout with dial indicator. Replace camshaft if runout exceeds .010" (.25 mm). Measure backlash

between camshaft gear and crankshaft gear. If backlash exceeds .0039" (.10 mm), replace camshaft gear. Standard value of backlash is .0004-.0020" (.01-.05 mm).

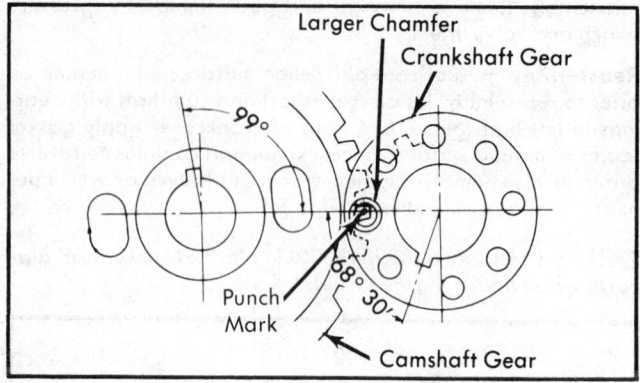

Fig. 5   Align Camshaft with Crankshaft as Shown

VALVE TIMING

With crankcase halves split, install crankshaft and camshaft so punch mark on camshaft gear is visible through chamfered hole in crankshaft gear.

ENGINE OILING

Crankcase Capacity — 1600 cc engine: 3.5 quarts (upper level) and 2.5 quarts (lower level). 1800 cc engine: 4.0 quarts (upper level) and 3.0 quarts (lower level).

Oil Filter — Full-flow.

Normal Oil Pressure — 1600 cc engine: 35 psi (2.5 kg/cm²) @ 500 RPM, 57 psi (4.0 kg/cm²) @ 2500 RPM. 1800 cc engine: 50 psi (3.5 kg/cm²) @ 500 RPM, 57 psi (4.0 kg/cm²) @ 2500 RPM.

Pressure Regulator Valve — Non-adjustable, opens at 57-64 psi (4.0-4.5 kg/cm²).

ENGINE OILING SYSTEM

Oil is pressure fed by a camshaft driven trochoid type oil pump. Pump incorporates an oil relief and by-pass valve in its body. Oil pump is located externally on engine. Oil from pump passes from main oil gallery to journals of camshaft and crankshaft. From there, oil goes to main bearings, pistons pin bearings and cylinder walls. Oil passes through valve lifters and push rods to oil rocker arms.

OIL PUMP

Removal — Remove four attaching bolts and pull pump and filter forward. Remove oil filter from pump.

Disassembly — 1) Remove screws, lift cover and rotor from pump body. Remove "O" ring. Remove by-pass spring and ball. Unscrew plug and remove washers, spring and pressure relief valve.

2) Measure rotor-to-drive gear and rotor-to-body clearance. Measure rotor side clearance and measure diameters of rotor and drive gear. Replace any component that exceeds wear limits.

3) Inspect relief valve spring, valve and pump body for wear or damage.

1600 & 1800 4-CYLINDER (Cont.)

NOTE — *Make sure oil pump shaft is aligned with slot in camshaft when reassembling.*

Reassembly — Reassemble in reverse order, using all new gaskets and "O" rings.

Installation — Install oil filter on pump. Using rearward movement reinstall oil pump and four attaching bolts.

Oil Pump Clearances	
Application	**Clearance In. (mm)**
Rotor-to-Drive Gear	.0008-.0047 (.02-.11)
Outer Rotor-to-Body	.0012-.0051 (.03-.13)
Rotor Side Clearance	.0009-.0083 (.15-.21)

Oil Pump Dimensions	
Application	**Dimension In. (mm)**
Drive Gear O.D.	1.1693-1.1709 (29.70-29.74)
Rotor O.D.	1.5957-1.5968 (40.53-40.56)
Relief Valve Spring Free Length	1.851 (47.10)

ENGINE COOLING

THERMOSTAT

Thermostat — On Federal Sedan, Hatchback and Hardtop models with automatic transmission, thermostat begins to open at 182-188°F (83.5-86.5°C) and fully opens at 208°F (98°C). On all other models, thermostat begins to open at 188-193°F (86.5-89.5°C) and fully opens at 212°F (100°C).

Coolant Capacity — 5.6-5.8 quarts.

WATER PUMP

Removal — Drain coolant and disconnect main radiator outlet hose. Remove drive belt and attaching bolts, remove water pump.

Disassembly — 1) Remove four screws attaching cover plate and gasket. Remove pulley and locking clip.

2) Withdraw shaft, impeller and mechanical seal from pump body. Press pump shaft from impeller.

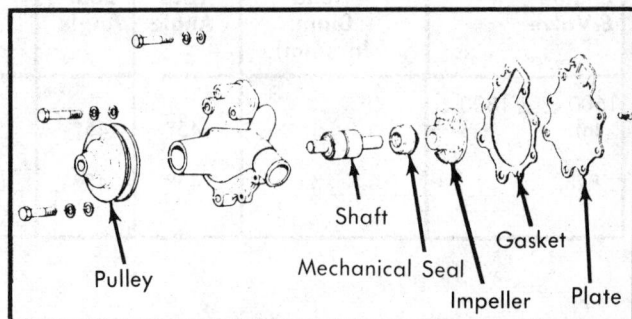

Pulley — Shaft — Mechanical Seal — Gasket — Impeller — Plate

Fig. 6   Exploded View of Water Pump

Reassembly — 1) Using an arbor press, press pump shaft into pump body until locking clip may be installed. Apply sealing compound to edge of mechanical seal and in housing with carbon ring facing toward impeller.

2) Press impeller onto shaft until impeller-to-body clearance is .020-.028" (0.5-0.7 mm). Press on bearing outer race, not shaft. Support impeller side of pump shaft and press on pulley until distance between center of pulley groove and rear face of pump housing is 2.406-2.429" (61.1-61.7 mm) for 1800 cc engine or 2.524-2.547" (64.1-64.7 mm) for 1600 cc engine.

Installation — Install water pump together with slotted clip, water pipe, and water by-pass pipe as a unit. Gradually tighten bolts alternately and evenly in several steps to prevent leakage. The clamps for the water hose should be positioned low to prevent interference with the EGR pipe.

ELECTRIC COOLING FAN

All models are equipped with an electric cooling fan motor. 4-WD models use a combination of electric fan, engine drive fan and forced cooling (water cooling). All other models utilize electric fan and forced cooling (water cooling).

ENGINE SPECIFICATIONS

GENERAL SPECIFICATIONS										
Year	Displ.		Carburetor	HP at RPM	Torque (Ft. Lbs. at RPM)	Compr. Ratio	Bore		Stroke	
	cu. ins.	cc					in.	mm	in.	mm
1981										
1600 cc	97	1595	2-Bbl.	67@5200	81@2400	9.01:1	3.62	92	2.36	60
1800 cc	109	1781	2-Bbl.	71@4400	94@2400	8.7:1	3.62	92	2.64	67

Subaru Engines

1600 & 1800 4-CYLINDER (Cont.)

ENGINE SPECIFICATIONS (Cont.)

VALVES							
Engine & Valve	Head Diam. In. (mm)	Face Angle	Seat Angle	Seat Width In. (mm)	Stem Diameter In. (mm)	Stem Clearance In. (mm)	Valve Lift In. (mm)
1600 cc & 1800 cc Int.	.....	45°	45°	.028-.051 (.7-1.3)	.3130-.3136 (7.950-7.965)	.0014-.0026 (.035-.065)	.....
Exh.	.....	45°	45°	.039-.071 (1.0-1.8)	.3128-.3134 (7.945-7.960)	.0016-.0028 (.040-.070)	.....

PISTONS, PINS, RINGS						
	PISTONS	PINS		RINGS		
Engine	Clearance In. (mm)	Piston Fit In. (mm)	Rod Fit In. (mm)	Rings	End Gap In. (mm)	Side Clearance In. (mm)
1600 cc & 1800 cc	.0004-.0016 (.010-.040)	.00004-.00067 (.001-.017)	.0002-.0016 (.005-.040)	No. 1	.0079-.0138① (.20-.35)	.0016-.0031③ (.04-.08)
				No. 2	.0079-.0138① (.20-.35)	.0012-.0028③ (.03-.07)
				No. 3	.0079-.0354② (.20-.90)	.....

① — Limit .0591" (1.5 mm).
② — Limit .07987" (2.0 mm).
③ — Limit .0059" (.15 mm).

CRANKSHAFT MAIN & CONNECTING ROD BEARINGS							
	MAIN BEARINGS				CONNECTING ROD BEARINGS		
Engine	Journal Diam. In (mm)	Clearance① In. (mm)	Thrust Bearing	Crankshaft End Play② In. (mm)	Journal Diam. In. (mm)	Clearance③ In. (mm)	Side Play④ In. (mm)
1600 cc Front & Rear	1.9668-1.9673 (49.957-49.970)	.0004-.0014 (.010-.035)	Center	.0016-.0054 (.040-.137)	1.7715-1.7720 (44.995-45.010)	.0008-.0028 (.020-.070)	.0028-.013 (.07-.33)
Center	1.9673-1.9678 (49.970-49.982)	.0004-.0012 (.010-.030)					
1800 cc Front & Rear	2.1636-2.1642 (54.995-54.970)	.0004-.0012 (.010-.030)	Center	.0016-.0054 (.040-.137)	1.7715-1.7720 (44.995-45.010)	.0008-.0028 (.020-.070)	.0028-.013 (.07-.33)
Center	2.1636-2.1642 (54.995-54.970)	.0004-.0010 (.010-.025)					

① — Limit front and rear .0022" (.055 mm); Limit center .0018" (.045 mm).
② — Limit .0118" (.30 mm).
③ — Limit .0039" (.10 mm).
④ — Limit .016" (.40 mm).

1600 & 1800 4-CYLINDER (Cont.)
ENGINE SPECIFICATIONS (Cont.)

CAMSHAFT

Engine	Journal Diam. In. (mm)	Clearance In. (mm)①	Lobe Lift In. (mm)
1600 cc Front & Center	1.0236-1.0243 (26.000-26.018)	.0010-.0023 (.025-.059)	.2262 (5.745)
1800 cc Front & Center	1.2598-1.2605 (32.000-32.018)	.0010-.0023 (.025-.059)	.2262 (5.745)
1600 cc & 1800 cc Rear	1.4173-1.4180 (36.000-36.018)	.0010-.0023 (.025-.059)	.2262 (5.745)

① — Limit — .0039" (.1 mm).

VALVE SPRINGS

Engine	Free Length In. (mm)	PRESSURE Lbs. @ In. (kg @ mm)	
		Valve Closed	Valve Open
1600 cc & 1800 cc Inner	1.921 (48.8)	19.0-22.1@1.476 (8.6-10.0@37.5)	41.7-48.3@1.122 (18.9-21.9@28.5)
1600 cc & 1800 cc Outer	1.783 (45.3)	32.9-38.1@1.555 (14.9-17.3@39.5)	112.5-127.9@1.201 (51.0-58.0@30.5)

TIGHTENING SPECIFICATIONS

Application	Ft. Lbs. (N·m)
Cylinder Head	
Step 1	22 (30)
Step 2	43 (58)
Step 3	47 (64)
Connecting Rod Nuts	29-31 (39-42)
Crankshaft Pulley	39-42 (47-54)
Crankcase Plug	46-56 (63-76)
Crankcase Halves	
6 mm Bolts	3-4 (4-5)
8 mm Bolts	17-20 (23-27)
10 mm Bolts	29-35 (39-48)
Intake Manifold	13-16 (18-22)
Flywheel	30-33 (41-45)
Rocker Arm	47 (64)

Toyota Engines

3A-C 4-CYLINDER

ENGINE CODING

ENGINE IDENTIFICATION

Engine serial number and code are stamped on left side of block.

Engine Identification	
Application	**Code**
Tercel (1452 cc)	3A-C

ENGINE, CYLINDER HEAD & MANIFOLDS

ENGINE

Removal — 1) Disconnect negative battery cable. Remove hood, air cleaner and, on models with automatic transmission, grille. Wrap drive shaft boots with shop towels.

2) Drain cooling system and remove hoses and oil cooler lines (if so equipped). Loosen fan shroud and remove radiator. Remove exhaust pipe and bracket, differential plate bolts and oil cooler pipe (if so equipped).

3) Disconnect ignition coil cable and all engine-to-chassis electrical connections at engine. Disconnect carburetor linkage, fuel lines and heater hoses.

4) On models with manual transmission, remove starter cable and windshield washer tank. On models with automatic transmission, remove starter and torque converter cover. On all models, support transmission with a floor jack and remove engine mounts.

5) Attach hoist to engine hangers and, with hoist supporting engine, remove transaxle bolts. On models with manual transmission, remove engine. On models with automatic transmission, remove 4 bolts to torque converter. Pull engine about 2" (50 mm) forward, disconnect torque converter and remove engine. On all models, suspend clutch or converter housing.

Installation — To install, reverse removal procedure, assuring that all adjustments and fluid levels are checked prior to starting engine.

MANIFOLDS

NOTE — Intake and exhaust manifolds are removed and installed as an assembly.

Removal — Remove air cleaner. Disconnect fuel and vacuum lines at carburetor. Disconnect choke and throttle linkage at carburetor. Remove heat insulator, PCV valve and PCV hose. Disconnect exhaust pipe at manifold. Remove manifold retaining nuts and bolts; remove manifold.

Installation — To install, reverse removal procedure, ensuring that mating surfaces are clean and new gaskets are used. Tighten 2 center bolts first, then tighten the remainder in a front-rear, top-bottom star pattern.

CYLINDER HEAD

Removal — 1) Drain cooling system and remove upper radiator hose. Remove manifold and carburetor assembly. Disconnect heater hose at rear of head. Remove rocker arm cover.

2) Remove spark plug wires, distributor and fuel pump. Position crankshaft to TDC by aligning mark on pulley to "0" mark on lower timing belt cover. Remove drive belt, water pump pulley and alternator.

3) Using a puller, remove crankshaft pulley. Remove timing belt covers and water pump. Mark position of camshaft timing sprocket and timing belt. Remove timing belt.

NOTE — Do not bend or twist belt. Keep belt free of oil, water, or steam.

4) Loosen rocker arm support bolts in 3 or 4 steps and in sequence shown in Fig. 1. Remove rocker arm assembly and camshaft timing sprocket. Remove camshaft bearing caps in same general sequence as rocker arm supports and arrange in order.

5) Measure camshaft thrust clearance. Remove camshaft and distributor drive gear. Loosen cylinder head bolts in 2 or 3 steps and in sequence shown in Fig. 2. Lift head from engine.

Installation — 1) Ensure that mating surfaces are clean, then install new gasket and head. Tighten head bolts gradually in 2 or 3 steps as shown in Fig. 2.

2) Install distributor drive gear on camshaft. Install camshaft on head making sure that arrows on bearing caps face front. Apply grease to and install front oil seal.

3) Install front bearing cap and tighten all bearing cap bolts gradually in 3 or 4 steps. Check camshaft thrust clearance and adjust to specifications. Continue installation in reverse order of removal.

CAUTION — When installing bearing caps, insure that front marks and imprinted numbers match.

Fig. 1 Rocker Arm Tightening Sequence
(Loosen in Reverse Sequence)

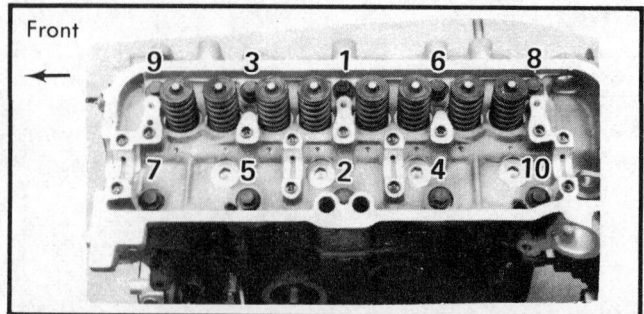

Fig. 2 Cylinder Head Tightening Sequence
(Loosen in Reverse Sequence)

3A-C 4-CYLINDER (Cont.)

CAMSHAFT

TIMING BELT

Removal — 1) Remove water pump drive belt and pulley. Position crankshaft to TDC by aligning mark on pulley to "O" mark on lower timing belt cover.

2) Using a puller, remove crankshaft pulley. Remove upper and lower timing belt covers. Mark position of camshaft timing sprocket and timing belt. Remove timing belt.

Inspection — 1) If belt is severed, check timing gear gasket for damage or improper installation. If belt teeth are cracked or damaged, check to see if camshaft is locked.

2) If there is noticeable wear or cracks on belt face, check for nicks on idler pulley lock. If there is damage or wear on only one edge of belt, check belt guide and alignment of each pulley.

Installation — 1) Loosen timing belt idler pulley and move toward the left as far as possible. Using care not to excessively bend or twist timing belt, install timing belt.

2) Turn crankshaft 2 revolutions and align timing mark. Measure timing belt tension as shown in *Fig. 3* and adjust with timing belt idler pulley. Complete installation by reversing removal procedure.

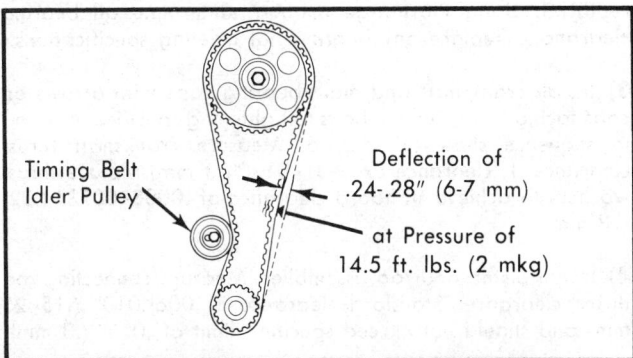

Timing Belt Idler Pulley

Deflection of .24-.28" (6-7 mm)

at Pressure of 14.5 ft. lbs. (2 mkg)

Fig. 3   Measuring Timing Belt Tension

CAMSHAFT

Removal — 1) Remove air cleaner and rocker arm cover. Remove front cover assembly and timing belt. See *TIMING BELT*. Loosen rocker arm support bolts in 3 to 4 steps and in reverse order of sequence shown in *Fig. 1*. Remove rocker arm assembly.

2) Remove camshaft timing sprocket. Remove camshaft bearing caps in same general sequence as rocker arm supports and arrange in order.

3) Remove camshaft and distributor drive gear. Check cam lobe height. Check camshaft for maximum runout of .0024" (.06 mm).

NOTE — *Rotate camshaft one turn clockwise and divide maximum gauge difference by 2.*

Installation — 1) Using plastigage, adjust bearing caps to clearance specifications. Make sure arrows on bearing caps face front. Apply grease to and install front oil seal.

2) Install front bearing cap and tighten all bearing cap bolts gradually in 3 or 4 steps. Check camshaft thrust clearance and adjust to specifications. Continue installation in reverse order of removal.

CAUTION — *When installing bearing caps, insure that front marks and imprinted numbers match.*

VALVES

VALVE ARRANGEMENT

I-E-E-I-I-E-E-I

ROCKER ARM ASSEMBLY

Removal — 1) Remove air cleaner and rocker arm cover. Loosen rocker arm support bolts in 3 to 4 steps and in reverse order of sequence shown in *Fig. 1*. Remove rocker arm assembly.

2) Check arm-to-shaft clearance by twisting on shaft. Little or no movement should be felt. If worn excessively, disassemble and check. If clearance exceeds .0024" (.06 mm), replace rocker arm and/or shaft.

NOTE — *Disassemble and mark all parts for reassembly in proper order. Loosen adjusting screws and nuts prior to installation of assembly.*

Installation — To install, reverse removal procedure. Tighten rocker arm support bolts in 3 to 4 steps and in sequence shown in *Fig. 1*.

VALVES & VALVE SPRINGS

1) Mark each valve and, using valve spring compressor, remove valves, valve retainers, retainer locks, springs and valve stem oil seals.

2) Using inside micrometer, measure inside diameter of valve guide at several places (use maximum wear point for calculation). Measure valve stem diameter and subtract difference from valve guide inside diameter. If valve stem clearance exceeds specifications, replace valve and guide.

3) Using a caliper type ruler, measure valve spring free length and check for squareness within .079" (2.0 mm). Using a spring tester, measure tension of each spring at specified height. Replace springs that do not meet specifications.

VALVE GUIDE SERVICING

1) Break off valve guide bushing at snap ring and remove snap ring. Heat cylinder head to approximately 176-212°F (80-100°C) and drive out bushing toward combustion chamber.

2) Re-heat cylinder head and install new guides from top of head. Drive guide in until snap ring makes contact. Using a .28" (7.0 mm) reamer, ream valve guides to provide proper clearance.

VALVE CLEARANCE ADJUSTMENT

1) With No. 1 piston at TDC of compression stroke, adjust cylinder numbers 1 & 2 intake valves and cylinder numbers 1 & 3 exhaust valves to specified clearance.

2) Rotate crankshaft one full turn (360°) clockwise to align timing mark on damper with "O" mark on timing cover. Adjust cylinder numbers 3 & 4 intake valves and cylinder numbers 2 & 3 exhaust valves to specified clearance.

Toyota Engines

3A-C 4-CYLINDER (Cont.)

NOTE – *Valves should be adjusted with engine at normal operating temperature. Cold specifications are provided for initial settings after assembly.*

Valve Clearance Specifications		
Valve	Hot	Cold
	In. (mm)	In. (mm)
Intake	.008 (.20)	.007 (.18)
Exhaust	.012 (.30)	.011 (.28)

PISTONS, PINS & RINGS

PISTON & ROD ASSEMBLY

Removal – With cylinder head and oil pan removed, machine ring ridge from top of cylinder. Mark rods and caps for correct assembly, then remove rod caps. Cover rod bolts with short lengths of hose to prevent crankshaft damage, then push piston/rod assembly out of block.

NOTE – *Ridge on cylinder wall must be removed before removing piston and rod assembly from block or damage to piston ring lands may result.*

Installation – Lubricate piston, cylinder and journal with clean engine oil. Position rings on piston as illustrated in *Fig. 4* and apply ring compressor. Install piston/rod assembly in proper position with notch on connecting rod facing forward. Align rod and cap marks and tighten rod caps to specification.

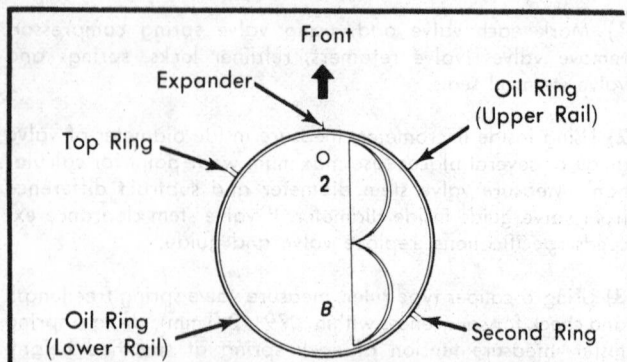

Fig. 4   Correct Piston Ring Gap Arrangement

FITTING PISTONS

Measure piston diameter at right angle to piston pin center line and at room temperature. Normal piston diameter is 3.047" (77.4 mm). Measure cylinder bore at top and bottom of wear

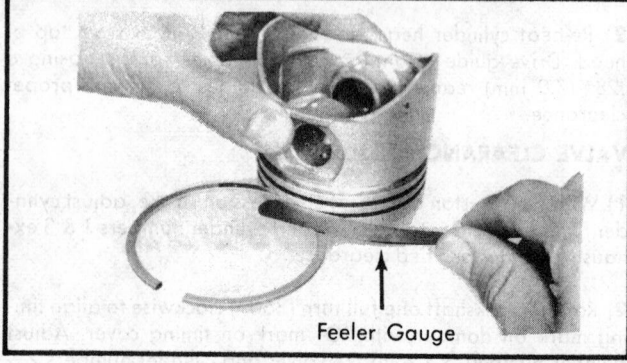

Fig. 5   Measuring Ring Groove Clearance

area and center of bore, in line with and at 90° to crankshaft. Standard bore is 3.053" (77.5 mm) with a wear limit of .008" (.2 mm). Maximum taper and out of round is .001" (.02 mm). If not within specifications, rebore and/or replace pistons. Measure ring end gap at bottom of ring travel. Check clearance of ring in ring groove. See *Fig. 5*.

PISTON PINS

Using a press and piston pin removal tool set, press piston pin out of piston and connecting rod. Lightly coat piston pin and pin hole with engine oil. Press in pin until centered in connecting rod.

CRANKSHAFT MAIN & CONNECTING ROD BEARINGS

MAIN & CONNECTING ROD BEARINGS

1) Prior to disassembly, mark main and connecting rod bearing caps for reassembly in their original positions and check crankshaft end play and connecting rod side play. Remove piston and connecting rod assemblies. Remove main bearing caps and remove crankshaft.

2) Measure crankshaft main and rod journal diameter. Check crankshaft for maximum runout of .0024" (.06 mm). If any measurement exceeds specifications, crankshaft must be replaced. Using Plastigage method, determine all bearing clearances. Replace any bearing not meeting specifications.

3) Install crankshaft and main bearing caps with arrows on caps facing front. Tighten bolts to tightening specifications and in sequence shown in *Fig. 6*. Measure crankshaft thrust clearance. If clearance exceeds .012" (.3 mm) replace thrust washers to achieve standard clearance of .0008-.0073" (.02-.18 mm).

4) Install piston and rod assemblies. Measure connecting rod thrust clearance. Standard clearance is .006-.010" (.15-.25 mm) and should not exceed specified limit of .012" (.3 mm).

Fig. 6   Main Bearing Tightening Sequence (Loosen in Reverse Order)

CRANKSHAFT FRONT OIL SEAL

Drive out seal from engine front cover using screwdriver. Using oil seal tool, drive new seal into cover making sure that seal goes in straight.

3A-C 4-CYLINDER (Cont.)

REAR MAIN BEARING OIL SEAL

Remove oil seal from case by driving out with a scewdriver. Using oil seal tool, drive new seal into cover making sure that seal goes in straight. Lightly coat seal lip with multi-purpose grease.

ENGINE OILING

Crankcase Capacity (Drain and Refill) — 3.7 qts. (Includes filter).

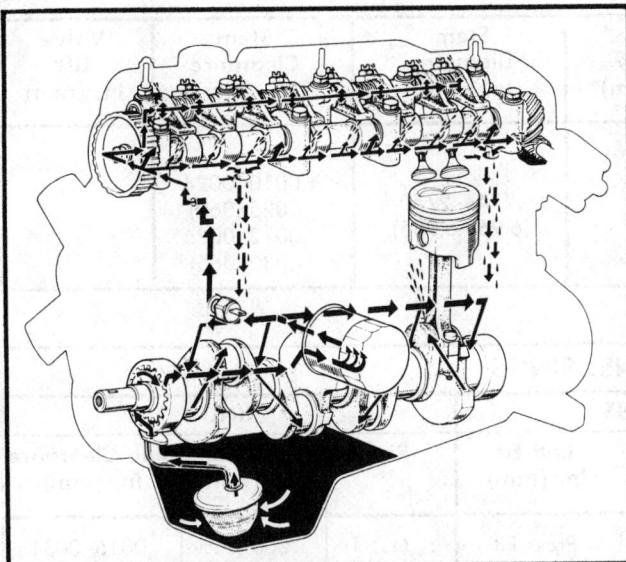

Fig. 7 Engine Oiling System

OIL PUMP

Removal — Remove timing covers and timing belt. See *TIMING BELT*. Remove oil pan and strainer. Remove oil pump and disassemble by removing (in order) cover, drive gear, driven gear, oil seal and relief valve. See *Fig. 8*.

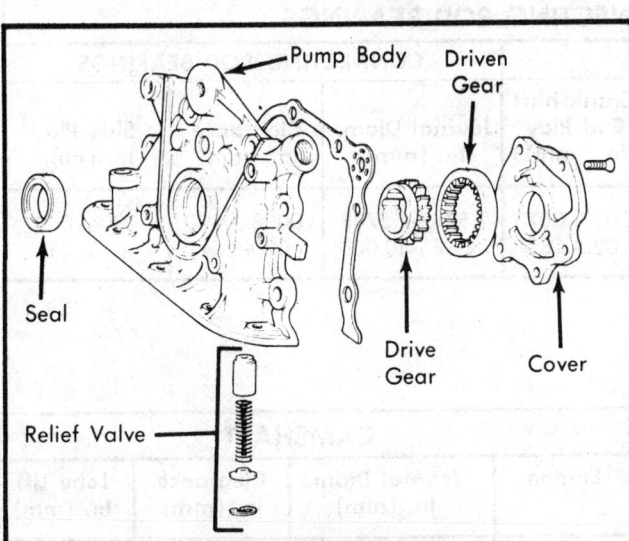

Fig. 8 Exploded View of Oil Pump and Pressure Relief Valve Assembly

Inspection — Check gears for wear or damage. Install new oil seal using proper seal tool. Measure clearances between gear tip of drive gear and driven gear, side clearance, and gear-to-body clearance. If any clearance exceeds specifications replace necessary part(s). Check relief valve for wear or damage.

Installation — To install, ensure that mating surfaces are clean and use new gasket. Reverse removal procedures to complete installation.

Oil Pump Specifications	
Application	**In. (mm)**
Gear Tip Clearance	
Drive Gear	.004-.010 (.10-.25)
	Limit .013 (.35)
Driven Gear	.002-.012 (.05-.31)
	Limit .013 (.35)
Gear Side Clearance	.001-.003 (.03-.08)
	Limit .004 (.10)
Gear-to-Body Clearance	.004-.007 (.10-.19)
	Limit .008 (.20)

ENGINE COOLING

Coolant Capacity — Approximately 5.5 quarts.

Thermostat — Starts to open at 176-183°F (80-84°C) and is fully open at 203°F (95°C).

Radiator Cap — 13 psi (.9 kg/cm²).

Fan Thermoswitch — Operates at 181-194°F (83-90°C).

WATER PUMP

Removal — Drain cooling system. Remove pulley and drive belt. Remove water pump and disassemble by removing (in order) pulley seat, shaft and bearing, rotor and seals. Before pressing out shaft and rotor, heat water pump body to about 167-185°F (75-85°C).

Inspection — Check all parts for cracks, damage or excessive wear and replace if necessary.

Installation — To install, use new gasket on clean mating surfaces and reverse removal procedures.

TIGHTENING SPECIFICATIONS	
Application	**Ft. Lbs. (N·m)**
Camshaft Sprocket Bolt	29-39 (39-53)
Connecting Rod Cap Nuts	26-32 (36-44)
Crankshaft Pulley Bolt	80-94 (109-128)
Cylinder Head Bolts	40-47 (54-64)
Flywheel Bolts	55-61 (75-83)
Main Bearing Cap Bolts	40-47 (54-64)
Manifold Nuts	15-21 (20-29)

Toyota Engines

3A-C 4-CYLINDER (Cont.)

ENGINE SPECIFICATIONS

GENERAL SPECIFICATIONS

Year	Displ.		Carburetor	HP at RPM	Torque (Ft. Lbs. at RPM)	Compr. Ratio	Bore		Stroke	
	cu. ins.	cc					in.	mm	in.	mm
1981	88.6	1452	1x2-Bbl	60@4800	75 @ 2400	9.0:1	3.05	77.5	3.03	77.0

VALVES

Engine & Valve	Head Diam. In. (mm)	Face Angle	Seat Angle	Seat Width In. (mm)	Stem Diameter In. (mm)	Stem Clearance In. (mm)	Valve Lift In. (mm)
1452 cc Intake	.....	44.5°	45°	.055 (1.4)	.2744-.2750 (6.969-6.985)	.0010-.0024 (.025-.060)	.....
Exhaust	.....	44.5°	45°	.055 (1.4)		.0012-.0026 (.030-.065)	.....

PISTONS, PINS, RINGS

Engine	PISTONS	PINS		RINGS		
	Clearance In. (mm)	Piston Fit In. (mm)	Rod Fit In. (mm)	Rings	End Gap In. (mm)	Side Clearance In. (mm)
1452 cc	.004-.005 (.10-.12)	Press Fit	Press Fit	No. 1	.008-.015 (.20-.40)	.0016-.0031 (.04-.08)
				No. 2	.006-.013 (.15-.35)	.0012-.0028 (.03-.07)
				Oil	.004-.024① (.10-.60)	.....

① — For TP type rings; Riken type — .012-.035" (.30-.90 mm).

CRANKSHAFT MAIN & CONNECTING ROD BEARINGS

Engine	MAIN BEARINGS				CONNECTING ROD BEARINGS		
	Journal Diam. In. (mm)	Clearance In. (mm)	Thrust Bearing	Crankshaft End Play In. (mm)	Journal Diam. In. (mm)	Clearance In. (mm)	Side Play In. (mm)
1452 cc	1.889-1.890 (47.98-48.00)	.0005-.0019 (.012-.049)	Center	.0008-.0073 (.020-.185)	1.5742-1.5748 (39.985-40.000)	.0008-.0020 (.020-.051)	.006-.010 (.15-.25)

VALVE SPRINGS

Engine	Free Length In. (mm)	PRESSURE Lbs. @ In. (kg @ mm)	
		Valve Closed	Valve Open
1452 cc	1.756 (44.60)	52.0@1.520 (23.6@38.6)	.....

CAMSHAFT

Engine	Journal Diam. In. (mm)	Clearance In. (mm)	Lobe Lift In. (mm)
1452 cc	1.101-1.102 (27.97-27.99)	.0015-.0029 (.037-.073)	1.553 (39.45)

3TC 4-CYLINDER

ENGINE CODING

ENGINE IDENTIFICATION

Engine can be identified by first group of numbers and letters in engine serial number. Engine serial number is located on left side of cylinder block behind dipstick.

Engine Identification	
Application	**Code**
Corolla (1770 cc)	3TC

ENGINE, CYLINDER HEAD & MANIFOLD

ENGINE

NOTE — *Following general procedures may not apply to all vehicles equipped with 3TC engine.*

Removal — 1) Disconnect and remove battery. Drain cooling system and disconnect hoses and tubes at radiator. Hood may be removed to provide greater access to engine and increased clearance when removing engine. Remove radiator. Remove air cleaner and disconnect accelerator torque rod, bond cable and clutch hose bracket.

2) Disconnect heater hoses and coolant temperature gauge wiring from engine. Disconnect all engine-to-chassis electrical connections at engine. Disconnect fuel line at pump and exhaust pipe at manifold flange. Remove starter. If equipped with automatic transmission, remove 6 torque converter mounting bolts through service holes at front side of drive plate and ring gear.

3) Attach suitable sling to engine and take up slack. Remove engine-to-transmission mounting bolts and left and right engine mount nuts. Lift engine from vehicle. Use caution to avoid damage to clutch and brake fluid reservoirs.

Installation — Screw alignment dowel in rear of engine to ease alignment. If equipped with automatic transmission, screw alignment dowel in one of the lower torque converter mounting holes. Lower engine into position, replace mounting bolts and nuts, and reverse removal procedure.

INTAKE MANIFOLD

Removal — Remove air cleaner and brackets. Disconnect fuel line and throttle controls at carburetor. Disconnect all remaining tubes and lines from carburetor and manifold. Beginning at ends and working toward center, loosen manifold bolts and nuts in several steps. Remove intake manifold assembly with carburetor attached.

Installation — Install new gasket on clean mating surfaces and install manifold. Tighten bolts and nuts in several steps, beginning at lower center and working toward ends in a criss-cross pattern.

EXHAUST MANIFOLD

Removal — Remove air cleaner and intake heat tube. Disconnect exhaust pipe at manifold flange. Loosen bolts and nuts in several steps, beginning at ends of manifold. Remove manifold.

Installation — Install manifold with new gasket to clean mating surfaces. Beginning in center and working outward, tighten nuts and bolts in several steps to specified torque.

CYLINDER HEAD

Removal — Drain cooling system and remove manifolds as previously described. Set No. 1 cylinder at TDC on compression stroke. Remove spark plug wires by pulling on rubber boots. Remove rocker arm cover and loosen cylinder head bolts in several steps in reverse of tightening sequence. Lift off rocker arm assembly and take out push rods, keeping them in order for installation. Remove head.

Installation — Ensure that mating surfaces are clean and install new head gasket. Place push rods in proper positions. Loosen rocker arm adjusting screw lock nuts and install rocker arm assembly. Tighten head bolts in several steps in the sequence shown and continue installation in reverse order of removal.

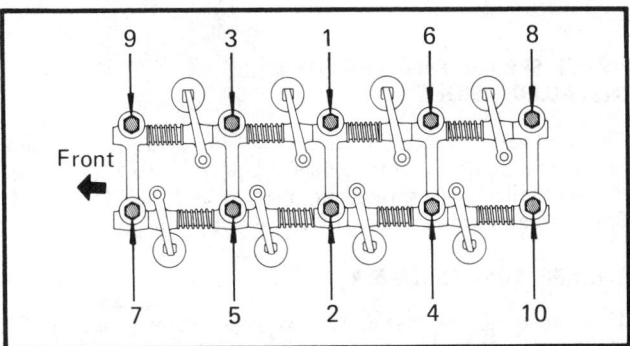

Fig. 1 Cylinder Head Tightening Sequence (Loosen in Reverse Order)

VALVES

VALVE ARRANGEMENT

Right Side — All intake.
Left Side — All exhaust.

VALVE GUIDE SERVICING

NOTE — *Manufacturer recommends using new valve guides whenever valves are replaced.*

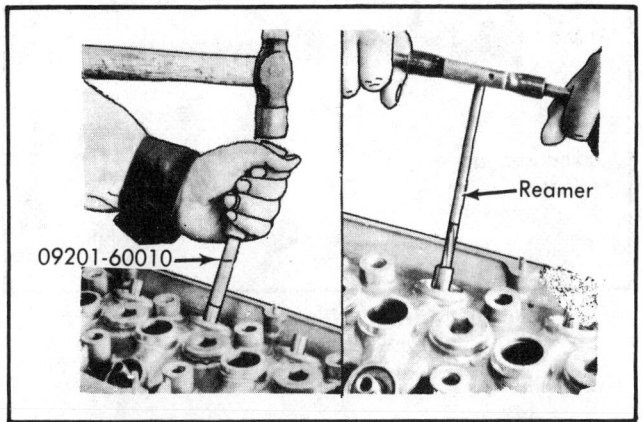

Fig. 2 Removing Valve Guide Bushing and Reaming to Proper Clearance

3TC 4-CYLINDER (Cont.)

1) Measure clearance between valve stem and valve guide bushing. If clearance is greater than .003" (.08 mm) for intake or .004" (.10 mm) for exhaust, replace valve and/or guide bushing.

2) Break off upper half of valve guide and heat cylinder head to 176-212°F (80-100°C). Using guide replacement tool (09201-60011), drive out guide bushing toward combustion chamber.

3) Apply thin coat of oil to guide and guide hole. Drive guide in until snap ring contacts head. Ream guide to achieve proper clearance.

VALVE STEM OIL SEALS

Cup type oil seals are used on all valves. Do not use old seals when valves have been removed. To install, lubricate valve stem and insert in cylinder head. Again lubricate valve stem and carefully push oil seal over valve guide.

NOTE — *Do not push down on top of seal; use pressure on seal sides only.*

VALVE SPRING FREE LENGTH & INSTALLED HEIGHT

Check all valve springs for correct free length, load length and squareness. Spring squareness should be within 075" (1.9 mm). When installed valve spring height should be 1.484" (37.7 mm). Spring free length should be 1.657" (42.08 mm).

ROCKER ARM ASSEMBLY

1) Remove cylinder head. Remove rocker arm assembly. To disassemble, remove 4 retainer springs at each corner, both end supports, compression springs and 2 end rocker arms.

2) Remove remaining middle 3 supports, 4 rocker arms and springs off rocker support shafts. Clearance between rocker arms and shaft should be .0024" (.060 mm) maximum.

NOTE — *Mark all parts to reassemble in order. Place washer between rocker arm and support number three (center).*

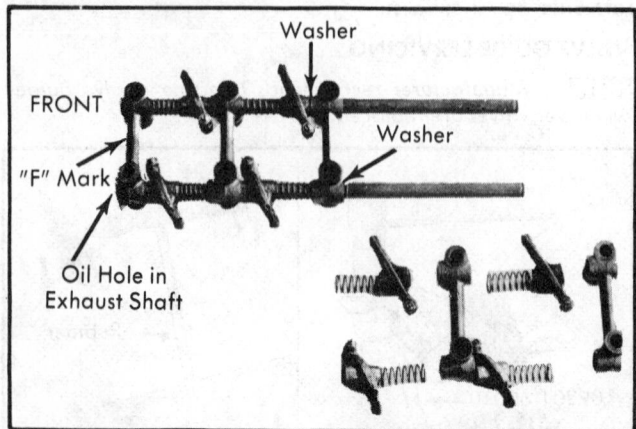

Fig. 3 Partially Disassembled View of Rocker Arm Assembly

VALVE LIFTERS

Inspect lifters and check clearance in bore. If clearance exceeds .004" (.10 mm), select oversize lifter and ream lifter bore to obtain clearance of .001-.002" (.02-.05 mm).

VALVE CLEARANCE ADJUSTMENT

NOTE — *Check with engine at normal operating temperature.*

Set number 1 cylinder to TDC on compression stroke. Adjust intake valves on number 1 and 2 cylinders, exhaust valves on number 1 and 3 cylinders. Turn crankshaft one revolution (360°) and adjust intake valves on number 3 and 4, exhaust valves on number 2 and 4 cylinders.

Valve Clearance Adjustment	
Valve	In. (mm)
Intake	.008 (.20)
Exhaust	.013 (.33)

PISTONS, PINS & RINGS

OIL PAN

Removal — 1) Disconnect left and right engine front mounts. Raise vehicle and support on stands. Remove engine undercover and right side stiffener plate. Remove stabilizer bar and oil pan bolts.

2) Place jack under clutch housing and raise slightly, taking care not to pull lower radiator hose. Lower oil pan and remove oil pump bolts. Pull oil pan and pump forward and outward.

Installation — Apply liquid sealer to 4 corners of oil pan gasket. To complete installation, reverse remove procedure.

PISTON & ROD ASSEMBLY

Removal — With oil pan and cylinder head removed, mark connecting rod and cap for correct assembly and take off bearing cap nuts. Tap studs lightly to loosen caps and remove bearing caps. Push piston/rod assembly out through top of cylinder block.

NOTE — *Cover rod bolts with short pieces of hose to prevent damage to crankshaft.*

Installation — Install piston rings on piston with ring gaps spaced as shown in *Fig. 4*. Code letter and number on ring should face UP. Lubricate piston, crankshaft and cylinder walls. Using suitable ring compressor, insert pistons in cylinders, making sure that notch in piston top is toward front of engine. Use hose pieces on studs to protect crankshaft. Install rod caps and tighten to specifications.

NOTE — *After tightening each cap, check rotation condition of crankshaft.*

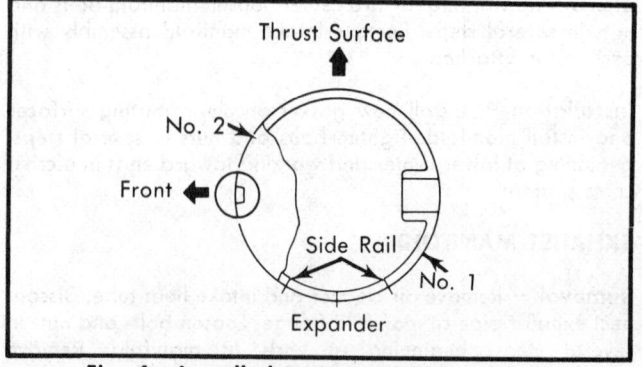

Fig. 4 Installed Position of Piston Rings

3TC 4-CYLINDER (Cont.)

FITTING PISTONS

1) Measure piston at right angle to pin center line, .40" (11 mm) below bottom ring. Standard piston diameter is 3.3437-3.3457" (84.92-84.98 mm). Oversize pistons are available .50" (13.0 mm), .75" (19.0 mm) and 1.00" (25.4 mm).

2) Measure cylinders at top, center and bottom of bore in two directions. If wear exceeds .008" (.20 mm) on any one cylinder, rebore all cylinders for oversize pistons.

3) Insert piston rings into cylinders and measure end gap at lower part of cylinder where wear is smallest. Measure clearance between ring and ring groove.

PISTON PIN REPLACEMENT

Check pin fit by trying to rock piston at right angle to pin. If any movement is felt, piston and pin must be replaced. Use suitable press and adapter (09221-25013) to press out piston pin. Install piston and pin to connecting rod so that notch in piston top is on same side of rod as trademark on rod center.

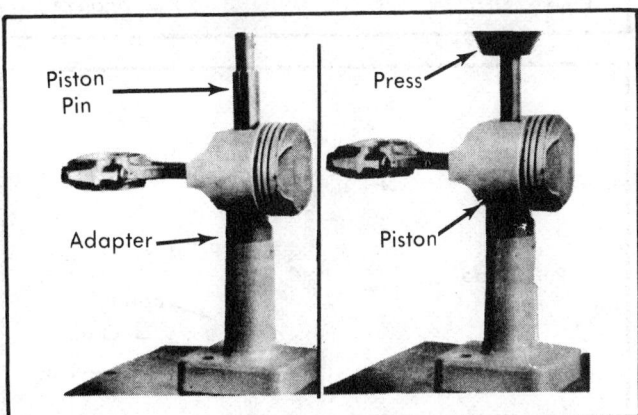

Fig. 5   Piston Pin Removal and Installation with Press and Adapter

CRANKSHAFT MAIN & CONNECTING ROD BEARINGS

MAIN & CONNECTING ROD BEARINGS

Use Plastigage method to measure bearing clearance. Clearance limit is .003" (.08 mm). Taper and out-of-round limit is .0004" (.01 mm). If limits are exceeded, crankshaft must be ground for undersize bearings. Bearings are available .002" (.05 mm), .010" (.25 mm) and .020" (.50 mm) undersizes.

THRUST BEARING ALIGNMENT

Measure crankshaft end play at center bearing. If end play exceeds limit of .012" (.30 mm), install replacement thrust bearings. Bearings are available in standard and oversizes of .005" and .010" (.125 and .250 mm).

NOTE — Oil groove on bearing faces toward center.

REAR MAIN BEARING OIL SEAL

Remove oil seal retainer and drive out old oil seal. Apply grease to seal inner lip and take care not to damage this surface. Using suitable tool (09250-10011), drive new seal into place. Replace oil seal retainer with new gasket.

ENGINE FRONT COVER

Removal — Remove water pump and fan assembly. Remove air pump. Set No. 1 cylinder at TDC on compression stroke, so key in crankshaft is facing straight upward. Remove crankshaft pulley with suitable puller (09213-31021). Remove bolts from pan into cover and cover into block, then carefully remove cover from engine.

Installation — Ensure that mating surfaces are clean and install new gasket between cover and block. Use new section of pan gasket if old gasket at bottom has been damaged. Apply suitable sealer at corners and place cover in position. Install cover bolts and drive pulley into position with suitable tool (09214-60010). Complete assembly in reverse of removal procedure.

FRONT COVER OIL SEAL

With front cover removed from engine, pry out old oil seal. With suitable driver (09223-22010), drive new seal in position until it is about even with timing gear cover. Before installing on engine, coat seal lip with multi-purpose grease.

CAMSHAFT

TIMING CHAIN & GEAR

Removal — With front cover off, remove camshaft gear retaining bolt. Remove camshaft gear, timing chain and crankshaft gear by pulling out evenly. Maximum elongation of chain is 11.47" (291.4 mm) with 11 lbs. (5 kg) tension.

Installation — Chain tensioner and plunger should be removed before installing timing chain and gears. Ensure that crankshaft and camshaft keys are pointing UP. Assemble chain and gears with marks aligned as illustrated and install as an assembly. Tighten camshaft timing gear bolt and install chain tensioner. Install remaining components in reverse order of removal.

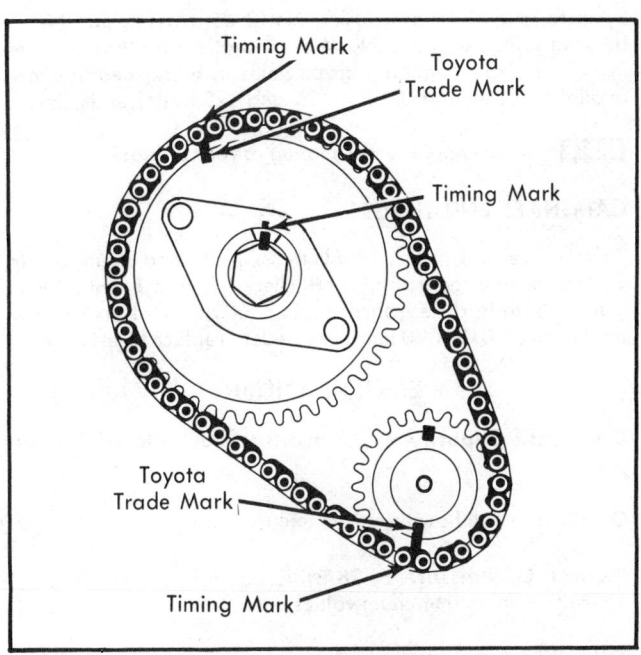

Fig. 6   Timing Chain and Sprocket Alignment Marks

Toyota Engines

3TC 4-CYLINDER (Cont.)

TIMING CHAIN TENSIONER & DAMPER

1) Inspect surfaces of tensioner plunger and bore of tensioner body. To test clearance, lubricate plunger and insert it into plunger body. Cover two oil passages with fingers and pull plunger. Vacuum strong enough to return plunger should be felt.

2) Measure thickness of tensioner head and chain damper wall. Head should be minimum .492" (12.5 mm) and chain damper should be minimum .20" (5.0 mm).

3) Install chain tensioner, then install damper. Clearance between chain and damper should be .020" (.5 mm) when properly installed.

NOTE — *Chain tensioner must be filled with oil after replacing tensioner or timing chain.*

CAMSHAFT

Removal — With cylinder head, timing chain cover and timing chain assembly removed, remove distributor and fuel pump. Lift out tappets and mark position for installation. Remove camshaft thrust plate. Insert timing gear retaining bolt and pull out camshaft slowly while turning.

Installation — Lubricate all bearing journals and insert camshaft. Place camshaft thrust plate in position with marked side outward. Install thrust plate retaining bolts. Install remaining components in reverse order of removal, ensuring that all timing marks are aligned.

CAMSHAFT BEARINGS

1) Using suitable bearing remover tool (09215-25010), pull out bearings 1, 2 and 5 toward front and bearings 3 and 4 toward rear. Using same tool, install new bearings in the following order: No. 4 using No. 1 as a guide, No. 2 using No. 1 as a guide and No. 3 using No. 5 as a guide.

2) Install No. 1 bearing using No. 2 as a guide and No. 5 bearing using No. 1 and No. 4 as guides. Ensure that oil holes in bearings are aligned with oil holes in block. Bearings are available .005" and .010" (.125 and .250 mm) undersize.

NOTE — *Apply liquid sealer to plug at rear of block.*

CAMSHAFT END THRUST

To measure end thrust, install thrust plate and timing gear. Tighten timing gear bolt and check clearance with feeler gauge. Standard clearance is .0028-.0059" (.071-.149 mm) If maximum of .012" (.30 mm) is exceeded, replace thrust plate.

ENGINE OILING

Crankcase Capacity — 3.5 quarts without filter; 4.0 quarts with filter.

Oil Filter — Full flow type with integral relief valve.

Normal Oil Pressure — 28 psi (2 kg/cm²) at idle; 43 psi (3 kg/cm²) running (minimum values).

Oil Pressure Regulator Valve — Begins to open at 51-63 psi (3.6-4.4 kg/cm²).

OIL PUMP

Oil pump is driven by bottom of distributor shaft. With oil pan off, remove mounting bolt and pull pump from engine. Remove cover and strainer, and check clearances. Inspect relief valve for scoring or wear and replace as necessary. Drive rotor and driven rotor have punch marks on cover side for assembly identification. Assemble pump and check operation by submerging suction end in clean engine oil and turning shaft clockwise with a screwdriver. Oil should come out discharge hole. Close hole with thumb and turn shaft as before. Shaft should be difficult to turn.

Oil Pump Specifications	
Application	In. (mm)
Rotor Tip Clearance	.0016-.0063 (.040-.160)
Limit	.0098 (.248)
Rotor Side Clearance	.0012-.0035 (.030-.088)
Limit	.0059 (.149)
Rotor-to-Body Clearance	.0039-.0063 (.099-.160)
Limit	.0098 (.248)

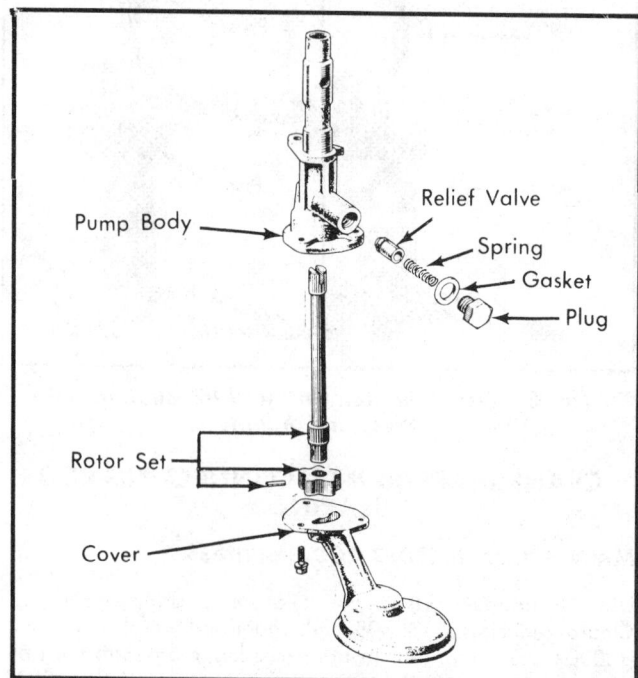

Fig. 7   Exploded View of Oil Pump and Pressure Relief Valve Assembly

ENGINE COOLING

Thermostat — Wax pellet type thermostat with opening temperature of 187-194°F (86-90°C). Fully opened at 212°F (100°C).

COOLANT DRAINING

Engine must be cool, then remove radiator cap. Loosen drain plugs at bottom of radiator and left side of engine block and drain coolant. To refill, make sure both drains are closed and

Toyota Engines

3TC 4-CYLINDER (Cont.)

fill radiator wth coolant. Start and run engine until warm, then top off radiator with coolant. Fill reservoir half full, then install radiator and reservoir caps.

Coolant Capacity — 8.4 quarts with manual transmission; 8.5 quarts with automatic transmission.

WATER PUMP

Removal & Installation — Drain cooling system and remove fan belt. Remove fan and drive pulley. Remove radiator hose, by-pass hose and heater hose from pump. Remove mounting bolts and lift pump from engine. To install, ensure that mating surfaces are clean and use new gasket. Reverse removal procedures to complete installation.

ENGINE SPECIFICATIONS

GENERAL SPECIFICATIONS

Year	Displ. cu. ins.	cc	Carburetor	HP at RPM①	Torque (Ft. Lbs. at RPM)②	Compr. Ratio	Bore in.	mm	Stroke in.	mm
1981	108	1770	1x2-Bbl.	70 @ 2400	93 @ 2400	9.0:1	3.35	85	3.08	78

① — California: 73@5000.
② — California: 90@2600.

VALVES

Engine & Valve	Head Diam. In. (mm)	Face Angle	Seat Angle	Seat Width In. (mm)	Stem Diameter In. (mm)	Stem Clearance In. (mm)	Valve Lift In. (mm)
1770 cc Intake	.....	44.5°	45°	.047-.063 (1.2-1.6)	.3136-.3142 (7.97-7.98)	.0010-.0024 (.025-.061)	.....
Exhaust	.....	44.5°	45°	.047-.063 (1.2-1.6)	.3136-.3142 (7.97-7.98)	.0012-.0026 (.030-.066)	.....

PISTONS, PINS, RINGS

Engine	PISTONS Clearance In. (mm)	PINS Piston Fit In. (mm)	Rod Fit In. (mm)	RINGS Rings	End Gap In. (mm)	Side Clearance In. (mm)
1770 cc	.002-.003 (.05-.07)	Press Fit	Press Fit	No. 1	.004-.010 (.10-.25)	.0008-.0024 (.02-.06)
				No. 2	.006-.012 (.15-.30)	.0006-.0022 (.015-.055)
				Oil	.008-.028 (.20-.70)	.....

CRANKSHAFT MAIN & CONNECTING ROD BEARINGS

Engine	MAIN BEARINGS Journal Diam. In. (mm)	Clearance In. (mm)	Thrust Bearing	Crankshaft End Play In. (mm)	CONNECTING ROD BEARINGS Journal Diam. In. (mm)	Clearance In. (mm)	Side Play In. (mm)
1770 cc	2.282-2.284 (57.976-58.000)	.0009-.0019 (.024-.048)	Center	.0008-.009 (.02-.22)	1.8888-1.8898 (47.976-48.000)	.0009-.0019 (.024-.048)	.006-.010 (.16-.26)

Toyota Engines

3TC 4-CYLINDER (Cont.)

ENGINE SPECIFICATIONS (Cont.)

CAMSHAFT			
Engine	Journal Diam. In. (mm)	Clearance In. (mm)	Lobe Lift In. (mm)
1770 cc		.0010-.0026 (.025-.066)	.....
No. 1	1.829-1.830 (46.46-46.48)		
No. 2	1.819-1.820 (46.21-46.23)		
No. 3	1.809-1.810 (45.96-45.98)		
No. 4	1.800-1.801 (45.71-45.73)		
No. 5	1.790-1.791 (45.46-45.48)		

TIGHTENING SPECIFICATIONS	
Application	Ft. Lbs. (N·m)
Camshaft Sprocket	51-79 (69-107)
Camshaft Thrust Plate	8-11 (11-15)
Connecting Rod Caps	29-36 (39-49)
Crankshaft Pulley	47-61 (64-83)
Cylinder Head Bolts	62-68 (84-92)
Exhaust Manifold	22-32 (30-44)
Flywheel	42-47 (57-64)
Intake Manifold	14-18 (19-24)
Main Bearing Caps	53-63 (72-86)

VALVE SPRINGS			
Engine	Free Length In. (mm)	PRESSURE (LBS.) Lbs. @ In. (kg @ mm)	
		Valve Closed	Valve Open
1770 cc	1.657 (42.1)	57.9@1.484 (26.3@37.7)	.....

Toyota Engines

4K-C 4-CYLINDER

ENGINE CODING

ENGINE IDENTIFICATION

Engine serial number and code is stamped on right side of block above oil filter. First 3 digits are engine code.

Engine Identification	
Application	Code
Starlet	4K-C

ENGINE, CYLINDER HEAD & MANIFOLDS

ENGINE

NOTE — *Engine removal and installation procedures were not available from manufacturer for Starlet models.*

MANIFOLDS

NOTE — *Aluminum intake and cast iron exhaust manifolds are removed as an assembly.*

Removal — Remove air cleaner. Disconnect fuel and vacuum lines at carburetor. Disconnect choke and throttle linkage at carburetor. Remove heat insulator, PCV valve and PCV hose. Disconnect exhaust pipe at manifold. Remove manifold retaining nuts and bolts and take off manifold.

Installation — To install, reverse removal procedure, ensuring that mating surfaces are clean and new gaskets are used. Front engine hanger is installed on top front stud between intake and exhaust manifold. Tighten 2 center bolts first, then top front, bottom rear, bottom front and top rear in that order.

CYLINDER HEAD

Removal — **1)** Drain cooling system and remove upper radiator hose. Remove manifold and carburetor assembly as previously outlined. Disconnect heater hose at rear of head. Remove rocker arm cover. Loosen rocker arm support bolts in 3 or 4 steps. Follow sequence of front, rear, front center and rear center bolt.

2) Remove bolts and shaft assembly. Remove push rods and keep in order for reassembly in original position. Disconnect spark plug wires. Loosen and remove head bolts in 2 or 3 steps as shown in *Fig. 1.* Lift head from engine.

Installation — Ensure that mating surfaces are clean, then install new gasket with "front" side facing up. Continue assembly in reverse order of removal. Tighten head bolts gradually in 2 or 3 steps as shown in *Fig. 1.* Install push rods and rocker shaft assembly, then adjust valves.

NOTE — *When installing rocker shaft assembly, be sure adjusting screws are backed off about 2 turns.*

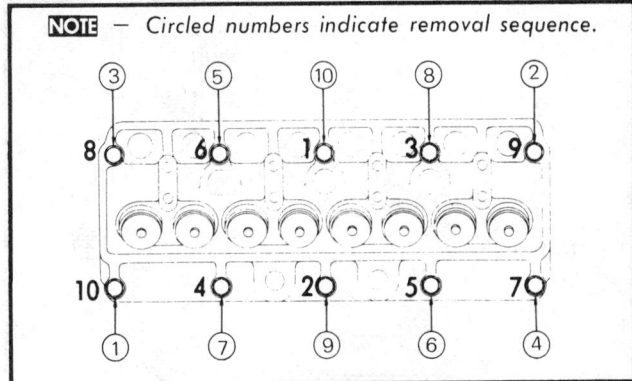

Fig. 1   Tighten Cylinder Head in Sequence Shown (Remove in Reverse Order ① Through ⑩)

VALVES

VALVE ARRANGEMENT

E-I-I-E-E-I-I-E

VALVE GUIDE SERVICING

1) Measure valve guide inner diameter and valve stem outer diameter. If difference exceeds .003" (.08 mm) for intake or .004" (.10 mm) for exhaust valves, replace valves and/or guides.

NOTE — *Cylinder head should be heated to about 212°F (100°C) before removal or replacement of valve guide.*

2) To replace valve guide, break off upper portion of guide at snap ring. Drive remaining portion of guide out of head through combustion chamber with suitable driver (09201-60011).

3) Install snap ring on guide and install from top with driver. Drive in until snap ring contacts head. Guide projects .07" (18 mm) when properly installed. Ream guide for proper stem clearance.

NOTE — *Oversize guides .002" (.05 mm) larger than original guides are available if required to obtain proper tightness between guide and head.*

VALVE STEM OIL SEALS

Valve stem oil seal fits over guide and stem, under spring assembly.

VALVE SPRINGS

Removal — Use compressor (09202-43012) to compress valve springs and retainers. Remove valve spring retainer locks (keepers), then remove retainer, spring, seal and washer. Mark and remove valves and components for reassembly.

Installation — Install components in original location and order. Use new seals on valve stems. Compress springs and install keepers.

NOTE — *Some engines may have a spring shield under retainer and "O" ring seal on valve stem above keepers.*

Toyota Engines

4K-C 4-CYLINDER (Cont.)

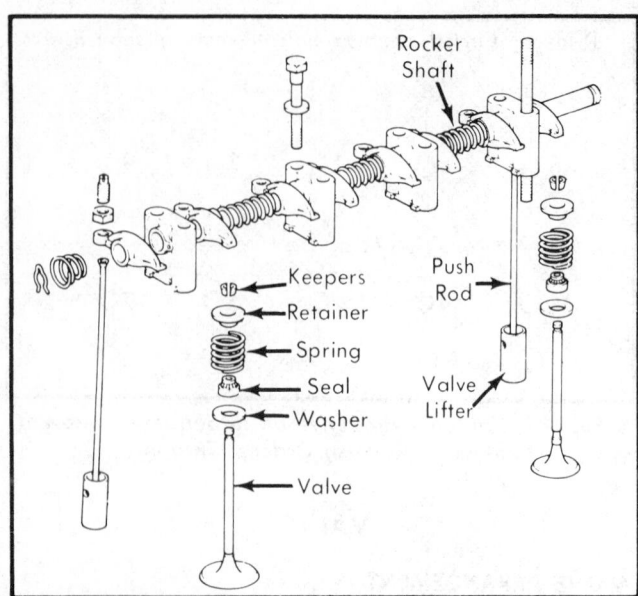

Fig. 2 **Exploded View of Valve Train Components**

VALVE SPRING INSTALLED HEIGHT

1) With valve spring removed, check length under specified load (see specifications) in a spring tester. Check free length. If less than 1.83" (46.5 mm), replace valve spring.

2) Check valve spring squareness with a steel square. If spring is out of square more than .063" (1.6 mm), replace spring.

ROCKER ARM ASSEMBLY

Disassembly – 1) Remove valve cover. Remove rocker arm assembly retaining bolts in sequence of front, rear, front center and rear center bolts. Remove rocker arm assembly. Remove retaining clips from both ends of rocker arm shaft. Remove conical springs, rocker arms, springs and support stands.

2) Thoroughly clean and inspect all components. Check rocker arm-to-shaft clearance. If clearance exceeds .0024" (.061 mm), replace rocker arms or shafts as necessary. Reface valve end of rocker arm if worn. Lubricate all components before assembly.

Reassembly – Assemble rocker arm assembly in reverse order of disassembly. Install rocker arm so that protruding side of valve end of rocker arm faces support stand.

VALVE TAPPET SERVICE

Check clearance between valve tappet and bore in crankcase. If clearance exceeds .004" (.1 mm), replace tappet with an oversize tappet. Oversize tappet is .002" (.05 mm) over standard. Ream bore in crankcase until clearance of .0006-.0020" (.015-.029 mm) is obtained.

VALVE CLEARANCE ADJUSTMENT

With number 1 cylinder at TDC on firing stroke, adjust clearance on valves number 1, 2, 3, and 5. Rotate crankshaft one revolution (360°) and set valves number 4, 6, 7, and 8. Set clearances COLD to: Intake – .005" (.13 mm), Exhaust –

.009" (.23 mm). If setting HOT, use following clearances: Intake – .008" (.20 mm), Exhaust – .012" (.30 mm).

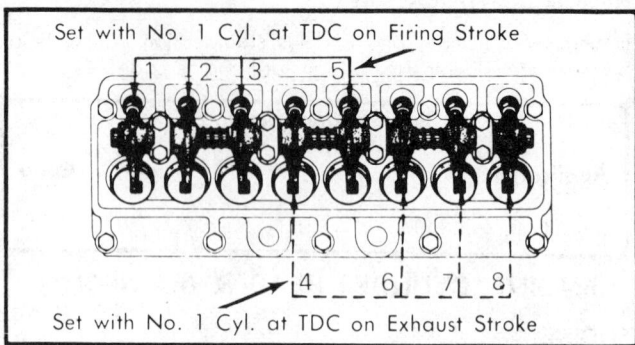

Fig. 3 **Valve Clearance Adjustment Follows Order Shown**

PISTONS, PINS & RINGS

OIL PAN

NOTE – *Engine must be removed to remove oil pan.*

Removal & Installation – With engine out of vehicle, drain any remaining oil from pan. Remove pan retaining nuts and bolts and take off oil pan. Before installation, clean mating surfaces and apply sealer. Install pan with new gasket and tighten to specifications.

PISTON & ROD ASSEMBLY

NOTE – *Remove ridge from top of cylinder bore before removing pistons.*

Removal & Installation – 1) With engine out of vehicle, remove cylinder head and oil pan. Remove connecting rod cap with bearing half and push piston and connecting rod assembly up and out through top of block. Mark rod and cap to ensure installation in original position.

2) Mark piston to insure that it is installed in same cylinder. To install piston and rod assembly, make sure ring gaps are in correct position (see illustration). Coat piston and rings with oil.

3) Compress piston rings with a ring compressor and install piston and rod assembly in crankcase with notch in piston facing front of engine. Make sure bearings are properly seated in connecting rod and cap and apply oil to crankshaft journal.

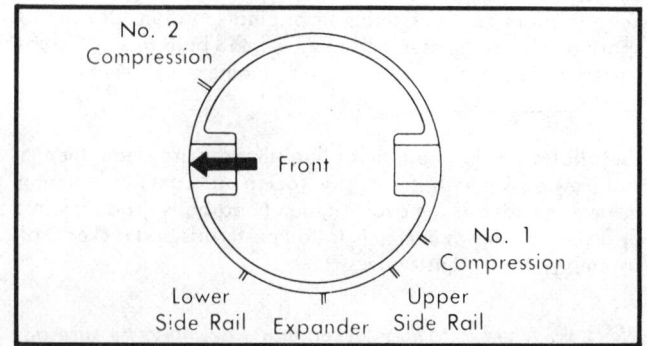

Fig. 4 **Arrange Piston Ring Gaps as Shown**

4K-C 4-CYLINDER (Cont.)

4) Make sure bearing in connecting rod is properly seated against crankshaft journal. Install connecting rod cap in correct position and tighten nuts to specifications. Install cylinder head, oil pan and engine as previously outlined.

PISTON PIN REPLACEMENT

1) Remove circlips from pin hole in piston. Heat piston to approximately 158-176°F (70-80°C). Drive out piston pin. Make sure pins, pistons and connecting rods are marked for reassembly to each other.

2) Thoroughly clean and inspect all components. Piston pin should push fit through piston when piston is heated. If fit is too loose, replace piston and pin.

3) Check piston pin-to-connecting rod clearance. If more than .002" (.05 mm), replace bushing. Press bushing out and install new bushing with press and driver (09222-30010). Make sure to align bushing and connecting rod oil holes. Refinish new bushing with pin hole grinder.

NOTE — *Pin coated with oil should be a thumb press fit at normal temperature.*

4) Thoroughly lubricate all components before assembly. Position piston on connecting rod with notch in piston and front mark on connecting rod facing the same direction. Heat piston and install piston pin and circlips.

FITTING PISTONS

1) Measure cylinder bores in 3 places at 90° to and parallel with crankshaft. If more than .008" (.20 mm) over standard, cylinders must be rebored. Pistons and rings are available in .020", .030" and .040" (.50, .75 and 1.00 mm) oversize.

2) Measure diameter of piston .60" (15 mm) from bottom of skirt at 90° to piston pin. Standard diameter is 2.953-2.955" (75.00-75.05 mm). Normal clearance is .0012-.0020" (.03-.05 mm).

3) Check piston rings for wear or damage and replace as necessary. Check piston ring gap in cylinders and piston ring side clearance in pistons (see specifications). Install rings on pistons with marks on rings up and make sure ring grooves in pistons are clean.

CRANKSHAFT MAIN & CONNECTING ROD BEARINGS

MAIN & CONNECTING ROD BEARING SERVICE

1) With engine mounted on suitable workstand, remove piston and rod assemblies as previously outlined. Remove crankshaft pulley bolt and take off crankshaft pulley with suitable puller (09213-31021). Remove timing chain cover and rear oil seal retainer. Remove camshaft sprocket and timing chain.

2) Remove oil pump. Remove main bearing caps with bearing halves and remove crankshaft. Crankshaft timing sprocket and pilot bearing in rear of crankshaft may be removed if desired.

3) Thoroughly clean and inspect crankshaft. Blow out all oil passages with compressed air. Check crankshaft for runout by checking center main bearing journal with a dial indicator. If runout exceeds limit of .0016" (.04 mm), it must be replaced.

4) Measure main and connecting rod journals. If limit of .0004" (.01 mm) out-of-round or wear is exceeded, crankshaft must be reground or replaced. Main bearings are available in .010" and .020" (.25 and .50 mm) undersize. Connecting rod bearings are available in .010", .020" and .030" (.25, .50 and .75 mm) undersizes.

5) Main and connecting rod bearing clearance is checked by the Plastigage method. To check connecting rod bearing clearance, make sure bearing halves and crankshaft journals are thoroughly clean. Place a piece of Plastigage wire on journal being checked. Install connecting rod cap and tighten nuts to specifications.

6) Remove connecting rod cap and check flattened wire against scale on back of Plastigage package to determine clearance. Main bearing clearance is checked in same manner. If rod bearing clearance is more than standard, a .002" (.05 mm) undersize bearing is available. If clearance is excessive with undersize bearing, crankshaft must be ground to next undersize. The limit of bearing clearance on both main and connecting rod bearings is .004" (.1 mm).

7) Check crankshaft end play with number 3 main bearing cap and original thrust washers installed. Pry crankshaft back and forth and measure clearance with a feeler gauge. Standard clearance is .002-.009" (.04-.22 mm) with a maximum limit of .012" (.3 mm). Excessive clearance may be reduced with washers .002" (.125 mm) or .004" (.250 mm) oversize. Install thrust washers with grooves toward crankshaft.

8) Install bearing halves in crankcase and main bearing caps. Lubricate bearings and install crankshaft. Install main bearing caps with arrows toward front and tighten cap bolts in 3, 2, 4, 5, 1 order.

NOTE — *Tighten bolts in 2 or 3 steps, checking crankshaft turning resistance after each step.*

9) Install remaining components in reverse order of removal, noting proper alignment of timing marks. See *TIMING CHAIN REPLACEMENT in this Article.*

CRANKSHAFT REAR OIL SEAL

Removal & Installation — With flywheel removed, unbolt and take off seal retainer. Drive old seal out of retainer from smooth side. Drive new seal into position with suitable tool (09250-10011). Coat seal lips with multi-purpose grease and install seal assembly.

ENGINE FRONT COVER OIL SEAL

Removal & Installation — Remove crankshaft pulley and pull out old seal with suitable puller (09308-10010). Install new seal with driver (09223-22010). Lubricate seal lips and install crankshaft pulley.

TIMING CHAIN REPLACEMENT

1) With timing chain installed on engine, attach a spring scale to chain. Pull out on chain with pressure of 22 lbs. (10 kg). Check distance between chain tensioner plunger and tensioner body.

Toyota Engines

4K-C 4-CYLINDER (Cont.)

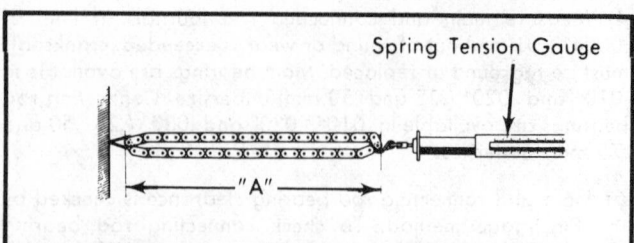

Fig. 5   Checking Timing Chain Elongation Using Spring Tension Gauge

2) If clearance exceeds .531" (13.5 mm), chain and sprockets must be removed and checked. Remove camshaft sprocket bolt and remove sprocket and chain. Pull crankshaft sprocket from crankshaft.

3) Secure 1 link of timing chain and attach spring tension gauge to opposite end. See Fig. 5. With 11 lbs. (5 kg) tension applied to chain, distance "A" should be no more than 10.7" (272 mm). If distance is more than specified, replace chain.

4) Place chain on crankshaft sprocket and measure diameter. If less than 2.34" (59 mm), replace sprocket. Measure camshaft sprocket in the same manner. If less than 4.48" (114 mm), replace sprocket.

5) To correctly install sprockets and timing chain, set No. 1 piston to TDC of compression stroke. Align camshaft dowel pin with mark on thrust plate. Align chain timing marks with those on sprockets.

6) Install timing chain and sprockets together. See Fig. 6. Apply a light coat of oil to crankshaft sprocket bolt and tighten. Install chain tensioner and vibration damper. Install timing chain cover.

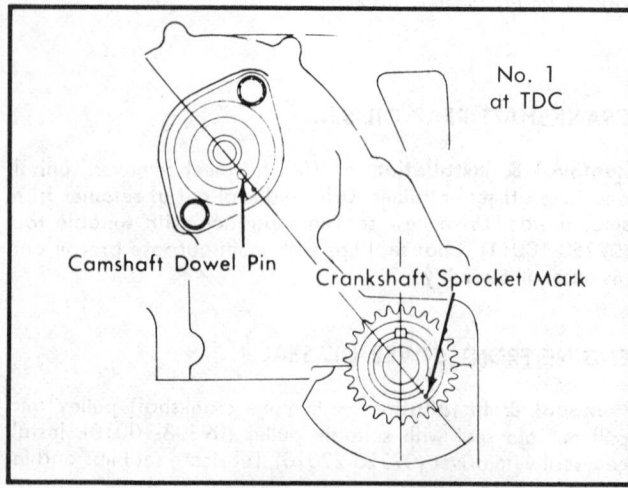

Fig. 6   Aligning Marks for Timing Chain and Sprocket Installation

TIMING CHAIN TENSIONER & DAMPER

1) Inspect surfaces of tensioner plunger and bore of tensioner body. To test clearance, lubricate plunger and insert it into plunger body. Cover two oil passages with fingers and pull plunger about half way out. Vacuum strong enough to return plunger should be felt.

2) Measure thickness of tensioner head and chain damper wall. Head should be minimum .47" (12 mm) and chain damper should be minimum .28" (7 mm).

CAMSHAFT

CAMSHAFT

With camshaft sprocket and timing chain removed, take off camshaft thrust plate. Remove front end plate from engine block. Remove tappets (valve lifters) and distributor if not previously removed. Pull camshaft straight out, using care not to damage bearings or journals.

NOTE — A head bolt may be screwed into end of camshaft to provide gripping surface for removal.

Check camshaft runout at number 2 journal by using ½ of the largest difference shown by dial indicator. Maximum runout limit is .0012" (.03 mm), and maximum journal out-of-round or taper is .0008" (.02 mm).

CAMSHAFT BEARINGS

Measure camshaft journal diameter and subtract from measured diameter of bearing bore to determine clearance. Bearings should be replaced if clearance exceeds .004" (.1 mm). Journals may be ground and .005" (.125 mm) or .010" (.250 mm) undersized bearings installed if necessary. To replace bearings, remove expansion plug from rear of engine. Use bearing replacement tool (09215-22010) to remove old bearings and insert new ones.

CAUTION — Oil holes in bearings must be aligned with oil holes in cylinder block. Install new expansion plug, coated with sealer, when all bearings have been installed.

CAMSHAFT END THRUST

Check clearance between thrust plate and first bearing journal. If clearance exceeds .012" (.3 mm), replace thrust plate.

NOTE — If clearance is still excessive after replacing thrust plate and installing sprocket, it will be necessary to replace the camshaft.

CAM LOBE LIFT

Total height of camshaft lobe is 1.436-1.440" (36.47-36.57 mm) for intake lobe. Height of exhaust lobe is 1.432-1.436" (36.37-36.47 mm). If less than 1.424" (36.17 mm) for intake or 1.420" (36.07 mm) for exhaust lobes, replace camshaft.

ENGINE OILING

Crankshaft Capacity — 3.7 quarts with filter.

Oil Filter — Full flow, mounted on outside of crankcase next to distributor.

Normal Oil Pressure — With engine at 212°F, 28.4 psi @ 300 RPM, 42.6 psi @ 3000 RPM.

Pressure Regulator Valve — Mounted in oil pump. See Oil Pump.

4K-C 4-CYLINDER (Cont.)

ENGINE OILING SYSTEM

Oil is circulated through the engine by pressure provided by a trochoid rotor type oil pump. Pump is mounted on bottom of crankcase and is driven by camshaft through the distributor drive. Oil is drawn from oil pan and is circulated through a full flow oil filter into the main oil gallery. Oil is then distributed to main and connecting rod bearing journals and camshaft bearing journals. Cylinders and piston pins are lubricated by oil squirting from hole in connecting rod. Oil is supplied to timing chain by oil from timing chain tensioner. Oil flows from number 2 cam bearing journal to rocker arm shaft to lubricate rocker arms. Excess oil from rocker arm shaft lubricates valves and valve stems.

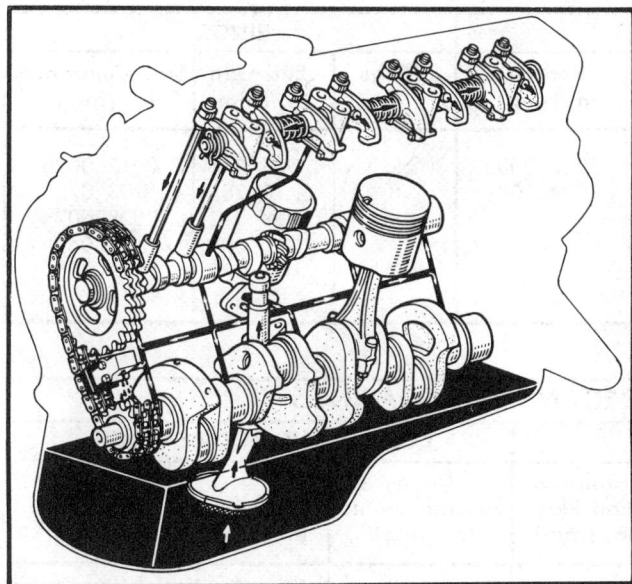

Fig. 7 Engine Oiling System

OIL PUMP

1) Remove oil pan and oil pump. Remove oil strainer, pump cover and pressure regulator plug from side of pump body. Remove spring, piston and rotors from pump body. Thoroughly clean and inspect all components. Check rotor tip clearance.

2) If tip clearance is more than .008" (.20 mm), replace rotors. Check clearance between drive rotors and cover. Place a straightedge on mating surface of pump body. Insert feeler gauge between straightedge and drive rotor.

3) If clearance exceeds .006" (.15 mm), replace cover, pump body or rotors. Check clearance between outer rotor and pump body with feeler gauge. If more than .008" (.20 mm) replace pump body or rotors. Check pressure regulator spring and piston for wear or damage. Replace as necessary.

4) To assemble pump, reverse disassembly procedure. Install rotors with punch marks toward body (upward). With pump assembled, submerge in clean motor oil and rotate drive shaft to check flow of oil from outlet port. Install pump and mounting bolt. Install oil pan.

Oil Pump Specifications	
Application	**In. (mm)**
Rotor Tip Clearance	.002-.006 (.04-.16)
	Limit .008 (.2)
Rotor Side Clearance	.001-.004 (.03-.09)
	Limit .006 (.15)
Rotor-to-Body Clearance	.004-.006 (.10-.16)
	Limit .008 (.2)

ENGINE COOLING

Coolant Capacity — 6.0 quarts.

Thermostat (Low Temperature Model) — Begins to open at 177°F (80°C) and fully opens at 203°F (95°C).

Thermostat (High Temperature Model) — Begins to open at 187°F (86°C) and fully opens at 212°F (100°C).

Radiator Cap — 11-15 psi.

WATER PUMP

Removal & Installation — Drain cooling system and loosen drive belt. Disconnect radiator and heater hoses at pump. Remove mounting bolts and take off water pump. To install, clean mating surfaces, coat new gasket with sealer and install water pump.

NOTE — *Cooling fan is electrically driven and may run at any time the ignition is on if coolant temperature is high. It may be necessary to remove fan and shroud to provide greater access to the water pump.*

ENGINE SPECIFICATIONS

GENERAL SPECIFICATIONS										
	Displ.				**Torque (Ft. Lbs. at RPM)**	**Compr. Ratio**	**Bore**		**Stroke**	
Year	**cu. ins.**	**cc**	**Carburetor**	**HP at RPM**			**in.**	**mm**	**in.**	**mm**
1981	78.7	1290	2-Bbl.	58@5200	67@3600	9.0:1	2.95	75	2.87	73

Toyota Engines

4K-C 4-CYLINDER (Cont.)
ENGINE SPECIFICATIONS (Cont.)

VALVES

Engine & Valve	Head Diam. In. (mm)	Face Angle	Seat Angle	Seat Width In. (mm)	Stem Diameter In. (mm)	Stem Clearance In. (mm)	Valve Lift In. (mm)
1290cc Intake	.....	44.5°	45°	.047-.067 (1.2-1.7)	.3136-.3142 (7.965-7.980)	.0012-.0026 (.030-.065)	.....
Exhaust		44.5°	45°	.047-.071 (1.2-1.8)	.3134-.3140 (7.960-7.975)	.0014-.0028 (.035-.070)	.....

PISTONS, PINS, RINGS

Engine	PISTONS	PINS		RINGS		
	①Clearance In. (mm)	Piston Fit In. (mm)	Rod Fit In. (mm)	Rings	End Gap In. (mm)	Side Clearance In. (mm)
1290cc	.001-.002 (.03-.05)	①	.0002-.0003 (.004-.008)	No.1	.004-.011 (.10-.28)	.0012-.0028 (.03-.07)
				No.2	.004-.012 (.10-.30)	.0008-.0024 (.02-.06)
				Oil	.008-.035 (.2-.9)	.....

① — Push fit with piston and pin heated to 158-176°F (70-80°C).

CRANKSHAFT MAIN & CONNECTING ROD BEARINGS

Engine	MAIN BEARINGS				CONNECTING ROD BEARINGS		
	Journal Diam. In. (mm)	Clearance In. (mm)	Thrust Bearing	Crankshaft End Play In. (mm)	Journal Diam. In. (mm)	Clearance In. (mm)	Side Play In. (mm)
1290cc	1.968-1.969 (49.976-50.000)	.0006-.0016 (.016-.040)	No. 3	.0016-.0095 (.040-.242)	1.653-1.654 (41.976-42.000)	.0006-.0016 (.016-.040)	.008-.012 (.20-.30)

VALVE SPRINGS

Engine	Free Length In. (mm)	PRESSURE Lbs. @ In. (kg @ mm)	
		Valve Closed	Valve Open
1290cc	1.831 (46.5)	70.1 @ 1.512 (312 @ 38.4)	.....

TIGHTENING SPECIFICATIONS

Application	Ft. Lbs. (N·m)
Cylinder Head Bolts	40-47 (55-64)
Manifold Nuts	15-21 (20-29)
Main Bearing Cap Bolts	40-47 (55-64)
Connecting Rod Cap Nuts	29-37 (39-50)
Camshaft Sprocket Bolt	40-47 (55-64)
Crankshaft Pulley Bolt	55-75 (75-102)
Flywheel Bolts	40-47 (55-64)

	INCH Lbs. (N·m)
Camshaft Thrust Plate Bolts	48-84 (5-10)

CAMSHAFT

Engine	Journal Diam. In. (mm)	Clearance In. (mm)	Lobe Lift In. (mm)
1290cc Journal No. 1	1.701-1.702 (43.21-43.23)	.0010-.0026 (.025-.066)	.....
No. 2	1.691-1.692 (42.96-42.98)	.0016-.0030 (.040-.070)	
No. 3	1.681-1.682 (42.71-42.73)	.0010-.0026 (.025-.066)	
No. 4	1.671-1.672 (42.46-42.48)	.0016-.0030 (.040-.096)	

22R 4-CYLINDER

ENGINE CODING

ENGINE IDENTIFICATION

Engine serial number is stamped on left side of cylinder block, behind the alternator. Last group of numerals and letters designates engine type.

Engine Identification	
Application	Code
Celica, Corona & Pickup (2189 cc)	22R

ENGINE & CYLINDER HEAD

ENGINE

Removal — 1) Remove hood and disconnect cable from negative battery terminal. With engine cool, drain cooling system. Remove air cleaner and cover carburetor. Remove radiator, shroud, hoses and upper bracket. If equipped with air conditioning, remove compressor and condenser but DO NOT disconnect refrigerant hoses.

2) Disconnect following hoses: Fuel hose from carburetor, water by-pass hose from carburetor coil housing, brake booster hose from intake manifold, heater hoses from engine, air injection tube at rear of engine and emission control hoses from carburetor and intake manifold.

NOTE — *Label all emission control hoses for identification, to ensure proper installation.*

3) Disconnect accelerator linkage from carburetor. If equipped with automatic transmission, disconnect automatic transmission throttle cable. Raise vehicle and drain engine oil. Remove starter and disconnect exhaust pipe at manifold. Disconnect wires from oil pressure switch and sending unit.

4) Remove 2 transmission stiffener plates and engine undercover. Place block of wood on jack and put jack under transmission. If equipped with automatic transmission, disconnect cooler lines from engine and remove 6 torque converter mounting bolts through service holes at rear of engine. On all models, remove transmission housing mounting bolts.

5) Remove motor mount bolts (above crossmember). Disconnect wiring from coil, alternator, and water temperature sending unit. If equipped with power steering, remove pump and move to one side. Disconnect hoses from air pump. Attach sling to engine and lift carefully from vehicle. If equipped with automatic transmission, ensure that converter remains with transmission.

Installation — 1) Lower engine into position ensuring that engine is aligned with transmission and motor mount supports. On manual transmission models, install motor mount and transmission housing mounting bolts.

2) On automatic transmission models, install guide pin in the torque converter and align with one of the drive plate holes. Align upper starter stud with hole in starter housing on engine. Align sleeves on block with converter housing. Install motor mount bolts and remove hoisting sling. Install 2 longest bolts in upper converter housing. Install 6 torque converter bolts finger tight, then to final torque.

3) To complete installation on all models, reverse removal procedure and check for leaks.

CYLINDER HEAD

Removal — 1) Disconnect battery and drain cooling system. Disconnect exhaust pipe at manifold flange. Remove air cleaner and cover carburetor. Remove all hoses and linkages to intake manifold, carburetor and cylinder head. Remove distributor with cap and wires. Remove fuel pump. Remove cylinder head cover and set No. 1 piston to TDC on compression stroke.

2) Paint mating marks on camshaft sprocket and timing chain. Remove rubber half circle seal and cam sprocket retaining bolt. Pull distributor drive gear and fuel pump drive cam off of sprocket. Remove sprocket from camshaft, allowing sprocket and chain to rest in cylinder head. Remove chain cover bolt, then remove cylinder head bolts in reverse of tightening sequence. *See Fig. 1.*

3) Pry equally at front and rear of rocker arm assembly to clear locating dowels. Lift head carefully to clear locating dowels but *DO NOT PRY BETWEEN HEAD AND BLOCK*. Drain engine oil due to coolant which will run into pan during head removal.

Installation — Apply liquid sealer at 2 front corners of block and position head gasket over locating dowels. Place head in position and turn camshaft so dowel is at top. Install rocker arm assembly over locating dowels and tighten head bolts in 3 steps in the sequence shown in *Fig. 1*. Continue installation in reverse of removal sequence, ensuring that valve and ignition timing is properly set.

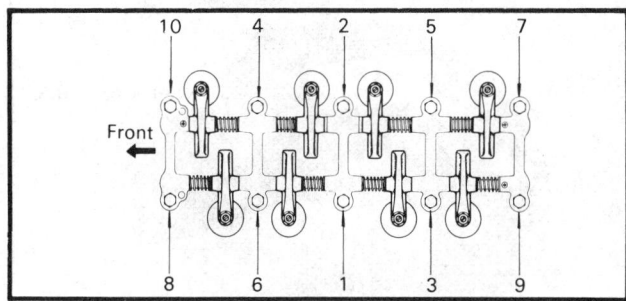

Fig. 1   Cylinder Head/Rocker Arm Bolt Tightening Sequence (Loosen in Reverse Order)

CAMSHAFT

TIMING CHAIN

Removal — 1) Remove cylinder head and oil pan. Remove radiator, drive belts, air pump and alternator bracket. Remove crankshaft pulley and timing chain cover assembly.

2) Remove chain from damper sprocket and remove cam sprocket and chain. Using puller (09213-36010), remove both oil pump drive and chain sprocket. Check chain, sprockets, tensioner and chain dampers for wear and replace as necessary. With chain stretched tight by hand, maximum distance between 17 links should be 5.79" (147.0 mm).

Installation — 1) Turn crankshaft until shaft key is at TDC. Position chain with chromed link over sprocket in line with sprocket mark as illustrated. Chain must be positioned between the 2 dampers.

22R 4-CYLINDER (Cont.)

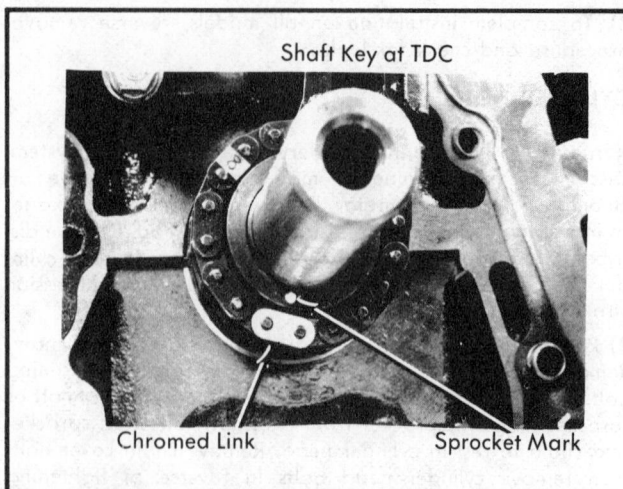

Fig. 2   Aligning Crankshaft Sprocket and Timing Chain

2) Install cam sprocket in chain so that timing mark on sprocket is located between 2 chromed links. Slide oil pump drive spline over crankshaft key. Install cover assembly with new gasket over dowels and pump spline.

Fig. 3   Aligning Camshaft Sprocket and Timing Chain

3) Continue installation in reverse of removal procedure and set camshaft timing as follows: With No. 1 cylinder at TDC on compression stroke, position camshaft so that dowel on sprocket flange is at 12 o'clock position. Complete assembly procedure.

CAMSHAFT

With cylinder head and rocker arm assembly removed, remove camshaft bearing caps and lift out camshaft. Camshaft bearing clearance may be checked using Plastigage method. If clearance exceeds specifications, replace cylinder head and/or camshaft. To install, reverse removal procedure. Install bearing caps in numbered order with arrows pointing toward the front. Adjust valve timing.

VALVE TIMING

Valve timing is determined by the relationship between the camshaft and the crankshaft. Turn crankshaft to position No. 1 piston at TDC (align mark on crankshaft with pointer on chain cover). Turn camshaft to locate dowel pin and stamped mark on camshaft at 12 o'clock position. Install timing gear and chain on camshaft. A locating pin may be needed to stretch chain and a hammer may be needed to drive on gear. Tighten timing gear bolts to specifications.

VALVES

VALVE ARRANGEMENT

Left Side — All exhaust.

Right Side — All intake.

VALVE GUIDE SERVICING

1) Measure clearance between valve stem and guide. If clearance exceeds specifications, valve guides must be replaced. If valve guide being replaced has a snap ring installed, break guide using brass punch and hammer. Using driver tool (09201-60011), drive old guide down through combustion chamber.

NOTE — *Only replacement valve guides have snap rings.*

2) Drive in new valve guide from top of head until snap ring contacts cylinder head. Guide should have .75" (19 mm) protrusion above cylinder head. Ream new valve guide to provide proper stem clearance.

VALVE STEM OIL SEALS

1) Using a suitable spring compressor, remove valve keepers. Withdraw spring retainer and springs. Remove valve stem oil seal from end of valve guide.

2) Slide a new oil seal over valve stem, using care not to damage seal as it passes over keeper grooves. Force seal over end of valve guide. Reverse removal procedure for remaining components.

VALVE SPRINGS

Check valve spring free length and squareness. If less than 1.8" (45.8 mm) long or out of square more than .07" (1.9 mm), replace spring. Use a spring tester and measure tension at installed height. Replace spring if less than specified.

ROCKER ARM ASSEMBLY

If rocker arms appear loose, disassemble rocker arm assembly and measure rocker arm-to-shaft clearance. Clearance should be .0004-.0020" (.01-.05 mm), with a maximum limit of .0031" (.08 mm). If clearance exceeds maximum limit, replace rocker arms and/or shafts. Reassemble in reverse of disassembly, noting that all rocker arms are identical, but that all rocker stands are different.

22R 4-CYLINDER (Cont.)

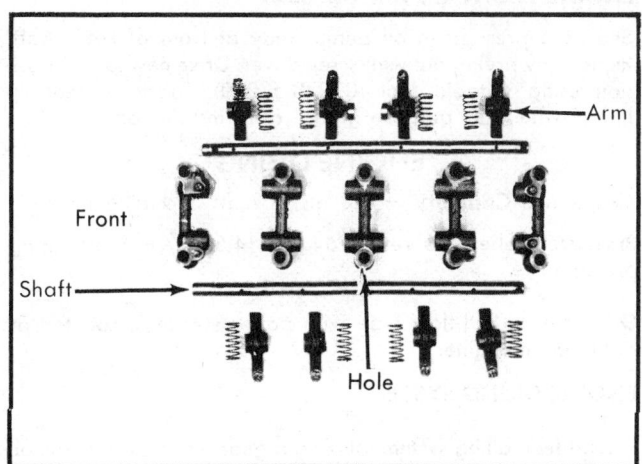

Fig. 4   Disassembled View of Rocker Arm Assembly

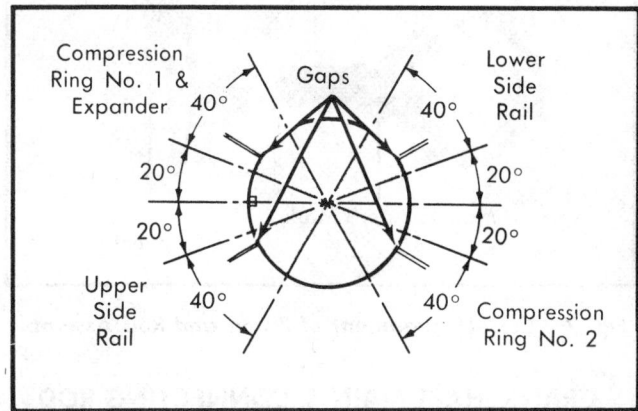

Fig. 5   Correct Piston Ring Gap Arrangement

VALVE CLEARANCE ADJUSTMENT

1) Engine should be at normal operating temperature. Remove valve cover and set No. 1 piston on TDC at compression stroke. Measure clearance between rocker arm and valve stem. Adjust intake valves 1 and 2 to .008" (.20 mm) and exhaust valves 1 and 3 to .012" (.30 mm).

2) Rotate crankshaft one complete revolution and align timing mark at TDC. Adjust intake valves 3 and 4 to .008" (.20 mm) and exhaust valves 2 and 4 to .012" (.30 mm).

PISTONS, PINS & RINGS

OIL PAN

Removal — Drain engine oil, then remove engine undercover and detach steering idler arm bracket. On all Pickups except 4-WD, remove pitman arm and front crossmember. On Celica and Corona, remove engine shock absorber (if so equipped) and engine mount bolts. Jack engine up about 1" (25 mm). On all models, remove pan bolts and nuts, then take off pan and gasket.

Installation — Place gasket on pan and apply sealer to 4 corners where front cover and rear seal retainer join cylinder block. Install pan. To complete installation, reverse removal procedure.

PISTON & ROD ASSEMBLY

Removal — With cylinder head and pan removed, machine ring ridge from top of cylinder. Mark rods and caps for correct assembly, then remove rod caps. Cover rod bolts with short length of hose to prevent crankshaft damage, then push piston/rod assembly out of block.

Installation — Lubricate piston, cylinder and journal with clean engine oil. Position rings as illustrated and apply ring compressor. Stamped mark on ring must face upward. Install piston/rod assembly in proper position with notch on piston top facing forward.

PISTONS & RINGS

1) Measure cylinder bore at top and bottom of wear area and center of bore, in line with and at 90° to crankshaft. Standard bore is 3.6220-3.6232" (91.998-92.029 mm) with a wear limit of .008" (.20 mm). Maximum taper and out of round is .0008" (.20 mm).

2) Measure piston at right angle to skirt and 1.02" (26 mm) below center of pin. If not within specifications, rebore cylinder and/or replace pistons. Measure ring end gap at bottom of ring travel. Check clearance of ring in land groove.

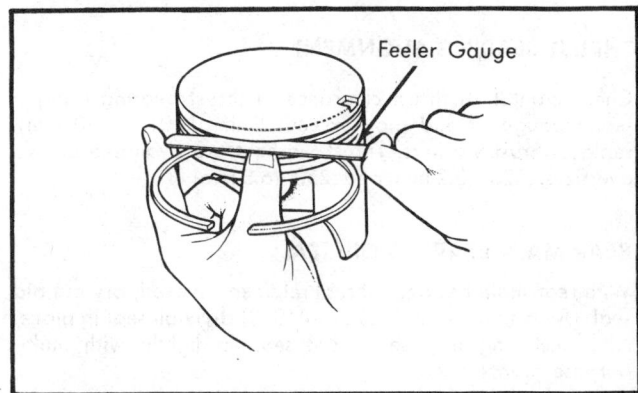

Fig. 6   Measuring Ring Groove Clearance

PISTON PINS

Removal — Heat piston to 176°F (80°C) and push piston pin out of piston and connecting rod. Piston pin should push through connecting rod with thumb pressure when rod is at 68°F (20°C). If pin is too loose in rod, press out bushing from connecting rod using press tool (09222-30010). Install and hone new bushing.

NOTE — *Piston and pin are a matched set. Use new snap rings for reassembly.*

Installation — Heat piston to 176°F (80°C) and position piston and connecting rod so mark on rod and indent on piston crown face same direction. Push piston pin into piston and rod assembly.

Toyota Engines

22R 4-CYLINDER (Cont.)

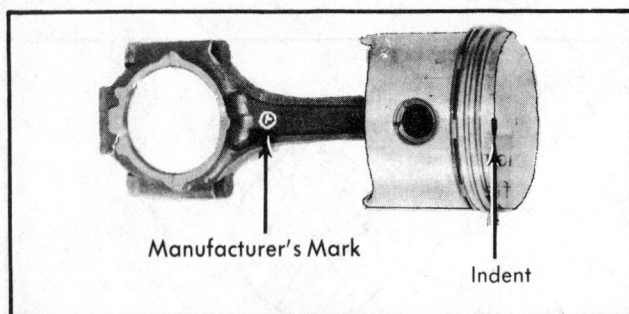

Fig. 7   Correct Alignment of Piston and Rod Assembly

CRANKSHAFT MAIN & CONNECTING ROD BEARINGS

MAIN & CONNECTING ROD BEARINGS

1) Measure crankshaft runout at center bearing journal. If runout exceeds .004" (.1 mm), replace crankshaft. Inspect all journals for wear or scoring. Check for out-of-round or taper. If crankshaft is worn excessively, grind journals for undersize bearings.

2) Measure bearing clearances using Plastigage method. If clearance exceeds specifications, grind journals for undersize bearings. Both main and connecting rod bearings are available .010" (.25 mm) undersize.

THRUST BEARING ALIGNMENT

Check crankshaft thrust clearance at thrust bearing using a feeler gauge. If end play exceeds limit of .012" (.30 mm), replace thrust washers. Thrust washers are available in two oversizes, .125" (3.2 mm) and .250" (6.3 mm).

REAR MAIN BEARING OIL SEAL

With rear main bearing oil seal retainer removed, pry out old seal. Using suitable tool (09223-41010) drive oil seal in place. After installing new seal, coat seal lip lightly with multi-purpose grease.

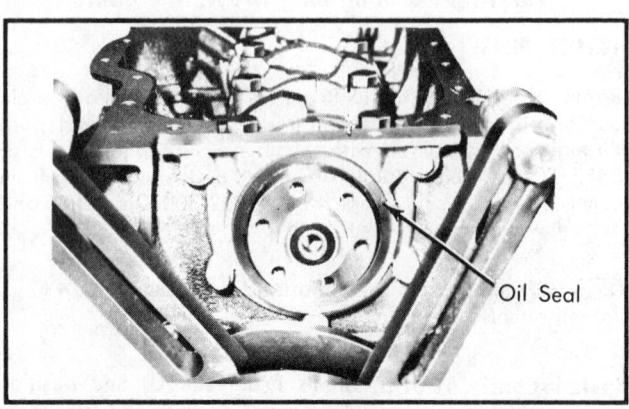

Fig. 8   Installed View of Rear Seal and Retainer

ENGINE FRONT COVER OIL SEAL

Seal is a press fit in oil pump body at front of crankshaft. Remove by prying out with screwdriver. Drive new seal in position using suitable tool (09223-50010). Lubricate seal lip lightly with multi-purpose grease after installation.

ENGINE OILING

Crankcase Capacity — 4.0 qts; 4.9 qts. including filter.

Pressure Relief Valve — 64 psi (4.5 kg/cm^2) operating pressure.

Oil Filter — Full-flow type with paper elements. Located at right side of engine.

ENGINE OILING SYSTEM

Forced feed oiling system utilizing a gear and crescent type oil pump driven from front of crankshaft. Oil from oil pan is pumped through a full flow oil filter and then to oil galleries in cylinder block. Oil is fed to crankshaft bearings, timing chain assembly, camshaft and rocker arm assembly.

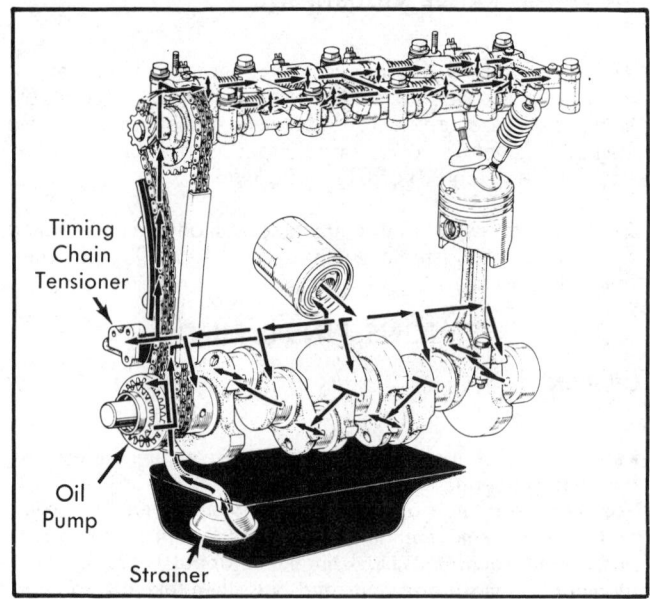

Fig. 9   Engine Oiling System

OIL PUMP

Oil Pump Specifications	
Application	**Clearance In. (mm)**
Drive Gear-to-Crescent	
Standard	.0087-.0098 (.22-.25)
Wear Limit	.012 (.30)
Driven Gear-to-Crescent	
Standard	.0059-.0083 (.15-.21)
Wear Limit	.012 (.30)
Driven Gear-to-Body	
Standard	.0035-.0059 (.09-.15)
Wear Limit	.008 (.20)
Gear Faces-to-Body	
Standard	.0012-.0035 (.03-.09)
Wear Limit	.0059 (.15)

Toyota Engines

22R 4-CYLINDER (Cont.)

Removal — Remove oil pan and strainer. Remove drive belts and crankshaft pulley. Remove 5 bolts and oil pump assembly. Remove oil pump drive spline from crankshaft and "O" ring from engine block. Remove relief valve plug, spring and piston from pump body. Remove driven and drive gear from pump body.

Installation — Reassemble pump and lubricate seal lip. Install new "O" ring in block and apply sealer to upper bolt. Install and tighten pump. Complete installation in reverse of removal procedure.

ENGINE COOLING

Thermostat — On Federal models except Cab and Chassis Pickup, starts to open at 190°F (88°C) and is fully open at 212°F (100°C). On Calif. models and all Cab and Chassis Pickups, starts to open at 180°F (82°C) and is fully open at 203°F (95°C).

Cooling System Capacity — 8.9 qts.

Radiator Cap — 11-15 psi (7.5-1.05 kg/cm²).

WATER PUMP

Removal & Installation — Drain cooling system and loosen alternator pivot adjusting bolts. Pivot alternator toward engine to loosen drive belt. Remove fluid coupling, pulley and fan belt. Remove 7 bolts and 2 nuts and take pump off engine. To install, use new gasket on clean mating surfaces and reverse removal procedure.

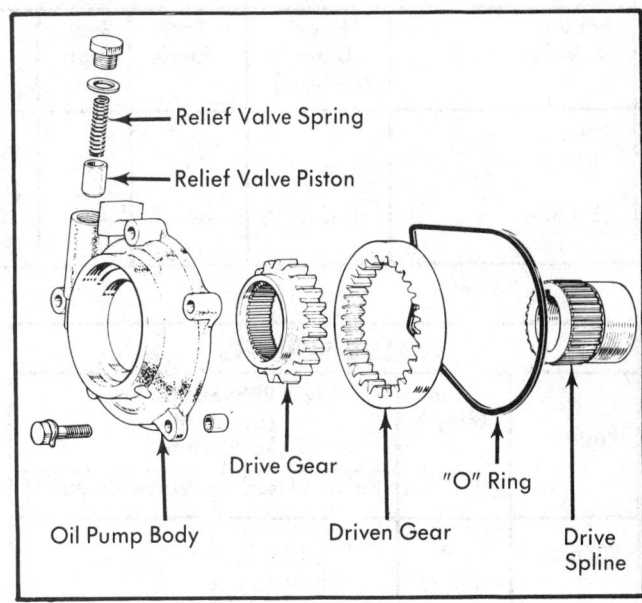

Fig. 10 Exploded View of Oil Pump

ENGINE SPECIFICATIONS

GENERAL SPECIFICATIONS

Year	Displ. cu. ins.	Displ. cc	Carburetor	HP at RPM	Torque (Ft. Lbs. at RPM)	Compr. Ratio	Bore in.	Bore mm	Stroke in.	Stroke mm
1981	144.4	2366	1x2 Bbl.	96@4800	122@2800	9.0:1	3.62	92.0	3.50	89.0

PISTONS, PINS, RINGS

Engine	PISTONS Clearance In. (mm)	PINS Piston Fit① In. (mm)	PINS Rod Fit② In. (mm)	RINGS Rings	RINGS End Gap In. (mm)	RINGS Side Clearance In. (mm)
2366 cc	.0020-.0028 (.050-.071)	Press Fit	.0002-.0004 (.005-.011)	No. 1 No. 2 Oil	.0110-.0157 (.28-.40) .0110-.0157 (.28-.40) .0018-.0315 (.30-.80)	.008 (.20) .008 (.20) .....

① — Push fit with piston heated to 176° F (80° C).
② — Push fit with piston at room temperature.

CRANKSHAFT MAIN & CONNECTING ROD BEARINGS

Engine	MAIN BEARINGS Journal Diam. In. (mm)	MAIN BEARINGS Clearance In. (mm)	MAIN BEARINGS Thrust Bearing	MAIN BEARINGS Crankshaft End Play In. (mm)	CONNECTING ROD BEARINGS Journal Diam. In. (mm)	CONNECTING ROD BEARINGS Clearance In. (mm)	CONNECTING ROD BEARINGS Side Play In. (mm)
2366 cc	2.3614-2.3622 (59.98-60.00)	.0010-.0022 (.025-.055)	Center	.0008-.0087 (.020-.220)	2.0862-2.0866 (52.989-52.999)	.0010-.0022 (.025-.055)	.0063-.0102 (.160-.259)

Toyota Engines

22R 4-CYLINDER (Cont.)
ENGINE SPECIFICATIONS (Cont.)

VALVES							
Engine & Valve	Head Diam. In. (mm)	Face Angle	Seat Angle	Seat Width In. (mm)	Stem Diameter In. (mm)	Stem Clearance In. (mm)	Valve Lift In. (mm)
2366 cc Intake	.....	44.5°	45°	.047-.063 (1.19-1.60)	.3138-.3145 (7.970-7.988)	.0008-.0024 (.0020-.060)	.....
Exhaust	.....	44.5°	45°	.047-.063 (1.19-1.60)	.3136-.3142 (7.965-7.980)	.0012-.0026 (.030-.066)	.....

VALVE SPRINGS			
Engine	Free Length In. (mm)	PRESSURE Lbs. @ In. (kg @ mm)	
		Valve Closed	Valve Open
2366 cc	1.80 (45.7)	55@1.59 (25@40.5)	.....

CAMSHAFT			
Engine	Journal Diam. In. (mm)	Clearance② In. (mm)	①Lobe Lift In. (mm)
2366 cc	1.2984-1.2992 (32.98-33.0)	.0004-.0020 (.010-.050)	Int. 1.680 (42.68) Exh. 1.682 (42.74)

① — Total Lobe Height.
② — End play is .0031-.0071" (.08-.18 mm)

TIGHTENING SPECIFICATIONS	
Application	Ft. Lbs. (N·m)
Camshaft Bearing Bolts	13-16 (18-22)
Camshaft Sprocket Bolt	51-65 (69-88)
Connecting Rod Cap Bolts	40-47 (54-64)
Crankshaft Pulley Bolt	102-130 (139-177)
Cylinder Head Bolts	53-63 (72-86)
Exhaust Manifold	29-36 (39-49)
Flywheel Bolts	73-86 (99-117)
Intake Manifold	13-19 (18-26)
Main Bearing Cap Bolts	69-83 (94-113)

L 4-CYLINDER DIESEL

ENGINE CODING

ENGINE IDENTIFICATION

Engine Identification tag is located on engine valve cover and contains engine identification code.

Engine Identification	
Application	Code
Pickup	L

ENGINE & CYLINDER HEAD

ENGINE

Removal — 1) Remove hood, air cleaner and both batteries. Drain cooling system, disconnect radiator hoses, fan shroud, radiator and remove from vehicle. If equipped with air conditioning, remove drive belt, compressor bracket bolts and lay compressor aside. Remove fan belt, fan and fan pulley.

2) Disconnect fuel hoses from injection pump, heater hoses at left side of engine and vacuum reservoir hose. If equipped with air conditioning, disconnect idle-up vacuum hose. Disconnect wires to alternator, starter, oil pressure switch, thermo switch and terminal "B" from glow plug relay No. 1. Disconnect wiring harness to engine at left fender.

3) Disconnect accelerator wire from injector pump. Using proper tool (Toyota No. 09305-20012), remove transmission shift lever from inside vehicle. Raise vehicle, drain engine oil and remove engine cover panel. Disconnect wire to back-up light switch. Disconnect engine shock absorber, remove drive shaft and disconnect speedometer cable.

4) Disconnect clamp from exhaust pipe at transmission housing. Disconnect exhaust pipe mount nuts at manifold and remove clutch slave cylinder. Lower vehicle and remove engine mount bolts. Place jack under transmission and remove rear engine mount at crossmember. Attach chain to engine brackets and position hoist over engine. Remove engine and transmission together as a unit.

CAUTION — *If vehicle is equipped with air conditioning, take care not to damage condenser. Make sure engine is clear of all wiring and hoses.*

Installation — If transmission was separated from engine, attach transmission to engine and reverse removal procedure to complete installation.

CYLINDER HEAD

Removal — 1) Using starter, turn engine over until No. 1 cylinder is at TDC on compression stroke. Disconnect negative battery terminals. Remove glow plug bracket and glow plugs. Disconnect injection and fuel pipes and remove from engine. Using suitable wrench, remove injection nozzle holders and linkage pipe. Arrange in order for correct reassembly.

2) Remove intake manifold bolts and remove manifold. Remove exhaust manifold bolts and remove manifold. Remove fan belt, fan and fan pulley. Remove crankshaft damper bolts

and using suitable puller, remove damper. After removing timing belt cover and belt guide, remove valve cover. Loosen idler pulley and remove timing belt and idler pulley.

NOTE — *If timing belt is to be re-used, mark belt and camshaft gear and injection pump pulley and belt before removing belt, to ensure correct reassembly.*

CAUTION — *Release tension on timing belt before removing attaching bolts to crankshaft pulley, camshaft pulley and injection pump pulley. Do not bend or twist belt and keep belt free from oil, water or steam.*

3) After removing attaching bolts, select suitable puller and remove crankshaft timing pulley. Using proper wrench to hold injection pump drive pulley from turning, remove bolt. Using puller, remove pulley being careful not to drop pulley as it will spring out. Using proper wrench to hold camshaft timing gear from turning, remove bolt. Using puller, remove timing gear.

4) Remove No. 2 oil seal retainer and loosen rocker arm attaching bolts gradually in reverse order of sequence shown in *Fig. 1*. Remove rocker arm assembly and camshaft. Loosen cylinder head bolts gradually in reverse order of sequence shown in *Fig. 2*. Remove cylinder head.

Installation — Clean cylinder block holes out using compressed air. Ensure that all mating surfaces are clean and free from oil, grease, dirt and all foreign materials. Position head on block. Coat head bolts lightly with engine oil, install bolts and tighten. Reverse removal procedure to complete installation.

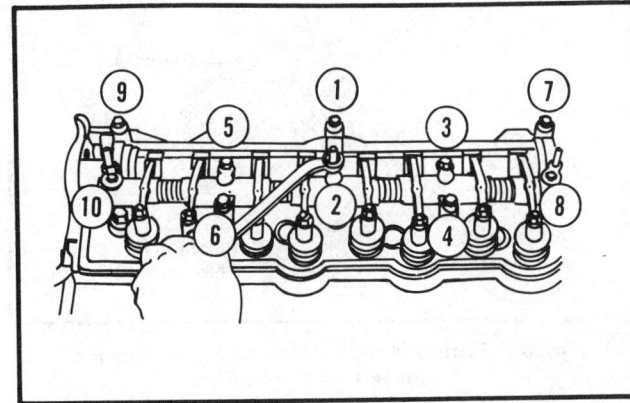

Fig. 1   Rocker Arm Assembly Tightening Sequence
(Loosen in Reverse Order to Disassemble)

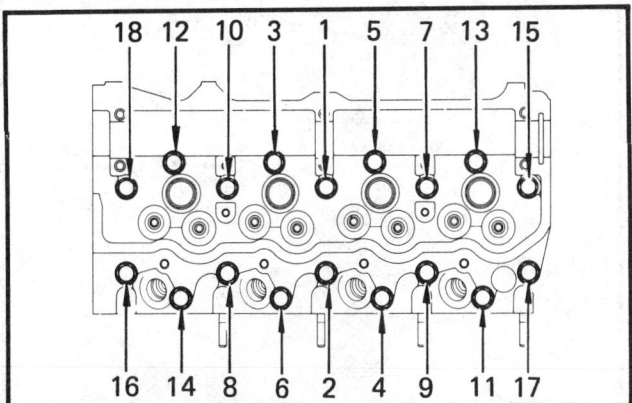

Fig. 2   Cylinder Head Tightening Sequence
(Loosen in Reverse Order to Disassemble)

Toyota Engines

L 4-CYLINDER DIESEL (Cont.)

CAMSHAFT

TIMING BELT

Removal — 1) Using starter, turn engine over until No. 1 piston is at TDC on compression stroke. Disconnect negative battery terminals. Remove fan belt, fan and pulley. Remove damper attaching bolt and using puller, remove damper.

2) Remove necessary attaching bolts and remove timing chain cover and belt guide. Loosen idler pulley bolt and remove timing belt.

Installation — 1) Before installing a new belt, remove idler pulley and spring. Check idler pulley to make sure it turns freely and smooth. Check the free length of idler pulley spring. Length of spring should be 1.563" (39.70 mm). Under 8.8 lbs (4 kg) tension, spring should measure 2.05" (52.0 mm) in length.

2) Check camshaft timing pulley, injection pump pulley and crankshaft pulley for wear or damage. Install idler pulley loose enough so it may be moved side to side by hand. Check alignment of timing marks on each pulley as shown in *Fig. 3*. Injection pump timing is normally retarded.

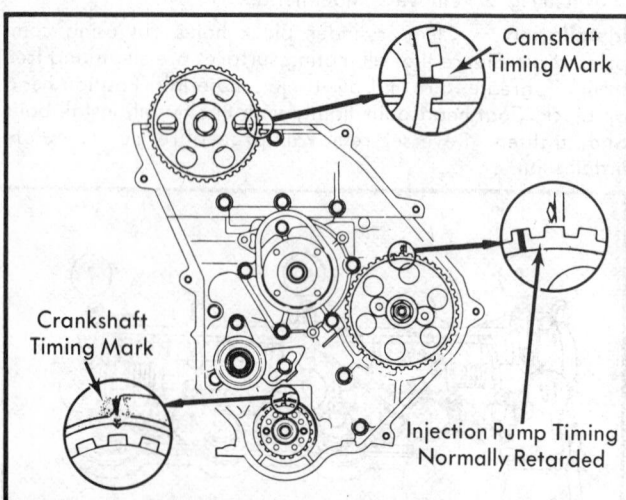

Fig. 3   Timing Mark Alignment Before Turning Crankshaft 2 Revolutions

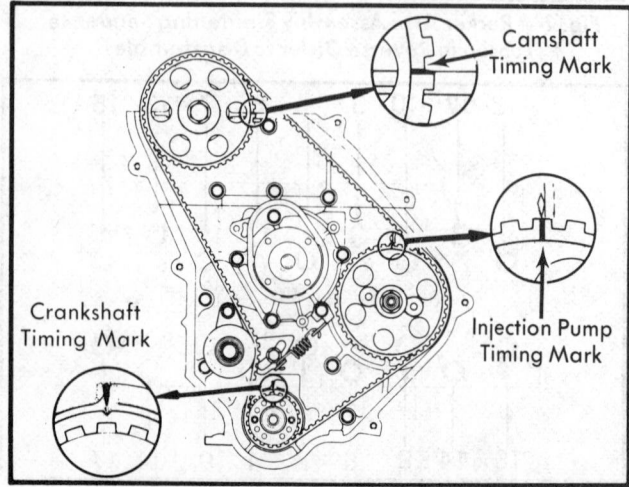

Fig. 4   Timing Mark Alignment After Turning Crankshaft 2 Revolutions

3) Install timing belt and idler spring. Turn the crankshaft 2 revolutions clockwise from TDC to TDC. While turning crankshaft make sure idler pulley bracket is moving. Ensure that each pulley aligns with marks shown in *Fig. 4*. Tighten timing belt idler pulley bolt. Reverse removal procedure to complete installation.

CAUTION — *Before installing timing belt, engine should be cold. Always turn crankshaft clockwise.*

CAMSHAFT

Removal — 1) Before removing camshaft, measure camshaft bearing clearance using Plastigage method. Clearance should be between .0009-.0030" (.022-.076 mm) with a limit of .004" (.10mm). With timing belt removed, loosen valve cover attaching bolts and remove valve cover. Gradually loosen rocker arm assembly bolts in reverse order of sequence shown in *Fig. 1*.

2) Remove rocker arm assembly and remove camshaft. Using proper gauge, measure camshaft runout. If runout is in excess of .0016" (.040 mm) camshaft must be replaced. Measure camshaft lobe height. If lobe height is less than 1.681" (42.69 mm) for intake and 1.689" (42.90 mm) for exhaust, camshaft must be replaced.

Installation — Install camshaft with Woodruff key facing straight upward. Loosen adjusting screw lock nuts on rocker arm assembly and install rocker arm assembly. Reverse removal procedures to complete installation.

VALVE TIMING

See *TIMING BELT* procedures for this information.

VALVES

VALVE ARRANGEMENT

E-I-E-I-E-I-E-I (Front-to-rear).

VALVES & VALVE SEATS

Removal & Installation — 1) Using valve spring compressor tool, compress spring and remove valve keepers, and remove valve assembly keeping disassembled parts in order for proper reassembly. Resurface valve face and tip if necessary or replace valve(s).

2) Using a 45° cutter, resurface valve seat. If seat position is too high, use a 45° cutter first, then follow with a 60° cutter. If seat position is too low, use a 45° cutter first, then follow with a 30° cutter. After valves, valve seats and valve guides have been serviced, reverse removal procedure to complete installation.

VALVE GUIDE SERVICING

1) With head disassembled, measure inside diameter of valve guide at several places using a dial indicator. Measure valve stem diameter and subtract the difference where clearance is the largest. If clearance exceeds the limit, replace both valve and valve guide. To replace valve guide, position proper tool on guide and drive out guide from top end toward combustion chamber.

L 4-CYLINDER DIESEL (Cont.)

2) Before installing new guide, make sure that hole in head is clean and apply a thin coat of oil to guide hole. Using suitable tool, drive guide into head until tip of guide protrudes .642-.657" (16.30-16.68 mm) above top of cylinder head. Using correct size reamer, ream intake valve guide clearance to .0008-.0022" (.020-.055 mm) and exhaust valve guide clearance to .0016-.0030" (.040-.076 mm).

VALVE SPRINGS

Valve springs must be square within .079" (2.00 mm). Using proper caliper measuring tool, measure spring free length. Spring free length should be within 1.8091-1.8327" (45.951-46.550 mm). Replace spring(s) that are not within specified installed height. Installed height is 1.547" (32.29 mm) at 53.4 lb. (24.2 kg) load.

VALVE CLEARANCE ADJUSTMENT

Turn crankshaft until No. 1 piston is at TDC on compression stroke. Adjust cylinders No. 1 & 2 intake valves and cylinders No. 1 & 3 exhaust valves. Turn crankshaft 360°. Adjust cylinders No. 3 & 4 intake valves and cylinders No. 2 & 4 exhaust valves.

NOTE — *Valve adjustment should be made with engine at normal operating temperature.*

Valve Clearances		
Application	**Hot** In. (mm)	① **Cold** In. (mm)
Intake	.010 (.25)	.011 (.27)
Exhaust	.014 (.36)	.015 (.38)
① — Initial setting only.		

NOTE — *Injection pump timing should be checked. Refer to TUNE-UP Section for necessary procedures.*

ROCKER ARM ASSEMBLY

Removal — Remove valve cover, and loosen rocker arm assembly attaching bolts in reverse of sequence shown in *Fig. 1*. Remove rocker arm assembly and check rocker arm-to-shaft clearance. If worn excessively, disassemble and measure clearance between the rocker arm and shaft. See Rocker Arm Assembly Chart.

Installation — After all clearances have been checked, reverse removal procedures to complete installation. *See Fig. 5.*

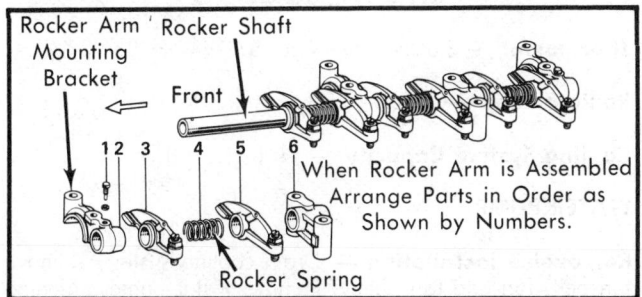

Fig. 5   Rocker Arm Shaft Assembly

Rocker Arm Assembly Chart	
Application	**Specification** In. (mm)
Oil Clearance	.0008-.0024 (.020-.060)
Limit	.004 (.10)
Rocker Arm Bore	
Limit	.7323 (18.600)
Shaft Diameter	
Limit	.7260 (18.440)

NOTE — *Align oil hole of front rocker support with rocker shaft oil hole.*

PISTONS, PINS, & RINGS

PISTON & ROD ASSEMBLY

Removal & Installation — **1)** With cylinder head, oil pan and oil screen removed, mark connecting rods and caps for identification, to ensure proper reassembly. Remove connecting rod caps and place a short piece of hose on connecting rod stud to prevent damage to crankshaft journal.

2) Push piston and rod assembly out of the top of cylinder bore. After piston and cylinder block have been serviced, reverse removal procedure to complete installation.

NOTE — *If carbon has built up at top of piston travel area in cylinder block, it may be necessary to use a ridge reamer to remove carbon before removing piston and rod assembly.*

FITTING PISTONS

1) Inspect cylinder liner walls for deep scratches or damage. If necessary, rebore cylinder liners all the same size. Standard bore size is 3.5433-3.5445" (89.999-90.030 mm), with a wear limit of .008" (.20 mm). If damage is excessive or bore measurement exceeds limits, replace cylinder liners.

2) Measure piston diameter in thrust direction 1.34" (34.0 mm) up from skirt bottom edge. Measurement must be made at normal temperature of 68°F (20° C). Measure cylinder bore and subtract the piston size to obtain correct piston clearance. Piston clearance should be .0014-.0022" (.035-.055 mm).

PISTON RINGS

After correct size rings have been selected, install rings on piston using proper ring expander tool. Measure ring end gap. Measure ring side clearance and space rings on piston as shown in *Fig. 6*.

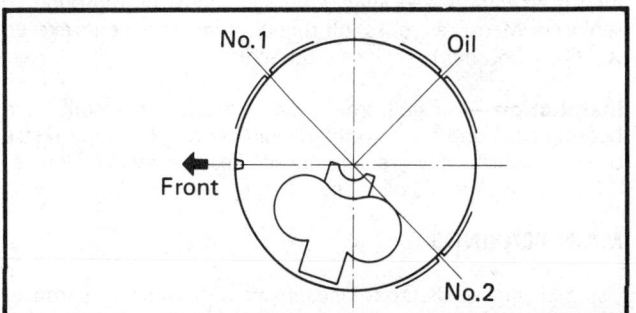

Fig. 6   Piston Ring Gap Spacing

Toyota Engines

L 4-CYLINDER DIESEL (Cont.)

PISTON PINS

Removal & Installation — 1) Piston pin fit is checked by rocking piston at right angle to pin. If any movement is felt, replace piston and pin. Heat piston to 140° F (60° C) and remove snap rings. Using suitable tool, remove pin. Measure oil clearance between bushing and piston pin.

2) Clearance should be .0002-.0005" (.005-.012 mm), with a limit of .0020" (.050 mm). If clearance exceeds limits, replace bushing and grind bore with a pin hole grinder. Heat piston to 140° F (60° C), install piston pin and push into piston hole with thumb pressure.

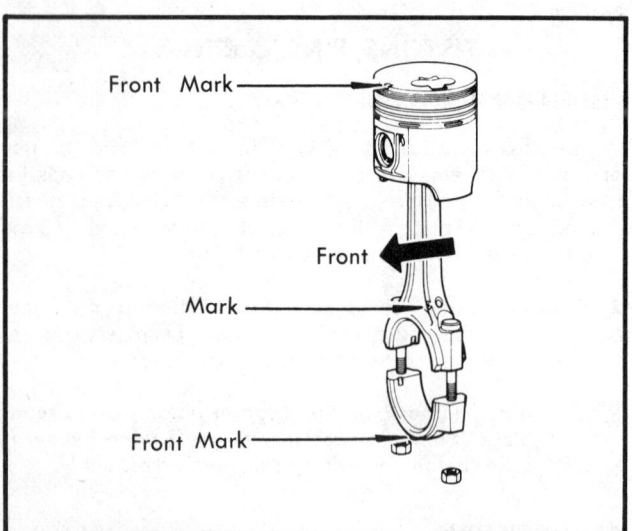

Fig. 7 Piston and Rod Assembly Installation

CRANKSHAFT

Removal — 1) With cylinder head off and pistons removed, measure crankshaft thrust clearance. Standard thrust clearance is .0016-.0098" (.040-.248 mm), with a wear limit of .012" (.30 mm). If clearance exceeds limits, replace thrust bearings as a set.

2) Oversize bearings are available in .005" (.125 mm) and .009" (.250 mm). Loosen crankshaft bearing bolts gradually, starting with center bearing, alternating and working toward the ends. Remove bearing caps and keep them in order to ensure proper reassembly.

Inspection — Inspect crankshaft for excessive wear or damage. Measure connecting and main journal diameters. If measurements exceed limits crankshaft must be reground or replaced. Measure crankshaft runout. If measurements exceed .0024" (.060 mm), replace crankshaft.

Installation — Install crankshaft in block and install main bearing caps and bolts. Tighten main bearing bolts in reverse order in which they were removed. Reverse removal procedure to complete installation.

MAIN BEARINGS

Using Plastigage method, measure main journal oil clearance. Clean journal, cap and bearing. Lay a strip of Plastigage across journal, install cap and tighten cap bolts. Remove cap bolts, cap and measure Plastigage at widest point. If clearance is not within specifications, replace bearings.

ENGINE OILING

Crankcase Capacity — 6.1 qts. with filter; 5.1 qts. without filter.

Oil Filter — Replaceable spin-on type filter is mounted on right side of engine block.

OIL PUMP

Removal — Disconnect negative battery terminal. Remove fan belt, fan and fan pulley. Remove damper attaching bolt and using puller, remove damper. Disconnect lower radiator hose and remove timing case attaching bolts. Remove timing chain cover. Remove oil pump plate attaching screws, and disassemble oil pump.

Inspection — Inspect gears and pump body for damage or excessive wear. Measure body clearance, tip clearance of driven and drive gears and side clearance.

Installation — Reverse removal procedure to complete installation, making sure to assemble drive and driven gears to pump body with triangular marks facing pump plate side. Apply Loctite to oil pump plate retaining screws.

Oil Pump Specifications	
Application	**Clearance In. (mm)**
Body Clearance	.0024–.0059 (.060–.149)
Limit	.008 (.20)
Side Clearance	.0012–.0035 (.030–.088)
Limit	.0059 (.149)
Tip Clearance	
Drive Gear-Crescent	.0087–.0098 (.220–.248)
Driven Gear-Crescent	.0059–.0083 (.149–.210)
Limit	.012 (.30)

ENGINE COOLING

Thermostat — Starts to open at 187-194° F (86-90° C).

Radiator Cap — 17 psi (1.2 kg/cm^2).

Cooling System Capacity — 11.1 qts.

WATER PUMP

Removal & Installation — Drain cooling system. Remove fan belt, fan and fan pulley. Remove water pump attaching bolts and remove water pump. Clean gasket surfaces and reverse removal procedure to complete installation.

Toyota Engines

L 4-CYLINDER DIESEL (Cont.)

TIGHTENING SPECIFICATIONS

Application	Ft. Lbs. (N·m)
Camshaft-to-Timing Pulley	69-75 (94-102)
Connecting Rod Cap	37-43 (50-58)
Crankshaft Pulley	69-75 (94-102)
Flywheel	84-90 (114-122)
Head Bolts	84-90 (114-122)
Main Bearing Cap	71-81 (97-110)
Manifold	
Intake	8-11 (11-15)
Exhaust	11-15 (15-20)
Rocker Arm Support	11-15 (15-20)

ENGINE SPECIFICATIONS

GENERAL SPECIFICATIONS

Year	Displ. cu. ins.	Displ. cc	Carburetor	HP at RPM	Torque (Ft. Lbs. at RPM)	Compr. Ratio	Bore in.	Bore mm	Stroke in.	Stroke mm
1981 2188 cc	133.3	2188	F.I.	.....	.....	.....	3.54	90.0	3.39	86.0

VALVES

Engine & Valve	Head Diam. In. (mm)	Face Angle	Seat Angle	Seat Width In. (mm)	Stem Diameter In. (mm)	Stem Clearance In. (mm)	Valve Lift In. (mm)
2188 cc Intake	.....	44.5°	44.5°	.051-.063 (1.29-1.60)	.3336-.3342 (8.473-8.488)	.0008-.0022 (.020-.055)	.....
Exhaust	.....	44.5°	44.5°	.051-.063 (1.29-1.60)	.3328-.3335 (8.453-8.470)	.0016-.0030 (.040-.076)	.....

CRANKSHAFT MAIN & CONNECTING ROD BEARINGS

Engine	MAIN BEARINGS Journal Diam. In. (mm)	MAIN BEARINGS Clearance In. (mm)	MAIN BEARINGS Thrust Bearing	MAIN BEARINGS Crankshaft End Play In. (mm)	CONNECTING ROD BEARINGS Journal Diam. In. (mm)	CONNECTING ROD BEARINGS Clearance In. (mm)	CONNECTING ROD BEARINGS Side Play In. (mm)
2188 cc	2.4402-2.4409 (61.981-61.998)	.0012-.0028 (.030-.071)	No. 3	.002-.010 (.040-.248)	2.0858-2.0866 (52.98-53.00)	.0012-.0028 (.030-.071)	.0031-.0079 (.078-.200)

PISTONS, PINS, RINGS

Engine	PISTONS ①Clearance In. (mm)	PINS Piston Fit In. (mm)	PINS Rod Fit In. (mm)	RINGS Rings	RINGS End Gap In. (mm)	RINGS Side Clearance In. (mm)
2188 cc	.0014-.0022 (.035-.056)	Push Fit	.....	No. 1	.0078-.0157 (.198-.398)	.0024-.0039 (.060-.099)
	.....	.....	.....	No. 2	.0118-.0197 (.299-.500)	.0016-.0031 (.040-.078)
	.....	.....	.....	Oil	.0118-.0197 (.299-.500)	.0012-.0028 (.030-.071)

Toyota Engines

2F 6-CYLINDER

ENGINE CODING

ENGINE IDENTIFICATION

Engine number is stamped on right side of cylinder block above starter motor. First two digits indicate engine type.

Engine Identification	
Application	Code
Land Cruiser (4230 cc)	2F

ENGINE, CYLINDER HEAD & MANIFOLDS

ENGINE

Removal — **1)** Drain crankcase and cooling system and remove battery. Remove hood and tip grill forward. Disconnect radiator and heater hoses and remove radiator. Remove air cleaner and ducting and cover carburetor. Disconnect throttle and choke controls to carburetor. If equipped with air conditioning, dismount compressor and condenser but DO NOT disconnect hoses.

2) Disconnect alternator and ignition wiring between engine and chassis. Tag all vacuum and emission control hoses for identification and disconnect from engine. If equipped with power steering, remove pump and reservoir from engine and tie out of way, but do not disconnect hoses.

3) Remove engine and transmission undercovers. Remove front propeller shaft and winch drive shaft. Place jack or suitable supporting device under transmission and transfer case. Remove bolts attaching transmission and transfer case to engine bell housing. Disconnect exhaust pipe from manifold and fuel line at pump.

4) Attach suitable hoist and sling to engine and remove engine mount bolts and nuts. Move engine forward and up very carefully to avoid damage to engine compartment components.

Installation — Use guide dowels in transmission bolt holes and lower into position. Use care when aligning clutch assembly over transmission pilot shaft. Continue installation in reverse sequence of removal.

INTAKE & EXHAUST MANIFOLDS

Removal — **1)** Disconnect battery and remove air cleaner. Disconnect throttle rod, choke rod, accelerator wire, vacuum line, and fuel line from carburetor.

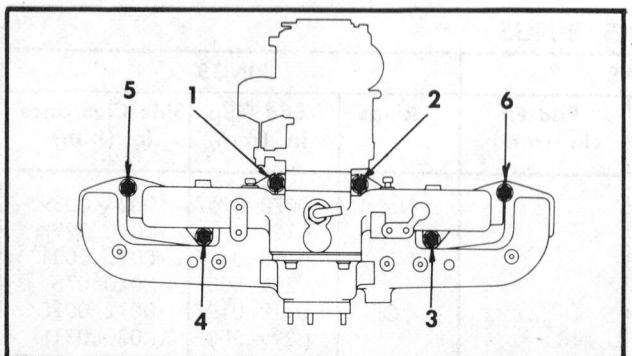

Fig. 1 Manifold Tightening Sequence

2) Disconnect magnetic valve wire from ignition coil terminal and remove carburetor assembly. Disconnect exhaust pipe from exhaust manifold. Remove manifold nuts, manifolds and gaskets.

Installation — Thoroughly clean all gasket surfaces and install new gaskets. Install manifold assembly and gradually tighten bolts working from center out. Install remaining components in reverse of removal procedure.

CYLINDER HEAD

Removal — Drain cooling system and remove intake and exhaust manifold as previously described. Disconnect spark plug wires and remove cylinder head cover. Remove rocker arm assembly and take out push rods, keeping them in order for installation. Loosen head bolts in 2 or 3 steps in reverse of tightening sequence and remove head.

Installation — Ensure that all mating surfaces are clean and place new head gasket on cylinder block. Ensure that mating oil hole on push rod side is between No. 4 and 5 cylinder. Install cylinder head and tighten bolts in 2 or 3 steps in the sequence illustrated. Complete installation in reverse sequence of removal.

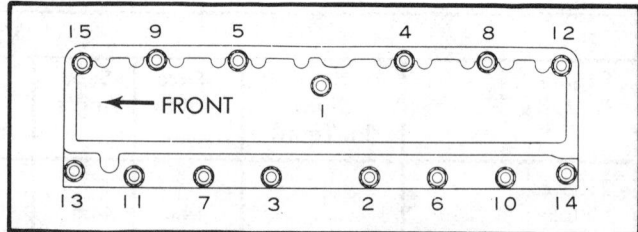

**Fig. 2 Cylinder Head Tightening Sequence
(Loosen in Reverse Order)**

VALVES

VALVE ARRANGEMENT

E-I-I-E-E-I-I-E-E-I-I-E

VALVE GUIDE SERVICING

1) Check clearance between valve stems and valve guides. If clearance exceeds .004" (.10 mm) for intake or .005" (.12 mm) for exhaust, replace valve and/or valve guide.

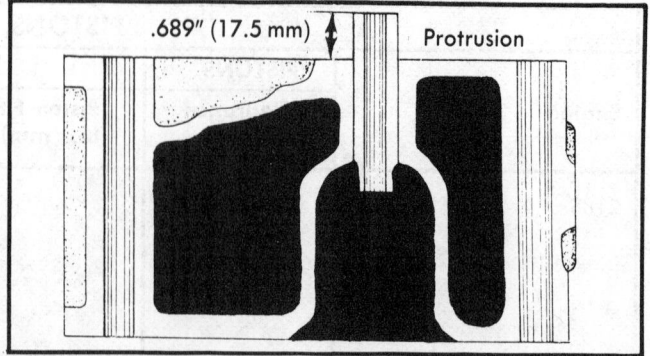

Fig. 3 Valve Guide Installation

2F 6-CYLINDER (Cont.)

2) To replace valve guide, drive toward combustion chamber with suitable tool (09201-60011). Use same tool to drive new guide in from top of cylinder head. When properly installed guide should extend .689" (17.5 mm) from top of cylinder head. Intake valve guide length is 2.13" (54 mm) and exhaust guide is 2.32" (59 mm) long. After installing, ream guide for proper clearance.

VALVE SPRINGS

Removal — Using suitable compressor, compress valve spring and remove retainer locks (keepers). Release compressor and remove spring retainer, spring, valve stem oil seal and spring seat. Remove valves and keep in order. Check spring squareness, free height and tension at installed height. Spring should be square within .079" (2 mm).

Installation — Insert valve into valve stem guide, and install valve spring seat, valve spring, valve stem oil seal and valve spring retainer onto valve stem. Compress valve spring using suitable valve spring compressor and install valve spring retainer locks. Make sure retainer locks seat properly in valve stem groove.

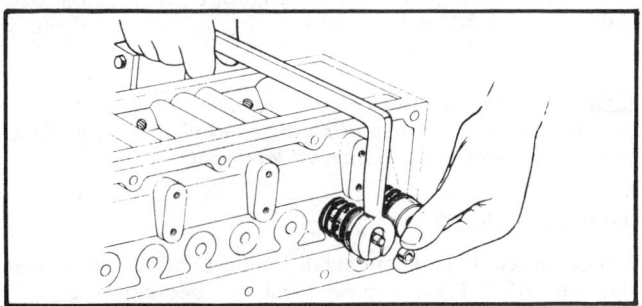

Fig. 4   Removing and Installing Valve Springs

ROCKER ARM ASSEMBLY

1) Check rocker arms and shaft for damage or wear. If clearance is excessive, replace bushing and ream to provide a clearance of .0007-.0015" (.017-.037 mm). When replacing bushing make sure oil hole in bushing lines up with oil hole in rocker arm.

2) Install rocker arms, springs and rocker shaft supports onto valve rocker shaft, then install valve rocker shaft lock springs.

NOTE — *There are two types of rocker arms and two types of rocker supports. Rocker support with oil hole is installed in the fourth position. Boss of rocker supports should face forward.*

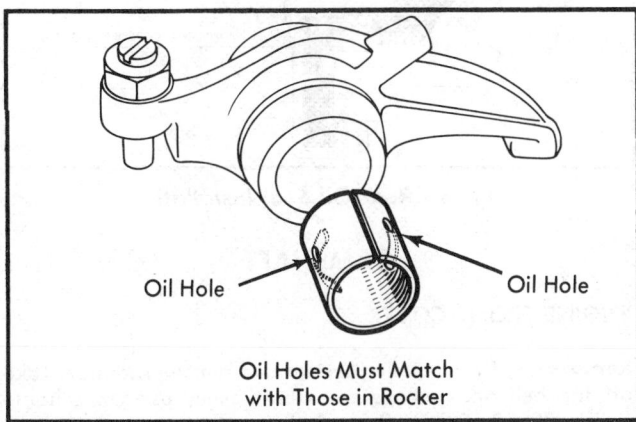

Oil Hole   Oil Hole

Oil Holes Must Match
with Those in Rocker

Fig. 5   Rocker Shaft Bushing Alignment

VALVE CLEARANCE ADJUSTMENT

1) Set No. 1 piston at TDC of compression stroke and align timing mark with pointer. Adjust valves 1,2,3,5,7 and 9 (as numbered from front).

2) Rotate crankshaft one complete turn and again align timing mark with pointer. Adjust remaining valves 4,6,8,10,11 and 12.

Valve Clearance Specifications	
Valve	**Clearance (Hot) In. (mm)**
Intake	.008 (.20)
Exhaust	.014 (.35)

PISTONS, PINS & RINGS

OIL PAN

Removal — Remove engine undercovers, and remove flywheel side and undercover. Remove front propeller shaft. Drain oil, remove oil pan attaching bolts and oil pan.

Installation — Thoroughly clean all gasket mating surfaces. Apply liquid sealer onto both oil pan gasket surfaces, install oil pan and tighten bolts. Reverse removal procedure for remaining components.

PISTON & ROD ASSEMBLY

Removal — With cylinder head and oil pan removed, remove connecting rod caps and remove bearings. Push piston and rod assembly up through cylinder block. Mark all components with cylinder numbers for correct reassembly.

NOTE — *Cover rod bolts with a short piece of hose during removal and installation to prevent damage to crankshaft.*

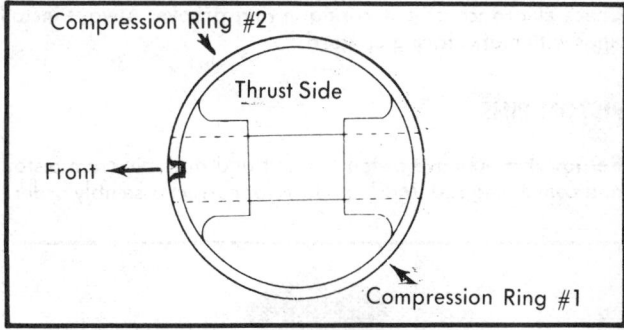

Compression Ring #2

Thrust Side

Front ←

Compression Ring #1

Fig. 6   Piston Ring Gap Spacing

Installation — Lubricate piston and rings and position ring gaps as illustrated. Use a ring compressor and install piston/rod assembly in proper position. Notch on piston must face FRONT and Toyota trademark on rod should face REAR. Oil hole in rod will face right (camshaft) side. Install bearings and caps.

NOTE — *Check for smooth rotation of crankshaft after tightening each bearing cap.*

FITTING PISTONS

1) Measure cylinder bores and pistons to be fitted. Measure piston with micrometer at bottom of skirt at right angles to piston pin. If clearance exceeds specifications, replace piston.

Toyota Engines

2F 6-CYLINDER (Cont.)

2) If cylinder bore is worn or tapered beyond specifications, cylinder must be bored and oversize pistons installed. Oversize pistons are available in .020" .040" and .060" (.50, 1.00 and 1.50 mm).

Cylinder Bore Specifications	
Application	Wear Limits In. (mm)
Standard Bore	3.701-3.703 (94.00-94.05)
Bore Wear Limit	.008 (.20)
Taper	.0008 (.020)
Difference Between Cyls.	.002 (.05)

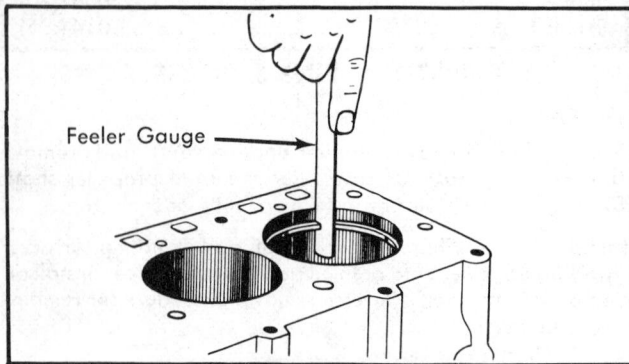

Fig. 7   Measuring Ring End Gap

3) Use .001-.002" (.03-.05 mm) feeler gauge with pull scale to check clearance of oversize pistons. Force of 2.2-5.5 lbs. (1.0-2.5 kg) must not be exceeded when pulling feeler gauge from cylinder.

4) Measure piston ring gaps in cylinder. If cylinder has not been bored, check gap with ring in lowest part of cylinder. Check clearance of piston ring in ring groove. Always install rings with marks facing upward.

PISTON PINS

Removal — Remove piston pin bolt and push pin from piston and connecting rod. Mark all parts for correct assembly order.

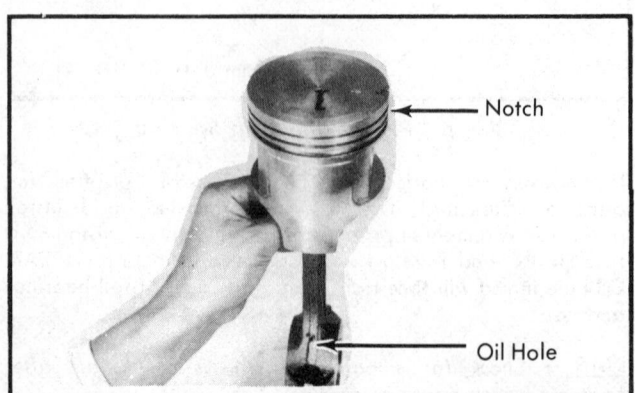

Fig. 8   Piston and Rod Assembled Properly

Installation — Position piston and connecting rod so that when notch on top of piston faces forward, oil hole in connecting rod faces camshaft side. Push pin into assembly and

center pin in piston. Center connecting rod between piston pin bosses and tighten piston pin bolt.

CRANKSHAFT MAIN & CONNECTING ROD BEARING

MAIN & CONNECTING ROD BEARINGS

1) Thoroughly clean crankshaft and blow out oil passages with compressed air. Check crankshaft for runout with a dial indicator on second or third main bearing journal. If runout exceeds .004" (.10 mm), straighten or replace crankshaft.

2) Check main and connecting rod bearing journals for taper or out-of-round. If taper or out-of-round exceeds .0004" (.01 mm), crankshaft must be ground to next undersize.

3) Main and connecting rod bearing clearance is checked by the Plastigage method. If clearance exceeds specifications, replace bearings. If crankshaft wear is excessive and clearance cannot be brought to specifications by use of new standard size bearings, crankshaft must be reground to next undersize. Bearings are available in .002", .010", and .020" (.05, .25, and .50 mm) undersize.

NOTE — *All main bearings are different. No. 1 (Front) and No. 4 (Rear) have oil holes and must be installed toward block. Arrow on connecting rod cap must face front.*

THRUST BEARING

Check crankshaft end play at No. 3 main bearing. If clearance exceeds .012" (.3 mm), replace crankshaft bearings.

REAR MAIN BEARING OIL SEAL

To install oil seal without disassembling engine, pry out oil seal with a screwdriver. Use crankshaft rear oil seal replacer tool (09223-60010) to drive new seal into place.

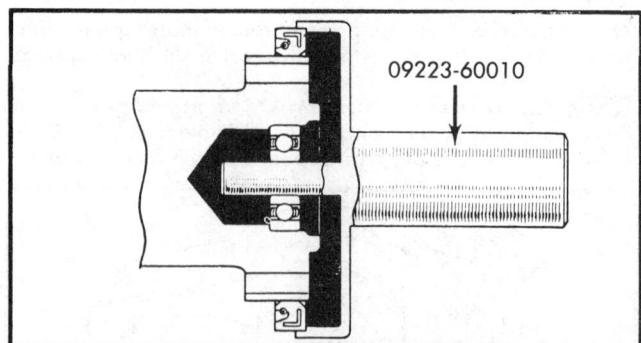

Fig. 9   Rear Oil Seal Installation

CAMSHAFT

ENGINE FRONT COVER

Removal — Drain cooling system and remove radiator. Take off fan belt and remove crankshaft pulley using a suitable puller (09213-60015). Remove timing gear cover bolts and take off cover.

2F 6-CYLINDER (Cont.)

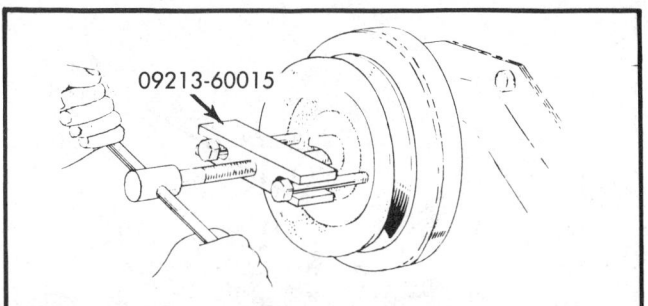

Fig. 10   Crankshaft Pulley Removal

09213-60015

Installation — Install cover and gasket. Ensure that bolts of proper length are used and screw in finger tight. Use liquid sealer on threads of lower 2 bolts. Drive pulley into position with suitable tool (09214-60010) to locate cover properly. Tighten cover bolts.

FRONT COVER OIL SEAL

Pry old oil seal out using screwdriver. Install new oil seal so that open end of seal is toward inside of timing gear cover. Drive seal in place with suitable tool (09515-35010).

Fig. 11   Front Oil Seal Installation

CAMSHAFT

Removal & Installation — Remove timing gear cover and slide oil slinger out from crankshaft. Remove 2 bolts retaining camshaft thrust plate to cylinder block by working through holes in camshaft timing gear. Remove camshaft by pulling out through front of block. Use care not to damage camshaft bearings or journals. To install, reverse removal procedure and set valve timing.

NOTE — *Ensure timing gear oil nozzle is positioned to direct oil onto timing gears. Stake into place with a punch.*

CAM LOBE HEIGHT

Measure height of cam lobe. If wear exceeds specification limit, replace camshaft. Intake lobe limit, 1.496" (38 mm); Exhaust lobe limit, 1.492" (37.9 mm).

CAMSHAFT BEARING

1) Inspect camshaft for runout. If runout exceeds .0059" (.15 mm), replace camshaft. Inspect camshaft journals and bearings for wear or damage. If clearance exceeds

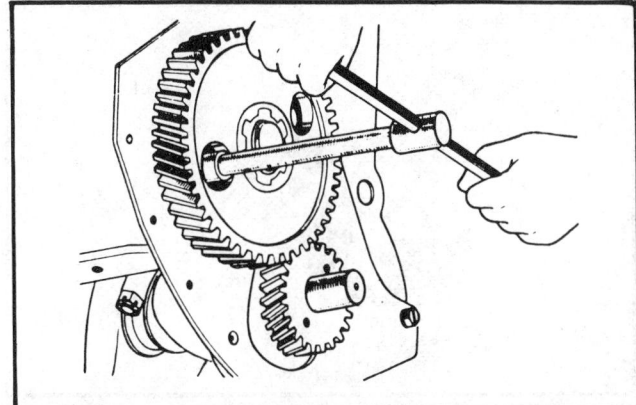

Fig. 12   Removing Crankshaft Thrust Plate Bolts

specifications, replace camshaft bearings and/or regrind camshaft. Bearings are available in standard .010" and .020" (.25 and .50 mm) oversizes.

2) Drive out camshaft rear expansion plug from cylinder block. Remove front and No. 2 bearing using Camshaft Bearing Remover (Tool 09215-60010). Place front and second bearing adapters against rear of respective bearing and place tool against front part of cylinder block.

3) Insert replacer shaft into the 3 parts and screw retainer nut onto replacer shaft. Hold slotted part of shaft with wrench to prevent shaft from turning. Front and No. 1 bearings will be pulled out to front by screwing in retainer nut with another wrench.

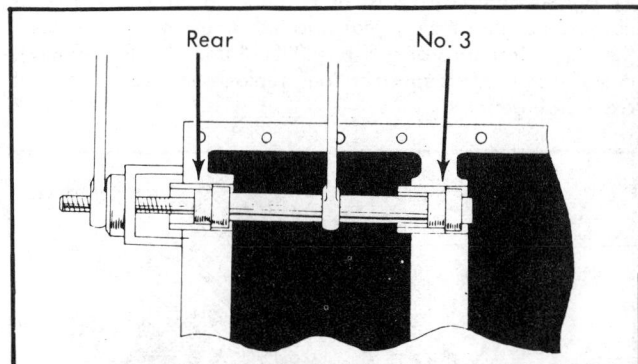

Rear   No. 3

Fig. 13   Typical Camshaft Bearing Removal Procedure (No. 3 and Rear Bearings Shown)

4) Remove No. 3 and rear bearing toward rear of block using tool in same manner as for front and No. 1 bearing. When installing new bearings, ensure that oil holes of bearing match up with oil holes in cylinder block.

5) When new bearings have been installed, measure to obtain proper clearance. Only a very light cut is required to ream bearings to proper size. Coat rear expansion plug with sealer and reinstall plug in block.

CAMSHAFT END THRUST

Measure end thrust with feeler gauge. Thrust should be .0079-.0103" (.200-.261 mm). If thrust exceeds .012" (.30 mm), replace camshaft thrust plate.

Toyota Engines

2F 6-CYLINDER (Cont.)

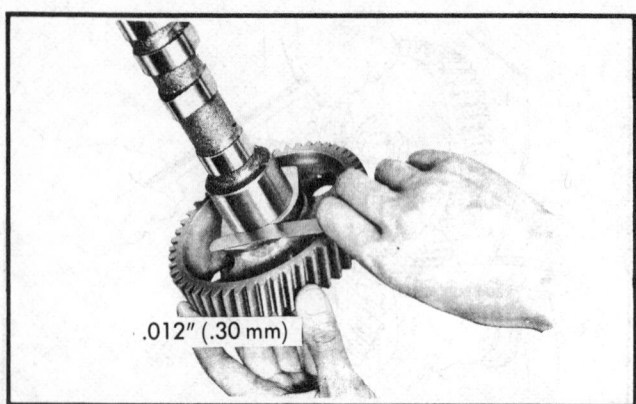

Fig. 14 Measuring Camshaft End Thrust

CRANKSHAFT TIMING GEAR

Remove pulley key from crankshaft. Using suitable puller (09213-60015), pull off crankshaft gear. To reinstall, drive on gear using suitable driver (09214-60010). Make sure timing mark on gear faces outward.

VALVE TIMING

1) With crankshaft timing gear installed, oil camshaft journals and bearings and insert camshaft. Align mating mark on camshaft timing gear with mark on crankshaft timing gear and push camshaft into position. No. 6 cylinder should be at TDC on compression stroke. If oil nozzle was removed, refit with oil hole facing down (toward gears).

2) Tighten camshaft thrust plate retaining bolts to specifications. Check that timing gear backlash does not exceed .008" (.20 mm). Standard backlash is .0020-.0047" (.050-.119 mm). If backlash exceeds specifications, replace both camshaft and crankshaft gears.

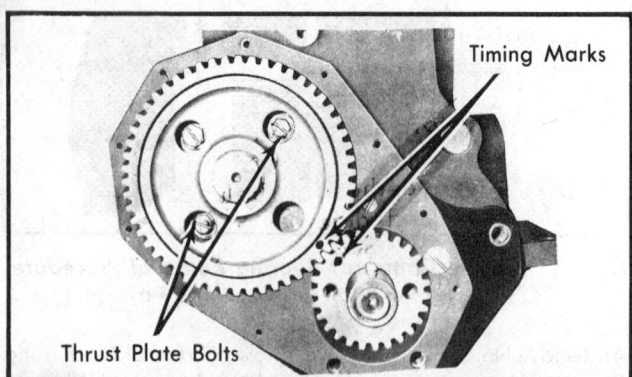

Fig. 15 Timing Mark Alignment

ENGINE OILING

Crankcase Capacity — 7.4 quarts (8.2 quarts with filter).

Oil Filter — Full flow cartridge type with integral relief valve.

Normal Oil Pressure — Pressure maintained at 50-64 psi (3.5-4.5 kg/cm²) by safety valve in oil pressure regulator.

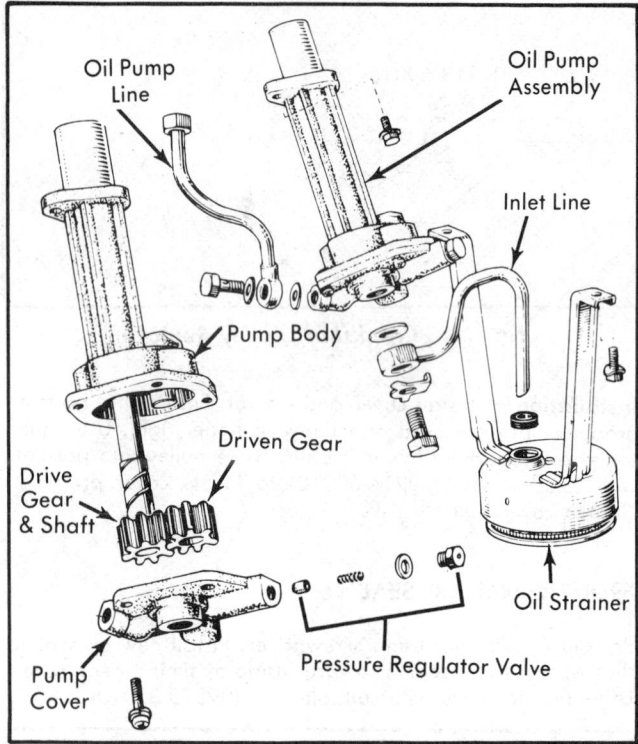

Fig. 16 Exploded View of Oil Pump Assembly

Pressure Regulator — Located in oil pump, non-adjustable.

ENGINE OILING SYSTEM

Force-feed system ensures positive lubrication through oil holes and galleries in engine block.

OIL PUMP

Removal — With oil pan removed, remove bolts attaching oil strainer to crankcase. Remove oil pump mounting bolt and oil pump line. Remove pump from engine. Remove cover and inspect gears and housing for proper clearances. Replace worn or damaged components.

Installation — Prior to installing assembled pump, check operation by submerging inlet line in fresh engine oil. Turn shaft clockwise with a screwdriver and check for oil flow from discharge hole. Cover discharge hole with thumb and turn as before. Turning resistance should be felt. Install pump on engine, noting that lower end of distributor drive shaft aligns with oil pump shaft. To complete installation, reverse removal procedure.

Oil Pump Specifications		
Application	Standard In. (mm)	Wear Limit In. (mm)
Gear-to-Housing Clearance	.0043-.0071 (.109-.180)	.008 (.20)
Gear Backlash	.0020-.0028 (.050-.071)	.0375 (.952)
Gear Side Clearance .	.0012-.0035 (.030-.088)	.0059 (.149)
Cover Wear		.0059 (.149)

Toyota Engines

2F 6-CYLINDER (Cont.)

ENGINE COOLING

Thermostat — Wax pellet type. Begins to open at 180°F (82°C) and is fully opened at 203°F (95°C).

Radiator Cap — 11-15 psi (75-1.05 kg/cm2).

Coolant Capacity — Approximately 16.9 quarts.

WATER PUMP

Removal — Drain cooling system and loosen alternator adjusting bar. Remove fan, fan pulley and fan belt. Remove lower radiator hose and heater hose from pump. Remove water pump retaining bolts, pump and gasket.

Installation — Ensure that mating surfaces are clean and free from pitting or damage. Install pump with new gasket and tighten mounting bolts. Complete installation in reverse sequence of removal and adjust belt tension.

ENGINE SPECIFICATIONS

GENERAL SPECIFICATIONS

Year	Displ. cu. ins.	Displ. cc	Carburetor	HP at RPM	Torque (Ft. Lbs. at RPM)	Compr. Ratio	Bore in.	Bore mm	Stroke in.	Stroke mm
1981	257.9	4230	1x2-Bbl.	125@3600	200@1800	8:3:1	3.70	94	4.00	101.6

VALVES

Engine & Valve	Head Diam. In. (mm)	Face Angle	Seat Angle	Seat Width In. (mm)	Stem Diameter In. (mm)	Stem Clearance In. (mm) ①	Valve Lift In. (mm)
4230 cc Intake	1.81 (46.0)	45.5°	45°	.055 (1.4)	.3138-.3144 (7.970-7.985)	.0012-.0024 (.030-.060)	.....
Exhaust	1.48 (37.5)	45.5°	45°	.067 (1.7)	.3134-.3140 (7.960-7.975)	.0016-.0028 (.040-.071)	.....

① — Wear limits: Intake — .004" (.10 mm), exhaust — .005" (.12 mm).

PISTONS, PINS, RINGS

Engine	PISTONS Clearance In. (mm)	PINS Piston Fit In. (mm)	PINS Rod Fit In. (mm)	RINGS Rings	RINGS End Gap In. (mm)	RINGS Side Clearance In. (mm)
4230 cc	.0012-.0020 (.034-.050)	.0003-.0005 (.008-.012)	Locked in Rod	No. 1	.0079-.0157 (.200-.398)	.0012-.0028 (.030-.071)
				No. 2	.0079-.0157 (.200-.398)	.0008-.0024 (.020-.060)
				Oil	.0074-.0197 (.200-.500)	.0016-.0075 (.040-.190)

CRANKSHAFT MAIN & CONNECTING ROD BEARINGS

Engine	MAIN BEARINGS Journal Diam. In. (mm)	MAIN BEARINGS Clearance In. (mm)	MAIN BEARINGS Thrust Bearing	MAIN BEARINGS Crankshaft End Play In. (mm)	CONNECTING ROD BEARINGS Journal Diam. In. (mm)	CONNECTING ROD BEARINGS Clearance In. (mm)	CONNECTING ROD BEARINGS Side Play In. (mm)
4230 cc No. 1	2.6367-2.6376 (66.972-66.996)	.0008-.0017 (.020-.044)	No. 3	.002-.006 (.06-.16)	2.1252-2.1260 (53.98-54.00)	.0008-.0024 (.020-.060)	.004-.009 (.11-.23)
No. 2	2.6957-2.6967 (68.472-68.496)						
No. 3	2.7548-2.7557 (69.972-69.996)						
No. 4	2.8139-2.8148 (71.472-71.496)						

Toyota Engines

2F 6-CYLINDER (Cont.)

ENGINE SPECIFICATIONS (Cont.)

VALVE SPRINGS			
Engine	Free Length In. (mm)	PRESSURE (LBS.) Lbs. @ In. (kg @ mm)	
		Valve Closed	Valve Open
4230 cc	2.028 (51.5)	71.7@1.693 (32.5@43.0)	.....

CAMSHAFT			
Engine	Journal Diam. In. (mm)	Clearance In. (mm)	Lobe Lift In. (mm)
4230 cc No. 1	1.8810-1.8888 (47.777-47.975)	.001-.003 (.025-.075)	.....
No. 2	1.8289-1.8297 (46.455-46.475)		
No. 3	1.7699-1.7707 (44.955-44.975)		
No. 4	1.7108-1.7116 (43.455-43.475)		

TIGHTENING SPECIFICATIONS

Application	Ft. Lbs. (N·m)
Camshaft Thrust Plate Bolts	8-11 (11-15)
Connecting Rod Bearing Caps	35-54 (48-73)
Crankshaft Main Bearing Caps	
No. 1 - No. 3	91-108 (124-147)
No. 4	76-94 (103-128)
Crankshaft Pulley	116-144 (158-196)
Cylinder Head	84-97 (114-132)
Flywheel Bolts	58-79 (79-107)
Manifold Nuts	29-36 (39-49)
Piston Pin Bolt	40-50 (54-68)
Rocker Arm-to-Cyl. Head	
8 mm Bolt	15-21 (20-29)
10 mm Bolt	22-32 (30-44)

5M-E 6-CYLINDER

ENGINE CODING

ENGINE IDENTIFICATION

Engine number is stamped on a machined pad on the right side of engine block. Engine code is also printed on a sticker attached to cylinder head cover.

Engine Identification	
Application	**Code**
Cressida & Supra (2563 cc)	5M-E

ENGINE, CYLINDER HEAD & MANIFOLDS

ENGINE

Removal — 1) Disconnect battery and drain cooling system. Remove hood and fan shroud. Remove radiator hoses, radiator, heater hoses and all oil cooler hoses. Remove oil pressure sending wire and alternator wiring.

2) Remove air cleaner and air intake ducting. Disconnect brake booster vacuum hose. Disconnect distributor primary wiring and coil secondary wiring. Label and disconnect all fuel lines, vacuum hoses and electrical wiring running between engine and engine compartment.

3) Disconnect starter wiring and accelerator connecting rod. If equipped with manual transmission, disconnect clutch flexible hose from master cylinder tube and cap hose end to prevent fluid leakage. On all models, disconnect power steering feed hose.

4) Raise front and rear of vehicle with jack and support on stands. Disconnect exhaust pipe from manifold and remove exhaust pipe supports and insulator. Disconnect speedometer drive cable and back-up light wiring.

5) On manual transmission models, remove console box and gear shift lever. On automatic transmission models, remove connecting rod swivel nut and disconnect control rod from shift lever.

6) On all models, remove propeller shaft and plug rear of transmission to prevent oil leakage. Take off rear engine undercover and remove front engine mounts. Support transmission with jack and remove rear engine mount and crossmember.

7) Lower jack supporting transmission and remove stands. Using an engine hoist, remove engine and transmission assembly from vehicle.

Installation — To install, reverse removal procedure and note the following: Check all fluid levels and linkage adjustments prior to starting engine.

INTAKE MANIFOLD

Removal — 1) Disconnect battery and drain coolant. Remove air cleaner and distributor cap. Remove radiator inlet

hose and heater hoses. Disconnect temperature gauge sending wire and fuel line.

2) It is necessary to remove air intake chamber with throttle body prior to intake manifold removal. Mark all vacuum, coolant and fuel hoses for identification and disconnect from air chamber. Disconnect intake connector, cold start injector, throttle link and throttle wire for automatic transmission. Remove mounting bolts and lift air chamber off of manifold.

3) Disconnect fuel injection wiring connectors and remove wiring clamps. Remove 4 bolts and pull out fuel delivery pipe with injectors. Remove pressure regulator at center of manifold, EGR valve, and disconnect remaining hoses. Remove mounting bolts and lift off manifold.

CAUTION — *When disconnecting delivery pipe and injectors, use container to catch the large amount of gasoline which will be expelled.*

Installation — Thoroughly clean all gasket surfaces and install new gaskets. Install manifold assembly and gradually tighten bolts working from center out. Install remaining components in reverse of removal procedure.

NOTE — *When installing injectors, lubricate "O" rings and insulators with gasoline.*

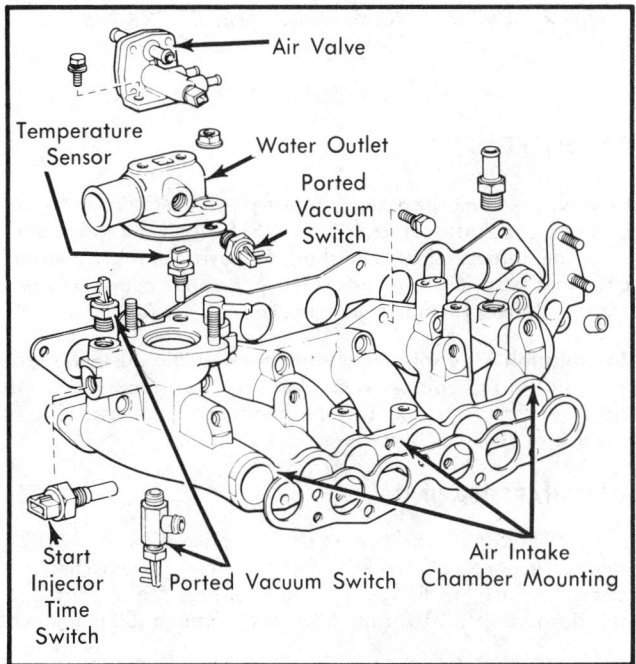

Fig. 1 Toyota 5M-E Intake Manifold Assembly

CYLINDER HEAD & ROCKER ARMS

Removal — 1) Remove intake and exhaust manifolds. Remove heater and by-pass hoses attached to head. Remove spark plugs and cylinder head cover. Turn crankshaft so that number 1 piston is at TDC on firing stroke and note that mating marks are aligned on timing gear and timing chain.

5M-E 6-CYLINDER (Cont.)

NOTE — *If timing is over 4 degrees BTDC, replace timing chain.*

2) Remove chain tensioner, then remove timing gear bolt noting that bolt has *LEFT* hand threads. Loosen head/rocker shaft bolts a little at a time in reverse of tightening sequence illustrated. Lift off rocker arm assembly, then lift head straight up from block.

Installation — Clean all gasket surfaces and apply sealer to cylinder head, around oil holes in the block, and in area of timing chain cover and block. Install new gasket. Clean all foreign matter from bolt holes and place cylinder head on block. Make sure valve adjusting screws have been loosened and install rocker shaft assembly. Install bolts and tighten in several steps according to the sequence illustrated. Align timing marks and reverse removal procedure to complete assembly.

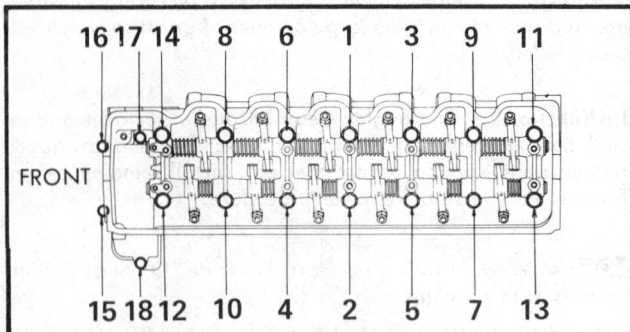

Fig. 2 Cylinder Head/Rocker Arm Bolt Tightening Sequence (Loosen in Reverse Order)

CAMSHAFT

CAMSHAFT

Removal — Remove rocker arm assembly. *See Cylinder Head.* Remove camshaft sprocket bolt (LEFT hand threads) and separate sprocket from camshaft. Remove camshaft bearing caps and keep in order for assembly. Remove camshaft from head and check for maximum runout of .0024" (.060 mm).

Installation — Lubricate camshaft bearing journals and place camshaft in position. Assemble bearing caps in original positions with arrow marks toward front. Complete assembly in reverse of removal procedure.

CAMSHAFT BEARINGS

Inspect bearings for wear or damage. Check that oil clearance does not exceed .004" (.10 mm). When checking clearance, use Plastigage method. Bearings are available in standard, .002", .010" and .020" (.05, .25 and .50 mm) oversizes.

CAMSHAFT END THRUST

Install camshaft in cylinder head and tighten all bearing caps. Attach dial indicator and check end thrust at flange end. Maximum clearance is .012" (.3 mm). Specified standard clearance is .003-.007" (.08-.18 mm).

CAM HEIGHT

Measure cam height. Minimum for intake is 1.696" (43.08 mm). Minimum for exhaust is 1.699" (43.15 mm). If height is less than specified, replace camshaft.

ENGINE FRONT COVER

Remove crankshaft damper attaching bolt and remove damper using suitable puller (09213-41013). Remove oil pan and remove front cover bolts and front cover. Use liquid sealer on front cover gaskets when assembling.

ENGINE FRONT COVER OIL SEAL

Inspect oil seal lip and replace if worn or damaged. Pry old seal out without damaging cover or retainer. Install seal using replacer tool (09223-50010). Apply multipurpose lubricant to seal lip.

TIMING CHAIN

Removal — After performing procedures set forth in Step **1)** in Valve Timing procedure, remove cylinder head cover, rocker arm shafts and camshaft. Remove cylinder head. Remove crankshaft damper attaching bolt and remove damper using puller. Remove oil pan, timing chain cover and timing chain.

Installation — **1)** Inspect chain, sprockets and tensioner. Position crankshaft sprocket so that key is pointed straight toward cylinder head and Toyota mark is in line with pump sprocket shaft. Install timing chain with white links aligned with punchmarks on crankshaft gear and pump gear. See Fig. 3.

NOTE — *Do NOT confuse index marks. Plated or white links align with punch marks on gears. Toyota symbol marks align with each other.*

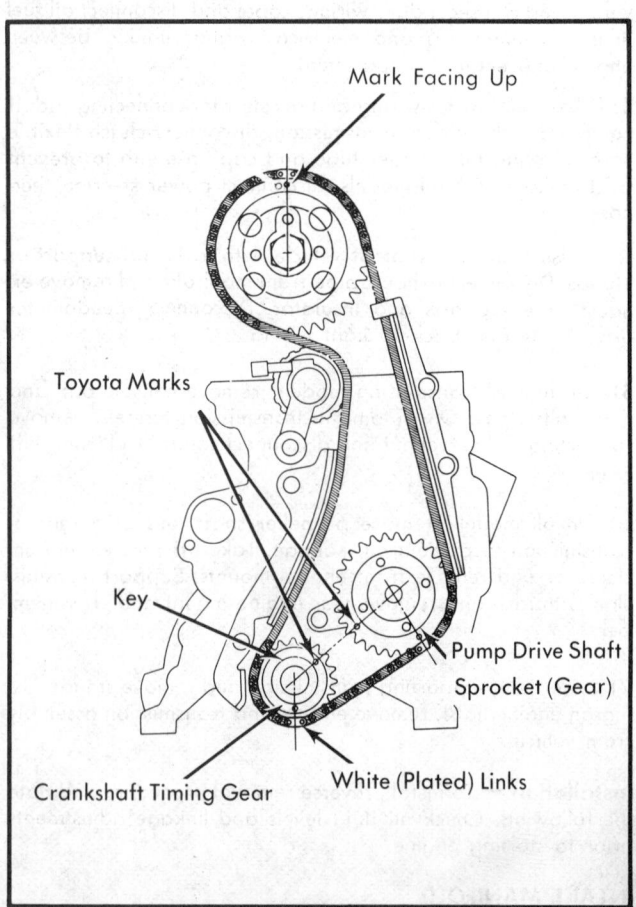

Fig. 3 Timing Chain with Pump Sprocket and Crankshaft Marks Aligned

5M-E 6-CYLINDER (Cont.)

2) Insert bolt in collar and install both chain vibration dampers and guide. With head and camshaft in position, assure that camshaft flange pin is aligned with embossed mark on rocker support number 1. Align mating link on chain with punch mark on camshaft drive gear and install drive gear on camshaft. Note that attaching bolt has LEFT hand threads.

3) Adjust timing chain tension by first rotating engine in normal direction (clockwise) until chain is at most slack position. Loosen tensioner locknut, then turn adjusting screw clockwise until resistance is felt. Loosen screw 2 full turns and tighten lock nut. If chain is noisy after starting engine, loosen adjusting screw ½ turn more. See *Valve Timing*.

OIL PUMP SHAFT

1) With front cover and timing chain removed, use puller (09213-36010) to remove pump shaft sprocket. Remove thrust plate bolt and pull pump shaft from cylinder block. Replace and tighten sprocket on shaft, then check end play between gear and plate with feeler gauge. If beyond limits, replace thrust plate.

2) Check bearing bore diameter with inside micrometer and journal diameter with outside micrometer. Standard clearance is .0010-.0026" (.025-.066 mm). If clearance exceeds .0031" (.08 mm), replace bearings with special tool (09233-41010).

Oil Pump Shaft Specifications	
Application	**In. (mm)**
Out-of-Round & Taper Limit	.0004 (.01)
Thrust Clearance	
Standard	.002-.005 (.05-.13)
Wear Limit	.012 (.30)
Bearing Clearance	
Standard	.0010-.0026 (.025-.066)
Wear Limit	.003 (.08)

VALVE TIMING

1) Rotate crankshaft in normal direction (clockwise) so that number 1 piston is at TDC on compression stroke. Check that camshaft flange timing pin is aligned with embossed mark on rocker support. (Timing chain cover graduation should indicate 0° mark aligned with notch in pulley.)

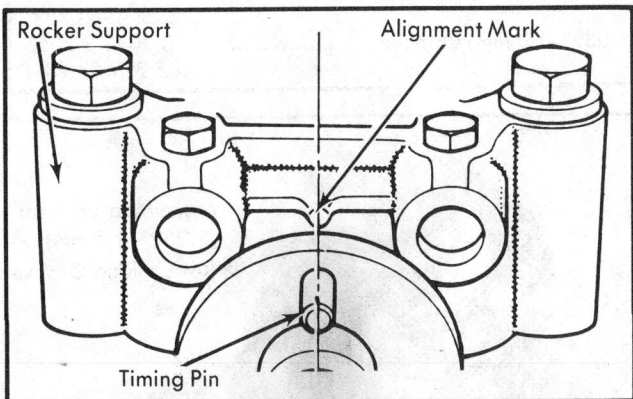

Fig. 4 Camshaft Flange Straight Pin Aligned with Support For Installation of Camshaft Gear

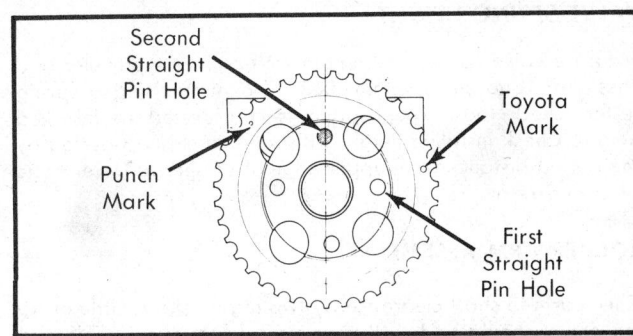

Fig. 5 Front View of Camshaft Gear with Alignment Marks and Straight Pin Holes

2) If marks are not as described, turn crankshaft until timing pin is in line with embossed mark and note timing cover graduation. Remove chain tensioner and timing gear set bolt. If timing was retarded 3 to 9 degrees, remove gear and install to second straight pin hole with piston at TDC. Install and adjust chain tensioner and recheck valve timing.

NOTE — *Movement of straight pin to No. 2 hole and No. 3 hole advances valve timing in steps of 6° each.*

VALVES

VALVE ARRANGEMENT

Left Side — All Intake.

Right Side — All Exhaust.

VALVE GUIDE SERVICING

1) Break off valve guide bushing at snap ring and remove snap ring. Heat cylinder head to approximately 176-212°F (80-100°C) and drive out bushing toward combustion chamber.

2) Allow head to cool and measure cylinder head bushing bore. If bore is .5118-.5224" (12.999-13.268 mm) use standard size valve guide. If bore measurement is in excess of .5224" (13.268 mm), use .05" (1.2 mm) oversize valve guide.

NOTE — *If cylinder head bore exceeds .5224" (13.268 mm), machine bore size to .5138-.5145" (13.050-13.068 mm).*

3) Measure installed height of .650" (16.5 mm) for intake guide and .551 (14 mm) for exhaust guide. Hand ream guide bore to provide specified stem clearance.

NOTE — *Valve guide replacement is recommended whenever new valves are installed.*

VALVE STEM OIL SEALS

Intake seals are slightly longer than exhaust valve seals and must not be switched. To install, assemble in order: plate washer, oil seal, inner and outer springs, and valve spring retainer. With suitable tool (09202-43011), install retainer locks.

VALVE & VALVE SPRING

Mark each valve and using valve spring compressor, remove valves, valve retainers, retainer locks, springs and valve stem oil seals. When replacing valve springs, closed coil ends face toward cylinder head.

Toyota Engines

5M-E 6-CYLINDER (Cont.)

VALVE SPRING HEIGHT

Measure valve spring free length with caliper type ruler and check for squareness within .063" (1.6 mm). Using a spring tester, check load when spring is compressed to installed height. Check installed height with valve in closed position by measuring distance from upper edge of washer to lower edge of spring retainer.

ROCKER ARM ASSEMBLY

Check arm-to-shaft clearance by twisting on shaft. Little or no movement should be felt. If movement is felt, disassemble and inspect. Bushings may be replaced and finished to give standard clearance of .0005-.0013" (.012-.033 mm) using pin hole grinder. Assemble rocker arm assembly, starting with rocker support number 1. Install on head and tighten bolts in sequence shown in Fig. 2.

NOTE — Disassemble and mark all parts for reassembly in proper order. Loosen adjusting screws and nuts prior to installing rocker arm assembly.

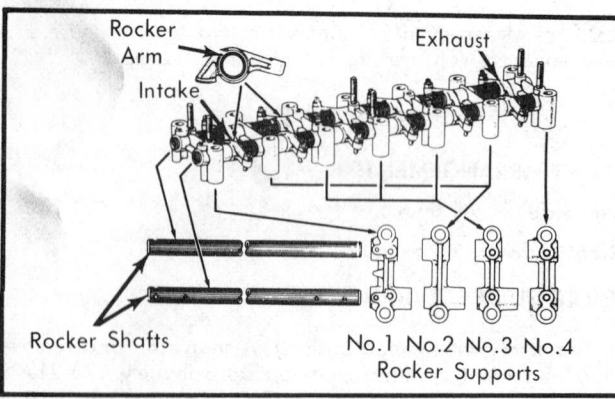

Fig. 6   Assemble Rocker Arm Assembly as Shown (Start with Rocker Support No. 1)

VALVE CLEARANCE ADJUSTMENT

NOTE — Before performing valve lash adjustment, ensure that engine is at normal operating temperature.

1) With No. 1 piston at TDC of compression stroke, adjust intake valves 1, 2, and 4, and exhaust valves 1, 3, and 5 to specified clearance.

2) Rotate crankshaft one turn (360°) clockwise and adjust intake valves 3, 5 and 6, and exhaust valves 2, 4 and 6.

Valve Clearance Specifications	
Valve	**In. (mm)**
Intake	.011 (.28)
Exhaust	.014 (.35)

PISTONS, PINS & RINGS

PISTON & ROD ASSEMBLY

Removal — With cylinder head and oil pan removed, remove connecting rod caps and remove bearings. Push piston

and rod assembly up through cylinder head side. Mark all components with cylinder numbers for correct reassembly.

NOTE — If there is a ridge at top of cylinder, remove by using a ridge reamer before removing piston and rod assembly.

Installation — 1) Apply oil to piston and piston rings. Install rings with mark on side of ring facing upwards. Position piston ring gaps shown in illustration. Using suitable ring compressor, install piston and rod assembly in cylinder block. Make sure mark on piston faces front.

2) Replace connecting rod caps with mating marks aligned. Tighten nuts evenly in 2 or 3 steps and check connecting rod side play.

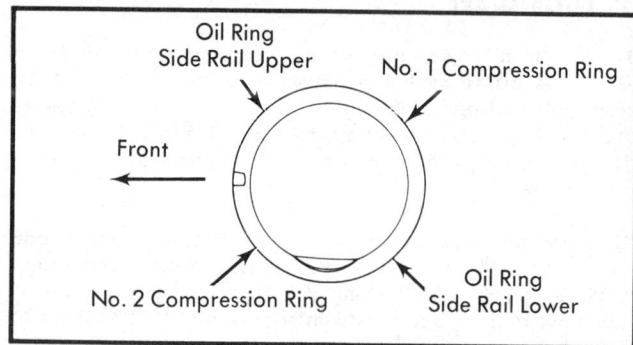

Fig. 7   Position Ring Gaps as Shown for Installation

FITTING PISTONS

Measure top, center and bottom of cylinder bore with dial indicator. If wear exceeds .008" (.20 mm) or taper and out-of-round exceeds .0008" (.020 mm), cylinders must be rebored. Bore in sequence number 1, 3, 6, 4, 2 and 5 cylinders. Last cut of boring bar should not remove more than .0020" (.050 mm). Finish to final dimension by honing the last .0008" (.020 mm).

Piston Diameter Table	
Application	**Piston O.D.** **In. (mm)**
Standard	3.2650-3.2669 (82.931-82.979)
.020" (.50 mm) Oversize	3.2846-3.2866 (83.428-83.479)
.030" (.75 mm) Oversize	3.2945-3.2965 (83.680-83.731)
.039" (1.0 mm) Oversize	3.3043-3.3063 (83.929-83.980)

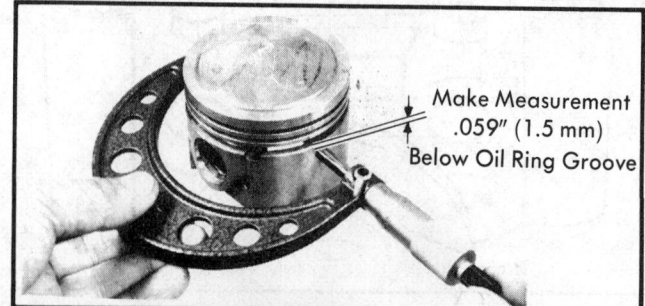

Fig. 8   Measure Piston as Shown at 68°F (20°C)

5M-E 6-CYLINDER (Cont.)

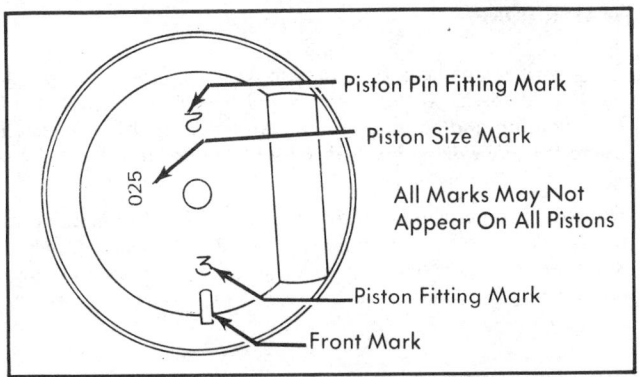

Fig. 9 Typical Reference Marks on Piston Head

NOTE — *Allow bore to cool after boring and honing to avoid erroneous readings while measuring. Cool measurement of piston and bore should provide .0020-.0028" (.05-.07 mm) for proper clearance.*

PISTON PINS

Removal — Remove circlips in piston pin hole with needle nose pliers. Heat piston to about 140°F (60°C) and remove pin by tapping lightly with plastic hammer. Keep piston, pin and rod together as a set.

Installation — Install one circlip in piston and heat to about 140°F (60°C). Align piston notch with rod mark and push pin in with thumb. Install remaining circlip.

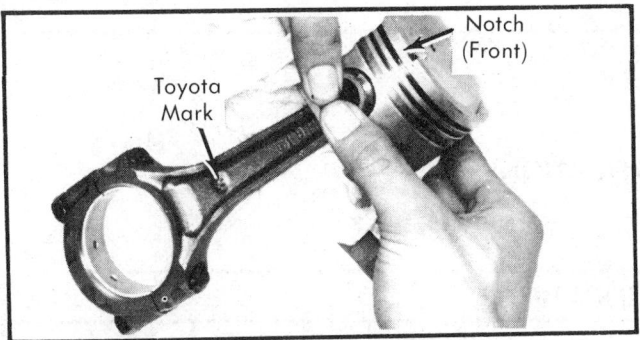

Fig. 10 Notch on Piston and Mark on Rod Must Face Same Direction When Installing Piston Pin

MAIN & CONNECTING ROD BEARINGS

1) Measure connecting rod side play with dial indicator. If greater than .012" (.30 mm), rod must be replaced. Wipe off bearing journal, then check clearance with Plastigage. If clearance exceeds .003" (.08 mm) and cannot be corrected with .002" (.05 mm) undersize bearings, or if taper or out-of-round exceeds .0008" (.020 mm), crankshaft must be ground to next undersize measurement.

2) Check crankshaft runout with dial indicator. If runout exceeds .0024" (.060 mm), correct or replace crankshaft. Check main bearing journal for taper and out-of-round. Check main bearing clearance using Plastigage. If required, crankshaft may be reground for undersize bearings. Undersize bearings for main and connecting rods are available in .002" (.05 mm), .010" (.25 mm) and .020" (.50 mm) as well as standard.

THRUST BEARING

Measure crankshaft end play with center (number 4) main bearing and cap installed. If clearance exceeds .012" (.30 mm), replace thrust washers to achieve standard clearance of .0020-.0098" (.050-.248 mm). Standard thickness of thrust washer is .115" (2.92 mm) with .005" (.13 mm) and .010" (.25 mm) oversizes available.

NOTE — *Install thrust washers with oil grooves facing outward*

REAR MAIN OIL SEAL

Inspect oil seal lip and replace if worn or damaged. Pry old seal out without damaging cover or retainer. Install seal using replacer tool (09223-41010). Apply multipurpose lubricant to seal lip.

ENGINE OILING

Pressure Relief Valves — There are 3 relief valves in the engine oiling system. The pressure relief valve in the oil pump opens at 71-85 psi (5.0-6.0 kg/cm²), the oil regulator valve-to-cooler opens at 38-50 psi (2.7-3.5 kg/cm²), and the relief valve in the filter opens with a pressure difference of 1-17 psi (.8-1.2 kg/cm²).

Oil Filter — Full flow spin-on type.

Crankcase Capacity — 4.9 qts. with filter, 4.3 qts. without filter.

ENGINE OILING SYSTEM

System is force feed with full-flow filtering unit. Pressure is delivered by a gear-driven oil pump. From filter oil travels through cylinder block passages by which internal components are lubricated. An external oil cooler is mounted at the upper left front of the radiator. It receives oil from the regulator mounted on the block, cools and returns the oil to the pan.

OIL PUMP

Removal — Remove oil pan, oil pump attaching bolts and remove oil pump. Disassemble pump by removing (in order) snap ring, spacer, drive shaft gear, Woodruff key, pump cover, pump shaft sub-assembly, driven gear, relief valve plug, gasket, spring and relief valve.

Inspection — After making proper clearance checks given in *Oil Pump Specifications Chart*, clean and inspect components and reverse disassembly procedure. Pump may be checked for operation by immersing screen in oil and turning shaft clockwise. Oil should discharge from pump outlet.

Installation — After inspection is finished, reverse removal procedure to complete reassembly and installation.

Oil Pump Specifications		
Application	**Standard In. (mm)**	**Wear Limit In. (mm)**
Body Clearance	.0012-.0024 (.030-.060)	.0079 (.20)
Gear Backlash	.020-.024 (.50-.60)	.035 (.88)
Side Clearance	.0012-.0035 (.030-.088)	.0059 (.149)

Toyota Engines

5M-E 6-CYLINDER (Cont.)

WATER PUMP

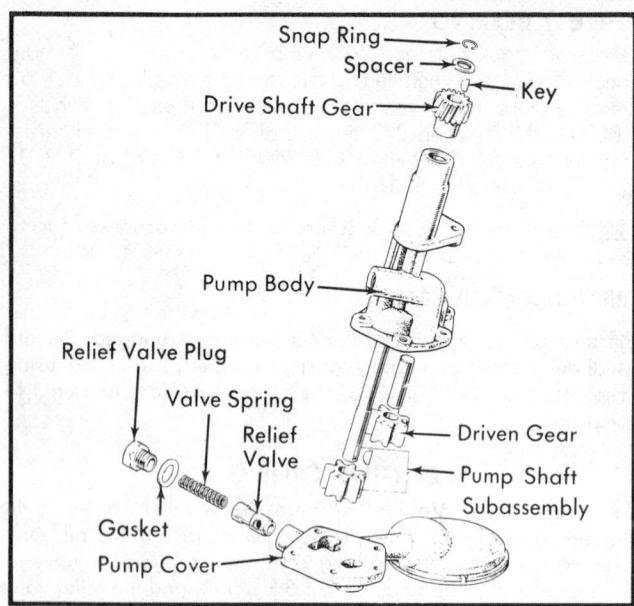

Fig. 11 *Exploded View of Gear Driven Oil Pump*

NOTE — *It is not necessary to remove complete water pump housing to service water pump. Pump cover may be removed from housing and housing may be left on cylinder block. Install pump to body with water drain hole facing down.*

Remove fluid coupling and fan assembly. Remove fan belt and pulley. Remove 5 cover bolts and take off cover assembly. Replaces seals and bearings as required. Use new gasket and reverse removal procedure.

ENGINE COOLING

Thermostat — Wax pellet type, begins to open at 176-183°F (80-84°C) and should open to more than .32″ (8 mm) at 203°F.

Radiator Cap — 12.8 psi (.9 kg/cm²).

Cooling Capacity — 11.6 quarts.

TIGHTENING SPECIFICATIONS

Application	Ft. Lbs. (N·m)
Camshaft Bearing Cap	13-16 (18-22)
Camshaft Timing Gear (L.H. Thread)	47-54 (64-73)
Chain Tensioner	22-28 (30-38)
Connecting Rod Cap	31-34 (42-46)
Crankshaft Pulley	98-119 (133-162)
Cylinder Head	
8mm Bolts	11-15 (15-20)
10mm Bolts	55-61 (75-83)
Exhaust Manifold	13-16 (18-22)
Flywheel	51-57 (69-78)
Intake Manifold	10-15 (14-20)
Main Bearing Caps	72-78 (98-106)

ENGINE SPECIFICATIONS

GENERAL SPECIFICATIONS

Year	Displ. cu. ins.	Displ. cc	Carburetor	HP at RPM	Torque (Ft. Lbs. at RPM)	Compr. Ratio	Bore in.	Bore mm	Stroke in.	Stroke mm
1981	156.4	2563	Fuel Inj.	108 @ 4800	136@2400	8.5:1	3.15	80	3.35	85

VALVES

Engine & Valve	Head Diam. In. (mm)	Face Angle	Seat Angle	Seat Width In. (mm)	Stem Diameter① In. (mm)	Stem Clearance In. (mm)	Valve Lift In. (mm)
2563 cc Intake	.....	44.5	45°	.039 (1.0)	.3138-.3144 (7.970-7.985)	.0010-.0024 (.025-.060)	.....
Exhaust	.....	44.5	45°	.039 (1.0)	.3134-.3140 (7.960-7.975)	.0014-.0028 (.035-.070)	.....

① — Wear limit for intake — .004″ (.10 mm), exhaust — .005″ (.13 mm).

Toyota Engines

5M-E 6-CYLINDER (Cont.)

ENGINE SPECIFICATIONS (Cont.)

VALVE SPRINGS ①			
Engine	Free Length In. (mm)	PRESSURE Lbs. @ In. (kg @ mm)	
		Valve Closed	Valve Open
2563 cc Inner	1.77 (44.9)	14.1-17.2@1.49 (6.4-7.8@37.9)	.....
Outer	1.84 (46.9)	37.3-46.5@1.63 (17.1-21.1@41.4)	.....

① — If valve spring is out of square more than .063" (1.6 mm), replace spring.

CAMSHAFT			
Engine	Journal Diam. In. (mm)	Clearance In. (mm)	Runout In. (mm)
2563 cc	1.3378-1.3384 (33.979-33.995)	.0007-.0022 (.017-.057)	.0024 (.060)

PISTONS, PINS, RINGS						
	PISTONS	PINS		RINGS		
Engine	Clearance In. (mm)	Piston Fit In. (mm)	Rod Fit In. (mm)	Rings	End Gap In. (mm)	Side Clearance In. (mm)
2563 cc	.0020-.0028 (.050-.071)	.....	.0002-.0004 (.005-.011) Limit .0006 (.015)	No. 1 No. 2 Oil	.0039-.0110 (.10-.28) .0039-.0110 (.10-.28) .0079-.0200 (.20-.50)	.0012-.0028 (.03-.07) .0008-.0024 (.02-.09)

CRANKSHAFT MAIN & CONNECTING ROD BEARINGS							
	MAIN BEARINGS				CONNECTING ROD BEARINGS		
Engine	Journal Diam. In. (mm)	Clearance In. (mm)	Thrust Bearing	Crankshaft End Play In. (mm)	Journal Diam. In. (mm)	Clearance In. (mm)	Side Play In. (mm)
2563 cc	2.3617-2.3627 (59.988-60.012)	.0013-.0023 (.034-.058)	No. 4	.002-.010 (.05-.25)	2.0463-2.0472 (51.976-52.000)	.0008-.0021 (.021-.053)	.012 (.30)

Triumph Engines

TR7 4-CYLINDER

ENGINE CODING

ENGINE IDENTIFICATION

Engine number is stamped on cylinder head and may be seen by looking down between intake manifold branches. Number can be broken down as shown in the following example:

CK12345UCA

1st and 2nd Digits — "CV" denotes carbureted models.
"CK" denotes fuel injected models.

3rd through 7th Digits — Serial number.
Suffixes — "U" denotes Federal.
"UC" denotes California.
"A" denotes automatic transmission.

ENGINE, CYLINDER HEAD & MANIFOLD

ENGINE

Removal — 1) Disconnect battery and bottom radiator hose, allowing coolant to drain. Remove hood, radiator, air cleaner duct and air cleaner hot air hose. Disconnect heater hoses at firewall and brake booster vacuum hose at intake manifold. Disconnect vapor canister hoses from canister, cooling system expansion hose from thermostat housing and anti-run-on valve hose from intake manifold.

2) Disconnect all electrical leads, fuel lines, cables, and linkages from engine. Remove shift boot, release bayonet cap securing lever to transmission extension, and remove gearshift lever. Raise front and rear of vehicle and place on stands. Disconnect propeller shaft from transmission.

3) Disconnect wiring from transmission and remove exhaust downpipe from manifold. Disconnect speedometer cable and remove clutch slave cylinder. Remove nut securing the left-hand engine mount to the subframe. Remove complete engine torque strap assembly (if equipped), and disconnect wiring from starter. Release wiring harness from clutch housing clips. Remove clutch housing bolts necessary to remove clips, and release clutch hydraulic line.

4) Remove engine ground strap and hood lock from firewall. Relieve pressure from air conditioning system (if equipped) and disconnect hoses from compressor. Using a lifting sling with a 23" (58.4 cm) leg to rear lift eye and a 18" (45.7 cm) leg to front eye, raise hoist to remove weight of engine.

5) Disconnect right side engine mount and remove five bolts securing rear crossmember to body. Raise rear of vehicle. Hoist engine and remove left side engine mount. Continue raising engine and work it away from vehicle.

Installation — To install, reverse removal procedure.

INTAKE MANIFOLD

Removal — Disconnect battery ground cable. Drain cooling system, including cylinder block. Remove air ducts and air cleaner. Disconnect all hoses, wiring and control cables from intake manifold and fuel rail. Remove distributor cap. Remove 6 manifold attaching bolts. Lift off manifold and fuel rail as an assembly.

Installation — To install manifold, reverse removal procedure.

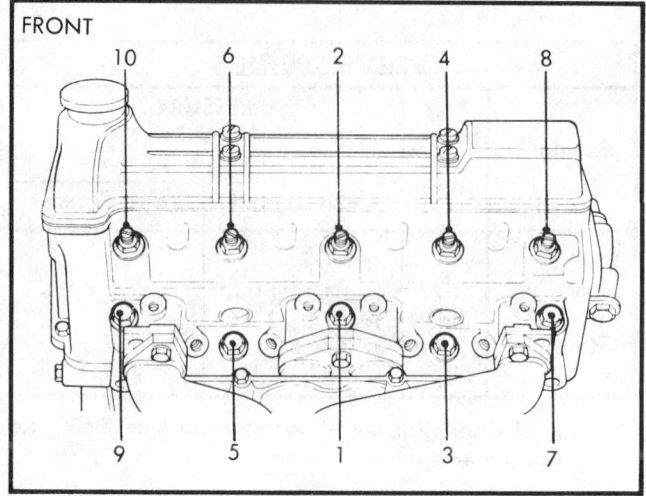

Fig. 1   Cylinder Head Tightening Sequence

CYLINDER HEAD

Removal — 1) Remove intake manifold. Then, remove camshaft cover and semi-circular grommet to gain access to camshaft sprocket nut. Crank engine until camshaft sprocket bottom bolt is accessible and remove bottom bolt. Anchor camshaft sprocket to support bracket. Crank engine so that timing mark on camshaft flange is in line with groove in camshaft front bearing cap and distributor rotor points to manifold rear attachment bolt hole in cylinder head.

2) Unlock and remove top sprocket retaining bolt. Disconnect air hose from air injection check valve and disconnect water pipe from thermostat housing. Disconnect exhaust pipe from manifold. Remove the two cylinder head to timing cover nuts and bolts. Loosen cylinder head nuts and bolts in reverse order of tightening sequence. See *Fig. 1*. Remove cylinder head complete with exhaust manifold.

Installation — To install, reverse removal procedure and tighten bolts to specification in sequence shown in *Fig. 1*.

CAMSHAFT

ENGINE FRONT COVER & OIL SEAL

1) Disconnect battery and remove crankshaft pulleys after first loosening drive belts and removing cooling fan. Remove alternator and mounting brackets. If equipped, remove air pump, diverter valve, brackets, and air conditioning compressor strut.

2) Remove two bolts and nuts securing front cover to cylinder head. Remove four bolts securing compressor to engine and three compressor adjusting bolts (if equipped). Remove two front oil pan bolts. Remove front cover center attachment bolt and bottom left side bolt. Remove front cover and gaskets and pry out old seal.

3) Dip new seal in engine oil and with lip facing inward, tap in squarely into front cover until flush with cover. Install front cover on engine in reverse of removal procedure using new gaskets.

TR7 4-CYLINDER (Cont.)

NOTE — *Front oil seal may be replaced with front cover installed by first removing crankshaft pulleys and prying out old seal.*

CAMSHAFT

1) Disconnect battery and remove camshaft cover. Crank engine until camshaft timing mark is 180° from groove in camshaft front bearing cap. Unlock and remove exposed camshaft sprocket retaining bolt. Crank engine so that timing mark on camshaft flange is exactly in line with groove in camshaft front bearing cap. Secure sprocket to support bracket with a suitable nut.

2) Unlock and remove remaining sprocket retaining bolt. Evenly loosen camshaft bearing cap nuts and remove bolts and washers. Check that bearing caps are numbered for identification and remove caps. Remove camshaft. To install, reverse removal procedure making sure timing marks are correctly aligned.

INTERMEDIATE SHAFT

1) Disconnect battery and remove fresh air duct, radiator, air conditioning condenser (if equipped), engine front cover, intake manifold, water pump cover and impeller, fuel pump, and camshaft cover. Crank engine so that timing mark on camshaft flange is in line with groove on front bearing cap. See *Fig. 3*. Remove distributor cap, and check that rotor points to last intake manifold bolt hole in cylinder head, indicating No. 1 piston is at TDC.

2) Remove the distributor, hydraulic chain tensioner and adjustable timing chain guide. Remove two Allen head screws and withdraw intermediate shaft keeper plate. Lift timing chain clear of sprocket and pull out intermediate shaft (complete with sprocket). Clamp intermediate shaft in a vise and remove sprocket retaining bolt, tab washer and sprocket. To install, reverse removal procedure, making sure valve timing is set correctly and adjusting timing chain tension.

TIMING CHAIN

1) Remove engine front cover, camshaft cover and distributor cap. Disconnect camshaft sprocket as described under *Camshaft Removal*. Make sure that camshaft timing marks are aligned when engine is TDC, No. 1 cylinder compression stroke. Remove hydraulic chain tensioner and guide plate.

2) Remove locking bolt from adjustable chain guide and common bolt securing adjustable guide and camshaft sprocket support bracket. Remove adjustable guide. Remove bolt securing camshaft support bracket and fixed guide while holding camshaft sprocket. Remove fixed guide and release chain from intermediate shaft and camshaft sprockets. Remove (upward) camshaft sprocket and bracket along with timing chain. To install, reverse removal procedure and check valve and intermediate shaft timing.

3) Set chain tension as follows: Insert a .100″ (2.54 mm) feeler gauge between chain slipper and tensioner body. See *Fig. 2*. Loosen three chain guide retainer bolts and press down on timing chain guide between camshaft and intermediate shaft sprockets until feeler gauge is a sliding fit. Hold guide in this

position and tighten adjustable guide bolt first, then two remaining bolts. Remove feeler gauge and continue reassembly.

VALVE TIMING

Crank engine until timing mark on crankshaft pulley coincides with zero mark on front cover scale. At this time, distributor rotor should point to rear bolt securing intake manifold to cylinder head and timing mark on camshaft flange is in line with groove in camshaft front bearing cap. To adjust timing it is necessary to remove timing chain. See *Fig. 3*.

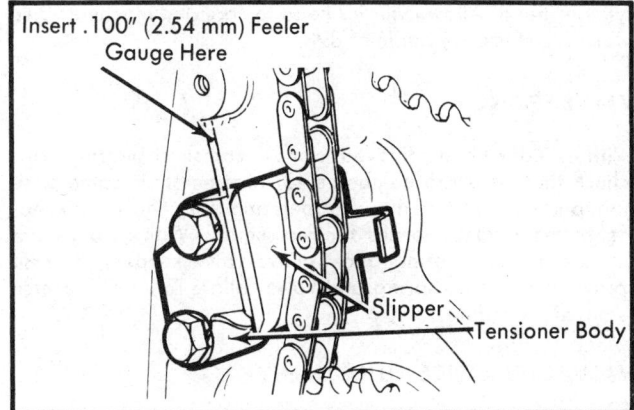

Insert .100″ (2.54 mm) Feeler Gauge Here

Slipper

Tensioner Body

Fig. 2 Adjusting Timing Chain Tension

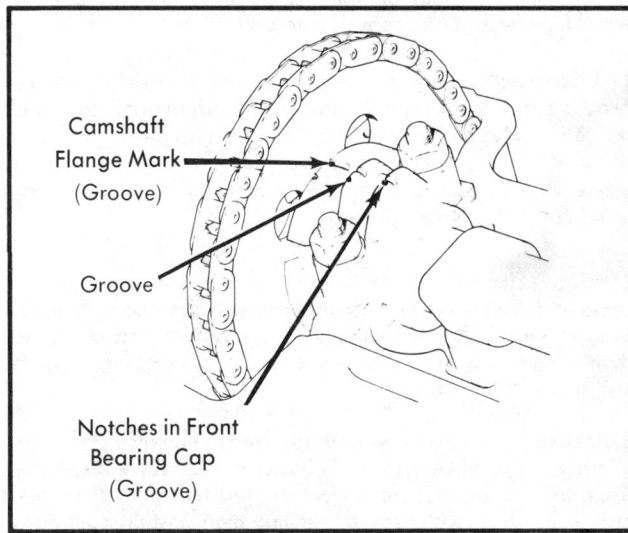

Camshaft Flange Mark (Groove)

Groove

Notches in Front Bearing Cap (Groove)

Fig. 3 Camshaft Timing Mark Alignment

VALVES

VALVE ARRANGEMENT

E-I-I-E-E-I-I-E (front to rear).

VALVE GUIDE SERVICING

1) Inspect valve guide wear by inserting a new valve, lifting it slightly from its seat, and rocking sideways. Movement of valve head across seat should not exceed .020″ (.508 mm).

2) If replacement is required, use valve guide removal and installation tool S-60A and adapters to remove and replace valve guide. After guides are installed, ream out guide using a .3130″ (7.95 mm) reamer.

TR7 4-CYLINDER (Cont.)

VALVE SEAT INSERT SERVICING

1) If valve seat inserts are too badly damaged to be refaced, replace inserts as follows: Machine-out existing inserts taking care not to damage insert bores in cylinder head. Machine intake valve seat bore to a diameter of 1.665-1.666" (42.29-42.32 mm) or exhaust valve seat bore to a diameter of 1.329-1.330" (33.75-33.78 mm).

2) Heat cylinder head uniformly to a temperature of 356°F (180°C) and immediately install new valve seats squarely into cylinder head. Allow cylinder head to cool and machine valve seats to an inclusive angle of 89°.

VALVE SPRINGS

With cylinder head removed, remove camshaft bearing caps (check that caps are numbered for reassembly in same position) and camshaft. Remove tappets and adjusting shims keeping them in correct order for reassembly. With spring compressor, depress spring and remove valve keepers. Release spring and remove spring and valve collar. To install, reverse removal procedure.

VALVE CLEARANCE ADJUSTMENT

NOTE — *This operation may be performed with cylinder head on the bench. When on the bench, turn camshaft using a wrench on hexagon at rear of camshaft.*

1) Disconnect battery and remove camshaft cover if cylinder head is installed on engine. Loosen camshaft bearing caps and retighten to specifications. Rotate camshaft or engine and check and record clearance of each valve using a feeler gauge between cam heel and tappet. Maximum clearance exists when cam lobe is straight up.

2) If all clearances are correct, adjustment procedure is completed. If any clearances are incorrect, proceed as follows: Remove camshaft and withdraw each tappet and adjusting shim where clearance requires adjustment, keeping tappets and shims in sequence.

3) Measure shim thickness and add measured valve clearance to arrive at total clearance. Subtract proper valve clearance from total clearance to determine needed shim thickness. Install tappets with correct shims then install camshaft. Recheck valve clearance and install camshaft cover.

Valve Clearance Specifications	
Application	**In. (mm)**
Intake	.008 (.2)
Exhaust	.018 (.5)

PISTONS, PINS & RINGS

OIL PAN

1) Disconnect battery and remove fresh air duct and fan shroud. Raise vehicle and drain engine oil. Remove two bolts securing coupling plate on bottom of oil pan to clutch housing. Remove engine torque strap assembly. Support front of engine using hoist or jack.

NOTE — *A bracket, made of angle iron, may be fabricated to bolt into lower timing cover bolt holes. Engine may then be supported by a jack via the fabricated bracket.*

2) Remove two engine right side mounting bolts, then remove left side engine mounting to sub-frame nut. Remove oil pan nuts and bolts. Raise engine sufficiently to enable oil pan, complete with left side engine mounting and cross-member to be removed. To install, reverse removal procedure.

PISTON & ROD ASSEMBLY

Connecting rods and rod caps are numbered. Note positioning and location before disassembly.

Removal — With oil pan and cylinder head removed, unscrew rod nuts and withdraw bearing caps. Place protective sleeves over rod bolts and push out rod and piston. Rotate crankshaft as necessary to gain access to piston and rod assemblies.

Installation — 1) Stagger piston ring gaps, lubricate pistons and rings and, using a ring compressor, place piston in cylinder bore, ensuring that raised flat portion of piston crown is toward right side of engine (viewed from driver's seat).

NOTE — *Some pistons may have arrows stamped on both sides of skirt, on the piston pin bore side, to indicate direction of pin off-set. Ensure that these arrows point to right side of engine also. Alternatively some pistons may have an arrow on the crown. These piston assemblies must be installed with arrow pointing to front of engine.*

2) Install bearing halves in connecting rod and cap and pull connecting rod onto crankpins. Install bearing caps to their respective numbered connecting rod making sure the bearing keeper recesses in connecting rods and caps are on the same side. Install new nuts and tighten.

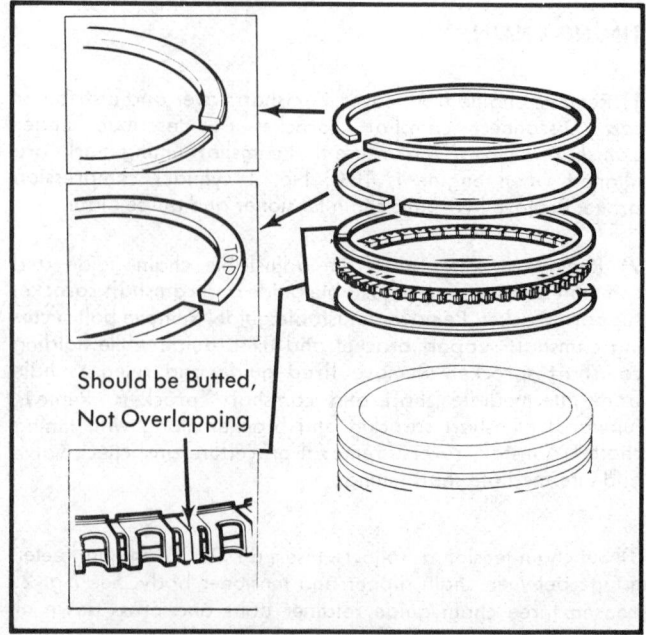

Should be Butted, Not Overlapping

Fig. 4 View Showing Correct Piston Ring Installation

TR7 4-CYLINDER (Cont.)

PISTON PIN REPLACEMENT

1) Remove circlips from pistons and extract piston pin. Separate piston from connecting rod. Inspect connecting rod bushing for wear and replace if necessary.

2) Using a press, remove worn bushing and install replacement. Ensure oil hole in new bushing is aligned with hole in connecting rod. Ream bushing to .9377-.9380" (23.818-23.825 mm)

FITTING PISTONS

Inspect and measure cylinder for wear or taper. Measure piston diameter and determine if clearance is correct. Install expanding ring in bottom groove of piston with ends butting but not overlapping. From bottom of piston install bottom rail and from top, upper rail. Install middle ring with word "TOP" facing upward. See *Fig. 4*. Install upper compression ring and stagger ring gaps.

NOTE — *Oversize rings are available in .010 and .020" (.254 and .508 mm) oversizes.*

CRANKSHAFT MAIN & CONNECTING ROD BEARINGS

MAIN & CONNECTING ROD BEARINGS

1) Remove engine and separate engine and transmission. Remove clutch, flywheel, engine rear adapter plate, oil pan and dipstick. Remove rear main bearing oil seal, timing chain cover, oil pickup screen and oil slinger. Remove crankshaft sprocket, drive key and shims.

2) Remove connecting rod bearing caps and slightly push up connecting rod assembly but do not dislodge it from cylinder. Remove upper and lower connecting rod bearings and install protectors over connecting rod bolts. Remove timing chain and main bearing caps. Lift out crankshaft. Remove pilot bushing, upper and lower main bearing inserts and thrust washers.

3) Examine all bearing journals and determine if regrinding is necessary. When regrinding crankshaft, do not grind journal diameter to less than specified minimum diameter. Examine each bearing half and replace any damaged bearings. Bearings are available in various oversizes. To install, reverse removal procedure making sure that grooves in thrust washers face outward.

Minimum Crankshaft Regrind Diameters	
Application	**In. (mm)**
Main Journal	2.0860-2.0865 (52.984-52.997)
Connecting Rod	1.7100-1.7105 (43.434-43.447)

CRANKSHAFT END PLAY

Using a feeler gauge or dial indicator, measure crankshaft end play by levering crankshaft back and forth. Value must be within specifications. If not, thrust washers are available in various oversizes.

REAR MAIN BEARING OIL SEAL

1) Disconnect battery and remove transmission, clutch and flywheel. Remove two rear oil pan bolts, loosen two right side rear and one left side rear oil pan bolts. Remove six bolts securing rear main bearing oil seal housing to crankcase. Press oil seal out of housing.

2) Lubricate outer diameter of new seal and press it squarely into housing with lip facing crankshaft. Clean gasket area and install new gasket using sealing compound. Lubricate crankshaft and carefully ease seal housing into position on two dowels. Install six retaining bolts noting that two lower bolts are longer. Evenly tighten bolts then install two pan bolts removed previously. Tighten all oil pan bolts and continue assembly in reverse of disassembly.

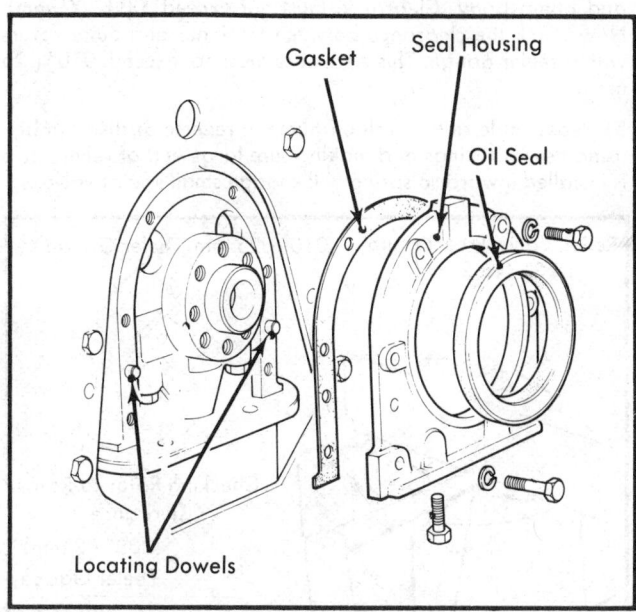

Fig. 5   Exploded View of Rear Main Bearing Oil Seal

ENGINE OILING

ENGINE OILING SYSTEM

Oil is drawn from engine by a rotor type pump which discharges via a nonadjustable relief valve to a full-flow filter. Cylinder bores, pistons and piston pins are splash lubricated. All other components are oiled through drilled passages.

Crankcase Capacity — 9.5 pts. (including filter).

Oil Filter — Full-flow, paper element type filter.

Oil Pressure Relief Valve — Nonadjustable.

OIL PUMP

NOTE — *Use care when removing slave cylinder that clutch release mechanism doesn't become dislodged. If mechanism does dislodge, transmission will have to be removed to repair it.*

1) Disconnect battery and raise vehicle. Remove 2 bolts securing clutch slave cylinder to clutch housing. Leave hydraulic line attached and wire slave cylinder out of way.

Triumph Engines

TR7 4-CYLINDER (Cont.)

2) Remove clutch housing nut and bolt, then remove four oil pump retaining bolts and washers. Remove pump from engine complete with hexagonal drive shaft. Remove "O" ring. To disassemble pump, first remove drive shaft. Remove two screws and lift off pump cover from body. Remove pump rotors and "O" ring. Remove cotter pin from pump body and pull out relief valve plug, spring and valve. Remove "O" ring from relief valve plug.

3) Clean all components and install rotors in pump body, ensuring that chamfered edge of outer rotor is at driving end of rotor pocket. Place a straight edge across pump body and with a feeler gauge check clearance between rotor and straight edge. This clearance should be .004" (.1 mm)

4) With a feeler gauge, check clearance between outer rotor and pump body. Clearance must not exceed .008" (.2 mm). Now check the clearance between the inner and outer rotors with a feeler gauge. This clearance must not exceed .010" (.25 mm).

5) Reassemble and install oil pump in reverse of disassembly, using new "O" rings and making sure large end of relief valve is installed inward so spring will engage small end of valve.

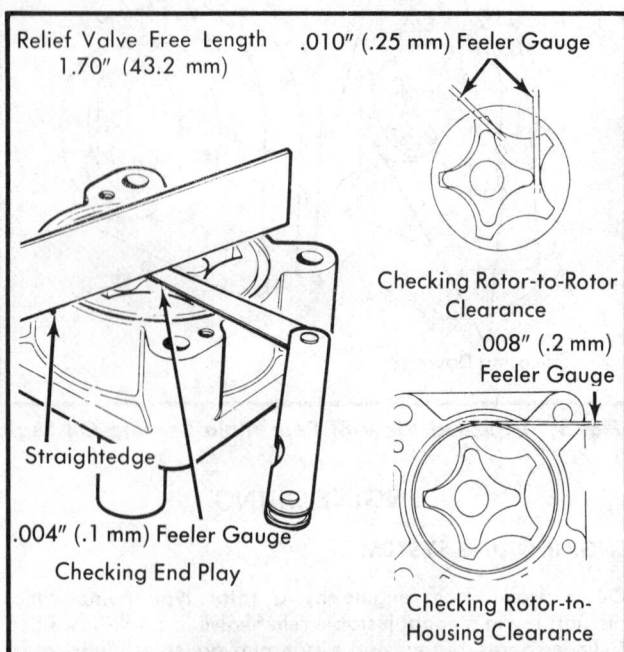

Fig. 6   View Showing Oil Pump Checking Points

ENGINE COOLING

WATER PUMP

1) Disconnect battery and remove intake manifold. Disconnect hoses from water pump cover and remove three bolts securing pump cover to engine. Lift off cover and gaskets. Turn impeller center bolt clockwise until either water pump is released from intermediate shaft drive gear and can be removed, or center bolt is removed. If center bolt comes out, use impact tool (4235A) and adapter (S4235A/10) to remove pump.

2) To overhaul pump, remove center bolt if not previously removed. Use a drift and support tool to remove impeller from shaft. Invert pump assembly (drive gear up) and drift shaft from housing. Remove "O" ring, graphite seal, water slinger, oil seal and circlip from pump shaft. Again invert shaft and drift shaft from bearing. Remove oil slinger. Remove "O" rings from housing.

3) To assemble, reverse disassembly procedure using new seals and "O" rings and noting the following: Make sure oil slinger dish is towards gear. Flat face of oil seal should face bearing. Dish of water slinger should be towards bearing. Install graphite seal with flat face towards bearing.

4) Place pump in housing. Make sure that pump and intermediate shaft gear mesh correctly and pump is seated properly. Clean gasket surfaces thoroughly, and temporarily install pump cover. Using feeler gauges, check that gap between pump cover and engine is equal. Equalize gap by adjusting bolts.

CAUTION — *Use of force or impact to seat pump will damage the pump and graphite seal.*

5) Select water pump cover gaskets to equal the gap noted in step 4) plus .010-.020" (.25-.5 mm) to provide running clearance. Remove pump cover, install selected gaskets, reinstall cover and tighten bolts to specifications. Complete installation in reverse of removal procedure.

Thermostat — Begins to open at about 190°F (88°C).

Cooling System Capacity — 15.5 pts. (including heater).

Radiator Cap — 15 psi (1.05 kg/cm²).

TIGHTENING SPECIFICATIONS

Application	Ft. Lbs. (N·m)
Camshaft Bearing Caps	14 (19)
Camshaft Sprocket Bolt	10 (14)
Connecting Rod Bolts	45 (61)
Crankshaft Pulley Bolt	120 (163)
Cylinder Head Bolts (Nuts)	50 (68)
Flywheel-to-Crankshaft	45 (61)
Idler Shaft Sprocket Bolt	38 (52)
Intake Manifold	20 (27)
Main Bearing Caps	65 (88)
Timing Chain Support Brackets & Guides	20 (27)
Timing Chain Tensioner-to-Block	9 (12)

ENGINE SPECIFICATIONS

GENERAL SPECIFICATIONS

Year	Displ.		Carburetor	HP at RPM	Torque (Ft. Lbs. at RPM)	Compr. Ratio	Bore		Stroke	
	cu. ins.	cc					in.	mm	in.	mm
1981 Fuel Injected	122	1998	Fuel Inj.	88.6@5000	105@4000	8.0:1	3.56	90.3	3.07	78.0

TR7 4-CYLINDER (Cont.)

ENGINE SPECIFICATIONS (Cont.)

VALVES							
Engine & Valve	Head Diam. In. (mm)	Face Angle	Seat Angle	Seat Width In. (mm)	Stem Diameter In. (mm)	Stem Clearance In. (mm)	Valve Lift In. (mm)
1998 cc Intake	1.560 (39.62)	45°	42.5°	.....	.3103-.3113 (7.881-7.907)	.0017-.0023 (.043-.058)	.....
Exhaust	1.280 (32.51)	45°	42.5°	.....	.3098-.3106 (7.87-7.89)	.0014-.0030 (.035-.076)	.....

PISTONS, PINS, RINGS						
	PISTONS	PINS		RINGS		
Engine	Clearance In. (mm)	Piston Fit In. (mm)	Rod Fit In. (mm)	Rings	End Gap In. (mm)	Side Clearance In. (mm)
1998 cc	.0005-.0015 (.013-.038)	0-.0004 (0-.010)	.0001-.0006 (.003-.015)	No. 1	.015-.025 (.39-.64)	.0019-.0039 (.048-.082)
				No. 2	.015-.025 (.39-.64)	.0015-.0025 (.038-.064)
				Oil	.015-.055 (.39-1.40)	Ends Butted

CRANKSHAFT MAIN & CONNECTING ROD BEARINGS							
	MAIN BEARINGS				CONNECTING ROD BEARINGS		
Engine	Journal Diam. In. (mm)	Clearance In. (mm)	Thrust Bearing	Crankshaft End Play In. (mm)	Journal Diam. In. (mm)	Clearance In. (mm)	Side Play In. (mm)
1998 cc	2.1260-2.1265 (54.000-54.013)	.0012-.0022 (.030-.055)	No. 3	.003-.011 (.08-.28)	1.7500-1.7505 (44.450-44.463)	.0008-.0023 (.020-.058)	.006-.013 (.15-.33)

VALVE SPRINGS			
Engine	Free Length In. (mm)	PRESSURE Lbs. @ In. (kg @ mm)	
		Valve Closed	Valve Open
1998 cc	1.60 (40.40)	.....	.....

VALVE TIMING				
	INTAKE		EXHAUST	
Engine	Open (BTDC)	Close (ABDC)	Open (BBDC)	Close (ATDC)
1998 cc	16°	56°	56°	16°

TR8 V8

ENGINE CODING

ENGINE IDENTIFICATION

Engine number is stamped on cylinder head on left side of engine and may be viewed by looking down between intake manifold branches. Codes are as follows:

Engine Identification Codes	
Application	**Engine Code**
Carbureted	
Federal	
Man. Trans.	10E00001A
Auto. Trans.	11E00001A
Calif.	
Man. Trans.	12E00001A
Auto. Trans.	13E00001A
Fuel Injection	
Man. Trans.	14E00001A
Auto. Trans.	15E00001A

ENGINE, CYLINDER HEAD & MANIFOLDS

ENGINE

NOTE — *Remove engine and transmission as an assembly.*

Removal — 1) Disconnect battery, drain coolant from radiator and engine block, and remove hood. Remove fresh air duct, alternator belt and alternator. If equipped, remove air conditioning compressor, leaving hoses attached. Tie compressor to one side.

2) Remove gear shift lever boot and flange assembly. On fuel-injected engines, remove airflow meter, disconnecting pipe at plenum chamber.

3) On carbureted engines, remove cold air inlet hose from temperature control valves. Remove valves. Remove hot air hoses from air boxes.

4) On all models, disconnect heater hoses at firewall. Disconnect throttle cable from throttle linkage. Disconnect brake servo hose at intake manifold plenum chamber. Release clips securing hose to air boxes.

5) On carbureted engines, disconnect float-chamber vent pipe and engine breather pipe from charcoal canister. Remove rubber cover from starter motor lead and remove lead from terminal.

6) Disconnect starter motor and alternator harness multi-plug, located near radiator expansion tank. Disconnect cooling system hoses from thermostat housing. Disconnect all electrical leads from ignition coil.

7) On carbureted engines, disconnect fuel inlet pipe at filter. On fuel injected engines, depressurize fuel system and disconnect inlet pipe from fuel rail.

8) Remove connector from cooling fan switch. Raise front of vehicle until bottom of radiator is approximately 3 ft. (.9 m) above floor. Support body on stands. Raise rear of car and support on stands. Drain engine oil.

9) Disconnect back-up light wires at multi-plug connector. Loosen muffler front joint and balance pipe clamps. Remove rear rubber "O" rings from brackets, and remove muffler and tailpipe assembly front down pipes.

10) Mark propeller shaft and transmission flange position. Remove 4 bolts and nuts securing propeller shaft drive flange to transmission drive flange. Remove speedometer cable clamp bolt and cable. Disconnect clutch slave cylinder hydraulic pipe from hose.

11) Remove clutch hose bracket from clutch housing. Remove intermediate steering shaft lower 2 bolts. Loosen lock nuts holding brake hoses to front suspension struts. Remove steering arm front bolt and both rear steering arm lower caliper bolts. Remove remaining caliper bolts and calipers.

12) Remove 6 nuts securing damper and spring assemblies to inner wing valances. Remove power steering pipe bracket from subframe. Drain power steering fluid, and seal all pipes and housing ports.

13) Lower rear of vehicle. Place jack under subframe and raise to take the weight. Fit an engine lifting harness to engine and raise with mobile hoist to support weight of engine.

14) Remove engine mounting bolts and nuts. Remove subframe nuts, lower rubber bushings and spacers. Lower the subframe and suspension assemblies and remove from vehicle. Remove steering intermediate shaft.

15) Place jack under transmission, supporting weight, and remove engine rear mounting crossmember from body. Lower engine and transmission assembly, and remove from beneath vehicle.

Installation — To install engine and transmission assembly, reverse removal procedure. Be sure to refill and bleed power steering system and to refill cooling system and crankcase.

CARBURETED INTAKE MANIFOLD

Removal — 1) Drain cooling system and remove fresh air duct. Disconnect top hose and expansion hose from thermostat housing.

2) Disconnect hose from diverter valve and brake servo hose from manifold nipple, releasing it from clips. Remove plug from cooling fan switch. Remove distributor vacuum pipe from left-hand carburetor and remove bolt and clip. Disconnect hose from back of distributor capsule.

3) Disconnect vacuum hose from right-hand carburetor (to EGR valve). Disconnect air cleaner interconnecting pipe from left-hand air cleaner box. Remove asbestos-wrapped EGR valve pipe completely. Disconnect engine breather hose from right-hand valve cover flame trap.

4) Disconnect float-chamber vent hose from canister and left-hand carburetor. Unclip spark plug leads from air cleaners.

TR8 V8 (Cont.)

Disconnect air temperature control valve from both air cleaners. Disconnect throttle cable from carburetor linkage, and remove kickdown cable bracket (vehicles with automatic transmissions).

5) Disconnect heater hoses from front and rear of manifold. Disconnect coolant temperature sensor lead. Disconnect purge air filter line from left-hand valve cover and remove filter from clip. Disconnect main fuel line filter and release front clip.

6) Disconnect carburetor countershaft link rod from left-hand carburetor by moving sleeves outward. Remove 12 intake manifold bolts and lift off manifold complete with carburetors and air cleaners.

7) Clean outside of manifold gasket, making sure all coolant is removed. Remove front and rear gasket clamps, and lift off and discard gasket and gasket seals. Clean threads of manifold bolts.

Installation – 1) Apply silicon grease to each side of new gasket seals. Install seals in position, with ends engaged in notches formed between cylinder heads and block.

2) Apply Hylomar PL 32M sealing compound (or equivalent) to 4 corners of new gasket, on cylinder head side around area of water passage joints. Fit gasket with word, "FRONT" towards front of engine. Fit gasket clamps in place, but do not fully tighten clamp bolts.

3) Apply sealing compound to manifold side of gasket as in step 2). Locate intake manifold in position on cylinder heads. Coat intake manifold bolt threads with thread lubricant-sealant (3M EC 776 or equivalent). Install bolts, tightening evenly, beginning at the center and working outward. Tighten gasket clamp bolts.

4) Reverse remaining removal procedures to complete installation.

FUEL INJECTION INTAKE MANIFOLD

Removal – 1) Drain cooling system and remove fresh air duct. Disconnect top hose and expansion hose from thermostat housing. Remove plenum chamber, airflow meter and extra air valve.

2) Disconnect pipes and filters from manifold, placing them to one side. Disconnect temperature switches, sensors and thermotime switch. Remove injectors.

3) Remove 12 intake manifold bolts and lift off manifold. Clean outside of manifold gasket, making sure any accumulation of coolant is removed. Remove 2 bolts and front and rear gasket clamps. Lift off clamps and discard gasket. Remove and discard gasket seals and clean threads of manifold bolts.

Installation – To install intake manifold and gasket, follow installation instructions for carbureted intake manifold.

CYLINDER HEAD

Removal – 1) Remove intake manifold and gasket. Remove spark plug leads from valve cover clamp. On carbureted models, move check valve aside and remove air temperature

control valve and hoses. Also remove heat chamber from exhaust manifold.

2) Remove dipstick tube bracket from left-hand valve cover. Remove dipstick and tube. Remove valve cover screws and lift off valve cover. Remove right-hand valve cover. Remove 4 bolts to remove each rocker shaft assembly. Remove push rods. Mark and disconnect leads from spark plugs.

3) Remove 3 bolts attaching air conditioning compressor to left-hand cylinder head and bolts attaching air pump and alternator mounting bracket to right-hand cylinder head. On left-hand head removals, remove exhaust manifold bolts to gain access to head bolts. On right-hand head removals, disconnect exhaust front pipe from manifold.

4) Loosen and remove 14 cylinder head bolts, reversing the tightening sequence. *See Fig. 1.* Lift off cylinder head (also exhaust manifold on right-hand head removal). Remove and discard gasket.

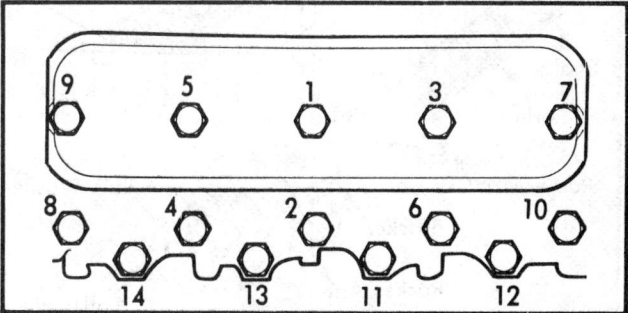

Fig. 1 Cylinder Head Bolt Tightening Sequence
(Loosen in Reverse Order Shown)

5) Wash and wire brush cylinder head bolts in solvent (3M No. 2 or equivalent) to completely remove sealant. Examine bolts and replace any with signs of thread damage or elongation. Never install bolts more than 4 times.

Installation – 1) Clean cylinder head and block mating surfaces. Install a new gasket with word, "TOP", up. DO NOT use sealant on gasket surfaces.

2) Position cylinder head over dowel pins in block. Coat threads of cylinder head bolts with lubricant-sealant (3M EC 776 or equivalent). Use various length bolts in proper locations, as follows:

Cylinder Head Bolt Locations	
Application	**Bolt Numbers**
Long bolts	Nos. 1, 3 and 5
Medium bolts	Nos. 2, 4, 6, 7, 8, 9 and 10
Short bolts	Nos. 11, 12, 13, and 14

3) After installing cylinder head bolts in the proper location, tighten bolts evenly and gradually in sequence shown in *Fig. 1.*

TR8 V8 (Cont.)

VALVES

VALVE ARRANGEMENT

E-I-E-I-I-E-I-E (both banks front to rear).

ROCKER ARM ASSEMBLY

Disassembly — Remove cotter pin from end of shaft and remove plain washer, wave washer, rocker arms, brackets and springs. See *Fig. 2*. Store components in correct sequence for reassembly.

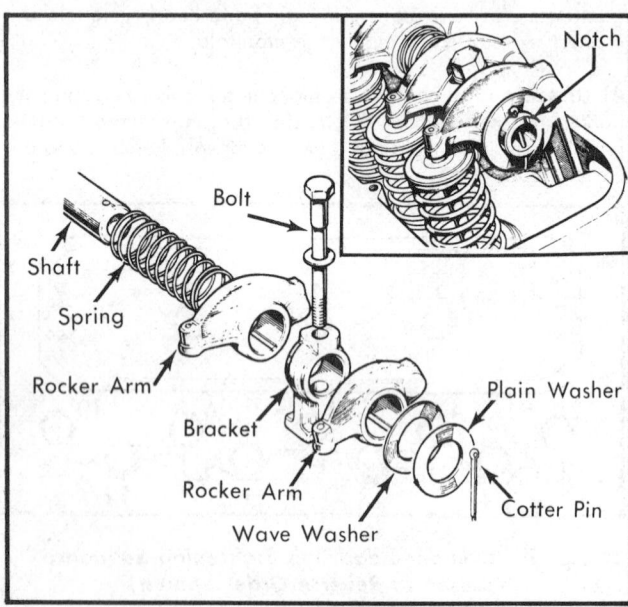

Fig. 2   Rocker Shaft Assembly Sequence (Inset Shows Notch on Shaft End)

Reassembly — 1) If new rocker arms are being installed, be sure to remove protective coating from each oil feed hole and push rod seat. Assemble plain washer against cotter pin in end of shaft. Install wave washer against plain washer.

NOTE — *Two different rocker arms are used and must be installed so that valve ends of arms slope away from brackets.*

2) Assemble rocker arms, brackets and springs in sets on rocker shaft. Compress springs and other components and install wave washer, plain washer and cotter pin in end of shaft.

3) Each rocker shaft is notched at one end and on one side only. The notch must be at top of shaft and toward front of the engine on right-hand side and toward rear of engine on left-hand side. See *Fig. 2*.

VALVE GUIDE SERVICING

1) Using a valve guide remover (274401), drive old guides out from combustion chamber side. Install specified spacer for valve guide drift (605774) on valve spring seat in top of cylinder head. See *Fig. 3*.

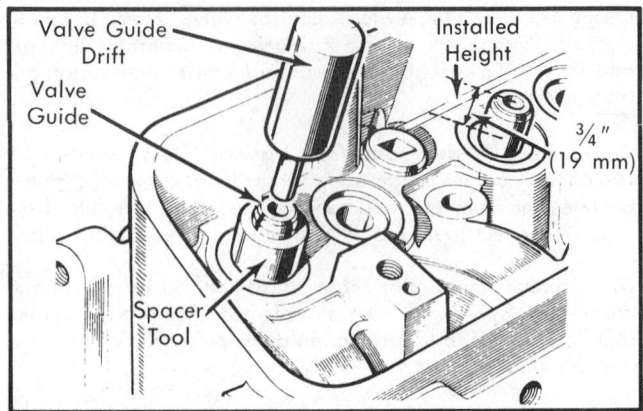

Fig. 3   Installing New Valve Guides

2) Lubricate new valve guide and insert into spacer. Using valve guide drift (600959), drive guide into cylinder head until drift bottoms against spacer. Installed guide should be ¾" (19 mm) above step surrounding valve guide boss.

NOTE — *Valve guides for service have an outside diameter .001" (.02 mm) larger than bore to provide an interference fit.*

VALVE SEAT INSERTS

1) Remove old seats, if necessary, by grinding them until thin enough to be cracked and pried out. Heat cylinder head evenly to approximately 150°F (65°C). Press new insert into recess in cylinder head.

NOTE — *Outside diameter of standard intake valve seat inserts is 1.6825-1.6838" (42.735-42.768 mm). Exhaust valve inserts are 1.4350-1.4545" (36.918-36.994 mm). Inserts for service are available in 2 oversizes, having .010" (.25 mm) and .020" (.50 mm) larger outside diameters.*

VALVE SERVICING

Removal — With cylinder heads removed, use valve spring compressor (276102 or equivalent) to remove valve locks. Keep components in proper order for later installation. Clean combustion chambers with a soft wire bush. Clean valves and valve guide bores. Regrind or install new valves, as necessary. If valves must be ground to a knife-edge to obtain a true seat, install new valves.

Installation — Lubricate valve stems and guides with engine oil. Insert each valve into its guide. Position valve springs on cylinder head (install new springs if compression tests prove springs are weak). Locate cap over top of spring. Compress spring with spring compressor (276102) and install valve lock. Install cylinder heads after rocker arm assembly and valves have been checked for proper assembly and ease of operation.

HYDRAULIC TAPPET SERVICING

1) Drain cooling system and remove fresh air duct. Remove intake manifold and valve covers. Remove rocker shaft assemblies. Remove push rods and keep in sequence for later installation. Remove tappets and store them with their respective push rods.

TR8 V8 (Cont.)

NOTE — *If tappets cannot be removed from bore, remove camshaft and remove tappet from bottom of bore.*

2) Inspect hydraulic tappets for blow holes or scoring. Replace if badly scored or grooved, or if blow hole would permit oil leakage from lower chamber. Some wear is permitted just above lower end of tappet body. This results from side thrust of cam against tappet body as tappet moves vertically in its guide.

3) Inspect cam contact surface of tappets. A round wear pattern is normal, as tappets rotate. A non-rotating tappet will have a square wear pattern, requiring tappet replacement. Be sure new tappets rotate freely in cylinder block before completing reassembly.

4) Install new tappets also if area of push rod contact is rough or otherwise damaged. Replace any push rods having a rough or damaged ball end seat.

NOTE — *Tappet noise is normal after an overhaul, due to oil drainage from tappet assemblies. If noise is excessive, run engine at 2500 RPM for a few minutes to eliminate noise.*

PISTONS, PINS & RINGS

OIL PAN

Removal — 1) Disconnect battery. Remove both cylinder heads and gaskets. Attach engine lifting brackets to second inboard cylinder head stud holes on each bank of block. Support engine weight (MS 53/3 supporting tool), so that 4 engine mounting nuts and bolts can be removed from subframe.

2) Raise engine about 1½" (38 mm). Raise vehicle and drain engine oil. Remove oil pan coupling plate bolts, oil pan bolts and oil pan. Remove oil pick-up strainer and oil pan baffle plate.

Installation — To install oil pan, reverse removal procedure.

PISTON & CONNECTING ROD ASSEMBLIES

NOTE — *Connecting rods and caps are not marked for reassembly reference. Be sure to mark caps for later reassembly to their respective rods. Also piston and rod assemblies must be marked for later assembly in their respective bores.*

Removal — Remove connecting rod caps. Screw guide bolts (605351) on to connecting rod bolts. Push connecting rod and piston assembly upward and remove from top of cylinder bore. Remove guide bolts.

Installation — 1) Position applicable crankshaft journal at BDC. Place upper bearing shell in connecting rod. Retain by screwing guide bolt (605351) on connecting rod.

2) Insert connecting rod and piston assembly into its respective bore. Dome-shaped bosses on connecting rods must face toward front of engine for right-hand bank of cylinders and toward rear of engine for left-hand bank. See Fig. 4. When connecting rods are installed, dome-shaped bosses will face each other.

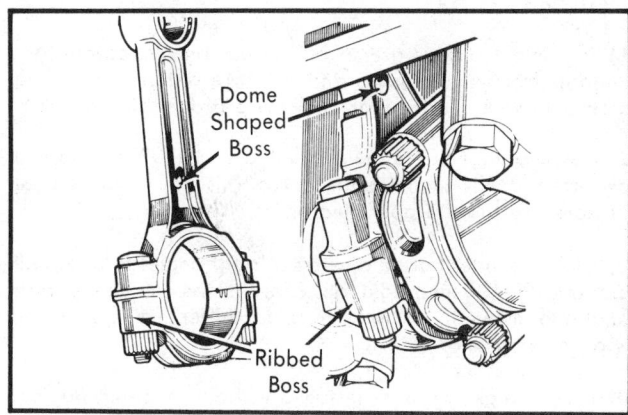

Fig. 4   Connecting Rod Positioning Marks

3) Position oil control piston rings so gaps are all on one side, between piston pin and thrust face. See Fig. 5. Ring rail gaps should be 1" (25 mm) to each side of expander ring gap.

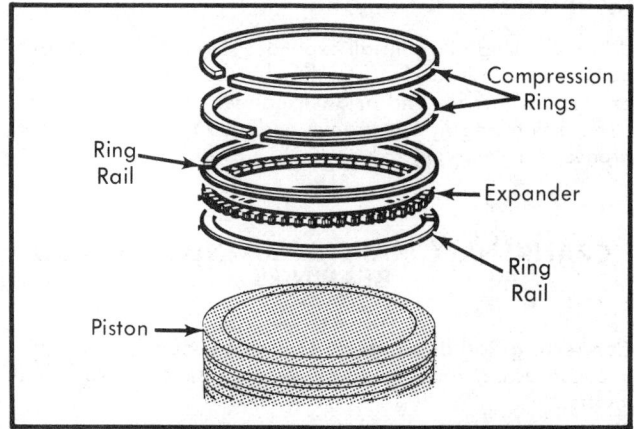

Fig. 5   Positioning Piston Rings

4) Position compression rings so their gaps are on opposite sides of piston, between piston pin and thrust face. Using a ring compressor, install piston and rod into its bore.

5) Install bearing lower shell into its connecting rod cap. Position cap and shell on its respective connecting rod, making sure ribbed edge of cap is toward front of engine on right-hand bank of cylinders and toward rear of engine on left-hand bank. See Fig. 4. Tighten connecting rod cap. Check for proper end play and free movement on crankshaft.

PISTON PINS

Removal & Installation — 1) Install piston and connecting rod on pressing tool (605350). Using a drift from tool set, press pin from piston and rod.

2) Locate piston pin guide on pressing tool (605350). Position piston and connecting rod on tool. Insert piston pin into piston and over guide. Position drift on piston pin and press pin in until it strikes shoulder of guide.

3) Make sure piston moves freely on piston pin and that no damage occurred during pressing. Install assemblies in their respective bores.

TR8 V8 (Cont.)

FITTING PISTONS

1) If original pistons are to be reused, remove carbon and deposits from ring grooves and compare piston and cylinder diameters with specifications to assure proper clearances.

2) If new pistons are to be installed, a single .001" (.025 mm) oversize piston is available for service. This may require honing of bore to obtain proper clearances.

3) Check cylinder bore diameters at right angles to piston pin 3.5-4.0" (90-100 mm) from top. Check piston diameter at right angles to piston pin at bottom of skirt. Difference in diameters is piston clearance.

4) If new rings are to be installed without reboring, deglaze cylinder walls in a cross-hatch pattern so as not to increase bore diameter. Install compression rings in cylinder bore to check end gaps. Also install compression rings in their respective grooves (chrome ring in top groove, stepped ring in second groove), and check clearance in grooves.

PISTON RINGS

When installing rings, install expander ring in bottom groove, making sure ends touch each other, but do not overlap. Install one ring rail above and below expander ring. Install chrome compression ring in top groove and stepped ring in second groove, with marking "T" or "TOP" upward.

CRANKSHAFT MAIN & CONNECTING ROD BEARINGS

Connecting Rod Bearings — 1) Position upper bearing shell into connecting rod and install on its respective crankshaft journal.

NOTE — *Make sure rod is correctly installed as outlined in steps **2)** and **5)** of PISTON & CONNECTING ROD ASSEMBLIES.*

2) Install Plastigage (605238) across center of lower half of crankshaft journal. Install bearing on connecting rod cap and install cap to rod. Do not rotate crankshaft while Plastigage is installed.

3) Compare Plastigage reading with specified bearing clearance. If wear limit is exceeded, install new bearings.

Crankshaft Main Bearings — 1) With oil pan removed, remove bolts retaining main bearing caps 2, 3 and 4 complete with upper and lower bearing shells. Inspect caps, bearing shells and crankshaft journals for damage.

NOTE — *Do not remove all 5 main bearing caps at once, since weight of crankshaft would distort front and rear oil seals. Only caps 2, 3 and 4 are identified by number. Keep upper and lower bearing shells together as matched sets.*

2) Using Plastigage method, check main bearing clearances and replace bearings as necessary. Check crankshaft journals for out-of-round. If more than .0015" (.038 mm), grind crankshaft to next undersize or replace crankshaft.

3) Install upper bearing shell 3 (thrust bearing) to cylinder block. Upper shells have central oil hole and must be lubricated prior to installation. *See Fig. 6.* Install with locking slot end trailing. Then, install upper shells 2 and 4 in same manner.

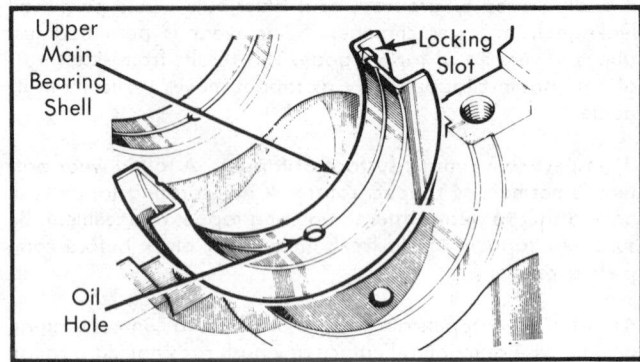

Fig. 6 Installing Upper Main Bearing Shell

4) Assemble lower shells to bearing caps, lubricate and install. Be sure all locking slots are together on right-hand side of engine. Tighten main bearing caps 2, 3 and 4 to specifications.

5) After main bearings 2, 3 and 4 have been checked and either reinstalled or replaced, remove main bearing caps 1 and 5 complete with lower bearing shells. Remove upper bearing shells. Discard main bearing side seals.

NOTE — *Main bearings 1 and 5 should be checked for proper clearance, using Plastigage method. Check crankshaft journals for damage and out-of-round in same manner as for bearings 2, 3 and 4.*

6) Install front upper bearing shell (with central oil hole) and place lower bearing shell in main bearing cap 1. Install to cylinder block. Be sure locking slots are together on right-hand side of engine. Tighten to specifications.

REAR MAIN BEARING & OIL SEAL

NOTE — *Oil seal is replaced with engine-transmission assembly removed, permitting removal of crankshaft. Seal may also be replaced with engine installed, by removing transmission, clutch and flywheel.*

1) With other 4 main bearing caps installed, install upper bearing shell in cylinder block. Install new side seals to rear main bearing cap. *See Fig. 7.* Do not cut seals to length, but permit them to extend ⅝" (1.5 mm) above bearing cap face.

2) Apply Hylomar PL 32M sealing compound (or equivalent) to rearmost half of rear main bearing cap or its cylinder block mating surface. Lubricate bearing half and side seals with clean engine oil.

3) Install rear main bearing cap snugly, but not completely, making sure it is squarely seated on cylinder block. Back off each main bearing cap bolt 1 turn.

4) Position seal guide (RO 1014) on crankshaft flange. Be sure oil seal guide and crankshaft journal are completely clean. Coat seal guide and oil seal journal with clean engine oil.

TR8 V8 (Cont.)

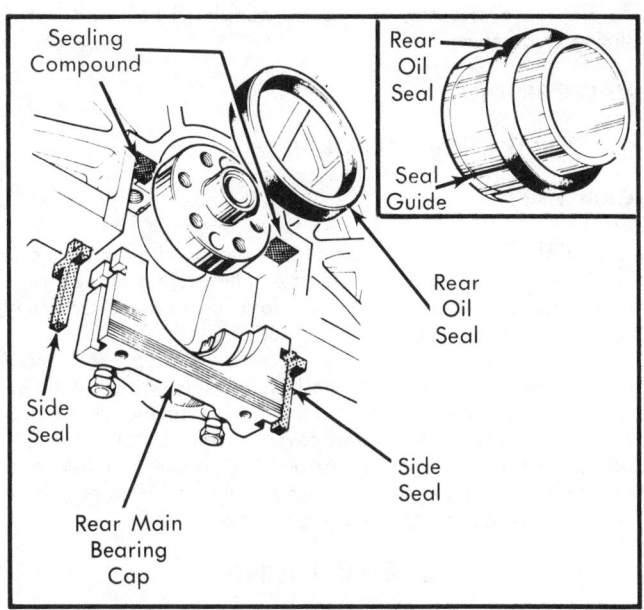

Fig. 7   Installing Rear Main Bearing Cap With Oil Seals

NOTE — *Be sure lubricant covers entire outer surface of oil seal guide, preventing lip from turning back during assembly. Do not handle oil seal lip at any time.*

5) Place oil seal on seal guide with lipped surface toward engine. By hand, push oil seal fully and squarely into recess formed in bearing cap and cylinder block, until it is seated against machined step in recess. Remove seal guide.

6) Tighten rear main bearing cap to specifications and check crankshaft end play. Complete reassembly or installation of engine-transmission assembly.

CAMSHAFT

TIMING GEAR COVER

NOTE — *If not equipped with air conditioning, disregard references to such components.*

Removal — 1) Disconnect battery, drain cooling system and turn crankshaft so No. 1 cylinder is at TDC. Remove crankshaft pulleys, alternator drive belt tension strap and radiator bottom hose (from water pump). Remove air intake left-hand hose on carbureted engines to gain access to power steering bolts. Remove power steering pump.

2) Disconnect electrical lead from oil pressure switch. On carbureted models, loosen air pump belt tension and remove air pump and belt. Disconnect heater inlet hose from water pump and outlet hose from rear of timing gear cover. Remove water pump.

3) Remove electrical leads from distributor, ballast resistor and coil. Remove distributor cap and set it aside. Disconnect vacuum pipe from distributor capsule. Remove top radiator hose from thermostat housing.

4) Remove timing gear cover bolts and single nut and washer. Remove 2 bolts securing oil pan to cover. Loosen 2 adjacent oil

pan bolts. Remove timing gear cover, complete with distributor, oil pump and filter. *See Fig. 8.* Remove gasket. Clean bolt threads with solvent (3M No. 2).

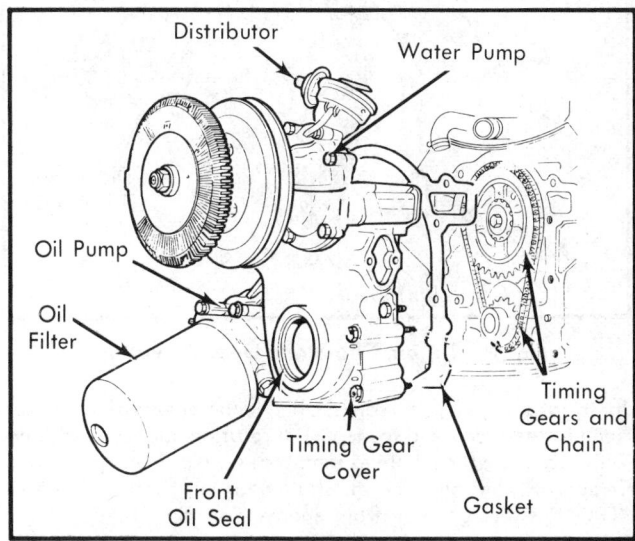

Fig. 8   Removing Timing Gear Cover Assembly

Installation — 1) To install, reverse the removal procedure. Be sure cylinder block and cover mating surfaces are clean. Coat both sides of new gasket with Hylomar PL 32M (or equivalent) and position on block or cover. Apply lubricant-sealer (3M EC 776 or equivalent) to threads of timing gear cover bolts.

2) Set distributor rotor arm to approximately 30° BTDC and install cover on cylinder block. Tighten bolts and nut with washer to specifications. Complete reversal of removal procedure.

TIMING GEAR COVER OIL SEAL

Removal — 1) Remove crankshaft pulleys. Remove fan and viscous coupling on non-air conditioned models. Screw extractor tool (18G 1328) into seal.

2) Turn center bolt clockwise to remove seal. Remove seal from extractor and discard seal.

Installation — 1) Clean seal housing in cover. Lubricate outside diameter of seal with clean engine oil. Using care not to damage seal, start seal into cover.

2) Fit adapter (18G 1291/5) to main tool (18G 1291/4) and screw bolt into crankshaft. Turn lock nut clockwise, drawing seal in until flush with cover. Remove tool and adapter. Lubricate seal lip with engine oil and install crankshaft pulleys.

TIMING CHAIN AND GEARS

Removal — With timing cover removed and No. 1 piston at TDC, remove distributor drive gear. *See Fig. 9.* Remove spacer and both gears with chain, keeping components assembled.

CAUTION — *Do not rotate engine shafts if rocker shafts are installed, as damage could result.*

TR8 V8 (Cont.)

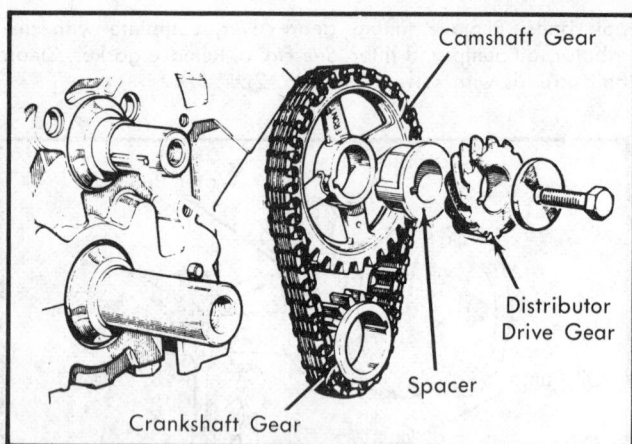

Fig. 9   Timing Chain and Gear Assembly

Installation — 1) If crankshaft and/or camshaft have not been rotated, proceed to step **3)**. If rotation has occurred (and with rocker shaft assemblies removed) set No. 1 piston at TDC. Temporarily install only camshaft gear on shaft with word, "FRONT", facing away from engine. See Fig. 10.

2) Turn camshaft until timing mark on gear is at lower 6 o'clock position. See Fig. 10. Remove camshaft gear without disturbing camshaft. Place camshaft and crankshaft gears in chain so their timing marks align.

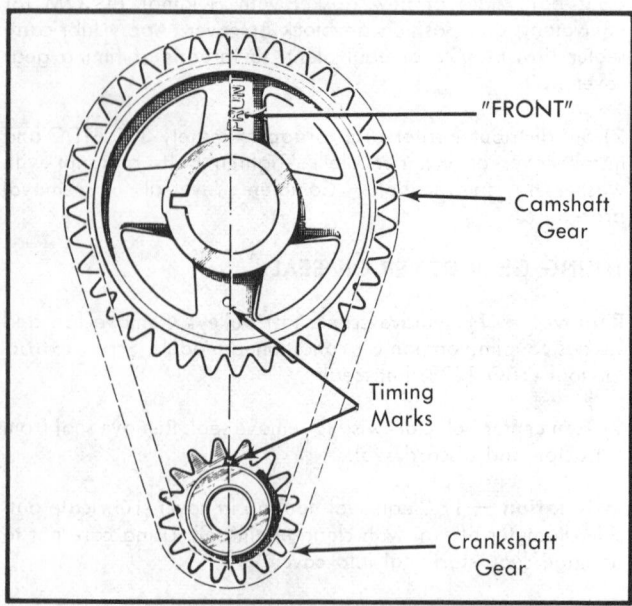

Fig. 10   Setting Valve Timing

3) Engage chain and gear assembly on camshaft and crankshaft key locations. Check that camshaft key is parallel to shaft axis for proper lubrication of distributor drive gear. Diameter of shaft including key should not exceed 1.187" (30.15 mm).

4) Again, check timing marks for proper alignment. Install spacer with flange toward front. Install distributor drive gear, making sure annular grooved side is to the rear (toward spacer).

5) Tighten distributor drive gear (camshaft) bolt and install timing gear cover.

VALVE TIMING

See TIMING CHAIN AND GEARS

CAMSHAFT

Removal — Remove intake manifold, timing chain and gears, valve covers and rocker shaft assemblies. Remove push rods and tappets, identifying them for later reassembly. Carefully remove camshaft from cylinder block.

Installation — Lubricate 5 camshaft journals and carefully insert camshaft into cylinder block. Install timing chain and gears, timing gear cover and cover oil seal. Install 8 tappets and push rods, rocker shaft assemblies, intake manifold and gasket. Install remaining components removed from engine or vehicle, as required for intake manifold removal.

ENGINE OILING

Crankcase Capacity — 5.4 quarts with filter. Normal drain and refill, 4.7 quarts.

Oil Filter — Disposable, full-flow type.

Pressure Relief Valve — Non-adjustable. Located in oil pump.

Normal Oil Pressure — 35 psi (2.46 kg/cm^2) at 2400 RPM.

OIL PUMP

A high capacity gear-type pump, driven by distributor shaft, which is geared to distributor drive gear on camshaft. Pump takes oil from pan, through a strainer and pumps it through oil filter to lubricate engine components.

Removal — Remove oil filter. Disconnect electrical lead from oil pressure switch. Remove bolts attaching oil pump cover assembly to timing gear cover. See Fig. 11. Lift off cover and gasket and slide out oil pump gears.

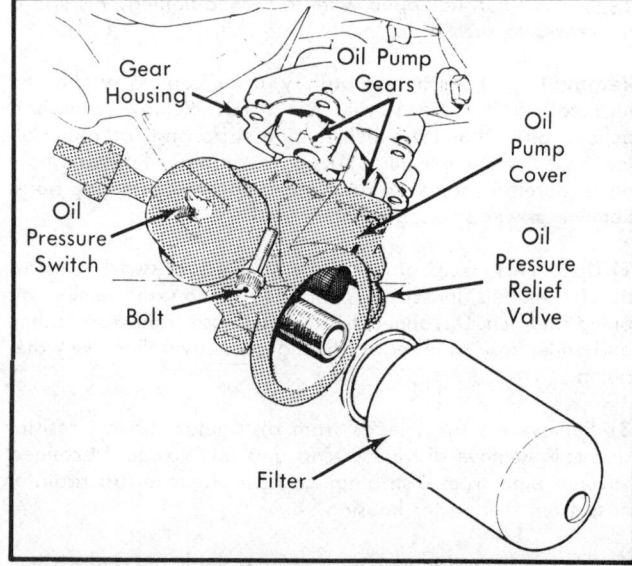

Fig. 11   Removing Oil Pump Cover from Housing

TR8 V8 (Cont.)

Inspection — Clean gears and inspect for wear or scoring. Replace worn gears. Remove oil pressure relief valve and inspect parts for wear. Replace spring if sides of spring are worn. Be sure valve moves freely in its bore, but has no side movement.

NOTE — *To check pump gears and housing for wear, install gears and shaft into timing gear cover. Place straightedge across face of gears and insert feeler gauge between straightedge and cover. If clearance is less than .0018" (.05 mm), check timing gear cover gear housing for wear.*

Installation — **1)** Lubricate and install pressure relief valve assembly. Fully pack oil pump gear housing with petroleum jelly (no other grease is suitable). Install oil pump gears, so petroleum jelly is forced into every cavity between teeth of gears.

CAUTION — *Unless pump is fully packed as indicated, pump may not prime itself upon reassembly and engine start-up. Use care when removing oil filter to replace filter immediately. If not replaced quickly, oil can drain from pump requiring pump removal and priming.*

2) Place a new gasket on oil pump cover and position cover on timing gear cover. Install and tighten bolts evenly and alternately. Connect electrical lead to oil pressure switch and install new oil filter. Check oil level in crankcase and bring to proper level.

ENGINE COOLING

Thermostat — Opens at 190°F (88°C).

Cooling System Capacity — 11.5 quarts with header tank; 10.5 quarts with expansion tank.

Radiator Cap — 15 psi (1.05 kg/cm²).

WATER PUMP

Removal — **1)** Disconnect battery and drain cooling system. Remove left-hand top hose from thermostat housing and other hoses from water pump.

2) Remove 4 bolts common to water pump and timing gear cover. Remove remaining 6 water pump bolts. Move air pump drive belt adjusting strap aside. Lift off water pump and gasket.

Installation — **1)** Clean water pump and timing gear cover mating surfaces. Grease gasket lightly and position on timing gear cover. Clean threads of mounting bolts and smear them with lubricant-sealant (3M EC 776).

2) Be sure 2 dowels are free of burrs. Install water pump over dowels and install bolts. Tighten evenly. Replace all hoses previously removed, install coolant and connect battery cables.

THERMOSTAT

Removal — Disconnect battery. Drain only radiator by disconnecting bottom hose. Remove top hose from thermostat housing. Remove 2 bolts and lift thermostat housing cover from intake manifold. See *Fig. 12*. Remove thermostat and gasket.

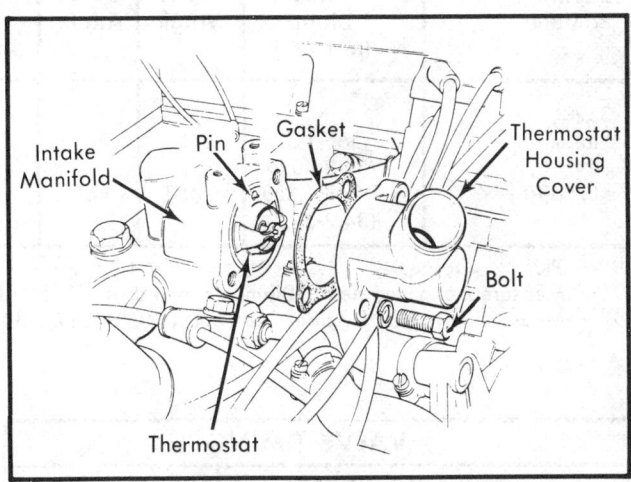

Fig. 12   Removing Thermostat and Gasket

Inspection — Note number stamped on thermostat, indicating temperature at which thermostat should be fully open. Place thermostat and a thermometer in water and heat, noting temperature at which thermostat opens. Install or replace, as necessary.

Installation — Clean gasket mating surfaces, and install thermostat with pin at 12 o'clock position. See *Fig. 12*. Install new gasket and position thermostat housing cover. Install and tighten bolts evenly. Connect hoses and battery.

TIGHTENING SPECIFICATIONS

Application	Ft. Lbs. (N·m)
Connecting Rod Cap	35 (48)
Cylinder Head	
Bolts 1 through 10	70 (95)
Bolts 11 through 14	50 (68)
Exhaust Manifold	16 (22)
Flexible Plate-to-Crankshaft	60 (82)
Flywheel-to-Crankshaft	60 (82)
Intake manifold	30 (41)
Rear Main Bearing	70 (95)
Other Main Bearings	55 (75)
Rocker Shaft Bracket	30 (41)
Vibration Damper	210 (286)

Triumph Engines

TR8 V8 (Cont.)
ENGINE SPECIFICATIONS

GENERAL SPECIFICATIONS										
Year	Displ.		Carburetor	HP at RPM	Torque (Ft. Lbs. at RPM)	Compr. Ratio	Bore		Stroke	
	cu. ins.	cc					in.	mm	in.	mm
1981	215.0	3528	①175CDSET	133@4750	.....	8.15:1	3.50	88.9	2.80	71.1
	215.0	3528	②Fuel Inj.	148@4750	.....	8.15:1	3.50	88.9	2.80	71.1

① – Twin 1-Bbl. side-draft carburetors.　② – Lucas digital electronic.

VALVES							
Engine & Valve	Head Diam. In. (mm)	Face Angle	①Seat Angle	②Seat Width In. (mm)	③Stem Diameter In. (mm)	④Stem Clearance In. (mm)	Valve Lift In. (mm)
3528 cc							
Intake	1.565-1.575 (39.8-40.0)	45°	46°	.060 (1.575)	.3402-.3412 (8.6-8.7)	.0010-.0030 (.02-.07)	.39 (9.9)
Exhaust	1.348-1.358 (34.2-34.5)	45°	46°	.060 (1.575)	.3397-.3407 (8.6-8.7)	.0020-.0004 (.05-.10)	.39 (9.9)

① – Plus ¼ degree.　② – Wear Limit .078" (2.0 mm).
③ – Measured at valve head. Diameter increases .0005" (.012 mm) away from head.
④ – Measured at top of guide. Subtract .0005" (.012 mm) for bottom of guide clearance.

VALVE TIMING				
	INTAKE		EXHAUST	
Engine	Open (BTDC)	Close (ABDC)	Open (BBDC)	Close (ATDC)
3528 cc	30°	75°	68°	37°

VALVE SPRINGS			
Engine	Free Length	PRESSURE (LBS.)	
		Valve Closed	Valve Open
3528 cc	.....	66.5-73.5 @ 1.577"	.....
	.....	123.5-136.5 @ 1.350"	.....
	.....	168.5-183.5 @ 1.187"	.....

PISTONS, PINS, RINGS						
	PISTONS	PINS		RINGS		
Engine	Clearance In. (mm)	Piston Fit In. (mm)	Rod Fit In. (mm)	Rings	End Gap In. (mm)	Side Clearance In. (mm)
3528 cc	①.0007-.0013 (.018-.033) ②.0016-.0028 (.04-.08) ③.0296-.0350 (.73-.88)	.0001-.0003 (.002-.007)	Press Fit	No. 1	.017-.022 (.44-.57)	.003-.005 (.08-.13)
				No. 2	.017-.022 (.44-.57)	.003-.005 (.08-.13)
				Oil	.015-.055 (.38-1.40)	.....

① – At bottom of skirt.　② – At top of skirt.　③ – At top land.

CRANKSHAFT MAIN & CONNECTING ROD BEARINGS						
	MAIN BEARINGS				CONNECTING ROD BEARINGS	
Engine	Journal Diam. In. (mm)	①Clearance In. (mm)	Thrust Bearing	Crankshaft End Play In. (mm)	Journal Diam. In. (mm)	①Clearance In. (mm)	Side Play In. (mm)
3528 cc	2.2992-2.2997 (58.39-58.41)	.0009-.0024 (.023-.061)	No. 3	.004-.008 (.10-.20)	2.0000-2.0005 (50.80-50.81)	.0006-.0022 (.015-.055)	.006-.014 (.15-.37)

① – Wear limit .003" (.08 mm).

JETTA, RABBIT, RABBIT PICKUP & SCIROCCO 4-CYLINDER

ENGINE CODING

ENGINE IDENTIFICATION

Engine identification number is stamped on left side of engine block near ignition distributor.

Engine Identification	
Application	Code
All Models	EN

ENGINE, CYLINDER HEAD & MANIFOLDS

ENGINE

NOTE — *Engine and transmission must be LOWERED out of vehicle as an assembly.*

Removal — 1) Disconnect battery cable at battery. Loosen fuel filler cap to relieve tank pressure. Remove rubber duct connecting throttle valve assembly to mixture control unit. Drain coolant by removing hose from thermostat flange and disconnect radiator fan motor and thermoswitch. Remove radiator with fan motor and ducts.

NOTE — *Never drain coolant when engine is hot.*

2) On air conditioned vehicles, remove air conditioner compressor and tie aside without disconnecting hoses. On all models, disconnect the following electrical connectors: Alternator, thermoswitch, oil pressure switch, warm-up regulator, coolant temperature sensor, coil and condensor wires, cold start valve, auxiliary air regulator and starter solenoid harness.

3) Remove intake air pre-heating duct. Remove injectors. Remove fuel lines for cold start valve and warm-up regulator. Disconnect remaining fuel, coolant, emission control and vacuum lines and position out of the way. Disconnect and remove accelerator linkage from engine.

NOTE — *When disconnecting fuel lines or components, have a container ready to catch leaking fuel in case system is still under pressure.*

4) Disconnect speedometer cable and ground cable from transmission. Detach selector cable and bracket on automatic transmission models. Detach clutch cable from clutch operating lever on manual transmission models. On all models, disconnect starter wires and back-up light switch. Raise vehicle.

5) Remove exhaust flex-pipe nuts or spring clip. On manual transmission models, remove shift lever from shift linkage. On all models, remove starter. Disconnect drive shafts from drive flanges. Remove horn and place out of the way. Remove engine front mount. Lower vehicle and remove axle nuts.

6) Raise vehicle and disconnect lower ball joints from bearing housings. Remove drive shaft while holding strut assembly away from vehicle. Reconnect ball joints and lower vehicle onto wheels. Attach lifting sling (US 1105) to engine and lift slightly. Remove complete rear mount.

7) Remove right front wheel. On manual transmission models, remove relay shaft and gearshift lever rods. On all models, remove bolts holding side mounts to body and lower engine/transmission assembly to dolly. Raise vehicle to clear engine and remove assembly from beneath vehicle.

Installation — To install, reverse removal procedures using caution to observe all tightening specifications.

NOTE — *Mounts must be properly aligned and free of tension before tightening.*

CYLINDER HEAD & MANIFOLDS

Removal — 1) Disconnect duct connecting throttle valve housing to mixture control unit. Remove radiator cap. Remove thermostat housing from water pump. Remove thermostat and drain cooling system.

2) Remove camshaft drive belt. Remove injectors from manifold tubes. Disconnect all hoses, cables and wires attached to throttle valve housing and intake air distributor. Disconnect exhaust pipe.

3) Remove nuts and bolts that hold exhaust manifold and intake manifold (air intake distributor) to cylinder head. Remove manifolds. Remove any screws, bolts or clips attaching air conditioning components to cylinder head (if equipped).

4) Remove upper alternator mounting bolt and adjusting bracket. Disconnect all coolant hoses. Disconnect temperature gauge wire. Remove spark plug wires and spark plugs. Remove wire from oil pressure sending unit.

5) Remove valve cover. Remove head bolts in reverse order of installation. Remove cylinder head. If head is stuck, pry off with a block of wood placed in each outboard exhaust port.

CAUTION — *Never drain coolant while engine is hot. Doing so could cause engine block or cylinder head to warp.*

Installation — To install, reverse removal procedure and note the following: Make sure head gasket is positioned with "OBEN" mark facing up. Tighten head bolts in sequence and steps shown.

JETTA, RABBIT, RABBIT PICKUP & SCIROCCO 4-CYLINDER (Cont.)

Cylinder Head Tightening Steps	
Application	**Ft. Lbs. (N·m)**
Step No. 1	22 (30)
Step No. 2	44 (60)
Step No. 3	55 (75) Plus ¼ Turn

NOTE — *Polygon (12 point) socket head bolts are set to final torque while cold and do not need to be retightened when hot. Tighten in sequence to 55 ft. lbs. (75 N·m) plus an additional ¼ turn.*

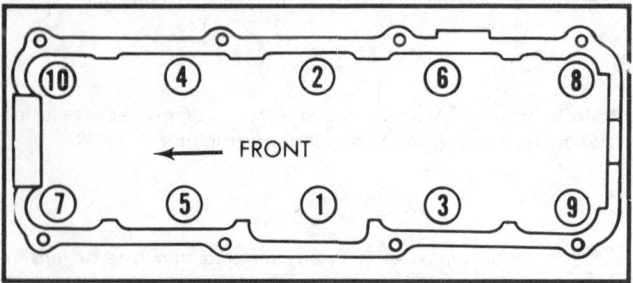

Fig. 1 Cylinder Head Tightening Sequence
(Loosen in Reverse Order)

CAMSHAFT

TIMING BELT

NOTE — *Sprockets DO NOT have to be removed to replace camshaft drive belt.*

Removal — Remove alternator belt, water pump pulley, and upper and lower drive belt covers. If equipped, remove air conditioning compressor drive belt. Loosen belt tensioner, and work belt off sprockets toward front of engine.

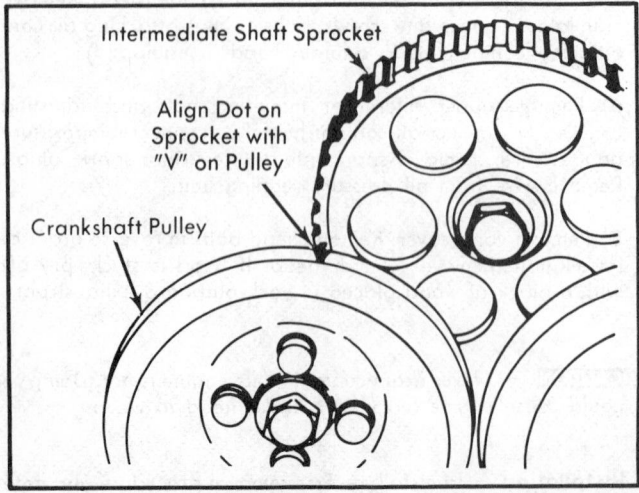

Intermediate Shaft Sprocket

Align Dot on Sprocket with "V" on Pulley

Crankshaft Pulley

Fig. 2 Intermediate Shaft Index Mark Aligned with Notch on Crankshaft Pulley

Installation — 1) Rotate camshaft sprocket until index punch mark on camshaft sprocket is lined up with top surface of valve cover mounting flange on spark plug side of head. Rotate crankshaft and intermediate shaft until index punch mark on intermediate shaft sprocket aligns with "V" notch on crankshaft pulley.

2) Use care not to move any sprocket. Fit belt on bottom first and then at top so there is no slack between sprockets. Tighten tensioner so belt can just be twisted 90° halfway between camshaft and intermediate sprockets. Tighten adjuster lock nut and reverse removal procedure for remaining components.

CAMSHAFT

Removal — 1) Remove camshaft cover. Loosen and remove bearing caps in following sequence: 5, 1, and 3, then loosen bearing caps 2 and 4 diagonally. Bearing caps are numbered front to rear.

2) Check camshaft end play. Remove camshaft and lift out cam followers. Install camshaft using only bearing caps 1 and 5. Fit dial indicator so tip of gauge touches front of camshaft. Pry camshaft back and forth. Reading should not exceed .006" (.15 mm). If end play is beyond limits, replace either camshaft or cylinder head.

3) Check camshaft runout. Fit dial indicator so gauge pin is against camshaft center journal. Turn camshaft and record runout range. Runout must not exceed .0004" (.01 mm). Replace camshaft as necessary.

4) Inspect camshaft lobes for wear. Worn lobes usually indicate lack of lubrication. Check engine oiling passages to make sure they are not restricted. Replace worn camshafts and worn discs.

5) Inspect cam followers for signs of seizure or lack of lubrication. If any aluminum particles from head are found on cam followers, replace followers. Cylinder head must be replaced if any follower bores are worn or excessively rough.

Installation — Lightly lube cam follower bores, then fit followers in their original bores. Install adjusting discs. Place camshaft on cylinder head. Loosely attach No. 2 and No. 4 bearing caps. Gradually tighten caps. Fit No. 5 and No. 3 bearing caps. Install new oil seal in front of camshaft. Install No. 1 bearing cap. Make sure all caps are torqued to proper specifications.

VALVE TIMING

With timing belt removed as previously described, rotate crankshaft and intermediate shaft until index mark (punch mark) on intermediate shaft is positioned in "V" notch on crankshaft pulley. See Fig. 2. This is firing point of No. 1 cylinder. Next, turn camshaft until timing mark on rear of camshaft sprocket is in line with top of cylinder head cover flange. See Fig. 3. Replace timing belt.

JETTA, RABBIT, RABBIT PICKUP & SCIROCCO 4-CYLINDER (Cont.)

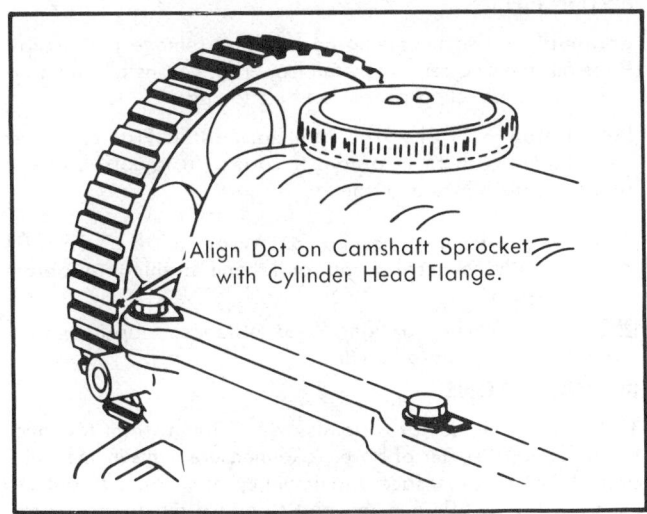

Fig 3   Index Mark on Camshaft Sprocket Aligned with Cylinder Head Flange

(within image) Align Dot on Camshaft Sprocket with Cylinder Head Flange.

VALVES

VALVE ARRANGEMENT

E-I-E-I-I-E-I-E (front to rear).

VALVE GUIDE SERVICING

1) Clean valve guides before making measurements. To measure guide, attach a suitable mounting device with a dial gauge (VW689/1) to mounting surface of cylinder head. Insert a new valve until end of stem is flush with end of valve guide.

2) Rock valve head against dial indicator and check amount of rock recorded. Maximum allowable rock is .039" (1 mm) for intake valves and .051" (1.3 mm) for exhaust valves. Proper valve guide diameter is .315"-.316" (8.01-8.04 mm).

3) Use a press and suitable adaptor (10-206) to remove and install valve guides. To remove guides, press out from combustion chamber side of head.

4) Coat new valve guides with engine oil. Press new guides into cold head from camshaft side. Make sure shoulder of guide meets firmly with top of cylinder head. Ream guides to uniform inside diameter.

CAUTION — *Do not use more than 1 ton pressure once guide shoulder is seated or shoulder may break.*

VALVE SPRINGS

NOTE — *Although normal maintenance on valve system is performed with head removed, it is possible to replace stem seals, keepers, retainers or broken springs with cylinder head installed.*

Removal (Head Installed) — With camshaft and tappets removed, turn crankshaft until piston of cylinder you are working on is at BDC. Apply steady air pressure of at least 85 psi through spark plug hole adapter to keep valves seated. Compress spring with suitable tool (VW 541) and remove valve keepers. Remove and replace damaged or worn parts.

Removal (Head Removed) — With camshaft and tappets removed, use suitable compressor (VW 541) to depress retainer and remove keepers. Take out retainer and springs.

Installation — Check springs on spring tester and inspect for cracks or distortion. Reverse removal procedure and note the following: Lower edge of valve spring retainer should be chamfered to prevent valve stem scoring. If necessary, grind a chamfer using stone or other suitable tool. When installing the springs, make sure closely spaced coils of outer springs are against spring seats.

VALVE STEM OIL SEALS

With tappet, adjuster pad, keepers, springs, and spring seats removed, extract valve stem oil seal. When installing new seal, first position protective plastic sleeve on valve stem, lubricate seal, and use a suitable mandrel (10-204) to push seal onto valve guide.

VALVE CLEARANCE ADJUSTMENT

1) Adjust valves with engine at normal operating temperature. Clearance adjustments are to be checked and made according to firing order. Using a wrench on the crankshaft pulley bolt, turn clockwise to bring No. 1 piston to TDC (cam lobes pointing up). Determine valve clearance by inserting a feeler gauge between cam lobe heel and adjusting disc.

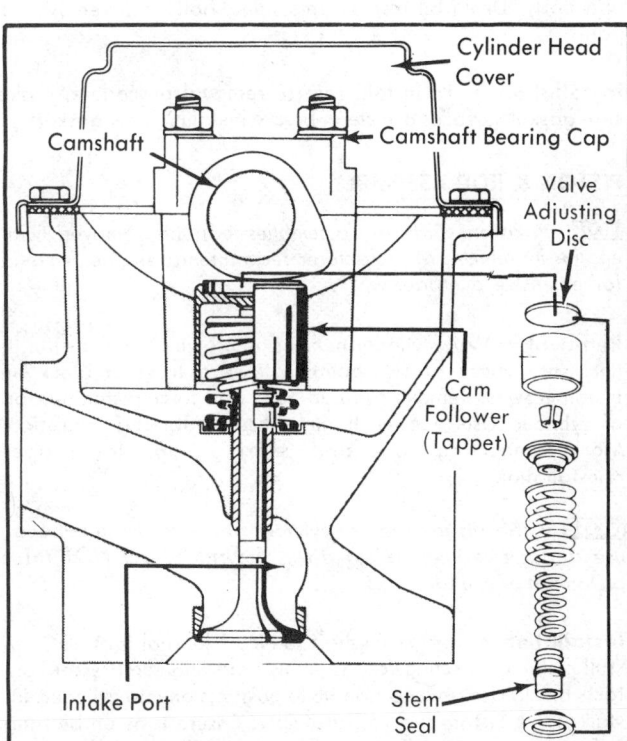

Fig. 4   Assembled View of Valve and Camshaft

(within image) Cylinder Head Cover — Camshaft Bearing Cap — Valve Adjusting Disc — Cam Follower (Tappet) — Camshaft — Intake Port — Stem Seal

Volkswagen Engines

JETTA, RABBIT, RABBIT PICKUP & SCIROCCO 4-CYLINDER (Cont.)

2) Rotate crankshaft pulley 180° at a time, and check cylinders No. 3, No. 4 and No. 2, consecutively. If necessary, adjust to specifications by installing thicker or thinner adjusting discs. Discs are available in 26 different thicknesses in increments of .0019″ (.05 mm). Disc thickness is stamped on the bottom, and ranges from .1181″ (3.0 mm) to .1673″ (4.25 mm). To install, press cam follower down with follower depressing tool (VW 546). Remove old disc with special pliers (VW 208), and insert new disc with stamped thickness marking toward cam follower.

Valve Clearance Specifications	
Application	**In. (mm)**
Intake	
Hot	.008-.012 (.20-.30)
Cold	.006-.010 (.15-.25)
Exhaust	
Hot	.016-.020 (.40-.50)
Cold	.014-.018 (.35-.45)

NOTE — *Cold settings are given for reference, as initial settings to be used during cylinder head rework. Final adjustments are made at normal operating temperature, and should be rechecked after approximately 1000 miles of operation.*

PISTONS, PINS & RINGS

OIL PAN

Removal — On Rabbit and Scirocco, drain oil, remove bolts and remove oil pan. On Dasher, support engine from above with support bar and threaded rod. Remove nuts holding engine mounts on subframe and bolts holding subframe to body. Pull subframe downward to separate engine mounts and body. Drain oil, remove mounting bolts and remove oil pan.

Installation — To install, reverse removal procedure. Make sure gasket surfaces are clean before installing new gaskets.

PISTON & ROD ASSEMBLY

NOTE — *Piston and rod assemblies can be removed with engine in vehicle. Manufacturer recommends engine removal for extensive overhaul work.*

Removal — Mark cylinder number on crown of each piston. If necessary, mark arrows pointing toward front of block on piston crowns. Remove rod cap bolts and force piston out top of cylinder. Use wooden hammer handle for this operation. Mark connecting rods and bearing caps for proper reinstallation.

NOTE — *If a ridge at top of cylinder prevents piston removal, use a ridge reamer to cut down the ridge. DO NOT force piston out of cylinder.*

Installation — Turn crankshaft so No. 1 journal is at BDC. Install piston connecting rod assembly until ring compressor contacts block. Use a wood handle to push piston into cylinder. Install No. 4 Piston and rod assembly. Ensure tabs on bearing halves engage notch in rod and cap. Install and tighten caps on rods 1 and 4. Turn crankshaft 180° and install No. 2 and 3 rod assemblies and rod caps.

PISTON PINS

Removal — Use needle-nosed pliers to remove pin circlips. Press out pin and remove piston from rod. For installation purposes, note direction piston is fitted to rod.

Installation — **1)** Check pin fit in each piston. Piston pin must be a thumb-push fit in piston. If correct fit is not obtained, replace both pin and piston.

2) Check pin fit in connecting rod. Wear limit is .0015″ (.04 mm). Rebush connecting rod and hone bushing to obtain correct clearance.

NOTE — *If pin is too tight, heat piston to approximately 140°F (60°C) in an oil bath.*

FITTING PISTONS

1) Measure cylinder at 3 points: ⅜″ (10 mm) from top and bottom, and at center of bore. Take measurements in line with, and at 90° to thrust face. Maximum cylinder taper or out-of-round is .0016″ (.04 mm) beyond standard dimensions. If excessive, cylinder reboring and oversize pistons are necessary.

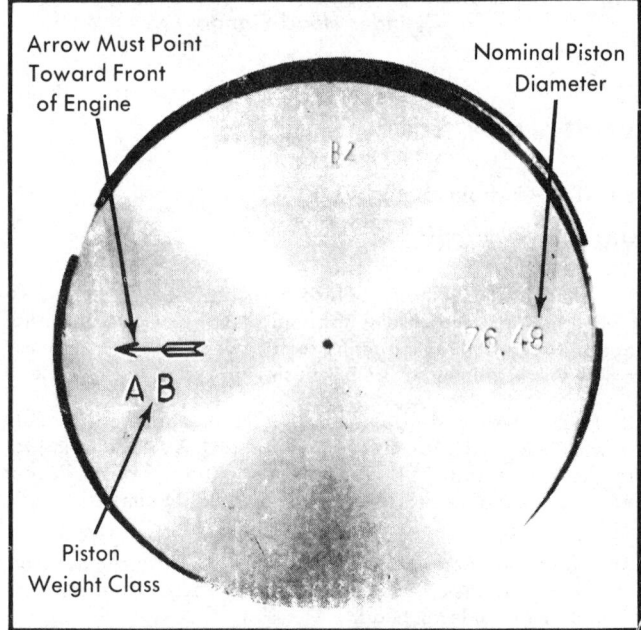

Fig. 5   Codes Stamped on Piston Head

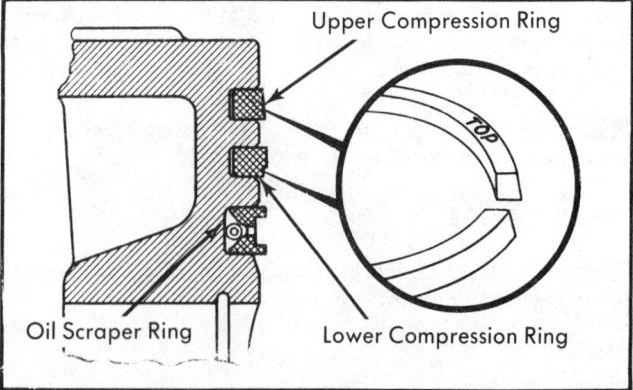

Fig. 6   Piston Ring Installation — Word TOP Must Face Piston Crown

2) Measure pistons at .63″ (16 mm) from bottom of piston skirt (measuring 90° to pin bore). Combining this measure-

JETTA, RABBIT, RABBIT PICKUP & SCIROCCO 4-CYLINDER (Cont.)

ment with measurement of corresponding cylinder bore, note piston-to-cylinder clearance. If this exceeds .0028" (.07 mm), oversize pistons must be installed.

3) Place rings squarely in cylinder bore about .60" (15 mm) down from top edge and measure end gap. Install rings on piston and measure side clearance. Position ring gaps 120° offset to each other (start with oil ring gap directly to the rear). Ensure stamp mark "TOP" on rings is facing upward.

CRANKSHAFT MAIN & CONNECTING ROD BEARINGS

MAIN & CONNECTING ROD BEARINGS

1) Push crankshaft toward one end and measure crankshaft end play at No. 3 (thrust) bearing. Main bearing caps are stamped "1" to "5" (front to rear), and must be returned to original positions upon reassembly. Measure end play (side play) of connecting rods. Remove all bearing caps and check bearing clearance using Plastigage method.

2) Measure crankshaft journals with a micrometer to determine journal out-of-round and taper. The maximum allowable wear is .0012" (.03 mm). Install main bearing inserts with oil groove in the engine block, making sure anti-rotation tabs engage in saddle notches. Lubricate new bearings, place crankshaft in block, and install lower main shells and caps in proper order.

Crankshaft Journal Diameters		
Size	**Main Bearing In. (mm)**①	**Rod Bearing In. (mm)**①
Standard	2.25 (53.97)	1.810 (45.97)
1st US	2.115 (53.72)	1.800 (45.72)
2nd US	2.105 (53.47)	1.790 (45.47)
3rd US	2.095 (53.22)	1.780 (45.22)

① — Journal diameter is ± .0004" (.01 mm).

REAR MAIN BEARING OIL SEAL

NOTE — *Rear main bearing oil seal may be replaced with engine in vehicle. Transmission and flywheel must be removed.*

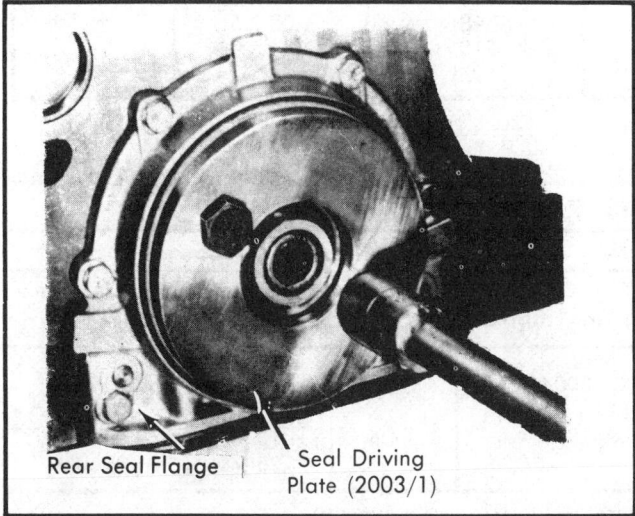

Rear Seal Flange | Seal Driving Plate (2003/1)

Fig. 7   Using Special Tool to Install Rear Main Oil Seal

Insert a large screwdriver between crankshaft flywheel flange and inside lip of oil seal. Pry out old seal. Install seal guide sleeve (2003/2A or equivalent) over crankshaft flange. Start new seal over guide sleeve, and into recess in seal carrier. Remove guide sleeve and bolt seal driving plate (2003/1 or equivalent) to flywheel mounting flange. Tighten bolts evenly to bring seal flush with carrier.

FRONT MAIN BEARING OIL SEAL AND INTERMEDIATE SHAFT OIL SEAL

Remove camshaft belt. Remove crankshaft sprocket. Pry seal from seal carrier, being careful not to damage carrier. Use removing tool (10-219 or equivalent) to remove seal. *See Fig. 8.* Using installing tool (10-203 or equivalent), press in new seal until flush with seal carrier. If tool 10-203 was used, remove it and using aluminum part of tool, press seal in until recessed .080" (2.0 mm) in seal carrier.

NOTE — *Same procedure applies to intermediate shaft oil seal except: Remove intermediate shaft sprocket. Only press new seal in until flush with seal carrier.*

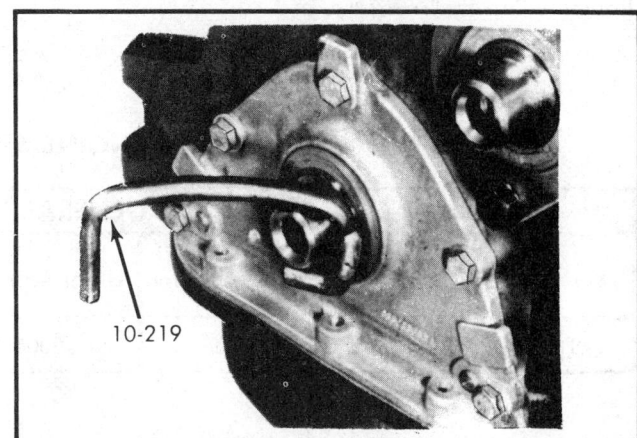

10-219

Fig. 8   Using Special Tool to Remove Front Oil Seal

ENGINE OILING

Crankcase Capacity — 4.3 quarts (4.7 quarts with filter change).

Oil Filter — Replaceable spin-on type.

Normal Oil Pressure — Minimum of 28 psi (1.97 kg/cm²) with engine at normal operating temperature.

ENGINE OILING SYSTEM

Oiling system is a pressure feed type. A gear oil pump lifts oil from pan and pressure feeds it to crankshaft journals, camshaft bearings, and intermediate shaft. Other parts of system receive oil mist or splash for lubrication.

OIL PUMP

Removal — **1)** With oil pan removed (see *OIL PAN* in this article), remove pump mounting bolts. Remove oil pump, leaving pickup tube attached.

2) Separate pickup tube from pump. Check oil pump gear backlash. Clearance should be between .002-.008" (.05-.20 mm). If specification is exceeded, replace gears or pump.

Volkswagen Engines

JETTA, RABBIT, RABBIT PICKUP & SCIROCCO 4-CYLINDER (Cont.)

3) Measure oil pump gear end play. If end play exceeds .006" (.15 mm), replace pump.

Installation — To install, reverse removal procedure. Make sure all mating surfaces are clean before installing gaskets. Oil pump drive shaft must align with distributor drive gear.

ENGINE COOLING

Cooling System Capacity — 7.3 quarts on Rabbit Pickup, 4.9 quarts on all other models.

Thermostat — Begins to open at 176°F (80°C), fully open at 201°F (94°C).

Radiator Cap — 17-19 psi.

WATER PUMP

NOTE — *The front portion of water pump (shaft, seals, bearing, and housing) can be replaced separately. To do this camshaft drive belt and sprockets must be removed. To avoid removing drive belt, remove water pump as an assembly.*

Removal — Drain coolant with engine cool. Remove alternator belt and alternator. Remove air injection pump belt (if equipped). Disconnect hoses from water pump and remove bolt holding camshaft drive belt cover to water pump. Remove water pump bolts and pump assembly.

Installation — To install, reverse removal procedure and make sure to use new "O" ring in recess in pump mounting flange.

NOTE — *Do not use sealer between water pump mounting flange and engine block.*

ENGINE SPECIFICATIONS

GENERAL SPECIFICATIONS

| Year | Displ. | | Carburetor | HP at RPM | Torque (Ft. Lbs. at RPM) | Compr. Ratio | Bore | | Stroke | |
	cu. ins.	cc					in.	mm	in.	mm
1981	105	1715	Fuel Inj.	74@5000	90@3000	8.2:1	3.13	79.5	3.40	86.4

VALVES

Engine & Valve	Head Diam. In. (mm)	Face Angle	Seat Angle	Seat Width In. (mm)	Stem Diameter In. (mm)	Stem Clearance In. (mm)	Valve Lift In. (mm)
1715 cc							
Intake	1.338 (33.9)	45°	45°	.079 (2.0)	.314 (7.98)	.001-.002 (.03-.05)	....
Exhaust	1.220 (31.0)	45°	45°	.095 (2.4)	.313 (7.95)	.002-.003 (.05-.07)	....

PISTONS, PINS, RINGS

| Engine | PISTONS | PINS | | RINGS | | |
	Clearance In. (mm)①	Piston Fit In. (mm)	Rod Fit In. (mm)②	Rings	End Gap In. (mm)③	Side Clearance In. (mm)④
1715 cc	.0012 (.03)	Push Fit	.0004-.0008 (.01-.02)	Comp.	.012-.018 (.30-.45)	.0008-.002 (.02-.05)
				Oil	.010-.016 (.25-.40)	.0008-.002 (.02-.05)

① — Wear limit .027" (.07 mm). ② — Wear limit .0015" (.04 mm). ③ — Wear limit .039" (1 mm).
④ — Wear limit .006" (.15 mm).

CRANKSHAFT MAIN & CONNECTING ROD BEARINGS

Engine	MAIN BEARINGS				CONNECTING ROD BEARINGS		
	Journal Diam. In. (mm)	Clearance In. (mm)	Thrust Bearing	Crankshaft End Play In. (mm)	Journal Diam. In. (mm)	Clearance In. (mm)	Side Play In. (mm)
1715 cc	2.124-2.125 (53.96-53.98)	.001-.003 (.025-.076)	No. 3	.003-.007 (.07-.17)	1.809-1.810 45.96-45.98)	.0011-.0035 .028-.088)	.014 (.37)

① — Wear limit .007″ (.17 mm).
② — Wear limit .015″ (.37 mm).
③ — Wear limit .0047″ (.12 mm).
④ — Wear limit indicated.

CAMSHAFT

Engine	Journal Diam. In. (mm)	Clearance In. (mm)①	Lobe Lift In. (mm)
1715 cc	.....	.0008-.002 (.02-.05)	.....

① — End play .006″ (.15 mm)

VALVE SPRINGS

Engine	Free Length In. (mm)	PRESSURE Lbs. @ In. (kg @ mm)	
		Valve Closed	Valve Open
1715 cc Inner	....	46-51 @ .719 (21-32 @ 18.3)	....
Outer	....	96-106 @ .916 (43.5-48 @ 22.3)	....

TIGHTENING SPECIFICATIONS

Application	Ft. Lbs. (N·m)
Timing Belt Tensioner Lock Nut	33 (45)
Intermediate Sprocket Bolt	①59 (80)
Crankshaft Sprocket Bolt	59 (80)
Water Pump Pulley Bolts	15 (20)
Crankshaft Pulley Bolts	15 (20)
Drive Plate-to-Crankshaft Bolts	①55 (75)
Connecting Rod Cap Bolts	②33 (45)
Main Bearing Cap Bolts	②48 (65)
Cylinder Head Bolts	③55 (75) plug ¼ turn
Ball Joints	36 (49)
Axle Nuts	173 (235)
Manifolds-to-Cylinder Head Bolts	18 (25)
Water Pump Bolts	15 (20)

① — Use Loctite.
② — To check clearance, tighten to 26 ft. lbs. (35 N·m) only.
③ — In 3 steps. See text.

Volkswagen Engines

VANAGON 4-CYLINDER

ENGINE CODING

ENGINE IDENTIFICATION

Engine code number is stamped on crankcase below breather, near coil. First two digits of cast number are engine code.

Engine Identification	
Application	**Engine Code**
Vanagon (1970 cc)	CV

ENGINE, CYLINDER HEAD & MANIFOLD

ENGINE

Removal — 1) Disconnect battery. Remove air cleaner with air flow sensor and air intake duct. Remove rubber boot to heater booster. Disconnect electrical wiring from the following components: alternator, distributor and oil pressure sending unit. Disconnect plug at control unit. Pull oil dipstick. Disconnect vacuum hose from brake booster. Disconnect all remaining vacuum hoses and electrical wiring leads running between engine and engine compartment.

2) Remove nuts of upper engine mounting bolts and disconnect accelerator cable. On automatic transaxle models, remove plug on top of transaxle housing, pull ATF dipstick and remove ATF filler tube grommet. Remove three 8 mm bolts of torque converter through hole on top off transaxle housing.

NOTE — *To gain access to bolts of torque converter, engine must be rotated until each bolt appears in hole on top of transmission housing. Use adapter (3052) to turn engine crankshaft.*

3) On all models, remove heater flap housing bolt; clamp fuel line and detach. Also clamp fuel line from pressure regulator and detach. Disconnect wiring from starter. On manual transaxle models, loosen transaxle mount bolt at front of transaxle. On automatic transaxle models, loosen accelerator cable at selector lever and detach. Loosen transaxle mount bolt at front of transaxle.

4) On all models, place a support (VW785/1) under transaxle. Place a floor jack under engine. Raise jack until engine is just supported. Remove nuts from lower engine mounting bolts. Remove bolts from engine carrier. Lower engine/transaxle assembly until transaxle rests on support (VW785/1). Slide engine assembly slightly to rear until it clears input shaft. Remove engine from transaxle and lower engine with floor jack.

Installation — To install, reverse removal procedure and note the following: Replace all self-locking nuts. On manual transaxle models, check clutch release bearing for wear; lubricate splines on main drive shaft, contact points of clutch release bearing and clutch release lever. Adjust accelerator cable at full throttle position. On automatic transaxle models, adjust accelerator cable.

INTAKE MANIFOLD

Removal — 1) Fuel injection manifold can be removed with engine in vehicle. Remove air cleaner, hoses, and pressure switch.

2) Disconnect wires on fuel injectors and remove two screws. Pull injectors off with plate and retainer. Make sure locating bushings are removed from manifold. Disconnect hoses on injectors and remove.

3) Remove intake manifold cover plate. Remove nuts and washers securing manifold to cylinder heads. Lift up on manifold and pull from tubes on air distributor.

Installation — To install manifold, reverse removal procedure and note the following: Use new gaskets and tighten intake manifold mounting nuts uniformly. Make sure gray protective cap on injector is to rear and cap is to front.

CYLINDER HEAD

NOTE — *Engine must be removed from vehicle and manifolds removed, before removing cylinder heads. If cylinders are not to be removed, use retaining device to keep cylinders from pulling free.*

Removal — 1) Remove rocker arm cover and gasket. Remove rocker arm shaft retaining nuts, loosening gradually one at a time to relieve spring tension evenly. Remove rocker arm assemblies.

2) Remove push rods, keeping in order for reassembly. Loosen cylinder head nuts gradually working in sequence from outside toward center.

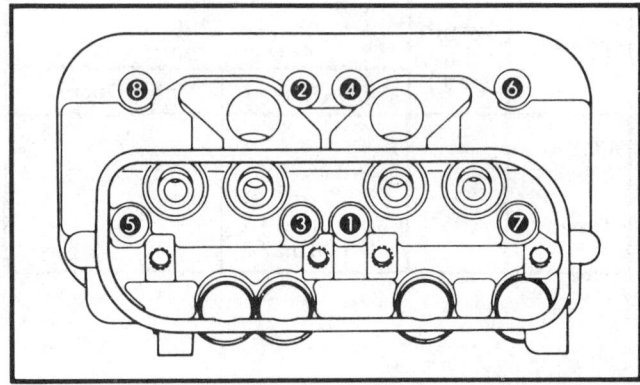

Fig. 1 Cylinder Head Bolt Tightening Sequence

Installation — 1) Place new metal gasket rings in peripheries of combustion chambers and install head over cylinder studs. Tighten nuts lightly by hand and then to specifications in 2 steps following sequence shown in *Fig. 1*.

2) Install push rod through top of cylinder head with black sealing ring at bottom and white ring at top. Install remaining components in reverse order of removal. Ensure push rod tube retaining wire bears against end of tubes and engage slots in rocker arm supports before installing cylinder head cover.

VALVES

VALVE ARRANGEMENT

E-I-I-E (both banks)

Volkswagen Engines

VANAGON 4-CYLINDER (Cont.)

VALVE GUIDE SERVICING

Mount head in VS 4401A. Place new valve in guide with stem flush with end of guide. With dial indicator, measure valve rock at valve head. If rock exceeds .047" (1.2 mm), replace valve and/or guide. Guides must be removed by drilling out with shouldered drill to a depth of 1.575-1.968" (40-50 mm). Drive out remaining part of guide. To install, coat new guide with engine oil and press in using US 4410. Ream to proper clearance after installation.

CAUTION — *DO NOT use a hammer and drift to replace guides due to the danger of damage to the cylinder head.*

VALVE SPRINGS

NOTE — *Valve spring may be removed with cylinder head installed. Apply constant air pressure (minimum 85 psi) to cylinder through spark plug hole to hold valve in place while compressing spring.*

Removal — Remove cylinder head cover and rocker arm shaft. Install suitable valve spring compressor tool (VW311s with cylinder head removed, VW653/2 with cylinder head installed). Compress spring retainer and spring and remove valve keepers. Release compressor and remove spring retainer and spring.

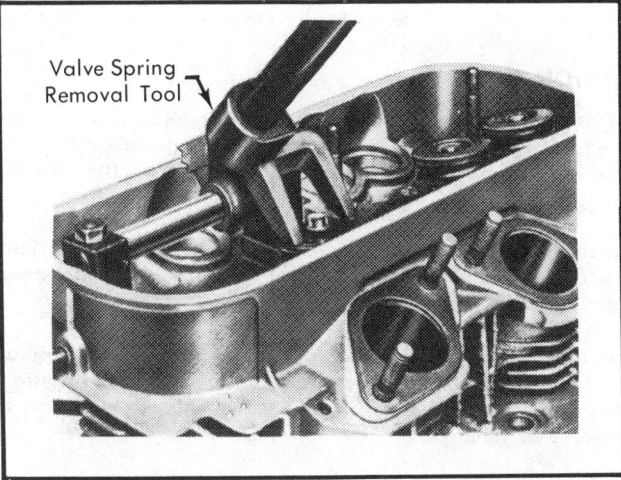

Fig. 2   Using Special Tool VW311s to Remove Valve Spring

Installation — Install valve, valve spring, and valve spring retainer. Compress spring and install valve keepers.

NOTE — *Install spring with closely spaced coils against cylinder head.*

ROCKER ARM ASSEMBLY

Removal — Disengage wire valve cover clip. Remove valve cover. Remove 4 rocker shaft retaining nuts. Each side has two separate shafts. Make sure mounting nuts are gradually and evenly loosened until spring tension is relieved.

Inspection — Check rocker arms and shafts for wear. If inside diameter of rocker arm is worn more than .789" (20.0 mm),

replace rocker arm. If diameter of rocker shaft is worn to less than .783" (19.9 mm), replace rocker shaft.

Installation — To install, reverse removal procedure and note: Make sure push rod tube retaining wire is reinstalled. Adjust valve clearance.

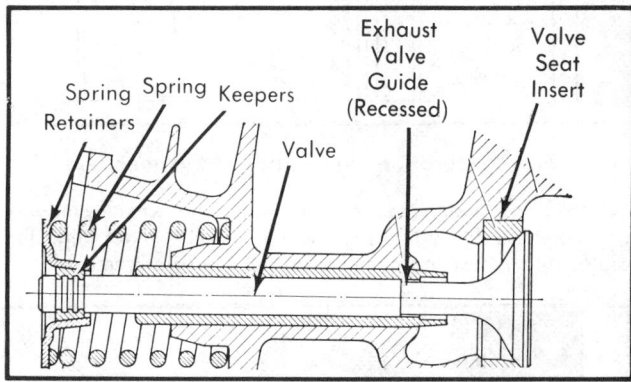

Fig. 3   Sectional View of Valve with Related Parts

HYDRAULIC VALVE LIFTERS

NOTE — *Valve lifters may be removed and installed without removing or disassembling engine.*

Removal — Valve covers, rocker arms, push rods and push rod covers must be off of engine. Remove lifters by withdrawing with a magnetic tool. Mark all lifters for installation in original position.

Installation — Ensure that lifters are filled with oil and reverse removal procedure. Back off adjusting screws in rocker arms until threaded part is flush with bottom of rocker arm. Proceed as in *Valve Clearance Adjustment.*

VALVE CLEARANCE ADJUSTMENT

Loosen all adjusting screws until flush with bottom of rocker arm. Hand turn crankshaft until number 1 cylinder is in firing position (number 1 firing mark on distributor body and rotor aligned). Turn adjusting screws for both rocker arms of number 1 cylinder until tips just touch valve stems (zero clearance). Tighten screws 2 additional turns and tighten locknuts. Turn crankshaft so rotor moves counterclockwise in 90° increments and repeat adjustment for number 2, 3 and 4 cylinders.

PISTONS, PINS & RINGS

CYLINDERS

Removal — Remove engine and remove cylinder head. **NOTE** — *Mark cylinders to insure they are reinstalled in original position.* Remove deflector plates from bottom of cylinders and pull cylinders from pistons.

Installation — 1) Check seating surfaces of cylinders on both ends. Make sure seating areas are perfectly clean and true before installing cylinders. Stagger ring gaps 120° apart so that oil ring gap faces upward when cylinder is installed.

2) Apply oil to cylinder, piston rings and piston pin. Compress rings with suitable ring compressor (US 1008A). Install new sealing gasket on crankcase side and slide cylinder over piston.

Volkswagen Engines

VANAGON 4-CYLINDER (Cont.)

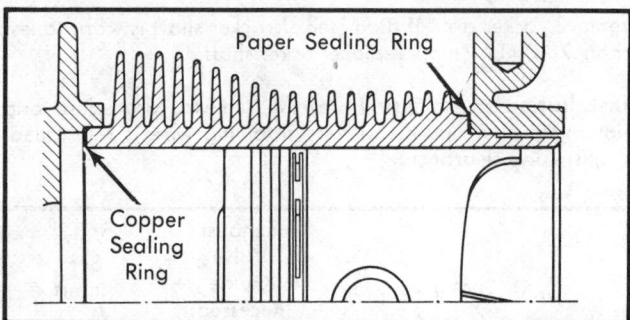

Fig. 4 Location and Seating of Cylinder Seal

3) Make sure studs do not contact cooling fins when cylinder is completely seated against crankcase. Install cylinder deflector plates and remaining components in reverse of removal.

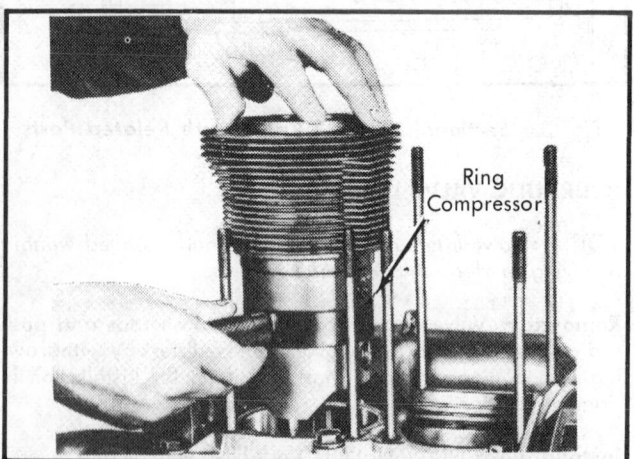

Fig. 5 Installing Cylinder Assembly into Case

FITTING PISTONS

1) With piston and cylinder removed, measure clearance between piston and cylinder. Check piston size at bottom of skirt and 90° to piston pin. Check cylinder size at several points throughout cylinder, using largest reading to determine clearance.

2) If clearance exceeds .008" (.20 mm) replace piston and cylinder as a set. New piston must be of the same weight grade as original or within 10 g of original piston weight. Piston size, weight and installation position are marked on top of

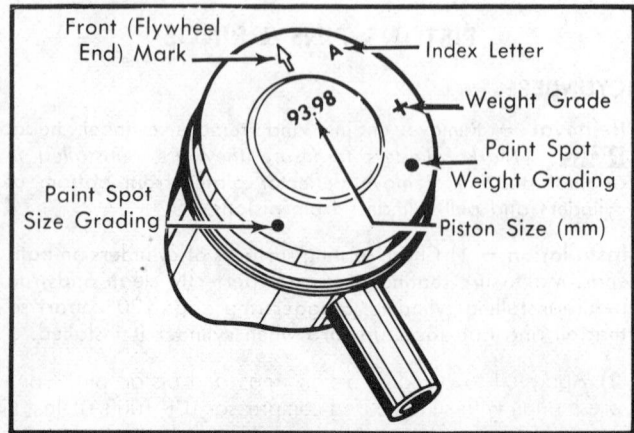

Fig. 6 Top View of Piston with Detail of Piston Markings

piston. Pistons and cylinders are available in .020" (.5 mm) and .040 (1.0 mm) oversizes. *See Fig. 6.*

NOTE — *Piston alone may be replaced with one of matching size. Only pistons of same size and weight grade should be installed in same engine.*

3) New piston rings are size graded to match piston/cylinder sets. Measure ring gap with ring installed approximately ³⁄₁₆" in cylinder. If ring end gap exceeds .035" (.90 mm) for compression rings or .037" (.95 mm) for oil scraper, replace.

4) Install rings on piston and measure ring side clearance using feeler gauge. If clearance exceeds .005" (.12 mm) on upper and middle rings or .004" (.10 mm) on oil scraper ring, piston must be replaced.

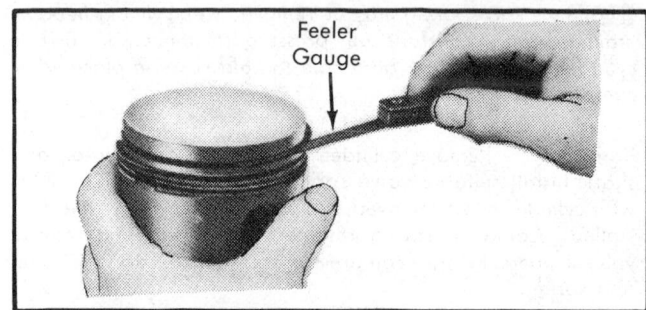

Fig. 7 Measuring Piston Ring Side Clearance with Feeler Gauge

PISTON PINS

Removal — Remove cylinders and mark pistons before removing for proper installation. Using suitable pliers (VW122b), remove piston pin circlips and push piston pin out of piston.

Installation — **1)** Check fit of pin in piston. At room temperature piston pin should be light push fit. If pin is too loose, both pin and piston must be replaced.

2) Install one circlip in piston on side facing flywheel. Position piston on connecting rod and push piston pin through piston. Replace remaining circlip. Replace remaining components in reverse of removal.

NOTE — *Piston may be heated to ease pin installation.*

CRANKSHAFT MAIN & CONNECTING ROD BEARINGS

CRANKCASE

Crankcase must be taken apart to replace connecting rods, connecting rod bearings and main bearings. It is also necessary to disassemble crankcase to remove crankshaft, camshaft, and camshaft bearings.

Disassembly — **1)** Remove engine from vehicle and remove cylinder heads, cylinders, and pistons. Remove flywheel or drive plate, and crankshaft pulley. Remove distributor, distributor drive shaft and fuel pump.

2) Remove oil cooler, oil filter and bracket, and oil pump assembly. *See Oil Pump Removal.* Remove rear engine carrier crossmember, bonded rubber mountings, and fan hub. Remove oil pan and oil filler pipe mounting bracket bolt.

VANAGON 4-CYLINDER (Cont.)

3) Remove six 10 mm main bearing nuts and bolts and five 8 mm nuts and bolts from crankcase flange. Using spring clips, clamp tappets in right half of crankcase and lift off right hand crankcase half.

CAUTION — *Never insert tools between crankcase flanges to separate halves. If stuck together, use rubber hammer to loosen right hand half from left.*

Reassembly — 1) Thoroughly clean and inspect both crankcase halves. Remove old sealing compound from mating surfaces and from all bolts, studs and washers. Blow out oil passages with compressed air. Check studs for tightness and check oil suction pipe for tightness.

2) Install crankshaft with connecting rods, in lett side crankcase half, making sure dowel pins are properly seated in bearings. Install camshaft. *See Camshaft Installation.* Install camshaft plug using liquid sealer all around plug. Spread liquid sealer over mating surfaces of crankcase halves.

3) Using spring clips, clamp tappets in right hand half of crankcase to join crankcase halves. Coat main bearing bolt heads (10 mm) with sealer and install in crankcase.

NOTE — *Install plastic dampers (part No. 021 101 107) on shank of main bearing bolts whether or not originally equipped.*

4) Coat the sealing nuts for main bearing bolts with sealer and install nuts with sealing rings outward. Tighten main bearing nuts and bolts and hand turn crankshaft to check for free movement. Coat bolt heads and nuts of 8 mm bolts with sealer, then install and tighten.

5) Check crankshaft end play. *See Thrust Bearing Alignment.* Install new crankshaft oil seals. *See Front Crankshaft Oil Seal Replacement and Rear Crankshaft Oil Seal Replacement.* Install remaining components in reverse of removal procedure.

MAIN & CONNECTING ROD BEARING SERVICE

1) With crankshaft and connecting rod assembly removed, remove snap ring securing distributor drive gear and crankshaft gear to crankshaft. Remove distributor drive gear and crankshaft gear by pressing or using suitable mandrel (VW457). Remove number 3 bearing. Remove connecting rods.

2) Thoroughly clean and inspect crankshaft. Blow out oil passages with compressed air. Check runout of crankshaft. If runout exceeds .0008" (.020 mm), regrind crankshaft to next undersize.

3) Check crankshaft journals for wear. If journals are worn more than .0012" (.030 mm), regrind crankshaft to next undersize. Lubricate and install number 3 bearing.

4) Heat crankshaft gear to approximately 176° F (80° C) in an oil bath and install on crankshaft over Woodruff key. Chamfer on gear bore must face number 3 main bearing journal. Install spacer, distributor drive gear and lock ring (circlip).

5) Using Plastigage method, check main and connecting rod bearings. If main bearing clearance on Nos. 1 and 3 exceeds .007" (.18 mm), .0067" (.17 mm) on No. 2, or .0075" (.19 mm) on No. 3; replace bearing. If clearance on any connecting rod bearing exceeds .007" (.15 mm), replace bearing.

6) Install numbers 1, 3 and 4 main bearings on crankshaft. *See Step 4)* for number 3 main bearing installation. Install lower bearing half of number 2 in crankcase, ensuring that dowel in crankcase engages hole in bearing half. Turn bearings on crankshaft to properly position oil holes and dowel holes. In-

stall bearing halves in cap and rod so that tangs in shells engage notches in rod bore. Fit to crankshaft with numbers on rod and cap on same side. Forged mark on rod must face UP when crankshaft is installed.

NOTE — *Lightly tap both sides of connecting rod with hammer to eliminate slight pinching of bearing shells when installing connecting rod.*

7) Check connecting rod side play with feeler gauge. If side play exceeds .0275" (.70 mm), replace connecting rod. Install crankshaft and connecting rod assembly as previously outlined. Check crankshaft end play. *See Thrust Bearing Alignment.*

Connecting Rod

Feeler Gauge

Crankshaft

Fig. 8   Using a Feeler Gauge to Check Connecting Rod Side Clearance

CRANKSHAFT END PLAY

NOTE — *Crankshaft end play is checked with engine assembled.*

1) Install flywheel with 2 shims, but do not install "O" ring and crankshaft oil seal. Attach dial indicator to crankcase and measure back and forth movement of crankshaft.

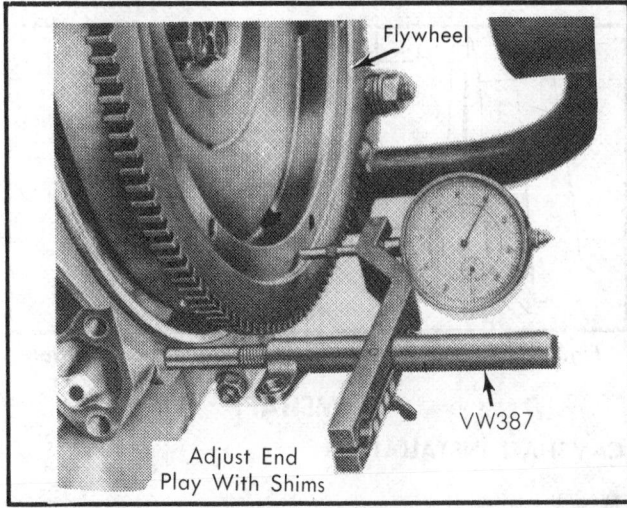

Flywheel

VW387

Adjust End Play With Shims

Fig. 9   Using a Dial Indicator to Check Crankshaft End Play

Volkswagen Engines

VANAGON 4-CYLINDER (Cont.)

2) Calculate necessary thickness of third shim. Install third shim and recheck end play. Thickness of shim is etched on face of shim, always use three shims to obtain correct end play.

Thrust Bearing Shims	
MM Markings on Shim	**Inch Equivalent**
.24 mm	.0095"
.30 mm	.0118"
.32 mm	.0126"
.34 mm	.0134"
.36 mm	.0142"
.38 mm	.0150"

3) With correct shim thickness determined, install crankshaft oil seal. *See Front Crankshaft Oil Seal.* Install flywheel, tighten bolts as required, and recheck crankshaft end play.

CRANKSHAFT REAR OIL SEAL

Removal & Installation — Remove blower impeller and pull impeller hub off crankshaft with suitable tool (VW185). Pry old seal out, using caution to avoid scratching shaft or crankcase. Clean recess and chamfer edges of seal seat, if necessary. Coat outside of seal lightly with sealer and start into position by hand. Press into final position with tool (VW190) and lightly lubricate fan hub before completing installation.

CRANKSHAFT FRONT OIL SEAL

Removal & Installation — Remove flywheel and carefully pry out old seal. Clean seat and chamfer edges if necessary. Apply thin film of sealer to outside edges and start seal into recess by hand. Seal lip must point toward crankcase. Complete installation with tool (VW191). Lubricate contact surface on flywheel and install flywheel.

DISTRIBUTOR DRIVE INSTALLATION

When crankcase has been assembled and remaining components installed, distributor drive must be installed. Rotate crankshaft until No. 1 piston is at TDC of compression stroke. Align timing mark on pulley with 0° mark on ignition timing scale. Insert distributor drive with slot at a 12° angle to center line of engine. Small segment of slot faces coil side. *See Fig. 10.*

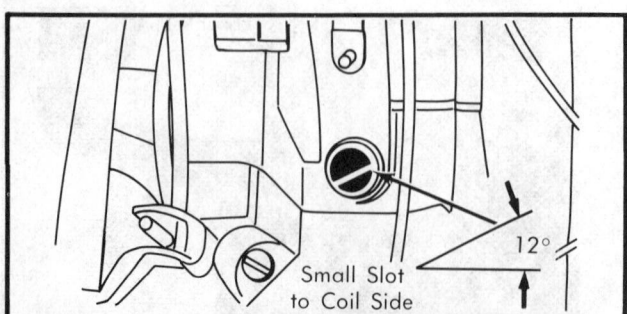

Fig. 10   Engine Distributor Drive Installation Position

CAMSHAFT

CAMSHAFT INSTALLATION

1) With camshaft removed, check riveting of camshaft gear to camshaft. Check camshaft for maximum runout of .0015" (.040 mm). If beyond limit, replace camshaft.

2) Check gear backlash with camshaft and crankshaft installed in crankcase half. Correct backlash is .002" (.05 mm). Gears have correct fit when crankshaft is rotated backwards and camshaft does not try to lift out of bearings.

Fig. 11   Position of Camshaft Timing Gear

3) If camshaft rises out of bearings, teeth on camshaft gear have the wrong pitch radius for crankshaft gear. Camshafts with gears that have various pitch radii are available. Pitch radius is stamped on inner face of timing gear.

4) Install camshaft with "O" stamped in tooth on outside of camshaft gear between 2 teeth with punch marks on crankshaft gear. Assemble crankcase halves as previously outlined. *See Fig. 11.*

CAMSHAFT END PLAY

Camshaft end play is checked with camshaft installed in crankcase half. Measure back and forth movement of camshaft with a dial indicator. If end play exceeds .006" (.16 mm), replace camshaft and/or bearings.

VALVE TIMING

Install camshaft with "O" stamped in tooth on outside of camshaft gear between 2 teeth with punch marks on crankshaft gear. *See Fig. 11.*

ENGINE OILING

Oil Capacity — 3.2 qts. Add .5 qt. with filter change.

Oil Pressure — 29 psi (2.04 kg/cm^2) at 2000 RPM with engine at 176°F (80°C).

Oil Filter — Full-flow, throw-away type oil filter.

Pressure Regulator Valves — Oil pressure relief valve, used to protect oil cooler from excessive pressure, is located in crankcase under oil filter. Oil pressure control valve, used to control oil pressure to bearings, is located in crankcase below oil breather. Oil pressure relief spring should have length of 1.54" (39 mm) at 15-19 lbs. (6.8-8.8 kg) load. Oil pressure control valve spring should have a length of 1.02" (26 mm) at 3¾-4⅜ lbs. (1.7-2.0 kg) load.

Volkswagen Engines

VANAGON 4-CYLINDER (Cont.)

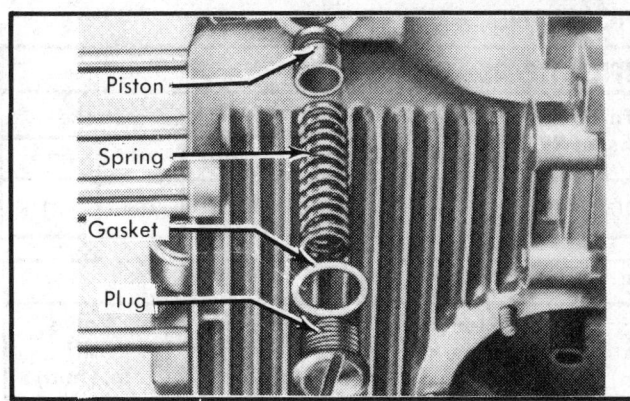

Fig. 12 Exploded View of Relief Valve Components

ENGINE OILING SYSTEM

Full pressure lubrication system utilizing a gear-type oil pump and installed in rear of engine and driven by camshaft. Oil is pumped through oil filter, oil cooler and into main oil passages in crankcase. Crankshaft main and connecting rod journals are oiled through cross-drilled oil passages in the crankcase. Oil is pumped to camshaft through oil passages that also lubricate valve tappets. Oil flows through push rods to lubricate rocker arms and shafts. Valve stems are lubricated by splash oil from rocker arms. Excess oil flows back into crankcase through push rod tubes. Cylinder walls and piston pins are lubricated by splash oil.

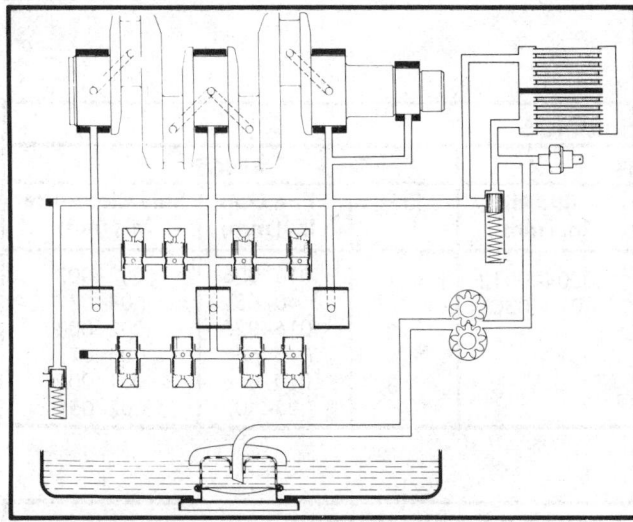

Fig. 13 Distribution of Oil For Engine Lubrication

OIL COOLER

To remove oil cooler, remove cooling air fan housing, three 6 mm nuts with washers attaching oil cooler to rear of crankcase, and bolts attaching oil cooler support strap. Remove support strap and oil cooler as unit. Always use new rubber seals when installing oil cooler.

OIL PUMP

Removal — Remove engine. Remove 4 nuts holding oil pump housing. Using 2 levers, pry oil pump out of crankcase. Oil pump insert can be removed with puller (VW803). *See Fig. 15.*

Inspection — Check housing for excessive wear, mainly in gear seating portions. Measure gear backlash for wear.

Backlash must not exceed .008″ (.20 mm). Replace bearing plate if scored.

Installation — Hand turn oil pump drive shaft until fully engaged in camshaft. Rotate crankshaft two revolutions. Pump plate should now be aligned with camshaft. Refit new gasket and reverse removal procedure for remaining components.

ENGINE COOLING

Thermostat — At 185-194°F (85-90°C), thermostat length should be at least 1¹³⁄₁₆″ (46 mm) measured from shoulders on bellows shaft.

COOLING SYSTEM

Engine is cooled by a radial blower mounted to rear end of crankshaft. Blower draws air through opening in blower shroud at rear of engine. Blower shroud is two-piece unit, mounted around blower and attached to crankcase. As air is drawn in, it is directed over finned cylinders and cylinder heads by deflector plates. As engine warms up, thermostat opens flaps completely to allow total flow of air.

BLOWER SHROUD REMOVAL

1) Remove engine as previously outlined. Remove ignition timing scale, fan with crankshaft pulley and alternator belt.

2) Disconnect cooling air control cable from control flap shaft. Remove four nuts attaching blower shroud to crankcase and pull assembly to rear and off engine. To install, reverse removal procedure. Adjust air flap control cable by pushing flaps into closed position and tighten cable.

3) Disconnect flap actuating cable from control shaft. Remove nuts securing shroud to crankcase and remove both halves of blower shroud.

4) To install, reverse removal procedure. Adjust air flap control by pushing flaps into closed position and tighten cable control.

5) Install drive belt and tighten alternator into proper belt tensioning position. Belt should have .4-.6″ (10-15 mm) deflection when pressed firmly in middle with thumb. Install cover plates and engine.

TIGHTENING SPECIFICATIONS

Application	Ft. Lbs. (N•m)
Connecting Rod Nut	25 (34)
Crankcase Half Nuts (8 mm)	14 (19)
Crankcase Half Sealing Nuts (10 mm)	25 (34)
Cylinder Head Nuts	22 (30)
Rocker Shaft-to-Cylinder Head Nuts	11 (15)
Heat Exchanger-to-Cylinder Head	16 (22)
Oil-Pan-to-Crankcase Nuts	9 (12)
Drive Plate-to-Crankshaft	65 (90)
Hub-to-Crankshaft Bolt	22 (30)
Fan-to-Hub	14 (19)
Engine-to-Transmission	22 (30)
Oil Pump-to-Crankcase	18 (25)
Oil Cooler-to-Crankcase	14 (19)
Flywheel-to-Crankshaft	80 (110)
Torque Converter-to-Drive Plate	18 (25)
Pressure Plate-to-Flywheel	18 (25)

Volkswagen Engines

VANAGON 4-CYLINDER (Cont.)
ENGINE SPECIFICATIONS

GENERAL SPECIFICATIONS

Year	Displ.		Carburetor	HP at RPM	Torque (Ft. Lbs. at RPM)	Compr. Ratio	Bore		Stroke	
	cu. ins.	cc					in.	mm	in.	mm
1981	120	1970	Fuel Injection	67@4200	101@3000	7.3:1	3.70	94	2.80	71

VALVES

Engine & Valve	Head Diam. In. (mm)	Face Angle	Seat Angle	Seat Width In. (mm)	Stem Diameter In. (mm)	Stem Clearance In. (mm)	Valve Lift In. (mm)
1970 cc							
Int.	1.547 (39.3)	29.5	30°	.070-.086 (1.80-2.20)	.313 (7.95)	.018 (.46)	.....
Exh.	1.299 (33.0)	45°	45°	.070-.098 (2.00-2.50)	.351 (8.92)	.014 (.35)	.....

VALVE SPRINGS

Engine	Free Length In. (mm)	PRESSURE Lbs. @ In. (kg @ mm)	
		Valve Closed	Valve Open
1970 cc Int. & Exh.	.....	168-186@1.14 (76-84@29)	.....

CAMSHAFT

Engine	Journal Diam. In. (mm)	Clearance In. (mm)	Lobe Lift In. (mm)
1970 cc	.9839-.9843 (24.991-25.001)	.0008-.0020 (.020-.051)	.....

PISTONS, PINS, RINGS

Engine	PISTONS	PINS			RINGS		
	Clearance In. (mm)	Piston Fit In. (mm)	Rod Fit In. (mm)	Rings	End Gap In. (mm)	Side Clearance In. (mm)	
1970 cc	.001-.002 (.02-.05)	①	.0004-.0012 (.010-.030)	1	.016-.026 (.40-.65)	.002-.003 (.04-.07)	
				2	.016-.026 (.40-.65)	.002-.003 (.04-.07)	
				3	.010-.016 (.25-.40)	.001-.002 (.02-.05)	

① — Push fit with light thumb pressure at room temperature.

CRANKSHAFT MAIN & CONNECTING ROD BEARINGS

Engine	MAIN BEARINGS				CONNECTING ROD BEARINGS		
	Journal Diam. In. (mm)	Clearance In. (mm)	Thrust Bearing	Crankshaft End Play In. (mm)	Journal Diam. In. (mm)	Clearance In. (mm)	Side Play In. (mm) ①
1970 cc No. 1	2.3609-2.3617 (59.967-59.987)	.0016-.0039 (.041-.099)	No. 1	.0027-.0050 (.07-.13)	1.9677-1.9685 (49.98-50.00)	.0008-.0027 (.020-.069)	.004-.016 (.10-.41)
2	2.3609-2.3617 (59.967-59.987)	.0012-.0035 (.030-.089)					
3	2.3609-2.3617 (59.967-59.987)	.0016-.0039 (.041-.099)					
4	1.5739-1.5748 (39.977-40.025)	.0020-.0039 (.051-.099)					

① — Limit .028″ (.7 mm).

DASHER, RABBIT, RABBIT PICKUP & VANAGON 4-CYLINDER DIESEL

ENGINE CODING

ENGINE IDENTIFICATION

Engine identification is stamped on left side of cylinder block on machined pad near No. 3 cylinder.

Engine Identification	
Application	**Code**
Vanagon	CS
All Others	CR

ENGINE, CYLINDER HEAD & MANIFOLDS

ENGINE

NOTE — *Manufacturer recommends that engine/transmission assembly be LOWERED out of Rabbit models as a unit.*

Removal (Rabbit & Pickup) — 1) Disconnect ground strap at battery and open coolant expansion tank. Open heater valve and drain all coolant from system at thermostat flange. Remove radiator with fan. Remove alternator and detach fuel filter from body.

NOTE — *Never drain coolant while engine is hot.*

2) Disconnect wires for fuel shut-off solenoid, glow plugs, oil pressure switch and coolant temperature sensor. Disconnect hoses for heater and expansion tank. Remove fuel supply and return lines and disconnect accelerator cable with bracket from injection pump. Disconnect cold start cable.

3) On air conditioned vehicles, remove air conditioner compressor and mounting brackets and set out of way without disconnecting hoses. On all models, disconnect wires from starter and back-up light switch and ground from transmission mount. On manual transmission models, detach clutch cable and remove relay shaft lever.

4) Remove exhaust flex pipe nuts or spring clips. Disconnect drive shafts from drive flanges. Remove starter, horn, oil filter and front engine mount. Remove axle nuts and disconnect lower ball joints from bearing housings, then remove drive shaft while holding strut assembly away from vehicle.

NOTE — *Remove axle nuts with vehicle sitting on ground.*

5) Reconnect ball joints so vehicle may be lowered onto wheels. Remove complete rear mount. Remove right front wheel. Attach suitable sling (US 1105) to engine and lift slightly. On manual transmission models, remove relay shaft and gearshift lever rods.

6) On all models, remove bolts holding side mounts to body. Lower engine/transmission assembly to dolly. Raise vehicle to clear and remove assembly.

Installation — To install, reverse removal procedures noting that fuel supply and return union screws are not interchanged. Fuel return pipe union screw is marked "OUT" on hex. head.

Removal (Dasher) — 1) Disconnect battery ground strap and open heater valve. Drain cooling system by removing thermostat and remove thermoswitch connector. Remove radiator with fan and shroud. Disconnect fuel supply and return lines at injection pump.

2) Detach accelerator cable and bracket from pump body. Disconnect cold start cable. Disconnect wires for fuel shut off solenoid, coolant temperature sensor, oil pressure switch, and glow plugs. Disconnect coolant and vacuum hoses. Disconnect clutch cable from bracket and lever on manual transmission models.

3) Loosen right engine mount at top and bottom. Remove alternator. Remove entire front engine mount and loosen left engine mount at top. Remove exhaust pipe from manifold and bracket from transmission. Remove starter. Remove engine/transmission bolts and flywheel cover plate bolts.

4) Install support bar under transmission and attach suitable engine sling (US 1105). Raise engine until assembly hits steering rack housing and remove left engine mount. Detach engine from transmission. Lift from vehicle while at the same time turning to clear body.

Installation — Ensure that dowel bushings fit block properly and install intermediate plate on bushings. (Use grease to stick plate to block.) Place starter on engine carrier before installing engine. Complete installation in reverse sequence of removal. Ensure that all mounts, cables and pipes are aligned and tightened without tension.

Removal (Vanagon) — 1) Disconnect battery ground cable. Remove top of air cleaner. Remove lower engine cover. Open coolant expansion tank cap. Disconnect lower hose from water pump at connecting pipe to radiator. Disconnect center hose from water pump.

2) Disconnect wiring from oil pressure switch, temperature sensors and glow plugs. Disconnect all remaining fuel, coolant, emission control and vacuum lines and position out of way. Disconnect accelerator cable from pump lever and bracket. Disconnect cold start cable.

3) Disconnect wire from fuel shut-off solenoid. Remove coolant reservoir. Remove oil fill cap and dipstick. Remove nuts from rear engine mounts (leave bolts in place). Remove all (7) engine/transmission mounting bolts. Remove bolts. Remove support member. Support engine with a crane and adapter (3058 or equivalent).

4) Remove nuts from front engine mount and remove engine mount bolts. Lower engine/transmission assembly until engine can be separated from transmission. Support transmission, remove engine from transmission and lower out of vehicle.

Installation — To install, reverse removal procedures noting that fuel supply and return union screws are not interchanged. Fuel return pipe union screw is marked "OUT" on hexagonal head.

CYLINDER HEAD & MANIFOLDS

NOTE — *Cylinder head may be removed and installed with engine in vehicle. Complete removal and installation procedures for Vanagon not available from manufacturer.*

Volkswagen Engines

DASHER, RABBIT, RABBIT PICKUP & VANAGON 4-CYLINDER DIESEL (Cont.)

Removal — 1) Remove air cleaner and ducting, then drain cooling system. Remove camshaft drive belt. Unbolt thermostat housing from water pump. Disconnect battery ground strap.

NOTE — *Do NOT drain coolant while engine is hot.*

2) Disconnect accelerator cable from injection pump. Detach fuel lines at injectors by unscrewing unions. Disconnect wire from glow p'ig bus, temperature sending wire and any other wires which could interfere with removal of cylinder head.

3) Remove spring clips holding exhaust pipe to manifold using clip remover tool (3059 or equivalent). Unbolt exhaust pipe support from engine/transaxle assembly (if equipped). From underneath vehicle, remove bolts and nuts holding exhaust manifold to cylinder head. Remove manifold from head.

4) Disconnect coolant hoses from head and remove any other hoses which may interfere with head removal. Remove cylinder head cover bolts and retaining plate. Carefully lift off cover and gasket. Loosen head bolts in reverse order of tightening sequence. See *Fig. 2*. Lift off head. Remove injectors and glow plugs to prevent damage while working on head.

5) Remove combustion chamber inserts by placing drift through injector hole and tapping out with hammer. Prior to installation, pre-chamber inserts must be reinstalled. When installing injectors, new heat shields must be installed between each injector and cylinder head. Place new shield in position with recess upward, toward injector. Tighten injector.

NOTE — *Combustion chamber inserts are NOT supplied as spare parts on latest models. If inserts are damaged it will be necessary to replace cylinder head.*

Installation — 1) Clean gasket surface and ensure that cylinder head and block are not warped. Maximum distortion of .004" (.010 mm) is allowed. If installing on original piston and block assembly select a new head gasket that has the same marks as the original.

2) To determine proper gasket, measure projection of piston above block when at TDC. Select proper gasket from following table:

Available Cylinder Head Gaskets

Piston Projection in Inches (mm)	Gasket Thickness in Inches (mm)	Identification Notches
.025-.032 (.63-.82) ...	.055 (1.40)	1
.033-.036 (.83-.92)	.059 (1.5)	2
.037-.040 (.93-1.02) ..	.063 (1.6)	3

Gasket must be installed with word "OBEN" facing up.

CAUTION — *Due to the aluminum construction of the head, do not use metal brushes or scrapers to clean gasket sealing surface or combustion chambers. Use solvent and wooden or plastic scrapers to remove foreign material. Do not mar piston tops when cleaning cylinder block. Ensure that all bolt holes and cylinder bores are absolutely free of debris prior to installing head or bolts.*

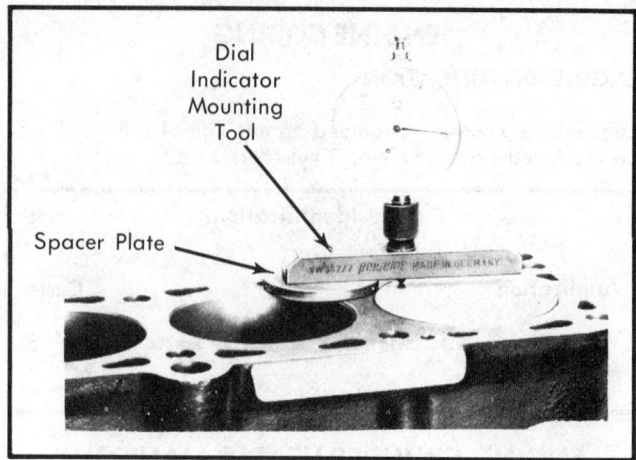

Fig. 1   Measuring Piston Projection

3) Lower head carefully onto gasket. Use guide pins (3070) or 2 of the outermost bolts and washers to keep gasket and head aligned with block. Tighten bolts in the sequence shown in *Fig. 2* and in steps shown in table. To complete installation, reverse removal procedure.

4) On Vanagon, turn bolts an additional ½ turn after step No. 3 of table. Run engine to operating temperature. Stop engine and tighten bolts an additional ¼ turn. After 1000 miles, retighten another ¼ turn.

5) On all other models, run engine until warm and recheck final torque. After 1000 miles, loosen bolts 30° and retighten again to 66 ft. lbs. (90 N·m).

Cylinder Head Bolt Tightening

Application	Ft. Lbs. (N·m)
Step No. 1	
Vanagon	29 (39)
All Others	35 (48)
Step No. 2	
Vanagon	43 (58)
All Others	50 (68)
Step No. 3	
Vanagon	54 (73)
All Others	66 (90)

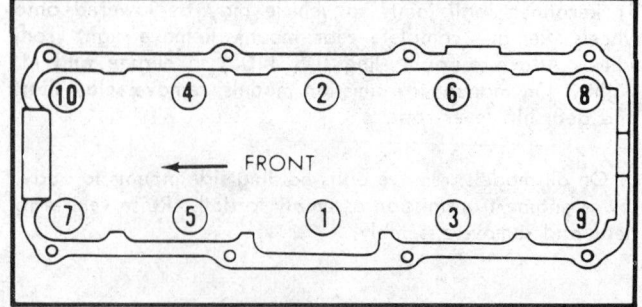

Fig. 2   Cylinder Head Tightening Sequence (Loosen in Reverse Order)

DASHER, RABBIT, RABBIT PICKUP & VANAGON 4-CYLINDER DIESEL (Cont.)

CAMSHAFT

TIMING BELT

NOTE — *Sprockets do not have to be removed to replace drive belt.*

Removal — 1) Loosen alternator and remove V-belt. Remove crankshaft V-belt pulley. Remove air cleaner and ducting. Remove drive belt and cylinder head cover. Remove timing plug on top of bell housing. Rotate engine to bring No. 1 piston to TDC. Check that TDC mark on flywheel is aligned with reference.

2) Using locking tool (2065A for Vanagon, 2065 for other models) lock camshaft in positon. Align tool by turning camshaft until one end of tool touches cylinder head. Measure gap at other end with feeler gauge. Insert feeler gauges of ½ thickness measured between tool and cylinder head at each end of tool.

3) Lock injection pump sprocket at TDC with special pin (2064). Loosen belt tensioner and remove timing belt from sprockets.

CAUTION — *Do not turn camshaft or crankshaft with drive belt removed.*

Installation — 1) Ensure that flywheel is still aligned with TDC mark. With camshaft and injection pump locked in place, loosen camshaft sprocket bolt ½ turn. Lightly tap camshaft gear loose from camshaft. Install drive belt so there is no slack between camshaft sprocket and injection pump and injection pump and crankshaft sprocket.

2) Tighten tension adjuster just enough to keep belt firmly in place. Remove injection pump locking pin. Adjust belt tension by turning tensioner until scale reads 12-13 on tension adjuster tool (VW 210). Tighten camshaft sprocket bolt and tensioner adjuster lock nut. Remove lock from camshaft.

3) Turn crankshaft 2 revolutions in direction of engine rotation. Using a rubber hammer, strike belt once between camshaft sprocket and injection pump sprocket. Recheck belt tension and install remaining components in reverse order of removal. Check injection pump timing.

CAMSHAFT

Removal — Remove timing belt. Loosen bearing caps in following sequence: 5, 1, and 3, then loosen caps 2 and 4 diagonally. Bearing caps are numbered front (sprocket end) to rear (flywheel end).

Inspection — 1) Number and remove cam followers, then reinstall camshaft using only end (1 and 5) bearing caps. Check axial play of camshaft with dial indicator. If play exceeds .006″ (.15 mm), either head or camshaft is worn and must be replaced.

2) To measure camshaft bearing clearance, install caps one at a time and check with either a dial indicator or Plastigage. Check camshaft runout by installing shaft between centers and applying dial indicator at center bearing journal. Runout must not exceed .0004″ (.01 mm) when camshaft is rotated.

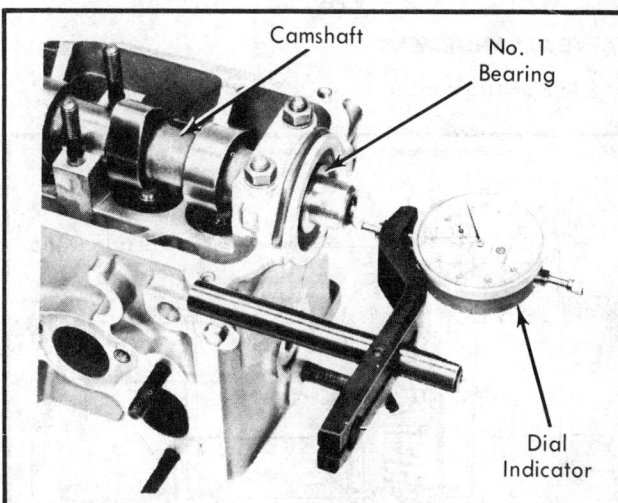

Fig. 4   Measuring Camshaft End Play

3) Inspect cam lobes, followers, and all bearing surfaces. Ensure that all oil passages are clean. Replace any components showing signs of pitting, galling or signs of seizure.

Installation — Lightly lubricate all components for assembly. Install cam followers in original bores with matching adjusting discs. Place camshaft and number 2 and 4 bearing caps in position with cam lobes of No. 1 cylinder pointing upward. Gradually tighten all 4 bearing cap nuts until camshaft is fully seated; then install caps 5, 3, and 1. Use seal installer (10-203 or equivalent) to install front oil seal and complete installation in reverse order of removal.

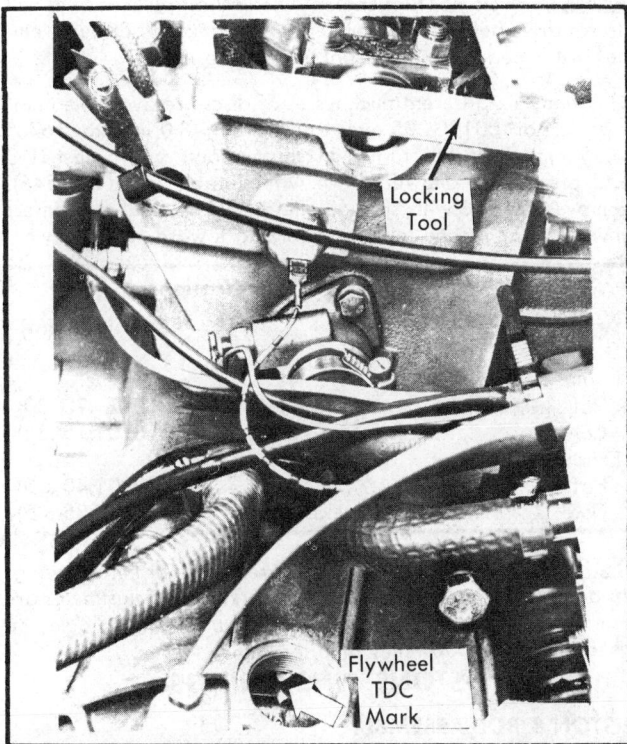

Fig. 3   Flywheel TDC Mark and Camshaft Locking Tool

DASHER, RABBIT, RABBIT PICKUP & VANAGON 4-CYLINDER DIESEL (Cont.)

VALVE TIMING

See TIMING BELT procedures in this article.

INJECTION PUMP TIMING

1) To check injection pump timing, set crankshaft to TDC on No. 1 cylinder and align marks on flywheel and clutch housing. Check marks on injection pump sprocket and mounting plate.

2) If timing needs adjustment, remove plug from injection pump cover and install adapter and dial indicator in place of plug. Preload dial indicator to .097" (2.5 mm).

3) Turn engine slowly counterclockwise until dial indicator needle stops moving. Zero indicator. Turn engine clockwise until TDC mark on flywheel is lined up with reference mark.

4) Check dial indicator against specifications listed in table. If out of adjustment, loosen bolts on mounting plate and support. Turn pump to adjust timing and tighten bolts.

Injection Pump Timing Specifications	
Application	**Range in Inches (mm)**
Dasher	① .033-.037 (.83-.93)
Rabbit & Rabbit Pickup	
With no paint dot	① .033-.037 (.83-.93)
With yellow paint dot	② .043-.047 (1.1-1.2)
Vanagon	① .031-.035 (.78-.88)
① — Set to .034" (.86 mm).	
② — Set to .045" (1.15 mm).	

VALVES

VALVE ARRANGEMENT

E-I-E-I-I-E-I-E (front to rear).

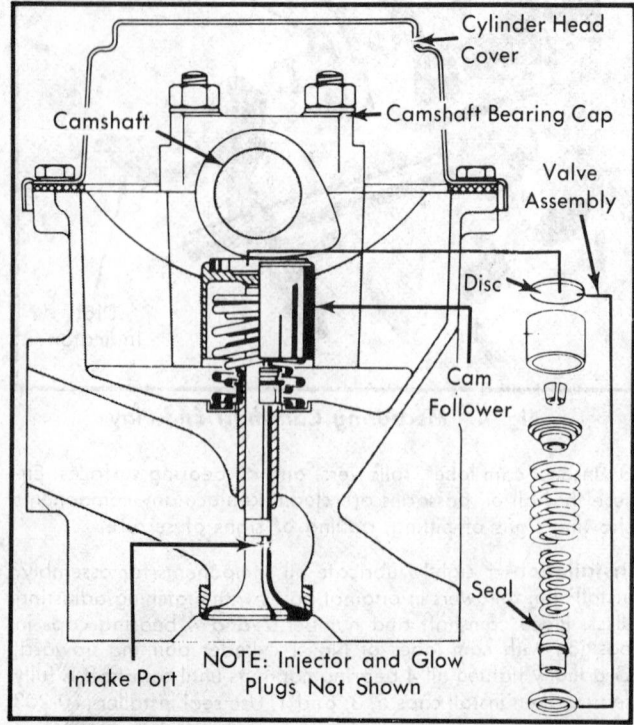

Fig. 5   End View of Camshaft and Valve Assembly

VALVE GUIDE SERVICING

1) To check for wear, insert NEW valve in clean valve guide until stem end is flush with spring end of guide. Use dial indicator to check that lateral (rocking) movement is no more than .051" (1.3 mm) when moved back and forth against indicator.

2) Prior to replacing worn guides, check that head is not cracked and that valve seats can be refaced. Press out old guides and coat new guides with oil. Press new guides in up to shoulder but do not use more than one ton of pressure once shoulder is seated. Hand ream guides to proper uniform diameter of .315-.316" (8.013-8.035 mm).

VALVE STEM SEALS AND SPRINGS

NOTE — *It is possible to replace valve springs and seals with head installed provided camshaft and tappets are removed. Piston of cylinder concerned must be at top dead center position.*

Use suitable spring compressor to depress spring and retainer. Remove keepers, then remove retainer and springs. Remove stem seal. Use protective sleeve over valve stem and install new seal. Complete assembly in reverse order of disassembly.

VALVE CLEARANCE ADJUSTMENT

1) Engine should be near operating temperature (coolant at about 95°F (35°C). Rotate crankshaft so that cam lobes for No. 1 cylinder (curb side) point upward. Check intake and exhaust clearance between heel of cam lobe and follower.

2) Use crankshaft pulley to rotate crankshaft 180° at a time and check No. 3, No. 4, and No. 2 clearance. If clearances are not within specifications, use thinner or thicker adjusting discs to increase or decrease clearance.

CAUTION — *Do not turn engine by camshaft pulley as this will stretch drive belt. Use a wrench to turn crankshaft or push vehicle in 4th gear to move crankshaft/valve train.*

3) Twenty-six different thicknesses of discs are available in increments of .0019" (.05 mm) from .1181" (3.0 mm) to .1673" (4.25 mm). To install, turn crankshaft about ¼ turn past TDC and press cam follower down with suitable tool (VW 546). Remove old disc with special pliers (VW 10-208) and insert new disc with etched thickness marking toward cam follower.

Valve Clearance Specifications	
Application	**In. (mm)**
Intake	
Hot	.008-.012 (.20-.30)
Cold	.006-.010 (.15-.25)
Exhaust	
Hot	.016-.020 (.40-.50)
Cold	.014-.018 (.35-.45)

NOTE — *Cold settings are given for reference as initial settings to be used during cylinder head rework. Final adjustments are made at normal operating temperatures and should be checked after 1000 miles of operation.*

PISTONS, PINS & RINGS

PISTON & ROD ASSEMBLY

Removal — Mark cylinder number on crown of each piston. If necessary, mark arrows pointing toward front of block on

DASHER, RABBIT, RABBIT PICKUP & VANAGON 4-CYLINDER DIESEL (Cont.)

piston crowns. Remove rod cap bolts and force piston out top of cylinder using wooden hammer handle. Mark rods and bearing caps for proper installation.

NOTE — *If ridge at top of cylinder prevents piston removal, use ridge reamer prior to further disassembly. DO NOT force piston out of cylinder.*

Installation — Turn crankshaft so No. 1 journal is at BDC. Install piston/rod assembly until ring compressor contacts block. Guide rod over journal and use wooden handle of hammer to push piston into cylinder. Repeat with No. 4 piston and rod assembly ensuring that tabs on bearing halves engage notches in respective rod and cap. Tighten caps on rods 1 and 4, then rotate crankshaft 180° and install No. 2 and No. 3 piston/rod assemblies.

PISTON PINS

Removal — Use needle-nose pliers to remove circlips. Press out pin and remove piston, noting direction piston is fitted to rod. If pin is too tight, heat piston to approximately 140°F (60°C) and then press out.

Installation — Check piston/pin fit for thumb push fit. Connecting rod/pin wear limit is .0015" (.04 mm). Connecting rod may be rebushed and honed to proper size if required. If pin is too loose in piston, replace both pin and piston.

FITTING PISTONS

Measure cylinder at 3 points: ⅜" (10 mm) from top and bottom, and at center of bore. Measure in line with and at 90° to thrust face. Cylinder wear limit is .0015" (.04 mm) out of round. If limit is exceeded, cylinders must be honed and new pistons fitted.

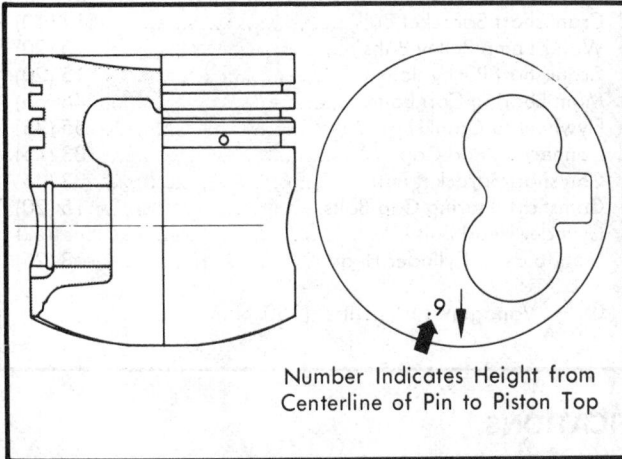

Number Indicates Height from Centerline of Pin to Piston Top

Fig. 6   Side and Top View of Diesel Piston

CRANKSHAFT MAIN & CONNECTING ROD BEARINGS

MAIN & CONNECTING ROD BEARINGS

1) Push crankshaft toward one end and measure end play at No. 3 (thrust) bearing. Main bearing caps are numbered "1"

through "5" with "1" at drive belt end and "5" at flywheel end. Measure connecting rod end play (side play). Check all bearing clearances with Plastigage, tightening bearings to 26 ft. lbs. (35 N·m).

2) Measure crankshaft journals to determine size and any out-of-round. Maximum allowable out of round is .0012" (.03 mm). Install main inserts with bearing half having oil groove into block. Lubricate bearings and install caps in original positions.

Crankshaft Journal Diameters		
Size	**Main Bearing In. (mm)①**	**Rod Bearing In. (mm)①**
Standard	2.125 (53.97)	1.810 (45.97)
1st US	2.115 (53.72)	1.800 (45.72)
2nd US	2.105 (53.47)	1.790 (45.47)
3rd US	2.095 (53.22)	1.780 (45.22)

① — Journal diameter is ±.0004" (.01 mm).

REAR MAIN BEARING OIL SEAL

NOTE — *Rear main bearing oil seal may be replaced with engine in vehicle. Transmission and flywheel must be removed.*

Removal — Insert screwdriver between crankshaft and flywheel flange and inside lip of seal. Pry seal out.

Installation — Install guide sleeve tool 2003/2A (or equivalent) over crankshaft flange. Start new seal into recess in carrier. Remove guide sleeve. Fit drive plate 2003/1 (or equivalent) and seat seal by tightening bolts.

FRONT MAIN BEARING OIL SEAL AND INTERMEDIATE SHAFT OIL SEAL

NOTE — *Diesel engine intermediate shaft rotates counterclockwise and utilizes a different seal than the gas engine. Arrow pointing counterclockwise on seal indicates correct application for Diesel model.*

Removal — Remove camshaft belt and crankshaft sprocket. On Vanagon, screw seal extractor 2085 (or equivalent) into seal to remove. On all others, pry seal from carrier using care not to damage carrier. Use seal extractor 10-219 (or equivalent) to remove seal.

Installation — Coat seal lips with oil and press into carrier until flush. Use special tool 10-203 (or equivalent). Remove steel sleeve from carrier and use aluminum part of the tool to drive seal in to a depth of .08" (2 mm) from front of carrier.

NOTE — *Same procedures are used for intermediate shaft seal except that intermediate shaft sprocket is removed. Seal is pressed in only until flush with carrier.*

Volkswagen Engines

DASHER, RABBIT, RABBIT PICKUP & VANAGON 4-CYLINDER DIESEL (Cont.)

ENGINE OILING

Crankcase Capacity		
Application	With Filter Change	Without Filter Change
Dasher	3.7 quarts	3.2 quarts
Rabbit & Rabbit Pickup	4.7 quarts	4.2 quarts
Vanagon	4.2 quarts	3.7 quarts

Oil Filter — Replaceable spin-on type.

Normal Oil Pressure — Minimum of 28 psi@2000 RPM and at normal operating temperature.

ENGINE OILING SYSTEM

Gear type oil pump provides oil for pressure feed to crankshaft journals, camshaft bearings, and intermediate shaft. A larger, heavy-duty oil filter and revised oil pump drive are used in the Diesel. Other lubrication characteristics are similar to the spark ignition engines.

OIL PUMP

Removal — Drain oil and remove oil pan. Remove pump mounting bolts and pump along with pick-up tube. Install in vise and remove pick-up tube.

Inspection — Check oil pump gear backlash with feeler gauge. Clearance should be between .002-.008" (.05-.20 mm). Measure pump gear end play using machinist's square and feeler gauge for .006" (.15 mm) clearance or less. If specifications are exceeded, replace gears or pump.

Installation — To install, assure that all mating surfaces are clean, install gaskets and reverse removal procedure.

ENGINE COOLING

Cooling System Capacity	
Application	Quarts
Dasher	5.9
Rabbit & Rabbit Pickup	7.3
Vanagon	16.9

Thermostat — Begins to open at 185°F (85°C) on Vanagon and 176°F (80°C) on all others. Fully open at 221°F (105°C) on Vanagon and 201°F (94°C) on all others. Fan thermoswitch starts fan at 200-208°F (93-98°C).

Radiator Cap — 11-16 psi for Vanagon, 17-19 for all others.

CAUTION — *Never drain the coolant while the engine is hot. Cylinder head or engine block could warp if not allowed to cool prior to draining.*

WATER PUMP

Removal — Drain cooling system. Disconnect battery ground cable and unplug alternator wires. Remove alternator and bracket. Disconnect thermostat housing and hoses from water pump. Remove bolts holding pump to camshaft belt cover and engine block and remove pump.

Installation — To install, reverse removal procedure and use new "O" ring in recess in pump mounting flange.

NOTE — *Do NOT use sealer between water pump mounting flange and engine block.*

TIGHTENING SPECIFICATIONS	
Application	Ft. Lbs. (N·m)
Timing Belt Tensioner Lock Nut	33 (45)
Intermediate Sprocket Bolt	33 (45)
Crankshaft Sprocket Bolt	①81 (110)
Water Pump Pulley Bolts	15 (20)
Crankshaft Pulley Bolts	15 (20)
Main Bearing Cap Bolts	48 (65)
Flywheel-to-Crankshaft Bolts	55 (75)
Connecting Rod Caps	33 (45)
Camshaft Sprocket Bolt	33 (45)
Camshaft Bearing Cap Bolts	15 (20)
Cylinder Head Bolts	See Text
Manifolds-to-Cylinder Head	18 (25)

① — Vanagon 110 ft. lbs. (150 N·m).

ENGINE SPECIFICATIONS

GENERAL SPECIFICATIONS										
Year	Displ.		Carburetor	HP at RPM①	Torque (Ft. Lbs. at RPM)②	Compr. Ratio	Bore		Stroke	
	cu. ins.	cc					in.	mm	in.	mm
1981 Diesel	97.0	1588	Fuel Inj.	52@4800	71.5@3000	23:1	3.012	76.5	23.40	86.40

① — Vanagon 48@4200 RPM.
② — Vanagon 71.5@2000 RPM.

DASHER, RABBIT, RABBIT PICKUP & VANAGON 4-CYLINDER DIESEL (Cont.)
ENGINE SPECIFICATIONS (Cont.)

VALVES

Engine & Valve	Head Diam. In. (mm)	Face Angle	Seat Angle	Seat Width In. (mm)	Stem Diameter In. (mm)	Stem Clearance In. (mm)	Valve Lift In. (mm)
1588 cc Diesel Intake	1.338 (40)	45°	45°	.079 (2.0)	.314 (7.97)	.051 (1.30)	.....
Exhaust	1.220 (31.0)	45°	45°	.095 (2.4)	.313 (7.95)	.051 (1.30)	.....

PISTONS, PINS, RINGS

Engine	PISTONS Clearance① In. (mm)	PINS Piston Fit In. (mm)	Rod Fit In. (mm)	RINGS Rings	End Gap In. (mm)②	Side Clearance In. (mm)③
1588 cc Diesel	.001 (.03)	Push Fit	.0004-.0008 (.01-02)	No. 1	.012-.020 (.30-.50)	.002-.004 (.06-.09)
				No. 2	.012-.020 (.30-.50)	.002-.003 (.06-.08)
				No. 3	.010-.016 (.25-.40)	.001-.002 (.03-.06)

① — Wear limit .028″ (.07 mm). ② — Wear Limit .039″ (1.0 mm).
③ — Wear limit Nos. 1 and 2, .008″ (.20 mm), No. 3, .006″ (.15 mm).

CRANKSHAFT MAIN & CONNECTING ROD BEARINGS

Engine	MAIN BEARINGS Journal Diam. In. (mm)	Clearance In. (mm)①	Thrust Bearing	Crankshaft End Play In. (mm)②	CONNECTING ROD BEARINGS Journal Diam. In. (mm)	Clearance In. (mm)③	Side Play In. (mm)
1588cc Diesel	2.124-2.125 (53.96-53.98)	.001-.003 (.03-.08)	No. 3	.003-.007 (.07-.17)	1.880-1.881 (47.76-47.78)	.0011-.0035 (.028-.088)	.014 (.37)

① — Wear Limit .007″ (.17 mm).   ② — Wear Limit .015″ (.37 mm).   ③ — Wear Limit .0047″ (.12 mm).

VALVE SPRINGS

Engine	Free Length In. (mm)	PRESSURE Lbs. @ In. (kg @ mm) Valve Closed	Valve Open
1588 cc Diesel Inner	.....	46-51@.719 (21-23@18.3)	.....
Outer	.....	96-106@.875 (43.5-48@22.3)	.....

CAMSHAFT

Engine	Journal Diam. In. (mm)	Clearance In. (mm)①	Lobe Lift In. (mm)
1588 cc Diesel	.....	.0008-.002 (.02-.05)	.....

① — End play .006″ (.1 mm)

Volvo Engines

B21F & B21FT 4-CYLINDER

ENGINE CODING

ENGINE IDENTIFICATION

Engine identification number is located on camshaft timing belt cover. Last 3 digits identify engine.

Engine Identification	
Application	**Code**
Models DL, GL, GLT (2130 cc)	
USA Federal	
Man. Trans.	498-920
Auto. Trans.	498-921
California	
Man. Trans.	498-892
Auto. Trans.	498-893
USA/California (MPG)	
Man. Trans.	498-896
Auto. Trans.	498-897
USA/California (Turbo)	
Man. Trans.	498-898

ENGINE, CYLINDER HEAD & MANIFOLDS

ENGINE

Removal —1) Remove battery. Disconnect windshield washer hose and engine compartment lamp. Remove hood. Remove rubber boot and snap ring at base of gearshift lever (manual transmission only).

2) Remove cap from expansion tank. Open radiator drain cock and drain coolant. Disconnect lower radiator hose at radiator, crankcase ventilation hose at cylinder head, and upper radiator hose at engine. Detach expansion tank hoses from radiator. Disconnect oil cooler lines for automatic transmission at radiator. On Turbo, disconnect oil cooler lines. Remove fan shroud screws, disconnect radiator, and lift radiator and fan shroud from vehicle.

3) Remove air cleaner and hose assembly. Loosen tensioner nut and remove belt from air pump. Disconnect hoses at pump and remove pump and bracket assembly. Remove vacuum pump after disconnecting hoses, including hose to brake power cylinder. Remove tensioner bar bolts, drive belt and power steering pump.

4) If equipped with air conditioning, remove crankshaft pulley and A/C drive belt. Reinstall pulley loosely. Disconnect and remove compressor and bracket.

5) Mark and disconnect four vacuum hoses at engine and two carbon filter hoses. Remove wire or connector from distributor, high tension lead from coil, and starter motor cables and clutch cable clamp from starter.

6) Detach wiring harness from voltage regulator. Disconnect throttle cable at pulley and A/C wire at solenoid on intake manifold.

7) Remove fuel cap to relieve pressure, and remove fuel hoses from filter and return pipe. Remove guard plate for ballast resistor, and disconnect two wire connectors from intake manifold micro switch, four in wiring harness, and two at ballast resistor.

8) Disconnect heater hoses at firewall and drain oil from engine. Remove exhaust pipe flange nuts and gasket. Remove front engine mounting bolts and front exhaust pipe mounting bracket. Disconnect gearshift control rod (automatic transmission) or clutch cable (manual transmission).

9) Disconnect speedometer cable, propeller shaft U-joint, and gearshift selector from control rod. If manual transmission has overdrive, disconnect wire to gearshift selector. Using a wooden block, place jack under transmission. Remove transmission support member.

10) Attach lifting yoke assembly (5035) to three engine lifting eyes, and adjust lifting beam (2810) to its rearmost position. Hoist slightly to release front engine mount dowels. Check for wires or hoses, and disconnect as necessary. Adjust lifting beam to forward position and lift engine from car.

Installation — To install, reverse removal procedure and check for proper installation of all lines, hoses and electrical leads.

INTAKE & EXHAUST MANIFOLDS

Removal — **1)** Disconnect battery ground cable, then remove air bellows from CI unit to intake manifold. Disconnect PCV hoses at intake manifold and flame arrester. Disconnect vacuum pump hose at intake manifold. Disconnect diverter valve hoses. Disconnect air pump with tensioner and position to one side.

2) Disconnect the following fuel lines: control pressure regulator (one hose), cold start injector (one hose), distributor pipe to engine (two hoses) front fuel filter to engine (two hoses), and injector hoses (four hoses). Disconnect wiring at control pressure regulator, cold start injector, and auxiliary air valve.

3) Remove air injection pipe. Disconnect throttle cable from intake manifold. Disconnect charcoal canister hoses and EGR valve hose from intake manifold. Remove intake manifold brace, attaching nuts, and intake manifold. Disconnect transmission fill pipe from flywheel housing (automatic transmissions only). Remove attaching nuts and exhaust manifold.

Installation — To install, reverse removal procedure and use new manifold gaskets. Tighten nuts and bolts to specifications.

CYLINDER HEAD

Removal — **1)** Drain cooling system at radiator and cylinder block. Disconnect battery ground cable. Disconnect upper radiator hose at engine. Disconnect air bellows between CI unit and air cleaner. Remove PCV hoses from intake manifold and oil trap on block. Disconnect vacuum pump hose at intake manifold.

2) Disconnect diverter valve hoses. Remove air pump and bracket. Disconnect the following fuel lines: control pressure regulator (one hose), cold start injector (one hose), distributor pipe to engine (two hoses), front fuel filter to engine (two hoses), and injector hoses (four hoses).

3) Disconnect wires at following components: control pressure regulator, cold start injector, auxiliary air valve, and temperature sender. Disconnect throttle cable from intake manifold. Disconnect charcoal canister hoses and EGR valve

B21F & B21FT 4-CYLINDER (Cont.)

hose from intake manifold. Disconnect transmission fill pipe from transmission housing (automatic transmissions only).

4) Remove water pipe rear clamp from manifold. Remove exhaust manifold to exhaust pipe attaching nuts. Remove intake manifold brace. Disconnect spark plug cables at plugs, then disconnect upper water hose at firewall. Remove timing belt cover, slacken drive belt tensioner and remove drive belt. Remove valve cover and cylinder head bolts. Lift cylinder head from engine.

Installation — 1) Install new head gasket with "TOP" mark upward. Be sure all contact surfaces are clean. Position cylinder head over gasket.

2) Dip head bolts and washers in engine oil before installation. Install and tighten bolts in sequence shown in *Fig. 1*.

3) Adjust valves. Reverse remainder of removal procedure and make final valve adjustment after running engine for 10 minutes. *See Valve Clearance Adjustment*. Retorque cylinder head bolts.

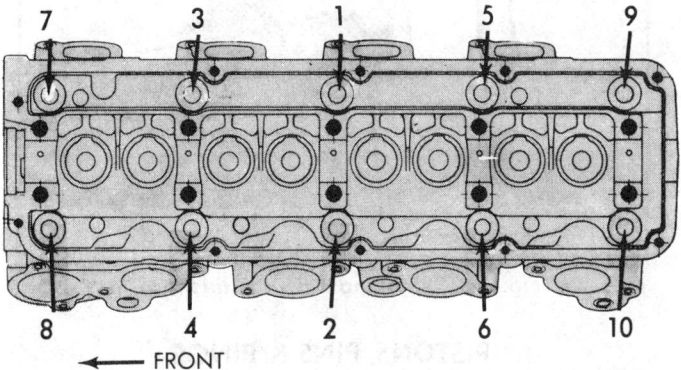

Fig. 1 Cylinder Head Tightening Sequence

CAMSHAFT

Removal — 1) Remove valve cover and gasket. Check and note markings on camshaft bearing caps. Remove center bearing cap and install holder tool (5021) to hold camshaft in place while removing remaining bearing caps.

2) Remove timing belt cover and slacken drive belt tensioner. Pull off drive belt and remove camshaft sprocket. Remove remaining bearing caps and take out front camshaft oil seal. Release screw on holder tool and lift out camshaft.

Installation — Ensure that dowel for sprocket is UP (12 o'clock position) and lubricate all bearing and friction surfaces. To complete installation, reverse removal procedure.

DRIVE BELT INSTALLATION

1) Install belt tensioner if previously removed. Align notch in crankshaft belt guide with timing mark on front cover. Rotate intermediate shaft so timing mark on sprocket aligns with mark on belt guard. Align marks on camshaft belt guide with timing mark on valve cover.

2) New drive belts have yellow markings. Two lines should fit toward crankshaft marks and next mark toward intermediate shaft mark. Place belt over crankshaft sprocket first, then intermediate shaft. Stretch belt on tension side and fit over camshaft sprocket. Slide back of belt inside tension roller.

3) Loosen nut on belt tensioner to permit spring tension to act against drive belt. Recheck timing marks for proper location and tighten tensioner nut. Attach pulley to front hub on crankshaft.

VALVES

VALVE ARRANGEMENT

E-I-E-I-E-I-E-I — Front to Rear.

VALVE GUIDE SERVICING

Removal & Installation — Heat cylinder head to 140° F (60° C) and press old guides out with drift (2818). To install, use intake guide drift (5027) and exhaust guide drift (5028) to press in new guides. Press in until drift contacts cylinder head to give proper height above cylinder head. Installed height for intake guide is .610"±.004" (15.5±.1 mm) and .709"±.004" (18.0±.1 mm) for exhaust guide.

NOTE — *Ensure that replacement guide is same size as old guide. At least 2000 lbs. (907 kg) force should be required to press in new guide; if not, head must be fitted with oversize guide.*

Fig. 2 Timing Marks for Crankshaft, Intermediate Shaft and Camshaft

B21F & B21FT 4-CYLINDER (Cont.)

VALVE SPRINGS

Removal & Installation — With cylinder head removed, compress valve springs using suitable valve spring compression tool, and remove valve retainers. Disassemble valve spring components and place valves in order in suitable valve rack. To install, place valves in position, fit valve guide seal, valve spring, upper washer and retainer.

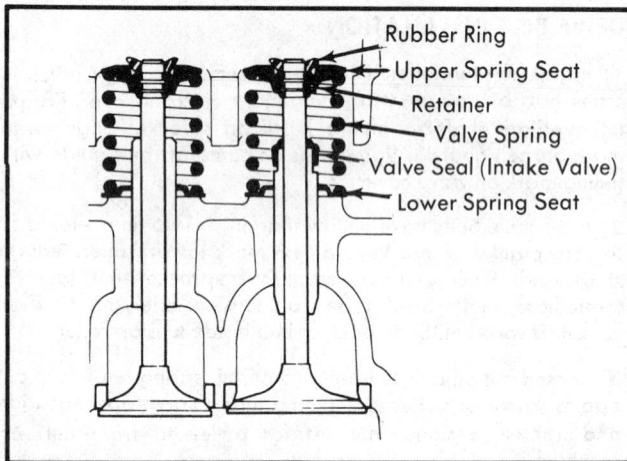

Rubber Ring
Upper Spring Seat
Retainer
Valve Spring
Valve Seal (Intake Valve)
Lower Spring Seat

Fig. 3   Valve and Guide Assembly

VALVE SPRING INSTALLED HEIGHT

Valve spring ends must be square. Installed height of valve spring cannot exceed specifications. Measure spring height from base of spring pad on cylinder head to underside of spring retainer.

VALVE CLEARANCE ADJUSTMENT

1) Valve clearance is adjusted with engine off, and may be done either warm or cold. Remove valve cover. Turn crankshaft center bolt until camshaft is in position for firing No. 1 cylinder. Both cam lobes should point up at equally large angles. Pulley timing mark should be on 0°.

2) Using feeler gauge, check valve clearance of No. 1 cylinder, measuring between camshaft lobe and discs. Intake and exhaust valves should have same clearances:

Valve Clearances	
When Checking	**In. (mm)**
Cold engine	.012-.018" (.30-.45 mm)
When Setting	**In. (mm)**
Cold Engine	.014-.016" (.35-.40 mm)
Hot Engine	.016-.018" (.40-.45 mm)

3) If clearance is incorrect, line up notches in valve depressors, so they are at right angles to engine center line. Install valve adjustment tool (5022) and turn handle downward until depressor groove is just above edge of cylinder head. Remove adjusting disc with special pliers (5026).

4) Using micrometer, measure thickness of disc. Then determine proper thickness required of new disc to bring clearance within specifications. For example: Measure existing clearance and subtract correct clearance. Difference should be added to thickness of old disc to determine thickness of new disc required. Discs are available in thicknesses ranging from .130" (3.30 mm) to .177" (4.50 mm) in increments of .002" (.05 mm).

5) Discs should be oiled and installed with marks down. Remove valve adjustment tool (5022), rotate crankshaft to correct firing position for No. 3 cylinder and repeat procedure. Then adjust valve clearance for No. 4 and No. 2 cylinders. When all four cylinders have been adjusted, turn camshaft a few turns and recheck valve clearance at all cylinders.

6) Position gasket on cylinder head and install valve cover.

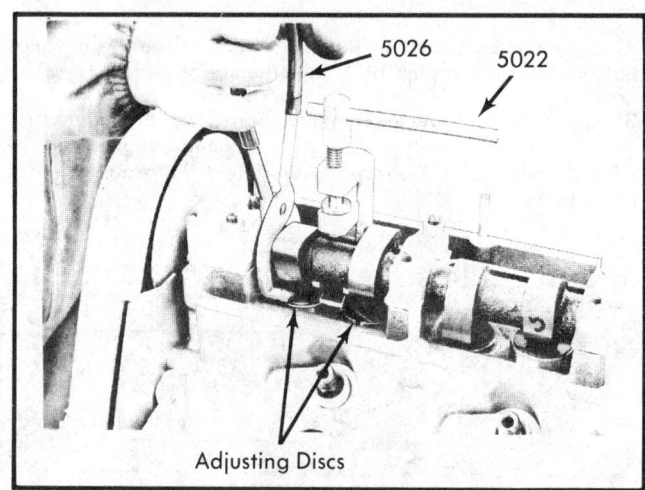

5026   5022

Adjusting Discs

Fig. 4   Removing Valve Adjusting Discs

PISTONS, PINS & RINGS

OIL PAN

Removal — 1) Raise and support front of vehicle. Remove splash guard. Remove engine mount nuts from underside of crossmember. Disconnect steering shaft at steering gear. Remove steering "U" joint lower bolt, loosen upper bolt and slide "U" joint up on shaft.

2) Position lifting tools (5006, 5033 and 5115) and lift engine slightly. See *Fig. 5*. Take out crossmember bolts. Lower crossmember. Remove left engine mount. Remove support bracket (located between rear of oil pan and clutch housing). Remove oil pan bolts. Turn and lower oil pan.

Installation — To install oil pan, reverse removal procedure.

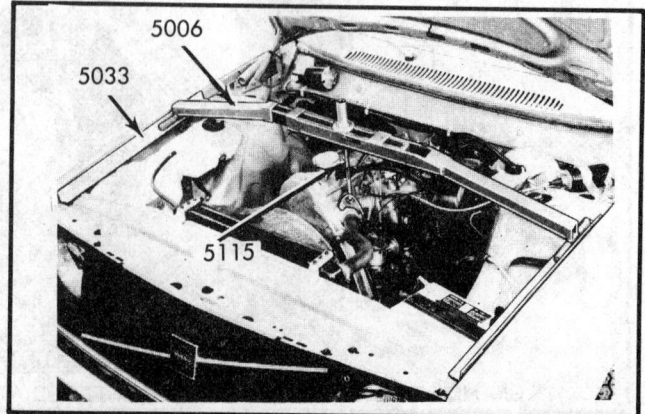

5006
5033
5115

Fig. 5   Lifting Tools Installed for Oil Pan Removal

B21F & B21FT 4-CYLINDER (Cont.)

PISTON & ROD ASSEMBLY

Removal — Remove cylinder head, oil pan and oil pump. Be sure connecting rods and caps are properly marked, so they may be reinstalled in original location. Remove carbon ridge from cylinder bores. Remove rod cap, and using wooden hammer handle, push piston out top of cylinder bore. Reinstall rod cap on piston and rod from which removed.

Installation — 1) Remove rod cap from connecting rod. Secure piston pin with retaining rings. Be sure "TOP" mark on rings is facing top of piston and end gaps are 120 degrees from each other and rings are properly installed. Install bearings in connecting rods and caps. Lubricate cylinder bores, pistons and bearings.

Fig. 7   Thumb Pressure Piston Fit

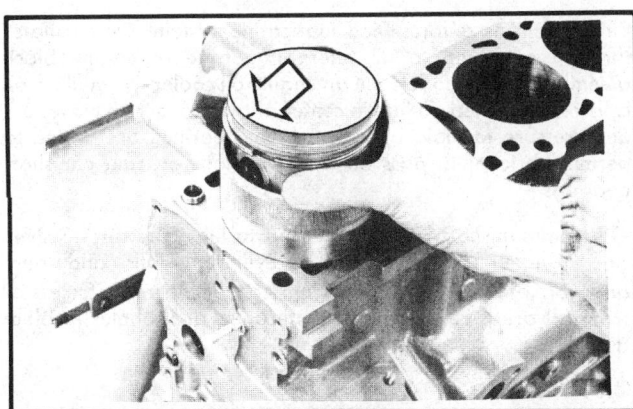

Fig. 6   Installation of Piston in Cylinder Block

2) Using piston ring compressor (5031), insert rod and piston into bore, with mark on top of piston and on connecting rod toward front of engine.

3) Using wooden hammer handle, tap lightly on top of piston. Align marks and tighten end caps. Install oil pump, oil pan and cylinder head.

FITTING PISTONS

Measure piston diameter at right angle to piston pin bore and .25" (7 mm) from lower edge. Measure cylinder bore at several positions. If difference exceeds clearance specifications, oversize pistons are available.

PISTON PINS

Piston pins are available in .002" (.05 mm) oversize from standard diameter. If replacement oversize pins are needed, piston pin hole should be reamed out to correct measurement using suitable reaming tool. Use reamer fitted with pilot guide, take only small cuts at a time. Pin fit is correct when pin can be pushed through connecting rod hole by hand, with only light resistance.

CRANKSHAFT MAIN & CONNECTING ROD BEARINGS

MAIN & CONNECTING ROD BEARINGS

Removal & Installation — 1) Remove oil pan and related parts. *See Oil Pan Removal.* Identify and mark connecting rod caps and main bearing caps to ensure correct replacement.

2) Remove connecting rod caps and push pistons towards top of cylinders. Remove main bearing caps (one at a time) and thoroughly clean all bearing surfaces.

3) Measure all journals, using a micrometer. Out-of-roundness on connecting rod bearings should not exceed .003" (.07 mm) and on main bearings, it should not exceed .002" (.05 mm). If values obtained are close to, or in excess of wear limits, crankshaft must be reground to next suitable undersize.

4) If all journals check out to standard size, refit with replacement bearings. Reinstall main bearing caps, refit connecting rods to crankshaft and tighten all nuts and bolts to specifications. Reassemble engine in reverse order of removal.

REAR MAIN BEARING OIL SEAL

Removal & Installation — 1) Remove transmission, clutch, and flywheel from engine. Remove two bolts from oil pan (into rear flange). Slacken two bolts on each side of flange, and remove flange. Use a suitable drift (2817) to remove oil seal.

2) Clean flange area thoroughly and inspect seal mating surface of crankshaft. Install new seal to flange using drift (2817).

NOTE — *If a new crankshaft has been installed, screw center bolt of tool in fully and install seal at outer position of flange. If crankshaft has not been replaced, install seal with center bolt of tool screwed out a couple of turns.*

3) Oil new seal and install flange with new gasket to cylinder block. Install attaching bolts and tighten. Install oil pan attaching bolts and tighten. Install flywheel, clutch, and transmission.

ENGINE FRONT COVER OIL SEAL

Removal — 1) Remove fan shroud, fan belt and fan pulley. Remove water pump pulley and camshaft drive belt cover. Remove crankshaft hub, sprocket and belt guide. Remove

B21F & B21FT 4-CYLINDER (Cont.)

sprocket from intermediate shaft. Detach wiring harness across front of engine. Remove two oil pan bolts from base of front cover and loosen two on each side of them. Remove drive belt guard plate and front cover.

2) Using suitable tool (5025) press out intermediate shaft seal from front cover. Using similar tool (5024) press out crankshaft seal. Use same tools to install new seals.

Installation — 1) Using new gasket, install front cover. Install oil pan, drive belt guard plate, and wiring harness.

2) Using tool (5024), install crankshaft seal. Using similar tool (5025), install intermediate shaft seal in front cover. Install inner belt guide on camshaft (collar facing away from belt). Install camshaft sprocket, aligning notch with dowel on camshaft. Install outer belt guide, washer and center bolt. Hold sprocket with holder tool (5034) and tighten bolt.

3) Install sprocket on intermediate shaft, aligning notch with dowel on shaft. Use tool (5034) to hold shaft while tightening center bolt.

4) Install belt guide and sprocket on crankshaft. Install front hub and tighten bolt. Install drive belt and complete installation of previously removed parts.

ENGINE OILING

Crankcase Capacity — B21F with filter change 4.0 quarts. Without filter change 3.5 quarts. B21F (Turbo) with filter change 4.7 quarts. Without filter change 4.2 quarts.

Oil Filter — Full-flow canister, disposable type.

Engine Oil Cooler — An engine oil cooler is used on vehicles equipped with turbo. It is air cooled and located at the side of the radiator. An engine oil thermostat, located at the oil cooler fitting, controls oil temperature.

Normal Oil Pressure — 35-85 psi (2.6-6.0 kg/cm^2) at 2000 RPM with engine at normal operating temperature.

ENGINE OILING SYSTEM

Engine utilizes a force-feed lubricating system. Oil circulates through oil pump to oil filter on outside of engine block assembly. Turbo models use an engine oil cooler. From filter, oil is forced to drilled gallery in center of block, where it moves under pressure to main bearings. Main bearings are drilled to permit lubricant to pass on to connecting rod and camshaft bearings.

Oil from camshaft bearings is used to lubricate discs, valves, and cylinder head assembly. Cylinder walls and rings are lubricated by the splash from connecting rods. Excess oil from all areas returns to sump through drain holes in block assembly.

OIL PUMP

1) Remove oil pan and related parts. *See Oil Pan Removal.* Pull oil pump out of engine, disassemble and clean all parts

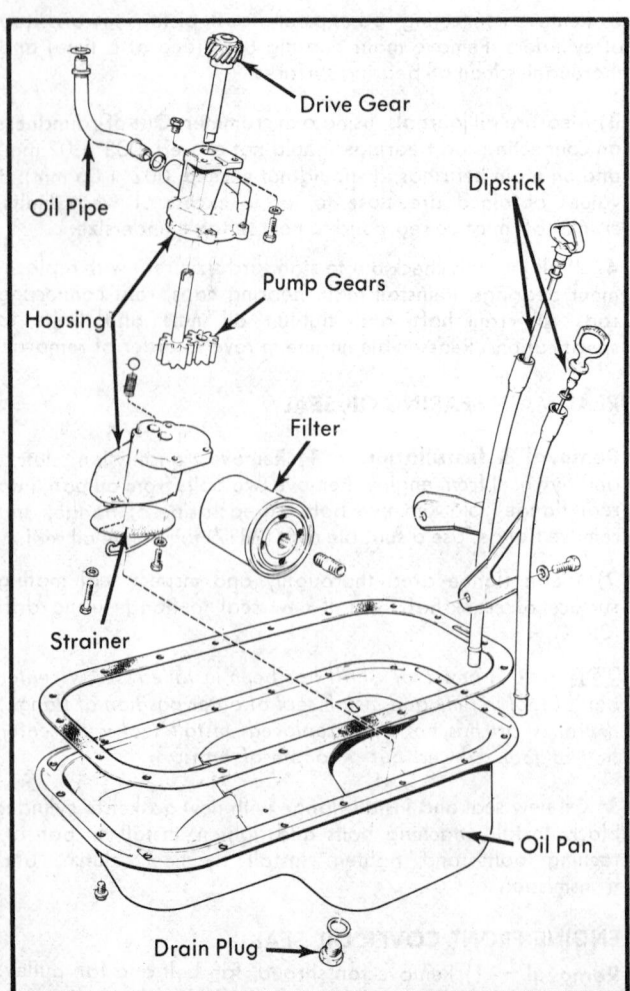

Fig. 8 Oiling System Components

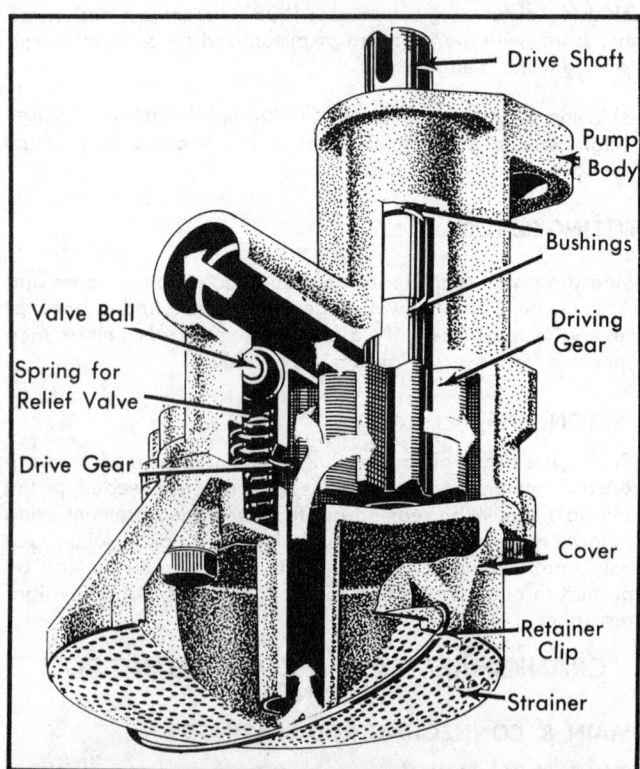

Fig. 9 Cutaway & Operational View of Oil Pump Assembly

B21F & B21FT 4-CYLINDER (Cont.)

thoroughly. Check all parts for excessive wear or signs of fatigue.

2) Measure backlash (clearance) between pump gears. It should be .006-.014" (.15-.35 mm). Also measure end play of gears. Allowable end play is .0008-.0048" (.02-.12 mm). If any parts show excessive wear or play, replace necessary components. Drive shaft and gear are matched set and must be replaced as an assembly.

3) Reinstall oil pump, making sure that sealing rings on oil delivery pipe are securely in place. Be sure oil pump properly engages pump drive shaft. Replace oil pan and related components.

ENGINE COOLING

WATER PUMP

Removal & Installation — 1) Remove expansion tank cap, open engine block drain cock, and disconnect lower radiator hose at radiator. Remove fan shroud and fan. Loosen alternator and air pump and remove drive belts.

2) Remove water pump pulley, timing gear cover, and lower radiator hose. Remove retaining bolt and slide coolant pipe rearward. Remove pump.

3) Clean all surfaces. Place new sealing ring on coolant pipe. Install new gasket when mounting pump. Install other components previously removed. Fill with coolant.

Thermostat — Standard wax type (marked 87°) opens at 189°F (87°C); fully open at 207°F (97°C).

Cooling System Capacity — 10 qts.

TIGHTENING SPECIFICATIONS	
Application	Ft. Lbs. (N·m)
Cylinder Head Bolts	
Step 1	37 (50)
Step 2	52 (70)
Step 3	① 66 (90)
Main Bearing Caps	85-91 (115-124)
Connecting Rod Caps	43-48 (58-65)
Camshaft Bearing Caps	13-16 (18-22)
Exhaust pipe-to-turbo	16-19 (22-26)
Exhaust & Intake Manifold Bolts	15 (20)
FLywheel Bolts	47-54 (64-73)
Engine Mount Bolts	15 (20)
Sprockets	
Camshaft	37 (50)
Intermediate Shaft	37 (50)
Crankshaft	122 (166)
Fan Bolt	33 (45)
Drive Belt Tensioner Nut	37 (50)

① —After tightening to this specification, run engine until it reaches normal operating temperature and retorque to this specification. Retorque after 600-1200 miles.

ENGINE SPECIFICATIONS

GENERAL SPECIFICATIONS										
Year	Displ.		Carburetor	HP at RPM	Torque (Ft. Lbs. at RPM)	Compr. Ratio	Bore		Stroke	
	cu. ins.	cc					in.	mm	in.	mm
1981 B21F	130.0	2130	Fuel Inj.	107@5250	114@2500	9.3:1	3.623	92	3.150	80
B21FT (Turbo)	130.0	2130	Fuel Inj.	133@5400	150@3750	7.5:1	3.623	92	3.150	80

VALVES							
Engine & Valve	Head Diam. In. (mm)	Face Angle	Seat Angle	Seat Width In. (mm)	Stem Diameter In. (mm)	Stem Clearance In. (mm)	Valve Lift In. (mm)
B21F & B21FT Turbo Int.	1.732 (44)	45.5°	44.75°	.068-.092 (1.7-2.3)	.3134-.3138 (7.96-7.97)	.0012-.0024 (.030-.060)	.44 (11.2)
Exh.	1.278 (35)	45.5°	44.75°	.068-.092 (1.7-2.3)	.3122-.3126 (7.93-7.94)	.0024-.0035 (.060-.090)	.44 (11.2)

Volvo Engines

B21F & B21FT 4-CYLINDER (Cont.)
ENGINE SPECIFICATIONS (Cont.)

PISTONS, PINS, RINGS						
	PISTONS	PINS		RINGS		
Engine	Clearance In. (mm)	Piston Fit In. (mm)	Rod Fit In. (mm)	Rings	End Gap In. (mm)	Side Clearance In. (mm)
2130 cc & 2130 Turbo	.0004-.0012 (.010-.030)	Push Fit	Push-fit	2 Comp. Oil	.0138-.0217 (.35-.55) .010-.016 (.25-.40)	.0016-.0028 (.040-.072) .0012-.0024 (.030-.062)

CRANKSHAFT MAIN & CONNECTING ROD BEARINGS							
	MAIN BEARINGS				CONNECTING ROD BEARINGS		
Engine	Journal Diam. In. (mm)	Clearance In. (mm)	Thrust Bearing	Crankshaft End Play In. (mm)	Journal Diam. In. (mm)	Clearance In. (mm)	Side Play In. (mm)
2130 cc & 2130 Turbo	2.4981-2.4986 (63.451-63.464)	.0011-.0033 (.028-.083)	.....	.0015-.0058 (.037-.147)	2.1255-2.1260 (53.987-54.000)	.0009-.0028 (.024-.070)	.006-.014 (.15-.35)

CAMSHAFT			
Engine	Journal Diam. In. (mm)	Clearance In. (mm)	Lobe Lift In. (mm)
2130 & 2130 Turbo	1.1437-1.1445 (29.050-29.070)	.0012-.0028 (.030-.071)	.....

VALVE SPRINGS			
Engine	Free Length In. (mm)	PRESSURE Lbs. @ In. (kg @ mm)	
		Valve Closed	Valve Open
2130 & 2130 Turbo	1.77 (45)	63.72@1.50 (29.33@38)	160-178@1.06 (73-81@27)

Volvo Engines

B28F V6

ENGINE CODING

ENGINE IDENTIFICATION

Engine identification number is located on the front left side of engine block, below the exhaust manifold, and above the power steering pump bracket. Vehicle Identification number (VIN) is located on top of instrument panel at lower left of windshield.

Engine Identification Numbers		
Application	Man. Trans.	Auto. Trans.
GLE & Coupe (2849 cc)		
Federal	498640	498641
California	498638	498639

ENGINE, CYLINDER HEADS, & MANIFOLDS

ENGINE

Removal — 1) Remove gearshift lever (manual) or place lever in "P" (automatic). Remove battery, hood, air cleaner, and engine splash guard.

2) Drain cooling system (each side of block), and disconnect all coolant hoses. Disconnect automatic transmission oil cooler pipes at radiator. Remove radiator and fan shroud. Disconnect heater hose at intake pipe, power brake hose at intake manifold, and vacuum pump hose at pump. Remove vacuum pump.

3) Disconnect fuel hoses at filter and return pipe. Disconnect wiring harness and relay connectors. Remove high tension lead from distributor and heater hoses at fire wall. Disconnect carbon filter hose at filter, and hose from EGR valve. Remove connector at voltage regulator and wire clamp. Disconnect connector for distributor, throttle cable, vacuum amplifier hose at T-pipe, and wax thermostat hoses.

4) Remove hose from air pump to backfire valve and wires from solenoid valve and micro switch. Remove nuts from both exhaust manifold flanges. Remove A/C compressor and drive belt without disconnecting hoses. Drain engine oil. Remove power steering pump and belt.

5) Remove nuts from front engine mounts. Remove exhaust pipe clamps (front exhaust pipe with catalytic converter). Disconnect shift control lever at automatic transmission.

6) Disconnect slave cylinder from clutch (manual transmission) and detach speedometer cable. Disconnect propeller shaft. Put stands under front of car, and using wooden block, place jack under oil pan. Remove transmission attachment member.

7) Using suitable sling and hoist, lift engine/transmission assembly from car.

NOTE — When removing engine, check for hoses and wires not previously removed.

Installation — To install, reverse removal procedures.

CYLINDER HEAD & MANIFOLDS (ENGINE IN VEHICLE)

Removal — 1) Disconnect battery ground cable. Remove air cleaner and disconnect throttle cable. Disconnect kick-down cable (automatic transmission) and remove pipe from EGR valve and intake manifold. Disconnect vacuum hose at EGR valve. Remove oil filler cap and stuff rag in filler hole. Disconnect crankcase ventilation pipe from intake manifold and remove intake manifold front, gaskets, and rubber rings.

2) Disconnect fuel line and connector from cold start injector. Disconnect vacuum hose, connector and two fuel lines from control pressure regulator. Disconnect hoses, pipes and electrical connectors, and remove auxiliary air valve. Remove connector at fuel distributor and wiring harness. Disconnect high tension leads from spark plugs and injectors from holders in both banks.

3) Disconnect vacuum hose at distributor, and remove vacuum, carbon filter, diverter valve, power brake, and heater hoses at intake manifold. Disconnect wires at throttle micro switch and solenoid valve, and fuel lines from filter and return pipe. Remove fuel distributor.

4) Disconnect EGR valve hose from throttle housing. Remove cold start injector and pipe. Remove intake manifold and rubber rings. Remove splash guard under engine and drain coolant from both sides of block. Remove air pump, vacuum pump and vacuum hoses at thermostat. Disconnect upper radiator hose and remove A/C compressor (do not remove hoses).

5) Remove distributor and EGR valve and bracket. Disconnect relay connectors and remove rear A/C bracket. Remove lower radiator hose at water pump and hoses from pump to cylinder heads. Disconnect supply hose from cylinder heads, and separate air manifold at rear of engine. Remove backfire valve and air hose. Remove valve covers.

6) On left side, remove four upper timing gear cover bolts and Allen head screw (not camshaft center bolt). On right side, remove four upper timing gear cover bolts and cover plate. Remove exhaust pipe clamps from under vehicle, and remove oil dipstick tube. Remove exhaust pipe flange nuts and exhaust manifold. Remove cover plates at rear of cylinder heads.

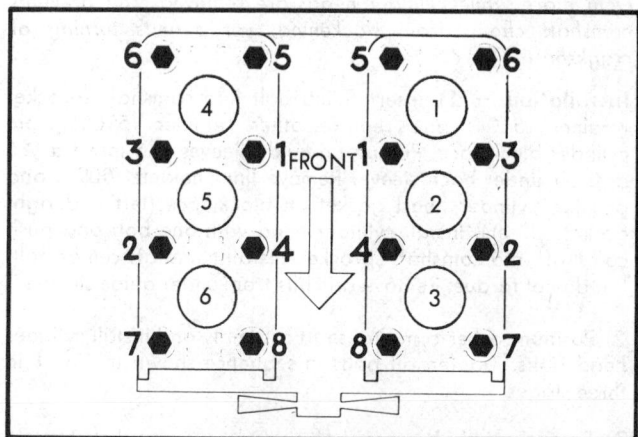

Fig. 1 Sequence for Removing and Installing Cylinder Head Bolts

Volvo Engines

B28F V6 (Cont.)

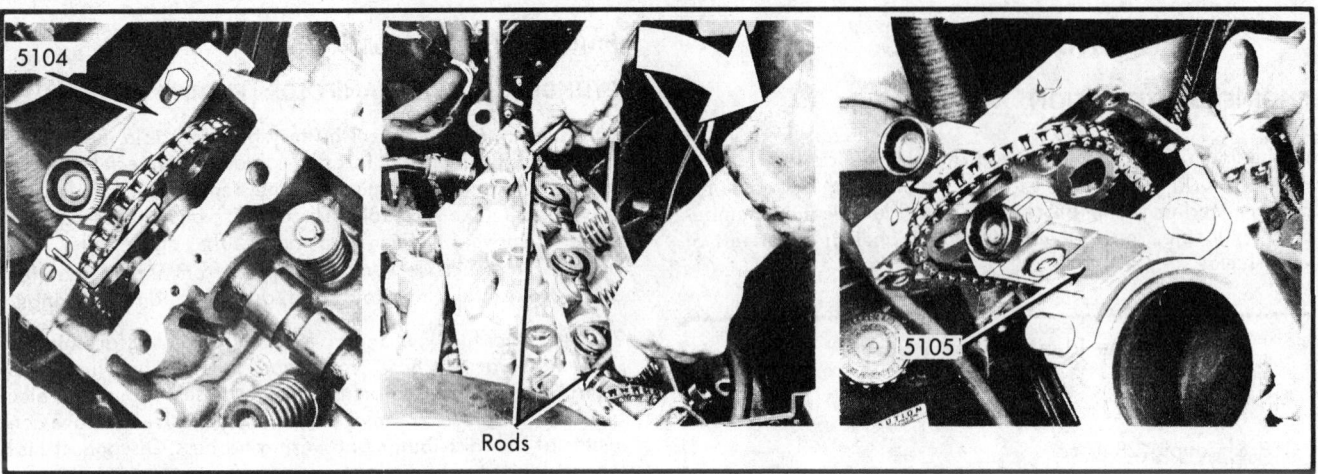

Fig. 2   Special Tools for Removing Cylinder Heads

7) Rotate each camshaft until large hole in sprocket aligns with rocker arm shaft. Remove rocker arm and shaft assembly by removing bolts in sequence shown in *Fig. 1*. Loosen bolt and push camshaft lock fork to one side.

8) Install tool to hold camshaft sprocket in place (5104). With tool installed, remove camshaft center bolt and slide camshaft to rear. Be sure camshaft stud is free from sprocket.

NOTE — *If tool is not used, camshaft chain will slacken and be held by chain tensioner. Sprocket then cannot be pulled upward when installing camshaft. If this should occur, timing gear cover must be removed for access to chain tensioner.*

9) Insert two 12" long rods into cylinder head bolt holes, *Fig. 2*, and push downward to loosen cylinder head from block. Do not attempt to remove cylinder head by lifting straight upward. If liners are not to be removed, be sure they do not separate from their seals in lower liner seat. If seals are damaged, coolant will enter crankcase. Lift out cylinder head carefully.

10) Tap guide sleeves flush with block face and remove gasket. Install liner holders (5093) to secure liners against seat seals. Clean gasket surfaces and install camshaft retaining tool (5105). After tool is securely in place, remove fixing bolt from previously installed tool (5104). See *Fig. 2*.

NOTE — *Sprocket retaining tool (5105) should be kept securely in place while cylinder heads are removed. This prevents camshaft chains from slackening, yet permits turning of crankshaft.*

Installation — **1)** Insert fixing bolt into camshaft sprocket retainer (5104) and remove other retainer (5105) from cylinder block face. Pull up on guide sleeves and insert a ⅛" drill bit under each sleeve. Remove liner holders (5093) and position cylinder head gasket on block face (left and right gaskets differ). Install cylinder head with one bolt and push camshaft into camshaft sprocket. Install camshaft center bolt, but do not torque. Remove drill bits from under guide sleeves

2) Position rocker arm and shaft assembly and install cylinder head bolts. Tighten all bolts in sequence shown in *Fig. 1* in three stages:

3) Torque camshaft center bolt and remove sprocket retainer (5104). Center lock fork over camshaft and tighten. Back off all cylinder head bolts in sequence, *Fig. 1*. Tighten to 11-14 ft.

lbs. Using protractor (5098) on standard socket, torque head bolts as follows:

Cylinder Head Tightening Specifications	
Sequence	**Ft. Lbs. (N·m)**
Step 1	7 (10)
Step 2	22 (30)
Step 3	44 (60)

- Starting with bolt one, take up slack of tool. Set protractor so "0" mark aligns with rocker arm and shaft assembly.

- Tighten bolt 116-120°.

- Repeat procedure in proper tightening sequence on other head bolts.

- After engine is assembled, run engine for 15 minutes and cool and for 30 minutes.

- Back off head bolts once more and torque to 11-14 ft. lbs.

- Using protector again torque to 113-117° in sequence.

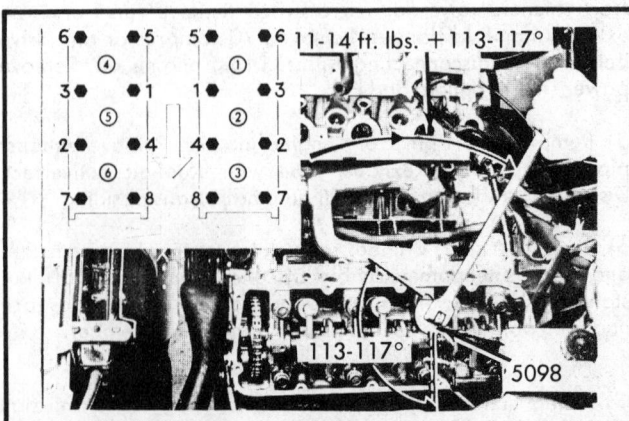

Fig. 3   Final Torquing of Cylinder Head Bolts
After Running and Cooling Engine

B28F V6 (Cont.)

4) Install remainder of components in reverse order of removal procedure, noting the following:

- Before installing valve cover, adjust valves (cold setting).

- When installing distributor, rotor should initially point to clamp clockwise from mark on distributor housing.

- Crankshaft should still be in position for firing No. 1 cylinder following valve adjustment. When distributor is pushed into place, rotor will point to mark on housing. See *Fig. 4 & 5.*

- Use new gaskets and rubber sealing rings.

- Firing order is 1-6-3-5-2-4.

- Be sure to fill engine with oil and coolant. Retorque cylinder head bolts after assembly is completed.

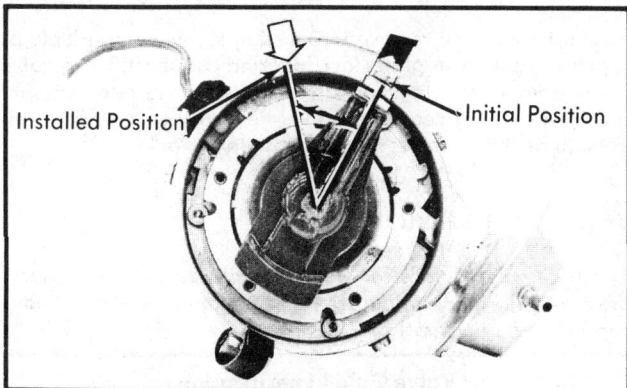

Fig. 4   Distributor Rotor Position Prior to Final Positioning

CAMSHAFT

CAMSHAFT

Removal & Installation — With cylinder head removed, remove lock fork and rear cover plate. Pull camshaft out from rear of head. To install, place camshaft in from rear of cylinder head. Note that camshaft for right bank has distributor drive gear at rear end. Install lock fork at front and cover plate at rear of head.

TIMING GEAR COVER

Removal — Remove both valve covers, lock flywheel (5112), and remove crankshaft nut. Remove pulley while key is on top of shaft (prevents dropping key in crankcase). Use puller (5069) to remove crankshaft seal. Remove timing gear cover.

Installation — Clean surfaces and place gaskets on block and timing gear cover. Install cover and tighten bolts to 7-11 ft. lbs. Install crankshaft seal (drift 5103). Block flywheel with locking tool (5112), install pulley and tighten crankshaft nut to 118-132 ft. lbs.

CHAINS & SPROCKETS

Removal — 1) Remove timing gear cover, oil pump chain, sprocket, oil pump and gears. Turn each tensioner lock ¼ turn counterclockwise and push in piston to slacken camshaft chains. Remove both tensioners, strainers, and curved and straight dampers. Remove camshaft sprockets and chains.

2) Stuff rag in holes near crankcase to keep key from falling in crankcase. Remove outer sprocket and inner double sprocket from crankshaft (either by hand or with puller).

Installation — 1) Place key in crankshaft. Oil sprocket and shaft. Install double sprocket (drift 4028) with mark outward. Install spacer ring and outer key. Install oil pump sprocket, strainers and chain tensioners, and curved and straight dampers.

2) Rotate crankshaft so key aligns with camshaft in left bank (No. 1 cylinder at TDC). Position camshaft so key points upward (rocker arms for No. 1 cylinder rock). Place chain on camshaft sprocket so that link between two white lines is centered over camshaft sprocket timing mark. Place chain on inner crankshaft sprocket so timing mark on sprocket is aligned with white mark on chain. Install left camshaft sprocket onto camshaft so that pin on sprocket slips into recess in camshaft. Chain should be stretched on tension side. Use screwdriver to hold sprocket and tighten center bolt to 51-59 ft. lbs.

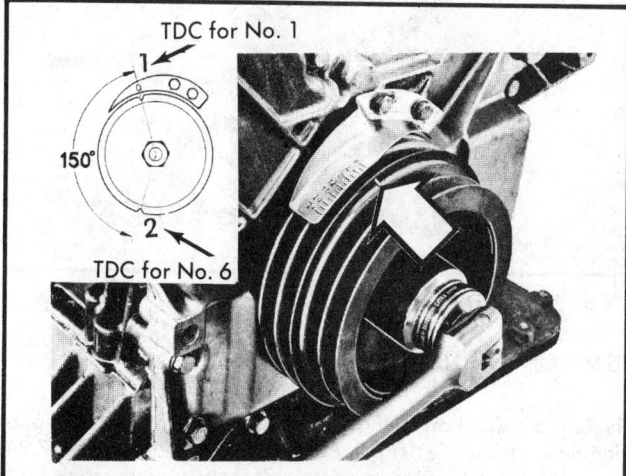

Fig. 5   Adjusting Crankshaft to Firing Position for No. 1 Cylinder

3) Rotate crankshaft clockwise 150° so that key points straight downward. Set right camshaft so keyway is in position shown in *Fig. 6.* Place chain on sprocket so link between

Fig. 6   Right Camshaft Keyway and Timing Marks

Volvo Engines

B28F V6 (Cont.)

white lines on chain aligns with sprocket timing mark. Place chain on crankshaft center sprocket so that chain and sprocket timing marks align. Fit sprocket on camshaft with chain stretched on tension side. Pin on sprocket should slip into camshaft recess. Use screwdriver to hold sprocket and torque center bolt to 51-59 ft. lbs.

4) Turn lock on each chain tensioner ¼ turn clockwise. Tension chains by rotating crankshaft 2 full turns in direction of rotation (clockwise). Remove crankshaft nut. Markings on chains and sprockets will no longer align. Reassemble oil pump, install chain and chain sprocket. Install timing gear cover after removing rag from crankcase holes.

Fig. 7   Locating Top Dead Center for No. 1 Cylinder

IGNITION TIMING PLATE

1) Rotate crankshaft so that mark No. 1 is at 20° mark on ignition timing plate. *See Fig. 5.* Remove plug and insert ⁵⁄₁₆" (7.94 mm) drill bit or similar rod into hole and against crankshaft counterweight. *See Fig. 7.* Rotate crankshaft in direction of normal rotation until drill bit can be pressed into recess in counterweight (TDC for No. 1 cylinder).

NOTE — *Do not drop drill bit into engine. Use drill or pin up to 10" long.*

2) Loosen two bolts and adjust ignition timing plate so that "0" mark is aligned with pulley mark. Tighten two bolts, remove drill bit or rod and install plug. Check camshaft setting. Valve clearance should be .028" (.7 mm). Intake valves for cylinders No. 1 and 6 should open between 6 and 12 degrees on crankshaft vibration damper.

ROCKER ARM ASSEMBLY

Removal — Mark rocker assemblies as to which head they belong. Remove lock ring from end of shaft, and remove rocker arms, shaft supports, spacer sleeves, and springs. Keep all parts in order for correct assembly. Remove the lock bolt and rocker shaft support from rocker shaft. Check shaft-to-arm clearance. New part clearance is .0005-.0021" (.012-.054 mm). New shaft diameter is .7858-.7866" (19.96-19.98 mm). Replace worn parts as necessary.

Installation — Install rocker shaft support on rocker shaft with lubricating holes pointing downward. The flat top surface should face toward lock ring groove in other end of shaft. Tighten lock bolt. Install thick spacer, exhaust rocker arm, thin spacer, intake rocker arm, spring, and rocker shaft support, in order. After installing 2 more such sets, install lock ring in rocker shaft groove.

VALVES

VALVE ARRANGEMENT

Right Bank .... E-I-E-I-E-I (Front-to-Rear)
Left Bank .... I-E-I-E-I-E (Front-to-Rear)

VALVE STEM OIL SEALS AND VALVE SPRINGS

With cylinder head removed from engine, remove spark plugs, injectors, rear cover plate, lock fork and camshaft. Using valve spring compressor, remove valve collets, spring retainer, spring, lower spring seat and valve. Remove valve guide seal from guide. Place valves in order in suitable rack.

VALVE GUIDE SERVICING

1) Check valve guides for wear. If replacement is necessary, press out old guide using drift (2818). Ream hole in cylinder head to oversize class 1 or 2:

Valve Guide Specifications	
Application	**Diameter In. (mm)**
Cylinder Head Hole, Class 1 ...	.5193-.5209 (13.19-13.23)
Cylinder Head Hole, Class 2	5311-.5327 (13.49-13.53)
Valve Guide, Class 1	①.5228-.5232 (13.28-13.29)
Valve Guide Class 2	①.5346-.5350 (13.58-13.59)
① — Oversize Valve Guides Shown	

2) Using drifts (5108 for intake; 5109 for exhaust), press in new guides. Ream guides to .3150-.3158" (8.00-8.02 mm). Check for burrs and be sure valves move freely in guides.

RECONDITIONING VALVES

After inspection, grind valves, mill or grind valve seats, and lap valves with grinding paste, as necessary. Check valve springs for proper length and tension. Install seals, valves, spring seats, spring, and spring retainers. Compress spring and install collets. Remove tool, and reinstall all parts previously removed from cylinder head.

VALVE CLEARANCE ADJUSTMENT

1) Rotate crankshaft with 1⁷⁄₁₆" (36 mm) wrench to bring No. 1 piston to TDC. *See Fig. 5.* In this position, both rocker arms for No. 1 cylinder should have clearance and not rock. Check and adjust the following cylinders for clearance: Intake valves on cylinders 1, 2, and 4; exhaust valves on cylinders 1, 3, and 6 (*White valves in Fig. 8*).

Volvo Engines

B28F V6 (Cont.)

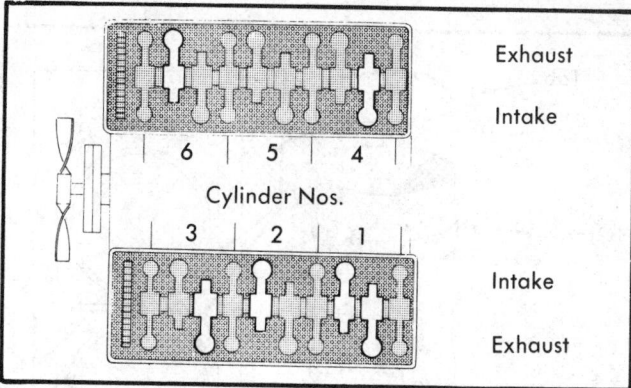

Fig. 8   Valve Clearance Adjustment Sequence

Valve Clearance Specifications①

Valve	In. (mm)
Intake	.004-.006" (.10-.15 mm)
Exhaust	.010-.012" (.25-.30 mm)

① — Specifications are for a cold engine.

2) Rotate crankshaft one full turn so marking is again opposite 0° mark. Rocker arms for No. 1 cylinder will now rock. Check and adjust the following cylinders for clearance:

Intake valves on cylinders 3, 5, and 6; exhaust valves on cylinders 2, 4, and 5 (Gray valves in Fig. 8).

PISTONS, PINS & RINGS

LOWER CRANKCASE

Removal — Remove oil pan and gasket, oil strainer and baffle plate. Remove 14 crankcase bolts and 8 main bearing nuts. Lift off lower crankcase. Install main bearing cap retainers (5096) on two outer bearings.

Installation — 1) Install rubber ring for oil channel. Clean and apply sealing compound to crankcase and block surfaces. Remove main bearing cap retainers and install lower crankcase.

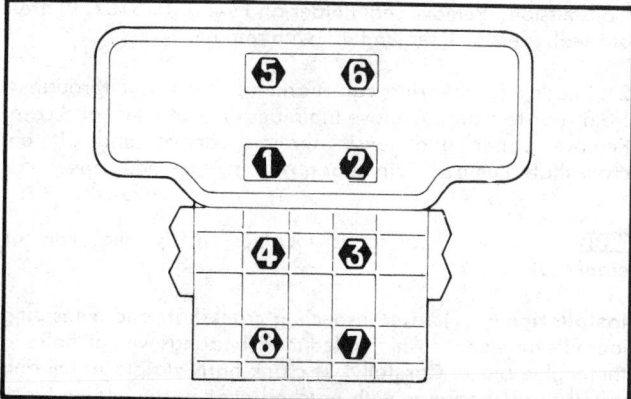

Fig. 9   Tightening Sequence for Main Bearing Nuts

2) Be sure crankcase and block are flush at rear end and tighten main bearing nuts to 22 ft. lbs. (3.1 mkg) torque. Use sequence shown in *Fig. 9*, then back off No. 1 nut and retorque to 22-25 ft. lbs. (3.1-3.5 mkg). Using protractor tool (5098), tighten nut an additional 73-77°. Continue in sequence, backing off each nut, torque tightening, and then angle tightening to specifications.

3) Tighten 14 lower crankcase bolts to 11-15 ft. lbs. Install baffle plate, oil strainer, gasket and oil pan.

PISTON & ROD ASSEMBLIES

Removal — 1) Remove lower crankcase and cylinder heads. Install cylinder liner holders (5093) to keep liners from being pushed out with piston. Check connecting rod and crankshaft markings so piston assemblies can be installed in their original positions. Connecting rods are marked "A" through "F" from rear of engine to front. Remove cap nuts and bearing cap and push piston assembly out through top of bore. Remove big end bearing.

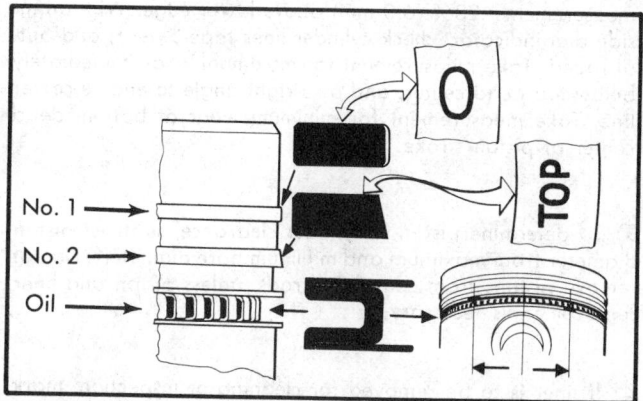

Fig. 10   Piston Ring Location and Markings

2) Remove piston rings and clean ring grooves and piston of any carbon deposits. Measure the side clearance and end gap of piston rings with a feeler gauge. Replace any components not within specifications.

Installation — 1) Install piston rings with end gaps at 120° angles from each other. Offset the gaps on the oil control rings. Note position marking on compression rings, and install with markings pointing up. See *Fig. 10*.

2) Lightly lubricate rings, and, using installation tool (5106) press piston into proper bore. Make sure that stamped arrow on top of piston is pointing toward the front of engine. This will introduce a clearance between the big end bearing and the crankshaft journal. This clearance should be positioned behind for cylinders 1, 2, and 3, and in front for cylinders 4, 5, and 6. Install bearing cap, and tighten to 33-37 ft. lbs. (4.6-5.1 mm).

PISTONS & LINERS

1) Pistons and liners are available only as matched sets. Pistons are classified by diameter in 3 catagories. Marking on piston top is either A, B, or C, and corresponds to liners marked 1, 2, or 3 respectively. The liners are marked in the recesses at the top of the liner. Pistons and piston pins are also

B28F V6 (Cont.)

classified by diameters, with blue, red, and white markings being used instead of numbers for proper matching.

Piston and Liner Diameters

Piston Designation	Diameter In. (mm)
"Mahle" A	3.5815-3.5819 (90.97-90.98)
"Mahle" B	3.5819-3.5823 (90.98-90.99)
"Mahle" C	3.5823-3.5827 (90.99-91.00)

Liner Designation	Diameter In. (mm)
"1" (for piston A)	3.5827-3.5831 (91.00-91.01)
"2" (for piston B)	3.5831-3.5835 (91.01-91.02)
"3" (for piston C)	3.5835-3.5839 (91.02-91.03)

2) Measure piston diameter at right angles to pin bore. Take measurements .236" (6.0 mm) above lower edge. With an inside dial indicator, check cylinder liner taper, wear, and out-of-round. Take measurement for maximum wear immediately below top dead center, and at a right angle to engine center line. Take measurement for minimum wear at bottom dead center of piston stroke.

3) To determine piston-to-cylinder clearance, subtract piston diameter from maximum and minimum bore diameters. Do not remove pistons from connecting rods, unless piston and liner replacement is necessary.

4) If liner is to be removed for cleaning or inspection, mark liner and block with colored pen. Do not damage gasket surface. Remove liner holders and pull up liners. When installing liners, be sure contact surfaces on block and liner are clean and without defect. Install No. 1 liner first (without shims) using previous pen markings for alignment. Tighten liner by hand, using two liner holders (5093). Using dial indicator, measure liner height above block at three points. Largest measurement should not exceed smallest measurement by more than .002" (.05 mm). Liner should be as close to .0091" (.23 mm) above block face as possible. Use correct shims to achieve dimension:

Liner Shim Thicknesses①

Color	Thickness — In. (mm)
Blue	.0028-.0041 (.070-.105)
White	.0033-.0047 (.085-.120)
Red	.0041-.0055 (.105-.140)
Yellow	.0051-.0065 (.130-.165)

① — Use same thickness shims for all liners.

5) Install shims with color marking up and positioned as shown in *Fig. 11*. Inner tabs on shims should be in liner groove.

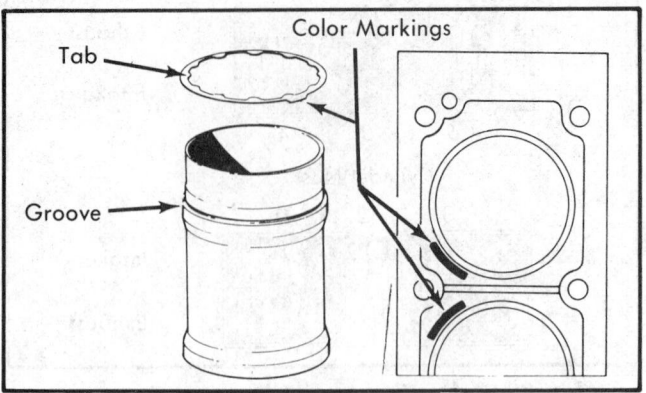

Fig. 11   Positioning Shims on Liners

6) After shimming, install four liner holders (5093) for each bank. Again measure each liner at three points. Largest and smallest dimensions should be within .002" (.05 mm). Measure three liners at points shown in *Fig. 12*. Difference in measurements between points "1" and "2" and between "3" and "4" should not exceed .0016" (.04 mm). If height difference is excessive, change shims.

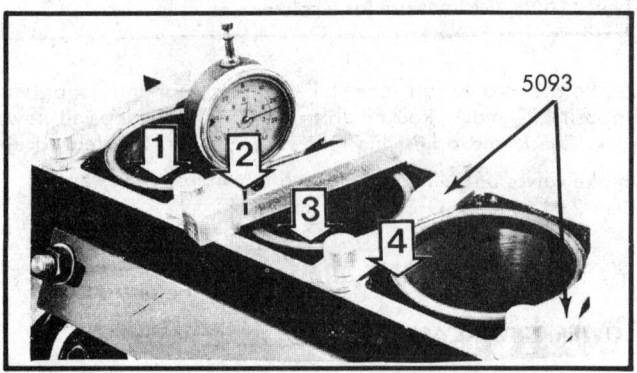

Fig. 12   Checking Liner Height Above Block Face

CRANKSHAFT MAIN & CONNECTING ROD BEARINGS

MAIN AND CONNECTING ROD BEARINGS

Removal — 1) Remove oil pan, lower crankcase, cylinder heads, clutch, drive plate or flywheel, spacer (automatic transmission) and input shaft pilot bearing (manual transmission). Remove seal holder and use drift (5107) to press out seal. Press new seal in flush with retainer.

2) Check main bearing cap markings (marked 1 through 4, from rear-to-front). Remove main bearing retainers and caps. Remove upper and lower thrust bearings and lift out crankshaft. Remove main bearings from block and caps.

NOTE — *Thrust bearing is located on flywheel end of crankshaft.*

Installation — 1) After inspecting crankshaft and measuring journals for wear, position oiled main bearings with oil holes to the engine block. Carefully set crankshaft into place. Oil and install thrust bearings with notched ends in the engine block groove. Oil and install unnotched thrust bearings on the crankshaft.

Volvo Engines

B28F V6 (Cont.)

2) Noting that cap identification number faces front of engine, lubricate bearing shell and position in bearing cap. Install bearing cap and bearing retainers (5096). Using a dial indicator, measure crankshaft end play and install thrust washers to bring end play to .0028-.0106" (.07-.27 mm).

3) Oil remaining bearing shells, place in caps, and install, noting that cap number points toward front of engine. Install main bearing retainer on rear main cap, and one nut on each remaining bearing cap to keep them in place until ready to install lower crankcase. Install lower crankcase and torque main caps. *See Lower Crankcase.*

ENGINE OILING

Crankcase Capacity — 6.8 quarts with oil filter change, and 6.3 quarts without filter change.

Oil Filter — Full-flow type, disposable, spin-on element.

Oil Pressure — With engine warm and a new filter installed, minimum 26 psi@900 RPM, and 58 psi@3000 RPM.

ENGINE OILING SYSTEM

Engine utilizes a force-feed lubrication system. Oil moves from oil pan through strainer to oil pump and full-flow oil filter mounted outside of engine block assembly. Oil is pressure fed from filter to drilled galleries in block.

Lubricant moves under pressure to main bearings, which are drilled to pass oil on to connecting rod and camshaft bearings, upward in block to rocker arm shafts. Excess or run-off oil drains back down into oil pan through drain holes in cylinder head. Cylinder walls and piston rings are lubricated by splash from connecting rods.

OIL PUMP

The oil pump is stocked as a complete unit (housing cover with impeller, and relief valve). Inspect housing, cover, and gears for damage and wear. Replace if necessary.

Removal — Remove both valve covers, crankshaft pulley, and timing gear cover. Remove oil pump drive sprocket and chain. Loosen the 4 retaining bolts, and lift out oil pump and gears.

Installation — Place gears on shaft, and oil the housing, gears and shaft. Install pump assembly, ensuring pump gears and shafts are centered in housing before tightening bolts. Install pump drive sprocket and chain. Install remaining components in reverse of removal order.

ENGINE COOLING

Thermostat — Wax-type. Begins to open at 176-181° F (80-83° C); fully open at 194-201° F (90-94° C). Marking, 180° F (82° C).

Cooling System Capacity — All models, 11.5 quarts.

Radiator Cap — 9-12 psi.

WATER PUMP

Removal & Installation — 1) Drain coolant from both sides of block. Remove intake manifold, 2 expansion tank hoses from radiator, upper radiator hose and automatic transmission oil cooler pipes. Remove fan shroud, radiator and fan.

2) Remove hoses from pump to block. Remove fan belts, water pump pulley, and remaining hose clamps. Remove senders from water pump, and pump from block. Remove cover and thermostat and cover from body. Install in reverse order.

Oil Pump Specifications

Dimension Application	Inches (mm)
Gear Width, Class 1	1.2167-1.2175 (30.905-30.925)
Gear Width, Class 2	1.2175-1.2183 (30.925-30.945)
Housing Width, Class 1	1.2185-1.2195 (30.975-31.010)
End Play	.0010-.0033 (.025-.084)
Clearance (Tooth-to-Housing)	①.0043-.0073 (.110-.185)
Backlash	①.007-.011 (.17-.27)
Bearing Clearance, Driving Shaft	.0006-.0021 (.015-.053)
Bearing Clearance, Trailing Shaft	.0006-.0021 (.015-.053)
Relief Valve Spring Length, No Load	3.52 (89.5)

① — Excluding bearing clearance.

TIGHTENING SPECIFICATIONS

Application	Ft. Lbs. (N·m)
Camshaft Center Bolt	51-59 (69-80)
Crankshaft Pulley Nut	118-132 (160-180)
Cylinder Head Bolts	
Step 1	7 (10)
Step 2	22 (30)
Step 3	①44 (60)
Connecting Rod Cap Nuts	33-37 (45-50)
Exhaust Manifold Bolts	7-11 (10-15)
Flywheel Bolts	33-37 (45-50)
Intake Manifold Bolts	7-11 (10-15)
Main Bearing Nuts	②22-25 (30-34)
Lower Crankcase Bolts	11-15 (15-20)
Transmission-to-Engine	30-36 (41-49)

① — Retorque using protector after Step 3, once engine is completed.
② — Tighten to spec. given PLUS an additional 75°.

Volvo Engines

B28F V6 (Cont.)

ENGINE SPECIFICATIONS

GENERAL SPECIFICATIONS

Year	Displ.		Carburetor	HP at RPM	Torque (Ft. Lbs. at RPM)	Compr. Ratio	Bore		Stroke	
	cu. ins.	cc					in.	mm	in.	mm
1981 B28F	174	2849	Fuel Inj.	130@5500	159@2750	8.8:1	3.58	91.0	2.87	73

VALVES

Engine & Valve	Head Diam. In. (mm)	Face Angle	Seat Angle	Seat Width In. (mm)	① Stem Diameter In. (mm)	① Stem Clearance In. (mm)	Valve Lift In. (mm)
2849 cc Intake	1.73 (44)	30°	30°	.067-.083 (1.7-2.1)	.3140-.3146 (7.97-7.99)	.0004-.0018 (.010-.046)	.2364 (6.004)
Exhaust	1.46 (37)	30°	30°	.079-.094 (2.0-2.4)	.3136-.3142 (7.96-7.98)	.0008-.0022 (.020-.056)	.2364 (6.004)

① — Stem diameter gets larger from disc toward collet end of valve, where measurement above is taken.

PISTONS, PINS, RINGS

Engine	PISTONS	PINS		RINGS		
	Clearance In. (mm)	Piston Fit In. (mm)	Rod Fit In. (mm)	Rings	End Gap In. (mm)	Side Clearance In. (mm)
2849 cc	Mahle .0008-.0016 (.020-.040)	Push Fit .0004-.0006 (.010-.015)	Press Fit .0008-.0016 (.020-.041)	Comp. 1	.016-.022 (.40-55)	.0018-.0029 (.045-.074)
				Comp. 2	.016-.022 (.40-.55)	.0010-.0021 (.025-.054)
				Oil	.015-.055 (.38-1.4)	.0004.0092 (.009-.233)

CRANKSHAFT MAIN & CONNECTING ROD BEARINGS

Engine	MAIN BEARINGS				CONNECTING ROD BEARINGS		
	Journal Diam. In. (mm)	Clearance In. (mm)	Thrust Bearing	Crankshaft End Play In. (mm)	Journal Diam. In. (mm)	Clearance In. (mm)	Side Play In. (mm)
2849 cc	2.7576-2.7583 (70.043-70.062)	.0015-.0035 (.038-.088)	.....	.0028-.0106 (.070-.270)	2.0578-2.0585 (52.267-52.286)	.0012-.0031 (.030-.080)	.008-.015 (.20-.38)

CAMSHAFT

Engine	Journal Diam. In. (mm)	Clearance In. (mm)	Lobe Lift In. (mm)
2849 cc Front	1.5921-1.5931 (40.440-40.465)	① .0014-.0033 (.035-.085)	.....
2nd	1.6157-1.6173 (41.040-41.065)		
3rd	1.6394-1.6404 (41.640-41.665)		
4th	1.6630-1.6640 (42.240-42.265)		

① — End play should be .0028-.0057" (.070-.144 mm).

VALVE SPRINGS

Engine	Free Length In. (mm)	PRESSURE Lbs. @ In. (kg @ mm)	
		Valve Closed	Valve Open
2849 cc	1.854 (47.1)	52-60@1.57 (24-27@40)	135-152@1.181 (61.3-68.9@30.0)

Volvo Engines

D24 6-CYLINDER DIESEL

ENGINE CODING
ENGINE IDENTIFICATION

Code for Volvo 6-cylinder diesel is D24. Engine serial number is located under vacuum pump on left side of engine block. Vehicle Identification Number (VIN) is located on top of instrument panel at lower left of windshield.

Engine Identification	
Application	**Code**
D24 Auto. Trans.	498705
D24 Man. Trans.	498704

ENGINE & CYLINDER HEAD

ENGINE

Removal – 1) Disconnect battery. Disconnect windshield washer hoses and remove hood. Remove lower radiator hose, drain coolant, and remove coolant hoses attached to engine. Remove radiator, expansion tank, and any attached hoses. Disconnect accelerator cable and vacuum lines.

2) Disconnect wires at main terminal, glow plug relay, and voltage regulator and hang out of way. Remove power steering belt and pump with brackets, and hang out of the way with hoses attached. Remove and plug fuel lines at filter and injection pump

3) Remove cooling fan and spacer, pulleys, and drive belts. Disconnect exhaust pipes at front and rear manifolds and remove air cleaner and ducting. Drain engine oil. Disconnect driveshafts, speedometer cable, and gear lever from transmission. On vehicles with manual transmission, disconnect clutch cable and pull out from clutch lever and housing. Position jack under transmission, raise slightly, and remove transmission crossmember. Detach engine mounts.

4) Attach lift 2810, and hooks 5185 and 5186, or a suitable lifting device to engine. Move hoist to rear position on beam 2810, and hoist engine enough to off-load left engine mount. Remove jack from under transmission. Move hoist to front position and carefully lift out engine, ensuring all wires and hoses clear assembly.

Installation – To install engine, reverse removal procedures.

CYLINDER HEAD

Removal – 1) Remove splash guard, expansion tank cap, and lower radiator hose. Drain radiator and disconnect battery. Remove radiator, fan, spacer, pulleys and fan belt. Remove drive belt for power steering. Remove valve cover and front and rear timing belt covers. Disconnect all wires to cylinder head.

2) Remove air cleaner and attached hoses. Disconnect vacuum pump and move to wheel housing. Remove vacuum pump plunger from cylinder head. Remove and plug fuel delivery pipes and disconnect cold start device. Set No. 1 piston to TDC, (timing mark on flywheel at "0"). Loosen water pump retaining bolts to relieve tension on timing gear belt, and remove belt.

3) Use wrench 5199 to hold camshaft drive gear in place, and remove center retaining bolt. Camshaft MUST NOT rotate, or damage to valves and pistons could result. Tap gear loose

from camshaft tapered end. Remove injection pump drive belt by loosening retaining bracket bolts. Use wrench 5199 to hold rear camshaft sprocket, and remove center retaining bolt. Tap gear loose from camshaft.

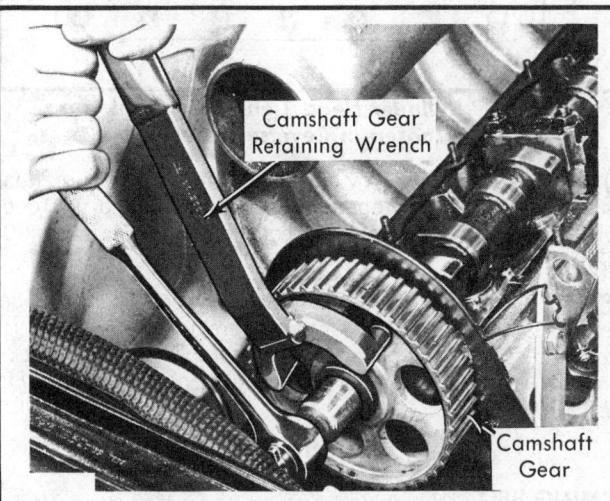

Fig. 1   Using Camshaft Gear Retaining Wrench

4) Loosen cylinder head bolts in reverse order of tightening sequence. Carefully lift cylinder head from engine, making sure rear glow plug clears injection pump bracket, and valves do not touch cylinder walls. Set cylinder head on wooden blocks so it does not rest on the valves.

Installation – 1) Clean all mating surfaces and check that cylinder head is not warped. Maximum allowable distortion is .002" (.05 mm) diagonally, and .008" (.2 mm) crosswise.

NOTE – *Cracks between valve seats not wider than .02" (.5 mm) do not warrent replacement of cylinder head, as they do not impair engine function.*

2) Select a head gasket with the same number of notches as previous gasket, unless pistons, rods, or crankshaft were disassembled or repaired. Then piston projection above engine block must be measured. Use a dial indicator to measure each piston while at TDC, and select proper gasket from the following table:

Available Cylinder Head Gaskets		
Piston Projection In. (mm)	**Notches**	**Gasket Thickness**
.026-.031 (.67-.80) 1		.055" (1.4 mm)
.032-.035 (.81-.90) 2		.059" (1.5 mm)
.036-.040 (.91-1.02) 3		.063" (1.6 mm)

3) Set No. 1 piston at TDC. Set camshaft for injection on cylinder No. 1 (both cam lobes of No. 1 cylinder should point up at equally large angles). Use stop tool 5190 to lock camshaft in place. Install aligning dowels 5189 in outer bolt holes. Remove rear glow plug to protect it from hitting injection pump. Carefully set cylinder head into place. Install the head bolts with new washers, coned side facing up and threads and washers oiled. Torque cylinder head bolts in 2 stages:

Stage 1 .... 30 ft. lbs. (40 N·m)
Stage 2 .... 65 ft. lbs. (90 N·m)

Volvo Engines

D24 6-CYLINDER DIESEL (Cont.)

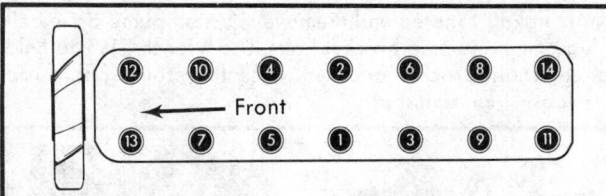

Fig. 2   Cylinder Head Tightening Sequence (Loosen in Reverse Order)

4) Complete installation by reversing removal procedure. Run engine until it reaches operating temperature, and retorque cylinder head bolts in proper sequence to 65 Ft. Lbs. (90 N•m).

NOTE — *After 600-1200 miles, cylinder head bolts must be retorqued. Vacuum pump and plunger must be removed to gain access to cylinder head bolt. With the engine cool, slacken each bolt individually by 30°, and then tighten to 65 Ft. Lbs. (90 N•m).*

CAMSHAFT

TIMING BELT

Removal — 1) Disconnect battery. Disconnect lower radiator hose and drain coolant. Remove coolant hoses attached to head. Remove coolant hoses attached to head. Remove radiator, expansion tank cap, and engine splash guard. Remove fan, spacers, pulleys and fan belt. Remove drive belt for power steering. Remove valve cover, and front and rear timing belt covers. Disconnect all wires to cylinder head.

2) Using a 1 1⁄16" (27 mm) wrench on crankshaft pulley bolt, bring No. 1 cylinder to TDC. Remove vibration damper center bolt using wrench 5187 to hold damper from turning. Remove Allen screws and pull off vibration damper. Remove lower belt shield. Loosen water pump bolts and remove gear belt.

NOTE — *Idler pulley must be replaced when replacing timing gear belt. Use puller 5202 or equivalent to remove pulley.*

3) Using holding tool 5199 to keep camshaft from moving, remove center bolt on camshaft rear gear and tap gear off camshaft. Install camshaft locking gauge 5190 in groove on rear of camshaft. Position a .008" (.2 mm) feeler gauge under left (injection pump) side of locking gauge. Remove camshaft front gear using holding tool 5199 to keep camshaft from turning while removing center bolt.

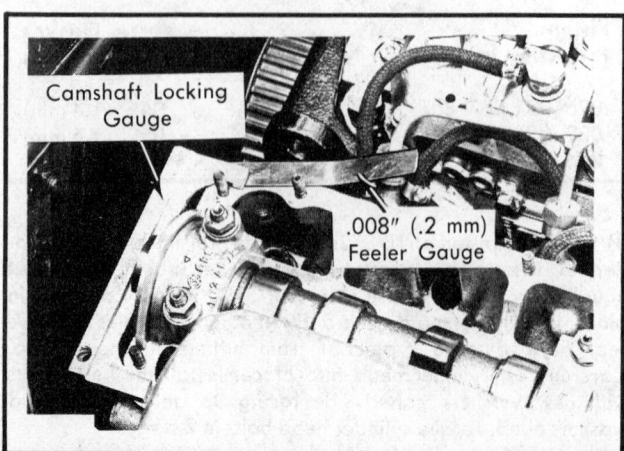

Fig. 3   Using Camshaft Locking Gauge to Set Engine Timing

Installation — 1) Making sure gear belt is fitted securely to all gears, install gear belt and camshaft front gear together. Install center bolt finger tight so gear can rotate. Camshaft must not rotate. Install lower belt shield and vibration damper using sealing agent 277961-9 (or equivalent) on damper center bolt.

2) Check that No. 1 piston is at TDC and timing mark on flywheel is on "0". Adjust gear belt tension to 12-13 on tension gauge 5197 using the water pump for adjustment. Strike the belt heavily by hand and recheck tension.

3) Using wrench 5199 to hold gear, tighten camshaft front gear center bolt. Remove gauge 5190 and install rear camshaft gear without moving camshaft. Install injection pump drive belt and adjust belt tension to 12-13 on tension gauge 5197. Reverse removal procedure to complete installation.

CAMSHAFT

Removal — With camshaft drive sprockets and vacuum pump removed, and engine at TDC, remove bearing caps 1 and 4. Alternately loosen cap nuts on caps 2 and 3. Lift out camshaft and remove seals.

Installation — 1) Lightly lubricate bearings and contact surfaces. Install gauge 5190 on camshaft rear and position camshaft on cylinder head. Cam lobes for cylinder No. 1 should point up at equally large angles. Install bearing caps 2 and 3 and tighten cap nuts alternately. Use gauge 5190 to guide rear end when tightening. Remove gauge.

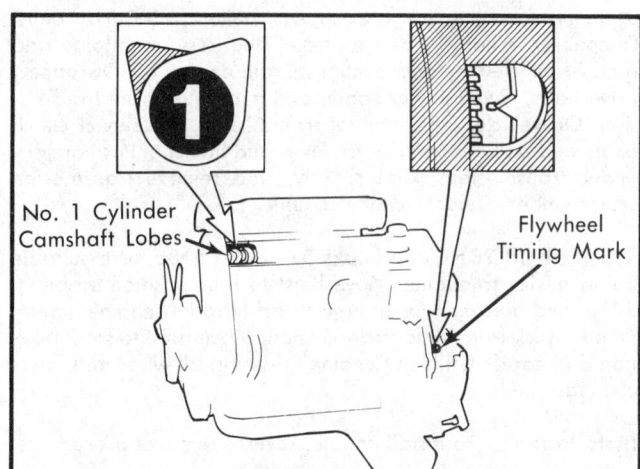

Fig. 4   No. 1 Cylinder, Top Dead Center Reference Mark

2) Install new oil seals on camshaft, but do not press them to bottom. Make sure seals are not cocked. Install bearing caps 1 and 4. Use adaptor 5200 and press seals into final position. Reverse removal procedure to complete installation.

INJECTION PUMP

Removal — 1) Pinch off hoses to cold start device and disconnect. Disconnect accelerator cable and automatic transmission kickdown cable (if equipped). Remove rear timing gear cover, vacuum pump, and fuel delivery pipes. Plug all fuel lines and connections to prevent contamination of fuel system. Disconnect wire at stop valve. Turn crankshaft pulley to bring No. 1 piston to TDC. Loosen injection pump bracket bolts to relieve belt tension and remove drive belt. Tighten one bolt to retain pump in an upright position.

Volvo Engines

D24 6-CYLINDER DIESEL (Cont.)

2) Loosen camshaft rear gear center bolt enough to allow gear to rotate on camshaft without letting camshaft rotate. Lock injection pump gear with stop 5193, and remove gear nut. Using puller 5204, remove injection pump gear. Remove bolts retaining front injection pump bracket to engine. Bracket comes out with pump. Remove Allen screws retaining injection pump, and remove pump.

Installation — To install, reverse removal procedure, noting that mark on injection pump and bracket coincide, and shaft key is correctly installed before replacing gear.

Pump Timing — 1) To check pump timing remove rear timing belt cover and set No. 1 piston to TDC. Disconnect cold start device by loosening the screw nearest the lever, and pushing lever forward. Rotate sleeve 90° and push lever back against stop. DO NOT loosen clamp screw at end of cable.

2) Install a dial indicator with adaptor 5194 in place of plug at injector pump distributor. Set dial indicator with .08" (2 mm) preload between plunger and pump shaft. Turn crankshaft counterclockwise until dial indicator is at minimum reading. Set dial indicator to zero and turn crankshaft to bring No. 1 piston back to TDC. Dial indicator reading should now be .028" (.70 mm).

3) If necessary, loosen injection pump retaining screws and turn pump to obtain proper setting. Tighten screws and rotate crankshaft 2 complete turns, bringing No. 1 piston back to TDC. Dial indicator should still read .028" (.07 mm). Readjust and recheck as necessary to obtain proper setting. Remove dial indicator, and install timing gear cover and cold start device.

VALVES

VALVE ARRANGEMENT

E-I-E-I-E-I-E-I-I-E-I-E-I-E   (front to rear)

VALVE CLEARANCE ADJUSTMENT

1) Remove valve cover and rotate crankshaft so that No. 1 piston is at TDC, and cab lobes point up. Flywheel mark should be at "0". Check intake and exhaust clearance between heel of cam lobe and cam follower. Check remaining cylinders in firing order sequence.

2) If adjustment is required, turn the crankshaft ¼ turn clockwise from piston TDC, as there is no room to depress valves. Using depressor tool (5196), press down valve depressor and remove disc with special pliers (5195).

3) Calculate thickness of disc required to reach proper setting. Discs are available in thicknesses of .130-.167" (3.30-4.25 mm) in increments of .002" (.05 mm). Lubricate and position new disc with stamped marking down. Rotate crankshaft several times and recheck all settings. Install valve cover.

Valve Clearance Specifications	
Application	**In. (mm)**
Intake	
Hot	.008-.012 (.20-.30)
Cold	.006-.010 (.15-.25)
Exhaust	
Hot	.016-.020 (.40-.50)
Cold	.014-.018 (.35-.45)

VALVE GUIDE SERVICING

1) With cylinder head removed from engine, and camshaft and lifters removed, attach a valve spring compressor to valve. Compress valve spring and remove retaining lock, upper valve spring washer, valve springs, and valve. Remove valve guide seals and lower valve spring washers.

2) Using a dial indicator, measure valve guide clearance by placing a new valve in guide bore with a valve stem end edge to edge with valve guide. Use proper intake or exhaust valve for bores as stem diameters are different.

3) Rock valve back and forth and observe dial indicator reading. Clearance must not exceed .051" (1.3 mm). If clearance is excessive, replace valve guides. Press out old guides from combustion chamber side of cylinder head using a drift (5218 or equivalent).

4) Oil replacement valve guide and press in place from camshaft side of cylinder head until guide flange bottoms in cylinder head. Do not use more than 1 ton force, or flange may break off of guide. Ream guides using hand reamer (5224 or equivalent).

NOTE — *Valves and seats must be reground if valve guides are replaced.*

5) Replace valve components, camshaft, and cylinder head in reverse order of removal.

PISTONS, PINS, & RINGS

PISTON & ROD ASSEMBLY

Removal — 1) With oil pan and cylinder head removed, mark each piston assembly for proper installation. Ream any ridge from cylinder bores using a ridge reamer. Place a rag on top of piston to collect cuttings.

2) Remove connecting rod cap and bearing shells, and push piston assembly out through top of cylinder bore.

Installation — 1) Fit bearing shells in connecting rod and rod cap. Lubricate cylinder bores, pistons, and bearing shells. Turn crankshaft so that journal for piston being serviced is at bottom of stroke.

2) Using a ring compressor, fit piston to bore noting that arrow on piston crown faces forward. Push piston down, and locate connecting rod to crankshaft. Fit rod cap to connecting rod and tighten new nuts. Install all pistons and check that crankshaft rotates freely.

FITTING PISTONS

1) Using a bore indicator, measure each cylinder bore at 3 points, both parallel and at right angles to crankshaft. Measure .393" (10 mm) from top, bottom, and at center of cylinder bore. The cylinder bore reading must not deviate by more than .002" (.04 mm) from basic value.

2) Measure piston diameter at right angle to piston pin .590" (15 mm) from lower edge. Subtract reading from that taken of cylinder bore. If specification is exceeded reboring or oversize pistons must be used.

NOTE — *Pistons with rounded edges on pressure side may not be used again. Round edges are caused by faulty injectors, which must be serviced before installation.*

Volvo Engines

D24 6-CYLINDER DIESEL (Cont.)

3) Place each piston ring squarely into bottom of cylinder bore and measure ring gap. Place ring approximately .59" (15 mm) from lower edge of cylinder.

PISTON PINS

Removal & Installation — 1) Remove circlips retaining piston pin. Push out pin with a drift. If pin moves stiffly, heat piston to approximatley 140°F (60°C). Assemble in reverse order.

2) If piston pin bushing warrants replacement, press bushing out using drift (5017 or equivalent). Press in new bushing until edges are flush with connecting rod. Drill out lubricating hole in bushing and ream bushing with a reamer. Piston pin must be loose, but still able to slide through hole with slight resistance.

PISTON RINGS

Removal — Using ring pliers, remove rings from piston. Remove any carbon deposits from ring lands and piston.

Installation — Fit expander ring in lowest groove of piston. Fit oil ring so ring gap is opposite spring opening. Install lower compression ring with "Top" marking upward. Install upper compression ring. Turn compression rings so all gaps are 120° apart. Do not turn oil control ring.

CRANKSHAFT MAIN & CONNECTING ROD BEARINGS

MAIN & CONNECTING ROD BEARINGS

Removal — Check markings on main and connecting rod bearings and remark if necessary. Using Plastigage method check main and connecting rod bearing clearance. If clearance is excessive, replace bearings. Do not mix old and new bearings. Replace in sets only.

Installation — Fit main bearing shells in engine block and main bearing caps. Install bearing shells with oil hole to engine block. Lubricate bearings and place crankshaft in position. Fit main bearing caps with No. 1 toward vibration damper and No. 7 toward flywheel. See *Piston and Rod Assembly* for connecting rod installation procedure.

Crankshaft Front Seal — With vibration damper removed, pull old seal from housing using puller 5205 (or equivalent). Grease seal lips, and press into place by hand. Use adapter 5200, a thick washer and camshaft center bolt to press seal into housing until seated.

Crankshaft Rear Seal — With flywheel removed, pry out old seal with a screwdriver. Coat seal contact surfaces and lips with oil and hand start into position. Tap seal into housing until it bottoms, using drift 5208 (or equivalent).

ENGINE OILING

Crankcase Capacity — 7 quarts with filter change, and 6.2 quarts without filter change.

Oil Filter — Replaceable spin-on type.

Normal Oil Pressure — Minimum of 28 psi@2000 RPM with engine at normal operating temperature.

ENGINE OILING SYSTEM

Gear-type oil pump pressure lubricates pistons, piston pins, and crankshaft. Three nozzles in the head distribute oil to cam lobes, valve depressors and vacuum pump piston.

OIL PUMP

The oil pump cannot be removed without removing the engine. No repairs can be made in the vehicle. The oil pump must be replaced as an assembly as there are no separate replaceable parts.

ENGINE COOLING

Cooling System Capacity — 10 quarts

Thermostat — Begins to open at 186°F (87°C), and is fully open at 236°F (102°C).

WATER PUMP

Removal — Remove timing belt as described in *TIMING BELT* in this article, making sure to mark belt position on belt, camshaft and crankshaft gears. Also, mark belt as to which parts face upward and forward. Remove protective plate and pump retaining bolts, and remove water pump.

Installation — Making sure all gasket surfaces are clean, lightly grease a new "O" ring and fit it to the pump. DO NOT use any other sealing agent. Install the pump with the longest retaining bolt in the upper hole. Reverse removal procedure to complete installation.

TIGHTENING SPECIFICATIONS

Application	Ft. Lbs. (N·m)
Camshaft Gear Center Bolt	33 (45)
Camshaft Gear Bolt (Rear)	74 (100)
Camshaft Pulley Nut	255 (350)
Cylinder Head Bolts	
Step 1	30 (40)
Step 2	65 (90)
Connecting Rod Cap Nuts	45 (61)
Exhaust Manifold Bolts	18 (25)
Flywheel Bolts	55 (75)
Intake Manifold Bolts	18 (25)
Main Bearing Cap Bolts	48 (65)
Transmission-to-Engine	35 (48)
Pump Gear	33 (45)

Volvo Engines

D24 6-CYLINDER DIESEL (Cont.)
ENGINE SPECIFICATIONS

GENERAL SPECIFICATIONS

Year	Displ.		Carburetor	HP at RPM	Torque (Ft. Lbs. at RPM)	Compr. Ratio	Bore		Stroke	
	cu. ins.	cc					in.	mm	in.	mm
1981 D24	145	2383	Fuel Inj.	82@4800	105.5@2800	23.5:1	3.01	76.5	3.40	86.4

PISTONS, PINS, RINGS

Engine	PISTONS	PINS		RINGS		
	Clearance In. (mm)①	Piston Fit In. (mm)	Rod Fit In. (mm)	Rings	End Gap In. (mm)②	Side Clearance In. (mm)
2383 cc	.0012-.0019 (.03-.05)	Push Fit	Close Running Fit	Comp 1	.012-.020 (.30-.50)	.0023-.0035③ (.06-.09)
				Comp 2	.012-.020 (.30-.50)	.0019-.0031③ (.05-.08)
				Oil	.010-.016 (.25-.40)	.0011-.0023④ (.03-.06)

① — Wear limit .0051″ (.13 mm) ② — Wear limit .040″ (1.0 mm)
③ — Wear limit .0078″ (.2 mm) ④ — Wear limit .0059″ (.15 mm)

CRANKSHAFT MAIN & CONNECTING ROD BEARINGS

Engine	MAIN BEARINGS				CONNECTING ROD BEARINGS		
	Journal Diam. In. (mm)	Clearance In. (mm)①	Thrust Bearing	Crankshaft End Play In. (mm)②	Journal Diam. In. (mm)	Clearance In. (mm)③	Side Play In. (mm)
2383 cc	2.283 (58.0)	.0006-.0029 (.016-.075)	No. 4	.003-.007 (.07-.18)	1.88 (47.8)	.0006-.0024 (.015-.062)	.0157 (.40)

① — Wear Limit .0063″ (.16mm)   ② — Wear limit .010″ (.25 mm)   ③ — Wear limit .0047″ (.12 mm)

VALVES

Engine & Valve	Head Diam. In. (mm)	Face Angle	Seat Angle	Seat Width In. (mm)	Stem Diameter In. (mm)	Stem Clearance In. (mm)①	Valve Lift In. (mm)
2383 cc Intake	1.417 (36.0)	44.5°	45°	.079 (2.0)	.314 (7.97)	.0118 (.30)	.335 (8.5)
Exhaust	1.221 (31.0)	45°	45°	.094 (2.4)	.313 (7.95)	.0118 (.30)	.354 (9.0)

① — Wear limit .05″ (1.3 mm)

CAMSHAFT

Engine	Journal Diam. In. (mm)	Clearance In. (mm)①	Lobe Lift In. (mm)
2383 cc Front	1.257-1.258 (31.92-31.95)	.002-.004 (.05-.10)	.....
Others	1.786-1.795 (29.94-29.96)		

① — End play .006″ (.15 mm)

VALVE SPRINGS

Engine	Free Length In. (mm)	PRESSURE Lbs. @ In. (kg @ mm)	
		Valve Closed	Valve Open
2383 cc Inner	1.33 (33.9)	16.2@1.13 (.72@28.6)	49.4@.72 (2.2@18.3)
Outer	1.58 (40.2)	40.0@1.28 (1.8@32.6)	102.5@.89 (4.5@22.3)

Section 7
CLUTCHES

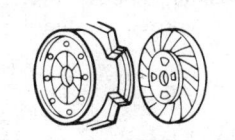

Contents

Clutches

CLUTCH TROUBLE SHOOTING

CONDITION & POSSIBLE CAUSE	CONDITION & POSSIBLE CAUSE
Chattering or Grabbing • Incorrect lever adjustment. • Oil or grease on facings. • Loose "U" joint flange. • Worn input shaft spline. • Binding pressure plate. • Binding release lever. • Binding disc hub. • Glazed facings. • Unequal pressure plate contact. • Bent clutch disc. • Uneven spring pressure. • Incorrect transmission alignment. • Loose facings. • Scored pressure plate. • Worn pressure plate, disc or flywheel. • Clutch disc hub sticking on shaft. • Worn or binding release levers. • Broken or weak pressure springs. • Sticking clutch pedal. • Incorrect disc facing. • Engine loose in chassis. **Spinning** • Dry or worn bushings. • Misaligned clutch housing. • Bent or distorted clutch disc. • Warped pressure plate. • Excessive pedal free play. **Dragging** • Oil or grease on facings. • Incorrect lever adjustment. • Incorrect pedal adjustment. • Dust or dirt on clutch. • Worn or broken facings. • Warped clutch disc. • Clutch disc hub binding on shaft. • Binding pilot bushing. • Sticking release bearing sleeve. • Warped pressure plate. **Whirring** • Incorrect pedal free play. • Incorrect transmission alignment.	**Rattling** • Weak or broken release lever spring. • Damaged pressure plate. • Broken clutch return spring. • Worn splines in clutch disc hub or transmission input shaft. • Worn clutch release bearing. • Dry or worn pilot bushing. • Unequal release lever contact. • Incorrect pedal free play. • Warped clutch disc. **Slipping** • Pressure plate springs worn or broken. • Worn facing. • Incorrect clutch alignment. • Oil or grease on facings. • Warped clutch disc. • Warped or scored pressure plate. • Binding release lever. • Binding clutch pedal. **Squeaking** • No lubrication in release bearing. • Worn release bearing. • Dry or worn pilot bushing. • Pilot bearing turning in crankshaft. • Worn input shaft bearing. • Incorrect transmission alignment. • No lubrication between clutch fork and pivot. • No lubrication in torque shaft. **Heavy, Stiff Pedal** • Dry or binding linkage components. • Sticking release bearing sleeve. • Dry or binding pedal hub. • Pedal interference with floorboard or mat. • Rough, dry or binding pivot ball, or fork pivots. **Grinding** • Dry release bearing. • Worn or dry pilot bearing. • Worn input shaft bearing.

Clutches

AUDI 4000

DESCRIPTION

Clutch is single plate dry disc type, using a diaphragm type pressure plate and a pre-lubricated clutch release bearing. Clutch is cable actuated.

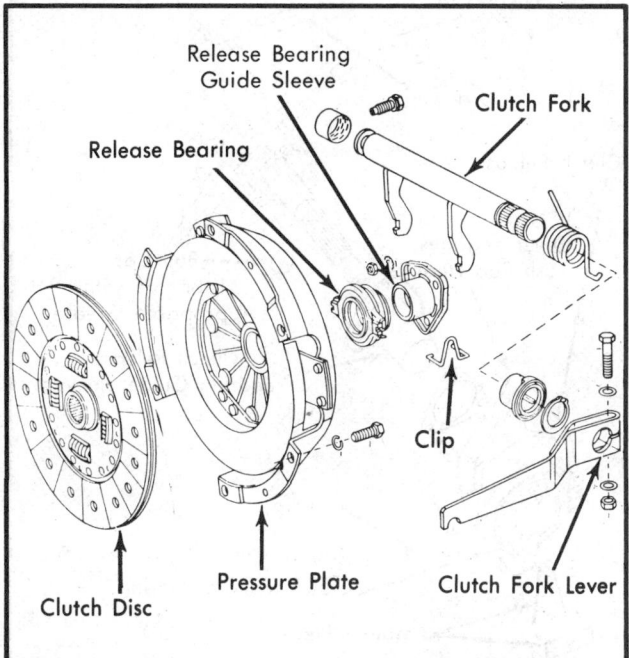

Fig. 1 Exploded View of Clutch Assembly

REMOVAL & INSTALLATION

CLUTCH ASSEMBLY

Removal — **1)** Disconnect negative battery cable. Disconnect exhaust header pipe at manifold and bracket on transmission. Remove upper transmission-to-engine bolts and engine support bolts. Disconnect backup light wiring and remove air cleaner.

NOTE — *On models equipped with a 5 cylinder engine and 5 speed transmission, the engine must be supported from above while removing and installing transmission.*

2) Remove bolt mounting shift assembly coupling to rear of transmission shifting shaft and separate assemblies. Unhook clutch cable at release lever. Disconnect speedometer.

3) Disconnect axle drive shafts at inner drive flanges. Remove starter. Take out front clutch housing cover plate. Remove remaining transmission-to-engine bolts. On some models, removal of certain steering brackets is necessary to remove transmission.

4) Support transmission with suitable jack. Remove transmission rear mounts and brackets. Remove front support bolts. Pry transmission away from engine and slide it out of vehicle.

5) Install holding tool (10-201) to flywheel and index (mark) pressure plate and flywheel. Loosen pressure plate bolts ¼ turn at a time in a diagonal pattern. Slide pressure plate off flywheel dowels and separate clutch disc.

Installation — To install, reverse removal procedure and note: Use clutch alignment tool to fit pressure plate and clutch. Make sure alignment marks are observed.

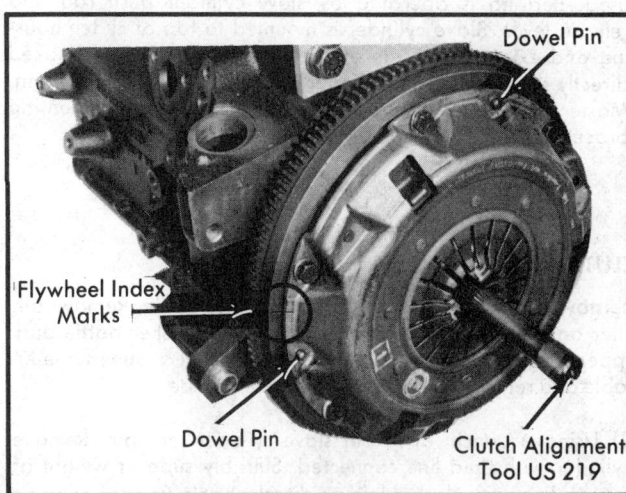

Fig. 2 Aligning Clutch Assembly Reference Marks for Reinstallation

CLUTCH RELEASE BEARING

1) With transmission separated from engine, remove spring clips securing release bearing to clutch fork. Bearing is pre-lubricated; do not wash in any cleaning solution.

2) Rotate bearing and check for roughness or noise, replace as necessary. Apply Molykote paste to bearing contact points on clutch fork. To install, reverse removal procedure.

PILOT BEARING

Lock flywheel to prevent rotation. Install suitable remover (10-202) and remove pilot bearing. Install bearing with suitable installer (VW207C) and seat bearing until distance from flywheel recess to bushing edge is ¹⁄₁₆" (1.5 mm). Lubricate bearing.

ADJUSTMENT

CLUTCH PEDAL FREE PLAY

Adjust clutch pedal free play by loosening and adjusting both counternuts at clutch cable. Pedal will have .59" (15 mm) free play when properly adjusted. On some models, counternuts are replaced by spring clips.

TIGHTENING SPECIFICATIONS

Application	Ft. Lbs. (N·m)
Clutch Assembly-to-Flywheel Bolts	18 (25)
Transmission-to-Engine Bolts	40 (55)

Clutches

AUDI 5000

DESCRIPTION

Clutch is a single plate, dry disc type. Pressure plate is a diaphragm spring type. A pre-lubricated release bearing is used. Bearing is operated by slave cylinder push rod and release lever. Slave cylinder is mounted to top of clutch housing and extends to inside of housing. Clutch pedal is hooked directly to clutch master cylinder push rod fork via a clevis pin. Master cylinder is secured to clutch/brake pedal mounting brace.

REMOVAL & INSTALLATION

CLUTCH ASSEMBLY

Removal – 1) Disconnect battery ground cable. Remove air filter on diesel models. Remove windshield washer bottle and upper engine-to-transmission bolts. Disconnect speedometer cable and remove torsion clip from slave cylinder.

2) Using a punch, drive out slave cylinder lock pin. Remove cylinder with fluid line connected. Suitably support weight of engine. Remove splash shield on diesel models. Remove exhaust pipe heat shield and disconnect exhaust pipe at manifold.

3) Disconnect axle drive shafts at transaxle and hang out of way. Disconnect back-up light wire. Pry off both shifting and adjusting rods. Remove lower engine-to-transmission mounting bolts.

4) Take out starter. Remove subframe cover shield. Slightly raise transmission. Remove transmission support bolts and bushings from both sides of subframe, then loosen both rear subframe mounting bolts. Remove right side transmission bracket. Remove transmission off dowels and take out of vehicle.

5) Index mark position of pressure plate in relation to flywheel. Insert flywheel retainer tool. Loosen pressure plate mounting bolt evenly in a diagonal pattern until pressure is relieved. Remove pressure plate and clutch disc.

Installation – To install, reverse removal procedure and note following: Clutch disc spring cage must face pressure plate. Clutch disc must slide freely with no radial play on input shaft. Lubricate input shaft splines with appropriate grease. Align pressure plate index marks. Use clutch disc alignment tool to center disc.

RELEASE BEARING & LEVER

Removal – Remove transmission. Remove cap bolt (attaching 2 retainer pieces) at lower edge of release lever. Slide release lever and bearing out of slave cylinder push rod and off guide sleeve. Disengage circlip and retainer clips keeping release bearing to lever. Separate bearing from lever. If necessary, guide sleeve can also be removed.

Inspection – Check clutch release bearing for wear or unusual noise. Do not wash bearing in solvent. If bearing is excessively noisy, replace.

Installation – To install, reverse removal procedure and note: Lubricate ball cap located in clutch housing with appropriate grease. Make sure clutch release lever locates directly into slave cylinder push rod tip. Push rod tip should be lubricated.

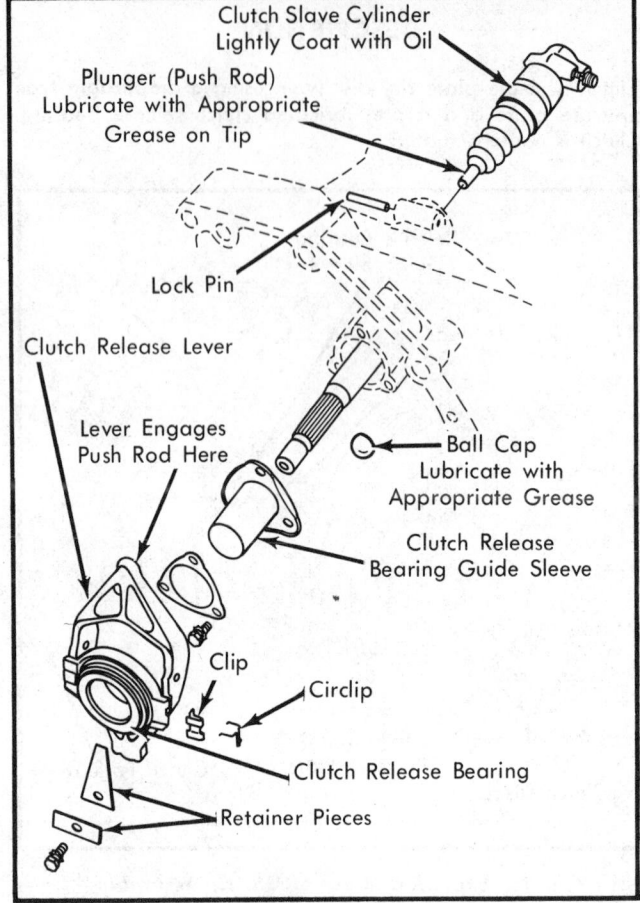

Fig. 1 Clutch Release Bearing with Related Components

MASTER CYLINDER

Removal – Disconnect and plug fluid lines. Separate cylinder from clutch pedal by removing clevis pin. Remove 2 bolts mounting master cylinder to pedal bracket and take out cylinder.

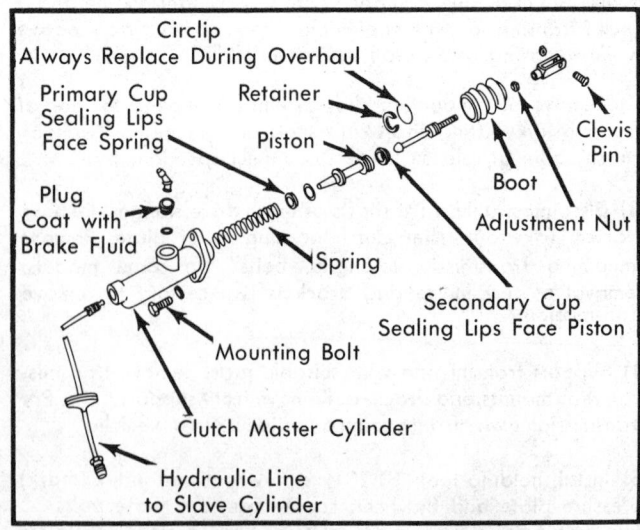

Fig. 2 Exploded View of Master Cylinder

Clutches

AUDI 5000 (Cont.)

Installation — Reverse removal procedure and bleed air from fluid line.

SLAVE CYLINDER

Removal — Working from under vehicle, drive out slave cylinder lock pin located on top of transmission. Slide cylinder back until push rod clears, then maneuver cylinder until fluid line can be disconnected and plugged.

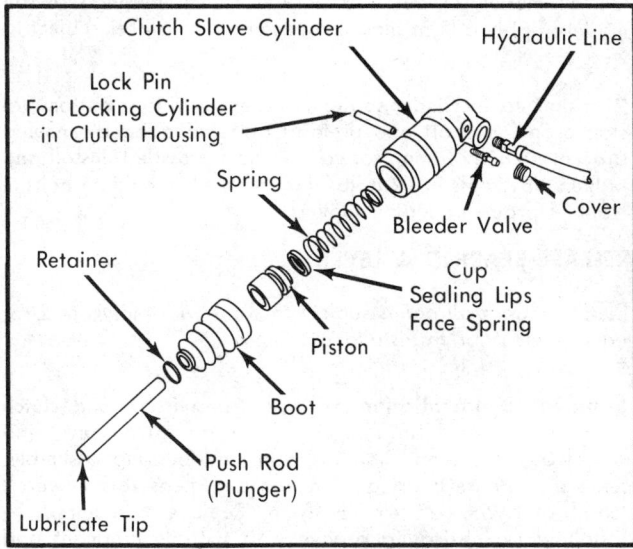

Fig. 3 Exploded View of Slave Cylinder

Installation — To install, reverse removal procedure. Coat outer surface of cylinder with oil before inserting into place. Bleed air from fluid line.

ADJUSTMENTS

CLUTCH PEDAL

Adjust master cylinder push rod so that in the rest position clutch pedal stands ⅜" (10 mm) above brake pedal.

NOTE — *If clutch pedal is correctly adjusted but fails to properly return, check hydraulic system for air, a tight pedal bushing or jammed return spring.*

HYDRAULIC SYSTEM BLEEDING

Use only pressure bleeding equipment to bleed system. Follow manufacturer's instructions.

TIGHTENING SPECIFICATIONS	
Application	**Ft. Lbs. (N·m)**
Pressure Plate Bolts	18 (24)
Drive Shaft-to-Transmission Bolts	32 (43)
Engine-to-Transmission Bolts	
Upper Bolts	40 (54)
Lower Bolts	
Inner 2 Bolts	33 (45)
Outer 2 Bolts	14 (19)
Starter Bolts	40 (54)

Clutches

BMW

320i
528i
633CSi
733i

DESCRIPTION

Clutch is dry single disc type using a diaphragm spring pressure plate. System is hydraulically operated by a clutch housing mounted slave cylinder and a firewall mounted master cylinder. Slave cylinder automatically adjusts for disc wear.

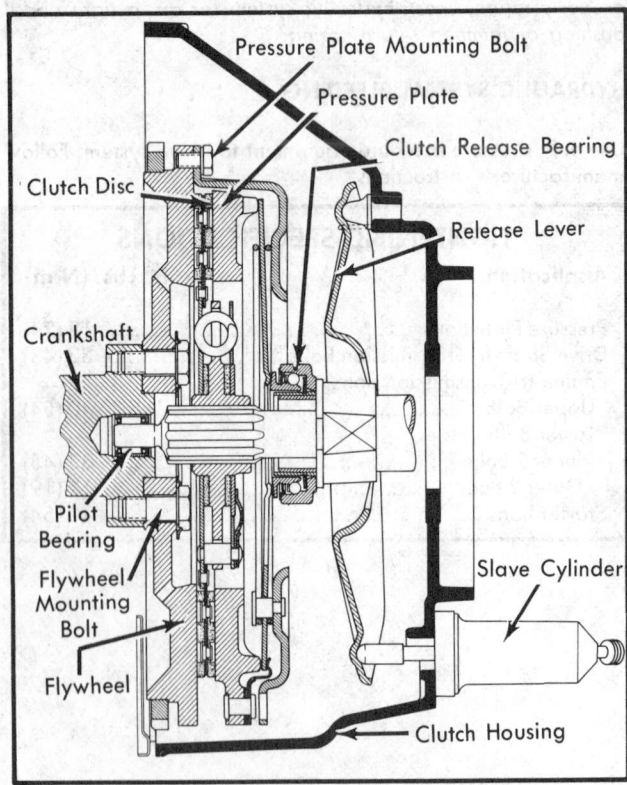

Fig. 1 Typical BMW Clutch Assembly

REMOVAL & INSTALLATION

CLUTCH ASSEMBLY

Removal – 1) On 320i models only, engage reverse gear. On all models, detach selector rod from gearshift lever. From inside vehicle, lift shift lever dust boot and remove circlip holding lever in place. Remove shift lever. Detach any exhaust system components which may interfere with transmission removal.

2) Fit clamp tool (26 1 011) to propeller shaft coupling and remove bolts holding coupling to transmission shaft coupler. Remove heat shield and detach bearing center bracket. On 733i, remove web under propeller shaft tunnel. On all models, remove center support bearing and bend propeller shaft so it can be removed from front coupling and placed out of way.

3) Support transmission and detach crossmember from body. Disconnect speedometer cable and housing from transmission. Detach clutch slave cylinder from clutch housing, leaving hydraulic line attached. Disconnect any electrical connections

from transmission and remove transmission mounting nuts. Remove transmission.

4) Remove flywheel inspection cover and bolts securing clutch housing to engine. Loosen pressure plate bolts one turn at a time and remove clutch assembly.

Installation – 1) Usng an alignment tool (21-2-100 or equivalent), install clutch disc and pressure plate. Tighten mounting bolts 1 turn at a time to 16-17 ft. lbs. (22-23 N·m). On all models except 320i, install clutch housing. On all models, apply a light film of grease on all surfaces subject to wear.

2) Install slave cylinder so that bleeder screw is at bottom. Install propeller shaft and preload center bearing by moving bracket .078" (2.0 mm) forward in slots provided. Install and tighten NEW nuts to 72 ft. lbs. (98 N·m) while holding bolts in front of propeller shaft coupling.

RELEASE BEARING & LEVER

NOTE – *Coat all points subject to wear with Molykote 2 (or equivalent) prior to installation.*

Removal & Installation – With transmission and clutch housing removed from engine, remove spring from pivot end of release arm and slide off arm and bearing assembly. Separate release bearing from arm and measure for overall length of 1.95±.02" (49.5±.4 mm). Replace as required. To install, pack lubricating groove with suitable lubricant and reverse removal procedure.

CLUTCH MASTER CYLINDER

Removal – Remove trim under left side of instrument panel. On 320i models, remove accelerator cable. Remove bolt attaching master cylinder push rod to clutch pedal. Siphon off brake fluid from reservoir until level is below clutch master cylinder supply port and detach hydraulic lines from clutch master cylinder. On 733i models only, remove windshield washer tank. On all models, remove mounting bolts at firewall and remove master cylinder from vehicle.

Installation – To install, reverse removal procedures and bleed hydraulic system. On 633CSi and 733i, ensure that pedal over-center spring is engaged in pedal guide before attaching push rod.

CLUTCH SLAVE CYLINDER

Removal & Installation – Siphon fluid from reservoir and detach slave cylinder from housing. Disconnect hydraulic line and remove cylinder. To install, reverse removal procedure ensuring that cylinder is mounted with bleeder screw at bottom. Fill reservoir and bleed system.

OVERHAUL

CLUTCH MASTER CYLINDER

Slide dust boot off and remove circlip holding push rod. Remove piston assembly and clean master cylinder and parts with alcohol. Inspect cylinder bore for corrosion or scoring; replace if required. Lubricate internal parts with brake fluid and reassemble. Adjust push rod length to approximately 5.5" (140 mm). See *Fig. 2.*

Clutches

BMW (Cont.)

NOTE – *Coat all pivot points on clutch pedal assembly with Molykote 2 (or equivalent) prior to assembly.*

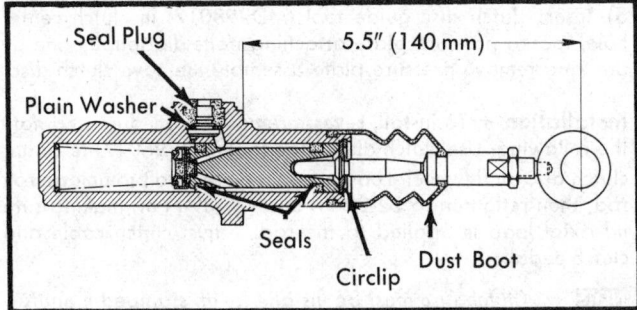

Fig. 2   Sectional View of Clutch Master Cylinder

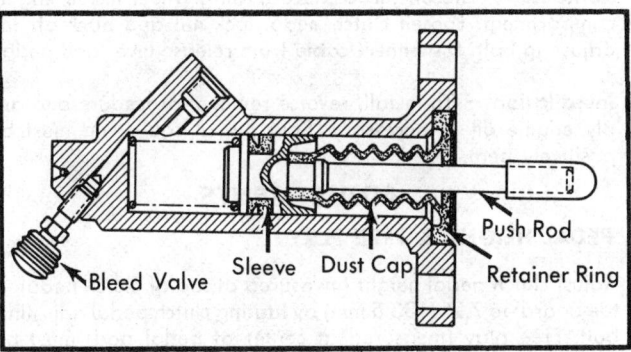

Fig. 3   Sectional View of Clutch Slave Cylinder

CLUTCH SLAVE CYLINDER

Remove retaining ring and take out push rod and boot. Remove piston and clean all internal parts with alcohol. Inspect bore for scoring and corrosion; replace if necessary. Lubricate all internal parts with brake fluid and reassemble.

ADJUSTMENT

NOTE – *Clutch free play is automatically adjusted for disc wear.*

HYDRAULIC SYSTEM BLEEDING

Ensure that fluid reservoir is full and attach bleeder hose to bleed screw on slave cylinder. Submerge end of hose in partly filled container of brake fluid and pump clutch pedal about 10 times. Hold pedal down on last stroke and loosen bleeder screw to allow air to escape. Close bleeder screw and repeat until air is bled from system.

TIGHTENING SPECIFICATIONS

Application	Ft. Lbs. (N·m)
Slave Cylinder-to-Clutch Housing Bolts	18-20 (24-27)
Clutch-to-Flywheel Bolts	16-17 (22-23)
Clutch Housing-to-Engine Bolts	
8 mm Bolts	18-20 (24-27)
10 mm Bolts	35-38 (47-51)
Cover-to-Clutch Housing Bolts	
6 mm Bolts	6-7 (8-9)
8 mm Bolts	18-20 (24-27)

CHRYSLER CORP. IMPORTS — FRONT-WHEEL-DRIVE MODELS

Champ
Colt

DESCRIPTION

Clutch is a diaphragm spring, single disc type. Operation is controlled mechanically by a cable. Clutch release bearing is sealed and permanently lubricated.

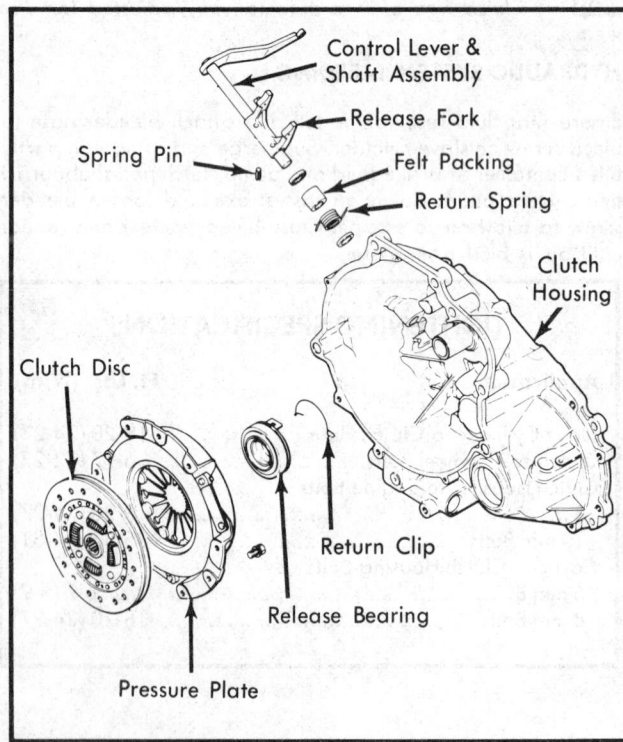

Fig. 1 Exploded View of Champ & Colt Clutch Assembly

REMOVAL & INSTALLATION

CLUTCH ASSEMBLY

Removal — 1) From inside engine compartment, disconnect negative cable from battery. Remove the following from transaxle:

- Clutch cable
- Speedometer cable
- Backup light switch harness
- Starter motor
- Four top engine-to-transaxle bolts

2) Raise vehicle and remove front wheels. Remove under cover, shift rod and extension. Drain transaxle fluid. Disconnect drive shafts from transaxle.

CAUTION — *Drive shaft retaining rings should be replaced with new ones on reassembly. Also, use care not to damage drive shaft boots.*

3) Disconnect range selector cable (if equipped). Remove engine rear cover.

4) Support engine with a suitable lifting device, then remove remaining engine-to-transaxle mounting bolts. Remove trans-

axle mount insulator-to-transaxle mount bolt. Remove and lower transaxle assembly from vehicle.

5) Insert clutch disc guide tool (MD998017) in clutch center hole, loosen pressure plate attaching bolts diagonally one by one and remove pressure plate assembly. Remove clutch disc.

Installation — To install, reverse removal procedure and note the following: Use clutch disc guide tool (MD998017) to center clutch disc on flywheel. Loosen front roll rod bolt to unload roll rod, then retighten to 22-29 Ft. Lbs. (29-39 N·m) making sure no axial load is applied to the rod. Adjust clutch cable and clutch pedal.

NOTE — *Clutch disc must be installed with stamped manufacturer's mark on pressure plate side.*

CLUTCH CABLE

Removal — Loosen the cable adjusting wheel inside engine compartment. Loosen clutch pedal lock nut and back off the adjusting bolt. Disconnect cable from release lever and pedal.

Installation — To install, reverse removal procedure and apply engine oil as necessary. Split pin at cable end must be positively bent.

ADJUSTMENTS

PEDAL HEIGHT & FREE PLAY

Adjust clutch pedal height (measured at top of clutch pedal to toe board) to 7.2" (183.5 mm) by turning clutch pedal adjusting bolt. Free play (measured at center of pedal pad) must be .8-1.2" (20-30 mm).

CLUTCH CABLE

Pull outer cable out toward engine compartment and adjust clearance between adjusting nut and holder to .20-.24" (5-6 mm). With pedal properly adjusted, pedal travel should be 5.7" (145 mm).

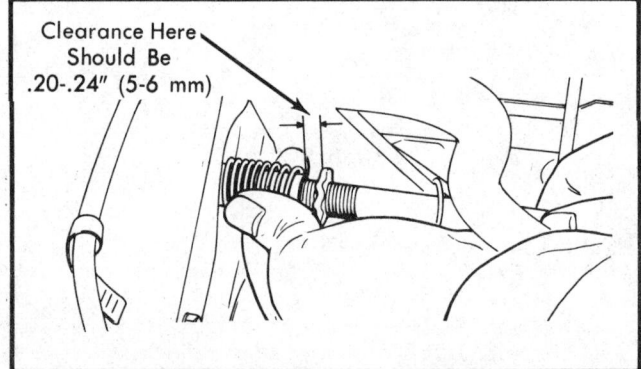

Fig. 2 Clutch Cable Adjustment

TIGHTENING SPECIFICATIONS

Application	Ft. Lbs. (N·m)
Clutch Cover-to-Flywheel	11-15 (15-20)
Transaxle-to-Engine	
8 mm Bolts	22-25 (30-34)
10 mm Bolts	32-40 (43-54)

CHRYSLER CORP. IMPORTS — REAR-WHEEL-DRIVE MODELS

Arrow Pickup
Challenger
Ram-50 Pickup
Sapporo

DESCRIPTION

Clutch is a diaphragm spring, single disc type. Operation is controlled mechanically by a cable. Clutch release bearing is sealed and permanently lubricated.

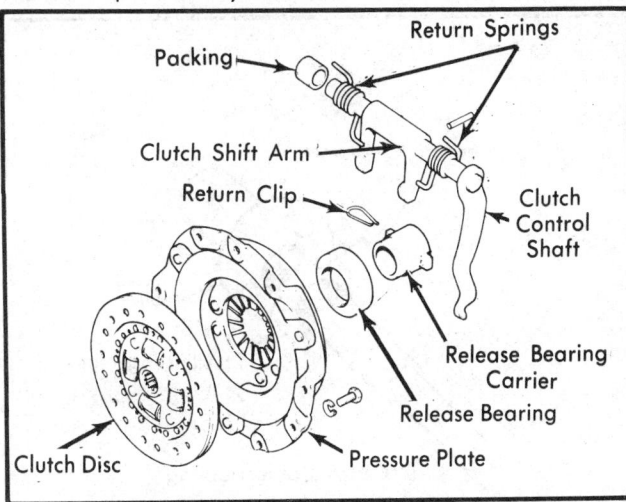

Fig. 1   Exploded View of Clutch Assembly

REMOVAL & INSTALLATION

NOTE — *Procedure is general for all models. Some steps do not apply to all models.*

CLUTCH ASSEMBLY

Removal — **1)** Disconnect battery ground cable. Remove air cleaner assembly. Remove starter. Insert rag between rocker cover and firewall.

2) From inside vehicle, remove console box (if equipped); remove back bone carpet. Remove dust cover retaining plate. Remove extension housing attaching bolts and control lever assembly.

NOTE — *Lever should be in 2nd gear on 4-speed transmissions and in 1st gear on 5-speed transmissions.*

3) Raise and support vehicle on jack stands; drain transmission fluid. Disconnect propeller shaft-to-differential pinion flange bolts. Remove center bearing (if equipped) and remove propeller shaft from transmission. Disconnect speedometer cable and backup light connector from transmission. Disconnect exhaust pipe from exhaust manifold and clutch cable from transmission. Support rear of engine on safety stands. With a service jack placed under transmission, remove rear engine support bracket.

NOTE — *Place jack under transmission oil pan, with the support area as wide as possible.*

4) Remove bell housing cover and remaining transmission-to-bell housing mounting bolts. Pull transmission assembly rearward from engine and remove from vehicle.

NOTE — *Use care not to twist front end of main drive gear.*

5) Insert clutch centering tool (MD998017) into clutch center hole to prevent dropping clutch disc. Alternately loosen clutch attaching bolts diagonally and evenly and remove clutch cover assembly. Separate pressure plate and clutch disc.

Installation — To install, reverse removal procedure and note the following: Use clutch centering tool (MD998017) to center clutch disc on flyweel. Apply lubricant to clutch disc splines and input shaft splines.

NOTE — *Clutch disc must be installed with stamped manufacturer's mark on pressure plate side. Also, be sure to keep disc facing, flywheel and pressure plate clean, dry and free of grease and oil.*

CLUTCH CABLE

Removal — Loosen cable adjusting wheel inside engine compartment, then loosen clutch pedal lock nut. Remove clutch cable from control lever, then from clutch pedal lever and remove from vehicle.

Installation — To install clutch cable, reverse the removal procedure and note following: Apply engine oil as necessary to install cable. Some models are equipped with insulating pads. Fit pads where cable routes near intake manifold and at rear side of engine mount.

CLUTCH RELEASE BEARING & SHIFT ARM

Removal — With transmission removed, remove return clip on transmission side, then slide off release bearing carrier and release bearing. Using a $\frac{3}{16}$" punch, remove shift arm spring pin and control lever assembly, then remove the shift arm and return springs. See *Fig. 2*.

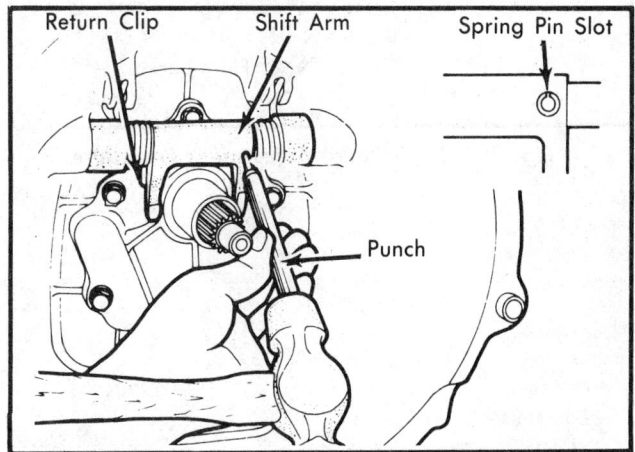

Fig. 2   Removing and Installing Shift Arm Spring Pins

Installation — **1)** Insert lever and shaft into transmission case from left side. Place shift arm, felt packings and return springs on shaft assembly.

2) Apply grease to inside of bushing and oil seal lips. Apply engine oil to felt packings. Align shift arm pin holes and control shaft pin holes. Drive spring pins into position. See *Fig. 2*.

NOTE — *Spring pin slot direction must be at right angle to control shaft centerline.*

Clutches

CHRYSLER CORP. IMPORTS — REAR-WHEEL-DRIVE MODELS (Cont.)

ADJUSTMENTS

PEDAL HEIGHT ADJUSTMENT

Rotate clutch pedal adjusting bolt (at top of clutch pedal) so that pedal height is as indicated in table. Pedal height is measured between floor board and top of clutch pedal pad.

Clutch Pedal Height and Travel		
Application	Height In. (mm)	Travel In. (mm)
Pickup Trucks		
2000 cc Engine	6.5 (166)	5.5 (140)
2600 cc Engine	6.9 (176)	5.9 (150)
All Others	7.1 (180)	5.8 (148)

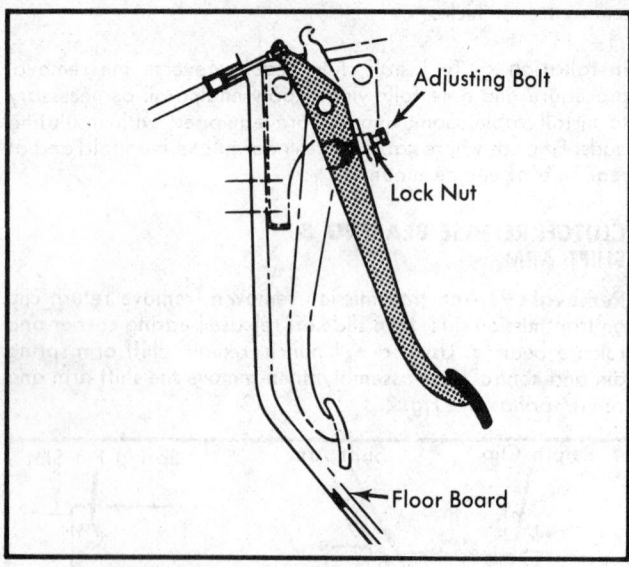

Fig. 3   Clutch Pedal Adjustment Procedure

CLUTCH CABLE

Pull clutch cable housing toward engine compartment. Rotate cable adjusting nut until .12-.16" (3-4 mm) clearance is obtained between adjusting nut and holder. Clutch pedal free play should be .8-1.4" (20-35 mm) for pickups and .6-.8" (15-20 mm) for all other models.

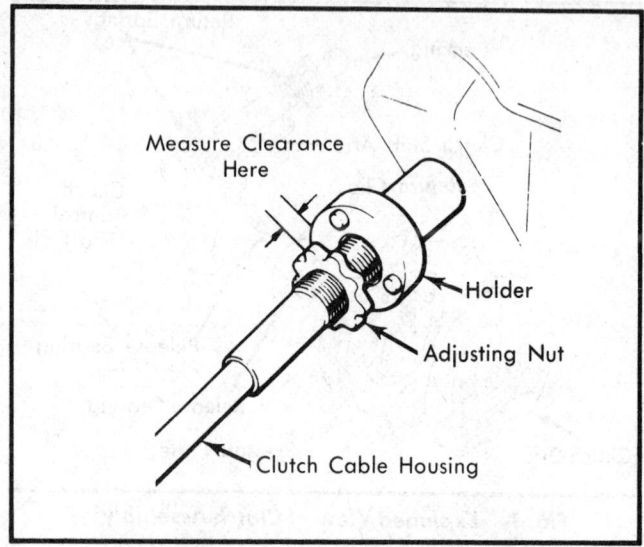

Fig. 4   Clutch Cable Adjustment Point

TIGHTENING SPECIFICATIONS	
Application	Ft. Lbs. (N·m)
Transmission-to-Engine Flange Bolts	32-39 (43-53)
Starter Bolts	16-23 (22-31)

COURIER

Pickup

DESCRIPTION

Clutch is of single dry disk type. Clutch assembly consists of clutch disc, clutch cover and pressure plate assembly, and clutch release mechanism. Clutch housing also acts as the transmission input shaft bearing retainer, and contains the input shaft bearing oil seal and a selective fit thrust washer for controlling input shaft end play. Clutch release mechanism is hydraulic, consisting of a firewall mounted master cylinder and a slave cylinder mounted on flywheel housing. To control clutch engagement, a one-way valve is mounted on clutch master cylinder to control the flow of return fluid when pressure on clutch is released.

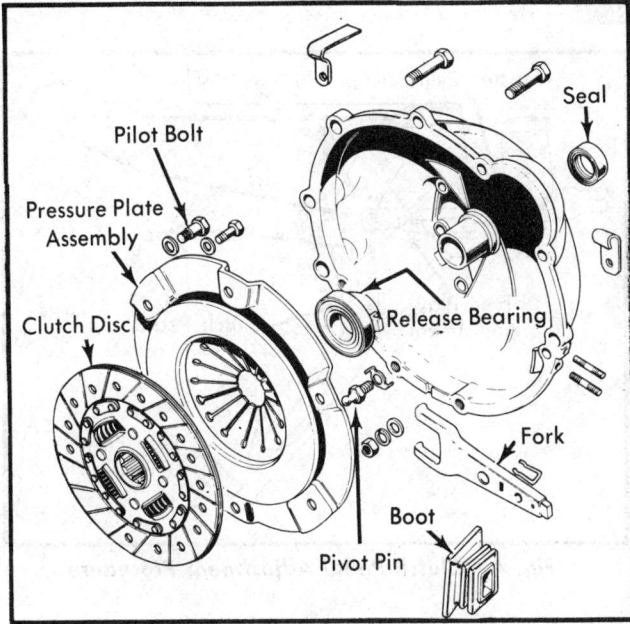

Fig. 1 Exploded View of Clutch Assembly with Detail of Internal Components

REMOVAL & INSTALLATION

CLUTCH ASSEMBLY

Removal — 1) Disconnect negative battery cable. Place transmission in neutral. On 5-speed transmission, remove boot retaining screws. Remove bolts attaching the retainer cover to the gearshift lever retainer and pull gearshift lever, shim and bushing up and away from retainer.

2) On 4-speed transmission, lift boot and remove screws, lock washer and flat washers attaching gearshift tower to the extension housing. Remove shift lever, tower and gasket as an assembly along with 2 shift lever boots.

3) On all models, cover opening and raise vehicle. Disconnect drive shaft and drive shaft center bearing supporting nuts and washers (if equipped). Disconnect drive shaft from transmission and install a plug in extension housing to prevent fluid leakage.

4) Disconnect exhaust pipe brackets from transmission case and clutch housing. Remove exhaust pipe and catalytic assembly. Disconnect clutch release lever return spring. Remove clutch release cylinder and secure it to the side. Remove speedometer cable from extension housing.

5) Disconnect wiring from transmission and starter. Support engine with a jack and remove starter. Support transmission and remove

bolts, lock washers and flat washers attaching transmission to the engine rear plate. Remove crossmember attaching nuts and bolts at transmission and frame side rails and remove crossmember.

6) Lower engine jack and remove transmission by sliding rearward and downward. Mark location of 2 pilot bolt holes on flywheel and pressure plate. Remove clutch attaching bolts and clutch assembly.

NOTE — *Transmissions have aluminum cases. Install flat washer between case and attaching bolt or nut.*

Installation — To install, reverse removal procedure and note: Align clutch disc and flywheel with centering tool. Install pressure plate and bolts finger tight, then tighten bolts a few turns at a time in a criss-cross pattern. Bleed hydraulic system and adjust clutch pedal free play.

RELEASE LEVER & BEARING

Removal — With transmission removed, disconnect release collar spring and slide out release lever, boot and bearing. Inspect all parts for wear or damage.

Installation — To install, apply lubricant to input shaft bearing retainer of clutch housing and pivot bolt. Seat release lever on pivot. Apply lubricant to bearing contact surface of lever. Install release bearing and hook release collar spring. Lubricate face of release bearing. Lever and bearing must operate freely.

CLUTCH MASTER CYLINDER

Removal — Disconnect and plug hydraulic lines. Remove master cylinder attaching nuts. Remove master cylinder.

Installation — To install, start pedal push rod into cylinder, then position cylinder against firewall. Install and tighten attaching nuts. Connect hydraulic line. Bleed hydraulic system and check pedal free play.

CLUTCH SLAVE CYLINDER

Removal — Disconnect hydraulic fluid inlet line at slave cylinder. Unhook release lever from push rod. Remove nuts attaching slave cylinder to clutch housing and remove cylinder.

Installation — Locate cylinder on studs in housing. Tighten nuts. Connect fluid inlet line. Fill master cylinder and bleed hydraulic system. Hook clutch release lever into slave cylinder push rod.

OVERHAUL

CLUTCH MASTER CYLINDER

1) Clean outside of cylinder, drain fluid and remove dust boot. Using a screwdriver, remove piston stop ring and washer. Remove piston, piston cup and return spring from cylinder.

2) Wash all parts in clean alcohol or brake fluid. Check all rubber components and replace if damaged, worn, softened or swollen. Check cylinder bore for wear or damage, and check clearance between cylinder bore and piston. Replace cylinder or piston if clearance is more than .004" (.102 mm).

3) To assemble, dip piston and cups in clean brake fluid and reverse disassembly procedure. When assembled, fill reservoir with fluid and operate piston with a screwdriver until fluid is ejected at outlet fitting.

COURIER (Cont.)

CLUTCH MASTER CYLINDER ONE-WAY VALVE

Disassembly — Remove cap from side of clutch master cylinder. *See Fig. 2.* Slide out washer, one-way valve and spring.

Reassembly — Position spring along with one-way valve into cylinder housing. Fit cap and washer.

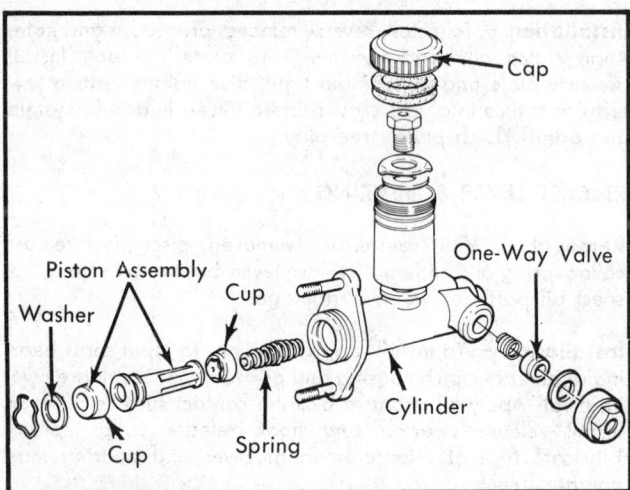

Fig. 2 Exploded View of Clutch Master Cylinder Assembly and One-Way Valve

SLAVE CYLINDER

Disassembly — 1) Clean outside of housing. Remove dust boot and clutch release rod.

2) Remove piston assembly and return spring. Remove bleeder screw cap, bleeder screw and steel ball.

Inspection — Check cylinder bore and piston for roughness, wear or scoring. Clearance between cylinder bore and piston should be .004" (.102 mm). Replace piston or cylinder if specification is exceeded.

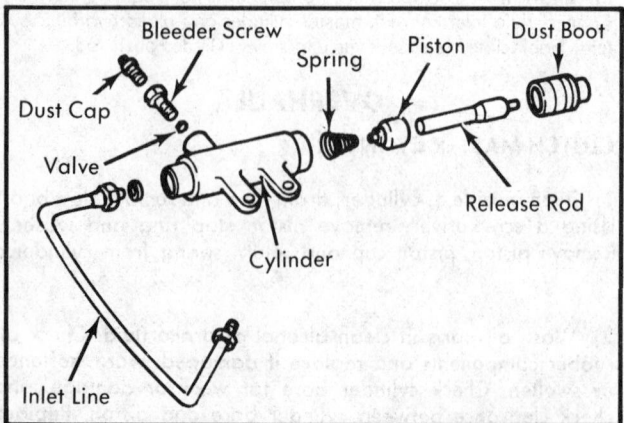

Fig. 3 Exploded View of Courier Slave Cylinder

Reassembly — 1) Lightly coat piston and cups with brake fluid. Fit cups to piston. Install piston into cylinder.

2) Install release rod and boot. Place steel ball into cylinder. Screw in bleeder and fit dust cap.

ADJUSTMENTS

CLUTCH PEDAL

Pedal free play is adjusted by loosening lock nut on push rod and rotating rod until .79-1.18" (20-30 mm) free travel is obtained at pedal pad. *See Fig. 4.* Tighten lock nut when adjustment is completed.

NOTE — *Free travel includes travel in master cylinder.*

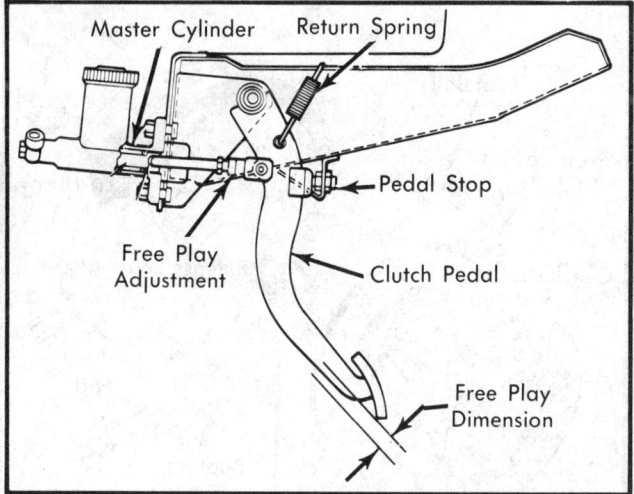

Fig. 4 Clutch Pedal Adjustment Procedure

HYDRAULIC SYSTEM BLEEDING

Remove rubber cap from bleeder valve and attach a bleeder tube and fixture to bleeder screw. Place other end of tube in a glass jar of brake fluid and open bleeder screw. Depress clutch pedal and allow to return slowly. Continue pumping action until air bubbles cease to appear in glass jar, then close bleeder screw. Install rubber cap on bleeder screw and fill master cylinder.

NOTE — *During bleeding, master cylinder must be kept ¾ full of brake fluid.*

TIGHTENING SPECIFICATIONS

Application	Ft. Lbs. (N·m)
Clutch Housing-to-Engine	
2000 cc Engine	34-45 (46-61)
2300 cc Engine	28-40 (38-54)
Pressure Plate-to-Flywheel	14-20 (19-27)
Slave Cylinder-to-Clutch Housing	12-17 (16-23)
Pivot Pin	23-34 (31-46)
Master Cylinder Attaching Bolts	14-18 (19-24)

Clutches

DATSUN — EXCEPT 310

DESCRIPTION

Clutch is dry, single disc type. All models use a diaphragm spring type pressure plate and pre-lubricated clutch release bearing. Clutch is operated by a firewall mounted master cylinder and a clutch housing mounted slave cylinder. All models except 210 have a non-adjustable slave cylinder assembly. On 210 models, a threaded push rod and lock nut enable adjustment at the slave cylinder.

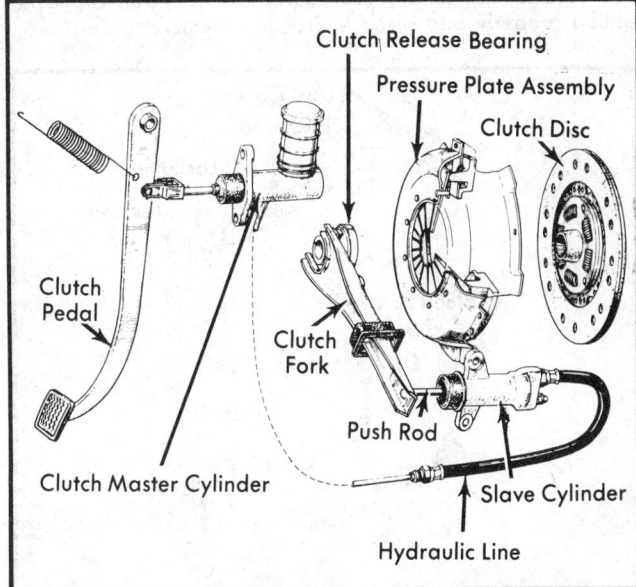

Fig. 1 Typical Datsun Hydraulically Operated Clutch System

REMOVAL & INSTALLATION

CLUTCH ASSEMBLY

NOTE — *Removal procedure is general. Some steps may not apply to all models.*

Removal — 1) Disconnect negative battery cable and accelerator linkage. Remove console box and place transmission shift lever in neutral. Remove control lever boots, snap ring (nut, if required), and shift lever pin. Remove shift control lever.

2) Raise and support vehicle on safety stands and disconnect exhaust pipe from manifold. If required, remove bolts mounting exhaust pipe bracket to extension housing or rear engine crossmember. Remove exhaust pipe insulator (if equipped) and lay over exhaust pipe.

3) Disconnect back-up light, neutral, overdrive and transmission controlled spark connectors (if equipped). Disconnect speedometer cable on all except 4-WD models. On 4-WD models, remove primary and front propeller shafts, and front differential carrier crossmember.

NOTE — *Index mark propeller shafts and companion flanges prior to removal.*

4) Remove slave cylinder. On all except 4-WD, separate center support bearing (if equipped) from crossmember and remove

propeller shaft. On all models, plug rear extension of transmission after removing propeller shaft to prevent loss of transmission fluid.

5) Support engine on suitable jack. Support transmission with transmission jack, then loosen rear engine mount attaching bolt and remove rear engine mounting bracket. Remove starter. Remove engine-to-transmission bolts. With engine supported and transmission mounted on transmission jack, slide transmission rearward and remove from vehicle.

6) Install clutch alignment tool and loosen pressure plate bolts one turn at a time. Use a criss-cross pattern to loosen bolts until spring pressure is relieved. Remove pressure plate and clutch disc.

NOTE — *Be sure to keep disc facing, flywheel and pressure plate clean, dry and free of grease and oil.*

Installation — To install, reverse removal procedure and note the following:

- Lubricate clutch disc splines with small amount of multipurpose grease.
- Slip clutch assembly over guide dowels.
- Use clutch aligning tool to center disc and pressure plate.
- Tighten bolts one turn at a time in a criss-cross pattern.
- Adjust linkage and pedal.
- Check and refill transmission lubricant.
- Bleed clutch hydraulic system and replenish fluid.

CLUTCH MASTER CYLINDER

Removal & Installation — Disconnect master cylinder push rod at clevis. Disconnect hydraulic line to slave cylinder. Remove cylinder attaching bolts and remove cylinder. Remove master cylinder dust cover if equipped. On 280ZX models only, remove windshield washer tank and clear fuel injection resistor before removing master cylinder. To install, reverse removal procedure, bleed hydraulic system and adjust pedal height and free play.

CLUTCH DAMPER (810)

Removal & Installation — Remove hydraulic lines from clutch damper. Remove clutch damper from bracket. To install, reverse removal procedure, bleed hydraulic system and adjust pedal height and free play.

CLUTCH SLAVE CYLINDER

Removal & Installation — Remove clutch fork return spring (if equipped). Disconnect hydraulic line from cylinder, remove bolts attaching cylinder to clutch housing, and remove slave cylinder. To install, reverse removal procedure, bleed hydraulic system and adjust pedal height and free play.

CLUTCH RELEASE BEARING & LEVER

Removal — With transmission removed from vehicle, remove dust boot from clutch housing. Disconnect release lever retaining spring or return spring, as required, and retaining clips holding release bearing to lever. Remove bearing and lever through front of clutch housing. Remove bearing from collar using a puller.

DATSUN – EXCEPT 310 (Cont.)

Installation – To install, reverse removal procedure and note the following: Apply multi-purpose grease to inside surface of bearing collar, release bearing contact points, release bearing, ball pin in clutch housing, and ball contact points on release lever.

OVERHAUL

NOTE – *Master cylinders and slave cylinders may be supplied by more than one manufacturer. Parts are not interchangeable. Ensure that overhaul kit matches cylinder.*

CLUTCH MASTER CYLINDER

1) With master cylinder removed, remove filler cap and drain fluid. Remove dust cover and stopper ring. Remove push rod and stopper. Remove supply valve stopper, then take out piston, spring seat and return spring.

2) Clean all parts in clean brake fluid and inspect for wear or damage. If cylinder-to-piston clearance exceeds .006" (.15 mm) replace defective part. Replace piston cup and dust cover during overhaul. To assemble, coat all parts with brake fluid and reverse disassembly procedure. Bleed hydraulic system and adjust pedal height.

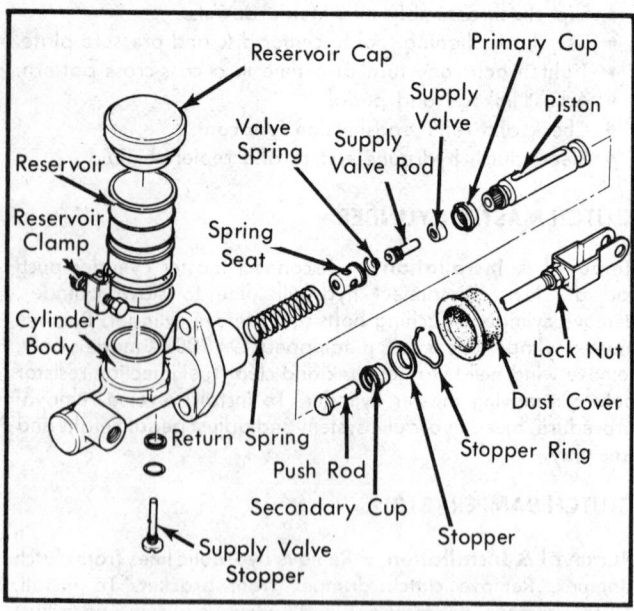

Fig. 2   Exploded View of Clutch Master Cylinder

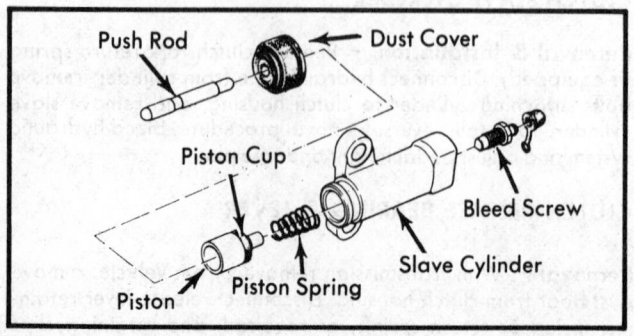

Fig. 3   Exploded View of Clutch Slave Cylinder Assembly (Except 210)

CLUTCH SLAVE CYLINDER

1) With slave cylinder removed, remove push rod and dust cover. Remove piston, piston cup and piston spring as an assembly. Remove bleeder screw.

2) Clean all parts in clean brake fluid and inspect for wear or damage. If cylinder-to-piston clearance exceeds .006" (.15 mm), replace defective part. Replace piston cup and dust cover during overhaul. To assemble, coat all parts with brake fluid and reverse disassembly procedure. Ensure piston cup is installed properly and bleed hydraulic system.

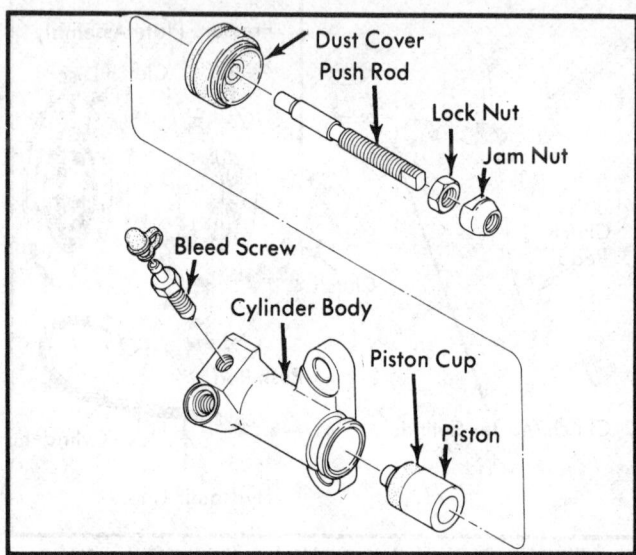

Fig. 4   Exploded View of 210 Clutch Slave Cylinder

CLUTCH DAMPER (810)

NOTE – *Do not let oil touch damper rubber.*

1) Remove four cover attaching screws. Remove damper rubber, piston and piston cup. Clean all parts in brake fluid. Check cylinder bore and piston for wear or damage. If cylinder-to-piston clearance exceeds .006" (.15 mm), replace defective part.

2) Check condition of piston cup. Always replace piston cup during overhaul. Check damper rubber for cracks, deformation and elasticity and replace if necessary.

3) To assemble, lubricate all parts in brake fluid and reverse disassembly procedure. Bleed hydraulic system and adjust pedal height and free play.

Pedal Height Specifications	
Application	**In. (mm)**
200SX	6.61-6.85 (168-174)
210	5.63-5.87 (143-149)
280ZX	7.99 (203)
510	6.34-6.57 (161-167)
810	7.17-7.32 (182-186)
Pickup	6.73-6.97 (171-177)

Clutches

DATSUN − EXCEPT 310 (Cont.)

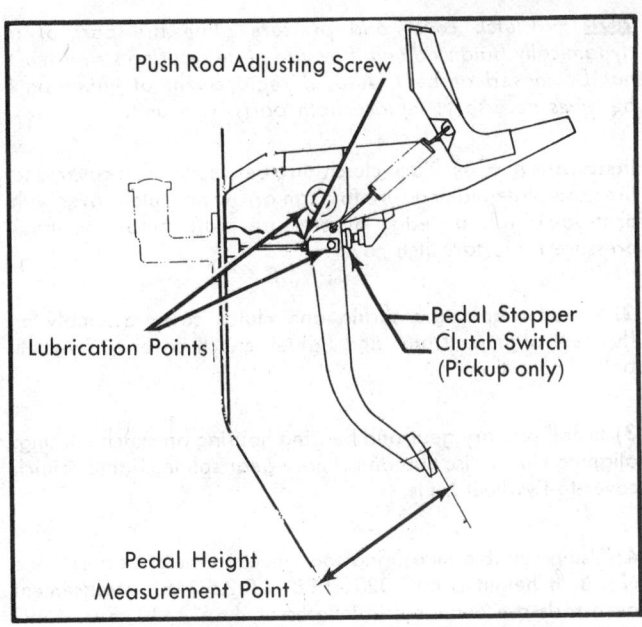

Fig. 5   Clutch Pedal Height Measurement and Free Play Adjustment Locations (Exc. 280ZX)

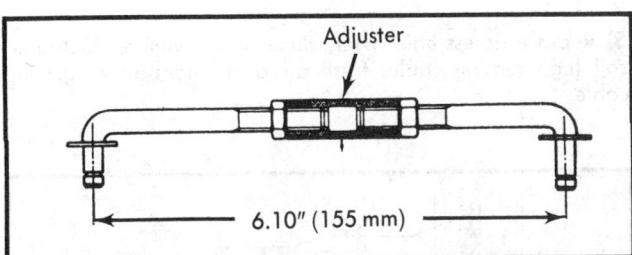

Fig. 6   280ZX Clutch Pedal Adjusting Rod Measurement

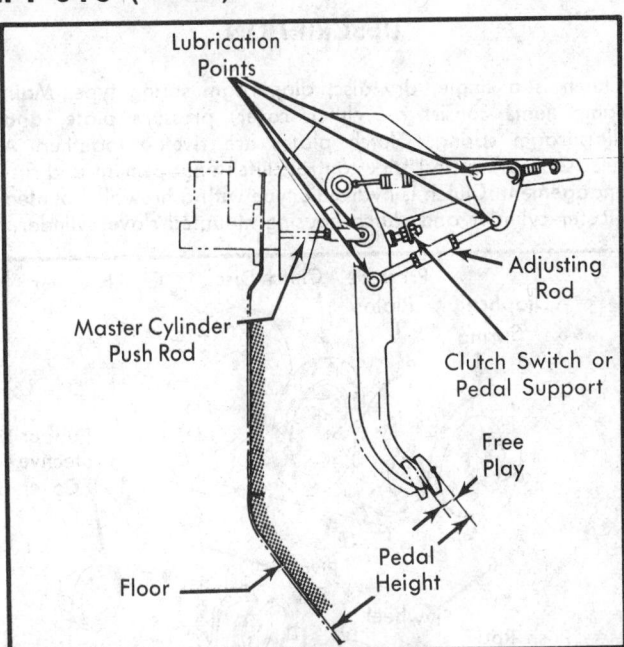

Fig. 7   280ZX Clutch Pedal Height Measurement and Free Play Adjustment Locations

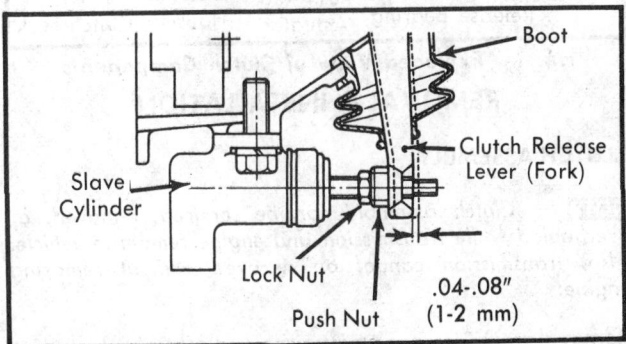

Fig. 8   Clutch Fork Free Play Adjustment Location for Datsun 210

ADJUSTMENT

PEDAL HEIGHT & FREE PLAY

Adjust pedal height on all models except 280ZX and Pickup by turning pedal stopper adjusting nut. Pickup models are adjusted by turning clutch switch adjusting nut. Adjustment on 280ZX models is made by first setting adjusting rod length to 6.10" (155 mm). See Fig. 6. Then adjust master cylinder push rod so that pedal height is 8.11" (206 mm). And finally turn pedal stopper or clutch switch until pedal height is down to 7.99" (203 mm). See Fig. 7. On all models, free play is adjusted to .04-.20" (1-5 mm) by turning master cylinder push rod in or out.

CLUTCH FORK FREE PLAY (210)

Loosen lock nut and push rod nut and turn push rod until release bearing lightly touches clutch diaphragm spring. Turn rod back (in opposite direction) about 1¼ turn and tighten lock nut. This provides about .04-.08" (1-2 mm) clearance between push nut and lever. Work clutch pedal several times and recheck pedal play.

HYDRAULIC SYSTEM BLEEDING

NOTE — On all models except 810, bleed slave cylinder. On 810 models equipped with clutch damper, bleed clutch damper then slave cylinder.

Fill reservoir with brake fluid. Fit bleeder hose to bleeder screw. Place opposite end of hose into a clear container partially filled with brake fluid. Pump clutch pedal two or three times and hold to floor. Break bleeder screw loose and allow air to vent. Close bleeder screw and allow pedal to return. Repeat procedure until no air bubbles are present in discharged fluid.

TIGHTENING SPECIFICATIONS

Application	Ft. Lbs. (N·m)
Clutch-to-Flywheel Bolts	12-15 (16-21)
Engine-to-Transmission Bolts	
210	12-16 (16-22)
510	29-35 (39-47)
All Others	32-43 (43-58)

Clutches

DATSUN 310

DESCRIPTION

Clutch is a single, dry disc, diaphragm spring type. Main components consist of: clutch cover, pressure plate, and diaphragm spring. Clutch plates are riveted together. A release bearing and fork control clutch engagement and disengagement. Clutch is hydraulic type with a firewall mounted master cylinder and clutch housing mounted slave cylinder.

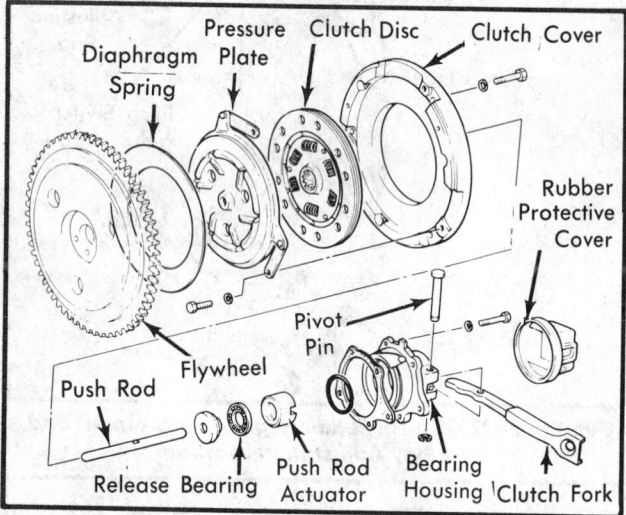

Fig. 1 Exploded View of Clutch Components

REMOVAL & INSTALLATION

CLUTCH ASSEMBLY

NOTE – *Clutch assembly can be serviced, removed, or overhauled while transmission and engine remain in vehicle. Also, transmission cannot be removed without removing engine.*

Removal – 1) Disconnect battery ground cable, fresh air duct and high tension cable between coil and distributor. Remove fuel filter from bracket. Remove clutch slave cylinder. Remove access hole cover from right wheel well and detach dust cover. Remove clutch release fork pivot pin and retaining clip through access hole and remove release fork.

2) Remove bearing housing attaching bolts. Remove bearing housing and primary drive gear assembly through access hole. See *Fig. 2.* Remove upper clutch housing inspection cover. Rotate ring gear with suitable tool and loosen clutch cover attaching bolts evenly. Lift out clutch cover assembly and diaphragm spring through inspection cover opening. Remove diaphragm spring and bolts securing pressure plate straps to clutch cover. Remove disc.

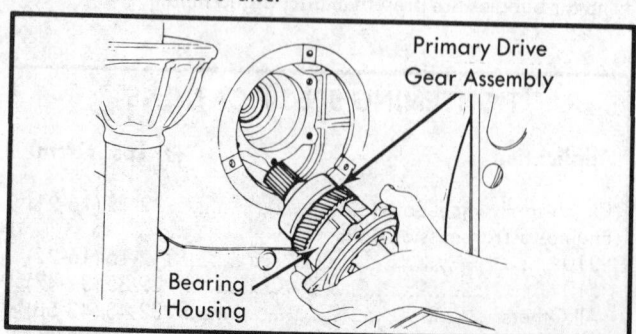

Fig. 2 Removing Primary Drive Gear Assembly

NOTE – *Clutch cover and pressure plate are part of a dynamically balanced unit. Pressure plate securing straps must not be moved or bent. Also, if replacement of either part becomes necessary, replace both parts as a unit.*

Installation – 1) Place clutch disc between clutch cover and pressure plate making sure to align arrow on clutch cover with protruding tab on edge of pressure plate before securing pressure plate to clutch cover.

2) Install diaphragm spring and clutch cover assembly on flywheel alignment pins and tighten clutch cover to flywheel bolts finger tight.

3) Install primary gear and bearing housing on clutch housing, aligning clutch disc hub on primary gear spline. Tighten clutch cover-to-flywheel bolts.

4) Using suitable measuring tool, measure height at "D". See *Fig. 3.* If height is not .020"–.098" (.5-2.5 mm), replacement push rods are available in lengths of 4.45" (113 mm), 4.49" (114 mm) and 4.53" (115 mm) to correct height at "D". Install clutch fork, rubber cover, pivot pin and retaining clip on bearing housing.

5) Replace access hole cover, clutch slave cylinder, fuel filter, coil high tension cable, fresh air duct and battery ground cable.

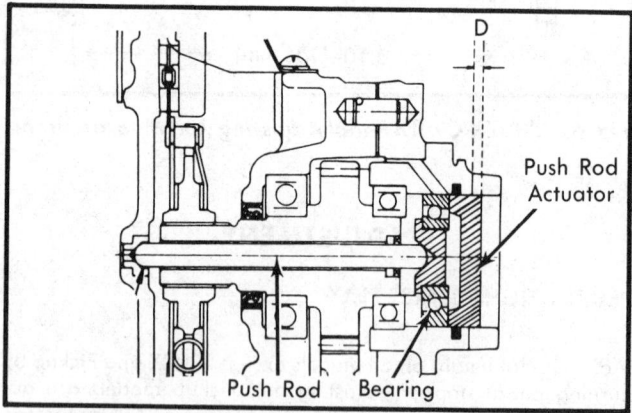

Fig. 3 Pressure Plate Push Rod Measurement

RELEASE BEARING

Removal – Remove clutch slave cylinder. Separate release lever by removing pivot pin. Remove bearing housing. Remove "O" ring, push rod actuator and bearing from bearing housing. Hold bearing and rotate outer race. Replace if operation is rough or noisy.

Installation – To install, reverse removal procedure and apply multi-purpose grease to sliding parts of release lever.

CLUTCH MASTER CYLINDER

Removal & Installation – Disconnect master cylinder push rod at clevis. Disconnect hydraulic line to slave cylinder. Remove cylinder attaching bolts and remove cylinder. To install, reverse removal procedure, bleed hydraulic system and adjust pedal free play.

DATSUN 310 (Cont.)

SLAVE CYLINDER

Removal & Installation — Disconnect clutch hose from slave cylinder. Remove slave cylinder attaching bolts and remove cylinder. To install, reverse removal procedure and bleed hydraulic system.

OVERHAUL

MASTER CYLINDER

Disassembly — Remove filler cap and drain fluid. Remove dust cover and stopper ring. Remove push rod and stopper. Remove supply valve stopper, then take out piston, spring seat and return spring.

Cleaning & Inspection — Clean all parts in clean brake fluid and inspect for wear or damage. If cylinder-to-piston clearance exceeds .006″ (.15 mm), replace defective part. Replace piston cup and dust cover during overhaul.

Reassembly — To assemble, coat all parts with brake fluid and reverse disassembly procedure. Bleed system and adjust pedal height.

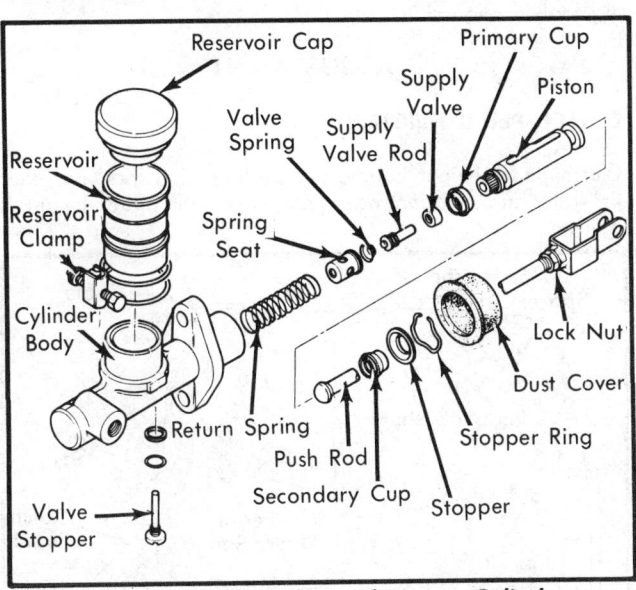

Fig. 4   Exploded View of Master Cylinder

SLAVE CYLINDER

Disassembly — Remove push rod and dust cover. Remove piston, piston cup and piston spring as an assembly. Remove bleeder screw.

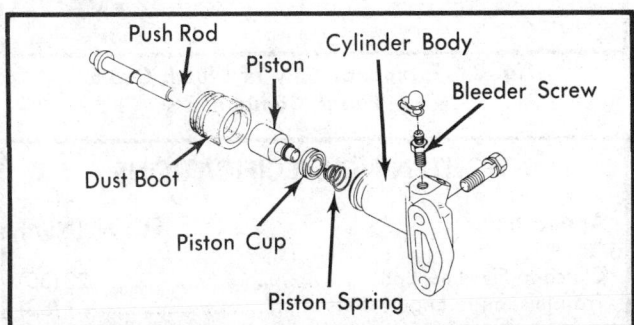

Fig. 5   Exploded View of Clutch Slave Cylinder

Cleaning & Inspection — Clean all parts in clean brake fluid and inspect for wear or damage. If cylinder-to-piston clearance exceeds .006″ (.15 mm), replace defective part. Replace piston cup and dust cover during overhaul.

Reassembly — To assemble, coat all parts with brake fluid and reverse disassembly procedure. Ensure piston cup is properly installed and bleed system.

ADJUSTMENTS

CLUTCH PEDAL HEIGHT & FREE PLAY

Adjust pedal height by turning pedal stopper. Correct height is 7.05-7.28″ (179-185 mm). See Fig. 6. Tighten lock nut. Adjust master cylinder push rod so pedal free play is .04-.20″ (1-5 mm). Tighten lock nut.

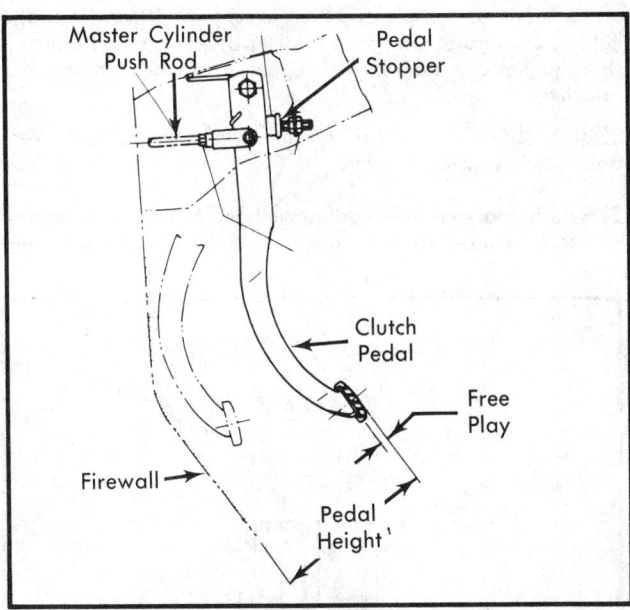

Fig. 6   Pedal Height and Free Play Measurement

HYDRAULIC SYSTEM BLEEDING

Fill reservoir with brake fluid. Fit bleeder hose to bleeder screw. Place opposite end of hose into clear container partially filled with brake fluid. Pump clutch pedal 2 or 3 times and hold to floor. Loosen bleeder screw and allow air to vent. Close bleeder screw and allow pedal to return. Repeat procedure until no air bubbles are present in discharged fluid.

TIGHTENING SPECIFICATIONS

Application	INCH Lbs. (N·m)
Clutch Cover Assy.-to-Flywheel Bolt	60-84 (7-10)
Pressure Plate Strap Bolt	84-108 (10-13)
Bearing Housing-to-Clutch Housing Bolt	48-84 (6-10)
Clutch Housing Cover Bolt	48-84 (6-10)
	Ft. Lbs. (N·m)
Slave Cylinder-to-Clutch Housing Bolt	22-30 (30-40)

Clutches

FIAT BRAVA

DESCRIPTION

Clutch is a dry, single disc type using a diaphragm spring pressure plate. Clutch disc is a conventional friction lining kind. Clutch operation is accomplished by a control cable attached at upper end directly to clutch pedal and lower end to clutch release fork.

REMOVAL & INSTALLATION

CLUTCH ASSEMBLY

Removal — 1) Disconnect battery ground cable and remove exhaust pipe-to-manifold clamp. From inside vehicle, pry up center insert of console and disconnect wiring from cigarette lighter. Disengage gear shift retainer by pulling shift lever up sharply. Remove handle with upper boot and center piece attached.

NOTE — *DO NOT twist shift lever while removing to prevent damage to plastic retainer.*

2) Release parking brake adjustment and raise lever to highest position. Remove rubber handle from parking brake lever.

Remove center console and lower boot retaining ring. Pull back carpet and insulation material. Remove rear screws in plastic tunnel cover and lift to free and remove lower boot. Place gear shift in neutral and remove selector lever locking ring bolts and locking ring.

3) Raise and support vehicle on safety stands. Install compressor (A70025) on flexible coupling and disconnect propeller shaft. Remove protection shield and bracket and secure propeller shaft out of way. Disconnect electrical wires from rear of transmission. Place transmission jack under transmission and support engine. Remove starter bolts. Disconnect clutch linkage and speedometer cable.

4) Remove flywheel cover bolts, then remove exhaust pipe support and place out of way. Remove transmission support mount. Remove engine-to-transmission bolts. Pull transmission rearward, tilting to slide input shaft out of clutch. Lower transmission to floor. Index mark clutch position on flywheel, then remove clutch.

Installation — To install clutch and transmission assembly, reverse removal procedure and note the following: Clutch disc must be installed with protrusion on hub facing transmission. Lubricate input shaft splines sparingly with oil and use centering tool to align clutch disc.

ADJUSTMENT

CLUTCH PEDAL HEIGHT

Clutch pedal height is adjusted by loosening lock nut (near firewall) and rotating adjustment nut until pedal height is adjusted.

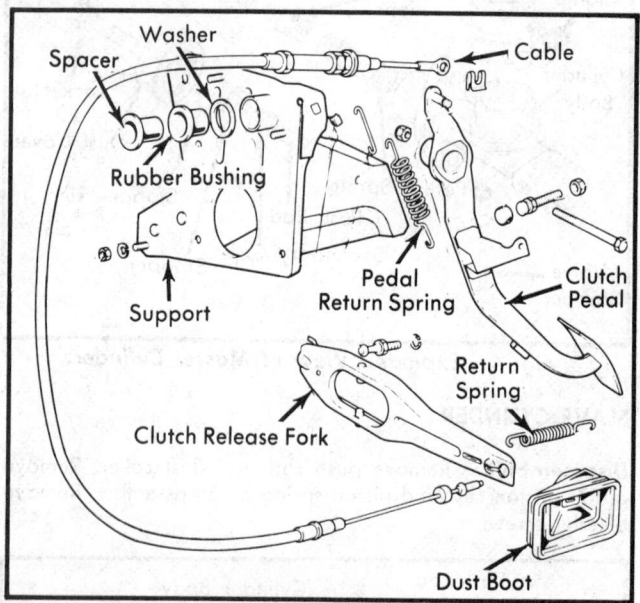

Fig. 2 Exploded View of Clutch Cable & Pedal Components

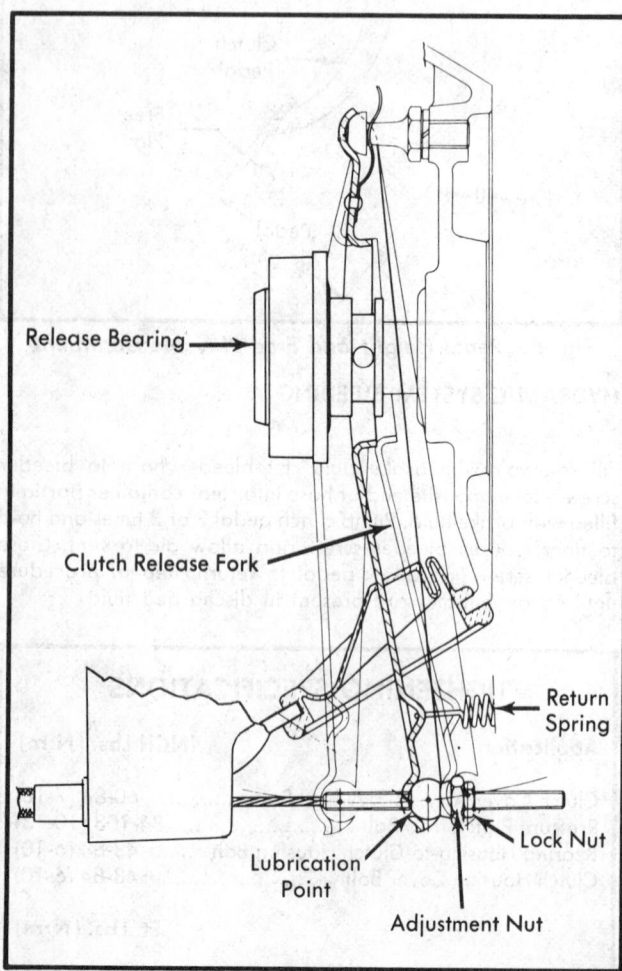

Fig. 1 Clutch Actuating Components

TIGHTENING SPECIFICATIONS

Application	Ft. Lbs. (N·m)
Clutch-to-Flywheel Bolts	22 (30)
Transmission-to-Engine Bolts	61 (83)

Clutches

FIAT SPIDER 2000

DESCRIPTION

Clutch is a dry, single-disc, diaphragm spring type. Clutch is engaged or disengaged through a cable which is actuated by the clutch pedal. Mechanism is self-adjusting to compensate for wear and there is no pedal free play.

REMOVAL & INSTALLATION

CLUTCH ASSEMBLY

Removal — 1) From inside driver's compartment, press down on gearshift lever and pry out retaining ring with screwdriver. Remove transmission cover. Raise and support vehicle.

2) From under vehicle, disconnect propeller shaft from transmission and remove safety cross strap. Remove propeller shaft center pillow block. Disconnect speedometer drive from transmission. Disconnect all electrical leads from transmission case. Disconnect clutch fork return spring and remove adjusting rod.

3) Remove inspection cover from bottom of clutch housing. Disconnect exhaust pipe support bracket from rear of transmission and remove starter from clutch housing. Position a suitable transmission holding fixture (A. 70509) to a floor jack and position under transmission.

4) Remove bolts securing transmission to engine and remove rear crossmember. With transmission supported by jack, pull to rear until input shaft clears release bearing. Lower jack when transmission is clear and remove from under vehicle. Remove clutch assembly from flywheel after marking their relationship for reinstallation.

Installation — To install transmission and clutch assembly, reverse removal procedure and note the following: Use centering tool to align clutch and flywheel. Lubricate transmission input shaft splines sparingly.

ADJUSTMENT

CLUTCH PEDAL HEIGHT

Loosen lock nut and rotate adjustment nut until clutch pedal height reaches desired level.

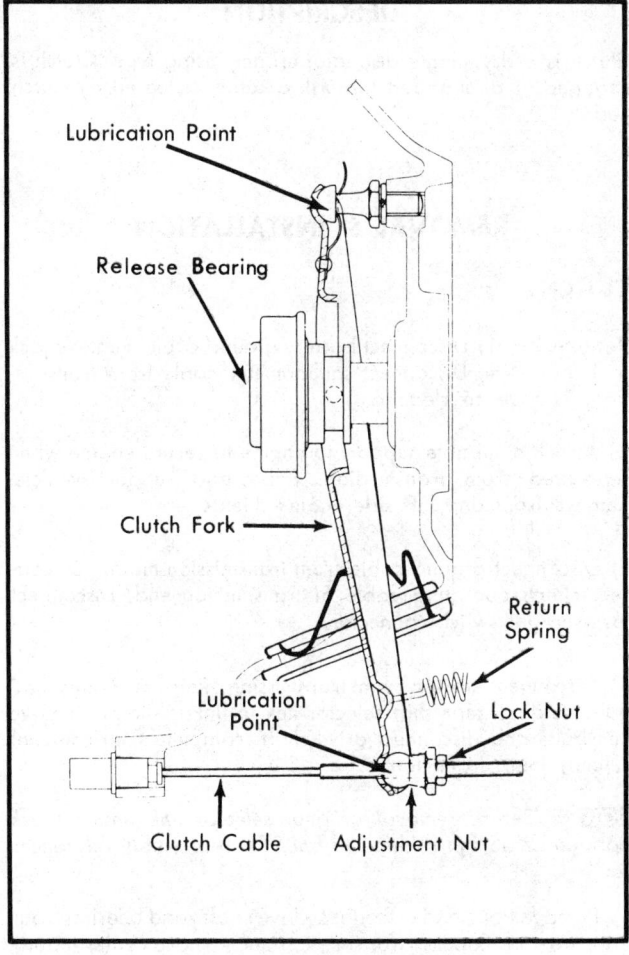

Fig. 1 Clutch Actuating Components Showing Cable Adjustment Point

TIGHTENING SPECIFICATIONS

Application	Ft. Lbs. (N·m)
Clutch-to-Flywheel Bolts	22 (30)
Transmission-to-Engine Bolts	61 (83)

Clutches

FIAT STRADA

DESCRIPTION

Clutch is a dry, single disc, diaphragm spring type. Clutch is engaged or disengaged through a cable, actuated by clutch pedal.

REMOVAL & INSTALLATION

CLUTCH

Removal — **1)** Disconnect battery ground cable. Remove jack and spare tire. Disconnect speedometer cable from transmission. Remove air cleaner.

2) Attach a suitable support to engine to secure engine when separated from transmission. Raise and support vehicle. Remove front and left side engine shields.

3) Disconnect ground cable from transmission mount. Disconnect clutch operating cable at transmission end. Disconnect reverse light switch connector.

4) Disconnect starter from transmission. Remove 2 nuts and bolts holding gear shift selector link to linkage joint. Remove hex bolts and disconnect drive shaft (complete with constant velocity joint) from flange.

NOTE — *Before removal of gear selector link, index mark position of slots in relation to bolts for reassembly reference.*

5) Remove bolts and disconnect drive shafts and bearing from transmission. Support transmission and remove center mount bolt. Remove transmission bracket and flywheel guard.

6) Remove remaining nuts and bolts attaching transmission to engine. Disconnect left side rubber mount and bracket, and lower transmission out of vehicle. Index mark clutch cover and flywheel, and loosen attaching bolts alternately and evenly. Remove clutch assembly.

Installation — With protruding portion of clutch assembly facing away from flywheel, loosely assemble clutch assembly to flywheel. Use clutch aligning tool (70210) to center clutch disc. Tighten clutch cover bolts alternately and evenly. To complete installation, reverse removal procedure.

CLUTCH CABLE

Removal — Remove spring clip from pin on clutch pedal. Remove cable eyelet from pin. At transmission end of cable, remove lock nut, adjusting nut and block. Remove threaded cable end from lever and remove bushing. Remove bolts at cable housing flange and remove cable.

Installation — Grease inside diameter of cable eyelet. Install in reverse order of removal. Adjust pedal height if necessary.

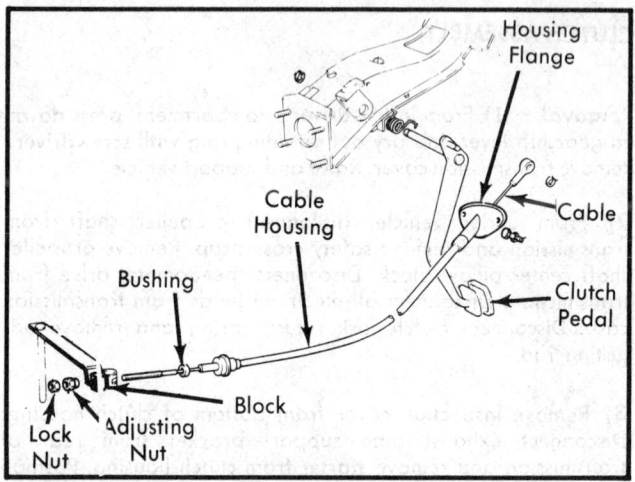

Fig. 1 Clutch Cable Components

ADJUSTMENT

CLUTCH PEDAL HEIGHT

Clutch pedal height should be 1.18" (30 mm) lower than brake pedal. If height is not to specification, loosen adjustment lock nut and rotate adjusting nut until pedal height is as specified.

TIGHTENING SPECIFICATIONS

Application	Ft. Lbs. (N·m)
Clutch Cover-to-Flywheel Bolt	28 (38)
Transmission-to-Engine Bolt	58 (79)
Starter-to-Clutch Housing Bolt	18 (24)
C.V. Joint-to-Axle Shaft Bolt	31 (42)

Clutches

FIAT X1/9

DESCRIPTION

Clutch is a dry, single plate, diaphragm spring type. Clutch actuation is hydraulic, using a firewall mounted master cylinder and a clutch housing mounted slave cylinder. A prelubricated clutch release bearing is also used.

REMOVAL & INSTALLATION

CLUTCH ASSEMBLY

Removal — 1) Disconnect positive battery cable. Remove air cleaner and carburetor cooling duct. From inside engine compartment, separate slave cylinder from transmission case. Install engine support. Remove upper transmission-to-engine mounting bolts.

2) Working from under vehicle, remove any guards which may interfere with transmission removal. Disconnect shifting flexible link and swing it out of the way. Disconnect backup light wires and seat belt warning system wire. Remove starter and exhaust pipe. Disconnect ground strap.

3) Remove nuts from the hub end of half shaft. Remove attaching hardware mounting suspension control arm to supports. Free half shaft from hub end and fix other end to transmission to prevent premature disconnection.

4) Remove the following items: Flywheel cover, engine crossmember support, and lower engine-to-transmission bolts. Remove transmission/differential from below vehicle. Mark clutch position on flywheel and remove clutch.

Installation — To install, reverse removal procedure using suitable tool (A. 70210) to center clutch assembly.

CLUTCH MASTER CYLINDER

Removal — Steering column must be removed to gain access to clutch master cylinder. Disconnect and cap master cylinder hydraulic line. Remove two bolts attaching cylinder to support plate. Withdraw cylinder from actuating rod and remove from vehicle.

Installation — To install, reverse removal procedure and bleed hydraulic system.

CLUTCH SLAVE CYLINDER

Removal — Remove slave cylinder hydraulic hose and union. Disconnect cylinder push rod from clutch release bearing fork. Slightly compress return spring and remove two mounting bolts; slowly withdraw cylinder from support plate.

Installation — To install, reverse removal procedure ensuring slave cylinder snugly fits against support and that hydraulic system is bled.

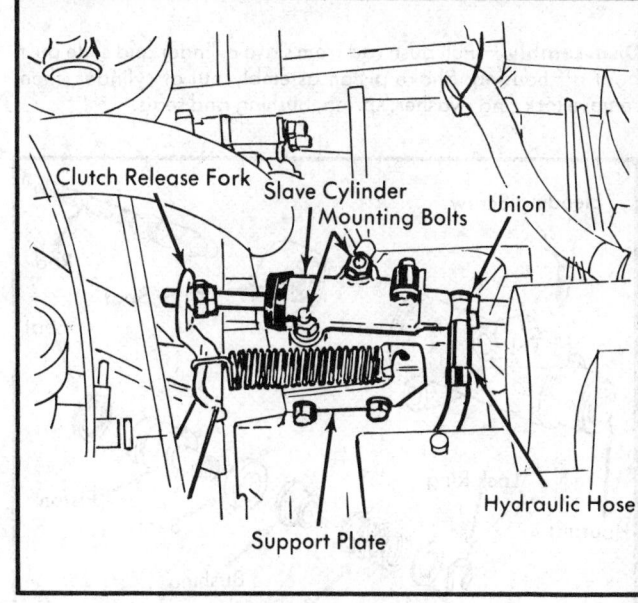

Fig. 1   Clutch Slave Cylinder Location

ADJUSTMENT

CLUTCH PEDAL HEIGHT & FREE PLAY

Clutch pedal height is adjusted by turning pedal stopper until total pedal travel is 6.75" (171 mm). Free play is adjusted to 1.25" (32 mm), by turning adjusting nut on slave cylinder.

OVERHAUL

CLUTCH MASTER CYLINDER

Disassembly — Ease rubber dust boot back and remove snap ring, using long nosed pliers. Remove seal and complete plunger assembly. Pull out remaining gasket, seal and spring.

Reassembly — Lightly coat all components with brake fluid. Insert spring and seal into position. Fit piston assembly and seal, then install snap ring. Slip boot over cylinder housing.

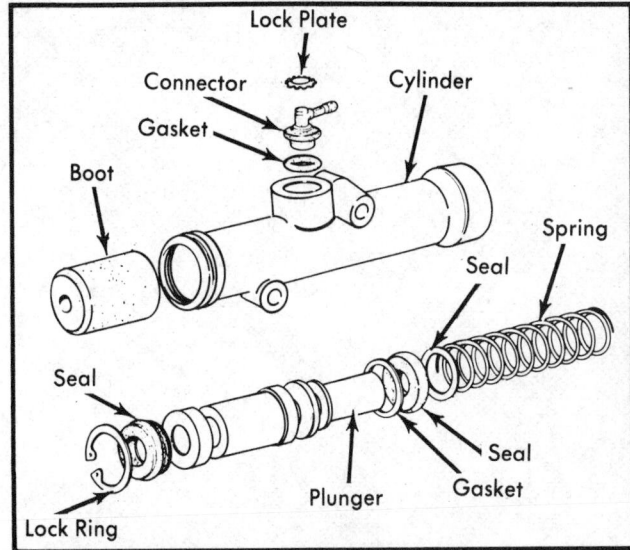

Fig. 2   Exploded View of Clutch Master Cylinder

FIAT X1/9 (Cont.)

CLUTCH SLAVE CYLINDER

Disassembly — Pull push rod from slave cylinder and slide dust boot off housing. Shake piston assembly out of cylinder, then remove lock ring, washer, spring, bushing and seals.

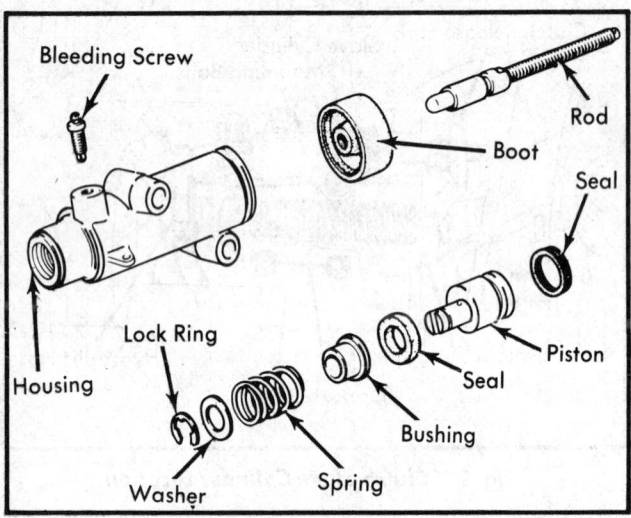

Fig. 3 Exploded View of Clutch Slave Cylinder

Reassembly — Lightly coat all components with brake fluid before reassembly. Insert rear seal, and piston assembly. Refit spring, washer, and lock ring. Install dust boot and push rod.

TIGHTENING SPECIFICATIONS

Application	Ft. Lbs. (N·m)
Clutch-to-Flywheel Bolts	11 (15)
Clutch Release Fork Bolt	18 (24)
Slave Cylinder Push Rod Adjusting Nut	18 (24)
Slave Cylinder Support Plate-to-Transmission Case Bolt	18 (24)
Support Plate-to-Transmission Case Stud Nut	18 (24)
Transmission-to-Engine Bolts	56 (76)

Clutches

HONDA ACCORD & PRELUDE

DESCRIPTION

Clutch is a single plate, dry disc type. Clutch assembly consists of clutch disc, clutch cover and pressure plate assembly, and clutch release mechanism. Clutch release mechanism is hydraulic, consisting of a firewall mounted master cylinder and a slave cylinder mounted to clutch housing. Clutch release fork free play is adjustable.

REMOVAL & INSTALLATION

CLUTCH

Removal — 1) Disconnect battery ground at transmission. Put gear shift in Neutral. Disconnect following electrical wiring.

- Positive battery cable at starter.
- Black/White wire from starter solenoid.
- Yellow/Green wire from water temperature sending unit.
- Black/Yellow and yellow wires from ignition timing thermosensor.
- Green/Black and yellow wires from back-up light switch.
- Red/Blue wires (Accord) or Pink/Blue wires (Prelude) from distributor.

2) On Prelude, remove speedometer cable clip and cable without disassembling gear holder. On all models, remove clutch slave cylinder with hydraulic line attached. Remove transmission side starter mount bolt and upper transmission mounting bolts.

3) Raise and support vehicle, and drain transmission fluid. Remove front wheels. On Prelude, remove engine shields, remove nut and washer from each end of stabilizer bar, remove both brackets and stabilizer bar.

4) On Accord, place transmission jack securely beneath transmission. Remove fender well shield from right front wheel well. Remove bolt securing speedometer drive holder and pull assembly out of transmission. Disconnect shift lever torque rod from clutch housing, then remove bolt from shift clevis.

5) On all models, disconnect right and left lower arm ball joints and tie rod end ball joints using ball joint remover. Turn each steering knuckle to its most outboard position. With screwdriver, pry constant velocity (CV) joint out approximately 1/2" (13 mm) then pull axle out of transmission housing. Repeat this procedure on opposite side.

6) On Accord, remove center beam. On Prelude, disconnect shift lever torque rod from clutch housing. Remove bolt from shift lever clevis, and jack up engine. Remove front and rear torque rods, then rear torque rod brackets.

7) On Accord, remove transmission stopper bracket from front of clutch housing. Remove upper torque arm. Remove the three M10 x 1.25 x 55 bolts from rear engine mount. Remove clutch cover, engine side starter bolts and starter. Remove front transmission mounting bolt and pull transmission away from engine block to clear dowel pins, then lower on transmission jack.

8) On Prelude, remove engine damper bracket and engine damper from center beam. Remove rear engine mount and bracket. Place a 1" x 2" x 4" (25 x 50 x 100 mm) block of wood between center beam and oil pan, lower jack and rest engine on center beam.

9) Remove engine side starter bolts and starter. Remove remaining transmission bolts, and pull transmission away from engine until mainshaft clears pressure plate. Lower transmission from vehicle.

10) On all models, check diaphragm for wear at release bearing contact area by inserting alignment tool (07974-6890100). Measure clearance between tool and fingers of spring with feeler gauge. Maximum limit is .04" (1.0 mm). Install holding device on ring gear and loosen pressure plate bolt 2 turns at a time in a criss-cross pattern. Remove pressure plate bolts and separate clutch disc.

Installation — To install, reverse removal procedure and note: Ensure flywheel dowels align with pressure plate dowel holes. Use clutch disc alignment tool (07974-6890100) and tighten pressure plate bolts in a criss-cross pattern. Refill transmission with SAE 10W-40 oil.

CLUTCH MASTER CYLINDER

Removal — Separate clutch pedal operating rod from master cylinder push rod by removing through pin at clevis. Disconnect and plug hydraulic lines. Remove nuts mounting master cylinder to firewall. Make sure brake fluid does not spill on painted surfaces.

Installation — To install, reverse removal procedure and bleed hydraulic system.

CLUTCH SLAVE CYLINDER

Removal — Disconnect hydraulic line from slave cylinder. Unhook return spring. Separate threaded rod from end of slave cylinder. Remove slave cylinder mounting bolts and take cylinder off clutch housing.

Installation — To install, reverse removal procedure and bleed hydraulic system.

CLUTCH RELEASE FORK AND BEARING

Removal — With transmission removed, separate slave cylinder push rod from release fork. Remove boot and carefully remove fork retainer clip. Pull fork through clutch housing from inside. Remove bearing retainer clip and pull bearing assembly from sleeve. If worn, bearing may be driven from holder and a new bearing installed using driver (7949-6110000) and attachment (07974-6890300). Radius side of bearing must go on holder first.

Installation — Coat all contact areas lightly with grease. Attach bearing and holder to fork with retainer clips. Install fork and sliding bearing assembly onto sleeve. Ensure that fork snaps onto pivot bolt and install boot. Move release fork back and forth to check for freedom of movement.

OVERHAUL

MASTER CYLINDER

NOTE — *The master cylinders used on Accord and Prelude differ in external appearance. Overhaul procedures are similar.*

Disassembly & Reassembly — 1) Remove boot and take off snap ring. Cover open end of cylinder with a shop rag and force piston out with compressed air. Bend spring retainer tabs and separate piston, cups, retainer, return spring and valve assembly.

2) Clean all parts with brake fluid and check for wear or damage. If cylinder bore-to-piston clearance exceeds .006" (.15 mm), replace defective part. Replace all rubber parts during overhaul. Reassemble by reversing disassembly procedure. Rotate piston during installation.

Clutches

HONDA ACCORD & PRELUDE (Cont.)

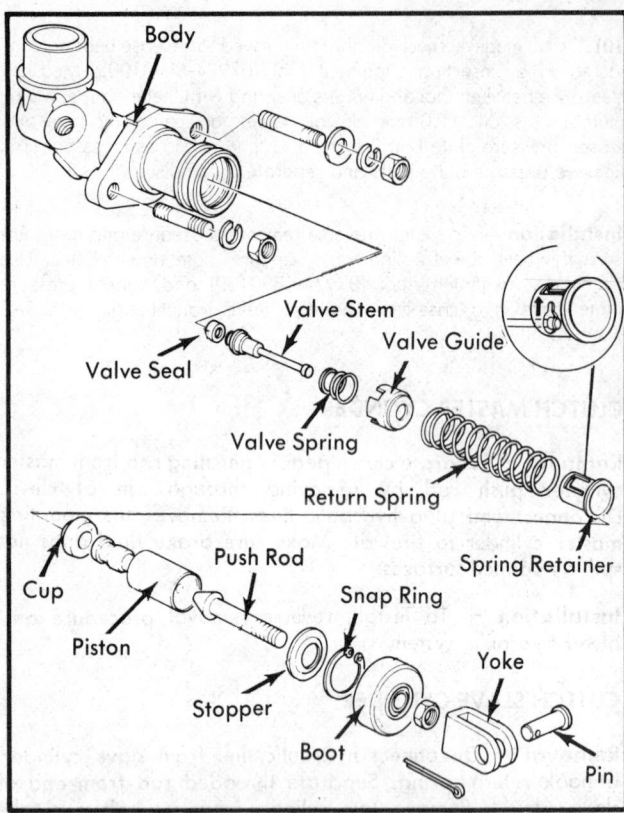

Fig. 1 Exploded View of Accord Master Cylinder. Prelude Cylinder is Similar Except Fluid Reservoir Is Separate From Cylinder Body

CLUTCH SLAVE CYLINDER

Disassembly & Reassembly — 1) Remove push rod and dust boot. Cover open end of cylinder with a shop rag and force piston out with compressed air. Remove piston cup and bleed screw.

2) Clean all parts in brake fluid and check for wear or damage. If cylinder bore-to-piston clearance exceeds .006" (.15 mm), replace defective part. Replace all rubber parts dur-

ing overhaul and coat all parts with brake fluid prior to reassembly. To reassemble, reverse disassembly procedure and insert piston with rotating motion.

ADJUSTMENT

CLUTCH PEDAL HEIGHT AND FREE PLAY

Adjust clutch pedal height to 7.24" (184 mm) by rotating pedal stop bolt in direction necessary to achieve specified height. Adjust pedal free play clearance (between clutch pedal push rod and master cylinder) to .05-.13" (1-3 mm) by loosening lock nut on push rod and rotating push rod.

CLUTCH RELEASE FORK FREE PLAY

Release fork free play should be .08-.10" (2.0-2.6 mm). To adjust, loosen lock nut and hold push rod end nut stationary while rotating push rod with screwdriver. Turn clockwise to decrease free play; counterclockwise to increase free play.

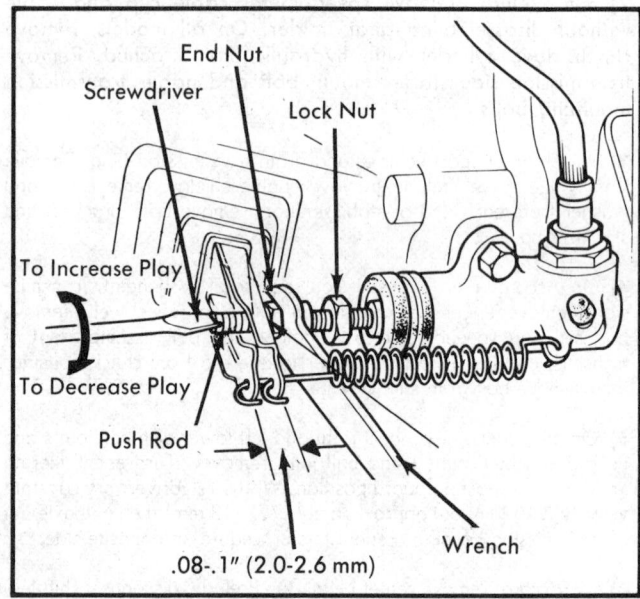

Fig. 3 Clutch Release Fork Adjustment Locations

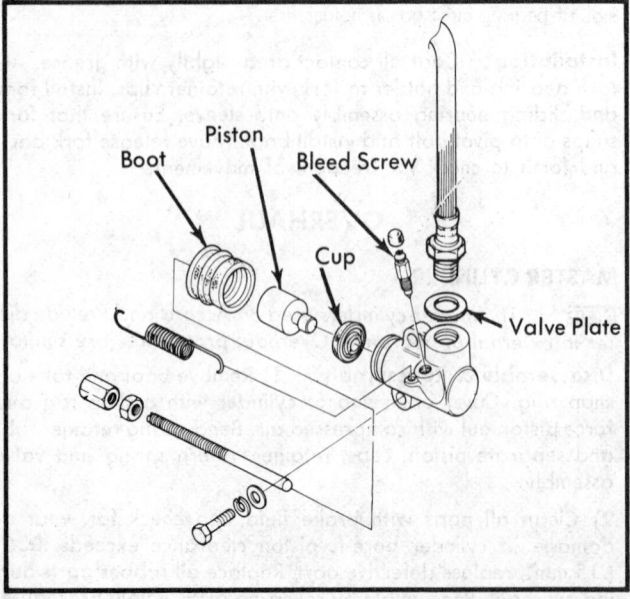

Fig. 2 Exploded View of Slave Cylinder

TIGHTENING SPECIFICATIONS

Application	Ft. Lbs. (N•m)
Flywheel-to-Crankshaft Bolts	80 (109)
Pressure Plate-to-Flywheel	
Accord	7-10 (10-14)
Prelude	19 (26)
Front and Rear Torque Rod Bolts	54 (73)
Center Beam Bolts (Accord)	14-18 (19-23)

Clutches

HONDA CIVIC

DESCRIPTION

Clutch is single plate dry disc type, using a diaphragm spring to engage pressure plate. Clutch has a mechanical release system consisting of clutch pedal, cable, clutch release lever, and release bearing.

REMOVAL & INSTALLATION

CLUTCH

Removal — **1)** Disconnect battery ground at transmission. Release steering lock and put gear shift lever in neutral. Disconnect following engine compartment wiring:

- Positive battery cable at starter.
- Black/White wire from starter solenoid.
- Yellow/Green wire from water temperature sending unit.
- Black/Yellow and yellow wires from ignition timing thermosensor.
- Green/Black and yellow wires from back-up light switch.

2) Remove speedometer cable clip and cable but do not disassemble speedometer gear holder. Disconnect clutch cable at release arm and remove transmission side starter mounting bolt. Remove top transmission mounting bolt and forward bolt for rear torque arm bracket.

3) Raise and support vehicle and drain transmission oil. Remove front wheels and stabilizer bar mounting brackets. Disconnect lower support arms at ball joints OR at pivot bolts. Disconnect tie rod end ball joints.

4) Turn right side steering knuckle outward as far as it will go and pry inboard constant velocity (CV) joint out of transmission housing approximately ½" to force spring clip out of differential gear splines. Pull axle out the rest of the way and repeat for left side. Disconnect shift lever torque rod from clutch housing. Slide pin retainer back and drive spring pin out with punch, then disconnect shift rod.

5) Place a jack under engine with a wooden block between jack pad and engine, then raise engine enough to take weight off mounts. Remove both front and rear torque rods and rear torque rod brackets. Remove engine damper bracket from transmission and remove rear engine mount with its bracket.

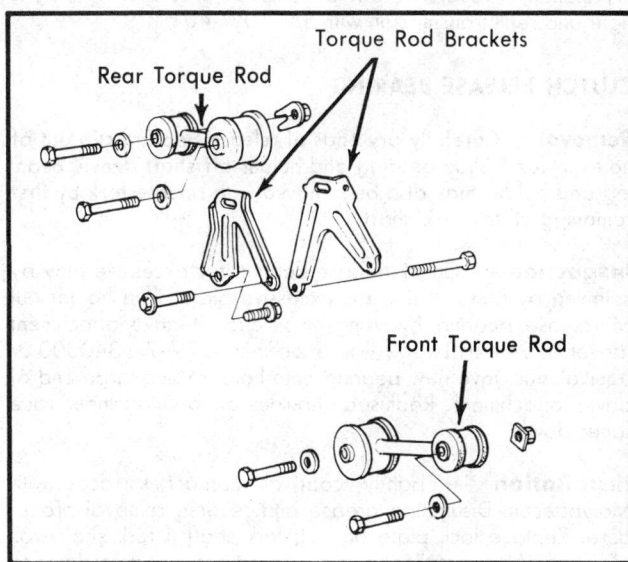

Fig. 2   Torque Rod and Bracket Components

6) Place a 1" x 2" x 4" block of wood between center beam and oil pan, then lower jack so that engine rests on center beam. Remove engine side starter mounting bolt, then remove starter and lower through chassis. Remove 2 remaining transmission mounting bolts. Raise transmission enough with transmission jack to take weight off engine and pull away from engine. Lower transmission clear of engine.

7) Install ring gear holder to keep flywheel from turning. Loosen pressure plate mounting bolts 2-turns at a time in a criss-cross pattern to prevent warping. Remove pressure plate and clutch disc.

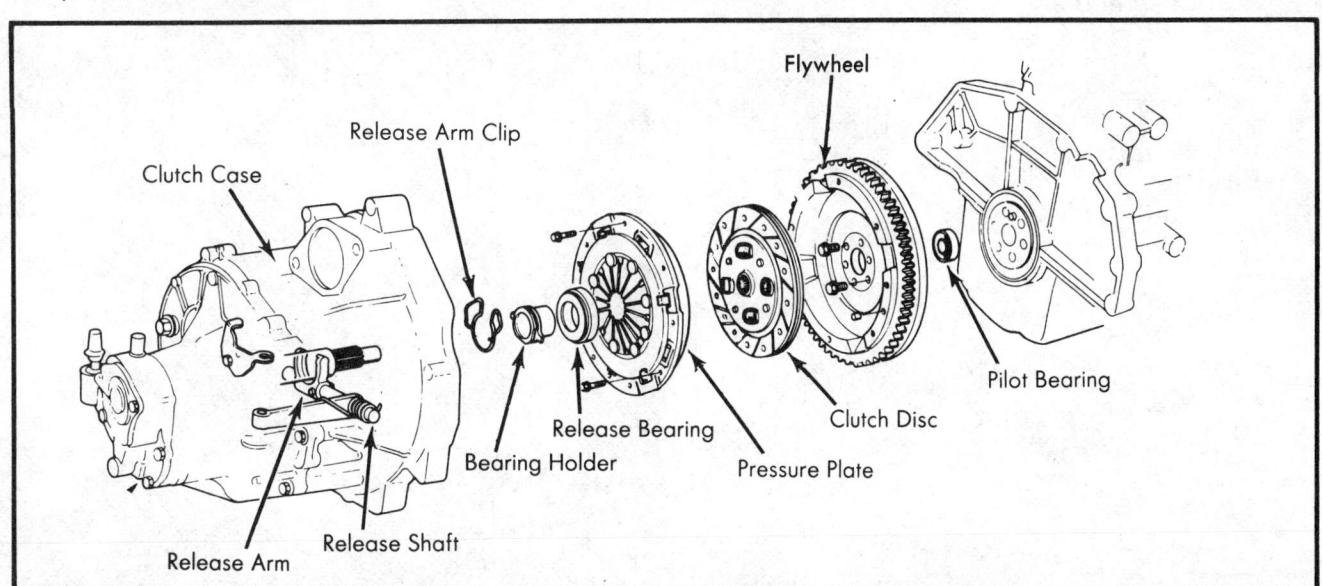

Fig. 1   Exploded View of Clutch Assembly

HONDA CIVIC (Cont.)

Installation — Use clutch alignment tool (07944-6340000 or equivalent) and install disc and pressure plate. Tighten bolts 2 turns at a time in a criss-cross pattern. Ensure that 2 dowel pins are installed in clutch housing, then complete installation in reverse order of removal. Ensure drain plug is tight and refill transmission with SAE 10W-40 oil.

CLUTCH RELEASE BEARING

Removal — Carefully pry ends of release bearing clip out of holes in fork. Slide bearing and holder off shaft sleeve. Bearing and holder may also be removed with release fork by first removing clutch fork shaft.

Inspection — Check release bearing for excessive play by spinning by hand. If there is excessive play, drive holder out of release bearing by using small end of drive attachment (driver 07949-6110000 with attachment 07947-6340300 or equivalent). Drive new bearing onto holder using large end of driver attachment. Radiused shoulder on bearing inner race faces down.

Installation — Lightly coat all contact surfaces with Molybdenum Disulphide grease and reverse removal procedure. Replace lock plate on shift fork shaft if fork shaft was removed. After installation, pull release arm up, then down to ensure fork fits against bearing holder and holder slides freely on sleeve.

NOTE — *Do not bend release bearing clips any further than necessary during removal or installation of bearing holder.*

ADJUSTMENT

CLUTCH PEDAL

Ensure that pedal return spring holds clutch pedal against stop pad. Turn adjusting nut in or out to give 7/16-9/16" (4.4-5.4 mm) free play at release arm. Free play at pedal should be 3/8-

1 3/16" (10-30 mm) and disengagement height should be at least 1 3/16" (30 mm) from floor. If pedal play and/or pedal disengagment height exceed these specifications, clutch components may require replacement.

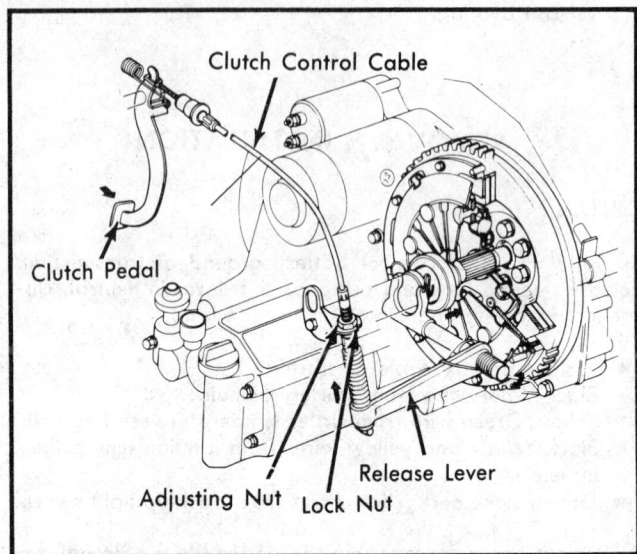

Fig. 3 Clutch Adjustment Point for Civic

TIGHTENING SPECIFICATIONS

Application	Ft. Lbs. (N.m)
Flywheel-to-Crankshaft	50 (68)
Front and Rear Torque Rod Bolts	54 (73)

	INCH Lbs. (N.m)
Pressure Plate-to-Flywheel	108 (12)

Clutches

ISUZU I-MARK

DESCRIPTION

The clutch assembly is a single plate, dry disc type, using a diaphragm spring to engage pressure plate. Clutch has a mechanical release system consisting of clutch pedal, cable, yoke and release bearing.

REMOVAL & INSTALLATION

CLUTCH

Removal — 1) Disconnect battery ground cable. Remove shift lever assembly. Loosen clutch cable adjusting nuts at left side of engine compartment. Remove upper starter mounting nuts at left side of engine compartment. Remove upper starter mounting nut and starter wiring. Raise and support vehicle front and rear.

2) Remove propeller shaft. Disconnect speedometer cable. Remove clutch cable. Remover starter lower bolt and remove starter. Disconnect exhaust pipe from manifold and remove exhaust pipe bracket. Remove flywheel inspection cover.

3) Remove rear transmission support mounting bolt. Support transmission under case and remove rear transmission support from frame. Lower transmission and position about 4" (100 mm) lower than when mounted. Disconnect back-up light. Disconnect coasting cut fuel switch (gasoline models only).

4) Remove transmission housing to engine block bolts. Move transmission straight back and lower away from vehicle. Index mark clutch assembly to flywheel for reassembly reference. Install aligning tool (J-24547 or equivalent) and remove retaining bolts evenly in a criss-cross pattern.

Installation — Using aligning tool (J-24547 or equivalent) install clutch assembly in original position and tighten bolts evenly in a criss-cross pattern. To complete installation, reverse removal procedure noting the following: Lubricate drive gear shaft with a slight coat of grease before installing. Readjust clutch pedal free travel as outlined in this story.

RELEASE BEARING

Removal — With clutch assembly removed, remove release bearing to yoke retaining springs and remove release bearing with support. Remove release yoke from transmission ball stud.

Installation — Lubricate ball stud and install release yoke. Lubricate support and install release bearing and support to release yoke with retaining springs. Install clutch assembly.

CLUTCH CABLE

Removal — Loosen clutch lock and adjusting nuts. Raise vehicle and remove return spring from release yoke. Remove clutch cable from release yoke and slide it through retaining bracket. Disconnect cable from clutch pedal and remove.

Installation — Slide cable through firewall and install clutch pedal. Install cable in original position through retaining bracket to release yoke. Install clutch return spring. Adjust clutch cable and tighten lock nut. See Adjustments in this Article.

PILOT BEARING

Removal — With clutch assembly removed, remove pilot bearing from crankshaft using puller (J-23907 or equivalent).

Installation — Install the pilot bearing in crankshaft using driver (J-26516 or equivalent) so that it is fitted against the bottom face of the bearing fitting hole. Install the remaining parts by reversing the removal procedure.

ADJUSTMENTS

CLUTCH PEDAL HEIGHT

Adjust setting of clutch switch so that pedal height from floor is approximately 6.2" (157.5 mm). Lock switch in position with lock nut.

CLUTCH PEDAL FREE TRAVEL

Loosen lock and adjusting nuts on clutch cable. Pull cable forward toward front of vehicle to take up slack. Turn adjusting nut inward until pedal free travel is approximately 5⁄8" (16 mm). Tighten lock nut.

TIGHTENING SPECIFICATIONS

Application	Ft. Lbs. (N•m)
Pressure Plate-to-Flyweel	14 (19)
Release Yoke Ball Stud	29 (39)

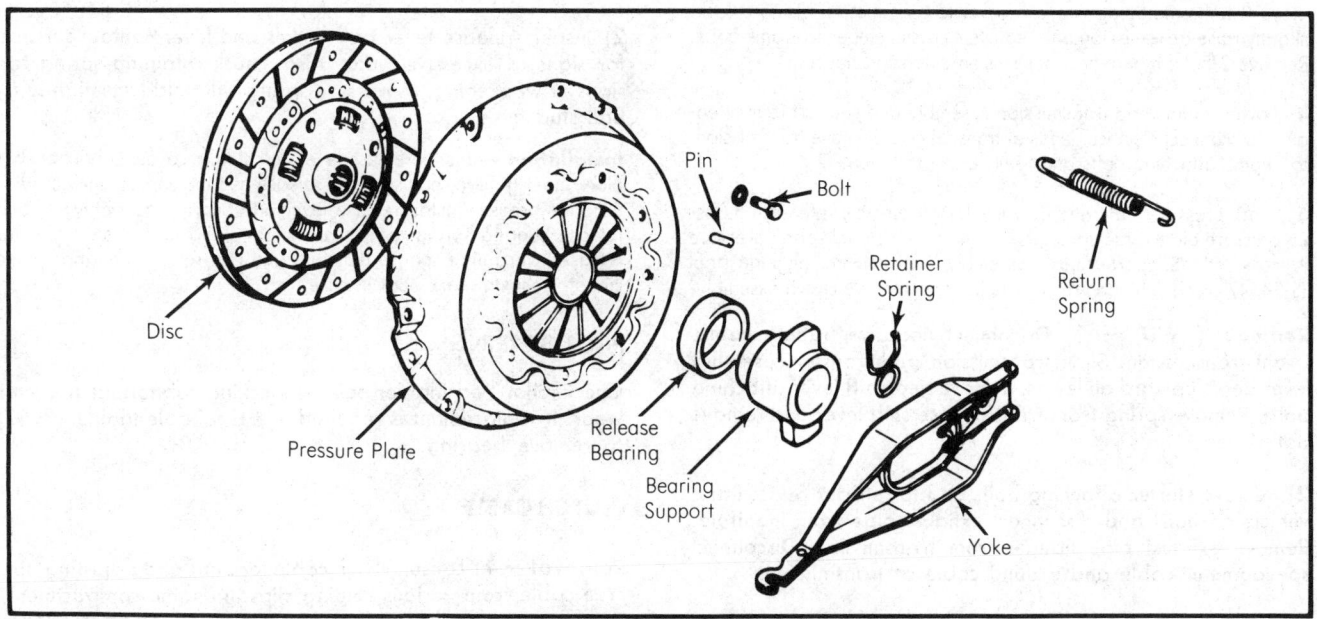

Fig. 1 Exploded View of Clutch Assembly

Disc

Pressure Plate

Release Bearing

Bearing Support

Pin

Bolt

Retainer Spring

Return Spring

Yoke

Clutches

ISUZU P'UP & LUV

Pickup

DESCRIPTION

Clutch assembly is a single dry disc type using a diaphragm spring pressure plate with a pre-lubricated release bearing. Clutch release lever is cable actuated. Cable is hooked to release lever and clutch pedal.

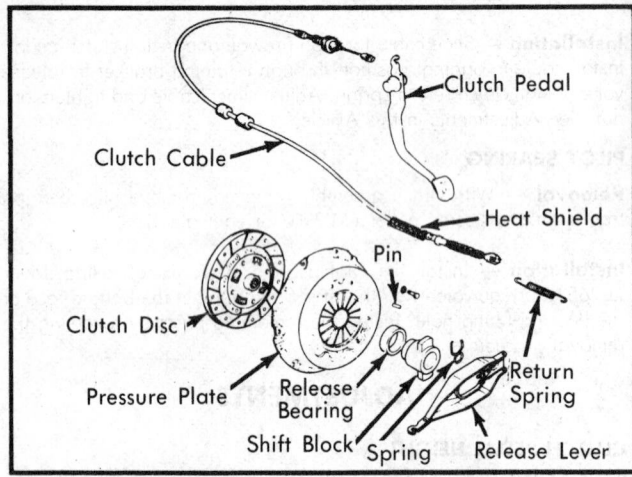

Fig. 1   Exploded View of P'UP & LUV Clutch Assembly

REMOVAL & INSTALLATION

CLUTCH ASSEMBLY

Removal (2WD) — 1) Disconnect negative battery cable. Slide gearshift lever boot up on lever, remove gearshift lever attaching bolts and remove lever assembly. Remove starter attaching bolts and lay starter aside.

2) Raise vehicle on hoist and disconnect exhaust pipe hanger at transmission. Disconnect speedometer cable at transmission and disconnect ground strap. Place a pan in position to catch oil and remove propeller shaft.

3) Remove 2 lower flywheel inspection cover mounting bolts. Remove 2 bolts mounting frame bracket to rear mount. Using a jack, slightly raise transmission and remove 4 crossmember-to-frame bolts. Remove 2 bolts mounting transmission extension housing.

4) Lower engine and transmission assembly and support rear of engine. Disconnect electrical leads at transmission. Remove transmission-to-engine attaching bolts and remove transmission.

5) Mark pressure plate and flywheel for reassembly reference. Loosen pressure plate attaching bolts 1 turn at a time until spring pressure is released. Support clutch assembly with clutch aligning tool (J-24547 or equivalent), remove bolts, and remove clutch assembly.

Removal (4WD) — 1) Disconnect negative battery cable. Drain transmission. Slide transmission and transfer case shift lever boots upward on levers. Remove gearshift lever attaching bolts. Remove spring from transfer case shift lever and remove both levers.

2) Remove starter attaching bolts and lay starter aside. Raise vehicle on hoist and disconnect exhaust pipe from manifold. Remove exhaust pipe hanger from transmission. Disconnect speedometer cable and ground cable at transmission.

3) Disconnect propeller shaft at differential and remove from vehicle. Disconnect front propeller shaft at both ends. Remove

return spring at clutch fork. Disconnect clutch cable from clutch fork and pull forward through stiffener bracket.

4) Remove 2 lower bolts mounting flywheel guard. Remove 3 frame bracket-to-transmission rear mount bolts and nuts. Raise engine slightly and remove rear mounting bolts from transfer case. Remove side case attaching bolts and remove case.

5) Remove stud bolt from transfer case. Lower engine and transmission and support rear of engine. Disconnect electrical connectors from transmission. Remove shift cover and gasket from top of transfer case. Remove transmission-to-engine bolts and remove transmission.

NOTE — *When removing transmission, turn side case fitting face of transmission case down and pull transmission back to clear clutch shaft. Tip transmission downward and remove transmission.*

6) Mark pressure plate and flywheel for reassembly reference. Loosen pressure plate attaching bolts 1 turn at a time until pressure is relieved. Support clutch assembly with a clutch aligning tool (J-24547 or equivalent) and remove clutch assembly.

Installation (All Models) — Apply a thin coat of Lubriplate (or equivalent) to clutch disc splines. Install clutch assembly to flywheel, matching alignment marks made during disassembly. Use clutch alignment tool (J-24547 or equivalent) to center clutch. Install and tighten attaching bolts. To complete installation, reverse removal procedure.

RELEASE BEARING, SHIFT BLOCK & RELEASE LEVER

Removal — Remove release lever from transmission case. Disengage release bearing to lever retaining springs. Slide out release bearing with shift block. Remove release lever from transmission ball stud.

Inspection — 1) Check release bearing for noise or lubricant loss by spinning bearing. Replace bearing if either condition exists.

2) Inspect release lever ball socket and lever contact surface for signs of excessive wear. Also, check retaining spring for signs of weakening. Make sure spring will hold lever tightly to ball stud.

Installation — Install release lever ball stud in cover. Lubricate shift block inner groove, ball seat and release bearing contact surface with graphite grease. Install release lever and bearing assembly. Attach release bearing spring to lever and spring clip to ball stud. Ensure release lever fully engages ball stud and that release bearing moves smoothly. Install fork boot in case.

PILOT BEARING

Check pilot bearing for seizing, sticking, abnormal noise or wear. If replacement is required, use a suitable tool (J-23907) to remove bearing.

CLUTCH CABLE

Removal — 1) Loosen clutch cable lock nut and adjusting nut. Free cable from various routing clips in engine compartment. Working under vehicle, disengage return spring from release lever.

Clutches

ISUZU P'UP & LUV (Cont.)

2) Disconnect cable from bracket and pull cable forward through bracket. Separate cable from clutch pedal and pull cable into engine compartment with damper rubber.

Installation — To install, reverse removal procedures and note the following: Ensure cable is not bent sharply or kinked. Keep lock and adjustment nuts loosened when installing.

ADJUSTMENT

CLUTCH CABLE

Pull cable into engine compartment. Rotate adjuster nut until washer damper assembly is brought back into contact with firewall. Work clutch pedal several times. Pull cable out again and fully tighten nut. Back adjusting nut off until there is about .196" (5 mm) between adjusting nut and boot. See *Fig. 2*. Tighten lock nut.

CLUTCH PEDAL HEIGHT

With clutch switch on pedal bracket, adjust pedal height to 6.40-8.85" (164-174 mm).

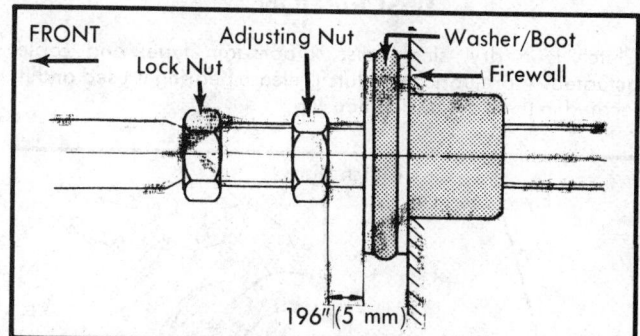

Fig. 2   Clutch Cable Adjustment Gap

TIGHTENING SPECIFICATIONS

Application	Ft. Lbs. (N·m)
Pressure Plate-to-Flywheel	13 (18)
Ball Stud-to-Front Cover	30 (41)

Clutches

MAZDA GLC

DESCRIPTION

Clutch is a dry, single disc, diaphragm type, and cable actuated. A prelubricated clutch release bearing is used and is located in the transmission housing.

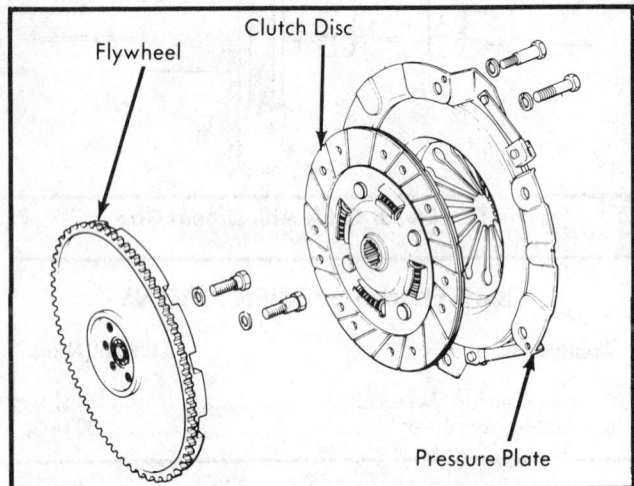

Fig. 1 Exploded View of Clutch Assembly

REMOVAL & INSTALLATION

CLUTCH ASSEMBLY

Removal (FWD) — 1) Disconnect negative battery cable. Disconnect speedometer cable. Remove the 2 clutch cable brackets and disconnect cable from release lever. Remove water pipe bracket and harness clips. Raise and support front of vehicle. Drain transaxle fluid.

2) Remove wheels. Remove under and side covers. Remove lower arm ball joint. Ensure driveshaft ball joint is not bent to maximum extent and pull shaft straight out of transaxle by pulling caliper toward operator. Take care not to damage oil seal.

3) Set engine support (49 E301 025) on the engine hanger and lift engine. Separate shift control rod and shift rod. Remove extension bar from transaxle. Remove crossmember. Separate left front mounting rubber and transcase.

4) Remove starter motor. Support transaxle with a jack. Remove transaxle mounting bolts and remove transaxle. Install disc centering tool (49 E301 310) and flywheel holding tool. Remove bolts from pressure plate evenly and alternately. Separate pressure plate and clutch disc.

Removal (RWD) — 1) Disconnect battery ground cable. Place gearshift lever in neutral and remove lever and hardware. Raise and support vehicle and drain transmission. Disconnect and remove propeller shaft. Disconnect speedometer cable, back-up light and exhaust pipe hanger on clutch housing.

2) Remove exhaust pipe support bracket from clutch housing and disconnect clutch cable from release lever. Remove clutch housing splash guard. Remove starter. Disconnect exhaust pipe hanger from extension housing. Place jack under rear of engine, protecting oil pan with a block of wood.

3) Disconnect transmission support member. Remove engine-to-transmission attaching bolts and carefully slide transmission

back until it can be lowered from the vehicle. Install flywheel holding tool and loosen pressure plate mounting bolts evenly until assembly can be removed. Separate clutch disc and pressure plate.

Installation (All Models) — Lightly lubricate input shaft splines. Use clutch aligning tool to center clutch assembly. Clutch cover and flywheel alignment marks must be aligned when assembling. Tighten pressure plate bolts. To complete installation, reverse removal procedure.

CLUTCH RELEASE BEARING & FORK

Removal & Installation (FWD) — Disconnect return spring from fork. Twist the release lever and separate from fork. Remove release bearing. Remove bolt holding release lever and fork together. Pull release lever and remove return spring, key and release fork. To install, apply grease to contact areas and reverse removal procedure.

Removal & Installation (RWD) — Loosen and remove bolt attaching release shaft to transmission. Slide bearing off bearing cover. Remove shaft from clutch housing. To install, coat all contact surfaces with grease and reverse removal procedures.

NOTE — *On FWD models, release bearing and collar are constructed as a single unit. On both models, bearing is prelubricated and should not be washed in any cleaning solution or solvet.*

CLUTCH CABLE

Removal & Installation (FWD) — Remove lock nut, adjusting nut, plain washer, damper and roller from release lever. See Fig. 4. Pull cable out of bracket. Remove cover from inner

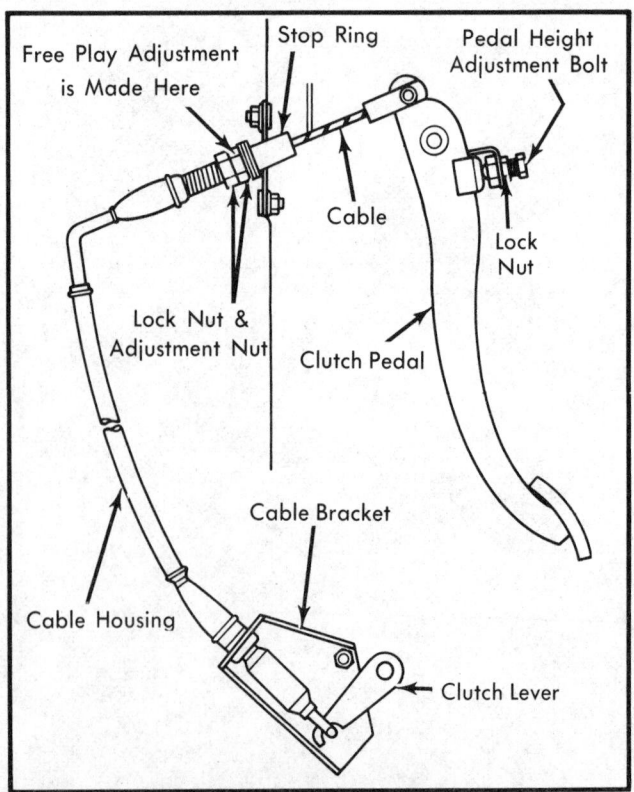

Fig. 2 Installed View of Clutch Cable (RWD Models) with Adjustment Locations

MAZDA GLC (Cont.)

panel. Disconnect cable from pedal assembly. Disconnect cable from release lever and remove cable. To install, reverse removal procedure. Grease bushings, pedal hook and roller. Seal boot to firewall and adjust pedal play.

Removal & Installation (RWD) — Loosen cable lock nut and adjustment nut. Pull cable through toward clutch pedal and disconnect from pedal. Push cable through stop ring in engine compartment and disconnect from cable at clutch lever. Remove retainer ring at bracket, separate cable housing at bracket and remove cable. To install, reverse removal procedure.

PILOT BEARING

Removal & Installation (All Models) — Pilot bearing is pressed into flywheel. Remove using puller. To install, lubricate bearing and install using driver.

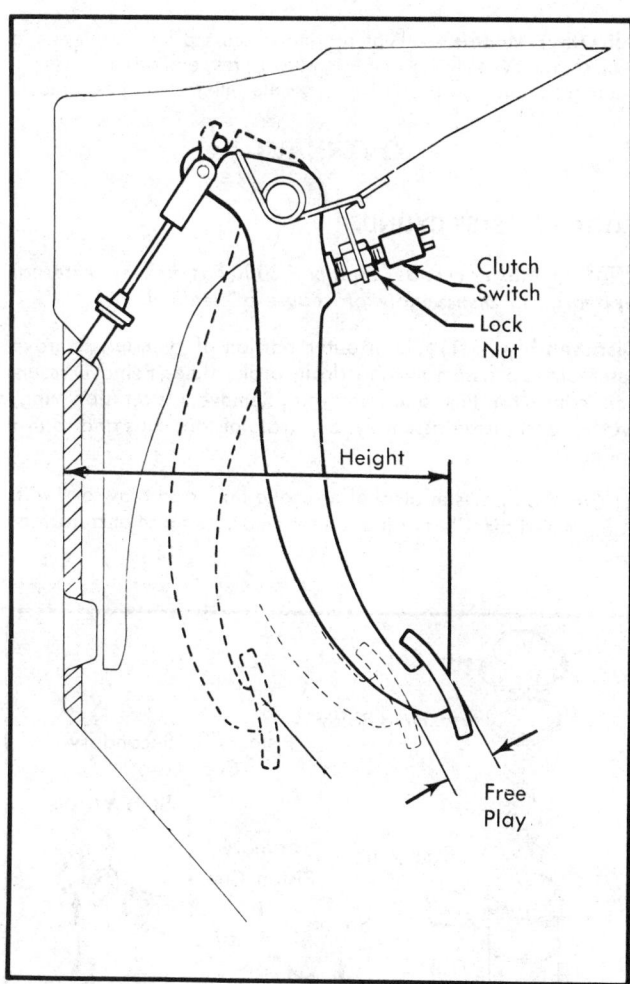

Fig. 3 Clutch Pedal Adjustment (FWD Models)

ADJUSTMENTS

CLUTCH PEDAL HEIGHT & FREE PLAY

Pedal Height (FWD) — Remove cover under dashboard. Adjust pedal height to 9.05-9.25" (230-235 mm) by loosening lock nut and rotating clutch switch until correct height is obtained. Tighten lock nut and install cover. See *Fig. 3*.

Pedal Height (RWD) — Adjust pedal height to 7.5-7.7" (190-195 mm) by loosening lock nut and rotating adjusting bolt until correct height is obtained. Tighten lock nut. See *Fig. 2*.

Free Play (FWD) — Free play should be .43-.67" (11-17 mm) and is set at release lever. Turn adjusting nut until gap is as specified when release lever is depressed and roller is pulled as shown in *Fig. 4*. Tighten lock nut.

Free Play (RWD) — Clutch pedal free play should be .39-.59" (10-15 mm) and is adjusted by setting release cable clearance at engine compartment side of firewall. Loosen lock nut, pull outer cable and turn adjusting nut until clearance is .06-.09" (1.5-2.3 mm). Tighten lock nut and check pedal free play. See *Fig. 2*.

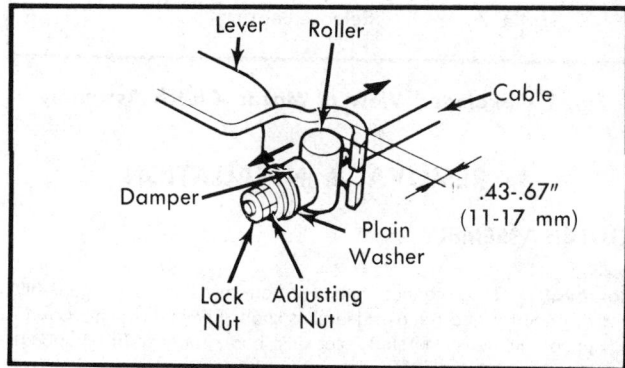

Fig. 4 Detail of Release Lever and Cable (FWD Models)

TIGHTENING SPECIFICATIONS

Application	Ft. Lbs. (N·m)
Flywheel-to-Crankshaft	60-65 (82-88)
Pressure Plate-to-Flywheel	13-20 (18-27)

MAZDA 626, RX7 & B2000 PICKUP

DESCRIPTION

Clutch is a dry, single disc, diaphragm spring type. Clutch system is hydraulic using a firewall mounted master cylinder and a slave cylinder attached to clutch housing. Release bearing is pre-lubricated and sealed.

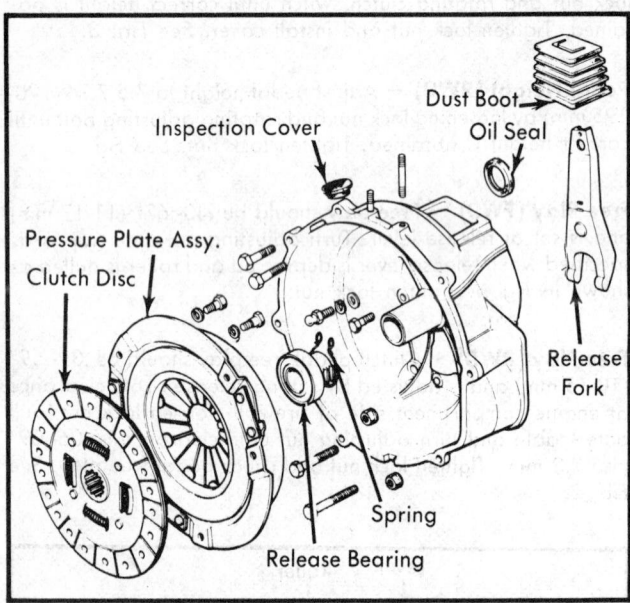

Fig. 1 Exploded View of Mazda Clutch Assembly

REMOVAL & INSTALLATION

CLUTCH ASSEMBLY

Removal — 1) Disconnect negative battery cable. Place gearshift lever in neutral and remove gearshift knob. Remove console box (if equipped). Remove gearshift lever dust boot, retainer (if equipped) and gearshift lever. B2000 gearshift lever components include wave washer, shim and bushing. On RX7, remove air cleaner.

2) On all vehicles, raise and support vehicle and drain transmission. Disconnect and remove propeller shaft. Disconnect and/or remove under covers and exhaust and emission control components as required. Remove clutch slave cylinder and place out of the way without removing fluid line. Disconnect and remove starter, speedometer cable, back-up lights and other electrical connections.

3) Place jack under rear end of engine, protecting oil pan with wooden block. Position transmission jack under transmission and remove transmission-to-engine mounting bolts. If equipped, remove transmission-to-crossmember bolts, crossmember-to-frame bolts and crossmember.

4) Slide transmission back until input shaft is cleared and remove from vehicle. Install flywheel holding tool and loosen pressure plate mounting bolts evenly until assembly can be removed. Separate clutch disc and pressure plate. Remove release bearing and fork.

Installation — To install, reverse removal procedure and note: Lightly coat input shaft splines with grease and use clutch alignment tool to center clutch assembly. Clutch cover and flywheel "O" alignment marks must be aligned at installation.

CLUTCH MASTER CYLINDER

Removal & Installation — Disconnect hydraulic line from master cylinder. Remove nuts mounting cylinder to firewall. Unhook clutch pedal from cylinder push rod. Remove cylinder. To install, reverse removal procedure and bleed hydraulic system.

CLUTCH SLAVE CYLINDER

Removal & Installation — Raise vehicle and support. Disconnect fluid hose. Remove nuts mounting slave cylinder to clutch housing and slide off cylinder. To install, reverse removal procedure and bleed clutch.

PILOT BEARING

RX7 — Remove bearing and seals with slide hammer (49 1285 071 or equivalent). Use driver (49 0823 72A or equivalent) to install new bearing. Apply multipurpose grease and install seal.

All Other Models — Pilot bearing is pressed into flywheel. To replace, remove flywheel and using arbor press and driver, press old bearing out and new bearing in. Lubricate with multipurpose grease.

OVERHAUL

CLUTCH MASTER CYLINDER

NOTE — *Master cylinder used on B2000 has different external appearance. Disassembly procedure is identical.*

Disassembly — 1) Clean outer portion of cylinder. Remove reservoir cap assembly and drain brake fluid. Remove reservoir connector link and reservoir. Remove piston stop ring, washer and piston assembly. Separate piston, cups and return spring.

2) Clean all parts in alcohol or brake fluid and blow dry with compressed air. Check all parts for wear, damage or deforma-

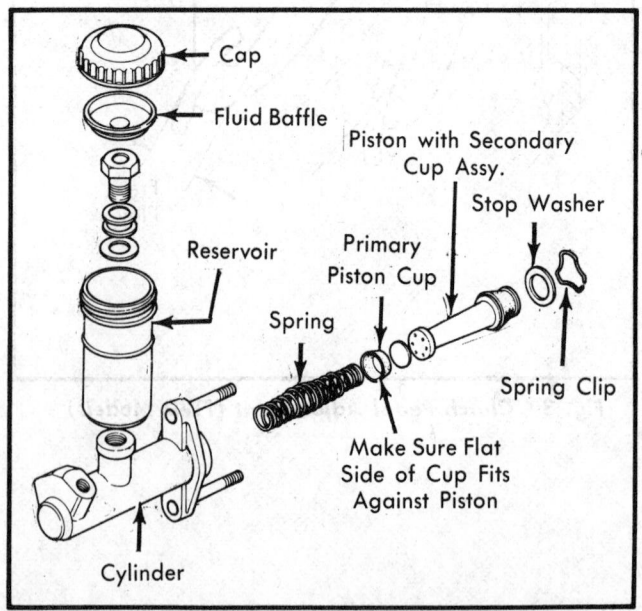

Fig. 2 Exploded View of Clutch Master Cylinder

MAZDA 626, RX7 & B2000 PICKUP (Cont.)

tion. If cylinder bore-to-piston clearance exceeds .006" (.15 mm), replace defective part. Replace parts as required and coat all components with brake fluid before assembly.

Reassembly — Reverse disassembly procedure and note: Install primary cup with flat side of cup against piston and ensure compensating port is open. After assembly, fill reservoir with clean brake fluid and operate piston with screwdriver until fluid is ejected at outlet port.

CLUTCH SLAVE CYLINDER

1) Clean outside of cylinder. Remove dust boot and release rod. Remove piston and cup assembly from cylinder, using compressed air if required. Remove spring, bleeder screw and valve. Clean all parts in brake fluid or alcohol and dry with compressed air.

2) Check all parts for wear or damage. If cylinder bore-to-piston clearance exceeds .006" (.15 mm), replace piston or cylinder. To reassemble, reverse disassembly procedure.

NOTE — *Before assembly, coat pistons and cups with clean hydraulic fluid.*

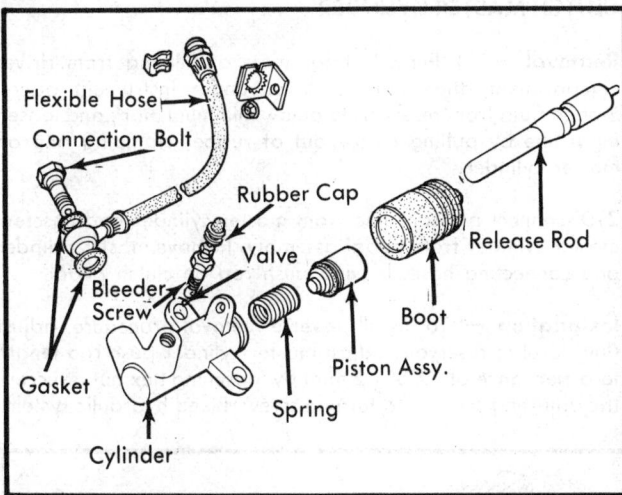

Fig. 3   Exploded View of Typical Slave Cylinder

ADJUSTMENTS

CLUTCH PEDAL FREE PLAY

Adjust clutch pedal free play (measured at pedal pad) to .02-.12" (0.6-3.0 mm) by loosening lock nut and turning pedal stopper bolt. Tighten lock nut. When free play is correct, pedal

height should be 7.5-7.7" (190-195 mm) on RX7, 7.6-7.8" (193-198 mm) on 626 and 8.5-8.7" (215-220 mm) on B2000 models.

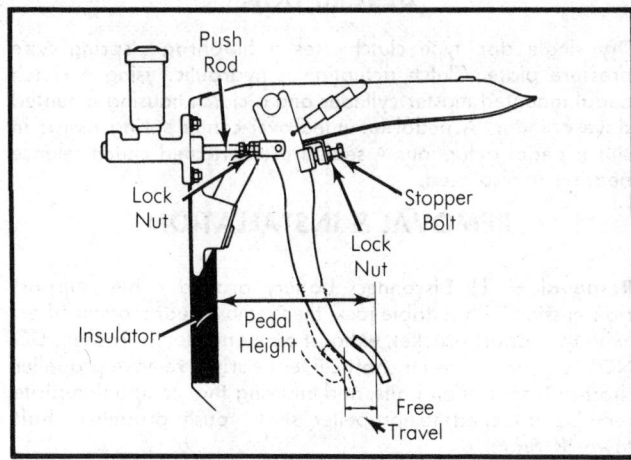

Fig. 4   Clutch Adjustment Locations

HYDRAULIC SYSTEM BLEEDING

1) Clutch hydraulic system must be bled whenever a fluid line has been disconnected or air has entered system. To bleed system, remove bleed screw cap at slave cylinder and attach a hose. Place opposite end in a jar partially filled with brake fluid. Check master cylinder fluid reservoir often during bleeding process and maintain level at ¾ full.

2) Open bleed screw, depress clutch pedal and allow pedal to return slowly. Continue operation until no air bubbles are seen in discharged fluid. Close bleeder screw, remove hose and attach dust cap to bleed screw.

TIGHTENING SPECIFICATIONS

Application	Ft. Lbs. (N•m)
Flywheel-to-Crankshaft (Piston Engines)	112-117 (152-159)
Flywheel-to-Eccentric Shaft (Rotary Engines)	289-362 (393-492)
Clutch-to-Flywheel	13-20 (18-27)

MERCEDES-BENZ

240D

DESCRIPTION

Dry single disc type clutch uses a diaphragm spring type pressure plate. Clutch actuation is hydraulic, using a clutch pedal mounted master cylinder and a clutch housing mounted slave cylinder. A pedal mounted over-center spring assists in clutch pedal actuation. A sealed prelubricated clutch release bearing is also used.

REMOVAL & INSTALLATION

Removal – 1) Disconnect battery ground cable, support transmission with suitable jack, then remove rear crossmember, exhaust support bracket, exhaust pipe and clamp. Loosen, DO NOT remove, propeller shaft center bearing, remove propeller shaft-to-transmission bolts, and ensuring that companion plate remains attached to propeller shaft, push propeller shaft towards rear.

2) Remove tachometer drive from rear of transmission. Remove clutch slave cylinder and pull towards the rear with lines connected, until rod is released from clutch housing. Remove shift linkage from transmission shift levers. Remove starter.

3) Remove transmission-to-intermediate flange attaching bolts (removing two upper bolts last). Pull transmission out horizontally, until input shaft is clear of clutch. Then remove in a downward direction.

4) Loosen pressure plate attaching bolts 1 to 1½ turns at a time until tension is released, then remove all bolts, pressure plate and clutch disc.

Installation – 1) To install, place slave cylinder and line above transmission, then, using an aligning tool, center clutch disc on flywheel and install pressure plate. Tighten bolts 1 to 1½ turns at a time until tight.

NOTE – *When installing propeller shaft to transmission, raise engine and transmission with suitable jack. Tighten propeller shaft center bearing clamp nut to 22-29 ft. lbs (30-39 N·m).*

CAUTION – *During installation, make sure that clutch is fully pulled into recess in flywheel.*

2) To complete installation, reverse removal procedure. Bleed slave cylinder and check hydraulic fluid level. Check clutch adjustment and shift linkage adjustment.

RELEASE BEARING & LEVER

Removal – Remove release bearing from bearing tube on front transmission cover. Move release lever down and to the left, then pull from ball pin on clutch housing.

Installation – To install, apply suitable lubricant to all bearing and lever contact surfaces, and reverse removal procedure.

CLUTCH MASTER CYLINDER

Removal – 1) Remove floor mats and lining from driver compartment, then remove cover under instrument panel. Siphon fluid from reservoir to below minimum mark and loosen input line by pulling elbow out of rubber clamping ring on master cylinder.

2) Disconnect pressure line from master cylinder and unscrew master cylinder from pedal assembly. Remove master cylinder and connecting hose, leaving push rod on clutch pedal.

Installation – To install, reverse removal procedure, adjust fluid level in reservoir, adjust master cylinder push rod length to a clearance of .008" (.2 mm) by loosening hex nut of eccentric adjusting screw and turning screw. Bleed hydraulic system.

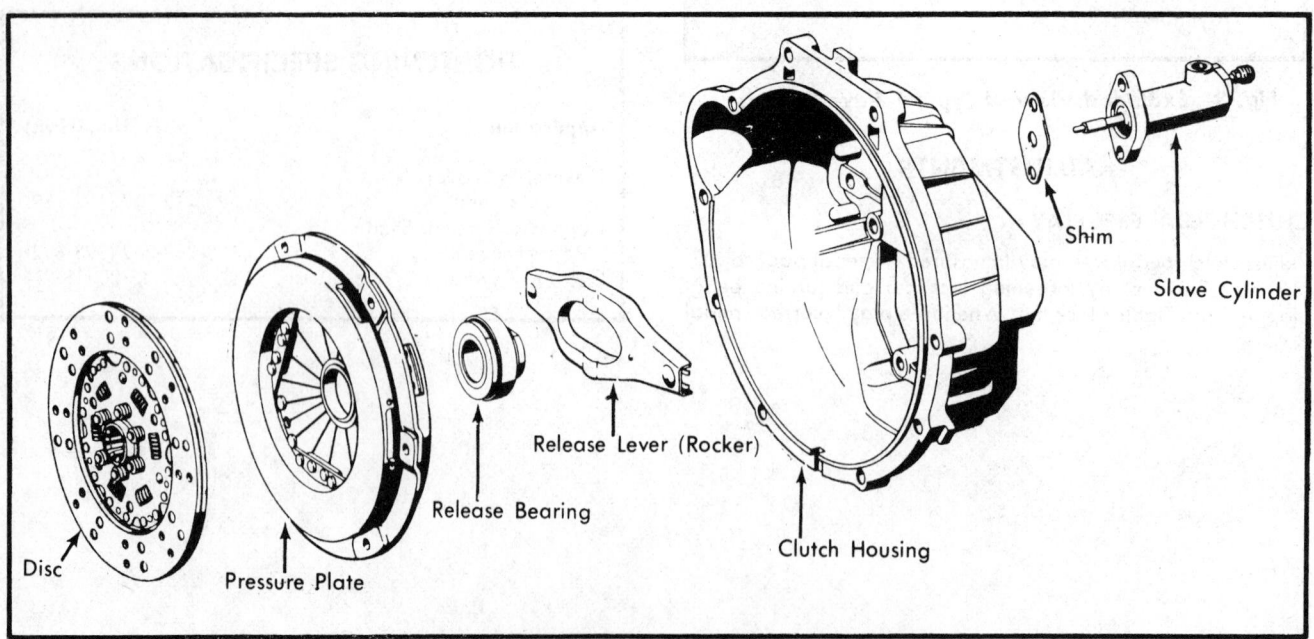

Fig. 1   Mercedes-Benz 240D Clutch Assembly

MERCEDES-BENZ (Cont.)

CLUTCH SLAVE CYLINDER

Removal — Disconnect hydraulic line from slave cylinder, then plug line with a rubber cap to prevent loss of fluid. Remove bolts attaching cylinder to clutch housing, then remove slave cylinder and push rod from housing as an assembly.

NOTE — *Take care not to lose plastic shim installed between cylinder and housing. Shim is recessed to accommodate inspection gauge.*

Installation — To install, place shim with grooved end against clutch housing and hold in position. Insert slave cylinder with push rod into clutch housing, and install and tighten mounting bolts. Connect hydraulic line to cylinder and bleed hydraulic system.

NOTE — *Wear on clutch disc may only be checked using special inspection gauge inserted in groove of plastic shim. Disc is serviceable if notches on gauge disappear in flange. If notches remain visible, wear limit is exceeded and disc must be replaced. See illustration.*

ADJUSTMENT

OVER CENTER SPRING

Adjust nuts at bottom of over center spring so that spring length measured across retainers is 2.05" (52.5 mm). Improper adjustment will result in failure of pedal to return when released or excessive pressure required to depress pedal.

HYDRAULIC SYSTEM BLEEDING

With Pressure Bleeder — 1) Connect pressure line of bleeder to opened bleeder screw of slave cylinder. Fluid reservoir of vehicle should be almost empty so brake fluid can flow from bottom upward through system, allowing air to escape in upward direction.

2) Make sure bleeder is set at lowest possible pressure, and watch reservoir to prevent overflow of fluid. When fluid approaches maximum level in reservoir, remove bleeder and close bleeder screw. Adjust fluid level in reservoir, if necessary, to maximum level in reservoir.

With Assistance of Brake System — 1) Check fluid level in reservoir and make sure it is at maximum level. Place a hose on bleeder screw of right front brake caliper and open screw. Press down on brake pedal until hose is filled with brake fluid and no more air bubbles are showing.

2) Place opposite end of hose on clutch slave cylinder bleeder screw, and open screw. Keep pressure on brake pedal. Close bleeder screw on caliper and release brake pedal. Repeat operation until no more air bubbles appear at fluid reservoir.

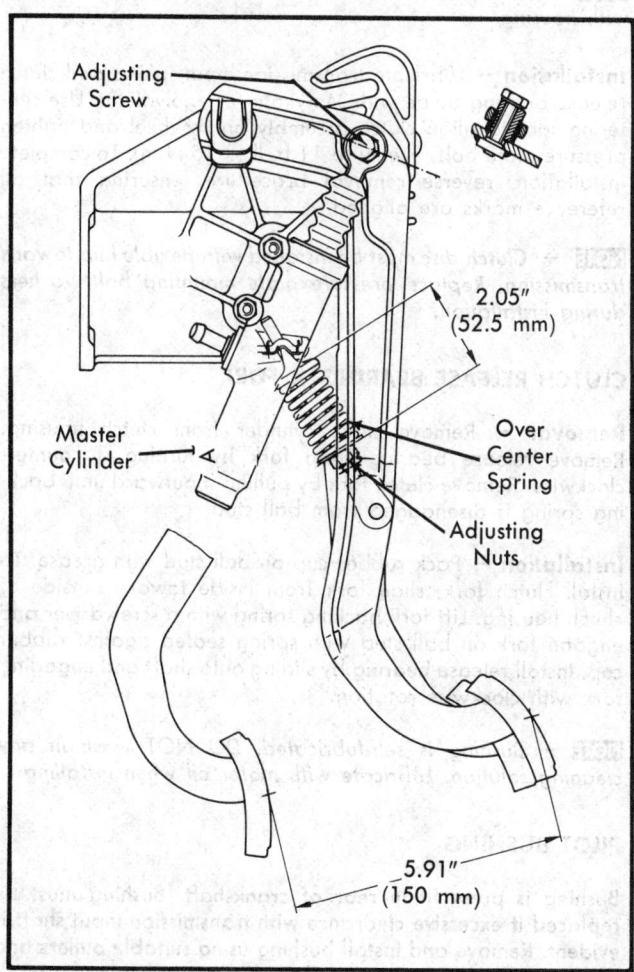

Fig. 2 *Clutch Pedal Assembly with Master Cylinder and Over Center Spring*

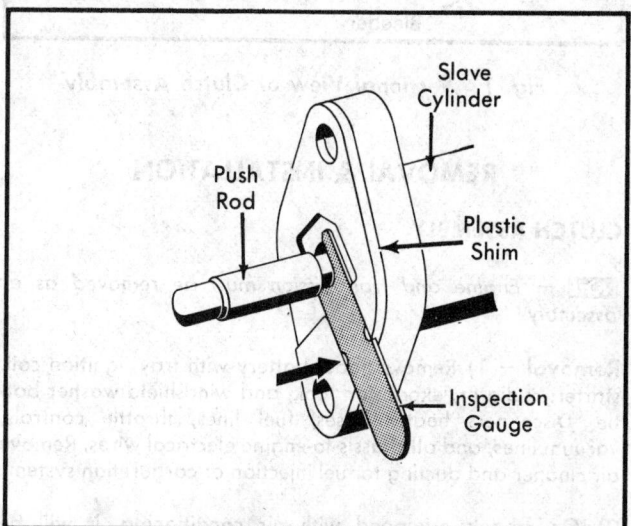

Fig. 3 *Checking for Clutch Disc Wear*

PEUGEOT

504
505
604

DESCRIPTION

Clutch is a dry, single disc, diaphragm spring type. Clutch actuation is hydraulic, using a firewall mounted master cylinder and a bell housing mounted slave cylinder. A pre-lubricated clutch release bearing is also used. Due to hydraulic system design, no adjustments, with the exception of bleeding hydraulic system, is necessary.

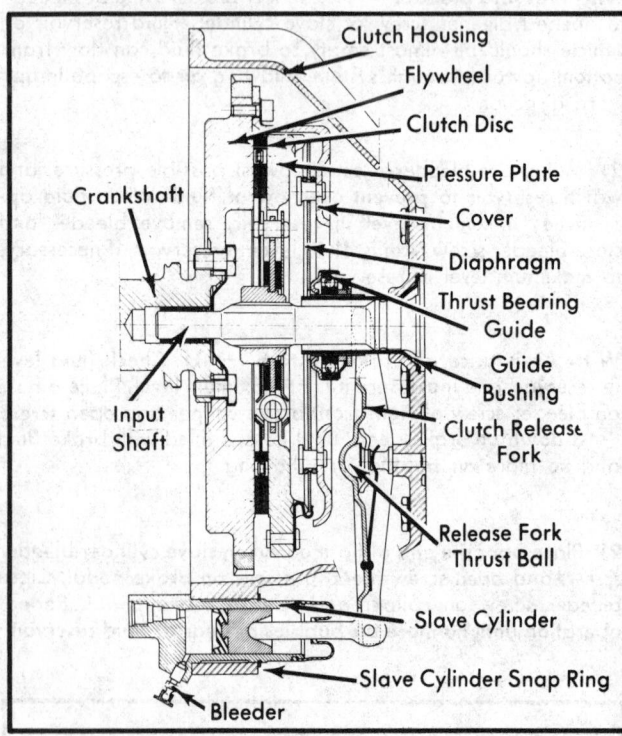

Fig. 1   Sectional View of Clutch Assembly

REMOVAL & INSTALLATION

CLUTCH ASSEMBLY

NOTE – *Engine and transmission must be removed as an assembly.*

Removal – **1)** Remove hood, battery with tray, ignition coil, starter, radiator, expansion tank, and windshield washer bottle. Disconnect heater hoses, fuel lines, throttle controls, vacuum lines, and all chassis-to-engine electrical wires. Remove air cleaner and ducting to fuel injection or carburetion system.

2) On models equipped with air conditioning, it will be necessary to remove and set aside under hood components of the air conditioning system. DO NOT disconnect hoses or pressure connections. Disconnect electrical leads to compressor, pressure switch, thermostat, and electric cooling fan. Free receiver-drier, condenser and compressor from their mountings and move to right side of vehicle.

3) If equipped with power steering, remove power steering pump and set aside without disconnecting hoses. On all models, remove upper clutch housing-to-engine mounting bolts and inspection plates. Disconnect exhaust pipe from manifold and remove muffler and exhaust pipe supporting brackets with heat deflector.

4) Attach suitable hoisting sling and raise engine until transmission contacts tunnel. On 604 models, fit propeller shaft tube support between muffler and body and tighten to support tube slightly. Remove steering coupling clamp bolts and replace with slightly longer bolts. Lower front cross member about 1.2" (30 mm) with steering rack attached.

5) On 504 and 505, attach transmission support tool (8.0125) and tighten to support transmission. On all models, remove lower clutch housing-to-engine bolts. Pull engine slightly forward and carefully lift from vehicle. Attach engine to suitable workstand and mark pressure plate and flywheel for reassembly reference. Remove pressure plate mounting bolts evenly and remove clutch assembly.

NOTE – *Clutch slave cylinder and release assembly remains with housing.*

Installation – Lubricate transmission input splines and clutch release bearing guide with Molykote (or equivalent). Use centering tool to align clutch assembly on flywheel and tighten pressure plate bolts evenly to 11 ft. lbs. (15 N·m). To complete installation, reverse removal procedure, ensuring that all reference marks are aligned.

NOTE – *Clutch disc must be installed with flexible hub toward transmission. Replace pressure plate mounting bolt washers during installation.*

CLUTCH RELEASE BEARING & FORK

Removal – Remove slave cylinder from clutch housing. Remove release bearing from fork by turning it counter-clockwise. Remove clutch fork by pulling it outward until backing spring is disengaged from ball stud.

Installation – Pack rubber cup on ball stud with grease. To install clutch fork, slide fork from inside toward outside of clutch housing. Lift fork backing spring with a screwdriver and engage fork on ball stud with spring seated against rubber cup. Install release bearing by sliding onto shaft and engaging fork with clockwise rotation.

NOTE – *Bushing is self-lubricated. DO NOT wash in any cleaning solution. Lubricate with motor oil when installing.*

PILOT BUSHING

Bushing is press fit in rear of crankshaft. Bushing must be replaced if excessive clearance with transmission input shaft is evident. Remove and install bushing using suitable pullers and drivers.

CLUTCH MASTER CYLINDER

Removal & Installation – Disconnect and plug master cylinder hydraulic lines from fluid reservoir and to slave cylinder. Remove bolts securing master cylinder to pedal assembly and

PEUGEOT (Cont.)

remove master cylinder. To install, reverse removal procedure and bleed hydraulic system.

CLUTCH SLAVE CYLINDER

Removal & Installation — Disconnect hydraulic line at slave cylinder. Remove snap ring securing cylinder in clutch housing, then slide slave cylinder from clutch housing mounting. To install, reverse removal procedure and bleed hydraulic system.

NOTE — *Overhaul procedures for clutch slave cylinder and master cylinder not provided by manufacturer.*

ADJUSTMENT

HYDRAULIC SYSTEM BLEEDING

Fabricate bleed tube using suitable rubber hose, clamps and adaptor from suitable bleeder kit (ARC 50). Attach hose to slave cylinder bleeder and pressure bleeder (ARC 50 or equivalent) to bleed tube. Adjust bleed pressure to 25.6 psi (1.8 kg/cm²). Open bleed screw and observe fluid level in master cylinder. Close bleed screw when fluid reaches specified level.

PORSCHE

911SC
924
928

DESCRIPTION

The 928 model uses a dual disc dry clutch and a diaphragm spring type pressure plate. All other models use a single disc dry clutch with the diaphragm spring type pressure plate. The 924 Turbo and 928 clutches are hydraulically operated and self adjusting, while the 911SC and 924 models are mechanically operated through an adjustable cable.

REMOVAL & INSTALLATION

CLUTCH ASSEMBLY

Removal (911SC) — 1) Raise and support vehicle. Disconnect negative battery cable and remove air cleaner. Loosen engine block vent hose at engine and plug vent cover hole. If equipped with air conditioning, detach compressor and place out of way but DO NOT disconnect hoses.

2) Remove relay plate cover and disconnect the engine wires at relay plate, adapter plug, relay plate socket, and ignition control unit. Remove fuel hoses at filter and return line. Disconnect accelerator linkage.

3) Remove rear center tunnel cover in passenger compartment. Slide boot forward over shift selector rod and disconnect coupling from inner shift rod. Disconnect speedometer sensor wires in tunnel. Drain engine oil and plug hoses on engine and oil tank.

4) Remove heater hoses at exchangers. Remove rear stabilizer. Disconnect ground strap at body and battery wires at starter. Disconnect accelerator linkage from pedal and clutch cable at transmission. Remove axle shafts from flanges at transmission.

5) Place suitable jack under engine/transmission assembly and lift slightly, using caution to prevent damage to secondary air injection pipes. Loosen transmission and engine mounting bolts and carefully lower assembly from vehicle.

6) Remove circlip from clutch release lever shaft and pull off lever and rubber ring. Remove mounting bolts and pull transmission from engine. Mark pressure plate and flywheel for reassembly and insert alignment tool. Loosen bolts 1 or 2 turns at a time in a diagonal pattern and separate clutch assembly from engine.

Removal (924 & 924 Turbo) — 1) Disconnect ground strap at battery. Loosen and remove clutch cable at holder, and remove holder nut. Use engine support (VW 10-222) to suspend engine on front transport eyelets. Loosen and remove bottom engine guard.

2) Remove catalytic converter and muffler. Push back dust boot, remove lock wire from bolt on shift linkage and unscrew bolt. Lift and fold back dust boot and inner cover on shift lever. Remove clamp and shift knob. Remove circlip from shift lever. Pull off shift rod and spring washer from pin of shift lever. Turn shift lever 180° and remove attaching bolts and lever.

3) Press down insulation sheet and push shift rod forward into cavity of tunnel approximately 12" (300 mm). Remove plug from central tube housing. Push back protective tube for shift

rod so it is outside of central tube housing. Open tab on protective tube with a screwdriver. Loosen and remove coupling screws through opening.

4) Move coupling toward transmission. Detach axle shafts and suspend in a horizontal position. Remove wires from back-up light switch. Position jack underneath transmission with adapter plate (US 618 and 618/1). Engage points on adapter plates in take-up bores of transmission. Remove transmission-to-central tube housing flange bolts.

5) Remove transmission mount bolts. Lower transmission and central tube until central tube rests on rear axle. Remove transmission. Push back shift rod. Disconnect oxygen sensor wire at plug and remove from clips. Move exhaust pipe holders and rubber mounts out of brackets bolted to central tube.

6) Remove front exhaust pipe and heat shields (if equipped). Remove central tube-to-clutch housing bolts. Push central tube toward rear to rest on transmission carrier, turning 90° to ease operation. Remove clutch housing attaching bolts.

7) Move clutch housing back and turn until clutch release lever is located below cast boss on oil pan. Push clutch housing forward, tilt down rear end slightly and remove. Loosen pressure plate attaching bolts evenly and alternately and remove clutch assembly from flywheel. Separate clutch disc from pressure plate.

Installation (911SC, 924 & 924 Turbo) — 1) Ensure that marks on flywheel and clutch are aligned and tighten pressure plate bolts 1 turn at a time in a diagonal pattern. Use a clutch centering tool to center disc. If installing new clutch, balancing marks on clutch and flywheel should be offset 180°.

2) On 911SC models, pull release lever in opposite direction of engine when transmission is installed on engine. There must be at least .78" (20.0 mm) clearance between release lever and transmission housing.

3) On all models, complete installation by reversing removal procedure. On 924, check that insulation sheet on central tube is positioned correctly. Inside flange to insulation distance should be 17.75" (500 mm). Install shift lever to transmission at an angle of 85°.

NOTE — *Use care when guiding central tube into clutch housing.*

Removal (928) — 1) Disconnect battery ground strap. Remove lower body brace. Remove clutch slave cylinder, leaving line attached. Remove lower clutch housing with starter attached and suspend from stabilizer bar. Remove catalytic converter.

2) Remove coupling screws and push coupling back on drive shaft. If equipped with long coupling, remove plug from central tube to reach rear bolt. Remove release bearing sleeve mounting bolts and push sleeve toward flywheel. Mark pressure plate, intermediate ring and flywheel for reassembly reference.

3) Drive dowel pins in direction of pressure plate with a punch until they are beyond centering bore of flywheel. Check visually at opening on intermediate plate. Loosen pressure plate mounting bolts evenly 1 or 2 turns at a time until free. Disconnect release lever at ball stud and remove pressure

PORSCHE (Cont.)

plate, clutch discs, release bearing sleeve and short driveshaft as an assembly.

Installation (928) — 1) Assemble and install clutch as a unit. Prior to installation, push intermediate plate at the 3 adjusting elements in direction of release bearing to preload pressure plate. To assemble, place pressure plate on a level plate in a press. Slide clips (US 8039) under bolt heads.

2) Check protrusion of centering pins. They should protrude .12" (3 mm) over bearing surface of intermediate plate. Push intermediate plate in the direction of release bearing on the 3 adjusting elements. Assemble the clutch, noting that disc with the long hub is installed in the rear and that hubs face release bearing. Mount marks on discs 180° from each other.

3) Drive pressure plate on to centering pins of intermediate plate with a plastic hammer far enough that drive plate between them can still be moved with short drive shaft. Recheck protrusion of centering pins. Lubricate contact areas and guide centering pins on to flywheel.

4) Insert mounting bolts and screw in uniformly until clutch is held tightly. Ensure pressure plate marks and intermediate plate markings are 180° from each other and tighten bolts. Ensure short drive shaft moves easily and remove clips from under pressure plate bolt heads. To complete installation, reverse removal procedure.

CLUTCH RELEASE BEARING

Removal (911SC & 928) — Bearing is removed with pressure plate. Remove by laying pressure plate on bearing and removing snap ring on flywheel side of clutch fingers. Remove bearing along with washers.

Removal (924 & 924 Turbo) — With clutch removed, detach bearing spring clips from release lever. Move lever forward and take bearing off of guide tube.

Installation (All Models) — Apply thin coat of suitable lubricant to guide tube and friction surfaces and reverse removal procedures.

Fig. 1   911SC Clutch Adjusting Mechanism

ADJUSTMENT

CLUTCH ADJUSTMENT

911SC — Clutch free play must be checked at transmission adjusting lever due to auxiliary clutch spring. With cable snug, adjust play at lever to .040" (1.0 mm). Clutch pedal travel may be adjusted at stop on floor plate. Release travel should be .965-1.004" (24.5-25.5 mm) when measured at cable end.

924 — With release bearing against diaphragm spring, lower end of cable should be 5.36-5.52" (136.0-140.0 mm) when measured from lower edge of cable holder to pin at release lever. To adjust, turn outboard release lever on shaft and tighten in position. Adjust cable with counternuts on holder to give .8-1.0" (20.0-25.0 mm) free play at clutch pedal.

924 Turbo & 928 — No adjustment is necessary due to automatic adjustment by slave cylinder. There must be .02" (.5 mm) play between end of push rod and master cylinder piston. This gives approximately .12" (3.0 mm) free play at pedal pad. If necessary, correct play by adjusting push rod.

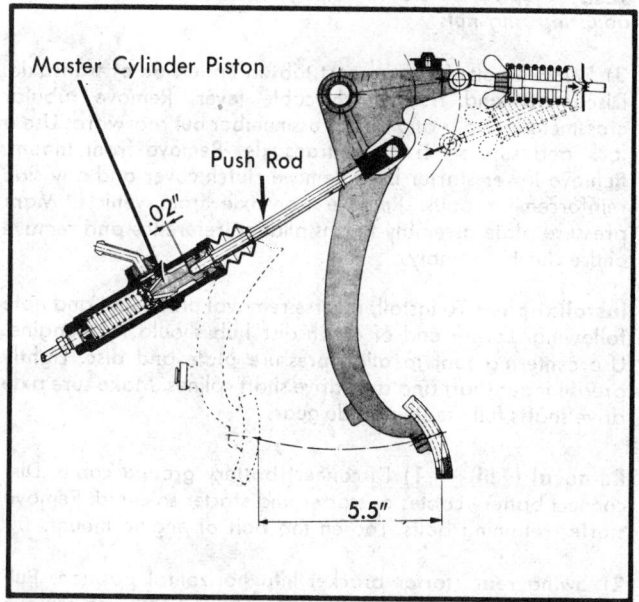

Fig. 2   924 Turbo & 928 Clutch Push Rod Adjustment

PEDAL ADJUSTMENT

NOTE — *Pedal adjustment procedures not available from manufacturer for other models.*

911SC — 1) With engine running and warm, reverse gear must be able to be engaged silently when pedal is fully depressed. Release lever should move .6" (15.0 mm) to completely release clutch. If cable housing rests on bottom of guide clamp when pedal is fully depressed, inner cable must be adjusted at yoke end.

2) Measure from threaded cable end of yoke to outer edge of lock nut. Adjust if not within .7-.9 (17.0-22.0 mm). If arc of cable is too large and allows cable to come out of guide clamp when pedal is released, inner cable must be shortened at yoke end.

RENAULT

Le Car
18i

DESCRIPTION

Clutch system is single disc dry plate type. Main components are: Disc, diaphragm spring operated pressure plate, ball bearing type clutch release bearing, release fork, and pilot bearing. Clutch operation is mechanical through cable actuation.

REMOVAL & INSTALLATION

CLUTCH ASSEMBLY

Removal (Le Car) – 1) Disconnect battery. Disconnect speedometer cable from transmission. Remove water pump belt, camshaft belt and air injection components. Remove both upper starter bolts (it may be necessary to use special wrench Ele. 565).

2) Remove clutch housing mounting bolts. Take off calipers and support out of way. Disconnect tie rods at steering rack end. Disconnect upper ball joints. Separate axle drive shafts by pulling stub axle out and down.

NOTE – *Be careful not to damage oil seal lips on differential adjusting ring nuts.*

3) Remove bolts from support tab on underside of transaxle. Disconnect and free clutch cable lever. Remove tubular crossmember bolts and slide crossmember out rearward. Use a jack and support front of transaxle. Remove front mount. Remove lower starter bolt. Remove clutch cover and any side reinforcement bolts. Remove transaxle from vehicle. Mark pressure plate assembly for installation reference and remove entire clutch assembly.

Installation – To install, reverse removal procedure and note following: Larger end of clutch disc hub should face engine. Use centering tool to align pressure plate and disc. Lightly grease input shaft and axle drive shaft splines. Make sure axle drive shafts fully seat into side gears.

Removal (18i) – 1) Disconnect battery ground cable. Disconnect battery cables at starter and starter solenoid. Remove starter retaining bolts. Loosen top bolt of engine mount.

2) Swing rear starter bracket into horizontal position. Pull starter back as far as it will go, rotate starter 90° and remove starter. Disconnect clutch cable from fork and remove housing stop.

3) Place support spacers (T. Av. 509.01) between lower shock retaining bolts and lower suspension arm shafts. Remove front wheels. Remove front brake calipers.

4) Using a drift punch and hammer, tap roll pins out of side gears. Remove steering ball joint nut. Using extractor tool, remove cone from ball joint housing.

5) Remove upper ball joint nut using extractor tool. Tilt stub axle carrier to free drive shaft from side gear. Do the same for other side. Disconnect back-up light wires, emission control wires and speedometer cable from transmission.

6) Disconnect gearshift linkage. Remove clutch protective cover. Support transmission with jack. Remove left and right transmission supports. Remove transmission retaining bolts. Pull transmission rearward and remove transmission from vehicle.

7) Mark pressure plate assembly for installation reference and remove entire clutch assembly.

Installation – To install, reverse removal procedure and note the following: Larger end of clutch disc hub should face engine. Use centering tool to align pressure plate and disc. Lightly grease input shaft and axle drive shaft splines. Make sure axle drive shafts fully seat into side gears.

CLUTCH CABLE

Removal – Disconnect cable from lever on transaxle. Free transaxle end of cable from sleeve stop. From inside vehicle, remove clutch pedal retaining clip and cable-to-pedal clevis pin. Slide pedal off of pivot rod, free cable from sleeve stop on pedal bracket, and remove cable.

Installation – To install, reverse removal procedure and note the following: Lubricate pedal bores and retaining pins with Molykote BR 2 lubricant. Adjust clutch free play.

CLUTCH RELEASE BEARING & FORK

Removal – With transaxle removed, disconnect the return spring from release bearing and fork, and slide bearing off transmission input shaft. Using a suitable tool (Emb. 384), extract fork retaining roll pins. Remove fork shaft, fork, and return spring.

Installation – 1) Lubricate fork shaft with Molykote BR 2 grease. Slide shaft into transaxle housing (fitted with rubber seal) and through release fork and return spring.

2) Align holes in shaft with those in fork and install roll pins, making sure that pins protrude $\frac{1}{32}$" on forward side of fork. Lubricate bearing sleeve and fork fingers with Molykote BR 2 grease, and slide bearing onto transmission input shaft.

3) Install return spring, placing ends in holes of release bearing support and in fork. Lubricate bearing face and portion of clutch diaphragm spring which bearing contacts with Molykote BR 2 grease. Install transmission and adjust clutch free play.

PILOT BEARING

Removal – Remove transaxle, clutch assembly and flywheel. Using a suitable tool (Mot. 11), extract bearing from crankshaft.

Installation – Using a suitable driver, install pilot bearing into crankshaft. Install flywheel, clutch assembly and transaxle. Adjust clutch free play.

OIL SEAL

Removal – Remove transaxle from vehicle. Remove the clutch housing attaching bolts and separate clutch housing from transmission. Using a suitable tool, remove oil seal from clutch housing.

RENAULT (Cont.)

Installation — Fit oil seal into place over special tool B. Vi. 526 or 488. Coat paper gasket with sealer. Place tool inside clutch release bearing guide to spread seal lip. Refit clutch housing on transaxle and slide tool along clutch shaft, then remove tool. Tighten clutch housing nuts.

ADJUSTMENT

CLUTCH FREE PLAY

Loosen lock nut. Turn adjusting nut to obtain free travel at end of release lever of ⅛-5⁄32" (3-4 mm).

TIGHTENING SPECIFICATIONS

Application	Ft. Lbs. (N·m)
Flywheel-to-Crankshaft	
Le Car	35 (48)
18i	67-81 (91-111)
Clutch Housing-to-Transmission	
Le Car	
8 mm Bolts	15 (20)
10 mm Bolts	30 (41)
18i	
8 mm Bolts	18 (24)
10 mm Bolts	26 (35)

Clutches

SAAB

DESCRIPTION

Clutch is dry, single plate, diaphragm spring type. Primary components are: Disc, pressure plate assembly, and release bearing. Release bearing is a special design ball bearing with elongated outer ring which presses directly against diaphragm when clutch pedal is let out. Clutch operation is hydraulic. Clutch pedal operates on a master cylinder which is connected to slave cylinder. Slave cylinder is located inside clutch cover around input shaft. Slave cylinder acts directly on release bearing. Clutch adjustment is automatic.

REMOVAL & INSTALLATION

CLUTCH ASSEMBLY

Removal – 1) Drain coolant. Remove hood. Disconnect negative battery terminal. Disconnect wiring harness from fan housing and the following electrical leads: Ignition coil, oil pressure switch, temperature switch, headlight wiper motor and thermal fan switch on radiator.

2) Disconnect radiator hoses. Remove grille and radiator. On all models, remove clutch housing cover, and install suitable spacer (8390023) between cover and diaphragm spring.

NOTE – Clutch pedal must be depressed to fit spacer.

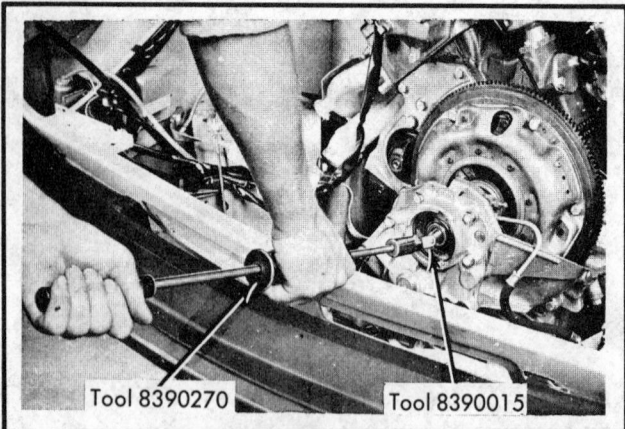

Fig. 1   Pulling Input Shaft Using Special Tools

3) Remove retaining ring and seal cap from input shaft. Remove plastic propeller from input shaft. Insert a bolt into clutch shaft and install tool 8393175. Withdraw the shaft as far as possible.

4) Remove slave cylinder retaining bolts. Remove pressure plate mounting bolts and remove pressure plate, clutch disc, slave cylinder (hydraulic line attached) and release bearing as an assembly.

NOTE – Make sure diaphragm spring does not damage slave cylinder sleeve.

Fig. 2   Lifting Out Clutch Assembly – Illustration Shows Relationship of Clutch Assembly to Surrounding Engine Components

NOTE – Before beginning clutch installation make sure input shaft seal is in good condition. Seal is located inside slave cylinder in primary gear case. Seal forms a direct bond with sealing surface of input shaft.

CAUTION – Make sure diaphragm spring does not damage slave cylinder sleeve during installation.

Installation – 1) Reassemble clutch assembly and loosely install two pressure plate retaining bolts.

NOTE – Hardened side of release bearing faces diaphragm spring.

2) Bolt slave cylinder guide sleeve to primary gear casing. Install input shaft and make sure it engages clutch disc splines and bearing. Install plastic propeller, seal cap and retaining ring to input shaft.

3) Tighten clutch assembly (pressure plate) to flywheel. Depress clutch pedal and remove spacer. With pedal depressed, install sliding lock ring toward slave cylinder. Complete installation by reversing removal procedure.

NOTE – DO NOT depress clutch pedal farther than necessary. Seal lip may be pressed too far, causing a hydraulic leak and seal damage.

CLUTCH MASTER CYLINDER

Removal & Installation – Remove hydraulic line at rear of cylinder. From under instrument panel in vehicle, remove access cover on left side. Remove push rod pin at clutch pedal. Remove master cylinder retaining nuts from firewall. From engine compartment, remove fluid supply line from top of cylinder and position so fluid does not leak. Remove master cylinder. To install, reverse removal procedure and bleed system.

CLUTCH SLAVE CYLINDER

NOTE – Slave cylinder removal is accomplished during clutch assembly removal. See Clutch Assembly Removal in this article.

Clutches

SAAB (Cont.)

OVERHAUL

CLUTCH MASTER CYLINDER

Disassembly — Pull back sealing bellows and remove retaining ring. Remove push rod and washer. Remove piston, convex washer, piston seal, and spring. Inspect cylinder bore for wear or damage. Replace complete assembly if cylinder is worn or damaged. Replace seal if worn or swollen.

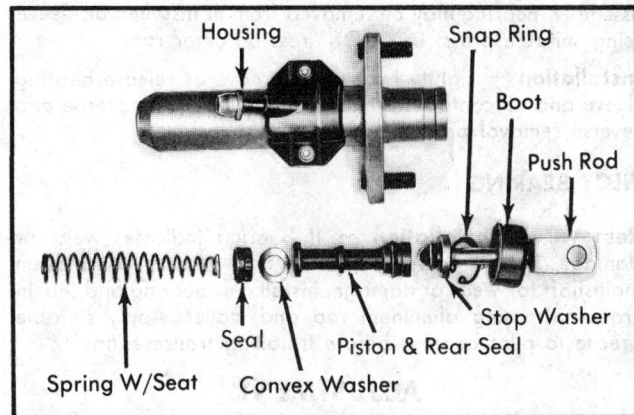

Fig. 3 Exploded View of Clutch Master Cylinder

Reassembly — Install return spring and spring retainer. Lubricate piston and seals with Girling Rubber Grease No. 3 . Install seals, convex washer and piston. Install push rod followed by washer and retaining ring. Install sealing bellows.

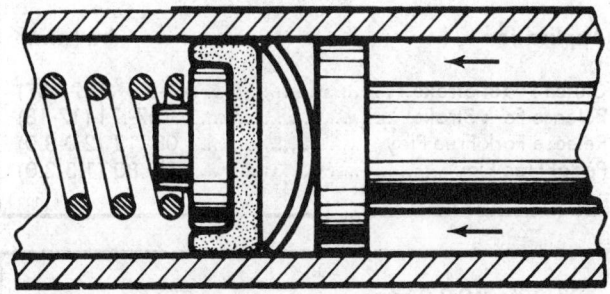

Fig. 4 Cut-Away View of Clutch Master Cylinder Bore Showing Convex Washer Correctly Installed. Convex Side MUST Face Master Cylinder Piston

CLUTCH SLAVE CYLINDER

Disassembly — 1) Remove clutch release bearing from slave cylinder.

2) Set slave cylinder with release bearing end facing up. Press cylinder sleeve out.

3) Remove "O" ring from sleeve.

4) Remove piston and lip seal.

NOTE — *Before beginning reassembly, lightly coat lip seal and piston (not "O" ring) with Caster Rubber Grease (or equivalent).*

Reassembly — 1) Fit "O" ring to sleeve flange.

2) Slide seal lip on sleeve.

3) Coat sleeve flange with brake fluid. Insert sleeve into cylinder. Push seal lip part way into cylinder.

4) Guide sleeve and cylinder together by pushing on piston until lock rings and "O" ring are fitted.

5) Place slave cylinder on support and seat sleeve into cylinder.

6) Fit release bearing to piston.

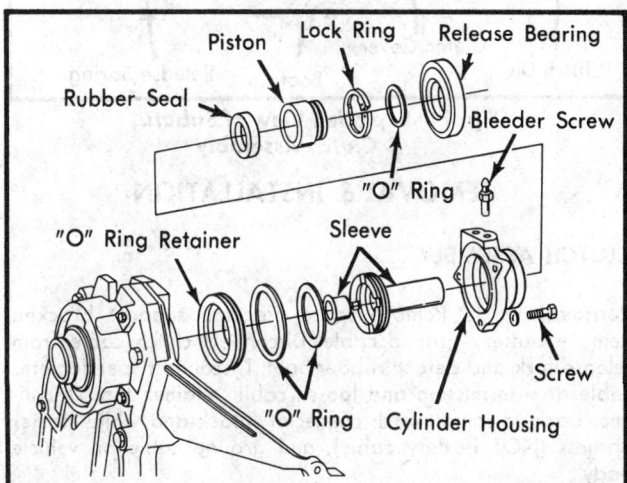

Fig. 5 Exploded View of Clutch Slave Cylinder

ADJUSTMENT

HYDRAULIC SYSTEM BLEEDING

1) Connect a ¼" hose to slave cylinder bleeder screw, and place opposite end in a container partially filled with hydraulic fluid. Fill master cylinder reservoir with hydraulic fluid. Open bleeder screw on slave cylinder ½ turn.

2) Place a coolant system tester over filler opening of master cylinder. Pump tester until all air has been removed from system. Close slave cylinder bleeder screw and check to see that all air has been expelled by depressing clutch pedal.

SUBARU

DL
GL
GLF

DESCRIPTION

Clutch is a single dry disc type with a diaphragm spring pressure plate. Actuation is mechanical through a cable. Sealed release bearing requires no lubrication.

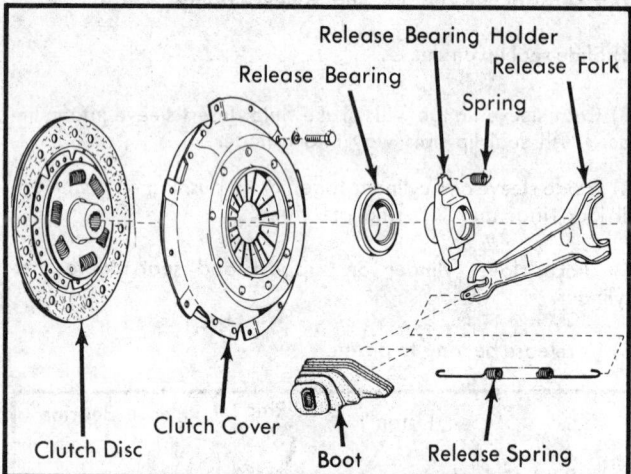

Fig. 1   Exploded View of Subaru Clutch Assembly

REMOVAL & INSTALLATION

CLUTCH ASSEMBLY

Removal — 1) Remove spare tire and support bracket. Remove battery ground cable. Disconnect clutch cable from release fork and detach rubber boot. Disconnect speedometer cable at transmission and loosen cable retainer clip. Disconnect back-up lamp switch connector, black and white starter harness (NOT battery cable), and ground cable on vehicle body.

2) Remove starter with battery cable attached. Remove upper engine-to-transmission bolts and loosen lower nuts. Loosen transmission side torque rod stopper nut by about .4" (10 mm) and tighten engine side nut by the same amount. On 4-WD models, separate both the gear selector and 4-WD selector system from the transmission.

3) On all models, raise and support front end of vehicle and remove front exhaust pipe assembly. On 4-WD models, remove transmission cover and rear drive shaft. Plug rear of transmission to prevent oil from running out. Remove exhaust cover and gearshift system from all except 4-WD models.

4) On all models, remove stabilizer, then lower both left and right transverse links. Drive spring pins from inner ends of axle shafts and push wheels out until axles separate from driving splines. Remove clamp on left side of hand brake cable. Remove nuts from transmission mounting pads.

5) Support transmission with a jack and remove crossmember. Remove nuts securing transmission to engine and move transmission away from engine. Ensure that mainshaft clears engine and lower transmission from vehicle. Remove pressure plate mounting bolts and take off clutch assembly.

Installation — Using alignment tool, place disc and pressure plate in position on flywheel. Ensure that there is a gap of 120° between "O" marks on flywheel and pressure plate. Tighten bolts to 12 ft. lbs. (16 N·m) gradually in a criss-cross pattern. Reverse removal procedure to complete installation.

CLUTCH RELEASE BEARING

Removal — With transmission separated from engine, disconnect return springs from transmission and remove bearing assembly. Bearing may be removed from or installed on sleeve using suitable press. DO NOT press on outer race.

Installation — Lightly coat inner groove of release bearing sleeve and all contact surfaces with multi-purpose grease and reverse removal procedures.

PILOT BEARING

Removal & Installation — If bearing indicates wear or damage, extract bearing and oil seal. Inspect transmission mainshaft for wear or damage. Install new bearing and seal in crankshaft using aluminum rod and mallet. Apply suitable grease to pilot bearing before installing transmission.

ADJUSTMENT

CLUTCH FREE PLAY

Remove fork return and adjust spherical nut so that there is .08-.12" (2.0-3.0 mm) play at fork end. Use care not to twist cable during adjustment. Attach return spring and ensure that cable is routed without kinks or sharp bends.

Clutch Adjustment Specifications	
Application	**In. (mm)**
Clutch Pedal Stroke	5.1-5.4 (129-137)
Release Fork Stroke	.67-.71 (17-18)
Release Fork Free Play	.08-.12 (2.0-3.0)
Pedal Free Play	.50-.80 (1.3-2.0)

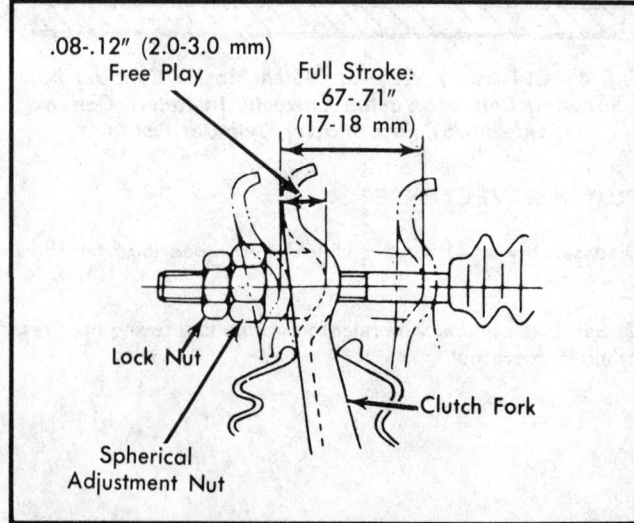

Fig. 2   Clutch Cable Adjustment Locations and Specifications

Clutches

TOYOTA CELICA, COROLLA, CORONA, PICKUP, STARLET & SUPRA

DESCRIPTION

Clutch is a dry, single plate, diaphragm spring type which is hydraulically operated by a firewall mounted master cylinder and clutch housing mounted slave cylinder. The slave cylinder used on 4-WD Pickup is adjustable; all others are non-adjustable and clearance is automatically compensated for by internal design of cylinder.

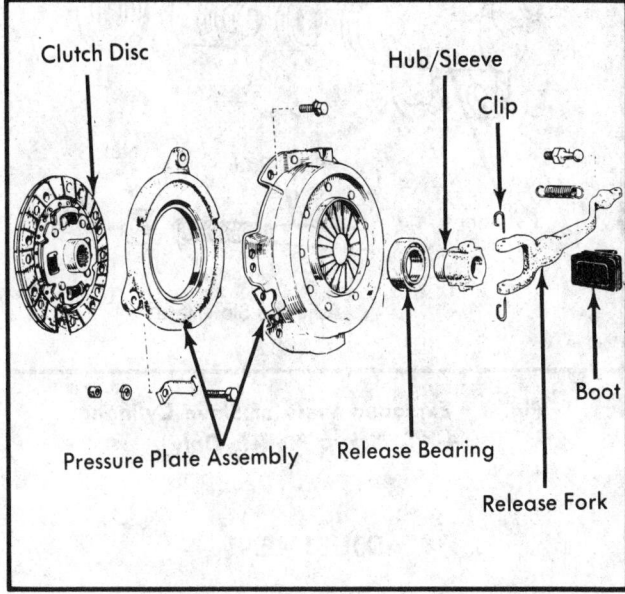

Fig. 1 Exploded View of Typical Clutch Arrangement. Pressure Plate Assembly and Hub/Sleeve Retainer Springs May Vary Between Models.

REMOVAL & INSTALLATION

CLUTCH ASSEMBLY

NOTE — Clutch removal procedures are of a general nature written to cover all Toyota models.

Removal — 1) Disconnect battery cable. Remove air cleaner and drain cooling system, then disconnect top radiator hose. Disconnect accelerator control rod linkage. Remove shift lever boot and shifter assembly. Remove starter.

2) Raise vehicle and support at front and rear with jack stands. If equipped, remove protective cover from under engine.

3) Remove clutch slave cylinder, but only disconnect hydraulic line if necessary. Disconnect exhaust pipe support bracket from mounting and separate exhaust pipe from manifold. Disconnect speedometer cable and electrical leads from transmission.

4) Scribe index marks on drive shaft and coupling for reinstallation reference, then remove drive shaft. Insert suitable plug into extension housing to prevent oil spillage.

5) Support engine with suitable jack, using a wooden block to protect oil pan. Support transmission with transmission jack and remove rear support crossmember. Lower transmission jack slightly and remove transmission-to-engine bolts. Pull transmission to rear; lower and remove from vehicle.

6) Index mark clutch assembly and flywheel for reassembly reference. Loosen bolts securing clutch assembly, alternately and evenly until pressure plate is released. Separate clutch disc and pressure plate.

Installation — To install, reverse removal procedure and note the following: Use a suitable aligning tool to center clutch disc on flywheel. Tighten clutch pressure plate attaching bolts alternately and evenly in a diagonal progression. With transmission installed, adjust clutch.

CLUTCH MASTER CYLINDER

Removal & Installation — Disconnect master cylinder push rod at clutch pedal by removing cotter pin and clevis. Disconnect hydraulic line at cylinder. Remove cylinder attaching nuts and remove cylinder from firewall. To install, reverse removal procedure and adjust pedal height, free play and bleed hydraulic system.

CLUTCH SLAVE CYLINDER

Removal & Installation — Raise and support vehicle on safety stands. Disconnect hydraulic line and clip. Remove slave cylinder attaching nuts and remove slave cylinder. To install, reverse removal procedure and bleed hydraulic system.

CLUTCH RELEASE BEARING

Removal — With transmission removed, check release bearing for freedom of rotation with bearing still installed on hub. To remove, disconnect spring clips from bearing collar and slide bearing off transmission input shaft. Use a press to remove and install bearing on sleeve.

Installation — Slide bearing and collar over transmission input shaft and secure to release lever with new retaining clips. Apply grease to diaphragm spring contact points before installing transmission.

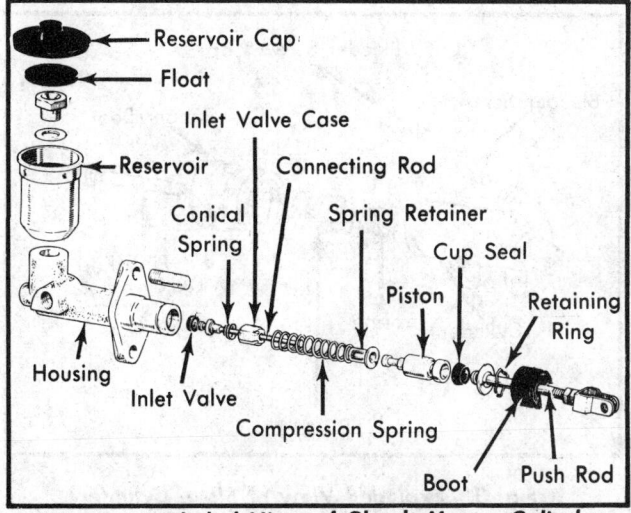

Fig. 2 Exploded View of Clutch Master Cylinder

TOYOTA CELICA, COROLLA, CORONA, PICKUP, STARLET & SUPRA (Cont.)

OVERHAUL

CLUTCH MASTER CYLINDER

Disassembly — With cylinder removed from vehicle, clamp it into a soft jawed vise. Remove reservoir, snap ring and push rod. Pull out piston, cup and remaining internal components. Further disassemble piston by prying up spring retainer and separating retainer from piston.

Cleaning & Inspection — Wash all parts in clean brake fluid and dry with compressed air. Master cylinder bore-to-piston clearance should not exceed .006" (.15 mm). Check compression spring for distortion or weakening and reservoir for damage. Ensure reservoir vent hole is open. Replace defective parts as required.

Reassembly — Dip cylinder cups into clean brake fluid or coat with rubber grease before assembly. Assemble piston components in reverse order of disassembly. Install piston assembly, push rod and reservoir into master cylinder.

CLUTCH SLAVE CYLINDER

Disassembly — Remove rubber boot and push rod. Remove piston assembly and spring from bore. If necessary, remove bleeder screw.

Cleaning & Inspection — Wash all parts in clean brake fluid and dry with compressed air. Slave cylinder bore-to-piston clearance should not exceed .006" (.15 mm). Replace defective parts. Replace piston cups during overhaul.

Reassembly — Install piston cups on piston and coat with brake grease. Install spring and piston assembly into cylinder bore and install rubber boot (protruded part down). Install push rod and bleeder screw.

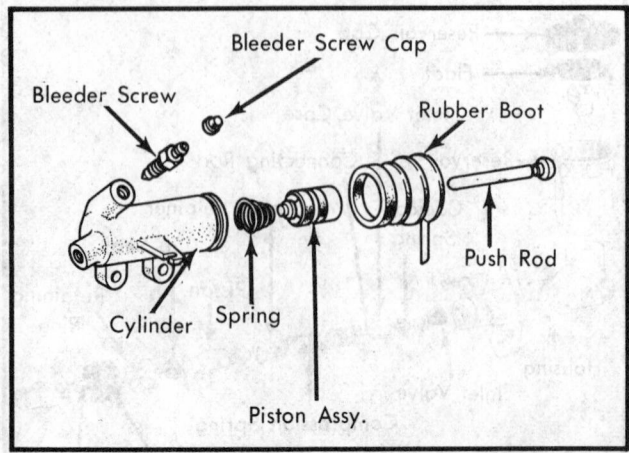

Fig. 3 Exploded View of Slave Cylinder (External Design Differs Among Models)

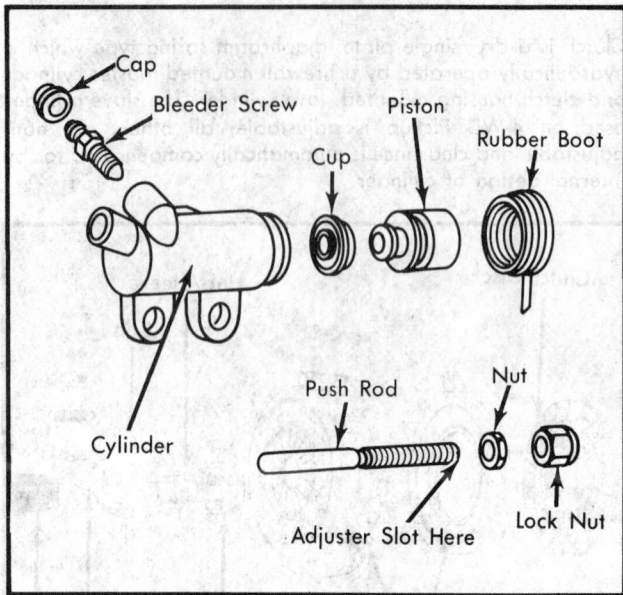

Fig. 4 Exploded View of Slave Cylinder (4-WD Pickup Models Only)

ADJUSTMENT

PEDAL HEIGHT

Adjust pedal stop bolt at top of pedal assembly until specified pedal height is obtained. Height is measured from floor mat to top of pedal pad.

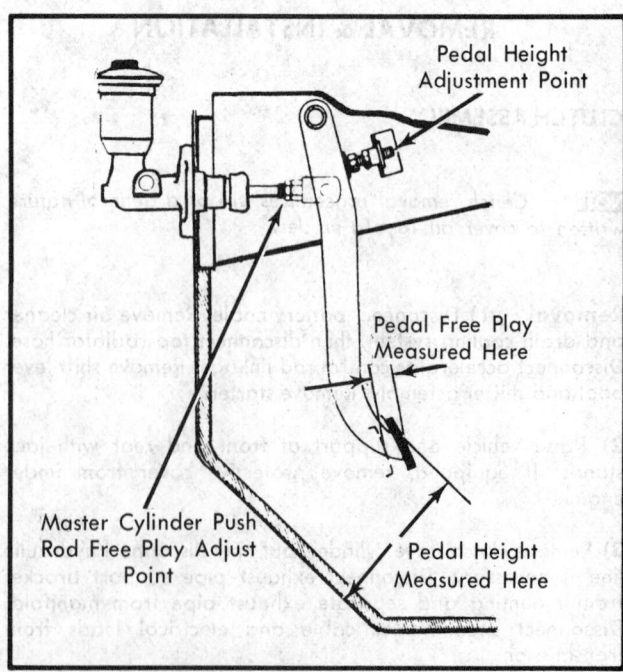

Fig. 5 Pedal Height and Free Play Measuring Points

TOYOTA CELICA, COROLLA, CORONA, PICKUP, STARLET & SUPRA (Cont.)

Pedal Height Specifications

Application	Height In. (mm)
Celica & Supra	6.3-6.7 (159.5-169.5)
Corolla	6.9-7.3 (175-185)
Corona	6.5-6.9 (166-176)
Pickup	6.0-6.4 (152-162)
Starlet	7.0 (178)

Pedal Free Play

Application	In. (mm)
Celica, Corolla & Corona	.5-.9 (13-23)
2-WD Pickup & Supra	.2-.6 (5-15)
4-WD Pickup	1.0-1.8 (25-45)
Starlet	.8-1.4 (20-36)

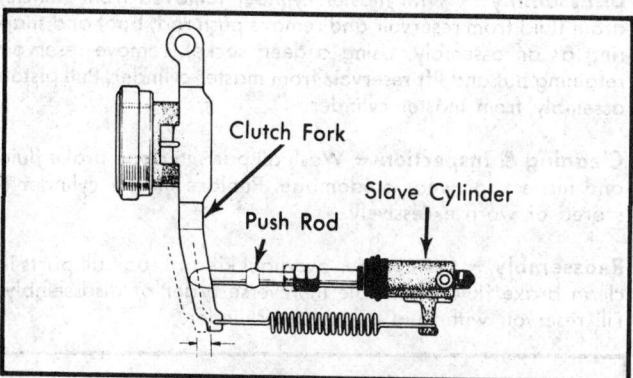

**Fig. 6 Clutch Fork Free Play Adjustment
(4-WD Pickup Models Only)**

PEDAL FREE PLAY

Except 4-WD Pickup — To adjust free play (measured at pedal pad), loosen lock nut on master cylinder push rod and turn push rod in or out until free play is within specifications. Tighten lock nut.

4-WD Pickup — Prior to adjusting pedal free play as described for other models, adjust clutch fork free play. To adjust fork free play, loosen lock nut on slave cylinder push rod and screw push rod in or out to obtain .08-.12" (2-3 mm) free play at clutch fork. Tighten lock nut and adjust pedal free play to 1.0-1.8" (25-45 mm).

HYDRAULIC SYSTEM BLEEDING

1) Raise and support vehicle on safety stands. Check master cylinder reservoir often during bleeding operation; add fluid as required. Remove slave cylinder bleeder screw cap and connect flexible hose to bleeder and immerse opposite end of tube in jar partially filled with brake fluid.

2) Pump clutch pedal several times. With pedal depressed, loosen screw ½ turn, exhaust air and close before pressure is depleted. Repeat operation until no air bubbles are seen in discharged fluid. Close bleeder screw on down stroke of pedal. Check system for leaks and fill master cylinder reservoir.

TIGHTENING SPECIFICATIONS

Application	Ft. Lbs. (N·m)
Clutch Housing-to-Engine	
Supra	22-23 (30-31)
All Others	36-58 (49-79)
Pressure Plate-to-Flywheel	11-15 (15-20)

Clutches

TOYOTA LAND CRUISER

DESCRIPTION

Clutch is a dry single disc type using a diaphragm type pressure plate. Clutch is hydraulically operated by a firewall mounted master cylinder and a clutch housing mounted slave cylinder. A prelubricated sealed release bearing is used.

REMOVAL & INSTALLATION

CLUTCH ASSEMBLY

Removal — 1) Drain transmission oil, transfer case oil, and fuel tank. Remove transmission undercover and disconnect front and rear driveshafts, power take-off shaft, speedometer cable and parking brake cable. Remove front seat with frames and console box. Remove rear heater tube clamp and shift lever knobs.

2) Remove fuel tank cover and fuel tank. Remove shift lever dust boots and transmission cover. Disconnect front drive indicator wire harness, transfer switch wire harness, and vacuum hoses (if equipped). Disconnect back-up light switch harness.

3) Using suitable tool (09305-60010), remove shift lever hold down nut and lift out shift lever. Support transmission assembly with rope and floor jack. Remove bolts attaching transmission to engine and lower assembly from vehicle.

4) Disconnect clutch fork return spring and remove slave cylinder, but do not disconnect hydraulic line unless necessary. Remove release bearing retaining clips, and release bearing with collar. Remove clutch lever assembly.

5) Mark pressure plate and flywheel for reassembly reference. Loosen clutch attaching bolts one turn at a time until spring pressure is released, then remove bolts and clutch assembly

Installation — To install, reverse removal procedure and note the following: Use suitable aligning tool to center disc on flywheel. Tighten clutch attaching bolts alternately and evenly. After reinstallation, adjust clutch fork free play and bleed hydraulic system if necessary.

CLUTCH MASTER CYLINDER

Removal — Remove clevis pin connecting master cylinder push rod to clutch pedal. Disconnect hydraulic line from cylinder body and plug opening. Remove cylinder attaching bolts at firewall and remove master cylinder. **CAUTION** — *Do not allow fluid to spill on painted surfaces.*

Installation — To install, reverse removal procedure, adjust pedal height and clutch pedal free play, and bleed hydraulic system. Check hydraulic system for leaks.

CLUTCH SLAVE CYLINDER

Removal — Plug master cylinder reservoir cap. Disconnect clutch return spring from hanger. Disconnect flexible hose from metal line and remove clip. Remove slave cylinder retaining bolts and remove slave cylinder.

Installation — To install, reverse removal procedure, adjust clutch fork free play and bleed hydraulic system.

CLUTCH RELEASE BEARING

Removal & Installation — With clutch assembly removed, remove release bearing from hub with suitable bearing remover/installer (0931500021). To install bearing, lubricate with multi-purpose grease and seat bearing with the remover/installer.

PILOT BEARING

Removal & Installation — With clutch assembly removed, check pilot bearing in end of crankshaft for roughness or noise during rotation. If defective, remove using a suitable puller (09303-55010). To install, lubricate bearing with multi-purpose grease and insert into crankshaft using driver (09304-47010).

OVERHAUL

CLUTCH MASTER CYLINDER

Disassembly — With master cylinder removed from vehicle, drain fluid from reservoir and remove push rod, boot and snap ring as an assembly. Using a deep socket, remove reservoir retaining nut and lift reservoir from master cylinder. Pull piston assembly from master cylinder.

Cleaning & Inspection — Wash all parts in clean brake fluid and inspect for wear or damage. Replace master cylinder if scored or worn excessively.

Reassembly — Use cylinder overhaul kit and soak all parts in clean brake fluid. Assemble in reverse order of disassembly. Fill reservoir with fluid and bleed cylinder.

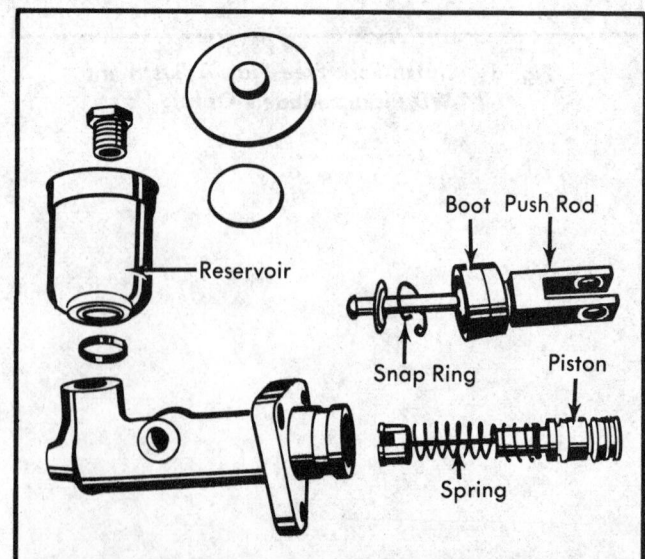

Fig. 1 Exploded View of Clutch Master Cylinder

CLUTCH SLAVE CYLINDER

Disassembly — Remove push rod assembly and rubber boot from cylinder body. Withdraw cylinder piston and cup seal. Loosen and remove bleeder screw.

Clutches

TOYOTA LAND CRUISER (Cont.)

Cleaning & Inspection — Wash all parts in clean brake fluid and inspect for wear or damage. If slave cylinder bore-to-piston clearance exceeds .006" (.15 mm), replace defective part. Replace piston cups during overhaul.

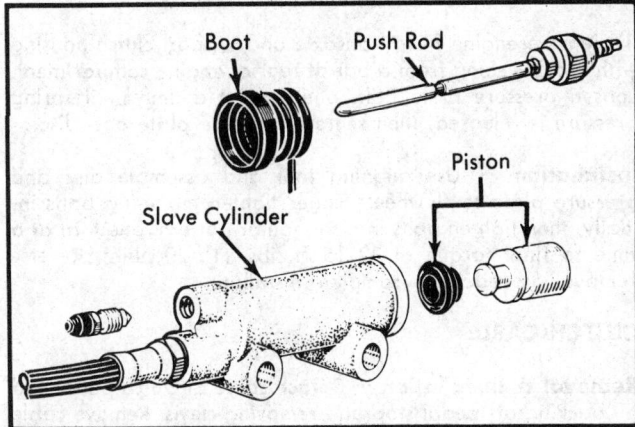

Fig. 2 Exploded View of Clutch Slave Cylinder

Reassembly — Soak all parts in clean brake fluid before reassembly. Reverse disassembly procedure and install boot with protruded part down.

ADJUSTMENTS

PEDAL HEIGHT

Pedal height is measured from floor to top of pedal pad. To adjust, loosen lock nut and turn stop bolt to give pedal height of 8.5" (215 mm).

PEDAL FREE PLAY

Clutch pedal free play is that distance of free movement before master cylinder push rod contacts piston. To adjust, loosen lock nut and turn push rod to obtain 1.9-2.0" (48-51 mm) free play. Tighten lock nut.

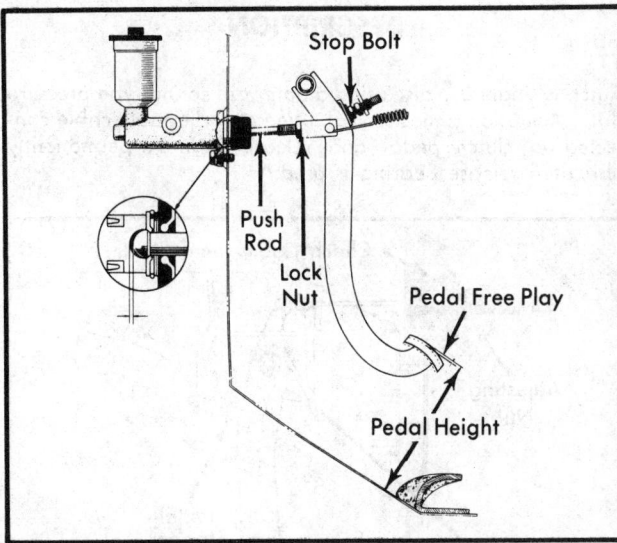

Fig. 3 Pedal Height Measuring and Adjustment Points

CLUTCH FORK FREE PLAY

To adjust clutch fork free play, loosen lock nut at slave cylinder and turn push rod tip while holding push rod nut with suitable wrench. Free play should be .12-.16" (3-4 mm). Tighten lock nut and check clutch pedal free play.

HYDRAULIC SYSTEM BLEEDING

1) Connect a flexible tube to slave cylinder bleeder screw, and place opposite end in a container partially filled with brake fluid.

2) Pump clutch pedal several times. With pedal depressed, loosen bleeder screw one-third to one-half turn and allow air to bleed out. Tighten bleeder screw.

3) Continue operation until air bubbles are no longer seen in fluid being discharged into container. Tighten bleeder screw securely and install cap. Check fluid level in master cylinder reservoir, and check system for leaks.

Clutches

TOYOTA TERCEL

DESCRIPTION

Clutch is single dry disc using diaphragm spring type pressure plate. Actuation is mechanical, using an adjustable cable connected to clutch pedal and release fork. A permanently lubricated release bearing is used.

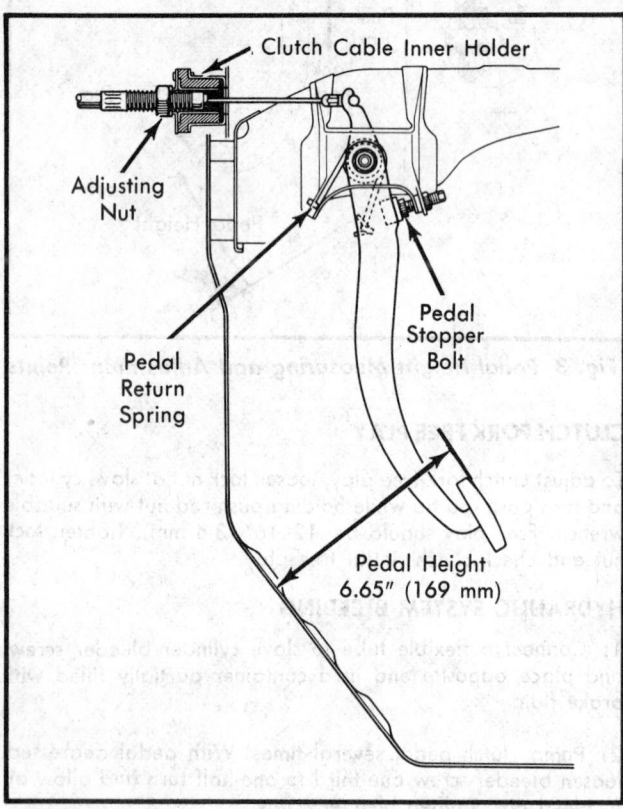

Fig. 1 Pedal Height and Free Play Adjustment

REMOVAL & INSTALLATION

CLUTCH ASSEMBLY

NOTE — *Engine must be removed to replace clutch assembly.*

Removal — 1) Remove engine hood, air cleaner case and battery negative terminal. Drain cooling system and wrap drive shaft boots with shop towels. Disconnect solenoid valve, water temperature switch and electric cooling fan connectors. Remove differential side plate stiffener bolts and exhaust pipe.

2) Remove radiator and windshield washer tank. Disconnect heater, fuel and brake booster hoses. Disconnect accelerator, choke and clutch release cables. Disconnect high tension wire from coil, alternator "B" terminal and connector from alternator and starter cable at starter.

3) Ensure that no bonding wires are connected from engine to chassis and disconnect engine mounts and engine shock absorber at lower right front of engine. Attach engine hoisting sling to engine and support differential with a jack. Remove engine to transaxle mounting bolts.

4) Remove engine from transaxle and support clutch housing with a cable slung from a bar at rear of engine compartment. Loosen pressure plate bolts one turn at a time until spring pressure is released, then remove pressure plate and disc.

Installation — Use aligning tool and assemble disc and pressure plate to flywheel. Finger tighten mounting bolts initially, then tighten bolts in a triangular pattern, one turn at a time to final torque of 11-15 ft. lbs. (15-20 N·m). Reverse removal procedure to complete installation.

CLUTCH CABLE

Removal & Installation — Detach cable at clutch pedal end by backing off pedal stop and removing clevis. Remove cable from release fork and free from engine compartment. To install, lubricate clevis attachment points with multipurpose grease and reverse removal procedure. Adjust pedal stop.

CLUTCH RELEASE BEARING

Removal & Installation — With engine removed from vehicle, remove retaining clips from bearing collar and clutch fork. Slide assembly from transmission. If bearing does not rotate smoothly, press off collar with driver (09315-00010). Use press and driver (09315-00021) to install new bearing on sleeve. Lightly grease inner groove of bearing collar and all contact surfaces and reverse removal procedures.

PILOT BEARING

Removal & Installation — If pilot bearing is worn or damaged, pull from crankshaft with puller (09303-35010). Coat new bearing with multipurpose grease and drive into crankshaft with installer (090304-12012).

ADJUSTMENTS

PEDAL HEIGHT

Measure distance from floor panel to upper surface of clutch pedal. Adjust pedal stopper bolt to give 6.65" (169 mm) pedal height.

CLUTCH PEDAL FREE PLAY

With release bearing contacting pressure plate, pedal play should be .08-1.10" (2-28 mm). To adjust, pull slightly on release cable and turn adjusting nut. Ensure that adjusting nut protrusion and cable holder inner notch are aligned, then depress pedal several times and recheck pedal play.

TRIUMPH

TR7
TR8

DESCRIPTION

Clutch is dry, single plate, diaphragm spring type. Clutch actuation is hydraulic, using a firewall mounted master cylinder and a clutch housing-mounted slave cylinder. Due to self-adjusting feature of clutch assembly, no adjustment, with the exception of bleeding hydraulic system, is necessary.

REMOVAL & INSTALLATION

CLUTCH ASSEMBLY

Removal (TR7) — **1)** Raise and support vehicle. Disconnect battery ground cable. Remove gear shift lever assembly. Index mark and separate propeller shaft from transmission. Disconnect exhaust pipe at intake manifold (pipe may have to be completely removed).

2) Disconnect speedometer cable and all electrical wires attached to transmission. Remove starter heat shroud. Place a jack (with wood block) under oil pan. Remove slave cylinder without disconnecting fluid line. Hang cylinder out of way.

3) Remove 2 bolts holding oil pan plate to clutch housing. Remove 4 nuts keeping transmission rear crossmember to body. Slightly lower engine. Remove starter.

4) Remove nuts and bolts mounting clutch housing to engine. Support transmission with appropriate jack. Slide back transmission/clutch housing assembly and remove from vehicle.

5) Index mark pressure plate with flywheel. Loosen 6 pressure plate mounting bolts evenly (a few turns at a time). Slide out pressure plate with clutch disc.

Removal (TR8) — **1)** Disconnect battery. Remove gear shift lever assembly. Raise and support vehicle. Remove exhaust system, leaving tail pipes loosely in place. Disconnect oxygen sensors (if so equipped). Index mark and separate propeller shaft from transmission. Place a jack (with wood block) under oil pan. Raise engine.

2) Remove 2 bolts holding oil pan plate to clutch housing and bolt holding clutch pipe to rear engine plate. Remove heat shield and slave cylinder without disconnecting fluid line. Support cylinder out of way. Remove nuts attaching transmission rear crossmember to body. Lower engine.

3) Disconnect and remove speedometer cable. Disconnect wiring harness plug. Remove all but 3 clutch housing bolts. Remove 4 bolts holding flywheel cover to clutch housing. Support transmission with appropriate jack and remove 3 remaining clutch housing bolts. Slide back transmission/clutch housing assembly and remove from vehicle.

4) Index mark pressure plate with flywheel. Loosen 6 pressure plate mounting bolts evenly (a few turns at a time). Slide out pressure plate with clutch disc.

Installation (All Models) — Reverse removal procedure and note the following: Ensure index marks on pressure plate align with those on flywheel. Use clutch aligning tool to center clutch disc. Tighten clutch bolts evenly and gradually.

CLUTCH MASTER CYLINDER

Removal — **1)** Disconnect hydraulic line and drain fluid. Plug open port and line.

2) Disconnect clevis mounting push rod to clutch pedal.

3) Remove 2 nuts mounting master cylinder to firewall and remove master cylinder.

Installation — Reverse removal procedure and bleed hydraulic system.

CLUTCH SLAVE CYLINDER

Removal — Raise and support vehicle. Disconnect and plug hydraulic line and remove slave cylinder.

NOTE — *Do not move operating rod in a forward direction. Forward movement may cause release lever to dislodge. Transmission removal would then become necessary for installation of release lever.*

Installation — Reverse removal procedure and note: Slave cylinder must be mounted with bleed screw ABOVE fluid pipe. Bleed hydraulic line.

CLUTCH RELEASE BEARING

Removal — With transmission assembly removed, use crow's foot wrench and remove clutch release lever pivot from clutch housing. Remove release lever, complete with pivot bolt and release bearing.

Installation — Reverse removal procedure, making sure fork and collar engage evenly.

OVERHAUL

CLUTCH MASTER CYLINDER

Disassembly — **1)** Remove master cylinder. Pull up rubber boot and remove snap ring. Slide out push rod and washer.

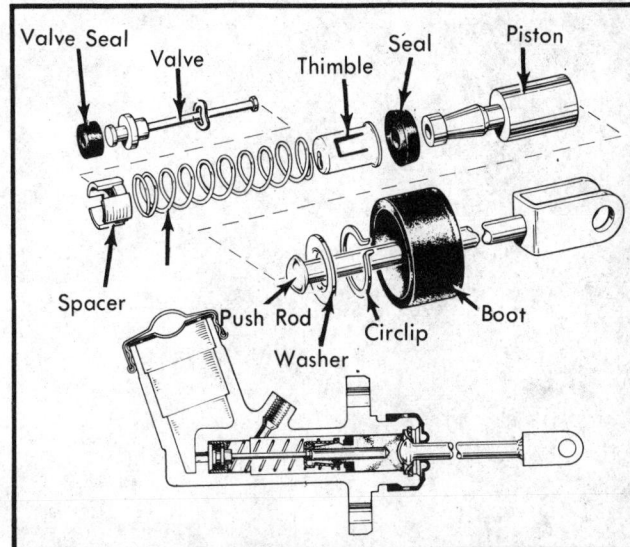

Fig. 1 Exploded View of Master Cylinder

TRIUMPH (Cont.)

2) Pull out piston, spring, and seal as an assembly. It may be necessary to use air pressure to force out assembly.

3) Straighten spring thimble prong, then remove thimble and spring from piston. Disengage valve stem from slot in thimble. Slip spacer off valve stem. Remove valve seal.

Reassembly — 1) Fit spacer, spring and thimble to valve stem. Fit new seal to piston with lip facing spring. Put spring thimble on piston and depress thimble prong.

2) Lubricate master cylinder bore with brake fluid and slide seal assembly, spring and piston into place. Reverse disassembly procedure to assemble remaining components.

CLUTCH SLAVE CYLINDER

Disassembly — Remove slave cylinder and pull off dust cover. Remove circlip, then take out piston, seal and spring.

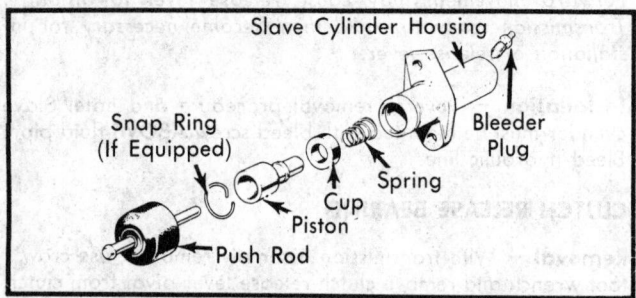

Fig. 2   Exploded View of Slave Cylinder

Inspection — Look at cylinder bore and piston for signs of damage. Replace either or both parts if wear is excessive.

Reassembly — Reverse removal procedure, lubricating parts with brake fluid and fitting small end of spring to piston.

ADJUSTMENT

HYDRAULIC SYSTEM BLEEDING

1) Fill master cylinder. Attach bleed tube to bleed valve on slave cylinder. Submerge free end of tube in container of brake fluid.

2) Slowly depress pedal to force air out. Close bleed valve and let pedal rise unassisted. Check that fluid level does not drop too low, and repeat until no more air bubbles are visible.

TIGHTENING SPECIFICATIONS

Application	Ft. Lbs. (N·m)
Clutch Assembly-to-Flywheel	22 (30)
Clutch Housing-to-Transmission	32 (44)
Slave Cylinder-to-Clutch Housing	21 (29)

Clutches

VOLKSWAGEN DASHER

DESCRIPTION

Clutch is single plate dry disc type, using a diaphragm type pressure plate and a pre-lubricated clutch release bearing. Clutch is cable actuated.

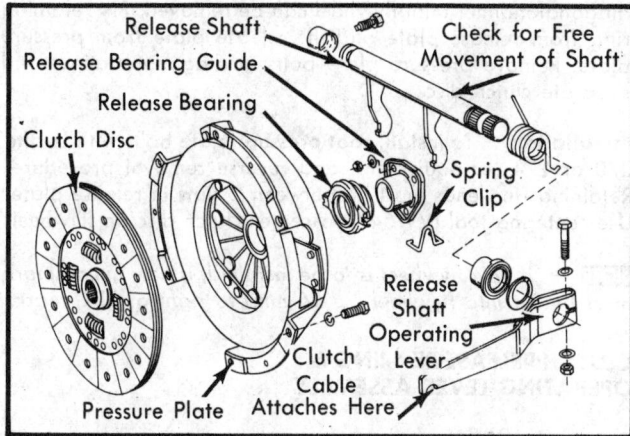

Fig. 1   Exploded View of Clutch Assembly

Fig. 2   View Showing Clutch Assembly Alignment on Flywheel

REMOVAL & INSTALLATION

TRANSAXLE & CLUTCH ASSEMBLIES

Removal — 1) Disconnect battery ground cable from battery. Disconnect exhaust pipe at manifold. Disconnect exhaust pipe bracket from rear of transaxle.

2) Disconnect gear shift lever and shift linkage. Disconnect back-up light wires. On some models there is a bolt mounting gear shift linkage to transaxle that must be removed.

3) Loosen clutch cable adjustment nut and disengage clutch housing from left side engine mount. Separate clutch cable from operating lever. Disconnect speedometer cable.

4) Disconnect front wheel axle drive shafts at transaxle. Suspend drive shafts with wire out of way. Remove starter.

5) Remove clutch housing front cover plate. Remove bolts mounting transaxle-to-engine. Place a jack under transaxle for support. Unbolt transaxle carrier from body. Slide transaxle to rear until input shaft is clear of clutch assembly. Lower out transaxle.

6) Lock flywheel to prevent rotation and index mark pressure plate and flywheel. Loosen pressure plate bolts ¼ turn at a time, working in a diagonal pattern. Slide pressure plate off dowels on flywheel.

Installation — 1) Using a clutch alignment tool, fit pressure plate with clutch. Make sure alignment marks are observed. Loosely attach assembly with 6 bolts.

NOTE — *If replacement pressure plate has white paint spot, it is a balance mark and should be 180° from countersunk hole or 180° from white paint mark on flywheel.*

2) Tighten pressure plate bolts in criss-cross pattern about 2 turns at a time.

3) Position transaxle to engine. Loosely fit bolts holding transaxle carrier to body. Reverse removal procedure to install remaining components.

CLUTCH RELEASE BEARING

Removal & Installation — With transaxle removed, remove spring clips without removing bearing from release shaft. Slide bearing off bearing guide. To install, roughen plastic guide sleeve with emery cloth, but do not lubricate. Lubricate metal guide sleeve with molybdenum disulphide paste. Coat pivoting points between bearing and operating shaft with multi-purpose grease. Position bearing to shaft and install spring clips.

NOTE — *Bearing is pre-lubricated, DO NOT wash in solvent.*

CLUTCH CABLE

Removal & Installation — Loosen cable adjusting nuts and free clutch cable housing from support bracket. Separate cable from clutch operating lever (mounted on side of clutch housing). Disconnect cable at pedal and force cable and housing into passenger compartment and remove. To install new cable, reverse removal procedure and adjust pedal free play.

NOTE — *If new clutch cable has been installed, make sure to recheck clutch pedal free play after 300 miles.*

PILOT BEARING

Removal & Installation — Lock flywheel to prevent rotation. Install suitable remover (10-202) and remove pilot bearing. Install bearing with suitable installer (VW207C) and seat bearing until distance from flywheel recess to bushing edge is 1/16" (1.5 mm). Lubricate bearing.

ADJUSTMENT

CLUTCH PEDAL FREE PLAY

Clutch pedal free play (measured at pedal pad) should be 5/8" (16 mm). To increase measurement, loosen top adjusting nut until specification is obtained. Tighten bottom nut until locked against bracket. To decrease measurement, loosen bottom adjusting nut until specification is obtained. Tighten top nut until locked against bracket.

TIGHTENING SPECIFICATIONS

Application	Ft. Lbs. (N·m)
Clutch Assembly-to-Flywheel	18 (24)
Clutch Lever-to-Transmission	18 (24)
Drive Shaft-to-Transmission	33 (45)
Transmission-to-Engine	40 (54)

Clutches

VOLKSWAGEN JETTA, RABBIT, RABBIT PICKUP & SCIROCCO

DESCRIPTION

Clutch is a single plate dry disc type, using a diaphragm type pressure plate and a transmission mounted clutch release bearing. Clutch is cable operated.

REMOVAL & INSTALLATION

TRANSAXLE & CLUTCH ASSEMBLY

Removal — 1) Disconnect battery ground strap and attach an engine support assembly. Remove left transaxle mount bolts and mount. Disconnect back-up light wires, speedometer drive cable (plug hole) and clutch cable.

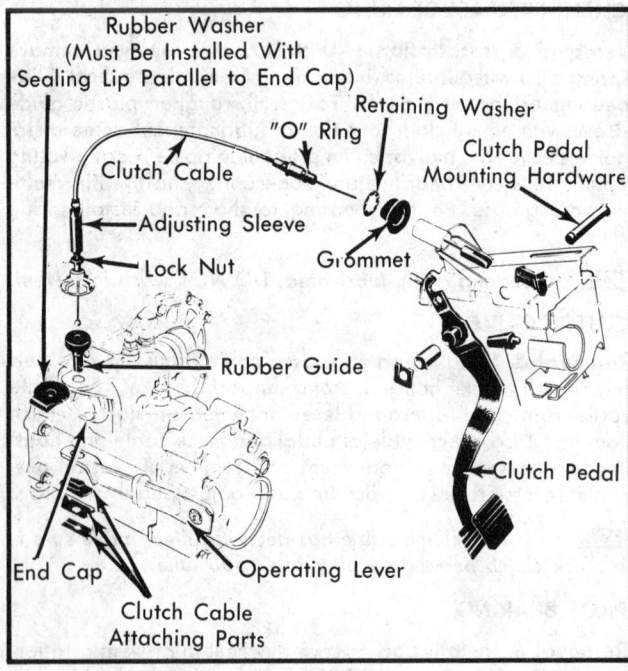

Fig. 1 Clutch Cable Routing & Adjusting Location

2) Remove upper clutch housing-to-transaxle bolts. Remove starter. Align flywheel lug with boss on bell housing (models equipped with flywheel which has cutouts). Disconnect shift linkage at rod lever and relay lever and remove front selector rod.

NOTE — *Vehicles with cutouts in flywheel can be identified by a stud/nut at right engine-to-transaxle mounting position. Flywheel on this type vehicle MUST be aligned before separating engine/transaxle.*

3) Remove exhaust pipe bracket. Remove transaxle rear mount and support transaxle on suitable jack. Disconnect left and right drive shafts at transaxle and wire up out of way. Remove large plate cover bolts (plate remains on engine). Remove small cover bolts and cover.

4) Remove right engine-to-transaxle bolt (stud/nut). Vehicles with cutouts in flywheel, pull transaxle away from engine to clear dowels and lower and remove transaxle. On all other vehicles, pull transaxle away from engine; cocking engine so

right side drive flange clears flywheel. Lower and remove transaxle.

5) With transaxle removed from engine, install holding tool (VW558) to ring gear or pressure plate. Remove bolts in a diagonal manner until flywheel can be removed. Pry retaining ring from release plate and lift release plate from pressure plate. Remove pressure plate bolts in diagonal manner and separate clutch disc.

Installation — To install, coat pressure plate bolts with Loctite 270 or 271 (or equivalent) and reverse removal procedure. Retaining ring ends must be between 2 slots in release plate. Use centering tool (VW547) to center clutch disc on flywheel.

NOTE — *If new flywheel is to be installed, a new timing mark must be cut into flywheel ¼" (6 mm) to right of TDC mark.*

CLUTCH RELEASE BEARING & OPERATING LEVER ASSEMBLY

Removal — 1) Remove 4 bolts and washers mounting clutch release cover to the far left end of transaxle case. Cover is waffle patterned. Remove 2 circlips located at each side of clutch lever.

2) Pull operating lever and release shaft assembly out of case. Lift return spring along with clutch lever out of transaxle case. Take out release bearing, guide sleeve and push rod. Check all seals and bearing; replace defective parts.

Installation — 1) Coat ends of push rod with multi-purpose grease and insert back into position. Grease sliding surface of bearing and guide sleeve.

2) Position return spring and clutch lever inside transaxle case. Return spring center hook should fit on top of clutch lever lug. Spring end hooks must point down to hold clutch lever away from release bearing.

3) Lightly coat release shaft with multipurpose grease. Fit shaft. Work operating lever until splines on release shaft mesh with those in clutch lever.

4) Install circlips. Make sure when operating lever is in normal position that return spring has tension. Fit gasket and cover.

ADJUSTMENT

CLUTCH PEDAL FREE PLAY

Clutch pedal free play should be 9/16-1" (15-25 mm) at clutch pedal and ¼" (6 mm) at operating lever. To adjust, loosen clutch cable lock nut in engine compartment. Turn adjusting sleeve until correct measurement is obtained and tighten lock nut. Operate clutch pedal several times and check free play.

TIGHTENING SPECIFICATIONS

Application	Ft. Lbs. (N·m)
Cover Plate	11 (15)
Drive Shaft-to-Transmission	32 (44)
Flywheel Bolts	14 (19)
Pressure Plate Bolts	54 (73)
Transmission-to-Engine	47 (64)

Clutches

VOLKSWAGEN VANAGON

DESCRIPTION

Clutch is dry, single disc, diaphragm spring type which is hydraulically operated by a firewall mounted master cylinder and a clutch housing mounted slave cylinder. Slave cylinder is non-adjustable and clearance is automatically compensated for by internal design of cylinder.

REMOVAL & INSTALLATION

CLUTCH ASSEMBLY

Removal – 1) Disconnect battery ground strap. Remove right upper engine/transmission bolt.

2) Remove hydraulic clutch line bracket from transmission but do not disconnect line. Remove slave cylinder from mounting bracket and suspend with wire.

3) Remove left upper engine/transmission bolt. Remove left lower engine/transmission nut. Remove left drive shaft hex bolts and remove drive shaft from transmission and suspend with wire.

4) Disconnect starter cables, remove right drive shaft hex bolts and suspend drive shaft with wire. Remove right side lower engine/transmission nut.

5) Support engine with chain or engine support (VW 785/1). Disconnect ground strap from near transmission mount. Remove front transmission mount from body.

6) Support transmission using jack (US 618 & US 618/5) and lower front of transmission by loosening engine support (loosen spindle on VW 785/1) until there is enough room to remove transmission. Separate transmission from engine and remove from vehicle.

7) Lock flywheel with VW 215C (or equivalent). Index mark pressure plate and flywheel for reassembly reference. Loosen pressure plate-to-flywheel bolts evenly in a diagonal fashion and remove clutch assembly.

Installation – Apply molybdenum disulphide grease to release bearing. Lubricate transmission input shaft with molybdenum disulphide powder. Position clutch disc against flywheel and align using a centering tool. Install pressure plate and tighten bolts evenly in a diagonal fashion. Replace transmission, reversing removal procedure and noting the following:

- Insert rear bolt for slave cylinder before installing.
- Position air deflector plates correctly.

CLUTCH RELEASE BEARING

Removal – Remove transmission as outlined in Clutch Assembly in this article. Pry off clip retainers from bearing and disengage spring clips. Remove release bearing by sliding off guide tube.

NOTE – *Do not wash bearing in solvent or cleaning solution. Wipe with dry cloth to clean.*

Installation – Lubricate release shaft and release bearing pivot points with molybdenum disulphide grease. Position bearing to shaft and install spring clips and retainers. Make sure clips are correctly positioned.

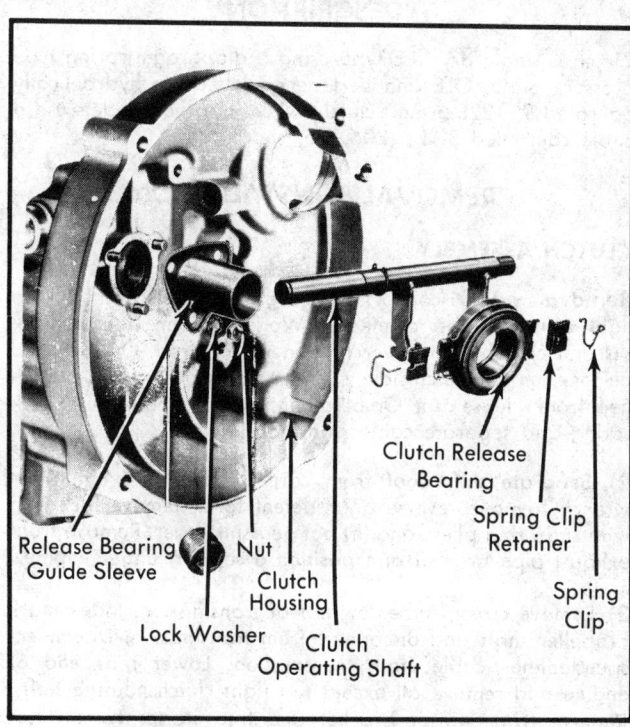

Release Bearing Guide Sleeve
Lock Washer
Nut
Clutch Housing
Clutch Operating Shaft
Clutch Release Bearing
Spring Clip Retainer
Spring Clip

Fig. 1 Clutch Release Bearing Assembly

CLUTCH MASTER CYLINDER

Removal & Installation – Disconnect master cylinder push rod at clutch pedal by removing cotter pin and clevis. Disconnect hydraulic line at cylinder. Remove cylinder attaching bolts and remove cylinder from firewall. To install, reverse removal procedure and pressure bleed the system following bleeder manufacturer's instructions.

CLUTCH SLAVE CYLINDER

Removal – Disconnect hydraulic line from slave cylinder. Disconnect slave cylinder push rod from clutch lever ball. Remove mounting bolts and remove cylinder.

Installation – Grease clutch lever ball lightly. Insert rear bolt to slave cylinder and install on vehicle. Install front bolt, attach hydraulic line and clutch lever. Pressure bleed system following bleeder manufacturer's instructions.

TIGHTENING SPECIFICATIONS

Application	Ft. Lbs. (N·m)
Engine-to-Transmission Nuts & Bolts	22 (30)
Drive Shaft-to-Transmission Bolts	33 (45)
Pressure Plate-to-Flywheel Bolts	18 (24)

Clutches

VOLVO

DL	GLE
GL	Bertone
GLT	Diesel

DESCRIPTION

Clutch is single dry disc type using a diaphragm spring type pressure plate. GLE and Bertone models use a hydraulically operated 9" (228.6 mm) clutch, while all other models use a cable controlled 8.12" (206 mm) clutch.

REMOVAL & INSTALLATION

CLUTCH ASSEMBLY

Removal – 1) Disconnect battery ground cable and back-up light wiring harness connector. Working from under vehicle, disconnect gear shift lever from gear shift rod. On GLE and Bertone, unbolt clutch slave cylinder from housing and disconnect from release arm. On all other models, unhook clutch fork spring and separate cable from housing.

2) Separate shift boot from carpet. Using a 4 mm Allen wrench, remove reverse gear detent fork. Remove lock ring with snap ring pliers and lift out gearshift lever. Remove front exhaust pipe bracket and position a support under engine.

3) Remove crossmember at rear of transmission. Index mark propeller shaft and disconnect from transmission. Disconnect speedometer cable from transmission. Lower rear end of engine and remove all except top right clutch housing bolts. Remove front starter bracket and free starter from clutch housing.

4) Install transmission jack and remove last clutch housing bolt. Pull transmission to rear and turn to clear propeller shaft tunnel. Lower transmission clear of vehicle. Loosen pressure plate bolts gradually in a diagonal pattern and remove clutch assembly.

Installation – To install transmission and clutch assembly, reverse removal procedure and note the following: Install clutch disc with long side of hub to rear using alignment tool (999 5111 or equivalent). Install pressure plate and tighten bolts gradually in a criss-cross pattern. Adjust clutch pedal play on all models except GLE and Bertone.

NOTE – *GLE and Bertone pressure plates have raised fingers and use a 1.43" (37 mm) long release bearing. Remaining model pressure plate fingers are straight and require the use of a 1.68" (43 mm) long release bearing. Pressure plates and bearings must never be mixed.*

CLUTCH CABLE

Removal – Remove return spring and disconnect clutch cable at clutch fork; extract cable. Remove cover panel under instrument cluster. Remove clevis pin at upper end of cable. Separate clutch fork adjustment mechanism from clutch housing, if necessary. Force cable out of rubber grommet located in firewall.

Installation – Insert new cable into rubber grommet, feed it through cable guide and attach at upper end with clevis pin. Position adjustment mechanism into clutch housing. Attach cable to clutch fork, then refit return spring.

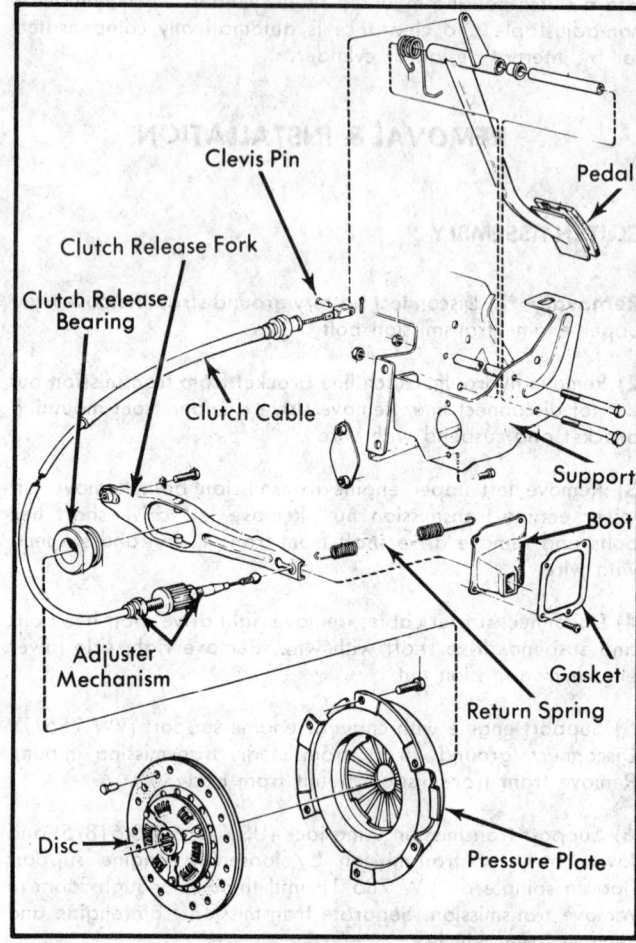

Fig. 1 Volvo Mechanical Linkage Clutch System

HYDRAULIC CLUTCH ACTUATION

Manufacturer does not provide maintenance instructions for hydraulically operated clutch linkage. There should be no free play in this type linkage.

PILOT BEARING

Remove retaining clip and remove bearing using puller (SVO 4090). Pack bearing with heat resistant grease and install into crankshaft using a driver. Install retaining clip.

ADJUSTMENT

CLUTCH FREE PLAY (EXCEPT GLE & BERTONE)

Using adjustment mechanism attached to clutch housing, set free play. Adjustment is correct when approximately .12" (3 mm) clutch fork free play is obtained.

Section 8
BRAKES

Contents

NOTE — ALSO SEE GENERAL INDEX

Brakes

BRAKE SYSTEM TROUBLE SHOOTING

CONDITION & POSSIBLE CAUSE	CONDITION & POSSIBLE CAUSE

Brake Chatter, Squeal or Squeak

- Dust on drums or rotors, or oil stained linings.
- Weak shoe return spring.
- Drum out of round.
- Excessively worn pads or shoes.
- Uneven rotor surface.
- Excessive lateral rotor runout.
- Excessive wheel bearing play.

Excessive Pedal Travel

- Excessive rotor runout.
- Brake fluid boil.
- Warped or excessively worn pads or shoes.
- Rear brakes out of adjustment.
- Power brake unit malfunction.

Poor Brake Operation

- Break lever stroke too long.
- Brake cable sticking.
- Excessive shoe-to-drum clearance.

Shoe When Pedal Applied

- Brake drum cracked or distorted.
- Uneven brake drum wear.
- Broken return spring.

Leaks in Caliper Piston Cylinder

- Damaged or excessively worn caliper piston seal.
- Deep scores or corrosion on surface of cylinder bore.

Rattling in Front Brakes

- Pad anti-rattle spring clip broken or missing.
- Excessive clearance between pads and caliper.

Pull When Brake Applied

- Incorrect tire pressure.
- Front end out of alignment.
- Unmatched tires.
- Restricted brake lines or hoses.

Excessive Pedal Pressure Required

- Linings coated with brake fluid, oil or grease.
- Entire pad not contacting rotor.
- Scored brake rotors.
- Incorrect pads.
- Seized piston.
- Power brake failing.

Low Pedal Effect

- Air in hydraulic system, brakes not properly bled.
- Hydraulic fluid leaking past primary cup in master cylinder.
- Bleeder screw not tight.

Uneven Braking

- Linings contaminated.
- Unmatched disc pads.
- One or more seized pistons.
- Incorrect tire pressure.
- Front wheels out of alignment.
- Brake hose or line clogged.
- Caliper alignment improper.

Brake Pedal Pulsation

- Excessive rotor lateral runout.
- Rotor not parallel.
- Wheel bearings out of adjustment.
- Rear drum out of round.

Spongy Pedal

- Air in brake system.
- Swollen brake hose(s).
- Brake fluid boiling point too low.
- Filler cap vent hole plugged.

Pedal Yield Under Slight Pressure

- Deteriorated check valve.
- External brake fluid leaks.
- Internal leak in master cylinder.

Brake Failure or Heavy Pedal

- Power unit diaphragm damaged.
- Check valve malfunctioning.
- Defective vacuum hose.
- Twisted air valve and valve rod plunger.

Brakes React Slowly

- Check valve malfunction.
- Vacuum hose blocked or broke.
- Air cleaner clogged or restricted.

Brake Drag or Slow Return

- Push rod out of alignment.
- Operating rod out of adjustment.
- Air valve and push rod plunger twisted.

Brake Servicing

HYDRAULIC BRAKE BLEEDING

DESCRIPTION

Hydraulic system bleeding is necessary any time air has been introduced into system. Bleed brakes at all 4 wheels if master cylinder lines have been disconnected or master cylinder has run dry. Bleeding may be done either by using pressure bleeding equipment or by manually pumping brake pedal and using bleeder tubes.

MANUAL BLEEDING

Fill master cylinder, then install bleeder hose to first bleeder valve to be serviced. See Bleeding Sequence. Place other end of hose in clean glass jar, partially filled with clean brake fluid, so end of hose is submerged in fluid. Open bleeder valve ¾-1 turn. Depress brake pedal slowly through its full travel (except as noted in Bleeding Sequence chart). Close bleeder valve, then release pedal. Repeat procedure until flow of fluid shows no signs of air bubbles.

NOTE — Check fluid level in master cylinder frequently during bleeding sequence to ensure air does not enter system.

PRESSURE TANK BLEEDING

Clean master cylinder cap and surrounding area, then remove cap. With pressure tank at least ⅓ full, connect master cylinder using suitable adapters. Attach bleeder hose to first bleeder valve to be serviced. See Bleeding Sequence. Place other end of hose in clean glass jar, partially filled with clean brake fluid, so end of hose is submerged in fluid. Open release valve on pressure bleeder. Unscrew valve ¾-1 turn, noting fluid flow. When fluid flow from bleeder valve into container is free of bubbles, close bleeder valve securely. Bleed remaining cylinders in correct sequence and in same manner. Remove pressure tank from master cylinder and check fluid level of master cylinder reservoir.

Bleeding Pressures①

Application	psi (kg/cm²)
BMW	
733i	56 (3.9)
All Others	28 (2.0)
Porsche	32 (2.3)
Renault	30 (2.1)
Volvo	50-60 (3.5-4.2)

① — For models not listed, refer to pressure tank manufacturer's specifications.

BLEEDING SEQUENCE

Before bleeding system, exhaust all vacuum from power unit by depressing brake pedal several times. Bleed hyraulic system in the following sequence:

Bleeding Sequence

Application①	Cylinder or Line
Audi & Volkswagen	RR, LR, RF, LF
BMW②	Longest Line First
Chrysler Corp. Imports	
Champ & Colt	LR, RF, RR, LF
All Others③	RR, LR, RF, LF
Courier④	Longest Line First
Datsun	
310	Master Cyl., LR, RF, RR, LF
810	RR, LR, RF, LF
Pickup	Master Cyl., Comb. Valve, Longest Line First
All Others	Master Cyl., Longest Line First
Fiat	Longest Line First
Honda	LF, RR, RF, LR
Isuzu & LUV	Shortest Line First
Jaguar⑤	LR, RR, Front
Mazda⑥	Longest Line First
Mercedes-Benz	Longest Line First
Peugeot⑦	Longest Line First
Porsche⑧	LR, RR, RF, LF
Renault	Longest Line First
Saab	LR, RF, RR, LF
Subaru	Master Cylinder., FR, RF, RR, LF
Toyota	Longest Line First
TR7 & TR8⑨	RF, LF, RR, LR
Volvo⑩	LF, RF, RR, LR

① — Before bleeding rear brakes, push brake pressure regulator in direction of rear axle.

② — The 528i and 633CSi have 3 bleed valves on each front caliper. Bleed lower inboard valve first, then other 2 at same time.

③ — Pickup models do not require bleeding of RR.

④ — Front and rear circuits are independent. Bleed each circuit separately.

⑤ — Engine running at idle speed.

⑥ — GLC has independant front and rear circuits. Bleed each circuit separately.

⑦ — If pressure tank is used, bleed all wheels at the same time.

⑧ — If equipped with inner and outer caliper bleed valves, bleed outer valves first, then inner valves.

⑨ — Remove pressure differential switch before bleeding.

⑩ — Rear wheels must be higher than front wheels. Front calipers are each equipped with 3 bleed valves. Bleed all 3 valves at same time.

Brakes

AUDI

4000
5000

DESCRIPTION

NOTE — *In this article, non-turbocharged Audi 5000 models are referred to as "5000"; turbocharged models are referred to as "Turbo".*

Brake system is hydraulically operated using a tandem master cylinder and power brake unit. Front brakes are sliding caliper disc. Rear brakes on Turbo models are sliding caliper disc; all other models use leading/trailing shoe drum brakes. Brake hydraulic system incorporates a brake pressure regulator to prevent premature lock-up of rear wheels. All service brake systems are self-adjusting. Parking brake is cable actuated on rear brake system.

ADJUSTMENT

STOP LIGHT SWITCH

On Turbo models, remove connector, loosen locknut and turn switch until tip is just touching brake pedal. Attach ohmmeter and turn switch until reading is infinite (switch open). Turn switch two additional turns and tighten lock nut. On all other models, loosen lock nut and turn switch until distance between tip and switch body is .087-.098" (2.2-2.5 mm). See *Fig. 1*. Tighten lock nut and check operation of switch.

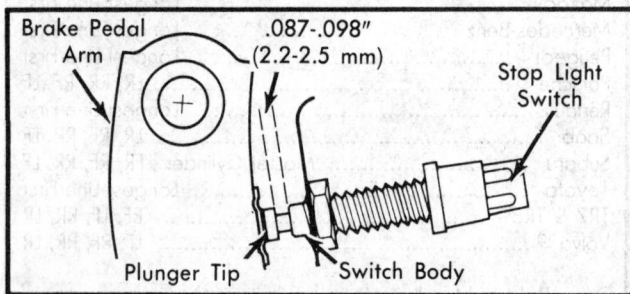

Fig. 1   Adjusting Stop Light Switch

PARKING BRAKE

NOTE — *Parking brake adjustment on Turbo is required only if rear calipers or parking brake parts are replaced.*

Turbo — Raise and support vehicle. Release parking brake lever and ensure parking brake levers at each rear wheel are resting on caliper stops (loosen parking brake cable adjustment if necessary). Depress brake pedal 40 times, then pull

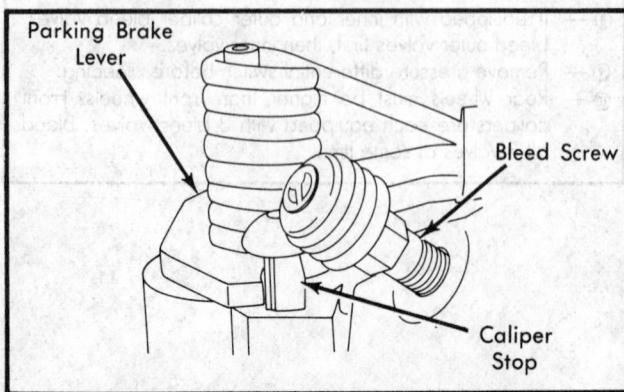

Fig. 2   Turbo Rear Disc Brake Caliper Parking Brake Lever Resting Position

parking brake lever up to 3rd notch. Tighten adjusting nut at equalizer until both wheels can just be turned by hand. Release parking brake lever and check that wheels rotate freely and levers on calipers return to stops. See *Fig. 2*.

Except Turbo — Raise and support vehicle. Firmly depress brake pedal once. Set parking brake lever at 3rd notch (2nd on 4000) from fully released position. Tighten adjusting nut at equalizer until both wheels can just be turned by hand. Release parking brake lever and ensure both wheels rotate freely.

BRAKE WARNING LIGHT

A dual warning light is mounted on dash. Light should glow when parking brake lever is pulled 1 notch and go off when lever is fully released (ignition on). To check circuit warning sensor, release parking brake (ignition on) and ensure light is off. Open bleeder screw on 1 wheel and depress brake pedal; light should glow.

BRAKE PRESSURE REGULATOR

Checking & Adjusting — 1) Regulator is located on rear frame. Empty vehicle, fill fuel tank and load driver's seat to 165 lbs. (74.8 kg). Bounce rear of car several times and allow vehicle to settle normally. Firmly depress brake pedal and release quickly; regulator should have moved.

2) Measure distance from top of tire rim to lower edge of fender lip (both sides). Install left spring tensioner. Raise vehicle on hoist and insert right spring tensioner (upper end only). Lower vehicle and bounce rear of car several times. Allow car to settle normally and attach right spring tensioner to axle.

NOTE — *Spring tensioners and measurement are not required if drive-on type hoist is used to support vehicle.*

3) Raise vehicle and check measurement; adjust if necessary. Connect 1500 psi (110 kg/cm²) gauge to left front caliper and another to right rear wheel cylinder (caliper). Bleed gauges and depress brake pedal firmly several times. Depress brake pedal until front gauge reaches specification listed in table. Check rear gauge reading.

Brake Pressure Regulator Pressures		
Application	Front Gauge psi (kg/cm²)	Rear Gauge psi (kg/cm²)
4000		
1st Reading	725 (51)	457-566 (32-40)
2nd Reading	1450 (102)	725-914 (51-64)
5000 & Turbo		
1st Reading	725 (51)	493-566 (35-40)
2nd Reading	1450 (102)	827-899 (58-63)

4) If pressures are consistently high at rear gauge, loosen regulator clamp bolt and REDUCE spring tension. If pressures were consistently low, INCREASE spring tension. If pressures cannot be obtained after adjustment, replace regulator.

AUDI (Cont.)

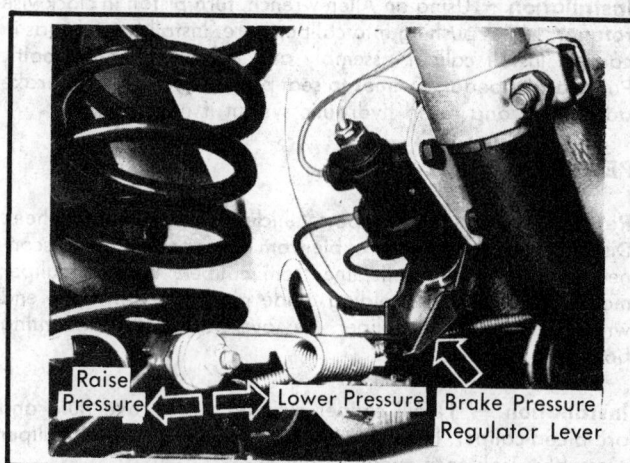

Fig. 3   Brake Pressure Regulator Adjustment
(Audi 4000 Regulator is Mounted in Reverse Direction)

REMOVAL & INSTALLATION

NOTE — *During removal or installation of brake pads or calipers, siphon small amount of brake fluid from master cylinder reservoir BEFORE pushing caliper piston into cylinder bore to prevent overflowing. Also, when reusing brake pads, mark the pads to ensure replacement in their original locations.*

NOTE — *Whenever brake pads or shoes are replaced and when brake rotors or drums are resurfaced or replaced, make sure the part is replaced or resurfaced on both sides of the vehicle to prevent uneven braking.*

FRONT DISC BRAKE PADS

Removal (5000) — Raise and support vehicle, remove tire and wheel. Remove plug from end of caliper guide pin. Remove Allen head bolts from top of caliper mounting frame. Thread 8 mm bolts into caliper guide pins and pull to remove guide pins. Remove caliper from mounting frame and lay aside. Remove brake pads (outer pad first) and push piston into housing.

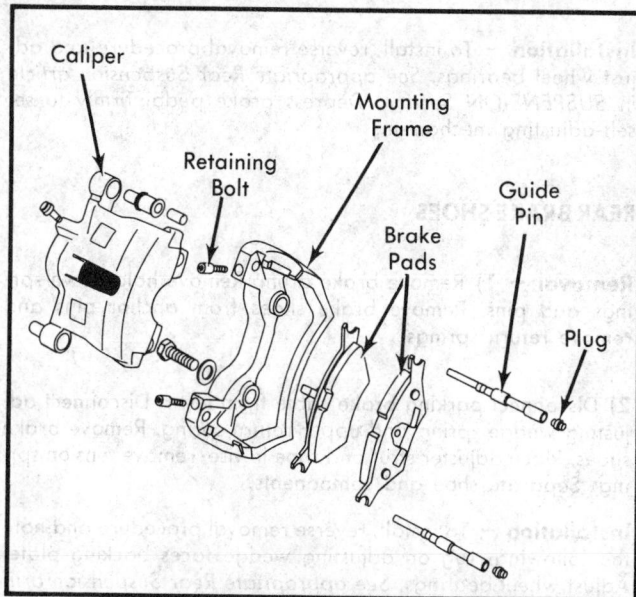

Fig. 4   Exploded View of Audi 5000
Front Disc Brake Assembly

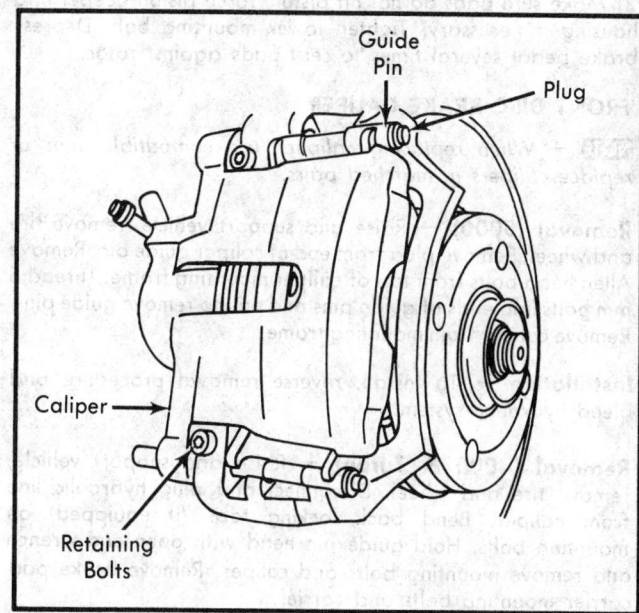

Fig. 5   Location of Guide Pins and Retaining Bolts

Installation — Install brake pads in caliper (inner pad first) making sure to align pegs on outer brake pad with holes in caliper. Install caliper assembly into mounting frame. Push caliper guide pins into mounting frame as far as possible. Install new Allen head guide pin retaining bolts in mounting frame and replace plugs in ends of guide pins.

Removal (4000 & Turbo) — 1) Raise and support vehicle; remove tire and wheel. Using hand pressure, force caliper to slide outward (toward outer wheel bearing) to seat piston in caliper bore.

2) Hold guide pin head with open end wrench while removing lower mounting bolt. Rotate caliper assembly upward. *See Fig. 6.* Remove disc pads from carrier.

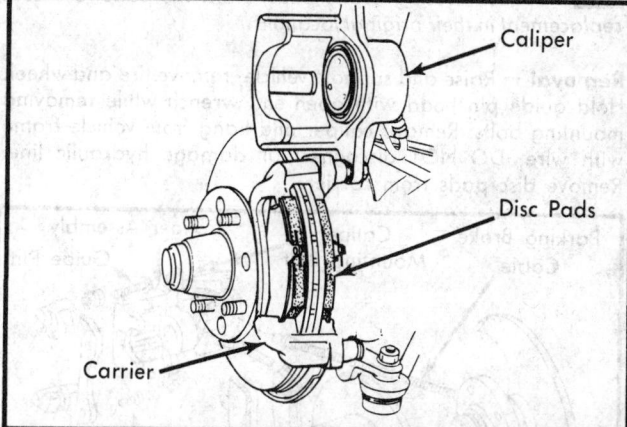

Fig. 6   Audi 4000 and Turbo Front Disc Pad Removal

Installation — 1) Clean area where pads rest. Make sure grommets on guide pins are not damaged. Guide pins must slide smoothly in housing. Install brake pads. Swing caliper housing down.

NOTE — *When replacing disc pads on Turbo and 4000 models, install head shield (furnished with repair kit) on piston side of inner pad.*

AUDI (Cont.)

2) Make sure pads do not hit piston; force piston deeper into housing if necessary. Tighten lower mounting bolt. Depress brake pedal several times to seat pads against rotor.

FRONT DISC BRAKE CALIPER

NOTE — *When replacing calipers, use compatible units or replace calipers in matched pairs.*

Removal (5000) — Raise and support vehicle, remove tire and wheel. Remove plug from end of caliper guide pin. Remove Allen head bolts from top of caliper mounting frame. Thread 8 mm bolts into ends of guide pins and pull to remove guide pins. Remove caliper from mounting frame.

Installation — To install, reverse removal procedure and bleed hydraulic system.

Removal (4000 & Turbo) — Raise and support vehicle; remove tire and wheel. Disconnect and plug hydraulic line from caliper. Bend back locking tabs (if equipped) on mounting bolts. Hold guide pin head with open end wrench and remove mounting bolts and caliper. Remove brake pad carrier mounting bolts and carrier.

Installation — To install, reverse removal procedure and bleed hydraulic system.

FRONT DISC BRAKE ROTOR

Removal — Raise and support vehicle; remove tire and wheel. Remove caliper as previously described and hang from vehicle frame with wire. DO NOT disconnect hydraulic line unless necessary. Remove screw securing rotor to spindle (4000) and pull rotor from spindle.

Installation — To install rotor assembly, reverse removal procedure. Bleed hydraulic system if necessary.

REAR DISC BRAKE PADS

NOTE — *When reusing brake pads, mark the pads to ensure replacement in their original locations.*

Removal — Raise and support vehicle; remove tire and wheel. Hold guide pin head with open end wrench while removing mounting bolts. Remove caliper and hang from vehicle frame with wire. DO NOT disconnect or damage hydraulic line. Remove disc pads from carrier.

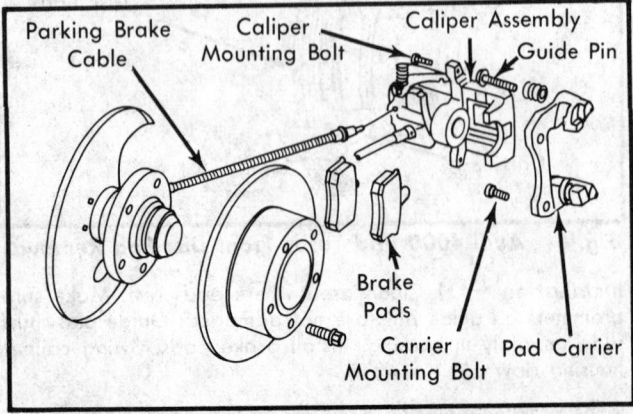

**Fig. 7 Exploded View of Audi Turbo
Rear Disc Brake Assembly**

Installation — Using an Allen wrench, turn piston in clockwise rotation while pushing into caliper bore. Install brake pads in carrier. Install caliper assembly and tighten mounting bolts. Pump brake pedal 40 times to seat pads. Check parking brake adjustment and bleed hydraulic system if necessary.

REAR DISC BRAKE CALIPER

Removal — Raise and support vehicle; remove tire and wheel. Disconnect parking brake cable from caliper assembly. Disconnect and plug hydraulic line from caliper. Remove caliper mounting bolts while holding guide pin head with open end wrench and remove caliper. Remove pad carrier mounting bolts and carrier.

Installation — 1) Fill caliper cylinder with brake fluid and pre-bleed caliper. Install brake pad carrier, then install caliper assembly. Tighten mounting bolts.

2) Reconnect hydraulic line and parking brake cable to caliper. Pump brake pedal 40 times to seat pads. Check parking brake adjustment and bleed hydraulic system.

REAR DISC BRAKE ROTOR

Removal — Raise and support vehicle; remove tire and wheel. Remove caliper as previously described and hang from frame with wire. DO NOT disconnect hydraulic line. Remove rotor from spindle.

Installation — To install, reverse removal procedure.

REAR BRAKE DRUM

Removal — Raise and support vehicle. Remove tire. Before removing right drum, release spring pressure on pressure regulator. Remove 1 wheel bolt. Using a screwdriver inserted through wheel bolt hole, push adjusting wedge upward. Reinstall wheel bolt. Remove wheel bearing hardware. Remove drum assembly without dropping thrust washer or outer bearing.

Installation — To install, reverse removal procedure and adjust wheel bearings. *See appropriate Rear Suspension article in SUSPENSION Section.* Depress brake pedal firmly to set self-adjusting mechanism.

REAR BRAKE SHOES

Removal — 1) Remove brake drum. Remove hold-down springs and pins. Remove brake shoes from anchor pins and remove return springs.

2) Disconnect parking brake cable from lever. Disconnect adjusting wedge spring and upper return spring. Remove brake shoes. Place adjuster strut and shoe in vise; remove tension spring. Separate shoe and components.

Installation — To install, reverse removal procedure and note the following: Lug on adjusting wedge faces backing plate. Adjust wheel bearings. *See appropriate Rear Suspension article in SUSPENSION Section.* Install drum and depress brake pedal firmly to set self-adjusting mechanism.

Brakes

AUDI (Cont.)

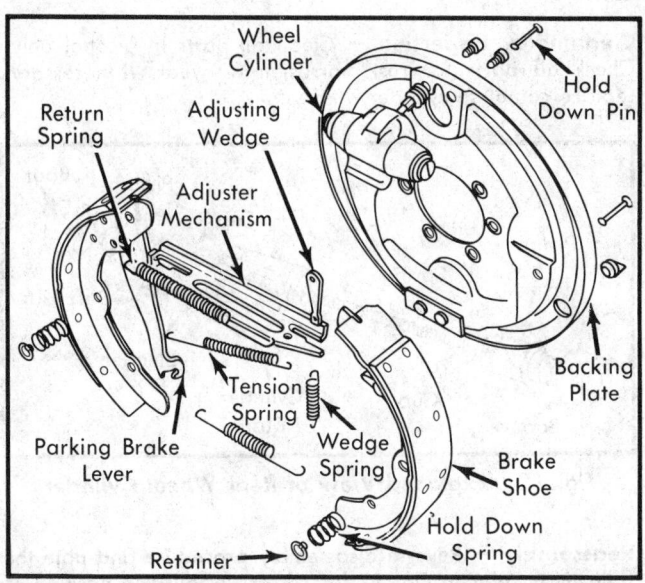

Fig. 8 Exploded View of Rear Drum Brake Assembly (Audi 4000 and 5000 Models)

MASTER CYLINDER

Removal — Siphon brake fluid from reservoir and remove hydraulic lines from master cylinder. Disconnect warning light electrical lead. Remove mounting bolts and separate master cylinder from power brake unit.

Installation — Replace "O" ring between master cylinder and power brake unit. Reverse removal procedure and bleed hydraulic system.

POWER BRAKE UNIT

Removal — Remove master cylinder from power brake unit. Remove pin at brake pedal and disconnect operating rod. Remove mounting nuts from firewall. Disconnect vacuum line and remove power unit.

Installation — To install, reverse removal procedure and note the following: Replace filter at operating rod end.

NOTE — Clevis and brake lever each have 2 holes. Install clevis pin only in holes nearest front of vehicle.

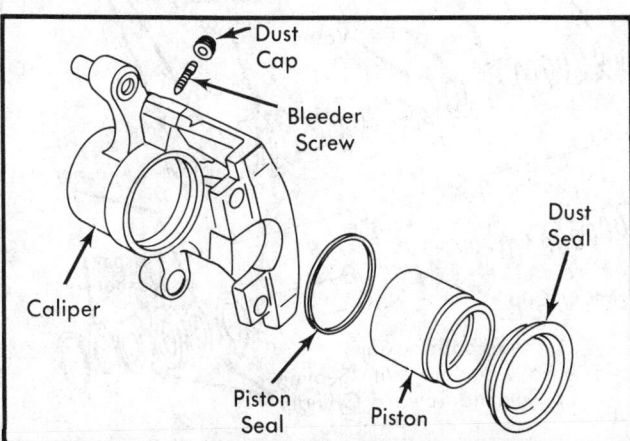

Fig. 9 Exploded View of Audi 5000 Front Disc Brake Caliper Assembly

CHECK VALVE

Large diameter side fits into power unit. To test, remove vacuum line and check valve. Blow into large diameter hole; valve should open. Blow into small diameter hole; valve should close. Replace if defective.

OVERHAUL

FRONT DISC BRAKE CALIPER

Disassembly — Remove brake pads and clean outside surfaces of caliper. Place a block of wood between piston and housing. Force piston out with compressed air and remove dust seal. Remove piston seal without damaging bore or groove.

Cleaning & Inspection — Clean all parts in alcohol only. Check cylinder bore and piston for wear or damage. Parts are serviced by replacement only. Boots, guide pins and other minor parts are only available with new pad carrier.

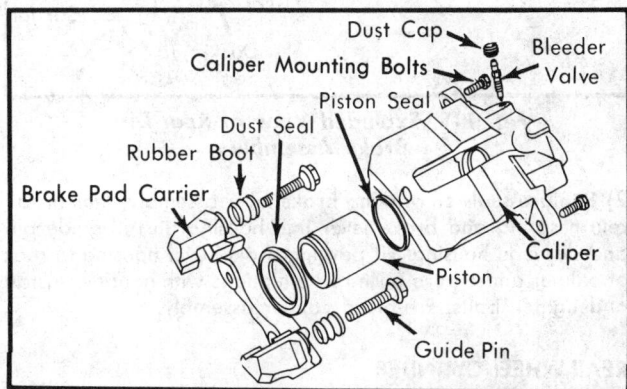

Fig. 10 Exploded View of Audi 4000 and Turbo Front Disc Brake Caliper Assembly

Reassembly — Coat piston, cylinder bore, and new seal with suitable brake paste. Fit seal into cylinder. Slide dust seal onto piston. Slowly insert piston into bore, fitting inner lip of dust seal into caliper housing groove. Fully seat piston in bore. Engage outer lip of dust seal into piston groove.

REAR DISC BRAKE CALIPER (TURBO)

Disassembly — 1) Remove caliper and clean outside surfaces. Remove parking brake lever housing bolts and housing. Remove guide pin and sleeve, then remove return spring and lever from housing. Remove and discard seal and "O" ring.

2) Using hand pressure, push piston out rear of caliper assembly. Remove push rod from rear of piston, then "O" ring, seals and spacer. Carefully remove piston seal without damaging bore or groove.

Cleaning & Inspection — Clean all parts in alcohol only. Check all parts for wear or damage. Guide pins, dust boots, seals, "O" rings and pad carrier are the only serviceable parts. Any damage to other parts requires replacement of caliper assembly.

Reassembly — 1) Coat piston, piston seal and parking brake guide pin with suitable brake paste. Fit seal into cylinder groove. Slide dust seal onto piston. Install spacer, "O" ring and seal onto push rod. Fit push rod into piston. Push piston into caliper bore from rear.

Brakes

AUDI (Cont.)

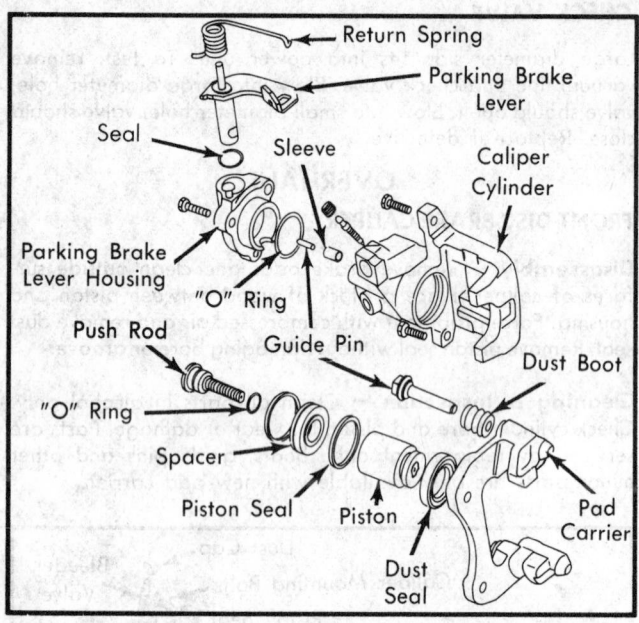

Fig. 11 Exploded View of Rear Disc Brake Assembly

2) Replace seals on parking brake lever assembly, then install return spring and brake lever into housing. Install guide pin and sleeve in housing. Fit parking brake lever housing to rear of caliper and ensure push rod pin aligns with housing. Install and tighten bolts. Pre-bleed caliper assembly.

REAR WHEEL CYLINDER

Disassembly — Thoroughly clean outside of cylinder. Remove boots, piston assemblies, cups and spring. Remove dust cap and bleeder screw.

Cleaning & Inspection — Clean all parts in alcohol only. Check all parts for rust, corrosion or wear. If necessary, replace complete cylinder.

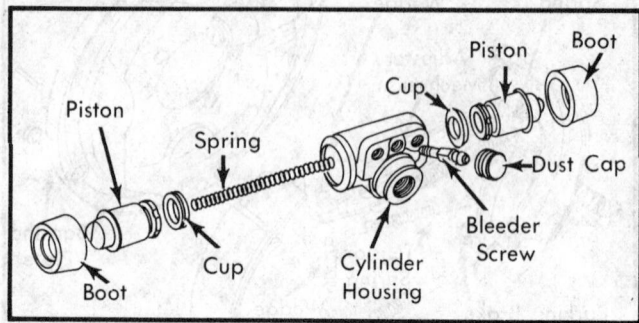

Fig. 12 Exploded View of Rear Wheel Cylinder

Reassembly — Reverse disassembly procedure and note the following: Refer to *Fig. 12* for correct installation position of wheel cylinder pistons.

MASTER CYLINDER

Disassembly — Remove "O" ring from master cylinder housing. Remove piston stop screw. Remove retaining ring and both pistons from housing. Remove pressure valves and reservoir from master cylinder housing. Disassemble piston assemblies as necessary.

Cleaning & Inspection — Clean all parts in alcohol and check for rust, corrosion, or other damage; replace parts as necessary. Make sure compensating and filler holes are not plugged.

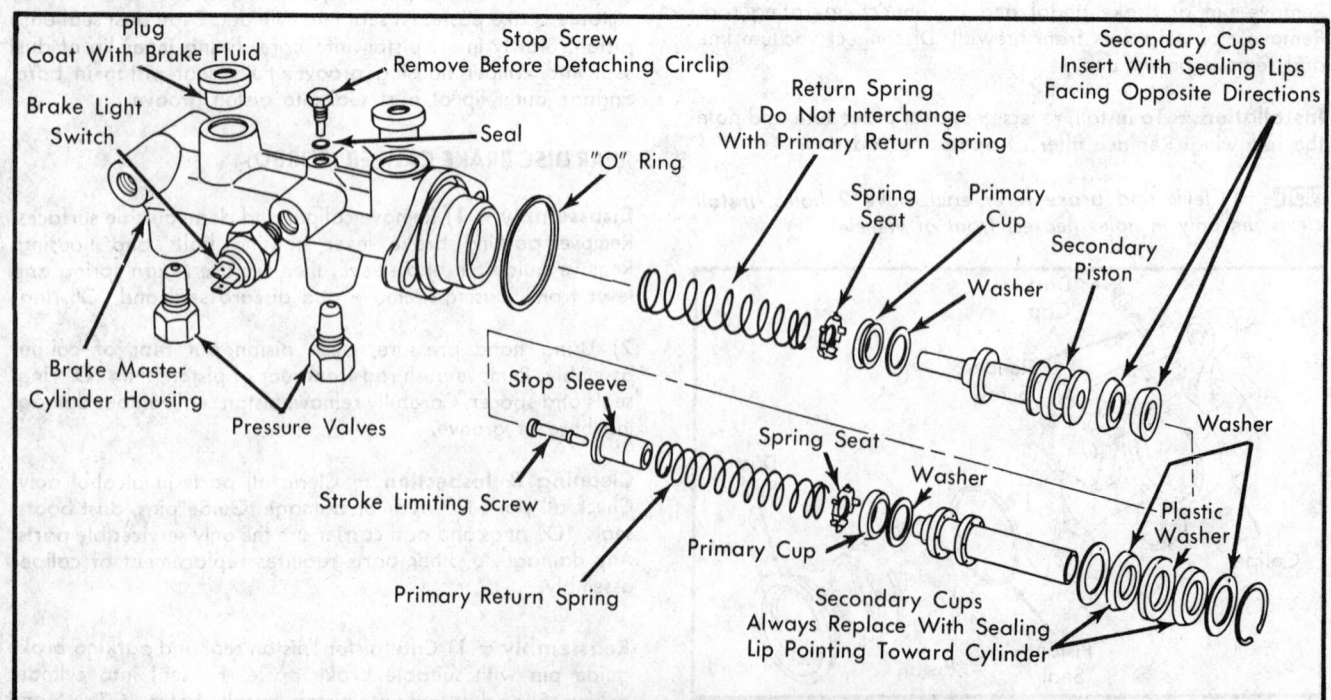

Fig. 13 Master Cylinder Component Relationship
(Audi 4000 Housing External Design Differs — Internal Parts Are Identical)

AUDI (Cont.)

Reassembly — Reverse disassembly procedure and note the following: Lubricate primary piston shaft with silicone grease and all other parts with brake cylinder paste. Replace all rubber parts. DO NOT interchange primary cup and piston seal; piston seal is identified by a groove and chamfered end.

POWER BRAKE UNIT

Manufacturer does not recommend overhaul of power brake unit. Replace as complete assembly if defective.

TIGHTENING SPECIFICATIONS

Application	Ft. Lbs. (N·m)
Caliper-to-Carrier Bolts	
4000 & Turbo (Front & Rear)	25 (34)
Carrier Mounting Bolts	
4000	36 (49)
Turbo	
Front	83 (112)
Rear	47 (64)
Caliper Mounting Frame Bolts (5000)	83 (112)
Caliper Guide Pin Retaining Bolts (5000)	18 (24)

DISC BRAKE SPECIFICATIONS

Application	Caliper Bore Diameter In. (mm)	Lateral Runout In. (mm)	Parallelism In. (mm)	Original Thickness In. (mm)	Minimum Refinish Thickness In. (mm)	Discard Thickness In. (mm)
Audi 4000	.....	.002 (.06)	.....	.472 (12)	.....	.394 (10)
Audi 5000	.....	.002 (.06)	.0008 (.02)	.866 (22)	.....	.787 (20)
Audi Turbo						
Front	.....	.002 (.06)	.0008 (.02)	.866 (22)	.....	.787 (20)
Rear	.....	.002 (.06)	.0008 (.02)	.394 (10)	.....	.315 (8)

DRUM BRAKE SPECIFICATIONS

Application	Wheel Cyl. Bore Diameter In. (mm)	Drum Diameter In. (mm)	Original Diameter In. (mm)	Maximum Refinish Diameter In. (mm)	Discard Diameter In. (mm)
Audi 4000	.....	7.874 (200)	7.874 (200)	7.894 (200.5)	7.913 (201)
Audi 5000	.....	9.055 (230)	9.055 (230)	9.094 (231)	9.134 (232)

Brakes

BMW

320i
528i
633CSi
733i

DESCRIPTION

Brake system is hydraulically operated using a tandem master cylinder and power brake unit. All models except 320i are equipped with 4 piston ATE front and rear disc calipers. The 320i is equipped with rear drum brakes and 2 piston Girling front disc brake calipers. Disc pad wear indicators are mounted on the instrument panel of 320i and 528i to indicate need for pad replacement. On 633CSi and 733i models, pad wear indicator lamp is component of "Check Control" system. An optional brake pressure regulator may be installed to reduce fluid pressure to rear brakes. Parking brake is cable actuated on drum brake of 320i and consists of internally mounted parking brake shoes on all rear disc brake systems.

ADJUSTMENT

REAR DRUM BRAKE SHOES

320i — Raise and support vehicle; release parking brake. While rotating tire, tighten brake adjusters (turn left adjuster counterclockwise; right adjuster clockwise) until brake shoes lock drum. Loosen each adjuster 1/8 turn or until wheel rotates without drag.

BRAKE PEDAL HEIGHT

Brake pedal height (measured from firewall to pedal pad center) should be 9.4-9.8" (239-249 mm) on 320i; 9.1-9.5" (230-241 mm) on 528i and 633CSi and 9.9-10.2" (251-260 mm) on 733i. To adjust pedal height, loosen stop light switch lock nut and position stop light switch out of way. Loosen brake operating rod lock nut and turn operating rod until correct pedal height is obtained. Tighten lock nut, reposition and adjust stop light switch and tighten stop light switch lock nut.

STOP LIGHT SWITCH

Stop light switch is located under instrument panel in front of brake pedal arm. To adjust stop light switch, loosen lock nut and turn adjusting nut so contact plunger just touches pedal arm and extended length of plunger is .20-.24" (5-6 mm). Tighten lock nut.

PARKING BRAKE

NOTE — *Before adjusting parking brake (except 320i), pull parking brake lever until resistance is felt, then 1 additional notch. With parking brake lever engaged as described, drive vehicle maximum of 1300 ft. (400 m).*

Except 320i — 1) Raise and support vehicle; remove tire and wheel and release parking brake. Insert a screwdriver into rotor inspection hole. Turn adjuster until parking brake shoes lock rotor, then back off adjuster 4-6 notches.

2) Working inside driver compartment, tighten adjustment nuts on lever until parking brake holds vehicle securely before fifth ratchet stop is reached.

320i — 1) Raise and support rear of vehicle. Fully release parking brake. Tighten brake shoes until wheel is locked. Back off adjusters about 1/8 turn or until wheel can just barely turn.

2) Work inside passenger compartment and tighten nuts on lever until parking brake holds vehicle securely before fifth ratchet stop is reached.

BRAKE WARNING LIGHT

A dual warning light is mounted on instrument panel. Light should glow when parking brake lever is pulled 1 notch (ignition on) and go off when lever is fully released. To check circuit warning sensor, fully release parking brake and ensure light is off (ignition on). Raise master cylinder filler cap; warning lamp should glow. If not, check bulb or circuit connections.

REMOVAL & INSTALLATION

DISC PADS

Removal — Raise and support vehicle. Remove wheel and tire. Disconnect pad wear sensors. Bend open fastener and pull out. Drive out retaining pin toward inside of vehicle. Remove cross spring. Using extractor tool, remove pads from caliper. If disc thickness has worn to .080" (2 mm), replace ends. Only replace pads in matched sets.

Installation — 1) Using a cylinder brush, clean guide surface and support surface in caliper. Siphon sufficient fluid from master cylinder reservoir to prevent overflowing, then press pistons to bottom of bores.

2) On rear calipers, ensure machined position of piston face makes a 20° angle with caliper wall. *See Fig. 1.* (Rotate piston with tool 341050 if necessary). On all calipers except 320i front calipers, install disc pads, shims (if required), cross spring and retaining pins. After installation, depress brake pedal several times to seat pads.

3) On 320i calipers, adjust shoulders of pistons so that guards are located at machined shoulders of piston. If necessary, use guard as adjusting template. Correct 20° position of piston with special tool 341060. Install pads, cross spring and retaining pins. Replace fastener, bending straight side. After installation, depress pedal several times to seat pads.

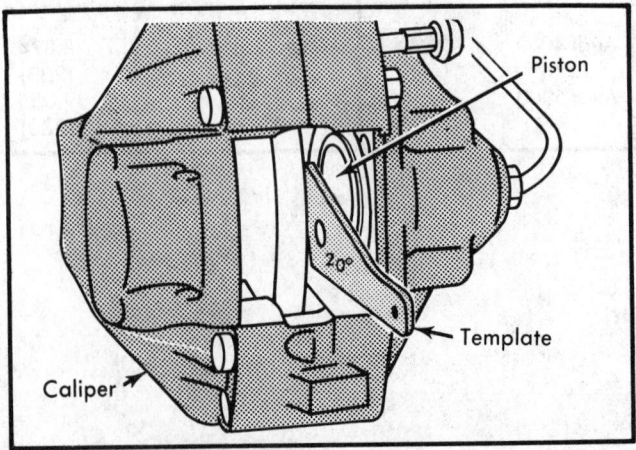

Fig. 1   Piston Alignment for Rear Brake Calipers

CALIPER ASSEMBLY

Removal — Drain brake fluid from master cylinder reservoir. Remove caliper mounting bolts. Disconnect disc pad wear in-

BMW (Cont.)

dicator electrical lead. Disconnect brake fluid inlet lines. Lift caliper off rotor.

Installation — Reverse removal procedure and bleed hydraulic system.

ROTOR

Removal — Raise and support vehicle; remove tire and wheel. On front calipers, separate bracket from strut. On all models, remove caliper and hang from frame with wire; DO NOT disconnect hydraulic line. On rear calipers, slip hydraulic line out of holding clamp. Remove rotor mounting bolt and remove brake rotor.

NOTE — *Front brake rotors are balanced; DO NOT remove or reposition balance clips. If any rotor must be replaced, replace rotors in axle sets.*

Installation — To install, reverse removal procedure.

PARKING BRAKE SHOES

Removal — With rear caliper and rotor removed, disconnect lower return spring using brake spring pliers. Turn retaining springs 90° using removal tool, then set spring aside. Pull brake shoes apart at bottom and lift upward.

Installation — To install, reverse removal procedure, adjust parking brake shoes and check operation.

BRAKE DRUM

Removal & Installation — Loosen brake adjuster cams. Remove countersunk Allen bolt and slide off brake drum. To install, reverse removal procedure and note: If one brake drum is reground, drum on other side must also be reground.

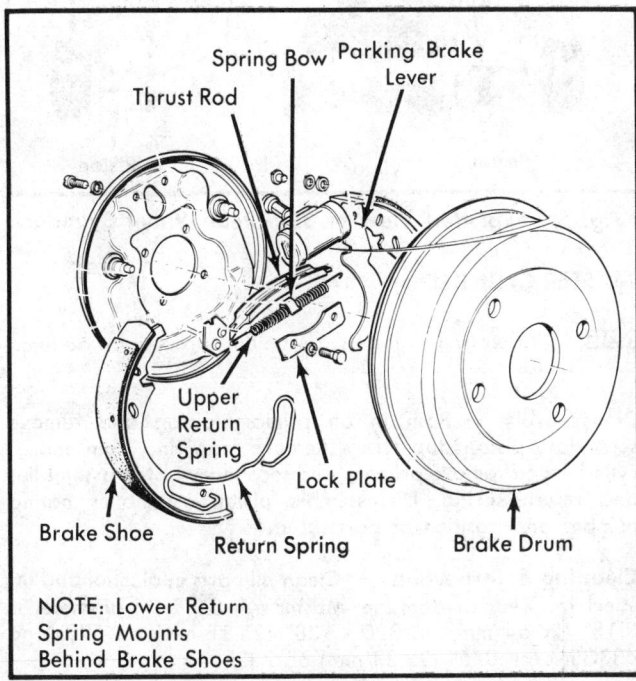

Spring Bow   Parking Brake
Thrust Rod   Lever

Upper
Return
Spring

Lock Plate

Brake Shoe   Return Spring   Brake Drum

NOTE: Lower Return
Spring Mounts
Behind Brake Shoes

**Fig. 2   Exploded View of Rear Drum
Brake Assembly**

BRAKE SHOES

Removal — Remove brake drum. Disengage mounting spring and hold-down spring clip from each shoe. Disconnect bottom return spring. Pull shoes apart and out of each wheel cylinder. Disconnect parking brake cable and remove brake shoes. If brake shoe lining has worn to .118" (3.0 mm) or less, replace brake shoes.

Installation — Reverse removal procedure and note: Connect long end of spring between parking brake lever and brake shoe.

MASTER CYLINDER

NOTE — *On 320i models only, mixture control unit must be removed to take off master cylinder.*

Removal — 1) Siphon off brake fluid from reservoir. On 320i, disconnect clutch hose connection. On 633CSi, remove air cleaner. On 528i and 633CSi, remove relay holder attaching bracket with all components still attached and position out of way.

2) Disconnect all hydraulic lines from master cylinder. Remove nuts mounting master cylinder to power booster. On 320i models, remove nuts mounting master cylinder support to inner fender panel. Remove support and master cylinder.

Installation — To install, reverse removal procedure and note: Make sure "O" ring on master cylinder is not damaged. An imperfect fit will not allow correct vacuum build-up.

POWER BRAKE UNIT

NOTE — *Power brake unit must be removed with master cylinder attached. On 320i, mixture control unit must be removed prior to removal of power brake unit.*

Removal — 1) Siphon brake fluid from master cylinder reservoir. On all models except 320i, remove left portion of lower dash panel. On all models, remove operating rod clevis pin from brake pedal arm. On 633CSi, remove air cleaner. On 528i and 633CSi, remove relay holder as previously described.

2) Disconnect and plug hydraulic lines at master cylinder, including clutch hose. Disconnect vacuum hose from power brake unit (hydraulic lines on 733i). Remove power brake unit mounting bolts. On 320i only, separate master cylinder support from inner fender panel. Remove power unit/master cylinder assembly from vehicle. Separate master cylinder from power brake unit.

NOTE — *On 733i models only, power steering pump also supplies hydraulic pressure through hydraulic accumulator to the power brake unit. If power steering fails, there will be sufficient pressure in the hydraulic accumulator to provide a few brake applications with full power.*

Installation — To install, mount master cylinder to power brake unit and reverse removal procedure. Bleed hydraulic system after installation.

Check Valve Replacement (Exc. 733i) — Check valve is located in vacuum line between power unit and intake manifold. To remove, loosen hose clamps, remove vacuum lines

BMW (Cont.)

and remove valve. To install, reverse removal procedure. Make sure arrow or black portion of valve faces intake manifold.

Filter Replacement (Exc. 733i) — With power brake unit removed from vehicle, pull back rubber dust boot. Remove retaining ring. Remove silencer and filter. To install, reverse removal procedure.

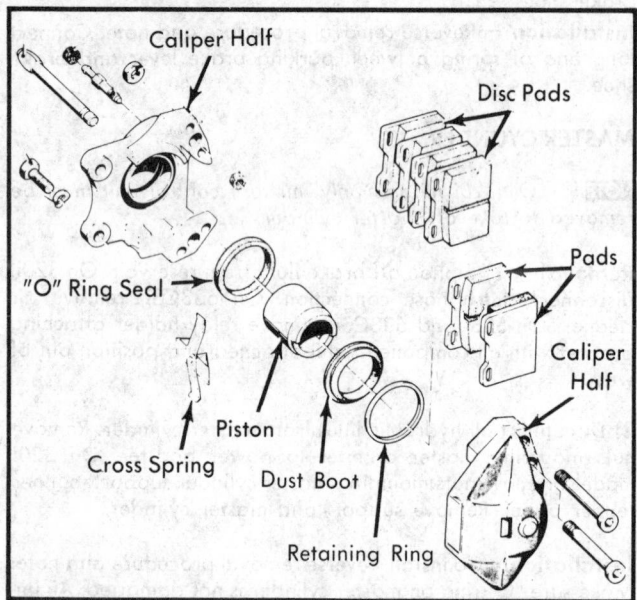

Fig. 3 Disassembled View of Dual Piston Caliper Used as Rear Caliper on 528i, 633CSi and 733i Models and Front Caliper on 320i Models Only

OVERHAUL

BRAKE CALIPER

NOTE — *DO NOT disassemble 4 piston caliper halves.*

Disassembly — With pads removed from caliper, remove retaining ring and dust boot. Using suitable clamp, hold one piston in position, insert wooden block in caliper cavity, then apply compressed air to fluid inlet to force out opposite piston. Repeat procedure for each piston. Remove piston seals without damaging caliper bore.

Cleaning & Inspection — Clean components in clean brake fluid and blow dry. Inspect caliper bore and pistons for wear or damage. Replace caliper assembly if corroded or worn; DO NOT hone. Replace piston seals and dust boots at each overhaul.

Reassembly — Coat pistons and calipers bores with brake cylinder paste. Install piston seals, then install pistons. Make sure pistons are not tilted when inserting. On 2 piston calipers ensure 20° piston angle is preset. Install dust boots and retaining rings.

REAR WHEEL CYLINDER

Disassembly — Remove dust boots and force out pistons and return spring. Separate and discard cylinder cups from pistons.

Cleaning & Inspection — Clean all parts in clean brake fluid. Check cylinder bore and dust boot retaining grooves for

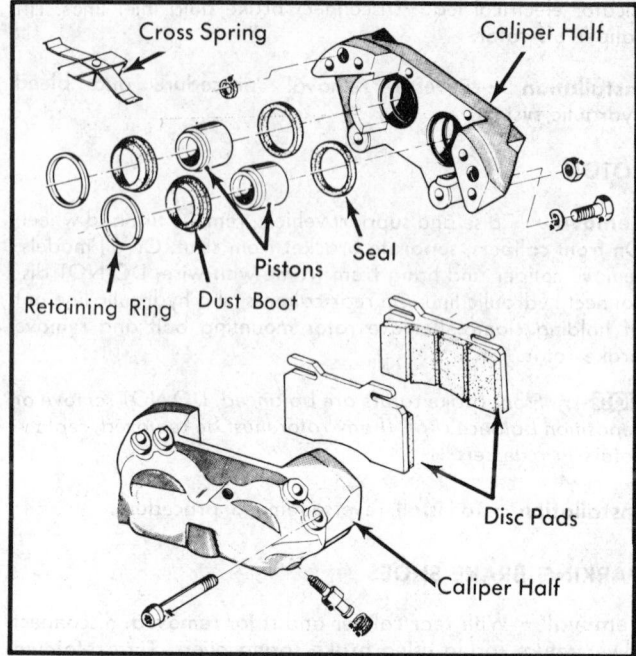

Fig. 4 Disassembled View of 4 Piston Caliper Used as Front Caliper on 528i, 633CSi and 733i

rust and corrosion. Replace wheel cylinder assembly if defective; DO NOT hone. Replace all rubber parts during overhaul.

Reassembly — Coat all parts with brake cylinder paste. Reassemble wheel cylinder by reversing disassembly procedure.

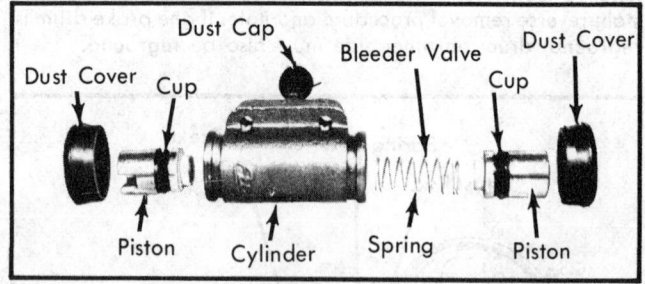

Fig. 5 Exploded View of 320i Rear Wheel Cylinder

MASTER CYLINDER

NOTE — *All master cylinders are similar, procedures outlined are general.*

Disassembly — Push in on primary piston and remove secondary piston stop screw. Remove snap ring from end of cylinder and remove primary and secondary piston assemblies and return spring. Dissassemble piston assemblies noting number and position of parts used.

Cleaning & Inspection — Clean all parts in alcohol and inspect for wear or damage. Master cylinder bore diameter is .812" (20.64 mm) on 320i, .938" (23.81 mm) on 528i and 633CSi and .875" (22.23 mm) on 733i.

NOTE — *Cylinders with surface defects in bores must be replaced; do not overhaul.*

BMW (Cont.)

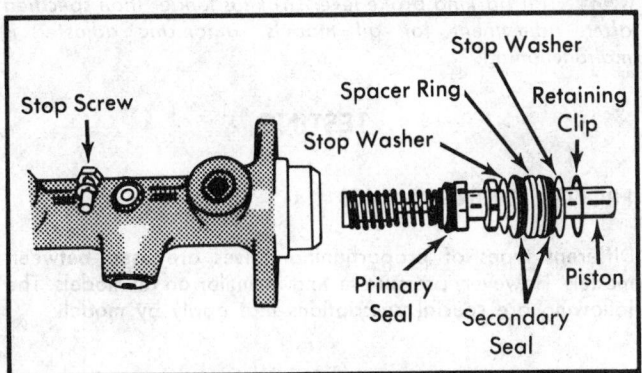

Fig. 6   *Master Cylinder Primary Piston Assembly*

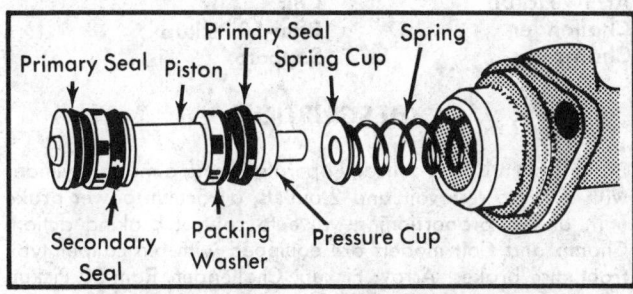

Fig. 7   *Master Cylinder Secondary (Front) Piston Assy.*

Reassembly — Reassemble piston assemblies using thin coating of ATE brake paste. Install piston assemblies into cylinder bore using a guide sleeve to prevent damage to seals. Install secondary piston stop screw, making sure piston is pushed fully forward before screw is installed and tightened. Install retaining ring in end of master cylinder bore.

TIGHTENING SPECIFICATIONS

Application	Ft. Lbs. (N·m)
Caliper Mounting Bolts	
Front	58-69 (79-94)
Rear	43-48 (58-65)
Rotor-to-Wheel Hub	
528i & 633CSi	11-13 (15-18)
733i	23-24 (31-33)
320i	36-42 INCH Lbs. (4-5 N·m)

DRUM BRAKE SPECIFICATIONS

Application	Wheel Cyl. Bore Diameter In. (mm)	Drum Diameter In. (mm)	Original Diameter In. (mm)	Maximum Refinish Diameter In. (mm)	Discard Diameter In. (mm)
320i Rear	.750 (19.05)	9.84 (250)	9.84 (250)	9.88 (251)	.....

DISC BRAKE SPECIFICATIONS

Application	Caliper Bore Diameter In. (mm)	Lateral Runout In. (mm)	Parallelism In. (mm)	Original Thickness In. (mm)	Minimum Refinish Thickness In. (mm)	Discard Thickness In. (mm)
320i						
Front	1.89 (48)	.008① (.2)	.0008 (.02)	.500 (12.7)	②	.461 (11.7)
528i						
Front	1.57 (40)	.008① (.2)	.0008 (.02)	.866 (22)	②	.827 (21)
Rear	1.65 (42)	.008① (.2)	.0008 (.02)	.374 (9.5)	②	.334 (8.5)
633CSi						
Front	1.57 (40)	.008① (.2)	.0008 (.02)	.866 (22)	②	.827 (21)
Rear	1.65 (42)	.008① (.2)	.0008 (.02)	.748 (19)	②	.709 (18)
733i						
Front	1.57 (40)	.006① (.15)	.0008 (.02)	.866 (22)	②	.827 (21)
Rear	1.30 (33)	.006① (.15)	.0008 (.02)	.394 (10)	②	.354 (9)

① — Installed on vehicle.
② — Machining of each braking surface is .020″ (.5 mm). Minimum rotor thickness must be observed.

Brakes

CHRYSLER CORP. IMPORTS

Arrow Pickup   Colt
Challenger   Ram-50 Pickup
Champ   Sapporo

DESCRIPTION

Brake system is hydraulically operated using a master cylinder with a single reservoir and 2 outlets, a vacuum power brake unit, and a proportioning valve to control braking action. Champ and Colt models are equipped with pin caliper type front disc brakes; Arrow Pickup, Challenger, Ram-50 Pickup and Sapporo are equipped with sliding caliper type front disc brakes. Rear brakes on all models are drum type although rear disc brakes are available as an option on Challenger and Sapporo models. All drum brakes are self adjusting. Parking brake cable actuates the rear drum brakes.

ADJUSTMENT

PEDAL HEIGHT & FREE PLAY

Back off stop light switch. Adjust pedal height (distance from top of pedal to floor board) by loosening lock nut and rotating master cylinder push rod (yoke, if equipped). DO NOT depress push rod. Tighten lock nut and ensure that brake pedal free play is .4-.6" (10-15 mm) on all models.

Pedal Height Specifications

Application	Pedal Height In. (mm)
Arrow Pickup & Ram-50 Pickup	6.5 (166)
Challenger & Sapporo	7.1 (180)
Champ & Colt	7.1-7.3 (180-185)

STOP LIGHT SWITCH

On Pickup models, adjust stop light switch until it just contacts brake pedal lever. On all other models, loosen lock nut and adjust switch-to-pedal arm clearance to .02-.04" (0.5-1.0 mm) and tighten lock nut. DO NOT depress master cylinder push rod during stop light switch adjustment.

PARKING BRAKE

Arrow Pickup & Ram-50 Pickup — Service brake adjustment must be accurate before making parking brake adjustment. Fully release parking brake and allow slack in rear cable to prevent brake shoe drag. Set balancer-to-crossmember clearance to 8" (203 mm) by adjusting turnbuckle. Balancer must be parallel with center line of vehicle. Brake lever stroke should be 16-17 notches at 66 lbs. force.

Challenger & Sapporo — When parking brake lever is pulled with a force of 45 lbs., the lever stroke should be 4-6 notches. If it is not, remove the accessory box and turn the adjusting nut until the specified number of notches is obtained with a pull of 45 lbs. force.

Champ & Colt — Remove parking brake lever cover and release brake lever. Adjust both cables to equal lengths, allowing enough slack in cables to prevent brake shoe drag. Properly adjusted parking brake lever stroke should be 6-7 notches at 44 lbs. force.

NOTE — *If parking brake lever stroke is longer than specified after adjustment for all models, automatic adjuster is malfunctioning.*

TESTING

PROPORTIONING VALVES

Different types of proportioning valves are used between models. However, pressure testing is similar on all models. The following are special descriptions that apply by model:

Arrow Pickup & Ram-50 Pickup — Valve accomplishes two functions: Improves braking efficiency by distributing braking force to front and rear wheels; increases braking force to rear wheels when large braking force is required or front brakes fail.

Challenger & Sapporo — Valve accomplishes three functions: Pressure control of rear service brakes; Deactivating rear brake pressure control when front service brakes fail; Trouble warning.

Champ & Colt — Valve body contains two separate proportioning valves and each valve must be checked separately. Valve body is identified with "A150" stamped on plug.

Pressure Test — Performed using two pressure gauges that measure at least 1500 psi. Hook one gauge to master cylinder rear side and one to rear wheel cylinder. Pressure readings should be as shown in chart. Replace defective part as required. DO NOT disassemble proportioning valve.

NOTE — *The proportioning valve on Champ and Colt models contains two valves; each must be tested separately.*

Brake Hydraulic Pressure Chart (psi)

Application	Wheel Cyl. Pressure	Master Cyl. Pressure
Arrow Pickup & Ram-50 Pickup		
B Valve	437-494	711
P Valve	668-754	966
Challenger & Sapporo		
With Rear Disc	674	853
With Rear Drum	532	711
Champ & Colt	519-590	953

Warning Light Test — To test warning light (if equipped), loosen bleeder screw of one wheel cylinder and depress brake pedal; warning light should come on. If not, check switch and wire connector.

Proportioning Valve Reset (Challenger & Sapporo Only) — After repairs on brake system, bleed brake lines. With all lines bled and bleeder valves secured, depress brake pedal hard. This will center valve and warning light should go out.

CHRYSLER CORP. IMPORTS (Cont.)

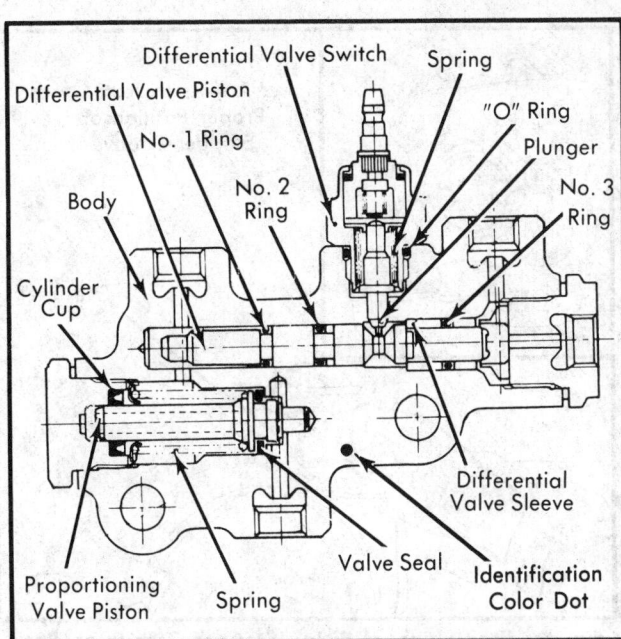

Fig. 1   Sectional View of Proportioning Valve (Challenger & Sapporo Shown, Others Similar)

REMOVAL & INSTALLATION

FRONT DISC BRAKE PADS

Removal (Champ & Colt) — Raise and support vehicle. Remove front wheel. Remove protector by prying up edge of clip at center of protector. Hold center of "M" clip, detach "M" clip from pad and its ends from retaining pins; remove clip. Remove retaining pins from caliper and remove "K" spring. Remove pads and anti-squeal springs from caliper by grasping backing plate area of pads with pliers.

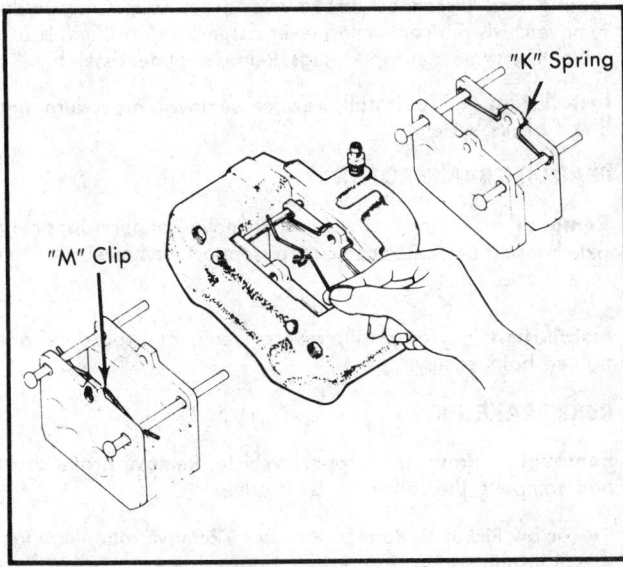

Fig. 2   Installing Spring and Clip on Brake Pads (Champ & Colt)

NOTE — *Replace all pads (left and right side) at same time.*

Installation — Press piston to bottom of bore using a suitable tool, install disc pads and retaining pins. Install "K" spring and

"M" clip, making sure positions are not reversed. See *Fig. 2.* Install pad protector with retaining clips on inner side of caliper.

Removal (All Others) — Raise and support vehicle. Remove front wheel. Remove retaining clip and pull out stopper plug. Loosen caliper assembly mounting bolts. Pull caliper assembly up and down in a diagonal manner and remove from mounting bracket. Remove inner and outer pad clips, then pull pads and anti-squeal shims from caliper support.

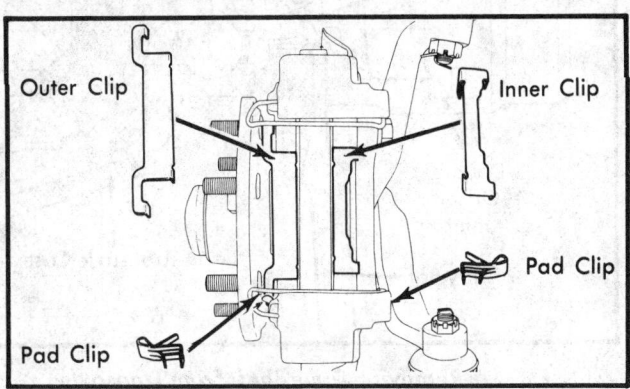

Fig. 3   Installing Pad Retaining Clips (Challenger, Sapporo & Pickups)

Installation — To install, reverse removal procedure and note the following: Press piston to bottom of caliper bore prior to pad installation. Ensure pad retaining clips are installed as shown in *Fig. 3.*

FRONT DISC BRAKE CALIPER

Removal (Champ & Colt) — Remove disc pads. Disconnect hydraulic line and remove bolts attaching caliper assembly to steering knuckle. Remove caliper assembly.

Installation — Reverse removal procedure, tighten caliper mounting bolts to specification and bleed hydraulic system.

Removal (All Others) — Remove disc pads. Pull out hose clip from strut area, then disconnect brake hose from caliper. Remove caliper.

Installation — To install, reverse removal procedure, tighten caliper mounting bolts to specification and bleed brake system.

FRONT DISC BRAKE ROTOR

Removal (Champ & Colt) — 1) Remove center cap, loosen drive shaft nut, lift vehicle and remove wheels. Remove under cover, then remove lower arm ball joint and strut bar from lower arm.

2) Drain transaxle fluid and remove caliper assembly. Insert pry bar between transaxle case and double offset joint outer case. Do not insert pry bar more than .28" (7 mm) to avoid damaging inner seal. Push pry bar toward center of vehicle to remove drive shaft from transaxle.

3) Using an axle shaft puller (Special Tool No. CT-1003), force the drive shaft out of hub. Remove knuckle, hub and rotor as an assembly by removing 2 bolts attaching knuckle to strut assembly.

CHRYSLER CORP. IMPORTS (Cont.)

4) Mount steering knuckle in a vise and drive out hub and rotor assembly with a soft hammer. Remove preload adjusting spacer from hub. Remove bolts attaching rotor to hub and remove rotor from hub assembly.

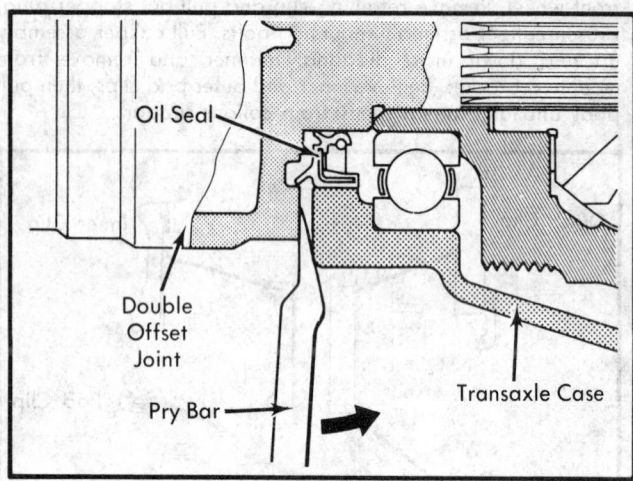

Fig. 4   Removing Drive Shaft From Transaxle
(Champ & Colt)

Installation — 1) Install rotor on hub and tighten bolts to specification. Hold outer bearing inner race with Special Tool MB990776-A and press hub into knuckle. Install new inner oil seal using Special Tools DT-1007-D and C-4171.

NOTE — *It will take a force of approximately 4400 lbs. (1996 kg) to press hub assembly into knuckle.*

2) Slide drive shaft into proper position and install knuckle assembly by reversing removal procedures.

NOTE — *If removal or replacement of bearings or races is necessary, see Chrysler Corp. Imports (FWD) article in SUSPENSION section.*

Removal (All Others) — With caliper assembly removed, remove hub dust cap, cotter pin, locknut (if used) and adjusting nut. Pull hub and rotor assembly from spindle using care not to drop outer wheel bearing. Remove hub to rotor attaching bolts and separate rotor from hub.

Installation — To install, reverse removal procedures and tighten hub-to-rotor bolts to specification. Bleed brake system if necessary and adjust wheel bearings. See *Chrysler Corp. Imports (FWD)* article in SUSPENSION Section.

REAR DISC BRAKE PADS

Removal — 1) Raise and support vehicle. Remove rear wheels. Remove caliper assembly dust cover. Disconnect parking brake cable from parking brake lever and from bracket.

2) Remove retaining pin and pull out stopper plug. Remove caliper assembly from rotor. Pull pads from caliper support.

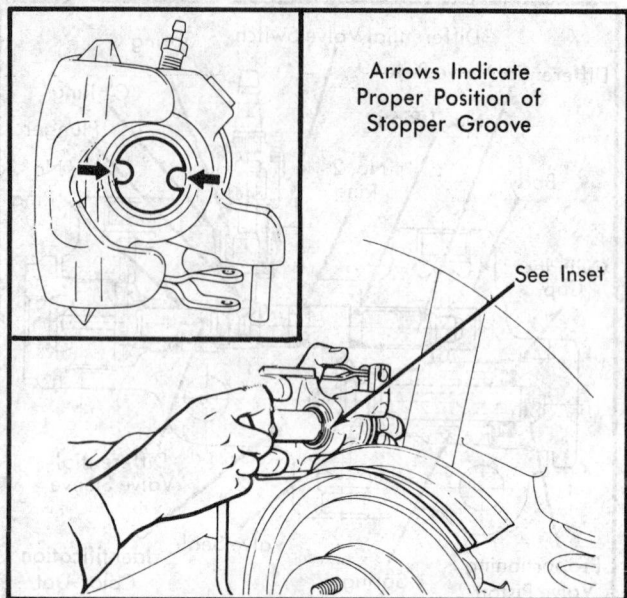

Fig. 5   Positioning of Piston Stopper Groove on Rear
Disc Brakes

Installation — To install, reverse removal procedure and note the following: Press the piston into its original position with clockwise rotation using a suitable driver. Ensure piston stopper groove is positioned as shown in *Fig. 5* so projection on back of pad will securely fit groove. Pad clips must be installed properly.

NOTE — *DO NOT use screwdriver to push piston into original position.*

REAR DISC BRAKE CALIPER

Removal — Remove disc pads. Pull out hose clip from axle housing and disconnect brake hose from caliper assembly. Remove clevis pin connecting lever assembly to parking brake cable, then remove stopper plugs. Remove caliper assembly.

Installation — To install, reverse removal procedure and bleed brake system.

REAR DISC BRAKE ROTOR

Removal — Remove disc pads. Remove caliper support-to-axle housing bolts. Remove caliper support. Remove rotor from axle shaft.

Installation — To install, reverse removal procedure and tighten bolts evenly.

REAR BRAKE SHOES

Removal — Raise and support vehicle. Remove brake drum and complete the following by model:

- Arrow Pickup & Ram-50 Pickup — Remove return springs, adjusting spring and lever. Remove shoes and adjuster as an assembly and separate. Remove parking brake cable from lever.

- Challenger & Sapporo — Remove hold down springs. Disconnect strut-to-shoe spring and upper shoe return spring end from trailing shoe. Remove trailing shoe and lower return spring. Hold adjuster latch down, pull adjuster lever

CHRYSLER CORP. IMPORTS (Cont.)

toward center of brake and remove leading shoe assembly. Remove upper shoe return spring and strut-to-shoe spring.

- Champ & Colt — Remove clip spring, shoe return spring, shoe-to-shoe spring and hold spring. Remove shoes and adjuster as an assembly and separate. Remove parking brake cable from lever.

Installation — 1) Reverse removal procedure and note the following: Apply brake grease to all shoe contact points, adjuster assembly, wheel cylinder and parking brake lever pin. Adjust amount of engagement of adjusting lever with strut, only after pulling lever fully toward center of brake. Note that adjusting lever and latch spring differ between right and left sides.

2) Champ and Colt models require check of parking brake cable to ensure it will not advance brake lever when released. Adjuster will malfunction if lever advances.

3) Pickups require check of adjuster after installation is complete. Adjuster lever should mesh with next tooth of adjuster when pulled and return to original position after wheel has moved one tooth. Adjuster assemblies differ between right and left sides.

MASTER CYLINDER

Removal — Remove sensor connector (if equipped). Disconnect brake lines from master cylinder. Slowly depress brake pedal several times to drain fluid from cylinder housing. Remove master cylinder from booster unit and separate reservoirs from housing.

Installation — Reverse removal procedure, check and adjust clearance between back of master cylinder piston and power brake push rod prior to installation. Clearance should be 0-.03" (0-.75 mm) for Pickup models, .004-.020" (0.1-0.5 mm)

for Challenger and Sapporo, and .006" (.015 mm) for Champ and Colt. Check and adjust pedal height and bleed brake system after installation.

POWER BRAKE UNIT
CHECK VALVE REPLACEMENT

NOTE — *Test Check valve before removal. Pull off vacuum hose on booster side of check valve. Place finger over check valve and crank engine. Vacuum should be felt.*

Removal — Remove hose clamps from both ends of check valve. Remove check valve clamp and remove check valve.

Installation — Coat both ends of check valve with sealer and install valve with arrow (identification mark) pointing toward intake manifold side. Install check valve clamp, vacuum hoses and secure hose clamps.

POWER BRAKE UNIT

Removal — Remove the brake master cylinder and disconnect vacuum hose from power brake unit. Disconnect brake pedal and operating rod of power brake unit. Remove 4 nuts attaching power brake unit to firewall from inside vehicle. Remove power brake unit.

Installation — Install power brake unit and tighten nuts to specification. Install brake master cylinder.

OVERHAUL

FRONT DISC BRAKE CALIPER

Disassembly (Champ & Colt) — Remove caliper attaching bridge bolts. Separate inner and outer caliper halves and remove torque plate. Remove retaining ring and dust seal. Apply compressed air to fluid inlet to remove piston. Remove piston seal without damaging caliper bore or seal groove.

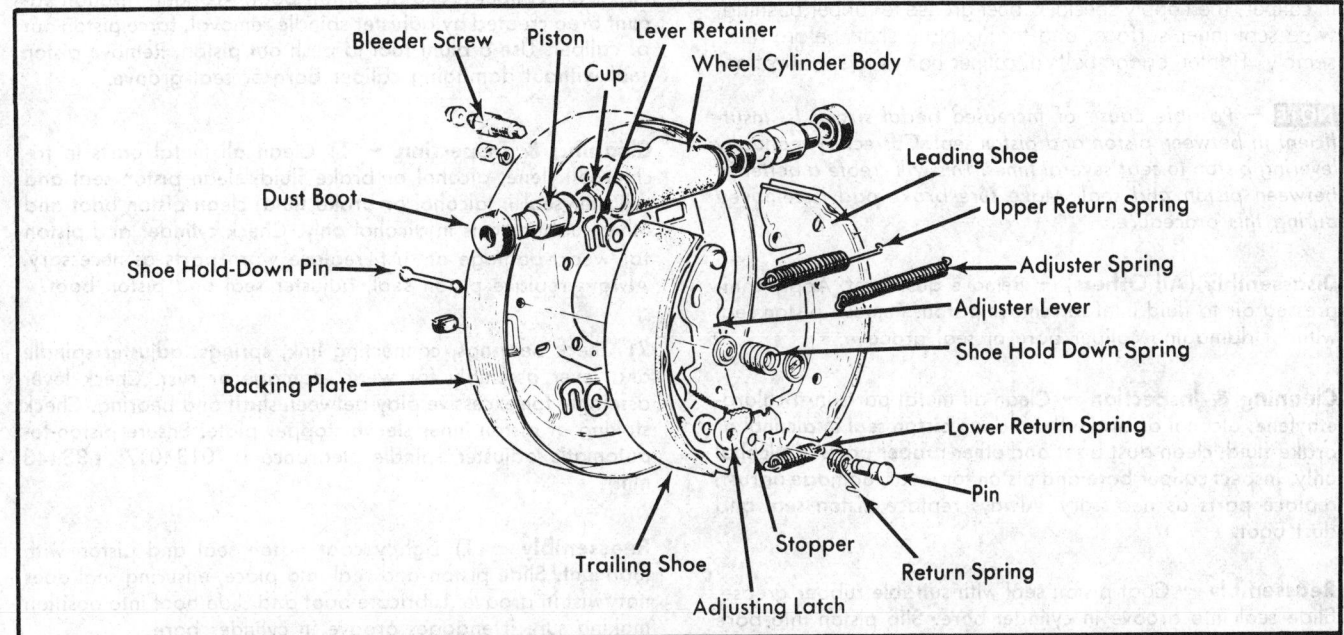

Fig. 6   Exploded View or Rear Brake Assembly for Component Relationship
(Challenger & Sapporo Shown, Others Similar)

CHRYSLER CORP. IMPORTS (Cont.)

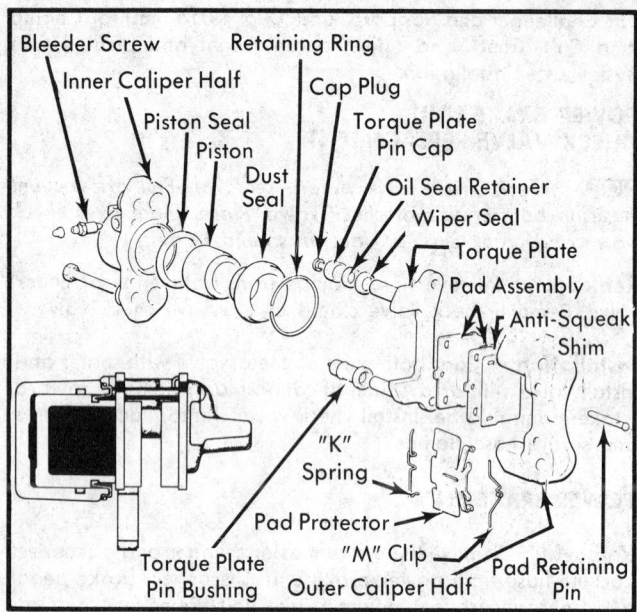

**Fig. 7   Disassembled View of Disc Brake Caliper
(Champ & Colt)**

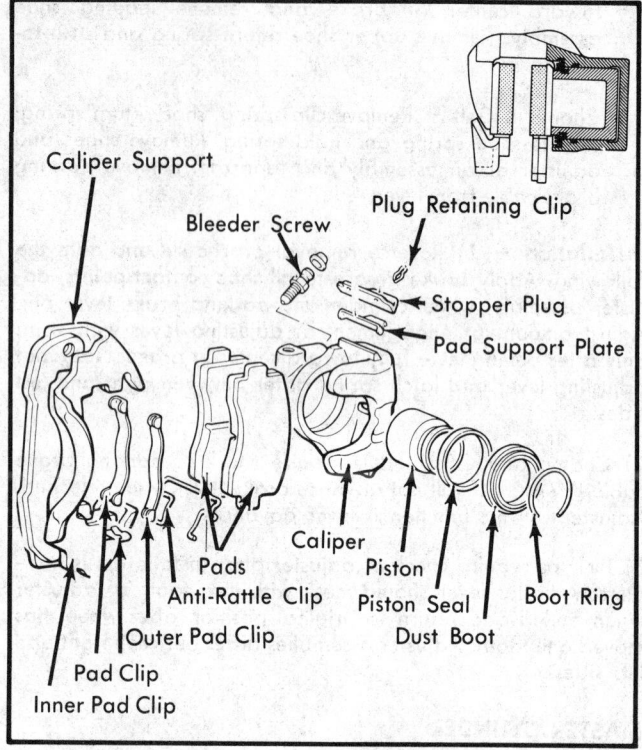

**Fig. 8   Exploded View of Front Disc Brake Caliper
(Challenger, Sapporo & Pickups)**

Cleaning & Inspection — Clean all metal parts in trichloro-ethylene, alcohol or brake fluid; clean piston seal in brake fluid or alcohol; clean dust seal and other rubber parts in alcohol only. Inspect caliper bore and piston for wear, damage or rust; replace parts as necessary. Always replace piston seal and dust seal.

NOTE — *Repair kits contain proper lubricants to be used during reassembly.*

Reassembly — Reverse disassembly procedure and note the following: Apply rubber grease to piston seal and brake fluid to piston when reassembling. If torque plate was removed from inner caliper half, clean torque plate shaft and shaft bore in caliper, then apply special rubber grease to rubber bushing, wipe seal inner surface, and torque plate shaft before reassembly. Tighten bridge bolts of caliper halves to specification.

NOTE — *Possible cause of increased pedal stroke is: Insufficient fit between piston and piston seal. Correct by manually levering piston to seat several times. This will create a better fit between piston and seal. Make sure brake pad is removed during this procedure.*

Disassembly (All Others) — Remove dust boot. Apply compressed air to fluid inlet to remove piston. Remove piston seal without damaging caliper bore or seal grooove.

Cleaning & Inspection — Clean all metal parts in trichloro-ethylene, alcohol or brake fluid; clean piston seal in alcohol or brake fluid; clean dust boot and other rubber parts in alcohol only. Inspect caliper bore and piston for wear, damage or rust; replace parts as necessary. Always replace piston seal and dust boot.

Reassembly — Coat piston seal with suitable rubber grease. Slide seal into groove in cylinder bore. Slip piston into bore making sure seal is not twisted. Lightly coat dust seal groove with recommended rubber grease. Fit dust boot into place. Refit cylinder to caliper.

REAR DISC BRAKE CALIPER

Disassembly — 1) Remove cap ring and take off lever cap. *See Fig. 9.* Remove retaining ring and spring, then pull out lever assembly. Slightly rotate automatic adjuster spindle, using pliers if necessary, and pull out assembly.

2) Using suitable bearing remover tool (MB990665), pull bearings from caliper. Take off piston boot. Working through vacant area created by adjuster spindle removal, force piston out of caliper. Use a blunt tool to push out piston. Remove piston seal without damaging caliper bore or seal groove.

Cleaning & Inspection — 1) Clean all metal parts in trichloroethylene, alcohol or brake fluid; clean piston seal and adjuster seal in alcohol or brake fluid; clean piston boot and other rubber parts in alcohol only. Check cylinder and piston for wear, damage or rust; replace worn parts as necessary. Always replace piston seal, adjuster seal and piston boot.

2) Check bearings, connecting link, springs, adjuster spindle and lever assembly for wear, damage or rust. Check lever assembly for excessive play between shaft and bearing. Check staking of piston inner sleeve stopper plate. Ensure piston-to-automatic adjuster spindle clearance is .013-.017" (.33-.43 mm).

Reassembly — 1) Lightly coat piston seal and piston with lubricant. Slide piston and seal into place, ensuring seal does not twist in groove. Lubricate boot and slide boot into position making sure it engages groove in cylinder bore.

NOTE — *Repair kit includes recommended lubricants.*

CHRYSLER CORP. IMPORTS (Cont.)

2) Using suitable bearing installation tool (MB990665), press in bearings until ends are flush with caliper body. Make sure mark on end of bearing faces out.

3) Coat automatic adjuster seal with recommended grease. Fit adjuster spindle and hardware in place until spindle turns freely. Make sure spring faces proper direction.

4) Press in connecting link spring washers with suitable tool (MB990666). Fit automatic adjuster spindle into place (spindle is not a press fit). Insert connecting link and lever assembly.

5) Fill lever cap with Niglube RX-2 (or equivalent), making sure all areas have significant amount of grease. Lightly grease stopper plug and caliper sliding surface. Assembly is ready for installation.

MASTER CYLINDER

Disassembly — Remove dust boot, retaining ring, stop washer and piston stop bolt. Withdraw primary piston assembly, secondary piston assembly and secondary return spring from master cylinder. Remove check valve caps, tube seats, check valves and check valve springs. Champ and Colt Hatchback master cylinders are equipped with two identical check valves.

NOTE — *DO NOT disassemble primary and secondary piston assembly.*

Cleaning & Inspection — Check master cylinder bore and piston for wear or other damage and replace as necessary. Check clearance between cylinder bore and piston; if clearance exceeds .006" (.15 mm), replace parts as necessary. Check all parts of primary and secondary piston assemblies and piston cups and springs; if any parts are found defective, replace components as assemblies.

Reassembly — Reverse disassembly procedure and note the following: Apply rubber grease to all parts (except boots) before reassembly. When assembled, check that return port is not blocked by piston cup when piston is located at return position.

NOTE — *Check valves differ between rear disc and rear drum models. Ensure correct check valve is properly installed.*

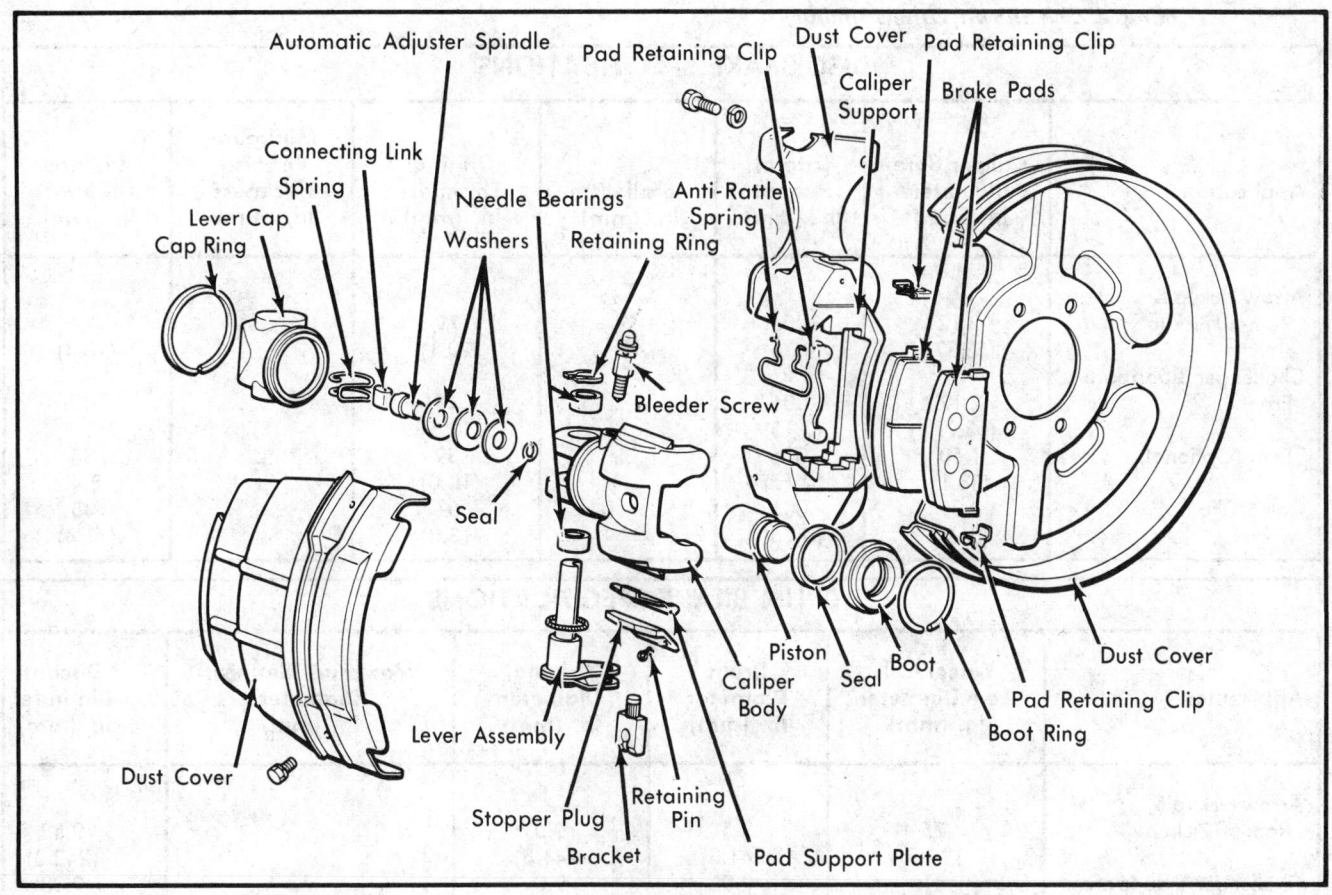

Fig. 9 Exploded View of Rear Disc Brake Caliper Assembly

CHRYSLER CORP. IMPORTS (Cont.)

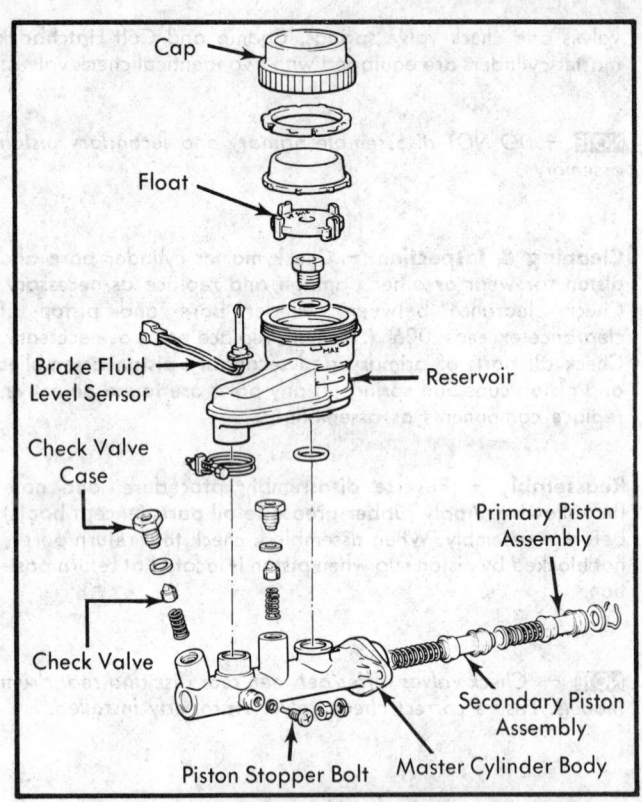

Cap
Float
Brake Fluid Level Sensor
Reservoir
Check Valve Case
Primary Piston Assembly
Check Valve
Secondary Piston Assembly
Piston Stopper Bolt
Master Cylinder Body

Fig. 10 Disassembled View of Master Cylinder (Champ & Colt Shown, Others Similar)

TIGHTENING SPECIFICATIONS

Application	Torque Ft. Lbs. (N·m)
Rotor to Hub Bolts	
Challenger & Sapporo	25-29 (34-39)
Champ & Colt	29-36 (39-49)
Pickup Models	34-38 (46-51)
Caliper Mounting Bolts	
Challenger & Sapporo	51-65 (69-88)
Champ & Colt	43-58 (59-78)
Pickup Models	51-65 (69-88)
Caliper Bridge Bolts	
Champ & Colt Only	58-69 (78-93)
Front Wheel Drive Components	
Drive Shaft Nut	87-130 (118-177)
Knuckle to Strut Assy.	54-65 (74-88)
Lower Arm to Ball Joint	69-87 (93-118)
Lower Arm to Strut Bar	69-87 (93-118)
Knuckle to Tie Rod	11-25 (15-33)

DISC BRAKE SPECIFICATIONS

Application	Caliper Bore Diameter In. (mm)	Lateral Runout In. (mm)	Parallelism In. (mm)	Original Thickness In. (mm)	Minimum Refinish Thickness In. (mm)	Discard Thickness In. (mm)
Arrow Pickup & Ram-50 Pickup	2.12 (53.97)	.006 (0.15)	.....	.79 (20.1)	.....	.72 (18.4)
Challenger & Sapporo Front	2.12 (53.97)	.006 (0.15)	.....	.49 (12.5)	.....	.43 (11.0)
Rear (Optional)	1.50 (38.1)	.006 (0.15)	.....	.39 (10.0)	.....	.33 (8.4)
Colt & Champ	2.01 (51.1)	.006 (0.15)	.....	.51 (13.0)	.....	.45 (11.4)

DRUM BRAKE SPECIFICATIONS

Application	Wheel Cyl. Bore Diameter In. (mm)	Drum Diameter In. (mm)	Original Diameter In. (mm)	Maximum Refinish Diameter In. (mm)	Discard Diameter In. (mm)
Arrow Pickup & Ram-50 Pickup	.75 (19.05)	9.5 (241.3)	9.5 (241.3)	.....	9.58 (243.3)
Challenger & Sapporo	.81 (20.64)	9.0 (228.6)	9.0 (228.6)	.....	9.08 (230.6)
Colt & Champ	.75 (19.05)	7.1 (180.0)	7.1 (180.0)	.....	7.20 (183.0)

COURIER

Pickup

DESCRIPTION

Brake system is hydraulically operated using a tandem master cylinder and vacuum power brake unit. Front brakes are sliding caliper disc; rear are leading/trailing drum. Brake system is protected by a pressure differential combination valve and warning light. If a leak occurs in front or rear brake system, or uneven fluid pressure develops, piston is moved off center, activating the warning light. Light will remain on until problem is corrected. Service brake systems are self-adjusting. Parking brake is cable actuated on rear wheels.

ADJUSTMENT

DRUM BRAKES

CAUTION — *Shoe-to-drum clearance must be made with brake drums at normal room temperature.*

1) Rear brakes are self-adjusting and require manual adjustment only after brake shoes have been replaced or adjusting rod length has been changed. To adjust, raise rear of vehicle and support on safety stands. Release parking brake and remove adjusting hole plugs from rear of backing plate.

2) Insert screwdriver through hole, rotate star wheel in direction of arrow stamped on backing plate until wheel locks. Insert a pointed tool through hole and push adjusting lever off star wheel. Back off star wheel 3 or 4 notches until wheel rotates freely without drag. Test drive vehicle after adjustment to ensure equal brake action.

NOTE — *Adjustment must be equal on both wheels.*

PEDAL FREE PLAY

Loosen lock nut on master cylinder push rod at clevis. Turn push rod in or out to obtain .33-.39" (8.5-10.0 mm) free play, measured at pedal pad. When clearance is correct, tighten lock nut.

STOP LIGHT SWITCH

Loosen lock nut and adjust stop light switch until it just contacts brake pedal stopper. DO NOT depress master cylinder push rod during stop light switch adjustment.

PARKING BRAKE

Adjust length of cable at equalizer so rear brakes are locked when parking brake lever is pulled out 5 to 10 ratchet clicks (1⅝-3⅛"; 40-80 mm). After adjustment, operate parking brake several times to ensure wheels rotate freely when parking brake is released.

NOTE — *Service brakes must be properly adjusted prior to adjusting parking brake.*

BRAKE WARNING LIGHT

A dual warning light is mounted on instrument panel. Parking brake light should glow when parking brake lever is pulled 1 notch (ignition on) and go off when lever is fully released. To check circuit warning sensor, fully release parking brake and ensure light is off (ignition on). Open 1 bleed screw and depress brake pedal; light should glow. Close bleed screw. To reset warning light; turn ignition on and depress brake pedal. Piston will center itself, causing the warning light to go off. Turn ignition off.

NOTE — *Warning light will glow after any repair on service brake system and will not go out until piston is centered in pressure differential valve.*

REMOVAL & INSTALLATION

DISC BRAKE PADS

Removal — Raise front of vehicle, support on safety stands and remove wheel. Remove locking spring clips and drive out stopper plates. Remove caliper body and anti-rattle spring from caliper bracket. Set caliper out of way; DO NOT allow caliper to hang from brake line. Remove disc pads and shims (if equipped). Note position of shims.

NOTE — *All pads must be replaced at same time.*

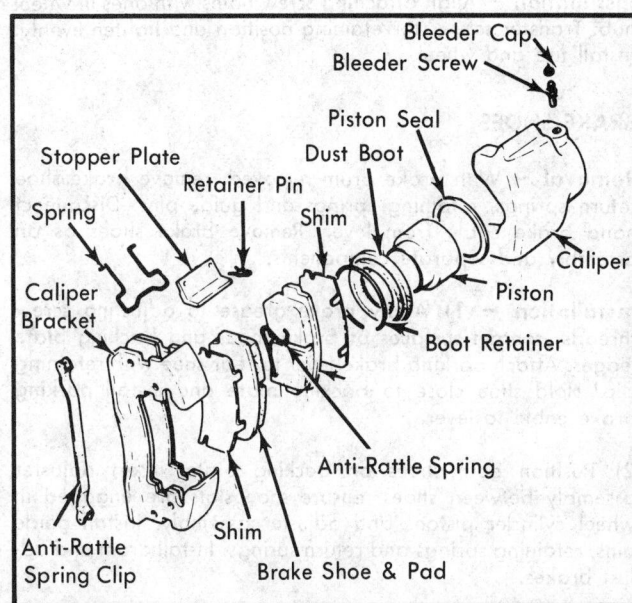

Fig. 1 Exploded View of Front Disc Brake

Installation — **1)** Pull bleeder cap off caliper and attach a tube to bleed screw. Open bleed screw and seat piston in bore with "C" clamp. Tighten bleed screw and remove clamp.

2) Install new pads and shims (if required) when pad thickness has worn to .276" (7 mm). Install anti-rattle spring and caliper body. Apply light coat of grease to stopper plates. Install plates and spring clips. Install wheel. Check brake fluid level and test brakes for proper operation.

FRONT DISC BRAKE CALIPER

Removal — Raise and support vehicle on safety stands; remove wheel. Remove clip at connection of flexible hose and

COURIER (Cont.)

brake line; separate and plug openings. Remove caliper bracket mounting bolts and remove entire assembly.

Installation — Reverse removal procedure, bleed brake system and centralize differential valve.

BRAKE ROTOR

Removal — With caliper assembly removed, remove dust cap, cotter pin, adjusting cap, adjusting nut, thrust washer and outer bearing. Remove hub and rotor assembly from spindle. Remove hub-to-rotor bolts and separate hub from rotor.

Installation — Reverse removal procedure, tighten hub-to-rotor bolts securely and adjust wheel bearings. *See Wheel Bearing Adjustment in WHEEL ALIGNMENT Section.*

BRAKE DRUM

Removal — Raise and support vehicle on safety stands; remove tire and wheel. Remove brake drum attaching screws and install them in tapered holes in brake drum. Turn screws in evenly to force drum away from wheel hub. Remove drum.

Installation — Align attaching screw holes with ones in wheel hub. Transfer screws to retaining position and tighten evenly. Install tire and wheel.

BRAKE SHOES

Removal — With brake drum removed, remove brake shoe return springs, retaining springs and guide pins. Disconnect hand brake cable from lever. Remove brake shoes as an assembly and separate components.

Installation — 1) Apply brake grease to adjusting screw threads, contact surfaces of brake shoes and backing plate ledges. Attach parking brake lever to rear shoe with retaining clip. Hold shoe close to backing plate and install parking brake cable to lever.

2) Position both shoes on backing plate, insert adjuster assembly between shoes; ensure shoe slots are engaged in wheel cylinder pistons and adjuster assembly. Install guide pins, retaining springs and return springs. Install drum and adjust brakes.

MASTER CYLINDER

Removal — Disconnect brake hydraulic lines and reservoir lines; plug all openings. Remove master cylinder-to-brake booster mounting nuts. Lift master cylinder outward and upward away from booster and push rod.

Installation — Reverse removal procedure and carefully guide push rod into master cylinder piston. Bleed brake system and check pedal free play.

PRESSURE DIFFERENTIAL VALVE

Removal — Disconnect warning light wire and hydraulic lines from combination valve. Remove mounting bolt and differential valve.

Installation — To install, reverse removal procedure and note the following: Bleed hydraulic system and center pressure differential valve.

POWER BRAKE BOOSTER

Removal — With master cylinder removed, disconnect vacuum line from booster. From inside vehicle, remove cotter pin attaching operating rod clevis to brake pedal, then remove mounting nuts from dash panel. Remove brake booster from engine compartment.

Installation — To install, reverse removal procedure and note the following: Install master cylinder, bleed hydraulic system, check pedal free play, center pressure differential valve and ensure proper brake operation.

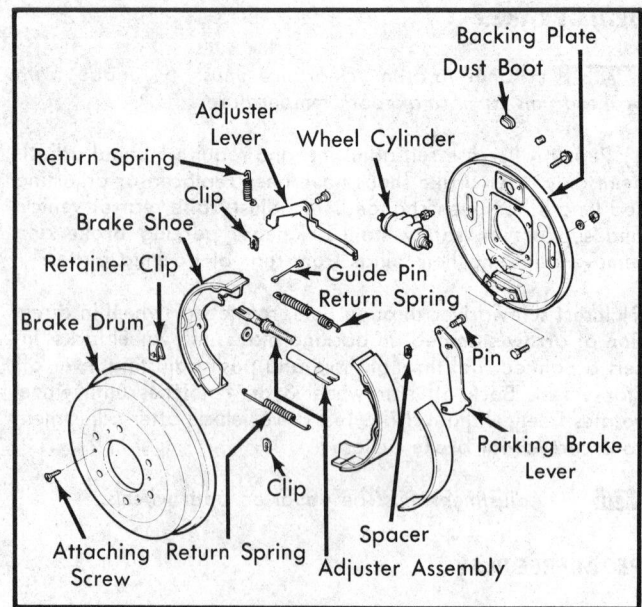

Fig. 2 Exploded View of Rear Brake Assembly

OVERHAUL

FRONT DISC BRAKE CALIPER

Disassembly — 1) Clean outside of caliper. Separate cylinder from bracket. Remove boot retainer and slide off dust boot. Force compressed air into brake line hole to remove piston from caliper.

2) It may be necessary to tap outside of piston housing with plastic hammer while applying air pressure to unseat piston. Dig out piston seal from inside caliper bore.

Cleaning and Inspection — Wash all disassembled parts in clean brake fluid and completely dry with compressed air. Inspect caliper bore and piston for scratches, grooves or rust. Minor imperfections can be eliminated with crocus cloth. Piston seal and dust boot must be replaced during each overhaul.

Reassembly — Lightly coat piston seal with brake fluid and insert into groove in caliper bore. Make sure seal is not twisted in groove. Lubricate piston and bore with brake fluid, then slide piston into place. Fit dust boot with flange seated in inner groove of caliper. Fit dust boot retainer.

COURIER (Cont.)

MASTER CYLINDER

Disassembly — 1) Drain brake fluid from reservoir and separate reservoir from master cylinder inlet ports. Remove primary piston snap ring and stop washer. Slide out primary piston, return spring and cup from bore.

2) Loosen secondary piston stop screw. Push secondary piston into cylinder bore with a screwdriver. Remove stop screw and "O" ring. Insert fabricated guide pin into stop screw hole. See Fig. 4.

3) Release pressure on secondary piston. Remove secondary return spring and cup. Use low air pressure if required. Remove brake line fittings, gaskets, check valves and springs.

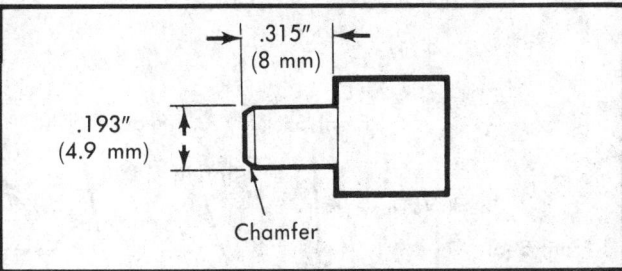

Fig. 4   Dimensions for Fabricating Guide Pin

2) Install secondary and primary cups to secondary piston. Insert fabricated guide pin into stop screw hole. Slide piston assembly and spring into cylinder; seat piston with screwdriver, remove guide pin and install stop screw and "O" ring. Release pressure on secondary piston.

3) Install cups to primary piston and insert piston assembly and spring into cylinder. Install washer and snap ring. Install reservoir and hoses to master cylinder.

POWER BRAKE BOOSTER

Disassembly — 1) Fit booster in vise with rod facing up and scribe index mark on both shells. Remove lock nut, clevis and dust boot. Rotate shell clockwise, unlocking it from front shell. Lift off shell complete with:

- Diaphragm
- Power Piston Assembly
- Valve Rod
- Plunger Assembly

2) Remove spring from front shell. From inside rear shell remove:

- Diaphragm
- Power Piston Assembly
- Valve Rod
- Plunger Assembly

3) Remove rear seal, with punch, from rear shell only if seal needs replacing. Take out air silencer retainer and air filter from power piston. DO NOT damage piston.

4) Press in valve rod and remove retainer key. Take valve rod and plunger assembly off power piston. Press out reaction disc. Slide push rod out of front shell.

Cleaning & Inspection — Wipe parts clean and inspect rubber parts for cuts, nicks or deformation. Inspect power piston for cracks, chipping, distortion and damaged seats. Inspect reaction disc, valve rod and plunger assembly and shells for nicks, dents or other damage. Inspect diaphragm for cuts. Replace defective parts.

Reassembly — 1) Apply brake fluid to inside of power piston bore and to surface of valve rod and plunger assembly. Insert valve rod and plunger assembly into power piston. Press in valve rod and align plunger groove with slot in power piston. Insert retainer key.

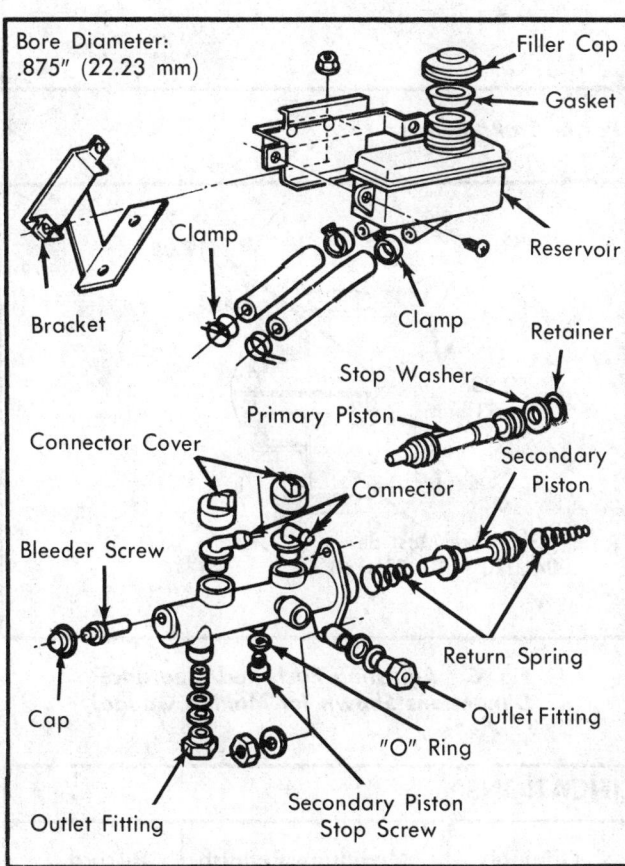

Fig. 3   Exploded View of Master Cylinder and Related Components

Cleaning & Inspection — Clean all parts in isopropyl alcohol and dry with compressed air. Check cups for wear, cracks or deformation. Check cylinder bore and pistons for wear, roughness or scoring. Replace defective parts. Check cylinder bore-to-piston clearance; if greater than .006" (.15 mm), replace pistons.

Reassembly — 1) Apply brake fluid to pistons and cups. Install check valves and springs, gaskets and brake line fittings in outlet holes.

NOTE — *Check valve with hole must be installed in outlet hole on side of master cylinder.*

COURIER (Cont.)

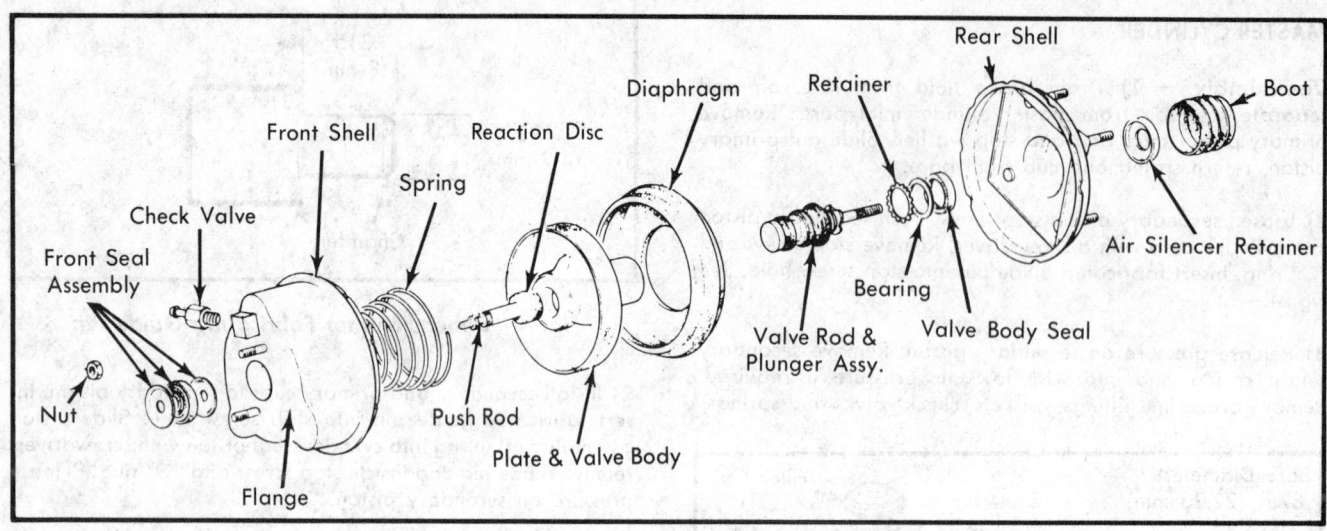

Fig. 5   Exploded View of Power Brake Booster

2) Install diaphragm on power piston; diaphragm must be seated in piston groove. Install air silencer and filter over valve rod and insert in power piston. Coat reaction disc surface with brake fluid and install in power piston.

3) Coat outer edge of diaphragm and rear shell seal with brake fluid. Carefully guide tube end of power piston through rear shell seal. Install push rod to front of power piston. Install return spring in front shell. Position rear shell over front shell, press down and rotate counterclockwise until scribe marks align.

4) Install dust boot, clevis and lock nut. Check push rod clearance with fabricated gauge. Clearance should be .004-.020″ (.10-.51 mm). See Fig. 6.

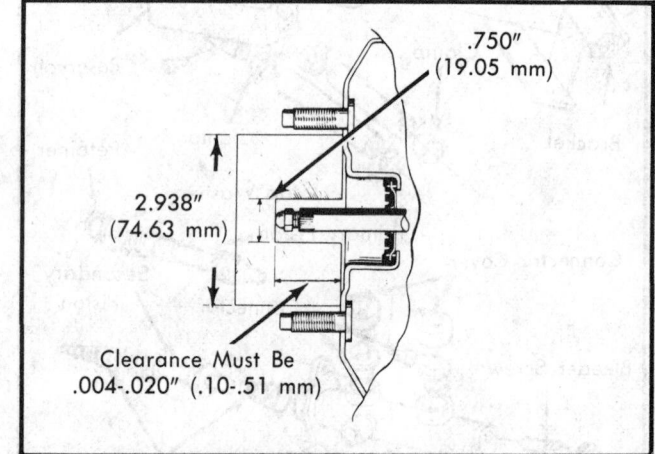

Fig. 6   Adjusting Push Rod Clearance (Dimensions Shown for Making Gauge)

DRUM BRAKE SPECIFICATIONS

Application	Wheel Cyl. Bore Diameter In. (mm)	Drum Diameter In. (mm)	Original Diameter In. (mm)	Maximum Refinish Diameter In. (mm)	Discard Diameter In. (mm)
Pickup	.875 (22.23)	10.236 (260)	10.236 (260)	10.276 (261)	.....

DISC BRAKE SPECIFICATIONS

Application	Caliper Bore Diameter In. (mm)	Lateral Runout In. (mm)	Parallelism In. (mm)	Original Thickness In. (mm)	Minimum Refinish Thickness In. (mm)	Discard Thickness In. (mm)
Pickup	2.125 (53.98)	.004 (.10)	.....	.472 (12)	.433 (11)	.....

Brakes

DATSUN 200SX, 280ZX & 810

DESCRIPTION

Brake system is hydraulically operated using tandem master cylinder and vacuum power unit. Front brakes of 280ZX are sliding caliper disc; rear brakes are fixed caliper, sliding yoke disc. Front and rear brakes of 200SX are fixed caliper, sliding yoke disc. Brake systems are equipped with a combination valve to prevent premature lockup of rear wheels. Service brake systems are self-adjusting. Parking brake is cable actuated on rear brake systems.

NOTE — *Rear disc brakes are optional equipment on 810 models. For models equipped with standard rear drum brakes, see appropriate story in this section.*

ADJUSTMENT

PEDAL HEIGHT & FREE PLAY

Adjust pedal height (measured from pedal pad to floor) to specification shown in table by moving stop light switch. Loosen operating rod lock nut and turn operating rod to attain proper height, tighten lock nut and adjust stop light switch. Pedal free play should be .04-.20" (1-5 mm). If specification is exceeded, adjust push rod length.

Pedal Height Specifications	
Application	**Pedal Height In. (mm)**
200SX	6.1-6.3 (155-161)
280ZX	
Man. Trans.	7.1-7.4 (181-187)
Auto. Trans.	7.5-7.7 (190-196)
810	6.5-6.7 (164-170)

STOP LIGHT SWITCH

Stop light switch is located under dash panel at brake pedal. Adjust travel during pedal height adjustment. After obtaining correct pedal height, position stop light switch until it just contacts brake pedal arm. Tighten lock nut.

PARKING BRAKE

200SX & 810 — Adjust parking brake by rotating turnbuckle. Rear wheels should lock when brake lever is pulled 7-8 notches with 44 lbs. (20 kg.) force. After releasing lever, ensure rear wheels rotate freely, rear cables are not slack and that rear brake toggle levers are in original positions.

280ZX — Adjust front cable adjusting nut so when parking brake lever is pulled with 60 lbs. (27 kg) force, lever stroke is 4-6 notches and rear wheels are locked. After releasing lever, ensure rear wheels rotate freely, rear cables are not slack and that rear brake toggle levers are in original positions.

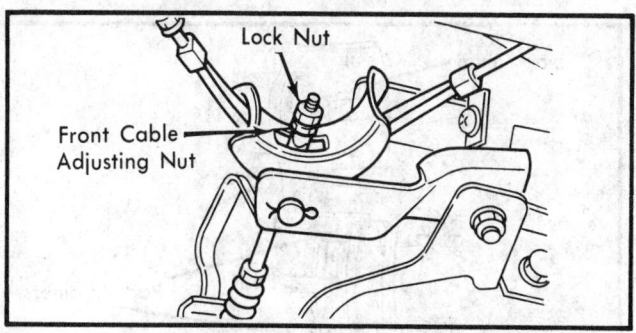

Fig. 1 Location for Adjusting 280ZX Parking Brake

BRAKE WARNING LIGHT

Light indicates parking brake is engaged and also warns of low brake fluid level. To adjust light operation with parking brake applied, bend switch plate down until light comes on when brake lever is pulled up 1 notch and goes out when lever is released (ignition on). To check warning light operation, release parking brake lever and raise master cylinder reservoir cap (ignition on). Warning light should glow. If not, check switch and wire connector.

REMOVAL & INSTALLATION

FRONT DISC BRAKE PADS

Removal (200SX) — Raise and support vehicle; remove tire and wheel. Remove retaining pin clips, retaining pins and pad springs. Remove pads from caliper assembly, using suitable pliers if necessary.

CAUTION — *DO NOT force piston groove inside piston seal. Piston seal could be damaged and caliper will have to be disassembled.*

Installation — **1)** Clean and apply P.B.C. grease to cylinder body yoke guide groove, yoke sliding contact points and piston end surface. Loosen bleeder screw and push outer piston into cylinder until piston end surface coincides with boot retaining ring end surface. Tighten bleeder screw and install inner brake pad.

2) Push inner piston into cylinder by pulling on yoke, then install outer pad. Install pad springs, retaining pins and clips. Depress brake pedal several times to seat pads and bleed hydraulic system if necessary.

Removal (280ZX & 810) — Raise and support vehicle. Remove tire and wheel. Remove lower pin bolt. Rotate caliper body upward. Remove pad retainers, shims and brake pads.

NOTE — *Do not pull caliper body away from rotor; use upper pin bolt as center of rotation.*

Installation — **1)** Clean piston and area around pin bolts with brake fluid. Install inner pad and seat piston by placing lever through opening in caliper body and pushing piston into bore. Apply brake grease to pad retainer points on caliper assembly and install outer pad and both shims.

DATSUN 200SX, 280ZX & 810 (Cont.)

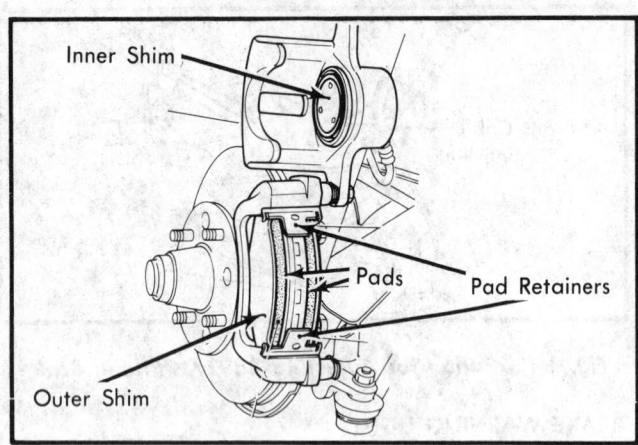

Fig. 2 Front Disc Brake Pad Retainer Location (280ZX & 810)

2) Install pad retainers. Rotate caliper body down into original position and install lower pin bolt. Tighten pin bolt and depress brake pedal several times to seat pads.

FRONT DISC BRAKE CALIPER

Removal — Raise and support vehicle. Remove wheel and tire. Disconnect and plug brake line from caliper. Remove caliper mounting bolts and remove caliper assembly.

Installation — To install, reverse removal procedure, tighten caliper bolts securely and bleed hydraulic system.

FRONT DISC BRAKE ROTOR

Removal — Remove caliper assembly as previously described and hang from frame with wire; DO NOT disconnect hydraulic line. Remove hub dust cap, "O" ring, cotter pin, adjusting cap and lock nut. Remove hub and rotor assembly from spindle without dropping outer bearing and washer. Remove outer bearing, washer and hub-to-rotor bolts. Separate rotor from hub.

NOTE — Avoid damage to hub dust cap "O" ring during removal of dust cap.

Installation — Reverse removal procedure and adjust wheel bearings. See Wheel Bearing Adjustment in SUSPENSION Section.

REAR DISC BRAKE PADS

Removal — Raise and support vehicle. Remove tire and wheel. Remove pin clip, then remove pad pins while holding anti-squeal springs with finger. Remove disc pads and shims (if equipped).

Installation — **1)** Apply brake grease to caliper body-to-pad clearance, yoke-to-pad clearance, pin-to-pad clearance, pin-to-bracket clearance and both sides of shims (200SX and 810). Apply silicon grease to friction surface of installing pads by pushing and turning outer piston clockwise until it retracts into caliper bore.

NOTE — Avoid damaging dust seal while turning outer piston.

2) Place lever between yoke and bore and move yoke until clearances to install pads are equal. Align outer piston so cut out portion is level. Install inner pad with protrusion of pad seated in piston cut out. Install shims on 200SX and 810. Install outer pad, anti-squeal springs, pad pins and pin clip. Depress brake pedal several times to adjust clearance. Pad-to-rotor clearance is correct when pedal stroke is constant. Add brake fluid and bleed hydraulic system.

REAR DISC BRAKE CALIPER

Removal — Disconnect hydraulic line from caliper and plug openings. Disconnect parking brake cable. Remove mounting bolts and remove caliper.

Installation — Reverse removal procedure and bleed hydraulic system if necessary. Depress brake pedal several times; when pedal stroke is constant, brake pad-to-rotor clearance is properly adjusted. Turn rotor to make sure no excessive drag is present.

REAR DISC BRAKE ROTOR

Removal — With caliper removed, pull rotor from axle stub.

Installation — Install rotor and caliper assembly. After installation, depress pedal until pedal stroke is constant to adjust pad-to-rotor clearance.

MASTER CYLINDER

Removal — Remove heat shield plate (if equipped). Disconnect brake fluid level gauge wiring and hydraulic lines from master cylinder. Remove master cylinder-to-power unit mounting nuts and remove master cylinder from power brake unit.

Installation — Reverse removal procedure, check pedal height and bleed hydraulic system.

POWER BRAKE UNIT

NOTE — Before removal, test check valve. Using brake booster tester, apply 7.9 in. Hg to brake unit side of check valve on 200SX. Apply 19.7 in. Hg to check valve on 810. If pressure drops more than .39 in. Hg in 15 seconds, replace check valve. Also, if valve does not open when pressure is applied to brake unit side of check valve, replace check valve. If valve is not defective, check brake system and vacuum lines for leaks. Replace if necessary.

Removal — Disconnect power unit push rod from brake pedal by removing clevis pin. Disconnect hydraulic lines from master cylinder, vacuum line from power unit, remove master cylinder mounting nuts, and remove master cylinder. Remove nuts attaching power unit to firewall, and remove power unit from engine compartment.

Installation — **1)** Reverse removal procedure and check push rod length, operating rod length and pedal height. Push rod length should be .38-.39" (9.75-10 mm) on 200SX and 810, and .37-.41" (9.5-10.5 mm) on 280ZX. Push rod on 200SX and 810 can NOT be adjusted. If not to specification, replace power unit. Adjust push rod length on 280ZX by turning tip of push rod.

Brakes

DATSUN 200SX, 280ZX & 810 (Cont.)

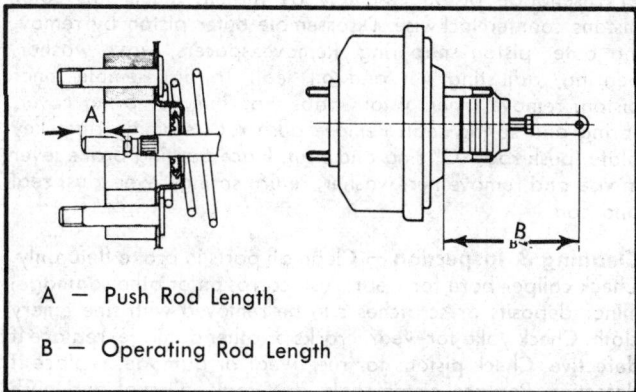

A — Push Rod Length

B — Operating Rod Length

**Fig. 3 Location for Measuring
Push Rod and Operating Rod Lengths**

2) Operating rod length should be 5.12" (130 mm) on 200SX, 5.63" (143 mm) on 280ZX and 5.71" (145 mm) on 810. Adjust operating rod length by loosening lock nut and turning operating rod to attain proper length. Tighten lock nut and clevis. Bleed system.

Check Valve Replacement — Check valve is located in vacuum line between intake manifold and power unit on firewall. To remove, disconnect retaining clip from firewall, remove hose clamps, separate hoses from valve, and remove check valve. To install, reverse removal procedure.

OVERHAUL

FRONT DISC BRAKE CALIPER

Disassembly (200SX) — With caliper and pads removed, drain any remaining fluid from cylinder. Remove gripper pin attaching bolts. Separate yoke and cylinder body. Remove yoke holder from piston. Remove retaining rings and dust seals from pistons. Push both pistons out in one direction. Remove piston seals. Remove gripper, if necessary.

Cleaning & Inspection — Clean all parts with brake fluid and check all components for wear or damage. If minor corrosion cannot be removed from cylinder bore with fine emery cloth, cylinder must be replaced. Replace all seals during overhaul.

NOTE — *Piston surfaces are plated and must be replaced if corroded or worn. DO NOT polish with emery cloth.*

Reassembly — 1) Install piston seals without damaging seals. Coat cylinder bore and pistons with brake fluid. Push outer piston into cylinder until piston end surface coincides with boot retaining ring end surface. DO NOT force piston groove inside piston seal. Push inner piston into cylinder bore by holding cylinder body and align piston yoke groove with cylinder yoke groove.

2) Apply brake grease to sealing surface of dust seal and install dust seal; clamping securely with retaining ring. Install yoke holder to inner piston. Install gripper to yoke. Apply 1% soap solution to inner gripper wall and drive gripper pin into position. Install yoke to yoke holder by supporting outer piston

end and pressing yoke into yoke holder with 44-66 lb. (20-30 kg) force. No clearance should be present between piston and yoke.

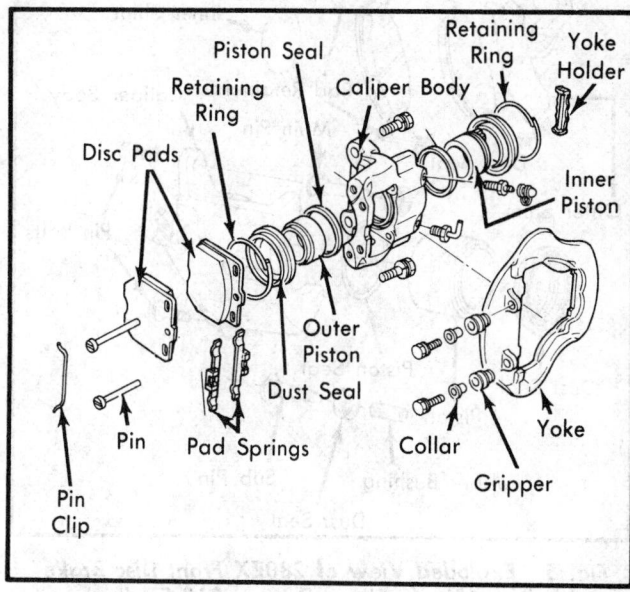

Fig. 4 Exploded View of 200SX Front Disc Brake Caliper

Disassembly (280ZX & 810) — Drain brake fluid from caliper body and clean exterior of caliper assembly. Remove pin bolts, separate caliper body from pad carrier and remove pad retainers and pads. Force piston and dust seal out of bore by applying compressed air to brake inlet. Remove piston seal without damaging seal and bore. Remove sub pin, main pin, sub pin bushing and seals.

Cleaning & Inspection — Clean all parts in brake fluid only. Check caliper bore for wear, rust, corrosion or other damage; minor deposits or scratches can be removed with fine emery cloth. Check pad carrier for wear, cracks or other damage; replace if defective. Check piston for rust, wear or damage; replace if defective. Check main pin and sub pin for wear, cracks or other damage; replace if defective. Replace piston seal and dust seals during overhaul.

Reassembly — 1) Apply brake fluid to sliding portions of piston and caliper bore. Apply rubber grease to inside of dust seals. Install piston seal in bore; install dust seal on piston and slide piston into caliper bore. Secure dust seal in piston groove and caliper groove.

2) Apply multi-purpose grease to sub pin rubber bushing, main pin and sub pin. Install seals, sub pin rubber bushing, sub pin and main pin. Apply brake grease to disc pad-to-carrier contact portions and mount pad carrier to caliper body. Install upper pin bolt, install disc pads, shims and rotate caliper down into position and install lower pin bolt. When caliper assembly is mounted on vehicle, turn rotor to ensure there is not excessive drag.

Brakes

DATSUN 200SX, 280ZX & 810 (Cont.)

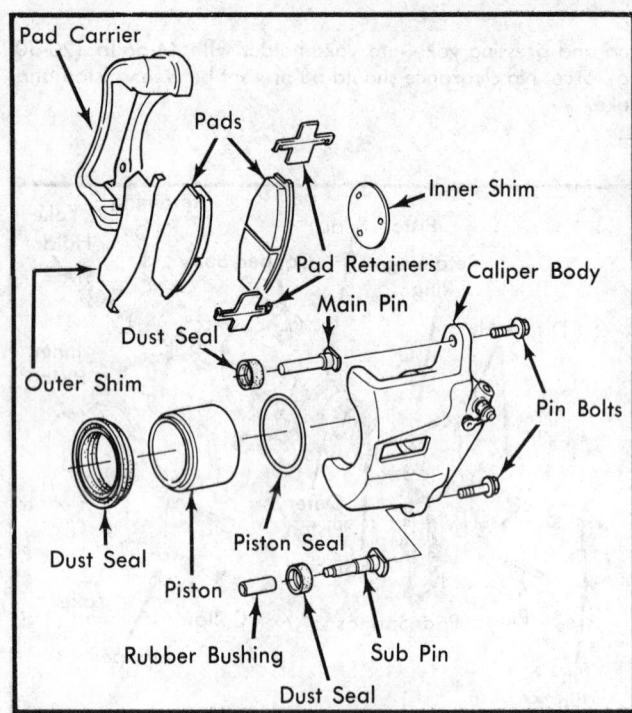

Fig. 5 Exploded View of 280ZX Front Disc Brake Caliper (Single Piston Design, 810 Similar)

REAR DISC BRAKE CALIPER

Disassembly — 1) Drain brake fluid from caliper body and clean exterior of caliper. Remove pads. Place caliper assembly on a work bench with yoke down; push in caliper body and separate caliper and yoke. Remove retaining rings and dust seals from piston ends. Push outer piston to remove piston assembly from caliper bore. Remove piston seals without damaging caliper bore.

2) Disengage piston assembly by turning inner and outer pistons counterclockwise. Disassemble outer piston by removing outer piston snap ring. Remove spacers, wave washer, bearing, adjusting nut and oil seal. To disassemble inner piston, remove inner piston snap ring. Remove spring cover, spring and spring seat. Remove push rod retaining ring, key plate, push rod, "O" ring and strut. Place parking brake lever in vise and remove nut, washer, return spring, lever, dust seal and cam.

Cleaning & Inspection — Clean all parts in brake fluid only. Check caliper bore for wear, rust, corrosion or other damage; minor deposits or scratches can be removed with fine emery cloth. Check yoke for wear, cracks or other damage; replace if defective. Check pistons for rust, wear or damage; replace if defective. Replace piston seals, dust seals, oil seal and push rod "O" ring during overhaul.

NOTE — *DO NOT use abrasives on piston plated surfaces.*

Reassembly — 1) Apply suitable grease to push rod groove, "O" ring, strut ends, oil seal, piston seals and inside dust seals. Install new oil seal on adjusting nut. See Fig. 7. Slide adjusting nut and seal into outer piston, then install bearing, spacer, wave washer, second spacer and secure components in position with outer piston snap ring.

2) Place cam inside inner piston and securely fit strut in cam hole. Install "O" ring on push rod without twisting "O" ring. Align square hole in key plate with push rod and slide assembly into inner piston bore; rounded portion of plate must seat in piston. Install push rod retaining ring. Position spring seat, spring and spring cover in position. Hold spring and spring cover in position with suitable drift and install inner piston snap ring.

NOTE — *Do not use excessive force on spring cover; cover will require replacement if deformed.*

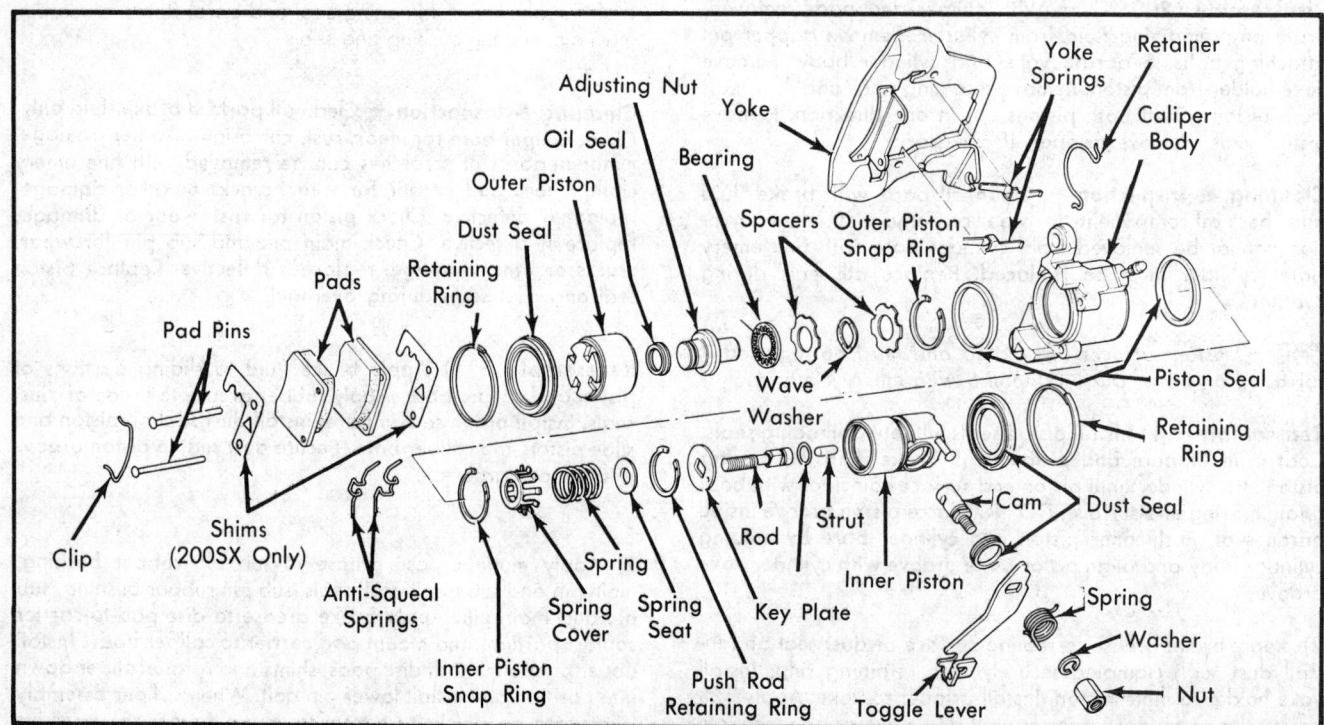

Fig. 6 Exploded View of Rear Disc Brake Caliper

DATSUN 200SX, 280ZX & 810 (Cont.)

3) Install toggle lever dust seal on cam (cam must face direction of parking brake operation) and align square hole in toggle lever on cam. Install return spring, lock washer and tighten nut. Reassemble piston assembly by turning clockwise. Coat sliding portions of piston assembly and caliper bore with brake fluid. Slide piston assembly into bore (outside piston first) from rear of caliper assembly. Install new dust seals and secure in position with retainer rings.

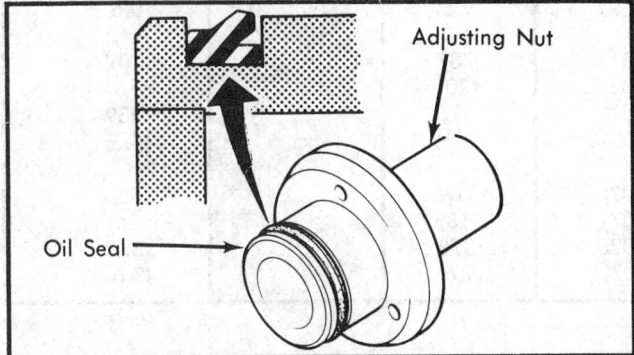

Fig. 7   Installation of Oil Seal on Rear Caliper Adjusting Nut

4) Install yoke springs to yoke. Coat yoke and caliper body frictional surfaces and caliper body pad pin holes with silicone grease. Align cut out portion of inner piston with yoke and reassemble yoke to caliper. Securely position retainer in piston groove.

5) Apply brake grease to caliper body-to-pad clearance, yoke-to-pad clearance, pad pin-to-pad clearance and pad pin-to-bracket clearance. Install pads, springs, pins and clip.

MASTER CYLINDER

Disassembly — Remove reservoir caps and filters; drain brake fluid. Remove snap ring and stopper bolt. Withdraw stopper, primary piston assembly, secondary piston assembly and springs. Remove check valve plugs and withdraw check valve assemblies.

NOTE — *Do not remove reservoir tanks. If tanks are removed for any reason, discard and install new tanks. Also, do not remove or disassemble brake fluid level gauge.*

Cleaning & Inspection — Clean all parts in brake fluid and check components for excessive wear or damage. If piston-to-cylinder clearance exceeds .006" (.15 mm) replace defective part. Caps, gaskets, packing and valves must be replaced during overhaul.

NOTE — *Master cylinders are produced by two companies and parts are not interchangeable. Ensure repair kit matches master cylinder. Only "Tokico" master cylinder is used on 200SX.*

Reassembly — Reverse disassembly procedure and note the following: Apply rubber grease to all rubber parts and brake fluid to remaining parts when assembling to prevent damage.

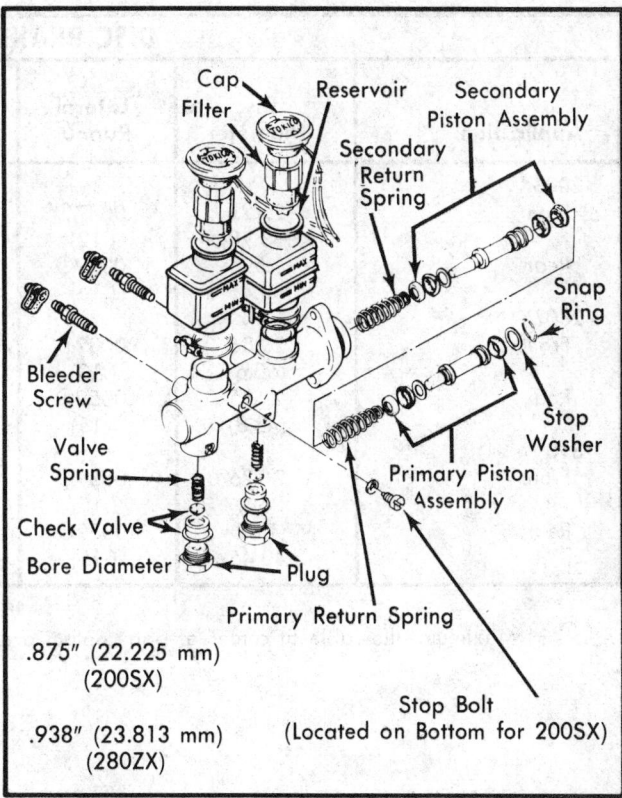

Fig. 8   Exploded View of Tokico Master Cylinder Nabco Master Cylinder is Similar But Has Different Piston Configuration for 280ZX

POWER BRAKE UNIT

NOTE — *Manufacturer does not recommend disassembly of this unit. If a problem is determined to be in power brake unit, complete assembly must be replaced. Do not disassemble power brake unit.*

TIGHTENING SPECIFICATIONS

Application	Ft. Lbs. (N.m)
Hub-to-Rotor Bolts	
200SX (Front)	28-34 (38-46)
280ZX (Front)	40-54 (54-73)
810 (Front)	36-51 (49-69)
Front Disc Brake Caliper	
200SX	
Yoke-to-Caliper Bolts	12-15 (16-20)
Caliper Mounting Bolts	53-72 (72-98)
280ZX	
Caliper-to-Carrier Bolts	16-23 (22-31)
Carrier-to-Mounting Bolts	53-72 (72-98)
810	
Main & Sub Pins	12-15 (16-20)
Rear Disc Brake Caliber	
Toggle Lever Nut	18-22 (25-30)
Caliper Mounting Bolts	28-38 (38-52)

Brakes

DATSUN 200SX, 280ZX & 810 (Cont.)

DISC BRAKE SPECIFICATIONS						
Application	Disc Diameter	Lateral Runout	Parallelism	Original Thickness	Minimum Refinish Thickness	Discard Thickness
200SX						
Front	2.125 (53.98)	.0047① (.12)	.0028 (.07)	.492 (12.5)	.....	.413 (10.5)
Rear	1.593 (40.46)	.0059① (.15)	.0028 (.07)	.378 (9.6)	.....	.339 (8.6)
280ZX						
Front	2.386 (60.6)	.0039① (.10)	.0012 (.03)	.787 (20)	.....	.709 (18)
Rear	1.685 (42.8)	.0059① (.15)	.0012 (.03)	.378 (9.6)	.....	.339 (8.6)
810						
Front	2.126 (54)	.0059① (.15)	.0028 (.07)	.709 (18)	.....	.630 (16)
Rear	1.59 (40.46)	.0059① (.15)	.0028 (.07)	.378 (9.6)	.....	.339 (8.6)

① — Maximum allowable at center of pad contact area.

Brakes

DATSUN 210, 310, 510, 810 & PICKUPS

DESCRIPTION

Brake system is hydraulically operated using tandem master cylinder and vacuum power unit. All models except 810 are equipped with single cylinder, dual piston, fixed caliper, sliding yoke type front disc brakes. 810 models are equipped with single piston sliding caliper disc brakes. Rear brake systems are duo-servo drum on pickups and leading/trailing drum on all other models. All models are equipped with combination valves to prevent premature rear wheel lock-up. The combination valve on pickups is mounted at a 10 incline on frame to change braking power of rear wheels in response to changes in load and brake fluid pressures. Parking brake systems are cable operated at rear wheels.

NOTE — *Some 810 models may be equipped with optional rear disc brakes. See article on Datsun 200SX, 280ZX & 810 4-Wheel Disc Brakes in this section for coverage of front and rear disc brakes.*

ADJUSTMENT

DRUM BRAKES

Pickups — Raise and support vehicle. Release parking brake and remove dust boot from backing plate. Lightly tap adjuster housing and move it forward. Rotate adjuster down with a screwdriver until drum locks. Back off adjuster 12 notches for correct shoe-to-drum clearance. Rotate brake drum by hand and ensure no excessive drag is present. Readjust clearance if necessary. Reinstall rubber boot and lower vehicle.

All Other Models — Drum brakes are self-adjusting and no adjustment in service is required.

PEDAL HEIGHT & FREE PLAY

Adjust pedal height (measured from pedal pad to floor) to specification shown in table by moving stop light switch. Loosen operating rod lock nut and turn operating rod to attain proper height, tighten lock nut and adjust stop light switch. Pedal free play should be .04-.20" (1-5 mm). If specification is exceeded, adjust push rod length.

Pedal Height Specifications	
Application	**Pedal Height In. (mm)**
210	5.6-5.9 (143-149)
310	7.1-7.3 (180-186)
510	6.1-6.3 (156-160)
Pickup	6.6-6.9 (168-174)

STOP LIGHT SWITCH

Stop light switch is located under dash panel at brake pedal. Adjust travel during pedal height adjustment. After obtaining correct pedal height, position stop light switch until it just contacts brake pedal arm. Tighten lock nut.

PARKING BRAKE

Pickup — Adjust parking brake by applying parking brake with 44 lbs. (20 kg) force to obtain lever stroke of 6-10 notches. Adjust equalizer link with adjusting nut until rear wheels are locked. Release parking brake. Ensure rear wheels turn freely. After adjustment, parking brake should operate smoothly without noise or drag.

All Other Models — Adjust parking brake by rotating turnbuckle. Rear wheels should lock when lever is pulled 7-8 notches with a force of 44 lbs. (20 kg). Release parking brake. Ensure rear wheels turn freely. After adjustment, ensure cables are slack and all parts are in origional positions.

BRAKE WARNING LIGHT

Light indicates parking brake is engaged. To adjust light operation, bend switch plate until light comes on when brake lever is pulled 1 notch and goes out when lever is released (ignition on). On all models except pickups, light also indicates low fluid level when parking brake is released. To check warning light operation, release parking brake and raise master cylinder reservoir cap. Warning light should glow; if not, check switch and wire connector.

REMOVAL & INSTALLATION

FRONT DISC BRAKE PADS

Removal — Raise and support vehicle; remove tire and wheel. Remove retaining clip and then remove pad pins while holding anti-squeal springs. Remove disc brake pads, using suitable pliers if necessary. Remove pad spring (210 and 310) and shims (310) with brake pads.

CAUTION — *DO NOT force piston groove inside piston seal. Piston seal could be damaged and caliper will have to be disassembled.*

Installation — **1)** Clean and apply P.B.C. grease or equivalent to cylinder body yoke guide groove, yoke sliding contact points and piston end surface. Loosen bleeder screw and push outer piston into cylinder until piston end surface coincides with boot retaining ring end surface. Tighten bleeder screw and install inner brake pad.

NOTE — *Make sure arrow mark on pad shims of 310 are installed in forward rotating direction.*

2) Push inner piston into cylinder by pulling on yoke, then install outer pad. Install anti-squeal springs, coil springs (210 and 310), retaining pins and clip. Depress brake pedal several times to seat pads, and bleed hydraulic system if necessary.

FRONT DISC BRAKE CALIPER

Removal — Raise and support vehicle; remove tire and wheel. Disconnect hydraulic line from caliper and plug all openings. On 310 models, remove strut assembly and knuckle arm mounting bolt. On all models, remove caliper mounting bolts and remove caliper.

Installation — To install, reverse removal procedure and bleed hydraulic system.

FRONT DISC BRAKE ROTOR

Removal (4WD Pickup) — 1) Raise and support vehicle. Remove tire and wheel. Remove caliper as previously

DATSUN 210, 310, 510, 810 & PICKUPS (Cont.)

described and hang from frame with wire. DO NOT disconnect hydraulic line. Set locking hub to "Lock" position and remove cover assembly bolts and cover.

2) Remove snap ring and remove clutch assembly by turning clockwise. Ensure lock pin is retained without damage. Remove drive shaft. Remove knuckle arm-to-knuckle bolt. Loosen but do not remove upper and lower ball joint nuts. Using ball joint tool (ST29020001), separate ball joints from spindle. Raise lower link with a jack and remove ball joint nuts. Remove knuckle assembly.

3) Straighten wheel lock washer and remove lock washer. Using lock nut remover (KV40102500), remove lock nut, lock washer and bearing washer. Push bearing support out of wheel hub. Using suitable puller, remove knuckle from hub. Remove hub-to-rotor bolts and remove rotor.

Installation — 1) Install hub-to-rotor bolts and tighten. Press knuckle onto hub, then install bearing support, bearing washer, lock washer and lock nut. Rotate hub several times to seat bearings and check bearing preload. Bend lock washer lip up into a lock nut groove.

2) Install spindle assembly and tighten suspension components. After installing drive shaft, check that axle shaft end play is .004-.012" (.1-.3 mm). Adjust axle shaft end play with proper thickness of snap ring. Mount caliper and tighten; bleed hydraulic system if necessary.

Removal (310) — With caliper removed, remove cotter pin. Remove hub nut from drive shaft end while holding hub with suitable tool. Using a puller, remove hub and rotor assembly. Remove hub-to-rotor bolts. With rotor supported on wooden blocks, remove hub from rotor with suitable press and drift.

Installation — To install, reverse removal procedure. Tighten hub-to-rotor bolts evenly and adjust wheel bearings. *See Wheel Bearing Adjustment in SUSPENSION Section.* Bleed hydraulic system.

Removal (All Other Models) — With caliper removed, remove hub dust cap, "O" ring, cotter pin, adjusting cap and lock nut. Remove hub and rotor assembly from spindle without dropping outer bearing and washer. Remove outer bearing and washer and hub-to-rotor bolts. Separate hub and rotor.

NOTE — *Avoid damaging dust cap "O" ring while removing hub dust cap.*

Installation — To install, reverse removal procedure. Tighten hub-to-rotor bolts evenly and adjust wheel bearings. *See Wheel Bearing Adjustment in SUSPENSION Section.* Bleed hydraulic system.

REAR BRAKE SHOES

Removal (Pickups) — 1) Raise and support vehicle on safety stands; remove tire and wheel. Loosen parking brake and remove brake drum. Remove retainers, anti-rattle springs, spring seats and anti-rattle pins.

2) Remove 2 return springs (lower). Open brake shoe outward, remove return spring (upper) and extension link. Remove brake shoes. Separate secondary shoe from toggle lever by removing pin.

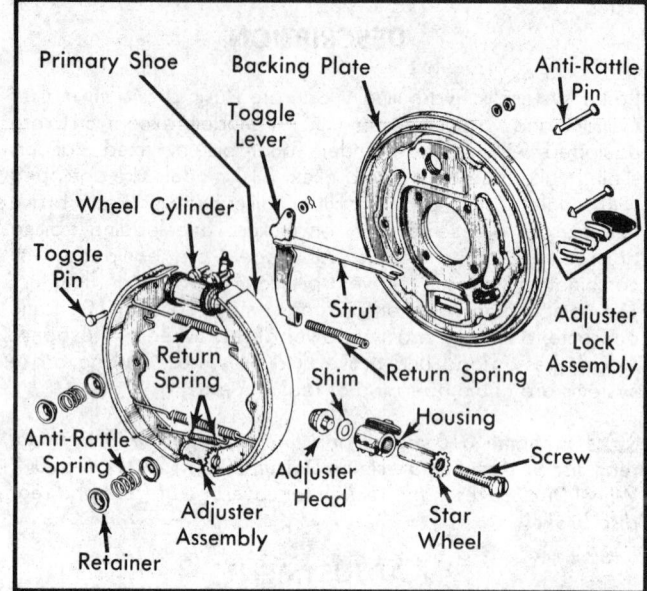

Fig. 1 Exploded View of Pickup Rear Brake Assembly

Installation — To install, reverse removal procedure and note the following: Apply brake grease to moving parts of adjuster assembly and all metal contact surfaces of brake shoes. Adjuster sliding resistance (measured with spring scale) should be 11-26 lbs. (5-12 kg); if not, install new adjuster shim.

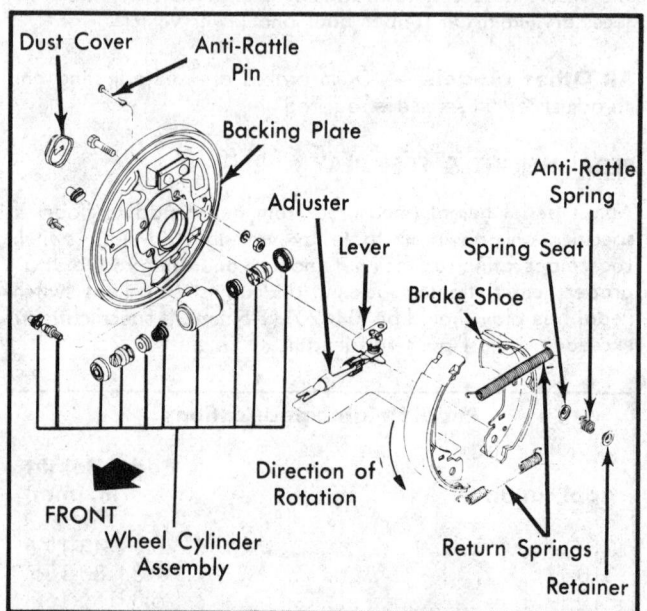

Fig. 2 Exploded View of Rear Brake Assembly (All Models Except Pickup)

Removal (All Other Models) — 1) Raise and support vehicle. Remove tire and wheel. Apply parking brake and remove stopper pin. Remove stopper from lever. Release parking brake and remove brake drum.

2) Remove parking brake cable from backing plate. Remove retainers, anti-rattle springs, pins and spring seats. Remove return springs and brake shoes. Remove dust cover and toggle lever with adjuster assembly.

Brakes

DATSUN 210, 310, 510, 810 & PICKUPS (Cont.)

Installation — Apply brake grease to all contact points and mating surfaces; reverse removal procedure to install brake shoes and note the following: Make sure adjuster operates properly, readjust shoe-to-drum clearance and bleed hydraulic system, if necessary.

MASTER CYLINDER

Removal — Disconnect electrical wiring at cylinder reservoir (if equipped). Disconnect and plug hydraulic lines at master cylinder and drain cylinder. Remove cylinder mounting nuts and remove master cylinder.

Installation — To install master cylinder, reverse removal procedure and note the following: Bleed hydraulic system and check pedal height.

POWER BRAKE UNIT

NOTE — *Before removal, test check valve. Using a brake booster tester, apply 19.7" (500 mm) of Hg to brake unit side of check valve. If pressure drops more than .39" (10 mm) of Hg for 310, 510 and 810 or .98" (25 mm) of Hg for 210 and Pickup in 15 seconds, replace check valve. Also, if valve does not open when pressure is applied to brake unit side of check valve, replace valve. If check valve is not defective, check brake system and vacuum lines for leaks; replace booster as an assembly.*

Removal — With master cylinder removed, disconnect vacuum line from power unit. From inside vehicle, disconnect pedal return spring, push rod from brake pedal, and power unit mounting nuts. Remove power unit from engine compartment.

Installation — Reverse removal procedure and adjust push rod length to .38-.39" (9.75-10.0 mm) by turning tip of push rod. Check pedal height and free play and bleed hydraulic system.

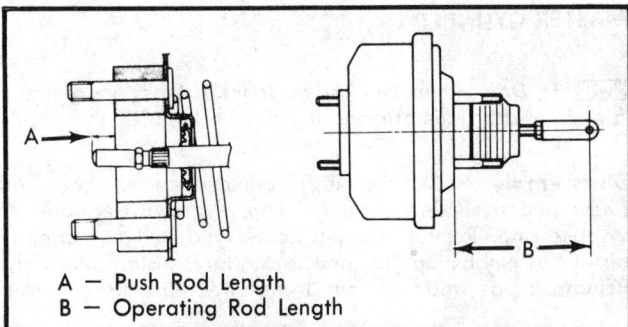

A — Push Rod Length
B — Operating Rod Length

Fig. 3 Location for Measuring Push Rod and Operating Rod Lengths

Operating Rod Lengths	
Application	**Length In. (mm)**
210 & 510	5.3 (135)
310	5.1 (130)
810	5.7 (145)
Pickup	10.8 (275)

Check Valve Removal — Check valve is located in vacuum line between intake manifold and power unit. To remove, disconnect retaining clip, remove hose clamps, separate hoses from valve and remove check valve. To install, reverse removal procedure.

OVERHAUL

FRONT DISC BRAKE CALIPER

NOTE — *For overhaul procedures of 810 front disc brakes, see article on Datsun 200SX, 280ZX and 810 4-Wheel Disc Brakes in this Section.*

Disassembly (510 & Pickup) — With caliper and pads removed, drain any remaining fluid from cylinder. Remove gripper pin attaching bolts. Separate yoke and cylinder body. Remove retaining rings and dust seals from piston. Push both pistons out in one direction on pickup. On 510, push pistons out by feeding compressed air into cylinder inlet gradually. Remove piston seals. Remove gripper, if necessary.

Cleaning & Inspection — Clean all parts with brake fluid and check all components for wear or damage. If minor corrosion can not be removed from cylinder bore with emery cloth, cylinder must be replaced. All seals must be replaced during overhaul.

NOTE — *Piston surfaces are plated and must be replaced if corroded or worn. DO NOT polish with emery cloth.*

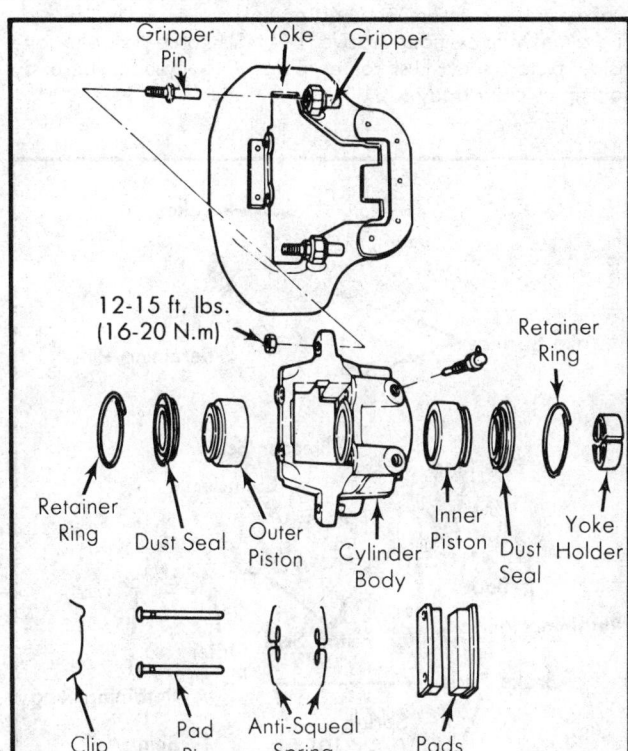

Fig. 4 Exploded View of Front Disc Brake Caliper (510 Shown, Pickup Similar)

Reassembly — 1) Install piston seals without damaging seals. Coat cylinder bore and pistons with brake fluid. Push outer piston into cylinder until piston end surface coincides with boot retaining ring end surface. DO NOT force piston groove inside piston seal. Push inner piston into cylinder bore by holding cylinder body.

DATSUN 210, 310, 510, 810 & PICKUPS (Cont.)

2) Apply brake grease to sealing surface of dust seal and install dust seal; clamping securely with retaining ring. Install yoke holder to inner piston. Install gripper to yoke. Apply 1% soap solution to inner gripper wall and drive gripper pin into position. Install yoke to yoke holder by supporting outer piston end and pressing yoke into yoke holder with 44-66 lb. (20-30 kg) force. No clearance should be present between piston and yoke.

Disassembly (210 & 310) — With caliper and pads removed, drain any fluid from cylinder. Tap the yoke lightly with a hammer to separate cylinder from yoke. Remove bias ring from inner piston, then remove retaining rings and boots from pistons. Push both pistons out by applying compressed air gradually. Remove piston seals. Remove yoke spring from yoke.

Cleaning & Inspection — Clean all parts with brake fluid and check all components for wear or damage. If minor corrosion cannot be removed from cylinder bore with emery cloth, cylinder must be replaced. Piston seals, dust covers and bias ring must be replaced during overhaul.

NOTE — *Piston surfaces are plated and must be replaced if corroded or worn. DO NOT polish with emery cloth.*

Reassembly — **1)** Apply brake fluid to cylinder bore and install piston seal. Insert bias ring into inner piston with rounded end in bottom of piston bore. Lightly coat piston with brake fluid and insert inner piston until yoke groove of bias ring aligns with cylinder groove. DO NOT force piston groove inside piston seal. Push outer piston into cylinder bore by holding cylinder body.

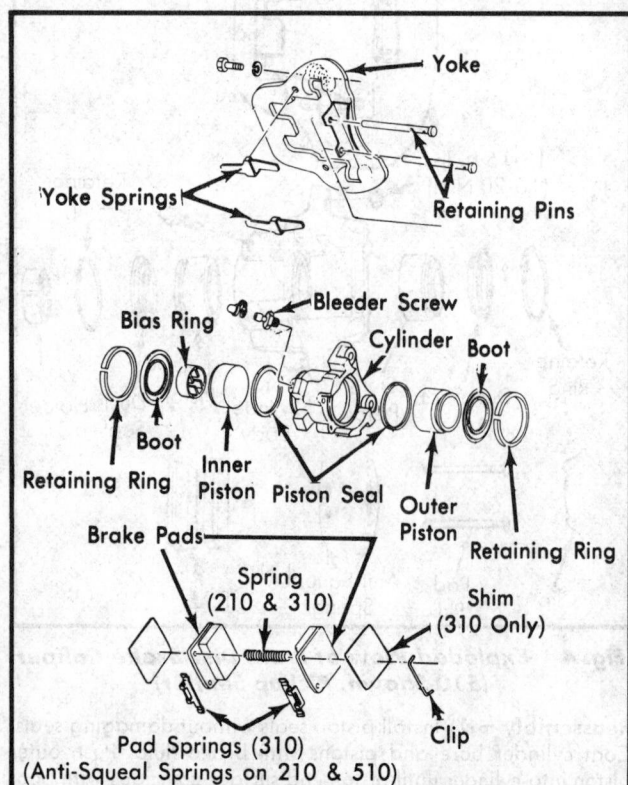

Fig. 5 *Exploded View of Front Disc Brake Caliper (210 & 310 Models)*

2) Install dust boots and retaining rings. Install yoke springs on yoke and bias springs to yoke. Apply P.B.C. grease (or equivalent) to yoke sliding surfaces of cylinder. Align bias ring so that it coincides with yoke. With yoke springs lightly inserted in cylinder groove, assemble cylinder body and yoke by tapping lightly.

REAR WHEEL CYLINDER

Disassembly — With rear wheel cylinder removed, remove dust covers and remove components.

Cleaning & Inspection — Clean all parts in brake fluid and check cylinder bore and pistons for excessive wear or damage. If piston-to-cylinder clearance is greater than .006" (.15 mm), replace necessary parts. Replace any torn or damaged rubber parts.

NOTE — *Wheel cylinders are produced by two companies and parts are not interchangeable. Ensure repair kit matches wheel cylinder.*

Reassembly — Apply brake fluid to cylinder bore, pistons and piston cups. Reverse disassembly procedure and install parts.

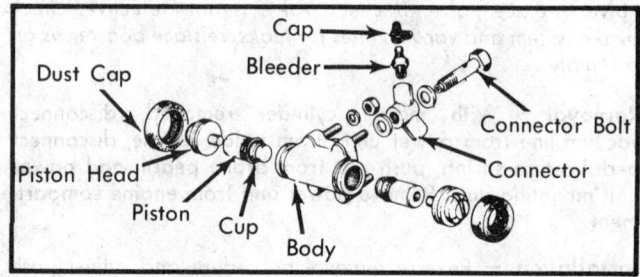

Fig. 6 *Exploded View of Typical Wheel Cylinder*

MASTER CYLINDER

NOTE — *Do not remove reservoir tanks. If tanks are removed for any reason, discard and install new tanks.*

Disassembly — Remove master cylinder reservoir caps and filters and drain brake fluid. Using a screwdriver, pry off stopper ring. Remove stopper screw and pull out primary piston assembly, spring and secondary piston assembly. Remove plugs and pull out front and rear check valves.

Cleaning & Inspection — Clean all parts in brake fluid and check components for excessive wear or damage. If piston-to-cylinder clearance is greater than .006" (.15 mm), replace necessary part. Caps, gaskets and valves must be replaced during overhaul.

NOTE — *Master cylinders are produced by two companies and parts are not interchangeable. Ensure repair kit matches master cylinder.*

Reassembly — Reverse disassembly procedure and note the following: Coat all parts with brake fluid (rubber parts with brake grease) when assembling.

DATSUN 210, 310, 510, 810 & PICKUPS (Cont.)

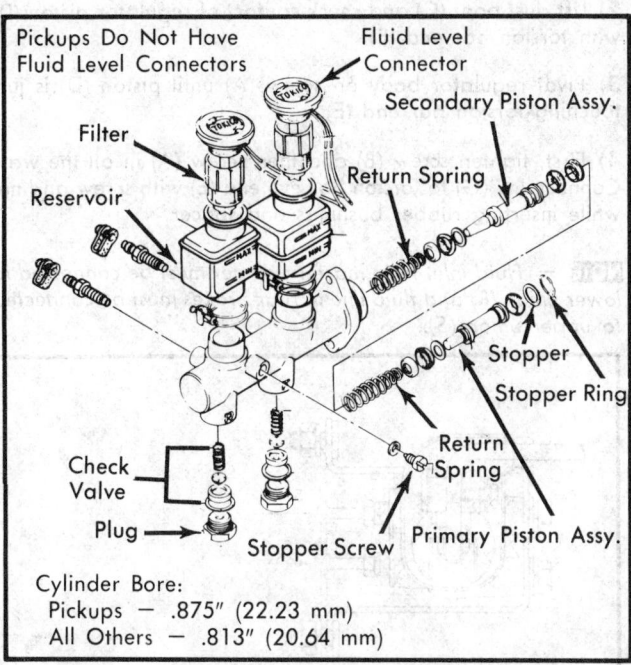

Pickups Do Not Have Fluid Level Connectors

Fluid Level Connector

Secondary Piston Assy.

Filter

Return Spring

Reservoir

Stopper

Stopper Ring

Check Valve

Return Spring

Plug

Stopper Screw

Primary Piston Assy.

Cylinder Bore:
Pickups — .875" (22.23 mm)
All Others — .813" (20.64 mm)

Fig. 7   Exploded View of Tokico Dual Reservoir Master Cylinder. Some Models Use Single Reservoir Cylinder. Nabco Cylinders Similar But Have Different Piston Configuration.

POWER BRAKE UNIT

NOTE — *Manufacturer does not recommend disassembly of this unit. If a problem is determined to be in booster unit, complete assembly must be replaced. Do not disassemble booster unit.*

TIGHTENING SPECIFICATIONS

Application	Ft. Lbs. (N m)
Hub-to-Rotor Bolts	
310	18-25 (25-34)
810	36-51 (49-69)
All Other Models	53-72 (72-98)
Caliper Mounting Bolts	
310	40-47 (54-64)
810	12-15 (16-20)
All Other Models	53-72 (72-98)
4WD Only	
Locking Hub	18-25 (25-34)
Drive Shaft-to-Carrier	20-27 (27-37)
Spindle Nut	87-108 (118-147)

DISC BRAKE SPECIFICATIONS

Application	Caliper Bore Diameter In. (mm)	Lateral Runout In. (mm)	Parallelism In. (mm)	Original Thickness In. (mm)	Minimum Refinish Thickness In. (mm)	Discard Thickness In. (mm)
210	2.012 (51.1)	.005 (.12)	.001 (.03)	.394 (10)	.....	.331 (8.4)
310	1.894 (48.1)	.005 (.12)	.001 (.03)	.378 (9.6)	.....	.339 (8.6)
510	2.012 (51.1)	.005 (.12)	.003 (.07)	.394 (10)	.....	.331 (8.4)
Pickups	2.125 (53.98)	.006 (.15)	.003 (.07)	.492 (12.5)	.....	.413 (10.5)

DRUM BRAKE SPECIFICATIONS

Application	Wheel Cyl. Bore Diameter In. (mm)	Drum Diameter In. (mm)	Original Diameter In. (mm)	Maximum Refinish Diameter In. (mm)	Discard Diameter In. (mm)
210	.813 (20.64)	8.00 (203)	8.00 (203)	.....	8.05 (204.5)
310	.687 (17.46)	8.00 (203)	8.00 (203)	.....	8.05 (204.5)
510 & 810 ①	.813 (20.64)	9.00 (228.6)	9.00 (228.6)	.....	9.06 (230)
Pickups	.625 (15.88)	10.00 (254)	10.00 (254)	.....	10.06 (255.5)

① — 810 wheel cylinder .875'' (22.23 mm) diameter.

Brava
Spider 2000
Strada
X1/9

DESCRIPTION

Brake system is hydraulically operated, using a tandem master cylinder and vacuum power brake unit. Spider 2000 and X1/9 models use single piston, sliding caliper, 4-wheel disc brakes. All other models are equipped with single piston, floating caliper front disc and leading/trailing rear drum brakes. All front and rear brake applications are self-adjusting. All models except X1/9 use pressure differential valves in rear brake circuits. All parking brakes are cable actuated and operate on rear brake application.

ADJUSTMENT

PARKING BRAKE

Pump service brakes several times to seat pistons, then fully release parking brake lever. Pull parking brake lever up 3-4 notches (3 notches on Brava and Strada). On Spider 2000 and X1/9 models, tighten nut on equalizer until rear wheels lock. X1/9 models have an opening provided in floor pan under body for access to equalizer. On Brava and Strada models, loosen lock nut located under parking brake handle and tighten adjusting nut until rear wheels lock. On all models, release parking brake and ensure rear wheels rotate freely. Repeat adjustment procedure if rear wheels drag.

BRAKE WARNING LIGHT

A dual warning light is mounted on dash. Light should glow when parking brake lever is pulled 1 notch and go off when lever is fully released (ignition on). To check circuit warning, release parking brake (ignition on) and ensure light is off. Lift master cylinder reservoir cover until level indicator is above fluid level; light should glow.

BRAKE PRESSURE REGULATOR

Brava — Install regulator and leave mounting bolts loose. Bring torsion bar (7) to dimension shown in *Fig. 1* from base of buffer end (11). Remove rubber boot (3) from regulator, then rotate regulator until piston (6) is just touching torsion bar (1). Tighten mounting bolts.

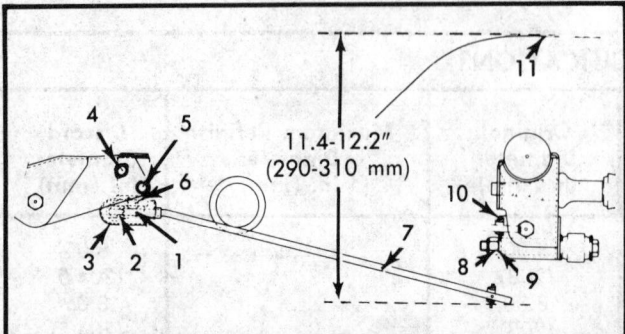

Fig. 1   Brake Pressure Regulator Measurement and Adjustment Points for Brava Models

Spider 2000 — 1) Bring end of torsion bar (E) to distance shown in *Fig. 2* from buffer resting surface. Use a jack to raise body to gain appropriate height, or place weight in passenger seat before tightening.

2) Lift dust boot (C) and check contact of regulator piston (D) with torsion bar end (E).

3) Pivot regulator body on screw (A) until piston (D) is just touching torsion bar end (E).

4) First, tighten screw (B) and then screw (A) in all the way. Connect link (G) to torsion bar eye end (E) with screw and nut while inserting rubber bushings and spacer.

NOTE — *Fluid inlet from master cylinder must be connected to lower union (R) and fluid line to rear brakes must be connected to upper union (S).*

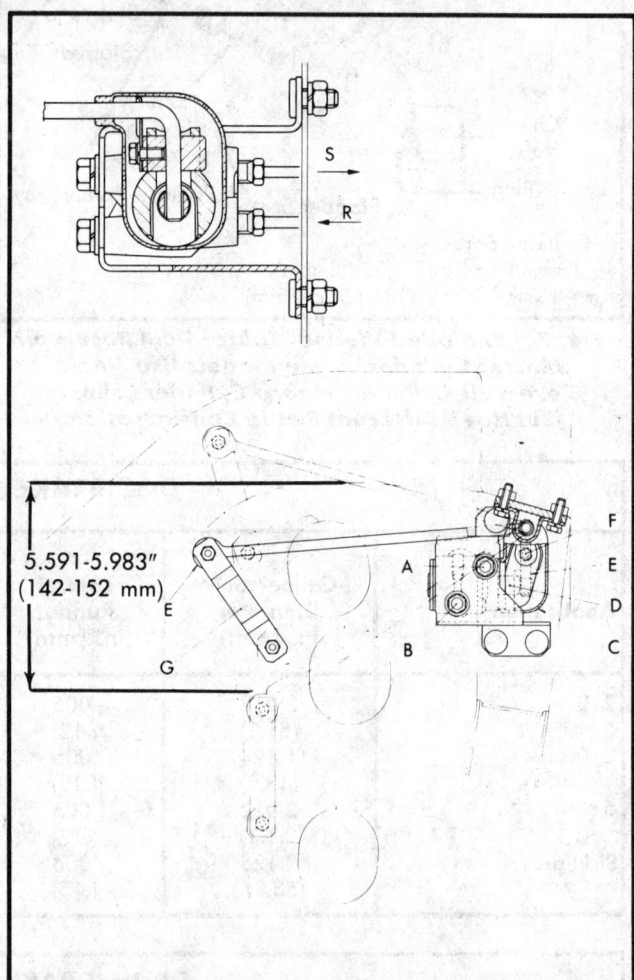

Fig. 2   Brake Pressure Regulator Measurement and Adjustment Points for Spider 2000

Strada — Raise and support vehicle. Loosen compensator (1) attaching bolts (7). Unclip plastic clamp and slide dust boot (9) from compensator. Disconnect torsion bar (3) from connecting link (4). Distance between center of suspension rubber buffer seat (2) and torsion bar end (3b) must be as shown in *Fig. 3*. Once specification is obtained, rotate compensator until piston (8) is just touching torsion bar (3a). Tighten bolts, connect torsion bar to connecting link. Slide dust boot onto compensator and secure with plastic clamp.

NOTE — *Vehicle must not be loaded if drive-on type lift is used to support vehicle.*

FIAT (Cont.)

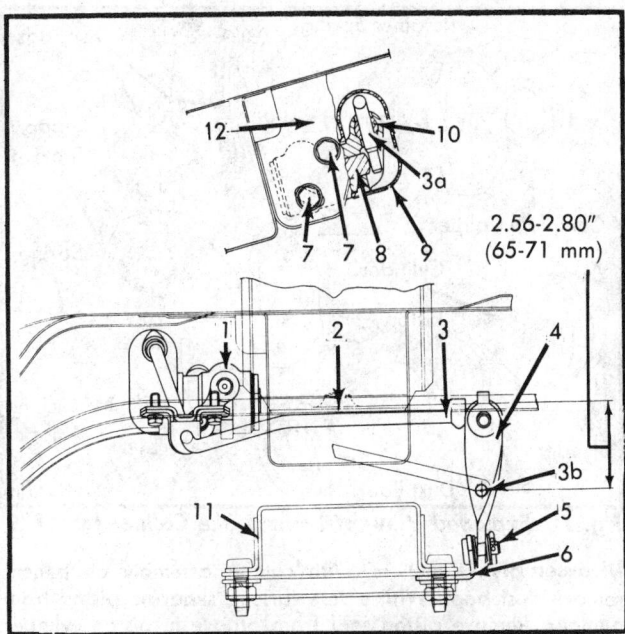

Fig. 3 Brake Pressure Regulator Measurement and Adjustment Points for Strada Models

2.56-2.80" (65-71 mm)

REMOVAL & INSTALLATION

DISC BRAKE CALIPERS & PADS

Removal — Raise and support vehicle; remove wheels. Plug master cylinder outlet ports. Disconnect brake line from caliper assembly. Remove cotter pins from locking blocks, drive out locking blocks and remove caliper. Take out disc pads and springs. On models with rear disc brakes, parking brake must be disconnected.

NOTE — *Pads MUST be replaced when worn to .079" (2 mm) from original thickness.*

Installation — To install caliper and pad assemblies, reverse removal procedures. Note that inside and outside pads may differ. Ensure distance between pad inner surfaces is not less than .413" (10.5 mm). In most instances 2 different types of pads are available. Do not mix pad types. Locking block contact areas must be lubricated with lithium based grease containing zinc oxide (N.L.G.C.).

BRAKE ROTOR

Removal — Remove caliper as previously outlined. Mount a dial indicator so plunger is .08" (2 mm) from outer edge of rotor and record runout. Remove caliper support bracket from support plate (front) or from axle housing (rear). Remove bolts mounting rotor to hub. Remove hub plate (if equipped), then using a puller or drift, remove rotor from hub.

Installation — Fit rotor onto wheel hub, install attaching bolts and tighten evenly.

REAR BRAKE DRUM

Removal — Raise and support vehicle; remove tire and wheel. Remove locating pin and attaching bolt. Remove brake drum, releasing shoe adjustment, if required.

Installation — To install, reverse removal procedure.

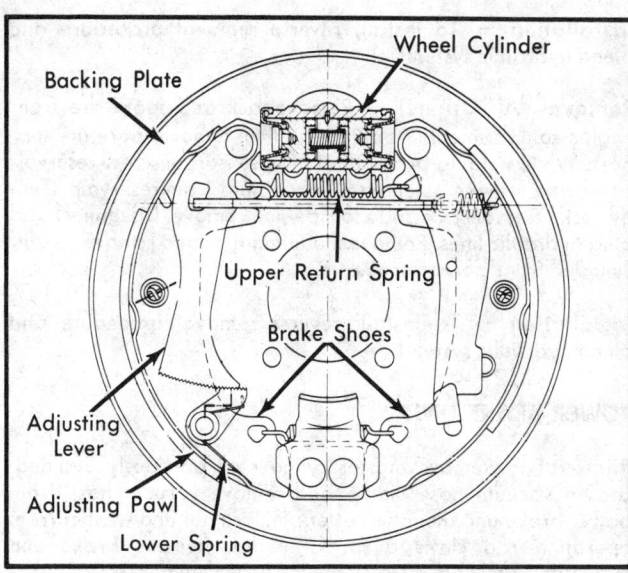

Fig. 4 Brava Rear Drum Brake Assembly

REAR BRAKE SHOES

Removal — **1)** Raise and support vehicle; remove tire and wheel. Remove brake drum. Retain wheel cylinder pistons in position with a clamp. Remove upper and lower return springs, shoe guide pins, springs and cups.

2) Disconnect parking brake cable from brake shoe link and remove brake shoes. Place brake shoes on work bench and remove self-adjusting lever by removing retaining clip on back of brake shoe. Remove adjusting pawl by removing spring retainer and spring, then remove adjusting pawl.

Installation — To install, reverse removal procedure and note the following: Longer return spring is upper return spring. Install brake shoes with ends correctly positioned in wheel cylinder pistons.

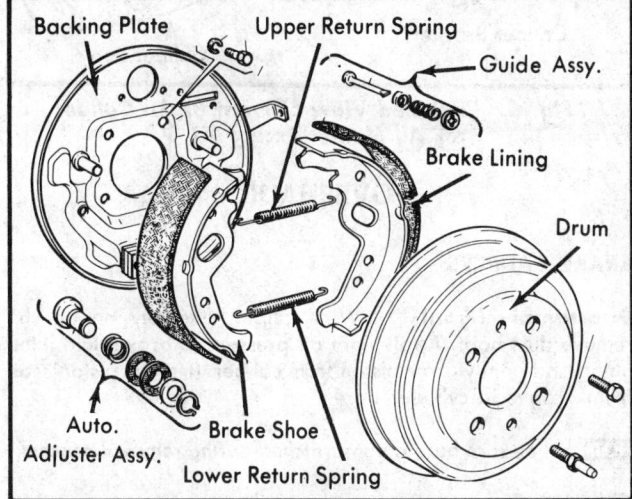

Fig. 5 Strada Rear Drum Brake Assembly

MASTER CYLINDER

Removal (X1/9) — Remove steering column. See *Steering Column Removal* in STEERING Section. Disconnect hydraulic lines from reservoir. Remove mounting nuts and slide unit off supports. Disconnect outlet lines from master cylinder.

Brakes

FIAT (Cont.)

Installation — To install, reverse removal procedure and bleed hydraulic system.

Removal (All Others) — Remove jack and spare tire from engine compartment (if equipped), then remove spare tire support. While holding brake fluid level sensor, unscrew reservoir cover and remove assembly. Siphon fluid from reservoir. Gently rock reservoir from side to side and remove. Disconnect and plug hydraulic lines. Remove mounting nuts and remove master cylinder from power brake unit.

Installation — To install, reverse removal procedure and bleed hydraulic system.

POWER BRAKE UNIT

Removal — Remove master cylinder as previously outlined. Loosen vacuum hose clamp and remove vacuum hose from power brake unit. Remove cotter pin, lock nut and washer from operating rod clevis at brake pedal. Remove brake unit mounting nuts and remove power brake unit.

Installation — To install, reverse removal procedure and note the following: After installing master cylinder, bleed hydraulic system.

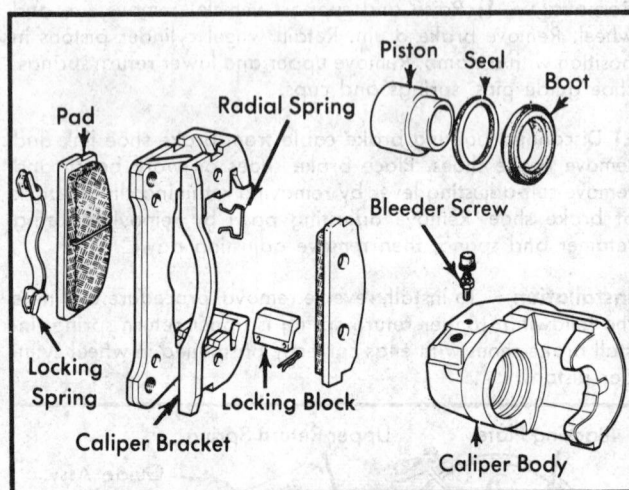

Fig. 6 Exploded View of Front Brake Caliper for All Models Except X1/9

OVERHAUL

BRAKE CALIPERS

Disassembly (Front) — With caliper assembly on bench, remove dust boot. Apply light air pressure to brake fluid inlet union and gently force piston from caliper. Remove piston seal from groove in cylinder bore.

NOTE — Be sure bore is not scratched during removal process.

Cleaning & Inspection — Clean all components in suitable solvent (Fiat LDC). Inspect each part for damage or excessive wear. Replace all piston seals and dust boots.

Reassembly — Fit piston seal in caliper. Insert piston to bottom end of cylinder bore. Position dust boot on caliper body. Fit caliper body into caliper bracket and reinstall on vehicle.

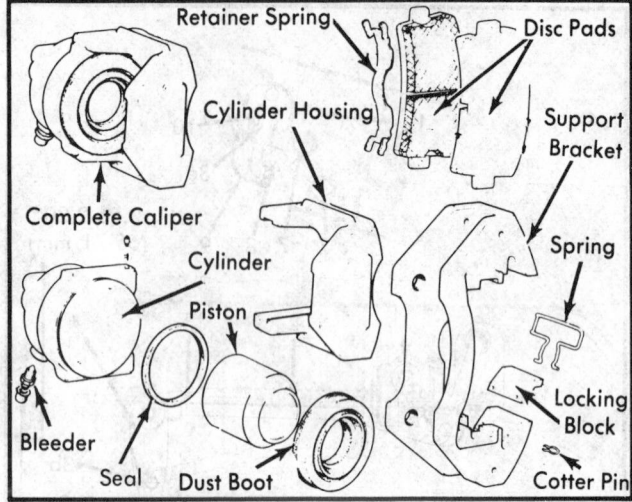

Fig. 7 Exploded View of Front Brake Caliper for X1/9

Disassembly (Rear) — With caliper assembly on bench, remove dust boot. With a screwdriver, separate piston from plunger. Remove piston seal from groove in piston cylinder bore. Remove cam lever, pivot pin, and lever. Lift out self-adjusting plunger, plunger seal, disc spring, and spring thrust washer.

Cleaning & Inspection — Clean all components in suitable solvent (Fiat LDC). Inspect each part for damage or excessive wear. Replace all piston seals and dust boots.

Reassembly — Fit self-adjusting plunger complete with seal, disc springs, and thrust washer. Fit parking brake cam lever complete with pivot pin. Fit pivot pin bushing and snap ring. Fit piston sealing ring into caliper cylinder. Screw piston into cylinder until fully seated. Align piston slot so it is opposite bleed connection. Refit dust boot.

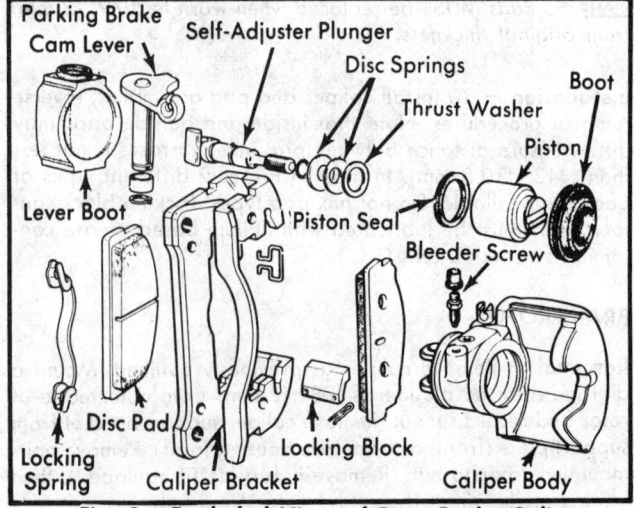

Fig. 8 Exploded View of Rear Brake Caliper Spider 2000 Shown — X1/9 Similar

MASTER CYLINDER

Disassembly — Remove connector(s) and cylinder bore dust boot. Remove stop bolt(s) and seal(s). Remove set screws and end plug (if equipped). Remove piston assemblies, return springs, cups, seals and spacers.

Inspection — Clean and thoroughly dry all parts, then inspect for wear or damage. Light scoring may be removed by hon-

FIAT (Cont.)

ing, make sure honing does not alter size of cylinder diameter. Replace all rubber pieces each time overhaul is performed.

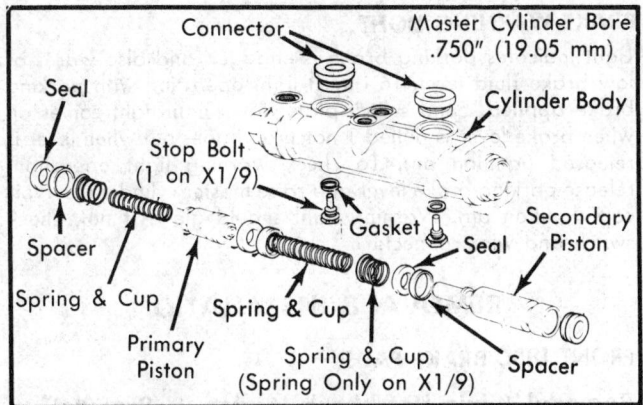

Fig. 9 Exploded View of Fiat Master Cylinder

Reassembly — To reassemble, reverse disassembly procedure and lightly coat all components with brake fluid before reassembly.

POWER BRAKE UNIT

NOTE — *The following procedure is for Strada models; all other models may require variations from the procedure outlined.*

Disassembly — **1)** Remove check valve and grommet from front shell. Place wooden blocks on both master cylinder mounting studs and 4 power brake mounting studs, then place unit in a vise. Slowly tighten vise until rear shell can be rotated clear of front shell locking tabs.

2) Separate front and rear shells. Slowly release vise until spring pressure is released, then remove power brake unit. Remove dust boot from rear shell. Remove filter assembly. Remove key to remove plunger and valve. Separate diaphragm from rear shell. Remove rear seal assembly.

3) Remove guide bushing front seal, vacuum piston, piston rod, backing plate and spring from front shell. DO NOT disturb adjustment of piston rod.

Inspection — Manufacturer recommends replacement of the following parts during overhaul: Backing plate, seals, filter assembly, diaphragm and boot. Inspect all other parts for wear or damage and replace as necessary.

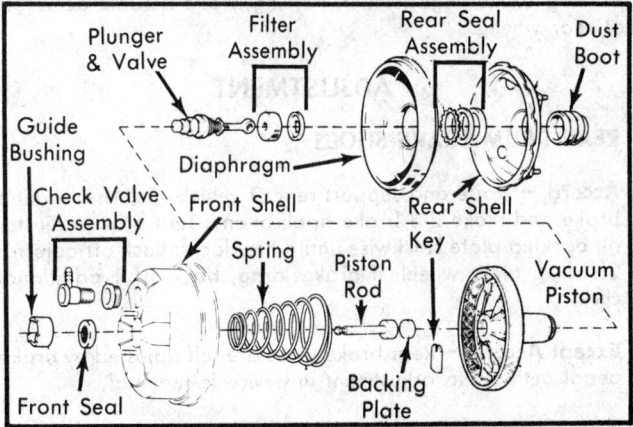

Fig. 10 Exploded View of Strada Power Brake Unit

Reassembly — To reassemble power brake unit, reverse disassembly procedure and note the following: After reassembly, adjust tip of push rod so it extends past the surface of front cover by .032-.040" (.825-1.025 mm). Adjust by turning nut.

DISC BRAKE SPECIFICATIONS

Application	Caliper Bore Diameter In. (mm)	Lateral Runout In. (mm)	Parallelism In. (mm)	Original Thickness In. (mm)	Minimum Refinish Thickness In. (mm)	Discard Thickness In. (mm)
Brava	1.89 (48)	.004 (.10)	.....	.425 (10.8)	.....	.386 (9.8)
Spider 2000 & X1/9						
Front	1.89 (48)	.006 (.15)	.....	.392-.400 (9.95-10.20)	.368 (9.35)	.354 (9.0)
Rear	1.34 (34)	.006 (.15)	.....	.392-.400 (9.95-10.20)	.368① (9.35)	.354 (9.0)
Strada	1.89 (48)	.10 (.25)	.....	.421-.429 (10.7-10.9)	.368 (9.35)	.354 (9.0)

① — Spider 2000 rear is .372" (9.45 mm).

DRUM BRAKE SPECIFICATIONS

Application	Wheel Cyl. Bore Diameter In. (mm)	Drum Diameter In. (mm)	Original Diameter In. (mm)	Maximum Refinish Diameter In. (mm)	Discard Diameter In. (mm)
Brava	.875 (22.2)	9.00 (228.6)	9.00 (228.6)	9.03 (229.4)	9.055 (230)
Strada	.687 (17.46)	7.30 (185.4)	7.30 (185.4)	7.335 (186.3)	7.355 (186.8)

Brakes

HONDA

Accord
Civic
Prelude

DESCRIPTION

Brake system is hydraulically operated using a tandem master cylinder and vacuum brake unit. All models are equipped with single piston, floating caliper, front disc brakes and leading/trailing rear drum brakes. All models use dual valve combination valves to prevent premature rear wheel lock-up. A brake warning light is mounted on the dash to indicate loss of brake fluid, uneven fluid pressure between brake systems and parking brake engagement. Parking brake is cable actuated at rear wheels.

ADJUSTMENT

REAR DRUM BRAKE SHOES

Accord — Raise and support rear of vehicle. Release parking brake and make 2-3 brake applications. Turn brake adjuster on backing plate clockwise until wheel locks. Back off adjuster 2 clicks, rotate wheel; if brakes drag, back off 1 additional click.

Except Accord — Rear brake shoes are self-adjusted by brake pedal action. No adjustment in-service is required.

PEDAL HEIGHT

Pedal height is measured from center of pedal pad to floor-board (without carpet). To adjust, loosen stop light switch lock nut and position switch out of way. Loosen power unit push rod lock nut and rotate push rod until pedal height is 7.25" (184 mm). Tighten lock nut, reposition and adjust stop light switch.

STOP LIGHT SWITCH

Stop light switch is located under dash, above brake pedal. To adjust, turn switch until plunger is fully depressed (threaded end touching pedal arm pad). Back off switch ½ turn and tighten lock nuts. Check that brake lights go off when pedal is released.

PARKING BRAKE

With rear brakes adjusted, raise and support rear of vehicle on safety stands. Loosen equalizer nut (located between rear lower control arms) and pull brake lever up 1 notch. Tighten adjusting nut until rear wheels drag slightly. Release brake lever; rear wheels should rotate freely. Rear wheels should lock when lever is pulled 4-8 notches on Civic and 3-7 notches on Accord and Prelude.

BRAKE WARNING LIGHT

Light indicates parking brake is engaged and also warns of low brake fluid level. To adjust light operation with parking brake applied, bend switch plate down until light comes on when brake lever is pulled 1 notch and goes out when lever is released (ignition on). To check warning light operation, release parking brake lever and raise master cylinder reservoir cap (ignition on). Warning light should glow; if not, check switch and wire connector.

REMOVAL & INSTALLATION

FRONT DISC BRAKE PADS

Removal (Civic Hatchback, Sedan & Prelude) — Raise and support vehicle. Remove tire and wheel. Remove lower caliper guide pin and pivot caliper body up out of way. Remove pads, pad shim and anti-rattle springs.

Installation — Install anti-rattle springs and pads. Install shim against outer pad. Loosen bleed screw, seat piston in caliper bore and tighten bleed screw. Rotate caliper body down and tighten lower caliper guide pin. Depress brake pedal several times to seat brake pads.

Removal (Civic Wagon & Accord) — Raise and support vehicle. Remove tire and wheel. Remove spring clips and guide plates. Remove caliper body and hang from frame with wire. DO NOT disconnect hydraulic line or allow caliper to hang from hydraulic line. Remove anti-rattle clips, pads and shims.

NOTE — *Shims for Accord must have high temperature grease (Dow Corning DC# 5 or equivalent) applied to red sides. Install red coated side against brake pad backing plate.*

Installation — Install pads. Place shim against outside shoe. Loosen bleed screw and push in piston so that caliper will fit over pads. Tighten screw. Install caliper on mount. Lubricate sliding surfaces of guide plates with silicon grease and install. Secure with spring pins. Depress brake pedal several times to seat pads.

FRONT DISC BRAKE CALIPER

Removal — Raise and support vehicle. Remove tire and wheel. Disconnect and plug hydraulic line at caliper. On Civic Hatchback and Sedan and Prelude, remove caliper guide pins and remove caliper. On Civic Station Wagon and Accord, remove spring pins and guide plates and remove caliper. Remove disc pads and remove caliper mounting bracket.

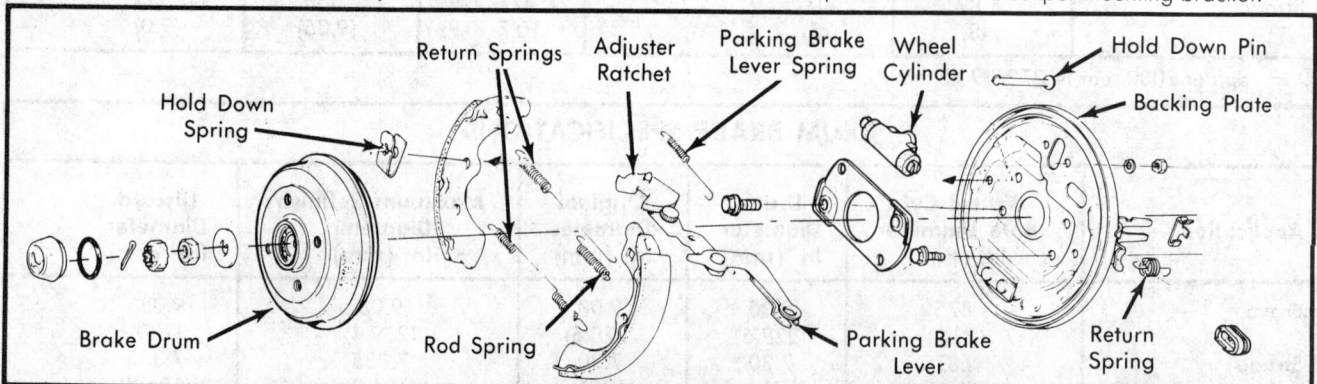

Fig. 1 Exploded View of Civic and Prelude Rear Brake Assembly

Brakes

HONDA (Cont.)

Installation — To install, reverse removal procedure and bleed hydraulic system.

DISC BRAKE ROTOR

NOTE — *Removal of hub requires replacement of spindle nut and wheel bearings. Install new parts and stake nut into position.*

Removal (Accord) — With caliper assembly removed, remove cotter pin and spindle nut. Using a slide hammer with hub puller attachment, remove hub and rotor assembly. Remove hub-to-rotor bolts and separate rotor from hub.

Installation — To install, reverse removal procedure. Tighten hub-to-rotor bolts evenly. Bleed hydraulic system if necessary.

Removal (Except Accord) — With caliper assembly removed, remove rotor retaining screw. Install two M8 x 1.25 x 12 mm bolts in existing holes. Alternately turn bolts 2 turns (to prevent warpage) until disc can be removed from hub.

Installation — To install, reverse removal procedure, tighten retaining screw securely and bleed hydraulic system, if necessary.

REAR BRAKE DRUM

Removal — Raise and support vehicle and remove rear wheels. Remove bearing retaining cap and rear axle nut, then remove brake drum.

NOTE — *If drum is difficult to remove, use slide hammer with hub puller attachment.*

Installation — To install, reverse removal procedure and tighten axle nut.

REAR BRAKE SHOES

NOTE — *All models use same basic brake design. Some minor variations may exist between systems.*

Removal — With brake drum removed, remove retaining clips and pins and return springs (note original position of return springs). Disconnect brake shoes from parking brake lever assembly and remove brake shoes.

NOTE — *Upper and lower return springs are not interchangeable.*

Installation — Apply light coat of grease to adjuster assembly, sliding surfaces of brake shoes and metal contact areas of backing plate. To install, reverse removal procedure, observing the precautions listed below for each model. Adjust and bleed brakes.

- Accord — Upper return spring has small loops and is installed between shoes with coils facing outward. Lower spring has larger loops and is installed with coils facing inward.

- Civic & Prelude — Upper return spring is identified by single coil. Before installing brake drum, release brake adjuster ratchet with screwdriver. Mark engaged teeth. Install drum and spindle nut. Depress brake pedal, remove drum and ensure ratchet has moved and brakes have self-adjusted.

MASTER CYLINDER

Removal — Disconnect hydraulic lines at master cylinder, remove retaining nuts, and remove master cylinder from power brake unit.

Installation — To install, reverse removal procedure and bleed hydraulic system.

POWER BRAKE UNIT

Removal — Disconnect vacuum hose at power brake unit, and hydraulic lines at master cylinder. Remove clevis pin retaining power brake unit push rod to brake pedal, and bolts attaching power unit to firewall, then remove power brake unit and master cylinder as an assembly.

Installation — To install, reverse removal procedure, tighten all bolts and bleed hydraulic system.

Check Valve Replacement — Check valve is located in vacuum line between brake unit and intake manifold. Before removal, test check valve. Disconnect valve from vacuum hose by removing clamps. Blow air through manifold side of valve; valve should not open. Repeat procedure on booster side of valve; valve should open. Replace defective valve and secure clamps.

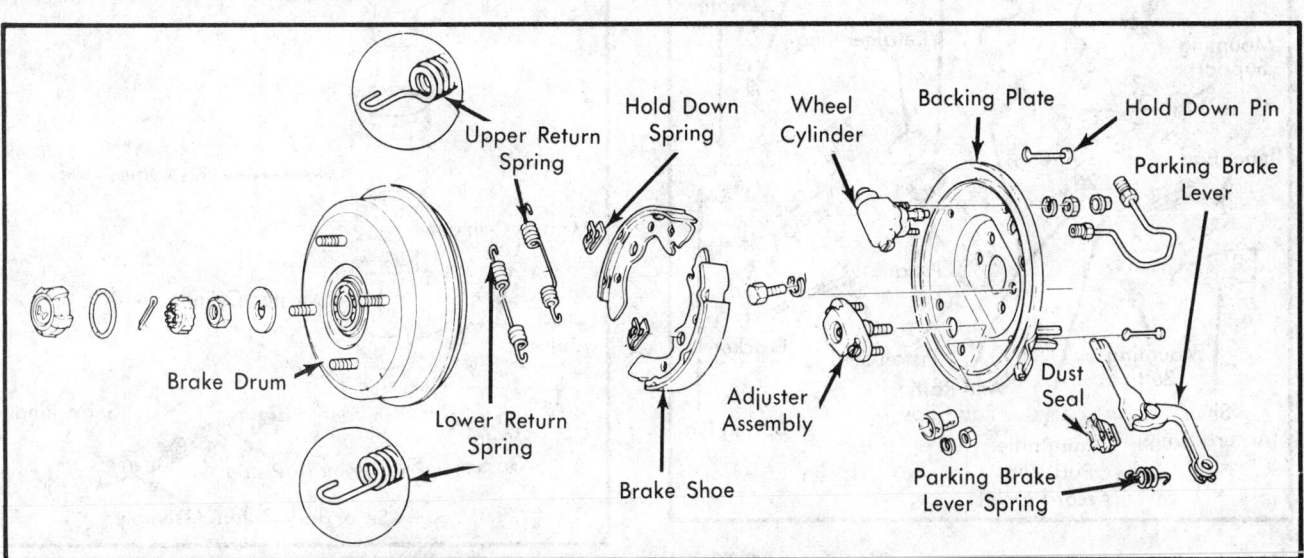

Fig. 2   Exploded View of Accord Rear Brake Assembly

HONDA (Cont.)

OVERHAUL

DISC BRAKE CALIPER

Disassembly — Remove retaining ring (if equipped), then remove piston boot. Place rags in front of piston and force piston out of caliper bore by applying light (30 psi) air pressure to brake fluid inlet port. Remove piston seal without damaging cylinder bore.

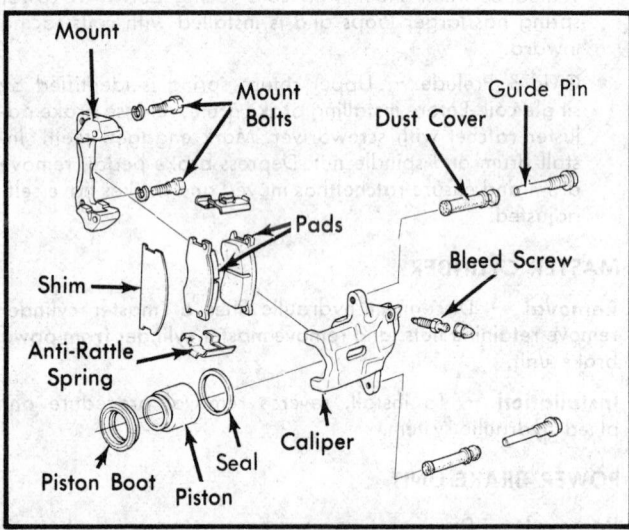

Fig. 3 Exploded View of Front Disc Brake Caliper (Civic Sedan and Prelude)

Cleaning & Inspection — Clean all parts in brake fluid and check for wear or damage. Check cylinder bore and pistons; replace if scratched or scored. Replace all rubber components during overhaul.

Reassembly — Apply brake fluid to caliper bore, piston surface and piston seal. Reverse disassembly procedure and make sure seals and boots are properly installed.

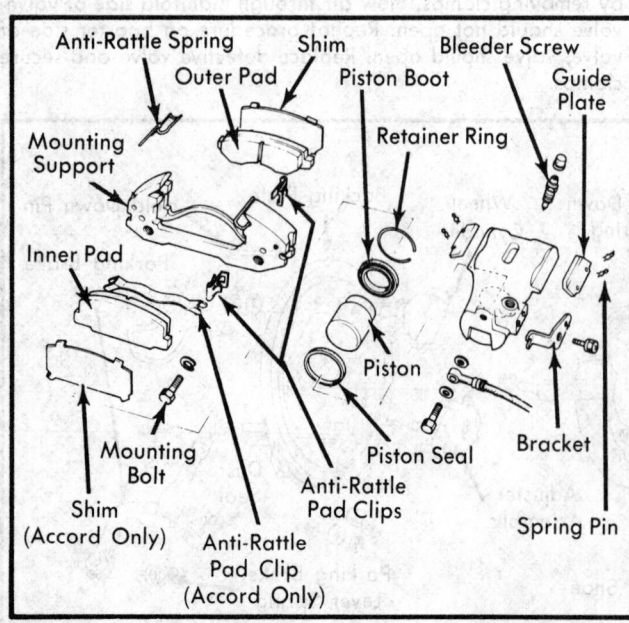

Fig. 4 Exploded View of Front Disc Brake Caliper (Accord Shown — Civic Station Wagon Similar)

REAR WHEEL CYLINDER

Disassembly — Remove dust seals and pistons. Remove cylinder cups from pistons. If necessary, remove bleeder screw.

Cleaning & Inspection — Clean all parts in brake fluid. Check for wear or damage. Replace any defective parts.

Reassembly — Coat cylinder bore, pistons and cups with brake fluid. Reverse disassembly procedure and install parts in cylinder bore. Install dust covers securely in cylinder body grooves.

NOTE — Lips of piston cups must face center of cylinder.

MASTER CYLINDER

Disassembly — 1) Remove reservoir cap assembly and drain brake fluid. Loosen retaining clamp and remove reservoir. Remove snap ring and stop bolt. Cover open end of master cylinder with a clean rag.

2) Place finger over stop bolt hole and secondary outlet port. Remove pistons by applying low pressure air to primary port. Piston assemblies must be replaced as complete units if disassembled.

Cleaning & Inspection — Clean all parts in brake fluid and check for wear or damage. Check master cylinder bore-to-piston clearance. If clearance exceeds .006" (.15 mm), replace defective part.

Reassembly — Coat all parts with brake fluid and reverse disassembly procedure. Rotate pistons while pushing into cylinder bore. Use suitable cup guide tool to compress secondary piston when installing snap ring.

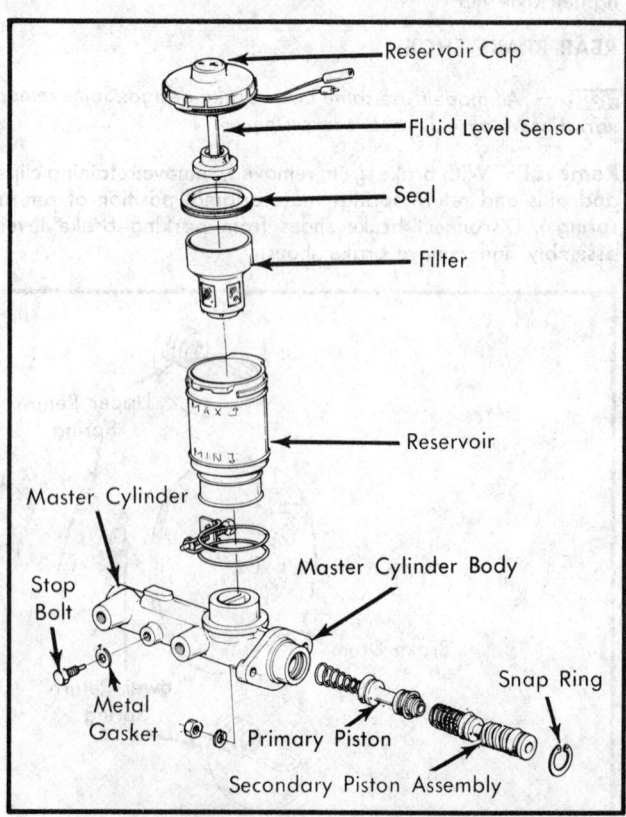

Fig. 5 Exploded View of Master Cylinder

HONDA (Cont.)

POWER BRAKE UNIT

NOTE — *Power brake units vary among models; overhaul procedures are the same for all models.*

Disassembly — **1)** Scribe an index mark across front and rear booster housings for reassembly reference. Remove lock spring and plate (except Accord). Remove master cylinder and output rod. To remove rear housing on Civic and Prelude, reinstall master cylinder mount nuts with lock nuts behind them.

2) Tighten nuts against each other on studs. Clamp power brake unit in vise by tightening vise against locked nuts on studs. Attach booster handles (07967-6340000) to rear housing with 4 nuts. Turn rear housing counterclockwise until locking tabs are free of slots on front housing.

CAUTION — *Housing assembly is spring loaded. Press down on handles while turning.*

3) To remove rear housing on Accord, carefully remove retaining bolts while holding housing. On all models, remove reaction cover, reaction ring, and reaction plates. Pry bushing retainer out of rear housing. Remove bushing and piston seal. Remove snap ring from push rod. Remove valve holder assembly from piston.

Cleaning & Inspection — Clean all parts in alcohol and dry with compressed air. Check all parts for wear or damage. Check booster piston for cracks or deformation. Replace all parts as indicated in illustration during overhaul.

Reassembly — **1)** Seat inner valve in groove of push rod and lubricate with silicon grease. Install outer valve on holder. Install push rod through valve holder and seat metal end of outer valve in groove of inner valve. Install inner and outer valve springs, spring seat, and felt silencer into valve holder and secure with circlip.

2) Slip filter over end of pushrod. Thread adjuster and lock nut onto shaft but do not tighten. Slip new diaphragm over piston and drive retaining ring into place. Apply silicon grease to inner and outer surfaces of piston tube. Press valve holder in power unit piston tube.

3) Apply silicon grease to piston seal. Install piston seal. Install bushing in rear housing and drive retainer in until seal bottoms. Slip diaphragm/piston assembly into rear housing. Install snap ring in groove of push rod. Install reaction plates, reaction ring and reaction cover.

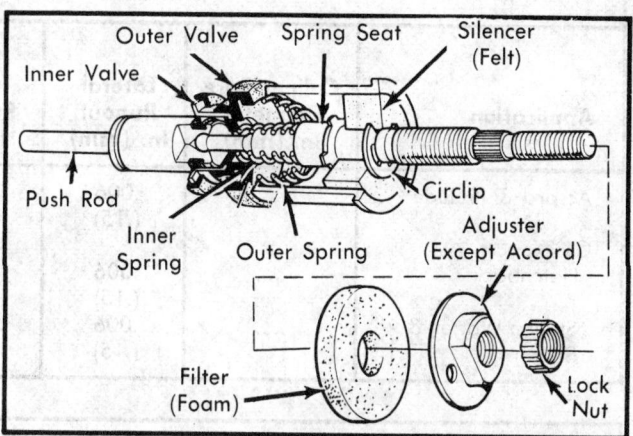

Fig. 7   Exploded View of Power Brake Valve Holder Assembly

NOTE — *Install reaction plates with rounded portion facing reaction ring. Install reaction ring with rubber end facing plates. Apply silicon grease to plates.*

4) Apply silicon grease to sealing lip and in groove of rod seal. Install new rod seal in front housing. To complete reassembly, reverse removal procedure. Before installing master cylinder to power brake unit, check master cylinder to push rod clearance. Place rod bolt adjusting gauge (67975-6570000) on master cylinder open end with knurled knob up.

5) Turn screw until it touches piston. Remove gauge from master cylinder and place on power brake unit with knurled knob down. Without moving adjusting screw position, measure distance between adjusting screw end and booster push rod. Clearance should be .004-.020" (.1-.6 mm) on Accord and .008-.016" (.2-.4 mm) on all others.

6) If clearance is not to specification, adjust on Accord by removing adjusting bolt, loosening lock nut and turning adjusting bolt to correct specification. On Civic and Prelude, set clearance by loosening star lock nut and turning adjuster.

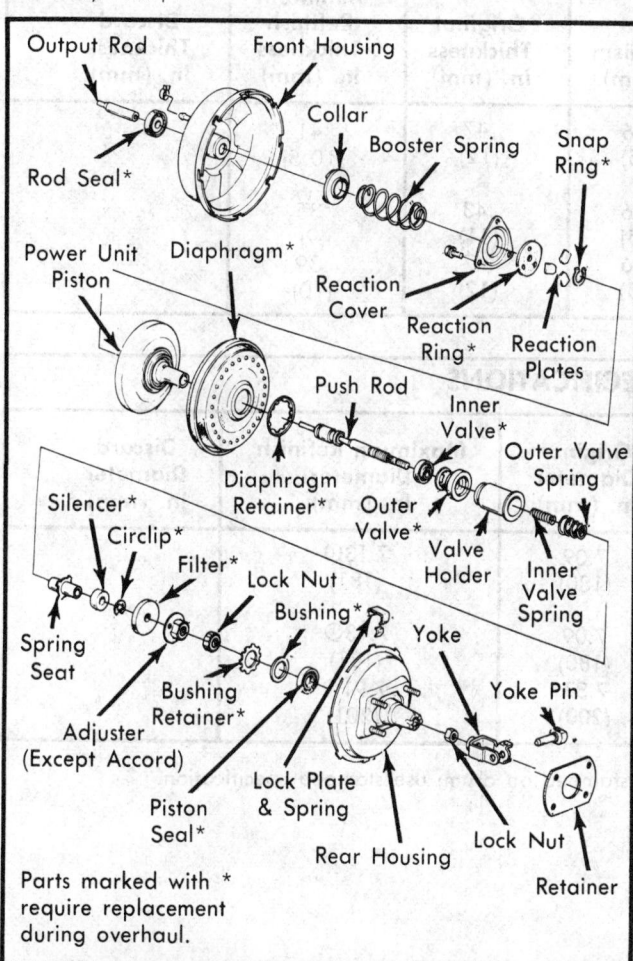

Fig. 6   Exploded View of Power Brake Unit (Civic and Prelude Shown — Accord Similar)

4) Remove circlip from valve holder assembly and disassemble valves. Pry off diaphragm retainer. Remove diaphragm from piston. Remove rod seal from front housing.

Brakes

HONDA (Cont.)

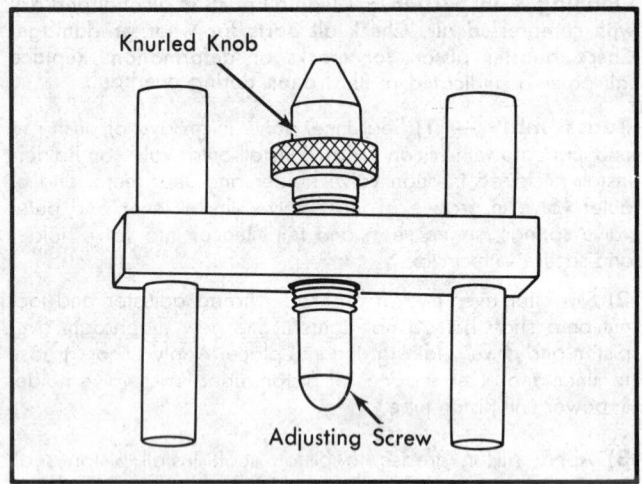

Knurled Knob

Adjusting Screw

Fig. 8   Push Rod Adjustment Gauge

TIGHTENING SPECIFICATIONS

Application	Ft. Lbs. (N.m)
Hub-to-Rotor Bolts	40 (54)
Caliper Mounting Bracket	56 (76)
Caliper Guide Pin Bolts	
Civic Hatchback	20 (27)
Prelude	13 (18)

DISC BRAKE SPECIFICATIONS

Application	Caliper Bore Diameter In. (mm)	Lateral Runout In. (mm)	Parallelism In. (mm)	Original Thickness In. (mm)	Minimum Refinish Thickness In. (mm)	Discard Thickness In. (mm)
Accord & Prelude	.....	.006 (.15)	.0006 (.015)	.47 (12)	.41 (10.5)	.....
Civic Hatchback	.....	.006 (.15)	.0006 (.015)	.43 (11)	.35 (9)	.....
Station Wagon & Sedan	.....	.006 (.15)	.0006 (.015)	.47 (12)	.39 (10)	.....

DRUM BRAKE SPECIFICATIONS

Application	Wheel Cyl. Bore Diameter In. (mm)	Drum Diameter In. (mm)	Original Diameter In. (mm)	Maximum Refinish Diameter In. (mm)	Discard Diameter In. (mm)
Accord & Prelude	.....	7.09 (180)	7.09 (180)	7.13① (181)	.....
Civic Hatchback & Sedan	.....	7.09 (180)	7.09 (180)	7.13① (181)	.....
Station Wagon	.....	7.87 (200)	7.87 (200)	7.91① (201)	.....

① — If maximum refinish diameter disagrees with specification stamped on drum; use stamped specification.

ISUZU

I-Mark

DESCRIPTION

Brake system is hydraulically operated using a tandem master cylinder and a vacuum operated power brake unit. All models are equipped with front disc and rear drum brakes. Rear brakes are of the leading/trailing type and have a self adjusting mechanisim. A combination valve is installed in engine compartment and includes a pressure limiting valve and a differential pressure switch (fail indicator). Parking brakes are cable operated and operate on rear wheels.

ADJUSTMENT

REAR DRUM BRAKE

Raise and support vehicle. Index mark wheel assembly and axle flange and remove wheel and tire. Remove brake drum. Measure inside diameter of brake drum with brake measuring tool (J-21177 or equivalent). Adjust brake shoes to brake drum dimension. Use a screwdriver to move auto adjuster lever to adjust. Install brake drum and wheel assembly. Lower vehicle.

PARKING BRAKE

Fully release parking brake lever. Check cable for free movement. Remove cable play by turning brake lever rod adjustment nut. Parking brake lever travel should be 8-10 notches.

PEDAL HEIGHT AND FREE PLAY

Adjust pedal free play by turning the push rod. Distance between upper face of brake pedal and carpet should be 6.73" (171 mm). Push the brake pedal by turning the stop light switch so that free play is eliminated. Tighten clevis lock nut and stop light switch lock nut.

REMOVAL & INSTALLATION

FRONT DISC PADS

Removal & Installation — Raise and support front of vehicle. Remove wheel and tire. Remove clips, pins, retaining spring, pad shims and brake pads. To install, apply P.B.C (Poly Butyl Caprysil) grease to face of pads and pad shims as shown in *Fig. 1*. Push pistons back into bores after slightly opening bleeder valves. Close valves. Assemble pad shims to brake pads with arrow pointing in direction of normal disc rotation. Install assembly to caliper. Install retaining spring, pins and clips. Install wheels and lower vehicle.

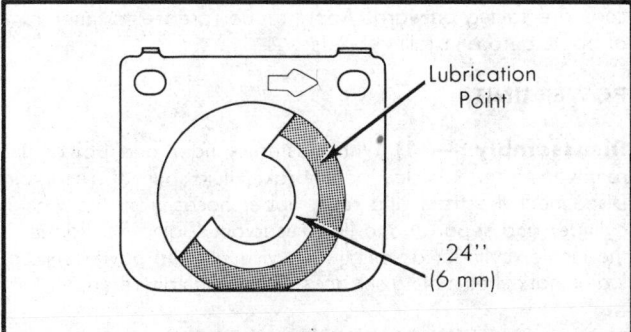

FRONT DISC CALIPER

Removal & Installation — Raise and support vehicle. Remove wheel and tire. Disconnect caliper hose from caliper and plug to prevent entry of dirt. Remove caliper mounting bolts and caliper. To install, reverse removal procedure.

FRONT DISC ROTOR

Removal & Installation — Raise and support vehicle. Remove tire and wheel. Remove caliper and suspend out of way. DO NOT allow to hang from hydraulic hose. Remove grease cap cotter key and spindle nut. Remove hub and disc assembly. Remove hub-to-rotor bolts and remove rotor from hub. To install, reverse removal procedure. Adjust wheel bearings. *See Wheel Bearing Adjustment in SUSPENSION Section.*

REAR BRAKE SHOES

Removal — Raise and support vehicle. Remove tire and wheel. Remove brake drum. Remove return springs and hold down pins, cups and springs. Move the automatic adjuster lever all the way in direction of expansion and disconnect the strut. Remove the primary shoe. Disconnect parking brake cable from parking brake lever and remove secondary shoe.

Installation — Install the secondary shoe, and install the parking brake cable to the parking brake lever. Install the primary shoe, strut and automatic adjuster lever. Install return springs, and shoe hold down springs, cups and pins. Install drum and adjust brake linings as outlined previously. Install wheel and lower vehicle.

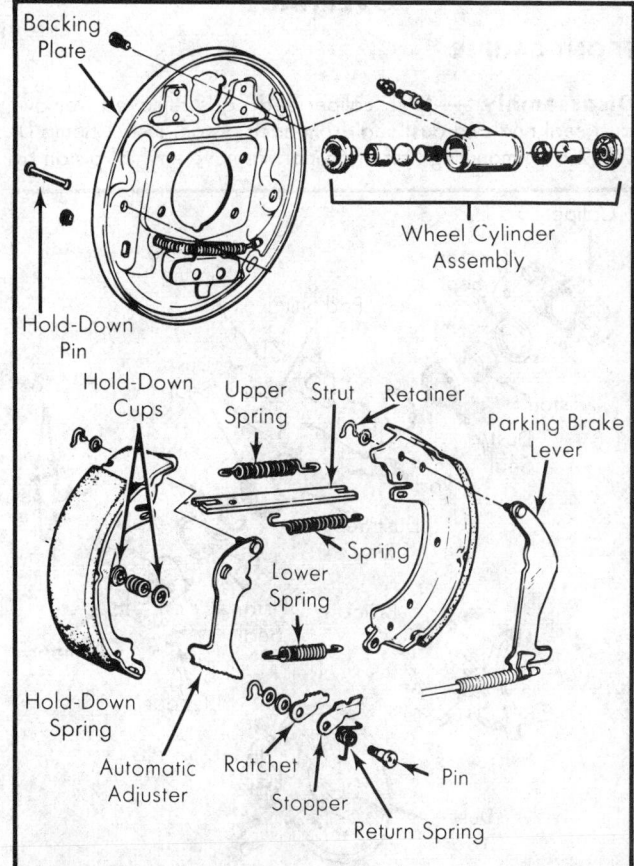

Fig. 1   Pad Shim Lubrication Point

Fig. 2   Exploded View of Rear Brake Assembly

ISUZU (Cont.)

MASTER CYLINDER

Removal — Disconnect hydraulic lines from master cylinder. Remove nuts securing master cylinder to power brake unit and support bracket. Remove bolts securing fluid reservoir bracket and remove master cylinder assembly and fluid reservoir.

Installation — Place master cylinder and reservoir in position with the fluid reservoir bracket and install bolts securing bracket to inner fender. Install nuts holding master cylinder to power brake unit and support bracket. Connect front and rear hydraulic lines to master cylinder. Bleed hydraulic system.

POWER BRAKE UNIT

Removal — Disconnect hydraulic lines from master cylinder. Cover and plug line ends. Remove master cylinder bracket bolts to cylinder and fender skirt and remove bracket. Remove vacuum hose clip and hose from check valve. Remove clevis pin and separate clevis from brake pedal arm. Remove power brake unit to dash panel retaining nuts and lift out power brake unit and master cylinder.

Installation — Install the master cylinder and power brake unit to the dash panel and support bracket. Connect hydraulic lines to master cylinder. Tighten master cylinder to power brake unit nuts, power brake to dash panel nuts and master cylinder support bracket bolt. Adjust brake pedal height and bleed brake system.

OVERHAUL

FRONT CALIPER

Disassembly — With caliper and pads removed, remove dust seal ring and dust seal from each piston. Install clamp (J-22429) on mounting half of caliper. Remove rim half piston by

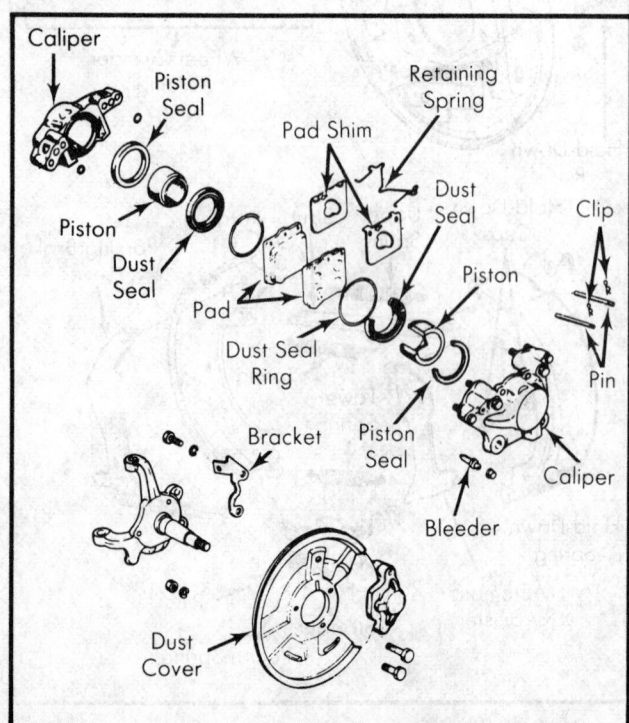

Fig. 3   Exploded View of Disc Brake Assembly

applying compressed air to brake line connection. Install clamp on rim half of caliper. Remove mounting half piston with compressed air. Remove piston seals from annular grooves in caliper piston bores.

Reassembly — Apply rubber grease to seal and cylinder wall and install new piston seal in cylinder. Carefully install piston to bottom of cylinder bore using finger pressure only. Install dust seal and seal ring. Assemble pad shim to brake pad with arrow pointing in direction of normal disc rotation and install in caliper. Install retaining spring pins and clips.

MASTER CYLINDER

Disassembly — Pour brake fluid out of reservoir. Disconnect the front and rear rubber hoses from the master cylinder and separate the fluid reservoir. Place the cylinder in a vise and remove pipe connector. Remove check valve, spring and retainer. Push in on primary piston with a screwdriver and remove secondary piston stop bolt and snap ring. Remove primary piston assembly, primary piston spring, secondary piston assembly and secondary piston spring.

Inspection — Measure master cylinder bore diameter and outside diameter of primary and secondary pistons. Standard bore diameter is .875" (22.2 mm). Clearance limit is .006" (.15 mm). Replace cylinder if damage is found or if clearance is beyond limit.

Reassembly — **1)** Lubricate parts with clean brake fluid. Assemble the spring check valve, gasket and pipe connector to the cylinder body and semi-tighten the pipe connector. Clamp cylinder in soft-jawed vise and tighten pipe connector. Install the primary piston spring and primary piston assembly into cylinder and set in position with snap ring.

2) Carefully note the direction of setting when assembling primary and secondary piston assembly into cylinder. Do not force piston into cylinder. Press primary piston all the way into position with a screwdriver and install secondary piston stop bolt with a gasket on the cylinder body.

WHEEL CYLINDER

Disassembly — Remove boots, pistons, piston cups, spring and bleeder screw from the wheel cylinder.

Inspection — Measure wheel cylinder bore and outside diameter of piston. Limit of clearance is .006" (.15 mm). Standard cylinder bore diameter is .812" (20.6 mm).

Reassembly — Lubricate the sliding parts of wheel cylinder with clean brake fluid. Assemble into cylinder so that piston cups are facing outward. Apply rubber grease to inner face of boots before installing boots.

POWER UNIT

Disassembly — **1)** With master cylinder and power unit removed from vehicle, pour brake fluid out of reservoir. Disconnect the front and rear rubber hoses from the master cylinder and separate the fluid reservoir. Clamp the flange of the master cylinder assembly in a vise with the power unit up. Index mark shell mating surfaces for reassembly reference.

2) Remove 4 nuts and spacer from rear shell of power unit. Loosen and remove lock nut and clevis from operating rod. Attach booster housing tool (J-9504-01) to rear shell and

ISUZU (Cont.)

carefully turn rear shell counterclockwise. Be careful as shell is under spring pressure. Maintain pressure on rear shell during removal.

3) Remove rear shell and diaphragm return spring. Remove boot from rear shell and remove diaphragm plate assembly. Remove retainer from rear shell and remove plate and seal. Remove diaphragm and silencer retainer from diaphragm assembly and remove valve plunger stopper key. Remove plunger assembly and reaction disc. Remove push rod, retainer and seal from front shell assembly.

Inspection — Clean and dry disassembled parts. Check diaphragm, boot and reaction disc from weakening, distortion or damage and replace as necessary. Check plunger assembly for wear. Replace if worn. Check diaphragm plate, check valve and vacuum hose for damage or wear and replace as necessary.

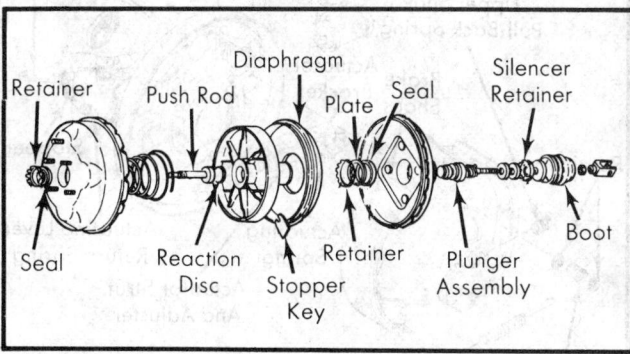

Fig. 4   Exploded View of Power Brake Unit

Reassembly — **1)** Apply silicon grease to the sliding faces of parts. Apply silicon grease to the seal fitting face of the rear shell and lipped portion and install plate, seal and retainer. Apply thin coat of silicon grease to the outer and inner faces of the diaphragm plate and the outer face of the poppet valve.

2) Install plunger assembly (with filter and silencer) making sure poppet valve is not projecting beyond the retainer. Push in on plunger and install valve plunger stopper key. Apply silicon grease to reaction disc and install in diaphragm plate.

3) Assemble diaphragm assembly to rear shell and install the boot and clevis. Install seal assembly to front shell. Apply silicon grease to sliding face of seal and push rod and install retainer and push rod. Temporarily secure master cylinder to front shell with nuts and lock washers. Clamp flanged portion of master cylinder in vise (front shell side up).

NOTE — *Do not tighten vise too tightly as damage to flange will result.*

4) Apply a thin coat of silicon grease to outer rim and contact faces of front and rear shells of diaphragm. Install diaphragm spring between front and rear shells. Using booster housing tool (J-9504-01) push in and rotate rear shell clockwise until it is fully seated with scribe marks aligned. Assemble push rod boot to rear shell. Make sure boot is fully installed in retainer and install spacer to rear shell.

CAUTION — *Before releasing tool, make sure rear shell is locked to front shell at all tabs.*

5) Loosely install push rod clevis lock nut and clevis. Remove assembly from vise and separate master cylinder from power brake unit. Position power brake unit in vise so that push rod is up. DO NOT clamp tightly. Measure distance between master cylinder mounting face of front shell and end of push rod. If necessary, adjust push rod to .733" (18.6 mm). Hold rod at serrated portion and turn threaded end.

TIGHTENING SPECIFICATIONS

Application	Ft. Lbs. (N.m)
Hydraulic Line Flare Nuts	12 (16)
Caliper-to-Steering Knuckle	36 (49)
Rotor-to-Hub	36 (49)
Master Cylinder-to-Power Brake Unit	10 (14)

DISC BRAKE SPECIFICATIONS

Application	Caliper Bore Diameter In. (mm)	Lateral Runout In. (mm)	Parallelism In. (mm)	Original Thickness In. (mm)	Minimum Refinish Thickness In. (mm)	Discard Thickness In. (mm)
I-Mark	.812 (20.6)	.006 (.15)	.....	.394 (10.0)	.338 (8.6)	.....

DRUM BRAKE SPECIFICATIONS

Application	Wheel Cyl. Bore Diameter In. (mm)	Drum Diameter In. (mm)	Original Diameter In. (mm)	Maximum Refinish Diameter In. (mm)	Discard Diameter In. (mm)
I-Mark	.812 (20.6)	9.00 (228.6)	9.00 (228.6)	9.04 (229.6)	9.055 (230.0)

Brakes

ISUZU P'UP & LUV

Isuzu P'UP
LUV Pickup

DESCRIPTION

Brake system uses a master cylinder with a single reservoir and two outlets, and a vacuum power brake unit. Front brakes are single piston, floating disc; rear brakes are duo-Servo type drum. A combination valve is used in all systems and is equipped with a fail indicator switch. If hydraulic pressure varies between front and rear systems, warning light on instrument panel will light. Warning light will glow until defect is repaired. Parking brake cable actuates the rear drums.

ADJUSTMENT

REAR DRUM BRAKE SHOES

Rear brakes self-adjust on reverse brake applications. No in-service adjustment is required. Initial adjustment must be made after changing brake linings or adjuster setting has been changed. To adjust, place vehicle on safety stands and follow one of the below methods:

Preferred Method — Remove brake drum. Measure drum diameter with drum-to-brake shoe gauge (J-21177); transfer gauge to brake shoes. Adjust star wheel until gauge just slides over linings. Install drum; lower car. Make final adjustment by making alternate forward and reverse brake applications until pedal height remains constant.

Alternate Method — With the brake drum installed, move the parking brake actuating lever until clicks indicating rotation of star wheel are no longer heard. With vehicle stationary, operate the parking brake repeatedly while depressing the brake pedal until sufficient pedal stroke is obtained.

PEDAL HEIGHT

Pedal height (measured from center of pedal pad to floorboard) should be 6.1-6.5" (154-164 mm). To adjust, disconnect negative battery cable and stop light switch electrical lead. Remove stop switch from bracket. Rotate push rod to obtain proper pedal height. Install and adjust stop light switch. Install electrical leads.

STOP LIGHT SWITCH

Stop light switch is located under dash, above brake pedal. To adjust, loosen lock nut and adjust clearance at switch housing (not actuating pin) and brake pedal tab to .02-.04" (.5-1 mm). Tighten lock nut.

PARKING BRAKE

NOTE — *Service brake must be properly adjusted prior to parking brake adjustment.*

1) With vehicle on a hoist and parking brake released, loosen lock nut on parking brake cable adjuster. Turn parking brake cable adjuster clockwise until actuating lever stopper on each rear brake is lifted completely off the flange plate.

2) Turn the adjuster counterclockwise until actuating lever stopper on each rear brake makes contact with the flange plate. Tighten lock nut on adjuster, then apply and release parking brake 3 or 4 times.

3) Parking brake lever stroke should be 12 to 13 notches when set firmly. Rear wheels should rotate freely with parking brake fully released. If either does not operate as described, repeat steps 1) and 2) until proper operation is obtained. Lower vehicle.

BRAKE WARNING LIGHT

A dual warning light is mounted on dash. Light should glow when parking brake lever is pulled 1 notch and go off when lever is fully released (ignition on). To check circuit warning sensor, release parking brake (ignition on) and ensure light is off. Open bleed screw on 1 wheel and depress brake pedal; light should glow.

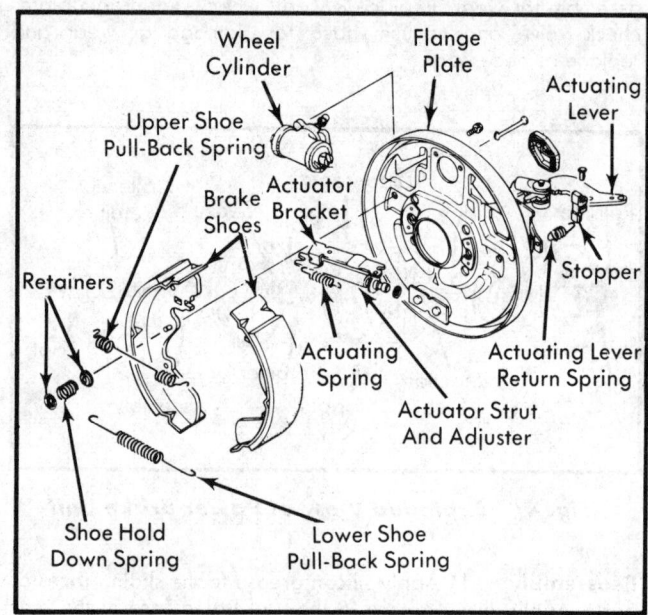

Fig. 1 Rear Brake Drum Assembly

REMOVAL & INSTALLATION

FRONT DISC BRAKE PADS

Removal — 1) Raise and support vehicle on safety stands; remove tire and wheel. Remove caliper stop spring pins and stops. Remove caliper from support and remove stop plates from caliper. Suspend caliper from frame with wire. DO NOT damage flex hose.

2) Remove pads and shims (mark pads if they are to be re-used). Remove anti-rattle springs from support. Replace pads if they have less than .039" (1 mm) of lining left. Always replace pads in axle sets.

Installation — Reverse removal procedure and note the following: Original pads must be installed in original position. Install pads to supports with wear indicators facing LOWER SIDE. Apply brake lubricant to shims, stop plates and caliper sliding surfaces.

NOTE — *Manufacturer recommends replacing stop plates and pins.*

FRONT DISC BRAKE CALIPER

Removal — Raise and support vehicle on safety stands; remove tire and wheel. Remove caliper stop spring pins and

ISUZU P'UP & LUV (Cont.)

stops. Disconnect hydraulic flex hose from brake line and plug openings. Remove caliper from support. Remove stop plates from caliper. Remove support mounting bolts and support assembly.

Installation — Reverse removal procedure and note the following: Apply brake grease to stop plates and caliper sliding surfaces. Flex hose identification stripe must follow a straight line with no binding. Install new stop plates and pins. Bleed hydraulic system.

FRONT DISC BRAKE ROTOR

Removal — With caliper removed, remove caliper support bolts and support. Remove grease cap, cotter pin, spindle nut retainer and nut. Remove hub and rotor assembly without dropping wheel bearings. Separate only if replacing either component.

Installation — Reverse removal procedures and adjust wheel bearings. See appropriate Front Suspension article in SUSPENSION Section. Tighten caliper support bolts evenly and bleed hydraulic system if necessary.

REAR BRAKE DRUM

Removal — Raise and support vehicle on safety stands; remove tire and wheel. Remove retaining screws and brake drum (neutralize shoes if required). Mark drum for reassembly reference.

Installation — To install drums, reverse removal procedures. Install drums in original position. Adjust brakes.

REAR BRAKE SHOES

Removal — 1) With drum removed, remove shoe pull-back springs, hold down springs, pins and retainers. Remove adjuster lever spring, adjuster cable and guide plate.

2) Remove adjuster lever and lever hold down spring. Remove brake shoes as an assembly. Separate primary and secondary shoes, adjuster, return spring and strut.

3) Separate parking brake lever and rear cable. Remove clip and washer and separate brake lever from secondary shoe.

Installation — Install parking brake lever to secondary shoe and rear cable to lever. Connect brake shoes together with return spring, and place adjuster screw into position, making sure star wheel is nearest secondary shoe. Install parking brake strut with spring on primary shoe end, then fit shoes to wheel cylinder push rods. Install hold down springs, self-adjuster assembly and return springs. Install drum and adjust and bleed hydraulic system.

MASTER CYLINDER

Removal — Disconnect battery ground cable. Disconnect hydraulic lines at master cylinder and cover ends to prevent entry of dirt. Remove bracket bolt at front end of cylinder, and nuts retaining cylinder to power unit, then remove master cylinder and gasket from power unit.

Installation — Reverse removal procedure, bleed hydraulic system and adjust pedal height if necessary.

POWER BRAKE UNIT

Removal — Disconnect battery ground cable. Disconnect hydraulic lines at master cylinder and cover ends to prevent entry of dirt. Remove bolts attaching bracket to master cylinder and fender and remove bracket. Disconnect vacuum line at power unit and place out of way. Disconnect brake pedal return spring and push rod. Remove nuts attaching power unit to firewall, and remove power unit and master cylinder as an assembly.

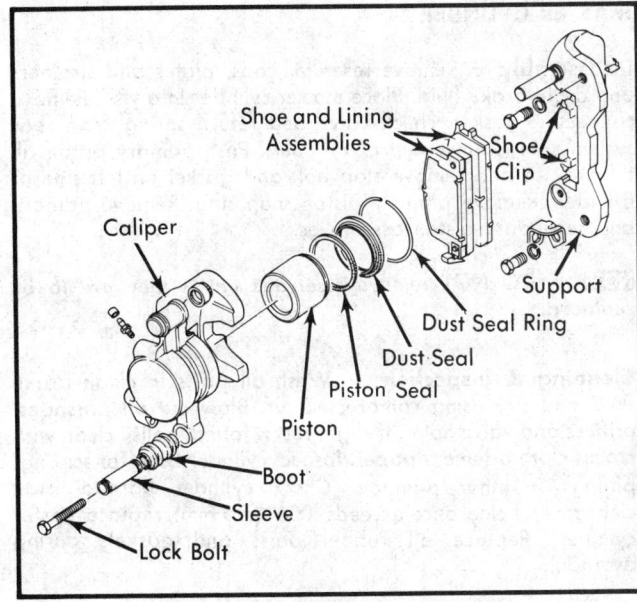

Fig. 2 Exploded View of Front Disc Brake Assy.

Installation — Reverse removal procedure, bleed hydraulic system and adjust pedal height if necessary.

OVERHAUL

FRONT DISC BRAKE CALIPER

Disassembly — Remove flex hose from caliper. Using pointed, but blunt instrument, remove seal from caliper. Place a block of wood between piston and caliper cavity wall, then apply enough compressed air pressure to force piston from cylinder. Remove and discard piston ring seal.

Cleaning & Inspection — Clean all parts in clean brake fluid and dry with filtered, dry, compressed air. Check cylinder bore and piston for wear, scuffing or corrosion. Replace if defective. Minor imperfections can be removed from caliper bore with crocus cloth. Replace dust seal and piston seal during overhaul.

NOTE — DO NOT polish piston outer surfaces with abrasive.

Reassembly — Lubricate piston seal and insert into caliper bore. Carefully insert piston into caliper assembly. Install dust seal on piston and caliper. Fit seal ring into dust seal.

WHEEL CYLINDER

Disassembly — Remove boots from cylinder ends. Remove pistons and cups. Remove expander springs, if equipped.

Cleaning & Inspection — Clean all parts in clean brake fluid. Inspect cylinder bore and pistons for rust, corrosion or

ISUZU P'UP & LUV (Cont.)

other damage. Replace defective parts. Check wheel cylinder bore-to-piston clearance. If clearance exceeds .006" (.15 mm), replace wheel cylinder assembly.

Reassembly — Lubricate cylinder bore with clean brake fluid. Install spring expander into bore. Install new cups with flat surfaces toward outside. Install new pistons into cylinder with flat surfaces facing center. DO NOT lubricate pistons, cups or boots prior to installation. Press new boots onto cylinder.

MASTER CYLINDER

Disassembly — Remove reservoir caps, plates and strainers and drain brake fluid. Place master cylinder in a vise. Remove connector, gasket, check valve and return spring from rear system side (front outlet of cylinder). Push primary piston all the way in and remove stop bolt and gasket on left side of cylinder. Remove primary piston snap ring. Remove primary and secondary piston assemblies.

NOTE — DO NOT remove reservoirs unless they are to be replaced.

Cleaning & Inspection — Wash all parts in clean brake fluid and dry using compressed air. Blow out all passages, orifices and valve holes. If slight rust is found, polish clean with crocus cloth or emery paper. Inspect cylinder bore for scoring, pitting or other damage. Check cylinder bore-to-piston clearance; if clearance exceeds .006" (.15 mm), replace master cylinder. Replace all rubber parts and gaskets during overhaul.

Reassembly — Lubricate cylinder bore and all parts with clean brake fluid, reverse disassembly procedure, and note the following: Use all new gaskets and seals when reassembling. When reassembly is complete, bench bleed master cylinder as follows: Install plugs in all outlet ports of cylinder, fill reservoirs with clean brake fluid, and press in and out on primary piston until air bubbles are no longer seen in fluid.

POWER BRAKE UNIT

Disassembly — 1) Remove master cylinder reservoir and drain remaining brake fluid from cylinder. Scribe alignment marks on front and rear shells to assure reassembly in original position. Clamp flange of master cylinder in a vise with power unit up. Loosen push rod clevis lock nut and remove clevis and lock nut, then remove push rod boot.

2) Place suitable wrench (J-9504) over rear shell mounting studs. Press down on wrench while rotating counterclockwise and remove rear shell, piston rod, power piston, return spring and spring retainer. Remove nuts and lock washers and separate master cylinder and power unit front shell, then remove and discard gasket.

NOTE — Power brake unit removal tool (J-9504) must be modified to fit brake unit.

NOTE — DO NOT disassemble push rod assembly; if defective, replace complete assembly.

3) Pry retainer off power piston and remove air silencer and filter, then remove rubber diaphragm from piston. Rotate power piston until push rod retainer slot is down, then press in on rod, allowing retainer to fall out of power piston. Remove push rod assembly and reaction disc.

4) If rear shell is defective, pry out seal retainer and remove spacer and seal assembly. If front seal is defective, pry out retainer and remove seal. If vacuum check valve is defective, remove using a twisting motion, then remove grommet.

NOTE — Do not clean parts with a mineral based solvent.

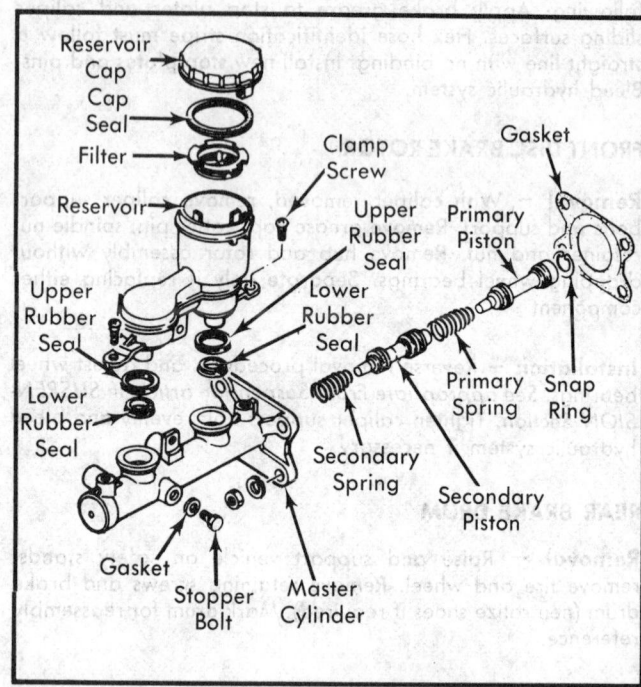

Fig. 3 Master Cylinder Assembly

Cleaning & Inspection — Clean all parts in denatured alcohol and blow dry with compressed air. Inspect inner surface of both shells for wear or damage; slight rust can be removed with fine emery cloth or crocus cloth. Inspect all parts for cracks, nicks, distortion or other damage; replace parts as necessary.

Reassembly — Reverse disassembly procedures and note the following: Apply a coat of silicone grease to parts before installation. When assembling front shell to rear shell, ensure marks made at disassembly are aligned. When reassembly is completed, remove master cylinder from power unit. Place suitable gauge (J-29759) over piston rod so that legs rest on master cylinder mounting surface. Piston rod should touch cut out portion of gauge. If rod must be adjusted, hold rod at serrated portion and turn threaded end.

TIGHTENING SPECIFICATIONS

Application	Ft. Lbs. (N·m)
Rotor-to-Hub	36 (49)
Support-to-Adapter	64 (87)
Steering Knuckle-to-Adapter	
LUV	
Large Bolt	55 (75)
Small Bolt	35 (48)
P'UP	29 (40)
Flange Plate-to-Axle Housing	55 (75)
Master Cylinder End Plug	47 (64)
Master Cylinder-to-Power Cylinder	10 (14)

Brakes

ISUZU P'UP & LUV (Cont.)

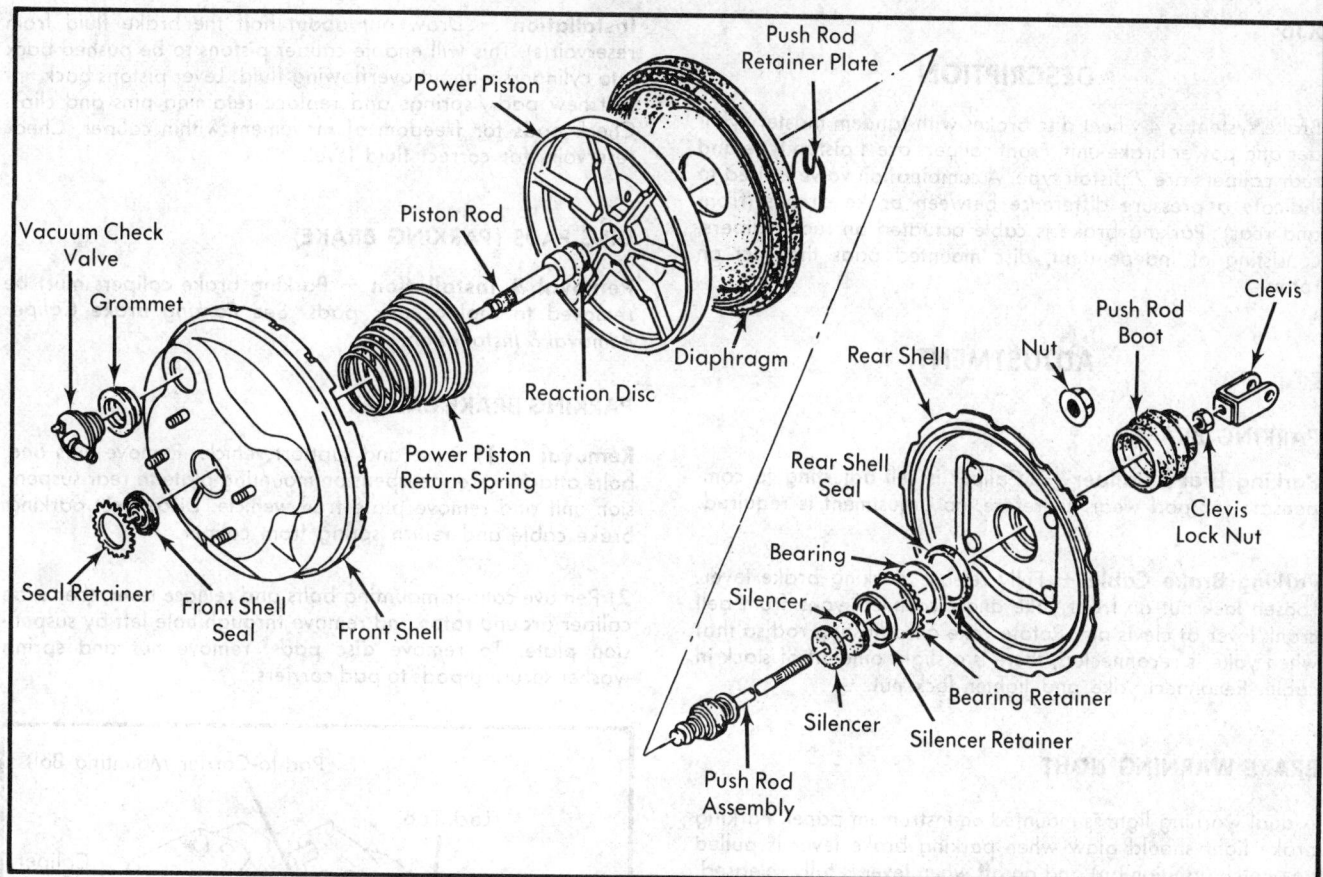

Fig. 4 Exploded View of Power Brake Assembly

DISC BRAKE SPECIFICATIONS

Application	Caliper Bore Diameter In. (mm)	Lateral Runout In. (mm)	Parallelism In. (mm)	Original Thickness In. (mm)	Minimum Refinish Thickness In. (mm)	Discard Thickness In. (mm)
LUV	①	.005② (.13)	.003 (.08)	.709 (18.0)	.668 (17.0)	.653 (16.6)
P'UP	①	.002 (.05)	.003 (.08)	.492 (12.5)	.453 (11.5)	.437 (11.1)

① — Information not available from manufacturer.
② — Max. rate of change must not exceed .001" (.03 mm) in 30°.

DRUM BRAKE SPECIFICATIONS

Application	Wheel Cyl. Bore Diameter In. (mm)	Drum Diameter In. (mm)	Original Diameter In. (mm)	Maximum Refinish Diameter In. (mm)	Discard Diameter In. (mm)
LUV	.750 (19.0)	10.0 (254.0)	10.0 (254.0)	10.059 (255.5)	10.079 (255.6)
P'UP	1.00 (25.4)	10.0 (254.0)	10.0 (254.0)	10.039 (255.0)	10.059 (255.5)

JAGUAR

XJ6

DESCRIPTION

Brake system is 4-wheel disc brakes with tandem master cylinder and power brake unit. Front calipers are 4 piston type and rear calipers are 2 piston type. A combination valve is used to indicate a pressure difference between brake circuits (front and rear). Parking brake is cable actuated on rear calipers, consisting of independent, disc mounted pads that act on rotor.

ADJUSTMENT

PARKING BRAKE

Parking Brake Caliper — Caliper is self-adjusting to compensate for pad wear, therefore, no adjustment is required.

Parking Brake Cable — Fully release parking brake lever. Loosen lock nut on front yoke and disconnect yoke from bell crank lever at clevis pin. Rotate yoke on adjusting rod so that when yoke is reconnected, there is a slight amount of slack in cable. Reconnect yoke and tighten lock nut.

BRAKE WARNING LIGHT

A dual warning light is mounted on instrument panel. Parking brake light should glow when parking brake lever is pulled one notch (ignition on) and go off when lever is fully released. To check circuit warning sensor, fully release parking brake and ensure light is off (ignition on). Open any bleed screw and light should glow. Close bleed screw, then release and reapply brake pedal; warning light should go out.

REMOVAL & INSTALLATION

DISC PADS (SERVICE BRAKES)

Removal — Raise vehicle and remove wheels. Remove pin clips, pad retaining pins, anti-chatter springs (if equipped) and lining pads.

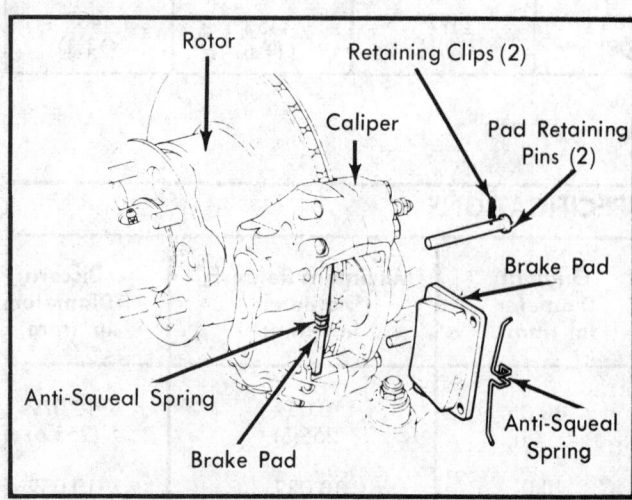

Fig. 1   Removing Front Disc Brake Pads

Installation — Draw out about half the brake fluid from reservoir(s). This will enable caliper pistons to be pushed back into cylinders without overflowing fluid. Lever pistons back, insert new pads, springs and replace retaining pins and clips. Check pads for freedom of movement within caliper. Check reservoirs for correct fluid level.

DISC PADS (PARKING BRAKE)

Removal & Installation — Parking brake calipers must be removed to replace disc pads. See *Parking Brake Caliper Removal & Installation.*

PARKING BRAKE CALIPER

Removal — 1) Raise and support vehicle. Remove nuts and bolts attaching rear suspension mounting plate to rear suspension unit and remove plate from vehicle. Disconnect parking brake cable and return spring from caliper.

2) Remove caliper mounting bolts and release lever, then slide caliper around rotor and remove through hole left by suspension plate. To remove disc pads, remove nut and spring washer securing pads to pad carriers.

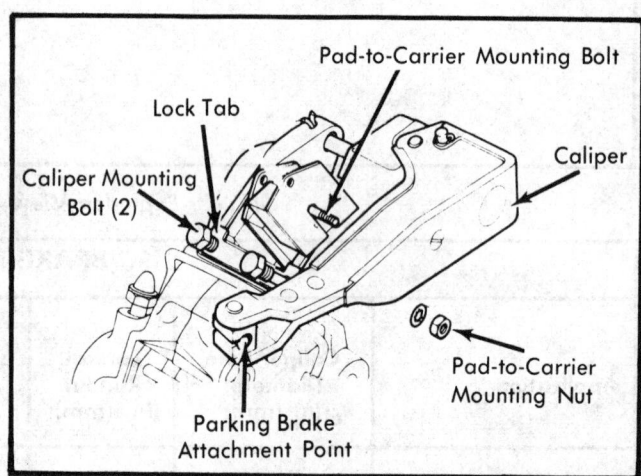

Fig. 2   Detail of Parking Brake Caliper

Installation — To install, reverse removal procedure and note the following: Adjust caliper if new pads have been installed or if caliper has been overhauled. Adjust by holding one pad carrier stationary and turning remaining carrier until there is a clearance of .75" (19 mm) between disc pad surfaces. Operate caliper actuating lever until adjuster ratchet stops clicking. Install remaining components and check operation of brakes.

SERVICE BRAKE CALIPER

NOTE — *Do not separate caliper halves for repair. If a leak exists between halves, replace caliper*

Removal (Front) — Raise vehicle and remove wheels. Disconnect caliper fluid line and plug. Discard locking wire from mounting bolts. Remove caliper.

NOTE — *Check position and number of shims between steering arm and caliper; replace shims in order.*

JAGUAR (Cont.)

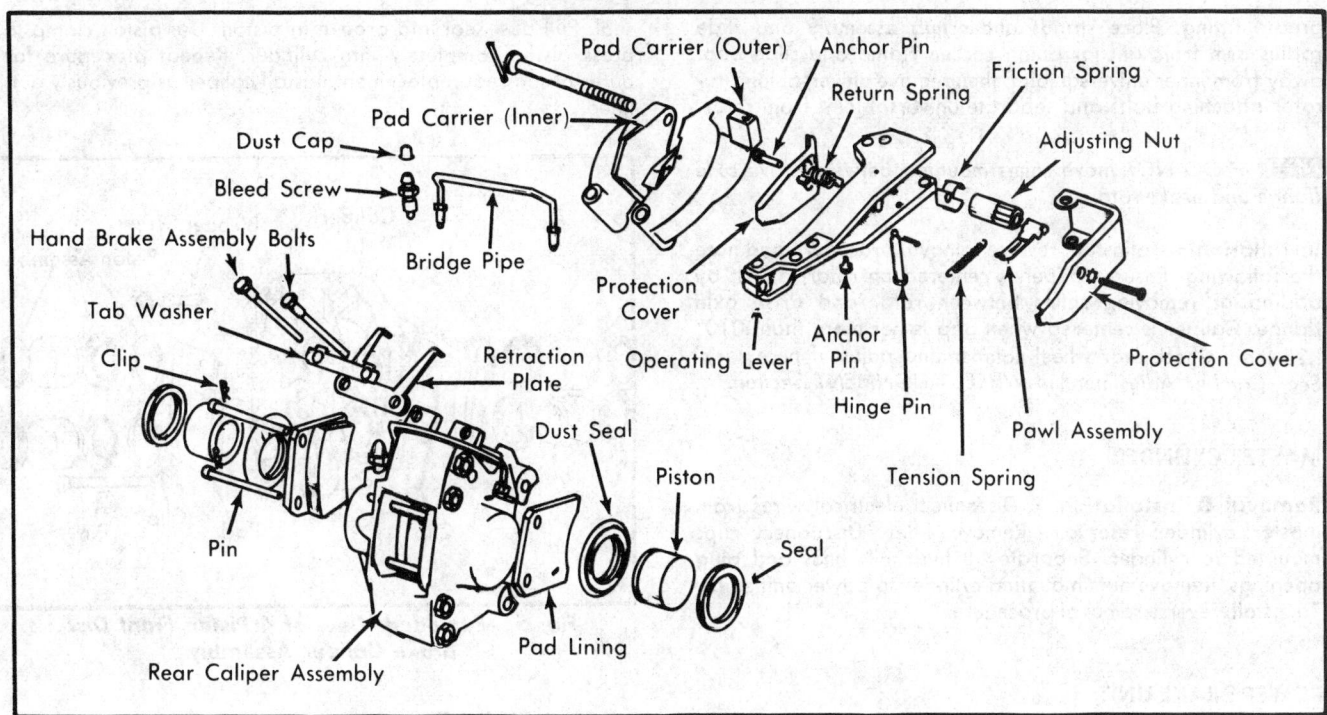

Fig. 3 Exploded View of Rear Brake Caliper with Detail of Parking Brake Assembly

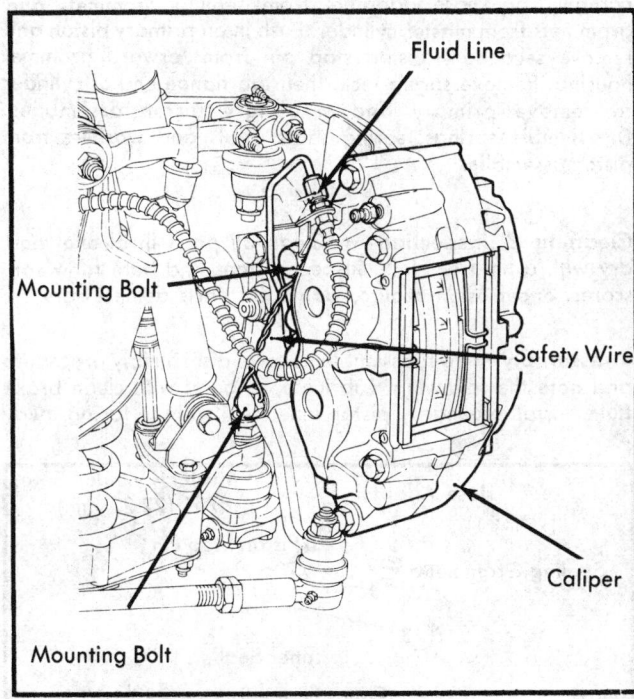

Fig. 4 Components to Remove to Allow Removal of Front Disc Brake Caliper

Installation — 1) Place caliper in position. If original caliper is being reinstalled, refit shims. Install mounting bolts and safety wire. Bleed brakes.

2) If new caliper is being used, check gap between caliper abutment and rotor face. Gap should be no more than .010″ (.25 mm). Gap on upper and lower abutment on SAME SIDE must be equal. If rotor is not centered, remove one caliper

mounting bolt and add or subtract shims as necessary. Repeat procedure on other bolt.

Removal (Rear) — Remove parking brake caliper as previously outlined. Disconnect and plug hydraulic line from caliper mounting bolts and lock wire. Slide caliper around brake rotor and out hole left by suspension plate.

Installation — Place caliper in position, install shims (if equipped) and secure bolts. Check rotor for centering between caliper. If necessary, adjust shims between drive flange and rotor. If shim adjustment is performed, rear wheel camber must be checked. *See Jaguar Rear Wheel Camber Adjustment in WHEEL ALIGNMENT Section.* Complete installation by reversing removal procedure.

BRAKE ROTOR

Removal (Front) — 1) Remove brake caliper as previously outlined. Remove hub-to-rotor attaching bolts and washers. Remove hub dust cap, then remove cotter pin, axle nut and washer from axle stub and remove hub.

2) Insert a punch through access hole in splash shield and lightly tap on it to free water deflector. Remove rotor assembly by sliding it from caliper jaws and over axle stub.

Installation — To install, reverse removal procedure. Pack hub and wheel bearings with grease and adjust wheel bearings. *See Wheel Bearing Adjustment in SUSPENSION Section.*

Removal (Rear) — Remove brake caliper as previously outlined. Disconnect shock absorber from lower mount and remove radius arm locking bolt and lower control arm outer

JAGUAR (Cont.)

grease fitting. Place stands under hub assembly and slide radius arm from anchor point. Loosen clamp and slide boot away from inner universal joint, then remove universal joint-to-rotor attaching bolts and separate universal joint from rotor.

NOTE — *DO NOT move shims mounted between drive axle flange and brake rotor.*

Installation — To install, reverse removal procedure and note the following: Ensure caliper is centered on rotor; adjust by adding or removing shims between rotor and drive axle flange. Caliper is centered when gap is not more than .010″ (.25 mm). Check rear wheel camber and adjust if necessary. *See Camber Adjustment in WHEEL ALIGNMENT Section.*

MASTER CYLINDER

Removal & Installation — Disconnect electrical wires from master cylinder reservoir. Remove filter. Disconnect clips mounted to cylinder. Separate all hydraulic lines and plug openings. Remove nuts mounting cylinder to power unit studs. To install, reverse removal procedure.

POWER BRAKE UNIT

Removal — 1) Disconnect battery. Disconnect and plug master cylinder lines. Pry vacuum hose from power unit. Remove fluid reservoir.

2) Remove bolt securing upper pedal box. Remove reservoir mounting bracket and stop light switch. Remove 6 bolts attaching pedal box. Remove brake pedal pad. Withdraw pedal box, master cylinder and power brake unit as an assembly, then separate.

Installation — To install, reverse removal procedure and bleed hydraulic system.

OVERHAUL

BRAKE CALIPER

NOTE — *DO NOT separate caliper halves for service; pistons and seals may be changed without splitting caliper. If a leak is detected between caliper halves, replace caliper as a unit.*

Disassembly — With disc pads removed, install a suitable piston clamp to retain outboard piston(s), then apply compressed air to fluid inlet port and remove inboard piston(s). Pull dust seal from piston(s) and caliper grooves. Carefully remove piston seal from cylinder.

NOTE — *Inboard piston(s) must be installed before outboard piston(s) can be removed.*

Cleaning & Inspection — Clean all parts in alcohol and inspect for wear or damage. Check cylinder bore and pistons for scratches, rust or corrosion; replace all damaged parts.

Reassembly — Coat cylinder, piston and seal with brake fluid before installing. Place piston seal in bore. Install dust seal over cylinder groove and carefully insert piston through dust

seal. Pull dust seal into groove in piston. Use piston clamp to press piston completely into cylinder. Repeat procedure for outer piston seal replacement. Install caliper as previously outlined.

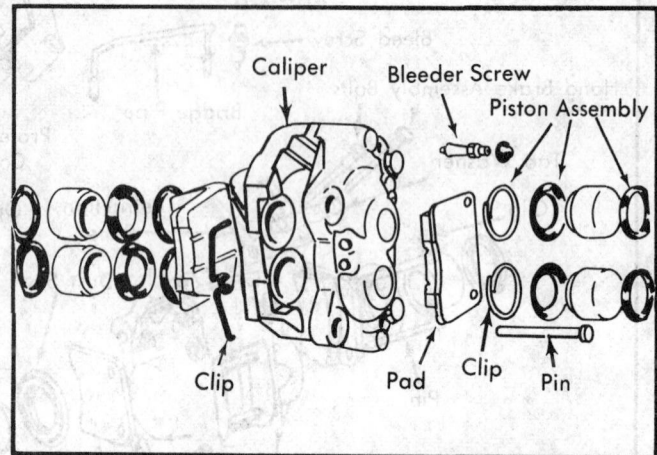

Fig. 5   Exploded View of 4 Piston Front Disc Brake Caliper Assembly

MASTER CYLINDER

Disassembly — With master cylinder removed from vehicle, carefully pry hose adapters from sealing grommets and grommets from master cylinder. Push in on primary piston and remove secondary piston stop pin from forward grommet housing. Remove spring lock, then tap flange end of cylinder to remove primary and secondary piston assemblies. Disassemble springs, spring seats, seals and washers from piston assemblies.

Cleaning & Inspection — Clean all parts in alcohol and dry with a lint-free cloth. Inspect pistons and bore for wear, scores, or corrosion; replace damaged parts as necessary.

Reassembly — To reassemble, reverse disassembly procedure and note the following: Lubricate all parts with clean brake fluid. Install secondary piston inner seal with lip facing away

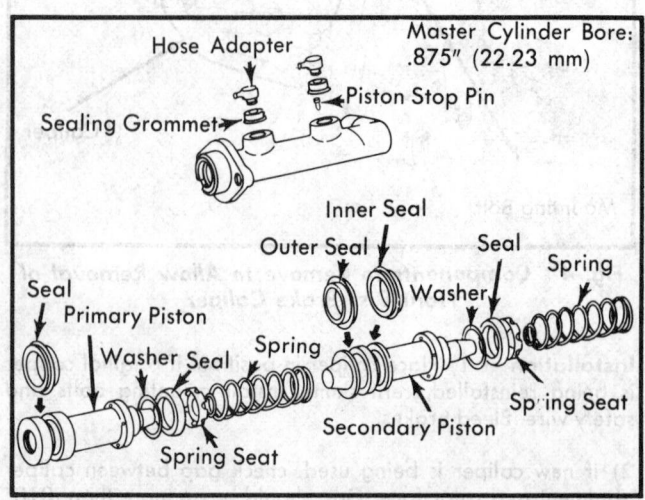

Fig. 6   Exploded View of Master Cylinder Assembly

JAGUAR (Cont.)

from primary piston and install outer seal with lip facing primary piston. Install primary piston seal with lip facing away from spring lock. Install master cylinder and bleed brake system.

POWER BRAKE UNIT

NOTE – *Power brake unit CANNOT be overhauled; if determined defective, replace entire unit.*

TIGHTENING SPECIFICATIONS

Application	Ft. Lbs. (N·m)
Caliper Mounting Bolts	
Front	50-60 (68-82)
Rear	49-55 (67-75)

DISC BRAKE SPECIFICATIONS

Application	Caliper Bore Diameter In. (mm)	Lateral Runout In. (mm)	Parallelism In. (mm)	Original Thickness In. (mm)	Minimum Refinish Thickness In. (mm)	Discard Thickness In. (mm)
XJ6						
Front	.....	.004 (.1)	.....	.950 (24.1)	.....	.....
Rear	.....	.004 (.1)	.....	.500 (12.7)	.....	.....

MAZDA

GLC
626
RX7
B2000 Pickup

DESCRIPTION

Brake system is hydraulically operated using a tandem master cylinder and power brake unit. Front brakes are floating caliper disc. Rear brakes on most models are leading/trailing drums. Floating caliper rear disc brakes are available on RX7 as an option. On all models, a combination valve is used to prevent premature lockup of rear wheels.

ADJUSTMENT

REAR DRUM BRAKE SHOES

GLC (RWD) — 1) Raise and support rear of vehicle. Release parking brake. Loosen the anchor pin lock nut and hold in position while turning anchor pin in proper direction until wheel is locked. See Fig. 1.

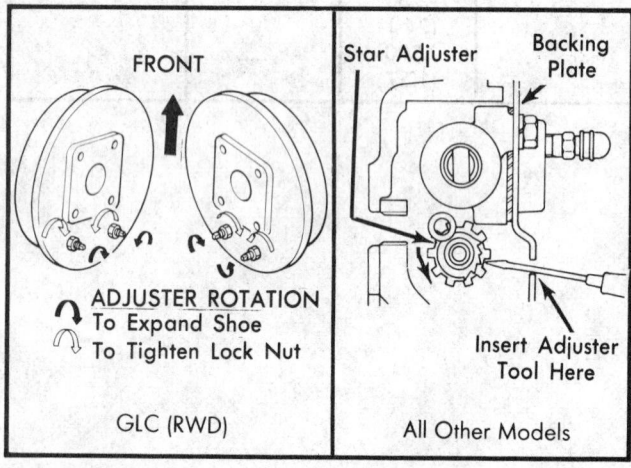

FRONT

Star Adjuster   Backing Plate

ADJUSTER ROTATION
To Expand Shoe
To Tighten Lock Nut

Insert Adjuster Tool Here

GLC (RWD)   All Other Models

Fig. 1 Rear Brake Shoe-to-Drum Adjustment

2) Back off anchor pin until wheel just turns freely. Hold the anchor in position and tighten lock nut. Repeat the procedure for each shoe and ensure adjustment is equal on both wheels.

All Other Models — Raise and support rear of vehicle. Release parking brake. Remove adjusting hole plugs from backing plate. Using a brake adjusting tool, rotate star wheel adjuster (direction marked on backing plate) until wheel locks. Back off adjuster 3-4 notches, until wheel rotates freely. Install adjusting hole plugs.

PEDAL HEIGHT & FREE PLAY

1) Pedal height (measured from fire wall to pedal pad center) should be as shown in chart. To adjust, disconnect negative battery cable and stop light switch connector. Loosen stop light switch lock nut and turn switch until correct pedal height is obtained. Tighten lock nut and connect electrical leads.

2) Pedal free play should be .28-.35" (7-9 mm). To adjust, loosen push rod lock nut and turn push rod until correct free play is obtained. Tighten lock nut.

Brake Pedal Height Adjustment	
Application	Height In. (mm)
GLC (FWD)	8.4-8.6 (210-220)
GLC (RWD)	
Man. Trans.	7.5-7.7 (190-195)
Auto. Trans.	7.7-7.9 (195-200)
626	7.2-8.2 (193-198)
RX7	7.5-7.7 (190-195)
B2000	8.1-8.3 (205-210)

STOP LIGHT SWITCH

Stop light switch is located under dash, above brake pedal. To adjust, disconnect battery ground cable and switch electrical lead. Turn switch until it contacts brake pedal arm. Check and adjust brake pedal height. Tighten lock nut and connect electrical connection and battery cable.

PARKING BRAKE

With service brakes properly adjusted, raise and support vehicle. On all models except B2000, remove parking brake lever boot and turn adjusting screw to lock rear wheels. Lever should be pulled 3-7 notches on GLC RWD, 5-9 notches on GLC FWD, 6-8 notches on RX7 and 5-7 notches on 626. Replace brake lever boot. On B2000, turn adjusting nut at equallizer (under vehicle) so rear wheels are locked when brake lever is pulled 5-10 notches. On all models, apply and release parking brake several times and make sure rear wheels rotate freely.

BRAKE WARNING LIGHT

B2000 — Light indicates parking brake is engaged and warns of brake system malfunction. To adjust light operation with parking brake applied, bend switch plate down until light comes on when brake lever is pulled 1 notch and goes out when lever is released (ignition on). To check warning light operation, release parking brake and ensure light is off (ignition on). Open bleeder screw on wheel and depress brake pedal; light should glow. Close bleeder screw and replenish brake fluid in master cylinder reservoir. With ignition on, depress brake pedal firmly to center combination valve piston. Light should go off; turn ignition off.

NOTE — Brake warning light on B2000 will glow whenever any repairs are made to service brake system. Combination valve piston must be centered using this procedure.

Except B2000 — Light indicates parking brake is engaged and also warns of low fluid level. Light should glow when parking brake lever is pulled 1 notch and go off when lever is fully released (ignition on). To check warning light operation, release parking brake lever and ensure light is off. Raise master cylinder reservoir cap and light should glow (ignition on). If not, check switch and wire connector.

REMOVAL & INSTALLATION

FRONT DISC BRAKE PADS

Removal - Raise and support vehicle. Remove wheel and tire. Disconnect pad wear indicator (if equipped). Detach brake hose from shock absorber (if necessary). On RX7 and

MAZDA (Cont.)

GLC FWD, remove lower caliper guide pin and pivot caliper body up out of way. On GLC RWD, 626 and B2000, remove spring clips and guide plates. Remove caliper body and hang from frame with wire. DO NOT disconnect hydraulic lines. On all models, remove anti-rattle springs (clips), pads and shims (if equipped).

Installation — To install, reverse removal procedure and note the following: Before mounting caliper, loosen bleed screw and seat piston. Tighten bleed screw. After pad installation, depress brake pedal several times to seat pads and bleed hydraulic system, if required.

NOTE — *Grease pad mounting support, caliper contact area, and shims with special grease (NLGI No. 2 or equivalent).*

REAR DISC BRAKE PADS

Removal — Raise and support rear of vehicle. Remove wheel and tire. Disconnect parking brake cable from caliper. Remove lower caliper attaching bolt. Lift up lower side of caliper. Remove anti-rattle spring. Remove disc brake pads and shims.

Installation — Using brake piston wrench (49 FA18 602), turn piston clockwise until piston is inserted into caliper fully. Position piston so that dowel on pad will seat in piston stopper groove. To complete installation, reverse removal procedure.

FRONT DISC BRAKE CALIPER

Removal — Raise and support vehicle. Remove wheel and tire. Disconnect and plug fluid line at caliper. On RX7, remove caliper guide pins and remove caliper. On all other models, remove spring clips and guide plates, then remove caliper. Remove disc pads as previously described and remove caliper mounting bracket.

Installation — To install, reverse removal procedure and bleed hydraulic system.

REAR BRAKE CALIPER

Removal — Raise the rear of vehicle and support with saftey stands. Remove tire and wheel. Disconnect parking brake cable from caliper. Disconnect brake hose. Remove caliper attaching bolt (lower side). Lift up caliper. Slide caliper toward inside of vehicle and remove caliper.

Installation — To install caliper reverse removal procedure and bleed hydraulic system.

FRONT DISC BRAKE ROTOR

Removal (Except GLC FWD) — With caliper assembly removed, remove wheel hub grease cap, cotter pin, lock plate and ring adjusting lock nut. Remove thrust washer and outer bearing from hub, then slide hub and rotor assembly from spindle. On B2000, remove hub-to-rotor bolts and separate rotor from hub.

Installation — To install, reverse removal procedure and tighten hub-to-rotor bolts evenly (B2000). Adjust wheel bearings. *See Wheel Bearing Adjustment in SUSPENSION Section.*

Removal (GLC FWD) — 1) Raise and support front of vehicle. Remove wheel and tire. Raise lock nut tab. Apply brakes to lock hub and remove drive shaft lock nut. Separate tie rod end from knuckle. Disconnect brake line from shock absorber.

2) Remove brake caliper assembly from knuckle and hang out of way. Remove ball joint and knuckle bolts and remove ball joint and knuckle from drive shafts as an assembly. Separate ball joints from knuckle. Remove wheel hub to rotor attaching bolts and using puller, remove rotor.

Installation — To install, reverse removal procedure.

REAR DISC BRAKE ROTOR

NOTE — *Removal and Installation procedures were not available.*

REAR BRAKE DRUM

Removal (Except GLC FWD) — Raise and support vehicle. Remove tire and wheel. Remove brake drum retaining screws and insert into tapped holes of brake drum. Turn screws evenly and force brake drum off flange.

Removal (GLC FWD) — Raise and support vehicle. Remove wheel and tire. Remove grease cap, nut and washer. Remove brake drum.

NOTE — *If it is difficult to remove drum, widen the shoe clearance by removing the lever stop. If necessary, disconnect the parking brake cable from lever and move lever to touch backing plate.*

Installation (All Models) — To install, reverse removal procedure. Tighten retaining screws evenly (if equipped). On GLC FWD, adjust wheel bearings. *See Wheel Bearing Adjustment in SUSPENSION Section.*

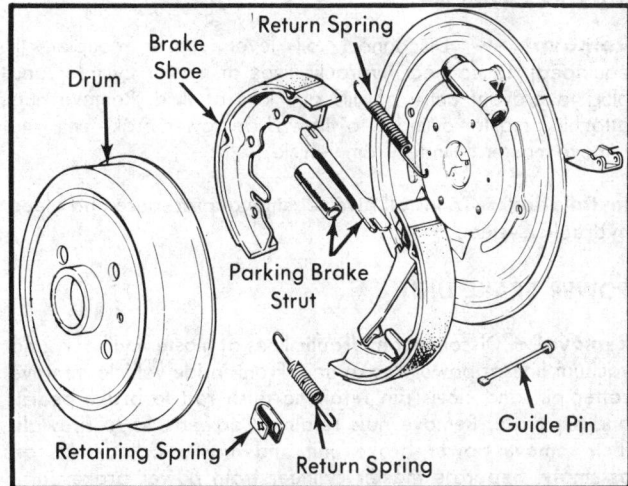

Fig. 2 Disassembled View of GLC (RWD) Rear Brakes. Other Models Similar.

REAR BRAKE SHOES

Removal (Except GLC FWD) — With brake drum removed, remove brake shoe return springs, retaining springs and guide pins. Remove brake shoes. Remove parking brake strut and disconnect parking brake cable from operating lever of secondary shoe.

Installation — 1) Lubricate adjusting screw threads and contact surfaces of shoes and backing plate with brake grease. In-

Brakes

MAZDA (Cont.)

stall parking brake operating lever to secondary shoe and secure with clip. Engage lever in parking brake cable.

2) Position operating strut between slots of shoes. Mount assembly to backing plate so slots in shoes are toward adjusting screws. Install return springs and retainer springs.

Removal (GLC FWD) — Remove brake drum. Remove trailing shoe hold-down spring and pin. Remove trailing shoe assembly. Remove return spring, anti-rattle spring and leading shoe hold down spring and pin. Remove leading shoe assembly.

Installation — Install in reverse order of removal. Be careful to move quadrant until it touches backing plate. Grease contact areas of brake shoes and backing plate. Adjust wheel bearings. *See Wheel Bearing Adjustment in SUSPENSION Section.*

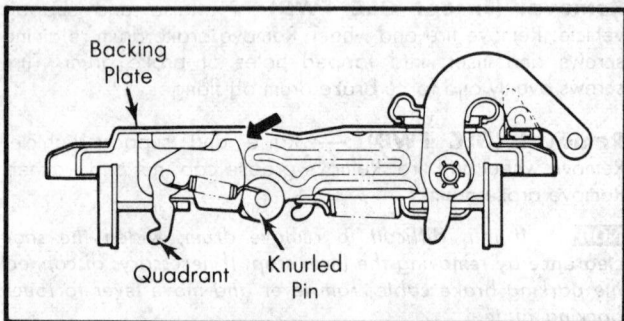

Fig. 3   GLC FWD Brake Quadrant

NOTE — *To move the quadrant, insert a screwdriver between knurled pin and quadrant and twist in direction of arrow.*

MASTER CYLINDER

Removal — Disconnect oil level sensor coupler (if equipped). Disconnect hydraulic lines at master cylinder and plug to prevent entry of dirt and loss of fluid. Remove nuts attaching master cylinder to firewall or power brake unit and remove master cylinder from vehicle.

Installation — To install reverse removal procedure and bleed hydraulic system.

POWER BRAKE UNIT

Removal — Disconnect hydraulic lines at master cylinder, and vacuum line at power brake unit. From inside vehicle, remove cotter pin and clevis pin retaining push rod to brake pedal, and separate. Remove nuts retaining power unit to firewall, then remove power brake unit and master cylinder as an assembly. Separate master cylinder from power brake unit.

NOTE — *On GLC FWD and RX7, remove master cylinder from power brake unit before removing power brake unit.*

Installation — To install, reverse removal procedure and bleed hydraulic system.

OVERHAUL

FRONT DISC BRAKE CALIPER

Disassembly — Thoroughly clean exterior of caliper and remove retainer and dust boot. Place a piece of wood in front

of piston, apply compressed air to fluid inlet and remove piston (tapping caliper with plastic hammer, if required). Remove piston seal without damaging caliper bore.

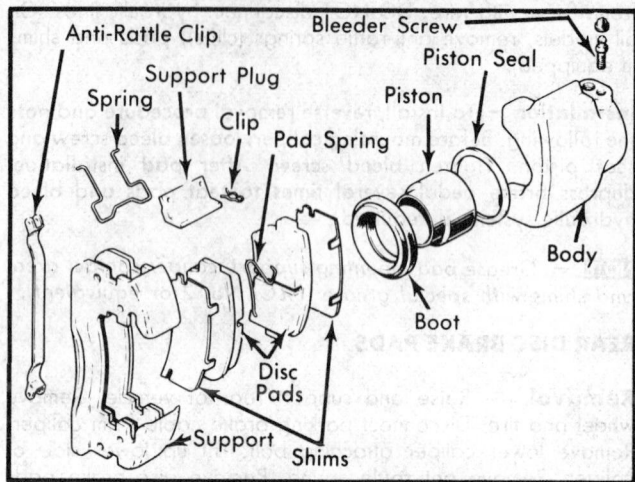

Fig. 4   Exploded View of B2000 Front Disc Brake Caliper

Cleaning & Inspection — Wash all parts in alcohol or brake fluid and air dry. Inspect cylinder bore and piston for scoring, scratches or rust. Replace defective parts. Minor damage may be removed with crocus cloth. Always replace dust boot and piston seal when caliper is disassembled.

Reassembly — Apply clean brake fluid to cylinder bore, piston and piston seal, then seat piston seal in caliper bore. Install piston carefully into cylinder bore and install dust boot and retainer.

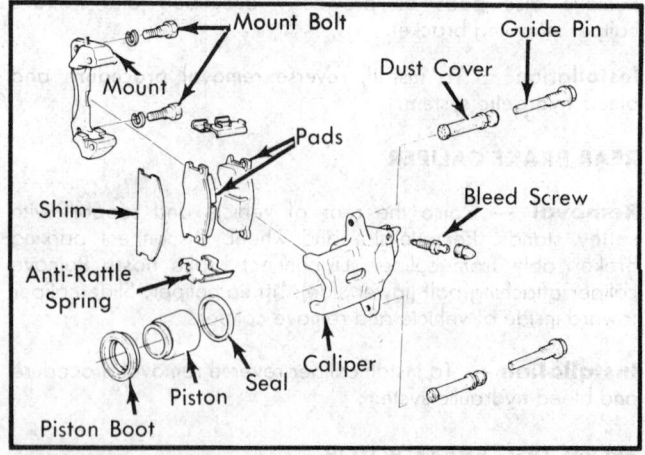

Fig. 5   Exploded View of RX7 Front Brake Caliper. GLC & 626 Similar. Pads, Shims & Mounts May Differ.

REAR DISC BRAKE CALIPER

Disassembly — Remove dust boot retainer and boot. Turn piston counterclockwise with disc brake piston wrench (49 FA18 602) and screw out piston. Remove piston seal. Remove boot retainer. Slip off boot. Remove snap ring. Compress conical spring in caliper with spring compressor (49 FA18 601), valve spring lifter arm, (49 FA18 601) and removing plate (49 E301 144). Remove parking brake crank, torsion spring and strut. Remove adjusting bolt and conical spring assembly. Press out needle roller bearings.

MAZDA (Cont.)

Inspection — Clean all parts in brake fluid or alcohol. Blow parts dry. Inspect caliper bore for scratches, scoring or rust. Minor damage can be eliminated by polishing with crocus cloth. Inspect needle roller bearing, strut, adjusting bolt and parking brake crank fror corrosion, wear or damage. Check torsion spring and conical spring for corrosion, weakness and damage. Check piston and sleeve nut for excessive play. It should be within .012-.020" (.3-.5 mm).

Reassembly — 1) Assemble the caliper in the reverse order of disassembly. Use new piston seals and dust seals. Three kinds of grease contained in seal kit must be used. White grease is for caliper slide bolts and mounting bolts. Orange grease is for bearings, adjusting bolt, strut and piston boot. Pink grease is for piston seal.

2) Lubricate the piston and caliper bore with clean brake fluid. Press in needle roller bearing so that arrow on bearing faces outward. Assemble conical spring and adjusting bolt. *See Fig. 6.* Install adjusting bolt assembly, strut and torsion spring in the caliper. Install piston using disc brake wrench as described under Disc Brake Pad Installation.

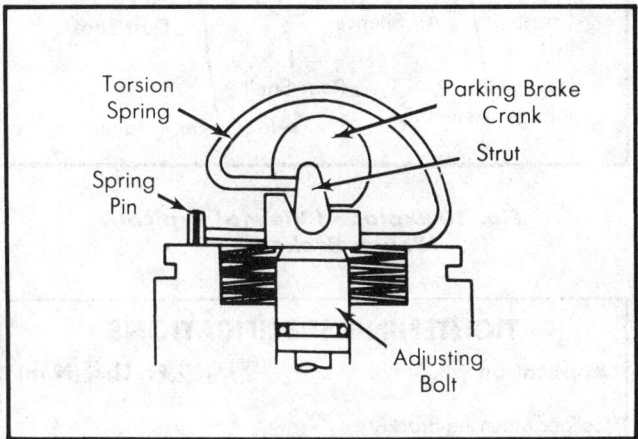

Fig. 6   Proper Installation of Conical Spring and Adjusting Bolt

WHEEL CYLINDERS

Disassembly — Remove dust boots. Remove pistons with adjuster assemblies. Press on 1 cylinder cup to force out filling blocks and return spring.

Cleaning & Inspection — Clean all parts in alcohol or brake fluid. Check cylinder bore and pistons for scores, roughness or wear. Check clearance between cylinder bore and pistons; replace if clearance exceeds .006" (.15 mm). Check cups for deformation; replace as necessary.

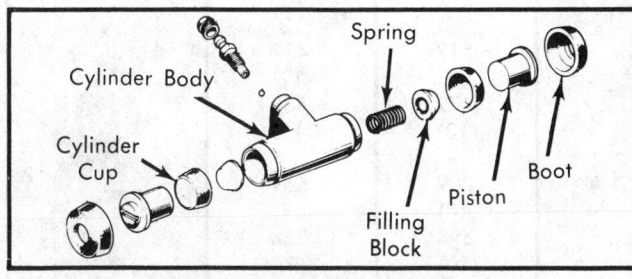

Fig. 7   Exploded View Wheel Cylinder

Reassembly — Reverse disassembly procedure and note the following: Coat all parts with clean brake fluid before reassembly. When installing cylinder cups, make sure flat side of cup faces outward.

MASTER CYLINDER

Disassembly — Thoroughly clean outside of master cylinder and pour out any remaining brake fluid. If equipped, remove reservoir and dust boot. Depress primary piston assembly. Remove retaining ring from rear of cylinder bore, and remove washer, primary piston assembly and return spring. Depress secondary piston, remove stop bolt (if equipped) and insert guide pin to prevent damage to secondary piston cup. Carefully withdraw secondary piston assembly and return spring. Remove fittings, check valves and springs.

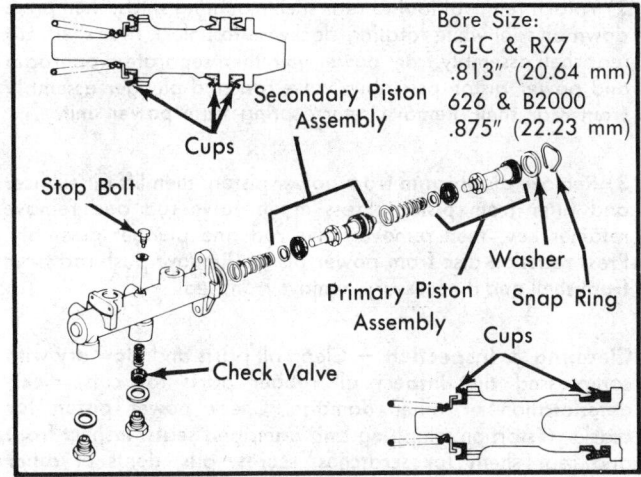

Fig. 8   Exploded View of Typical Master Cylinder. Some Models May Vary Slightly.

Cleaning & Inspection — Clean all parts in alcohol or brake fluid. Check all parts for scoring, roughness or wear. Check piston-to-cylinder clearance. If clearance exceeds .006" (.15 mm), replace parts as necessary. Remove all foreign matter from internal passages and recesses with compressed air. Check cylinder cups for deformation and replace as required.

Reassembly — Reverse disassembly procedure and note the following: Coat all parts with clean brake fluid before reassembly. Use new gaskets at all hydraulic unions. When assembled, make sure piston cups do not cover compensating ports. Make sure valve with hole in center faces front side outlet hole.

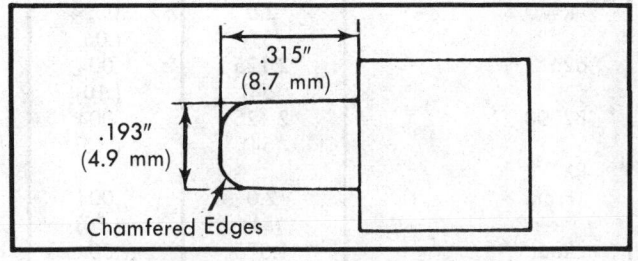

Fig. 9   Dimensions for Fabricating Guide Pin

Brakes

MAZDA (Cont.)

POWER BRAKE UNIT

NOTE — *Power brake units vary slightly between model application. The following overhaul procedures are general instructions which can be used if attention is paid to specific order of components.*

Disassembly — 1) Remove master cylinder and check valve from power unit, then place power unit in a vise with push rod up. Scribe alignment marks on front and rear shells to assure reassembly in original position. Remove clevis, lock nut and dust boot from rear shell.

CAUTION — *Separate front and rear shells carefully; spring tension may cause rear shell to release quickly.*

2) Attach removal tool to rear shell mounting studs, then press down on tool while rotating clockwise to unlock rear shell. Lift rear shell assembly from power unit, then separate diaphragm and power piston assembly, valve rod and plunger assembly from rear shell. Remove return spring from power unit.

3) Remove diaphragm from power piston, then lift air silencer and filter from piston. Press in on valve rod and remove retainer key, then remove valve rod and plunger assembly. Press reaction disc from power piston. Remove push rod from front shell and if necessary, remove front seal.

Cleaning & Inspection — Clean all parts and blow dry with compressed air. Inspect all rubber parts for cuts, nicks, deterioration or other damage. Check power piston for cracks, distortion, chipping and damaged seats. Inspect front and rear shells for scratches, scores, pits, dents or other damage. Replace any defective parts.

Reassembly — Reverse disassembly procedure. Apply clean brake fluid to parts before reassembly. When assembling rear shell to front shell, make sure index marks are aligned. Before installing master cylinder to power unit,

measure clearance between primary piston and power unit push rod. Clearance on RX7 should be .004-.012" (.1-.3 mm). On all other models, clearance should be .004-.020" (.1-.5 mm). If clearance is not to specifications, correct by adjusting push rod length.

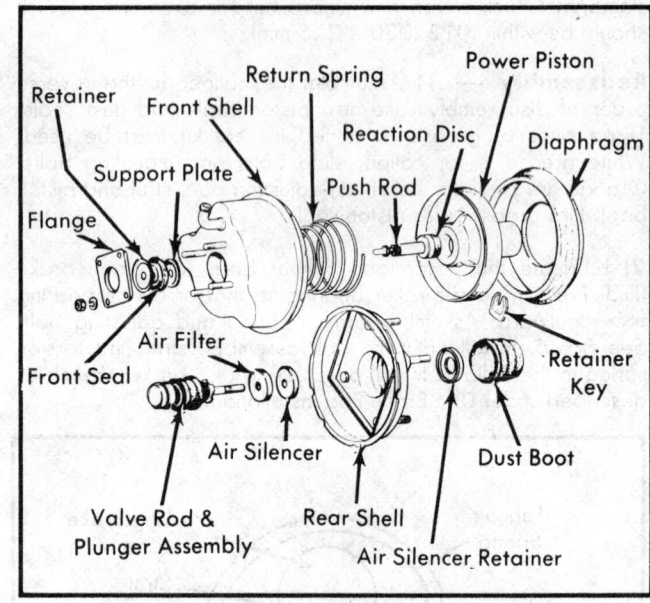

Fig. 10 Exploded View of Typical Power Brake Unit

TIGHTENING SPECIFICATIONS

Application	Ft. Lbs. (N.m)
Caliper Mounting Bracket	
B2000	40-47 (54-64)
GLC RWD	33-40 (45-54)
Caliper Guide Pin (626)	33-40 (45-54)

DISC BRAKE SPECIFICATIONS

Application	Disc Diameter	Lateral Runout	Parallelism	Original Thickness	Minimum Refinish Thickness	Discard Thickness
GLC						
FWD	2.125 (54)	.004 (.10)	.....	.433 (11)	.394 (10)	.....
RWD	2.0 (51)	.0024 (.06)	.....	.512 (13)	.472 (12)	.....
626	2.125 (54)	.004 (.10)	.....	.512 (13)	.472 (12)	.....
B2000	2.125 (54)	.004 (.10)	.....	.472 (12)	.433 (11)	.....
RX7						
Front	2.0 (51)	.004 (.10)	.....	.709 (18)	.669 (17)	.....
Rear	1.375 (35)	.004 (.10)	.....	.394 (10)	.354 (9)	.....

Brakes

MAZDA (Cont.)

DRUM BRAKE SPECIFICATIONS

Application	Wheel Cyl. Bore Diameter In. (mm)	Drum Diameter In. (mm)	Original Diameter In. (mm)	Maximum Refinish Diameter In. (mm)	Discard Diameter In. (mm)
GLC					
FWD	.688 (17.5)	7.09 (180)	7.09 (180)	7.13 (181)	.....
RWD	.750 (19)	7.87 (200)	7.87 (200)	7.91 (201)	.....
626	.813 (20.6)	9.00 (229)	9.00 (229)	9.04 (230)	.....
B2000	.875 (22)	10.24 (260)	10.24 (260)	10.28 (261)	.....
RX7	.750 (19)	7.87 (200)	7.87 (200)	7.91 (201)	.....

Brakes

MERCEDES-BENZ

240D
280 Series
300 Series
380 Series

DESCRIPTION

Service brake system utilizes 4-wheel disc brakes, hydraulically operated by a step-type or tandem master cylinder, connected to a power unit. Step-type master cylinder can be identified by a stop screw located on top center of master cylinder. Tandem master cylinder stop screw is located at bottom center of master cylinder. Cylinders are manufactured by Teves or Bendix and incorporate a 2 or 3-chamber reservoir with a fluid level sensor contact built into each chamber. Warning light is activated when fluid level is low. Parking brakes are cable actuated, internal expanding shoe-type, housed in rear brake rotors.

ADJUSTMENT

PEDAL HEIGHT & FREE PLAY

Pedal height (measured from pedal pad to pedal stop) should be 5.9" (150 mm). To adjust pedal height, loosen lock nuts and turn stop light switch until correct height is obtained. Tighten lock nuts. Pedal free play should be .2-.6" (5-15 mm).

STOP LIGHT SWITCH

Stop light switch is located under dash, above brake pedal. To adjust, loosen lock nuts and adjust switch so that contact button extends .24-.32" (6-8 mm). Tighten lock nuts.

PARKING BRAKE

Remove one wheel lug bolt at each rear wheel. Raise and support vehicle, and rotate wheels until lug bolt hole is positioned over parking brake adjuster (approximately 45° in upward and forward direction from wheel center). Using a screwdriver inserted through lug bolt hole, turn adjuster until wheel cannot be turned by hand. Back off adjuster until wheel can be turned by hand without restriction.

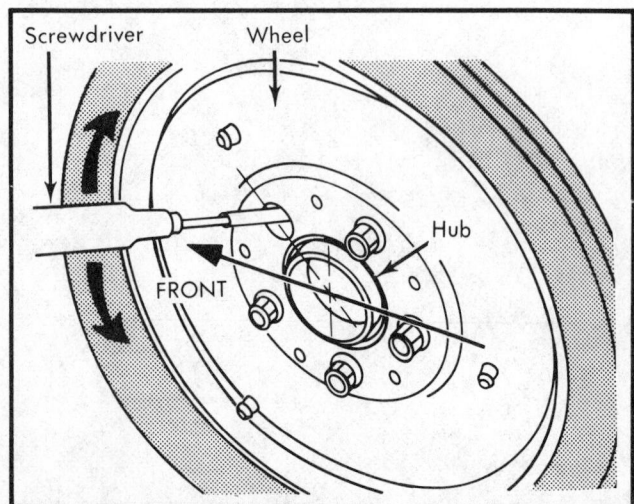

Fig. 1   Fitting Parking Brake Adjuster Tool Into Adjusting Mechanism

BRAKE WARNING LIGHT

A dual warning light is mounted on dash. Light should glow when parking brake lever is pulled 1 notch and go off when lever is fully released (ignition on). To check circuit warning sensor, release parking brake (ignition on) and ensure light is off. Open bleed screw on 1 wheel and depress brake pedal; light should glow. Close bleed screw, replenish brake fluid and bleed hydraulic system.

REMOVAL & INSTALLATION

DISC PADS

Removal — Raise vehicle, support with safety stands and remove wheels. If equipped, remove shaft cover plate from caliper and disconnect wear indicator wires. Drive out retaining pins toward inside of vehicle (on Bendix brakes, retaining pins have locking keys in pins) and remove cross spring. Loosen bleed fitting using suitable extractor tool, remove disc pads from caliper assembly.

NOTE — *All bolts are self-locking hex-head and should be used once only.*

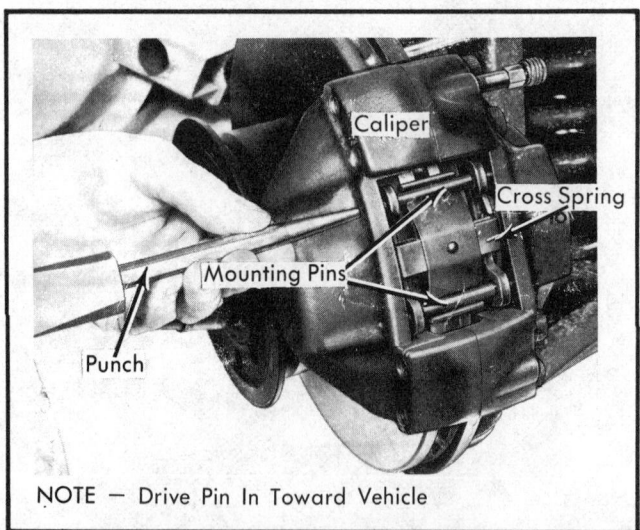

NOTE — Drive Pin In Toward Vehicle

Fig. 2   Knocking Out Disc Pad Mounting Pins On Teves Model Brakes

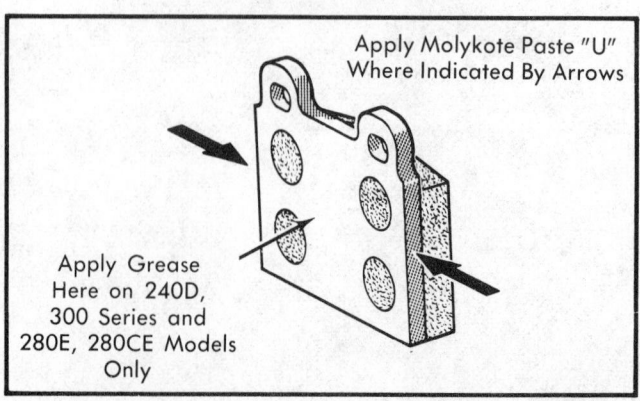

Fig. 3   Typical Mercedes-Benz Disc Brake Pad Illustration Shows Molykote Application Points

MERCEDES-BENZ (Cont.)

Installation — Using a cylinder brush, clean disc pad guide surface in caliper. Siphon sufficient fluid from master cylinder reservoir to prevent overflowing, then press pistons to bottom of bores. Install disc pads, cross spring and retaining pins. If equipped, install cover plate, retaining pin locking keys and wear sensor wires.

BRAKE CALIPER

Removal — Raise and support vehicle, and remove wheel. Disconnect brake lines at caliper assembly, and plug lines to prevent entry of foreign matter. Remove caliper attaching bolts, and remove caliper assembly from vehicle.

Installation — Reverse removal procedure ensuring that calipers are replaced in matched pairs from either manufacturer. Tighten all nuts and bolts and bleed hydraulic system.

BRAKE ROTOR

Removal (Front) — With caliper assembly removed, remove hub grease cap. Remove contact spring for radio shielding. Loosen clamping nut socket screw on wheel spindle. Remove clamping nut and washer. Remove wheel hub and rotor assembly. Remove bolts securing hub to rotor and remove rotor.

Installation — To install, reverse removal procedure, tighten all bolts and fittings evenly and bleed hydraulic system (if necessary). Adjust wheel bearings. *See Wheel Bearing Adjustment in SUSPENSION Section.*

Removal & Installation (Rear) — Remove rear wheel and caliper assembly, then pull rotor out from axle shaft flange. To install, reverse removal procedure, tighten all bolts and fittings evenly, and bleed hydraulic system if necessary.

Fig. 4 Assembled View of Rear Hub and Caliper

MASTER CYLINDER

Removal — Drain master cylinder brake fluid. Disconnect and plug brake lines, disconnect electrical wires. Remove bolts securing master cylinder to power booster and remove master cylinder.

Installation — Reverse removal procedure and note the following: Always replace rubber "O" ring seal between master cylinder and power unit. Bleed hydraulic system and check complete system for fluid leaks.

POWER BRAKE UNIT

Removal — Drain master cylinder and remove master cylinder from vehicle. Disconnect vacuum line at power brake unit and disconnect push rod at brake pedal. Remove power brake unit attaching hardware and remove assembly from vehicle.

Installation — To install, reverse removal procedure, tighten all nuts and bolts, and bleed hydraulic system.

OVERHAUL

BRAKE CALIPER

Disassembly — With caliper removed from vehicle and disc pads removed from caliper, remove dust cap from piston housing. Hold one piston in place using a suitable clamp, then apply compressed air to fluid inlet and remove opposite piston. Remove piston seal from groove of cylinder bore. Remove remaining piston and seal in same manner.

NOTE — *DO NOT separate caliper halves.*

CAUTION — *DO NOT polish chrome plated surfaces of pistons.*

Cleaning & Inspection — Remove deposits on pistons with a soft brass wire brush. Check cylinder bore of caliper for wear or damage. Small rust deposits may be removed with polishing cloth. Heavier deposits in front of piston seal groove may be removed with fine emery cloth.

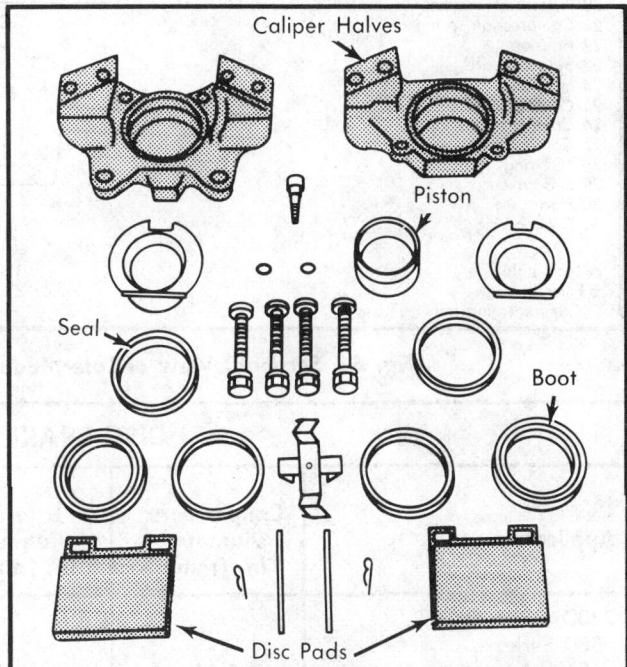

Fig. 5 Disassembled View of Typical Mercedes-Benz Brake Caliper

Reassembly — Coat piston and caliper bore with ATE brake cylinder paste (or equivalent), install piston seal into caliper bore and install piston. Install dust cap, then install heat shield into piston with recess in shield fitting into elevation of piston.

NOTE — *Elevation on piston MUST face downward and project at least .004" (.1 mm) above shield.*

Brakes

MERCEDES-BENZ (Cont.)

MASTER CYLINDER

CAUTION — *Bendix master cylinder, spray painted blue, cannot be repaired.*

Disassembly (Tandem and Step Tandem) — Remove reservoir, push piston in with screwdriver, then remove stop screw and "O" ring. Remove lock ring from housing, then remove piston, stop washer, 2 vacuum seals and intermediate ring. Remove intermediate piston by rapping lightly with a wooden board.

NOTE — *Teves reservoir only, remove cap, end covers, strainer, splash guard, "O" rings and contact inserts. Bendix model, remove strainer from cover. DO NOT remove contact inserts. All models, master cylinder diameter should be .937" (23.81 mm).*

Inspection — Clean all parts with alcohol or brake fluid. Check bore in housing and piston for scoring and rust. Small rust spots in housing may be removed with polishing cloth. Scored or badly rusted parts cannot be repaired, replace complete master cylinder.

Reassembly — Reverse disassembly procedure and bleed hydraulic system.

TIGHTENING SPECIFICATIONS

Application	Ft. Lbs. (N·m)
Caliper Mounting Bolts	
Front	83 (113)
Rear	65 (88)
Hub-to-Rotor Bolts	83 (113)

1 Container plug
3 Piston (push rod circuit)
4 Stop washer
5 Locking ring
6 Vacuum seal
7 Intermediate ring
8 Bearing ring
9 Filling washer
10 Primary sleeve
11 Supporting ring
12 Spring retainer
14 Connecting screw
15 Stop screw
17 Compression spring
18 Ring sleeve
19 Spring plate
20 Piston (intermediate piston)
21 Compression spring
22 Housing
23 Splash guard
24 Strainer
25 Closing cover
26 Compensating tank
27 Contact insert
28 "O" ring
29 End cover
30 Float
31 Sealing ring

A Leak hole
B Filler hole
C Compensating hole

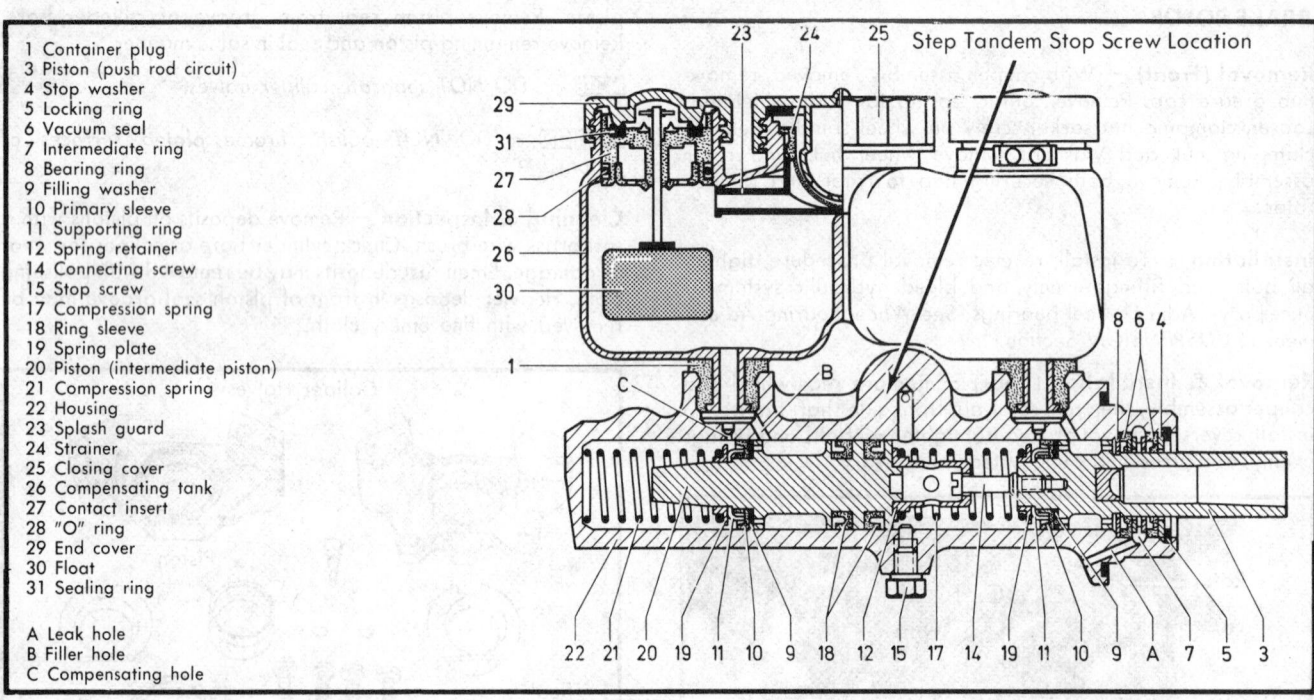

Fig. 6 Sectional View of Late Model Mercedes-Benz Tandem Master Cylinder

DISC BRAKE SPECIFICATIONS

Application	Caliper Bore Diameter In. (mm)	Lateral Runout In. (mm)	Parallelism In. (mm)	Original Thickness In. (mm)	Minimum Refinish Thickness In. (mm)	Discard Thickness In. (mm)
240D, 280E, 280CE, 300 Series						
Front	2.36 (60)	.005 (.12)	.0008 (.02)	.496 (12.6)	.....	.417 (10.6)
Rear	1.50① (38)	.005 (.12)	.0008 (.02)	.394 (10)	.....	.327 (8.3)
280SE & 380 Series						
Front	2.36 (60)	.005 (.12)	.0008 (.02)	.866 (22)	.....	.787 (20)
Rear	1.50 (38)	.005 (.12)	.0008 (.02)	.394 (10)	.....	.327 (8.3)

① — 300TD Caliper bore diameter — 1.65" (.42 mm).

PEUGEOT

504
505
604

DESCRIPTION

Brake system is hydraulically operated using a tandem master cylinder and power brake unit. The 504 is equipped with sliding yoke front disc brakes and rear drum brakes. All other models are equipped with 4-wheel sliding yoke disc brakes. All models are equipped with a load actuated compensator to provide equal fluid distribution to front and rear brakes. Parking brake is cable operated at rear wheels.

ADJUSTMENT

REAR DRUM BRAKE SHOES

Raise and support rear of vehicle. To adjust, rotate front adjustment eccentric clockwise until wheel locks, then back off until wheel just turns freely. Repeat procedure for rear adjustment eccentric, but rotate the eccentric counterclockwise.

NOTE — *Do not alter the adjustment of brake pedal.*

PARKING BRAKE

504 — Remove center console and raise and support vehicle. Fully release parking brake lever. Loosen lock nut at lever and tighten adjusting screw until wheels are locked with 4-7 notches of lever travel. Tighten lock nut and ensure wheels rotate freely with parking brake fully released.

Except 504 — Parking brake is self-adjusting and requires no in-service adjustment. Normal lever travel should be 7-13 notches.

BRAKE WARNING LIGHT

A triple warning light is mounted on instrument panel. Light will glow to indicate disc pad replacement, parking brake is engaged and brake fluid is low or malfunction exists in brake system. Light should glow when parking brake lever is pulled 1 notch and go off when lever is fully released (ignition on). To check circuit warning sensor, release parking brake (ignition on) and ensure light is off. Open bleed screw on 1 wheel and depress brake pedal; light should glow. Close bleed screw, replenish brake fluid and bleed hydraulic system.

REMOVAL & INSTALLATION

DISC BRAKE PADS

CAUTION — *Peugeot uses brake calipers from various manufacturers. Removal and Overhaul procedures may vary slightly. Disc pads and calipers MUST match for each axle application.*

Removal — Raise and support vehicle under frame; remove tire and wheel. Disconnect pad wear indicator electrical lead. Remove retaining spring and pins, then remove damper spring and brake pads.

NOTE — *Manufacturer recommends applying Permatex "High Tack" adhesive to back portion of pads prior to installation.*

Installation — 1) Remove small amount of brake fluid from master cylinder reservoir. Using suitable tool, press piston into cylinder bore. On rear calipers, rotate piston clockwise 1/8 turn

before pressing into cylinder. After piston is seated in bore of rear caliper, return piston to original position by rotating counterclockwise 1/8 turn.

2) On all calipers, install pads and damper spring. Damper spring of rear caliper MUST be installed with arrow (or hole) at top. On all brake calipers, reconnect pad wear indicator. Bleed hydraulic system.

DISC BRAKE CALIPER

Removal — Raise and support vehicle; remove tire and wheel. Remove disc pads as previously described. Remove and plug hydraulic line from caliper. On rear caliper, disconnect parking brake cable and casing from operating lever. On all calipers, remove mounting bolts and remove caliper assembly.

Installation — Mount caliper and install mounting bolts with new lock washers coated with Loctite (or equivalent). Complete installation by reversing removal procedure and ensure hydraulic hose is not twisted. Bleed hydraulic system.

FRONT DISC BRAKE ROTOR

Removal — Remove caliper mounting bolts and support out of way without disconnecting hydraulic line. Remove hub grease cap, adjusting nut, washer and outer wheel bearing. Remove hub and rotor assembly from spindle. Separate hub and rotor by removing attaching bolts and washers from rear of hub.

Installation — Apply Loctite (or equivalent) to new lock washers and tighten hub-to-rotor bolts. Complete installation by reversing removal procedure and adjust wheel bearings. *See Wheel Bearing Adjustment in SUSPENSION Section.*

REAR DISC BRAKE ROTOR

Removal — 1) Disconnect hydraulic line retaining clip on control arm. Remove pad electrical lead and disc pads. Remove caliper mounting bolts and support caliper out of way without disconnecting hydraulic line. Remove axle shaft nut. Align bearing housing access hole and remove bearing housing bolts.

2) Remove shaft, hub and rotor as an assembly. Remove drive shaft from hub assembly with suitable puller. Mount hub assembly in a padded vise and install suitable extractor and remove bearing housing nut with a 35 mm socket. Install suitable extractor and thrust pad and remove bearing housing. Remove hub-to-rotor bolts and separate assembly.

Installation — 1) Apply Loctite (or equivalent) to new lock washers and tighten hub-to-rotor bolts. Install bearing housing nut to bearing housing and tighten nut. Mount hub and rotor assembly on bearing housing. Coat drive shaft splines with Molykote 321 (or equivalent) and install drive shaft in hub.

2) Mount shaft, hub and rotor assembly on vehicle. Install new washers coated with Loctite (or equivalent) on bearing housing bolts and tighten bolts. Install axle nut and tighten. Mount caliper and install new washers coated with Loctite (or equivalent) on mounting bolts. Install brake pads.

REAR BRAKE DRUM

Removal — Raise and support vehicle; remove tire and wheel. Slide brake drum off brake assembly. It may be necessary to neutralize brakes by removing backing plate plug and pushing parking brake lever off the seat.

PEUGEOT (Cont.)

Installation — To install, reverse removal procedure.

REAR BRAKE SHOES

Removal — With brake drum removed, remove and discard hold down springs. Remove return springs, separate parking brake linkage from brake shoe and remove parking brake cable from operating lever. Remove brake shoes. Remove parking brake lever and strut from shoes.

Installation — To install, reverse removal procedure and note: Replace hold down springs during installation and ensure proper operation of parking brake.

MASTER CYLINDER

Removal & Installation — Using a siphon, drain brake fluid from master cylinder. Disconnect all hydraulic lines from master cylinder. Remove master cylinder-to-power brake unit attaching nuts and lift off master cylinder. To install, reverse removal procedure, fill master cylinder with new brake fluid and bleed hydraulic system.

OVERHAUL

FRONT DISC BRAKE CALIPER

Disassembly — Clamp caliper assembly in a soft-jawed vise and remove disc brake pads. Seat pistons in cylinder bore and remove thrust spring and yoke. Remove protector retaining clips and protectors. Force both pistons from cylinder bore and remove nylon spacer on yoke piston. Remove and discard piston seals.

Cleaning & Inspection — Clean all parts in denatured alcohol and check cylinder bore and pistons for wear, damage or scoring. If any defects are found, defective parts must be replaced. Replace piston seals during overhaul.

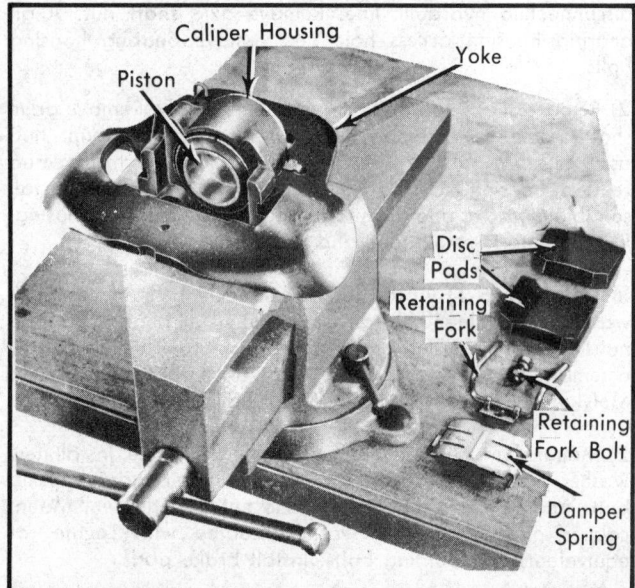

Fig. 1   Disassembling Front Disc Brake Caliper

Reassembly — Lubricate pistons and seals with suitable lubricant and install seals. Insert pistons in cylinder bore with nylon spacer seated against yoke piston. Install protectors and

retaining clips (thin clip on rotor side). Coat yoke and caliper sliding parts with Molykote 321 (or equivalent) and install yoke and thrust spring. Seat pistons in cylinder bore and install disc pads.

REAR DISC BRAKE CALIPER

Disassembly — **1)** Clamp caliper assembly in a soft-jawed vise and remove disc pads. Rotate piston clockwise 1/8 turn and seat piston assembly in cylinder bore. Remove thrust spring and yoke.

2) Remove parking brake lever return spring. Lift lever and remove nylon spacer. Remove protector retaining clips and protectors. Force piston assembly from cylinder bore. Remove and discard piston seals.

Cleaning & Inspection — Clean all parts in denatured alcohol and check cylinder bore and piston assembly for wear or damage. If any defects are found, replace defective part. Separate piston assembly and inspect wear compensation assembly. Replace piston seals during overhaul.

Reassembly — **1)** Lubricate piston assembly and seals with suitable lubricant and install seals. Insert piston assembly from rear of cylinder assembly without damaging piston seals. Install protectors and retaining clips (thin clip on rotor side). Raise parking brake lever and install nylon spacer. Install return spring.

2) Coat yoke and caliper sliding parts with Molykote 321 (or equivalent) and install yoke and thrust spring. Seat piston assembly in caliper bore, then rotate piston assembly counterclockwise to original position. Install disc pads.

MASTER CYLINDER

Disassembly — **1)** Mount master cylinder in a soft jaw vise. On Lockheed master cylinders, remove reservoir attaching screw from inside each reservoir and separate each reservoir from master cylinder. On Teves master cylinders, separate reservoir from master cylinder by pulling it from sealing grommets, then remove grommets.

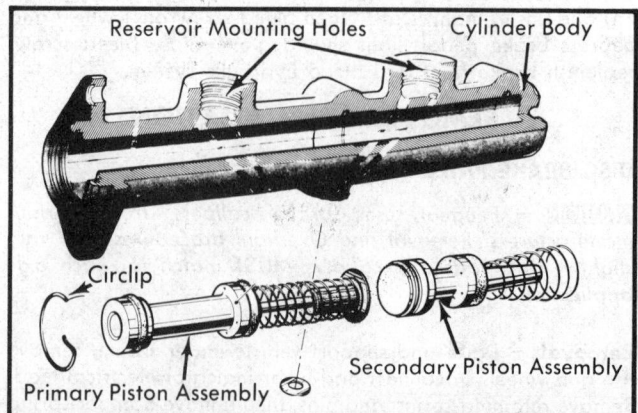

Fig. 2   Sectional View of Master Cylinder Assembly

2) On all master cylinders, remove piston stop screw. Remove piston circlip and stop washer, then extract primary piston assembly. Using compressed air, force out secondary piston assembly.

NOTE — *DO NOT disassemble piston assemblies; if piston or seals are damaged or worn, replace both piston assemblies.*

Brakes

PEUGEOT (Cont.)

Cleaning & Inspection – Wash all parts in denatured alcohol and dry with compressed air. Inspect all parts for wear, scoring, burrs or corrosion and replace as necessary.

NOTE – *DO NOT polish cylinder bore with emery cloth.*

Reassembly – Reverse disassembly procedure and note the following: Coat all parts with clean brake fluid prior to reassembly. After reassembly is completed, push in primary piston several times and ensure it returns fully and smoothly to its stop each time.

POWER BRAKE UNIT

NOTE – *Power brake unit is serviced as an assembly only. Do not attempt to overhaul.*

TIGHTENING SPECIFICATIONS

Application	Ft. Lbs. (N·m)
Caliper Mounting Bolts	
Front	51 (69)
Rear	31 (42)
Retaining Fork Bolt	13 (18)
Hub-to-Rotor Bolts	36 (49)
Bearing Housing Mounting Bolts	31 (42)
Rear Axle Shaft Nut	181 (246)

DRUM BRAKE SPECIFICATIONS

Application	Wheel Cyl. Bore Diameter In. (mm)	Drum Diameter In. (mm)	Original Diameter In. (mm)	Maximum Refinish Diameter In. (mm)	Discard Diameter In. (mm)
504 Rear	.....	11.00 (280)	11.00 (280)	11.06 (281)	11.08 (281.5)

DISC BRAKE SPECIFICATIONS

Application	Caliper Bore Diameter In. (mm)	Lateral Runout In. (mm)	Parallelism In. (mm)	Original Thickness In. (mm)	Minimum Refinish Thickness In. (mm)	Discard Thickness In. (mm)
504						
Front	.....	.003 (.07)	.0008 (.02)	.502 (12.75)	.443 (11.25)	.423 10.75)
505						
Front	.....	.003 (.07)	.0008 (.02)	.502 (12.75)	.443 (11.25)	.423 (10.75)
Rear	.....	.003 (.07)	.0008 (.02)	.472 (12.0)	.433 (11.0)	.413 (10.5)
604						
Front	.....	.003 (.07)	.0008 (.02)	.787 (20.0)	.748 (19.0)	.709 (18.0)
Rear	.....	.003 (.07)	.0008 (.02)	.472 (12.0)	.433 (11.0)	.413 (10.5)

PORSCHE

911SC
924
928

DESCRIPTION

Brake system is hydraulically operated using a tandem master cylinder and power brake unit. The 911SC and 928 models are equipped with 4-wheel disc brakes. 924 models use disc front and drum rear brakes (rear disc brakes are optional). All models use a brake warning light to detect pressure drop in brake circuit. 928 models also have a pad wear sensor, and 924 models have a fluid level sensor in reservoir.

ADJUSTMENT

REAR DRUM BRAKE SHOES

Raise and support vehicle. Release parking brake. Turn adjuster until a slight drag is felt when rotating brake drum. Back off adjuster until drum is just free to rotate.

BRAKE PEDAL TRAVEL & FREE PLAY

Brake Pedal Travel — Pedal travel (measured from pedal pad center to point of brake application) should be 1.19-1.56" (30-40 mm). To adjust pedal travel, loosen operating rod lock nut and rotate rod until correct pedal travel is obtained. Tighten operating rod lock nut.

Free Play — Pedal free play (measured from pedal pad center to floorboard) should be about ⅜" (10 mm). To adjust pedal free play, loosen operating rod lock nut and set free play to specification. Check pedal travel and tighten operating rod lock nut.

PARKING BRAKE

Except 924 Models — Raise and support vehicle; remove tire and wheel. Release parking brake lever and push caliper pistons and pads into caliper to allow rotor to turn freely. Loosen parking brake cable lock nuts until cable is slack. Working through access hole in parking brake drum, turn star wheel adjuster until rotor cannot be turned by hand. Adjust parking brake cable at rear cable end until it just begins to pull and tighten lock nuts. Back off star wheel adjuster until rotor turns freely without drag. Repeat operation on opposite wheel and check parking brake operation.

924 Models — Raise and support vehicle. Make sure service brakes are properly adjusted. From inside vehicle, pull parking brake lever up 3-4 notches and turn adjuster nut at base of brake lever until both wheels can be turned by hand.

BRAKE WARNING LIGHT

NOTE — *Warning light will glow after any repair on service brake system and will not go out until manually reset.*

A dual warning light is mounted on instrument panel. Parking brake light should glow when parking brake lever is pulled 1 notch (ignition on) and go off when lever is fully released. To check circuit warning sensor, fully release parking brake and ensure light is off (ignition on). Open 1 bleed screw and depress brake pedal; light should glow. To reset warning light, bleed hydraulic system and test service brakes. Disconnect and reconnect negative battery cable; warning lamp should go out.

REMOVAL & INSTALLATION

DISC PADS

NOTE — *Mark pads and calipers before removal. If pads are to be reused, they must be installed in original position. If only 1 pad (front or rear) needs replacing, all pads on same axle must be replaced.*

Removal — Raise and support vehicle; remove tire and wheel. Disconnect pad wear indicator electrical connection, if equipped. Remove retaining pin clip and retaining pins. On 911SC, squeeze spreader spring and remove disc pads. On all other models, remove inside brake pad with pad remover. Outside disc pad is guided by a tab on sliding caliper frame; remove outer pad by pushing frame out away from rotor and removing pad.

CAUTION — *If fluid level is too high in reservoir, overflow will result when pistons (during installation) are pushed back into calipers.*

Installation — Push piston back into caliper using suitable tool (P83), or wooden block. Remove anti-rotation locks (if equipped) and clean all parts with alcohol. Inspect all parts for damage or wear. Ensure piston 20° position is correct using suitable gauge (P84). Install remaining parts in reverse order of removal, replace parts as necessary.

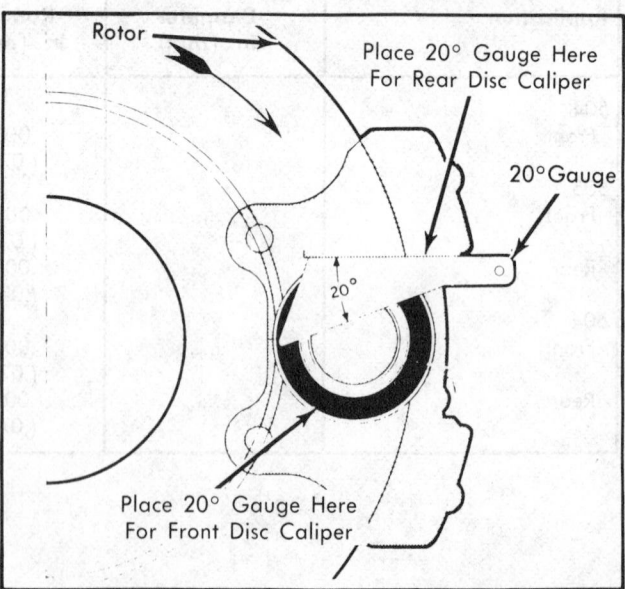

Fig. 1   Positioning Caliper Piston Using 20° Gauge

BRAKE CALIPER

CAUTION — *When any fluid fitting is disconnected, fluid will drain from reservoir through master cylinder and out open fitting. To avoid this, depress brake pedal far enough so piston cup will pass the compensating (resupply) port.*

Brakes

PORSCHE (Cont.)

Removal — Raise and support vehicle; remove tire and wheel. Remove brake pads as previously described and remove splash shield (if equipped). Disconnect and plug hydraulic line, remove caliper mounting bolts and remove caliper.

Installation — To install, reverse removal procedure and bleed hydraulic system.

BRAKE ROTOR

Removal — Raise and support vehicle; remove tire and wheel. Remove caliper as previously described and hang from frame with wire; DO NOT disconnect hydraulic line. On front brake rotors, remove dust cap, loosen clamp lock screw, then remove clamp nut and thrust washer. Remove rotor and wheel bearings as an assembly and separate. On rear brake rotors, remove rotor attaching bolts and remove rotor. Mark rotor and hub for reassembly reference, remove hub-to-rotor bolts (if equipped) and separate hub from rotor.

NOTE — *If rear rotor cannot be removed by hand, insert two 8 mm bolts into attaching screw holes and alternately tighten bolts to press rotor from hub.*

Installation — To install, reverse removal procedure. Bleed hydraulic system and adjust front wheel bearings. See *Wheel Bearing Adjustment* in *SUSPENSION* Section.

NOTE — *Rotors must be installed in original position due to cooling holes and internal ventilation channels. These holes and channels are different for right and left sides.*

REAR BRAKE SHOES

Removal — Raise and support vehicle and remove wheels. Using suitable puller (40-107) remove brake drum. Remove shoe hold down springs. Remove upper and lower return springs and pressure rod. Remove parking brake rod from brake shoe.

Installation — Reverse removal procedures and note the following: Lubricate adjusting screws and sliding surfaces of brake shoes lightly. Use new bearing pin and clip when installing parking brake lever.

PARKING BRAKE SHOES (REAR DISC BRAKE ONLY)

Removal — Raise and support vehicle; remove tire and wheel. Remove parking brake drum retaining screws and remove parking brake drum. Remove parking brake cable from shoes. Remove expander, shoe retaining springs and pins, then raise upper shoe and remove adjuster and spring. Remove lower shoe retainer and remove parking brake shoes.

Installation — To install, reverse removal procedure.

MASTER CYLINDER

Removal — On 911SC, raise and support vehicle and drain fluid from reservoir. Pull back on accelerator pedal to detach pedal from pad. Remove floor mat and floor board and withdraw boot from master cylinder. Remove underpanel covering front axle. On all models, remove hydraulic lines, electrical connections and reservoir tubes (if equipped). Remove mounting nuts and remove master cylinder.

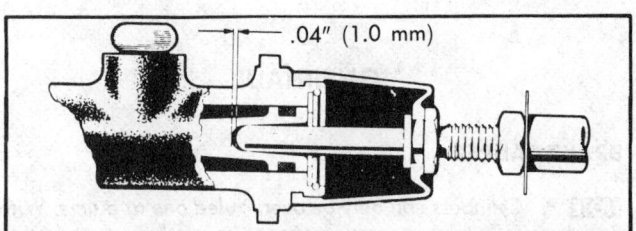

.04" (1.0 mm)

Fig. 3   Illustrating Push Rod-to-Master Cylinder Piston Clearance on 911SC Models

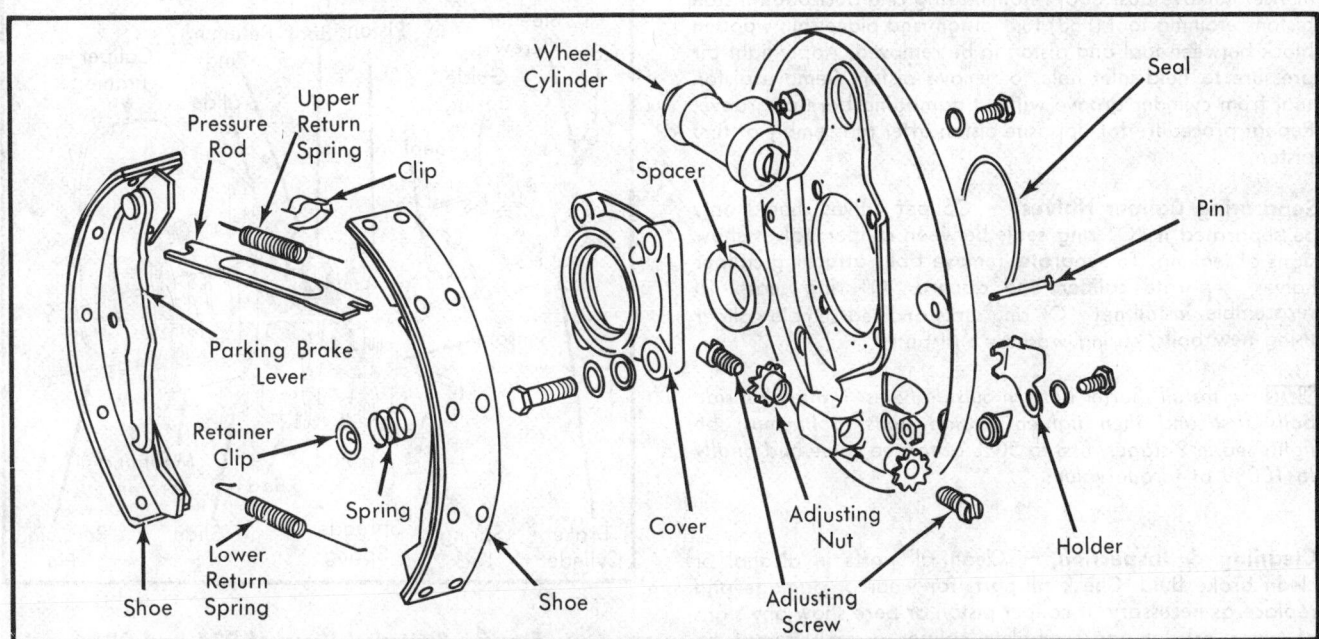

Fig. 2   Exploded View of 924 Rear Brake Assembly

Brakes

PORSCHE (Cont.)

Installation — To install, reverse removal procedure and note the following: On 911SC, be sure push rod is correctly installed and that clearance between push rod and piston is about .04" (1.0 mm). Use a sealing material on cylinder flange to prevent water leakage into driver's compartment. Bleed hydraulic system.

POWER BRAKE UNIT

NOTE — *Before removal, test check valve and power brake unit for operation. To check valve, pull off vacuum hose, place finger over check valve and crank engine; vacuum should be created. To check power brake unit, push on brake pedal several times with engine stopped, hold pedal down and start engine. If power brake unit is operating properly, brake pedal will drop sightly.*

Removal — With master cylinder removed, disconnect vacuum hose from power brake unit. Remove pin connecting power brake unit operating rod to brake pedal assembly, remove nuts and remove power brake unit from vehicle.

Installation — Reverse removal procedures and note the following: Apply suitable sealer to power brake unit mounting surface and vacuum line connections. Adjust pedal height and bleed hydraulic system.

OVERHAUL

BRAKE CALIPER

NOTE — *Cylinders can only be overhauled one at a time. With 1 piston removed, air pressure cannot be used to remove other piston.*

Disassembly (911SC) — Clamp caliper (by mounting flange) in vise. Remove dust boot retaining ring and dust boot. Install piston retaining tool (P83) to 1 piston and place thin wooden block between tool and piston to be removed. Apply light air pressure to fluid inlet hole to remove piston. Remove piston seal from cylinder groove without damaging bore or groove. Repeat procedure for opposite piston after reassembly of first piston.

Separating Caliper Halves — Caliper halves should only be separated if "O" ring seals between caliper halves show signs of leaking. To separate, remove bolts attaching caliper halves, separate caliper and discard "O" ring seals. To reassemble, install new "O" ring seals and reassemble caliper using new bolts, spring washers and nuts.

NOTE — *Install shorter bolts in outside holes. Tighten 2 inside bolts first and then tighten outside bolts. Bolts must be tightened in 2 stages; first to 50% of torque value and finally to 100% of torque value.*

Cleaning & Inspection — Clean all parts in alcohol or clean brake fluid. Check all parts for wear or damage and replace as necessary. If caliper piston or bore show any signs of wear or damage, complete caliper assembly must be replaced.

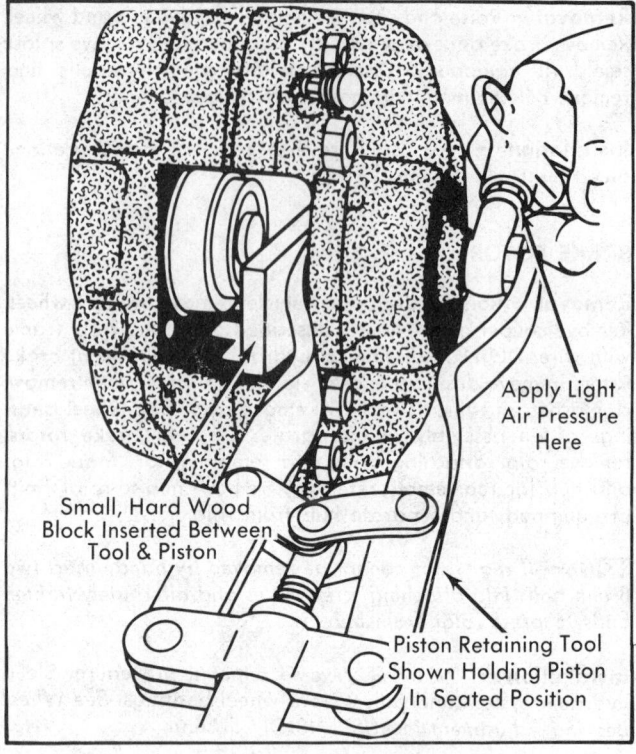

Fig. 4   Using Air Pressure to Remove 911SC Caliper Piston

Reassembly — Reverse disassembly procedure and note the following: Use new rubber components, dust cover retaining ring and pad retaining plates. Apply brake cylinder paste to piston and cylinder seal. Assure piston is straight with cylinder by using a suitable piston installing clamp. Check 20° position of piston with suitable gauge and correct using piston rotating pliers (if needed). Replace fluid inlet bolt and adapter seals.

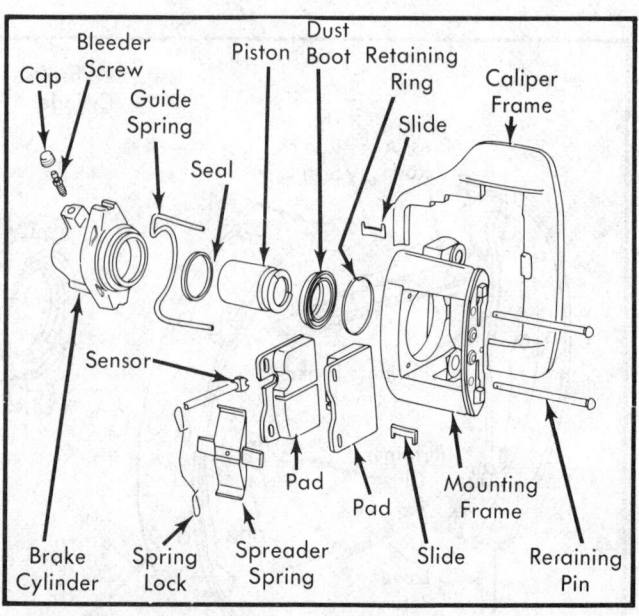

Fig. 5   Exploded View of 924 and 928 Brake Caliper Assembly

Brakes

PORSCHE (Cont.)

Disassembly (Except 911SC) — With disc pads removed, press caliper frame off mounting frame. Insert wooden block in caliper frame and force cylinder assembly off caliper frame with plastic hammer. Remove dust boot retaining ring and dust boot. Force piston out of caliper bore with light air pressure. Remove piston seal from cylinder groove without damaging groove or bore.

Cleaning & Inspection — Clean all parts in alcohol or clean brake fluid. Check all parts for wear or damage and replace as necessary. If caliper piston or bore show any signs of wear or damage, complete caliper assembly must be replaced.

Reassembly — To reassemble, reverse disassembly procedure and note the following: Use new rubber components, dust cover retaining ring and pad retaining plates. Apply brake cylinder paste to piston and cylinder seal. Assure piston is straight with cylinder by using piston installing clamp. Check 20° position.

MASTER CYLINDER

Disassembly — Push in on primary piston to remove lock ring, then remove stop plate and primary piston assembly. Remove piston stop screw and, using compressed air, remove secondary piston. Remove secondary piston support washer, spring seat and return spring. To remove hydraulic warning system assembly, remove sending unit and retaining bolt from master cylinder, and using compressed air, remove pistons and springs.

Cleaning & Inspection — Clean all parts with alcohol. Check all pistons and cylinders for out-of-round, corrosion or damage. Inspect all other parts for scoring, excessive wear, corrosion or other damage.

Reassembly — To reassemble, reverse disassembly procedure and note the following: Lightly coat all parts with brake cylinder paste before installation. Use new "O" ring seals on warning system sending unit and retaining bolt. Tighten all hydraulic lines and fittings. Bleed hydraulic system.

POWER BRAKE UNIT

Manufacturer does not recommend overhaul of power brake unit. Replace as complete assembly if defective.

TIGHTENING SPECIFICATIONS

Application	Ft. Lbs. (N·m)
Caliper Mounting Bolts	
911SC	50 (68)
924	60 (82)
928	61 (83)
Caliper Housing Bolts (911SC, Front)	43 (58)
Rotor-to-Hub Bolts	
911SC & 924	17 (23)
928	84 INCH Lbs. (10)

DRUM BRAKE SPECIFICATIONS

Application	Wheel Cyl. Bore Diameter In. (mm)	Drum Diameter In. (mm)	Original Diameter In. (mm)	Maximum Refinish Diameter In. (mm)	Discard Diameter In. (mm)
924 Rear	.750 (19.05)	9.05 (230)	9.05 (230)	9.09 (231)	9.11 (231.5)

DISC BRAKE SPECIFICATIONS

Application	Caliper Bore Diameter In. (mm)	Lateral Runout In. (mm)	Parallelism In. (mm)	Original Thickness In. (mm)	Minimum Refinish Thickness In. (mm)	Discard Thickness In. (mm)
911SC						
Front	1.89 (48)	.004 (.1)	.0008 (.02)	.807 (20.5)	.752 (19.1)	.728 (18.5)
Rear	1.49 (38)	.004 (.1)	.0008 (.02)	.787 (20.0)	.732 (18.6)	.708 (18.0)
924						
Front	1.89 (48)	.....	.....	.512 (13)	.472 (12)	.453 (11.5)
928						
Front	2.126 (54)	.004 (.1)	.0012 (.03)	.787 (20)	.756 (19.2)	.732 (18.6)
Rear	1.417 (36)	.004 (.1)	.0012 (.03)	.787 (20)	.752 (19.2)	.732 (18.6)

RENAULT

Le Car
18i

DESCRIPTION

Brake system is hydraulically operated using a tandem master cylinder and optional power brake unit. All models are equipped with front disc brakes and rear drum brakes. A pressure limiter valve is installed in rear brake circuit to prevent premature rear wheel lock-up. Parking brake is cable actuated on rear wheels.

ADJUSTMENT

REAR DRUM BRAKE SHOES

Le Car — Two adjusting lugs are located on backing plate. Using a wrench, turn front lug counterclockwise and rear lug clockwise until shoes just contact drum. Then back off adjustment until drum rotates freely.

18i — Adjust brake shoes by pressing down on brake pedal repeatedly.

BRAKE PEDAL FREE PLAY

Le Car — Brake pedal free play (measured at pedal pad center) should be .203" (5 mm). To adjust free play, loosen operating rod lock nut and rotate operating rod until specified free play is obtained. Tighten lock nut.

PARKING BRAKE

Le Car — Adjust service brakes, then fully release parking brake. Loosen lock nut on adjustment rod. Tighten adjustment nut until lining just meets drum. At this point, parking brake lever travel should be about 6 notches. Tighten lock nut and check operation.

18i — Place vehicle on a lift with parking brake handle released. Screw on equalizer nut until cable deflection between secondary cable and vehicle chassis is about .74" (20 mm). Check parking brake lever travel. It should move a minimum of 12 notches.

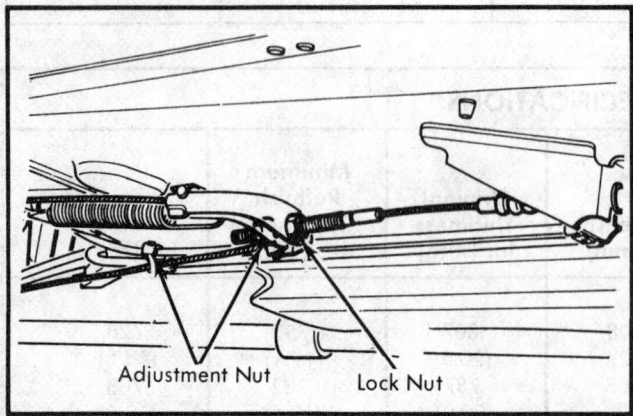

Adjustment Nut   Lock Nut

Fig. 1   Le Car Parking Brake Adjustment Points

BRAKE WARNING LIGHT

A dual warning light is mounted on instrument panel. Light should glow when parking brake lever is pulled 1 notch and go off when lever is fully released (ignition on). To check circuit warning sensor, release parking brake (ignition on) and ensure light is off. Raise master cylinder reservoir cap; light should glow. If not, check bulb or circuit connections.

REAR BRAKE PRESSURE LIMITER

NOTE — *Limiter must always be checked and adjusted with vehicle on level ground, fuel tank full, trunk empty and driver's seat occupied.*

1) To check limiter, remove 1 rear wheel cylinder bleeder screw and install a pressure gauge (Fre. 214-02 on Le Car, Fre. 214-04 on 18i) into vacant hole. Bleed system through screw on gauge. Depress brake pedal and check pressure at wheel cylinder.

2) Pressure on Le Car should be 405-465 psi (28.5-32.5 kg/cm²) and pressure on 18i should be 435-490 psi (30.6-34.5 kg/cm²). Release lock nut and tighten adjustment nut to increase pressure or loosen it to reduce pressure. Apply brake pedal several times and recheck adjustment. Remove pressure gauge and bleed system.

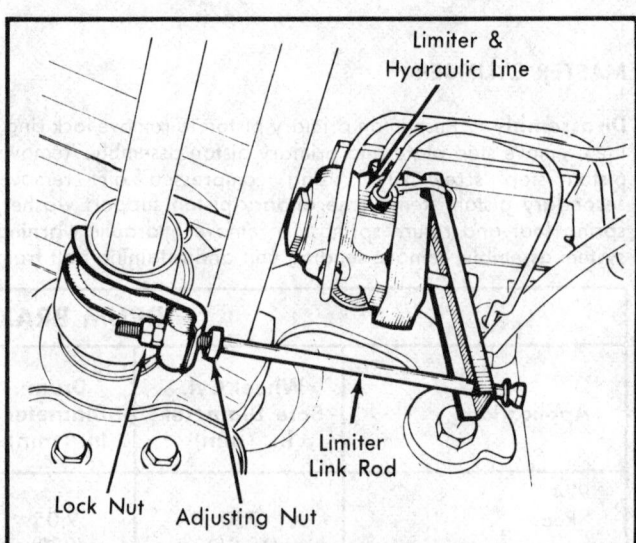

Limiter &
Hydraulic Line

Limiter
Link Rod

Lock Nut   Adjusting Nut

**Fig. 2   Pressure Limiter Adjustment Points
(Le Car Shown, 18i Similar)**

REMOVAL & INSTALLATION

FRONT DISC PADS

Removal & Installation (Le Car) — Caliper must be removed to remove brake pads. See Disc Brake Caliper Removal & Installation.

Removal (18i) — Raise and support vehicle. Disconnect pad wear warning light wires. Take out retaining clip and remove key. With a screwdriver, gently pry between rotor and caliper at outer pad to push caliper piston back slightly. Remove pads.

Installation — Push caliper piston back with clamp (Fre.823). Put the 2 anti-squeal pins in place on new pads. Position pads in caliper bracket and engage key after having chamfered entry end of key. Put clip on key. Reconnect wear-warning light wires. Press down brake pedal several times to seat pads.

Brakes

RENAULT (Cont.)

FRONT DISC CALIPER

Removal (Le Car) — Raise and support vehicle and remove front wheels. Remove spring clips and slide keys out of caliper and mounting bracket. Disconnect brake line fitting from flexible hose and remove hose retaining clip from body. Remove caliper from mounting bracket and disconnect flexible hose from caliper. Remove brake pads and pad spring from caliper.

Installation — To install, reverse removal procedure and note the following: Install longest pad spring on outside of caliper. Tighten all fittings and bleed hydraulic system.

Removal (18i) — Raise and support vehicle and remove wheel and tire. Remove brake pads. Disconnect hydraulic line. Remove 2 caliper bolts remove caliper.

Installation — To install, reverse removal procedure and bleed brake system.

FRONT DISC ROTOR

Removal (Le Car) — Remove caliper as previously described and remove caliper mounting bracket. Attach holding tool (Rou. 604 or Rou. 436-01) to wheel studs and remove axle shaft nut. Attach slide hammer to hub and remove hub and rotor assembly. Remove hub-to-rotor bolts and remove rotor from hub.

Installation — To install, reverse removal procedure and tighten hub-to-rotor bolts evenly. Bleed hydraulic system if required.

Removal (18i) — Raise and support vehicle and remove brake pads and caliper. Remove inset bolts and remove disc.

NOTE — In some cases it may be necessary to slightly loosen drive shaft nut in order to remove disc.

Installation — Put the new disc in place on hub and attach with bolts. If necessary, torque drive shaft nut while holding hub with hub locking tool (Rou. 604). Install the caliper and tighten bolts. Install brake pads.

REAR BRAKE DRUM

Removal (Le Car) — Raise and support vehicle. Remove hub grease cap, cotter pin, nut and washer. Back off brake shoe adjuster. Attach slide hammer and remove drum.

Installation — To install, reverse removal procedure. Lubricate wheel bearings and adjust. See Wheel Bearing Adjustment in SUSPENSION Section.

Removal (18i) — Loosen parking brake. Remove dust plug from backing plate. Put a screwdriver against parking brake lever and push to free its peg from brake shoe. Loosen lever by pushing toward rear. Remove grease cap, cotter pin, lock nut, drum hub nut and washer. Remove drum and outer wheel bearing.

Installation — 1) Grease bearings and place drum in place with outer bearing, drum hub and nut. Adjust bearings. See Wheel Bearing Adjustment in SUSPENSION Section.

2) Install castle lock nut and cotter pin. Put on grease cap filled with grease. Adjust brake shoes by pressing down on the brake pedal repeatedly. Adjust parking brake. Reinstall dust plug on backing plate.

REAR BRAKE SHOES

Removal & Installation — Remove wheel and brake drum from vehicle. Install wheel cylinder clamp, then remove upper brake shoe return spring. Disconnect parking brake cable from actuator lever. Remove parking brake actuator link and lower return spring. Unhook shoe hold-down springs and remove brake shoes. To install, reverse removal procedure.

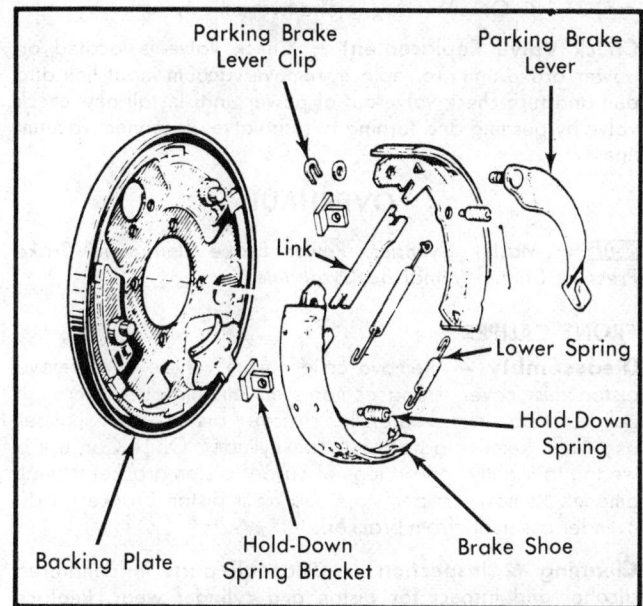

**Fig. 3   Exploded View of Brake Shoe Assembly
(Le Car Shown, 18i Similar)**

MASTER CYLINDER

Removal (Le Car) — Drain fluid from master cylinder and disconect and plug hydraulic lines. Remove pressure loss indicator bolt (if equipped). Disconnect push rod from brake pedal (without power brake unit). Remove mounting hardware and remove master cylinder.

Installation — To install, reverse removal procedure and adjust brake pedal free play. Bleed and adjust hydraulic system.

Removal (18i) — Drain fluid reservoir and remove the reservoir along with rubber hose rings. Unscrew brake lines and mark their positions on master cylinder. Remove 2 attaching nuts on brake booster. Remove master cylinder.

Installation — Check master cylinder operating clearance. The piston rod projection length should be .354" (9 mm). Attach master cylinder to brake booster. Attach hydraulic lines in the following order: right front wheel, left front wheel, left rear wheel and right rear wheel. Bleed brake system.

POWER BRAKE UNIT

NOTE — Power brake unit is not serviceable, only the air filter and check valve can be serviced.

Removal (Le Car) — Disconnect battery and remove fluid from master cylinder. Remove engine air cleaner (if necessary). Disconnect hydraulic lines at master cylinder, and remove pressure loss indicator valve bolt (if equipped). Disconnect vacuum hose and remove clevis from brake pedal. Remove power brake unit attaching nuts from pedal side of firewall. Remove master cylinder and power cylinder as an assembly. Separate master cylinder from power brake unit.

Brakes

RENAULT (Cont.)

Removal (18i) — Remove master cylinder from vehicle. Remove brake pedal push rod adjuster link pin. Remove brake booster attaching nuts on firewall. Remove brake booster from vehicle, saving support spacer.

Installation (All Models) — To install reverse removal procedure and adjust push rod-to-master cylinder clearance. Clearance should be .36" (9.13 mm) on Le Car and .35" (9.0 mm) on 18i. On all models, bleed hydraulic system.

Check Valve Replacement — Check valve is located on power brake unit. To replace, remove vacuum input line and pull and turn check valve out of power unit. Install new check valve by pushing and turning to seat valve. Reconnect vacuum line.

OVERHAUL

NOTE — *Master Cylinder, Power Brake Unit, and Brake Pressure Limiter cannot be Overhauled.*

FRONT CALIPER

Disassembly — Remove caliper from vehicle and remove piston dust cover. Using compressed air introduced through caliper fluid inlet, carefully remove piston from caliper assembly. Remove piston seal from cylinder. On Le Car, use a wedge to slightly spread legs of caliper piston bracket a small amount. Remove caliper stop peg from piston bracket. Slide cylinder assembly from bracket.

Cleaning & Inspection — Clean all parts in denatured alcohol and inspect for piston and cylinder wear. Replace worn parts as required. Replace all rubber seals during overhaul.

Reassembly — Lubricate cylinder bore, piston, and seals with brake fluid prior to reassembly. To reassemble, reverse disassembly procedure.

WHEEL CYLINDER

Disassembly & Reassembly — Remove dust boots, pistons, cups and spring. Examine components for damage or excessive wear. Replace worn parts as required. Before reassembly, dip pistons and cups in clean brake fluid.

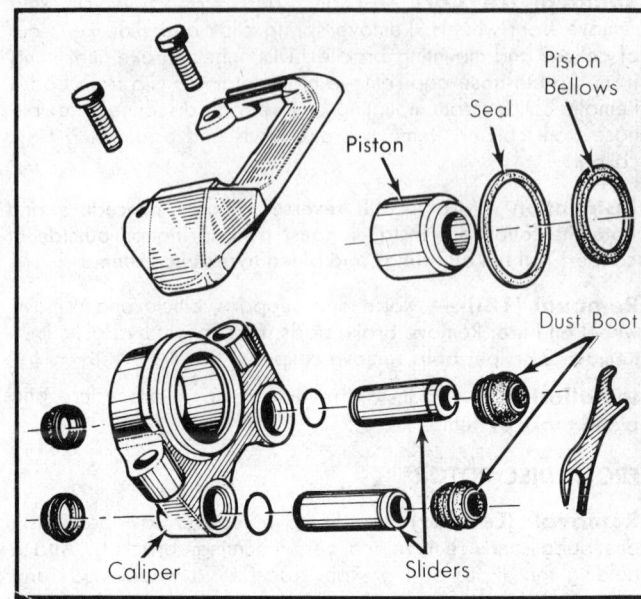

Fig. 4 Exploded View 18i Caliper Assembly

TIGHTENING SPECIFICATIONS

Application	Ft. Lbs. (N.m)
Caliper Bracket Bolts	
Le Car	50 (68)
18i	74 (101)
Caliper Attaching Bolts	
18i	44 (60)
Rotor-to-Hub	
Le Car	20 (27)
Drive Shaft Nut	
Le Car	90 (122)
18i	185 (252)

DRUM BRAKE SPECIFICATIONS

Application	Wheel Cyl. Bore Diameter In. (mm)	Drum Diameter In. (mm)	Original Diameter In. (mm)	Maximum Refinish Diameter In. (mm)	Discard Diameter In. (mm)
Le Car	.866 (22)	7.10 (180)	7.10 (180)	7.136 (181)	.....
18i	.866 (22)	8.996 (228.5)	8.996 (228.5)	9.035 (229.5)	.....

DISC BRAKE SPECIFICATIONS

Application	Disc Diameter	Lateral Runout	Parallelism	Original Thickness	Minimum Refinish Thickness	Discard Thickness
Le Car	1.772 (45)	.004 (.10)	.....	.395 (10)	①	.354 (9)
18i	1.890 (48)	.003 (.08)	.....	.472 (12)		.354 (9)

① — Rotor cannot be machined; it must be replaced.

Brakes

SAAB

DESCRIPTION

Service brake system is hydraulically operated by a tandem master cylinder and vacuum power brake unit acting on four-wheel disc brakes. Front calipers are sliding yoke Girling calipers; rear brakes are fixed yoke ATE calipers. Master cylinder contains level sensor which illuminates a warning lamp on instrument panel if fluid level becomes low. Brake circuit is double diagonal system (right front, left rear/left front, right rear). Parking brake is mechanically operated on FRONT brake caliper assemblies.

ADJUSTMENT

PARKING BRAKE

Before adjusting cable, apply brake lever several times to stretch cables. Rotate cable adjusting nuts located at rear of parking brake lever under plastic cover until distance between lever on front caliper and yoke is .019" (.5 mm). With engine switched off, pump brake pedal repeatedly until foot brake starts to operate. Pull parking brake lever up 5 notches. Continue to pump brake pedal until parking brake operates after being pulled up an additional 2-4 notches.

NOTE — *Parking brake cables are crossed, so to adjust left parking brake mechanism (cable), right adjusting nut must be rotated and vice versa.*

BRAKE WARNING LIGHT

Brake warning lights are mounted on instrument panel. Parking brake light should go on when parking brake lever is pulled 1 notch (ignition on) and go off when lever is fully released. To check lever indicator circuit, raise master cylinder filler cap. Warning light should glow. If not, check bulb, circuit connections and sensor.

REMOVAL & INSTALLATION

DISC BRAKE PADS

Removal (Front) — Raise and support vehicle. Remove tire and wheel. Rotate disc so that 1 of the recesses in the edge of disc is in line with brake pads. Remove damper spring, pin retaining clip and pad retaining pin. If retaining pin is difficult to remove, use tapping out tool (83 90 270) and removal tool (89 96 175). Withdraw brake pads.

Installation — 1) Rotate direct piston with brake piston key (89 96 043) at the same time brake piston is pressed into cylinder. If necessary, first siphon off ½ brake fluid from master cylinder to prevent overflow. Check that piston movement has not moved dust cover.

2) Check that yoke moves easily in groove in brake housing. Fit the new pads together with "U" pin retaining clip and damper spring. To complete installation, reverse removal procedure and adjust parking brake.

Removal (Rear) — Raise and support vehicle. Remove tire and wheel. Tap out brake pad retaining pins using a .11" (2.8 mm) drift. Remove retaining spring. Remove brake pads. If required, use extractor (89 95 043).

Installation — Use handle of brake piston key (89 96 043) and push pistons back far enough to install pads. Be careful not to overflow master cylinder. Fit pad retaining pins and pin retaining clip. To complete installation, reverse removal procedure.

NOTE — *Girling caliper brake pads are not interchangeable. Outer pads are identified by "V" notch.*

DISC BRAKE CALIPER

Removal — Raise and support vehicle and remove wheels and tires. Remove brake pads. On front wheel calipers, disconnect parking brake cable from lever on caliper. On all wheels, disconnect hydraulic line from hose, plug lines to prevent entry of dirt and loss of fluid. Remove caliper attaching bolts and lift off caliper.

Installation — To install, reverse removal procedure and note the following: Tighten all attaching bolts, bleed hydraulic system and adjust parking brake cables.

DISC BRAKE ROTOR

Removal — Remove brake pads and caliper, suspending caliper out of way. Do NOT allow caliper to hang from hydraulic line. Remove retaining screws and remove brake rotor.

Installation — To install, reverse removal procedure. Tighten all nuts and bolts and adjust parking brake if necessary.

MASTER CYLINDER

Removal — Disconnect electrical lead to warning switch on master cylinder. Disconnect clutch master cylinder hose from fluid reservoir, then plug reservoir nipple to prevent loss of fluid. Disconnect hydraulic lines from master cylinder. Remove master cylinder-to-power brake unit attaching nuts and lift off master cylinder.

Installation — To install, reverse removal procedure and bleed hydraulic system.

POWER BRAKE BOOSTER

Removal — Remove steering column bearing cover, ash tray and safety padding screw from inside vehicle. Remove safety padding screws from inside engine compartment. Disconnect all electrical leads, hydraulic and vacuum lines from master cylinder and power brake unit. Remove cotter pin from brake pedal push rod. Remove attaching nuts and lift off master cylinder and power brake unit as an assembly.

Installation — To install, reverse removal procedure and bleed hydraulic system.

Check Valve Replacement — Remove vacuum hose clamps at check valve and remove check valve from power unit. To install, reverse removal procedure.

Filter Replacement — Remove power brake unit from vehicle. Remove rubber dust boot and filter retainer. Withdraw silencer and filter from end of booster. To install, cut a slit in filter and slip over push rod. Reverse removal procedure and ensure slots in filter and silencer are 180° apart.

SAAB (Cont.)

OVERHAUL

CALIPER ASSEMBLY

Disassembly (Girling Type) — **1)** With caliper removed from vehicle, mount assembly in a soft jawed vise. Remove parking brake return spring. Separate yoke from caliper assembly. Remove spring and parking brake lever from yoke.

2) Remove retaining ring and dust boot, then using compressed air, force out indirect piston assembly from caliper. Press direct piston push rod and remove piston from caliper. Remove "O" rings and seal rings from caliper bore and pistons.

Cleaning & Inspection — Wash all parts, except indirect piston assembly, in clean brake fluid and dry with a lint-free cloth. Inspect all parts for corrosion, damage or wear; replace defective parts. Replace all rubber parts during overhaul.

NOTE — *Indirect piston assembly must be wiped clean only. DO NOT use any type of solvent or brake fluid.*

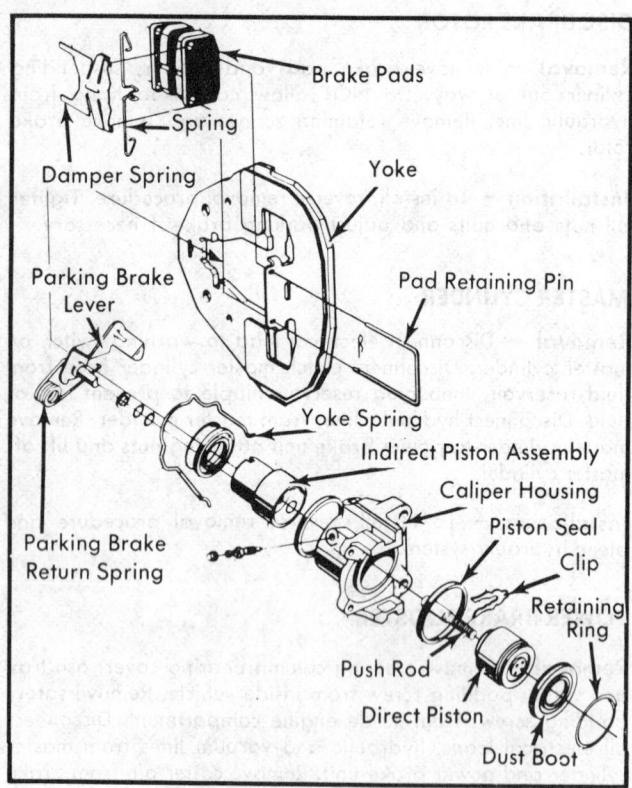

Fig. 1　Exploded View of Girling Caliper

Reassembly — **1)** Replace any worn, damaged or corroded parts. On indirect piston, replace "O" ring on push rod and "O" ring retainer at parking brake lever. Lubricate cylinder bore with brake fluid and fit new piston seals. Lubricate aperature for parking brake lever with parking brake mechanisim grease (89 94 782).

2) Fit anchor plate to push rod and push push rod into hole in indirect piston. Ensure recess in anchor plate comes immediately over spring in piston. Lubricate indirect piston and insert in caliper housing so recess for yoke is directly in line with groove in caliper housing.

3) In the same manner push the direct piston into cylinder and using brake piston key (89 96 043), screw together piston and push rod. Screw and push in the 2 pistons until the edges of dust cover grooves are flush with caliper. Fit new dust covers and retaining rings.

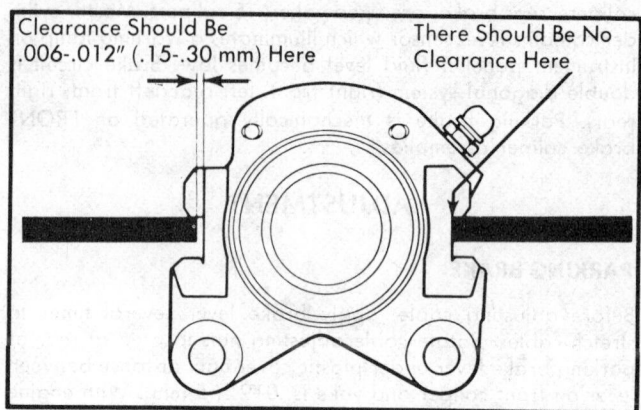

Fig. 2　Girling Caliper Clearance Measuring Points

4) Install yoke spring and parking brake lever to yoke. Brush brake yoke grease (Castrol-(45)30 08 612) on yoke sliding surfaces. Apply grease to seating surface of pad retaining disc in housing. Align yoke guide edges with grooves in brake housing. Lift the parking brake lever and fit end of axle pin into hole in indirect piston.

5) Install parking lever return spring. Check clearance between sliding surface of yoke and brake housing. No clearance is allowed on bleeder screw side. Opposite side must have .006-.012" (.15-.30 mm) clearance. *See Fig. 2.*

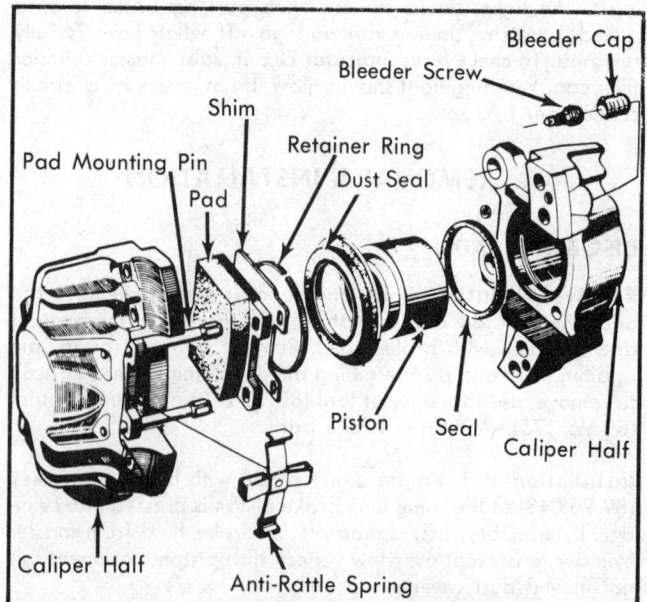

Fig. 3　Exploded View of ATE Caliper

Disassembly (ATE Type) — With caliper and pads removed, clean outer portion of caliper. Remove dust covers and retaining rings. Insert wooden block between pistons and carefully apply compressed air to fluid inlet port to force pistons out of cylinder bores. Remove piston seals from cylinder bores without damaging bores. Remove bleeder screw.

NOTE — *DO NOT separate caliper halves.*

SAAB (Cont.)

Cleaning & Inspection — Wash all parts in clean brake fluid. Inspect cylinder bores and pistons for corrosion, damage or wear. Replace defective parts. Replace all rubber parts during overhaul.

Reassembly — Coat all parts with clean brake fluid and install new piston seals in cylinder bores. Carefully install pistons into cylinder bores. Check piston position with template (89 953 42). *See Fig. 4.* Install rubber boots and retaining clips. Install bleeder screw and disc pads.

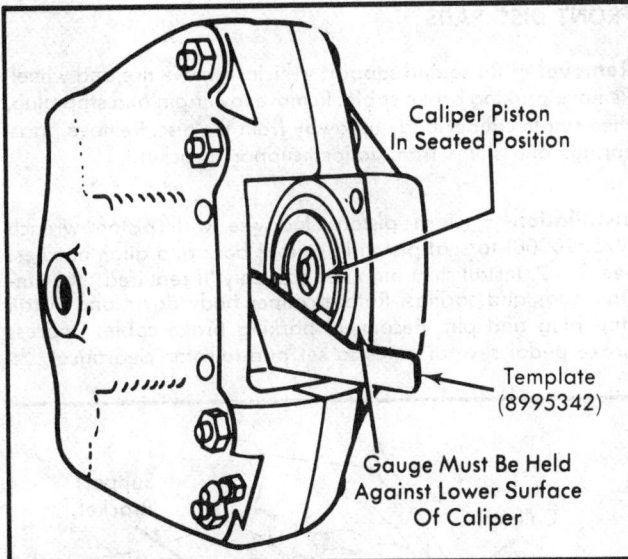

Fig. 4 Checking ATE Caliper Piston Position

MASTER CYLINDER

Disassembly — 1) With master cylinder removed from vehicle, drain brake fluid from reservoir. Mount cylinder in a soft jaw vise. Remove retaining pins and separate reservoir from master cylinder (pins may have to be driven out). Remove rubber seals from reservoir mounting holes in cylinder.

2) Push in on primary piston and pull secondary piston stop pin from forward reservoir mounting hole. Remove circlip and take out primary piston assembly and spring. Remove cylinder from vise and carefully knock it against a block of wood to remove secondary piston assembly and spring. Remove brake warning switch from master cylinder, then remove end plug and lift out warning valve assembly.

Cleaning & Inspection — Wash all parts in clean brake fluid and dry with a clean, lint-free cloth. Inspect all parts for corro-

sion, damage or wear; replace defective parts. Replace rubber parts during overhaul.

Reassembly — Reverse disassembly procedure. Coat all parts with clean brake fluid and use care not to damage seals during installation of pistons.

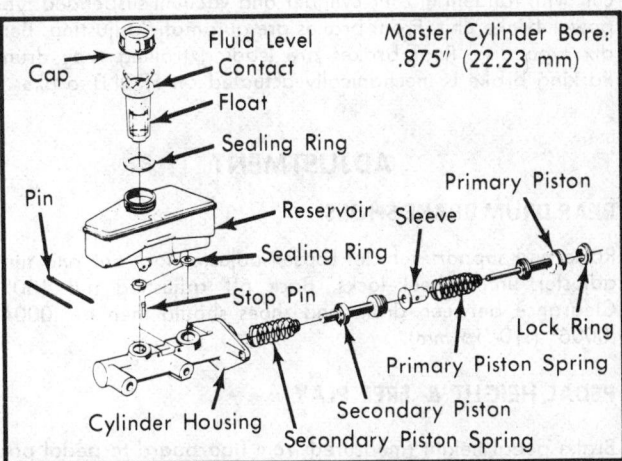

Fig. 5 Exploded View of Master Cylinder

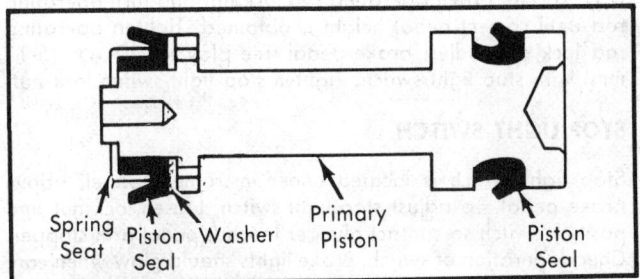

Fig. 6 Primary Piston Seal Installation

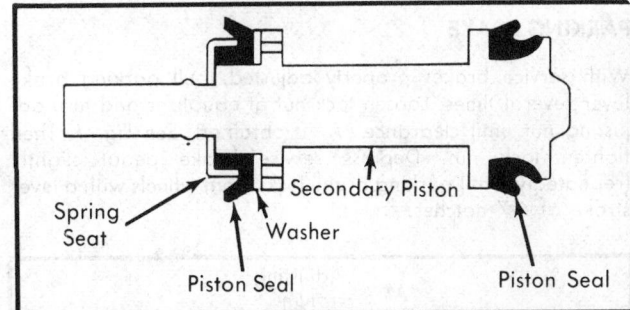

Fig. 7 Secondary Piston Seal Installation

DISC BRAKE SPECIFICATIONS

Application	Caliper Bore Diameter In. (mm)	Lateral Runout In. (mm)	Parallelism In. (mm)	Original Thickness In. (mm)	Minimum Refinish Thickness In. (mm)	Discard Thickness In. (mm)
900 Front	2.126 (54)	.004 (.10)	.441 (11.2)	.500 (12.7)	.461 (11.7)	.0006 (.015)
Rear	1.181 (30)	.004 (.10)	....	.413 (10.5)	.374 (9.5)	....

SUBARU

Hatchback   Sedan
Hardtop   Wagon

DESCRIPTION

Service brake system is a diagonally split, dual hydraulic circuit with tandem master cylinder and vacuum suspended type power brake unit. Front brakes are automatic adjusting, Bendix type disc. Rear brakes are leading/trailing type drum. Parking brake is mechanically actuated on FRONT brakes.

ADJUSTMENT

REAR DRUM BRAKE SHOES

Raise and support vehicle. Loosen adjuster lock nut and turn adjuster until wheel locks. Back off adjusting nut 180°. Clearance between drum and shoes should then be .0004-.0006" (.10-.15 mm).

PEDAL HEIGHT & FREE PLAY

Brake pedal height (measured from floorboard to pedal pad center) should be 5.3-5.9" (135-150 mm). To adjust pedal height, loosen stop light switch lock nut and position out of way. Loosen brake operating rod lock nut and turn operating rod until correct pedal height is obtained. Tighten operating rod lock nut. Adjust brake pedal free play to .20-.43" (5-11 mm) with stop light switch. Tighten stop light switch lock nut.

STOP LIGHT SWITCH

Stop light switch is located under instrument panel, above brake pedal. To adjust stop light switch, loosen lock nut and position switch so contact plunger touches pedal arm stopper. Check operation of switch. Brake lights should glow when contact plunger moves .07-.13" (1.8-3.3 mm). If not, adjust switch and tighten lock nut.

PARKING BRAKE

With service brakes properly adjusted, pull parking brake lever several times. Loosen lock nut at equalizer and turn adjusting nut until clearance "A" is obtained. See Fig. 1. Then tighten lock nut. Depress service brake pedal slightly (repeatedly) until parking brake locks front wheels with a lever stroke of 6-7 notches.

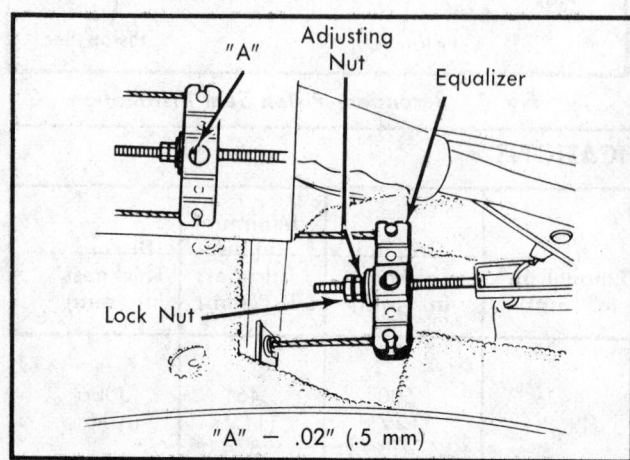

Fig. 1   Location for Adjusting Parking Brake

BRAKE WARNING LIGHT

A dual warning light is mounted on all models. Light should glow when parking brake is applied (ignition on). A sensor is also located in master cylinder reservoir to indicate low fluid level. To test sensor, remove reservoir cap to allow float to drop. Bulb should glow (ignition on and parking brake released).

REMOVAL & INSTALLATION

FRONT DISC PADS

Removal — Raise and support vehicle; remove tire and wheel. Remove parking brake cable. Remove lower pin and stop plug, then rotate caliper body up away from the disc. Remove pads, springs and shims from caliper support bracket.

Installation — Turn piston clockwise with piston wrench (925590000) to seat piston in caliper bore and align notches. See Fig. 2. Install shim on outer pad only (if required), then install pads and springs. Rotate caliper body down and install stop plug and pin. Reconnect parking brake cable. Depress brake pedal several times to set pad-to-rotor clearance.

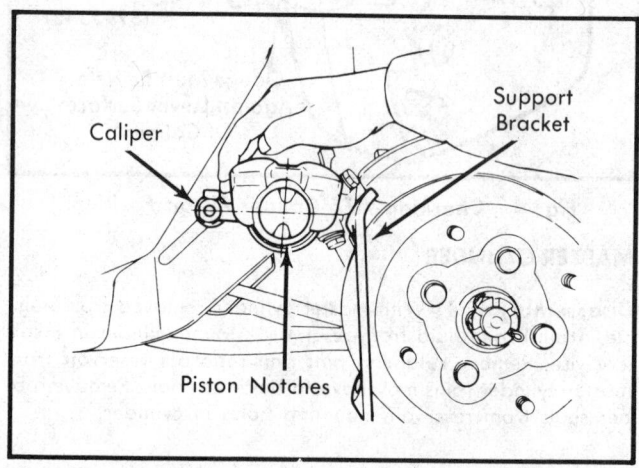

Fig. 2   Aligning Caliper Piston Notches for Replacing Disc Brake Pads

FRONT DISC CALIPER

Removal — Raise and support vehicle; remove tire and wheel. Remove pads as previously described. Disconnect and plug hydraulic line at caliper and remove parking brake cable. Remove caliper assembly. DO NOT remove support bracket unless rotor is being removed.

Installation — Apply silicone grease to lock pin and guide pin. Install caliper assembly, pads and parking brake cable. Install hydraulic line, then bleed hydraulic system.

FRONT DISC ROTOR

Removal — Raise and support vehicle; remove tire and wheel. Remove disc pads as previously described. Remove caliper assembly and hang from frame with wire; DO NOT disconnect hydraulic line. Remove caliper mounting bracket bolts and bracket. Using a puller, pull rotor and hub assembly from axle. Remove hub-to-rotor bolts and separate rotor from hub.

Brakes

SUBARU (Cont.)

NOTE — *Replace mounting bracket when rotor is replaced.*

Installation — To install, reverse removal procedure and tighten hub-to-rotor bolts evenly. Depress brake pedal several times to seat pads.

REAR BRAKE DRUM

Removal — Raise and support vehicle; remove tire and wheel. Remove dust cap and wheel bearing components (2-wheel drive). Remove cotter pin and castle nut on 4-wheel drive. Remove brake drum. Loosen brake adjustment if necessary and use puller if required to pull off brake drum.

Installation — To install, reverse removal procedure and adjust wheel bearings. *See Wheel Bearing Adjustment in SUSPENSION Section.*

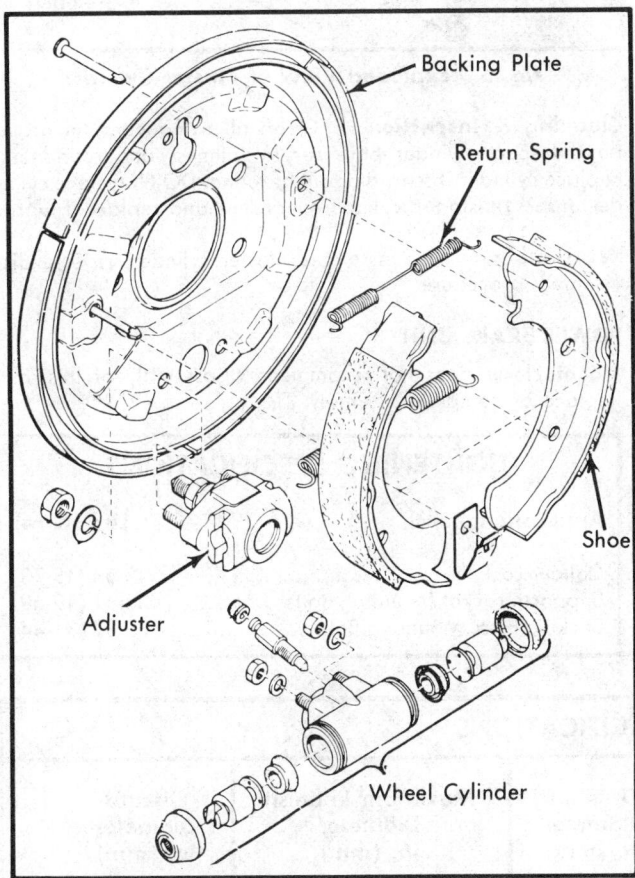

Fig. 3 *Exploded View of Rear Drum Brake Assembly*

REAR BRAKE SHOES

Removal — With brake drum removed, remove and plug hydraulic lines from wheel cylinder. Remove backing plate bolts and backing plate assembly. Separate shoes from backing plate by removing hold down springs. Disconnect lower end first and then remove upper end from cylinder. Separate return springs from shoes.

Installation — To install, reverse removal procedure and note the following: Return springs are installed with coils on inside of shoe assemblies (next to backing plate). Return springs are not interchangeable; lower spring is thicker diameter. Adjust brakes and bleed hydraulic system.

MASTER CYLINDER

Removal & Installation — Siphon brake fluid from reservoir. Disconnect warning light electrical connection. Remove hydraulic lines. Remove retaining nuts and remove master cylinder from power brake unit. To install, reverse removal procedure and bleed hydraulic system.

POWER BRAKE UNIT

Removal & Installation — From inside vehicle, remove cotter pin and disconnect push rod from brake pedal. Remove power brake retaining nuts from firewall. In engine compartment, remove master cylinder retaining nuts. Disconnect vacuum hose at power brake unit and wiring harness from master cylinder. Position master cylinder to one side without damaging hydraulic lines. Remove power brake unit. To install, reverse removal procedure and bleed hydraulic system.

OVERHAUL

FRONT CALIPER

Disassembly — **1)** Thoroughly clean exterior of caliper with clean brake fluid. Remove outer pad clip and bleed screw. Remove dust boot retainer and dust boot. Apply compressed air or liquid to fluid inlet and force piston out of caliper bore.

2) Carefully remove guide pin boot and piston seal. Remove parking brake lever cap ring and lever cap, then remove snap ring from lever and spindle assembly.

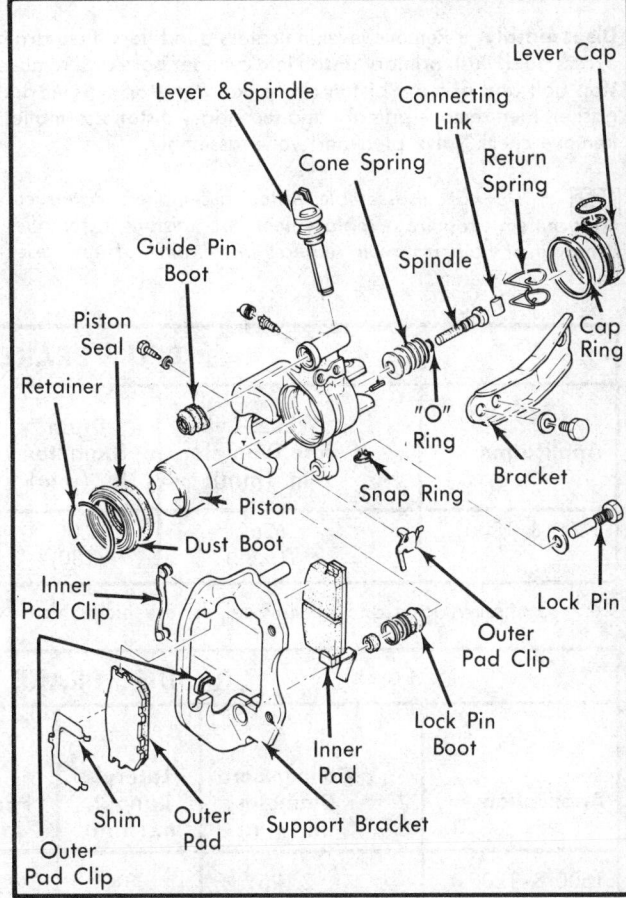

Fig. 4 *Exploded View of Front Disc Caliper Assembly*

SUBARU (Cont.)

3) Mount caliper assembly in soft-jaw vise and install puller (925471000) to release spring washer tension. With spring tension released, pull out lever and spindle. Remove puller and remove connecting link, return spring, spindle and cone spring.

Cleaning & Inspection — Clean all components with brake fluid and ensure that inner cylinder wall is not scratched or corroded. Replace any damaged parts.

Reassembly — **1)** Coat piston seal with silicone grease and insert into cylinder by hand. Coat piston, piston boots and cylinder wall with brake fluid; hand insert piston. Install boot and retainer.

2) Lightly coat spindle and "O" ring with silicone grease. Insert spindle and install spring washers with puller (925471000). Lubricate and install connecting link (thick side in slot.) Install parking brake lever assembly, snap ring, lever cap and retainer.

REAR WHEEL CYLINDER

Disassembly — Remove boot and take out piston with cup. DO NOT separate cup unless replacement is available.

Cleaning & Inspection — Clean all parts in brake fluid only. If cylinder is out of round or burred, replace as an assembly; DO NOT hone.

Reassembly — To reassemble, reverse disassembly procedure and ensure piston cup is not installed in reverse direction.

MASTER CYLINDER

Disassembly — Remove level indicators and filters, then drain excess fluid. Push primary piston into cylinder bore and remove stop bolt and primary piston circlip. Remove stop washer and gasket, then remove primary and secondary piston assemblies. Remove check valve plug and valve assembly.

NOTE — *Do not disassemble piston assemblies. Piston cup replacement requires replacement of piston assemblies. Removal of fluid reservoir requires installation of new reservoir.*

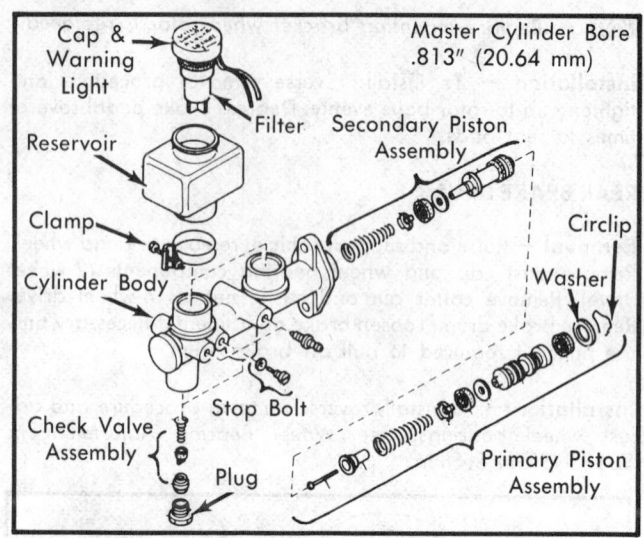

Fig. 5 Exploded View of Master Cylinder

Cleaning & Inspection — Clean all components in brake fluid. Inspect cylinder bore for smoothness and roundness. Replace cylinder if scored or out of round. DO NOT hone cylinder. Inspect piston-to-cylinder clearance and replace if worn.

Reassembly — To reassemble master cylinder, reverse disassembly procedure.

POWER BRAKE UNIT

Manufacturer does not recommend disassembly of this unit. Replace as complete assembly.

TIGHTENING SPECIFICATIONS

Application	Ft. Lbs. (N·m)
Caliper Lock Pin	33-54 (45-73)
Support Bracket Mounting Bolts	36-51 (49-69)
Backing Plate Mounting Bolts	23-32 (31-44)

DRUM BRAKE SPECIFICATIONS

Application	Wheel Cyl. Bore Diameter In. (mm)	Drum Diameter In. (mm)	Original Diameter In. (mm)	Maximum Refinish Diameter In. (mm)	Discard Diameter In. (mm)
1600 & 1800	.625① (15.88)	7.09 (180)	7.09 (180)	.....	7.17 (182)

① — Station Wagon and all 4-wheel drive vehicles have wheel cylinder bore of .687" (17.46 mm).

DISC BRAKE SPECIFICATIONS

Application	Caliper Bore Diameter In. (mm)	Lateral Runout In. (mm)	Parallelism In. (mm)	Original Thickness In. (mm)	Minimum Refinish Thickness In. (mm)	Discard Thickness In. (mm)
1600 & 1800	2.125 (53.97)	.004 (.10)	.....	.492 (12.5)	.....	.394 (10)

TOYOTA

Celica   Pickup
Corolla   Starlet
Corona   Supra
Cressida   Tercel
Land Cruiser

DESCRIPTION

Brake systems are hydraulically actuated using a tandem master cylinder and vacuum power brake unit. Power units vary among models and Land Cruiser and Cressida models use a separate vacuum pump to provide vacuum to power brake unit. Supra is equipped with 4-wheel disc brakes. All other models are equipped with front disc brakes and rear drum brakes. A load sensing proportioning valve is installed in rear circuit of all pickup models (except ½ ton) and Land Cruiser models. Rear brakes on Pickup and Land Cruiser models require adjustment; all other models are self-adjusting. All parking brakes are cable actuated and operate on rear brakes except Land Curiser. Parking brake on Land Cruiser operates on transfer case.

NOTE — Brake caliper applications vary among models. Check and compare calipers with those shown in this article for correct service procedures.

ADJUSTMENTS

DRUM BRAKES

Pickup & Land Cruiser — Raise and support vehicle on safety stands. Release parking brake and ensure wheel rotates freely. Remove plug from adjusting hole. Turn adjusting screw with suitable adjusting tool until wheel can not be turned. Depress brake pedal and ensure drum is locked. On Land Cruiser, back off adjuster 4-5 notches or until wheel turns with slight drag. On Pickup models, back off adjuster 10-12 notches or until wheel turns freely.

BRAKE PEDAL HEIGHT

Brake pedal height is measured from center of brake pedal to asphalt sheet under carpet. To adjust clearance, loosen stop light switch and lock nut on brake pedal push rod. Adjust pedal height by turning push rod. After setting pedal height, tighten lock nut, adjust stop light switch and tighten stop light switch lock nut. See Fig. 1.

Brake Pedal Height	
Application	**Height In. (mm)**
Celica, Corona & Supra	6.5-6.9 (165-175)
Corolla	6.9-7.3 (175-185)
Cressida	6.1-6.5 (154-165)
Land Cruiser	8.5 (215)
Pickup	6.2-6.6 (157-167)
Starlet	6.9 (175)
Tercel	6.4-6.5 (163-165)

BRAKE PEDAL FREE PLAY

Pedal free play is distance brake pedal travels before initial resistance of power brake push rod is contacted. To adjust pedal free play, stop engine and depress brake pedal several times to exhaust vacuum from power brake unit. Place a straightedge beside brake pedal, then press pedal down with fingers until initial resistance is felt. See Fig. 1. Free play should be .16-.28" (4-7 mm) for Tercel and .12-.24" (3-6 mm) for all others. If pedal travel is not as specified, adjust pedal height, start engine and confirm free play measurement. Check brake pedal height.

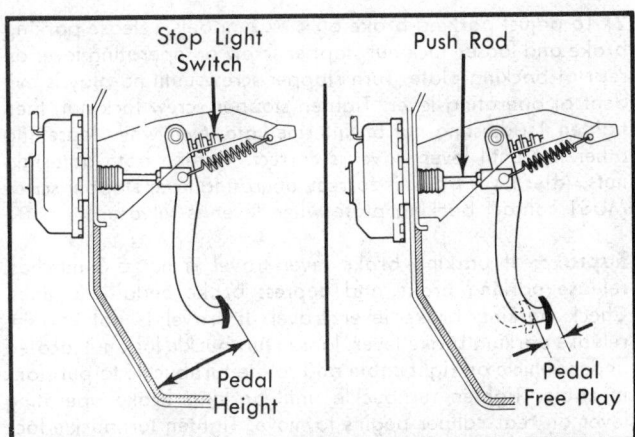

Fig. 1 Measuring Pedal Height and Free Play

PARKING BRAKE

NOTE — Before adjusting parking brake, release parking brake lever. Pull parking brake and count number of notches lever travels. If lever travel meets specifications, do not adjust parking brake. Pickup models require adjustment of service brakes before adjusting parking brake. On all other models, except Supra, if parking brake requires adjustment, first set brake shoe-to-drum clearance by depressing release knob on parking brake lever and operating lever several times. Recheck lever travel.

Celica, Corolla & Starlet — If parking brake lever travel is not 3-6 notches, remove console (if equipped), release parking brake, loosen lock nut and turn adjusting screw on lever until lever travel is correct. Tighten lock nut and install console (if equipped). Wheels should be locked when parking brake is applied and rotate freely when lever is released.

Corona — If parking brake lever travel is not 3-7 notches, release parking brake, loosen lock nut on turnbuckle (under vehicle) and rotate turnbuckle until travel is correct. Tighten lock nut. Wheels should be locked when parking brake is applied and rotate freely when lever is released.

Cressida — If parking brake lever travel is not 5-7 notches, release parking brake and loosen lock nut on turnbuckle located under vehicle on right cable. Rotate turnbuckle until .39" (10 mm) of threaded cable end is inside turnbuckle. Tighten lock nut. Remove slack from rear cables by loosening lock nut on equalizer and turning adjusting nut. Tighten lock nut. Wheels should be locked when parking brake is applied and rotate freely when lever is released.

Land Cruiser — Fully release parking brake and turn adjusting cam on back of backing plate (at rear of transfer case) until brake shoes seat against drum. Back off adjusting cam 1 notch at a time until drum locks when parking brake is applied and spins freely when released. After adjusting brake shoes, adjust parking brake travel to 12 notches by turning cable adjusting nut or turnbuckle. Wheels should be locked when parking brake is applied and rotate freely when lever is released.

Brakes

TOYOTA (Cont.)

Pickup — **1)** If parking brake lever travel is not 7-15 notches, adjust parking brake, AFTER adjusting service brakes. To adjust parking brake on 2-WD models, release parking brake and turn adjusting nut on intermediate lever (under vehicle) until lever travel is correct. Wheels should be locked when parking brake is applied and rotate freely when lever is released.

2) To adjust parking brake on 4-WD models, release parking brake and loosen lock nut stopper screw on operating lever on rear of backing plate. Turn stopper screw until no play is evident at operating lever. Tighten stopper screw lock nut, then tighten 1 adjusting nut on intermediate lever while loosening other nut until lever travel is correct. Tighten both adjusting nuts. After lever travel is correct, operating lever stopper screw MUST contact backing plate when lever is released.

Supra — If parking brake lever travel is not 5-8 notches, release parking brake and depress brake pedal 2-3 times. Check parking brake lever travel. If travel is not correct, release parking brake lever, loosen turnbuckle lock nut located under vehicle on right cable and rotate turnbuckle to put slack in cable. Tighten turnbuckle until parking brake operating lever on rear caliper begins to move. Tighten turnbuckle lock nut. Check parking brake operation.

NOTE — *With either operating lever pushed away from caliper, it should not move when opposite operating lever is pushed away from caliper. If it does, cable is too tight and parking brake must be readjusted.*

Tercel — If parking brake lever travel is not 2-5 notches, release parking brake and loosen lock nut on equalizer (under vehicle). Turn adjusting nut until lever travel is correct. Wheels should be locked when parking brake is applied and rotate freely when lever is released.

STOP LIGHT SWITCH

Stop light switch is located under dash, above brake pedal. To adjust, loosen lock nuts and adjust switch so contact button just touches brake pedal. Tighten lock nut and check pedal height.

BRAKE WARNING LIGHT

A dual warning light is mounted on dash of all vehicles except Pickups (single warning light). On all models, light should glow when parking brake lever is pulled 1 notch and go off when lever is fully released (ignition on). To check circuit warning on all models except Pickups, release parking brake (ignition on) and ensure light is off. Open bleed screw on 1 wheel and depress brake pedal; light should glow. Close bleed screw, replenish brake fluid and bleed hydraulic system.

LOAD SENSING PROPORTIONING VALVE (LAND CRUISER & PICKUPS, EXCEPT ½ TON)

1) Set rear axle load (including vehicle weight) to 1433 lbs. (650 kg) on 4WD pickup, to 2646 lbs. (1150 kg) on Land Cruiser and 1323 lbs. (600 kg) on all others. Install a load proportioning gauge (09705-29017 or 09709-29017) to front caliper and another to rear wheel cylinder on same side of vehicle.

2) Depress brake pedal and raise pressure on front gauge to 711 psi (50 kg/cm²). Do NOT depress brake pedal more than 1

time and do not release pedal while setting front pressure reeading. After 2 seconds, rear brake pressure should be 398-540 psi (28-38 kg/cm²) on pickups and 498-611 psi (35-45 kg/cm²) on Land Cruiser.

3) Depress brake pedal further and raise front brake pressure to 1138 psi (80 kg/cm²) on pickups and 1422 psi (100 kg/cm²) on Land Cruiser. Rear brake pressure should be 525-725 psi (37-51 kg/cm²) on pickups and 725-925 (51-65 kg/cm²) on Land Cruiser.

4) If pressure readings do not meet specifications, adjust load sensing proportioning valve by adjusting length of lower shackle. See *Fig. 2*. If rear pressure was low, lengthen distance "A". If rear pressure was high, shorten distance. Repeat test procedure and check pressure readings.

NOTE — *Turning the lower shackle 1 turn changes pressure reading 8.5 psi (.6 kg/cm²).*

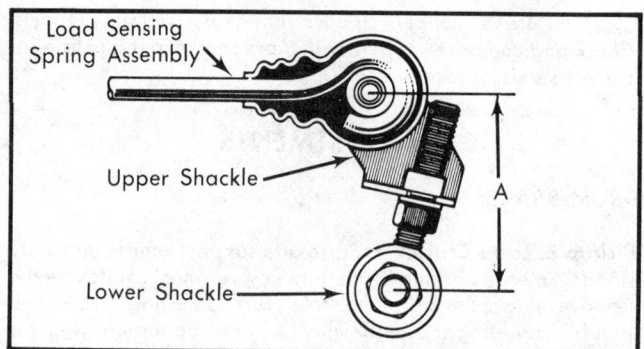

Fig. 2   Adjusting Load Sensing Proportioning Valve

5) If rear pressures do not conform to specifications after adjusting lower shackle, loosen valve body retaining nuts and reposition valve body. If rear pressure was high, raise valve body. If pressure was low, lower valve body. Tighten nuts and adjust length of lower shackle to standard length.

6) Standard length for 4WD pickup should be 4.72" (120 mm) and 3.07" (78 mm) for all other models. Repeat test procedure and check pressures. If pressures do not meet specifications, position valve body in upper most position and depress brake pedal to obtain readings shown on Load Sensing Proportioning Valve Specifications table. If measured value does not meet specifications shown in table, replace valve assembly.

Load Sensing Proportioning Valve Specifications

Front Reading psi (kg/cm²)	Rear Reading psi (kg/cm²)
Pickup	
71 (5)	71 (5)
711 (50)	280-337 (19.7-23.7)
1138 (80)	424-509 (29.8-35.8)
Land Cruiser	
71 (5)	71 (5)
365 (25)	148-205 (10.4-14.4)
835 (60)	312-411 (21.9-28.9)

TOYOTA (Cont.)

REMOVAL & INSTALLATION

NOTE — *Front disc calipers used on Toyota vehicles may vary between manufacturer and model. Refer to appropriate illustrations to assist in identification of caliper.*

FRONT DISC BRAKE PADS

Removal ("F" Type) — Raise and support vehicle. Remove tire and wheel. Remove spring clips and guide. Remove cylinder and suspend out of way without disconnecting hydraulic lines. Remove anti-squeal spring. Remove brake pads and guide plates. Remove anti-rattle springs and pad support plates.

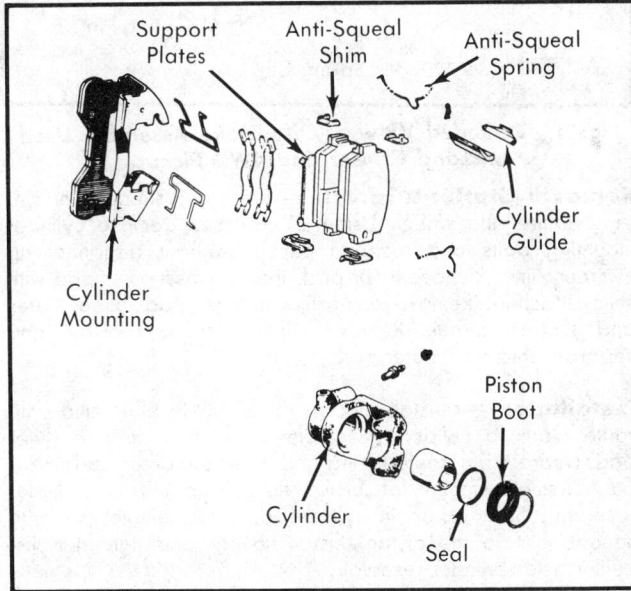

Fig. 3 Exploded View of "F" Type Disc Brake Used on Celica and Supra

Installation — Install support plates. Install pad guide plates and anti-rattle springs. Install brake pads and anti-squeal

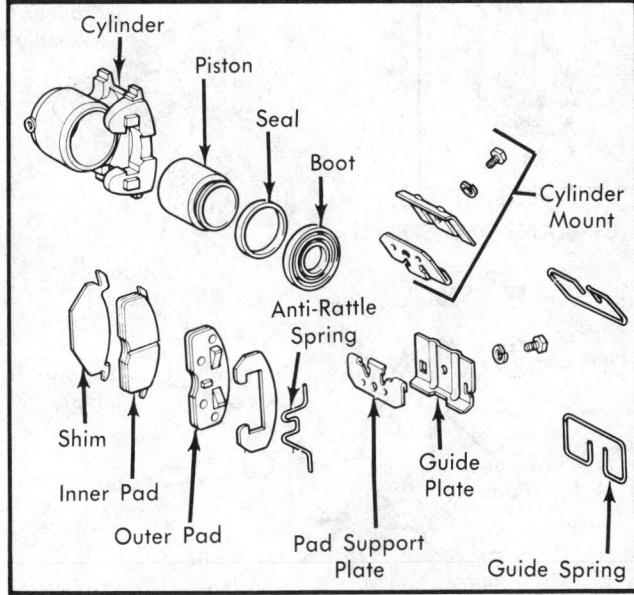

Fig. 4 Exploded View of "K" Type Disc Brake Used on Cab and Chassis Pickup

shims. Install cylinder over brake pads. Install cylinder guides and clips. Apply grease to cylinder guides.

Removal ("K" Type) — Raise and support vehicle; remove tire and wheel. Remove guide plates, support springs and pad support plates. Remove cylinder with outer pad attached and suspend from frame without disconnecting hydraulic line. Remove outer pad anti-rattle spring. Remove outer pad and shim (if equipped). Remove inner pad and shim (if equipped) from cylinder mount. See *Fig. 4*.

Installation — Clean piston and cylinder assembly, then seat piston in cylinder bore, opening bleed screw if necessary. Install inner pad and shim (if equipped) to cylinder mount. Install outer pad, shim (if equipped) and anti-rattle spring on cylinder. Apply brake grease to cylinder guides. Install cylinder (with outer pad installed) over inner pad, then install pad support plates, support springs and guide plates.

NOTE — *Larger side of support springs MUST face away from vehicle.*

Removal (Girling) — Raise and support vehicle; remove tire and wheel. Remove clip, pins, anti-rattle spring, pads and shims.

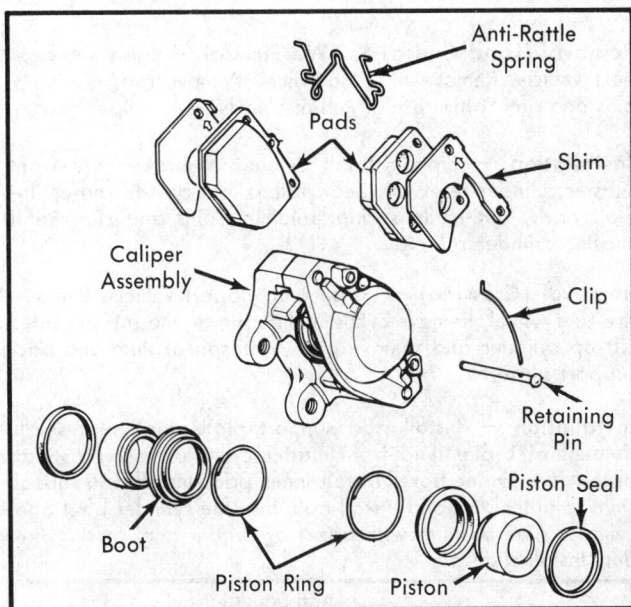

Fig. 5 Exploded View of Girling Type Disc Brake Used on Corona and Standard Pickups

NOTE — *Install anti-squeal shim on piston side only.*

Installation — Coat both sides of shim with brake grease. Remove small amount of brake fluid from master cylinder reservoir. Push pistons into cylinder bore. Install shims with arrows pointing in direction of forward rotation of disc. Install pads, springs, pins and clips. Refill master cylinder reservoir.

Removal & Installation (Corolla) — Raise and support vehicle; remove tire and wheel. Remove pad protector, anti-rattle springs, spring pins, pad and shims (if equipped). Clean dirt from pin portion of torque plate. To install, clean piston assembly and seat piston in cylinder bore. Insert pads and shims (if equipped). Install retaining pins, anti-rattle springs and protector.

TOYOTA (Cont.)

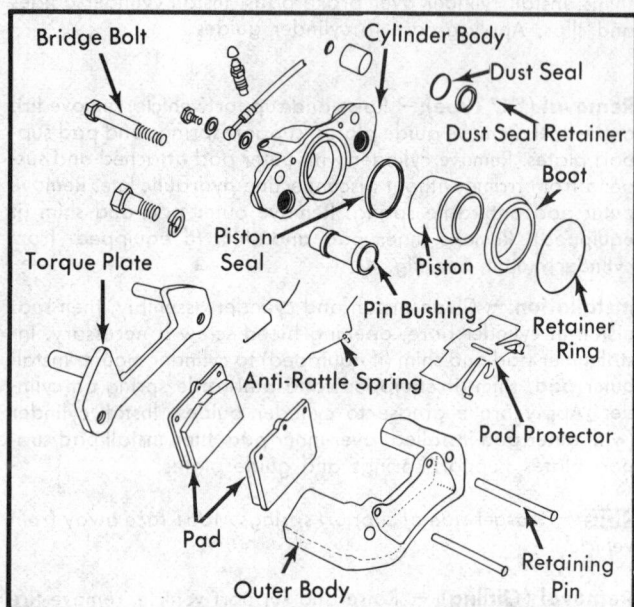

Fig. 6 Exploded View of Toyota or Sumitomo Type Disc Brake Used on Corolla

Removal (Land Cruiser & 4WD Pickup) — Raise and support vehicle. Remove tire and wheel. Remove clip, retaining pins and anti-rattle spring. Pull disc pads from caliper cavity.

Installation — Siphon small amount of brake fluid from master cylinder reservoir. Seat pistons into cylinder bores. Install pads, anti-rattle spring, retaining pins and clip. Refill master cylinder reservoir.

Removal (Cressida) — Raise and support vehicle. Remove tire and wheel. Remove cylinder slide pin on the sub pin side. Lift up cylinder and remove pads, anti-squeal shim and pad support plate.

Installation — Install pad support plate. Siphon a small amount of brake fluid from master cylinder reservoir. Seat piston in cylinder bore. Install inner pad. Install anti-squeal shim to outer pad and install pad. Insulate cylinder boot and cylinder slide bushing with paper or rubber and lower cylinder. Install slide pin.

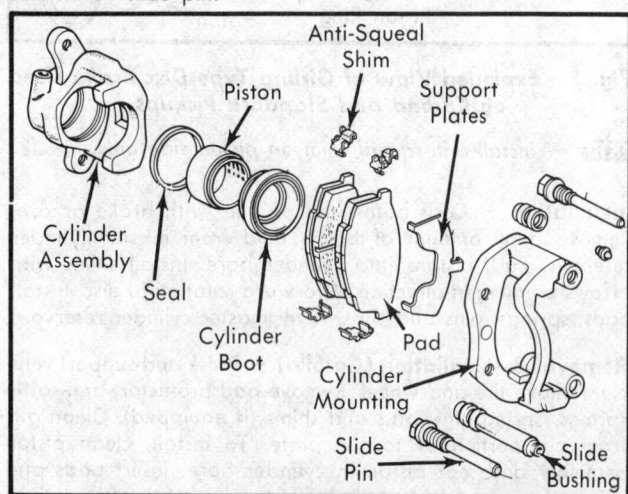

Fig. 7 Exploded View of Cressida Disc Brake

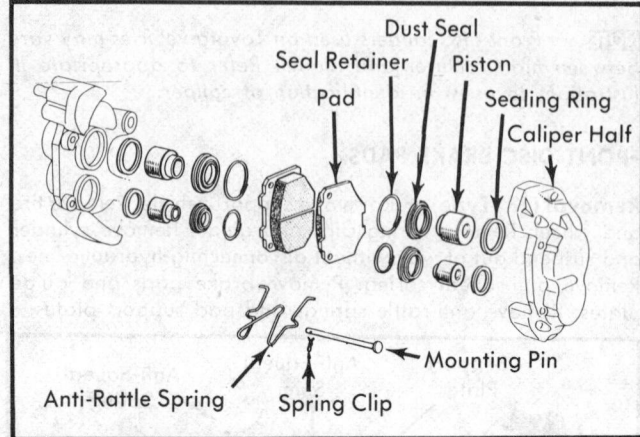

Fig. 8 Exploded View of Disc Brake Assembly Used on Land Cruiser and 4WD Pickup

Removal (Starlet & Tercel) — Raise and support vehicle; remove tire and wheel. Using 2 wrenches, remove cylinder mounting bolts and suspend caliper without disconnecting hydraulic line. Remove inner pad, then remove outer pad with shim attached. Remove anti-rattle springs, pad guide plates and support plates. Remove inner shim from piston and separate shim from outer pad.

Installation — Install support plate, guide plate and anti-rattle plate to caliper. Assemble anti-squeal shim to outer pad. Depress anti-rattle spring and assemble outer pad. Draw out a small amount of brake fluid from master cylinder reservoir. Seat piston in cylinder bore. Assemble the anti-squeal shim to the piston. Install caliper and tighten bolts. Refill master cylinder reservoir.

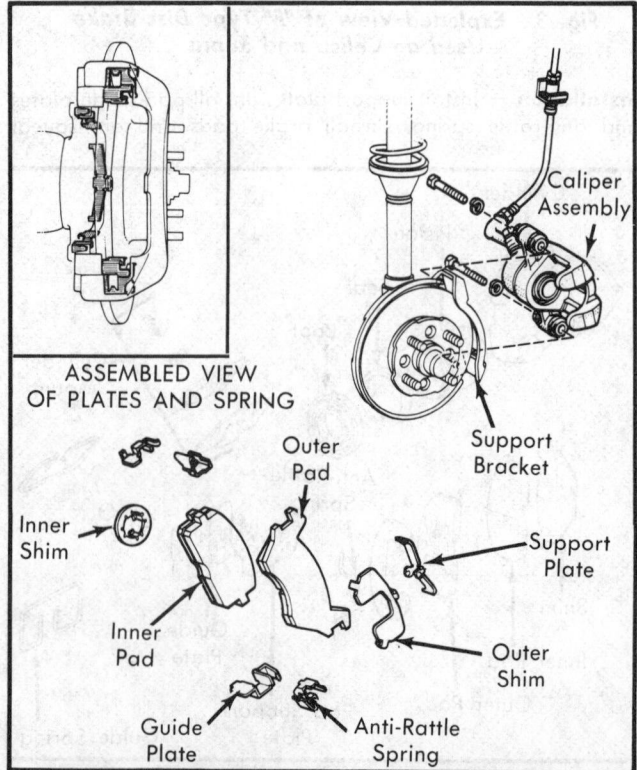

Fig. 9 Exploded View of Toyota Disc Brake Used on Starlet and Tercel

TOYOTA (Cont.)

FRONT DISC BRAKE CALIPER

Removal & Installation ("F" Type) — Raise and support vehicle; remove tire and wheel. Remove spring clips and guide plates. Disconnect hydraulic line and remove caliper. Remove brake pads as previously outlined. To install, apply brake grease to guides and reverse removal procedure. Bleed hydraulic system.

Removal & Installation ("K" Type) — Raise and support vehicle; remove tire and wheel. Disconnect hydraulic line and remove brake pads as previously outlined. Remove caliper. To install, reverse removal procedure and bleed hydraulic system.

Removal & Installation (Cressida, Starlet & Tercel) — Raise and support vehicle. Remove tire and wheel. Disconnect hydraulic line and remove caliper mounting bolts. Slide caliper off mounting bracket. To install, apply rubber grease to retaining pin dust boots and bushings. Reverse removal procedures and install caliper with NEW pins. Bleed hydraulic system.

Removal & Installation (All Others) — Raise and support vehicle; remove tire and wheel. Remove brake pads as previously outlined. Disconnect hydraulic line. Remove caliper mounting bolts and lift off caliper. To install, reverse removal procedure and ensure mounting bolts are tightened. Bleed hydraulic system.

FRONT DISC BRAKE ROTOR

Removal (Land Cruiser & 4WD Pickup) — Raise and support vehicle. Remove wheel and caliper assembly. Remove hub grease cap and snap ring. Remove free wheel nuts. Using a tapered punch, tap on slits of cone washers to remove. Remove free hub. Remove axle hub and disc.

NOTE — *Free wheel hub control handle must be set to "FREE" position for removal.*

Installation — To install, reverse removal procedure. Adjust wheel bearings. See *Wheel Bearing Adjustment in SUSPENSION Section.*

Removal (Tercel — 1) Raise and support vehicle; remove tire and wheel. Remove cotter pin and castellated cap. Depress brake pedal and loosen bearing lock nut. Remove caliper assembly as previously described and suspend from frame without disconnecting hydraulic line.

2) Disconnect tie rod end using remover (09610-20011). Using a jack, raise left lower arm assembly. Remove stabilizer bar and strut bar from lower arm. Remove bolt securing lower arm to crossmember and disconnect lower arm from crossmember.

3) Remove bearing lock nut and washer. Using puller (09950-20013), pull hub from drive axle shaft. Remove shock absorber-to-steering knuckle retaining bolt. Separate shock absorber from knuckle. Remove steering knuckle and hub assembly from vehicle with lower arm attached.

NOTE — *Before removing hub assembly, suspend drive axle shaft up so it does not fall or become damaged.*

4) Separate lower arm from steering knuckle. Remove inner dust shield and remove oil seal. Using hub remover (09608-16031), force hub out of steering knuckle. Place alignment

marks on hub and rotor for reassembly reference. Remove hub-to-rotor bolts and separate hub from rotor.

Installation— 1) Install new outer bearing if removed and adjust bearing preload. *See Wheel Bearing Adjustment in SUSPENSION Section.* Align marks made during removal and install hub to rotor. Tighten hub-to-rotor bolts evenly. Install spacer in steering knuckle, then install inner bearing and race.

2) Using installer (09636-20010), press steering knuckle onto hub with 2205 lbs. (1000 kg) of pressure. With pressure still applied, rotate steering knuckle to settle bearings. Using a spring pull scale, measure frictional force of steering knuckle with pressure still applied. Frictional force should be 13-26 ozs. (370-750 g).

3) Increase pressure to 7716 lbs. (3500 kg), rotate steering knuckle to settle bearings and measure frictional force. Force should be 13-40 ozs. (370-1120 g). If frictional force is not to specification, insert thinner spacer to raise force or thicker spacer to lower force.

4) Tap oil seal into steering knuckle until it is recessed .16" (4 mm) from end of steering knuckle. Install dust shield and coat oil seal lip with multi-purpose grease. Attach lower arm to steering knuckle. Place steering knuckle and lower arm into position and insert drive axle shaft into hub assembly. Attach steering knuckle to shock absorber. Loosely install bearing washer and lock nut.

5) Loosely install strut bar to lower arm. Align stopper on shock absorber with steering knuckle. Raise lower arm with a jack until steering knuckle contacts shock absorber stopper. Attach lower arm to crossmember and loosely install retaining bolt. Insert bolt to retain steering knuckle to shock absorber and tighten.

6) Connect stabilizer bar to lower arm and tighten nut. Connect and tighten tie rod to steering knuckle. Install disc brake caliper, depress brake pedal and tighten axle nut. Bounce vehicle several times to settle suspension, then tighten lower arm-to-crossmember bolt and strut bar with vehicle weight resting on suspension system. Check front alignment. See *WHEEL ALIGNMENT Section.*

Removal & Installation (All Others) — Raise and support vehicle. Remove tire and wheel. Remove caliper. Remove hub grease cap, cotter pin, washer and castellated nut. Carefully remove outer wheel bearing. Remove rotor and hub assembly and place alignment marks on rotor and hub for reassembly reference. Remove hub-to-rotor bolts and separate hub from rotor. To install, reverse removal procedure. Adjust wheel bearings. See *Wheel Bearing Adjustment in SUSPENSION Section.*

REAR DISC BRAKE PADS

Removal — Raise and support vehicle; remove wheel. Remove parking brake cable from brake lever. Remove cylinder guides and plates. Remove cylinder and hang out of way. DO NOT let cylinder hang by hydraulic line. Remove pad springs, shims and springs. Remove anti-rattle springs, pad guide plates and pad support plates.

Installation — Preset piston before installing pads by pushing and turning piston clockwise until it retracts into cylinder body. Install pad support plates, pad guide plates and anti-rattle springs. Install pads, shims and springs. Install cylinder, guides and plates. Install parking brake cable.

TOYOTA (Cont.)

NOTE — *Piston stopper groove and inner pad protrusion must be aligned.*

REAR DISC BRAKE CALIPER

Removal & Installation — Raise and support vehicle; remove wheel. Remove parking brake cable from brake lever. Remove cylinder guides and plates. Remove and plug hydraulic line at cylinder. Remove cylinder and mount. To install, reverse removal procedure and bleed brake system.

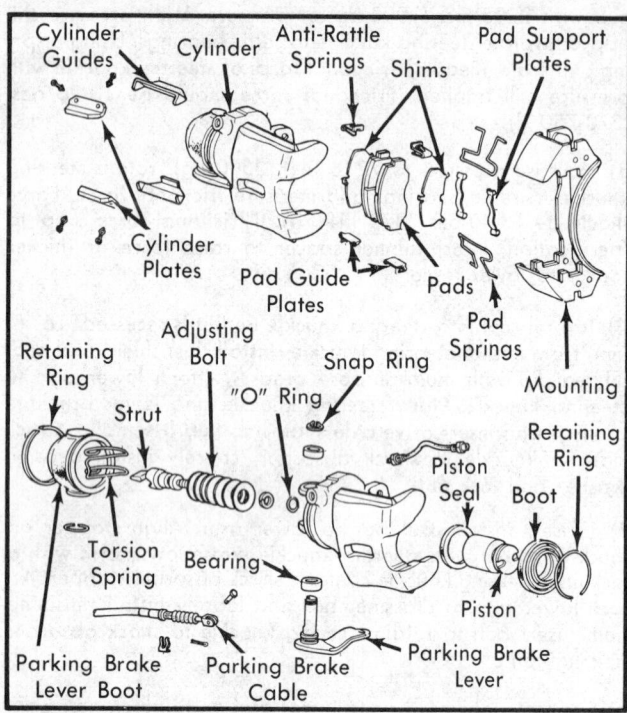

Fig. 10 Exploded View Supra Rear Disc Brake

REAR DISC BRAKE ROTOR

Removal & Installation — With wheel and caliper removed, slide rotor off axle flange. To install, reverse removal procedure and bleed brake system.

REAR BRAKE DRUM

Removal (All Models) — Raise and support vehicle; remove wheel. Remove set screws from brake drum (if equipped). Pull drum from axle flange. It may be necessary to loosen brake adjustment before removing drum.

Installation — On all models (except Land Cruiser) set brake shoe-to-drum clearance by measuring inside diameter of brake drum and diameter of brake shoes. Turn brake adjuster until difference between diameters is .02" (.6 mm). Install brake drum and adjust brakes if required.

BRAKE SHOES

Removal (Standard Pickup) — With brake drum removed, remove adjuster spring and adjuster. Remove front hold down spring and pin, then remove front shoe and anchor spring. Remove rear hold down spring and pin and remove rear shoe. Remove adjusting strut and spring from adjusting lever. Disconnect parking brake cable from lever. Using a screwdriver, remove "C" washers retaining parking brake lever and adjuster lever to rear shoe. Remove levers from shoe.

Installation — To install, reverse removal procedure and note the following: Install parking brake lever and adjuster lever to rear shoe with new "C" washers. After installation of brake assembly, move adjuster back and forth and ensure adjusting bolt moves. If not, check installation of brake assembly. Bleed hydraulic system.

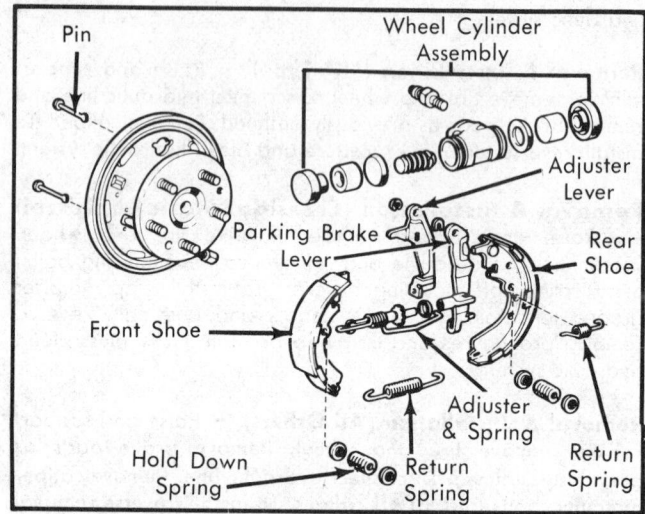

Fig. 11 Exploded View of Standard Pickup Rear Brake

Removal (Land Cruiser) — With brake drum removed, remove tensioner spring. Remove hold down pins and clips. Remove return springs and remove brake shoes.

Installation — Position brake shoes over wheel cylinders with front return spring hooked on inner side of shoe. Install rear return spring to outer side of shoe. Install hold down pins and clips. Adjust and bleed brakes.

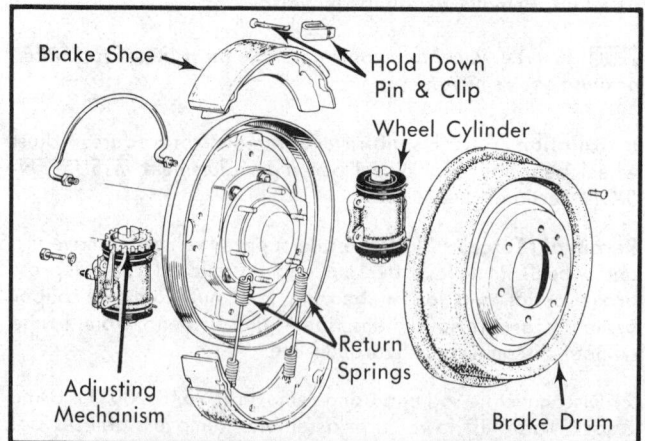

Fig. 12 Exploded View of Land Cruiser Rear Brake

Removal (Cab & Chassis Pickup & 4WD Pickup) — With brake drum removed, remove upper return springs. Remove adjuster cable, cable guide, adjuster lever and anchor plate. Remove adjuster lever tension spring and strut. Remove hold down springs and pins. Pull brake shoes from backing plate and separate adjusting mechanism and return spring. Disconnect parking brake cable from lever. Mount rear shoe in vise and remove "C" washer retaining parking brake lever to shoe. Remove parking brake lever.

Installation — To install, reverse removal procedure and note the following: Adjuster mechanisms are not interchangeable. Left-hand thread — right wheel; right-hand thread — left

TOYOTA (Cont.)

wheel. After installation of brake assembly, pull adjusting cable backward and release; adjusting bolt should move. If not, check installation of brake assembly. Install drum and adjust brakes.

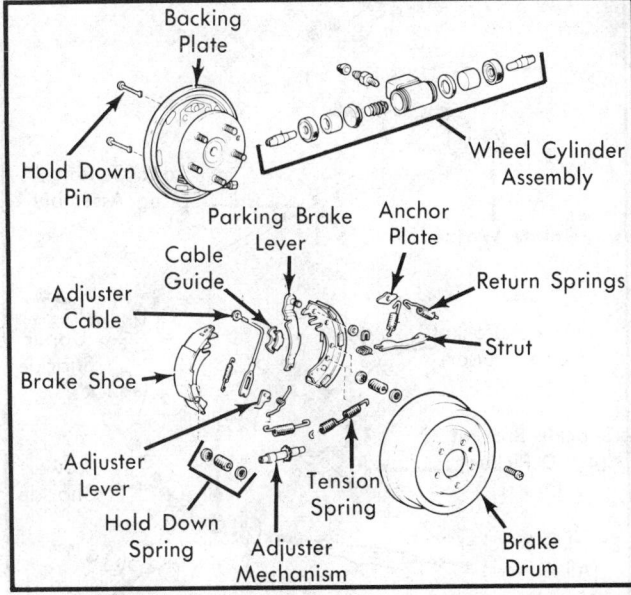

Fig. 13 Exploded View of Cab and Chassis and 4WD Pickup Rear Brake

Removal (Starlet and Tercel) — With brake drum removed, remove return spring. Remove hold down springs and pins. Disconnect front shoe from parking brake strut and disconnect lower spring. Remove front shoe. Disconnect parking brake lever return spring. Remove rear shoe from backing plate and disconnect parking brake cable from lever. Remove "C" washer retaining parking brake lever and adjusting lever to rear shoe, then remove levers from rear shoe. Remove "C" washer retaining parking brake lever on adjusting lever and separate levers.

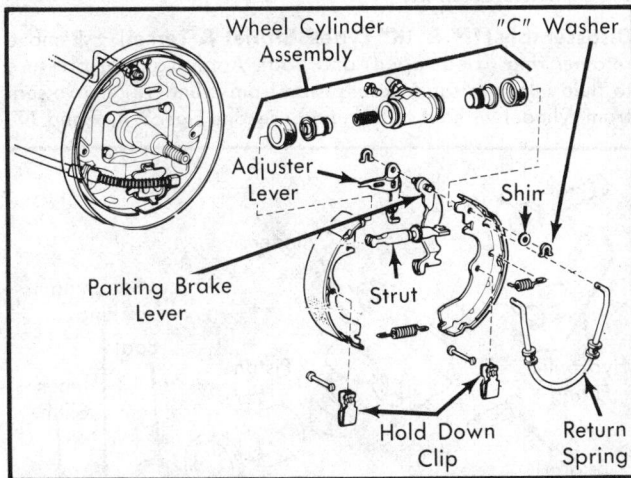

Fig. 14 Exploded View of Tercel Rear Brake (Starlet Similar)

Installation — **1)** Install parking brake lever onto adjusting lever with NEW "C" washer. Install lever assembly on rear shoe and retain in position temporarily with NEW "C" washer. Measure clearance between adjusting lever and rear of shoe.

Remove "C" washer and install correct shim(s) which will give a clearance of 0-.014" (0-.35 mm). Install and stake "C" washer and ensure lever moves.

2) Complete installation by reversing removal procedure and note the following: Adjuster mechanisms are not interchangeable. Left-hand thread — left wheel; right-hand thread — right wheel. Install drum and bleed hydraulic system.

NOTE — Shims are available in 6 sizes: .008" (.2 mm), .012" (.3 mm), .016" (.4 mm), .020" (.5 mm), .024" (.6 mm) and .035" (.9 mm). Shims may be installed in pairs to provide proper clearance.

Removal (All Others) — With brake drum removed, remove hold down pins and clips. Remove anchor spring and return spring. Remove front shoe and adjuster strut. Remove parking brake cable from parking brake lever. Remove rear shoe, parking brake lever and adjusting lever as an assembly. Remove "C" washer retaining parking brake lever and adjusting lever to rear shoe and separate levers from shoe.

Installation — Install adjusting lever and parking brake lever to rear shoe with NEW "C" washer. Measure clearance between lever and shoe. Remove "C" washer and install correct shim(s) which will give a clearance of 0-.014" (0-.35 mm). Install and stake "C" washer and ensure lever moves. Complete installation by reversing removal procedure and note the following: Adjuster mechanisms are not interchangeable. Left-hand thread — right wheel; right-hand thread — left wheel. Install drum and bleed hydraulic system.

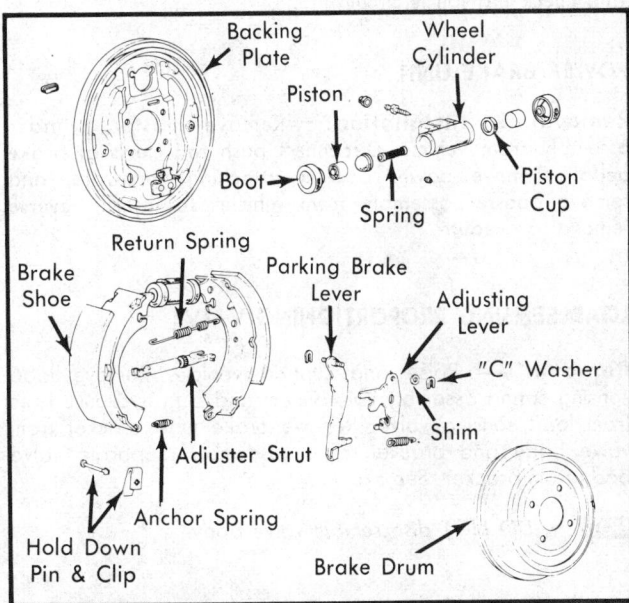

Fig. 15 Exploded View of Rear Brake Used on Celica, Corolla, Corona and Cressida

REAR BRAKE WHEEL CYLINDER

Removal (All Drum Brake Models) — With brake drum and shoes removed, disconnect hydraulic line from wheel cylinder. Remove mounting bolts and remove wheel cylinder.

Installation — To install, reverse removal procedure. Adjusting mechanisims on many models are not interchangable. Install adjusting mechanisim to the wheel from which it was removed.

TOYOTA (Cont.)

PARKING BRAKE

Removal (Land Cruiser) — Drain oil from transfer case. Disconnect front of drive shaft and wire out-of-way. Remove drum mounting nut and slide drum off splines. Remove return springs and tension springs, then take off hold down springs and pins. Disconnect parking brake cable from shoes.

Installation — To install, reverse removal procedure and note: Make sure lower tension spring is installed so it lies between back plate and shoes. Refill transfer case with 1.8 quarts of SAE 90. Tighten drum mounting nut and adjust parking brake.

MASTER CYLINDER

Removal & Installation — Disconnect electrical lead (if equipped). Disconnect and plug hydraulic lines. Remove master cylinder-to-power brake unit mounting nuts. Remove master cylinder. To install, reverse removal procedures and bleed brake system.

VACUUM PUMP

Removal (Cressida & Land Cruiser) — Disconnect vacuum line from pump assembly. Disconnect and plug oil lines. Remove mounting nuts and gently pry pump off studs. Tap with a plastic hammer if necessary.

Installation — To install, reverse removal procedure and note: Run engine at idle speed. Loosen screw at vacuum pump outlet and check that oil is circulating.

POWER BRAKE UNIT

Removal & Installation — Remove master cylinder assembly from vehicle. Disconnect push rod clevis at brake pedal. Remove power booster attaching hardware, and remove booster assembly from vehicle. To install, reverse removal procedure.

LOAD SENSING PROPORTIONING VALVE

Removal — Raise and support vehicle. Remove load sensing spring assembly. Disconnect and plug hydraulic lines from load sensing valve. Remove brake tube bracket from valve body and bracket as an assembly. Separate valve body from bracket. *See Fig. 16.*

NOTE — *DO NOT disassemble valve body.*

Installation — Wipe parts and inspect for rust or damage. Inspect valve piston pin and load sensing contact surface for wear (bottom of valve). Replace as an assembly if wear exceeds .028" (.7 mm). To install, reverse removal procedure and note the following: Apply rubber grease to all rubbing areas. Install new rubber plate on valve body side of spring. Adjust length of upper and lower shackle to original height. After installation, position valve body so valve piston lightly contacts load sensing spring. Bleed hydraulic system and check brake pressures.

NOTE — *DO NOT mistake valve side of load sensing spring for shackle side.*

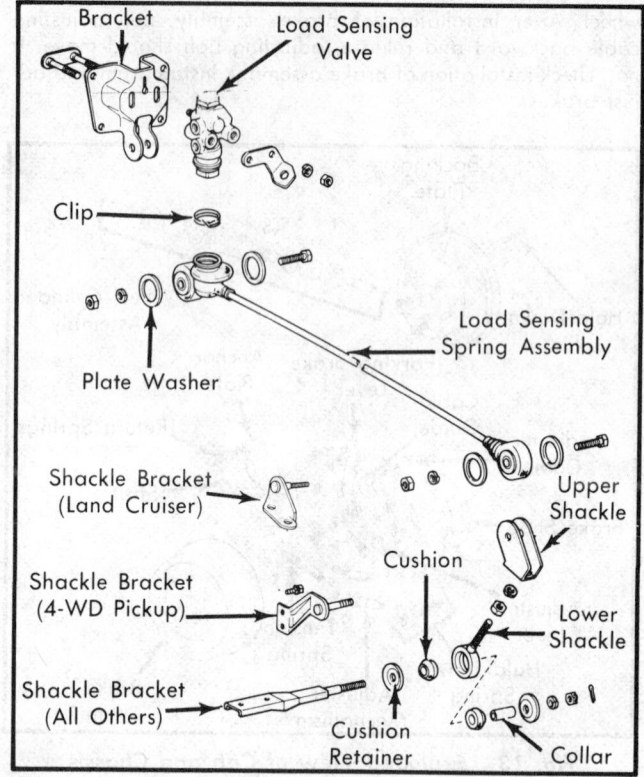

Fig. 16 Exploded View of Load Sensing Proportioning Valve

OVERHAUL

NOTE — *When overhauling caliper, wheel cylinder, or master cylinder assemblies, all rubber components should be replaced. If cylinder bores in any part are pitted, or scored more than light honing will repair, entire assembly should be replaced.*

DISC BRAKE CALIPER

Disassembly ("F" & "K" Types, Starlet & Tercel) — Remove retainer ring (if equipped) and boot. Apply light air pressure to fluid inlet port and expel piston from cylinder. Remove seal from cylinder without damaging bore. See Figs. 3, 4, 9 and 17.

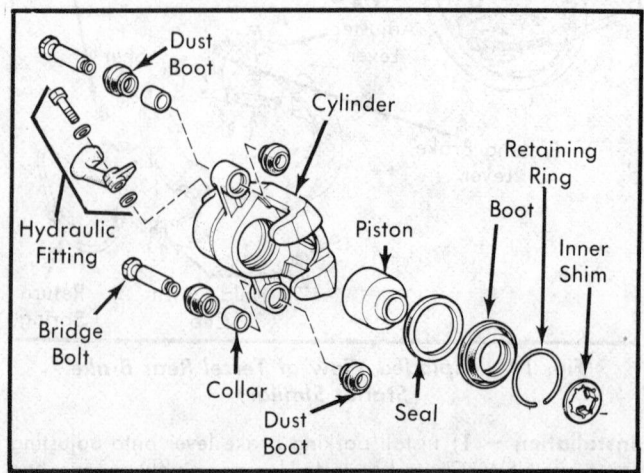

Fig. 17 Exploded View of Starlet and Tercel Caliper Assembly

TOYOTA (Cont.)

Cleaning & Inspection — Clean all parts in clean brake fluid. Inspect bore and piston for excessive wear or damage; replace defective parts.

Reassembly — Coat piston, seal and cylinder bore with rubber grease before reassembly. To reassemble, reverse disassembly procedure and note the following: On "K" type, install seal, fit boot to piston, then fit boot to cylinder and push piston into cylinder bore.

Disassembly (Corolla) — Loosen both bridge bolts (caliper half mounting bolts) and separate cylinder casting from outer body. Pull out torque plate. Remove retainer ring and boot. Force light air pressure through fluid inlet port and expel piston. From caliper, remove following: Piston seal, bushings, hole plug, retainers and dust seals. *See Fig. 6.*

Cleaning & Inspection — Clean all parts in alcohol or clean brake fluid. Inspect parts for excessive wear or damage; replace defective parts. If torque plate pins are excessively worn or if pin weld parts are abnormally corroded, caliper must be replaced.

Reassembly — 1) Ensure torque plate pins and bushing bores are clean and coat with grease furnished in repair kit. Coat piston seals and cylinder bore with rubber grease. Fit dust seal, retainers and bushings to cylinder.

2) Fit piston seal on cylinder and push piston in by hand. Install dust boot and ring. Reassemble torque plate pins in cylinder body. Make sure torque plate is free to slide smoothly. Install bridge bolts and tighten.

Disassembly (Land Cruiser & 4WD Pickup) — Remove dust seal retainer ring and seal. Insert small block of wood into cylinder cavity. Apply light air pressure to one side of cylinder to expel pistons; repeat on opposite side. Remove piston seals without damaging bores. *See Fig. 8.*

NOTE — *DO NOT separate caliper halves.*

Cleaning & Inspection — Clean all parts in clean brake fluid. Inspect pistons and cylinder bores for excessive wear, damage or corrosion; replace defective parts.

Reassembly — Lightly coat all parts with rubber grease Insert new piston seal, being careful that seals properly enter grooves. Fit piston and slide dust seal into position. With dust seal seated, fit retainer ring.

Disassembly (All Others) — Remove dust boot retainer ring and dust boot. Insert small wooden block between pistons and apply light air pressure to fluid inlet port to expel pistons. Remove seals without damaging bores. *See Fig. 5.*

NOTE — *DO NOT separate caliper halves.*

Cleaning & Inspection — Clean all parts in clean brake fluid. Inspect bores and pistons for excessive wear or damage; replace defective parts.

Reassembly — Coat piston seals, cylinder bores and pistons with brake grease. To reassemble, reverse disassembly procedure.

Disassembly (Supra Rear Caliper) — 1) Remove dust boot retaining ring and boot. Remove piston by turning it counterclockwise with remover (09719-14010). Remove piston seal from cylinder groove without damage to cylinder bore. *See Fig. 10.*

2) Remove retaining ring from parking brake lever boot. Pull boot back over parking brake lever and remove shaft retaining ring. Using arbor press and suitable remover (09719-14010), remove parking brake lever; separate boot from lever.

3) Remove torsion spring and strut. Mount caliper assembly in padded vise and remove bearings. Separate components and arrange for reassembly reference.

Cleaning & Inspection — Wash all parts in clean brake fluid. Inspect all parts for excessive wear, damage or corrosion; replace defective parts.

Reassembly — 1) Coat all parts with rubber grease. Install bearings. Fit new "O" ring and spring washer on adjusting bolt. Ensure "O" ring and washer do not touch. Install adjusting bolt and strut into bore with strut against raised side of bolt. Strut must be angled toward torsion spring retaining pin. Install torsion spring with formed loop seated around retaining pin.

2) Fit rubber boot to parking brake lever. Install parking brake lever with arbor press and suitable tool (09719-14010). Install shaft retaining ring. Pull boot over lever assembly and install retaining ring.

3) Install piston seal into cylinder bore. Install piston into cylinder bore by turning it clockwise with suitable installer (09719-14010J). Align piston with piston stopper groove; install dust boot and retaining ring.

MASTER CYLINDER

Disassembly — Remove reservoir(s), hose, and switches (if equipped). Mount cylinder in a soft-jawed vise. Remove dust boot and check valves. Push pistons into cylinder bore and remove stop bolt. Remove snap ring and withdraw piston assemblies. Remove unions, outlet plugs and other external components. Disassemble piston assemblies by removing springs, retainers and cups. *See Fig. 18.*

Cleaning & Inspection — Wash all parts in clean brake fluid and inspect for wear, damage or corrosion. Replace defective parts as required.

Reassembly — To reassemble, reverse disassembly procedure using all new rubber parts and lubricating all components with clean brake fluid.

VACUUM PUMP

Disassembly (Cressida & Land Cruiser) — Drive dowel pins from end cover toward case. Separate end cover. Continue to drive dowels through case and stop when flush with end frame. Remove end frame with pins still fitted. Remove both "O" rings and discard. Slide rotor and blades from case.

Inspection — Inspect end cover and casing for damage or wear. Casing bore must not be worn beyond 2.29" (5.8 mm). Check rotor-to-valve shaft spline play. Rotor wear must not exceed .095" (2.4 mm). Inspect rotor blades for the following wear limits. Height .46" (11.6 mm); length 1.374" (34.91 mm); width .272" (6.9 mm). Check end frame bushing and oil seal. Bushing bore must not exceed .635" (16.44 mm). Replace oil seal by prying out and pressing in new one.

Brakes

TOYOTA (Cont.)

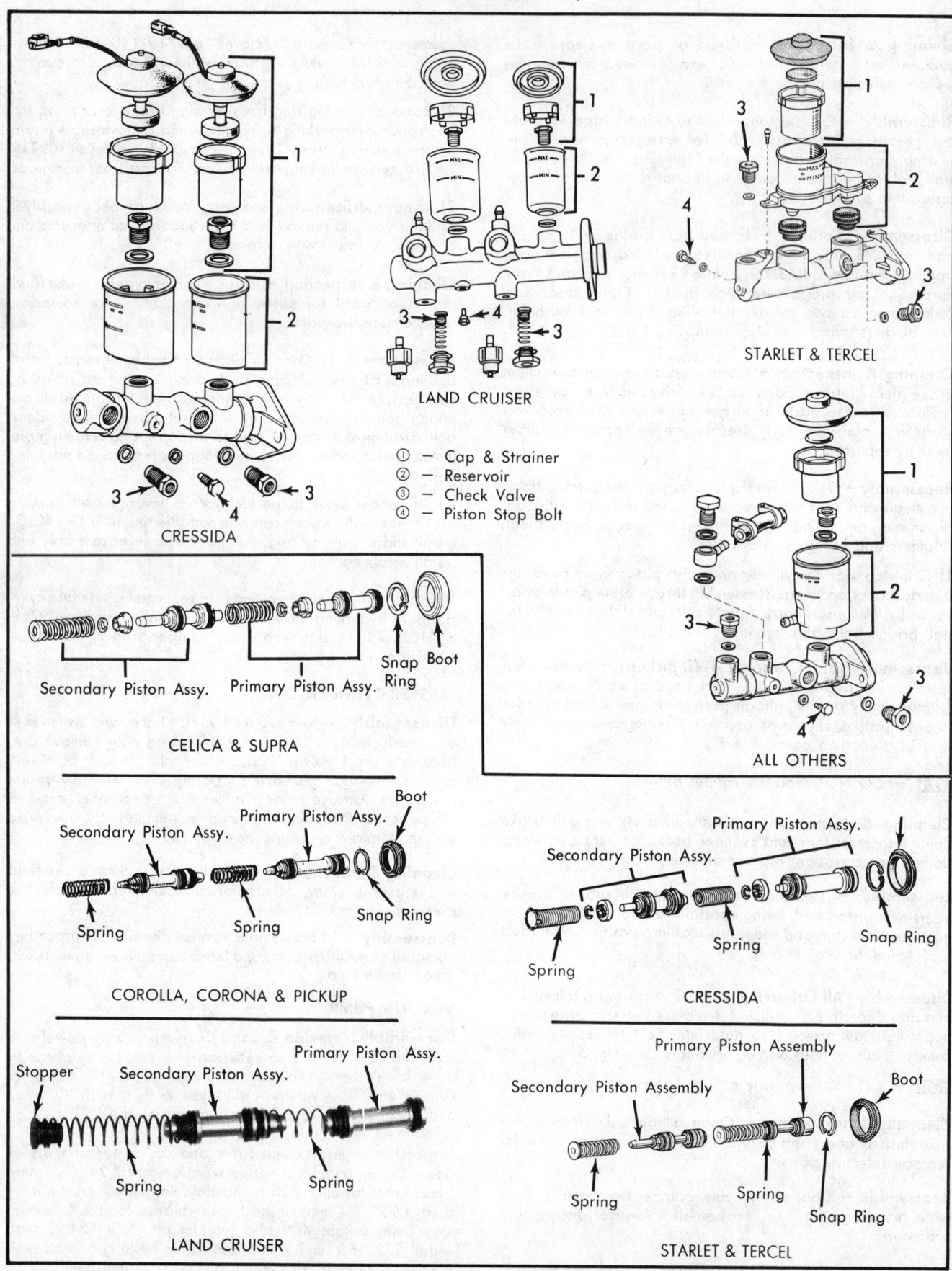

CRESSIDA

LAND CRUISER

① — Cap & Strainer
② — Reservoir
③ — Check Valve
④ — Piston Stop Bolt

STARLET & TERCEL

ALL OTHERS

CELICA & SUPRA
Secondary Piston Assy.
Primary Piston Assy.
Snap Ring
Boot

COROLLA, CORONA & PICKUP
Secondary Piston Assy.
Primary Piston Assy.
Boot
Spring
Spring
Snap Ring

CRESSIDA
Secondary Piston Assy.
Primary Piston Assy.
Spring
Snap Ring

LAND CRUISER
Stopper
Secondary Piston Assy.
Primary Piston Assy.
Spring
Spring

STARLET & TERCEL
Secondary Piston Assembly
Primary Piston Assembly
Boot
Spring
Spring
Snap Ring

Fig. 18   Exploded View Of Master Cylinders With Detail of Each Model's Piston Assemblies Shown

TOYOTA (Cont.)

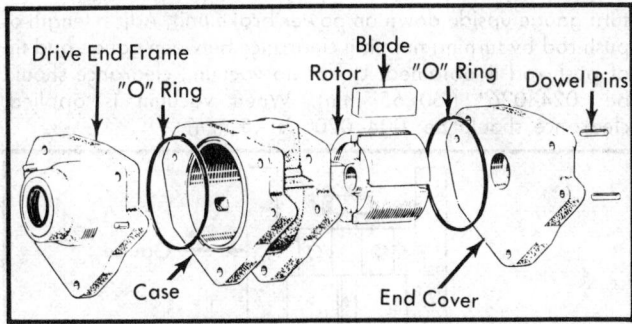

Fig. 19 Exploded View of Vacuum Pump

Reassembly — Lightly coat new "O" rings and insert into grooves. Refit rotor and blades. Drive in dowel pins.

POWER BRAKE UNIT

NOTE — *Power brake units are produced by several manufacturers and may vary slightly between model application. The following overhaul procedures can be used with minor attention to detail of specific booster being repaired. Refer to Figs. 20, 21 and 22.*

Disassembly — **1)** Remove check valve and grommet from front of unit (except Corolla, Pickup and Tercel), then remove push rod (except Land Cruiser). From rear of unit, remove clevis, nut and dust boot. Using a screwdriver, pry off retainer and remove filter and silencer pack.

NOTE — *Check valve on Corolla, Pickup and Tercel is located in vacuum line and is mounted on firewall.*

2) Place an alignment mark on front and rear shells for reassembly reference. Mount unit in suitable support to prevent internal spring pressure from forcing shells apart. On units equipped with clamping band, remove bolt and nut. Remove band and separate front and rear shells. On all other units, rotate front shell counterclockwise and separate front and rear shells.

3) On Land Cruiser, remove front diaphragm lock nut and separate front diaphragm assembly. Remove rear diaphragm retainer and center plate. Remove rear diaphragm lock nut and 4 hub bolts. Remove hub and separate rear diaphragm assembly. Remove push rod and spring, reaction disc, reaction disc hub and spring, valve body and "O" ring from rear shell.

4) On Aisin units, remove spring from front shell. Remove spring retainer, reaction plate and levers and "O" ring from diaphragm plate. Remove snap ring, then pull operating rod out through rear of diaphragm plate. Remove diaphragm retainer, then separate diaphragm and diaphragm plate. Remove star washer, seal and boot from rear shell.

5) On JKK units, remove push rod and spring from front shell. Remove diaphragm from diaphragm plate. Depress operating rod, remove stopper key, then pull out operating rod and reaction disc. Remove star washer, seal and bearing from rear shell.

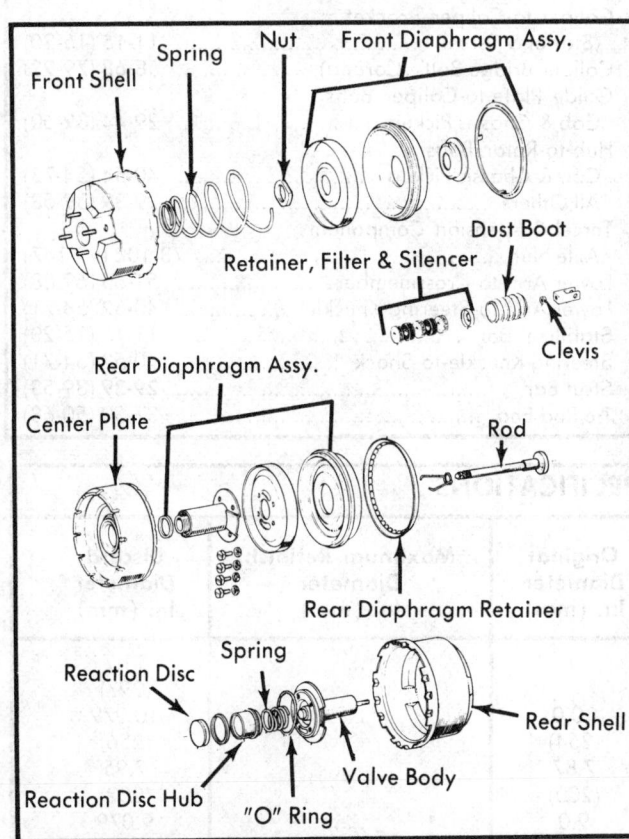

Fig. 20 Land Cruiser Power Brake Unit

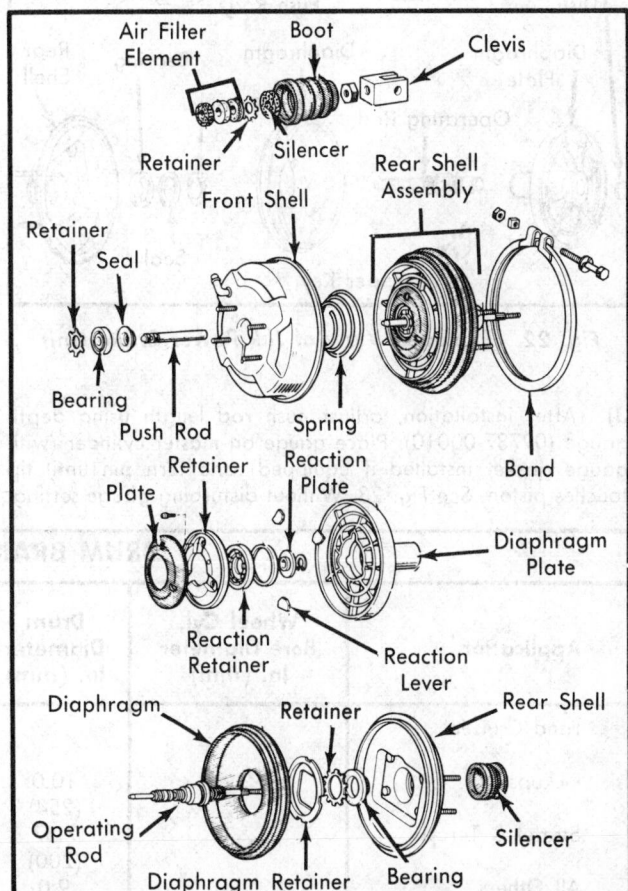

Fig. 21 Exploded View of Aisin Power Brake Unit

Brakes

TOYOTA (Cont.)

Cleaning & Inspection — Wash all parts in denatured alcohol. Inspect all components for wear or damage; replace defective parts. Replace all rubber parts during overhaul.

Reassembly — 1) Apply silicone grease to front and rear shell seals and reaction disc. Coat diaphragm edge with light coat of oil before final tightening. Shell halves must align with index marks.

2) Reassemble power brake unit by reversing removal procedure and note the following: On Aisin units, secure diaphragm to diaphragm plate by turning retainer 45°. On JKK units, rear seal must be seated .40-.43" (10-11 mm) from rear shell body. On Land Cruiser, fit reaction disc with protrusion directed toward valve body and install center plate on hub with large groove facing front side.

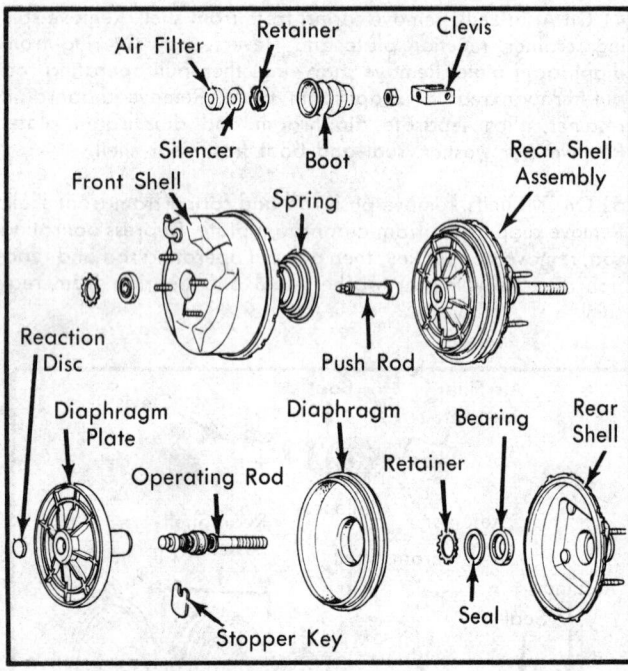

Fig. 22 Exploded View of Jkk Power Brake Unit

3) After installation, adjust push rod length using depth gauge (09737-00010). Place gauge on master cylinder (with gauge gasket installed if equipped) and turn pin until tip touches piston. *See Fig. 23.* Without disturbing gauge setting, turn gauge upside down on power brake unit. Adjust length of push rod by turning nut until clearance between gauge and tip of push rod is obtained. Under no vacuum, clearance should be .024-.026" (.60-.65 mm). When vacuum is applied, clearance should be .004-.020" (.1-.5 mm).

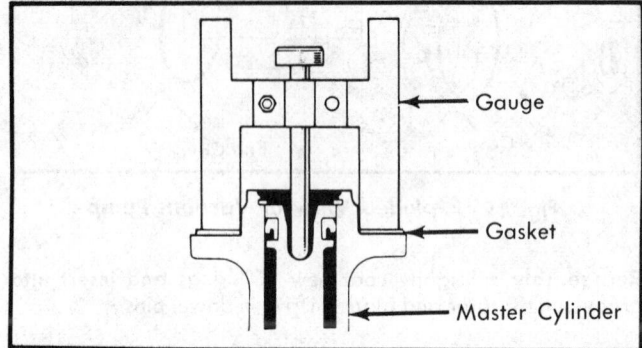

Fig. 23 Adjusting Push Rod Clearance With Gauge

TIGHTENING SPECIFICATIONS

Application	Ft. Lbs. (N·m)
Caliper Mounting Bolts	
Celica, Corolla & Supra	44-54 (60-73)
Corona, Cressida & 2WD Pickup	68-86 (92-117)
4WD Pickup	54-76 (73-103)
Land Cruiser	73-108 (99-147)
Caliper Bracket-to-Steering Knuckle	
Cab & Chassis Pickup	80-126 (109-171)
Tercel	33-39 (45-53)
Caliper-to-Caliper Bracket	
(Starlet & Tercel)	11-15 (15-20)
Caliper Bridge Bolts (Corolla)	58-68 (79-92)
Guide Plate-to-Caliper Bolts	
Cab & Chassis Pickup	29-44 (39-60)
Hub-to-Rotor Bolts	
Cab & Chassis Pickup	40-54 (54-73)
All Others	29-39 (39-53)
Tercel Suspension Components	
Axle Nut	73-108 (99-147)
Lower Arm-to-Crossmember	51-65 (69-88)
Lower Arm-to-Steering Knuckle	40-52 (54-71)
Stabilizer Bar	11-15 (15-20)
Steering Knuckle-to-Shock	40-52 (54-71)
Strut Bar	29-39 (39-53)
Tie Rod End	37-50 (50-68)

DRUM BRAKE SPECIFICATIONS

Application	Wheel Cyl. Bore Diameter In. (mm)	Drum Diameter In. (mm)	Original Diameter In. (mm)	Maximum Refinish Diameter In. (mm)	Discard Diameter In. (mm)
Land Cruiser	.....	.....	.....	.....	11.7 (297)
Pickups	.....	10.0 (254)	10.0 (254)	.....	10.079 (256)
Starlet & Tercel	.....	7.87 (200)	7.87 (200)	.....	7.95 (202)
All Others	.....	9.0 (228.6)	9.0 228.6)	.....	9.079 (230.6)

TOYOTA (Cont.)

DISC BRAKE SPECIFICATIONS						
Application	Disc Diameter	Lateral Runout	Parallelism	Original Thickness	Minimum Refinish Thickness	Discard Thickness
Cab & Chassis Pickup	.....	.006 (.15)	.....	.787 (20)	.....	.748 (19)
Other Pickups	.....	.006 (.15)	.....	.492 (12.5)	.....	.453 (11.5)
Land Cruiser	.....	.005 (.12)	.....	.787 (20)	.....	.748 (19)
Supra						
Front	.....	.006 (.15)	.....	.492 (12.5)	.....	.453 (11.5)
Rear	.....	.006 (.15)	.....	.394 (10)	.....	.354 (9)
Starlet & Tercel	.....	.006 (.15)	.....	.394 (10)	.....	.354 (9)
All Others	.....	.006 (.15)	.....	.492 (12.5)	.....	.453 (11.5)

TRIUMPH

TR7
TR8

DESCRIPTION

All models are equipped with front disc and rear drum brakes. A tandem master cylinder with 2 independent and complete hydraulic circuits is used on all models. A pressure differential valve is used on all models to detect low pressure in either front or rear brake circuit. When a pressure differential exists between the 2 circuits, the pressure differential valve will be positioned off-center and cause the brake failure warning lamp on instrument panel to glow. A vacuum servo unit is used for power braking. Parking brake is cable actuated on rear brakes.

ADJUSTMENT

DRUM BRAKES

NOTE — *Rear brakes on TR7 and TR8 models are equipped with self-adjusting mechanism incorporated in parking brake linkage.*

PARKING BRAKE

NOTE — *Adjustment of rear brakes will normally provide satisfactory parking brake adjustment. If cables are stretched, further adjustment is performed as follows:*

1) Raise and support rear of vehicle. Release parking brake lever. Disconnect parking brake cable clevis pins from operating levers on brake backing plates. With light finger pressure, push operating levers inward to ensure operating levers are in contact with brake shoes.

2) Align parking brake cable equalizer (located on right side of differential housing) ½" (12.5 mm) to left of vertical position. Adjust each clevis equal amounts until clevis pins can be easily inserted into operating levers. Secure clevis pins and check operation. Brakes should not drag. Parking brake lever travel should be 5-7 notches with 25 lbs. (11.4 kg) force applied to lever.

BRAKE WARNING LIGHT

NOTE — *Warning light will glow after any repair on service brake system and will not go out until manually reset by bleeding hydraulic circuit.*

A dual warning light is mounted on instrument panel. Parking brake light should glow when lever is pulled 1 notch (ignition on) and go off when lever is fully released. To check circuit warning sensor, fully release parking brake and ensure light is off (ignition on). Open 1 bleed screw and depress brake pedal; light should glow. To reset warning light, bleed hydraulic system and check operation of brakes. After bleeding brakes, turn ignition on; warning lamp should not glow. If warning lamp glows, center differential valve.

NOTE — *During bleeding process, use only short strokes to prevent differential valve from being forced off-center.*

DISC BRAKE PADS

Removal — Raise and support vehicle; remove tire and wheel. Remove retaining pins and springs. Lift out brake pads, complete with damper shims.

Installation — Clean surfaces of piston and caliper cavity. Ease caliper pistons into bores (with bleeder screw slightly open) to provide clearance. Insert new pads and shims. Smaller cut out faces up. Install retaining springs and pins.

DISC BRAKE CALIPER

Removal — Raise and support vehicle. Remove tire and wheel. Disconnect and plug hydraulic line at caliper. Remove 2 bolts and washers retaining steering arm and lower caliper mounting lug to stub axle. Push steering arm clear. Remove upper caliper mounting bolt and remove caliper.

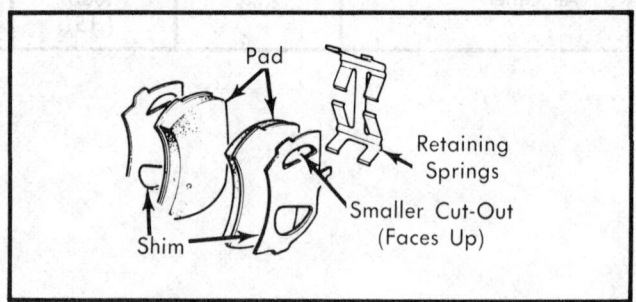

Fig. 1 Disc Brake Pad and Component Parts

Installation — To install, reverse removal procedure and bleed hydraulic system.

DISC BRAKE ROTOR

Removal — Raise and support vehicle; remove tire and wheel. Remove caliper without disconnecting hydraulic line and hang out of way. Remove grease cap, cotter pin, castellated nut and washer. Remove hub, complete with bearings and disc. Remove 4 hub-to-rotor bolts and separate hub from rotor.

Installation — To install, reverse removal procedures. Eliminate hub end play. Do NOT tighten hub more than 60 INCH lbs. (7 N·m). Adjust wheel bearings. See *Wheel Bearing Adjustment* in SUSPENSION Section.

REAR BRAKE DRUM

Removal — Raise and support vehicle. Remove tire and wheel. Remove 2 brake drum retaining screws. Release parking brake and remove brake drum. If drum is difficult to remove, release self-adjuster. To release, remove dust cover on backing plate and insert small screwdriver and engage slotted hole in small adjusting lever. Press lever down to release adjuster.

Installation — To install, reverse removal procedure. If brake adjustment was released, neutralize brakes, install brake drum and depress brake pedal to set shoe-to-drum clearance. Tighten retaining screws evenly.

Brakes

TRIUMPH (Cont.)

REAR BRAKE SHOES

CAUTION — *Upper and lower return springs and not interchangeable. Note position of each spring prior to removal.*

Removal — Remove brake drum. Remove cotter pin from parking brake lever on rear of backing plate. Separate lever from parking brake lever. Remove rear shoe anchor pins, spings and cups. Disconnect and remove lower return spring.

Installation — To install, reverse removal procedure. If brake adjustment was released, neutralize brakes, install brake drum and depress brake pedal to set shoe-to-drum clearance. Tighten retaining screws evenly.

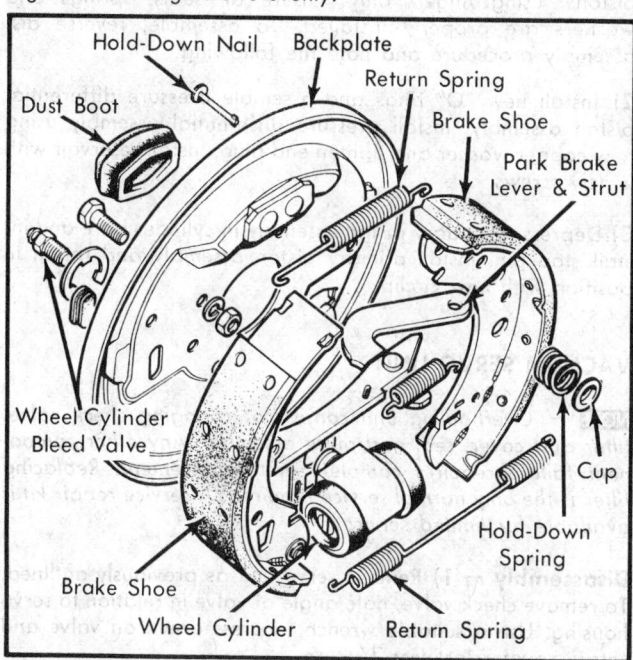

Fig. 2 Exploded View of Rear Assembly

MASTER CYLINDER

Removal — Disconnect all hydraulic lines and electrical connections (if equipped) from master cylinder. On models equipped with vacuum servo unit, remove mounting nuts and washers, then remove master cylinder. On models without vacuum servo unit, disconnect master cylinder push rod from brake pedal. Remove 4 mounting bolts securing master cylinder to firewall, then remove 2 bolts securing cylinder to front bracket. Remove master cylinder.

Installation — To install, reverse removal procedure and note the following: Bleed hydraulic system and check that pressure differential valve is centered.

VACUUM SERVO UNIT

Removal & Installation — Remove master cylinder as previously outlined. Disconnect vacuum hose from check valve. Remove clevis pin from servo operating rod and brake pedal lever. Remove 4 mounting nuts and washers, then remove servo. To install, reverse removal procedure.

PRESSURE DIFFERENTIAL VALVE

Removal & Installation — Disconnect electrical leads. Disconnect inlet and outlet lines and plug all ports to prevent loss of fluid and entry of dirt. Remove bolt securing valve and remove unit. To install, reverse removal procedure, bleed brakes and if necessary, center valve shuttle.

REAR BRAKE WHEEL CYLINDER

Removal & Installation — Remove brake shoes as previously outlined. Drain fluid and disconnect flexible hydraulic line at wheel cylinder. Remove wheel cylinder dust cover, retaining clip and spring plate. Remove wheel cylinder complete with parking brake operating lever. To install, reverse removal procedure and bleed hydraulic system.

NOTE — *Bleeder screw is installed on right wheel cylinder only. Left cylinder has fluid line installed in place of bleed screw to transfer fluid to right wheel cylinder. DO NOT interchange wheel cylinders.*

OVERHAUL

DISC BRAKE CALIPER

Disassembly — Using low air pressure, force pistons from caliper bores. If pistons are seized, the whole caliper assembly must be replaced. Carefully pry dust seal retainer from groove, using a blunt instrument. Take out dust seal and fluid seal.

Inspection — Clean caliper bores and inspect for deep scratches or pitting. Look at pistons and ensure they are not corroded or damaged. Replace components as necessary.

Reassembly — Fit new fluid seals into caliper bores, making sure they are properly located. Lightly coat bores with clean brake fluid. Insert pistons into caliper bores with approximately $\frac{5}{16}$" (7.9 mm) of each piston protruding from mouth of each bore. Fit new dust seal into retainer, then slide assembly, seal first, into mouth of bore. Fully seat pistons, ensuring retainers are not distorted.

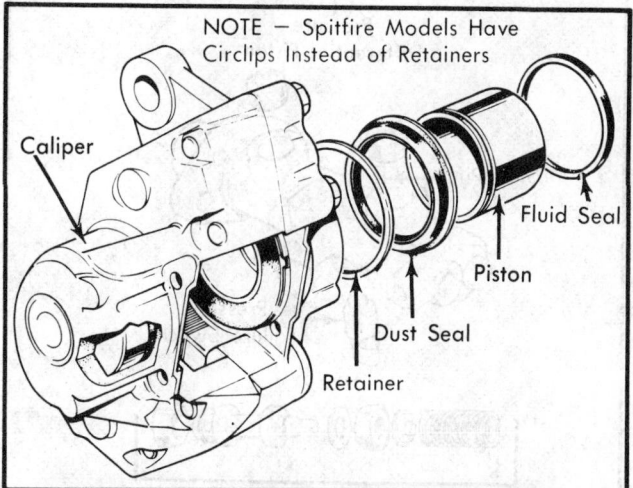

Fig. 3 Disassembled Front Disc Brake Caliper

REAR WHEEL CYLINDER

Disassembly — Remove wheel cylinder. Remove dust cover retaining ring and dust covers. Press on 1 piston to force pistons, seals and springs from cylinder.

Cleaning & Inspection — Clean all parts in alcohol or brake fluid and examine cylinder bore and piston for score marks, ridges or corrosion. If either bore or piston is damaged, replace entire cylinder assembly.

TRIUMPH (Cont.)

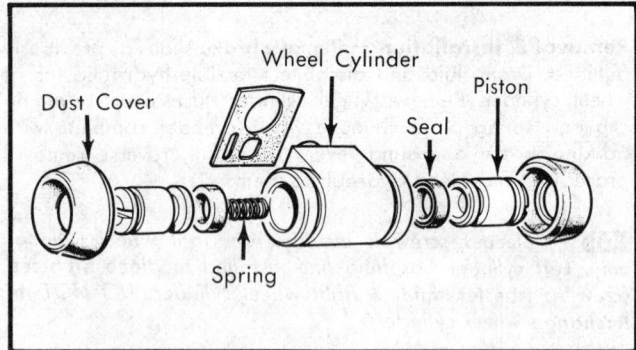

Fig. 4   Exploded View Wheel Cylinder

Reassembly — Install new seals on pistons. Lubricate seals, inside of cylinder and pistons with clean brake fluid. Reverse disassembly procedure to complete reassembly of wheel cylinder.

MASTER CYLINDER

Disassembly — 1) Drain and discard hydraulic fluid from reservoir. Remove reservoir from master cylinder. Note size and location of reservoir seals, remove seal from master cylinder. Remove metal cap and rubber boot from end of master cylinder.

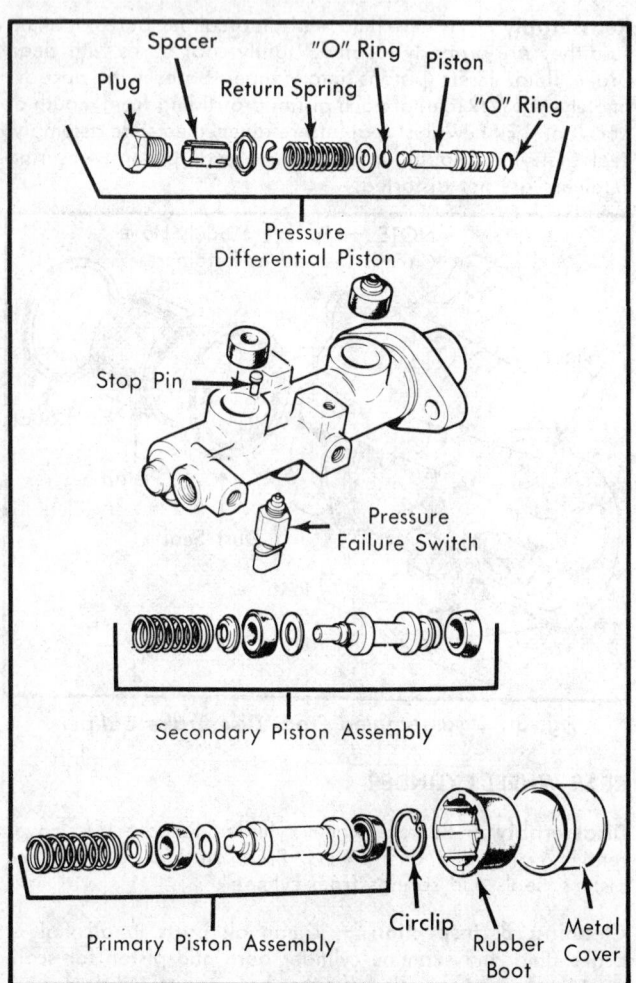

Fig. 5   Exploded View of Master Cylinder

2) Remove circlip and withdraw primary piston assembly. Unscrew pressure failure switch from cylinder body. Remove end plug and copper washer, withdraw spacer, return spring and pressure differential piston as an assembly.

3) Remove spring retainer. Separate spring and piston. Remove and discard "O" rings. Note size and position of all piston seals, washers and spring retainers. Remove seals using fingers only.

Reassembly — 1) Install seals on primary and secondary pistons, using fingers only. Ensure all seals, springs and washers are properly installed. To assemble, reverse disassembly procedure and note the following:

2) Install new "O" rings and assemble pressure differential piston assembly. Install pressure differential assembly using new copper washer and tighten end plug. Install reservoir with 2 new screws.

3) Depress secondary piston assembly in cylinder bore and install stop pin. Install primary piston assembly and retain in position with new circlip.

VACUUM SERVO UNIT

NOTE — *Overhauling unit consists of changing check valve, filter dust cover, seal and plate assembly. Any other component failure requires complete unit replacement. Replacing filter is the only normal service required. A service repair kit is available for limited service.*

Disassembly — 1) Remove servo unit as previously outlined. To remove check valve, note angle of valve in relation to servo housing. Use a suitable wrench to press down on valve and rotate counterclockwise 1/3 turn.

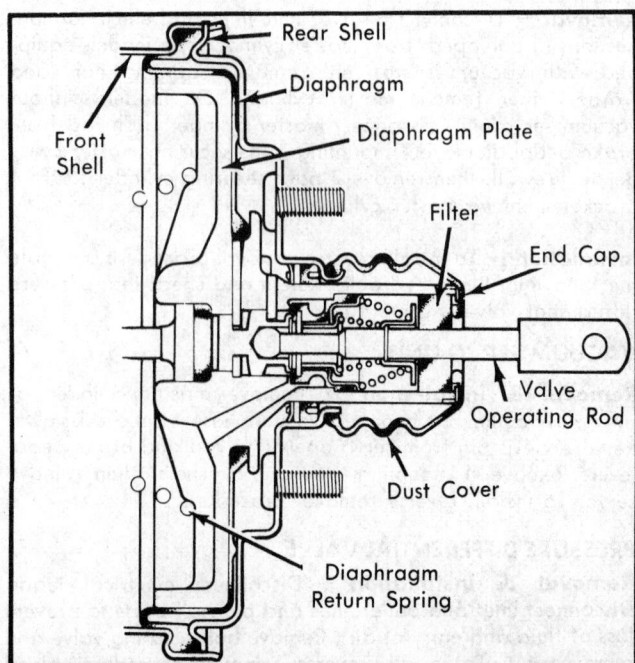

Fig. 6   Sectional View of Vacuum Servo Unit

Brakes

TRIUMPH (Cont.)

2) Remove filter by pulling back dust cover and pulling out filter. Do not remove valve operating rod. For ease of filter installation, cut new filter diagonally.

NOTE — *Servo push rod to master cylinder clearance is set by factory and secured with Loctite. No attempt should be made to alter setting.*

Reassembly — To reassemble components of servo unit, reverse disasssembly procedure.

TIGHTENING SPECIFICATIONS

Application	Ft. Lbs. (N·m)
Rotor-to-Hub	32 (44)
Caliper Mounting Bolts	74 (101)
Master Cylinder End Plug	33 (45)

Application	INCH Lbs. (N·m)
Reservoir-to-Master Cylinder	60 (7)
Master Cylinder-to-Pressure Reduction Valve	108 (12)

DRUM BRAKE SPECIFICATIONS

Application	Wheel Cyl. Bore Diameter In. (mm)	Drum Diameter In. (mm)	Original Diameter In. (mm)	Maximum Refinish Diameter In. (mm)	Discard Diameter In. (mm)
TR7 & TR8 5-Speed	.....	9.00 (229)	9.00 (229)	.....	9.05 (229.9)
All Others	.....	8.00 (203)	8.00 (203)	.....	8.05 (204.5)

DISC BRAKE SPECIFICATIONS

Application	Caliper Bore Diameter In. (mm)	Lateral Runout In. (mm)	Parallelism In. (mm)	Original Thickness In. (mm)	Minimum Refinish Thickness In. (mm)	Discard Thickness In. (mm)
TR7 & TR8	.....	.....	.....	.375 (9.5)	.....	.....

Brakes

VOLKSWAGEN

Dasher	Rabbit Pickup
Jetta	Scirocco
Rabbit	Vanagon

DESCRIPTION

Brake systems are hydraulically actuated using a tandem master cylinder and optional power brake unit. All models are equipped with front disc brakes and self-adjusting rear drum brakes. Jetta, Rabbit and Rabbit Pickup models are equipped with a brake proportional valve and all other models are equipped with a pressure regulator in rear brake circuit to avoid rear wheel lock-up. All models are equipped with cable actuated parking brake which operates on rear brakes.

ADJUSTMENT

PEDAL HEIGHT

Dasher — Pedal height is measured from center of brake pedal pad to bottom of steering wheel. To adjust, loosen clevis lock nut and turn push rod until distance is 23.8" (605 mm). Tighten lock nut.

PEDAL FREE PLAY

NOTE — *Pedal free play is adjusted at the power brake unit on all models except Dasher. Power brake unit (if equipped) must be removed to adjust free play.*

STOP LIGHT SWITCH

Jetta, Rabbit & Rabbit Pickup — Stop light switch is located under dash, above brake pedal. To adjust, loosen lock nuts and adjust switch so distance between brake pedal arm and switch body is .20-.24" (5-6 mm). Tighten lock nuts. See Fig. 1.

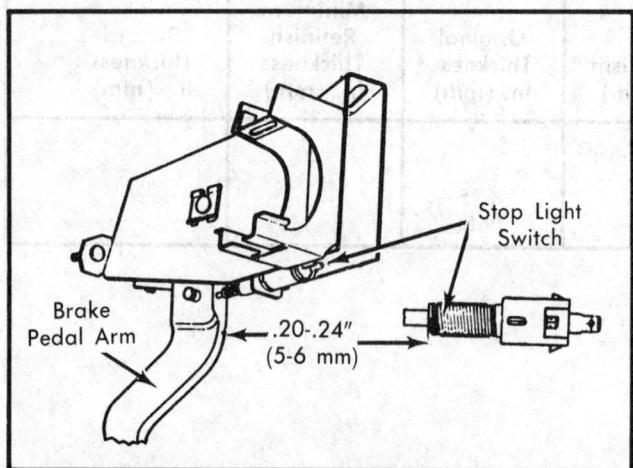

Stop Light Switch

Brake Pedal Arm

.20-.24" (5-6 mm)

Fig. 1 Adjusting Stop Light Switch on Jetta, Rabbit and Rabbit Pickup Models

PARKING BRAKE

Dasher & Vanagon — Raise and support vehicle and ensure rear brakes are properly adjusted. From under vehicle, loosen parking brake cable lock nut(s). Pull parking brake handle up 2 notches (2-4 notches on Vanagon) and tighten cable adjusting nut(s) until rear wheels lock. Tighten lock nut(s) and ensure rear wheels rotate freely with parking brake fully released.

All Others — Raise and support vehicle and ensure rear brakes are properly adjusted. Pull back rubber (plastic) boot at base of parking brake handle and loosen parking brake cable lock nuts. Pull handle up 2 notches and tighten each adjusting nut until rear wheels lock. Tighten lock nuts and refit boot. Ensure rear wheels rotate freely with parking brake fully released.

BRAKE WARNING LIGHT

A dual warning light is mounted on dash. Light should glow when parking brake lever is pulled 1 notch and go off when lever is fully released (ignition on). To check circuit warning operation, release parking brake (ignition on) and ensure light is off. Open bleed screw on 1 wheel and depress brake pedal; light should glow. Close bleed screw, replenish brake fluid and bleed hydraulic system.

NOTE — *Jetta, Rabbit and Rabbit Pickup models are equipped with warning sensor which is connected to brake proportioning valve. This sensor DOES NOT indicate fluid level in master cylinder. All other models are equipped with sensor which indicates fluid level in reservoir.*

BRAKE PROPORTIONING VALVE

Jetta, Rabbit & Rabbit Pickup — 1) Valve is located below master cylinder. Connect a 1500 psi (110 kg/cm²) gauge to left front caliper and another gauge to right rear wheel cylinder. Bleed gauges and depress brake pedal several times.

2) Apply brake pedal until front gauge reads indicated pressure for first reading in Brake Pressure Chart. Record rear gauge reading. Increase pedal pressure until front gauge reads indicated pressure for second reading. Record rear gauge reading. Remove gauges and bleed hydraulic system. If pressures do not meet specifications, replace proportioning valve.

BRAKE PRESSURE REGULATOR

Dasher & Scirocco — 1) Regulator is located on right rear frame on Dasher and left rear frame on Scirocco. Empty vehicle, fill fuel tank and load driver's seat to 165 lbs. Bounce car several times and allow vehicle to settle normally.

2) Measure distance from top of tire rim to lower edge of fender lip (both sides). Attach spring tensioners to hold vehicle in settled position. See Fig. 2. Raise and support vehicle, check measurement and adjust tensioners if required. Connect a 1500 psi (110 kg/cm²) gauge to left front caliper and another gauge to right rear wheel cylinder. Bleed gauges.

3) Pump pedal several times. Depress brake pedal until front gauge reads indicated pressure for first reading in Brake Pressure Chart. Record rear gauge reading. Increase pedal pressure until front gauge reads indicated pressure for second reading. Record rear gauge reading.

4) If both pressures were high on rear wheel, loosen regulator clamp bolt and REDUCE spring tension. INCREASE spring tension if pressures were too low. Replace pressure regulator if spring adjustment does not correct pressures.

NOTE — *Do NOT adjust spring tension with brake pedal depressed.*

VOLKSWAGEN (Cont.)

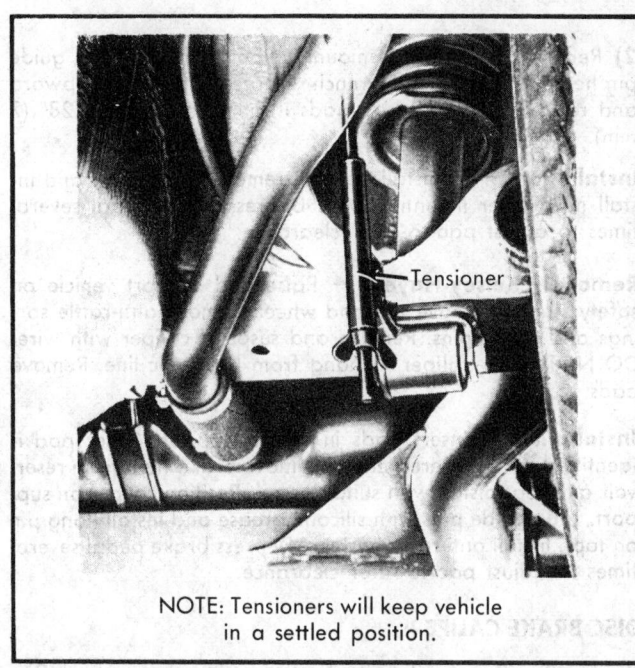

NOTE: Tensioners will keep vehicle
in a settled position.

Fig. 2   Tensioner Installed to Shock Absorber Mount

Vanagon — 1) Regulator is mounted on right rear frame. Raise and support vehicle and connect a 1500 psi (110 kg/cm²) gauge to left front caliper and another gauge to left rear wheel cylinder. Bleed gauges and depress brake pedal several times.

2) Remove regulator attaching nuts, then remove regulator from mounting studs. Depress brake pedal until front gauge reads indicated pressure for first reading in Brake Pressure Chart. Maintain pressure and tilt front of regulator down at a 30° angle. Increase pedal pressure until front gauge reads indicated pressure for second reading. Record rear gauge reading.

NOTE — *Do not damage brake lines when tilting regulator.*

3) If pressures are as specified in Brake Pressure Chart, return and secure regulator to proper position. Remove gauges and bleed hydraulic system. If pressures are not as specified, replace regulator.

Brake Pressure Chart		
Application	**Front Gauge** psi (kg/cm²)	**Rear Gauge** psi (kg/cm²)
Dasher		
1st Reading	710 (50)	440-497 (31-35)
2nd Reading	1422 (100)	753-810 (53-57)
Rabbit Pickup		
1st Reading	725 (51)	478-594 (34-42)
2nd Reading	1450 (102)	739-884 (52-62)
Vanagon		
1st Reading	725 (51)	725 (51)
2nd Reading	1450 (102)	798-943 (56-66)
All Other Models		
1st Reading	725 (51)	420-536 (30-38)
2nd Reading	1450 (102)	681-884 (48-62)

REMOVAL & INSTALLATION
FRONT DISC BRAKE PADS

NOTE — *ATE, Girling or Kelsey-Hayes calipers may be used on front disc brakes. Dasher is equipped with new type Girling calipers. Disc pads are interchangeable between ATE and Girling calipers only.*

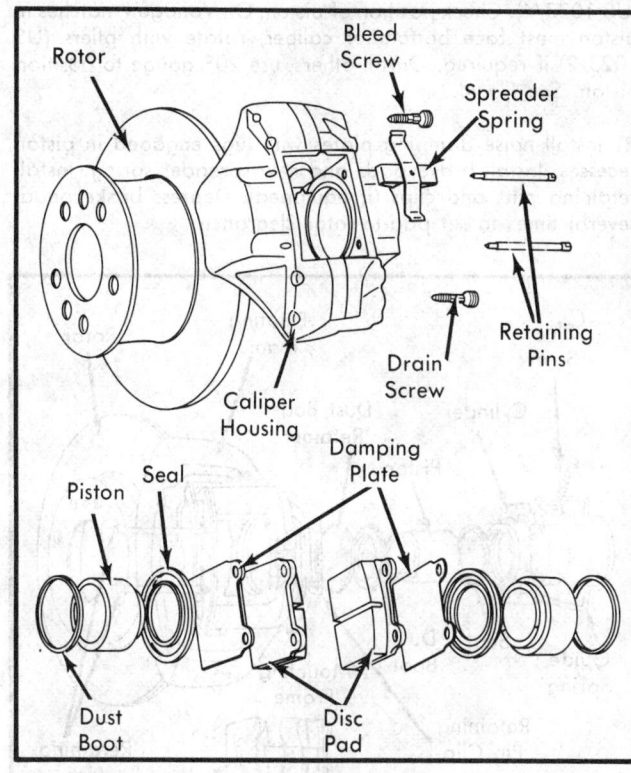

Fig. 3   ATE Disc Brake Assembly — Vanagon

Removal (ATE) — 1) Raise and support vehicle; remove tire and wheel. Remove retaining clip (if equipped) and remove retaining pins and spreader spring. Using a disc pad extractor (US 1023/3), remove inner brake pad.

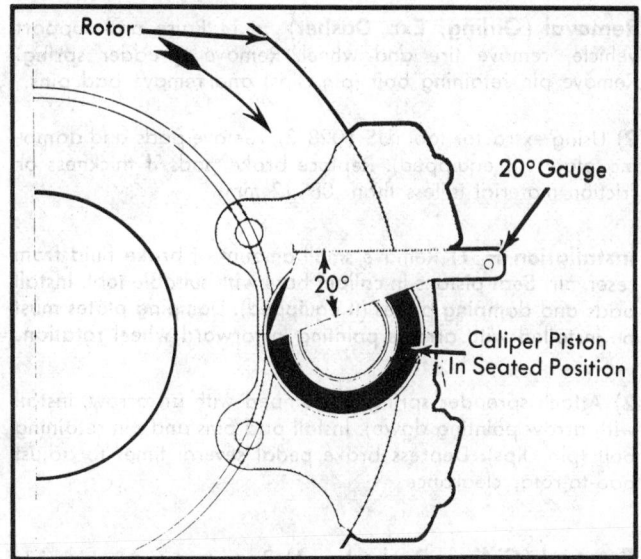

Fig. 4   Using a 20° Gauge to Position Piston in ATE Caliper Bore (Except Vanagon)

Brakes

VOLKSWAGEN (Cont.)

2) Separate outer pad from notch in piston, then extract outer brake pad. Remove damping plates. Replace brake pads if thickness is less than .08″ (2 mm) on Vanagon or .25″ (6 mm) on all other models.

Installation — 1) Siphon small amount of brake fluid from master cylinder reservoir. Seat piston in bore with compressor (US 1023/4). Check position of piston. On Vanagon, notches in piston must face bottom of caliper; rotate with pliers (US 1023/2) if required. On all others, use 20° gauge to position piston. *See Fig. 4.*

2) Install noise damping plates with lugs engaged in piston recesses. Install brake pads and new spreader spring. Install retaining pins and clips (if equipped). Depress brake pedal several times to set pad-to-rotor clearance.

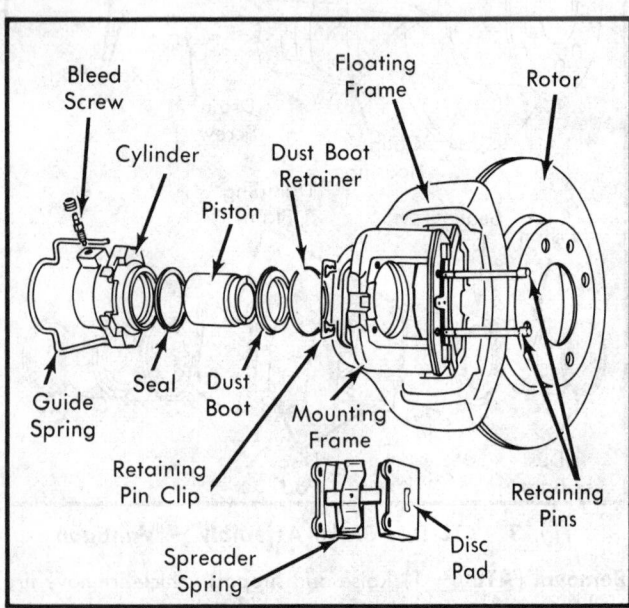

Fig. 5 ATE Disc Brake Assembly — Except Vanagon

Removal (Girling; Exc. Dasher) — 1) Raise and support vehicle; remove tire and wheel. Remove spreader spring. Remove pin retaining bolt (pin clips) and remove pad pins.

2) Using extractor tool (US 1023/3), remove pads and damping plates (if equipped). Replace brake pads if thickness or friction material is less than .08″ (2 mm).

Installation — 1) Remove small amount of brake fluid from reservoir. Seat pistons in caliper bore with suitable tool. Install pads and damping plates (if equipped). Damping plates must be installed with arrows pointing in forward wheel rotation.

2) Attach spreader spring (if stamped with an arrow, install with arrow pointing down). Install pad pins and pin retaining bolt (pin clips). Depress brake pedal several times to adjust pad-to-rotor clearance.

Removal (Girling; Dasher) — 1) Raise and support vehicle on safety stands; remove tire and wheel. Remove small amount of brake fluid from reservoir. Using hand pressure, seat piston in housing by pushing caliper toward outer bearing.

2) Remove lower caliper mounting bolt while holding guide pin head with open end wrench. Rotate caliper body upward and remove pads. Replace pads if lining is less than .28″ (7 mm).

Installation — To install, reverse removal procedure and install new lower mounting bolt. Depress brake pedal several times to adjust pad-to-rotor clearance.

Removal (Kelsey-Hayes) — Raise and support vehicle on safety stands; remove tire and wheel. Remove anti-rattle springs and guide pins. Remove and suspend caliper with wire. DO NOT allow caliper to hang from hydraulic line. Remove pads.

Installation — Insert pads in caliper support (inner pad is identified by chamfered ends). Remove brake fluid from reservoir and seat piston with suitable tool. Position caliper on support. Lube guide pins with silicone grease and install (long pin on top). Install anti-rattle springs. Depress brake pedal several times to adjust pad-to-rotor clearance.

DISC BRAKE CALIPER

Removal — Raise and support vehicle and remove wheel. Disconnect brake line from caliper and plug opening to prevent entry of dirt and foreign matter. Bend back locking tabs (if equipped) on mounting bolts. Remove caliper mounting bolts and take off caliper assembly.

Installation — To install, reverse removal procedure, using new lock plates and mounting bolts.

DISC BRAKE ROTOR

Removal (Vanagon) — Remove grease cap, cotter pin and loosen adjusting nut. Raise and support vehicle on safety stands. Remove wheel and tire. Remove wheel bearing hardware. Remove and suspend brake caliper. Pull hub and rotor from spindle without dropping bearing.

Removal (All Other Models) — Raise and support vehicle on safety stands. Remove wheel and tire. Remove and suspend brake caliper. Remove countersunk screw from between 2 wheel bolt holes. Pull rotor off hub.

Installation (All Models) — To install, reverse removal procedure. On Vanagon, adjust wheel bearings. *See Wheel Bearing Adjustment in SUSPENSION Section.*

REAR BRAKE DRUM

CAUTION — *Loosen and tighten spindle nut only with wheels on the ground.*

Removal (Vanagon) — Remove dust cap, cotter pin and loosen castellated nut. Raise and support vehicle; remove tire and wheel. Release parking brake at equalizer and back off adjuster. Remove drum retaining screws. Install puller and remove drum.

NOTE — *Drum must rotate freely during removal.*

Installation — To install, reverse removal procedure and ensure drum retaining screws are tight. Adjust parking brake and depress brake pedal several times to set self-adjusting mechanism.

Brakes

VOLKSWAGEN (Cont.)

Removal (All Others) – Raise and support vehicle. Remove 1 wheel bolt and push adjusting wedge upward with a screwdriver. Reinstall wheel bolt, remove wheel bearing hardware and remove drum assembly from spindle without dropping thrust washer or outer bearing.

Installation – To install, reverse removal procedure and adjust wheel bearings. *See Wheel Bearing Adjustment in SUSPENSION Section.* Apply brake pedal firmly several times to set self-adjusting mechanisim.

BRAKE SHOES

Removal (Vanagon) – **1)** With wheel and drum removed, remove hold down springs and pins. Disconnect parking brake cable from lever on brake shoe. Remove lower return spring and adjuster spring.

2) Move brake shoes out of lower support and remove return springs. Remove brake shoes as an assembly from backing plate without pulling pistons out of wheel cylinder. Separate brake shoes and disconnect parking brake lever from brake shoe. Remove lower support bolts and support.

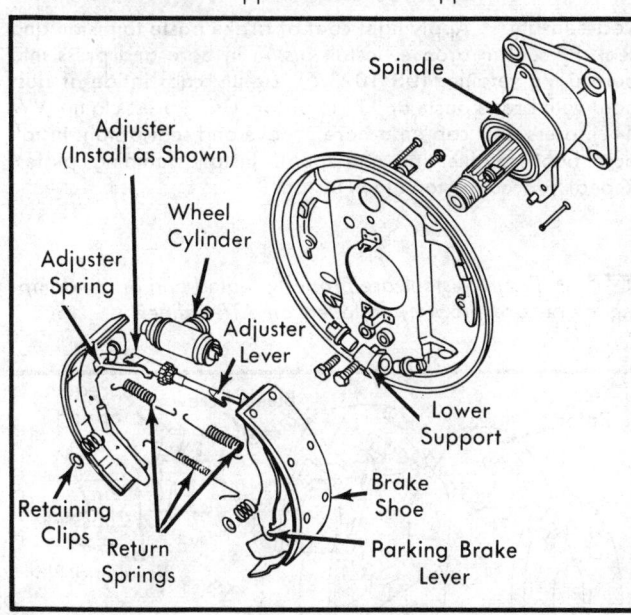

Fig. 6   Vanagon Rear Brake Assembly

Installation – **1)** To install, reverse removal procedure and note the following: After installing brake shoes, adjust brake shoes by setting distance (measured from outer surface of each brake lining) to 9.87" (250.7 mm).

2) Adjust parking brake at equalizer (there must not be any free play between parking brake lever on brake shoe and adjusting rod). Install brake drum and depress brake pedal several times to set self-adjusting mechanism.

Removal (All Others) – **1)** With drum removed, remove hold down springs and pins. Remove brake shoes from anchor pins and remove return spring.

2) Disconnect parking brake cable from lever. Disconnect adjusting wedge spring and upper return spring. Remove brake shoes. Place adjuster strut and shoe in vise; remove tension spring. Separate shoe and components.

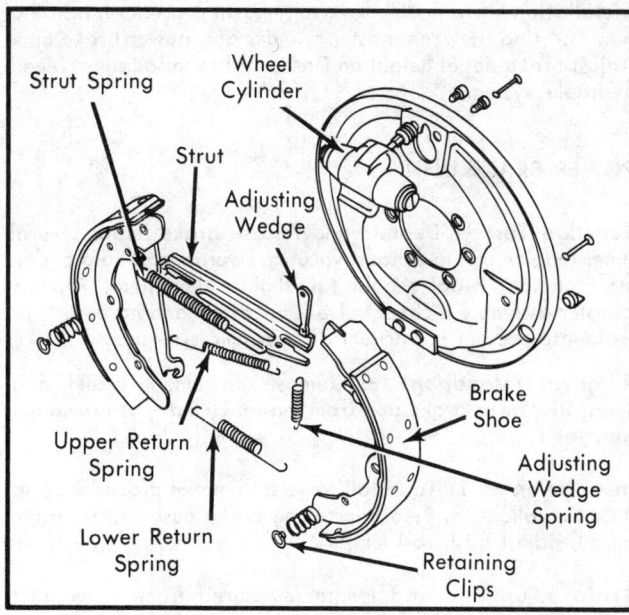

Fig. 7   Rear Brake Assembly (Except Vanagon)

Installation – To install, reverse removal procedures. Lug on adjusting wedge faces backing plate. Adjust wheel bearings. *See Wheel Bearing Ajustment in SUSPENSION Section.* Apply brake firmly to set self adjusting mechanism.

MASTER CYLINDER

NOTE – *Removal and installation of all master cylinders is basically the same. The following variations may apply: Location of cylinder, removal of wheel for accessibility, number of fluid connections, and number of electrical connections.*

Removal (Vanagon) – **1)** Remove instrument panel, then drain or siphon fluid from master cylinder reservoir. Disconnect fluid lines and electrical connections from master cylinder. Remove vacuum lines from power brake unit. Remove pedal and bracket assembly.

2) Disconnect brake push rod from brake pedal. Remove power brake unit and master cylinder assembly from pedal bracket. Remove master cylinder-to-power brake unit attaching bolts and remove master cylinder.

Installation – To install, reverse removal procedure and note the following: Install a new "O" ring between master cylinder and power brake unit. Adjust brake push rod length. *See POWER BRAKE UNIT.* Bleed hydraulic system.

Removal (All Others) – Drain or siphon fluid from reservoir. Raise and support vehicle and remove cover plate (if equipped). Disconnect fluid lines and electrical connections at master cylinder. On models without power unit, remove brake push rod from brake pedal. Remove master cylinder-to-power brake unit attaching bolts and remove master cylinder.

NOTE – *If spacers are used on attaching bolts, do not drop or lose spacers.*

VOLKSWAGEN (Cont.)

Installation — To install, reverse removal procedure. Install a new "O" ring between master cylinder and power brake unit. Adjust brake pedal height on Dasher. After installation, bleed hydraulic system.

POWER BRAKE UNIT

Function Test — Depress and release brake pedal several times (engine off) to exhaust vacuum. Depress and hold pedal; start engine. Pedal should fall slightly then hold. Replace booster assembly if check valve is operative and no defects or leaks are present in vacuum or hydraulic systems.

Removal (Vanagon) — Remove instrument panel and separate power brake unit from master cylinder as previously described.

Installation — 1) To install, reverse removal procedure and note the following: Before installing brake push rod to brake pedal, adjust push rod length.

2) To adjust push rod length (measured from power unit flange to centerline of push rod clevis), loosen lock nut and turn push rod until distance is 4.39" (111.5 mm). Tighten lock nut. Complete installation and bleed hydraulic system.

Removal (All Others) — Remove master cylinder from power brake unit as previously described. Disconnect brake push rod from brake pedal. Disconnect vacuum lines from power brake unit. Remove mounting nuts from firewall and remove power brake unit.

Installation — To install, reverse removal procedure. Always replace damping ring, washer, filter and "O" ring. Slots in damping washer and filter must be offset 180°.

CHECK VALVE

Function Test — Check valve is located in vacuum line between power brake unit and intake manifold. Blowing into large diameter side must unseat valve; valve must seat when test is performed on opposite side. Replace defective valve.

VACUUM BOOSTER
(CIS FUEL INJECTED MODELS ONLY)

1) An adjustable or non-adjustable vacuum booster is installed to increase vacuum to power brake unit. To check booster, warm engine until oil reaches 140°F. Install "T" connector between distributor vacuum unit and intake manifold. Gauge should read 7.4" (188 mm) vacuum with engine idling. If not, check vacuum lines for leaks.

2) If vacuum is as specified in step 1), check booster as follows: Remove and plug hose from right side of booster. Loosen lock nut (if equipped) and install vacuum gauge and hose. Gauge should read 11.8" (300 mm) vacuum with engine idling. Adjust screw in or out to obtain correct reading (if equipped). Replace defective booster.

VACUUM PUMP
(DIESEL ONLY)

Removal & Installation — Remove vacuum lines from upper housing. Remove unit from engine block. To install, reverse removal procedure and replace "O" ring at mounting base.

OVERHAUL

DISC BRAKE CALIPER

Disassembly (ATE & Girling; Vanagon) — 1) Remove disc pads and damping plates as previously described. Clamp mounting flange in a soft-jawed vise and remove dust boot retainer (if equipped) and dust boot.

2) Install piston retainer tool (US 1023/5) on 1 piston. Insert wooden block in caliper and remove piston with compressed air. Repeat procedure for opposite piston. Remove piston seals without damaging bore.

Cleaning & Inspection — Clean all parts in brake fluid. Check piston and caliper bore for wear or damage; replace as necessary. DO NOT split caliper housings; assembly must be replaced if split. Replace all parts included in repair kit.

Reassembly — Apply light coat of brake paste to piston and seal. Fit seal in groove, install piston in bore and press into bore using retainer (US 1023/5). Lightly coat inside of dust boot with brake paste and fit to piston. Using press clamp (VW 442), press dust cap onto bore groove and seat piston. Install dust boot retainer (if equipped). Install damping plates. Repeat procedure for other piston.

NOTE — *Ensure pistons are properly seated and piston damping plates are properly installed on ATE calipers.*

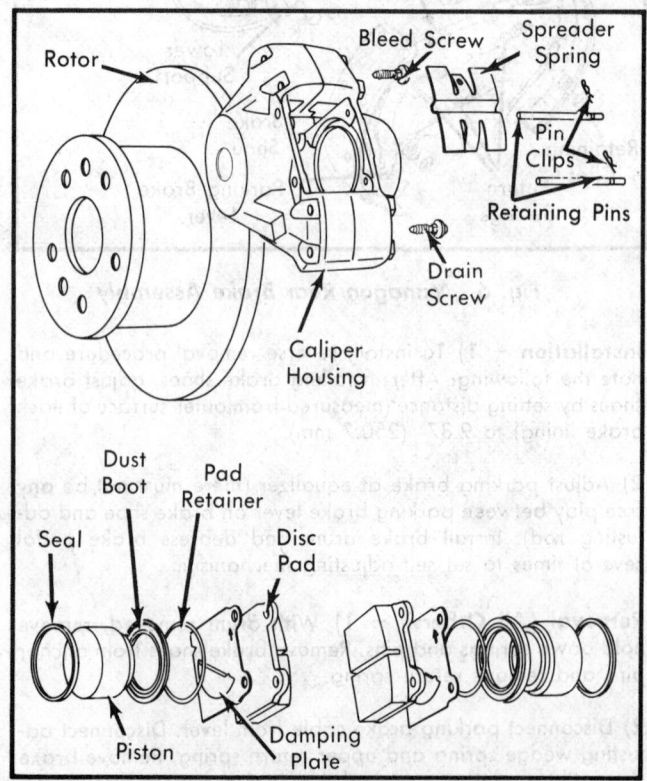

Fig. 8 Girling Disc Brake Assembly — Vanagon

VOLKSWAGEN (Cont.)

Disassembly (ATE; All Others) — 1) Remove disc pads as previously described. Press caliper frame off floating frame. Insert wooden block in floating frame and drive cylinder and guide spring off with brass drift.

2) Remove piston retaining ring and dust seal. Protect piston with wooden block and force piston out with compressed air. Remove piston seal without damaging bore.

Cleaning & Inspection — Clean all parts in brake fluid. Check piston and bore for wear or damage; replace as necessary. Replace all parts included in repair kit.

Reassembly — Reverse disassembly procedure and note the following: Coat piston with brake paste. Use a vise to seat piston. Use a brass drift to fit brake cylinder to floating frame. Make sure both grooves in mounting frame are pushed over ribs on floating frame. Make sure piston is properly positioned. *See Fig. 4.*

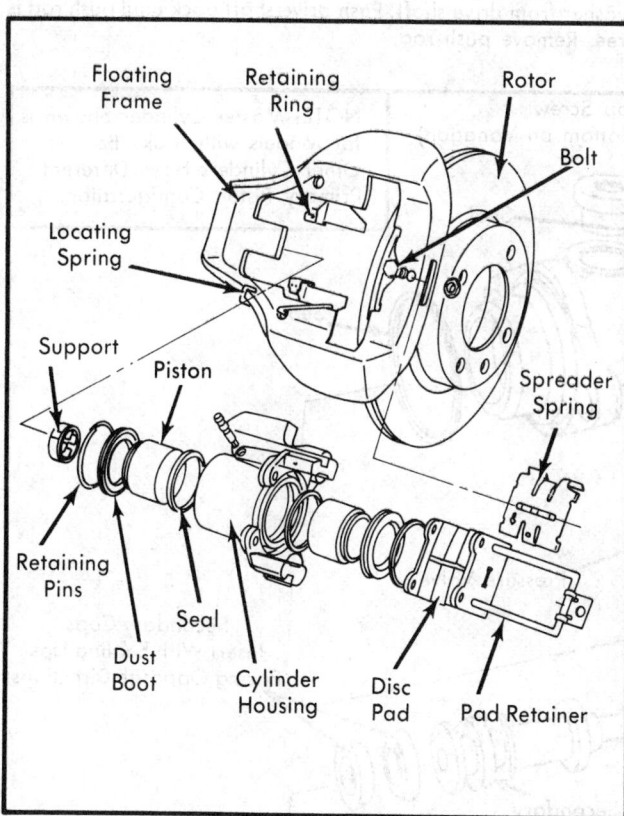

**Fig. 9 Girling Disc Brake Assembly
(Except Dasher and Vanagon)**

Disassembly (Girling; Except Dasher) — Press cylinder out of frame. Remove dust boot and retaining ring from each piston. Hold piston between padded jaws of vise and blow pistons out of bore with compressed air. Remove piston seals without damaging bore.

Cleaning & Inspection — Clean all parts in brake fluid. Check piston and caliper bore for wear or damage; replace as necessary. Replace all parts included in repair kit.

Reassembly — To reassemble, reverse disassembly procedure and note: Coat pistons and seals with brake paste before refitting.

Disassembly (Girling; Dasher) — Separate cylinder housing from pad carrier. Remove dust cap. Insert wooden block in housing and blow out piston with compressed air. Remove piston seal without damaging bore.

Cleaning & Inspection — Clean all parts in brake fluid. Check piston and bore; if corroded, pitted or scored, replace defective part. DO NOT use abrasives. Replace all parts included in repair kit.

Reassembly — Coat piston, cylinder bore and new seal with brake paste. Fit seal into cylinder. Slide dust seal onto piston, then slowly insert piston into cylinder, fitting inner lips of dust seal on housing groove. Fully seat piston into cylinder. Engage outer lip of dust seal on groove of piston.

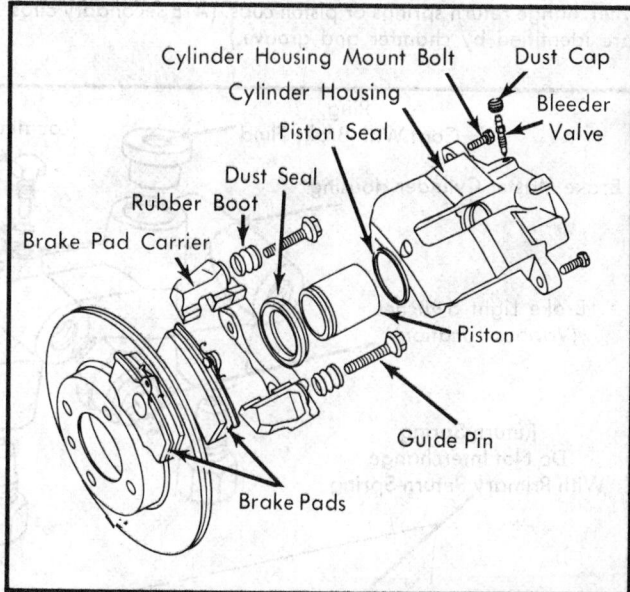

**Fig. 10 Girling Disc Assembly Used on Dasher
Kelsey-Hayes Disc Assembly is Similar**

Disassembly (Kelsey-Hayes) — Disconnect brake hose from caliper. Remove caliper from support assembly. Remove anti-rattle springs and guide pins. Remove support from spindle. Remove dust boot from piston. Place wooden block in caliper housing and blow piston out with compressed air. Remove piston seal without damaging bore. Remove guide pins and bushings, if required.

Cleaning & Inspection — Clean all parts in brake fluid. Check cylinder bore and piston for wear or corrosion; replace defective part. Replace all parts included in repair kit.

Reassembly — Coat seals, dust boot, cylinder bore and piston with brake paste. Coat guide pins with silicone grease. Reverse disassembly procedure and note the following: Seat dust boot with brass drift. Long guide pin is installed in top hole of caliper housing.

Brakes

VOLKSWAGEN (Cont.)

MASTER CYLINDER

NOTE — *Master cylinders differ in external design and primary piston configuration between power assist and non-power assist models. Disassembly procedures are the same.*

Disassembly — Remove dust boot (if equipped) and piston stop screw. Remove circlip and washer. Tap open end of cylinder and remove piston assemblies. Remove all external mountings and hardware from cylinder.

Cleaning & Inspection — Clean all parts with brake fluid or denatured alcohol. Check cylinder bore and pistons for wear; replace as complete assembly if defective. Replace all rubber parts during overhaul and use all parts included in repair kit.

Reassembly — Reverse disassembly procedure and note the following: Coat primary piston shaft with lubricant supplied in repair kit. Coat pistons and cups with brake paste. DO NOT interchange return springs or piston cups. (ATE secondary cups are identified by chamfer and groove.)

POWER BRAKE UNIT PRESSURE REGULATING VALVE & PROPORTIONING VALVE

NOTE — *Manufacturer recommends replacing each unit as complete assembly. DO NOT disassemble.*

VACUUM PUMP (DIESEL ONLY)

Disassembly — 1) Remove cover from upper housing and separate components. Remove upper housing retaining screws and separate housings. Remove diaphragm retaining nut and separate diaphragm and plates.

2) Remove drive shaft cover and gasket. Remove retainer and washer from drive shaft. Push drive shaft back until push rod is free. Remove push rod.

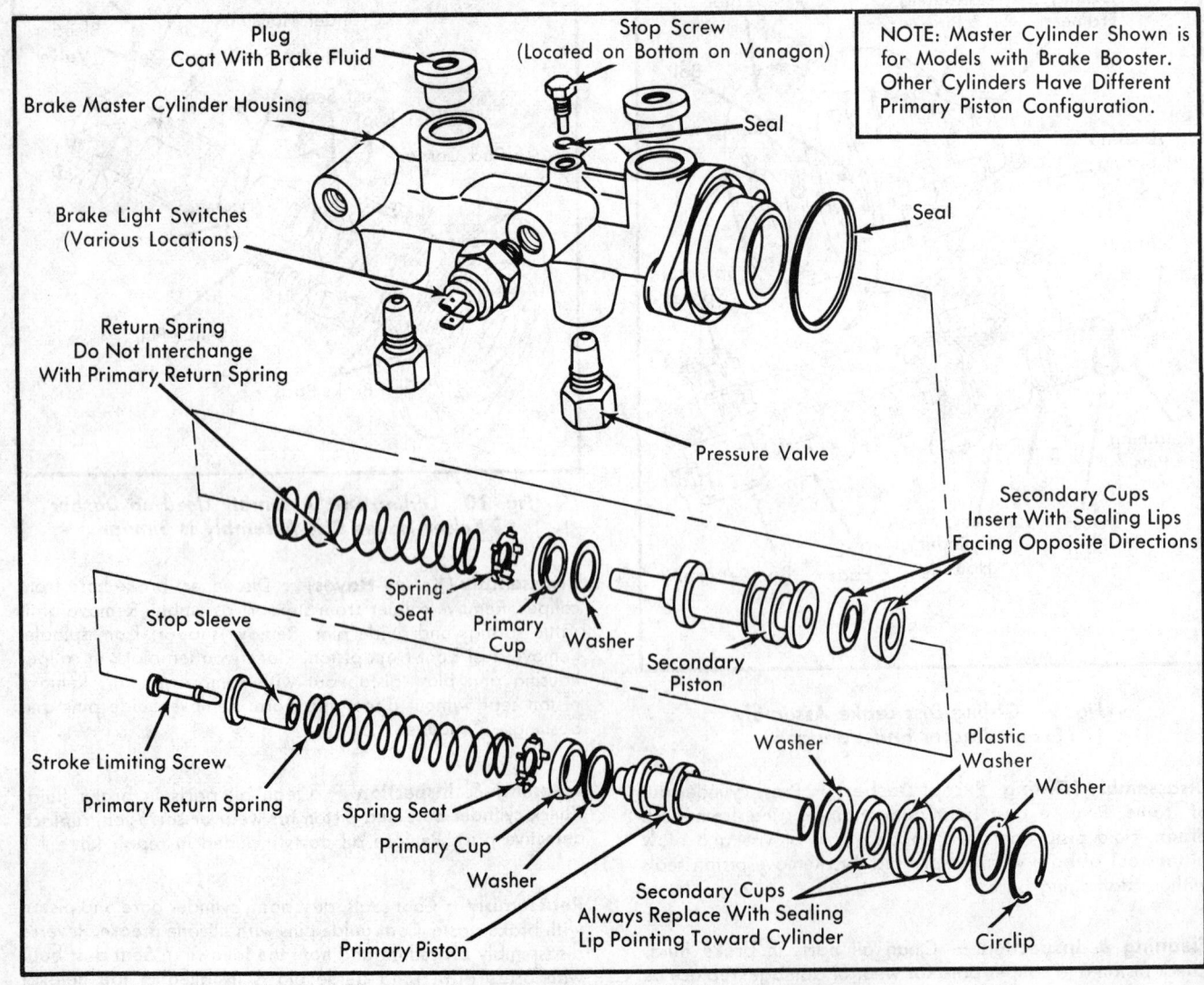

Fig. 11 Exploded View of Master Cylinder

VOLKSWAGEN (Cont.)

Cleaning & Inspection — Clean all parts in denatured alcohol and inspect body for cracks. Inspect diaphragm for cracks and deformation. Replace defective parts as required. Replace diaphragm retaining nut and all rubber parts during overhaul. Use all parts included in repair kit.

Reassembly — **1)** Reassemble diaphragm assembly with diaphragm molded center facing up. Coat new retaining nut with sealing compound and tighten to 60 INCH lbs. (7 N.m). Install upper housing plate with brake booster connection pointing straight up. Loosely install retaining screws.

2) Press and hold push rod into position. Tighten upper housing retaining screws. Push drive shaft into position and secure with washer and retainer. Replace spring sealing washers and install valves with spring seat toward housing. Replace gaskets and install covers.

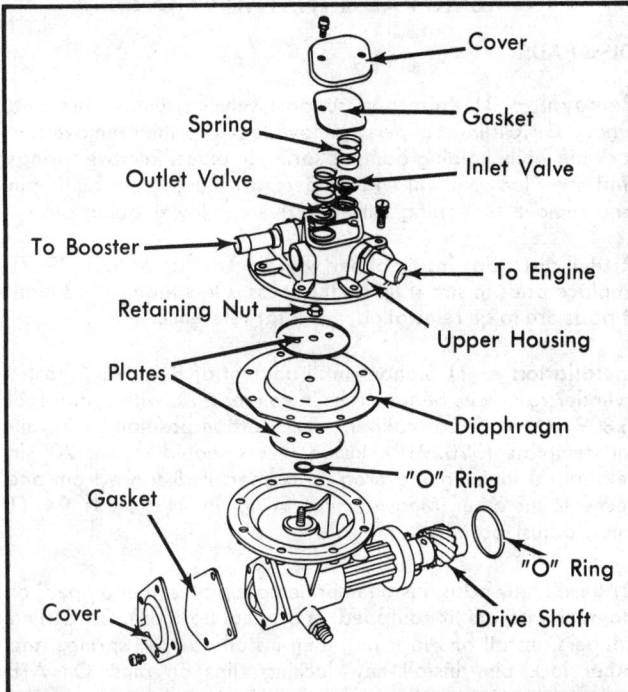

Fig. 12 Exploded View of Diesel Engine Vacuum Pump Assembly

TIGHTENING SPECIFICATIONS

Application	Ft. Lbs. (N·m)
Caliper Mounting Bolts①	
Dasher (Support Bolt)	43 (58)
Dasher (Caliper-to-Support Bolt)	25 (34)
Vanagon	118 (160)
All Others	36 (49)
Girling Caliper Pad Retainer Bolt	14 (19)
Kelsey-Hayes Guide Pins	30 (41)
Vanagon Rear Brake Shoe Support	48 (65)

① — New self locking bolts may be used in some cases. Tighten to 50 ft. lbs. (68 N·m).

DISC BRAKE SPECIFICATIONS

Application	Caliper Bore Diameter In. (mm)	Lateral Runout In. (mm)	Parallelism In. (mm)	Original Thickness In. (mm)	Minimum Refinish Thickness In. (mm)	Discard Thickness In. (mm)
Vanagon	.....	.004 (0.10)	.....	.512 (13)	.453 (11.5)	.433 (11)
All Others	.....	.004 (0.10)	.0008 (.02)	.472 (12)	.413 (10.5)	.393 (10)

DRUM BRAKE SPECIFICATIONS

Application	Wheel Cyl. Bore Diameter In. (mm)	Drum Diameter In. (mm)	Original Diameter In. (mm)	Maximum Refinish Diameter In. (mm)	Discard Diameter In. (mm)
Dasher & Rabbit Pickup	.....	7.87 (200)	7.87 (200)	7.90 (200.5)	7.91 (201)
Vanagon	.....	9.92 (252)	9.92 (252)	9.96① (253)	9.98 (253.5)
All Others	.....	7.08 (180)	7.08 (180)	7.10 (180.5)	7.13 (181)

① — Use oversize linings after turning drum .020″ (0.50 mm).

VOLVO

DL	GLE
GL	Bertone
GLT Turbo	Diesel

DESCRIPTION

Volvo models may be equipped with Girling calipers on all 4 wheels or Girling front calipers; ATE rear calipers. Service brakes are hydraulically operated by tandem master cylinder and vacuum power brake unit. Master cylinder distributes hydraulic pressure to distribution/warning valve. Distribution/warning valve equally distributes hydraulic pressure to each circuit. One circuit is lower front caliper pistons and right rear caliper; other circuit is upper front caliper pistons and left rear caliper. If hydraulic pressure differs between circuits, dash mounted light will glow. Each rear brake line has a pressure valve to prevent rear wheel lock-up. Parking brake is mechanically operated on rear wheel mounted, internal brake shoes.

ADJUSTMENT

PEDAL HEIGHT

Brake pedal height should be equal to clutch pedal. To adjust, loosen lock nut, remove cotter pin and turn push rod until height is equal. Replace cotter pin and tighten lock nut. Pedal travel should then be 5.7-6.5" (145-165 mm).

NOTE — *Pedal travel can only be measured during brake bleeding operation. See Hydraulic System Bleeding article in this section.*

STOP LIGHT SWITCH

Stop light switch is located under instrument panel, in front of brake pedal. To adjust, loosen retaining screws and position switch so contact plunger just contacts pedal arm. Measureable distance from switch body to pedal arm should be .08-.24" (2-6 mm). Tighten retaining screws.

PARKING BRAKE

NOTE — *Adjust parking brake when full application stroke of brake lever exceeds 3 or 4 notches.*

1) Remove center console rear ash tray, then working through ash tray hole, loosen parking brake cables adjusting screw until cables are slack. Raise and support rear of vehicle, then remove wheels. Align hole in parking brake drum with starwheel adjuster.

2) Tighten starwheel until drum can just be rotated by hand, then back off adjuster until drum just rotates freely. Install rear wheels. Tighten parking brake cable adjusting screw until parking brake is fully applied when lever is pulled 2 or 3 notches. Install ash tray and lower vehicle.

BRAKE WARNING LIGHTS

Brake Failure Light — This light will glow if pressure differential is exceeded or fluid level is low. Light will continue to glow until problem is corrected. Check calipers, hydraulic lines, master cylinder, power brake unit and vacuum pump for defects and repair as required.

Parking Brake Light — This light will glow when parking brake lever is pulled 1 notch and go out when fully released (ignition on).

REMOVAL & INSTALLATION

DISC PADS

Removal — 1) Raise and support vehicle; remove tire and wheel. On Girling calipers, remove lock clip then remove one lock pin while holding damper spring in place. Remove springs and other lock pin. On ATE calipers, drive out upper guide pin and remove tensioning spring. Drive out lower guide pin.

2) Pull disc pads from caliper with pad extractor tool (2917). Replace pads in sets if lining thickness is less than ⅛" (3 mm). If pads are to be reinstalled, mark for reference.

Installation — 1) Siphon small amount of fluid from master cylinder reservoir. Seat pistons in caliper bore with piston tool (2809). On ATE rear calipers, check piston position by installing template (SV02919). Piston recess should incline 20° in relation to lower guide area on caliper. If distance from one recess to the other (*Measurement "A" in Fig. 1*) exceeds .04" (1 mm), adjust position.

2) Install new pads, install intermediate plates (if equipped) or damper washers (if equipped) in original positions. On Girling calipers, install one lock pin, then install damper springs and other lock pin. Install new locking clips on pins. On ATE calipers, tap one guide pin into position, install new tensioning spring and install other guide pin while holding tensioning spring in position.

NOTE — *Install damper washers with small contact face toward pad. DO NOT install intermediate plates in calipers equipped with damper washers.*

3) After installation, depress brake pedal several times to seat pads against rotor. Ensure proper operation of brakes, install wheel and lower vehicle.

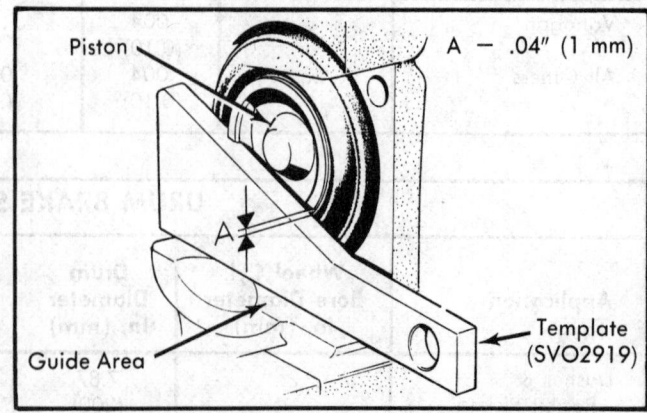

Fig. 1 Checking ATE Rear Caliper Piston Angle

CALIPER ASSEMBLY

Removal — Raise and support vehicle, and remove wheel. Disconnect brake line connections at caliper, and cap lines to prevent entry of foreign matter. Remove caliper mounting bolts and lift caliper from vehicle.

VOLVO (Cont.)

Installation – Position caliper assembly on mounting bracket, and install attaching bolts. After installing bolts, check clearance between disc pads and rotor on both sides of rotor; maximum deviation between sides should not exceed .022″ (.01 mm) for front calipers or .010″ (.25 mm) for rear calipers. If clearance is not within specifications, correct by adding shims to caliper. Connect hydraulic lines and bleed hydraulic system.

DISC BRAKE ROTOR

Removal & Installation – With caliper assembly removed, mount a dial indicator and check rotor runout. Runout must not exceed .004″ (.10 mm). Measure rotor thickness through one revolution; thickness variance must not exceed .0008″ (.02 mm). Unscrew rotor lock bolts and pull rotor from hub. To install, reverse removal procedure.

PARKING BRAKE SHOES

Removal – Remove center console rear ash tray and loosen parking brake cable adjusting nut until cables are slack. Raise

and support rear of vehicle and remove wheels. Remove caliper (without disconnecting hydraulic line) and support out of way, then remove rotor. Remove brake shoe return springs and lift off shoes and adjuster.

Installation – Reverse removal procedure and note the following: Replace brake drum (rotor) if out-of-round more than .008″ (.2 mm). Apply a thin coat of heat resistant graphite grease to brake shoe sliding surfaces and to adjusting starwheel. After installation, adjust parking brake. See *Parking Brake.*

MASTER CYLINDER

Removal & Installation – Disconnect hydraulic lines at master cylinder and cap openings to prevent entry of foreign matter. Remove cylinder attaching hardware, and remove cylinder assembly from vehicle. To install, reverse removal procedure, and bleed hydraulic system.

POWER BRAKE UNIT

Removal & Installation – With master cylinder removed, disconnect vacuum hose at power unit. From inside vehicle, disconnect push rod link at brake pedal and remove clutch pedal stop bracket. Remove power unit attaching nuts at firewall. Tilt power unit slightly forward and remove lock nut and yoke. Remove power unit from engine compartment. To install, reverse removal procedure and note: Install new gasket between power unit and firewall; discarding sealing putty (if equipped). Install vacuum hose connector facing down. Bleed hydraulic system.

Check Valve Replacement – Remove vacuum hose clamps at check valve, and remove check valve from vehicle. When installing check valve into vacuum hose, install valve with arrow on valve housing pointing toward intake manifold.

Filter Replacement – Remove power brake unit from vehicle. Remove rubber dust boot, and filter retainer washer. Withdraw silencer and filter from end of booster. To install, reverse removal procedure, making sure slots in filter and silencer are 180° apart.

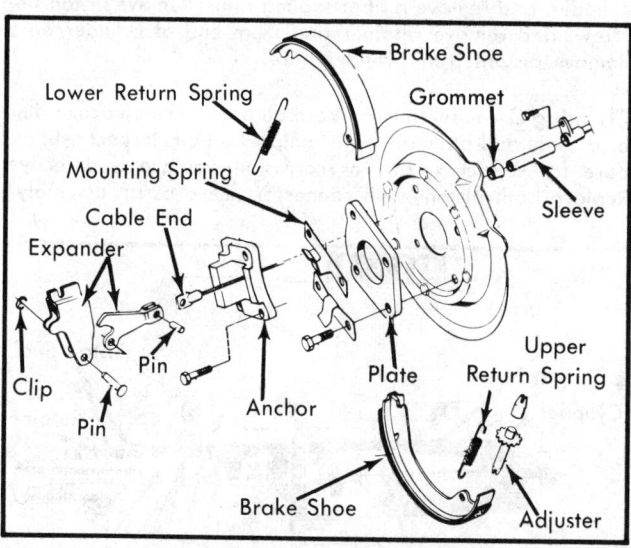

Fig. 2   Exploded View of Parking Brake Assembly

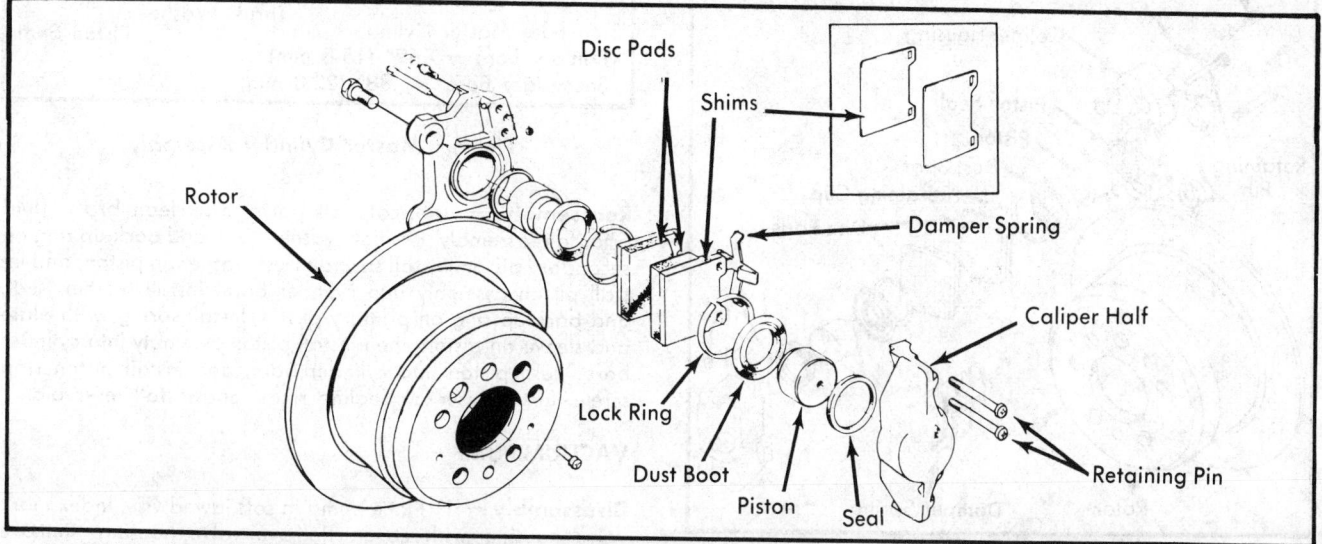

Fig. 3   ATE Rear Caliper Assembly

Brakes

VOLVO (Cont.)

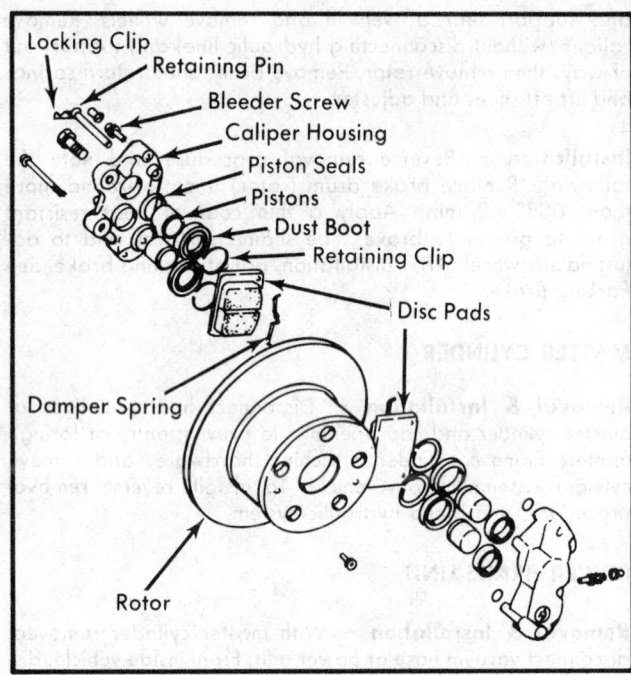

Fig. 4 Girling Front Caliper Assembly

VACUUM PUMP

Removal & Installation — Disconnect hoses at vacuum pump and remove mounting bolts and pump. Clean mating surfaces to remove gasket material, install new gasket and reverse removal procedure to complete installation.

OVERHAUL

BRAKE CALIPER

Disassembly — With caliper removed from vehicle, remove disc pads, piston dust covers and retaining clips. Insert wooden

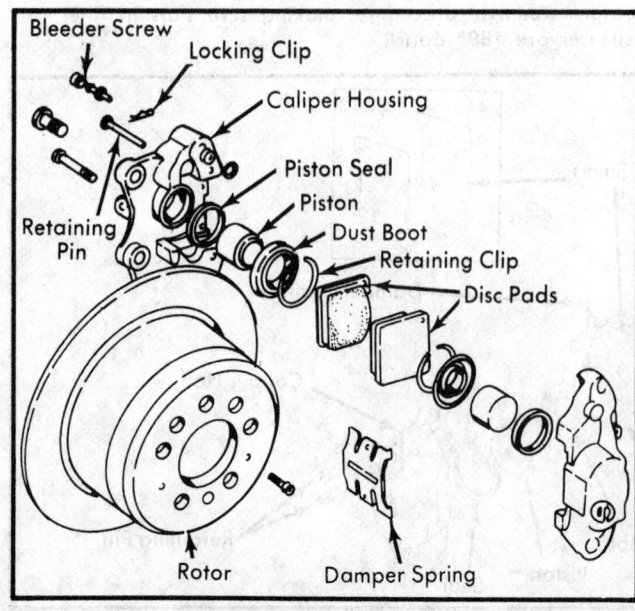

Fig. 5 Girling Rear Caliper Assembly

block into caliper housing and apply compressed air at fluid inlet ports to force pistons out of caliper. Remove piston seals from cylinder bore with blunt tool without damaging cylinder bore. Remove bleeder screw.

NOTE — *DO NOT separate caliper halves.*

Cleaning & Inspection — Clean all parts in brake fluid or alcohol. Inspect cylinder bores for scoring, rust or corrosion, replace if defective. Replace rubber seals and dust covers during overhaul.

Reassembly — Coat all parts with clean brake fluid and install new piston seals in cylinder bores. Carefully install pistons into cylinder bores. Check piston position on ATE rear brake calipers. Install rubber dust boots and retaining clips. Install bleeder screw and disc pads.

MASTER CYLINDER

Disassembly — Remove master cylinder from vehicle, and clamp mounting flange in a vise. Remove reservoir from cylinder, and remove rubber sealing rings. Remove piston stop screw, and remove retainer ring from end of cylinder bore. Remove pistons from cylinder bore.

Cleaning & Inspection — Wash all parts in clean brake fluid or alcohol and blow dry with compressed air. Inspect cylinder bore for scratches, rust or corrosion; replace if defective. Replace both pistons with connector sleeve as an assembly.

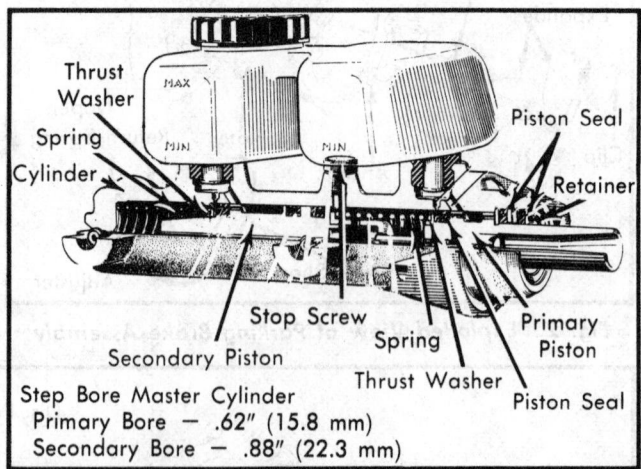

Fig. 6 Master Cylinder Assembly

Reassembly — Lubricate all parts with clean brake fluid prior to reassembly. Position washer, seal, and back-up ring on secondary piston. Install spring thrust washer on piston, and install piston assembly into cylinder bore. Install washer, seal, and back-up ring on primary piston. Install spring, with plate and sleeve on piston, then install piston assembly into cylinder bore. Push piston into cylinder bore, and install piston stop screw. Install reservoir sealing rings, and install reservoir.

VACUUM PUMP

Disassembly — 1) Place pump in soft jawed vise. Index mark valve housing with cover. Remove valve housing. Remove diaphragm, washers, and spring from pump.

Brakes

8-109

BRAKES

VOLVO (Cont.)

2) Turn pump over. Remove bottom cover. Remove actuating lever pin. Slide out pump lever, pump rod and nylon bushing.

Reassembly — 1) Place bushing on pump rod. Put rod in pump housing. Fit lever and pin. Install bottom cover and gasket.

2) Place washer and "O" ring on diaphragm screw. Remember to lightly coat end of screw with suitable thread locking compound. Install diaphragm assembly. Insert valve housing aligned with index marks. Fit valves and seals. Make sure domed side disc faces diaphragm. Install valve housing cover with spring and gasket.

TIGHTENING SPECIFICATIONS

Application	Ft. Lbs. (N·m)
Front Caliper Mounting Bolts	65-72 (88-98)
Rear Caliper Mounting Bolts	38-46 (52-63)

DISC BRAKE SPECIFICATIONS

Application	Caliper Bore Diameter In. (mm)	Lateral Runout In. (mm)	Parallelism In. (mm)	Original Thickness In. (mm)	Minimum Refinish Thickness In. (mm)	Discard Thickness In. (mm)
DL & GL Front	.....	.004 (.10)	.0008 (.02)	.563 (14.3)	.557① (14.1)	.....
Rear	.....	.004 (.10)	.0008 (.02)	.378 (9.6)	.331 (8.4)	.....
GLT Turbo, GLE, Bertone & Diesel Front	.....	.004 (.10)	.0008 (.02)	.945 (24.0)	.990① (22.8)	.....
Rear	.....	.004 (.10)	.0008 (.02)	.378 (9.6)	.331 (8.4)	.....

① — Minimum Refinish Thickness is stamped on all rotors. Adhere to stamped specifications.

Contents

Section 9
WHEEL ALIGNMENT

NOTE — ALSO SEE GENERAL INDEX.

Wheel Alignment

WHEEL ALIGNMENT TROUBLE SHOOTING

CONDITION & POSSIBLE CAUSE	CONDITION & POSSIBLE CAUSE
Uneven or Premature Tire Wear • Improper tire inflation. • Front end alignment out of tolerance. • Suspension and/or steering system components worn or damaged. • Toe-in incorrect. • Improper standing height. • Brake dragging. • Excessive wheel bearing play. • Poor driving habits. • Uneven or sagging springs. • Bent wheel. • Improper torsion bar adjustment. • Loose or worn wheel bearings. • Worn or defective shock absorbers. • Tires out of balance. • Bent wheel rotor. • Overloaded vehicle.	**Hard Steering** • Idler arm bushing too tight. • Ball joint tight or seized. • Steering linkage too tight. • Ball joints and steering linkage need lubrication. • Power steering fluid low. • Power steering drive belt loose or broken. • Power steering pump defective. • Steering gear not adjusted properly (sector shaft or worm gear too tight). • Incorrect wheel alignment (excessive caster). • Damaged steering gear or suspension components. • Bent steering knuckle or supports. **Vehicle "Wanders"** • Idler arm, ball joints or steering linkage worn or binding. • Strut rod or control arm bushings worn. • Loose or worn wheel bearings. • Improper tire pressure. • Stabilizer bar missing or defective. • Wheel alignment out of tolerance. • Broken springs. • Defective shock absorbers. • Damaged steering gear or suspension components.
Pulls to One Side • Improper tire inflation. • Brake dragging. • Mismatched tires (uneven diameter, different tread design or construction). • Broken or sagging spring or torsion bar. • Power steering valve not centered. • Front end alignment out of tolerance. • Defective wheel bearing. • Uneven sway bar links. • Bent frame. • Steering system bushings worn. • Idler arm bushing too tight. • Uneven loading.	**Front End Shimmy** • Tire out of balance. • Tire and/or wheel out of round. • Excessive wheel runout. • Insufficient or improper caster. • Worn suspenson or steering system components. • Defective shock absorbers. • Wheel bearings worn or loose. • Power steering reaction bracket loose. • Tire stiffness variation. • Steering gear rack or box mounting loose. • Steering gear adjustment loose. • Worn spherical joints (front wheel drive).

Radial Tire Lead — Some alignment problems involving "lead" or pull to one side have been caused by off-center belts on radial tires. To diagnose this problem inflate tires to recommended pressure and drive vehicle both directions on an uncrowned road. Observe and note any "lead", then switch front tires and road test again. If lead is corrected without roughness, leave tires in position. If roughness results, replace tires. If lead reverses, install a known good tire on one side and repeat road test. If lead remains, install a known good tire in place of other front tire. If lead remains, recheck alignment. It may be necessary to adjust caster so that leading side is 1° more positive than other side.

WHEEL ALIGNMENT SPECIFICATIONS

Application	Caster (Degrees)	Camber (Degrees)	Toe-In (Inches)	Remarks
AUDI				
4000				① — Toe-in given in degrees.
Front	$\frac{1}{2} \pm \frac{1}{2}$	$-\frac{2}{3} \pm \frac{1}{2}$	$\frac{1}{6} \pm \frac{1}{6}$ ①	② — $1\frac{1}{6} \pm \frac{2}{3}$ for Turbo.
Rear	.....	$-1 \pm \frac{1}{3}$	$\frac{1}{3} \pm \frac{1}{3}$ ①	
5000				
Front	$-\frac{1}{6} \pm \frac{2}{3}$ ②	$-\frac{1}{2} \pm \frac{1}{2}$	$\frac{1}{12}$ to $-\frac{1}{6}$ ①	
Rear	.....	$-\frac{1}{2} \pm \frac{1}{2}$	$\frac{1}{6}$ to $\frac{5}{12}$ ①	
BMW				
320i				
Front	$8\frac{1}{3} \pm \frac{1}{2}$	$0 \pm \frac{1}{2}$	$\frac{3}{64}$ to $\frac{3}{32}$	
Rear	.....	$-2 \pm \frac{1}{2}$	0 to $\frac{5}{64}$	
528i				
Front	$7\frac{2}{3} \pm \frac{1}{2}$	$\frac{1}{2} \pm \frac{1}{2}$	$\frac{3}{64}$ to $\frac{3}{32}$	
Rear	.....	$-2 \pm \frac{1}{2}$	0 to $\frac{5}{6}$	
633CSi & 733i				
Front	$9 \pm \frac{1}{2}$	$0 \pm \frac{1}{2}$	0 to $\frac{1}{16}$	
Rear	.....	$-1 \pm \frac{1}{2}$	$\frac{5}{64}$ to $\frac{9}{64}$	
CHRYSLER CORP. IMPORTS				
Arrow	$2\frac{1}{12} \pm \frac{1}{2}$	$1 \pm \frac{1}{2}$	$\frac{5}{64}$ to $\frac{15}{64}$	① — A toe-in to toe-out range.
Champ & Colt				
Hatchback	$\frac{5}{6} \pm \frac{1}{3}$	$\frac{1}{2} \pm \frac{1}{2}$	$\frac{5}{32}$ to $\frac{5}{64}$ ①	
Challenger & Sapporo	$2\frac{2}{3} \pm \frac{1}{2}$	$1\frac{1}{6} \pm \frac{1}{2}$	0 to $\frac{9}{32}$	
Colt Wagon	$2\frac{2}{3} \pm \frac{1}{2}$	$1\frac{1}{4} \pm \frac{1}{2}$	$\frac{5}{64}$ to $\frac{23}{64}$	
Arrow & Ram-50 Pickup	$2\frac{1}{2} \pm 1$	$1 \pm \frac{1}{2}$	$\frac{5}{64}$ to $\frac{23}{64}$	
COURIER				
Pickup	$\frac{3}{4}$ to $1\frac{1}{4}$	$\frac{1}{2}$ to $1\frac{1}{4}$	0 to $\frac{1}{4}$	
DATSUN				
200SX	$2\frac{1}{2} \pm \frac{3}{4}$	$\frac{1}{12} \pm \frac{3}{4}$	0 to $\frac{5}{64}$	① — $2\frac{3}{4} \pm \frac{3}{4}$ for Wagon.
210	$2\frac{5}{12} \pm \frac{3}{4}$ ①	$\frac{3}{4} \pm \frac{3}{4}$	$\frac{3}{64}$ to $\frac{1}{8}$	② — $1\frac{2}{3} \pm \frac{3}{4}$ for Wagon.
280ZX				③ — $-\frac{5}{6} \pm \frac{3}{4}$ for Wagon.
Front	$4\frac{11}{12} \pm \frac{3}{4}$	$\frac{1}{6} \pm \frac{3}{4}$	$\frac{3}{64}$ to $\frac{1}{8}$	④ — $1\frac{2}{3} \pm \frac{1}{2}$ for 4-WD.
Rear	.....	$\frac{2}{3} \pm \frac{3}{4}$	$\frac{5}{64}$ to $\frac{5}{32}$	
310				
Front	$1\frac{1}{6} \pm \frac{3}{4}$	$1 \pm \frac{3}{4}$	0 to $\frac{5}{64}$	
Rear	.....	$\frac{3}{4} \pm 1$	0	
510	$1\frac{5}{6} \pm \frac{3}{4}$ ②	$\frac{1}{2} \pm \frac{3}{4}$ ③	$\frac{3}{64}$ to $\frac{1}{8}$	
810				
Front	$1\frac{11}{12} \pm \frac{3}{4}$	$\frac{3}{4} \pm \frac{3}{4}$	0 to $\frac{3}{64}$	
Rear	.....	$1\frac{1}{6} \pm \frac{3}{4}$	$\frac{5}{32}$ to $\frac{35}{64}$	
Pickup	$1\frac{1}{3} \pm \frac{1}{2}$ ④	$\frac{1}{2} \pm \frac{1}{2}$	$\frac{13}{64}$ to $\frac{9}{32}$	
FIAT				
Brava	$3\frac{1}{4} \pm \frac{1}{2}$	$1 \pm \frac{1}{2}$	$\frac{5}{32}$ to $\frac{5}{16}$	① — Toe-out.
Spider 2000	$3\frac{1}{4} \pm \frac{1}{2}$	$\frac{1}{4} \pm \frac{1}{2}$	$\frac{5}{32}$ to $\frac{1}{4}$	
Strada				
Front	$2 \pm \frac{1}{2}$	$1\frac{1}{2} \pm \frac{1}{4}$	$\frac{3}{32}$ to $\frac{1}{8}$ ①	
Rear	.....	$1 \pm \frac{1}{2}$	0 to $\frac{1}{32}$	
X1/9				
Front	$7 \pm \frac{1}{2}$	$-\frac{1}{2} \pm \frac{1}{2}$	$\frac{1}{16}$ to $\frac{3}{16}$	
Rear	.....	$-1\frac{1}{4} \pm \frac{1}{2}$	$\frac{5}{32}$ to $\frac{1}{4}$	

Wheel Alignment

WHEEL ALIGNMENT SPECIFICATIONS (Cont.)

Application	Caster (Degrees)	Camber (Degrees)	Toe-In (Inches)	Remarks
HONDA				
Accord				① — Toe-out.
Front	$1\frac{1}{3}\pm1$	$\frac{1}{3}\pm1$	$\frac{3}{64}\pm\frac{5}{64}$①	② — Toe-in.
Rear	.....	.....	$\frac{3}{64}\pm\frac{5}{64}$②	③ — 1 ± 1 for Wagon.
Civic				
Front	$1\frac{3}{4}\pm1$③	0 ± 1	$0\pm\frac{1}{8}$①	
Rear			$\frac{5}{64}\pm\frac{5}{64}$②	
Prelude				
Front	$1\frac{1}{2}\pm1$	0 ± 1	$0\pm\frac{1}{8}$①	
Rear	.....	.....	$\frac{1}{8}$②	
ISUZU				
I-Mark	$5\frac{1}{6}\pm1\frac{1}{4}$	$\frac{1}{6}\pm\frac{3}{4}$	$\frac{5}{64}\pm\frac{11}{64}$	
P'UP	$\frac{1}{2}\pm\frac{1}{2}$	$\frac{1}{2}\pm\frac{1}{2}$	$\frac{5}{64}\pm\frac{5}{32}$	
JAGUAR				
XJ6				
Front	$2\frac{1}{4}\pm\frac{1}{4}$	$\frac{1}{2}\pm\frac{1}{4}$	$\frac{1}{16}$ to $\frac{1}{8}$	
Rear	.....	$-\frac{3}{4}\pm\frac{1}{4}$	0 to $\frac{1}{32}$	
LUV				
2-WD Pickup	$\frac{1}{2}$	$\frac{1}{2}$	$\frac{5}{64}$	
4-WD Pickup	$\frac{1}{3}$	$\frac{7}{12}$	$\frac{5}{64}$	
MAZDA				
GLC	$2\pm\frac{3}{4}$①	$1\pm\frac{1}{2}$②	0 to $\frac{1}{8}$	① — $1\frac{3}{4}\pm\frac{3}{4}$ for Wagon.
626	③	$1\frac{1}{4}\pm\frac{1}{2}$	0 to $\frac{15}{64}$	② — $1\pm\frac{1}{2}$ for Wagon.
RX7	④	$1\pm\frac{1}{2}$	0 to $\frac{15}{64}$	③ — $3\frac{2}{3}\pm\frac{3}{4}$ for right side,
B2000 Pickup	$1\pm\frac{1}{3}$	$\frac{3}{4}\pm\frac{1}{3}$	0 to $\frac{15}{64}$	$3\frac{1}{6}\pm\frac{3}{4}$ for left side.
				④ — $4\frac{1}{6}\pm\frac{1}{2}$ for right side,
				$3\frac{2}{3}\pm\frac{1}{2}$ for left side.
MERCEDES-BENZ				
280E, 300SD	$10\pm\frac{1}{2}$	$-\frac{1}{6}\pm\frac{1}{6}$	$\frac{1}{8}\pm\frac{3}{64}$	
All Others	$8\frac{3}{4}\pm\frac{1}{2}$	$0\pm\frac{1}{6}$	$\frac{1}{8}\pm\frac{3}{64}$	
PEUGEOT				
504	$2\frac{2}{3}\pm\frac{1}{2}$	$-\frac{2}{3}\pm\frac{1}{2}$	$\frac{5}{64}$ to $\frac{5}{32}$	
505	.....	$\frac{2}{3}\pm\frac{1}{2}$	$\frac{1}{8}$ to $\frac{5}{32}$	
604				
Front	$3\frac{1}{2}\pm\frac{1}{2}$	$\frac{1}{2}\pm\frac{3}{4}$	$\frac{5}{64}$ to $\frac{5}{32}$	
Rear	.....	$-1\frac{1}{2}\pm\frac{1}{2}$	$\frac{3}{64}$ to $\frac{5}{32}$	
PORSCHE				
911SC				
Front	$6\frac{1}{12}\pm\frac{1}{4}$	$\frac{1}{2}\pm\frac{1}{6}$	$0$①	① — Toe-in given in
Rear	.....	$0\pm\frac{1}{6}$	$\frac{1}{6}\pm\frac{1}{6}$①	degrees.
924				② — $\frac{5}{12}\pm\frac{1}{2}$ for
Front	$2\frac{3}{4}\pm\frac{1}{2}$	$-\frac{1}{3}\pm\frac{1}{4}$	$0\pm\frac{1}{6}$①	924 Turbo "Sport".
Rear	.....	$1\pm\frac{1}{2}$②	$0\pm\frac{1}{12}$①	
928				
Front	$3\frac{1}{2}\pm\frac{1}{2}$	$-\frac{1}{2}\pm\frac{1}{6}$	$0\pm\frac{1}{12}$①	
Rear	.....	$-\frac{2}{3}\pm\frac{1}{6}$	$\frac{1}{6}\pm\frac{1}{12}$①	
RENAULT				
Le Car				
Front	$12\frac{1}{2}\pm\frac{1}{2}$	$\frac{1}{2}\pm\frac{1}{2}$	$\frac{3}{64}$ to $\frac{3}{16}$	① — Toe-out given in
Rear	.....	$\frac{1}{2}\pm\frac{1}{2}$	$\frac{3}{64}$ to $\frac{1}{8}$	degrees.
18i				
Front	$3\pm\frac{1}{2}$	$0\pm\frac{1}{2}$	$\frac{1}{6}\pm\frac{1}{6}$①	
Rear	.....	$\frac{1}{4}\pm\frac{1}{4}$	$\frac{1}{8}\pm\frac{1}{8}$①	

WHEEL ALIGNMENT SPECIFICATIONS (Cont.)

Application	Caster (Degrees)	Camber (Degrees)	Toe-In (Inches)	Remarks
SAAB				
900	$2 \pm \frac{1}{2}$	$\frac{1}{2} \pm \frac{1}{2}$	$\frac{5}{64} \pm \frac{3}{64}$	
SUBARU				
Exc. 4-WD Wagon				① — $-1\frac{1}{4}$ to $\frac{1}{4}$ for Wagon.
Front	$-1\frac{1}{6}$ to $\frac{1}{3}$ ①	$1\frac{1}{2} \pm \frac{3}{4}$	$\frac{5}{64}$ to $\frac{5}{16}$	② — $1\frac{3}{4} \pm \frac{3}{4}$ for Wagon.
Rear	.....	$0 \pm \frac{3}{4}$	$0 \pm \frac{1}{8}$	
4-WD Wagon				
Front	$-1\frac{5}{12}$ to $\frac{1}{12}$	$1\frac{11}{12}$ to $3\frac{1}{3}$	$\frac{15}{64}$ to $\frac{15}{32}$	
Rear	.....	$-\frac{5}{12}$ to $1\frac{1}{12}$	$-\frac{1}{8}$ to $\frac{1}{8}$	
BRAT				
Front	$-3\frac{1}{4} \pm 1\frac{2}{3}$	$1\frac{1}{3} \pm \frac{3}{4}$	$\frac{5}{64}$ to $\frac{15}{64}$	
Rear	.....	$1\frac{1}{3} \pm \frac{3}{4}$	$\frac{5}{64}$ to $\frac{15}{64}$	
TOYOTA				
Celica	$1\frac{2}{3} \pm 1$	$\frac{11}{12} \pm 1$	$\frac{3}{64} \pm \frac{3}{64}$ ①	① — $\frac{5}{32} \pm \frac{3}{64}$ with power steering.
Corolla	$1\frac{3}{4} \pm \frac{1}{2}$ ②	$1 \pm \frac{1}{2}$	$\frac{1}{8} \pm \frac{1}{64}$ ③	② — $1\frac{1}{2} \pm \frac{1}{2}$ for Wagon.
Corona	$1\frac{1}{2} \pm \frac{1}{2}$	$1 \pm \frac{1}{2}$	$\frac{1}{8} \pm \frac{3}{64}$ ③	③ — $\frac{3}{64} \pm \frac{3}{64}$ with radial tires.
Cressida	$1\frac{1}{2} \pm \frac{1}{2}$	$\frac{5}{6} \pm \frac{1}{2}$	$\frac{1}{8}$	④ — $\frac{3}{64} \pm \frac{5}{64}$ with radial tires.
Land Cruiser	$1 \pm \frac{3}{4}$	$1 \pm \frac{3}{4}$	$\frac{7}{64} \pm \frac{5}{64}$ ④	⑤ — $\frac{1}{8} \pm \frac{3}{64}$ with radial tires.
2-WD Pickup	$1 \pm \frac{1}{2}$	$\frac{11}{12} \pm \frac{1}{2}$	$\frac{13}{64} \pm \frac{3}{4}$ ⑤	⑥ — Toe-in with radial tires $\frac{5}{64} \pm \frac{1}{32}$
4-WD Pickup	$3\frac{1}{2} \pm \frac{2}{3}$	$1 \pm \frac{2}{3}$	$\frac{5}{32} \pm \frac{3}{64}$ ③	⑦ — Station Wagon $1\frac{3}{4} \pm \frac{1}{3}$.
Starlet	$2 \pm \frac{1}{3}$ ⑦	$\frac{2}{3} \pm \frac{1}{3}$	$\frac{5}{32} \pm \frac{25}{64}$ ⑥	
Supra	$4\frac{1}{6} \pm \frac{1}{2}$	$\frac{5}{6} \pm \frac{1}{2}$	$\frac{1}{8} \pm \frac{3}{64}$	
Tercel				
Front	$2\frac{1}{6} \pm \frac{1}{2}$	$\frac{1}{2} \pm \frac{1}{2}$	$\frac{5}{64} \pm \frac{3}{64}$	
Rear	.....	$0 \pm \frac{1}{2}$	$0 \pm \frac{3}{64}$	
TRIUMPH				
TR7 & TR8	$3\frac{1}{2} \pm 1$	$-\frac{1}{4} \pm 1$	0 to $\frac{1}{16}$	
VOLKSWAGEN				
Dasher				① — Toe-in given in degrees.
Front	$\frac{1}{2} \pm \frac{1}{2}$	$\frac{1}{2} \pm \frac{1}{2}$	$\frac{1}{6}$ to $\frac{1}{4}$ ①	
Rear	.....	$-\frac{2}{3} \pm \frac{2}{3}$	$0 \pm \frac{5}{6}$ ①	
Jetta, Rabbit & Scirocco				
Front	$1\frac{5}{6} \pm \frac{1}{2}$	$\frac{1}{3} \pm \frac{1}{2}$	$\frac{1}{4} \pm \frac{1}{6}$ ①	
Rear	.....	$1\frac{1}{4} \pm \frac{7}{12}$	$\frac{1}{3} \pm \frac{1}{3}$ ①	
Rabbit Pickup				
Front	$1\frac{5}{6} \pm \frac{1}{2}$	$\frac{1}{3} \pm \frac{1}{2}$	$-\frac{1}{4}$ to $\frac{1}{6}$ ①	
Rear	.....	$0 \pm \frac{7}{12}$	$\frac{1}{3} \pm \frac{1}{3}$ ①	
Vanagon				
Front	$7\frac{1}{4} \pm \frac{1}{4}$	$0 \pm \frac{1}{2}$	$\frac{1}{6} \pm \frac{1}{4}$ ①	
Rear	.....	$-\frac{5}{6} \pm \frac{1}{2}$	$0 \pm \frac{1}{6}$ ①	
VOLVO				
All Models				① — $\frac{1}{2} \pm \frac{1}{4}$ for GLT.
Man. Steering	$2\frac{1}{2} \pm \frac{1}{2}$	$1\frac{1}{4} \pm \frac{1}{4}$ ①	$\frac{3}{16} \pm \frac{1}{16}$	
Pow. Steering	$3\frac{1}{2} \pm \frac{1}{2}$	$1\frac{1}{4} \pm \frac{1}{4}$ ①	$\frac{1}{8} \pm \frac{1}{16}$	

Wheel Alignment

AUDI

ADJUSTMENT

TIRE INFLATION (COLD)

Before attempting to check and adjust wheel alignment, ensure tires are properly inflated. Tire sizes and pressures can be found on a sticker located on side panel of left door on all models.

NOTE — *Vehicles must not be loaded down with passengers or any weight that would cause vehicle to lean or sag and affect riding height.*

CASTER

Caster angle is not adjustable. If caster is not within specifications, check suspension components for excessive wear or damage. Replace components as necessary to bring caster into specifications.

CAMBER

4000 — With vehicle properly positioned on alignment rack, measure camber angle. If not within specifications, loosen ball joint mounting bolts on control arm and install Wedge Tool (US 4490). Tighten adjusting nut to break joint loose from control arm. *See Fig. 1.*

NOTE — *When tool nut is loosened, weight of vehicle will move wheel to negative camber. After adjustment, retorque ball joint nuts to 47 ft. lbs. (64 N·m).*

5000 — Work under hood and loosen the 3 upper strut mounting nuts. Place a socket over suspension strut nut. Move strut around in slots until camber is correct. Tighten nuts to 14 ft. lbs. (19 N·m).

Fig. 1 Camber Adjusting Tool for Audi 4000

TOE-IN

Loosen adjustable tie rod lock nuts (5000) or clamp and lock nut (4000). Rotate threaded collar (5000) or rod (4000) until toe-in is within specifications. Tighten locking components. If necessary, remove steering wheel and reposition so wheel spokes are horizontal when front wheels point straight-ahead.

BMW

ADJUSTMENT

TIRE INFLATION (COLD)

Before attempting to check and adjust wheel alignment, ensure tires are properly inflated. Tire sizes and pressures can be found in the owner's manual.

CASTER & CAMBER

Before checking caster and camber, vehicle must be in loaded condition. *See Vehicle Loading Table.* If caster or camber are not within specifications, check suspension components for damage.

Vehicle Loading Table	
Application	①**Lbs. (kg)**
Each Front Seat	150 (68)
Rear Seat	150 (68)
Luggage Compartment	46 (21)

① — Fuel tank full.

TOE-IN

Before checking toe-in, vehicle must be in loaded condition. *See Vehicle Loading Table.* Check toe-in with front wheels in straight-ahead position. If not within specifications, loosen tie rod tubes until correct toe-in is obtained. Tighten clamping bolts.

CHRYSLER CORP. IMPORTS

ADJUSTMENT

TIRE INFLATION (COLD)

Before attempting to check and adjust wheel alignment, ensure tires are properly inflated. Tire sizes and pressures can be found in owner's manual.

CASTER

Pickups — To adjust caster, adjust by tightening upper arm shaft. A half turn of upper arm shaft will cause .049" (1.25 mm) front or rear movement of upper arm shaft, resulting in ¼° change in caster adjustment.

All Others — Caster, as a general rule, requires no adjustment. However, slight adjustment can be made by moving strut bar nut until specified caster angle is obtained.

CAMBER

Pickups — To adjust camber, hold upper arm shaft-to-crossmember bolt in position and remove nut from engine compartment side. Adjust number of shims between upper arm shaft and crossmember until correct camber specification is obtained.

All Others — Camber requires no adjustment. Steering knuckle is integral with strut assembly and camber is preset at

CHRYSLER CORP. IMPORTS (Cont.)

the factory. If camber is not within specifications, check suspension components for damage.

TOE-IN

Arrow, Champ & Colt Hatchbacks — Position wheels in straight-ahead position. If toe-in is not to specifications, loosen locking nuts on tie rod turnbuckles. Rotate buckles until toe-in is within specifications. Tighten lock nuts. Adjustment must be made equally to both sides of vehicle.

All Others — Position wheels in straight-ahead position. If toe-in is not to specifications, loosen locking nut on left tie rod turnbuckle. Rotate buckle until toe-in is within specifications. Tighten lock nut.

NOTE — *After adjusting toe-in, check difference in lengths of left and right tie rods. If difference exceeds .20" (5 mm), remove right tie rod and adjust length until difference is .20" (5 mm) or less.*

COURIER

ADJUSTMENT

TIRE INFLATION

Before attempting caster or camber adjustments, ensure tires are correctly inflated. Specifications are located on glove box door; especially consider radial tires, they require a different pressure than conventional tires.

NOTE — *Vehicle must be unloaded, except fuel, water, and oil should be at their proper levels.*

CASTER

To adjust caster, adjust shims between upper control arm and frame or turn control arm shaft until correct specifications are obtained.

CAMBER

To adjust camber, adjust shims between upper control arm and frame until correct specifications are obtained. Shims are available in the following sizes: .039" (1 mm), .063" (1.6 mm), .079" (2 mm) and .126" (3.2 mm).

TOE-IN

1) Raise vehicle until front wheels clear ground. Turn wheel by hand and scribe a line in center of each tire tread. Measure distance between marked lines in front of front wheel and at rear of front wheel. Both measurements must be taken at equal distances from ground.

2) If distance between wheels at rear is greater than that at front, but within specifications, adjustment is correct. If adjustment is wrong, loosen clamp bolts and adjust tie rod to specifications.

NOTE — *Tighten clamping bolts with bolts horizontal and below steering link to prevent interference with center steering link.*

DATSUN

ADJUSTMENT

TIRE INFLATION (COLD)

Before attempting to check or adjust wheel alignment, make sure that tires are properly inflated. Refer to manufacturer's specifications given in owner's manual.

CASTER

Pickup — Caster is adjusted by increasing or decreasing thickness of shims inserted between upper link spindle and upper link mounting bracket. Caster adjustment affects camber adjustment, if you change caster specification, camber specification is also changed.

NOTE — *Total thickness of shims must be within .236" (6.0 mm) and must not collectively total more than 3 individual shims. Difference of total thickness between front and rear must be within .079" (2.0 mm).*

All Others — Caster is preset at factory and cannot be adjusted. If not to specifications, check suspension for wear or damage and repair or replace components as necessary.

CAMBER

Pickup — Camber is adjusted by increasing or decreasing thickness of shims inserted between upper link spindle and upper link mounting bracket. If you change camber adjustment you also change caster adjustment.

NOTE — *Total thickness of shims must be within .236" (6 mm) and must not collectively total more than 3 individual shims. Difference of total thickness between front and rear shims must be within .079" (2 mm).*

All Others — Camber is preset at factory and cannot be adjusted. If not to specifications, check suspension for wear or damage and repair or replace components as necessary.

TOE-IN

810 — Place front wheel facing straight ahead. Ensure steering gear faces same direction. Adjust side rod (tie rod) so that steering gear side has a distance of 14.35" (364.5 mm) bet-

Wheel Alignment

DATSUN (Cont.)

ween ball joints. Adjust idler arm side so distance between ball joints is 14.19" (360.5 mm). Tighten clamp bolts after adjustment.

All Others — Place wheels in straight-ahead position, then make sure steering wheel and steering gear are also in straight-ahead position. Adjust toe-in by varying the length of steering side rods (tie rods). Loosen lock nuts and rotate rods evenly until toe-in is within specifications.

Toe-In Specifications①		
Application	Side Rod Length② In. (mm)	Tie Rod Length③ In. (mm)
200SX	2.8 (71)	
210	12.4 (315)	
280ZX		
Man. Steering	1.16 (29.5)	
Power Steering		14.42 (366.3)
310	5.24 (133)	
510	5.0 (127)	
810	1.42 (43)	
Pickup		
2-WD		13.07 (332)
4-WD		10.83 (275)

① — Pre-alignment adjustments if side rods or tie rods have been disassembled. For final adjustment specifications, see Wheel Alignment Specifications in this section.
② — From side rod lock nut-to-boot end of side rod.
③ — From center-to-center of tie rod ends.

FIAT

ADJUSTMENT

TIRE INFLATION (COLD)

Before attempting to check or adjust wheel alignment, make sure tires are properly inflated. Refer to manufacturer's specifications given in owner's manual.

CASTER

Brava & Strada — If caster is not to specifications, raise and support front of vehicle. Remove stabilizer bar (strut rod) to control arm nut and disconnect control arm from body. Remove end of stabilizer bar (strut rod) from control arm. To adjust caster, additon of shims between end of stabilizer bar (strut rod) and rubber pad of control arm will decrease caster angle. Removal of shims will increase caster angle. Reverse removal procedure and recheck caster.

Spider 2000 — If caster is not within specifications, raise front of vehicle and remove wheel and shock absorber. Using suitable tool (A.74174), compress spring to relieve lower control arm and loosen nuts holding control arm pivot bar to crossmember. To adjust caster, remove shims from front stud and move to rear stud to increase caster. To decrease caster, remove shims from rear stud and move shims to front stud. Reverse removal procedure and check caster.

X19 — If caster is not within specifications, adjust by adding or subtracting shims located between strut rod and strut support.

CAMBER

Brava & Strada (Front) — Camber is preset at factory and cannot be adjusted. If not to specifications, check suspension for wear or damage and repair or replace components as necessary.

Strada (Rear) — If rear camber is not within specifications, raise rear of vehicle and compress one end of leaf spring (shifting it from flexible guide anchoring spring to control arm). Remove guide and slowly release spring. Remove nuts attaching pivot to body and loosen screw to free adjustment shims. To increase camber, remove equal number of shims on both bolts attaching control arm to body. To decrease camber, add an equal number of shims on both bolts. Reverse removal procedure and recheck camber.

Spider 2000 — If camber is not within specifications, adjust by changing amount of shims. Raise front of vehicle, remove wheel and shock absorber. Using suitable tool (A.74174), compress spring to relieve lower control arm and loosen nuts holding control arm pivot bar to crossmember. To increase camber, remove equal amount of shims from both studs. To decrease camber, add an equal amount of shims to both studs. Reverse removal procedure and check camber.

NOTE — Adding or removing equal amount of shims will not affect caster.

X1/9 (Front & Rear) — Camber is nonadjustable. If not within specifications, inspect suspension for damage and repair or replace parts as necessary.

TOE-IN

NOTE — Lengthen tie rod to toe wheel in and shorten tie rod to toe wheel out.

Brava, Strada & X1/9 (Front) — Place front wheels in straight-ahead position. If toe-in is not to specifications, loosen sleeve locking nut on tie rods. To adjust, rotate tie rod until correct toe-in specifications are obtained. Hold tie rod in position and lock nut against tie rod sleeve.

Spider 2000 — Place front wheels in straight-ahead position. If toe-in is not within specifications, loosen 4 clamps securing sleeves on tie rods. Rotate tie rods in opposite direction (by equal amounts) to set toe-in to specifications. Tighten clamp nuts.

NOTE — Expansion slot in sleeve must coincide with clamp joint when clamp is fully tightened.

Strada (Rear) — If rear toe-in is not to specifications, raise rear of vehicle and compress one end of leaf spring (shifting it from flexible guide anchoring spring to control arm). Remove guide and slowly release spring. Remove nuts attaching pivot

FIAT (Cont.)

to body and loosen screws to free adjustment shims. To increase toe-in, add shims to rear screw or remove shims from front screw. To decrease toe-in, add shims to front screw or remove shims from rear screw.

X1/9 (Rear) — If rear wheel toe-in is not within specifications, loosen clamps securing sleeves to reaction rods. Adjust toe-in by lengthening or shortening reaction rods. Tighten clamps and recheck toe-in.

HONDA

ADJUSTMENT

TIRE INFLATION (COLD)

Before checking or adjusting wheel alignment, make sure tires are correctly inflated. Refer to manufacturers specifications located in glove box.

RIDING HEIGHT

Make sure tires are properly inflated. Measure from top of wheel opening to ground. If front height measurement is not within specifications, check rear height before attempting to repair front suspension. *See Riding Height Specifications table.*

Riding Height Specifications		
Application	**Front** In. (mm)	**Rear** In. (mm)
Accord		
LX	25.2 (639)	23.7 (603)
Hatchback	25.6 (651)	23.7 (603)
Sedan	25.4 (646)	23.7 (603)
Civic		
Hatchback	24.8 (631)	24.4 (620)
Wagon	25.1 (638)	25.7 (653)
Sedan	24.9 (632)	24.4 (620)
Prelude	24.4 (620)	24.2 (615)

CASTER

Caster is nonadjustable. If alignment is not within specifications, inspect for damaged parts and replace as necessary.

CAMBER

Camber is nonadjustable. If alignment is not within specifications, inspect for damaged parts and replace as necessary.

TOE-OUT

Front — Loosen lock nuts at each end of tie rods. Turn tie rod until toe-out is within specifications. Use same procedure for both sides. To center steering wheel after toe has been adjusted, turn both tie rods in same direction until steering wheel (spokes) are centered. Tighten lock nuts.

TOE-IN

Rear — To adjust toe-in, loosen lock nuts on radius arm adjusting bolts. Rotate adjusting bolt until toe is within specifications, then tighten lock nuts. On Accord models, each notch on cam plate is equal to .20" (5 mm). On Civic models, each notch on cam plate is equal to .63" (16 mm). On Prelude models, each notch on cam plate is equal to .60" (15 mm).

NOTE — *Notches on cam plate are for reference only. Do not use notches to equalize adjustments on rear radius rods.*

ISUZU

ADJUSTMENT

TIRE INFLATION (COLD)

Before attempting to check and/or adjust wheel alignment, make sure tires are properly inflated. Refer to owner's manual for manufacturer's specifications. Check front end for loose parts and front coil springs for correct riding height.

CASTER

Pickup — Caster angle is set by varying length of strut rod, by loosening and turning lock nuts.

All Other Models — Caster is not adjustable. If caster is not within specifications, check suspension components as necessary to bring caster into specifications.

CAMBER

Pickup — Camber is adjusted by adding or subtracting equal amount of shims from front and rear of bolts on upper control arm.

All Other Models — Camber may be adjusted by removing the upper ball joint, rotating it 180° and reinstalling ball joint. Approximately 1° of camber may be obtained.

TOE-IN

All Models — To adjust toe-in, center steering wheel, loosen lock nuts on tie rods and turn tie rods until toe-in is within specifications. Tighten tie rod lock nuts.

JAGUAR

ADJUSTMENT

TIRE INFLATION (COLD)

Before attempting to check or adjust wheel alignment, make sure tires are properly inflated. Refer to owner's manual for manufacturer's specifications.

RIDING HEIGHT

XJ6 (Front) — Check that vehicle is full of fuel, oil and water, and that tires are properly inflated. Press down on front bumper and slowly release, then lift up on bumper and slowly release. This will settle front suspension. Measure distance between center of outer headlight and ground on both sides of vehicle. Height should be 24.6" (611 mm) minimum. To adjust height, install or remove spring spacers from front coil springs.

Wheel Alignment

JAGUAR (Cont.)

NOTE – *Spring spacers are ⅛" (3.2 mm) thick and will change riding height approximately ⁵⁄₁₆" (7.9 mm).*

XJ6 (Rear) – Check that vehicle is full of fuel, oil and water, and that tires are properly inflated. Roll vehicle forward 3 car lengths to settle rear suspension system. Measure distance between lower surface of rear crossmember and ground on both sides of vehicle. Correct height should be 7.2-7.7" (183-195 mm). If height is not within specifications, replace all 4 rear springs.

PREPARATION FOR CASTER & CAMBER ADJUSTMENT

1) Ensure vehicle is on level ground and that tires are properly inflated. Before checking or adjusting caster or camber, fabricate 2 setting tools as shown in *Fig. 1*.

2) Compress front suspension and insert tools under upper control arms, adjacent to control arm rubber stops and over brackets welded to bottom of control arms.

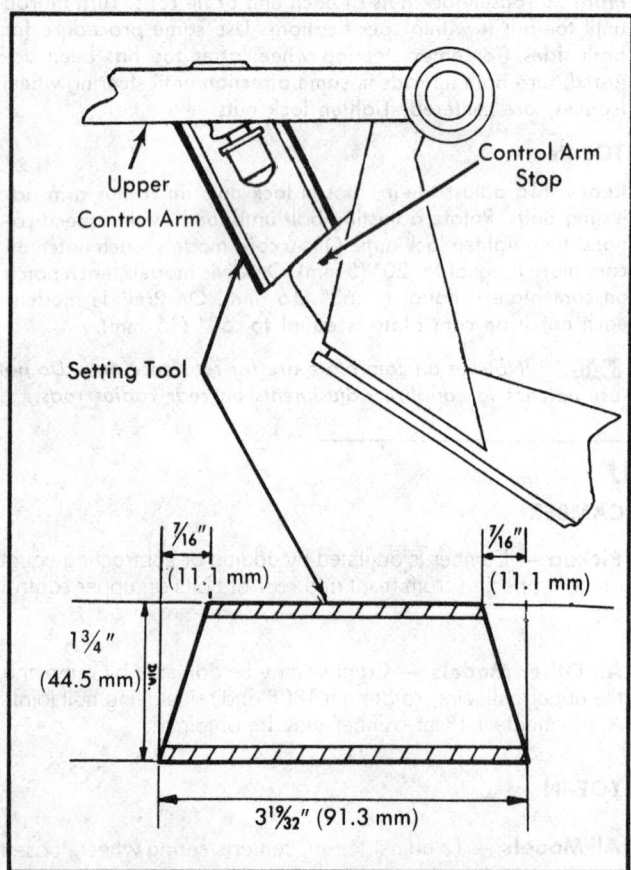

Fig. 1 Dimensions for Fabricating Setting Tools

3) Compress rear suspension and install setting links (J. 25) to lock rear suspension in place. See *Fig. 2*. Vehicle is now locked in half-loaded condition and caster and camber can be checked and adjusted.

CASTER

NOTE – *Before adjusting caster angle, make sure car is standing at normal riding height.*

XJ6 – If caster angle is not within specifications, adjust by moving shims on front and rear of upper control arm ball joint.

To increase caster, loosen bolts securing upper ball joint and move shims from rear of ball joint to front of ball joint. To decrease caster, reverse procedure. Tighten ball joint attaching bolts and recheck caster angle.

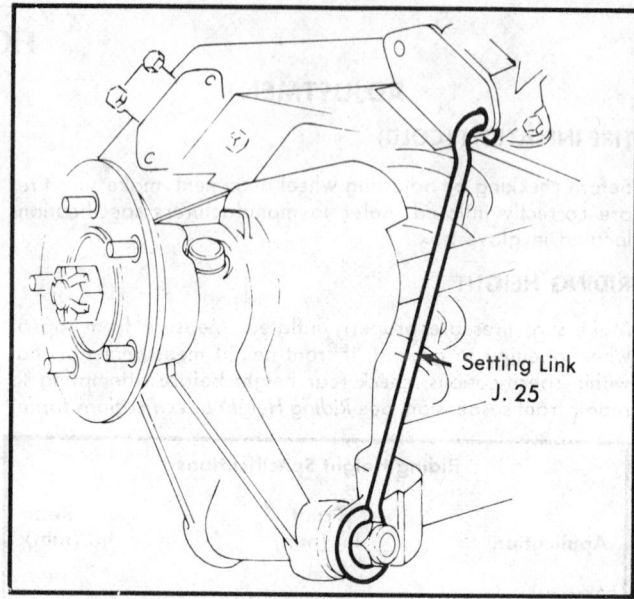

Fig. 2 Rear Suspension in Locked Position with Special Tool

CAMBER

NOTE – *Before attempting to check or adjust camber angle it will be necessary to make sure that vehicle is in half-loaded condition.*

XJ6 (Front) – Place wheels in straight-ahead position. Measure camber angle. Make sure front wheels are within ¼ ° of each other. Adjustment is accomplished by adding or subtracting shims. See *Fig. 3*. Adding shims increases camber angle. Make sure same number of shims are used on each bolt.

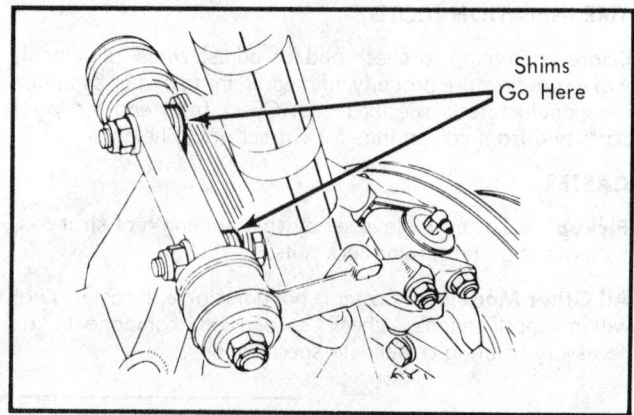

Fig. 3 Shim Placement for Front Camber Angle Adjustment

XJ6 (Rear) – Before checking rear wheel camber, rear suspension must be in the half-loaded position. See *Preparation for Caster & Camber Adjustment*. To adjust, remove suspension setting links (J. 25), raise and support rear of vehicle and remove wheels. Loosen nuts securing half-shaft to brake disc, then add or remove shims as required to bring camber angle within specifications.

JAGUAR (Cont.)

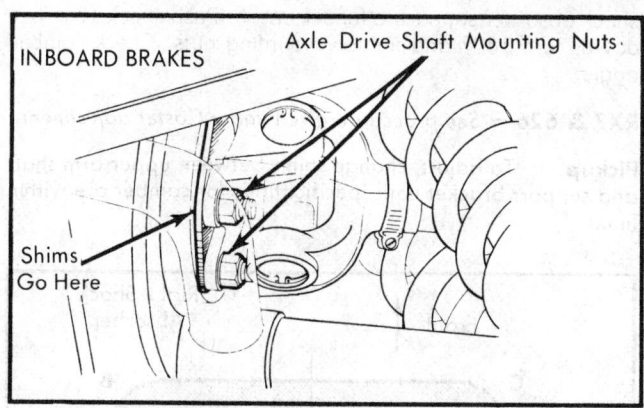

Fig. 4   Placement of Shims for Rear Camber Angle Adjustment

Labels in figure:
INBOARD BRAKES
Axle Drive Shaft Mounting Nuts
Shims Go Here

NOTE — *Addition of one .020" (.5 mm) shim will alter camber ¼°.*

TOE-IN

XJ6 — Place wheels in straight-ahead position. Remove grease nipple from rack adjuster nut. Put centralizing tool (12279) into locating hole. Push tool onto back of rack bar. Slowly turn steering wheel until tool drops into back of rack bar. Measure toe-in. If toe-in is not within specifications, adjust by loosening steering link lock nuts and rotating adjuster sleeves equal amounts, as necessary. Tighten lock nuts and recheck toe-in.

LUV

Riding Height Specifications

Application	Front In. (mm)	Rear In. (mm)
2-WD		
Standard	4.6 (116.8)	6.1 (155)
Long Wheelbase	4.6 (116.8)	7.5 (190)
4-WD	4.8 (122)	7.7 (195)

ADJUSTMENT

TIRE INFLATION

Before checking or adjusting wheel alignment, ensure tires are correctly inflated. Refer to manufacturer's specifications located in glove box or on right door lock pillar.

RIDING HEIGHT

1) Place vehicle on smooth level surface. Bounce vehicle several times. Raise vehicle and allow to settle at normal height. Measure distance as shown in *Fig. 1 and 2.*

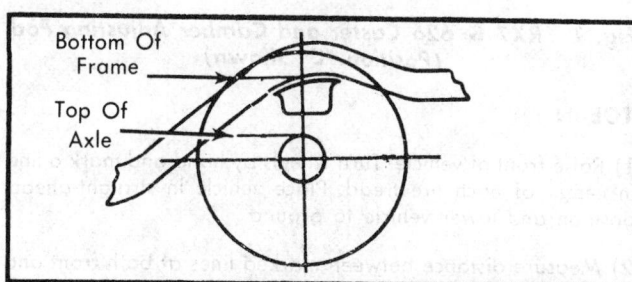

Fig. 1   Rear Suspension Riding Height Measuring Point

Labels in figure:
Bottom Of Frame
Top Of Axle

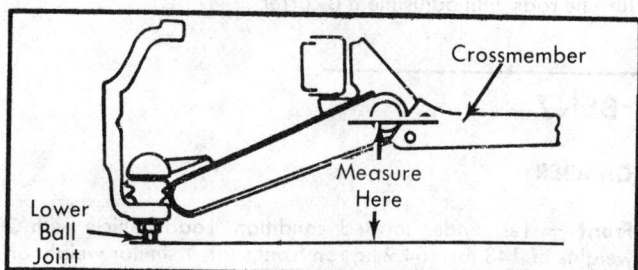

Fig. 2   Front Suspension Riding Height Measuring Point

Labels in figure:
Crossmember
Lower Ball Joint
Measure Here

NOTE — *Height check should be made with a full tank of gas, spare tire installed, and jack included. No passengers should be in vehicle.*

2) Difference between measurements of each side must not be more than ½" (12.7 mm). If an adjustment is necessary, it can be made at bolt on height control arm.

TORSION BAR SPRING HEIGHT

1) Park vehicle on level surface. Jounce vehicle several times and allow vehicle to return to settled position.

2) On 2-WD vehicles, measure buffer clearance (clearance between rubber bumper and lower control arm). Using bolt located on height control arm, adjust buffer clearance to about .866" (22 mm).

3) On all models, turn adjuster bolt on torsion bar until correct riding height specification is obtained.

NOTE — *Rotating bolt inward increases vehicle height.*

CAMBER & CASTER

Camber and caster adjustments may be made at same time with shims inserted between upper control arm pivot shaft and frame. Adding or subtracting equal number of shims at both front and rear pivot shaft bolts will decrease positive camber. Adding or subtracting shims from front to rear or rear to front pivot shaft bolts will change caster. Transfer of 1 shim from front to rear bolt will decrease positive caster.

TOE-IN

NOTE — *Toe-in must be adjusted after caster and camber adjustment.*

Toe-in can be adjusted by rotating the intermediate rod after loosening lock nuts. Rotate intermediate rod towards front of vehicle to reduce toe-in and towards rear of vehicle to increase toe-in until proper specification is obtained.

Wheel Alignment

MAZDA

ADJUSTMENT

TIRE INFLATION (COLD)

Before attempting to check or adjust wheel alignment, make sure tires are properly inflated. Refer to manufacturer's specifications given in owner's manual.

CASTER

GLC — Caster is not adjustable. If caster is not to specifications, inspect suspension for excessive wear or damage. Replace components as necessary.

RX7 & 626 — 1) Caster and camber angles are adjusted by changing position of shock absorber support. To adjust, remove 4 nuts attaching shock absorber support to fender apron. Raise front of vehicle and support with jack stands, then remove wheel on side to be adjusted.

2) Press shock absorber downward and change position of support according to table and *Fig. 1*. Tighten shock absorber support mounting nuts. Install wheel, lower vehicle and recheck caster and camber.

Caster and Camber Adjustment			
Adjustment		Variation	
	Shock Absorber Support	Caster	Camber
A	0	0	0
B	90°	½ °	0
C	180°	½ °	½ °
D	270°	0	½ °

Pickup — To adjust, change shims between upper arm shaft and support bracket or turn upper arm shaft until specifications are obtained.

CAMBER

NOTE — *On GLC wagon, camber is not adjustable. If camber is not within specifications, inspect suspension for excessive wear or damage. Replace components as necessary.*

GLC — Camber may be adjusted 1/2° negative or positive. Raise front end and support with jack stands. Remove front wheel, open hood and remove 2 mounting nuts attaching

shock absorber support to fender apron. Push shock absorber down, turn 180° and tighten mounting nuts. Check camber angle.

RX7 & 626 — *See procedure given under Caster adjustment.*

Pickup — To adjust, change shims between upper arm shaft and support bracket until specifications for camber are within limits.

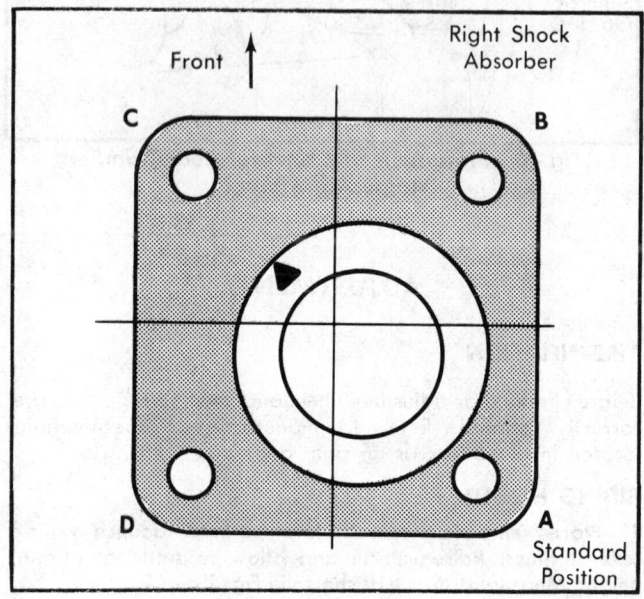

Fig. 1 RX7 & 626 Caster and Camber Adjusting Pad (Position "C" Shown)

TOE-IN

1) Raise front of vehicle. Turn wheels by hand and mark a line in center of each tire tread. Place vehicle in straight-ahead position and lower vehicle to ground.

2) Measure distance between marked lines at both front and rear of wheel. Make sure measurements are made equal distances from ground. Distance at rear of wheel should be .24" (6 mm) more than that at front wheels. Loosen lock nuts and turn tie rods until adjustment is correct.

MERCEDES-BENZ

ADJUSTMENT

TIRE INFLATION (COLD)

Before attempting to check or adjust wheel alignment, make sure tires are properly inflated. Refer to manufacturer's specifications given in owner's manual.

CASTER

Front — Test under loaded condition. Load vehicle with 2 weights of 143 lbs. (64.9 kg) on rear seat and a full tank of fuel. If caster is not to specifications, loosen lock nut on eccentric bolt on front side of lower control arm. To adjust, rotate eccentric bolt until caster angle is within specifications. Hold eccentric bolt in place and tighten lock nut.

CAMBER

Front — Test under loaded condition. Load vehicle with 2 weights of 143 lbs. (64.9 kg) on front seat, 1 similar weight on rear seat and a full tank of fuel. If camber is not within specifications, loosen lock nut of eccentric bolt on rear side of lower control arm. To adjust, rotate eccentric bolt until camber is within specifications. Hold eccentric bolt in place and tighten lock nut.

TOE-IN

Front — Place wheels in straight-ahead position. If toe-in is not within specifications, adjust by loosening lock nuts on outer steering links and rotating links to obtain specified toe-in. Make sure steering links are adjusted equally.

Wheel Alignment

PEUGEOT

ADJUSTMENT

TIRE INFLATION (COLD)

Before attempting to check or adjust wheel alignment, make sure tires are properly inflated. Refer to manufacturer's specifications given in owner's manual.

TOE-IN

Position wheels in straight-ahead position. If toe-in is not to specifications, loosen clamping bolts on the 2 steering links. To adjust, rotate 2 steering links simultaneously in either direction necessary to obtain specified toe-in. Tighten clamping bolt and recheck toe-in.

CAMBER & CASTER

Camber and caster are not adjustable. If alignment is not within specifications, inspect for damaged suspension parts and repair or replace as necessary.

PORSCHE

ADJUSTMENT

TIRE INFLATION (COLD)

Before attempting to check or adjust wheel alignment, make sure tires are properly inflated. Refer to manufacturer's specifications given in owner's manual.

RIDING HEIGHT

NOTE — *Riding height should be set with fuel tank full and spare tire included.*

911SC (Front) — 1) Checking or adjusting riding height can only be performed with vehicle on level surface. Mark center of front wheel hub cap (grease retainer cup). Bounce vehicle several times to settle suspension. Measure distance "A" shown in *Fig. 1.* Measure distance "B" shown in *Fig 1.* Difference between measurements (riding height) should be 3.7-4.1" (94-104 mm).

2) If necessary, loosen or tighten torsion bar adjusting bolt until correct height is obtained. Bounce vehicle several times and recheck height. Make sure difference between right and left side measurements does not exceed .20" (5 mm).

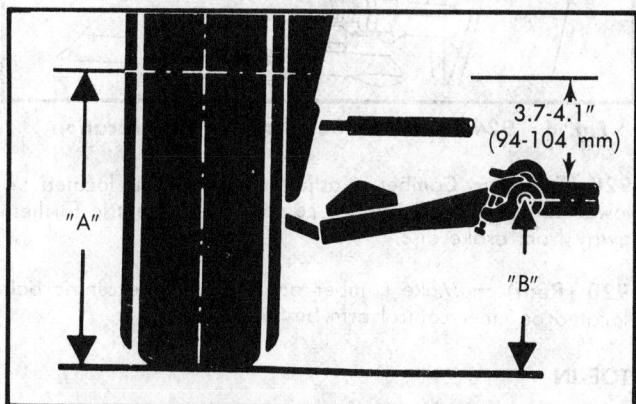

Fig. 1   Front Suspension Riding Height Measuring Points for 911SC

911SC (Rear) — Checking or adjusting riding height can only be performed with vehicle on level surface. Mark center of rear wheel. Bounce vehicle several times to settle suspension. Measure distance "a" shown in *Fig. 2.* Distance "a" plus 1.26-1.65" (32-42mm) equals "b"; however, distance "b" is difficult to measure because the torsion bar is mounted off center in its rubber bushing. Therefore it is necessary to measure distance "b1" and add .585" (14.8 mm), radius of bushing. This total should equal "b". After calculating "b", difference between "a" and "b" should be 1.26-1.65" (32-42 mm). Difference in

height from left to right should not exceed .20" (5 mm). If values are not within specifications, check front height and rear torsion bar adjustment. Correct as required.

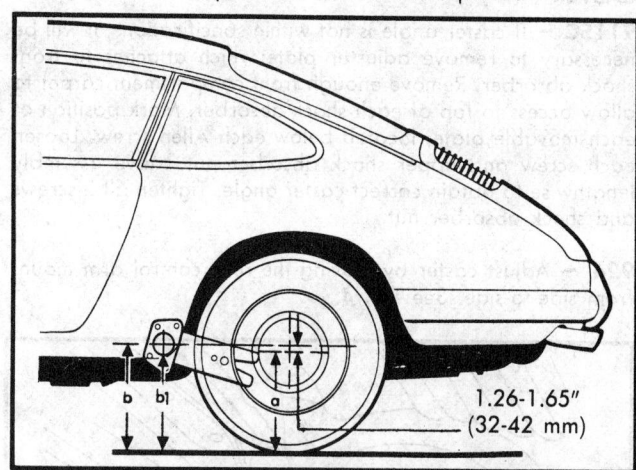

Fig. 2   Rear Suspension Riding Height Measuring Points for 911SC

924 (Rear) — Rear height is adjusted at 2-piece spring plate; spring plate removal is not required. Loosen mounting bolt and adjust vehicle height with eccentric bolt. See *Fig. 3.* Height should be .311-.319" (7.9-8.1 mm) when measured from torsion bar center to center of wheel.

NOTE — *If spring plate angle is 19° (with stabilizer bar) or 23° 40' (without stabilizer bar), vehicle height will be correct.*

Fig. 3   Location of 924 Rear Riding Height Adjusting bolt

Wheel Alignment

PORSCHE (Cont.)

928 (Front) — Park vehicle on level ground. Place wheels in straight-ahead position. Measure distance from boss (on forward underside of lower control arm) to ground. Distance should be about 7.48" (190 mm). Height is determined by coil spring and is not adjustable at front axle.

928 (Rear) — Place vehicle on level surface. Place front wheels in straight-ahead position. Measure distance from lower edge of crossmember (below camber adjusting cam) to ground. Distance should be 6.81-7.20" (173-183 mm).

- To adjust vehicle upward turn coil spring adjusting nut (located at under side of lower spring retainer) clockwise.
- Rear height must be adjusted to match front height. EXAMPLE: If front height is .394" (10 mm) too high, rear height must be raised .394" (10 mm).

CASTER

911SC — If caster angle is not within specifications, it will be necessary to remove adjuster plate which attaches to front shock absorber. Remove enough front compartment carpet to allow access to top of each shock absorber. Mark position of each movable plate, located below each Allen screw. Loosen each screw and upper shock absorber nut. Move assembly lengthwise to obtain correct caster angle. Tighten all 3 screws and shock absorber nut.

924 — Adjust caster by moving the rear control arm mount from side-to-side. See Fig. 4.

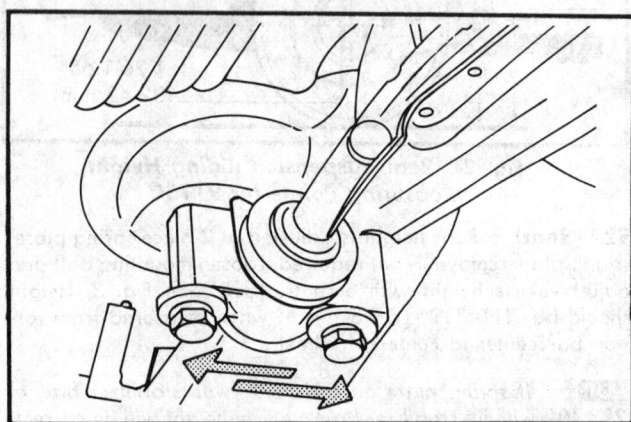

Fig. 4   924 Caster Adjustment Location

928 — Caster is adjusted at eccentric located on lower control arm. To adjust caster, use eccentric closest to brake disc.

CAMBER

911SC (Front) — If camber angle is not within specifications, it will be necessary to move adjuster plate which attaches to front shock absorber. Follow procedure outlined for adjusting caster and move assembly from side-to-side to obtain correct camber angle. Tighten all 3 screws and shock absorber nut.

911SC (Rear) — To obtain correct camber angle at rear wheels, it is necessary to adjust rear torsion bars first. See Torsion Bar Adjustment. Then, loosen nuts on retaining bolts and on eccentric bolt at rear axle flange. Turn camber eccentric until camber angle is within specifications. Tighten retaining nuts and eccentric bolt nuts.

924 (Front) — Adjust camber by turning eccentric bolt shown in Fig. 6.

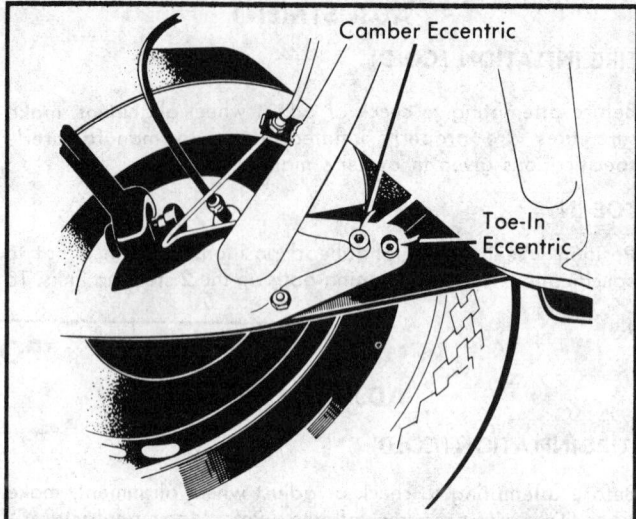

Fig. 5   911SC Rear Camber Adjustment Points

924 (Rear) — Loosen bolts between spring plate and diagonal arm flange. Bring camber to specification by turning eccentric.

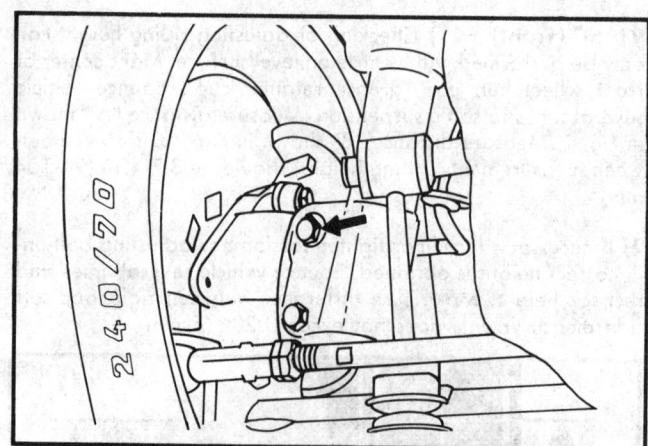

Fig. 6   924 Front Camber Eccentric Bolt Location

928 (Front) — Camber is adjusted at eccentric located on lower control arm. To adjust camber, use eccentric farthest away from brake disc.

928 (Rear) — Make camber adjustments at eccentric bolt located on inner control arm bushing.

TOE-IN

All Models (Front) — Place front wheels in straight-ahead position. Adjust left and right steering links (tie rods) equally to obtain specified setting. Coat each steering link with anti-corrosive compound after adjustment.

911SC (Rear) — To adjust rear wheel toe-in, loosen nuts on retaining bolts and adjusting eccentrics at rear axle flange. Turn toe-in eccentric until toe-in is set to specifications. Hold eccentric stationary and tighten all lock nuts.

924 (Rear) — Adjust toe-in by repositioning control arm flange in slots of spring plate. Use of special tool 1979 is suggested.

Wheel Alignment

PORSCHE (Cont.)

928 (Rear) — Rear toe-in adjustments are made at eccentric bolt located on front control arm bushing.

TORSION BAR ADJUSTMENT

911SC (Rear) — Place torsion bar into transverse tube with inner end splines first. Slip radius arm onto outer end splines of torsion bar. Place leveling tool (VW 261) on lower edge of door opening and adjust level so bubble is in center of glass. Check adjustment (degrees) of free hanging radius arm with same leveling tool. If not to specifications, adjust by turning torsion bar and radius arm in opposite directions. Adjustment of both radius arms must each equal $36\frac{3}{4}° \pm \frac{1}{4}°$.

RENAULT

ADJUSTMENT

TIRE INFLATION (COLD)

Before attempting to check or adjust wheel alignment, make sure tires are properly inflated. Refer to manufacturer's specifications given in owner's manual.

RIDING HEIGHT

NOTE — *Riding height should be set with fuel tank full and without additional weight in vehicle.*

Front — Checking or adjusting riding height can only be performed with vehicle on level surface. To calculate front riding height, measure distance from ground to center of wheel ("H_1" in *Fig. 1*) and distance from ground to front side member ("H_2" in *Fig. 1*) in line with wheel centers. Then subtract the measurements. Difference should be $1\frac{7}{8}$-$2\frac{5}{8}$" (48-68 mm), with the variation between right and left sides not to exceed $\frac{3}{8}$" (10 mm). To adjust front riding height, mark position of torsion bar in bracket, then remove and rotate torsion bar until correct riding height is obtained.

Rear — Rear riding height is calculated by measuring from ground to center of wheel ("H_4" in *Fig. 1*) and to punched out hole in rear side member (H_5" in *Fig. 1*). The difference in the measurements should be $\frac{1}{16}$-$\frac{9}{16}$" (1.5-14 mm) with variation between right and left sides not to exceed $\frac{3}{8}$" (10 mm). Adjust rear riding height in same manner as front riding height.

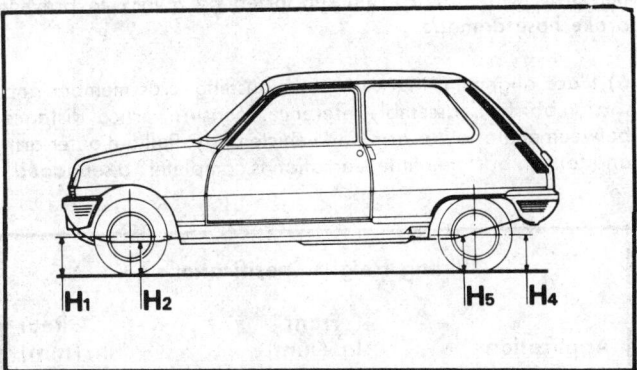

Fig. 1   Riding Height Measurement Points

CASTER

NOTE — *Caster is not adjustable on 18i models.*

Vehicle riding height must be calculated before adjusting caster. Caster angle corresponds to the difference in front and rear riding heights between "H_2" and "H_5" as shown in *Fig. 1*. After calculating the difference, refer to Caster Angle table for correct caster angle. To adjust caster angle, loosen both lower control arm mounting bolts and add or remove shims to adjust caster to specifications. The addition or removal of 1 shim equals about $1°$ change in caster angle.

NOTE — *Never use more than 2 shims between bushing and side member. Always check steering box height after caster adjustment.*

Le Car Caster Angle Specifications	
Difference Between "H_2" & "H_5"	Caster Angle
$1\frac{9}{16}$" (40 mm)	$12\frac{1}{2}°$
$2\frac{3}{8}$" (60 mm)	$12°$
$3\frac{3}{16}$" (80 mm)	$11\frac{1}{2}°$
$3\frac{15}{16}$" (100 mm)	$11°$
$4\frac{3}{4}$" (120 mm)	$10\frac{1}{2}°$
$5\frac{1}{2}$" (140 mm)	$10°$

CAMBER

NOTE — *Camber is not adjustable on 18i models.*

Camber angle is not adjustable. If not within specifications, inspect front suspension for wear or damage and repair or replace components as necessary.

TOE-IN

If toe-in is not to specifications, disconnect steering arm at rack end. Loosen lock nut on steering end fitting. To increase toe-in, unscrew end fitting. To decrease, screw in fitting. Tighten lock nut and connect steering arm. Recheck toe-in.

SAAB

ADJUSTMENT

TIRE INFLATION (COLD)

Before attempting to check or adjust wheel alignment, make sure tires are properly inflated. Refer to manufacturer's specifications given in owner's manual.

CASTER

To adjust caster, add or remove shims under upper control arm bushing brackets. Changing shims from front to rear bracket increases caster angle. Moving shims from rear to front decreases caster angle.

NOTE — *Same shim thicknesses removed from front must be placed under rear and vice versa. Change in caster also affects camber.*

CAMBER

To adjust camber, add or remove shims under upper control arm bushing brackets. Increasing shims under both brackets

SAAB (Cont.)

reduces camber angle and removing shims under both increases camber.

NOTE — *Always add or remove same thickness of shims at front and rear or caster angle will be affected.*

TOE-IN

With wheels in straight-ahead position, loosen steering link (tie rod) lock nut and turn adjustable sleeve until correct toe-in is obtained. Tighten lock nuts and recheck toe-in.

NOTE — *After adjustment of toe-in, measurement "A" (Fig. 1) of tie rod must not exceed 1.0" (25 mm) or 1.02" (26 mm) for power steering models. For tie rods opposite each other, the difference between measurements "A" must not exceed .08" (2 mm).*

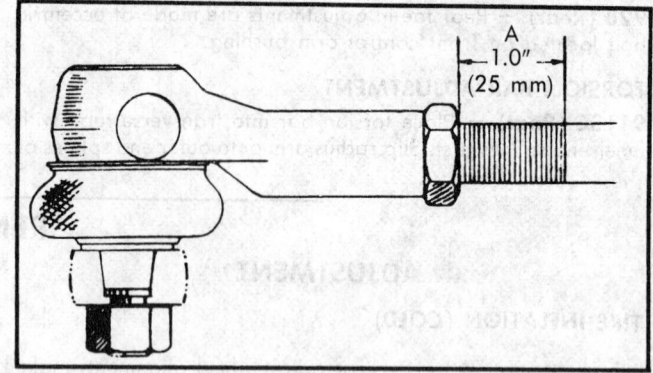

Fig. 1   View Showing Tie Rod Length Measurement

SUBARU

ADJUSTMENT

TIRE INFLATION (COLD)

Before attempting to check or adjust wheel alignment, make sure tires are properly inflated. Refer to manufacturer's specifications given in owner's manual.

RIDING HEIGHT

Front (All Models) — Place vehicle on level surface. Measure distance between ground and front end of transverse link attaching bolt. Adjust clearance by turning nuts (at same time) on strut until specified height is obtained. See *Riding Height Specifications* table.

Rear (4-WD) — Place vehicle on level surface. Measure the distance between ground and center of outer end face of torsion bar on BRAT and between ground and lowest point of crossmember pipe on all others. Adjust clearance by turning adjusting bolt clockwise to increase riding height and counterclockwise to decrease height. See *Riding Height Specifications* chart.

NOTE — *Adjusting bolt is accessible through service hole located in vehicle floor.*

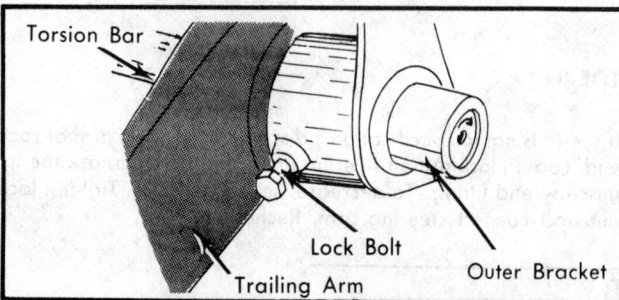

Fig. 1   Installed View of Torsion Bar Outer End Attachment

Rear (2-WD) — 1) Riding height is adjusted by changing the angle between trailing arm center line and markings on outer bracket. See *Fig. 1*. The trailing arm and outer bracket have full serrations around the torsion bar mounting hole, while torsion bar has 1 missing serration, thus allowing torsion bar to be inserted at any angle.

2) To increase riding height, turn outer end and inner end of torsion bar in direction opposite to cast-in arrow on outer end of bar. Height changes .20" (5 mm) with each shift in serration.

3) Initially set vehicle rear riding height by inserting torsion bar with its missing serrations aligned with markings on outer bracket surface and trailing arm inner surface. This should equal the approximate riding height. See *Riding Height Specifications* chart.

4) Measure riding height from center of trailing arm bushing to ground and determine numbers of teeth to be shifted on inner and/or outer serrations.

NOTE — *Vehicle must be in unloaded condition.*

5) At top of shock absorber, remove bolt attaching shock to body. Raise rear of vehicle and remove wheel. Remove lock bolt of outer bushing. Remove 3 bolts connecting outer and inner arms with brake drum supported by a jack to prevent brake hose damage.

6) Place alignment mark on outer bushing, crossmember and torsion bar for reassembly reference. Measure vertical distance between end of outer arm and vehicle body. Pull out outer arm and torsion bar until inner serration is completely disengaged.

Riding Height Specifications

Application	Front In. (mm)	Rear In. (mm)
1600 & 1800 (2-WD)		
Station Wagon	9.65-10.63 (245-270)	11.02-11.81 (280-300)
All Others	9.45-10.43 (240-265)	10.24-11.02 (260-280)
1600 & 1800 (4-WD)		
Hatchback	10.43-11.42 (265-290)	12.60-13.39 (320-340)
Station Wagon	10.63-11.61 (270-295)	13.19-13.98 (335-355)
BRAT	9.84-10.83 (250-275)	13.58-14.37 (345-365)

SUBARU (Cont.)

7) Rotate torsion bar and outer arm to shift matching of inner serration by appropriate pitches and engage inner serration with crossmember. Pull outer arm from torsion bar and rotate outer arm in opposite direction to shift matching of outer serration by appropriate pitches.

NOTE – *DO NOT disengage inner serration of torsion bar from crossmember.*

8) Install outer arm to torsion bar and crossmember, then measure vertical distance between end of outer arm and vehicle body. Change in this distance shows half of change in riding height clearance caused by adjustment.

9) Install 3 bolts connecting outer and inner arms. Repeat adjustment procedure on opposite wheel. Install wheels and lower vehicle. Install shock absorbers and outer bushing lock bolt. Check rear riding height adjustment. If correct, tighten lock bolt on outer bushing. If incorrect, repeat adjustment on each wheel.

CASTER

Caster angle is not adjustable. If angle is not to specifications, inspect suspension for wear or damage and repair or replace components as necessary.

CAMBER

Camber angle is not adjustable. If angle is not to specifications, inspect suspension for wear or damage. Repair or replace components as necessary.

TOE-IN

If toe-in is not within specifications, loosen both left and right tie rod lock nuts. Turn both tie rods an equal amount until specified toe-in is obtained.

TOYOTA

ADJUSTMENT

TIRE INFLATION (COLD)

Before attempting to check or adjust wheel alignment, make sure tires are properly inflated. Refer to manufacturer's specifications given in owner's manual.

CAMBER & CASTER

Pickup (2-WD) — If camber or caster angles are not within specifications, adjust by adding or removing shims between upper control arm shaft and front suspension crossmember. To increase camber, remove shims from upper control arm shaft bolts in equal amounts. To decrease camber, add shims to upper control arm shaft bolts in equal amounts. To increase caster, add shims to rear side of upper control arm shaft bolt or remove shims from front side. To decrease caster, remove shims from rear side of upper control arm shaft bolt or add shims to front side.

Land Cruiser & Pickup (4-WD) — Camber and caster are not adjustable. If not within specifications, inspect and repair or replace front suspension components as necessary.

Starlet — Caster adjustment is made by adding or subtracting spacers on the sway bar.

All Other Models — If caster angle is not within specifications, adjust by loosening nuts on strut rod and turning nuts to lengthen or shorten strut rod.

NOTE — *Camber is not adjustable except on Pickup models. If camber angle is not within specifications, check front end for bent or worn parts and replace as necessary.*

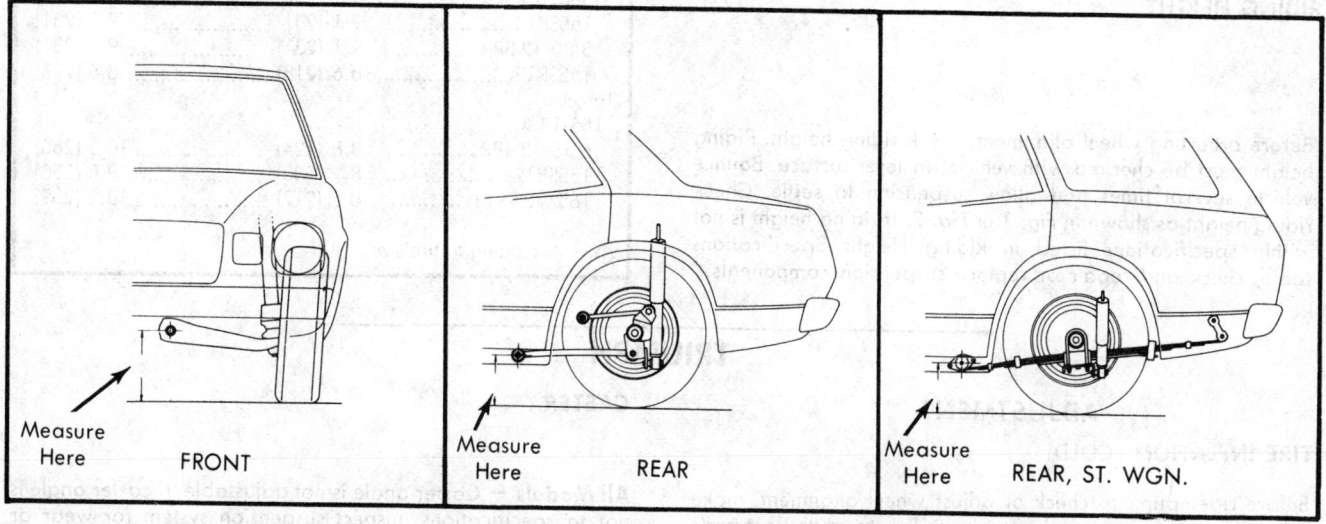

Fig. 1 Riding Height Measurement Points for All Models — Except Pickup & Land Cruiser

Wheel Alignment

TOYOTA (Cont.)

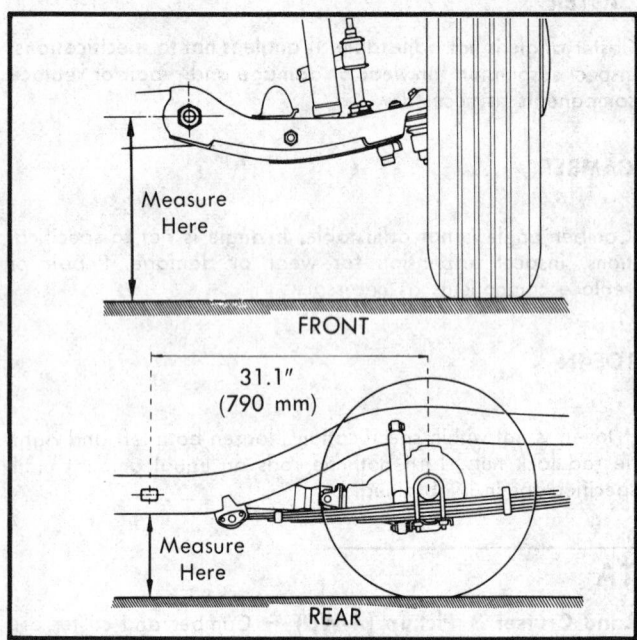

Measure Here

FRONT

31.1"
(790 mm)

Measure Here

REAR

Fig. 2 Riding Height Measurement Points for 2-WD Pickup Models

TOE-IN

All Models — If toe-in is not within specifications, loosen steering link (tie-rod) clamping bolts and rotate adjusting sleeves an equal amount until correct toe-in is obtained. Position clamp bolts at right angles to slot in tie rod and tighten bolts.

RIDING HEIGHT

Before adjusting wheel alignment, check riding height. Riding height must be checked with vehicle on level surface. Bounce vehicle several times and allow suspension to settle. Check riding height as shown in *Fig. 1* or *Fig. 2*. If riding height is not within specifications listed in Riding Height Specifications table, check and repair or replace suspension components.

Riding Height Specifications ①

Application	Front In. (mm)	Rear In. (mm)
Celica & Supra		
165SR14	9.2 (234)	9.3 (235)
175SR14	9.4 (239)	9.5 (240)
185/70SR14	9.3 (237)	9.4 (238)
Corolla		
Station Wagon		
165SR13	9.13 (232)	9.1 (232)
All Others		
6.45-13	9.3 (237)	9.5 (241)
165SR13	9.1 (230)	9.2 (234)
185/70SR13	9.1 (232)	9.3 (236)
185/70HR13	9.1 (232)	9.3 (236)
Corona		
Station Wagon		
5.60-13	9.1 (231)	8.9 (225)
6.45-13	9.0 (229)	8.8 (223)
165SR13	8.8 (223)	8.5 (217)
165SR14	9.3 (235)	9.0 (229)
175SR14	9.5 (241)	9.3 (235)
All Others		
5.60-13	9.1 (231)	9.2 (233)
6.45-13	9.0 (229)	9.1 (231)
165SR13	8.8 (223)	8.9 (225)
165SR14	9.3 (235)	9.3 (237)
175SR14	9.5 (241)	9.6 (243)
Cressida		
Sedan		
All Tires	9.1 (231)	9.6 (243)
Station Wagon		
All Tires	9.2 (233)	9.8 (248)
Pickup (2-WD)		
1/2 Ton		
7.00-14 6PR	10.3 (261)	11.4 (288)
185SR14 4PR	9.8 (250)	10.7 (270)
E78-14 (B)	10.0 (254)	11.1 (281)
ER78-14 (B)	9.9 (251)	10.7 (271)
3/4 Ton		
7.50-14 6PR	11.0 (278)	12.0 (305)
Starlet		
Sedan		
145SR13	9.0 (230)	9.0 (230)
Wagon		
6.15-13 6PR	9.2 (234)	9.3 (235)
155SR13	9.1 (231)	9.1 (231)
5.00-12 8PR	9.1 (231)	9.1 (231)
155SR12	8.6 (218)	8.6 (218)
Tercel		
155-13 &		
6.15-13 4PR	8.8 (224)	10.5 (266)
155SR12	8.2 (208)	9.8 (250)
165/70 SR13	8.5 (217)	10.2 (259)

① — According to tire size.

TRIUMPH

ADJUSTMENT

TIRE INFLATION (COLD)

Before attempting to check or adjust wheel alignment, make sure tires are properly inflated. Refer to manufacturer's specifications given in owner's manual.

CASTER

All Models — Caster angle is not adjustable. If caster angle is not to specifications, inspect suspension system for wear or damage and repair or replace components as necessary.

Wheel Alignment

TRIUMPH (Cont.)

CAMBER

All Models — Camber angle is not adjustable. If camber angle is not within specifications, inspect suspension system for wear or damage. Repair or replace components as necessary.

TOE-IN

All Models (Front) — Set front wheels in straight ahead position. If adjustment is necessary, loosen steering link (tie rod) lock nuts and gaiter clips. Rotate adjusting sleeves equal amounts until correct toe-in is obtained. Tighten lock nuts and recheck toe-in.

VOLKSWAGEN

ADJUSTMENT

TIRE INFLATION (COLD)

Before attempting to check or adjust wheel alignment, make sure tires are properly inflated. Refer to manufacturer's specifications given in owner's manual.

CASTER

Vanagon — If caster is not within specifications, adjust by changing length of strut bar at crossmember mount. After adjusting caster, check and adjust camber.

All Others — Caster angle is not adjustable. If not within specifications, inspect front suspension for wear or damage and repair or replace components as necessary.

CAMBER

Dasher (Front) — If camber is not within specifications, loosen nuts attaching ball joint to track control arm. To adjust, insert adjusting tool (40-200) in adjusting holes in control arm and pry ball joint sideways until camber is set to specifications. Tighten attaching nuts and recheck camber. Camber should not vary more than 1° between right and left sides.

NOTE — *Insert tool from front on right side and from rear on left side.*

Vanagon (Front) — If camber is not within specifications, loosen nut on upper control arm shaft and rotate shaft until camber angle is set to specifications. Tighten nut and recheck camber.

Vanagon (Rear) — If camber is not within specifications, loosen outer bolt on trailing arm and adjust camber by using a screwdriver to move trailing arm up or down. Tighten trailing arm bolt and recheck camber.

All Other Models (Front) — If camber is not within specifications, loosen nuts of suspension strut-to-wheel bearing housing mounting bolts. Turn eccentric bolt (upper mounting bolt) until specified camber angle is obtained. Tighten mounting bolt nuts and recheck camber.

All Other Models (Rear) — Rear camber is not adjustable. If camber angle is not within specifications, inspect rear suspension for wear or damage and repair or replace components as necessary.

TOE-IN

Vanagon (Front) — Place wheels in straight-ahead position and ensure lug on rubber washer of pinion shaft is aligned with notch in steering gear housing. Loosen lock nuts and rotate both tie rods equal amounts until toe-in specifications are obtained. Tighten lock nuts, ensure steering wheel is centered on steering shaft and that dust boots are not twisted.

Vanagon (Rear) — If toe-in is not to specifications, loosen inner bolt on trailing arm. Using a screwdriver, adjust toe-in by moving trailing arm forward or rearward until correct toe-in specification is obtained. Tighten trailing arm inner bolt.

All Other Models (Front) — Place wheels in straight-ahead position. Loosen lock nuts on adjustable tie rod end (if equipped). Hold axle boot to avoid twisting. Adjust tie rod until specified toe-in is obtained. Tighten lock nut and recheck toe-in.

All Other Models (Rear) — Toe-in is not adjustable. If toe-in is not within specifications, inspect rear suspension for wear or damage and repair or replace components as necessary.

VOLVO

ADJUSTMENT

TIRE INFLATION (COLD)

Before attempting to check or adjust wheel alignment, make sure tires are properly inflated. Refer to manufacturer's specifications given in owner's manual.

CASTER

Caster cannot be adjusted. If not within specifications, check front end components for damage.

CAMBER

If camber is not within specifications, loosen nuts at strut assembly upper attachment. Use special tool 5038 (or equivalent) at strut upper attachment to adjust camber. Tighten lock nuts. Recheck camber.

TOE-IN

Place wheels in straight-ahead position and loosen lock nut and rubber dust boot outer clamp. Turn tie rods until toe is within specifications. Make sure length of tie rods does not differ more than .08" (2 mm). Measure difference between groove in tie rod and lock nut.

Jacking & Hoisting

ALL MANUFACTURERS

NOTE — *These illustrations are not intended to represent exact structure of each vehicle's frame, underbody or body outline. They are presented only to give the mechanic some point of reference.*

FRAME & UNDERBODY

The following illustrations indicate areas (parts) of the underbody and frame which may be used to raise and support the vehicle, using either floor jack or hoist. These points are indicated by shaded areas on the frame. *See sample illustration.*

OUTERBODY

Those points designated on the outline of the body were specifically designed to facilitate the use of the vehicle's own jack, but may also be used to raise and support the vehicle by means of a floor jack or hoist. These jacking points are indicated by circular dots on the outline of the body. *See sample illustration.* If floor jack or hoist is employed, extreme care should be exercised to avoid damaging the outer body shell.

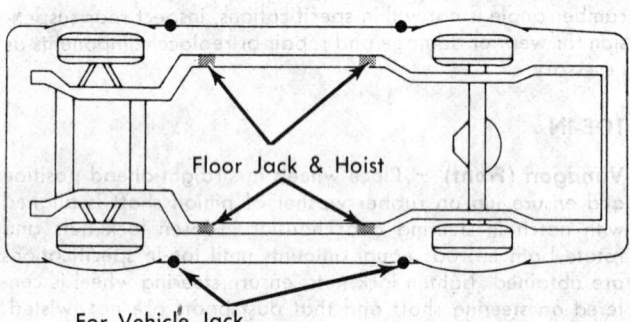

Fig. 1 Sample Jacking & Hoisting Points
(Typical Illustration)

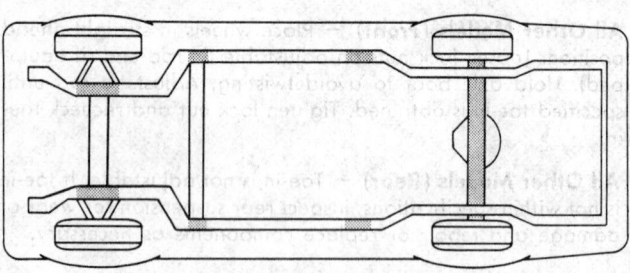

Arrow & Ram-50 Pickups

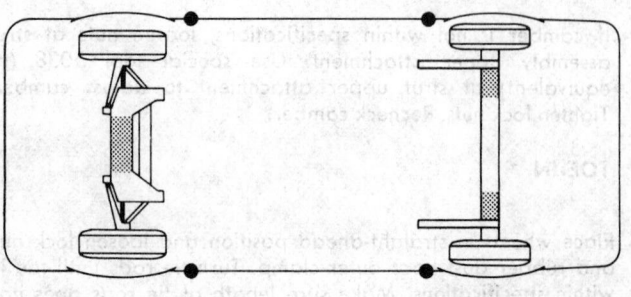

Audi

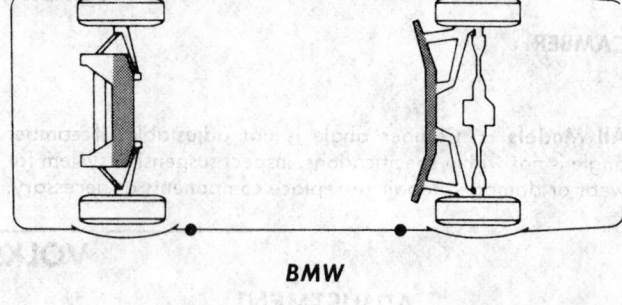

BMW

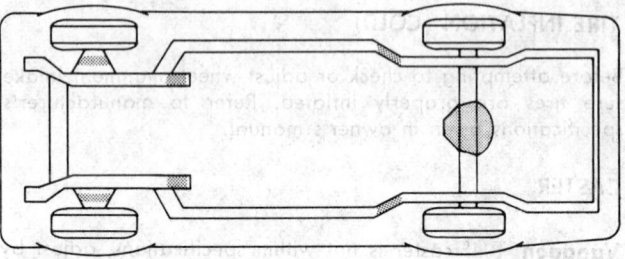

Challenger & Sapporo

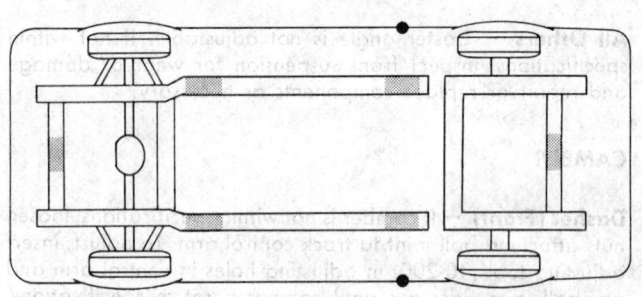

Champ & Colt Hatchbacks

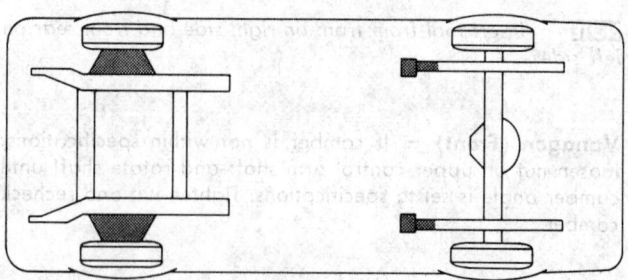

Courier

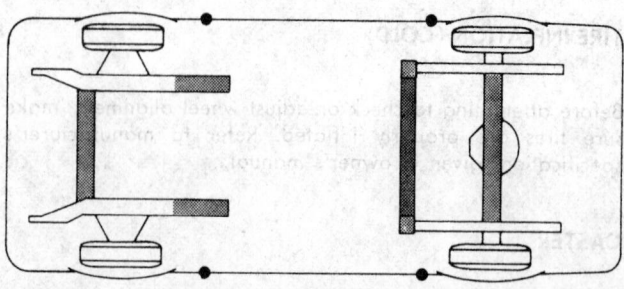

Datsun (Exc. Pickup & 310)

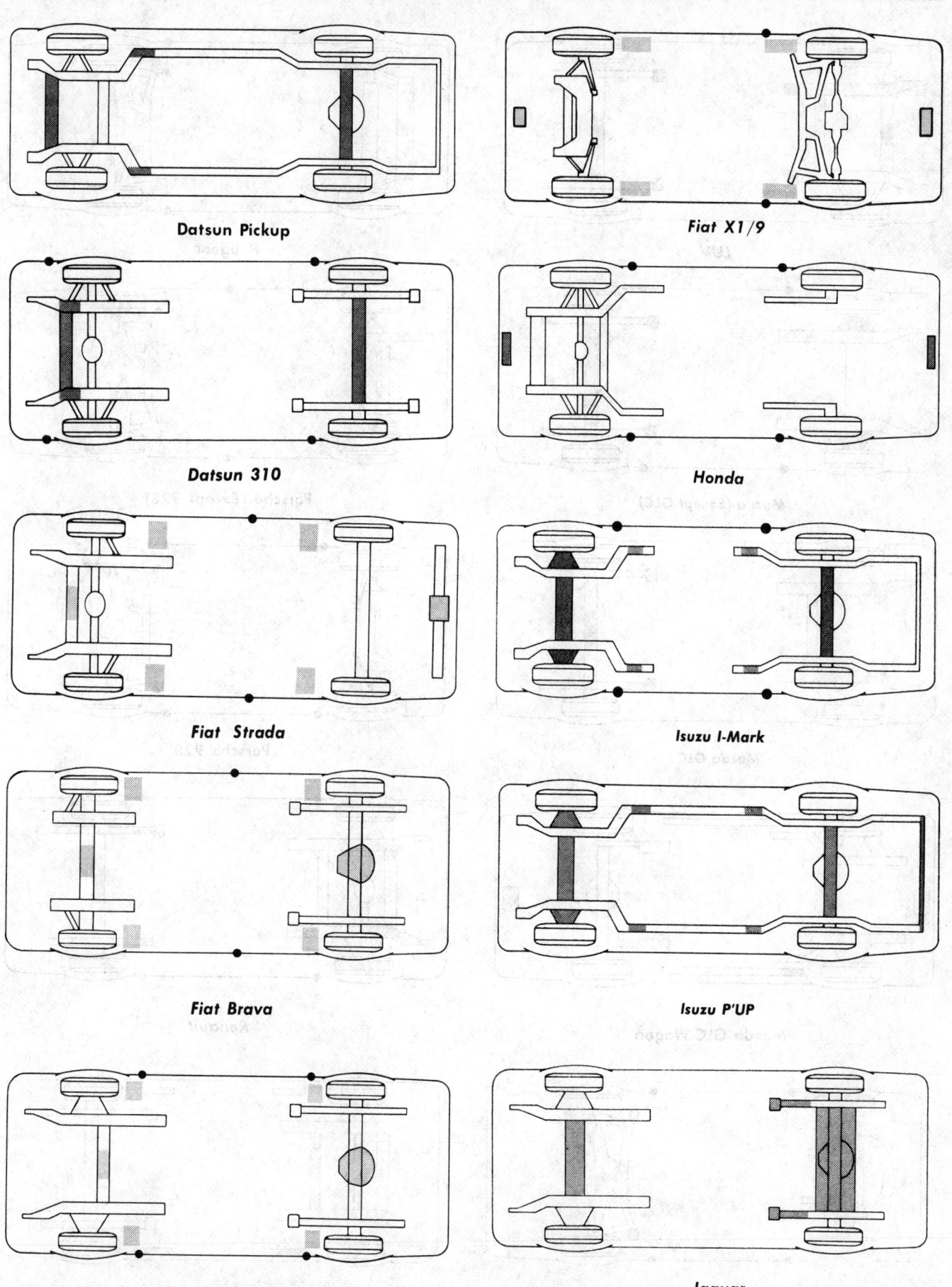

Datsun Pickup

Fiat X1/9

Datsun 310

Honda

Fiat Strada

Isuzu I-Mark

Fiat Brava

Isuzu P'UP

Fiat Spider 2000

Jaguar

Jacking & Hoisting

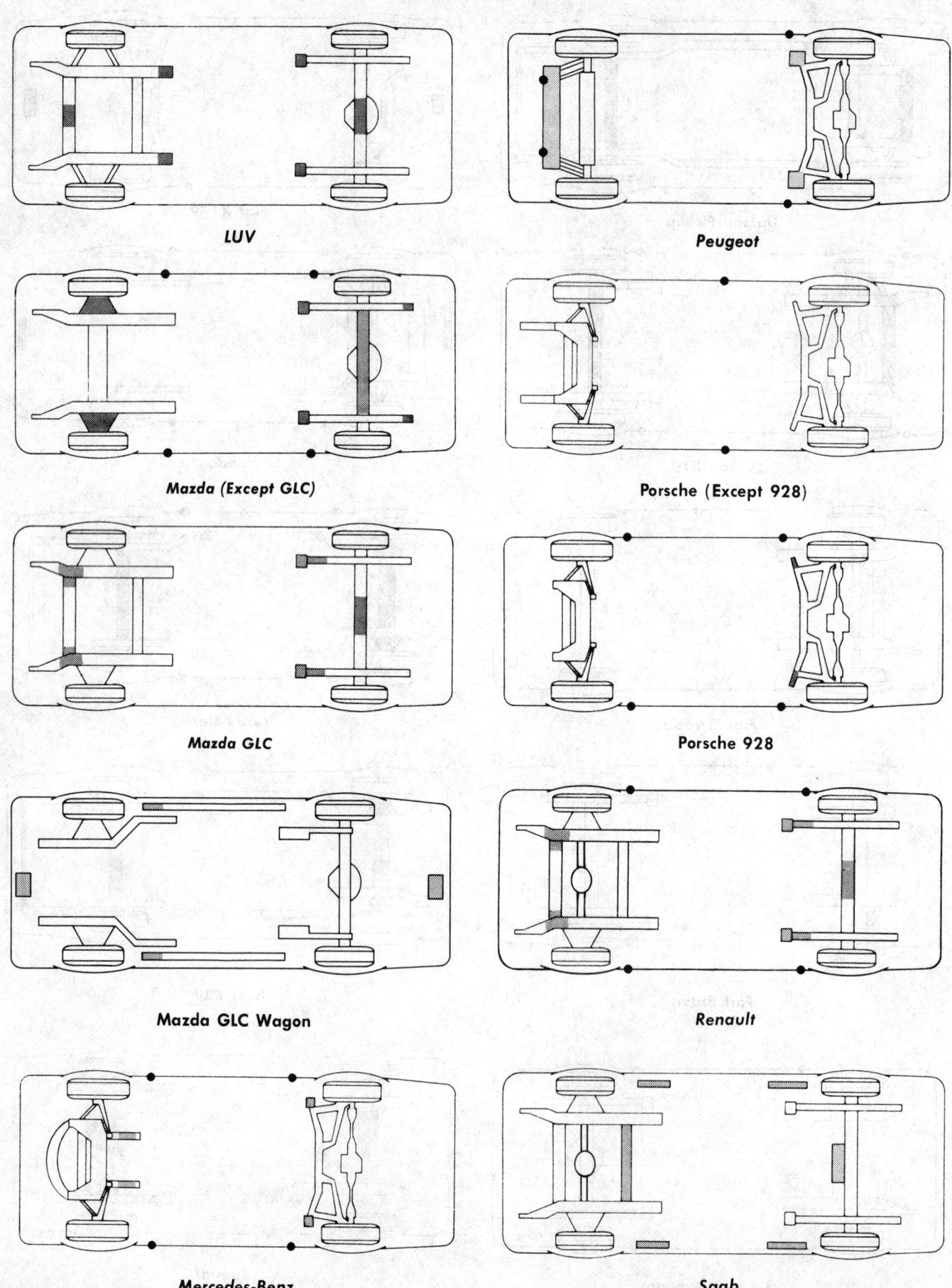

LUV

Peugeot

Mazda (Except GLC)

Porsche (Except 928)

Mazda GLC

Porsche 928

Mazda GLC Wagon

Renault

Mercedes-Benz

Saab

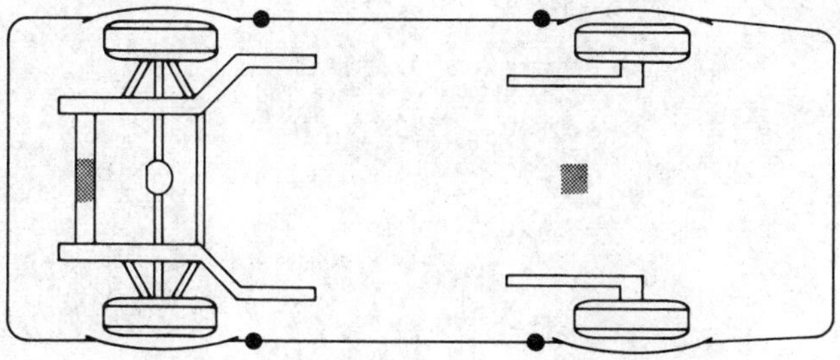

Subaru

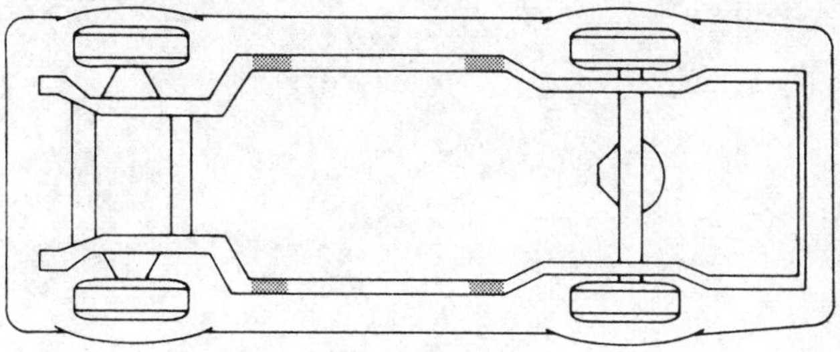

Triumph

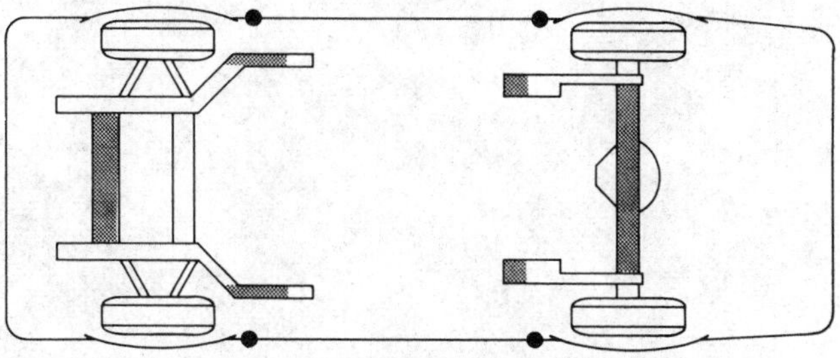

Toyota (Except Starlet, Tercel, Land Cruiser & Pickup)

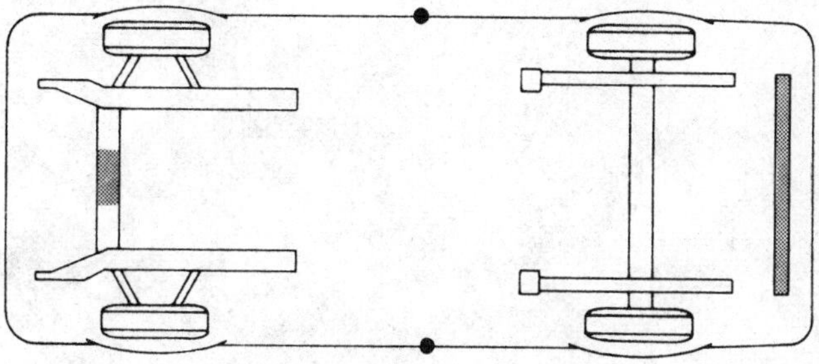

Volkswagen Rabbit Pickup

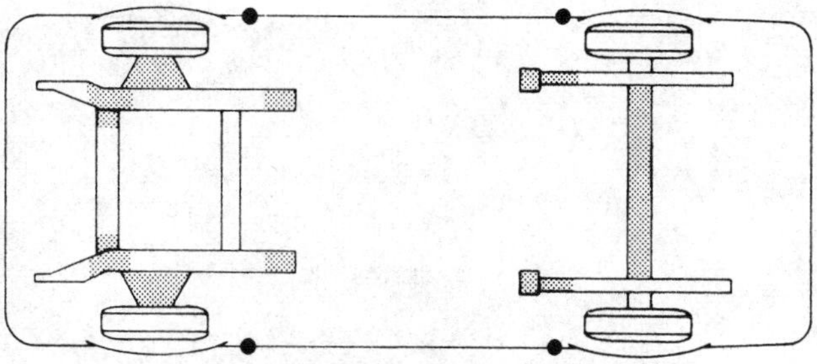

Toyota Starlet & Tercel

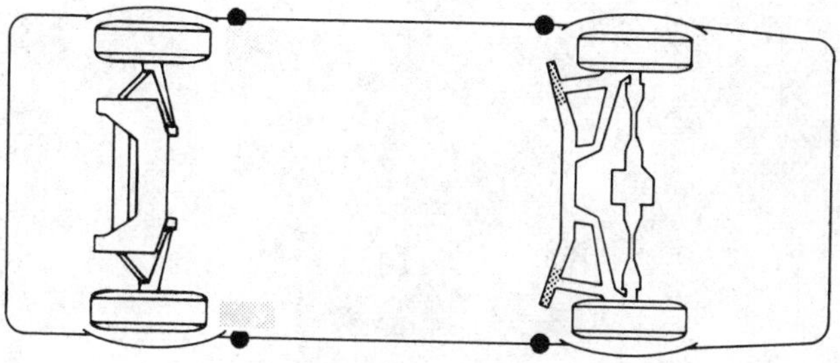

Volkswagen Vanagon

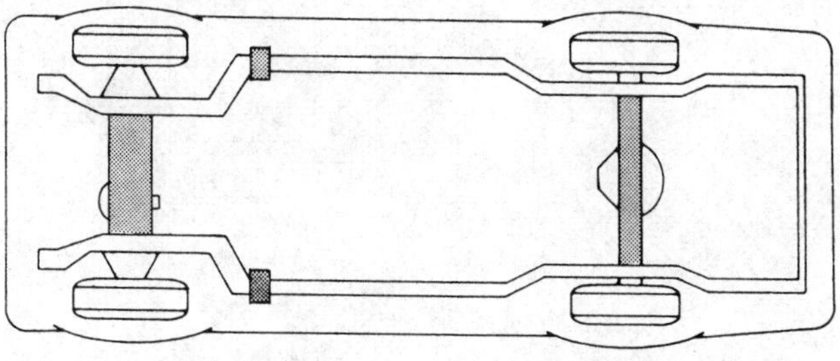

Toyota Land Cruiser & Pickup

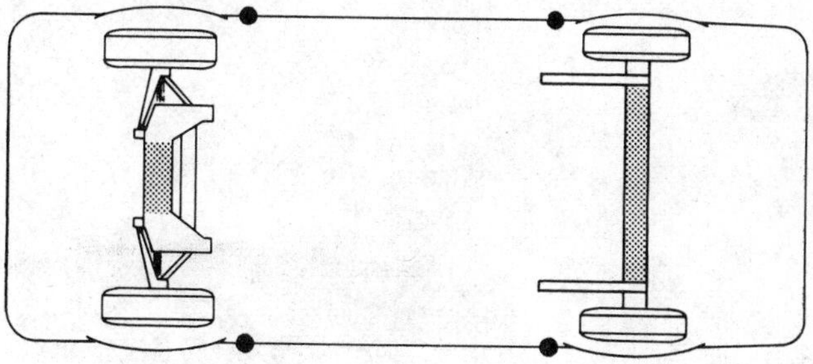

Volkswagen (Except Pickup & Vanagon)

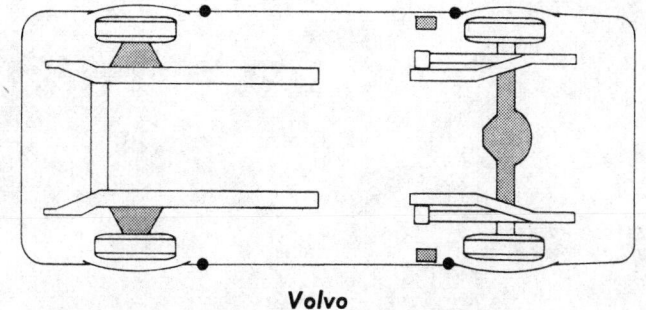

Volvo

Section 10
SUSPENSION

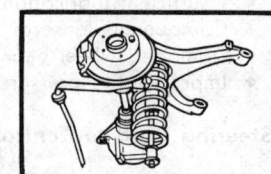

Contents

Suspension

SUSPENSION TROUBLE SHOOTING

CONDITION & POSSIBLE CAUSE	CONDITION & POSSIBLE CAUSE
Hard Steering • Tire pressure too low. • Front wheels out of alignment. • Lower control arm ball joint seized. **Pull to One Side** • Crossmember broken, cracked or loose. • Left and right side wheel base uneven. • Loose or excessively worn wheel bearings. • Loose wheel lug nuts. **Steering Wheel Wander** • Excessive ball joint wear. • Lower control arm and strut worn. • Lower control arm pivot bolt (shaft) loose or worn. • Lower control arm and strut damaged or worn.	**Body Roll** • Stabilizer broken or damaged. • Shock absorbers worn. **Noise** • Coil spring broken. • Bad shock absorber. • Insufficient lubrication. • Components loose or excessively worn. • Damaged wheel bearing. • Improper tire pressure. **Steering Hard to Control** • Broken front coil spring. • Defective shock absorber. • Loose control arm bushings. • Strut assembly loose. • Tire pressure. • Wheel alignment out of tolerance. • Damaged suspension links.

AUDI

4000
5000

DESCRIPTION

Suspension is independent type, having strut assembly, control arm and stabilizer bar. Strut assembly consists of shock absorber surrounded by a coil spring. It is attached to inner fender panel at top and is integral with steering knuckle at bottom. Lower control arm is connected by ball joint to steering knuckle and by bushing connection to frame (note configuration differences in *Fig. 1*). Stabilizer bar is connected by brackets to subframe and by bracket to control arm on 4000 and by bushing and bolt on 5000.

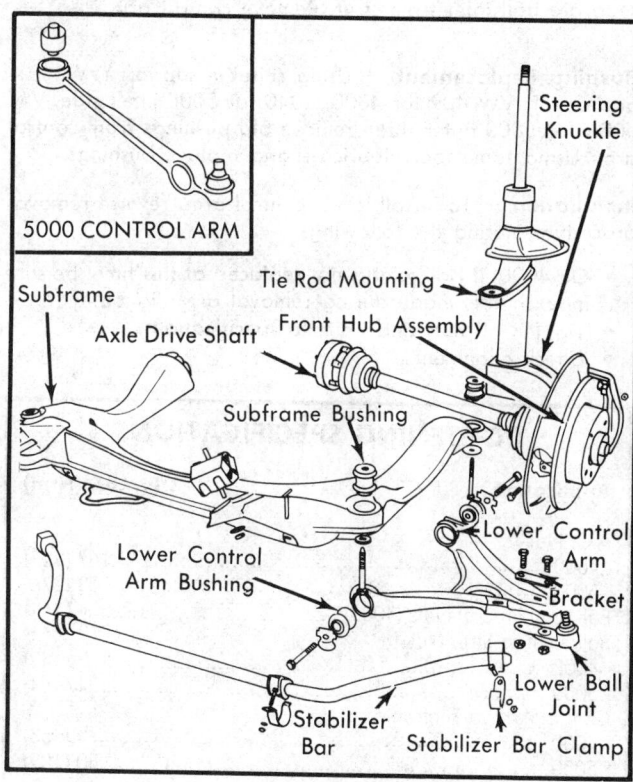

Fig. 1 *Exploded View of Audi Front Suspension*

ADJUSTMENTS

WHEEL ALIGNMENT SPECIFICATIONS & PROCEDURES

See Wheel Alignment Specifications and Procedures in WHEEL ALIGNMENT section.

WHEEL BEARING ADJUSTMENT

No adjustment required.

BALL JOINT CHECKING

Inspect ball joints for wear or excessive play. Replace as necessary.

REMOVAL & INSTALLATION

NOTE — *During any removal and installation procedure, if axle nut is removed or installed, do so with vehicle resting on ground at full curb weight.*

STRUT ASSEMBLY

NOTE — *When removing strut on 5000, install strut tool 2070 before removing. Mount tool retaining plate, tighten spindle and spindle nut until seated.*

Removal — 1) Loosen axle nut. Raise and support vehicle; remove wheel. Without detaching brake hose or line, unbolt caliper, remove brake hose bracket and suspend caliper out of way.

2) Detach stabilizer bar from sub-frame on 5000 and from lower control arm on 4000. Remove wheel bearing housing/ball joint clamp bolt on 4000.

3) Remove brake rotor and ball joint on 5000. On both models, use suitable tool and press off tie rod end. On 5000, remove ball joint from hub and using suitable puller attached to hub studs, press out drive shaft from hub.

4) On 4000, remove axle nut, push control arm down and pull drive shaft out of wheel bearing housing. On 5000, remove 3 nuts holding strut to body while holding strut from below. On 4000, loosen top nut on shock absorber while holding piston rod with hex wrench.

5) On 5000, pull hub off drive shaft. On both models, remove strut from vehicle.

Disassembly — 1) With strut assembly on bench, attach suitable spring compressor to coil spring and compress enough to remove upper piston rod retaining nut. Remove strut top plate.

2) Slowly release tension from coil spring and remove spring.

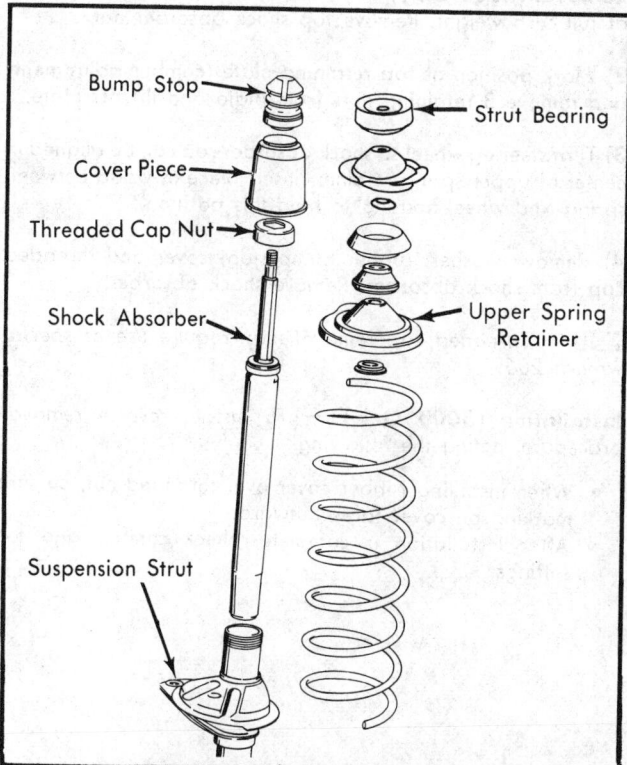

Fig. 2 **Disassembled View of Strut Assembly**
(4000 Shown; 5000 Similar)

Front Suspension

AUDI (Cont.)

3) Use suitable tool (40-201A, 4000; 2069, 5000) to remove threaded cap from top of shock absorber. Remove shock absorber.

Reassembly & Installation — To reassemble and install, do so in reverse of disassembly and removal procedure, noting the following:

- On 5000 models, be sure damping ring locating tabs are mated with indentations on upper spring retainers.
- If nuts or bolts are covered with undercoat or grease, clean threads thoroughly before installation.
- Drive axle splines must be grease-free. Also, apply a narrow ring of suitable locking compound (D6) around outer end of drive shaft splines and allow 1 minute to dry before installing.
- Tighten drive axle nut with vehicle resting on ground.

WHEEL BEARINGS

Removal — Remove strut assembly from vehicle. Press wheel hub from steering knuckle. Remove bearing retaining snap rings and press wheel bearing from knuckle. Press inner race from wheel hub.

NOTE — *Whenever wheel bearing is replaced, a new race must be used.*

Installation — Reverse removal procedure to install.

CAUTION — *When installing hub, be sure that tool contacts inner bearing race only.*

SHOCK ABSORBER (ON-CAR)

Removal (5000 Only) — **1)** Leave vehicle sitting on ground at full curb weight. Remove top shock absorber nut.

2) Mark position of top retaining plate (camber adjustment) and remove 3 retaining nuts from plate and lift off plate.

3) Turn steering wheel so shock absorber rod can be aligned in center of upper spring retainer (insert piece of wood between spring and wheel housing to hold this position).

4) Remove washer, rubber bump stop, cover and threaded cap from shock absorber. Remove shock absorber.

NOTE — *Threaded cap removal may require use of special wrench 2069.*

Installation (5000 Only) — To install, reverse removal procedure, noting the following:

- When installing rubber cover over threaded nut, be sure marking on cover faces outward.
- After installation is complete, check camber and toe settings.

LOWER CONTROL ARM

Removal — **1)** Raise and support front of vehicle. Place additional support under strut assembly.

2) Detach stabilizer bar from control arm. It may be necessary to remove stabilizer bar clamp bolts from frame to gain movement.

3) Loosen control arm mounting bolts. Remove axle drive shaft if necessary.

4) On 4000, index mark ball joint nuts and bracket. Remove ball joint mounting nuts, bolts and bracket (4000) and separate ball joint from strut. Remove control arm.

Bushing Replacement — Using suitable support (VW 401) and driver (VW 409 for 4000; 2040 for 5000 inner side, VW 408a for 5000 outer side), remove old bushings from control arm. Using same tools, lubricate and replace bushings.

Installation — To install lower control arm, reverse removal procedure, noting the following:

- On 4000, if ball joint is not replaced at this time, be sure index marks made during removal are aligned.
- Tighten all nuts and bolts to specifications.
- Check alignment.

TIGHTENING SPECIFICATIONS

Application	Ft. Lbs. (N·m)
Axle Nut①	
4000	167 (227)
5000	203 (276)
Ball Joint Bracket Nuts (4000)	47 (64)
Ball Joint-to-Strut Nut	
4000	36 (49)
5000	47 (64)
Control Arm-to-Subframe	
4000	43 (58)
5000	80 (109)
Shock Absorber Threaded Cap	
4000	109 (147)
5000	130 (177)
Shock Piston Rod Nut	
4000	36 (49)
5000	43 (58)
Stabilizer Bar Bracket	
4000	18 (24)
5000	76 (103)
Stabilizer Bar-to-Control Arm (5000)	80 (109)
Strut Upper Plate (5000)	18 (24)
Strut Upper Retaining Nuts (5000)	18 (24)

① — Always replace.

Front Suspension

S
U
S
P
E
N
S
I
O
N

BMW

320i
528i
633CSi
733i

DESCRIPTION

Strut type suspension consisting of a vertically mounted strut assembly. Strut assembly is mounted to chassis frame at top by means of a thrust bearing. Lower end of strut assembly is mounted to ball joint which is bolted to lower control arm. Strut assembly connects to ball joint by means of a steering knuckle which is bolted to strut assembly and ball joint. Strut assembly consists of a shock absorber built into strut tube. A coil spring is mounted on outside of strut assembly. A stabilizer bar is mounted to front of axle carrier (crossmember) and is connected at ends to lower control arms. On all models except 320i, a strut rod is connected to lower control arm and axle carrier.

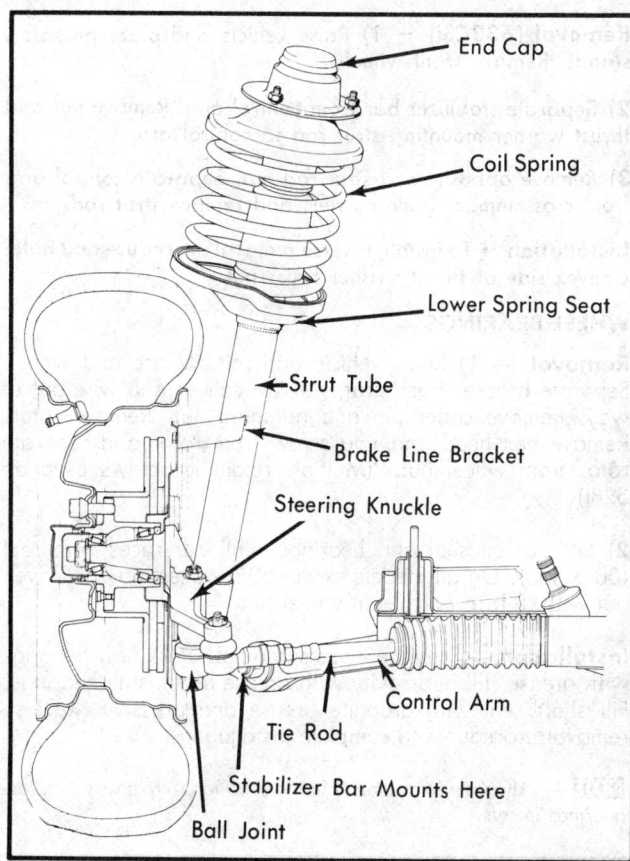

Fig. 1 BMW 320i Front Suspension Assembly

ADJUSTMENTS

WHEEL ALIGNMENT SPECIFICATIONS & PROCEDURES

See Wheel Alignment Specifications and Procedures in WHEEL ALIGNMENT Section.

WHEEL BEARING ADJUSTMENT

320i Models — While rotating wheel hub, tighten castle nut to 22-24 ft. lbs. (30-33 N•m), then rotate hub at least 2 more times. Loosen castle nut until bearing end play is noticed. Tighten castle nut to a maximum of about 24 INCH lbs. (3 N•m), then loosen to nearest hole and install cotter pin.

NOTE — After adjustment, slotted washer should move easily, without noticeable resistance.

528i, 633CSi & 733i Models — Tighten castle nut to 22-24 ft. lbs. (30-33 N•m) while continuously rotating wheel. Loosen castle nut until there is visible axial bearing play. Again rotate wheel and tighten nut, this time to 24 INCH lbs. (3 N•m). Insert cotter pin. Thrust washer should have movement with only slight resistance after adjustment.

BALL JOINT CHECKING

Axial movement of ball joint with pressure applied by leverage should be .055" (1.4 mm) or less. If play exceeds specifications replace control arm assembly.

REMOVAL & INSTALLATION

FRONT SUSPENSION ASSEMBLY

Removal — **1)** Raise and support vehicle. Remove front wheels. Detach brake line mounting brackets from strut tube. If equipped with brake wear sensor, unplug connector and remove ground wire at caliper. On all models, remove calipers and suspend out of way (with hydraulic lines connected). On 320i, disconnect stabilizer bar at frame.

2) Disconnect steering shaft pinch bolt at universal joint. Index mark shaft and separate from "U" joint. Drain power steering

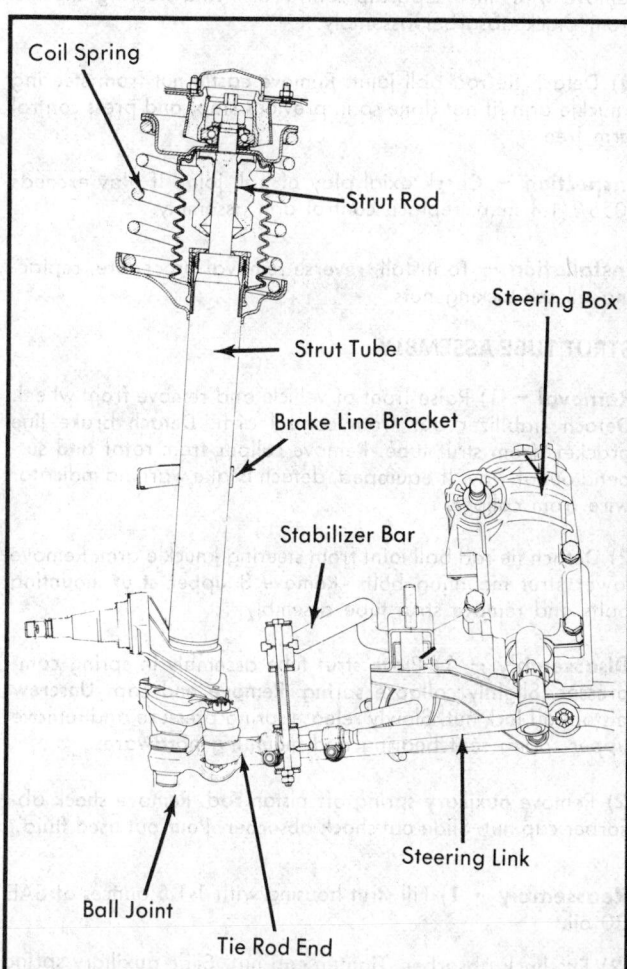

Fig. 2 BMW 528i, 633CSi and 733i Front Suspension

Front Suspension

BMW (Cont.)

unit, detach power steering hoses and plug openings. Remove nuts from engine dampers, heat shields and engine mounts (as equipped). Remove clamps from automatic transmission cooling lines (if equipped).

3) Check along front axle for engine ground wire. If attached at this location, remove wire. Detach top strut-to-fender mountings. Using overhead hoist to support engine and a floor jack to support suspension, detach right end of front axle from frame member and lower suspension from vehicle.

Installation — To install reverse removal procedure and note the following: Make sure shoulder of engine mount engages properly in opening. Reconnect steering shaft while front wheels are pointing straight ahead. Ensure steering shaft index marks are aligned and that mounting screw engages safety groove. Check wheel alignment and bleed power steering unit, if equipped.

LOWER CONTROL ARM

Removal — **1)** Raise vehicle and remove front wheel. Disconnect stabilizer link or bar from control arm. If strut rod connects to control arm, remove from arm.

2) Detach inner end of control arm from axle carrier. On models held with castle nut only, remove castle nut and press control arm from steering knuckle. If held with safety wire, remove wire, then separate control arm and steering knuckle from shock absorber assembly.

3) Detach tie rod ball joint. Remove castle nut from steering knuckle arm (if not done so in previous step) and press control arm free.

Inspection — Check axial play of ball joint. If play exceeds .055" (1.4 mm), replace control arm assembly.

Installation — To install, reverse removal procedure, replacing all self-locking nuts.

STRUT TUBE ASSEMBLY

Removal — **1)** Raise front of vehicle and remove front wheel. Detach stabilizer bar from control arm. Detach brake line brackets from strut tube. Remove caliper from rotor and suspend out of way. If equipped, detach brake warning indicator wire from caliper.

2) Detach tie rod ball joint from steering knuckle arm. Remove lower strut mounting bolts. Remove 3 upper strut mounting bolts and remove strut tube assembly.

Disassembly — **1)** Place strut tube assembly in spring compressor. Slightly collapse spring. Remove end cap. Unscrew piston rod lock nut. Slowly release spring pressure and remove upper spring seat bearing and mounting hardware.

2) Remove auxiliary spring off piston rod. Remove shock absorber cap nut. Slide out shock absorber. Pour out used fluid.

Reassembly — **1)** Fill strut housing with 1-1.5 ounces of SAE 30 oil.

2) Fit shock absorber. Tighten cap nut. Slide auxiliary spring into place. Guide coil spring into lower spring seat. Set upper bearing mount (upper spring seat) on top of coil spring. Slide

piston rod through opening, after extending rod as far as possible. Attach compressor and collapse spring enough to install upper mounting nut.

Installation — To install, reverse removal procedure and tighten all nuts and bolts.

STABILIZER BAR

Removal — Raise and support vehicle. Remove front wheels for easier access. Detach stabilizer link or bar from control arms. Remove stabilizer bar brackets and take stabilizer bar from vehicle.

NOTE — *Before installation, inspect bushings for excessive wear and replace as necessary.*

Installation — To install, reverse removal procedure.

STRUT ROD

Removal (633CSi) — **1)** Raise vehicle and place on safety stands. Remove front wheels.

2) Separate stabilizer bar from control arm. Remove nut and thrust washer mounting strut rod to control arm.

3) Remove opposite end strut rod nut. Separate control arm from crossmember (axle carrier) and remove strut rod.

Installation — To install, reverse removal procedure and note: Convex side of thrust washer faces nut.

WHEEL BEARINGS

Removal — **1)** Raise vehicle and remove tire and wheel. Separate bracket from strut, remove caliper and wire out of way. Remove cotter pin and retaining nut. Remove rotor. Remove hex head retaining screw from rotor and separate rotor from wheel hub. (Multiple retaining screws used on 528i).

2) Lift out oil seal and bearings. Pull out races with tool (00 8 550). On all models except 528i, races may be driven out with drift at notches in wheel hub.

Installation — Press new races into hub. Pack new bearings with grease, fill hub cavity with grease and install bearings. Fill shaft seal with graphite grease and press in. Reverse removal procedures to complete installation.

NOTE — *Always replace races with bearings and always replace bearings in sets.*

TIGHTENING SPECIFICATIONS

Application	Ft. Lbs. (N•m)
Axle Carrier-to-Body	
320i	32-35 (44-48)
528i, 633CSik & 733i	54-60 (73-82)
Control Arm-to-Axle Carrier	59-66 (80-90)
Shock Absorber Cap Nut	87-101 (118-137)
Stabilizer Bar Brackets	34-37 (46-50)
Stabilizer Bar or Link-to-Control Arm	
320i	50-65 (68-88)
528i & 633CSi	16-17 (22-23)
733i	18-20 (25-27)
Tie Rod Castle Nut	25-29 (34-39)

CHRYSLER CORP. IMPORTS — EXCEPT PICKUPS

Challenger
Champ
Colt
Sapporo

DESCRIPTION

Strut type suspension consisting of a vertically mounted strut assembly, lower control arm and stabilizer bar. Strut assembly is mounted to top of fender panel by a rubber insulator. On rear-wheel drive models, the strut assembly mounts at bottom to steering arm and pivots in ball joint. On front-wheel drive (FWD) models, the lower end of strut is bolted to a separate steering knuckle. On all models, a stabilizer bar and strut bars are attached to front chassis members and ends of lower control arms.

ADJUSTMENTS

WHEEL ALIGNMENT SPECIFICATIONS & PROCEDURES

See Wheel Alignment Specifications and Procedures in WHEEL ALIGNMENT Section.

WHEEL BEARING ADJUSTMENT

Rear Wheel Drive — Tighten spindle nut to 175 INCH lbs. (20 N•m). Loosen completely and retighten to 43 INCH lbs. (5 N•m).

Install cap and cotter pin. Do not back off nut more than 15° to accommodate cotter pin. If holes cannot be aligned within 15°, repeat procedure.

Front Wheel Drive — 1) Adjustment is obtained by using the correct wheel bearing preload spacer. To determine correct spacer, install spacer selection gauge (MB990959) in hub and tighten to 14 ft. lbs. (19 N•m).

2) Rotate tool several times to seat wheel bearings. Install dial indicator on tool and load approximately .2" (5 mm) of travel on dial indicator. Zero indicator.

3) Measure travel by holding threaded stud of special tool with a wrench, then back off nut slowly until travel no longer registers on dial indicator. Note reading.

4) Repeat procedure to ensure accurate reading. Average the readings and select proper spacer according to table.

BALL JOINT CHECKING

Remove ball joint assembly from vehicle. Check axial and radial play. If any measurable play is present, replace ball joint. Check starting torque required to rotate ball joint stud. Starting torque should be 108 INCH lbs. (12 N•m) on FWD models and 48-72 INCH lbs. (5-8 N•m) on all others. Check turning torque on FWD models. Torque required should be 24-48 INCH lbs. (3-5 N•m). If readings are not to these specifications, ball joints should be replaced.

REMOVAL & INSTALLATION

STRUT ASSEMBLY

Removal (FWD Models) — Raise and support front of vehicle. Remove wheel. Disconnect brake line from strut. Remove attaching nuts and bolts at ends of strut. Remove strut.

Removal (All Other Models) — 1) Raise and support vehicle. Remove wheel and tire. Disconnect brake line at strut and wheel well bracket and remove. Remove caliper and hub assemblies.

2) Remove strut assembly mounting nuts from both ends of strut and remove from vehicle.

Disassembly — 1) Clamp strut assembly in vise and use proper tool to compress coil spring. Remove dust cover. Remove nuts holding insulator to strut sub-assembly. Remove insulator and then coil spring.

2) If oil loss is found, disassemble sub-assembly after thoroughly cleaning it. Place sub-assembly vertically in vise. Use special wrench (CT-1112) to remove seal assembly. Compress piston rod to lowest position during this procedure.

3) Drain fluid. Using small screwdriver, remove square-cut "O" ring from rod and draw out rod assembly and guide. Remove guide from piston rod.

Reassembly — 1) Clean and replace all components as required. Apply hydraulic fluid to sliding surfaces. Insert piston rod in cylinder. Compress piston ring with fingers as it slides into cylinder.

2) Assemble cylinder and piston assembly with strut outer casing. Fill unit with approximately 8 oz. (FWD) or 14.5 oz. (all others) of new hydraulic fluid.

3) With guide flange at top, insert piston rod until guide flange contacts shock absorber cylinder end. Install "O" ring

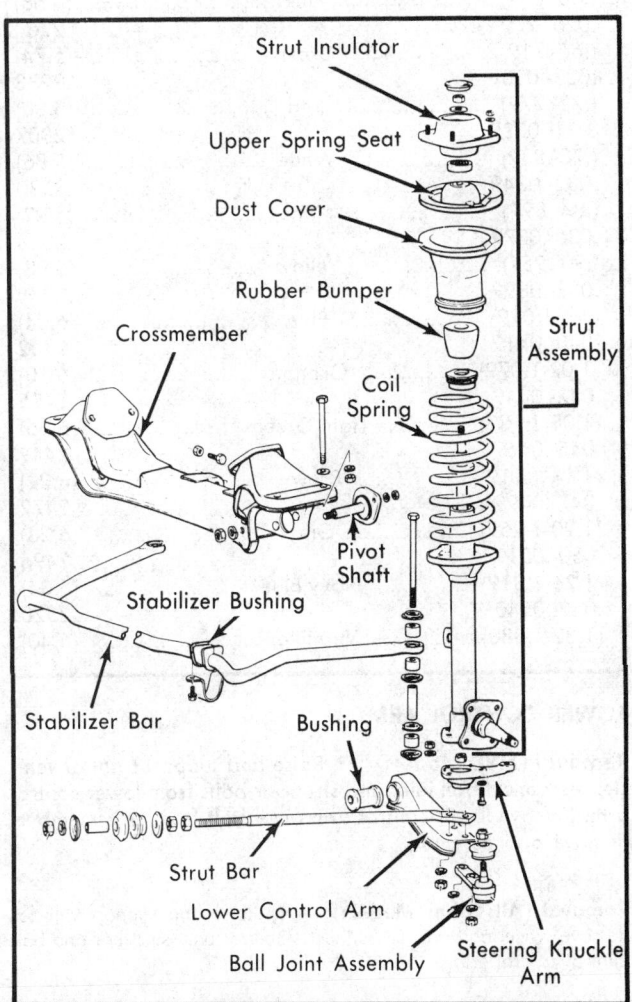

Fig. 1 Exploded View of Front Suspension (Rear-Wheel Drive Models)

Strut Insulator
Upper Spring Seat
Dust Cover
Rubber Bumper
Crossmember
Strut Assembly
Coil Spring
Pivot Shaft
Stabilizer Bushing
Stabilizer Bar
Bushing
Strut Bar
Lower Control Arm
Ball Joint Assembly
Steering Knuckle Arm

CHRYSLER CORP. IMPORTS − EXCEPT PICKUPS (Cont.)

between guide and strut outer cylinder (always use new "O" ring).

4) Cover piston rod end with seal guide (CT-1111B), slide in seal after applying oil to seal lip and tighten seal assembly until seal nut edge contacts strut outer cylinder.

NOTE − *Be sure to replace seal assembly when shock absorber has been disassembled.*

5) Attach compressor to coil spring and place spring onto strut assembly. Pull shock absorber fully out and position bumper rubber and spacer.

6) Align "D" shaped hole in spring seat upper assembly with indentation on piston rod. Install insulator assembly. Install self-locking nut and tighten temporarily.

NOTE − *If replacing coil springs, be sure to use same color-code class as original.*

7) After seating upper and lower end of coil spring on grooves of spring seats, remove spring compressor. Using special tool (CT-1112) tighten spring seat and self-locking nut to specified torque.

Installation (All Models) − Reverse removal procedures to install, noting the following: On rear wheel drive models, apply suitable sealer to flanged mating surfaces of strut mount and knuckle. Pack strut upper bearing with grease and install dust cap.

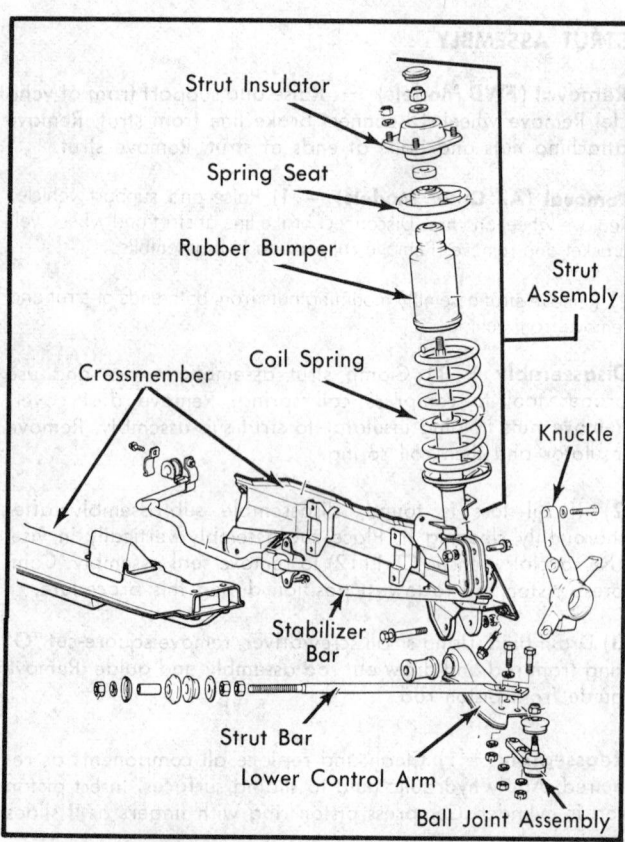

Fig. 2 Exploded View of Front Suspension (Front-Wheel Drive Models)

WHEEL BEARINGS

Removal (FWD Models) − **1)** Remove knuckle and hub assembly. Separate knuckle from hub (use soft hammer if necessary), remove

inner bearing and inner race from knuckle and preload adjusting spacer from hub. Separate rotor from hub.

2) Remove outer bearing inner race with drift and pry out inner and outer grease seals. Drive out bearing outer races.

Removal (All Other Models) − **1)** Raise and support vehicle. Remove tire and wheel, remove caliper assembly and wire out of way.

2) Pry off grease cup, remove cotter pin, cap and retaining nut. Remove hub and rotor assembly. Remove outer bearing inner race and drive out remaining races.

Installation − Reverse removal procedures to install, noting the following: Select wheel bearing preload adjusting spacer (FWD) and set bearing preload according to procedures given in "WHEEL BEARING ADJUSTMENT."

Wheel Bearing Preload Spacer		
Indicator Reading In. (mm)	**Spacer Color**	**Spacer Thickness** In. (mm)
.021-.0239 (.54-.500)	Light Blue	.2212 (5.62)
.024-.0259 (.60-.659)	Pink	.2236 (5.68)
.026-.279 (.66-.719)	Green	.2260 (5.74)
.028-.0309 (.72-.779)	Red	.2283 (5.80)
.031-.0329 (.78-.839)	White	.2307 (5.86)
.033-.0349 (.84-.899)	None	.2330 (5.92)
.035-.0379 (.90-.959)	Yellow	.2354 (5.98)
.038-.0399 (.96-1.019)	Blue	.2378 (6.04)
.040-.0419 (1.02-1.079)	Orange	.2402 (6.10)
.042-.0449 (1.08-1.139)	Light Green	.2425 (6.16)
.045-.0469 (1.14-1.119)	Brown	.2449 (6.22)
.047-.0499 (1.20-1.259)	Grey	.2472 (6.28)
.050-.0519 (1.26-1.319)	Navy Blue	.2496 (6.34)
.052-.0540 (1.32-1.380)	Vermilion	.2520 (6.40)

LOWER CONTROL ARM

Removal (FWD Models) − Raise and support front of vehicle. Disconnect ball joint and strut bar bolts from lower control arm. Remove lower control arm pivot bolt from crossmember. Remove arm assembly.

Removal (All Other Models) − **1)** Raise and support vehicle. Remove wheel and tire. Disconnect stabilizer bar, strut bar and ball joint at control arm.

2) Disconnect idler arm bracket from body and move steering linkage back. Remove control arm pivot bolt from crossmember and remove arm.

CHRYSLER CORP. IMPORTS — EXCEPT PICKUPS (Cont.)

NOTE — On all models, do not remove ball joint from steering knuckle unless ball joint is to be replaced.

Ball Joint Replacement (FWD) — Remove ball joint assembly from control arm. Press or drive ball joint from knuckle. Remove assembly. Reverse procedure to install new unit.

Ball Joint Replacement (All Other Models) — **1)** Remove wheel and tire. With brake hose connected, remove caliper assembly and wire out of way.

2) Press tie rod end from steering knuckle. Remove knuckle-to-strut retaining bolts and separate with plastic hammer.

3) Loosen ball joint retaining nut in knuckle arm. With nut partially installed to protect stud, tap ball joint from arm.

4) Reverse procedure to install new ball joint.

Installation (All Models) — To install, reverse removal procedure and note the following: On rear-wheel drive models, when connecting strut assembly to steering knuckle arm, apply suitable sealer to flanged mating surface. On all models, when installing lower control arms, tighten all nuts and bolts to specifications after vehicle has been lowered to ground.

STEERING KNUCKLE (FWD MODELS ONLY)

Removal — **1)** Raise and support front of vehicle. Remove wheel. Remove cotter pin, axle nut and washer. Remove underside cover. Remove strut bar and disconnect ball joint from lower control arm. Drain transaxle.

2) Insert a pry bar between the transaxle case and the shoulder of the constant velocity joint of axle shaft. Do not insert pry bar more than .28" (7 mm) to avoid damaging inner seal. Pry axle shaft from transaxle and support.

3) Using an axle shaft puller (CT-1003 or equivalent), force axle shaft out of hub and remove from vehicle. Remove brake assembly.

4) Using a tie rod puller, remove tie rod end from knuckle. Disconnect the knuckle from strut and remove hub and knuckle as an assembly.

Installation — To install, reverse removal procedure, noting the following: Replace the constant velocity joint retainer ring each time the axle shaft is removed from transaxle case.

STABILIZER & STRUT BAR

Removal — Raise vehicle and support on safety stands. Disconnect stabilizer and strut bars from mountings on lower control arm. Remove strut bracket from body mounting position. Remove stabilizer bracket on each side and take off stabilizer. Next, lift off strut bar after noting position of all washers and bushings.

Installation — Reverse removal procedures to install, noting the following: On FWD models, right side strut bar is marked with yellow. On all other models, check mark between bolt holes to determine right (R) and left (L) rods. Make sure distance from end of strut rod to outside edge of outer lock nut is 2.95" (75 mm) on FWD models, and 3.2" (81 mm) on all others.

TIGHTENING SPECIFICATIONS

Application	Ft. Lbs. (N•m)
Front Wheel Drive Models	
Drive Axle Nut	87-130 (118-177)
Strut-to-Knuckle Arm	54-65 (73-88)
Knuckle Arm-to-Ball Joint	40-51 (54-69)
Knuckle Arm-to-Tie Rod Ball Joint	11-25 (15-34)
Control Arm-to-Ball Joint	69-87 (94-118)
Control Arm-to-Crossmember	69-87 (94-118)
Strut Bar-to-Control Arm	69-87 (94-118)
Strut Bar-to-Crossmember	54-61 (73-83)
Stabilizer Bracket Bolts	22-29 (30-39)
Hub-to-Rotor	29-36 (39-53)
Rear Wheel Drive Models	
Strut-to-Knuckle Arm	58-78 (79-106)
Knuckle Arm-to-Ball Joint	43-52 (59-71)
Knuckle Arm-to-Tie Rod Ball Joint	25-33 (34-45)
Control Arm-to-Crossmember	58-69 (79-94)
Control Arm-to-Ball Joint	43-51 (59-69)
Stabilizer-to-Control Arm	10-14 (14-19)
Stabilizer Bracket Bolts	25-33 (34-45)
Strut Bar-to-Control Arm	43-51 (59-69)
Strut Bar-to-Bracket	54-61 (73-83)
Hub-to-Rotor	25-29 (34-39)

CHRYSLER CORP. IMPORTS — PICKUPS

Arrow Pickup
Ram-50 Pickup

DESCRIPTION

Independent front suspension with coil springs. Wheel is supported by steering knuckle mounted between upper and lower control arms by ball joints. Upper and lower control arms pivot on shafts connected to crossmember. The coil spring ends fit in pockets formed in crossmember and lower control arm. The shock absorber mounts between crossmember and lower control arm, inside the coil spring. A stabilizer bar and two strut bars mount to frame and connect to ends of lower control arms.

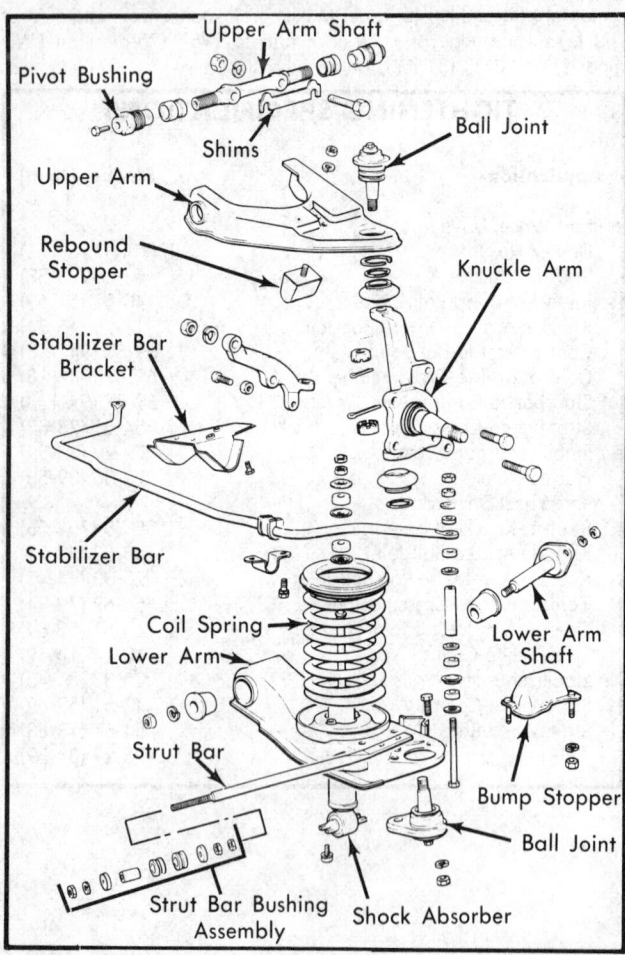

Fig. 1 Exploded View of Front Suspension Assembly

ADJUSTMENT

WHEEL ALIGNMENT SPECIFICATIONS & PROCEDURES

See Wheel Alignment Specifications & Procedures in WHEEL ALIGNMENT Section.

WHEEL BEARING ADJUSTMENT

Tighten adjusting nut to 22 ft. lbs. (30 N·m) to seat bearings. Loosen nut and tighten to 6 ft. lbs. (8 N·m). Install cotter pin.

NOTE — It is important that the adjusting nut be loosened not more than 30 to fit cotter pin.

BALL JOINT CHECKING

With components removed from vehicle, check upper ball joint for starting torque and lower ball joint for axial play. Starting torque should be 7-30 INCH lbs. (.8-3.4 N·m). Axial play should be .02" (.5 mm) or less. Replace as needed.

REMOVAL & INSTALLATION

SHOCK ABSORBERS

Removal — Raise and support front of vehicle. Remove upper shock mounting nuts and bushings. Remove lower shock mounting bolts and remove shock absorber.

Installation — To install, reverse removal procedure.

WHEEL BEARINGS

Removal — Raise vehicle and remove wheel and tire. Remove caliper assembly and wire out of way. Remove rotor with hub. Remove bearings, clean grease from hub and with a drift, drive out bearing races. Oil seal will be removed with inner race.

Installation — Coat bearing race outer surface evenly with bearing grease. Drive race into place. Pack bearings, fill oil seal and coat inner surface of hub evenly with grease. Install bearings and drive oil seal into place. Be careful not to deform seal. Fill bearing dust cap with grease and install. Reverse removal procedure to complete installation.

STEERING KNUCKLE

Removal — **1)** Raise and support front of vehicle. Remove wheel, brake assembly and hub.

2) Loosen nuts at forward end of strut bar, then disconnect it from control arm. Disconnect stabilizer bar from control arm. Remove shock absorber.

3) Using spring compressor, compress coil spring. Remove cotter pins and nuts from upper and lower ball joint studs. Use ball joint removal tool to disconnect ball joints from knuckle.

4) Loosen spring compressor slowly, and remove knuckle and coil spring.

Installation — To install, reverse removal procedure.

LOWER CONTROL ARM, COIL SPRING & BALL JOINT

Removal — **1)** Raise and support front of vehicle. Loosen nuts at forward end of strut bar. Disconnect stabilizer bar and strut bar from control arm. Remove shock absorber.

2) Use coil spring compressor to compress coil spring. Remove cotter pin and nut from lower arm ball joint stud.

3) Use ball joint tool to disconnect lower ball joint from knuckle. Loosen coil spring compressor and remove coil spring.

4) Remove lower arm pivot shaft and remove lower control arm.

Inspection — Inspect arm, bushings and ball joint for wear or damage. Replace defective parts as necessary.

Installation — To install, reverse removal procedure noting the following: Install pivot shaft to crossmember and tighten

CHRYSLER CORP. IMPORTS — PICKUPS (Cont.)

bolts, leaving shaft nut loose. Tighten shaft nut to specifications after vehicle has been lowered to the ground. The distance from the forward end of the strut bar to the face of the rear adjusting nut is 3.9" (100 mm).

UPPER CONTROL ARM & BALL JOINT

Removal — 1) Raise and support front of vehicle. Remove wheel and shock absorber. Use a coil spring compressor to compress the coil spring.

2) Remove cotter pin and nut from upper ball joint. Using a ball joint tool, disconnect ball joint from knuckle.

3) Remove bolts attaching upper control arm shatt to crossmember. Remove upper control arm as an assembly.

Inspection — Inspect arm, bushings and ball joint for wear or damage. Replace parts as necessary.

Ball Joint Replacement — Ball joints are removed and installed with a press and suitable adapters. The ball joint requires a minimum press load 2200 lbs. (998 kg) for removal and an initial 1550 lbs. (703 kg) during installation. Final press load required to seat ball joint is 11,000 lbs. (4989 kg). Install a new snap ring and dust cover on ball joint.

Installation — To install, reverse removal procedure, noting the following: Reinstall camber shims in original location between upper arm shaft and crossmember. Check wheel alignment.

TIGHTENING SPECIFICATIONS

Application	Ft. Lbs (N·m)
Shock Absorber Mount Bolts	6-9 (8-12)
Shock Absorber Mount Nuts	9-13 (12-18)
Lower Arm Shaft Nut	40-54 (54-73)
Strut Bar Lock Nut	54-61 (73-83)
Ball Joint-to-Lower Arm	22-30 (30-41)
Upper Ball Joint-to-Knuckle	43-65 (59-88)
Lower Ball Joint-to-Knuckle	87-130 (118-177)
Upper Arm Pivot Bushing	181-253 (246-344)
Upper Arm Shaft-to-Crossmember	
Produced Before 1/81	40-54 (54-73)
Produced 1/81 and After	72-87 (100-118)
Strut Bar-to-Lower Arm	51-61 (69-83)

Pickup

DESCRIPTION

Independent type suspension, consisting of upper and lower control arms and wheel spindle mounted between upper and lower arms by means of ball joints. Upper control arm pivots on a shaft attached to frame. Lower control arm pivots on a shaft mounted to crossmember. A coil spring is mounted between lower control arm and frame. Shock absorber is hydraulic, double-action type mounted inside coil spring.

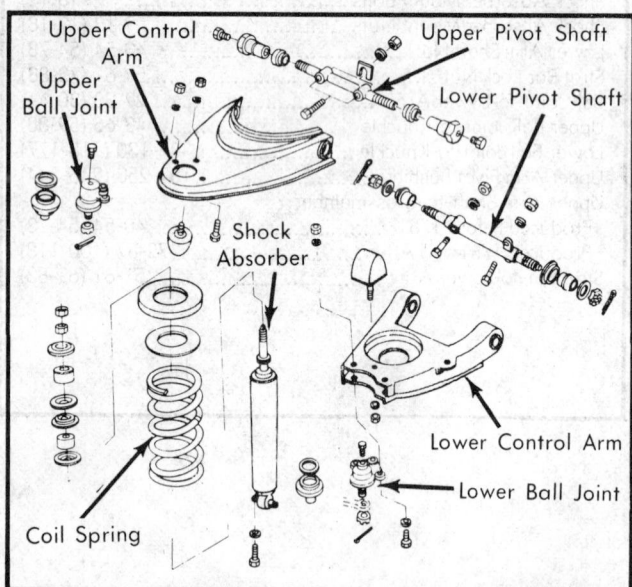

Fig. 1 Exploded View of Front Suspension Assembly

ADJUSTMENT

WHEEL ALIGNMENT SPECIFICATIONS & PROCEDURES

See Wheel Alignment Specifications and Procedures in WHEEL ALIGNMENT Section.

WHEEL BEARING ADJUSTMENT

All Models — While rotating wheel, hub and drum assembly, tighten adjusting nut to 17-25 ft. lbs. (23-34 N•m). Back adjusting nut off 1/4 turn and install retainer with new cotter pin. Check wheel rotation. If rough or noisy, inspect, clean or replace wheel bearings.

BALL JOINT CHECKING

Check working surfaces of ball joints and studs for wear or damage. End play should not exceed .031" (.8 mm). If end play is excessive, replace ball joint.

REMOVAL & INSTALLATION

SHOCK ABSORBERS

Removal — Remove nut, rubber bushing and washer attaching upper end of shock absorber to crossmember. Remove lower retaining bolts holding shock absorber to lower control arm. Remove shock absorber from vehicle.

Installation — To install, reverse removal procedure and tighten mounting bolts to specifications.

WHEEL BEARINGS

Removal — 1) Raise vehicle and remove wheel and tire. Remove grease cap, cotter pin, nut lock, adjusting nut and flat washer from spindle. Remove outer bearings.

2) Remove brake caliper and wire out of way. Pull hub and disc assembly from spindle. Remove and discard old grease seal. Remove inner bearings. Clean old grease from inner race, outer race and inside of hub with solvent.

3) Pull out races with tool or drive out with hammer and drift. Clean inside of hub and wheel spindle thoroughly with clean solvent to remove all old grease.

Installation — 1) Install new bearing races with tool (T56P-1217-A) or drift making sure that races are seated properly. Pack inside of hub with grease until flush with inside diameter of bearing races.

2) Pack wheel bearings with new grease and install inner bearing in hub. Coat new oil seal lightly with grease and install. Reverse removal procedures to complete installation. Adjust wheel bearings.

UPPER BALL JOINT & CONTROL ARM

Removal — 1) Raise and suitably support vehicle under lower control arm. Lower vehicle until arm is off rubber bumper stop. Remove tire and wheel. Remove cotter pin and nut attaching upper ball joint to spindle.

2) Tap with a hammer to break ball joint loose and separate it from spindle. Remove 3 retaining nuts and bolts and remove ball joint from control arm. Open hood and remove 2 upper arm retaining bolts. Remove control arm from vehicle.

Installation — Position ball joint in upper arm and tighten bolts. Install control arm in vehicle and tighten bolts. Install spindle on ball joint, tighten nut and install cotter pin. Install tire and wheel, remove safety stands and lower vehicle. Check wheel alignment.

LOWER CONTROL ARM, BALL JOINT & COIL SPRING

Removal — 1) Raise vehicle and place safety stands under frame behind both lower control arms. Remove wheel and tire. Remove lower shock absorber bolts and collapse shock absorber up into spring. Remove retaining bolt attaching stabilizer bar to lower control arm.

2) Install a floor jack under spring area of lower arm and raise arm to relieve spring pressure. Remove cotter pin and nut attaching lower control arm to spindle, strike tapered fit with hammer and separate ball joint from spindle.

3) Remove three bolts and nuts retaining ball joint to lower control arm and remove ball joint. Release jack and lower arm

COURIER (Cont.)

enough to remove coil spring. Remove three bolts and nuts retaining lower control arm to crossmember and remove arm from vehicle.

Installation — 1) Place lower control arm in position, install three retaining bolts and nuts, DO NOT tighten. Place coil spring in position in lower arm and hold in place with a "C" clamp. Place upper end of spring in pocket in frame and raise lower control arm with a jack.

2) Position ball joint in lower arm and tighten bolts. Raise lower control arm with jack enough to install ball joint in spindle, refit nut.

3) Tighten three lower arm retaining bolts left loose. Pull shock absorber down and tighten retaining bolts. Install stabilizer bar as previously outlined. Install tire and wheel, remove safety stands and lower vehicle. Check caster, camber and toe-in.

TIGHTENING SPECIFICATIONS

Application	Ft. Lbs. (N·m)
Upper Ball Joint Stud	47 (64)
Lower Ball Joint Stud	65 (88)
Ball Joint-to-Upper Arm	17 (23)
Ball Joint-to-Lower Arm	65 (88)
Shock Absorber	
Lower Mount	15 (20)
Upper Mount	①
Control Arm-to-Frame	
Lower	62 (84)
Upper	69 (94)
Lower Arm Shaft-to-Lower Arm	62 (84)
Bumper-to-Lower Arm	65 (88)
Bumper-to-Upper Arm	17 (23)

① — Distance from top of lock nut to top of shock absorber stud should be .26" (6.5 mm)

Front Suspension

DATSUN 200SX, 210, 280ZX, 510 & 810

DESCRIPTION

Strut type suspension consisting of a vertically mounted strut assembly, lower control arm, stabilizer bar and compression rod. Strut assembly is mounted at top to chassis frame by a thrust bearing and at bottom to lower control arm by a ball joint. Strut assembly consists of a shock absorber built into outer strut tube, a coil spring mounted on outside of strut tube, and a wheel spindle integral with bottom of strut tube. Compression rod is mounted between lower control arm and chassis. Stabilizer bar is mounted to front chassis member and is connected at end of lower control arm.

ADJUSTMENTS

WHEEL ALIGNMENT SPECIFICATIONS & PROCEDURES

See Wheel Alignment Specifications & Procedures in WHEEL ALIGNMENT Section.

WHEEL BEARING ADJUSTMENT

All Models — Tighten spindle nut to torque specifications in table. Spin wheel and retorque spindle nut. Loosen nut according to specifications in table and then tighten to align cotter pin hole. Check preload. If not to specification, repeat procedure until correct preload is acquired.

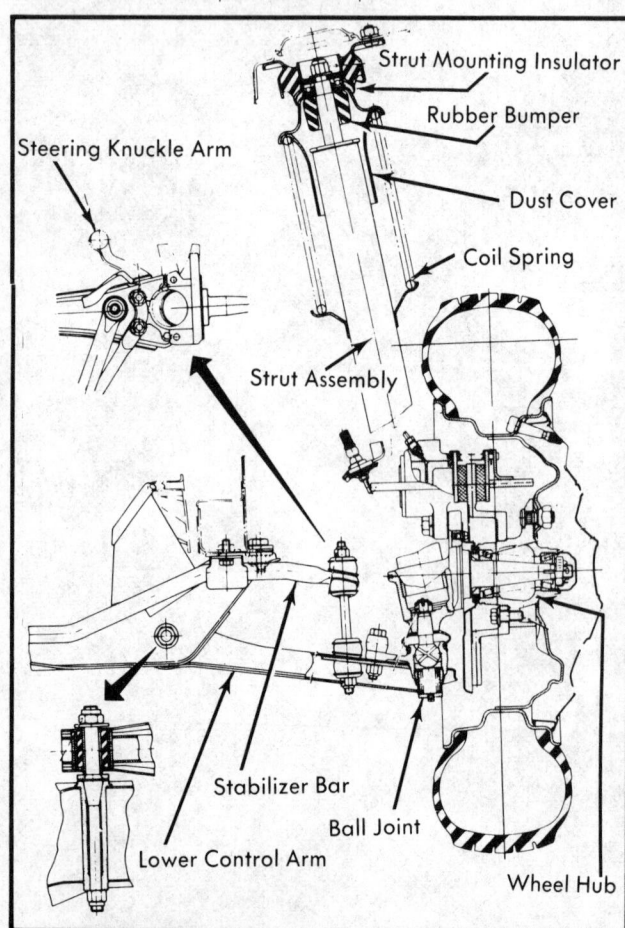

Fig. 1 Assembled View of 210 Front Suspension, (All Other Models Are Similar)

Wheel Bearing Adjustment			
	Torque		Preload
Application	Ft. Lbs. (N·m)	Loosen	Lbs. (N)
200SX, 810 .	18-22 (25-29)	60°	①1.5-3.3 (6.9-14.7)
210	22-25 (29-34)	90°	Less Than 2.6 (11.8)
280ZX	18-22 (25-29)	60°	Less Than 4.0 (17.7)
510	22-25 (29-34)	90°	Less Than 2.6 (11.8)

① — Figures given are for new wheel bearings. Used bearings are .4-1.8 (2.0-7.8).

BALL JOINT CHECKING

All Models — Remove lower control arm. Use appropriate gauge and attach it to top of ball joint stud nut. Measure force (INCH lbs.) required to turn ball joint stud. If measurement is not within specifications, replace ball joint.

Ball Joint Turning Torque		
	New	Used
Application	In. Lbs. (N·m)	In. Lbs. (N·m)
200SX	35-87 (3.9-9.8)	17-69 (2.0-7.8)
210, 510	35-87 (3.9-9.8)	Less Than 17 (2.0)
280ZX	22-69 (2.5-7.8)	Less Than 13 (1.5)
810	35-87 (3.9-9.8)	Less Than 13 (1.5)

REMOVAL & INSTALLATION

SPRING & STRUT ASSEMBLY

Removal — 1) Raise and support front of vehicle. Remove front wheels. Detach brake hose from bracket on front strut (if required). Remove caliper assembly retaining bolts and remove caliper from axle.

2) Remove bolts holding strut to knuckle arm. Detach knuckle arm from bottom of strut. If necessary, pry lower control arm away from strut to ease removal. Remove strut assembly.

3) Place jack under strut to support it when nuts are removed. Remove 3 nuts holding strut to hood ledge and remove strut and spring as an assembly.

Disassembly — 1) Thoroughly clean strut assembly. Fix assembly in suitable holding tool (KV48100300) and clamp tool in vise.

2) With spring compressor, press spring down just far enough to permit turning of strut mounting insulator and remove self-locking nut.

NOTE — Be sure spring tool evenly engages on at least 3 coils. Do not hit piston rod of strut with spring tool.

3) Take out strut insulator, bearing, dust seal, upper spring seat, spring and rubber bumper.

4) Push piston rod down until it bottoms. Remove gland packing using suitable wrench (ST35500001). Remove "O" ring from top of piston rod guide and lift out piston rod and cylinder.

DATSUN 200SX, 210, 280ZX, 510 & 810 (Cont.)

NOTE — *The piston rod, piston rod guide and cylinder are furnished as a matched set with precision mating surfaces.*

5) Drain fluid from inner and outer cylinder and discard. Wash all parts in solvent.

Reassembly — **1)** Install strut outer casing onto suitable holding tool (KV48100300). Install cylinder and piston rod assembly (shock absorber kit) in outer casing.

2) Where present, remove piston rod guide from cylinder. Pour in specified amount of new fluid (outer casing).

Strut Oil Replacement Amounts	
Application	**Oz.**
200SX, 210 & 810	11.0
280ZX	9.3
510	
Atsugi Brand	11.0
Kayaba Brand	13.3

3) Install piston rod guide (bushing), taking care not to damage guide with threaded portion of rod. On 210, 510 and 280ZX, install new "O" ring over rod guide. Lube inner edge of sealing lips of gland packing and install with gland packing guide (ST35520000).

4) To correctly bleed strut assembly, stand strut vertically with spindle end down and pull piston rod up to end of stroke. Turn strut assembly until spindle end is up and depress piston rod to end of stroke. Repeat several times until there is no variation of pressure between pushing and pulling piston rod.

5) Pull piston rod fully out and install rubber bumper. Place spring on lower spring seat and compress with proper tool (ST35651001). Lubricate dust seal and then install dust cover, spring seat, dust seal, mounting bearing and insulator.

6) Install new self-locking nut hand tight only (tighten to specification after unit is installed in vehicle). To prevent entry of dirt, apply a thick coat of multi-purpose grease around upper seal. After positioning spring between upper and lower seats, release spring compressor slowly. Raise rubber bumper to upper spring seat.

Installation — Reverse removal procedures to install.

WHEEL BEARINGS

Removal — **1)** Raise vehicle. Support with safety stands. Remove tire, wheel and splash guard. Remove caliper and wire out of way. Remove cap, cotter pin, adjusting cap and wheel bearing nut.

2) Remove wheel hub with rotor. Remove retaining bolts and separate wheel hub from rotor. Lift or pry out wheel bearings, washers and grease seals, then drive out bearing races.

Installation — Reverse removal procedures to install, noting the following: Make sure bearing races are fully seated. Pack hub, cap and bearings thoroughly with grease. Lubricate contact surface of grease seals, threaded part of spindle and bearing washer to bearing contact face before final assembly. Adjust wheel bearings.

LOWER CONTROL ARM & BALL JOINT

Removal — **1)** Raise vehicle. Support with stands. Remove tire, wheel and splash guard (if equipped).

2) Detach tie rod at ball socket. Remove steering knuckle arm bolts and separate arm from bottom of strut. Separate compression rod and stabilizer bar from lower control arm. Remove bolt connecting lower control arm to crossmember. Remove lower control arm with ball joint and knuckle arm.

3) Place arm in vise, loosen control arm ball joint bolts and remove ball joint (exc. 810). Place steering knuckle arm in vise and press out ball joint.

4) Remove bushing from lower control arm.

Installation — Press bushing into control arm. To install lower control arm, reverse removal procedure. Do not tighten nuts and bolts to final torque until weight of vehicle is on front wheels.

COMPRESSION & STABILIZER BARS

Removal — Raise vehicle and support with safety stands. Remove tire and wheel. Remove splash guard and back off nuts securing compression rod to mounting bracket. Remove bolts attaching compression rod to lower control arm. Remove rod. Remove nuts securing stabilizer bar to connecting rod. Remove stabilizer bracket bolts and brackets, and remove stabilizer bar.

Installation — Reverse removal procedures to install.

TIGHTENING SPECIFICATIONS	
Application	**Ft. Lbs. (N·m)**
Stabilizer Bar Bracket Bolts	
210	12-15 (16-20)
200SX & 510	23-31 (31-42)
280ZX & 810	20-27 (26-36)
Compression Rod-to-Lower Control Arm	
200SX, 210 & 510	37-44 (50-60)
280ZX & 810	33-40 (44-54)
Compression Rod Nut	33-40 (44-54)
Gland Packing Nut	
200SX & 810	72-87 (98-118)
210	58-80 (78-108)
280ZX & 510	72-94 (98-127)
Strut Self-Locking Nut	43-54 (59-74)
Lower Control Arm-to-Crossmember	
200SX	46-55 (63-75)
210 & 510	37-44 (50-60)
280ZX & 810	58-80 (78-108)
Ball Joint-to-Lower Control Arm	
200SX, 210 & 510	37-44 (50-60)
280ZX & 810	33-40 (44-54)
Knuckle Arm-to-Strut	53-72 (72-97)
Ball Joint-to-Knuckle Arm	
200SX, 280ZX & 810	71-88 (96-120)
210 & 510	40-72 (54-98)
Tie Rod Ball Joint	
200SX, 210 & 510	22-51 (29-69)
280ZX & 810	40-72 (54-98)

Front Suspension

DATSUN 310

DESCRIPTION

All models use a strut type front suspension system. Shock absorbers are built into each strut. Upper end of strut is mounted to inner fender panel. Lower end is connected by a ball joint to lower control arm. Control arm mounts at two points on subframe. Steering knuckle is removable from strut. Knuckle bolts to strut with four bolts and has a hole for axle drive shafts to pass through.

ADJUSTMENTS

WHEEL ALIGNMENT SPECIFICATIONS & PROCEDURES

See Wheel Alignment Specifications and Procedures in WHEEL ALIGNMENT Section.

WHEEL BEARING ADJUSTMENT

1) Loosen spindle nut and tighten to 87-145 ft. lbs. (118-196 N•m). Spin assembly several times in both directions to ensure smooth rotation.

2) Torque required to start rotation at spindle nut should be 6.9-24.3 INCH lbs. (.8-2.7 N•m). Preload may also be measured with a pull scale attached to one of the wheel studs. Force required should be 3.1-10.8 lbs. (13.7-48.1 N).

3) If preload is not to specifications, bearing spacer must be replaced. (See "Bearing Removal"). If any axial end-play is present in wheel bearing, or bearing preload is below specification, replace spacer with a smaller one. If bearing preload is greater than specification, a larger spacer must be installed.

BALL JOINT CHECKING

With ball joint removed and stud nut in place, check turning torque required to turn stud. If force required is less than 8.7 INCH lbs. (1.0 N•m) on a used joint, it should be replaced. Check end play with dial indicator at stud end. If end play exceeds .059" (1.5 mm), replace ball joint.

REMOVAL & INSTALLATION

CONTROL ARM

Removal — Raise and support vehicle with safety stands. Remove tire and wheel. Remove bolts securing lower control arm to ball joint. Take off nut mounting stabilizer bar to control arm. Disconnect control arm from subframe by removing two mounting bolts.

Inspection — Inspect arm for distortion. Replace control arm bushings using a press. Make sure new bushings extend evenly on both sides of hole.

Installation — To install, reverse removal procedure and note: Control arm bolts must be tightened with weight of vehicle on ground.

STEERING KNUCKLE

Removal — Raise vehicle and place on safety stands. Remove tire and wheel. Detach and plug brake line and remove brake caliper. Remove axle nut. Using a puller, remove stub axle and brake rotor assembly from axle shaft. Disconnect ball joint and support control arm. Remove 4 bolts securing steering knuckle to strut.

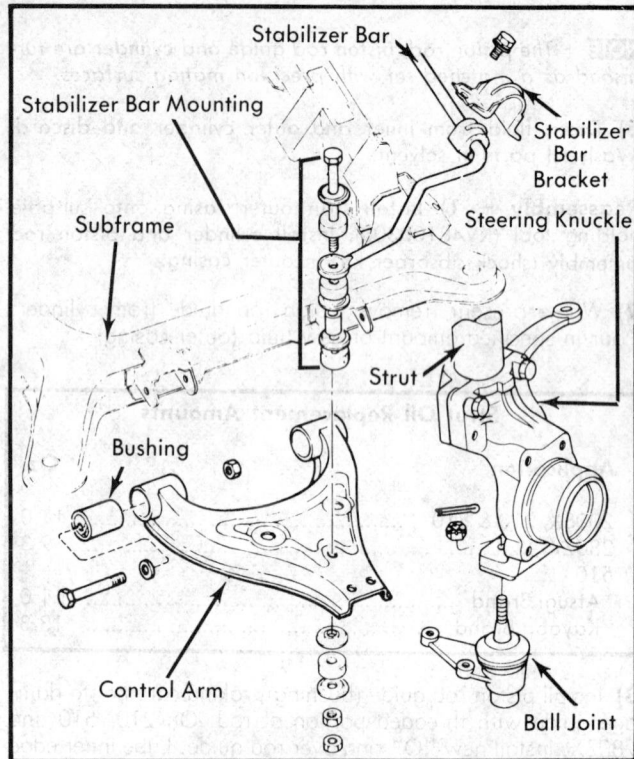

Fig. 1   Exploded View of Control Arm and Stabilizer Bar

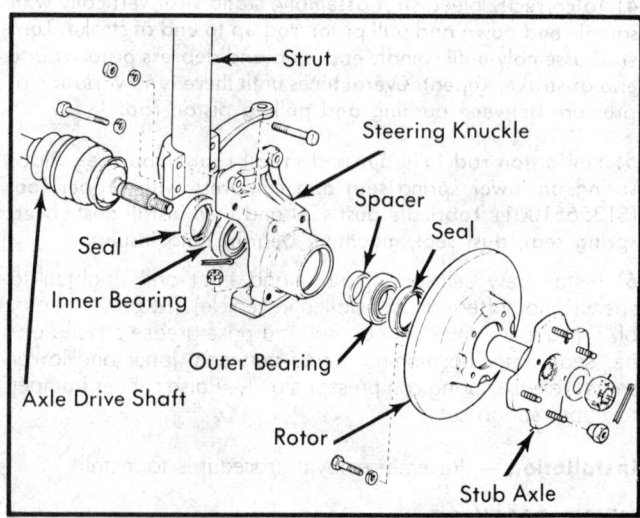

Fig. 2   Exploded View of Steering Knuckle and Strut

Installation — To install, reverse removal procedure and note: Adjust wheel bearings.

BALL JOINT

Removal — Raise vehicle and support on safety stands. Remove tire and wheel. Remove ball joint stud nut. Use ball joint driver and hammer to drive ball joint stud out of knuckle. Remove bolts securing ball joint to lower control arm.

NOTE — *Take care not to damage ball joint dust cover.*

Installation — To install ball joint, reverse removal procedure and make sure new cotter pin is installed. Replace ball joint dust cover if cracked.

DATSUN 310 (Cont.)

STABILIZER BAR

Removal — 1) Raise vehicle and support on safety stands. Support subframe with jack. Disconnect exhaust pipe from exhaust manifold and front body mount. Disconnect transmission control linkage and transmission support rod at transmission.

2) Remove stabilizer-to-control arm nuts. Loosen, but do not remove, subframe attaching bolts. Lower subframe just enough to allow removal of stabilizer bar clamp bolts from subframe. Remove stabilizer bar from vehicle.

Installation — To install, reverse removal procedure and replace any bushing that is worn or cracked.

STRUT ASSEMBLY

Removal — 1) Raise vehicle and suitably support with safety stands. Remove tire and wheel. Working from inside engine compartment, remove cap. Partially loosen lock nut mounting piston rod. Disconnect brake line and plug opening. Detach tie rod from steering knuckle.

2) Place safety stand under control arm for support. Remove four bolts mounting strut to steering knuckle. Remove three nuts keeping upper portion of strut to inner fender panel. Maneuver strut and coil spring assembly from vehicle.

Disassembly — 1) Place strut in a vise and use a spring compressor to slightly compress coil spring. Remove piston rod nut and all upper mounting hardware.

2) Push piston rod into cylinder until it bottoms. Remove packing gland bolt. Remove "O" ring, then slowly lift out piston rod and cylinder as a unit. Drain all fluid from inner cylinder and strut casing. Discard inner cylinder. Flush strut casing with solvent.

Inspection — Inspect all components for damage or excessive wear. Always replace packing gland and "O" ring.

Reassembly — 1) Install cylinder and piston rod in strut casing. Remove piston rod guide from cylinder. Add 7 oz. (210 cc) of strut oil to Atsugi struts or 7.4 oz. (220 cc) to K.Y.B. struts. Place piston rod guide in cylinder and install new "O" ring over rod guide. Install and tighten gland packing bolt.

NOTE – *Lubricate gland packing bolt sealing lips with multi-purpose grease.*

2) Bleed air from cylinder by pumping piston rod in and out until equal resistance is felt on inward and outward strokes. Refit coil spring on strut.

NOTE – *Install a new piston rod nut, but do not torque it until strut is installed in vehicle.*

Installation — To install strut assembly, reverse removal procedure and note following: Make sure all contact surfaces are clean and dirt free.

WHEEL BEARINGS

Removal — Remove steering knuckle. Remove bolts securing wheel hub to brake rotor. Using press and drift, separate rotor from hub. Remove and discard old oil seals. Press wheel bearing from hub. Remove wheel bearing from steering knuckle. Drive out bearing race with a brass drift fitted through notches in knuckle.

Installation — 1) Pack wheel bearings with grease. Install inner and outer bearing races.

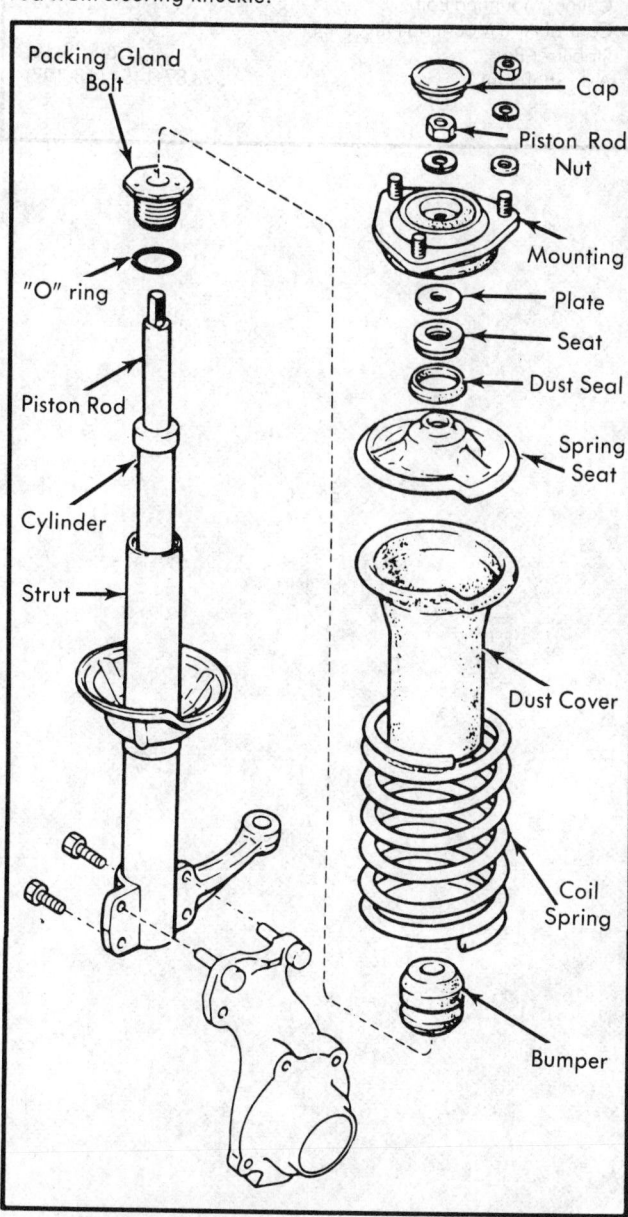

Packing Gland Bolt
"O" ring
Piston Rod
Cylinder
Strut
Cap
Piston Rod Nut
Mounting
Plate
Seat
Dust Seal
Spring Seat
Dust Cover
Coil Spring
Bumper

Fig. 3 Exploded View of Strut Assembly

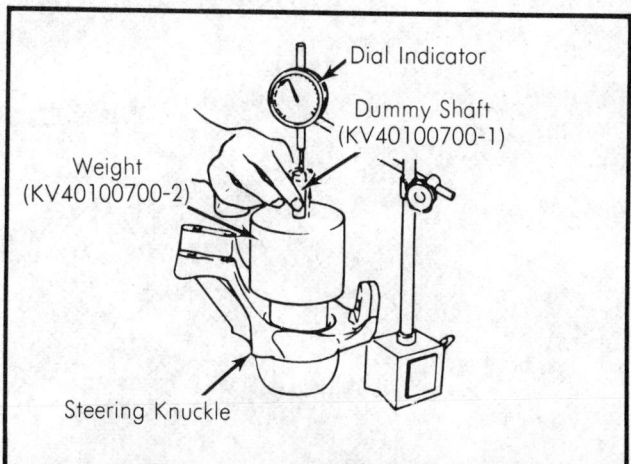

Dial Indicator
Dummy Shaft (KV40100700-1)
Weight (KV40100700-2)
Steering Knuckle

Fig. 4 Determining Required Spacer Thickness

Front Suspension

DATSUN 310 (Cont.)

2) Place outer bearing on base (KV40100700-3) and place steering knuckle over it so bearing seats in outer race. Then slide inner bearing over dummy shaft (KV40100700-1) and place shaft bearing in knuckle with end of shaft in outer bearing and inner bearing in inner race.

3) Slide weight (KV40100700-2) over dummy shaft and down onto knuckle. Turn knuckle back and forth to seat bearing. Assemble dial indicator with contact button resting on top of dummy shaft. Zero indicator. Pull upward on shaft until it reaches end of travel, rotate 1 revolution and record maximum deflection of indicator needle.

4) To determine required spacer thickness, add recorded dial indicator reading to metric thickness dimension stamped on side of flange on end of dummy shaft.

5) Select required spacer. Spacers are available in 18 sizes, ranging from .291-.293" (7.38-7.44 mm) to .331-.333" (8.40-8.46 mm) in .002" (.05 mm) increments. For size identification, spacers are numbered "05" (smallest size) through "22" (largest size).

6) Pack grease seal and bearings with bearing grease. Install outer grease seal and press outer bearing onto stub axle. Install rotor on stub axle. Place knuckle in position on stub axle,

install spacer and press inner bearing onto stub axle and knuckle assembly until it just bottoms. Install inner seal, then reinstall knuckle and wheel on vehicle.

NOTE — *Wheel bearings must always be replaced in complete sets including both bearings and races.*

TIGHTENING SPECIFICATIONS

Application	Ft. Lbs. (N·m)
Packing Gland Bolt	58-116 (79-158)
Piston Rod Nut	46-53 (63-72)
Strut-to-Steering Knuckle	24-33 (33-45)
Ball Joint Stud Nut	20-29 (27-39)
Ball Joint-to-Control Arm	40-47 (54-64)
Caliper Mounting Bolt	40-47 (54-64)
Control Arm Mounting Nut	42-51 (57-69)
Stabilizer Bar	6-9 (8-12)
Axle Shaft Nut	87-145 (118-197)

DATSUN PICKUP

DESCRIPTION

Front suspension is an independent type with upper and lower control arms which are connected by ball joints. This suspension also incorporates a torsion bar which connects to lower control arm inner end and to frame bracket, a strut rod which connects to lower control arm outer end and a stabilizer bar. A double-acting shock absorber is also used. See Fig. 1.

ADJUSTMENT

WHEEL ALIGNMENT SPECIFICATIONS & PROCEDURES

See Wheel Alignment Specifications & Procedures in WHEEL ALIGNMENT Section.

WHEEL BEARING ADJUSTMENT

2WD — 1) Tighten wheel bearing nut to 25-29 ft. lbs. (34-39 N•m). Turn wheel hub several times in both directions to seat wheel bearing. Retorque nut. Turn wheel bearing nut back 45°, install adjusting cap and tighten as required to line up grooves with hole in spindle.

2) Install cotter pin and measure bearing preload and axial play. Measure preload with pull gauge on any wheel stud. Axial play should be less than .003" (.08mm) and preload should be less than 2.6 lbs. (11.8 N) with old parts and 6.4 lbs. (28.4 N) with new parts. If not to specifications, repeat procedure until correct readings are obtained.

4WD — 1) With vehicle supported by jack stands and wheels removed, remove free-running hub and brake pads. Measure wheel bearing preload and axial play. If end play exceeds .004-.012" (.1-.3 mm) or preload exceeds 2.2-9.5 lbs. (9.8-42.2 N), bearings require adjustment.

2) To adjust bearing preload, replace wheel bearing collar with a thicker one (stamped number is higher by one) when preload is too high, or a thinner one (stamped number is lower by one) when preload is too low. See "Wheel Bearings — Removal" for procedure.

BALL JOINT CHECKING

Upper Ball Joint — With ball joint removed from vehicle and stud nut in place, check stud turning torque. If torque does not

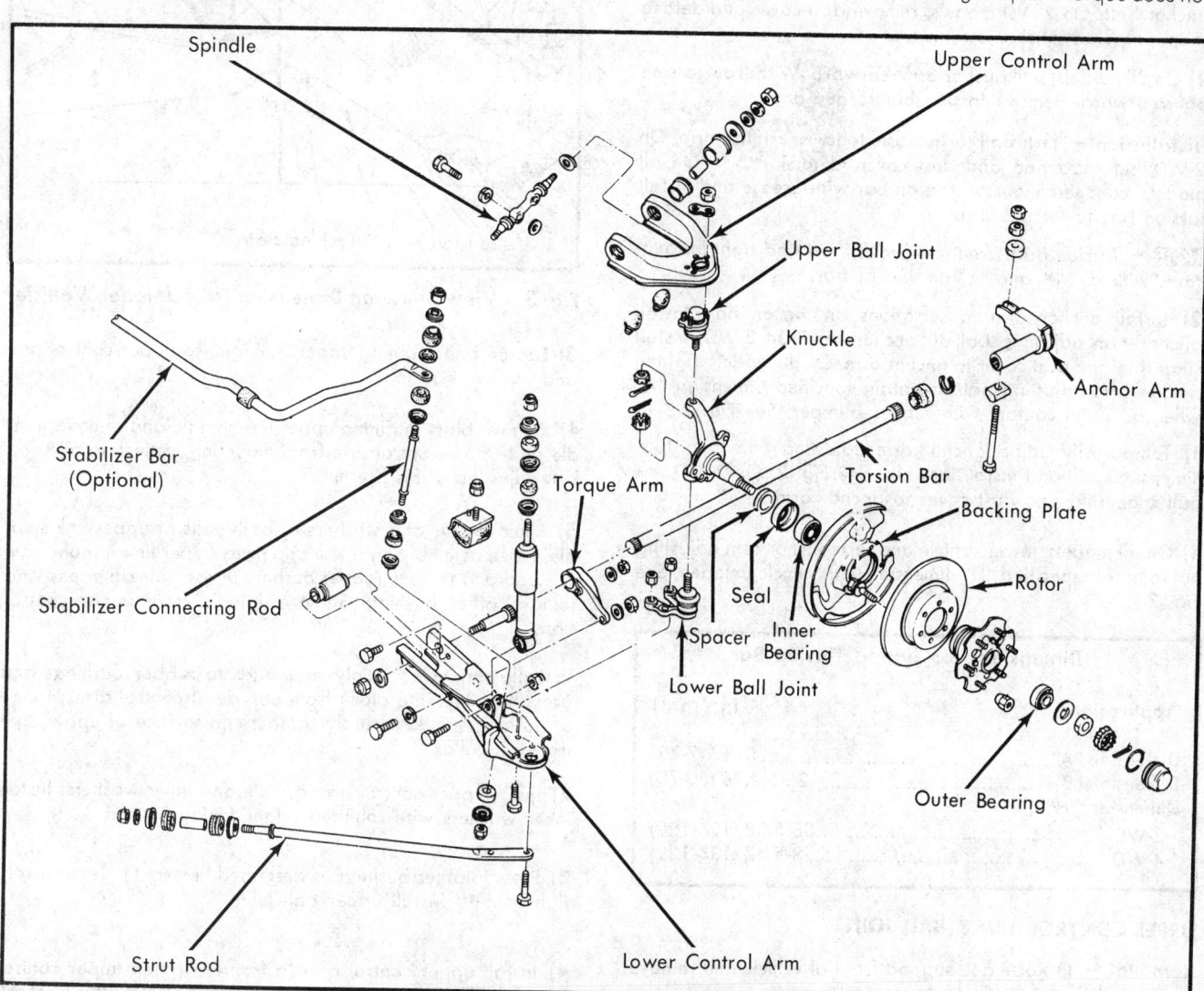

Fig. 1 Exploded View of Datsun Pickup Front Suspension (2-WD Shown, 4-WD Similar)

DATSUN PICKUP (Cont.)

meet specifications, 8.7-43.4 INCH lbs. (1.0-4.9 N•m), ball joint should be replaced. If dust cover is excessively cracked, replace ball joint.

Lower Ball Joint — Check ball joint end play in axial direction. If play exceeds .004-.039" (.1-1.0 mm) joint should be replaced. If dust cover is excessively cracked, replace ball joint.

REMOVAL & INSTALLATION

SHOCK ABSORBER

Removal — Turn steering wheel to either side to provide access to shock absorber. Disconnect upper and lower fixing nuts. Remove shock absorber, noting positions of mounting hardware.

Installation — To install, reverse removal procedure and tighten nuts and bolts to specifications.

TORSION BAR

Removal — 1) Raise and support vehicle. Remove torsion bar anchor bolt. On 2-WD models, remove dust cover and detach snap ring from anchor arm.

2) On all models, pull anchor arm rearward. Withdraw torsion bar rearward. Remove torsion bar torque arm.

Installation — 1) Install torque arm to lower control arm. On 2-WD, set snap ring and dust cover to torsion bar. On all models, coat serrations on torsion bar with grease and install torsion bar to torque arm.

NOTE — *Torsion bars are identified for left and right installations with an "R" and "L" on end of bar.*

2) Install anchor arm to serrations on torsion bar. Install anchor arm adjusting bolt to anchor arm. On 2-WD, install snap ring and dust cover to anchor arm. On all models, tighten anchor arm adjusting bolt to obtain specified dimension "A" when bar is in contact with rubber bumper. See *Fig. 2.*

3) Temporarily adjust anchor arm adjusting bolt to obtain dimensions "B" and install lock nut. See *Fig. 2.* On 2-WD, install snap ring and dust cover to anchor arm.

4) On all models, lower vehicle and turn anchor arm adjusting nut to obtain specified "H" dimension with vehicle unladen. See *Fig. 3.*

Dimensions for Setting Torsion Bar	
Application	**In. (mm)**
Dimension "A"	.28-.67 (7-17)
Dimension "B"	2.36-2.76 (60-70)
Dimension "H"	
2-WD	4.88-5.08 (124-129)
4-WD	5.28-5.47 (134-139)

UPPER CONTROL ARM & BALL JOINT

Removal — 1) Raise and support front of vehicle and remove wheel and tire. Jack up lower control arm.

2) Remove cotter pin and nut from upper ball joint and separate ball joint from steering knuckle with suitable tool.

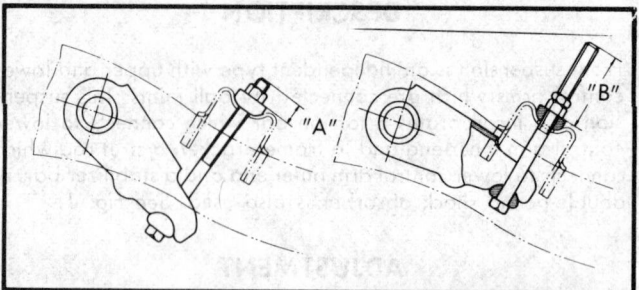

Fig. 2   View Showing Measuring Points for Installation of Anchor Pin

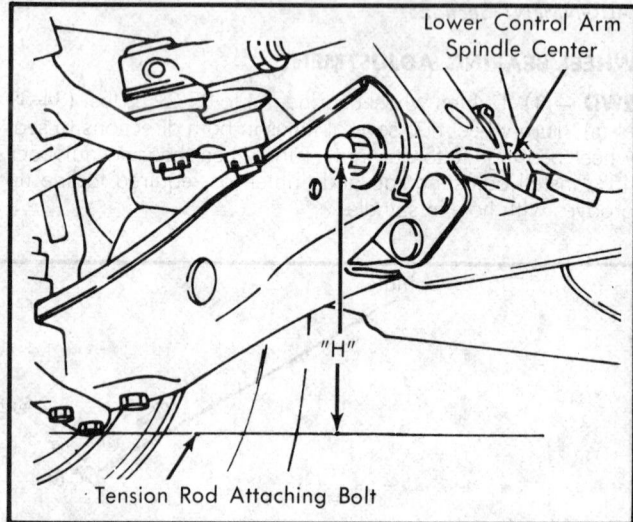

Fig. 3   View Showing Dimension "H" (Unladen Vehicle)

3) Loosen bolts holding upper ball joint to upper control arm and remove ball joint.

4) Remove bolts retaining upper link spindle and remove spindle and upper control arm from mounting, collecting all camber adjusting shims present.

5) Remove nuts and washers at both ends of upper link spindle. Place assembly on a vise and press upper link spindle from one end and remove rubber bushing. Press from other end and remove other bushing. Remove spindle from upper control arm.

Installation — 1) Apply soap suds to rubber bushings and press bushings into place from outside of control arm. Flange of bushing should securely contact end surface of upper control arm collar.

2) Insert upper control arm spindle and inner washers. Install inner washers with rounded edges facing inward.

3) Press in other bushing as described in step **1).** Temporarily tighten nuts. Install upper ball joint.

4) Install upper control arm to frame. Tighten upper control arm spindle with camber adjusting shims. After fitting, check dimensions "A" and "B" shown in *Fig. 4.* Dimension "A" should be 5.34-5.42" (135.6-137.6 mm), "B" should be 1.114" (28.3 mm).

DATSUN PICKUP (Cont.)

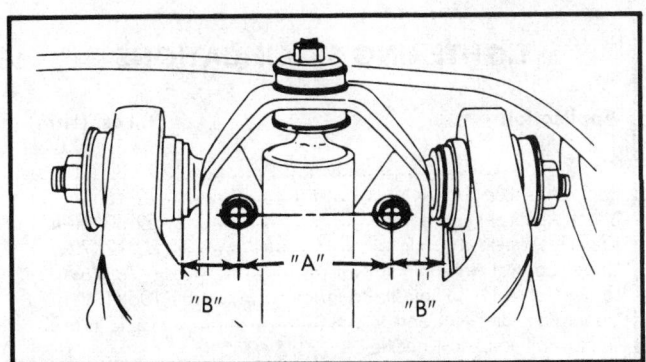

Fig. 4   Upper Control Arm Spindle Dimensions

5) Install upper ball joint to knuckle spindle. Make sure grease does not come into contact with tapered areas of ball joint knuckle spindle and threads of ball joint.

6) Install tire and wheel, lower vehicle and check height "H" of lower control arm. See *Fig. 3*. Check and adjust wheel alignment. See *appropriate article in WHEEL ALIGNMENT section*.

LOWER CONTROL ARM & BALL JOINT

Removal — 1) Raise and support front of vehicle. Remove wheel assembly. Remove torsion bar, and disconnect lower end of shock absorber from control arm.

2) Press out lower ball joint from knuckle. Disconnect stabilizer bar connecting rod from control arm. Remove torque arm from lower control arm.

3) Remove lower control arm spindle from control arm and remove control arm from frame. Remove lower ball joint nuts and bolts and remove ball joint from control arm.

4) Using a suitable drift, (KV40102000), drive out lower control arm bushings. See *Fig. 5*.

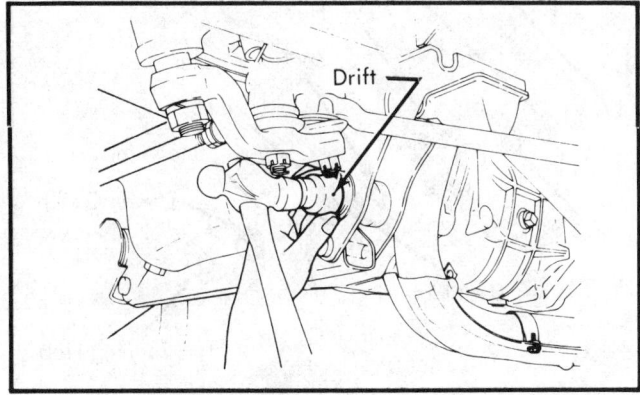

Fig. 5   Removing Bushings from Lower Control Arm

Installation — To install, reverse removal procedure, tightening nuts and bolts to specifications. Be sure grease does not contact tapered area of ball joint stud or knuckle hole and does not contact ball joint threads. Turn anchor bolt adjusting nut to obtain specified "H" dimension. See *Fig. 3*. Check and adjust wheel alignment. See *appropriate article in WHEEL ALIGNMENT section*.

STRUT ROD

Removal — Remove bolt holding strut rod to lower control arm and separate these parts. Remove nut attaching strut rod to bracket and remove rod with bushings, collar and washers.

Installation — To install, reverse removal procedure, noting the following: Swing strut rod a few times to settle bushings and washers; do not allow grease or oil to contact rubber bushings; tighten retaining nuts and bolts to specifications.

STABILIZER BAR

Removal — Remove nut holding stabilizer connecting rod to lower control arm. Remove bolt holding stabilizer mounting bracket to frame. Remove nut attaching stabilizer and connecting rod and remove these parts.

Installation — To install, reverse removal procedure and note the following; white mark painted on stabilizer bushing seat can be seen from both sides of vehicle when correctly installed.

WHEEL HUB, KNUCKLE & WHEEL BEARINGS

Removal — 1) On 2WD models, raise and support vehicle. Remove wheel and tire. Remove brake caliper assembly and wire out of way. Remove dust cap, cotter pin, adjusting cap and adjusting nut.

2) Remove wheel hub and rotor. Remove outside wheel bearing inner race and washer. Remove hub-to-rotor retaining bolts and separate hub from rotor. Remove wheel bearings and grease seals. Drive out wheel bearing outer races.

3) Remove knuckle arm and backing plate. Loosen (do not remove) ball joint retaining nuts. Separate ball joints from knuckle with tool (ST29020001). Jack up lower control arm and remove ball joint nuts. Remove knuckle.

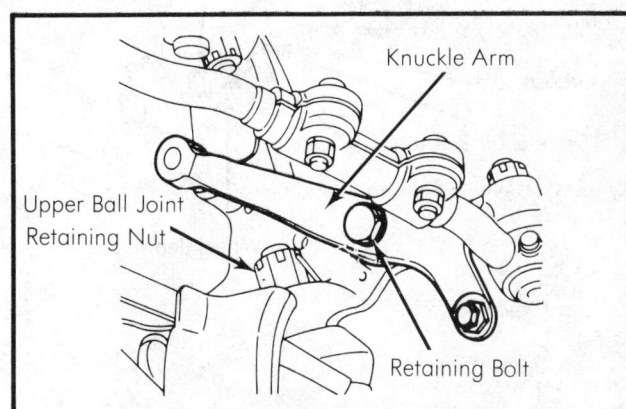

**Fig. 6   Knuckle Arm Location
(2WD Shown, 4WD Similar)**

4) On 4WD models, raise and support vehicle. Remove wheel and tire. Remove brake caliper assembly and wire out of way. Remove free-running hub assembly. Remove snap ring, drive clutch and stabilizer connecting rod bolt from lower control arm.

5) Remove bolts holding drive shaft to differential, (do not remove boots), and remove drive shaft from knuckle.

Front Suspension

DATSUN PICKUP (Cont.)

NOTE — *Turn steering wheel all the way right to remove right shaft and all the way left to remove left shaft.*

6) Remove knuckle arm retaining bolt. Loosen (do not remove) ball joint retaining nuts. Separate ball joints from knuckle with tool (ST29020001). Jack up lower control arm and remove ball joint nuts. Remove knuckle.

7) Straighen tangs on lock washer, remove lock nut with tool (KV40102500), and remove lockwasher and special washer. Push wheel bearing support from wheel hub.

8) Separate knuckle from hub with puller, remove wheel bearing collar and drive out inside wheel bearing outer race. Separate wheel hub from rotor.

9) Strike wheel hub projection against wood block to loosen bearing and press off bearing. Remove drive shaft bearing from wheel bearing support with drift.

Installation — Reverse removal procedures to install, noting the following: On 4WD models check wheel bearing adjustment as previously outlined before installing complete assembly in vehicle. On all models, always use new lock washers, grease seals and cotter pins.

TIGHTENING SPECIFICATIONS

Application	Ft. Lbs. (N·m)
Anchor Bolt	22-30 (30-41)
Shock Absorber Upper Nut	12-16 (16-22)
Shock Absorber Lower Nut	22-30 (30-41)
Knuckle Arm-to-Knuckle	53-72 (72-97)
Upper Control Arm Spindle Nut	56-76 (76-103)
Upper Control Arm Spindle-to-Frame	80-108 (109-147)
Upper Ball Joint-to-Control Arm	12-16 (16-22)
Upper Ball Joint-to-Knuckle	
2WD	58-72 (78-98)
4WD	36-65 (49-88)
Lower Control Arm-to-Frame	80-108 (109-147)
Lower Ball Joint-to-Control Arm	23-38 (38-52)
Lower Ball Joint-to-Knuckle	
2WD	87-123 (118-167)
4WD	43-72 (59-98)
Stabilizer Bar-to-Frame	12-16 (16-22)
Stabilizer Bar-to-Lower Control Arm	12-16 (16-22)
Strut Rod-to-Frame	87-116 (118-157)
Strut Rod-to-Lower Control Arm	28-38 (38-52)
Torque Arm-to-Lower Control Arm	
Inner Nut	26-33 (35-45)
Outer Nut	20-27 (26-36)
Drive Shaft-to-Differential (4WD)	20-27 (27-37)
Free-Running Hub (4WD)	18-25 (25-34)

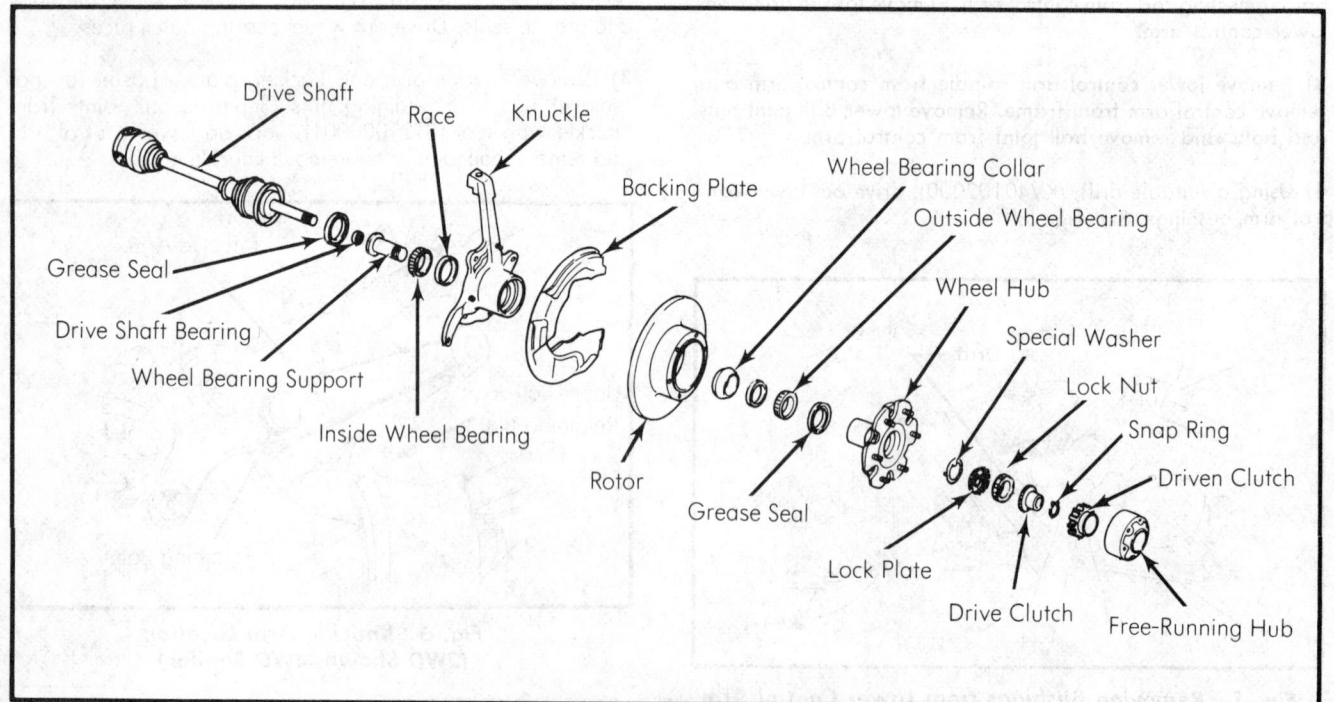

Fig. 7 Exploded View of 4WD Front Axle Assembly

Front Suspension

FIAT BRAVA

DESCRIPTION

Strut type front suspension consisting of a vertically mounted strut assembly. Strut assembly is mounted to body at the top by means of a rubber mount and lower end of strut is connected to steering knuckle. Strut assembly consists of hydraulic shock absorber with a coil spring mounted over outside. Lower control arm is connected to steering knuckle through ball joint and to front crossmember. A stabilizer bar is mounted to lower control arm and to frame.

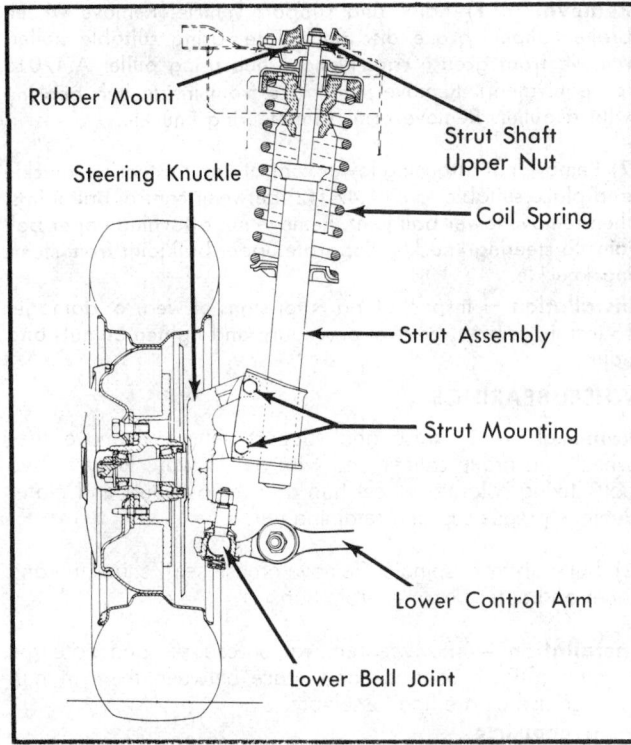

Fig. 1 Fiat Brava Front Suspension Assembly

Labels in figure:
- Rubber Mount
- Steering Knuckle
- Strut Shaft Upper Nut
- Coil Spring
- Strut Assembly
- Strut Mounting
- Lower Control Arm
- Lower Ball Joint

ADJUSTMENTS

WHEEL ALIGNMENT SPECIFICATIONS & PROCEDURES

See Wheel Alignment Specifications and Procedures in WHEEL ALIGNMENT Section.

WHEEL BEARING ADJUSTMENT

While rotating hub, tighten spindle nut to 14.5 ft. lbs. (20 N•m) to seat bearing. Loosen nut and retighten to 5 ft. lbs. (7 N•m). Loosen nut 30° and stake collar of spindle nut into machined slot on spindle. Check hub end play with dial indicator. Play should be .001–.004" (.025–.100 mm). If play exceeds this amount and wheel bearing is in good condition, repeat procedure until correct end play is obtained.

NOTE — Whenever spindle nut is removed, it MUST be replaced with a new one.

BALL JOINT CHECKING

With vehicle raised and supported under lower control arms, grasp wheel at top and bottom and try to shake wheel. If excessive movement is noted, remove control arm from vehicle and check ball joint for excessive play or damage to swivel and rubber boot. Control arm and ball joint are assembled as a unit. If ball joint is bad, replace control arm.

REMOVAL & INSTALLATION

FRONT SUSPENSION ASSEMBLY

Removal — 1) With vehicle on ground, remove upper nut and washer from strut shaft. Remove the 3 rubber mount nuts and washers. Remove rubber mount assembly. Install and tighten retaining tool (A74375) on strut shaft. Remove the 2 nuts and washers retaining strut to body.

2) Jack up vehicle and remove wheel. Disconnect brake hose from tube at clip on fenderwell. Disconnect tie rod from steering knuckle.

3) Position a jack under suspension assembly. Remove nut, washer and rubber bushing from end of sway bar. Remove nut, washer and bolt from control arm at frame. Remove arm from bracket. Push arm to rear to remove from sway bar end. Carefully lower suspension from vehicle.

Disassembly and Reassembly — 1) Disconnect control arm by removing ball joint stud nut and separating ball joint from steering knuckle. Remove strut assembly by removing nuts and bolts attaching assembly to steering knuckle.

2) Remove coil spring by using a coil spring compressor and removing retaining tool from strut shaft. Reassemble in reverse order of disassembly.

Installation — To install, reverse removal procedure and note the following: Lower vehicle to ground before removing retaining tool from strut shaft and installing rubber mount assembly.

WHEEL BEARINGS

Removal & Installation — 1) Raise vehicle. Remove tire and wheel. Remove brake caliper and wire out of way. Remove two bolts attaching rotor to hub and remove brake rotor and plate. Remove spindle nut and washer, then remove hub from spindle.

2) Remove outer bearing. Use puller to remove inner bearing and retainer. Press in new outer bearing, inner bearing and retainer. Pack area between bearings with grease. Reverse removal procedures to complete installation.

STRUT ASSEMBLY

Removal — With vehicle on ground, remove upper nut and washer from strut shaft. Remove the 3 rubber mount nuts and washers. Remove the rubber mount assembly. Install and tighten retaining tool (A74375) on strut shaft. Remove the 2 nuts and washers retaining strut to body. Raise vehicle, remove 2 strut-to-knuckle bolts and remove strut.

NOTE — To remove coil spring from strut, see Disassembly and Reassembly under Front Suspension Assembly.

Installation — To install, reverse removal procedure and note the following: Lower vehicle to ground before removing retaining tool from strut shaft and installing rubber mount assembly.

TIGHTENING SPECIFICATIONS

Application	Ft. Lbs. (N•m)
Ball Joint-to-Steering Knuckle	58 (79)
Control Arm-to-Crossmember	65 (88)
Strut Assembly-to-Knuckle	36 (49)
Strut Assembly-to-Upper Mount	43 (59)
Strut Upper Mount-to-Body	18 (25)
Stabilizer Bar-to-Crossmember	65 (88)
Stabilizer Bar-to-Control Arm	43 (59)

Front Suspension

FIAT SPIDER 2000

DESCRIPTION

Independent wishbone type suspension with coil springs and telescopic, hydraulic, double-acting shock absorbers. Shock absorbers are mounted inside coil springs between upper and lower control arms. Control arms are connected to steering knuckle with ball joints.

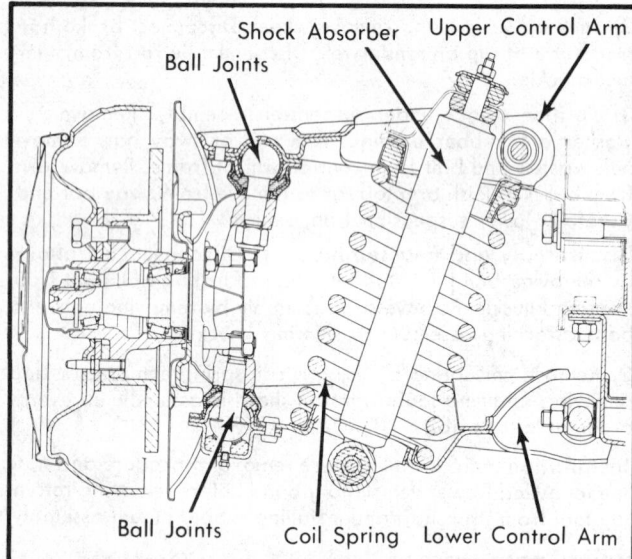

Fig. 1 Sectional View of Front Suspension Assembly

ADJUSTMENTS

WHEEL ALIGNMENT SPECIFICATIONS & PROCEDURES

See Wheel Alignment Specifications and Procedures in WHEEL ALIGNMENT Section.

WHEEL BEARING ADJUSTMENT

While rotating hub, tighten spindle nut to 14.5 ft. lbs. (20 N•m) to seat bearing. Loosen nut and retighten to 5 ft. lbs. (7 N•m). Loosen nut 30° and stake collar of spindle nut into machined slot on spindle. Check hub end play with dial indicator. Play should be .001–.004" (.025–.100 mm). If play exceeds this amount and wheel bearing is in good condition, repeat procedure until correct end play is obtained.

BALL JOINT CHECKING

With vehicle raised and supported under lower control arms, grasp wheel at top and bottom and try to shake wheel. If excessive movement is noted, remove control arm from vehicle and check ball joint for excessive play or damage to swivel and rubber boot. Control arm and ball joint are assembled as a unit. If ball joint is bad, the entire control arm must be replaced.

NOTE — Whenever spindle nut is removed, it MUST be replaced with a new one.

REMOVAL & INSTALLATION

FRONT SUSPENSION ASSEMBLY

Removal — 1) Raise and support vehicle. Remove wheels and shock absorbers. Compress coil spring with spring compressor to relieve tension from lower control arm.

2) Disconnect and cap brake lines. Using a puller, disconnect tie rod from steering knuckle arm. Remove pivot bolt and detach upper control arm from body. Remove nuts and bolts securing lower control arm to crossmember and remove suspension.

Installation — To install, reverse removal procedure. Tighten all nuts and bolts, bleed brakes and check wheel alignment.

STEERING KNUCKLE

Removal — 1) Raise and support vehicle. Remove wheel, brake caliper, brake disc and plate. Using suitable puller, remove front grease cap. Remove hub using puller A.47015 (or equivalent). Remove inner race from inside hub bearing with a puller. Remove arm from steering knuckle.

2) Remove nut attaching lower control arm to steering knuckle and place suitable tool (A.47042) between control ball joints, then remove lower ball joint. Remove nut attaching upper ball joint to steering knuckle. Separate upper ball joint from steering knuckle.

Installation — Inspect all parts for signs of wear or damage. To install, reverse removal procedure and tighten all nuts and bolts.

WHEEL BEARINGS

Removal — 1) Raise and support vehicle. Remove tire, wheel and brake caliper and wire out of way. Remove two bolts fixing rotor to wheel hub and remove hub and plate. Remove grease cup and retaining nut.

2) Pull hub from spindle. Remove grease seal, snap ring and inner and outer bearings from hub.

Installation — Reverse removal procedures and note the following: Pack bearings and space between them in hub with grease before final assembly.

COIL SPRINGS

Removal — Raise and support vehicle so suspension hangs freely. Remove wheels and shock absorbers. Disconnect stabilizer bar from lower control arm. Support lower control arm with a jack and disconnect lower ball joint stud from steering knuckle. Install suitable spring compressor and rotate lower control arm down carefully. Coil spring may now be removed.

Installation — To install, reverse removal procedure.

STABILIZER BAR

Removal — Remove front stabilizer bar by removing nuts and bolts securing bar to crossmember. Remove nuts and bolts attaching ends of stabilizer bar to lower control arms and remove stabilizer bar.

Installation — To install, reverse removal procedure.

TIGHTENING SPECIFICATIONS

Application	Ft. Lbs. (N•m)
Lower Control Arm Pin-to-Crossmember	43 (59)
Lower Control Arm-to-Crossmember	72 (98)
Upper Control Arm	65 (88)
Lower Shock Absorber	43 (59)
Steering Arm-to-Steering Knuckle	43 (59)
Brake Caliper	36 (49)
Crossmember-to-Side Member	69 (94)

Front Suspension

FIAT STRADA

DESCRIPTION

Suspension is independent, strut type. Consists of double-action shock absorbers with surrounding coil springs. Strut assemblies are mounted to inner fender panel at top and to steering knuckle at bottom. Steering knuckle is also bearing carrier for drive axles. Lower control arm is connected to knuckle by ball joint. On models with manual transmission, a reaction strut is connected to chassis and lower control arm. On models with automatic transmission, a stabilizer bar is used in place of reaction struts.

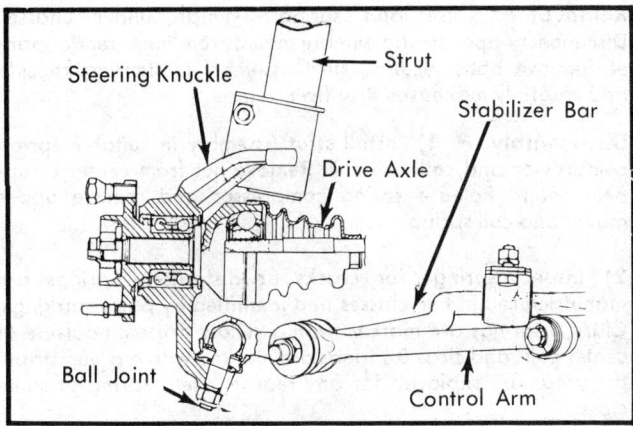

**Fig. 1 Strada Front Suspension
(Auto. Trans. Model Shown)**

ADJUSTMENTS

WHEEL ALIGNMENT SPECIFICATIONS & PROCEDURES

See Wheel Alignment Specifications and Procedures in WHEEL ALIGNMENT section.

WHEEL BEARING ADJUSTMENT

While rotating hub to seat bearing, tighten spindle nut to 159 ft. lbs. (216 N•m). Stake collar of spindle nut to spindle.

BALL JOINT CHECKING

Raise and support vehicle on drive-on type hoist. Using a jack, raise lower control arm. Insert ball joint gauge (A.96505) over ball joint. Lower edge of gauge must not touch threaded portion of bolt. If ball joint does not meet with this specification, replace control arm (includes integral ball joint).

REMOVAL & INSTALLATION

STRUT ASSEMBLY

Removal — Raise and support front of vehicle. Detach upper strut mount from fender panel. Remove bolts holding strut to steering knuckle. Pull knuckle down to separate and remove strut assembly.

Disassembly and Reassembly — Install spring compressor and compress spring enough to remove upper strut nut. Slowly release spring, remove strut assembly from compressor and separate all strut components. Inspect spring for cracks or other flaws and replace (in matched sets only) if needed. Reverse disassembly procedures to assemble.

NOTE — *If replacing coil springs, be sure same color-coded class of spring is installed (different colors show different weights).*

Installation — To install, reverse removal procedure, tightening nuts to specifications. Be sure lower mount nuts are tightened after vehicle is at curb weight.

WHEEL BEARINGS

Removal — 1) Remove hub, rotor and knuckle as an assembly from vehicle as outlined in Suspension Removal. It is not necessary to remove control arm or tie rod from vehicle. Remove retaining bolts (2), and separate rotor and plate from steering knuckle. Press hub (with outer bearing half) from knuckle.

2) Remove inner race from hub shaft. Pry out cap and retaining ring and press bearing from knuckle.

NOTE — *Bearing and seal, once removed, must be replaced with new parts.*

Installation — Install retaining ring and press new bearing into knuckle. Support bearing from opposite side and press in hub. Reverse removal procedures to complete installation.

CONTROL ARM, BUSHINGS & BALL JOINTS

Removal — Remove complete suspension assembly as outlined. Remove ball joint stud nut and separate from steering knuckle.

Disassembly — To replace control arm bushings, drill out metal sleeve from inside rubber bushings and remove bushings. If ball joint is defective, replace entire control arm assembly.

Reassembly — Place outer washer, bushing and sleeve on centering pin of suitable bushing installation tool. Place control arm over bushing. Position inner bushing and washer on control arm. Place this assembly in a vise and press into place. Sleeve will bellow out over washers, securing bushings in control arm.

Installation — To install, reverse removal procedure.

TIGHTENING SPECIFICATIONS

Application	Ft. Lbs. (N•m)
Front Axle-to-Hub Nut	159 (216)
Control Arm Pivot Bolt	29 (39)
Stabilizer Bar-to-Control Arm	51 (69)
Stabilizer Bar-to-Chassis	36 (49)
Ball Joint Nut	40 (54)
Strut Assembly Mount	
Upper	25 (34)
Lower	43 (59)

Front Suspension

FIAT X1/9

DESCRIPTION

Independent type front suspension consisting of lower control arms and hydraulic shock absorbers, surrounded by coil springs. Steering knuckle is attached to lower control arm at sealed ball joint. Shock absorber is attached to steering knuckle at bottom and to fender panel at top. Lower control arm pivots in rubber bushings attached to crossmember. Stabilizer bar is mounted to lower control arm and at front, to frame.

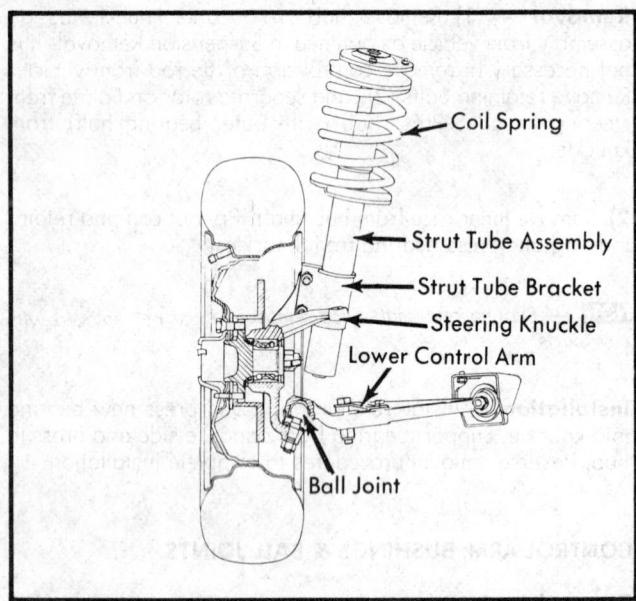

Fig. 1 Sectional View of Front Suspension Assembly

ADJUSTMENT

WHEEL ALIGNMENT SPECIFICATIONS & PROCEDURES

See Wheel Alignment Specifications and Procedures in WHEEL ALIGNMENT Section.

WHEEL BEARING ADJUSTMENT

Spin hub to seat bearing while tightening spindle nut to 112 ft. lbs. (152 N•m). Stake collar of spindle nut into machined slot on spindle.

BALL JOINT CHECKING

With vehicle raised and supported under lower control arms, grasp wheel at top and bottom and try to shake. If excessive movement is noted, remove control arm and check ball joint for excessive play or damage to swivel and rubber boot. Control arm and ball joint are assembled as a unit. If ball joint is bad, replace control arm.

REMOVAL & INSTALLATION

FRONT SUSPENSION ASSEMBLY

Removal — Raise and support vehicle; remove tire and wheel. Remove front disc brake caliper assembly. *See appropriate article in BRAKE section.* Remove bolts and plate holding shock absorber tube to steering knuckle. Separate shock absorber at top by removing upper mounting nuts. Disconnect lower control arm from stabilizer bar bracket and ball joint. Remove tie rod nut and force tie rod from steering knuckle. Maneuver assembly from vehicle.

Inspection — Check rubber bushings in control arm and replace any that appear worn. Inspect ball joints for excessive play or damage; replace as necessary.

Installation — To install suspension assembly, reverse removal procedure ensuring all nuts and bolts are properly torqued.

STRUT ASSEMBLY

Removal — Raise and support vehicle under chassis. Disconnect upper strut assembly mount from inner fender panel. Remove bolts securing strut assembly to steering knuckle and carefully maneuver strut from vehicle.

Disassembly — 1) Install strut assembly in suitable spring compressor and collapse coil. Remove nut from center of upper mount. Release spring compressor and remove upper mount and coil spring.

2) Inspect springs for cracks or distortion. Springs are manufactured in two classes and identified by paint markings. Class A springs are marked with a yellow stripe on outside of center coils and class B springs are marked with a green stripe. If springs are replaced for any reason, use a spring of same class.

Reassembly — Using same spring compressor as previously outlined, reverse disassembly procedure to assemble strut assembly.

Installation — To install strut assembly, reverse removal procedure. Do not tighten strut assembly lower mount until weight of vehicle is on ground.

WHEEL BEARINGS

Removal — 1) Raise vehicle and remove tire and wheel. Remove brake caliper and support bracket and wire out of way. Remove rotor, plate retaining bolt and centering stud.

2) Remove tie rod-to-knuckle nut, disconnect ball joint and pull tie rod out of way. Remove control arm-to-knuckle nut and separate. Remove strut lower mounting bolts and remove knuckle from vehicle.

3) Remove hub to knuckle retaining nut and press hub from knuckle. Remove bearing retaining ring nut and pull out bearing.

Installation — Reverse removal procedures to install, noting the following: Always use a new ring nut. Perform final tightening of suspension bolts with front end on ground and loaded.

CONTROL ARM, BUSHINGS & BALL JOINTS

Removal — Remove complete front suspension assembly as previously outlined. Remove ball joint stud nut and separate ball joint from steering knuckle with a suitable puller.

Disassembly — Inspect ball joint for wear or distortion. If ball joint is defective, complete control arm must be replaced. Inspect bearings for wear or damage. If defective, drill out metal sleeve from inside rubber bushing and extract bushing.

Front Suspension

FIAT X1/9 (Cont.)

Reassembly — Position outer washer, bushing and sleeve on centering pin of bushing installation tool. Place control arm over bushing and washer from opposite side. Place control arm, components and tool into a press. Position remaining tool components in sleeve and press into position.

Installation — Attach control arm to steering knuckle and tighten ball joint stud nut. Reverse removal procedure to complete installation.

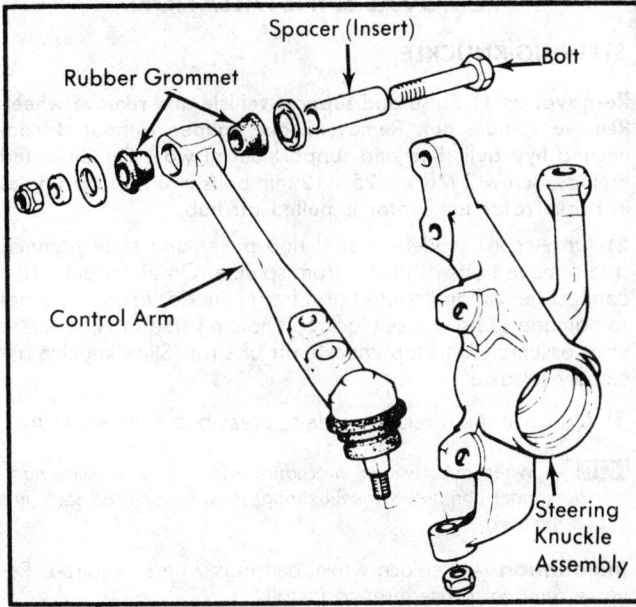

Fig. 2 Exploded View of Lower Control Arm Assembly

STABILIZER BAR

Removal — Raise and support vehicle. Disconnect stabilizer mounting bolt from lower control arm. Remove stabilizer at-taching hardware from front end of stabilizer and carefully maneuver bar from vehicle.

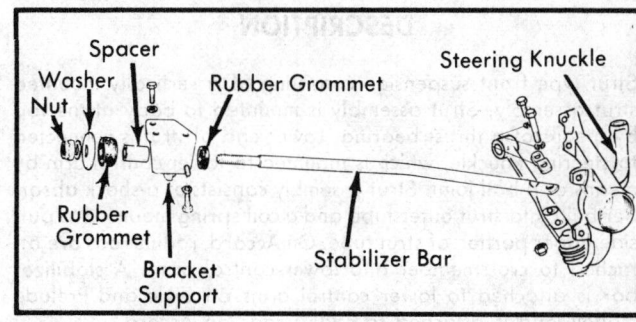

Fig. 3 Exploded View of Stabilizer Bar Assembly

Installation — To install stabilizer bar, reverse removal procedure noting the following: Replace any rubber grommet that appears distorted or severely worn.

TIGHTENING SPECIFICATIONS

Application	Ft. Lbs. (N·m)
Tie Rod Nut	58 (79)
Lower Control Arm-to-Crossmember	29 (39)
Stabilizer Bar-to-Lower Control Arm	51 (69)
Stabilizer Bar-to-Frame	51 (69)
Strut Mounting Nuts	
Upper and Lower	43 (59)
Wheel Bearing Ring Nut	43 (59)
Wheel Hub Nut	112 (152)

Front Suspension

HONDA

Accord
Civic
Prelude

DESCRIPTION

Strut type front suspension consisting of a vertically mounted strut assembly. Strut assembly is mounted to body at the top by means of a thrust bearing. Lower end of strut is connected to steering knuckle, which is mounted to lower control arm by means of a ball joint. Strut assembly consists of a shock absorber built into strut outer tube and a coil spring mounted to outside upper portion of strut tube. On Accord, radius rods are attached to crossmember and lower control arms. A stabilizer bar is attached to lower control arms on Civic and Prelude models and is attached to radius rods on Accord.

ADJUSTMENT

WHEEL ALIGNMENT SPECIFICATIONS & PROCEDURES

See Wheel Alignment Specifications & Procedures in WHEEL ALIGNMENT Section.

WHEEL BEARING ADJUSTMENT & INSPECTION

Adjustment — Wheel bearings are non-adjustable.

Inspection — Check axial end play and wheel wobble. Place dial indicator against wheel spindle and zero indicator. Grasp tire firmly and push in and out while observing indicator dial. End play should not exceed .020" (.5 mm) on Prelude models. There should be no end play on all others. To check wheel wobble, zero indicator against outer rim of wheel and shake wheel. Movement should not exceed .020" (.5 mm). If either reading exceeds specifications check spindle nut torque and bearings for damage. Replace as needed.

BALL JOINT CHECKING

Raise and support front of vehicle. Attach dial indicator to lower control arm with indicator tip on steering knuckle near ball joint. Place pry bar between lower control arm and steering knuckle. Push on pry bar and observe movement on dial indicator. Movement should not exceed .020" (.5 mm). Ball joint and control arm are serviceable as an assembly only. If ball joint exceeds limit, replace control arm.

REMOVAL & INSTALLATION

STEERING KNUCKLE

Removal — 1) Raise and support vehicle and remove wheel. Remove spindle nut. Remove brake caliper without disconnecting hydraulic line and support out of way. On Civic and Prelude, screw 2 M8 x 1.25 x 12 mm bolts into threaded holes in brake rotor until rotor is pulled off hub.

2) On Accord models: Install hub puller and slide hammer and remove hub with rotor from spindle. On all models: Disconnect tie rod and control arm from knuckle, taking care not to damage seals. Loosen lock bolt holding steering knuckle to strut assembly and tap knuckle off of strut. Slide knuckle assembly off axle.

3) On Civic and Prelude models, press hub from knuckle.

NOTE — *When hub removal procedure involves use of slide hammer, both inner and outer wheel bearings must be replaced each time hub is removed.*

Installation — Replace wheel bearings where required. Reverse removal procedures to install.

WHEEL BEARINGS

Removal — 1) With knuckle and hub removed from vehicle, remove splash guard and snap ring from knuckle. Remove inner grease seal, bearing and race. Press out outer race.

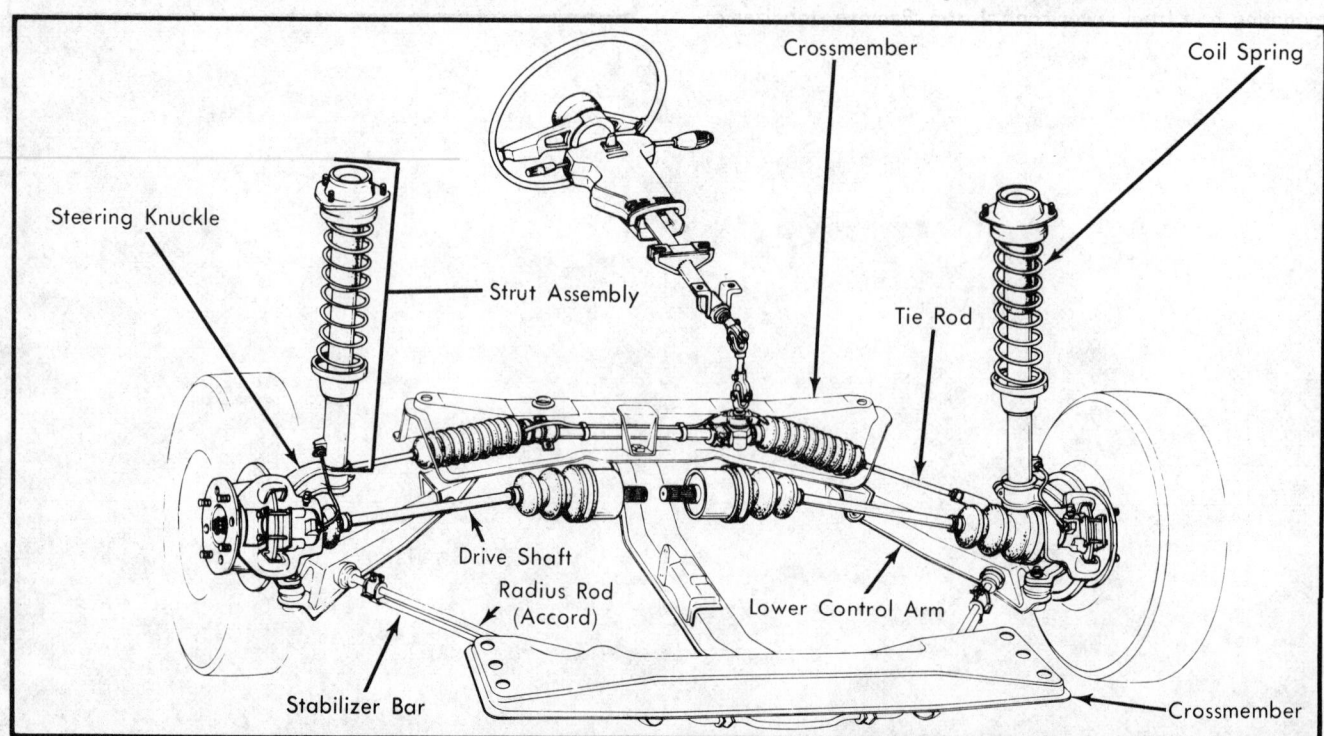

Fig. 1 Assembled View of Honda Front Suspension Showing Component Relationships

HONDA (Cont.)

2) Pull out outer bearing inner race and remove grease seal. Wash knuckle and hub thoroughly with clean solvent before reassembly.

Installation — 1) Press in bearing outer race. Pressure required must not exceed 5000 lbs. (22240 N). Pack bearings and coat races before installing bearings. Install outer bearing and race. Install snap ring securely in groove.

2) Pack grease seal groove and coat sealing lip with grease. Press in seal. Install splash guard, inner bearing and race. Reverse removal procedures to complete installation.

STRUT ASSEMBLY

Removal — Raise and support vehicle, then remove wheel. Disconnect brake line at strut assembly and remove retaining clip. On Prelude and Civic, remove brake caliper without disconnecting hydraulic line and support out of way. On all models, loosen lock bolt securing strut to steering knuckle and separate knuckle from strut. Remove nuts retaining upper end of strut to body and remove strut.

Disassembly — Using suitable tool, compress coil spring to relieve tension from upper shock absorber retaining nut. Remove nut, seals, spacers, etc. (noting arrangement), beneath upper mounting plate. Slowly remove pressure from spring and lift spring off. Shock absorber may now be replaced, if necessary.

Reassembly — Reverse disassembly procedure using *Fig. 2* as a guide. Coat both sides of needle bearing with grease. Check all components for signs of seepage and correct as needed.

Installation — Reverse removal procedure and note: Make sure slot in steering knuckle is engaged in tab on shock (strut) housing before seating it into steering knuckle.

LOWER CONTROL ARM

Removal — Raise and support vehicle. Remove front wheel. Disconnect lower ball joint from steering knuckle, using ball joint remover tool. Disconnect stabilizer retaining bolts and nuts from control arm (it may be necessary to loosen front stabilizer retaining brackets). Remove lower control arm pivot bolt and remove control arm.

Installation — To install, reverse removal procedure and note: On Accord models only, make sure bolt mounting lower control arm to crossmember is tightened with weight of vehicle on jack. This simulates normal riding height.

STABILIZER BAR

Removal — Remove stabilizer bar brackets from crossmember. On Civic and Prelude, remove stabilizer-to-control arm nuts and remove stabilizer bar. On Accord, remove stabilizer-to-radius rod bolts and remove stabilizer bar.

Inspection — Inspect all rubber bushings and metal sleeves for excessive wear or damage.

Installation — Reverse removal procedure and note the following: On Civic, install bar with white stripe on driver's side of vehicle and align inside edge of stripe with stabilizer bar bushing. On Prelude, notice that the right side stabilizer bracket bolts are longer than the left side bolts.

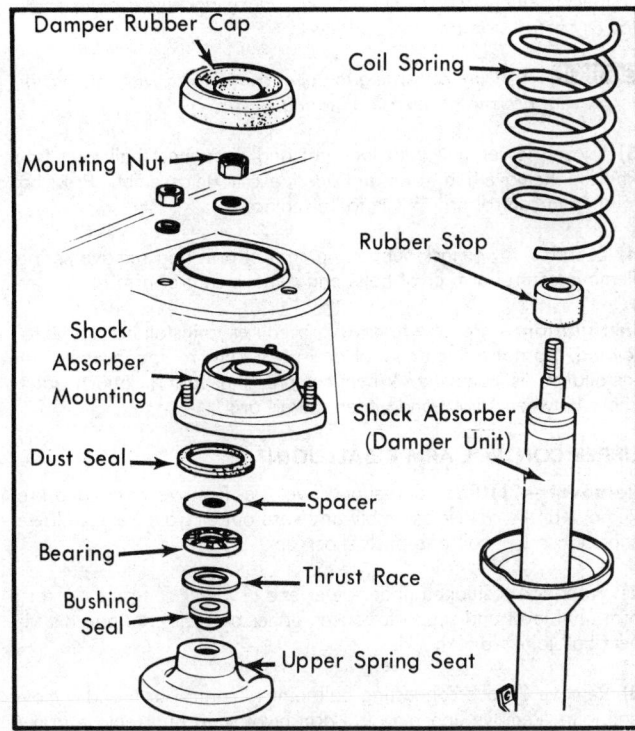

Fig. 2   Exploded View of Honda Strut Assembly (Accord Shown; Civic Models Similar)

TIGHTENING SPECIFICATIONS

Application	Ft. Lbs. (N·m)
Spindle Nut	108 (147)
Ball Joint	
Accord & Prelude	33 (45)
Civic	25 (34)
Control Arm-to-Crossmember	
Accord	36 (49)
Civic & Prelude	40 (54)
Strut-to-Knuckle	
Accord & Prelude	47 (64)
Civic	36 (49)
Strut-to-Body	
Accord (3)	22 (30)
Civic & Prelude (1)	33 (45)
Stabilizer-to-Control Arm	
Civic & Prelude	32 (44)
Stabilizer-to-Radius Rod	
Accord	16 (22)
Stabilizer-to-Body	
Accord	16 (22)
Civic	37 (50)
Prelude	28 (38)
Tie Rod End-to-Knuckle	32 (44)
Radius Rod-to-Control Arm	
Accord	40 (54)

Front Suspension

ISUZU I-MARK

DESCRIPTION

Independent type front suspension consisting of upper and lower control arms with steering knuckle mounted between control arms by means of ball joints. Upper control arm pivots on shaft through crossmember, lower arm pivots on shafts (2) through crossmember and frame. A coil spring is mounted between lower control arm and crossmember. Shock absorber is hydraulic, double-action type mounted between upper control arm and inner fender panel. A stabilizer bar is used to enhance stability and riding comfort.

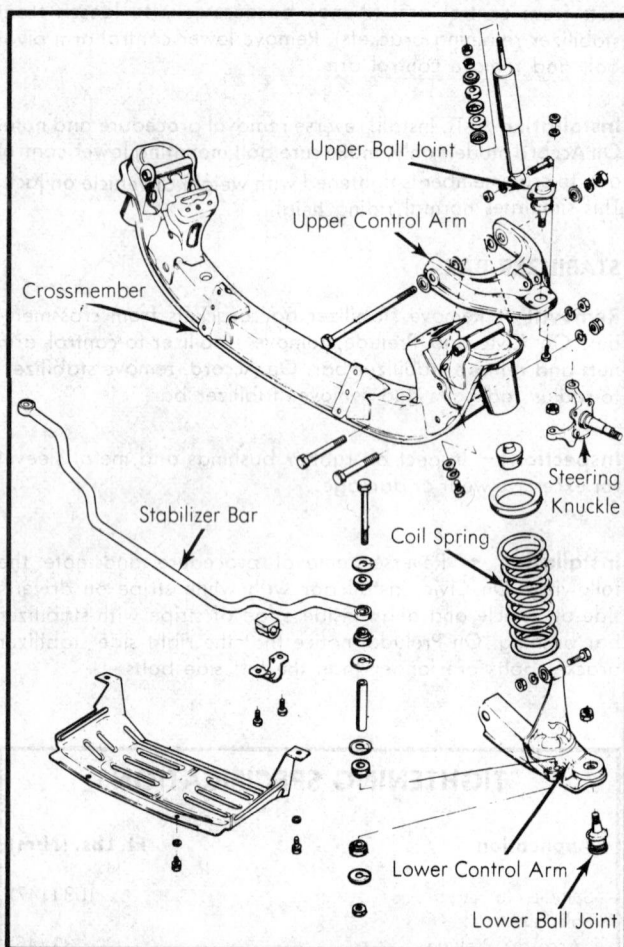

Fig. 1 Exploded View of I'Mark Front Suspension

ADJUSTMENT

WHEEL ALIGNMENT SPECIFICATIONS & PROCEDURES

See Wheel Alignment Specifications & Procedures in WHEEL ALIGNMENT Section.

WHEEL BEARING ADJUSTMENT

Raise and support vehicle. Remove grease cap and cotter pin. Loosen spindle nut. Tighten spindle nut to 22 ft. lbs. (30 N•m) while rotating wheel to seat bearings. Back off nut completely and tighten hand tight. Install cotter pin. Tighten nut as needed to align slot in nut with hole in spindle.

BALL JOINT CHECKING

Check ball joints for excessive movement or play. If axial play of lower ball joint exceeds .040" (1.0 mm) it should be replaced.

REMOVAL & INSTALLATION

SHOCK ABSORBERS

Removal — Raise and support vehicle. Remove wheel and tire. Remove lower shock retaining bolt from upper control arm. Remove upper retaining nut from inside engine compartment and remove shock.

Installation — Reverse removal procedures to install.

WHEEL BEARINGS

NOTE — *Wheel bearing removal procedure not available from manufacturer.*

STEERING KNUCKLE

Removal — 1) Raise and support vehicle. Remove wheel and tire. Remove lower shock absorber attaching bolt and push shock up and out of way. Remove brake caliper and wire up.

2) Press tie rod end ball joint from steering knuckle. Remove grease cap, cotter pin, hub nut and washer. Remove wheel hub with rotor. Remove dust plate retaining bolts and remove dust plate from knuckle.

3) With jack positioned under outer end of lower control arm, raise arm until level and support. Loosen upper and lower ball joint nuts and disconnect ball joints from knuckle. Remove steering knuckle.

Installation — Reverse removal procedures to install noting the following: Attach dust plate to knuckle before installing knuckle to ball joints.

LOWER CONTROL ARM, COIL SPRING & BALL JOINT

Removal — 1) Raise and support vehicle. Remove wheel and tire. Disconnect tie rod end from steering knuckle. Remove lower shock absorber bolt and push shock up.

2) Disconnect stabilizer bar from lower control arm. Remove brake caliper assembly and wire out of way. Place jack under outer end of lower control arm and lift until level.

CAUTION — *Secure coil spring to upper control arm with safety chain to prevent accidental release of spring.*

3) Loosen lower ball joint lock nut and disconnect ball joint from knuckle. Remove hub, rotor and steering knuckle assembly. Press ball joint from control arm if it is to be replaced.

4) SLOWLY lower jack supporting control arm and remove spring. Remove control arm pivot bolts and remove control arm.

Installation — Reverse removal procedures to install noting the following: Do not tighten control arm pivot bolts to specification until installation is complete. When compressing spring, attach safety chain between spring and upper control arm.

UPPER CONTROL ARM & BALL JOINT

Removal — 1) Raise and support vehicle. Remove wheel and tire. Remove brake caliper assembly and wire out of way. Remove lower shock absorber bolt and push shock up.

2) With jack positioned under outer end of lower control arm, raise arm until level and support. Loosen upper ball joint nut and disconnect ball joint from knuckle.

3) Remove 2 bolts connecting ball joint to control arm and remove ball joint. Remove upper control arm pivot shaft and remove arm.

Installation — Reverse removal procedures to install noting the following: When installing ball joint, be sure that the cut off side of

ISUZU I-MARK (Cont.)

mounting flange is towards outside of vehicle. Do not tighten pivot shaft bolt to specification until installation is otherwise complete. When installing control arm, make sure that the smaller washer is installed to the inside of the front arm and the larger washer is installed to the inside of the rear arm.

STABILIZER BAR

Removal — Raise and support vehicle. Remove engine splash guard. Remove stabilizer bar bolt and grommet assemblies from lower control arms. Remove stabilizer support clamps from body and remove stabilizer bar.

Installation — Reverse removal procedures to install.

TIGHTENING SPECIFICATIONS

Application	Ft. Lbs. (N·m)
Upper Control Arm Pivot Shaft	47 (64)
Upper Control Arm-to-Ball Joint	29 (39)
Upper Ball Joint-to-Steering Knuckle	47 (64)
Lower Control Arm Pivot Bolts	47 (64)
Lower Control Arm-to-Ball Joint	58 (79)
Lower Ball Joint-to-Steering Knuckle	58 (79)
Tie Rod Ball Joint-to-Steering Knuckle	29 (39)
Shock Absorber-to-Control Arm	29 (39)
Brake Caliper-to-Steering Knuckle	36 (49)

ISUZU P'UP & LUV

LUV
P'UP

DESCRIPTION

Independent type suspension, using torsion bars. Upper control arms are mounted to bracket which is part of shock tower. Lower control arm is mounted to crossmember. Ball joints attach both upper and lower control arms to steering knuckles, which are part of the front wheel spindle. Torsion bars are connected in front to lower control arm and at rear to frame crossmember. Back and forth movement of front suspension is regulated by a strut bar connecting lower control arm to frame, by means of a rubber bumper at frame end of strut. A stabilizer bar is attached to lower control arms and frame.

ADJUSTMENT

WHEEL ALIGNMENT SPECIFICATIONS & PROCEDURES

See Wheel Alignment Specifications & Procedures in WHEEL ALIGNMENT Section.

WHEEL BEARING ADJUSTMENT

1) Raise and support vehicle. On 4 wheel drive (4WD) models, place transfer shift lever in "2H" position and free wheeling hub in "FREE" position. Remove hub cover, then remove snap ring and shims from end of spindle. Remove free wheeling hub body and lock washer.

2) On 2 wheel drive (2WD) models, remove grease cap, cotter pin and nut retainer from spindle.

3) Rotate wheel and tighten spindle nut (hub nut) to 22 ft. lbs. (30 N•m) on 2WD and until hub locks on 4WD models. Turn hub 2 or 3 times to settle bearings. Loosen nut. Retighten nut finger tight and check that hub has no free play.

4) Attach a spring scale and measure starting force. Tighten spindle nut until a reading of 1.8-2.6 lbs. (8.0-11.6 N) is obtained. Make sure that the brake pads are not in contact with the rotor during this procedure.

5) On 2WD models, reassemble components in opposite order of removal. On 4WD models, install lock washer and free wheeling hub body and measure the clearance between free wheeling hub body and snap ring while pushing out on the axle shaft.

6) Select new spacer shims so that this clearance is less than .001" (.3 mm). Replacement shims are available in sizes .008, .01, .02 and .04" (0.2, 0.3, 0.5 and 1.0 mm). Install remaining components in reverse order of removal.

BALL JOINT CHECKING

With vehicle raised and supported under lower control arm, grasp wheel at top and bottom and try to move wheel. If movement exceeds .06" (1.5 mm), replace lower ball joint or upper control arm and ball joint assembly. New ball joints should have no visible play when checked.

REMOVAL & INSTALLATION

UPPER CONTROL ARM & BALL JOINT

Removal — 1) Raise and support vehicle with safety stands under lower control arms. Remove tire and wheel. Remove shock absorber dust cover. Remove upper ball joint cotter pin and nut.

2) Separate ball joint from steering knuckle and wire the knuckle and brake caliper assembly out of way. Do not allow assembly to hang from brake hose. Note number and placement of shims at upper control arm bracket.

3) Remove 2 bolts from upper pivot shaft. Remove upper stem retaining nut, retainer and rubber grommet. Depress shock absorber. Remove control arm from bracket.

4) If replacing pivot shaft and bushings, remove bolts from each end of pivot shaft. Remove lock washer, flat washer and plate. Press out pivot shaft and bushings.

Inspection — Check control arm and pivot shaft for cracks or distortion. Replace both pivot shaft and bushings if either is found defective. Replace ball joint and control arm as an assembly if either is defective.

Installation — 1) If pivot shaft and bushings have been removed, install pivot shaft and bushings on control arm using installer tool (J-29755). Install bolt with plate, washer and lock washer on each side of pivot shaft and tighten.

2) Install ball joint stud through knuckle. Install castle nut. Tighten to specifications, plus just enough more to install cotter pin. Mount control arm to chassis and install shims in equal thickness to those removed during disassembly.

3) Tighten bolt at thin shim pack first, then bolt at thicker shim pack. Install shock absorber dust cover, wheel and tire. Lower vehicle to ground.

LOWER CONTROL ARM & BALL JOINT

Removal — 1) Raise and support vehicle. Remove wheel and tire. Remove strut bar, torsion bar and stabilizer bar.

2) Detach lower end of shock absorber. Remove ball joint-to-control arm retaining bolts and separate ball joint from control arm. Remove control arm retaining nuts and bolts and remove control arm from vehicle.

Ball Joint Replacement (2WD Models) — Remove cotter pin and ball joint stud nut. Separate ball joint from knuckle. Remove bolts attaching ball joint to control arm (if still installed) and remove ball joint.

Ball Joint Replacement (4WD Models) — Follow Control Arm Removal procedures through separation of ball joint from control arm. Remove tie rod ends from knuckle. Remove cotter pin and ball joint stud nut. Separate ball joint from steering knuckle. Remove hub and knuckle assembly from axle shaft (do not allow assembly to hang by brake line). Remove ball joint.

Inspection — Check all parts for distortion, cracking or excessive wear. Replace all worn parts.

ISUZU P'UP & LUV (Cont.)

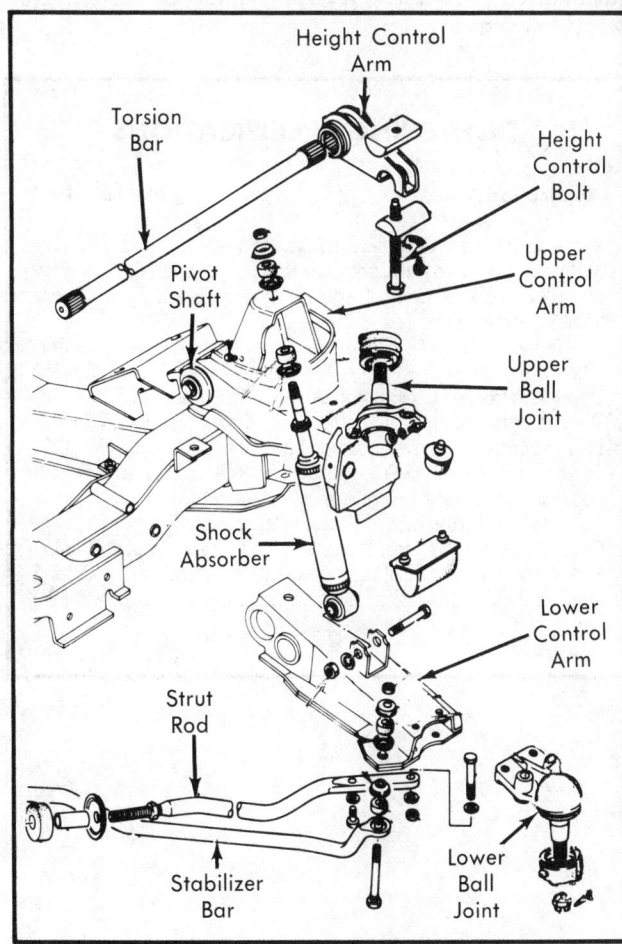

Fig. 1 Exploded View of Front Suspension (2WD Shown, 4WD Similar)

Installation (All Models) — Installation procedures are the opposite of removal except that the ball joint must be attached to the control arm before control arm installation.

SHOCK ABSORBER

Removal — Raise vehicle and support on safety stands. Remove shock absorber dust cover. Hold shock absorber upper stem with a wrench and remove retaining nut, retainer and rubber grommet. Remove shock absorber lower pivot bolt from lower control arm and remove shock absorber.

Installation — Check shock absorber and replace if necessary. Fully extend shock absorber, place lower retainer and grommet on stem and slide shock absorber into position. Install upper grommet and retainer on stem and tighten nut. Slide bolt through lower shock absorber mount and shock absorber. Install shock absorber dust cover, tighten mounting bolt and lower vehicle.

WHEEL BEARINGS

Removal (2WD) — 1) Raise and support vehicle. Remove wheel and tire. Remove brake caliper and support, and wire out of way. Remove grease cap, cotter pin, spindle nut retainer and spindle nut. Remove hub and rotor.

2) Remove outer bearing, pry out inner grease seal and remove inner bearing. Drive out bearing races as needed.

Installation — Reverse removal procedures to install. Always use new races with new bearings, always use new grease seals.

Removal (4WD) — 1) Raise and support vehicle. Remove wheel and tire. With transfer case shift lever in "2H" position and free wheeling hub in "FREE" position, remove hub cover retaining bolts (6) and remove hub cover assembly.

2) Remove snap ring and shims from end of spindle. Remove free wheeling hub body from hub assembly.

3) Remove brake caliper and support and wire out of way. Remove lock washer. Remove hub nut with wrench. Remove hub and rotor. Remove outer bearing from hub. Drive out inner grease seal and retaining ring (inner bearing will be removed in this process). Drive out bearing races as needed.

Installation — Reverse removal procedures to install. Adjust wheel bearings.

STABILIZER BAR

Removal — Raise vehicle and disconnect stabilizer bar from lower control arm. Remove brackets holding bar to frame and remove bar. Remove link bolt, spacers and rubber grommets from lower control arm or stabilizer bar. Inspect all parts for wear or damage and replace if necessary.

Installation — Bolt brackets to frame over rubber bushings installed over stabilizer bar but do not tighten. Connect link bolts to lower control arm, making sure washers are installed in correct position. Connect link bolts to stabilizer, and tighten to specifications. Tighten bracket bolts to specifications.

TORSION BAR

Removal — Raise vehicle and place safety stands under front of vehicle. Remove stopper plate (2WD only) and height control arm adjusting bolt. Mark position and remove height control arm from torsion bar and third crossmember (2WD), or torsion bar and bracket (4WD). Mark position and remove torsion bar from control arm.

Installation — 1) Thoroughly grease serrated portions at both ends of torsion bar. Raise lower control arm with jack to position rubber bumpers in contact with lower control arm. Install front end of torsion bar into control arm.

2) Install height control arm into position so its end reaches height control bolt (grease portion of height control arm which fits into frame).

3) Turn height control adjusting bolt to position marked during removal. Check riding height. See appropriate article in WHEEL ALIGNMENT section. Install stopper plate.

LOWER CONTROL ARM STRUT BAR

NOTE — Correct caster angle can be maintained by marking positions of strut rod nuts for reassembly reference.

Front Suspension

ISUZU P'UP & LUV (Cont.)

Removal — Raise vehicle and remove nuts, washers and rubber bushings from front side of strut bar. Remove 2 bolts holding strut bar to lower control arm and remove strut bar.

Installation — Place washer and bushing on strut bar and slide rod through frame bracket. Place second set of washers and bushings on end through bracket, then start on washer and one nut, but do not tighten. Bolt other end of strut to lower control arm and tighten to specifications. Lower vehicle and tighten bracket nut, install second nut and tighten to specifications.

STEERING KNUCKLE

Removal — 1) Raise vehicle and place safety stands under front of vehicle. Remove brake caliper assembly without disconnecting line and support out of way.

2) Remove hub and rotor assembly as outlined in Wheel Bearing Removal. Remove 4 retaining bolts around spindle and, on 2WD models, remove tie rod link, dust shield and adapter.

3) Remove cotter pins and castle nuts from upper and lower ball joints and separate ball joints from knuckle. Remove knuckle.

Installation — To install, reverse removal procedures. Adjust wheel bearings.

TIGHTENING SPECIFICATIONS

Application	Ft. Lbs. (N·m)
Stabilizer Bar-to-Bracket	55 (75)
Stabilizer Bar-to-Lower Control Arm	84 INCH Lbs. (10)
Strut Bar-to-Lower Control Arm	45 (61)
Strut Bar-to-Frame	
2WD	90 (122)
4WD	50 (68)
Upper Control Arm Pivot Shaft Bushings	87 (118)
Upper Control Arm Pivot Shaft-to-Frame	75 (102)
Lower Control Arm-to-Crossmember (2WD)	90 (122)
Lower Control Arm-to-Frame Bracket (4WD)	97 (132)
Ball Joint-to-Lower Control Arm	45 (61)
Ball Joint Stud Nuts	75 (102)
Shock Absorber (Upper)	14 (19)
Shock Absorber (Lower)	45 (61)
Rotor-to-Hub	36 (49)

JAGUAR

XJ6

DESCRIPTION

Suspension consists of upper and lower control arms, double acting hydraulic shock absorbers, coil springs, stabilizer bar and steering knuckles. The upper control arms are mounted inboard to fulcrum shafts and are mounted outboard to steering knuckles by upper ball joints. Lower control arms are mounted inboard to crossmember and outboard to steering knuckles by lower ball joints. Coil springs are mounted between lower control arms and crossmember. Shock absorbers are attached at the bottom to lower control arms and at the top to body. Stabilizer bar is attached to lower control arms and crossmember.

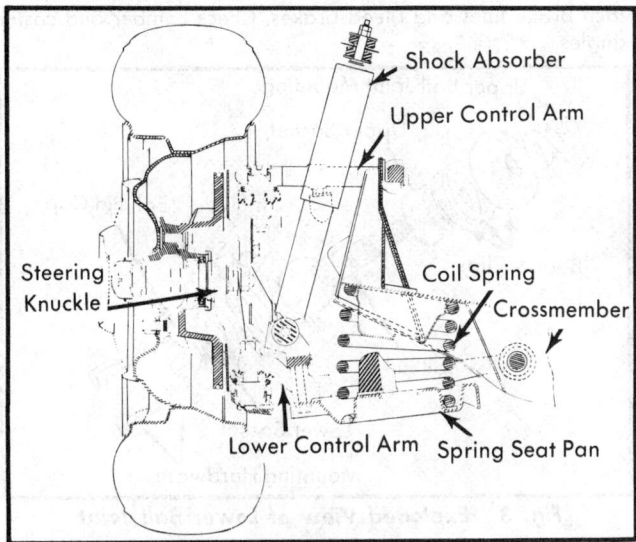

Fig. 1 Sectional View of Front Suspension Assembly

ADJUSTMENT

WHEEL ALIGNMENT SPECIFICATIONS & PROCEDURES

See Wheel Alignment Specifications and Procedures in WHEEL ALIGNMENT Section.

WHEEL BEARING ADJUSTMENT

While rotating hub, tighten nut until no end play is evident. Loosen nut a maximum of 120° to line up cotter pin and install pin. Check end play with dial indicator. If end play is not .002-006" (.05-.015 mm), adjust axle nut until correct end play is obtained.

BALL JOINT CHECKING

Inspect ball joints for any signs of excessive wear or damage. Replace as needed. Lower ball joint can be adjusted with shims. These shims are not to be used to compensate for worn ball joints, and are designed to provide adjustment during overhaul reassembly only.

REMOVAL & INSTALLATION

WHEEL BEARINGS

Removal — 1) Raise and support vehicle. Remove wheel and tire. Remove hub to rotor attaching bolts through holes in hub. Remove grease cap, cotter pin, axle nut and washer. Remove hub.

2) Remove grease seal and wheel bearings. Drive out bearing races.

Installation — Reverse removal procedure to install.

FRONT SUSPENSION ASSEMBLY

Removal — 1) Disconnect battery and remove air cleaners. Disconnect the upper end of shock absorber. Drain and discard power steering fluid. Disconnect and plug power steering inlet and outlet hoses.

2) Remove nuts securing engine mounts to brackets on frame crossmember. Disconnect rear crossmember mountings, then separate stabilizer bar from link. Turn steering column until pinch bolt holding lower "U" joint to pinion shaft is accessible. Remove pinch bolt.

3) Return steering to straight-ahead position. Set ignition to "LOCK" and remove key. Separate lower steering column from upper "U" joint, then from pinion shaft.

4) Raise and support vehicle. Remove front wheels. Disconnect brake hoses and lines. Detach ground strap from engine. Remove suspension mounting bolts. Collect and note location of all washers, spacers and bushings. Remove suspension assembly from vehicle.

Installation — To install, reverse removal procedure and note the following:

- Be sure brake lines and hoses are properly routed without bends or kinks.
- It may be helpful to remove protective heat shield covering boot on rack and pinion steering prior to positioning suspension into place.
- Be sure power steering reservoir is full before starting engine after installation.
- If additional information is required on steering column installation, see *appropriate article in STEERING section of this manual.*
- Bleed brake system.

SHOCK ABSORBERS

Removal — Detach upper shock absorber mounting. Raise and support vehicle. Remove front wheel if necessary for access to lower mounting. Remove lower shock absorber mounting and remove from vehicle.

Installation — To install, reverse removal procedure.

COIL SPRINGS

Removal — Raise and support vehicle, then remove tire and wheel. Fit a spring compressor (JD-6D & adaptor JD-6D-1) and collapse spring coil enough to allow load on pan seat to be relieved. Remove hardware mounting spring pan to lower control arm. Slightly loosen spring compressor and remove assembly complete.

NOTE — *Be sure to note number and location of any packing shims.*

Installation — To install coil spring, reverse removal procedure noting the following: Floor jack can be placed under lower ball joint to aid in aligning spring pan bolt. A maximum of three packers may be placed in spring pan and no more than two can be fitted on crossmember.

LOWER CONTROL ARM

Removal — 1) Remove complete suspension assembly as described in this article.

JAGUAR (Cont.)

2) With assembly on bench, detach tie rod ball joints from steering knuckle, then detach and remove steering rack from crossmember. Use spring compressor to remove coil spring. Separate upper ball joint, noting location of all caster shims. Detach lower ball joint.

3) Remove stabilizer bar support bracket and shock absorber lower mounting. Remove cotter pin and pivot shaft nut. Drive pivot shaft from crossmember and collect spacers. Remove lower control arm.

Installation — To install, reverse removal procedure. Do not tighten pivot shaft nut until vehicle is resting on ground at full curb weight.

UPPER CONTROL ARM

Removal — 1) Raise and support vehicle. Remove front wheel. Detach upper ball joint from control arm. Note number of all caster adjusting shims present.

2) Wire steering knuckle to coil spring and remove bolts holding upper control arm pivot shaft to vehicle. Note number and location of all camber adjusting shims. Remove control arm from vehicle.

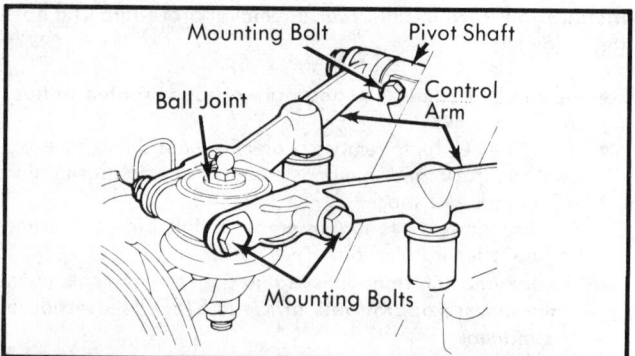

Fig. 2 Upper Control Arm Mounting Points

Installation — To install upper control arm, reverse removal procedure and tighten all nuts and bolts. Recheck wheel alignment.

STABILIZER BAR

Removal — Raise and support vehicle. Remove front wheels. Detach both ends of stabilizer bar from mounting links. Remove both mounting brackets from frame. Remove all mounting bushings from bar. Detach 1 tie rod end from steering knuckle and maneuver stabilizer from vehicle.

Installation — To install, reverse removal procedure, fully tightening stabilizer bar-to-link nuts after vehicle is resting on ground.

LOWER BALL JOINT

Removal — 1) Raise front of vehicle and place on safety stands. Remove wheel. Disconnect brake line from caliper and plug openings. Disconnect tie rod from steering arm. Twist stub axle carrier to gain access to bolts securing upper ball joint to control arm, then remove bolts. Note position and number of shims.

2) Remove nut mounting lower ball joint to control arm. Use tool JD 24 (or equivalent) to separate ball joint from control arm, then maneuver assembly from vehicle.

Disassembly & Reassembly — 1) Pry back tab washers and remove four screws keeping ball pin cap. Lift out ball pin. Release clip and remove upper socket from stub axle.

2) Clean all components and inspect for excessive wear or damage.

3) Install new upper socket to stub axle. Fit lip of boot clip in recess in socket. Lip MUST be near lower face of clip. Install new boot to clip and attach with plastic retaining ring. Grease new ball pin and put into position.

4) Put ball pin cap into vise and cut out lower socket. Clean shavings and fit new socket. Refit shims and replace ball cap. Fit four setscrews with lock tabs and tighten, continually checking ball joint movement.

5) If ball pin is loose in socket, remove shims. If pin is excessively tight, add shims until movement is correct. Movement should be slightly stiff.

Installation — Insert ball joint in lower control arm and tighten lock nut. Align stub axle with upper control arm and insert bolts (bolt heads MUST face front). Make sure packing pieces and shims are properly installed. Reconnect tie rod. Attach brake lines and bleed brakes. Check camber and caster angles.

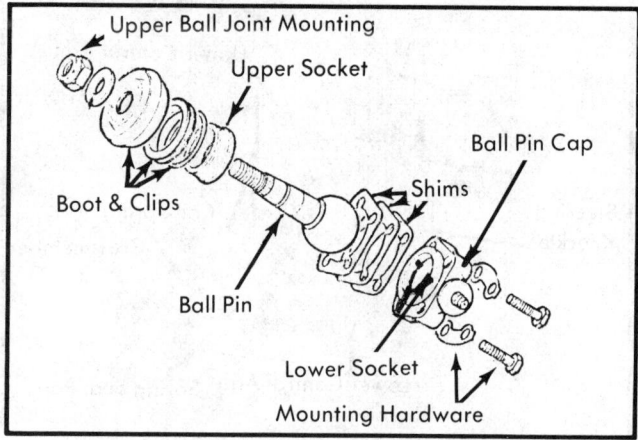

Fig. 3 Exploded View of Lower Ball Joint

UPPER BALL JOINT

NOTE — *Upper control arm ball joint cannot be overhauled. If ball joint is excessively worn, assembly must be replaced.*

Removal — 1) Raise vehicle and place on safety stands. Remove wheel. Twist steering to full lock position. Wire stub axle to crossmember to prevent tension on brake hose when ball joint is separated.

2) Remove bolt mounting upper ball joint to control arm. Note number of shims and position of packing pieces. Remove ball joint lock nut and separate ball joint from control arm. Maneuver assembly from vehicle. Withdraw ball joint from stub axle.

Installation — Apply grease to replacement ball joint and place in position in stub axle. Hold ball joint against taper fit washer and tighten retaining nut. Refit upper control arm mounting bolts (bolt heads must face forward) and caster shims. Check camber and caster angles.

TIGHTENING SPECIFICATIONS

Application	Ft. Lbs. (N·m)
Upper Pivot Shaft- to-Crossmember	49-55 (67-75)
Upper Ball Joint-to-Arm	26-32 (35-44)
Pivot Shaft-to-Upper Arm	45-55 (61-75)
Pivot Shaft-to-Lower Arm	32-50 (44-68)
Upper Shock Absorber	27-32 (37-44)
Lower Shock Absorber	32-36 (44-49)
Spring Pan	27-32 (37-44)
Stabilizer-to-Link	14-18 (19-25)
Tie Rod Nut	35-50 (48-68)

MAZDA GLC, 626 & RX7

DESCRIPTION

Independent hydraulic strut type suspension with coil springs. Strut assemblies mount between lower control arms and upper fender panels. Strut assemblies consist of: hydraulic shock absorbers (built into strut tube), coil springs around outside of strut tube housing, and a steering knuckle that is connected to both lower control arm and strut. Lower control arms pivot at crossmember and are connected by ball joints to steering knuckle. Rear wheel drive models are equipped with a stabilizer bar which is attached to the chassis at each end to the lower control arms. On 626 and RX7 models, tension rods are installed to maintain alignment and stability.

ADJUSTMENT

WHEEL ALIGNMENT SPECIFICATIONS & PROCEDURES

See Wheel Alignment Specifications & Procedures in WHEEL ALIGNMENT Section.

WHEEL BEARING ADJUSTMENT

Rear Wheel Drive Models (RWD) — 1) Raise and support vehicle. Remove wheel and tire. On RX7 models, tighten spindle nut until hub locks, then back off until hub rotates smoothly. On all other models, tighten spindle nut to 14-18 ft. lbs. (19-25 N•m).

2) Turn hub a few times to seat bearings. Loosen nut. Install one wheel bolt and attach spring scale. Gradually tighten spindle nut until a preload reading of 1.0-1.4 lbs. (4.5-6.2 N) on GLC and RX7, or .8-1.9 lbs. (3.6-8.5 N) on 626, is obtained.

Front Wheel Drive Models (FWD) — 1) With steering knuckle removed (see Wheel Bearing Removal) and outer bearing and spacer in place, attach spacer selector (49 B001 727) to knuckle.

2) Tighten selector nut to 145 ft. lbs. (197 N•m) by 35 ft. lb (48 N•m) increments, checking that knuckle turns smoothly at each step. Measure bearing preload at caliper mounting hole in knuckle. Preload should be .5-2.0 lbs (2.2-8.9 N). If not to specification, the spacer must be changed.

3) There are 21 spacers available from .2474" (6.285 mm) to .2794" (7.085 mm) in .0016" (.04 mm) increments. If preload is too high, increase spacer thickness. If it is too low, decrease thickness. Changing spacer thickness by one number will change preload by about .5-1.0 lbs. (2.2-4.5 N). Number is stamped on outer edge of spacer. Recheck preload after new spacer is installed.

BALL JOINT CHECKING

RWD Models — With strut assembly disconnected (GLC & 626) or control arm removed from vehicle (RX7), check ball joint dust boot for cracks or other damage. Rotate ball joint stud several times to settle joint. Attach knuckle arm and connect spring scale to tie rod hole in arm. Support knuckle with finger and measure starting force required to turn ball joint. If scale reading is less than .9 lbs. (4.0 N), replace ball joint and lower control arm as an assembly.

FWD Models — Raise and support vehicle. With control arm removed and ball joint assembly attached to knuckle arm, measure starting force required to turn ball joint. If scale reading is not 4.0-6.8 lbs. (17.8-30.3 N), replace ball joint assembly.

REMOVAL & INSTALLATION

LOWER CONTROL ARM

Removal (RWD Models) — 1) Raise and support vehicle. Remove wheel and tire.

2) Remove cotter pin from tie rod nut. Remove nut. Separate tie rod ball joint with puller.

3) Remove bolts mounting steering knuckle to strut tube. Disconnect stabilizer bar and tension rod (if equipped) from control arm.

Removal (FWD Models) — 1) Raise and support vehicle. Remove tire and wheel. Disconnect knuckle arm-to-control arm ball joint.

2) Remove control arm retaining bolts at frame and remove arm.

Installation — To install, reverse removal procedure.

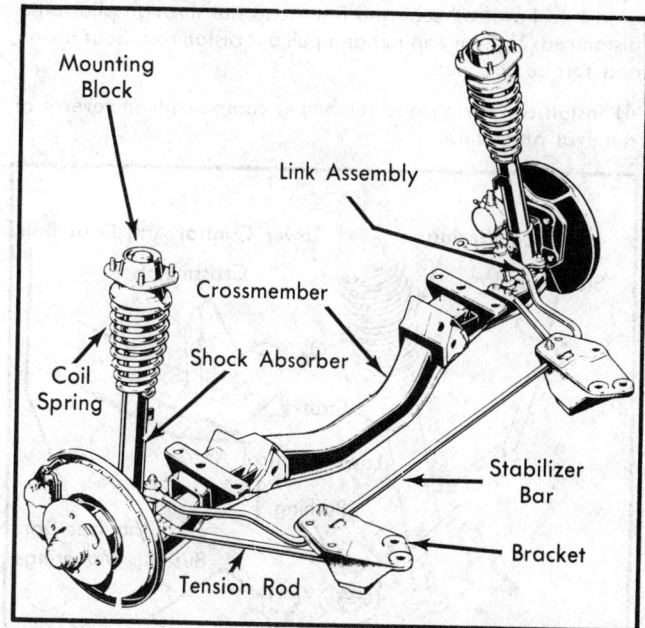

Mounting Block

Link Assembly

Crossmember

Shock Absorber

Coil Spring

Stabilizer Bar

Bracket

Tension Rod

Fig. 1   626 & RX7 Front Suspension Assembly

STRUT ASSEMBLY (RWD Models)

Removal — 1) Raise and support vehicle. Remove tire and wheel. Remove strut-to-fender panel nuts from inside engine compartment.

2) Remove brake hydraulic line mounting clip from strut housing. Remove brake caliper and wire out of way. Remove grease cap, cotter pin, nut lock and bearing from spindle. Pull off hub and brake assembly.

3) Remove backing plate. Remove strut-to-steering knuckle mounting bolts. Drop lower control arm down. Remove strut assembly and coil spring.

Disassembly — 1) Clamp strut in vise. Use spring compressor to collapse coil spring. Remove locknut and washer from top of piston rod.

2) Remove shock absorber support, spring seat and thrust bearing. Remove coil spring, dust boot and damper stopper.

3) Place strut in a soft jawed vise. Remove cap nut and seal. Pry "O" ring from guide rod. Pull piston rod and pressure tube assembly out of strut (reservoir tube). Remove strut from vise and drain fluid.

NOTE — Do not remove piston rod, guide or base valve from pressure tube. Service as a complete assembly only.

MAZDA GLC, 626 & RX7 (Cont.)

Inspection — Check reservoir tube for cracks or wear. Check all rubber parts for cracks or excessive damage. Inspect coil spring for signs of fatigue or damage. Replace parts as needed.

Reassembly & Installation — 1) Hold reservoir tube in vise. Insert pressure tube and piston rod assembly into tube. Pour hydraulic fluid into reservoir.

2) Install piston rod guide into pressure tube. Fit new "O" ring between rod guide and reservoir tube.

3) Fit a pilot (49 0259 590) over threads of piston rod. Apply grease to lip of oil seal and insert cap nut through pilot onto piston rod. Tighten cap nut and pull out piston rod. Seat piston and torque cap nut.

4) Install coil spring and remaining components in reverse of removal procedure.

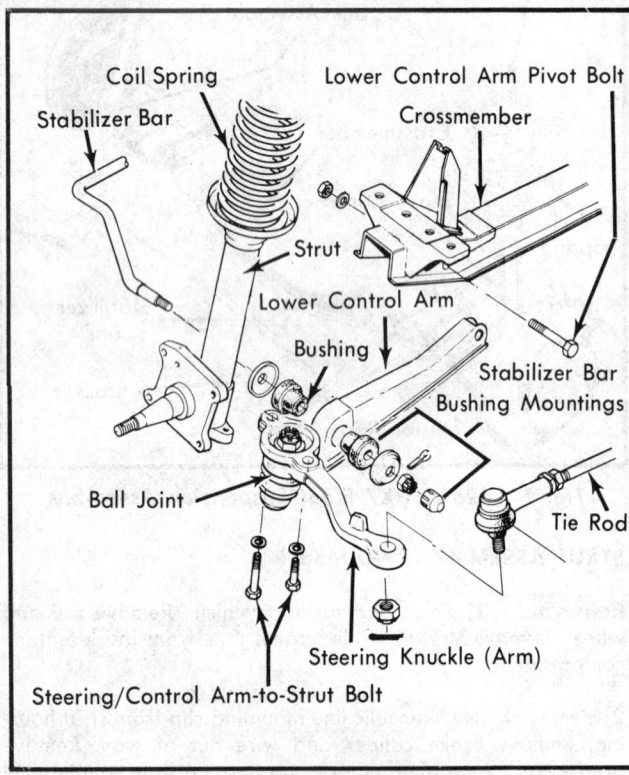

Fig. 2 Exploded View of GLC Front Suspension (RWD Models)

STRUT ASSEMBLY (FWD Models)

Removal — Raise and support vehicle. Remove tire and wheel. Remove brake line from bracket on strut. Remove retaining bolts from top and bottom of strut assembly and remove strut.

Disassembly — 1) Clamp strut in vise. Use spring compressor to collapse coil spring. Remove lock nut and washer from top of piston rod.

2) Remove shock absorber support and spring seat. Remove coil spring, dust boot and damper stopper. Disassembly is complete. Strut assembly is serviced as an assembly.

Inspection — Check all rubber parts for cracking or signs of wear. Inspect coil spring for signs of fatigue, cracks or other damage. Replace components as needed.

Reassembly & Installation — Reverse removal and disassembly procedures to assemble and install.

Strut Reservoir Volume	
Application	**Ounces**
RX7	7.61
GLC	8.45
626	8.15

WHEEL BEARINGS

Removal (FWD Models) — 1) Raise and support vehicle. Remove wheel and tire. Remove drive shaft lock nut. Separate tie rod ball joint from knuckle

2) Disconnect brake line from clip on strut, remove brake caliper assembly and wire out of way. Remove knuckle-to-strut attaching bolts and ball joint-to-control arm bolts. Remove knuckle and ball joint as an assembly. Separate ball joint from knuckle.

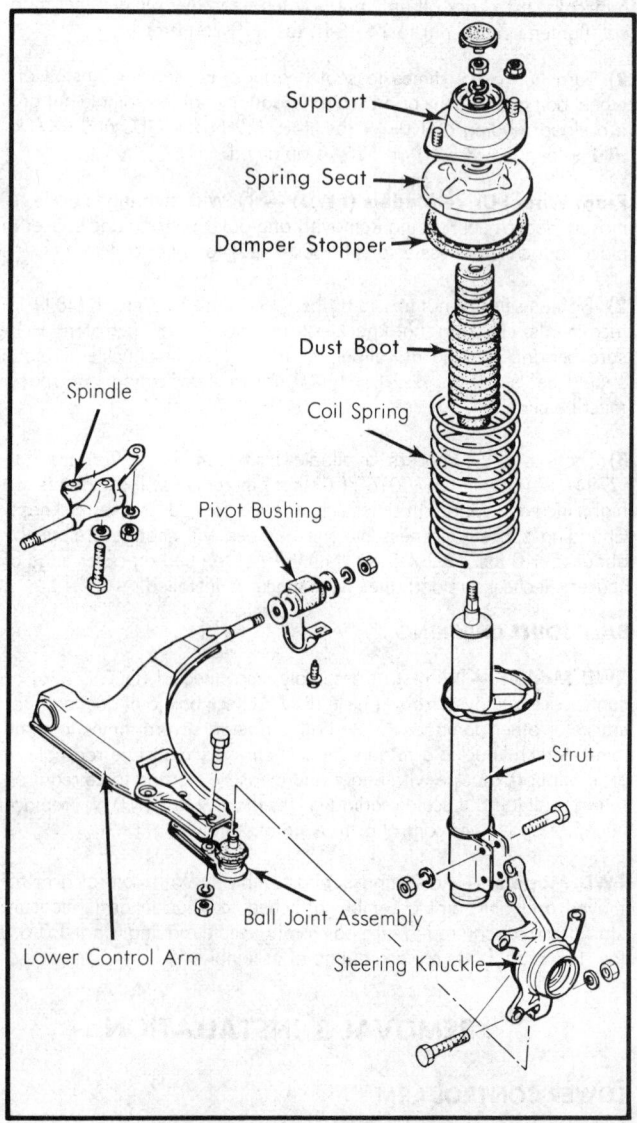

Fig. 3 Exploded View of GLC Front Suspension (FWD Models)

MAZDA GLC, 626 & RX7 (Cont.)

3) With wheel hub in vise, remove knuckle with puller (49 B001 726). Remove hub-to-rotor retaining bolts and separate hub from rotor. Remove bearing spacer and press outer bearing from hub.

4) Remove inner and outer grease seals. Remove inner bearing and drive out bearing races with drift. Inspect bearings and races for excessive wear or damage and replace as needed. Always use a new race with a new bearing.

Installation (FWD Models) — Reverse removal procedures to install. Check bearing preload.

Removal (RWD Models) — **1)** Raise and support vehicle. Remove wheel and tire. Remove brake caliper and wire out of way. Remove grease cap, cotter pin, nut lock, adjusting nut and bearing from spindle.

2) Remove rotor and hub assembly. Remove grease seal and inner bearing. Inspect bearing races for excessive wear or signs of damage. If replacement is required, drive out with drift.

Installation (RWD Models) — Reverse removal procedures to install. Check bearing preload.

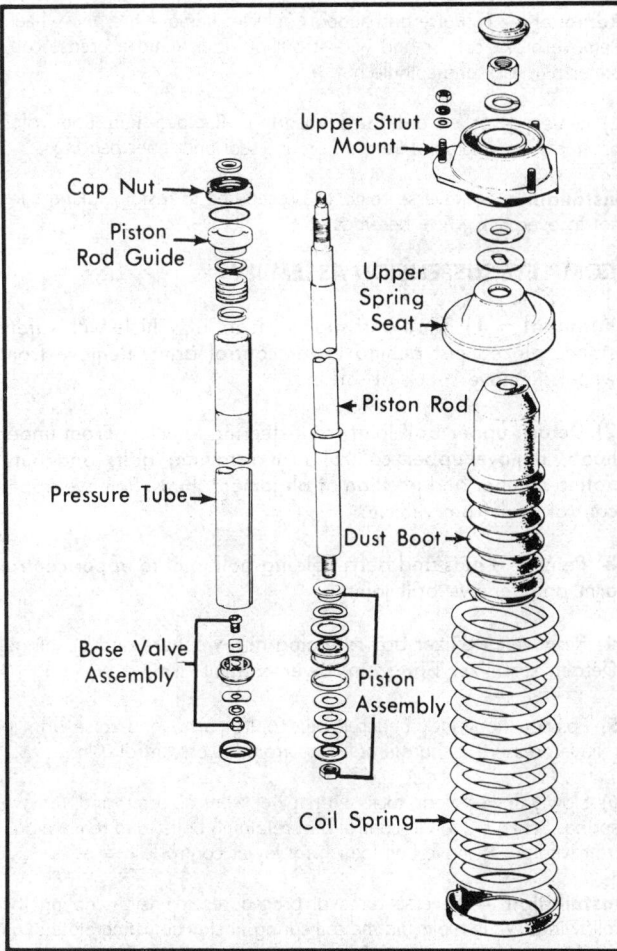

Cap Nut
Piston Rod Guide
Pressure Tube
Base Valve Assembly
Upper Strut Mount
Upper Spring Seat
Piston Rod
Dust Boot
Piston Assembly
Coil Spring

Fig. 4   Exploded View of Strut Asssembly (RWD Models Only)

TIGHTENING SPECIFICATIONS

Application	Ft. Lbs. (N·m)
RWD Models	
Control Arm-to-Frame	29-40 (39-54)
Steering Knuckle-to-Strut	
GLC	69-85 (94-116)
RX7 & 626	43-51 (59-69)
Ball Joint-to-Knuckle	
GLC	43-58 (59-79)
RX7	43-51 (59-69)
626	46-69 (63-94)
Knuckle-to-Tie Rod Ball Joint	22-33 (30-45)
Tension Rod-to-Control Arm	
RX7	40-50 (54-68)
626	48-58 (65-79)
Tension Rod Lock Nut	80-108 (109-147)
Strut Cap Nut	
GLC	72-94 (98-128)
RX7 & 626	36-43 (49-59)
w/cartridge	58-108 (79-147)
FWD Models	
Control Arm Spindle Nut	55-69 (75-94)
Control Arm Spindle-to-Frame	69-86 (94-117)
Control Arm Pivot Bushing Nut	55-69 (75-94)
Control Arm Pivot Bushing Bracket	37-45 (50-61)
Ball Joint-to-Control Arm	69-86 (94-117)
Ball Joint-to-Knuckle (Pinch Bolt)	33-40 (45-54)
Knuckle-to-Tie Rod Ball Joint	22-33 (30-45)
Knuckle-to-Strut	58-86 (79-117)
Strut Cap Nut	55-69 (75-94)
Axle Nut	116-174 (158-237)

Front Suspension

MAZDA B2000 PICKUP

DESCRIPTION

Independent type suspension, consisting of upper and lower control arms and wheel spindle mounted between upper and lower arms by means of ball joints. Upper control arm pivots on a shaft attached to frame; lower control arm pivots on a shaft mounted to crossmember. A coil spring is mounted between lower control arm and frame. Shock absorber is hydraulic, double-action type, mounted between lower control arm and frame inside coil spring. A stabilizer bar is also incorporated which connects to the lower control arm on each side by bushings and links.

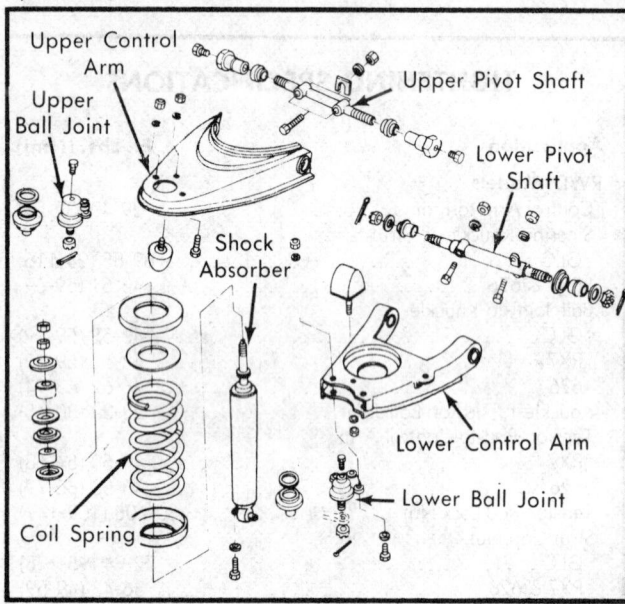

Fig. 1 Exploded View of Front Suspension Assembly for Component Identification

ADJUSTMENTS

WHEEL ALIGNMENT SPECIFICATIONS & PROCEDURES

See Wheel Alignment Specifications & Procedures in WHEEL ALIGNMENT section.

WHEEL BEARING ADJUSTMENT

Raise and support vehicle. Remove wheel and tire. Tighten spindle nut until hub locks, then back off just enough to allow smooth rotation of hub. Turn a few times to seat bearing and check bearing preload. Tighten spindle nut until a preload of 1.3-2.4 lbs. (5.8-10.7 N) is obtained.

BALL JOINT CHECKING

Check ball joint dust seal for wear or damage, and replace as needed. Check end play. If play exceeds .04" (1.0 mm), replace ball joint.

REMOVAL & INSTALLATION

SHOCK ABSORBERS

Removal — Remove nut, rubber bushing and washer attaching upper end of shock absorber to crossmember. Remove lower retaining bolts holding shock absorber to lower control arm, and remove shock absorber from vehicle.

Installation — Reverse removal procedure and tighten mounting bolts.

WHEEL BEARINGS

Removal — **1)** Raise and support vehicle. Remove tire and wheel. Remove brake caliper and wire it out of way. Remove grease cap, cotter pin, lock and spindle nut.

2) Remove washer and outer bearing. Remove hub and rotor assembly from spindle. Remove grease seal and inner bearing.

Installation — Reverse removal procedures to install, taking care not to overpack wheel bearings.

COMPLETE SUSPENSION ASSEMBLY

Removal — **1)** Raise and support front of vehicle with safety stands placed just behind lower control arms. Remove front wheel. Remove shock absorber.

2) Detach upper ball joint from steering knuckle. From under hood, remove upper control arm retaining bolts and nuts, noting number and position of alignment shims. Remove upper control arm from vehicle.

3) Remove 3 nuts and bolts holding ball joint to upper control arm and remove ball joint.

4) Remove stabilizer bar retaining nut, washers and bushings. Detach stabilizer bar from lower control arm.

5) Position floor jack under lower control arm, and raise arm to relieve pressure. Separate ball joint from lower control arm.

6) Slowly lower floor jack with lower control arm, and remove spring. Remove 2 lower control arm retaining bolts, and remove arm from vehicle. Remove ball joint from lower control arm.

Installation — Reverse removal procedures to install, noting the following: When replacing the coil spring, install adjusting plate(s) as needed to obtain equal road clearance on right and left sides. Never use more than three adjusting plates on any one side.

TIGHTENING SPECIFICATIONS

Application	Ft. Lbs. (N·m)
Ball Joint-to-Knuckle	51-65 (69-88)
Bal Joint-to-Lower Control Arm	60-70 (82-95)
Control Arm-to-Frame (Both)	54-69 (73-94)

MERCEDES-BENZ — EXCEPT 380SL & 380SLC

240D
280 Series
300 Series
380SEL

DESCRIPTION

Front suspension consists of upper and lower control arms, coil springs, shock absorbers, steering knuckles and a stabilizer bar.

ADJUSTMENTS

WHEEL ALIGNMENT SPECIFICATIONS & PROCEDURES

See Wheel Alignment Specifications and Procedures in WHEEL ALIGNMENT section.

WHEEL BEARING ADJUSTMENT

All Models — While rotating hub, tighten clamp nut until hub can just be turned. Loosen clamp nut and release bearing tension by striking steering knuckle spindle with plastic hammer. Using a dial indicator, check wheel bearing end play. End play should be .0004-.0008" (.01-.02 mm). Adjust clamp nut until end play is within limits. Tighten socket bolt of clamp nut. Washer between outer bearing and clamp nut should rotate when light pressure is applied.

BALL JOINT CHECKING

Check ball joint lateral and vertical movement. If any measureable lateral movement is observed, replace ball joint. Correct excessive or insufficient vertical movement by adding or removing washers.

REMOVAL & INSTALLATION

NOTE — Shock absorber mounts and stabilizer attachments should not be tightened or loosened unless vehicle is resting on ground.

SUSPENSION ASSEMBLY (ONE SIDE)

Removal — 1) Disconnect upper shock mount. Raise vehicle and support with jack stands under outer edge of lower control arms. Remove front wheel.

2) Remove coil spring, as described in this article. Use suitable tool to separate tie rod ball joint from steering knuckle arm.

3) Detach flexible brake hose from brake line at connection on fender well. Loosen plug connection of brake lining wear indicator on caliper. Remove bolts holding brake support to frame.

4) Support front axle half. Mark position of lower control arm eccentric to crossmember for reinstallation purposes. Remove eccentric bolt.

5) Remove stabilizer bar support from upper control arm. Remove hex bolt holding upper control arm bushing to body. Remove front suspension assembly.

Installation — 1) Position front suspension in vehicle and mount upper control arm to body and stabilizer bar, but do not fully tighten bolts. Raise opposite side of vehicle as required to obtain proper stabilizer bar position.

2) Attach upper control arm to frame crossmember. Attach brake support to frame. Reconnect brake line to hose and plug connection of caliper wear indicator.

3) Install coil spring. Install shock absorber loosely. Attach tie rod ball joint to steering knuckle arm.

4) Bleed brake system. Install front wheel and lower vehicle to ground.

5) Place eccentric bolt of camber adjustment to original position and tighten.

6) Tighten upper control arm-to-body bolt and stabilizer bar-to-control arm support bolt. Tighten shock absorber mounting bolts. Check axle height and front wheel alignment. See WHEEL ALIGNMENT section.

UPPER CONTROL ARM

NOTE — Loosen hex nuts on ball joints with coil spring installed ONLY when supporting jacks are under lower control arm and not body. If jack cannot be so positioned, remove coil spring.

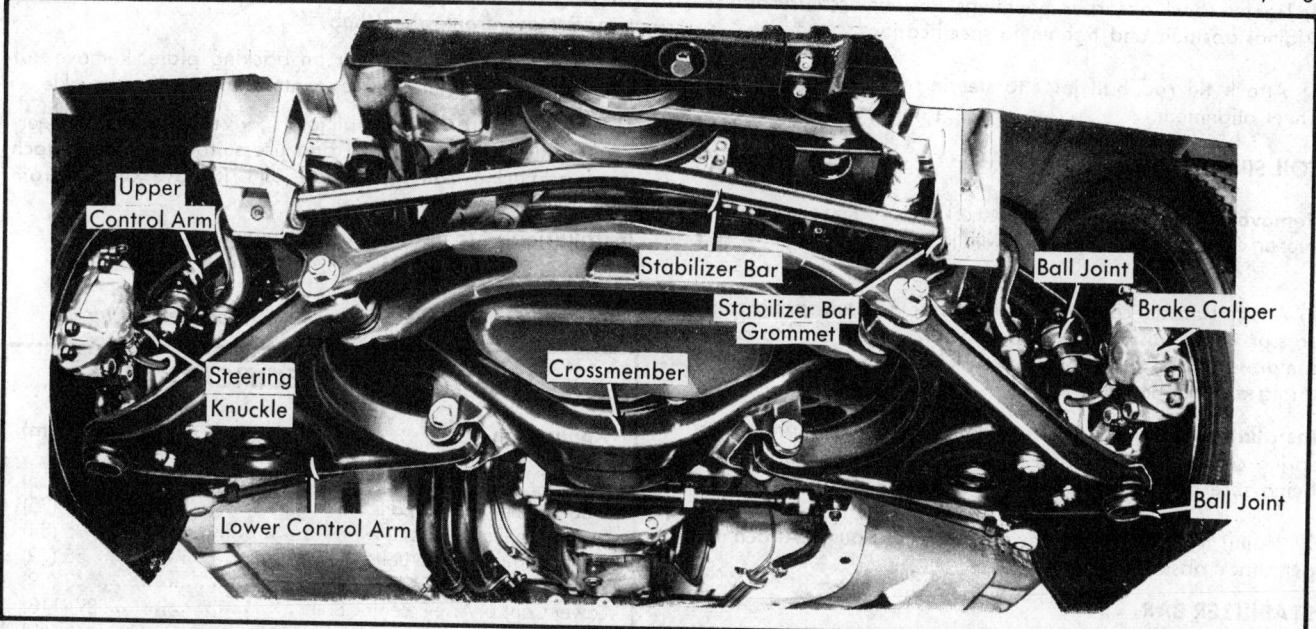

Fig. 1 Assembled View of Mercedes-Benz Front Suspension
(280 Series Shown; Others Similar with Major Difference in Stabilizer Bar Configuration and Mounting)

MERCEDES-BENZ – EXCEPT 380SL & 380SLC (Cont.)

Removal — 1) Raise vehicle and support under outer edge of lower control arms with jack stands.

2) Remove upper ball joint nut. Using suitable tool, detach ball joint from steering knuckle arm. Wire steering knuckle to frame so it will not drop.

3) Remove upper control arm support from stabilizer bar and from body. Remove upper control arm.

Installation — 1) Position upper control arm in vehicle and install control arm-to-body bolt. Connect upper ball joint to steering knuckle.

2) Mount stabilizer bar support to upper control arm, attaching bolt loosely. Lower vehicle to ground and tighten all bolts to specifications. Check front end alignment.

LOWER CONTROL ARM

Removal — 1) Loosen top shock absorber mount. Lower mount. Remove shock absorber. Raise vehicle and support with jack stands under outer edge of lower control arms.

2) Remove front wheel. Remove coil spring as described in this article. Detach tie rod ball joint from steering knuckle arm.

3) Mark position of lower control arm eccentric bolt and bushing to crossmember for reassembly reference.

4) Remove bolts holding brake support to frame. Remove lower control arm eccentric bolt. Detach lower ball joint from control arm. Remove lower control arm with brake support.

Installation — 1) Mount lower control arm to ball joint. Position control arm bushing to frame.

2) Attach brake support to frame. Install coil spring. Install shock absorber, loosely. Mount front wheel and lower vehicle to ground.

3) Tighten shock absorber mountings. Position eccentric bolt to original position and tighten to specifications.

4) Attach tie rod ball joint to steering knuckle arm. Check wheel alignment.

COIL SPRING

Removal — 1) Disconnect upper shock mount. Raise vehicle and support under lower control arms with jack stands. Remove wheel.

2) Attach suitable coil spring compressor. Tighten spring compressor while raising jack under lower control arm to assist compressing operation. Slowly lower jack and remove the coil spring and rubber mounting.

Installation — 1) Position rubber mount on coil spring. With spring compressed, position in vehicle. Slowly release spring, being sure it rests in mounting groove.

2) Mount front wheel and lower vehicle to ground. Attach upper shock absorber mount.

STABILIZER BAR

Removal — 1) Raise vehicle and support with jack stands under lower control arms. Remove front wheels.

2) Detach upper control arm support from stabilizer bar.

3) Remove master cylinder and booster. Remove heater hoses, air cleaner, regulator linkage, vacuum lines and electrical wiring as required to allow clearance for stabilizer bar removal.

4) Remove stabilizer bar mounting brackets and bushings. Remove end covers and remove stabilizer bar.

Installation — 1) Position stabilizer bar in vehicle and loosely attach bar support to upper control arm.

2) Position rubber bushings on stabilizer bar, with splits facing against frame. Install brackets loosely.

3) Attach left and right end covers and replace all hoses, linkage, wiring and brake components removed. Mount front wheels and lower vehicle to ground.

4) Tighten stabilizer bar-to-control arm support bolt. Tighten mounting brackets. Check front wheel alignment.

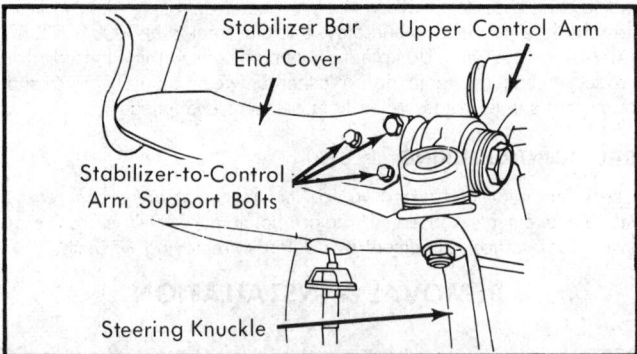

Fig. 2 Showing Attachment of Upper Control Arm and Stabilizer Bar

STEERING KNUCKLE

Removal — 1) Raise vehicle and support with jack stands under outer edge of lower control arms. Remove front wheels.

2) Detach steering knuckle arm from steering knuckle. Remove caliper from steering knuckle and suspend out of way with wire. Remove front wheel hub.

3) Loosen brake hose holder on backing plate. Remove nut from upper ball joint and separate from steering knuckle.

4) Remove nut from lower ball joint. Swivel upper end of steering knuckle slightly outward and use suitable tool to detach steering knuckle from lower ball joint. Remove knuckle from vehicle.

Installation — To install, reverse removal procedure.

WHEEL BEARINGS

NOTE – *Information not available from manufacturer.*

TIGHTENING SPECIFICATIONS

Application	Ft. Lbs. (N•m)
Shock Absorber Lower Mount	18 (25)
Stabilizer Bar Bracket Bolts	18 (25)
Steering Linkage Bolts	25 (34)
Steering Knuckle Arm Bolts	58 (79)
Upper Control Arm Eccentric Bolts	43 (59)
Lower Control Arm Eccentric Bolts	87 (118)
Upper Ball Joint Nut	43 (59)
Lower Ball Joint Nut	58 (79)

MERCEDES-BENZ 380SL & 380SLC

DESCRIPTION

Front suspension assembly is a coil spring type, having separately mounted coil springs and shock absorbers between upper and lower control arms. Other front suspension components include steering knuckle, tie rods and a stabilizer bar.

ADJUSTMENTS

WHEEL ALIGNMENT SPECIFICATIONS & PROCEDURES

See Wheel Alignment Specifications and Procedures in WHEEL ALIGNMENT section.

WHEEL BEARING ADJUSTMENT

All Models — While rotating hub, tighten clamp nut until hub can just be turned. Loosen clamp nut and release bearing tension by striking steering knuckle spindle with plastic hammer. Using a dial indicator, check wheel bearing end play. End play should be .0004-.0008" (.01-.02 mm). Adjust clamp nut until end play is within limits. Tighten socket bolt of clamp nut. Washer between outer bearing and clamp nut should rotate when light pressure is applied.

BALL JOINT CHECKING

Check ball joint lateral and vertical movement. If any measureable lateral movement is observed, replace ball joint. Correct excessive or insufficient vertical movement by adding or removing washers.

REMOVAL & INSTALLATION

NOTE — *Manufacturer requires that shock absorber mountings and stabilizer bar attachments not be loosened or tightened unless vehicle is resting on ground or axle is supported enough to simulate full vehicle load.*

SHOCK ABSORBERS

Removal — With vehicle on ground, detach upper and lower shock absorber mountings. Compress shock absorber to gain clearance and remove from vehicle.

Installation — To install, reverse removal procedure.

WHEEL BEARINGS

NOTE — *Information not available from manufacturer.*

COIL SPRING

Removal — 1) Loosen lower shock absorber mounting and stabilizer bar connecting linkage. Raise front of vehicle. Remove front wheel.

2) Mark position of lower control arm eccentric bolts on inner end of arm for reinstallation reference. Attach and engage a suitable coil spring compressor. Remove eccentric bolts.

3) Place suitable cradle-type support beneath lower control arm directly below coil spring position. Slowly lower cradle, allowing inner end of control arm to drop down, and remove coil spring.

Installation — To install, reverse removal procedure, fully tightening stabilizer bar mountings and lower shock absorber mounting after vehicle is resting on ground.

STABILIZER BAR

Removal — Loosen stabilizer bar connecting linkage from both lower control arms. Remove stabilizer bar-to-frame mounting brackets and remove stabilizer bar.

Installation — To install, reverse removal procedure.

STEERING KNUCKLE

Removal — 1) Install coil spring compressor on spring. Raise and support front of vehicle. Remove front wheel.

2) Remove bolt holding steering knuckle arm to steering knuckle. Detach flexible brake hose from brake line and plug openings. Remove caliper.

NOTE — *On some models, it may be possible to remove caliper from rotor and suspend out of way without detaching brake hose. This will eliminate necessity of bleeding brake system after installation.*

3) Remove nuts from upper and lower ball joint studs. Detach both ball joints from steering knuckle. Remove steering knuckle.

Installation — To install, reverse removal procedure, bleed brakes and check front wheel alignment.

UPPER CONTROL ARM

Removal — 1) Attach suitable spring compressor to coil spring. Raise and support front of vehicle. Remove front wheel.

NOTE — *Shock absorber remains installed.*

2) Remove bolt holding steering knuckle to steering knuckle arm. Detach brake hose from brake line and plug openings.

3) Remove nuts from upper and lower ball joint studs. Using suitable tool, detach upper ball joint from steering knuckle.

4) Remove both upper control arm mounting nuts and remove arm.

Installation — To install, reverse removal procedure. Bleed brakes and check front wheel alignment.

LOWER CONTROL ARM

Removal — 1) Loosen and detach lower shock absorber mounting. Raise front of vehicle and remove front wheel.

2) Detach steering knuckle arm from steering knuckle. Separate brake hose from brake line and plug openings. Remove brake hose retaining clip.

3) Remove coil spring as described in this article.

4) Remove nuts from upper and lower ball joint studs. Detach lower control arm from lower ball joint. Remove control arm.

Installation — Reverse removal procedures and note the following: Bleed brake system. Tighten shock absorber mounting bolts after vehicle is resting on ground. Check front wheel alignment.

TIGHTENING SPECIFICATIONS

Application	Ft. Lbs. (N•m)
Shock Absorber Lower Mount	14 (19)
Upper Ball Joint Nut	29 (39)
Lower Ball Joint Nut	29 (39)
Tie Rod Ball Joint Nut	14 (19)
Lower Control Arm-to-Frame	130 (177)
Steering Arm-to-Steering Knuckle	57 (78)
Upper Control Arm Clamping Bolt	21 (29)
Upper Control Arm-to-Body	60 (82)

PEUGEOT

504
505
604

DESCRIPTION

An independent, strut front suspension is used. Wheels are supported by steering knuckles that are attached to vertical strut assemblies. Lower control arms are attached to bottom of steering knuckles by ball joints. Inner ends of control arms pivot on front crossmember. Attached to lower control arms are strut rods that run forward to mounting points on front crossmember. Top of vertical strut assemblies are attached to inner fender panels. Coil springs fit into spring seats attached to strut assemblies. Hydraulic shock absorbers are built into strut assemblies. A stabilizer bar is mounted to frame and connected at ends to lower control arm.

ADJUSTMENTS

WHEEL ALIGNMENT SPECIFICATIONS & ADJUSTMENTS

See Wheel Alignment Specifications and Adjustments in WHEEL ALIGNMENT Section.

FRONT WHEEL BEARINGS

Raise and support vehicle. While rotating wheel or hub, tighten spindle nut to 29 ft. lbs. (39 N·m) on 505 and 604 models or 22 ft. lbs. (30 N·m) on 504 models. On all models, loosen spindle nut and retighten to 86 INCH Lbs. (10 N·m).

BALL JOINT CHECKING

NOTE — Information and procedures not available from manufacturer.

REMOVAL & INSTALLATION

FRONT STRUT ASSEMBLY

Removal — 1) Raise vehicle and place safety stands under front crossmember. Remove wheel. Remove brake caliper and suspend with a wire from underbody. DO NOT disconnect hydraulic line.

2) Separate tie rod from rear arm. Disconnect stabilizer bar at mounting on lower control arm. Remove control arm pivot bolt nut and tap bolt out. Remove nut mounting strut rod to control arm.

3) Place a jack under steering knuckle and remove bolts mounting strut to inner fender panel. Hold spring by one coil and lower jack to remove strut assembly.

Disassembly — 1) Install suitable strut holder and spring compressor to strut assembly. Mount assembly horizontally in vise and compress spring enough to unseat it. Hold shock absorber piston rod and remove top nut and retainer. Slowly release tension on spring. Remove upper spring seat assembly, coil spring and rubber boot from shock absorber rod.

2) Suspend strut assembly vertically in vise. Remove shock absorber gland nut. Pull up slowly on piston rod and remove piston rod assembly. Remove support cup with rod seal, thrust washer, upper spring and bushing "O" ring from piston rod.

3) Pry bumper and lower spring seat off strut housing. Take strut housing from vise and drain hydraulic fluid. Unscrew strut housing and remove compensator valve.

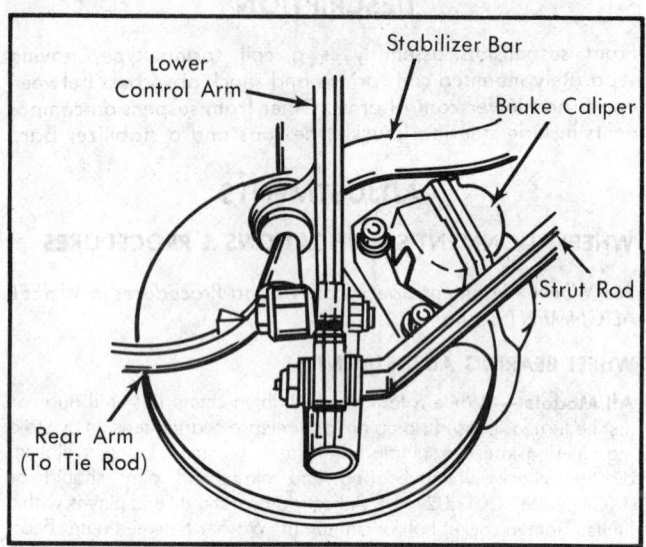

Fig. 1 Components That Must Be Disconnected Prior to Strut Assembly Removal

Cleaning & Inspection — Clean and inspect all parts for wear or damage; replace defective parts. All components indicated in Figs. 2 and 3 must be replaced during overhaul.

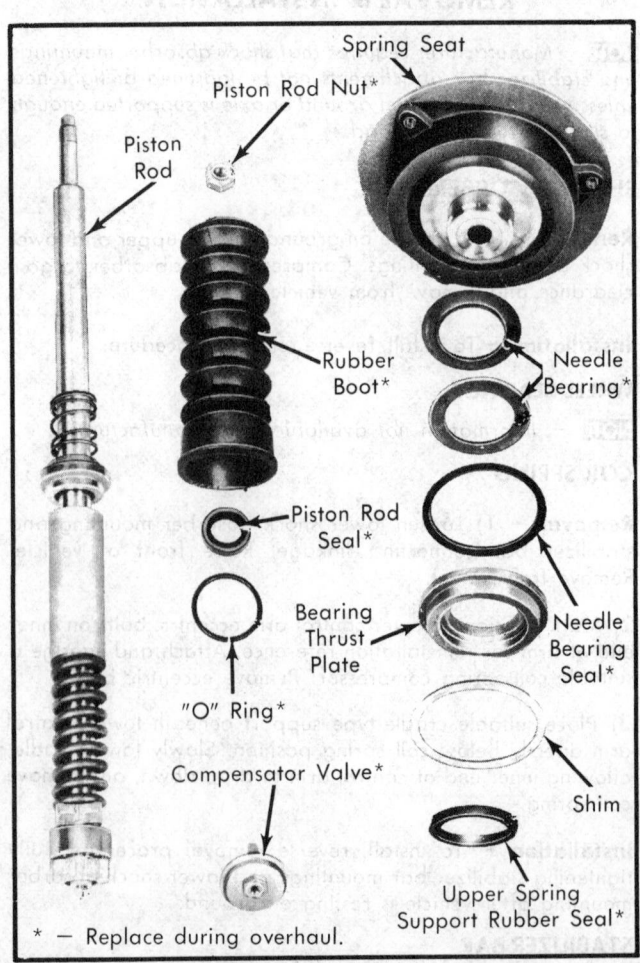

* — Replace during overhaul.

Fig. 2 Peugeot 504 and 604 Strut Assembly and Spring Seat Components

PEUGEOT (Cont.)

Reassembly — 1) Mount strut vertically in vise. Install recoil bumper with lower spring seat. Install compensator valve to shock absorber tube by lightly tapping with rubber mallet. Blow off valve, shock absorber tube and shock absorber inner housing with compressed air.

2) Fit shock absorber tube to strut housing. Fill shock absorber with 10 oz. (504 and 604) or 11 oz. (505) of Esso Oleofluid 40X (or equivalent). Slowly insert piston rod assembly into shock absorber tube. Clearance between upper shock absorber housing and upper bushing must be .12" (3 mm).

3) Install new "O" ring, then install upper spring and thrust washer (convex side up). Install new piston rod seal to cup. Position cup and seal over rod and force assembly down until thrust washer engages spring. Tighten gland nut. Check rod rotation and operation.

4) Install rubber dust boot. Fully extend piston rod and place holding clamp between bottom of dust boot and shock absorber cap nut. Place housing horizontally in vise. Fit new seal to bearing thrust plate. Reassemble upper spring seat components as shown in *Figs. 2 and 3*.

5) Install coil spring and upper spring seat. Install and tighten spring compressor until retainer and new locking nut can be installed. Tighten nut while holding rod.

Installation — 1) Mount assembled strut assembly and guide into position while raising steering knuckle with jack. Install upper mounting bolts. Retainer must be parallel with centerline of car.

2) Fit thrust washer, cup, and bushing to strut rod. Slide strut rod into control arm. Fit bushing cup and new stop nut.

3) Insert pivot bolt with bolt head facing rearward into position between control arm and front crossmember. DO NOT tighten nut. Refit stabilizer bar (nut end nearest front) to lower control arm. Install new washer and nut but DO NOT tighten.

4) Connect tie rod to rear arm. Tighten nut. Clean brake disc and refit brake caliper. Tighten mounting bolts after placing few drops of Loctite (or equivalent) on washers.

5) Refit wheel. Lower vehicle. Push in front suspension strut rod and tighten all nuts to final torque.

WHEEL BEARINGS

Removal — 1) Raise and support vehicle. Remove wheel. Remove brake cylinder and wire out of way. On 504 and 505 models, remove hub nut lock and hub nut. On 604 models, remove hub plug and nut. On all models, remove wheel hub. If inner bearing remains on spindle, remove with puller as necessary.

2) On 504 models with angular contact ball bearings, remove hub nut "O" ring and surplus grease from hub. On all models, fit hub to press and remove inner bearing with grease seal. Remove outer bearing and press out outer race.

Installation — Reverse removal procedures to install. Use press to install inner bearing, both bearing races, and grease seal. Whenever a bearing is replaced, a new bearing race must be used. Always treat bearings and races as matched sets.

STABILIZER BAR

Removal — With vehicle on ground, remove 2 bolts mounting stabilizer bar near front crossmember. Disconnect both links mounting stabilizer bar at connecting links. Guide bar from vehicle.

Installation — Fit cup, spacer and bushing to control link. Install stabilizer mounting bolts and spacers.

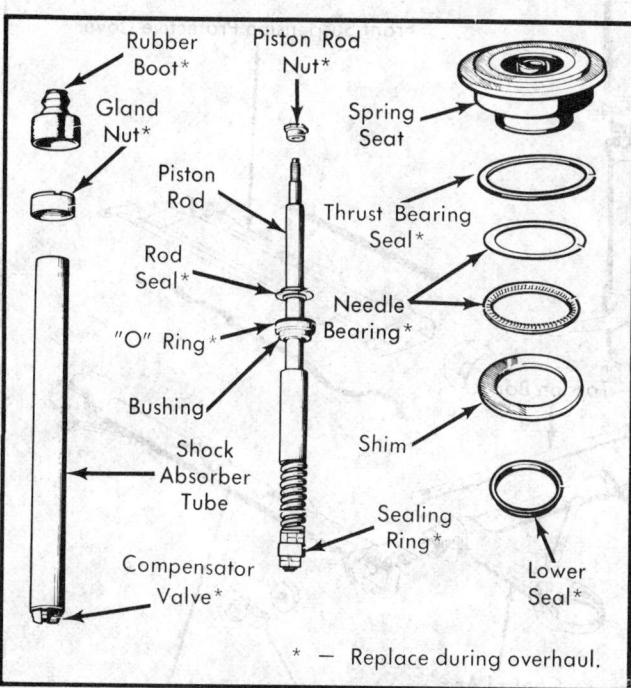

Rubber Boot*
Gland Nut*
Piston Rod Nut*
Spring Seat
Piston Rod
Thrust Bearing Seal*
Rod Seal*
Needle Bearing*
"O" Ring*
Bushing
Shim
Shock Absorber Tube
Sealing Ring*
Compensator Valve*
Lower Seal*

* — Replace during overhaul.

Fig. 3 Peugeot 505 Strut Assembly and Spring Seat Components

TIGHTENING SPECIFICATIONS

Application	Ft. Lbs. (N·m)
Shock Absorber Piston Nut	33 (45)
Shock Absorber Housing Nut	58 (79)
Rear Arm-to-Control Arm Nut	33 (45)
Rear Arm-to-Tie Rod Nut	31 (42)
Strut Rod-to-Control Rod Nut	33 (45)
Stabilizer Bar-to-Control Arm	33 (45)
Control Arm Pivot Bolts	33 (45)

Front Suspension

PORSCHE 911SC

DESCRIPTION

Independent strut type suspension with torsion bars. Strut assemblies are mounted to inner fender panels at top by thrust bearings. Bottom of strut assemblies are mounted to control arms by ball joints. Steering knuckle and shock absorbers are integral with individual strut assembly. Control arms pivot in mounts connected to body at front and in mounts integral with suspension crossmember at rear. Torsion bars anchor to control arm at front and to suspension crossmember at rear. Suspension crossmember also serves as mount for steering gear and is removable.

ADJUSTMENT

WHEEL ALIGNMENT SPECIFICATIONS & PROCEDURES

See Wheel Alignment Specifications & Procedures in WHEEL ALIGNMENT Section.

WHEEL BEARING ADJUSTMENT

Tighten spindle nut while rotating wheel to seat bearings. Back off nut until thrust washer can be moved sideways with light pressure from a screwdriver. Spindle nut should be tight enough to prevent any wheel hub axial play. Tighten pinch bolt, making sure that spindle does not change position.

BALL JOINT CHECKING

Check ball joints for any signs of unusual wear, damage or excessive play. If any is found, ball joint must be replaced.

REMOVAL & INSTALLATION
STRUT ASSEMBLY AND THRUST BEARING

Removal — 1) Raise vehicle and place safety stands under body. Remove wheel and tire. Remove brake rotor and brake caliper.

NOTE — *If necessary, refer to appropriate article in BRAKE SYSTEMS section.*

2) Remove tie rod end strut nut and separate tie rod end from steering arm. Unscrew adjusting screw from torsion bar adjusting lever and remove lever. Remove ball joint retaining bolt at bottom of strut assembly and push control arm down to separate strut assembly from ball joint.

3) Remove center nut from upper strut assembly mount from inside luggage compartment. Remove lock washer, tab washer and strut assembly. Mark position of pressure plates on fender panel and remove Allen head bolts and pressure plates. Remove thrust bearing and support.

NOTE — *Thrust bearing can be removed without completely removing strut assembly by disconnecting upper mount and pulling down on control arm to separate from thrust bearing.*

Installation — 1) Install thrust bearing and support. Place pressure plates in proper position and tighten Allen head bolts. Inspect strut assembly for leaks, if leak is discovered, strut assembly must be replaced.

2) Push rod to bottom of stroke, if flange does not bottom out against strut tube, replace strut assembly. There should be no variation of pressure when pushing in or pulling out on rod.

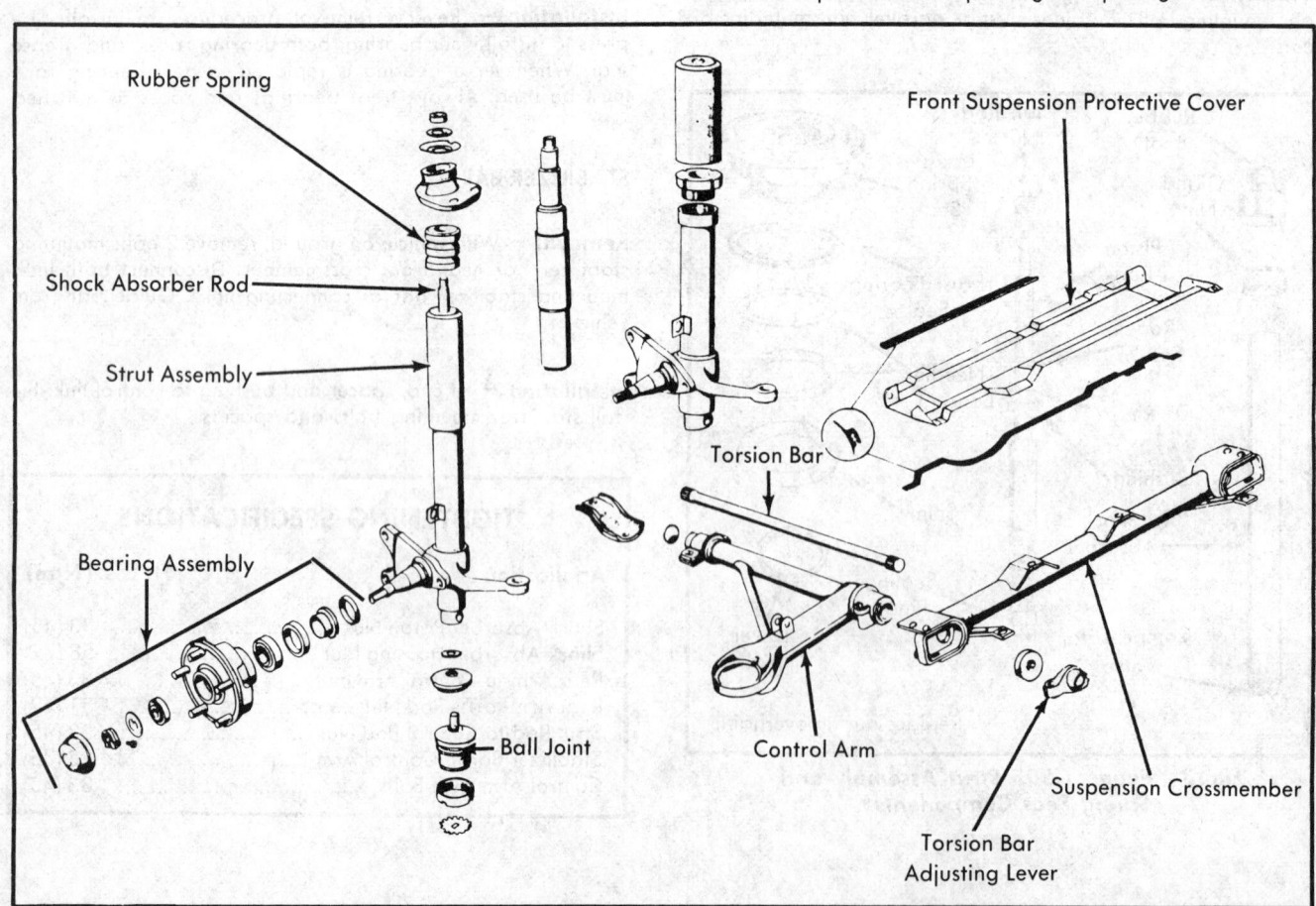

Rubber Spring

Shock Absorber Rod

Strut Assembly

Bearing Assembly

Ball Joint

Front Suspension Protective Cover

Torsion Bar

Control Arm

Suspension Crossmember

Torsion Bar Adjusting Lever

Fig. 1 Exploded View of Front Suspension Assembly

PORSCHE 911SC (Cont.)

3) Install strut assembly in proper position in vehicle. Install hollow rubber spring, new lock washer, and tighten nut. Fit strut assembly to ball joint and tighten nut.

NOTE — *Make sure steel washer is between ball joint and stud.*

4) Push control arm lever down to stop and install adjusting lever on torsion bar. Grease threads of adjusting screw with suitable grease and install screw. Make sure closing cover is correctly seated against adjusting lever.

5) Install tie rod and retighten nut. Install remaining components. See *appropriate article in BRAKE SYSTEM Section.* Tighten all nuts and bolts, bleed brake system, check wheel alignment and riding height.

WHEEL BEARINGS

Removal — 1) Disconnect brake line from caliper. Remove caliper. Remove grease cap, loosen spindle nut pinch bolt, remove spindle nut and remove wheel bearing thrust washer.

2) Remove hub and rotor assembly from vehicle. Press out outer wheel bearing (depending on equipment used, it may be necessary to separate rotor from hub), heat wheel hub to 250-300° F (120-150° C) and press out inner bearing and grease seal. Press out bearing races.

NOTE — *Several brands of bearings are used when vehicle is assembled. Bearings and races are not interchangeable between brands. Therefore, always replace bearings and races in matched sets.*

Installation — Reverse removal procedures to install. Adjust wheel bearings.

CONTROL ARM & BALL JOINT

Removal — 1) Raise vehicle and place safety stands under body. Remove wheel and tire. Remove adjusting screw from torsion bar lever and remove lever. Disconnect strut assembly from control arm as previously outlined. Remove rear control arm mounting bolt at suspension crossmember. Remove two bolts securing front control arm mount to body. Slide control arm with torsion bar out of suspension crossmember.

CAUTION — *If both control arms are being removed, reinstall rear control arm mounting bolt in suspension crossmember before removing opposite side.*

2) Secure control arm in a vise and remove ball joint retaining nut using a suitable wrench. Remove ball joint from control arm. Control arm should pivot smoothly in mounts. If control arm binds or is distorted, it must be replaced.

3) Inspect torsion bars for damaged serrations. Check sealing bellows on ball joint, replace if damaged or cracked. Remove sealing bellows with a flat chisel and install using suitable mandrel to press bellows on with.

Installation — 1) Install ball joint in control arm and tighten grooved nut. Secure nut by bending over tab on lock washer. Grease entire torsion bar and install in control arm. Place control arm in proper position in vehicle and tighten mounting bolts (front to rear).

2) Install strut assembly on ball joint and tighten retaining bolt. Push down on control arm until it contacts stops and install torsion bar seal and adjusting lever. Slide adjusting lever against torsion bar until it reaches stop. Grease adjusting bolt threads and install in lever. Make sure closing cover is correctly seated against adjusting lever. Install control arm protective cover. Install wheel and tire, lower vehicle and check riding height and wheel alignment.

SUSPENSION CROSSMEMBER

Removal — Raise vehicle and place safety stands under vehicle. Remove front axle protective cover. Remove steering gear bolts from crossmember. Remove rear control arm mounting bolts as previously outlined and remove suspension crossmember. Place crossmember on level surface and check for distortion. Inspect for cracks or damage.

Installation — Place crossmember in proper position in vehicle and install control arm mounting bolts as previously outlined. Install steering gear bolts and tighten. Install front suspension protective cover. Lower vehicle and check riding height and wheel alignment.

FRONT AXLE STABILIZER

Removal — Remove stabilizer shackles. Unbolt stabilizer lever retaining nuts and extract lever. Remove stabilizer mounting cover hardware and gently pry cover from vehicle.

Installation — Check all rubber grommets for signs of wear and replace components as necessary. Coat rubber parts with suitable lubricant. Reinstall stabilizer mounting cover, center stabilizer, then tighten attaching bolts. Seat stabilizer lever in position so stabilizer protrudes approximately .118" (3 mm) beyond lever. Tighten retaining nuts and install shackles.

FRONT AXLE ASSEMBLY

Removal — Disconnect brake hose and plug opening. Disconnect stabilizer bar at crossmember. Remove tie rod shield. Remove bolts at carrier and control arm brackets. Place jack under crossmember. Disconnect steering shaft. Remove upper strut mounting hardware. Carefully pull front axle assembly from vehicle.

Installation — To install, reverse removal procedure.

TIGHTENING SPECIFICATIONS

Application	Ft. Lbs. (N·m)
Strut Assembly-to-Ball Joint Securing Bolt	47 (64)
Strut Assembly Thrust Bearing	58 (79)
Pressure Plate Allen Head Bolts	34 (46)
Front Control Arm Mount	34 (46)
Control Arm & Suspension Crossmember Mounting Bolt	65 (88)
Steering Gear Bolts	34 (46)
Ball Joint-to-Control Arm Grooved Nut	108 (147)
Front Protective Clamp Allen Head Bolt	32 (44)
Suspension Protective Cover-to-Body Bolts	34 (46)
Suspension Protective Cover-to-Crossmember Bolts	11 (15)
Tie Rod End Strut Nuts	32 (44)

Front Suspension

PORSCHE 924

DESCRIPTION

Vehicle uses independent strut type front suspension. Lower control arms mount with a ball joint to steering knuckle. Back branch of control arm mounts to frame with "U" clamp around control arm pivot shaft. Front branch attaches to frame with bushings and pivot bolt. Strut assembly mounts at top to body with 3 nuts and at bottom to steering knuckle with 2 bolts. Tie rod mounts to steering knuckle with ball joint.

ADJUSTMENTS

WHEEL ALIGNMENT SPECIFICATIONS & PROCEDURES

See Wheel Alignment Specifications and Procedures in WHEEL ALIGNMENT Section.

WHEEL BEARING ADJUSTMENT

Tighten spindle nut while rotating wheel to seat bearings. Back off nut until thrust washer can be moved sideways with light pressure from a screwdriver. Spindle nut should be tight enough to prevent any wheel hub axial play. Tighten pinch bolt, making sure that spindle nut does not change position.

BALL JOINT CHECKING

Measure distance between upper edge of control arm and lower edge of steering knuckle using a vernier caliper. Place a lever under ball joint and pry upward. Record any movement. New ball joints should have no end play. Wear limit for older ball joints is .1" (2.5 mm).

REMOVAL & INSTALLATION

STRUT ASSEMBLY

Removal — 1) Raise vehicle so front suspension and front wheels are not supported.

2) Remove bolts mounting suspension strut to steering knuckle. Note that top bolt is one used to adjust front wheel camber.

3) Detach brake line from brake line bracket on strut. Remove brake caliper assembly and suspend out of way. Pry strut off of steering knuckle.

4) Support front suspension. Work inside engine compartment and remove strut upper mounting nuts. Guide assembly out of vehicle.

Disassembly — 1) Fit strut to spring compressor. Slightly collapse coil spring. Remove shock absorber piston rod nut. Take off the following:
- Stop
- Seal
- Bearing flange
- Bearing
- Spring seat

2) Slowly release spring pressure and remove coil spring. Lift off rubber buffer and protective sleeve. Hold shock absorber upright and work piston rod through entire stroke several times. Equal pressure must be felt in both directions. Remove cap nut and take out shock absorber.

Reassembly — 1) Place shock absorber in strut tube and fit cap nut. Slide on protective sleeve and buffer. Position coil spring into lower seat.

NOTE — If new coil spring is being installed, ensure that paint stripe color code matches that of spring on opposite side.

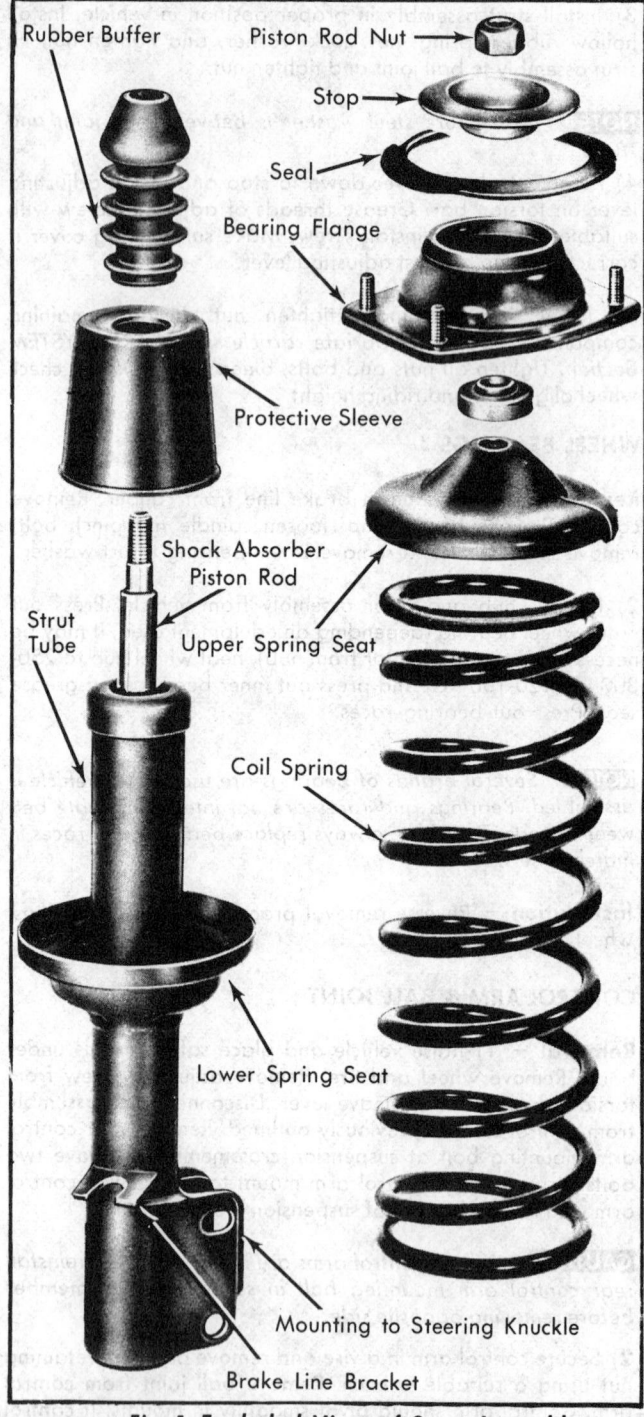

Fig. 1 Exploded View of Strut Assembly

2) Fit coil spring to compressor and collapse coil enough to allow piston rod threads to be exposed after upper mounting hardware is fitted. Tighten piston rod lock nut. Release spring pressure.

Installation — To install, reverse removal procedure and check front wheel alignment.

WHEEL BEARINGS

Removal — 1) Raise and support vehicle. Remove wheel. Remove grease cap and loosen spindle nut pinch bolt. Remove spindle nut, washer and outer wheel bearing.

PORSCHE 924 (Cont.)

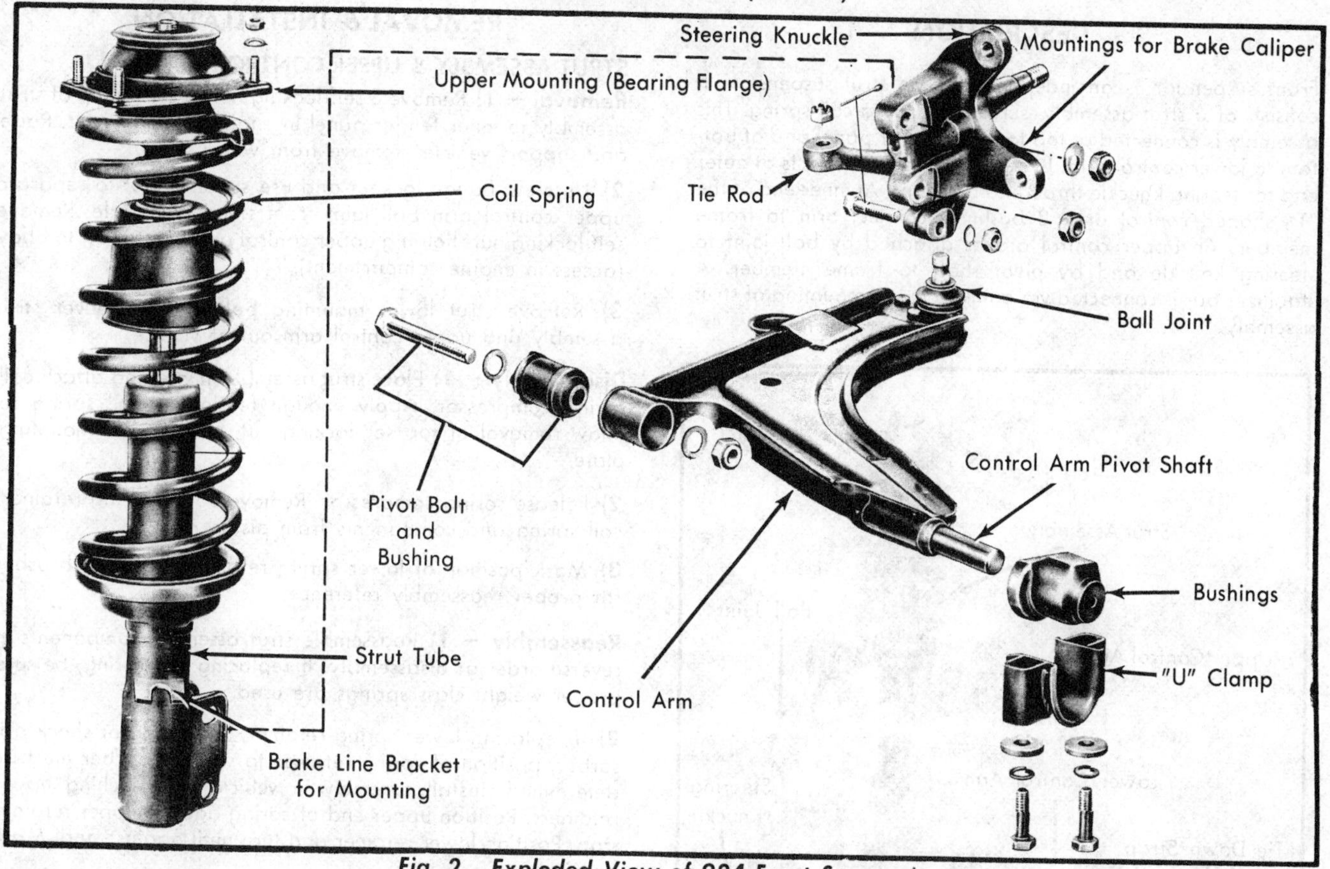

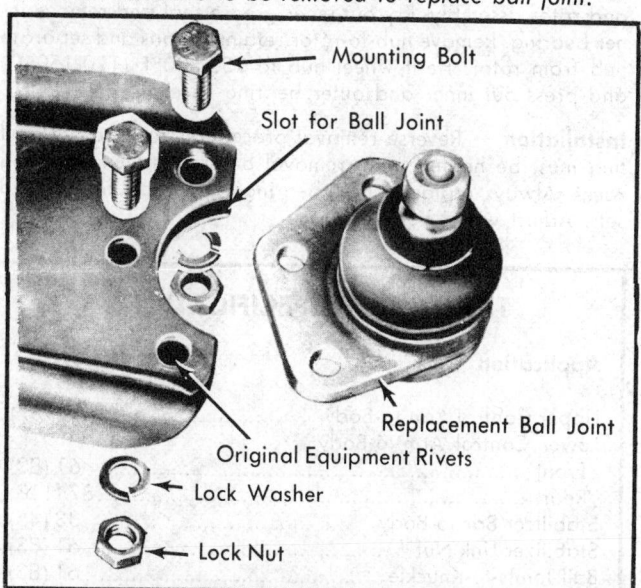

Steering Knuckle — Mountings for Brake Caliper

Upper Mounting (Bearing Flange)

Coil Spring — Tie Rod

Ball Joint

Control Arm Pivot Shaft

Pivot Bolt and Bushing

Bushings

"U" Clamp

Strut Tube

Control Arm

Brake Line Bracket for Mounting

Fig. 2   Exploded View of 924 Front Suspension

2) Remove brake caliper and wire out of way. Remove hub and rotor assembly. Pry off inner grease seal and remove inner bearing. Drive out bearing races if needed or if bearings are to be replaced.

Installation — If bearing or race is bad, replace in matched sets. Do not use new bearings with old bearing races. Reverse removal procedures to install. Adjust wheel bearings.

CONTROL ARM & BALL JOINT

NOTE — If there is enough access room to work, lower control arm does not have to be removed to replace ball joint.

Mounting Bolt

Slot for Ball Joint

Replacement Ball Joint

Original Equipment Rivets

Lock Washer

Lock Nut

Fig. 3   Ball Joint Location in Control Arm

Removal — 1) Raise vehicle and support so suspension is free. Remove pinch bolt mounting ball joint in bottom of steering knuckle. Pull ball joint out of steering knuckle.

2) If control arm is not being removed, drill through ball joint rivets with about 15/64" (6 mm) bit. Chisel off rivet heads. Fit new ball joint into slot on control arm and install bolts so heads are on top.

3) If control arm is being removed, take out mounting pivot bolt and "U" clamp housing inner pivot pin. Slide out control arm. For ball joint replacement, refer to step 2).

Inspection — Check control arm bushings. If bushings are bad they can be replaced. Press out worn bushings. Select new bushing and press into position. Make sure new bushings do not twist when seating into position.

Installation — To install, reverse removal procedure.

TIGHTENING SPECIFICATIONS

Application	Ft. Lbs. (N·m)
Control Arm-to-Crossmember	40-54 (54-73)
"U" Clamp Bolts	30 (41)
Tie Rod Castle Nut	22-36 (30-49)
Strut Piston Rod Nut	56-58 (76-79)
Strut-to-Steering Knuckle	51-72 (69-98)
Upper Strut Mount	15-21 (20-29)
Ball Joint-to-Control Arm (Replacement)	18 (25)
Ball Joint Pinch Bolt	36-43 (49-59)

Front Suspension

PORSCHE 928

DESCRIPTION

Front suspension is an independent type strut suspension. It consists of a strut assembly, surrounded by a coil spring. This assembly is connected at top to inner fender panel and at bottom to lower control arm. Lower control arm connects at outer end to steering knuckle through a ball joint. At inner end of the "T" shaped control arm, 2 bushings connect arm to frame member. An upper control arm is attached by ball joint to steering knuckle and by pivot shaft to frame member. A stabilizer bar is connected via a link to lower mounting of strut assembly.

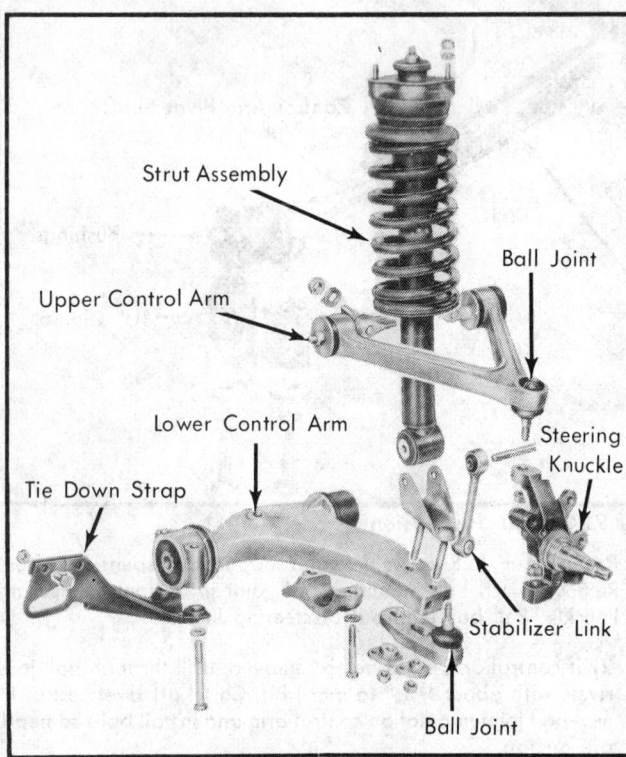

Fig. 1   Exploded View of Porsche 928 Front Suspension Assembly

ADJUSTMENTS

WHEEL ALIGNMENT SPECIFICATIONS & PROCEDURES

See Wheel Alignment Specifications and Procedures in WHEEL ALIGNMENT section.

WHEEL BEARING ADJUSTMENT

Tighten spindle nut while rotating wheel to seat bearings. Back off nut until thrust washer can be moved sideways with light pressure from a screwdriver. Spindle nut should be tight enough to prevent any wheel hub axial play. Tighten pinch bolt, making sure that spindle nut does not change position.

BALL JOINT CHECKING

Check ball joint and seal for signs of abnormal or excessive wear, damage or play. If any is found, replace ball joint.

REMOVAL & INSTALLATION

STRUT ASSEMBLY & UPPER CONTROL ARM

Removal — 1) Remove 3 self-locking nuts securing top of strut assembly to inner fender panel in engine compartment. Raise and support vehicle. Remove front wheel.

2) Unscrew flange locknut and use suitable tool to separate upper control arm ball joint from steering knuckle. Remove self-locking nuts holding upper control arm pivot shaft to body (access in engine compartment).

3) Remove strut lower mounting bolt and maneuver strut assembly and upper control arm out of vehicle.

Disassembly — 1) Place strut assembly in vise and attach coil spring compressor. Apply enough tension to coil spring to allow removal of top self-locking nut, washer and mounting plate.

2) Release spring compressor. Remove upper spring retainer, coil spring and components from piston rod.

3) Mark position of lower spring retainer to shock absorber for proper reassembly reference.

Reassembly — 1) Reassemble strut assembly components in reverse order of disassembly. If replacing coil spring, be sure proper weight class springs are used.

2) If replacing lower spring retainer, coil spring or shock absorber, position of spring retainer to shock absorber must be determined. Install assembly in vehicle by attaching upper retainers. Position upper end of spring against upper retainer stop. Position lower retainer and turn until against stop. Mark position.

3) Remove strut assembly back to vise and complete reassembly.

Installation — To install, reverse removal procedure.

WHEEL BEARINGS

Removal — 1) Raise and support vehicle. Remove wheel. Remove grease cap, loosen spindle nut pinch bolt and remove spindle nut. Remove thrust washer and outer wheel bearing.

2) Remove brake caliper and wire out of way. Remove hub and rotor assembly. Pry out inner grease seal and remove inner bearing. Remove hub-to-rotor retaining bolts and separate hub from rotor. Heat wheel hub to 250-300°F (120-150°C) and press out inner and outer bearing races.

Installation — Reverse removal procedures to install. Wheel hub must be heated as in removal before installing bearing races. Always replace wheel bearings and races in matched sets. Adjust wheel bearings.

TIGHTENING SPECIFICATIONS

Application	Ft. Lbs. (N·m)
Upper Control Arm-to-Body	101 (137)
Lower Control Arm-to-Body	
Front	61 (83)
Rear	87 (118)
Stabilizer Bar-to-Body	33 (45)
Stabilizer Link Nut	61 (83)
Ball Joints-to-Knuckle	61 (83)

RENAULT LE CAR

DESCRIPTION

Independent type suspension, consisting of upper and lower control arms with stub axles mounted between upper and lower control arms by ball joints. Upper control arm pivots on shaft attached to frame. Lower arm pivots on shaft secured to crossmember. Shock absorbers mount on body brackets at top and control arms at bottom.

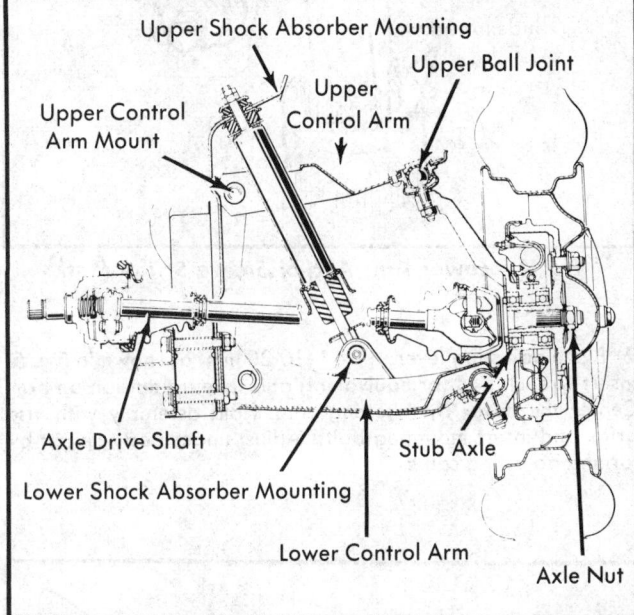

Fig. 1   Cut-Away View of Le Car Front Suspension

ADJUSTMENT

WHEEL ALIGNMENT SPECIFICATIONS & PROCEDURES

See *Wheel Alignment Specifications & Procedures* in WHEEL ALIGNMENT Section.

WHEEL BEARING ADJUSTMENT

No adjustment is necessary on wheel bearings. Tighten stub axle nuts to 90 ft. lbs. (122 N·m).

BALL JOINT CHECKING

Inspect ball joints for excessive wear or play. Replace as needed.

REMOVAL & INSTALLATION

SHOCK ABSORBERS

Removal — Raise and support vehicle. Remove lock nut, mounting nut, and bushing attaching shock absorber to upper bracket. Remove lower retaining bolt holding shock absorber to lower control arm. Remove shock absorber from vehicle.

Installation — To install, reverse removal procedure.

WHEEL BEARINGS

Removal — 1) Raise and support vehicle. Remove wheel. Remove brake caliper and caliper bracket. Attach tool (Rou.

604) to keep rotor from turning and loosen axle nut. Attach slide hammer at wheel studs and remove hub and rotor.

2) Remove hub-to-rotor retaining bolts. Separate hub from rotor. Pull outer bearing from inside of hub.

3) Disconnect tie rod ball joint from steering knuckle. Disconnect control arm ball joints from knuckle. Remove knuckle. Remove bearing cover from inside of knuckle. Press out inner bearing.

Installation — Reverse removal procedures to install noting the following: Use sealer when installing bearing cover to knuckle. Assemble hub and rotor to steering knuckle and install to stub axle as a complete assembly.

UPPER CONTROL ARM & BALL JOINT

Removal — Take out overflow tank and remove ignition coil. Using tool T. Av. 476 (or equivalent) disconnect upper ball joint. Remove nut from inboard edge of pivot shaft. Place a lock nut on outer end of pivot shaft and turn mounting nut to remove shaft. Pivot shaft will clear brake lines. Maneuver control arm from vehicle.

Inspection & Replacement — Inspect rubber bushings for cracks or distortion. Use a press and mandrel to remove and replace worn bushings. To replace ball joint, place control arm in a vise and drill out rivet heads. Fit new ball joint with shim placed on top of control arm. Tighten nuts and bolts (those that replaced rivets). Make sure bolt head is installed on dust cover side of joint.

Installation — To install, reverse removal procedure and note following: Apply a light coat of grease to pivot shaft before inserting in control arm. If ball joint has been replaced, check wheel alignment and steering box height.

LOWER CONTROL ARM & BALL JOINT

Removal — 1) Raise front of vehicle and place on safety stands. Remove stub axle nut. Disconnect and remove torsion bars. Disconnect sway bar from brackets and mounting on control arm. Separate bottom of shock absorber from mounting.

2) Remove lower control arm from crossmember. Put tool T. Av. 235 (or equivalent) in brake drum or hub. With a spacer located between thrust screw and axle drive shaft, force shaft inward and free ball joint from stub axle carrier.

NOTE — *Make sure axle drive shaft is not removed.*

Inspection & Replacement — 1) Inspect rubber bushings and sleeve inserts for cracks, excessive damage or wear. Use a mandrel and press to replace bushings. Make sure each bushing is centered and has adequate protrusion out each side of control arm.

2) Place control arm in suitable holding fixture (vise). Chisel or drill out rivet heads. Remove nuts, if necessary. Separate joint from control arm. Fit new ball joint into control arm. Make sure bolt heads face dust cover side.

Installation — To install, reverse removal procedure and note following: Make sure castor adjusting shims are under bushing. Check wheel alignment after reinstallation.

STUB AXLE

Removal — Raise vehicle and place on safety stands. Remove hub and disc assembly. Using tool T. Av. 476 (or equivalent)

RENAULT LE CAR (Cont.)

disconnect upper and lower ball joints, then separate steering arm ball joint. Use a slide hammer and withdraw drum/hub assembly. Make sure axle drive shaft does not drop.

Installation — Install stub axle into position while guiding ball joints into position. Pull drive shaft into carrier housing. Refit brake components. Tighten stub axle nut.

TORSION BAR

Removal — 1) Slide seat forward and tilt seat. Loosen lock nut and turn cam screw counterclockwise to zero. Raise vehicle and place on safety stands. Remove dust cover from adjusting lever. Fit special tool 545 (or equivalent) in adjusting lever. From inside vehicle, remove lever housing attachment bolts. Remove housing cover cam assembly from adjusting lever, then slowly release pressure on wrench.

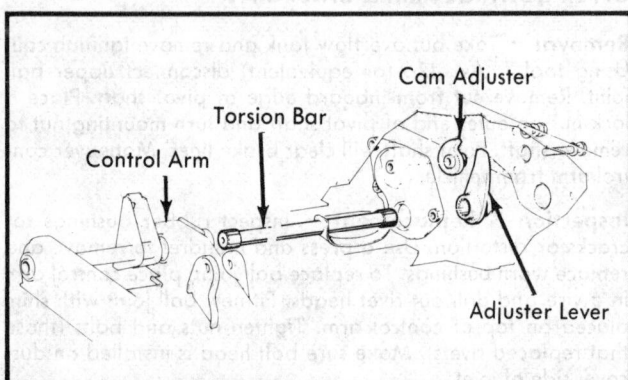

Fig. 2 Exploded View of Torsion Bar Assembly

2) Index mark position of adjusting lever with floor crossmember. Mark position of torsion bar on lower arm anchor sleeve. Disconnect stabilizer bar brackets. Remove bar from arm and check that mark made on lower arm anchor sleeve is aligned with punch mark on torsion bar. If punch marks do not align, count number of revolutions and spines displaced to align marks.

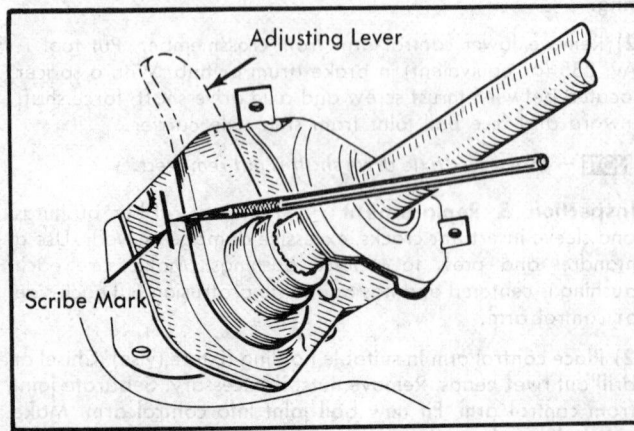

Fig. 3 Scribing Marks on Floor Crossmember

Installation — 1) Lightly grease torsion bar ends with grease. Reassemble cover seal, cam housing, and adjusting lever over torsion bar. Insert bar into lower control arm, aligning index mark made during removal. Fit adjusting lever on splines, aligning with mark on floor crossmember.

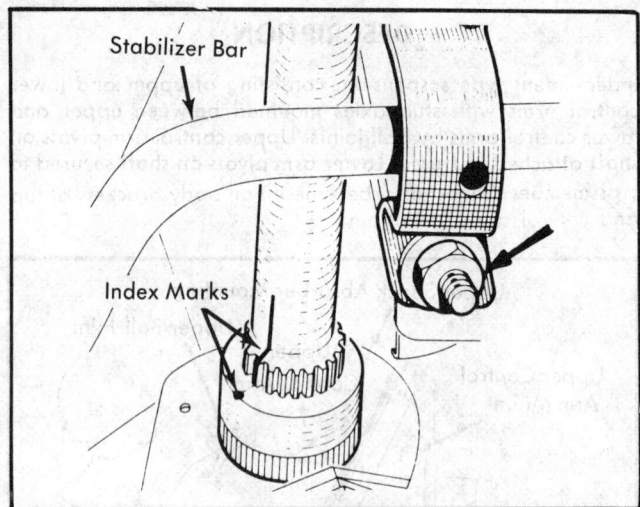

Fig. 4 Lower Arm Anchor Sleeve Scribe Mark

2) Place adjusting lever $\frac{3}{8}$-$\frac{3}{4}$" (10-20 mm) as shown in *Fig. 5*. Insert wrench 545 (or equivalent) and take up tension on bar. Center the cover by resetting cam. Hold assembly with vise grips and insert mounting bolts. Adjust under body height by turning adjusting cams.

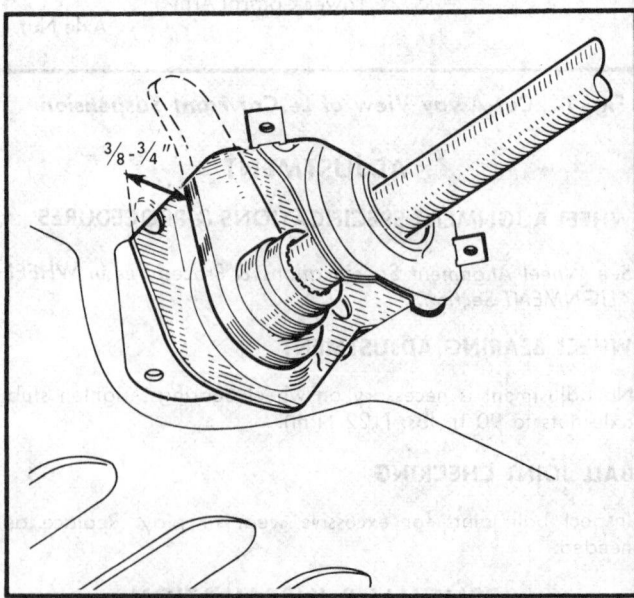

Fig. 5 Position of Adjusting Lever

TIGHTENING SPECIFICATIONS

Application	Ft. Lbs. (N·m)
Lower Shock Absorber Bolt	30 (41)
Lower Ball Joint	40 (54)
Upper Ball Joint	25 (34)
Lower Control Arm Nuts	75 (102)
Axle Nut	90 (122)

RENAULT 18i

DESCRIPTION

Coil spring front suspension utilizing upper and lower control arms. Hydraulic, double action shock absorber is mounted to inner fender panel at top and to upper control arm at bottom. Coil spring mounts around upper portion of shock absorber. Wheel hub and rotor are supported by a steering knuckle which is mounted between the control arms with ball joints. A stabilizer bar is used to aid vehicle control and stability.

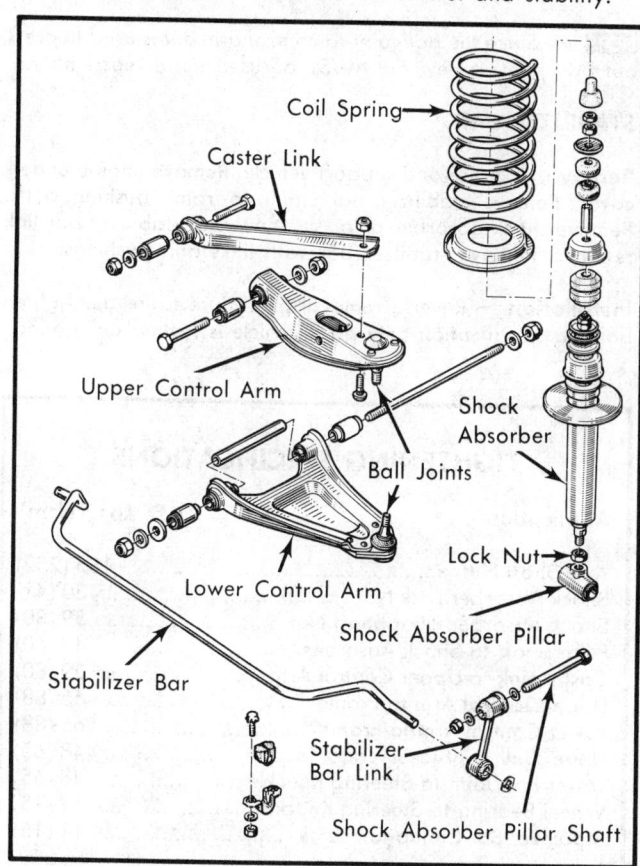

Fig. 1   Exploded View of 18i Front Suspension

ADJUSTMENTS

WHEEL ALIGNMENT SPECIFICATIONS & PROCEDURES

See Wheel Alignment Specifications and Procedures in WHEEL ALIGNMENT section.

WHEEL BEARING ADJUSTMENT

Wheel bearings are not adjustable. Tighten axle shaft nuts to 185 ft. lbs. (252 N·m).

BALL JOINT CHECKING

Inspect ball joints for excessive wear or play. Replace as needed. If rubber grease cup is cracked or otherwise damaged, ball joint must be replaced.

REMOVAL & INSTALLATION

SHOCK ABSORBER & COIL SPRING ASSEMBLY

Removal — 1) Raise vehicle and remove wheels. Place jack stand under lower control arm at ball joint. Lower vehicle until entire weight (for that side) is supported by stand.

2) Install spring compressor tool (Sus. 863) with clamps over next-to-last upper coil of spring. Lubricate threaded ends of clamps. Install nuts hand tight only.

3) Lower jack stands until coil spring separates from upper spring mounting cup. Spring should now turn by hand. Loosen shock absorber pillar shaft nut but do not remove bolt.

4) Remove upper shock mounting nut. Loosen lower shock lock nut. Unscrew shock from pillar and remove shock absorber, coil spring and tool.

5) Install inside type coil spring compressor (Sus. 594) and tighten to release spring compressor clamps. Loosen compressor and remove spring.

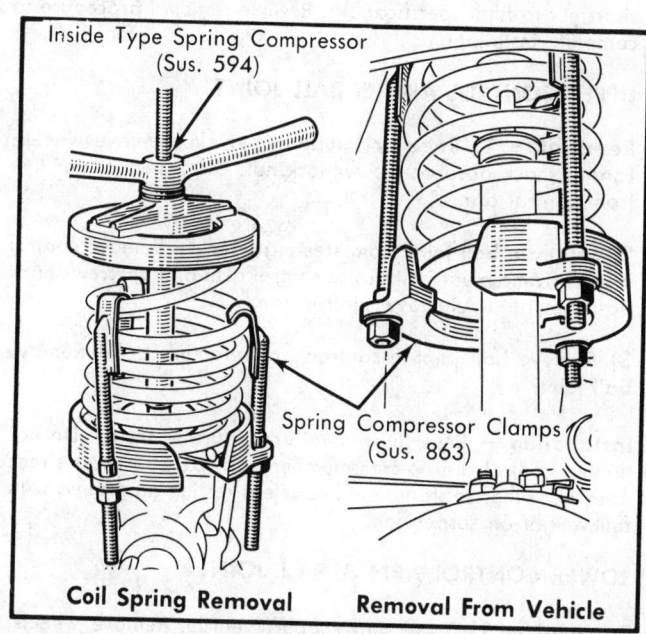

Coil Spring Removal   Removal From Vehicle

Fig. 2   Shock Absorber & Coil Spring Removal

Installation — 1) Compress spring with inside compressor (Sus. 594) and install compressor clamps. Remove inside compressor. Install shock absorber with coil spring and compressor.

2) Raise jack and screw shock tightly into pillar. Back off one turn. Install upper shock absorber bushings and cups in same position as before removal. Install upper nut hand tight.

3) Lower vehicle completely and bounce up and down a few times to settle suspension. Tighten upper nut, lower lock nut and pillar shaft nut to final specifications. Remove spring compressor.

WHEEL BEARINGS

Removal — 1) With vehicle on ground and parking brake engaged, remove hub cap and loosen axle shaft nut (do not remove nut). Raise and support vehicle. Remove wheels.

2) Remove brake pads and caliper assembly. Do not allow caliper to hang by brake line. Remove 2 hub-to-rotor retaining bolts with Torx type wrench. Remove brake rotor.

3) Remove axle shaft nut. Place 2 metal blocks between wheel hub and steering knuckle so that 2 wheel bolts can be used to

RENAULT 18i (Cont.)

press off hub. Install wheel bolts in hub and tighten gradually and alternately, pressing hub out of knuckle.

4) Remove 6 bearing-to-knuckle retaining bolts and remove bearing. Remove inner race from axle shaft. Remove outer bearing from wheel hub with puller.

Installation — 1) Install bearing inner race on axle shaft. Install bearing to steering knuckle. Press outer race into wheel hub. Pack bearing, races and grease seals with multi-purpose grease.

2) Position wheel hub on axle shaft and tap on with plastic hammer until axle shaft nut can be installed a few turns. Attach tool (Rou. 604) to keep hub from turning and tighten axle shaft nut to final specifications. Reverse removal procedure to complete installation.

UPPER CONTROL ARM & BALL JOINT

Removal — 1) Raise and support vehicle. Remove wheels. Loosen shock absorber lower lock nut. Disconnect caster link from control arm.

2) Separate ball joint from steering knuckle. Remove control arm-to-frame pivot bolt. Raise control arm and unscrew shock absorber pillar. Remove control arm.

3) Remove ball joint-to-control arm retaining bolts. Remove ball joint.

Installation — Reverse removal procedure to install. Do not tighten control arm-to-crossmember bolt, caster link or shock absorber pillar shaft nut until vehicle is resting on ground with full weight on suspension.

LOWER CONTROL ARM & BALL JOINT

Removal — 1) Raise and support vehicle. Remove wheels. Loosen ball joint-to-knuckle nut until it contacts axle shaft constant velocity joint. Press ball joint from knuckle by continuing to remove ball joint nut. Remove control arm pivot shaft bolts and pivot shaft. Remove arm from vehicle.

2) Punch out ball joint retaining rivets with cold chisel. Remove ball joint from control arm.

Installation — Install new ball joint with bolts supplied. Bolts must be installed with heads on top side of control arm. Reverse removal procedures to complete control arm installation. Do not torque pivot shaft bolt to final specification until vehicle is resting on ground.

NOTE — *Since the ball joint-to-control arm nut is used to press out ball joint, a new nut MUST be used upon reassembly.*

STABILIZER BAR

Removal — Raise and support vehicle. Remove engine undercover. Remove stabilizer bar clamp-to-frame bushing bolts. Remove shock absorber pillar shaft nut and stabilizer bar link retainer. Remove stabilzer bar with links and bushings.

Installation — Reverse removal procedure to install. Tighten bolts to specification only after vehicle is resting on ground.

TIGHTENING SPECIFICATIONS

Application	Ft. Lbs. (N·m)
Axle Shaft Nut	185 (252)
Shock Absorber Lock Nut	30 (41)
Shock Absorber Pillar Shaft Nut	59 (80)
Pillar Shaft-to-Shock Absorber	44 (60)
Caster Link-to-Upper Control Arm	59 (80)
Upper Control Arm-to-Frame	65 (88)
Lower Control Arm-to-Frame	65 (88)
Upper Ball Joint-to-Steering Knuckle	48 (65)
Lower Ball Joint-to-Steering Knuckle	48 (65)
Wheel Bearing-to-Steering Knuckle	11 (15)
Stabilizer Bar Clamp-to-Frame	11 (15)

Front Suspension

SAAB

900

DESCRIPTION

Independent front suspension with coil springs. Wheel is supported by steering knuckle mounted between upper and lower control arms by means of ball joints. Both upper and lower control arms pivot on shafts connected to body. Coil springs fit in pockets built into body at top and in supports attached to upper control arms at bottom. Hydraulic shock absorbers mount between lower control arm and body. If stabilizer bar is used, it is attached to frame and connected at ends to lower control arms.

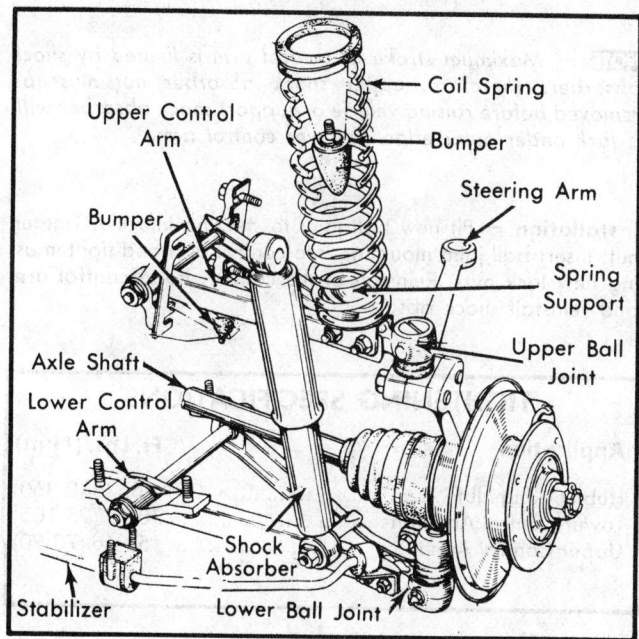

Fig. 1 Saab Front Suspension Assembly with Relationship of Components

ADJUSTMENT

WHEEL ALIGNMENT SPECIFICATIONS & PROCEDURES

See Wheel Alignment Specifications and Procedures in WHEEL ALIGNMENT Section.

WHEEL BEARING ADJUSTMENT

Front wheel bearings are not adjustable. Tighten front spindle nut to 246-261 ft. lbs. (335-355 N·m).

BALL JOINT CHECKING

1) Check ball joint wear with ball joints in unloaded, normal working position. Insert Saab tool (83 93 209) between upper control arm and chassis member before raising vehicle.

2) Raise vehicle off the ground and check ball joints for excessive play or looseness. DO NOT place jack under lower control arm when making this check.

REMOVAL & INSTALLATION

CONTROL ARMS

NOTE — *Engine must be removed prior to removing upper left control arm.*

Removal — 1) Remove upper shock absorber nut. Raise and support vehicle. Remove tire and wheel. If removing upper control arm, use a spring compressor (8995839) to remove coil

spring. Remove ball joint-to-control arm retaining bolts, providing support under steering knuckle housing to prevent brake line damage.

NOTE — *Remove shock absorber prior to jacking up 900 series vehicles; or by supporting shock in position with a jack placed under outer end of lower control arm.*

2) Remove control arm attaching bolts and control arm. If control arm bushings are being replaced, press them out using proper adapter and driver. Note amount and location of upper control arm spacers for reassembly reference.

Installation — 1) Replace worn or damaged components. If bearings have been removed from control arm, position onto control arm so when both nuts are tightened and locked, angle between arm and bearing will be as specified. Install control arm brackets. Install bearing locating bolts and spacers in upper arm. Tighten control arm bearings.

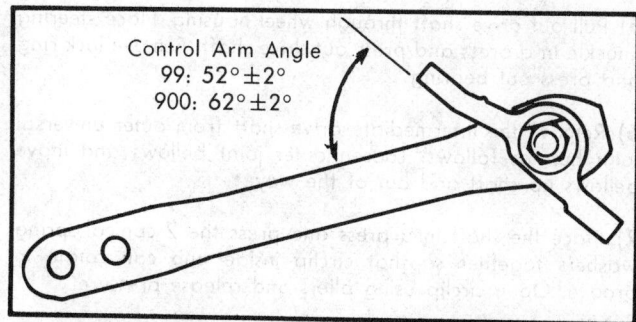

Fig. 2 Upper Control Arm-to-Bearing Angle

2) Install ball joint-to-control arm bolts. Correctly position upper spring spacer and support ring on upper control arm. Install compressed coil spring onto upper control arm with rubber buffer. Raise outer end of lower control arm slightly with a jack and install shock absorber. Tighten all mounting bolts. Install wheel and tire. Recheck wheel alignment.

Control Arm Specifications		
Application	**Upper Control Arm**	**Lower Control Arm**
900	60°-64°	16°-20°

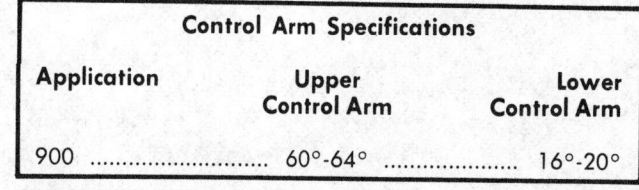

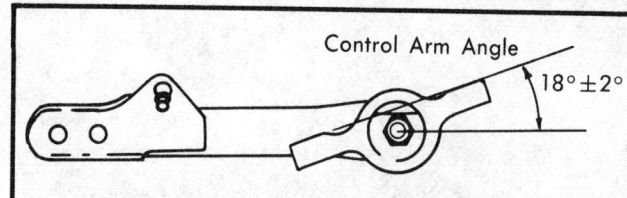

Fig. 3 Lower Control Arm-to-Bearing Angle

SHOCK ABSORBERS

NOTE — *Pneumatic shock absorbers require special handling to prevent personal injury. Drill a hole 3/8 - 5/8" (10-15 mm) from pressure chamber edge before discarding.*

Removal & Installation — Remove upper shock absorber nut before raising vehicle. Raise and support vehicle on safety stands; remove tire and wheel. Remove nuts securing shock absorber and remove shock. Save the washers and rubber parts for use in installation. To install, reverse removal procedure.

Front Suspension

SAAB (Cont.)

WHEEL BEARING

Removal — 1) Remove upper shock absorber nuts. Remove wheel and hub nut. Place a jack under end of lower control arm, raise car and secure with safety stands.

2) Rotate disc until recess in disc lines up with brake pads. Disconnect hand brake cable and remove brake housing. Using puller tool (89 96 084) remove hub and brake disc.

3) Remove large clamp around bellows of inner universal joint. Remove steering arm and upper ball joint using separator tool (8995409). Remove screws on lower control arm bracket.

4) Separate inner universal joint, fitting a cover in bellows to stop needle bearings from falling out and to keep dirt out of joint.

5) Pull out drive shaft through wheel housing. Place steering knuckle in a press and press out drive shaft. Remove lock ring and press out bearing.

6) Remove the intermediate drive shaft from outer universal joint hub as follows: Loosen outer joint bellows and move bellows up shaft and out of the way.

7) Place the shaft in a press and press the 2 conical spring washers together so that circlip inside hub can rotate in groove. Open circlip using pliers and release pressure.

8) Pull intermediate shaft out of hub together with spherical shaped washer, 2 cone shaped spring washers and shaft locking ring.

Installation — To install, reverse removal procedure.

BALL JOINTS

Removal — Raise and support vehicle; remove tire and wheel. Take weight off control arm travel stop (if equipped) and raise outer portion of lower control arm with a jack. Remove lower shock absorber mounting. Lower jack until drive shaft is aligned with body grommet. With jack under arm for support, remove caliper and hang out of way. Remove ball joint nut. Using suitable tool (8995409) separate ball joint from steering knuckle.

NOTE — Maximum stroke of control arm is limited by shock absorber. Therefore, upper shock absorber nut must be removed before raising vehicle or support shock absorber with a jack under outer edge of lower control arm.

Installation — Fit new ball joint to steering knuckle. Tighten nut. Insert ball joint mounting into control arm and tighten using new lock nuts. Reinstall brake caliper. Raise control arm and reinstall shock absorber.

TIGHTENING SPECIFICATIONS

Application	Ft. Lbs. (N·m)
Hub Locking Nut	251-265 (340-360)
Lower Control Arm Nuts	70-77 (95-105)
Upper Control Arm Nuts	54-66 (73-90)

Front Suspension

SUBARU

DL
GL
GLF

DESCRIPTION

Suspension is strut type, utilizing a hydraulic shock absorber/coil spring assembly forming a strut. Strut is secured at top to body and at bottom to steering knuckle. Steering knuckle pivots on ball joint attached to lower control arm. Lower control arms are attached to front crossmember. Radius rods are bolted to lower control arms and attached to rear crossmember with rubber bushings, washers and nuts. A stabilizer bar is attached to rear crossmember and to radius rods with clamps and rubber bushings.

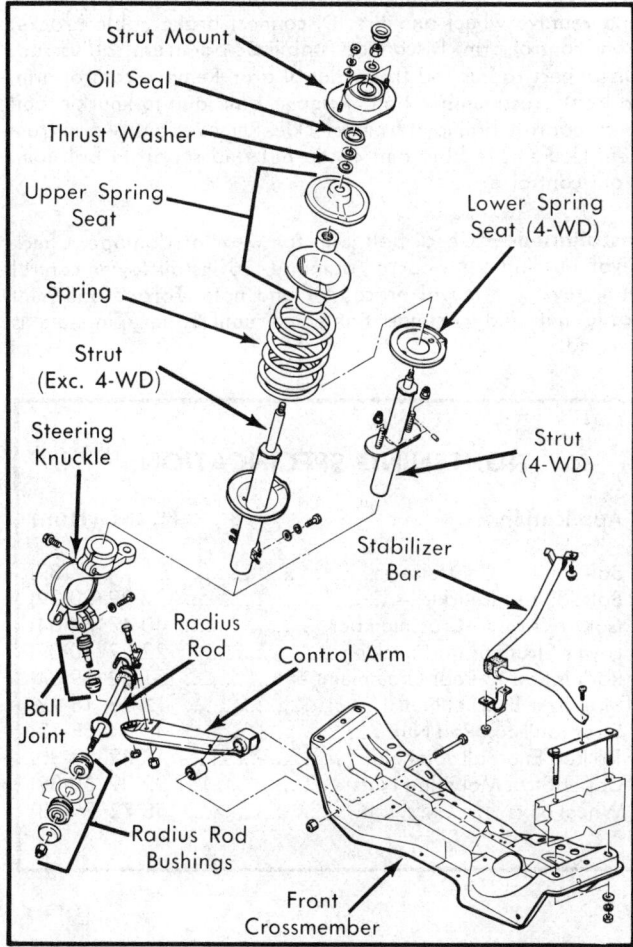

Strut Mount
Oil Seal
Thrust Washer
Upper Spring Seat
Spring
Strut (Exc. 4-WD)
Steering Knuckle
Lower Spring Seat (4-WD)
Strut (4-WD)
Radius Rod
Control Arm
Stabilizer Bar
Ball Joint
Radius Rod Bushings
Front Crossmember

Fig. 1 Exploded View of Subaru Front Suspension

ADJUSTMENTS

WHEEL ALIGNMENT SPECIFICATIONS & PROCEDURES

See Wheel Alignment Specifications and Procedures in WHEEL ALIGNMENT Section.

WHEEL BEARING ADJUSTMENT

Front wheel bearing is not adjustable. Tighten spindle nut (axle shaft nut) to 145 ft. lbs. (197 N·m). If cotter pin hole is not aligned, tighten further a maximum of 30° to align hole.

BALL JOINT CHECKING

Check ball joints for excessive play or looseness. Also check rubber boot for damage. Replace components as necessary.

REMOVAL & INSTALLATION

FRONT SUSPENSION

Removal — 1) Detach battery ground cable. Raise and support vehicle and remove front wheel(s).

2) Remove parking brake cable hanger from tie rod end, remove cable end from caliper lever, remove outer cable clip from caliper, remove cable bracket from housing and remove cable mounting bracket from lower control arm.

3) Disconnect brake hose from brake line and plug line. Drive out spring pins from inner ends of drive axles nearest transaxle housing.

4) Remove self-locking nut and bolt holding control arm to crossmember. Pull control arm downward from crossmember.

5) Use suitable tool to separate tie rod end from steering knuckle arm.

6) Detach radius rod from rear crossmember. Remove stabilizer bar brackets.

7) Remove upper strut assembly mounting nuts. Pull drive shaft from transaxle and remove suspension assembly from vehicle.

Installation — To install, reverse removal procedure, noting the following points:

- Be sure to align spring pin holes in drive axle before installing.
- When installing strut top mount, be sure stud marked "FRONT" is forward on Sedan, Hatchback and Hardtop models, and stud marked "VAN/4WD" is forward on Station Wagon and 4-WD models.
- When installing stabilizer, be sure slit in bushing is facing downward in clamp.
- Replace all self-locking nuts.
- Before installing radius rod bushing, soak it in soapy solution or rubber lubricant to assist installation.
- When installing castellated nuts on ball joints, tighten nut, as required, beyond specified torque setting to align cotter pin hole.
- Always use new spring pins for attaching inner end of drive shaft.
- Bleed brake system.

STRUT ASSEMBLY

Removal — 1) Detach battery ground cable. Raise and support vehicle. Remove front wheel. Disconnect brake hose from brake line, strut and brake caliper. Plug brake line.

2) Remove strut-to-knuckle bolts and pull strut out of knuckle. Remove upper strut mounting nuts. Remove strut from vehicle.

Disassembly — 1) Mount strut in spring compressor/holding fixture (925651000) and place in horizontal position. Compress spring until upper seat is separated from coil spring.

2) Use wrench portion of tool to hold upper mounting plate while removing self-locking nut from top end of strut. Remove thrust washer, oil seal and thrust bearing. Remove the upper spring seat from rod.

Front Suspension

SUBARU (Cont.)

3) Carefully remove tension from coil spring and remove tool and spring from strut.

Reassembly — To reassemble, reverse diassembly procedures, replacing self-locking nut with a new one. Place small amount of grease on thrust washer.

Installation — To install, reverse removal procedure, noting the following:

- Be sure upper strut mounting plate is facing in proper direction as described under "Front Suspension" installation procedure in this article.
- When reattaching brake line and hose, be sure to allow enough clearance from wheel apron.
- Bleed brake system.

WHEEL BEARING

Removal — **1)** Disconnect negative battery cable. Apply hand brake. Remove wheel cap, cotter pin and loosen castle nut and wheel nuts. Raise vehicle and support with stands.

2) Release parking brake. Disconnect parking brake cable from (inner end) lever of brake caliper. Remove clip of outer part of parking brake cable and disconnect cable from brake caliper.

3) Remove 2 retaining bolts to disc brake caliper assembly, and secure assembly out of the way. Remove 2 damper strut retaining bolts. Remove cotter pin and castle nut of tie rod end ball stud, and remove ball stud from knuckle arm housing using a puller.

4) Remove retaining bolt and separate transverse link from housing. Disconnect strut from housing. Remove castle nut on housing and remove disc and hub assembly from axle shaft.

5) Remove disc shield by removing retaining bolt. Attach puller tool (921121000) to housing and turn tool handle to pull housing off axle shaft.

6) Using a plastic hammer and aluminum or brass bar, tap on inner race to remove outer bearing and outer race to remove inner bearing.

Installation — To install, reverse removal procedure.

STABILIZER BAR

Removal — Raise front of vehicle, and support with safety stands. Remove clamps securing stabilizer bar to radius rod. Remove clamps attaching stabilizer bar to rear crossmember.

Installation — Check all bushings for wear or damage and replace as necessary. Check stabilizer bar for possible cracking. To install, reverse removal procedure.

LOWER CONTROL ARM

Removal — Raise front of vehicle, support with safety stands, and remove wheel and tire. Disconnect brake cable bracket from control arm. Disconnect stabilizer bar from radius rod. Disconnect radius rod from control arm. Remove control arm-to-front crossmember bolt. Remove ball joint-to-knuckle bolt and separate ball joint from knuckle. Remove control arm from vehicle. Remove ball joint castle nut and separate ball joint from control arm.

Installation — Check ball joint for wear or damage. Check pivot bushing for wear or damage. To install lower control arm, reverse removal procedure and note: Torque ball joint castle nut and continue tightening until cotter pin hole is aligned.

TIGHTENING SPECIFICATIONS

Application	Ft. Lbs. (N·m)
Ball Joint-to-Control Arm	29 (39)
Ball Joint-to-Knuckle	22-29 (30-39)
Control Arm-to-Crossmember	40-47 (54-64)
Lower Strut End-to-Knuckle	22-29 (30-39)
Radius Rod-to-Rear Crossmember	51-62 (69-84)
Stabilizer Bracket Nuts	13-16 (18-22)
Strut-to-Piston Rod Nut	43-54 (58-73)
Tie Rod End Ball Joint Nut	18-22 (24-30)
Upper Strut Mounting Nuts	22-29 (30-39)
Wheel Nuts	58-72 (79-98)

Front Suspension

TOYOTA CELICA, COROLLA, CORONA, CRESSIDA, STARLET & SUPRA

DESCRIPTION

Independent strut type suspension consisting of vertically mounted strut assemblies, lower control arms, strut rods and a stabilizer bar. Individual strut assembly is mounted at top to inner fender by a thrust bearing and at bottom to lower control arm by means of a ball joint. Strut assembly consists of a shock absorber built into strut outer tube, a coil spring mounted on outside of strut tube and a steering knuckle integral with bottom of strut tube. A strut rod is mounted between lower control arm and frame. A stabilizer bar is mounted to front frame members and connected at ends to lower control arms. The suspension crossmember that serves as support for all suspension components is removable.

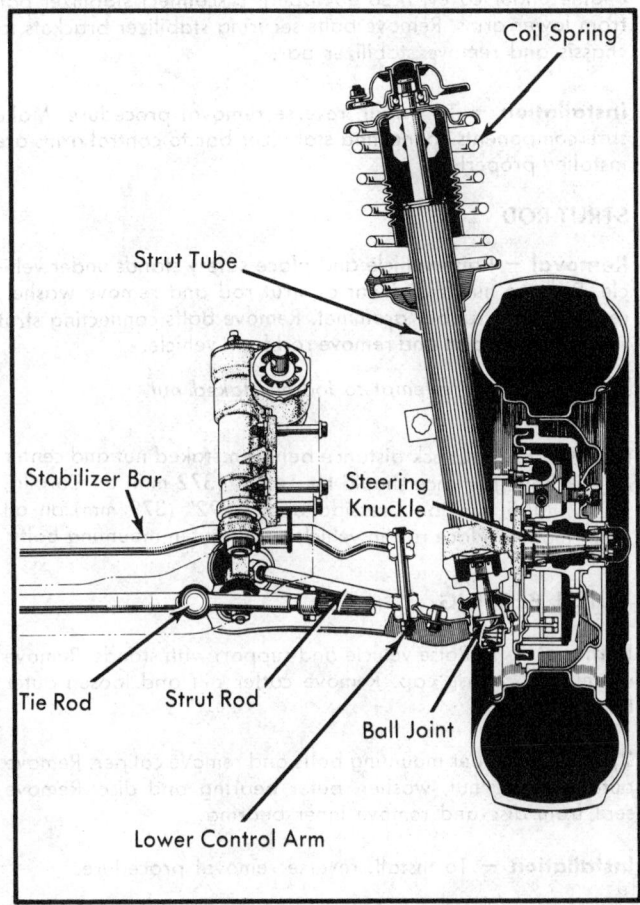

Fig. 1 Assembled View of Front Suspension Assembly (Corolla Shown; Other Models Similar)

Labels: Coil Spring, Strut Tube, Stabilizer Bar, Steering Knuckle, Tie Rod, Strut Rod, Ball Joint, Lower Control Arm

ADJUSTMENT

WHEEL ALIGNMENT SPECIFICATIONS & PROCEDURES

See Wheel Alignment Specifications & Procedures in WHEEL ALIGNMENT Section.

WHEEL BEARING ADJUSTMENT

1) Tighten nut to 22 ft. lbs. (30 N·m) on Celica, Cressida, Supra and Starlet models or to 19-23 ft. lbs. (26-31 N·m) for all other models while turning hub to seat bearings. Loosen nut until it can be turned with fingers. Tighten nut finger tight using a socket without a handle.

2) If not aligned for cotter pin installation, tighten until installation is possible. Preload at hub (while turning) should be within specifications listed in *Bearing Preload Specifications Table.*

Bearing Preload Specifications	
Application	**Preload Lbs. (kg)**
Celica, Corolla, Starlet & Supra	.7-1.5 (.3-.7)
Corona	.8-1.9 (.4-.9)
Cressida	2.2 (1.0)

BALL JOINT CHECKING

Check ball joints for damaged rubber boot, excessive looseness or play. If damaged or excessively worn, replace lower control arm with ball joint.

REMOVAL & INSTALLATION

STRUT ASSEMBLY

Removal — **1)** Raise and support vehicle. Remove front wheel. Disconnect brake tube and flexible hose.

2) Remove 3 nuts retaining top of strut assembly to vehicle. Remove bolts holding lower end of strut tube to steering knuckle.

3) Pull down on control arm to gain clearance and remove strut assembly (with brake and hub assembly attached) from vehicle.

Disassembly — **1)** Install assembly in vise, clamping portion of strut tube below flange.

2) Use suitable spring compressor to collapse spring enough to remove strut rod top nut. Relieve pressure and remove spring.

3) Using ring nut removing tool, remove ring nut. Remove gasket by picking out with a needle. Remove piston rod, rod guide and rebound stopper.

4) Remove cylinder from shell, and using a brass rod, remove base valve from cylinder.

NOTE — *Do not attempt to disassemble piston rod and valve.*

Reassembly — Thoroughly clean and inspect all components. Replace any damaged parts. Install shock absorber components into cylinder in reverse of disassembly procedure, noting the following:

- After installing piston nut, stake it in place.
- When installing base valve onto cylinder, use a soft-face hammer to drive into place.
- Add specified amount of new shock absorber oil to cylinder.
- Install new oil seal to ring nut.

TOYOTA CELICA, COROLLA, CORONA, CRESSIDA, STARLET & SUPRA (Cont.)

- Before fully tightening ring nut, pull piston rod out of cylinder about 3-4".
- Always use new self-locking nut on top of piston rod.

Shock Absorber Oil Capacities	
Application	**Ozs.**
Celica & Supra	11.0
Corolla	10.6
Corona	
13" (330 mm) Shock	10.6
14" (325 mm) Shock	11.0
Cressida	10.8
Starlet	8.1

Installation — To install strut assembly in vehicle, reverse removal procedure, noting the following:

- After top end of strut is attached to mounting, fill bearing recess, which protrudes into engine compartment, with multi-purpose grease.

CONTROL ARM

Removal — 1) Raise and support vehicle. Remove wheel. On Cressida, remove engine under cover and detach strut bar and stabilizer bar from lower arm.

2) On all models, remove strut assembly-to-knuckle mounting bolts. Push lower arm down and disconnect strut from knuckle arm. On Corolla, separate stabilizer bar and strut bar from lower arm.

3) On Celica, Corolla, Corona and Supra, disconnect knuckle arm from ball joint. On Celica, Supra and Corona, disconnect stabilizer bar and strut bar from lower arm. On Cressida, detach tie rod end from knuckle arm.

4) On all models, remove bolt holding lower arm to crossmember and remove lower arm.

Disassembly — 1) On Cressida, place control arm in a vise and use suitable puller to remove knuckle arm from ball joint.

2) On all models, pry dust cover from ball joint and discard (also discard dust cover snap ring or retaining wire).

3) Press bushing out of control arm toward front side of arm, using suitable press and arbor.

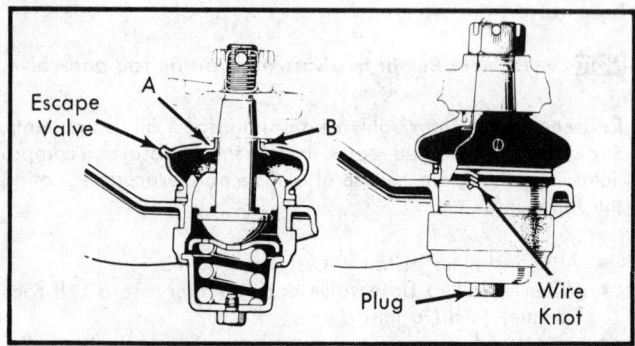

Fig. 2 Ball Joint and Dust Cover

Reassembly — 1) Use suitable support and press in new bushing. Apply ball joint grease to points "A" and "B" of new dust cover. See *Fig. 2*.

2) Install dust cover with escape valve facing rear of vehicle. Wind wire twice around dust cover and bend wire knot down, facing rear of ball joint.

3) Remove plug and install grease fitting. Fill ball joint with grease. Remove fitting and install plug.

Installation — To install, reverse removal procedure.

STABILIZER BAR

Removal — Remove strut rods from lower arms. Remove engine under cover, if so equipped. Disconnect stabilizer bar from lower arms. Remove bolts securing stabilizer brackets to chassis and remove stabilizer bar.

Installation — To install, reverse removal procedure. Make sure components connecting stabilizer bar to control arms are installed properly.

STRUT ROD

Removal — Raise vehicle and place safety stands under vehicle. Remove nut from front of strut rod and remove washer, retainer, and rubber grommet. Remove bolts connecting strut rod to control arm and remove rod from vehicle.

NOTE — *Do not attempt to loosen staked nut.*

Installation — Check distance between staked nut and center of bolt hole. Distance should be 14.64" (372 mm) on Corolla, 15.90" (405 mm) on Cressida and 14.92" (379 mm) on all other models. Place rod in vehicle and tighten mounting bolts.

WHEEL BEARING

Removal — 1) Raise vehicle and support with stands. Remove wheel and grease cap. Remove cotter pin and loosen outer bearing nut.

2) Remove caliper mounting bolts and remove caliper. Remove outer bearing nut, washer, outer bearing and disc. Remove seal from disc and remove inner bearing.

Installation — To install, reverse removal procedure.

CROSSMEMBER

Removal — 1) Remove engine under cover, if so equipped. Remove nuts holding both sides of crossmember to engine mounts. Raise and support vehicle on safety stands. Remove bolts holding lower arms to crossmember. On Corolla and Corona, remove engine shock absorber.

2) On all models, raise engine with chain or jack. On Cressida, disconnect stabilizer bar from lower arm. On all models, remove bolts securing crossmember to frame and remove crossmember.

Installation — To install, reverse removal procedure. Make sure components connecting stabilizer bar to control arms are installed in correct order.

Front Suspension

TOYOTA CELICA, COROLLA, CORONA, CRESSIDA, STARLET & SUPRA (Cont.)

TIGHTENING SPECIFICATIONS

Application	Ft. Lbs. (N·m)
Ball Joint-to-Knuckle Arm	51-65 (69-88)
Control Arm-to-Crossmember①	
Cressida	65-94 (88-128)
All Other Models	51-65 (69-88)
Control Arm-to-Stabilizer	11-15 (15-20)
Control Arm-to-Strut Rod	
Cressida	43-53 (58-72)
All Other Models	29-40 (39-54)
Knuckle Arm-to-Strut Tube	
Corolla	51-65 (69-88)
All Other Models	58-86 (79-117)
Piston Rod-to-Mounting Plate	29-40 (39-54)
Piston Rod Ring Nut	73-108 (99-147)

① — With vehicle at full curb weight.

Front Suspension

TOYOTA PICKUP

DESCRIPTION

Independent front suspension with torsion bars. Wheel is supported by steering knuckle mounted between upper and lower control arms by ball joints. Upper and lower control arms pivot on shafts connected to frame. Torsion bars mount in anchor arms at frame and in torque arms mounted to lower control arms. Strut bars mount at frame and at lower control arm ends. Hydraulic shock absorbers mount between lower control arms and frame. A stabilizer bar is mounted to frame and connected at ends to lower control arms.

ADJUSTMENT

WHEEL ALIGNMENT SPECIFICATIONS & PROCEDURES

See Wheel Alignment Specifications & Procedures in WHEEL ALIGNMENT Section.

WHEEL BEARING ADJUSTMENT

1) Tighten outer bearing nut to 22 ft. lbs. (30 N·m). Turn hub to right and left 2 or 3 times. Loosen nut until it can be turned by hand.

2) Using a socket, tighten nut as tight as possible by hand. Using a spring tension gauge, check bearing preload. Bearing preload should be 1.3-4.0 lb. (.59-1.8 kg).

3) If preload is less than specification, tighten nut and recheck preload. If preload is excessive, loosen nut and recheck. Install nut lock, cotter pin and grease cap.

BALL JOINT CHECKING

NOTE — *This procedure is performed with brake pedal depressed to prevent wheel bearing play.*

Jack up lower control arm until tire is off ground. Move tire up and down. Maximum ball joint vertical play should not exceed .091" (2.3 mm). Inspect ball joint dust cover for damage. Replace ball joints as necessary.

REMOVAL & INSTALLATION

SHOCK ABSORBERS

Removal — 1) Raise vehicle and place on jack stands under frame. Remove wheel and tire. Remove 2 nuts holding shock absorber to bracket. Remove washers and cushions from shaft of shock absorber.

2) Remove bolts securing shock absorber lower mount to control arm. Fully compress shock absorber, tilt forward and remove from vehicle.

Installation — To install, reverse removal procedure. Tighten all nuts and bolts.

TORSION BAR

Removal — 1) Raise and support front of vehicle. Remove wheel. Remove torsion bar boots at both ends and mark anchor arm and torque arm for correct spline alignment during reassembly.

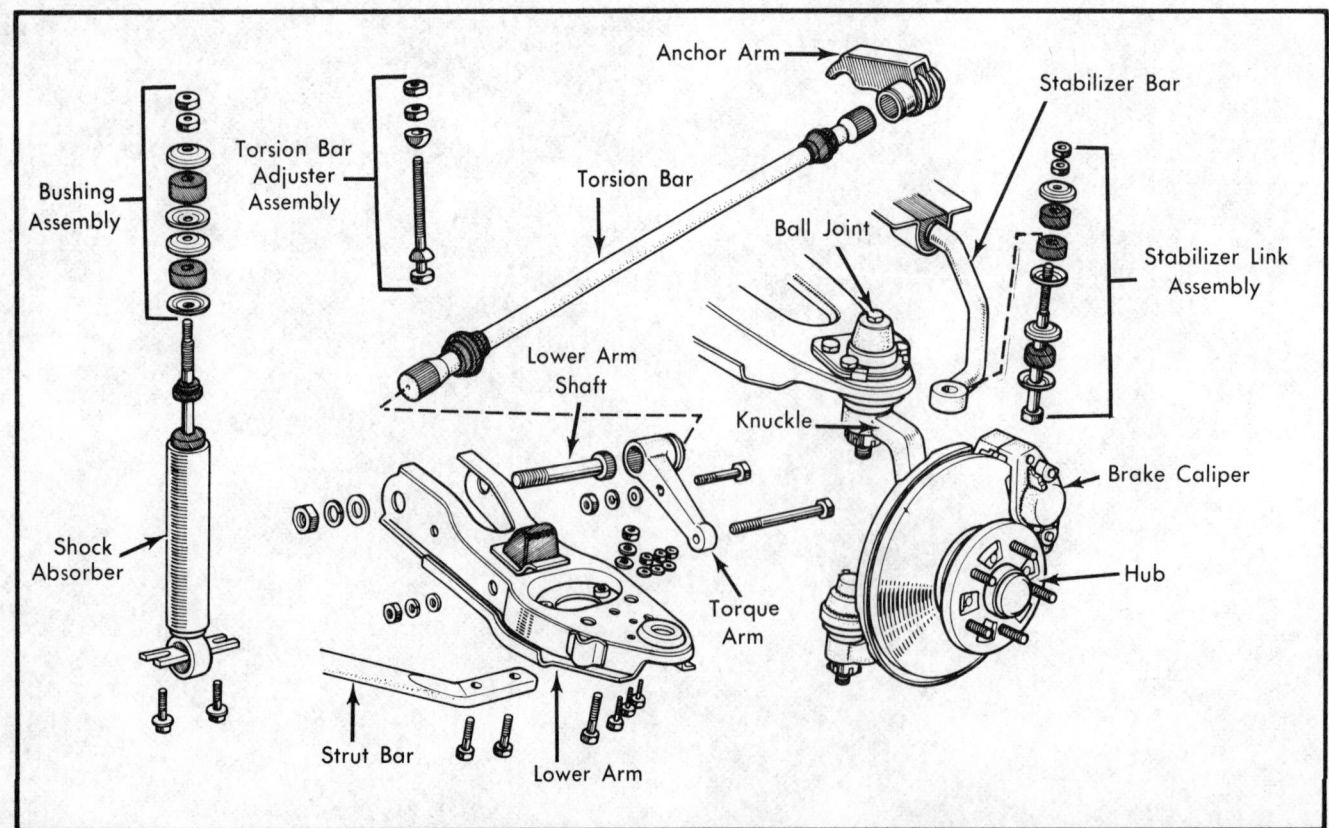

Fig. 1 Exploded View of Toyota Pickup Front Suspension

Front Suspension

TOYOTA PICKUP (Cont.)

2) Remove adjuster bolt lock nut. Measure distance from end of adjuster bolt to lower face of adjusting nut. Record distance for use during installation.

3) Place a jack under the anchor arm and raise slightly. Remove adjusting nut, lower jack slowly and remove the anchor arm and torsion bar.

Inspection — Inspect all parts for wear or damage. Check all splines carefully. Note that left and right torsion bars are not interchangeable.

Installation — 1) Grease splines prior to installation. When re-using old torsion bar, align marks on torsion bar with marks on torque arm and anchor arm and install.

2) When using new torsion bar, jack up front of vehicle and block tire up to height of 7.09-7.87" (180-200 mm). Lower jack until clearance between spring bumper on lower arm and frame is .51" (13 mm).

NOTE — *Place stands under vehicle for safety.*

3) Install new torsion bar so adjusting bolt protrusion is .31-1.10" (7.87-27.94 mm) for ½ ton vehicles and .43-1.22" (11-31 mm) for ¾ ton vehicles. Remove block from under wheel and lower front of vehicle until it rests on stands. Tighten adjusting nut until bolt protrudes 2.72-3.50" (69-89 mm).

4) With either old or new torsion bar, grease boot lips and install boots to torque arm and anchor arm. Remove stands and bounce vehicle several times to settle suspension. Adjust vehicle to standard height with adjusting nut. *See Riding Height Specifications in Wheel Alignment Section.* Using 2 wrenches, tighten lock nut.

NOTE — *If bolt protrusion is not 2.72-3.50" (69-89 mm), change the position of anchor arm spline and reassemble.*

UPPER CONTROL ARM & BALL JOINT

Removal — 1) Raise vehicle by placing jack under lower control arm. Place stands under frame and leave jack in place. Remove wheel. Remove cotter pin and nut from upper ball joint stud. Using a puller, separate ball joint from knuckle.

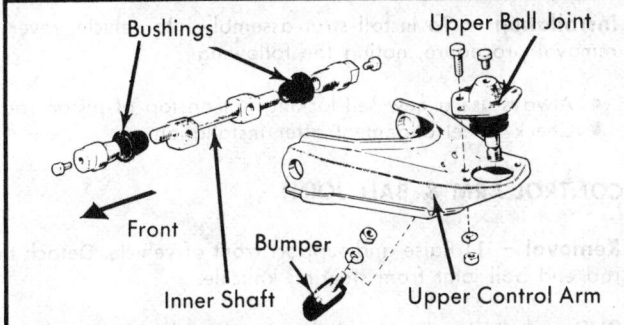

Fig. 2 Exploded View of Upper Control Arm Assembly

2) Remove bolts securing upper control arm shaft, noting size and number of shims between pivot shaft and frame. Remove control arm as an assembly. Remove bolts securing ball joint to control arm, and remove ball joint. Press off bushings using suitable adapters and remove shaft.

Installation — Inspect all components for wear or distortion. Install pivot shaft with offset mounting hole to front. Reverse removal procedure for installation, making sure wheel alignment shims are installed in correct position. Tighten all bolts and nuts to specifications. Check wheel alignment.

LOWER CONTROL ARM & BALL JOINT

Removal — 1) Raise and support vehicle. Remove wheel. Remove torsion bar and shock absorber. Disconnect stabilizer bar and strut bar from control arm.

2) Remove cotter pin and nut from lower ball joint stud and, using a puller, separate ball joint from steering knuckle. Remove torque arm and pivot shaft from control arm. Remove control arm from vehicle. Remove bolts securing ball joint to control arm and remove ball joint. Remove bushings from frame, if necessary.

Installation — To install, reverse removal procedure, noting the following: Tighten lower arm mount nut to specifications after vehicle has been lowered to the ground. Check wheel alignment.

WHEEL BEARING

Removal — Raise vehicle and support with safety stands. Remove wheels. Remove grease cap, cotter pin and nut lock. Remove disc brake caliper retaining bolts and remove caliper. Remove outer bearing nut, washer, outer bearing and disc. Remove grease seal from back of disc and remove inner bearing.

Installation — To install, reverse removal procedure.

STEERING KNUCKLE

Removal — 1) Raise and support vehicle. Remove wheel. Disconnect brake tube from brake caliper. Remove caliper from knuckle.

2) Remove cap, cotter pin, nut lock, nut and axle hub with rotor. Remove knuckle arm and dust cover. Suspend brake hose out of the way.

3) Remove cotter pins and nuts from ball joint studs. Use a puller and separate ball joints from steering knuckle. Remove knuckle.

Installation — To install, reverse removal procedure. Check wheel alignment.

TIGHTENING SPECIFICATIONS

Application	Ft. Lbs. (N·m)
Ball Joint-to-Lower Arm (8 mm)	15-21 (20-29)
Ball Joint-to-Lower Arm (10 mm)	29-39 (39-53)
Ball Joint-to-Upper Arm	15-21 (20-29)
Lower Arm-to-Frame	145-217 (197-295)
Lower Ball Joint-to-Steering Knuckle	87-123 (118-167)
Shock Absorber-to-Bracket	14-22 (19-30)
Shock Absorber-to-Lower Arm	11-15 (15-20)
Strut Bar-to-Lower Arm	55-75 (75-102)
Upper Ball Joint-to-Steering Knuckle	66-94 (90-128)
Upper Arm-to-Shaft	62-79 (84-107)
Upper Arm Shaft-to-Frame	51-65 (69-88)

Front Suspension

TOYOTA TERCEL

DESCRIPTION

Vehicles are equipped with front wheel drive and independent strut type suspension. Vertically mounted strut assemblies are surrounded by coil springs and mounted at inner fender at top and steering knuckle at bottom. Tie rod ends connect rack and pinion steering to steering knuckle. Lower ball joint connects knuckle to lower control arm which attaches to frame crossmember. Stabilizer bar attaches to lower control arm and crossmember in front of wheels and strut rod attaches to lower control arm and chassis to the rear of front wheels.

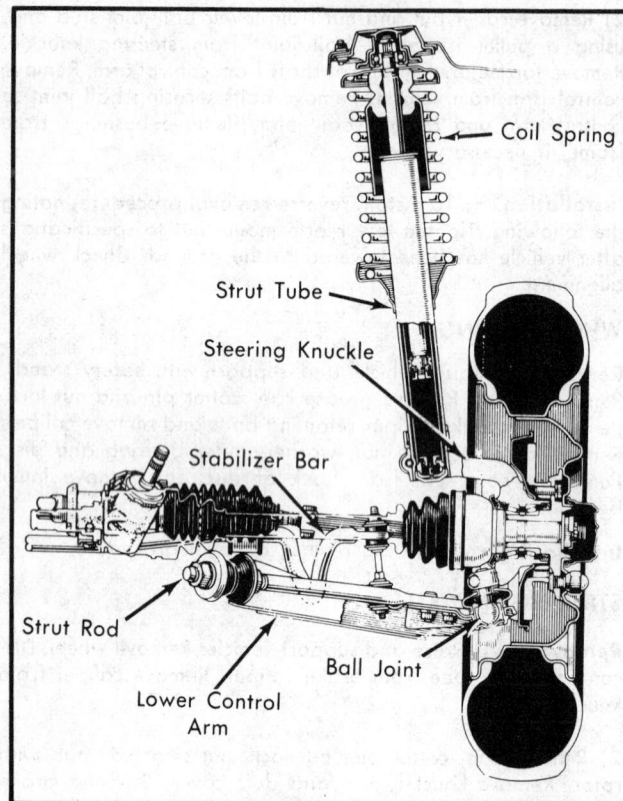

Coil Spring

Strut Tube

Steering Knuckle

Stabilizer Bar

Strut Rod

Ball Joint

Lower Control Arm

Fig. 1   Assembled View of Tercel Front Suspension

ADJUSTMENT

WHEEL ALIGNMENT SPECIFICATIONS & PROCEDURES

See Wheel Alignment Specifications & Procedures in WHEEL ALIGNMENT Section.

WHEEL BEARING ADJUSTMENT

Front wheel bearings are not adjustable. Check bearings for excessive play and replace as necessary.

BALL JOINT CHECKING

Raise front of vehicle. Place wooden block 7.09-7.87" (180-200 mm) in height under one front tire. Lower jack until there is about half a load on front coil springs. Place safety stand under vehicle. Insure that front wheels are in a straight ahead position and block them. Move lower arm up and down. Ball joint should have no vertical play. Repeat in same manner for other side.

REMOVAL & INSTALLATION

STRUT ASSEMBLY

Removal — 1) Raise and support vehicle. Remove wheel and tire. Remove brake caliper and suspend with wire. Disconnect stabilizer bar end from lower control arm.

2) Remove bolt attaching strut assembly to steering knuckle. Tap on knuckle with a hammer to separate it from lower end of strut. Remove 3 nuts holding top of strut to fender and remove strut from vehicle.

Disassembly — 1) Install assembly in a vise, clamping portion of strut tube below flange or use holding fixture (09714-16010).

2) Use suitable spring compressor to collapse spring enough to remove strut rod top nut. Relieve pressure on spring and remove spring, and disassemble shock absorber top end retaining components.

3) Using ring nut removing tool, remove ring nut. Remove gasket by picking out with a needle.

4) Withdraw piston and rod guide from cylinder. Remove cylinder from shell, and using brass rod, remove base valve from cylinder.

NOTE — *Do not attempt to disassemble piston rod and valve.*

Reassembly — Thoroughly clean and inspect all components. Replace any damaged parts. Install shock absorber components into cylinder in reverse order of disassembly, noting the following:

- When installing base valve into cylinder, use a soft face hammer to drive it into place.
- Fill shock absorber with 7.8 ounces (230 cc) new shock absorber fluid.
- After assembling rod guide, install new gasket.
- Apply multi-purpose grease to ring nut oil seal.
- Before fully tightening ring nut, pull out piston rod from cylinder 3-4".
- Assemble coil spring with paint mark downward.

Installation — To install strut assembly into vehicle, reverse removal procedure, noting the following:

- Always use a new self-locking nut on top of piston rod.
- Check wheel alignment after installation.

CONTROL ARM & BALL JOINT

Removal — 1) Raise and support front of vehicle. Detach tie rod end ball joint from steering knuckle.

2) Detach strut rod and stabilizer bar from lower control arm. Detach lower control arm ball joint from steering knuckle.

3) Remove control arm pivot bolt and remove control arm from vehicle.

NOTE — *On left side, jack up control arm to remove bolt.*

TOYOTA TERCEL (Cont.)

Bushing Replacement — Use suitable press to remove and install bushing. When installing, there must be no oil or grease on bushing or arm boss. Press only on flange of outer tube.

NOTE — *Control arm and ball joint are servicable as a unit only. If damaged, replace entire assembly.*

Installation — To install, reverse removal procedure, noting the following:

- Tighten the lower arm with vehicle weight on suspension.
- Check front wheel alignment.

STABILIZER BAR

Removal and Installation — Remove engine under cover. Remove stabilizer bar ends from control arms, noting bushing positioning, then remove bolts securing mounting brackets to chassis. Remove stabilizer bar. To install, reverse removal procedure, ensuring components connecting bar to control arms are installed in correct order.

STRUT ROD

Removal — Raise and support front of vehicle. Jack up lower control arm, remove nut from front of strut rod and remove washer, retainer, and rubber grommet. Remove bolts connecting strut rod to control arm and remove rod from vehicle.

Installation — Set distance between outer side of staked nut (inside retaining nut) and inner mounting bolt to 13.0" (330.4 mm). Place rod in vehicle and tighten mounting hardware.

WHEEL BEARINGS

Removal — 1) Raise vehicle and secure with safety stands. Remove front wheels. Remove cotter pin and adjusting nut cap. Remove 2 brake caliper retaining bolts and tie caliper out of the way with a piece of wire.

2) Remove bearing lock nut. Disconnect strut bar end by removing nut holding stabilizer bar-to-lower arm. Disconnect strut bar end by removing nut holding strut bar-to-lower arm.

3) Remove cotter pin and nut retaining tie rod-to-axle hub. Using tie rod puller tool (SST 09610-20012) remove tie rod from axle hub. Place jack under axle hub side of lower arm and raise vehicle slightly to relieve pressure on lower arm.

4) Do this only on one side at a time. Remove bolt holding lower arm-to-crossmember. Disconnect lower arm from crossmember. Remove the bolt holding axle hub to shock absorber.

5) Using puller tool (SST 09950-20014) pull axle hub from drive shaft. Separate shock absorber from steering knuckle and remove axle hub.

NOTE — *Take care not to damage boot.*

6) Remove bolt holding axle hub to lower arm. Separate axle hub from lower arm. Remove disc splash shield. Using puller tool (SST 09308-00010) remove oil seal from axle hub.

7) Using separator tool (SST 09608-16031) remove axle hub from steering knuckle. Remove inner bearing and spacer. Separate hub from disc by removing 4 bolts.

8) Place hub in a vise. Using a chisel and hammer, open a clearance between outer bearing and hub. Using a bearing puller (SST 09950-20014) remove outer bearing from hub. If necessary, remove any scratches on hub surface using an oil stone.

Installation — To install, reverse removal procedure.

SUSPENSION CROSSMEMBER

Removal — 1) Raise and support front of vehicle. Disconnect steering intermediate shaft pinch bolt. Remove engine under cover and detach tie rod end ball joints from steering knuckle.

2) Remove stabilizer bar. Remove lower control arm pivot bolt, and detach engine shock absorber from crossmember. Remove steering link housing brackets and remove steering assembly from vehicle.

3) Remove engine mounting nuts and prop up engine from below. Remove lower crossmember retaining bolts and remove crossmember.

Installation — To install, reverse removal procedure and note the following:
- For the left side, jack up lower control arm to install to crossmember.
- Lower and rock vehicle before tightening lower arm pivot bolts.
- Check front end alignment.
- Make sure components connecting stabilizer bar to control arms are installed in correct order.

TIGHTENING SPECIFICATIONS

Application	Ft. Lbs. (N·m)
Ball Joint-to-Steering Knuckle	40-52 (54-71)
Caliper Mounting Bolts	33-39 (45-53)
Control Arm-to-Crossmember①	51-65 (69-88)
Control Arm-to-Strut	40-52 (54-71)
Control Arm-to-Stabilizer	11-15 (15-20)
Control Arm-to-Strut Rod	29-39 (39-53)
Crossmember Mounting Bolts	30-39 (41-53)
Engine Mounting Bolts	26-39 (35-53)
Piston Rod Ring Nut	66-97 (90-132)
Piston Rod-to-Mounting Plate	29-39 (39-53)
Stabilizer Bar Brackets	22-32 (30-44)
Steering Link Brackets	22-32 (30-44)
Strut-to-Upper Mount	15-21 (20-29)
Tie Rod End-to-Steering Knuckle	37-50 (50-68)

① — With vehicle at full curb weight.

Front Suspension

TRIUMPH TR7 & TR8

DESCRIPTION

Suspension is strut type with a coil spring around strut tube. Strut is secured at top to inner fender and at bottom to control arm link. A stabilizer bar is connected to chassis and lower control link. Control arm links are mounted by a ball joint at stub axles and through bolts at chassis.

ADJUSTMENT

WHEEL ALIGNMENT SPECIFICATIONS & PROCEDURES

See Wheel Alignment Specifications and Procedures in WHEEL ALIGNMENT Section.

WHEEL BEARING ADJUSTMENT

Raise and support front of vehicle. Remove tire and wheel. Check hub for excessive end play. If adjustment is necessary, remove grease cap and cotter pin. Tighten spindle nut to 50 ft. lbs. (68 N·m), then back off 1 flat and install cotter pin.

BALL JOINT CHECKING

Inspect ball joints for excessive wear or play. Replace ball joints as necessary.

REMOVAL & INSTALLATION

LOWER CONTROL LINK

Removal — 1) Raise and support vehicle with safety stands. Remove tire and wheel. Remove mounting hardware from end of stabilizer bar. Remove bolts holding steering arm to stub axle and move out of way. Remove nut and separate ball joint. Remove bolt and nut securing lower control link to chassis, then take out link.

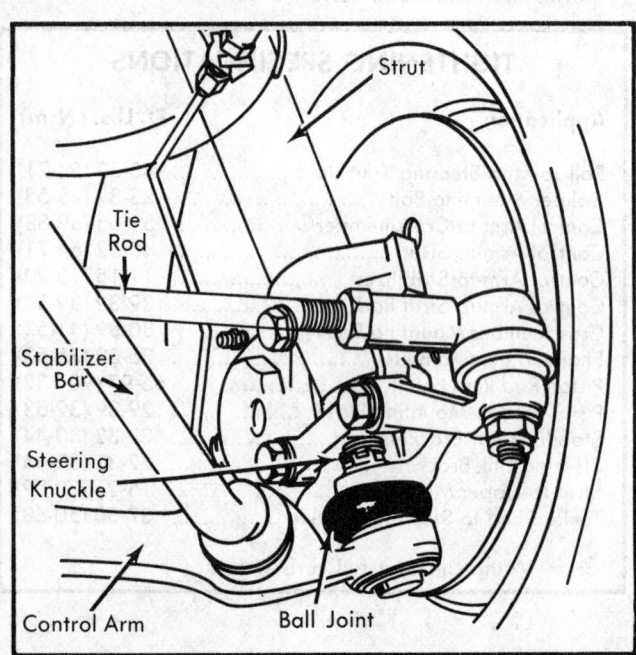

Fig. 1   Detail of Components to Remove in Order to Take Off Lower Control Link and Strut Assembly

2) Remove plastic and rubber ring from ball joint. Remove snap ring retaining ball joint housing to bottom link. Press or drive out ball joint and housing. Install new ball joint, fit snap ring, plastic, and rubber ring.

Installation — To install reverse removal procedure and tighten lower control link when vehicle weight is on ground.

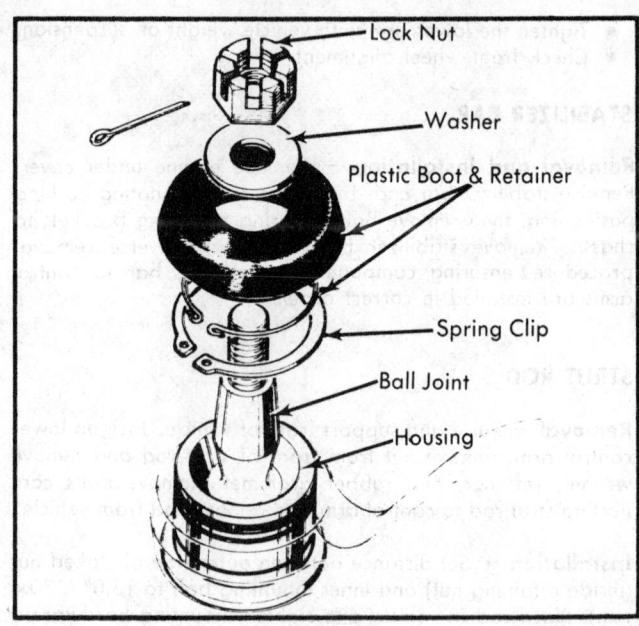

Fig. 2   Exploded View of Ball Joint Assembly

STRUT ASSEMBLY

Removal — 1) Raise vehicle and support with jack stands. Remove tire and wheel. Separate steering arm from stub axle assembly by removing two bolts. Disconnect brake hose from bracket on strut tube. Disconnect brake caliper and hang out of way.

2) Remove ball joint nut and separate from stub axle. Remove three nuts mounting strut assembly to inner fender panel. Pull strut downward and maneuver from vehicle.

3) Using a spring compressor, collapse coil and remove slotted nut from top of strut assembly. Take out spring pan complete with top mounting and swivel assembly. Remove spring from strut.

Disassembly — Using plug nut wrench (RTR359), remove plug nut. Slide shock absorber from strut tube.

Reassembly — Fit shock absorber to strut tube, then fit plug nut and tighten.

TRIUMPH TR7 & TR8 (Cont.)

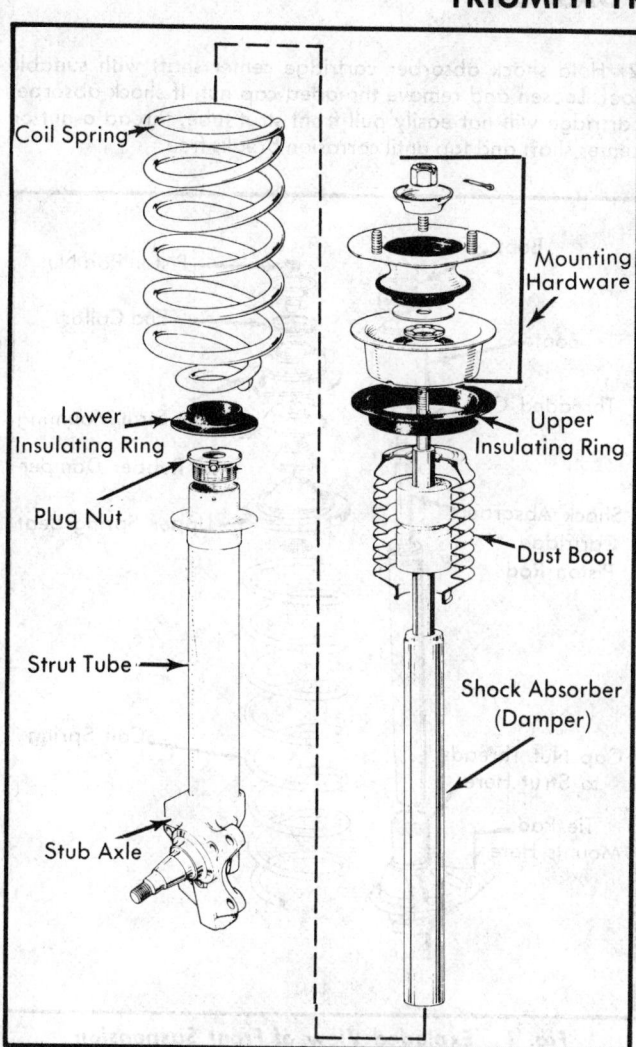

Coil Spring

Mounting
Hardware

Lower
Insulating Ring

Upper
Insulating Ring

Plug Nut

Dust Boot

Strut Tube

Shock Absorber
(Damper)

Stub Axle

Fig. 3 Disassembled View of Strut

Installation —1) Compress coil spring and ensure bumper stop is correctly positioned. Fully extend strut rod and fit the following: lower insulating ring, rubber seal, spring, upper insulating ring, and spring pan. Fit seal to thrust collar and place on upper spring pan.

2) Install plain washer (smearing first with light coating of grease) with ground surface facing spring pan. Insert rubber mounting to strut and secure with dished washer and slotted nut. To complete installation, reverse removal procedure. Bleed brake system.

WHEEL BEARINGS

Removal — 1) Raise vehicle and support with stands. Remove wheel and grease cap. Remove cotter pin and loosen outer bearing nut.

2) Remove caliper mounting bolts and remove caliper. Remove outer bearing nut, washer, outer bearing and disc. Remove seal from disc and remove inner bearing.

Installation — To install, reverse removal procedure.

STABILIZER BAR

Removal — Raise vehicle and place on safety stands. Remove bolts and brackets mounting stabilizer bar to chassis. Remove mounting nut and rubber bushing securing stabilizer bar to lower control link. Pull out stabilizer, adjusting vehicle height as necessary. If necessary, inner bushing and mounting bushings can now be removed and replaced.

Installation — Refit inner dished washer with dish facing bushing, then install inner bushing on each end of stabilizer bar. Insert stabilizer bar and fit outer rubber bushings with dished washers. Reinstall mounting brackets and tighten all nuts and bolts.

TIGHTENING SPECIFICATIONS

Application	Ft. Lbs. (N·m)
Stabilizer Bar-to-Chassis	37 (50)
Stabilizer Bar-to-Lower Control Link	59 (80)
Strut Mounting-to-Body	21 (29)
Strut-to-Mounting	44 (60)
Strut Tube Plug Nut	74 (101)
Tie Rod-to-Stub Axle	74 (101)

Front Suspension

VOLKSWAGEN DASHER

DESCRIPTION

Volkswagen Dasher is front wheel drive with independent strut type front suspension. Axles are supported by lower control arms, vertically mounted strut assemblies, and a stabilizer bar. Strut assemblies consist of double action shock absorbers with coil springs mounted over the outside. The top part of strut is attached to the inner fender panel and the lower portion is attached directly to steering knuckle. Tie rods are connected to supports under coil springs. Stabilizer bar is connected to lower control arms at each end and to crossmember below engine.

ADJUSTMENT

WHEEL ALIGNMENT SPECIFICATIONS & PROCEDURES

See Wheel Alignment Specifications & Procedures in WHEEL ALIGNMENT Section.

WHEEL BEARING ADJUSTMENT

Front wheel bearings are pressed into bearing housing and no adjustment is required.

BALL JOINT CHECKING

1) Raise and support front of vehicle and turn steering wheel to one side. Install suitable levering tool so that ball joint spring may be compressed.

2) With spring compressed, position a vernier caliper with lower jaw on ball joint stud and upper jaw on top of clamping bolt for ball joint stud. Note reading.

3) Slowly release tension from spring and note travel of caliper. This reading indicates ball joint play. If play exceeds .040" (1 mm) for new ball joints or .100" (2.5 mm) for used ball joints, replace ball joint.

REMOVAL & INSTALLATION

STRUT & COIL SPRING ASSEMBLY

Removal — 1) Loosen axle nut and wheel lugs. Raise and support vehicle; remove wheel and tire. Remove brake hose clips, disconnect brake caliper and move out of way.

2) Loosen bolt holding suspension ball joint stud in bottom of strut assembly. Using suitable tool, remove tie rod end from mounting under coil spring seat. Disconnect stabilizer bar from lower control arm.

3) Force lower control arm down until ball joint stud is removed from suspension strut. Remove axle nut. Support axle drive shaft, then pull strut outward and off of axle drive shaft. Remove both upper mounting nuts. Guide strut from vehicle.

Disassembly — 1) Place strut in a vise and install coil spring compressor. Tighten compressor until pressure is taken off upper retainer. Remove upper collar mounting nut. Take off upper mounting hardware. Release spring compressor and remove coil spring.

2) Hold shock absorber cartridge center shaft with suitable tool. Loosen and remove threaded cap nut. If shock absorber cartridge will not easily pull front strut tube, thread a nut on center shaft and tap until corrosion breaks free.

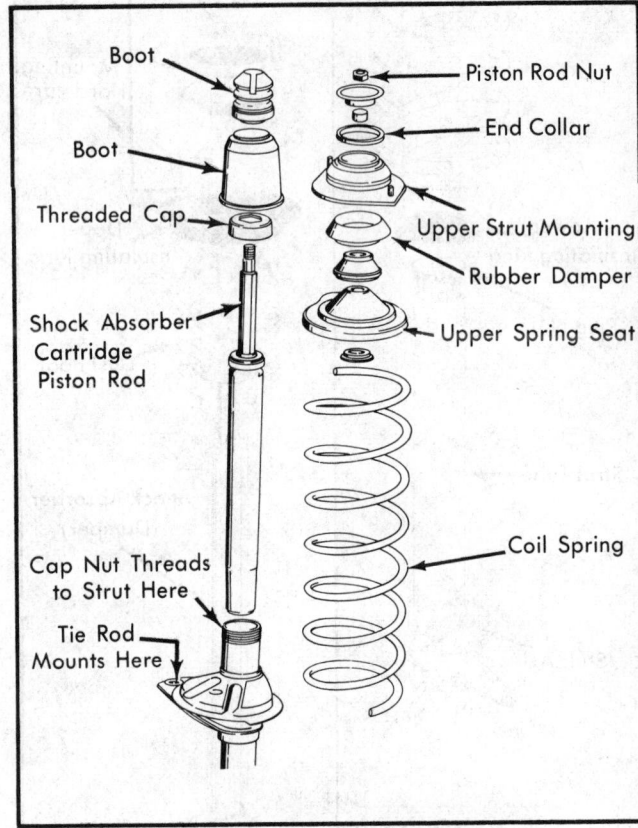

Fig. 1   Exploded View of Front Suspension Strut

Reassembly — To reassemble, reverse disassembly procedure, noting the following: Coil springs may be replaced individually, but paint stripe color of replacement spring must match stripe color of original spring.

Installation — To install, reverse removal procedure and note the following. When assembling ball joint to lower control arm always use a new bolt and nut. Face bolt head toward front of vehicle.

WHEEL BEARINGS

Removal — 1) Remove strut assembly from vehicle as previously described. Using a press, press wheel hub out of bearing.

NOTE — *Wheel bearing is destroyed in pressing out hub. Once either the wheel hub or bearing has been removed from suspension strut, a new bearing must be installed.*

2) Remove 2 circlips inside bearing housing (one at each end of bearing). Using a press tool, apply pressure to bearing outer race. Press out bearing toward outboard end of bearing housing.

Installation — To install, reverse removal procedure.

Front Suspension

VOLKSWAGEN DASHER (Cont.)

LOWER CONTROL ARM

Removal — **1)** Raise vehicle so that front wheel and suspension are not supported.

2) Disconnect stabilizer bar at control arm and subframe. Slide stabilizer bar out of vehicle.

3) Loosen ball joint clamp bolt. Force lower control arm down until ball joint stud is removed from suspension strut. Remove bolts mounting control arm to subframe. Guide arm from vehicle.

Bushing Replacement — **1)** Check bushing in control arm for signs of excessive wear or damage. If bushings are bad they can be replaced.

2) Support wide points on control arm. Press bushings from each side of control arm.

3) Select new bushings. Lightly coat each bushing with brake paste. Press bushing into position in control arm. Make sure bushing does not twist when pressing into place. Use bushing guide if necessary.

Installation — Reverse removal procedure and note: Use water pump pliers to compress clamps around bushing when trying to start bolts. Check front wheel alignment.

STABILIZER BAR

Removal — **1)** Raise vehicle and suitably support with safety stands. Remove brackets mounting stabilizer bar to lower control arm .

2) Loosen and remove "U" brackets mounting stabilizer bar to subframe. Guide stabilizer bar from vehicle. Inspect rubber bushings for damage or excessive wear and replace as necessay.

Installation — To install, reverse removal procedure. Install with end sections pointing down. Drive vehicle around the block before fully tightening clamp bolts.

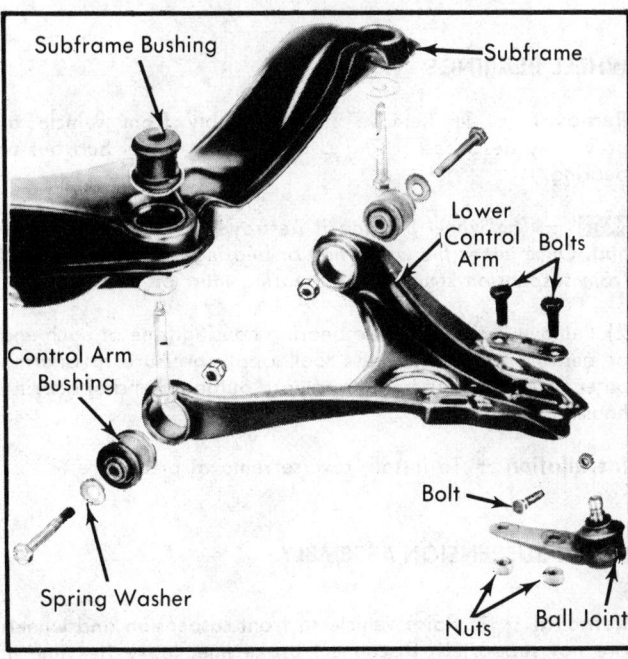

Fig. 2 Exploded View of Lower Control Arm

TIGHTENING SPECIFICATIONS

Application	Ft. Lbs. (N·m)
Axle Nut	
18mm Nut	145 (197)
20mm Nut	175 (238)
Ball Joint-to-Suspension Strut	36 (49)
Ball Joint-to-Lower Control Arm	47 (64)
Lower Control Arm-to-Subframe	50 (68)
Piston Rod Nut	43 (58)
Stabilizer Bar-to-Lower Control Arm	7 (10)
stabilizer Bar-to-Subframe	18 (24)
Shock Absorber Cap Nut	108 (147)
Tie Rod Castle Nut	29 (39)
Upper Strut Assembly-to-Body	18 (24)

Front Suspension

VOLKSWAGEN JETTA, RABBIT, RABBIT PICKUP & SCIROCCO

DESCRIPTION

Vehicles are equipped with front wheel drive and independent strut type front suspension. Axles are supported by lower control arms, and vertically mounted strut assemblies. Strut assemblies consist of double action shock absorbers with coil springs mounted over the outside. The top portion of strut is attached to inner fender panel and lower portion is attached directly to steering knuckle. Tie rods are connected to steering knuckle.

ADJUSTMENT

WHEEL ALIGNMENT SPECIFICATIONS & PROCEDURES

See *Wheel Alignment Specifications & Procedures* in WHEEL ALIGNMENT Section.

WHEEL BEARING ADJUSTMENT

Front wheel bearings are pressed into bearing housing and no adjustment is required.

BALL JOINT CHECKING

1) Raise and support front of vehicle and turn steering wheel to one side. Install suitable levering tool so that ball joint spring may be compressed.

2) With spring compressed, position a vernier caliper with lower jaw on ball joint stud and upper jaw on top of clamping bolt for ball joint stud. Note reading.

3) Slowly release tension from spring and note travel of caliper. This reading indicates ball joint play. If play exceeds .040" (1 mm) for new ball joints or .100" (2.5 mm) for used ball joints, replace ball joints.

REMOVAL & INSTALLATION

STRUT ASSEMBLY

NOTE — *Suspension strut does not need to be removed to replace end collar. Only requirement is to leave vehicle on ground.*

Removal — 1) Raise vehicle so front suspension and front wheels are not supported.

2) Remove bolts mounting suspension strut to steering knuckle. Note that top bolt is one used to adjust front wheel camber.

3) Remove brake caliper assembly and suspend out of way. Pry or force suspension strut out of steering knuckle.

4) Support front suspension by hand. Also, support lower control arm and related components. Work inside engine compartment and remove upper strut mounting nuts. Guide out strut assembly.

Disassembly — Fit strut to spring compressor. Slightly collapse coil spring. Remove shock absorber piston rod nut. Slowly release spring pressure. Take off upper mounting hardware and coil spring.

Reassembly — 1) Fit protective sleeve and buffer over piston rod.

NOTE — *Both coil springs must be of same class. If set cannot be matched, both springs will have to be replaced. Springs are color coded.*

2) Position coil spring into lower spring seat. Install the upper spring retainer. Fit entire assembly into spring compressor and collapse coil gradually until whole threaded portion of piston rod is exposed.

3) Put on bearing, rubber bumper and remaining upper mounting components. Hold piston rod and tighten piston rod lock nut.

Installation — Reverse removal procedure and check front wheel alignment.

WHEEL BEARINGS

Removal — 1) Remove strut assembly from vehicle as previously described. Using a press, press wheel hub out of bearing.

NOTE — *The wheel bearing is destroyed in pressing out the hub. Once either the wheel hub or bearing has been removed from suspension strut, a new bearing must be installed.*

2) Remove 2 circlips inside bearing housing (one at each end of bearing). Using a press tool, apply pressure to bearing outer race. Press out bearing toward outboard end of bearing housing.

Installation — To install, reverse removal procedure.

FRONT SUSPENSION ASSEMBLY

Removal — 1) Raise vehicle so front suspension and wheels are not supported. Disconnect brake line, leave flex line in place, and plug openings.

2) Remove tie rod castle nut. Press tie rod from steering knuckle. Remove bolts mounting inner portion of constant velocity joint to transaxle drive flange.

3) Remove lower control arm front pivot bolt. Remove 2 bolts mounting "U" shaped bracket holding control arm rear pivot.

NOTE — *On vehicles equipped with automatic transmissions, engine may have to be slightly raised to gain access to pivot bolts.*

4) Support suspension assembly. Remove upper strut mounting nuts located in engine compartment. Guide assembly from vehicle.

Installation — Reverse removal procedure and note: Make sure convex side of thrust washer faces pivot bolt head.

VOLKSWAGEN JETTA, RABBIT, RABBIT PICKUP & SCIROCCO (Cont.)

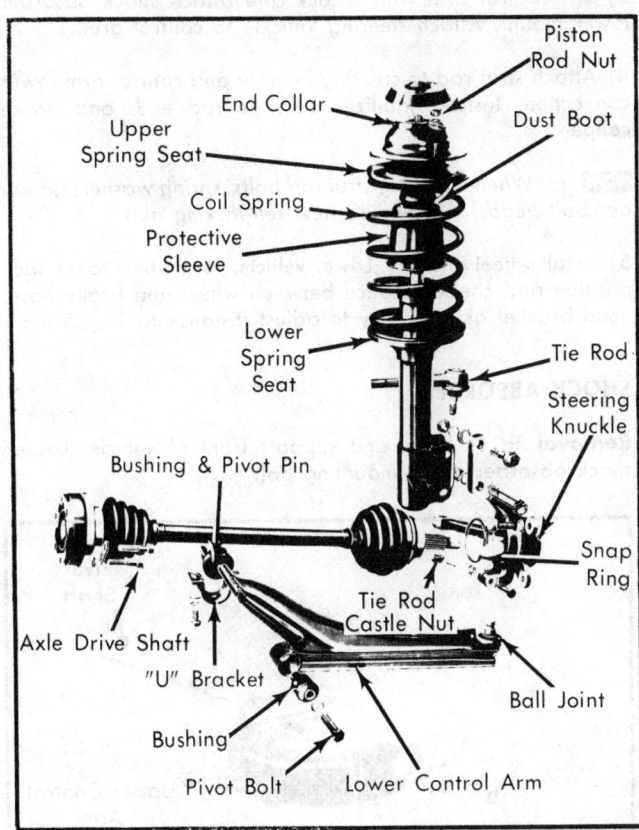

Fig. 1   Exploded View of Front Suspension Components

LOWER CONTROL ARM & BALL JOINT

NOTE — *Ball Joint can be replaced while control arm is in vehicle.*

Removal — 1) Raise vehicle and suitably support with front suspension free. Remove nut and clamp bolt mounting ball joint in bottom of steering knuckle. Force ball joint out of steering knuckle. Leave control arm hanging in mounts at subframe.

2) If control arm is not being removed, drill out 3 ball joint rivets with a 9/32" (7 mm) drill. After drilling it still may be necessary to chisel off rivet heads. Remove ball joint.

3) If control arm is being removed, take out pivot bolt and "U" bracket housing inner pivot pin. Slide out control arm.

NOTE — *On vehicles equipped with automatic transmissions, engine may have to be slightly raised to gain access to pivot bolts.*

Inspection — Check lower control arm bushings. If bushings are bad they can be replaced. Press out worn bushing. Select new bushing and press into position. Make sure bushing does not twist when seating into place.

Installation — Slide new ball joint into slot in control arm. Tighten ball joint mounting bolts. Refit lower control arm to subframe (chassis). Install ball joint into lower section of suspension strut.

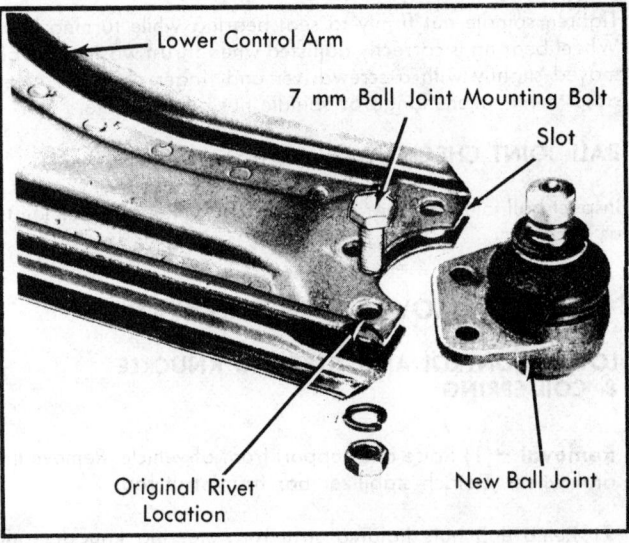

Fig. 2   New Ball Joint Installation Location in Lower Control Arm

TIGHTENING SPECIFICATIONS

Application	Ft. Lbs. (N·m)
Axle Shaft Nut	173 (235)
Axle Drive Shaft-to-Transaxle	32 (44)
Ball Joint Clamp Bolt-to-Steering Knuckle	36 (49)
Control Arm-to-Subframe (Chassis)	50 (68)
New Ball Joint-to-Control Arm	18 (24)
Piston Rod Nut	58 (79)
Pivot Pin "U" Bracket	32 (44)
Suspension Strut-to-Steering Knuckle	58 (79)
Suspension Strut-to-Inner Fender	14 (19)
Tie Rod Castle Nut	22 (30)

Front Suspension

VOLKSWAGEN VANAGON

DESCRIPTION

Front suspension consists of upper and lower control arms and ball joints, shock absorbers surrounded by coil springs, and steering knuckles. Strut rods attach to chassis and lower control arms, and stabilizer bar attaches to chassis and strut rod.

ADJUSTMENT

WHEEL ALIGNMENT SPECIFICATIONS & PROCEDURES

See Wheel Alignment Specifications and Procedures in WHEEL ALIGNMENT Section.

WHEEL BEARING ADJUSTMENT

Tighten spindle nut firmly to seat bearing while turning hub. Wheel bearing is correctly adjusted when thrust washer can be moved slightly with a screwdriver and finger pressure. After adjustment, peen flange of spindle nut over spindle.

BALL JOINT CHECKING

Inspect ball joint for wear or excessive play. Replace ball joints as necessary.

REMOVAL & INSTALLATION

LOWER CONTROL ARM, STEERING KNUCKLE & COIL SPRING

Removal – 1) Raise and support front of vehicle. Remove tire and wheel. Detach stabilizer bar from strut rod.

2) Remove 3 nuts holding strut rod, steering knuckle, and lower control arm together. Remove brake caliper and brake hose bracket.

NOTE – Strut rod length determines caster angle. If setting at body mounting is changed, caster must be readjusted.

3) Hang caliper from body with wire hook. Using suitable pressing tool, detach tie rod end from steering knuckle.

4) Remove upper ball joint from upper control arm. Detach steering knuckle from upper and lower control arms.

5) Loosen shock absorber lower mounting on lower control arm. Support lower control arm with a jack, and pull out shock absorber bolt from lower control arm.

6) Lower jack slowly and remove coil spring. Remove lower control arm pivot bolt and remove control arm from vehicle.

Bushing Replacement – Using suitable press and adapters, press out old bushings and press in replacements.

Installation – 1) Install lower control arm to vehicle with pivot bolt. Position coil spring so straight end is at bottom.

2) Attach damping ring to spring with tape. Install spring in control arm spring depression.

3) Lift control arm with a jack and attach shock absorber lower mount. Attach steering knuckle to control arm.

4) Attach strut rod to steering knuckle and control arm lower connection. Install stabilizer bar, tie rod end, and brake caliper.

NOTE – When installing strut rod bolts, spring washers go under bolt heads. Always use new self-locking nuts.

5) Install wheel and tire. Lower vehicle. Turn wheel to full-lock position and check distance between wheel and brake hose. Bend bracket as necessary to adjust distance to 1" (25 mm).

SHOCK ABSORBER

Removal – 1) Raise and support front of vehicle. Loosen shock absorber lower mounting bolt.

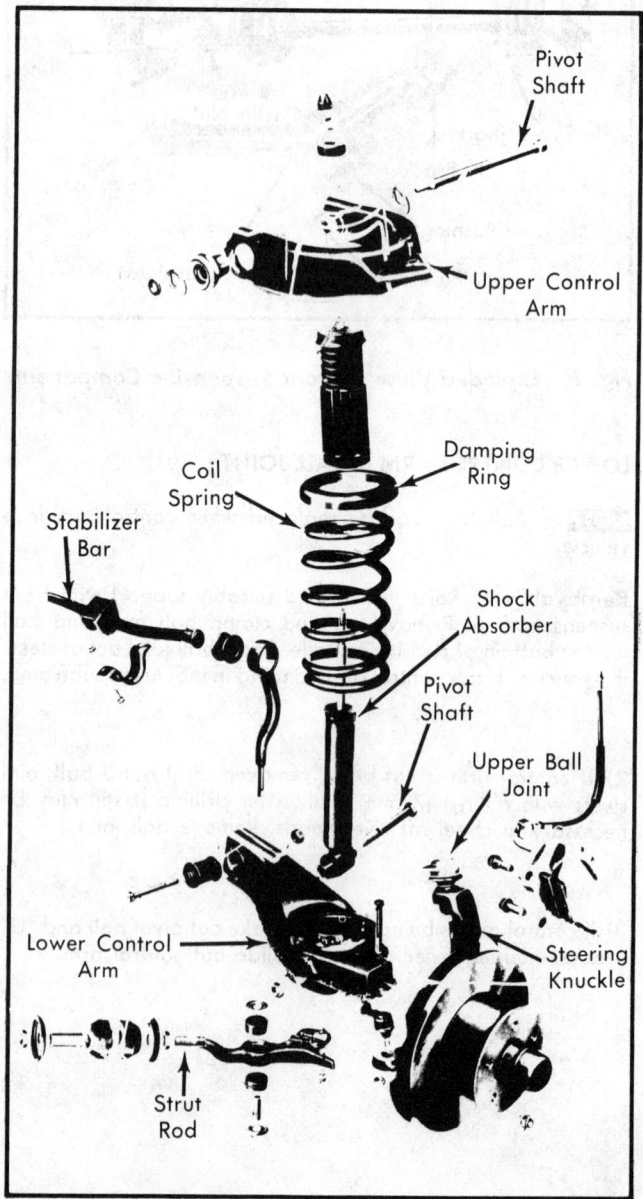

Fig. 1 Exploded View of Vanagon Front Suspension

VOLKSWAGEN VANAGON (Cont.)

2) Lower vehicle to ground and remove mounting bolt. Raise vehicle and remove shock absorber upper mounting hardware and remove shock absorber from vehicle.

Installation — With vehicle raised off ground, install shock absorber to upper mounting. Lower vehicle and attach shock absorber to lower control arm.

NOTE — *When lifting vehicle with shock absorber disconnected, avoid damaging upper ball joint.*

UPPER CONTROL ARM

Removal — 1) Raise and support vehicle. Remove tire and wheel. Remove bolts holding upper ball joint to upper control arm.

2) Swing steering knuckle carefully to one side. Note the position of upper control arm pivot shaft and remove from control arm. Remove control arm from vehicle.

Bushing Replacement — Note the position of and grind off spot welds holding in bushings. Using suitable press and adapters, press out old bushing and press in replacements. Secure bushing with spot welds in noted locations. Clean up welds and paint surface.

Installation — Lubricate pivot shaft with multi-purpose grease. Install upper control arm to body and position pivot shaft as noted during removal. Install ball joint to upper control arm. Install tire and wheel and lower vehicle.

NOTE — *Flat on pivot shaft must be vertical and face center of vehicle. Larger side of eccentric washer faces down.*

STABILIZER BAR

Removal & Installation — Disconnect stabilizer bar from strut rod. Remove bolts holding mounting bracket to chassis and remove stabilizer bar. To install, reverse removal procedure.

STRUT ROD

Removal & Installation — Disconnect stabilizer bar from strut rod. Remove 3 nuts holding strut rod, steering knuckle and lower control arm together. Remove hardware mounting strut rod to chassis and remove strut rod from vehicle. To install, reverse removal procedure and adjust caster.

NOTE — *When attaching strut rod, steering knuckle, and lower control arm, spring washers are to be installed under bolt heads. Always use new self-locking nuts.*

WHEEL BEARINGS

Removal — 1) Raise vehicle and support with stands. Remove wheel and grease cap. Remove cotter pin and loosen outer bearing nut.

2) Remove caliper mounting bolts and remove caliper. Remove outer bearing nut, washer, outer bearing and disc. Remove seal from disc and remove inner bearing.

Installation — To install, reverse removal procedure.

BALL JOINTS

Removal — Remove steering knuckle from vehicle. Using ball joint adapter tool (VW 267a), remove ball joint adapter from lower ball joint. Remove nuts securing ball joints to steering knuckle and using same tool, press out upper ball joint. Remove circlip from lower ball joint and use suitable press to press ball joint from steering knuckle.

Installation — 1) Press in ball joints with flat side of shoulder facing spindle. Attach adapter loosely to lower ball joint.

NOTE — *Do not tighten adapter fully. Adapter must be aligned with control arm when steering knuckle is installed or rubber boot will tear.*

2) Install steering knuckle to vehicle and tighten ball joints and adapter with new self-locking nuts.

TIGHTENING SPECIFICATIONS

Application	Ft. Lbs. (N·m)
Ball Joint Locking Nuts①	80 (109)
Brake Caliper-to-Mounting	115 (156)
Shock Absorber Top Nut	22 (30)
Stabilizer Bracket-to-Chassis	14 (19)
Stabilizer-to-Strut Rod	22 (30)
Strut Rod-to-Chassis	72 (98)
Strut Rod-to-Lower Control Arm①	
1st Tightening	47 (64)
2nd Tightening	51 (69)
Lower Control Arm Pivot Bolt	65 (88)
Tie Rod End-to-Steering Knuckle	22 (30)
Upper Ball Joint-to-Control Arm	43 (58)
Upper Control Arm Pivot Bolt	54 (73)

① — Always use new locking nuts.

Front Suspension

VOLVO

DL	GLE
GL	Bertone
GLT	Diesel

DESCRIPTION

Strut type suspension consisting of a vertically mounted strut assembly. Strut assembly is mounted to chassis frame at top by means of a thrust bearing. Lower end of strut assembly is mounted to a ball joint which is bolted to lower control arm. Steering knuckle is an integral part of strut assembly. Strut assembly consists of a shock absorber built into strut outer tube; a coil spring mounted on outside of strut assembly; and a spindle integral with bottom of strut. A stabilizer bar connects the control arms through rubber mounted links.

ADJUSTMENT

WHEEL ALIGNMENT SPECIFICATIONS & PROCEDURES

See *Wheel Alignment Specifications & Procedures* in *WHEEL ALIGNMENT* Section.

WHEEL BEARING ADJUSTMENT

While rotating hub, tighten nut to 50 ft. lbs. (68 N·m). Loosen nut 1/3 turn and check for hub rotating freely with no end play. If necessary to align cotter pin holes, loosen nut and install cotter pin.

BALL JOINT CHECKING

Maximum permitted axial play for lower ball joint is .12" (3 mm). Check ball joint by prying back and forth with a bar. If specifications are exceeded, replace ball joints.

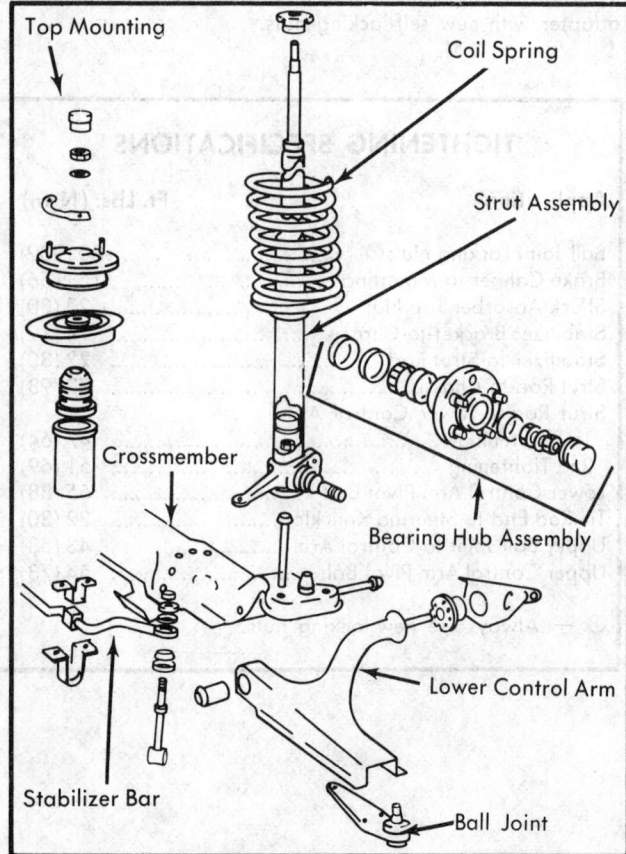

Fig. 1   Exploded View of Front Suspension Assembly

REMOVAL & INSTALLATION

CONTROL ARM

Removal — Raise vehicle and support on safety stands, then remove wheel and tire. Disconnect stabilizer bar-to-link assembly. Disconnect ball joint from control arm at three attaching bolts. Remove front attaching bolt for control arm. Remove bracket attaching rear of control arm to chassis, then remove control arm from vehicle. If control arm bushing is being replaced, press out using proper adapter (9995085) and driver (9995091).

Installation — Inspect all components for wear or damage. Use proper adapter (9995085) and driver (5555084) to install new bushings if necessary. If bushing in bracket is replaced, ensure that small slots on new bushing will point in a horizontal position when bracket is installed on vehicle. Install bracket, with control arm, to chassis but do not tighten bolts. Install front attaching bolt for control arm but do not tighten. Install ball joint to control arm and tighten bolts. Position a jack under control arm and raise so coil spring is compressed. Connect stabilizer bar to link. Tighten control arm attaching nuts and bolts. Install wheel and tire.

NOTE — *Tighten rear bushing nut with vehicle weight resting on wheel.*

SHOCK ABSORBER

Removal — **1)** Raise vehicle and support on safety stands, then remove wheel and tire. Position jack under control arm and raise slightly to provide support. Using a spring compressor, compress coil spring being sure to engage five coils with tool. Disconnect steering rod from steering arm and stabilizer bar from link at control arm. Remove bolt attaching brake line bracket. Remove cover on upper end of strut and spring assembly. Remove center nut using tool as indicated in *Fig. 2*.

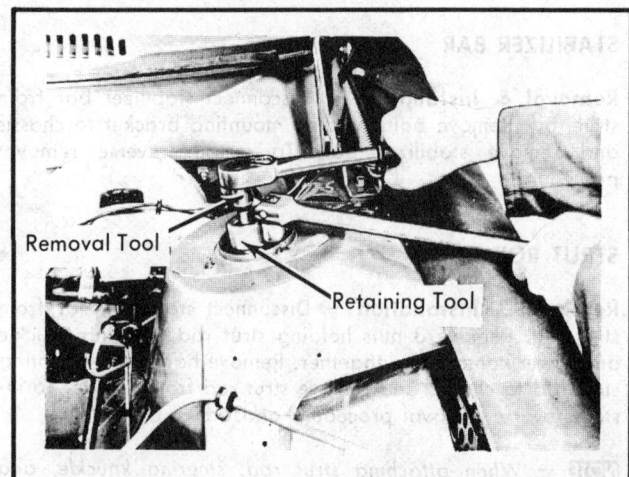

Fig. 2   View Showing Removal of Strut Assembly Center Nut

2) Lower jack supporting control arm while supporting strut assembly so brake lines and hoses are not damaged. Hook special tool (9995045) to strut assembly and stabilizer to support unit during remaining removal procedures. Remove the spring seat and rubber bumper. Remove coil spring with compressor tool attached. Remove shock absorber retaining nut while holding strut outer casing at the weld. Pull shock absorber from casing.

Front Suspension

VOLVO (Cont.)

Installation – 1) Install new shock absorber and retaining nut while holding strut outer casing at the weld. Pull shock absorber spindle to fully extended position. Install coil spring onto strut assembly making sure spring end is properly aligned on strut bracket. Install rubber bumper and install spring seat on coil spring. Guide strut assembly into upper mount and shock absorber spindle through upper mount. Connect stabilizer bar to stabilizer link.

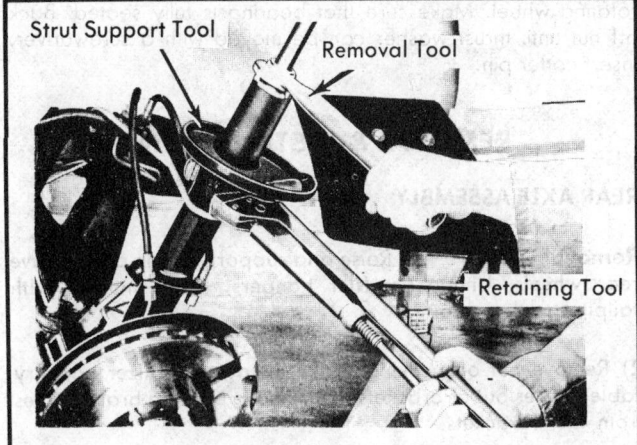

Fig. 3   View Showing Removal of Shock Absorber Nut

Strut Support Tool
Removal Tool
Retaining Tool

2) Position jack under control arm and raise slightly. Install and tighten washer and nut to shock absorber spindle while using proper retaining tool. Install cover, then connect brake line bracket to chassis. Connect steering arm to steering rod and remove coil spring compressor tool slowly. Install wheel and tire.

WHEEL BEARINGS

Removal – 1) Raise vehicle and support with stands. Remove wheel and grease cap. Remove cotter pin and loosen outer bearing nut.

2) Remove caliper mounting bolts and remove caliper. Remove outer bearing nut, washer, outer bearing and disc. Remove seal from disc and remove inner bearing.

Installation – To install, reverse removal procedure.

BALL JOINTS

Removal – Raise vehicle and support with safety stands. Loosen shock absorber nut. Remove 4 bolts attaching ball joint to strut assembly. Remove ball joint from control arm, then remove ball joint nut and separate from attachment.

Installation – Position new ball joint to attachment and tighten nut. Install ball joint assembly to strut assembly and to control arm. Tighten shock absorber retaining nut.

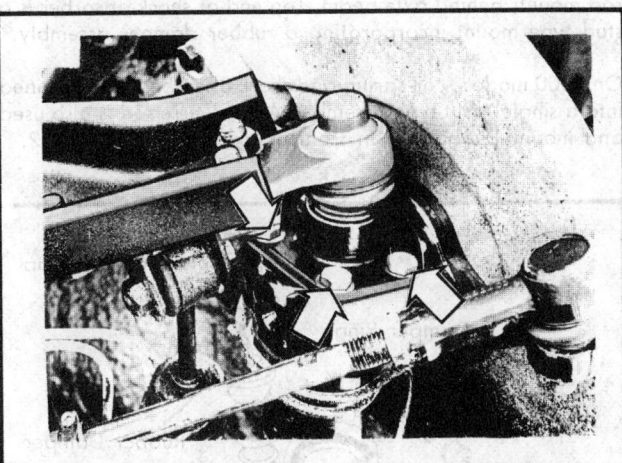

Fig. 4 View Showing Ball Joint Retaining Bolts

TIGHTENING SPECIFICATIONS

Application	Ft. Lbs. (N·m)
Ball Joint-to-Control Arm	70-95 (95-129)
Ball Joint Assembly-to-Strut	15-20 (20-27)
Ball Joint-to-Bracket	35-50 (48-68)
Control Arm Bracket-to-Frame	22-36 (30-49)
Control Arm Retaining Bolts	
Front	40-70 (54-95)
Rear	36-43 (49-58)

Rear Suspension

AUDI

4000
5000

DESCRIPTION

Suspension on all Audi models consists of coil springs, shock absorbers, transverse rod and trailing arms. Some design differences occur between models.

On 5000 models, rear suspension arrangement is illustrated in *Fig. 1*. On these models, coil spring is mounted directly on rear axle and shock absorber is mounted separately. Transverse rod mounts behind axle beam. Top end of shock absorber is a stud type mount incorporating a rubber damper assembly.

On 4000 models, coil spring and shock absorber are combined into a single, strut type assembly. A transverse rod is also used and mounts diagonally in front of axle beam. See *Fig. 2*.

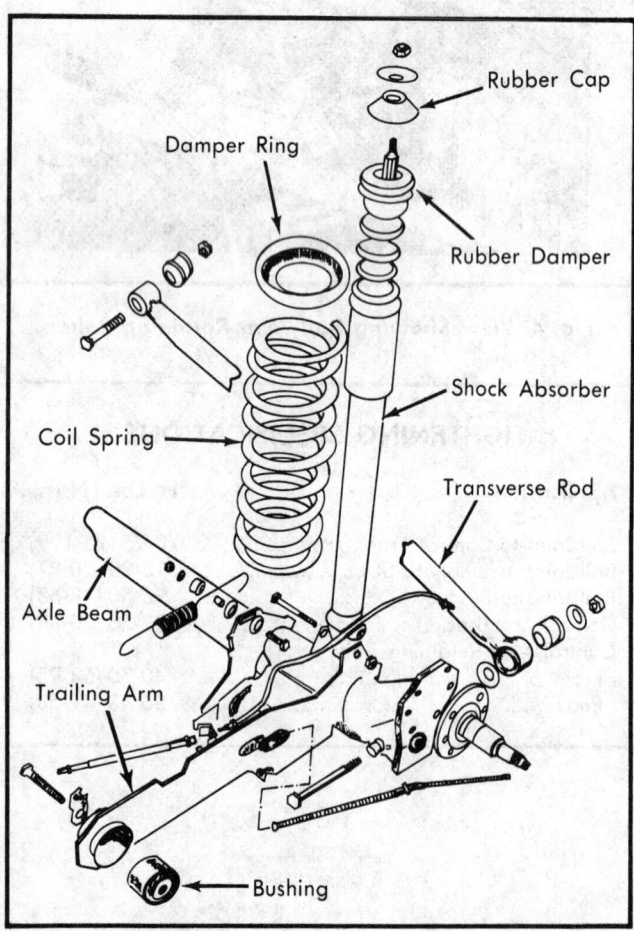

**Fig. 1   Exploded View of Audi 5000
Rear Suspension**

ADJUSTMENTS

WHEEL ALIGNMENT SPECIFICATIONS & PROCEDURES

See Wheel Alignment Specifications and Procedures in WHEEL ALIGNMENT Section.

WHEEL BEARING ADJUSTMENT

4000 Models — Remove grease cap, cotter pin and castle nut. Tighten spindle nut and loosen for adjustment. Adjust by lightly tightening spindle nut until plain washer (beneath spindle nut) can be just be moved from side to side with a screwdriver.

5000 Models — Tighten adjustment nut firmly while rotating wheel. Make sure that bearing is fully seated. Back off nut until thrust washer can be moved with a screwdriver. Insert cotter pin.

REMOVAL & INSTALLATION

REAR AXLE ASSEMBLY

Removal (4000) — 1) Raise and support vehicle and remove rear wheels. Unhook muffler hangers, lower muffler with tailpipe and secure.

2) Remove nut on parking brake linkage equalizer bar. Pry cable sleeves out of brackets and remove parking brake cables from their brackets.

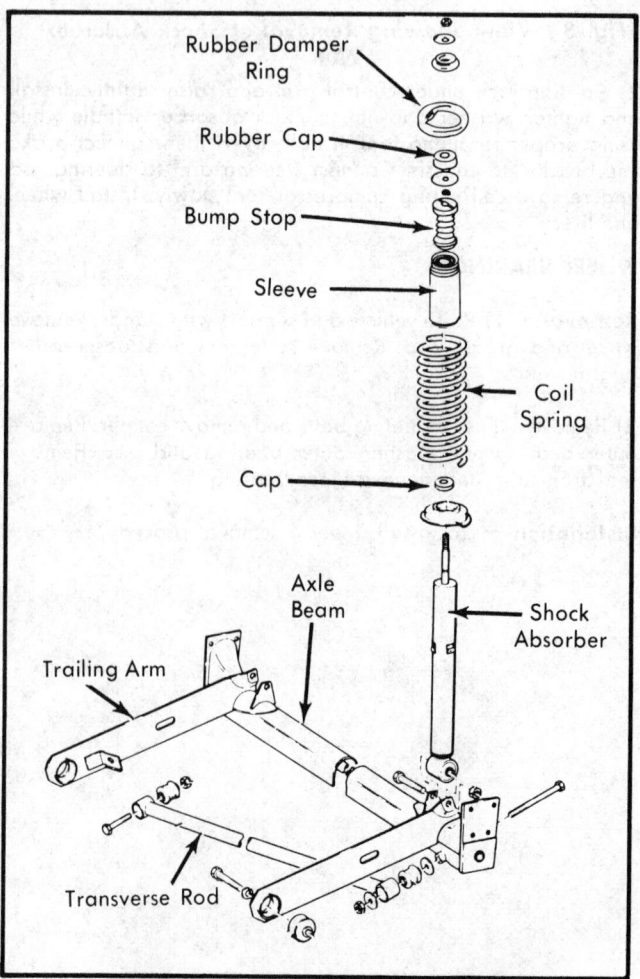

**Fig. 2   Exploded View of Audi 4000
Rear Suspension**

SUSPENSION

AUDI (Cont.)

3) Detach brake hoses and plug lines. Remove nuts from trailing arm mounting bolts, leaving bolts in place. Disconnect spring from brake pressure regulator.

4) Remove transverse rod mounting bolt, suspension strut mounting bolts, and trailing arm mounting bolts. Remove rear axle assembly while guiding parking brake cable over tailpipe and muffler.

Bushing Replacement (4000) — Place trailing arm in press and force bushing from arm. Reverse process to install new bushing. Make sure bushing slots are positioned horizontally in trailing arm.

Installation (4000) — 1) Raise and support vehicle. Place rear axle in position. Install both trailing arm bolts and hand tighten. Install rear wheels, lower vehicle and tighten trailing arm bolts with wheels on ground.

2) Install transverse rod, brake hoses, and spring for pressure regulator. Bleed brakes, attach parking brake cable and adjust.

Removal (5000) — 1) Loosen, but do not remove wheel bolts. Raise and support vehicle. Remove bolt from transverse rod at axle mounting. Detach right brake hose at coupling with steel tubing. Plug openings.

2) Detach brake pressure regulator spring (hooked to lower mounting bolt of shock absorber). Detach left brake hose at connection with tubing and plug openings.

3) Remove right fuel tank retaining strap. Remove parking brake cable from guide on fuel tank. Loosen left side parking brake cable bolt. Loosen parking brake adjusting nut and disconnect parking brake cable.

4) Remove rear mounting for exhaust system. Lower vehicle to ground. Remove both shock absorber top nuts. Using frame jack, raise vehicle slowly until coil spring can be removed from axle mountings. Remove rear wheels.

5) Remove trailing arm mounting bolts, with rear axle suitably supported on a jack. While slowly lowering axle assembly from vehicle, guide parking brake cable over exhaust pipe.

Bushing Replacement (5000) — Place trailing arm in press and force bushing from arm. Reverse process to install new bushing. Align cutouts with center axis.

Installation (5000) — 1) Raise vehicle and position rear axle in vehicle. Install and lightly tighten trailing arm mounting bolts. Install both rear wheels and lower vehicle to ground.

2) Position rubber damper rings on coil springs, jack up vehicle body, position springs and slowly lower body to hold springs (3 persons may be required to perform this step).

3) Tighten shock absorber top mounting nuts. Raise vehicle and check position of coil springs. If necessary, turn springs in mounting to correct their positions.

4) With vehicle resting on ground, tighten trailing arm bolts. Install transverse rod, brake hoses, spring for brake pressure regulator and fuel tank retaining strap.

5) Bleed brake system, attach and adjust parking brake cable.

TRANSVERSE ROD

Removal (All Models) — Raise and support vehicle. Remove nuts from transverse rod bolts and tap bolts out of holes. Inspect bushings and sleeves for wear and replace if necessary.

Installation (All Models) — To install, reverse removal procedure.

SHOCK ABSORBERS

NOTE — *Remove and install shock absorbers one at a time. Do not allow rear axle to hang from body mounts only.*

Removal (4000) — Loosen trunk sheet metal trim and remove shock absorber top protective cap. Remove upper mounting nut. Raise vehicle, remove lower mounting bolt and remove shock absorber.

Removal (5000) — Remove top shock absorber mounting. Remove lower mounting and shock.

Installation (All Models) — To install, reverse removal procedure. On 4000 models, be sure top protection cap is properly installed.

TIGHTENING SPECIFICATIONS

Application	Ft. Lbs. (N.m)
Shock Absorbers	
Upper	14 (19)
Lower	
4000	43 (58)
5000	40 (54)
Trailing Arm	
4000	72 (98)
5000	69 (94)
Transverse Rod	
4000	51 (69)
5000	65 (88)

BMW

320i
528i
633CSi
733i

DESCRIPTION

Independent type rear suspension with rear struts. Semi-trailing control arms pivot on crossmember and are integral with axle shaft bearing housing. Shock absorber (strut assembly) mounts to purchase on top of control arm and to body. A stabilizer bar is attached to each trailing arm and at two points on crossmember.

ADJUSTMENTS

WHEEL ALIGNMENT SPECIFICATIONS & PROCEDURES

See Wheel Alignment Specifications and Procedures in WHEEL ALIGNMENT Section.

REMOVAL & INSTALLATION

STRUT ASSEMBLIES (SHOCK ABSORBERS)

Removal (Exc. 733i) — Raise vehicle and remove rear wheel. Place jack under control arm. Disconnect shock at lower mounting. Remove centering shell and mounting nuts from top of shock absorber. Remove assembly from vehicle.

Removal (733i) — Remove rear seat backrest. Raise and support vehicle under control arms. Detach lower mounting. Remove package shelf and detach centering shell at wheel housing. Remove shock absorber from vehicle.

Disassembly (All) — Using spring compressor, collapse spring and remove centering shell. Remove coil spring and boot. Pull retainer and auxiliary spring off shock absorber. Inspect and replace any defective parts.

Reassembly (All) — Reverse disassembly procedure, making sure coil spring is properly aligned before releasing spring compressor. Vent opening on spring faces inside retainer.

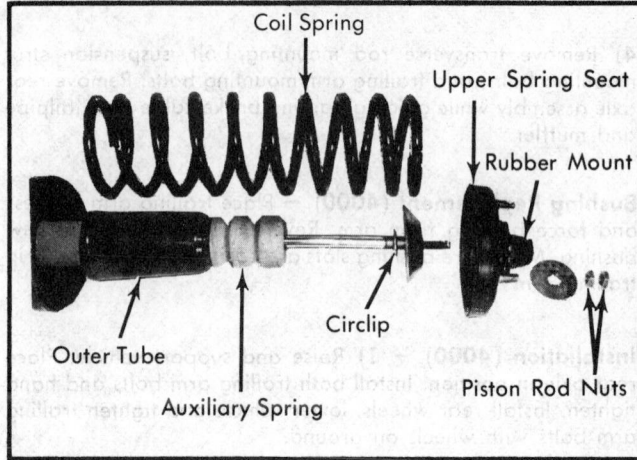

Fig. 2 Exploded View of BMW Rear Suspension Strut Assembly — 320i Shown

Installation (All) — To install, reverse removal procedure. Tighten bolts and nuts after vehicle is resting on ground.

SEMI-TRAILING CONTROL ARM

Removal (Exc. 733i) — **1)** Raise vehicle and remove rear wheels. Remove parking brake lever. Disconnect and plug brake line at union bracket. Detach brake pad wear sensor from right control arm (if equipped).

2) Remove stabilizer bar from control arm. Remove strut assembly (shock absorber) from vehicle. Disconnect axle drive shaft from bearing carrier. Place jack under control arm. Remove trailing arm pivot bolts at crossmember and lower arm to ground.

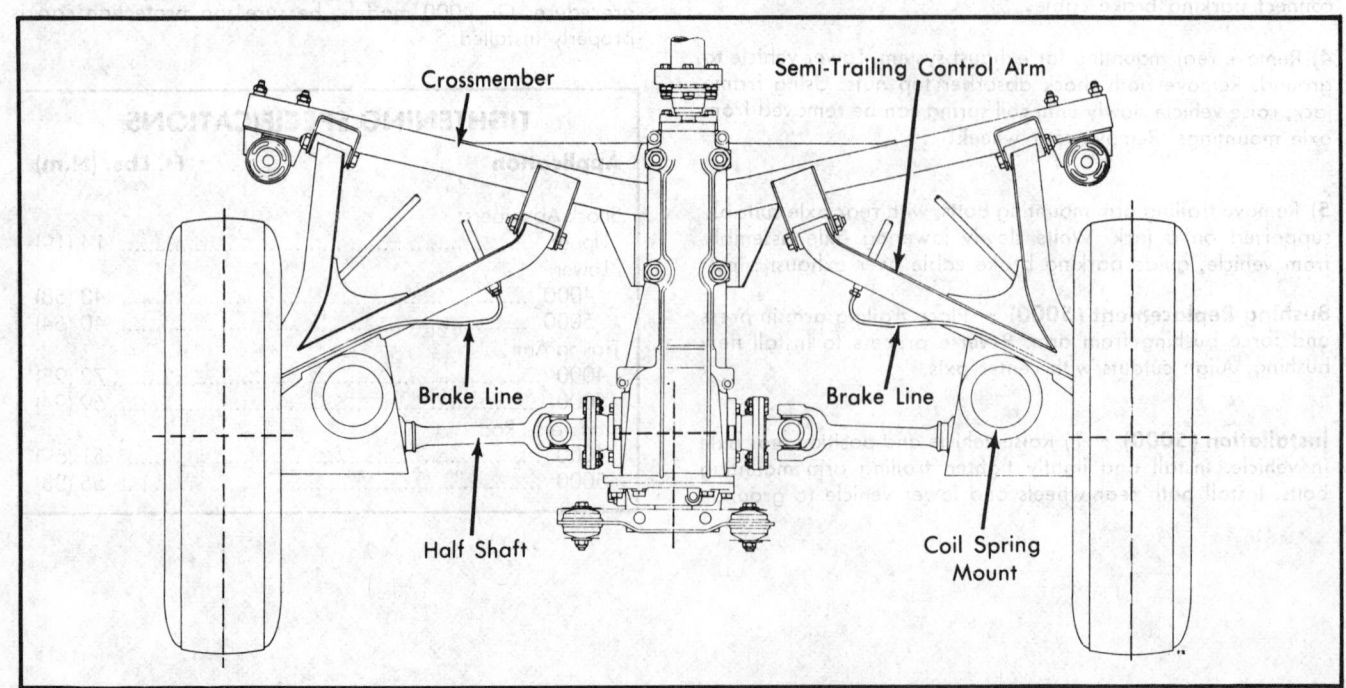

Fig. 1 Overhead View of BMW Rear Suspension

BMW (Cont.)

Removal (733i) – 1) Raise and support vehicle. Remove rear wheel. Pull up parking brake lever and detach output shaft at drive flange. Remove parking brake lever.

2) Using a syringe, draw off fluid from reservoir and detach and plug brake lines. Detach control arm from rear axle carrier. Detach shock absorber and remove control arm.

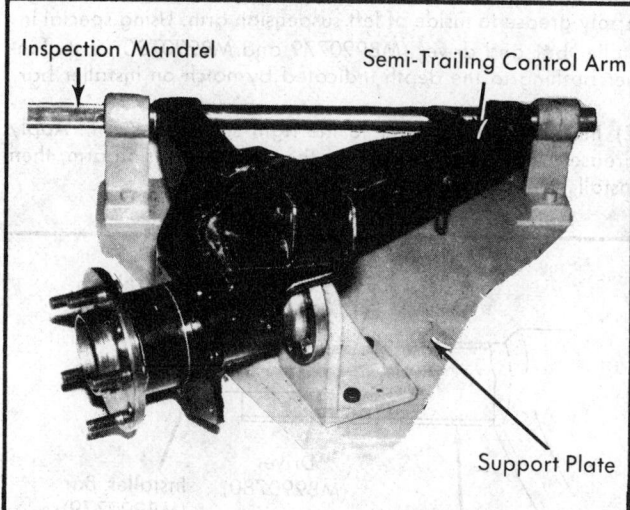

Inspection Mandrel

Semi-Trailing Control Arm

Support Plate

Fig. 3 Trailing Arm Fitted to Support Plate to Check Alignment

Inspection (All) – 1) Visually inspect bushings and replace as necessary. Before pressing out worn bushings, cut off collar. When pressing in new bushings, lubricate them with oil. Note that collared edge faces out.

2) Check trailing arm alignment. Place arm in support plate. See *Fig. 3.* Slide inspection mandrel through control arm to crossmember mounting bushings bores (bushings removed). If control arm is out of alignment it can be straightened if there is no other damage to arm.

Installation (All) – To install, reverse removal procedure and tighten nuts fully after vehicle is resting on ground. Bleed and adjust brakes.

TIGHTENING SPECIFICATIONS

Application	Ft. Lbs. (N.m)
Lower Shock Absorber Mount	
320i	36-39 (49-53)
528i, 633CSi & 733i	87-94 (118-127)
Upper Shock Absorber Mount	18-20 (24-27)
Trailing Arm-to-Crossmember	
320i	58-65 (79-88)
528i, 633CSi & 733i	49-54 (66-73)

Rear Suspension

CHRYSLER CORP. IMPORTS — FRONT-WHEEL-DRIVE MODELS

Champ
Colt

DESCRIPTION

Rear suspension is independent design and consists of left and right suspension arms, shock absorbers and coil springs. Suspension arms slide together on bushings. Suspension arms are attached to frame by shock absorbers and a clamp that utilizes bushings. Some models are equipped with a stabilizer bar which is attached to suspension arms near pivot points.

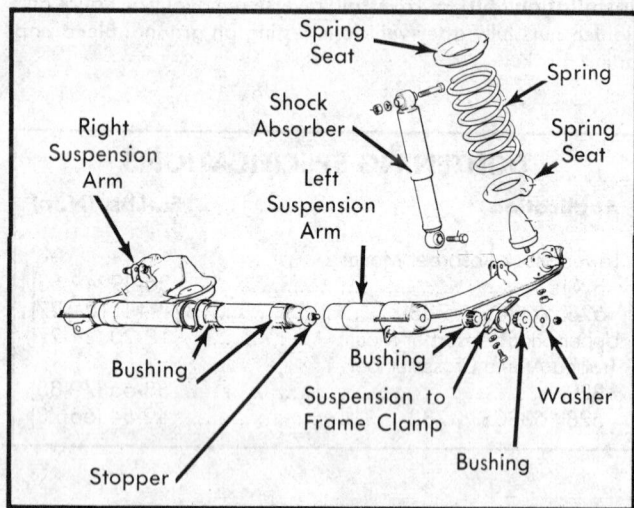

Fig. 1 Exploded View of Champ and Colt Hatchback Rear Suspension Assembly

ADJUSTMENT

WHEEL ALIGNMENT SPECIFICATIONS & PROCEDURES

See *Wheel Alignment Specifications and Procedures* in *WHEEL ALIGNMENT* Section.

WHEEL BEARING ADJUSTMENT

Tighten adjusting nut to 14 ft. lbs. (20 N·m). Loosen nut completely and then retighten to 48 INCH lbs. (5 N·m). Install cotter pin and dust cap.

REMOVAL & INSTALLATION

REAR SUSPENSION ASSEMBLY

Removal — 1) Raise and support rear of vehicle with jacks under frame. Remove rear brake assembly. Remove muffler. Raise suspension slightly.

2) Remove shock absorber, then lower jack and remove coil spring, Temporarily install shock absorber to suspension arm. Disconnect and plug brake hose at suspension arm.

3) Remove shock absorber and suspension clamp bolts. Remove suspension assembly from vehicle.

Disassembly — 1) With suspension assembly removed from vehicle, loosen nuts at both ends of suspension arms. Remove clamps washer and bushings. Remove dust cover (clamp).

2) On models with stabilizer bar, make an index mark at each end of bar in alignment with punch marks on brackets. On all models, separate suspension arms. Remove rubber stopper from right arm. Pry first bushing out of left arm. Using a punch and hammer, drive inner bushing out of left arm.

Reassembly — 1) Replace any worn or damaged bushings. Apply grease to inside of left suspension arm. Using special installer bar and driver (MB990779 and MB990780), install inner bushing to the depth indicated by notch on installer bar.

2) Install new dust cover to the right suspension arm. Apply grease to the inside surface of the right suspension arm, then install rubber stopper.

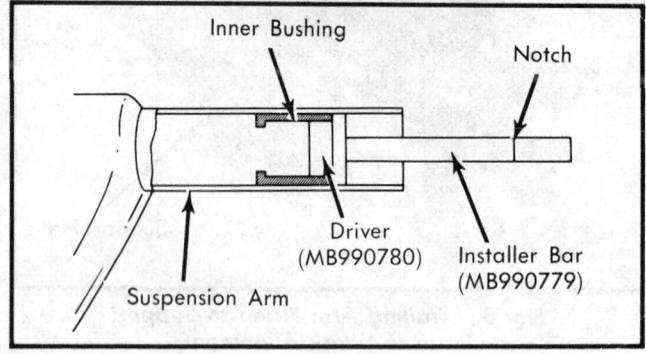

Fig. 2 Installing Inner Bushing to Suspension Arm

3) Slowly push right and left suspension arms together. Wipe off excess grease. On models with stabilizer bar, align index marks on bar ends with punch marks on brackets. On all models, install bushing, clamp and washer on suspension arms. Ensure that washer is installed with toothed side facing bushing.

4) Install nut on suspension arm. Pack dust cover with grease, then secure it to suspension arm with clamp.

Installation — 1) With suspension assembly in place, install clamp bolts. Install coil springs and shock absorbers. Temporarily tighten shock absorber bolts.

NOTE — *Make sure that upper and lower spring seats are installed correctly.*

2) Install rear brake assembly. Install wheels. Lower vehicle and tighten suspension arm end nuts and shock absorber bolts. Bleed and adjust brakes.

TIGHTENING SPECIFICATIONS

Application	Ft. Lbs. (N.m)
Shock Absorber	47-58 (64-79)
Suspension Arm End Nuts	47-54 (64-73)
Suspension Clamp-to-Frame	36-51 (49-69)

Rear Suspension

CHRYSLER CORP. IMPORTS — REAR-WHEEL-DRIVE MODELS

**Challenger
Sapporo**

DESCRIPTION

The rear suspension is of the 4-link coil spring type. The lower arm and upper control arm are attached to the rear axle housing brackets and to the body with individual bushings. Shock absorbers attach to the body and to the rear axle housing.

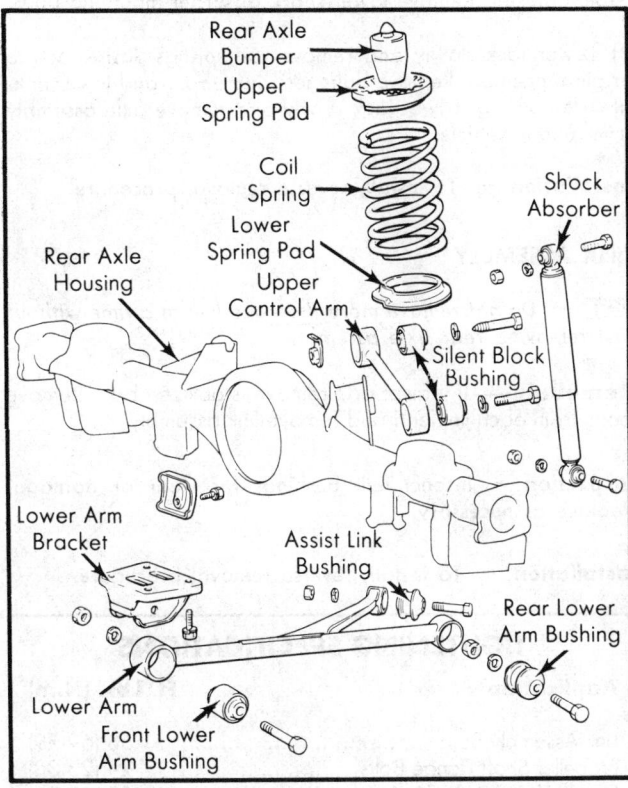

Fig. 1 Exploded View of Challenger & Sapporo Rear Suspension

REMOVAL & INSTALLATION
COIL SPRING & SHOCK ABSORBER

Removal — Raise vehicle and support body on safety stands. Place a floor jack under rear axle assembly and raise axle assembly slightly. Remove upper and lower shock absorber bolts and remove shock absorber. Lower jack and let axle assembly hang down. Remove coil spring.

Installation — Install coil springs so that the spring ends contact the spring stops in upper and lower spring pad. Install shock absorbers and loosely tighten bolts. Lower vehicle to ground and tighten shock absorber attaching bolts.

LOWER ARM & UPPER CONTROL ARM

Removal — Raise vehicle and support body with safety stands. Place a floor jack under rear axle assembly and raise slightly. Remove upper control arm attaching bolts and remove upper control arm. If equipped with rear drum brakes, remove parking brake rear cable from lower arm. Remove bolts that attach lower arm to rear axle housing and to bracket attached to body. Remove lower arms.

Bushing Replacement — Use an arbor press to replace any bushing, in the lower arms or upper control arm, that is damaged or deteriorated. When the new bushing is pressed into place, be sure that bushing extends out each end of arm equally.

Installation — Support rear axle housing with a floor jack. Install lower arms, being sure that right and left arms are installed on their proper sides. Install upper control arm and attaching bolts. If equipped with drum brakes, reconnect parking brake cable to lower arm.

TIGHTENING SPECIFICATIONS

Application	Ft. Lbs. (N.m)
Lower Arm-to-Lower Arm Bracket	94-108 (127-146)
Lower Arm-to-Axle Housing	
Inner Bracket	47-58 (64-79)
Outer Bracket	94-108 (127-146)
Shock Absorber Attaching Bolts	47-58 (64-79)
Upper Control Arm Bolts	94-108 (127-146)

Rear Suspension

DATSUN 200SX, 210 & 510

DESCRIPTION

Rear suspension is a coil spring and link type, consisting of coil springs, shock absorbers and 4 links which control axle movement.

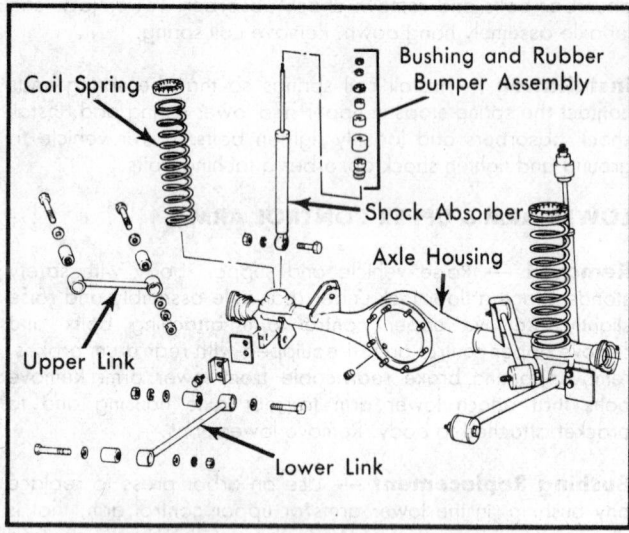

Fig. 1 Exploded View of Datsun 200SX, 210 & 510 Rear Suspension

REMOVAL & INSTALLATION

SHOCK ABSORBERS

Removal — From inside vehicle, remove upper shock absorber nut. Remove lower shock absorber bolt from bracket. Remove shock absorber.

Installation — To install, reverse removal procedure.

COIL SPRINGS

Removal — 1) Block front wheels. Raise and support rear of vehicle. Support the center of the differential with a jack.

2) Remove rear wheels. Remove shock absorber mount bolts from axle assembly. Lower axle assembly slowly and remove coil springs as they are extended.

Installation — To install, reverse removal procedure.

REAR AXLE ASSEMBLY

Removal — 1) Block front wheels. Raise and support rear of vehicle. Support center of differential with a jack. Remove rear wheels.

2) Disconnect propeller shaft, brake hose and parking brake cable adjuster. Remove lower shock absorber mounting bolts.

3) Lower jack slowly and remove coil springs. Raise jack to original position. Remove bolts securing upper and lower links at axle housing. Lower jack slowly and remove axle assembly from under vehicle.

Installation — To install, reverse removal procedure.

LINK ASSEMBLY

NOTE — Do not remove more than one link at a time without first removing rear axle assembly.

Removal — If equipped, remove stabilizer bar. Remove bolts from each link end and remove link assembly.

Inspection — Inspect link bushings for wear or damage. Replace as necessary.

Installation — To install, reverse removal procedure.

TIGHTENING SPECIFICATIONS

Application	Ft. Lbs. (N.m)
Link Assembly Bolts	51-58 (69-79)
Propeller Shaft Flange Bolts	17-24 (23-33)
Shock Absorber Lower Nuts	51-58 (69-79)
Shock Absorber Upper Nuts	11-14 (15-19)

DATSUN 280ZX & 810

DESCRIPTION

Rear suspension is of the semi-trailing arm, independent type. The rear wheel is supported by a spring and shock absorber strut assembly and the semi-trailing arm. The upper end of the strut is attached directly to the upper body. The lower end of the strut is attached to the end of the semi-trailing arm. The differential gear carrier is installed directly to the suspension subframe and a differential mounting bracket and insulator. The semi-trailing arm is installed on the subframe with rubber bushings and pivot bolts. The rear wheel bearing housing and lower strut mount bracket are welded to the end of the semi-trailing arm. 280ZX models have an additional rear stabilizer bar attached for added suspension control.

REMOVAL & INSTALLATION

STRUT & COIL SPRING

Removal — 1) Block front wheels. Raise rear of vehicle and support with stands.

2) Support semi-trailing arm with jack. Open trunk lid, remove cover and 3 nuts securing strut assembly to body. Lower jack gradually.

3) Disconnect strut by removing bolt at semi-trailing arm. Remove strut vehicle.

Disassembly — For coil spring removal, use a spring compressor (ST35651001 or equivalent). Compress spring until mounting insulator can be turned by hand. Remove self-locking

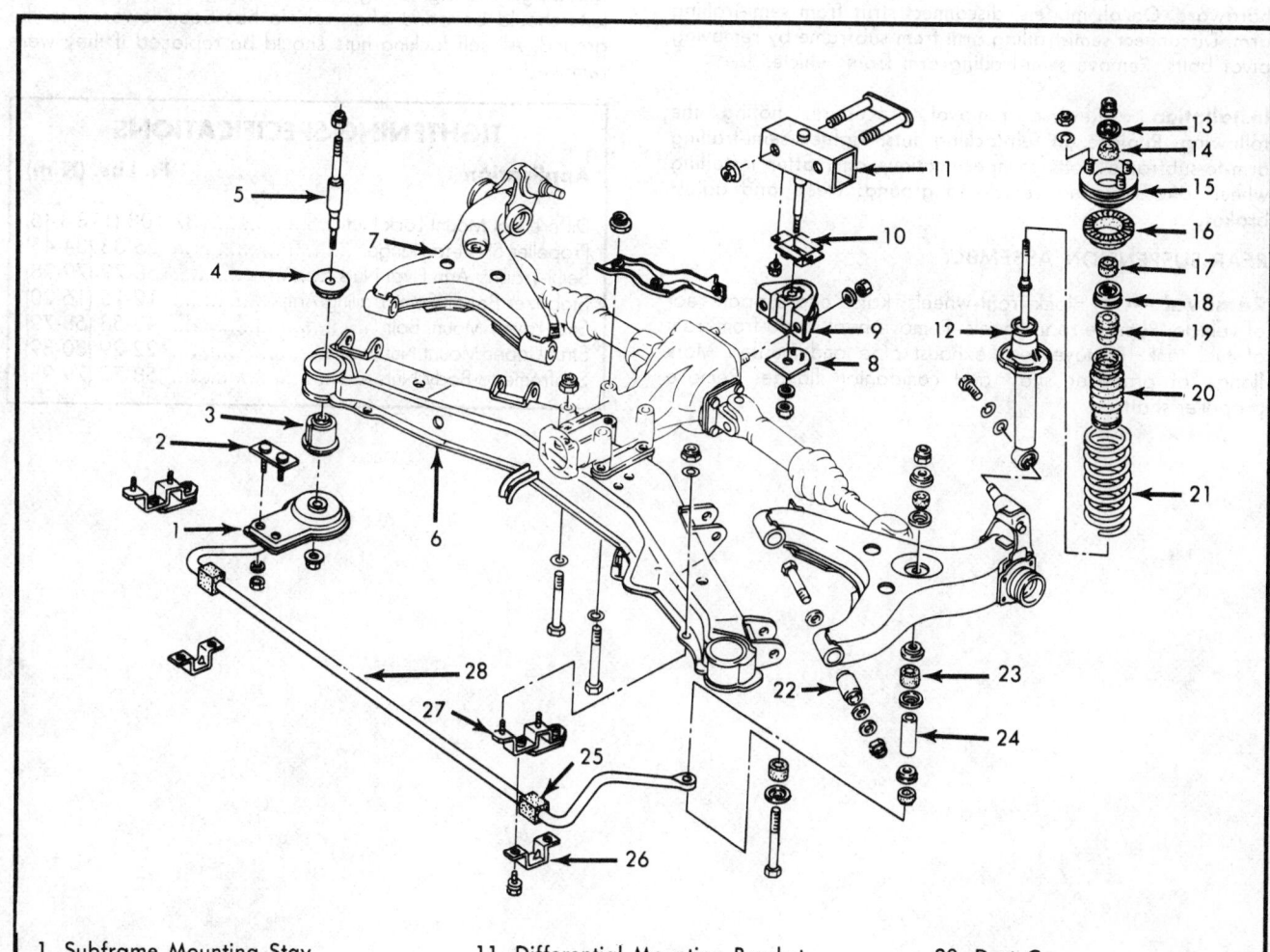

1. Subframe Mounting Stay
2. Subframe Mounting Bolt
3. Subframe Mounting Insulator
4. Subframe Mounting Washer
5. Suspension Mounting Bolt
6. Subframe
7. Semi-Trailing Arm
8. Differential Mounting Plate
9. Differential Mounting Insulator
10. Differential Mounting Adapter Plate*
11. Differential Mounting Bracket
12. Strut Assembly
13. Cupped Washer
14. Strut Mounting Bushing "A"
15. Strut Mounting Insulator
16. Spring Seat Cushion
17. Strut Mounting Bushing "B"
18. Bumper Cover
19. Rubber Bumper
20. Dust Cover
21. Coil Spring
22. Semi-Trailing Arm Bushing*
23. Stabilizer Bushing*
24. Stabilizer Collar*
25. Stabilizer Mounting Bushing*
26. Stabilizer Mounting Clip*
27. Stabilizer Mounting Bracket*
28. Stabilizer Bar*

* — 280ZX only.

Fig. 1 Exploded View of Datsun 280ZX & 810 Rear Suspension Assembly

Rear Suspension

DATSUN 280ZX & 810 (Cont.)

nut on strut shaft. Release spring compressor and remove coil spring.

Reassembly — Reverse disassembly procedure using a new self-locking nut on strut shaft.

Installation — Install strut assembly to upper body first, then connect lower end of strut to semi-trailing arm and tighten bolt to specifications.

SEMI-TRAILING ARM

Removal — **1)** Block front wheels, raise rear of vehicle and remove rear wheels. Disconnect brake line from hose at semi-trailing arm and brake assembly. Remove brake line. Disconnect axle shaft from stub shaft by removing the 4 flange bolts.

2) On 280ZX, remove stabilizer bar bolt and related hardware. On all models, disconnect strut from semi-trailing arm. Disconnect semi-trailing arm from subframe by removing pivot bolts. Remove semi-trailing arm from vehicle.

Installation — Reverse removal procedure, noting the following: Replace all self-locking nuts. Tighten semi-trailing arm-to-subframe bolts to specifications only after installing wheels and lowering vehicle to ground. Bleed and adjust brakes.

REAR SUSPENSION ASSEMBLY

Removal — **1)** Block front wheels. Raise and support rear of vehicle. Remove rear wheels. Remove heat shield from front of fuel tank. Remove rear exhaust pipe and muffler. Mark flange of propeller shaft and companion flange. Remove propeller shaft.

2) Disconnect and plug rear brake hoses at semi-trailing arms. Place a jack under center of suspension and differential assembly. Disconnect hand brake cables and lower strut ends.

3) Remove subframe nuts at body. Remove differential mount lock nut. Lower rear suspension assembly and remove from under vehicle.

Disassembly — **1)** Disconnect axle shafts from differential and stub shafts. Remove differential assembly from subframe. Remove pivot bolts and semi-trailing arms.

2) Insulator bushings can be removed with removal/installation tool (ST38280000 or equivalent).

Reassembly & Installation — Assemble and install in reverse order of disassembly and removal, while noting the following: Final tightening of semi-trailing arm pivot bolt lock nuts should be done after vehicle has been lowered to the ground. All self locking nuts should be replaced if they were removed.

TIGHTENING SPECIFICATIONS

Application	Ft. Lbs. (N.m)
Differential Mount Lock Nut	87-108 (118-146)
Propeller Shaft-to-Flange	25-33 (34-45)
Semi-Trailing Arm Pivot Nuts	58-72 (79-98)
Stabilizer Bar-to-Semi-Trailing Arm	12-15 (16-20)
Strut Lower Mount Bolt	43-58 (58-79)
Strut Upper Mount Nut	22-29 (30-39)
Subframe-to-Body Nuts	58-72 (79-98)

DATSUN 310

DESCRIPTION

Rear suspension is of the trailing arm, independent type and consists of a coil spring, shock absorber and trailing arm. The forward end of the trailing arm pivots at the body and is suspended by the coil spring. The shock absorber mounts adjacent to the spring and controls trailing arm movement.

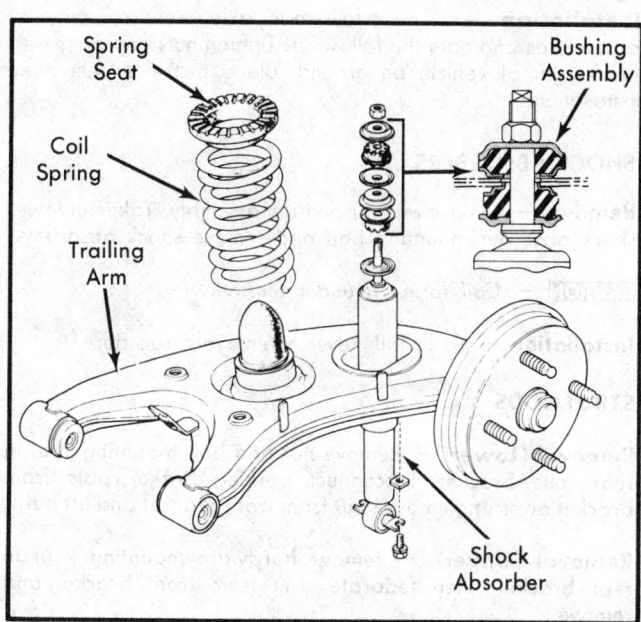

Fig. 1   Exploded View of Datsun 310 Rear Suspension

REMOVAL & INSTALLATION

SHOCK ABSORBER

Removal — Block front wheels. Raise and support rear of vehicle. Remove rear wheel. Support lower end of trailing arm securely with a jack. Remove nut and bolts from shock absorber ends. Lower jack slowly and remove shock absorber.

Installation — Install in reverse order of removal.

COIL SPRING

Removal — Block front wheels. Raise and support rear of vehicle. Remove rear wheel. Support lower end of trailing arm securely with jack. Remove shock absorber. Trailing arm can now be lowered completely and coil spring removed.

Installation — Install in reverse order of removal.

TRAILING ARM

Removal — 1) Block front wheels. Raise and support rear of vehicle. Place a jack under lower end of trailing arm. Remove rear wheel. Disconnect parking brake cable.

2) Remove hub cap, cotter pin and wheel bearing retaining nut. Remove brake drum with bearings. Disconnect and plug brake line. Remove brake assembly.

3) Remove shock absorber and coil spring. Remove pivot nuts and bolts. Remove trailing arm. Inspect pivot bushings and replace as necessary.

Installation — To install, reverse the removal procedure, noting the following: Final tightening of the pivot bolts should be performed after vehicle is lowered to ground. Bleed brake system.

TIGHTENING SPECIFICATIONS

Application	Ft. Lbs. (N.m)
Brake Backing Plate Bolt	18-25 (24-34)
Shock Absorber Lower Bolt	11-17 (15-23)
Shock Absorber Upper Nut	6-9 (8-12)
Trailing Arm Pivot Bolt	40-48 (54-65)
Wheel Bearing Lock Nut	29-33 (39-45)

FIAT BRAVA & SPIDER 2000

DESCRIPTION

Rear suspension consists of upper and lower struts, shock absorbers, coil springs, and a track bar. Lower struts mount near wheels under axle housing and at brackets on body just ahead of rear wheels. Upper struts mount to bracket on axle housing and to bracket on body. A track bar is connected to axle housing bracket on one end and to a frame bracket on the other. Shock absorber is encased by the coil spring.

REMOVAL & INSTALLATION

REAR SUSPENSION ASSEMBLY

Removal — 1) Raise vehicle and support with safety stands. Remove rear wheels. Disconnect propeller shaft from rear axle. Disconnect parking brake cable from cable housing

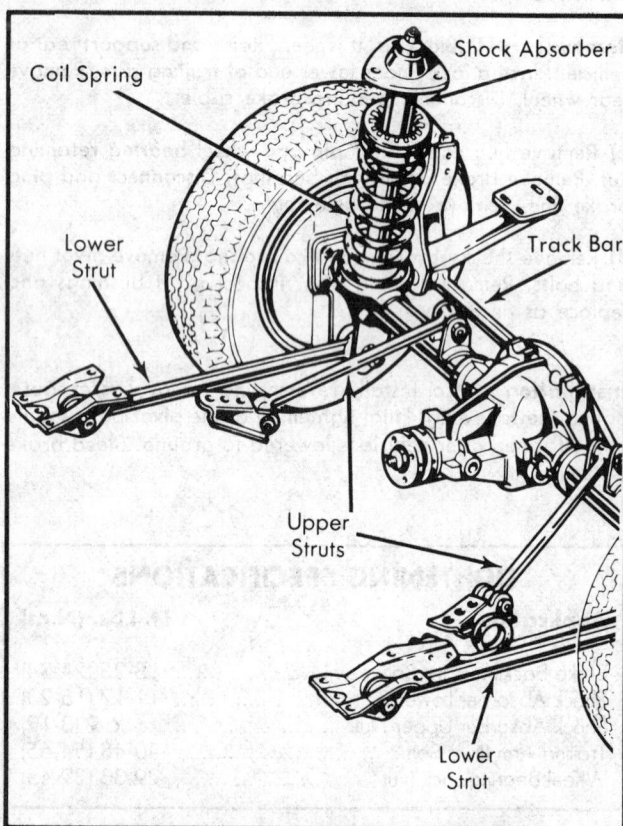

Fig. 1   Fiat Brava & Spider 2000 Rear Suspension Assembly

assembly. Disconnect track bar from body. Place a floor jack under axle assembly. Raise jack just enough to support axle assembly.

2) Disconnect lower strut rods from body bracket. Remove brake hose and brake regulator rod from bracket. Disconnect brake hose from "T" fitting on rear axle. Disconnect upper struts from frame bracket. Disconnect shock absorbers from upper mounts and remove upper mounts from body. Carefully lower rear axle assembly from vehicle.

Installation — To install rear axle, reverse removal procedures and note the following: Tighten nuts and bolts with full wieght of vehicle on ground. Bleed brake system after installation.

SHOCK ABSORBERS

Removal — Remove rear suspension assembly. Take out lower shock absorber mounting bolt and remove shock absorber.

CAUTION — *Coil spring is under tension.*

Installation — To install, reverse removal procedure.

STRUT RODS

Removal (Lower) — Remove nut and bolt mounting strut in rear axle bracket. Disconnect parking brake cable from bracket on strut. Remove strut from front bracket and lift out.

Removal (Upper) — Remove hardware mounting strut in rear bracket, then separate strut from front bracket and remove.

Installation (Upper and Lower) — To install, reverse removal procedure.

TIGHTENING SPECIFICATIONS

Application	Ft. Lbs. (N.m)
Shock Absorber-to-Lower Mount	36 (49)
Shock Absorber-to-Upper Mount	11 (15)
Strut Rod Bolts	58 (79)
Track Bar-to-Body	58 (79)
Track Bar-to-Rear Axle	72 (98)
Upper Shock Mount-to-Body	18 (24)

Rear Suspension

FIAT STRADA

DESCRIPTION

Independent type rear suspension utilizing a transverse leaf spring. Wheel bearing carriers are supported by control arms connected to chassis and by hydraulic double action shock absorbers connected at top to inner fender panel. Transverse leaf spring is connected to chassis at center and to control arms at outside.

ADJUSTMENT

WHEEL ALIGNMENT SPECIFICATIONS & PROCEDURES

See Wheel Alignment Specifications & Procedures in WHEEL ALIGNMENT Section.

WHEEL BEARING ADJUSTMENT

Tighten spindle nut to 159 ft. lbs. (216 N.m) and stake collar of spindle nut to spindle.

REMOVAL & INSTALLATION

SHOCK ABSORBER & CONTROL ARM

Removal — 1) Raise rear of vehicle, position safety stands under chassis and remove rear wheels. Disconnect and plug brake flex line. Disconnect retainer to remove torsion bar from connecting link. Disconnect parking brake cable from lever on back of backing plate.

2) Position a jack under control arm, raise slightly and disconnect upper shock absorber mount (accessible from inside luggage compartment). Lower control arm and repeat for the other side. Remove leaf spring rubber bumper. Remove 2 nuts to disconnect control arm pivot shaft from chassis and remove control arm from chassis, keeping track of shims as control arm is removed.

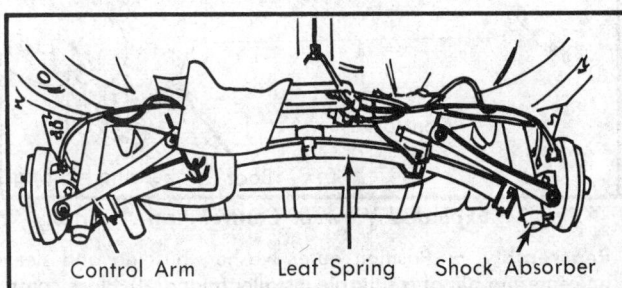

Control Arm   Leaf Spring   Shock Absorber

Fig. 1 Installed View of Rear Suspension Assembly

Installation — To install control arm and shock absorber, reverse removal procedure. Bleed brake hydraulic system. Tighten control arm pivot shaft nuts with weight of vehicle on rear wheels.

CONTROL ARM BUSHINGS

Removal — 1) Remove shock absorber and control arm as previously outlined. Remove pivot bolt securing control arm to bearing carrier and shock absorber mount.

2) Remove inner pivot shaft nuts at control arm. Using a press and suitable mandrel, press out on pivot shaft until bushing is partially removed. This allows for removing tool to properly center on opposite bushing.

3) Using same procedure, remove other bushing. Remove control arm from press and extract remaining bushing. Use a puller to remove bearing carrier bushings from control arm.

Installation — 1) Using same tools as used for removal in addition to a suitable spacer installed between inner legs of control arm, press bushings into control arm and onto pivot shaft. Use same tool used for removal to reinstall bearing carrier bushings into control arm.

2) Reinstall control arm, bearing carrier and shock absorber as previously outlined. Tighten control arm-to-bearing carrier pivot bolt with weight of vehicle on rear wheels.

TRANSVERSE LEAF SPRING

Removal — Raise rear of vehicle, position on safety stands and remove wheels. Place a jack under left end of spring and raise enough to release spring from rubber mounting pad on control arm. Remove cotter pin and disconnect rod linking spring to brake regulator (if equipped). Remove mount for rubber pad on bottom of control arm and lower jack to release spring. Repeat same procedure for opposite side. Remove two guides securing spring to chassis and remove spring.

Installation — Inspect spring making sure there are not any cracked or broken leaves. Inspect all rubber mounts and inter leaf shims for wear or damage. To install transverse leaf spring, reverse removal procedure.

TIGHTENING SPECIFICATIONS

Application	Ft. Lbs. (N.m)
Backing Plate-to-Bearing Carrier	18 (24)
Control Arm Pin Nuts	30 (41)
Control Arm-to-Bearing Carrier Pivot Bolt	58 (79)
Control Arm-to-Chassis Pivot Bolt	36 (49)
Leaf Spring Mounting Pad-to-Control Arm	22 (30)
Lower Shock Absorber Mount	43 (58)
Rear Wheel Spindle Nut	159 (216)
Upper Shock Absorber Mount	18 (24)

Rear Suspension

FIAT X1/9

DESCRIPTION

Fiat X1/9 is a rear engine mounted and rear wheel driven vehicle utilizing independent rear suspension. All rear suspensions consists of the following: Lower control arms, bearing housings and hydraulic, strut type, shock absorbers. Control arms are attached to chassis in rubber bushings and to bearing housing with a ball joint. Hydraulic strut assembly attaches to bearing housing just above axle shaft and mounts at top to inside of engine compartment. A reaction rod is also attached to bearing housing and is used to adjust rear wheel alignment.

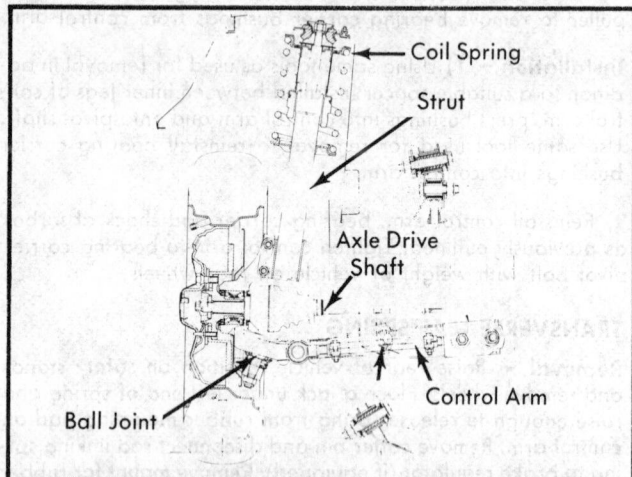

Fig. 1   Sectional View of Fiat X1/9 Rear Suspension Assembly

ADJUSTMENTS

WHEEL ALIGNMENT SPECIFICATIONS & PROCEDURES
See Wheel Alignment Specifications and Procedures in WHEEL ALIGNMENT Section.

WHEEL BEARING ADJUSTMENT
Tighten rear spindle nut to 112 ft. lbs. (152 N.m). After tightening, stake collar of spindle nut into machined slot on spindle.

REMOVAL & INSTALLATION

SUSPENSION ASSEMBLY

Removal — Raise and support vehicle. Remove tire and wheel. Remove rear brake caliper and disconnect parking brake cable. *See appropriate article in the BRAKE section.* Remove exhaust pipe. Note number and position of shims on control arm. Separate front and rear ends of lower control arm from chassis; do not lose shims. Remove hub nut and washer. Remove nuts mounting strut assembly at top. Slide suspension off axle shaft and secure axle to prevent pulling out of differential.

Installation — To install suspension assembly, reverse removal procedure. Make sure axle nut is properly torqued before lowering vehicle. Tighten all remaining bolts with weight of vehicle on all four wheels. Ensure correct amount of shims are installed.

STRUT ASSEMBLY

Removal — Raise and support vehicle; remove tire and wheel. Disconnect upper strut assembly mounts from inside

engine compartment. Remove bolts mounting strut to bearing housing and carefully maneuver strut assembly from vehicle.

Disassembly — 1) Using a suitable spring compressor, collapse spring coil. With spring compressed, remove nut from center of upper mount. Release spring compressor and remove upper mount and coil spring.

2) Inspect springs for cracks or distortion. Springs are manufactured in two classes and identified by paint marks. Class A springs are marked with a yellow stripe on outside of center coils and class B springs are marked with a green stripe. If springs are replaced, use one of same class.

Reassembly — Using same spring compressor as previously implemented, reverse disassembly procedure.

Installation — To install strut assembly, reverse removal procedure. Do not tighten strut assembly lower mount until weight of vehicle is on ground.

CONTROL ARM, BUSHINGS & BALL JOINTS

Removal — Remove complete front suspension assembly as previously outlined. Remove ball joint stud nut and separate ball joint from bearing housing using suitable puller.

Disassembly — Inspect ball joint for wear or excessive play. If ball joint is defective, replace complete control arm. Inspect bushings for wear or damage. If defective bushings are found, drill out bushing metal sleeve and force rubber from control arm.

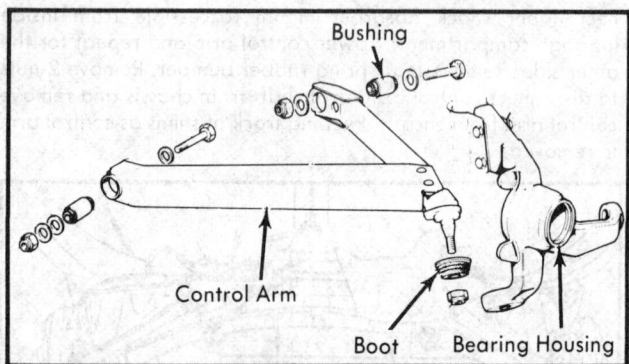

Fig. 2   Exploded View of Control Arm Assembly

Reassembly — Position outer washer, bushing and sleeve on centering pin of a suitable installer (mandrel). Place control arm over bushing and install bushing and washer for opposite side. Using suitable mandrel and necessary adaptors press in new bushing until properly seated. Repeat procedure for other side.

Installation — To install control arm, attach to bearing housing, tighten ball joint stud nut, and position suspension assembly as previously outlined.

TIGHTENING SPECIFICATIONS

Application	Ft. Lbs. (N.m)
Ball Joint Nut	72 (98)
Brake Caliper-to-Bearing Housing	36 (49)
Control Arm Pivot Pin Nut	72 (98)
Reaction Rod-to-Control Arm	51 (69)
Strut-to-Bearing Housing Bolts	43 (58)
Wheel Bearing Nut	43 (58)
Rear Wheel Spindle Nut	112 (152)

Rear Suspension

HONDA

Accord
Civic
  Except Wagon
Prelude

DESCRIPTION

Rear suspension system on all models is an independent type. Major components are: Control arm (lower), shock absorber with coil spring assembly, radius rod (Accord) or radius arm (Civic and Prelude) and rear hub carrier. Prelude models are equipped with a rear stabilizer bar.

REMOVAL & INSTALLATION

SHOCK ABSORBER

Removal — 1) Raise vehicle and suitably support on safety stands. Remove rear wheels. Disconnect brake line from bracket on shock absorber housing. Plug open ends and place lines out of way. Disconnect parking brake cable from lever on backing plate.

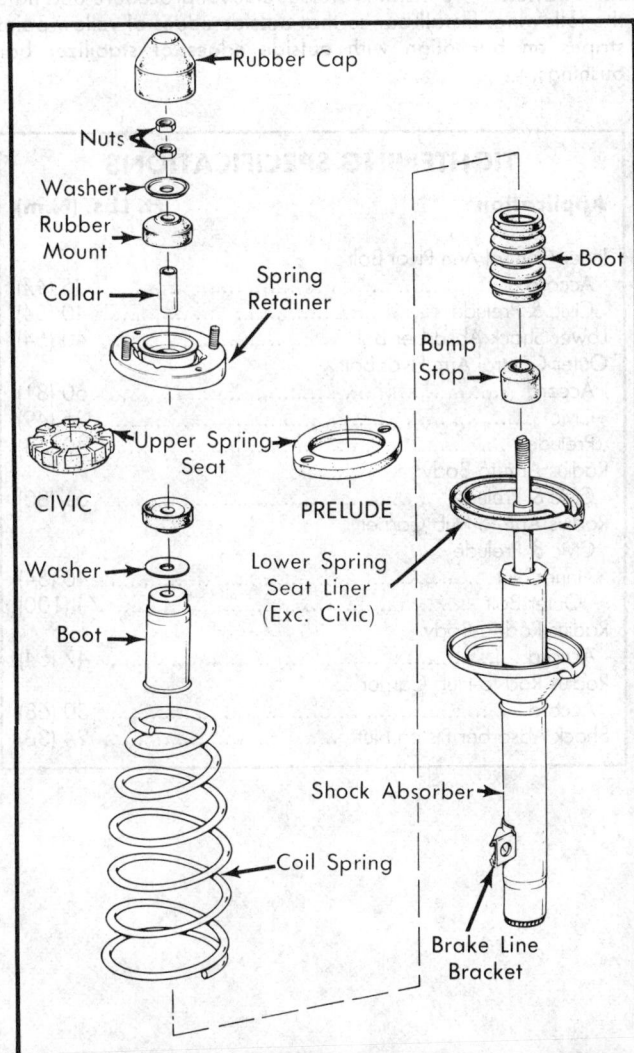

Fig. 1 Exploded View of Shock Absorber Assembly (Civic and Prelude Shown; Accord Similar)

2) On Prelude, remove nut from stabilizer bar connecting link. On Civic and Prelude, loosen control arm pivot bolt and front radius arm pivot bolt. On Accord, remove cotter pin and loosen outer control arm pivot bolt.

3) On all models, remove bolt mounting shock absorber to hub carrier. Remove 2 upper shock absorber retaining nuts. Lower shock absorber and coil spring from vehicle.

Disassembly — Fit spring compressor and slightly compress coils. Remove lock nut and piston rod center nut. Take off upper mounting hardware and coil spring.

Inspection — Check piston rod for smooth, even operation. Inspect for signs of oil leaks. Listen for noise or unusual binding during inspection.

Reassembly — Select new shock absorber. Fit coil spring to lower spring seat. Refit spring compressor. Collapse coil enough to insert upper mountings and tighten piston rod. Release coil spring.

Installation — To install, reverse removal procedure and note: Fit top of shock absorber first. Make sure tab on shock absorber engages slot in bearing carrier. Bleed brake system.

REAR WHEEL HUB CARRIER

Removal — Raise vehicle and place on safety stands. Remove wheel and brake drum. Disconnect and plug brake lines. Remove bolt mounting shock absorber to hub carrier. Disconnect control arm and radius rod or arm from hub carrier. Maneuver hub carrier from vehicle.

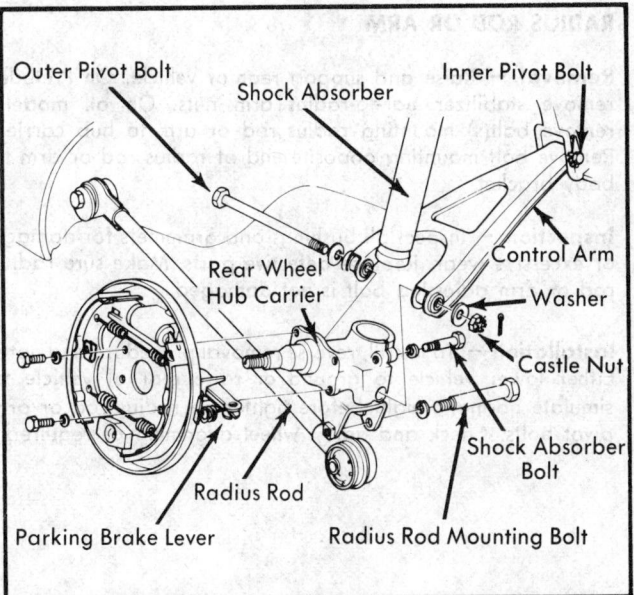

Fig. 2 Exploded View of Accord Rear Suspension

Installation — To install hub carrier, reverse removal procedure and note following: Bleed brake system and check rear wheel alignment.

Rear Suspension

HONDA (Cont.)

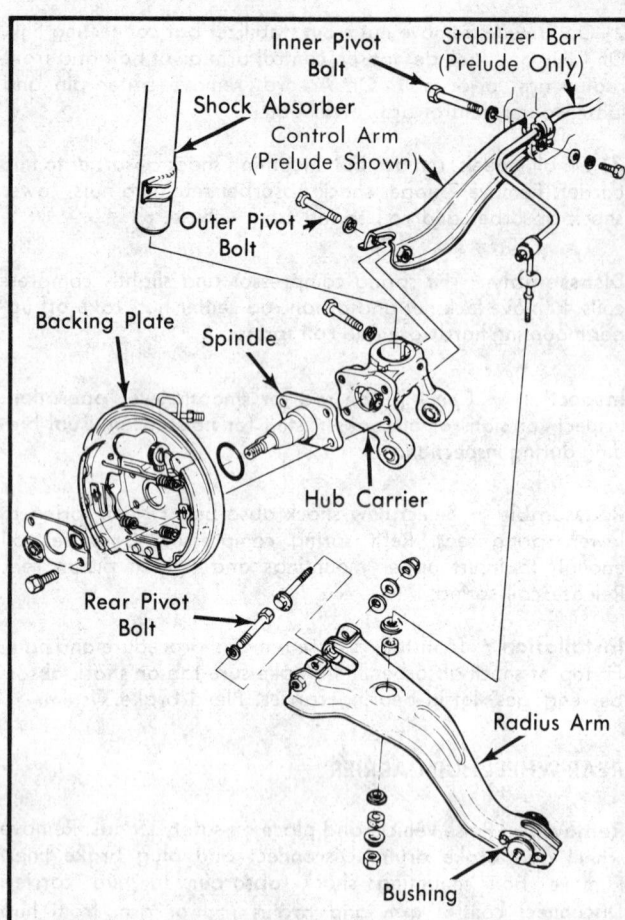

Inner Pivot Bolt

Stabilizer Bar (Prelude Only)

Shock Absorber

Control Arm (Prelude Shown)

Outer Pivot Bolt

Backing Plate

Spindle

Hub Carrier

Rear Pivot Bolt

Radius Arm

Bushing

Fig. 3 Exploded View of Civic and Prelude Rear Suspension

RADIUS ROD OR ARM

Removal — Raise and support rear of vehicle. On Prelude, remove stabilizer bar-to-radius arm nuts. On all models, remove bolt(s) mounting radius rod or arm to hub carrier. Remove bolt mounting opposite end of radius rod or arm to body bracket.

Inspection — Inspect all bushings and grommets for damage or excessive wear. Replace defective parts. Make sure radius rod or arm adjusting bolt is not damaged.

Installation — To install, reverse removal procedure and note: Either lower vehicle to ground or raise rear of vehicle to simulate normal weight before tightening radius rod or arm pivot bolts. Check and adjust wheel alignment as required.

CONTROL ARM

Removal — Raise vehicle and place on safety stands. Remove wheel and brake drum. Remove brake hoses from shock absorber mounting, then plug openings. Remove brake backing plate. Remove bolt mounting shock absorber to hub carrier. Remove both inside and outside control arm pivot bolts. Pull out control arm.

Inspection — Inspect all control arm bushings for damage or excessive wear. Replace any parts found defective. Always replace bolt lock tabs.

Installation — To install, reverse removal procedure and note following: Bleed brake system and check rear wheel alignment.

STABILIZER BAR (PRELUDE ONLY)

Removal — Remove stabilizer bar-to-radius arm nuts. Remove bolts attaching stabilizer bar to body. Maneuver stabilizer bar out of vehicle.

Installation — To install, reverse removal procedure and note the following: Install bar so that outside edges of yellow paint stripes on bar align with outside edges of stabilizer bar bushings.

TIGHTENING SPECIFICATIONS

Application	Ft. Lbs. (N.m)
Inner Control Arm Pivot Bolt	
Accord	35 (47)
Civic & Prelude	40 (54)
Lower Shock Absorber Bolt	40 (54)
Outer Control Arm Pivot Bolt	
Accord	60 (81)
Civic	36 (49)
Prelude	40 (54)
Radius Arm-to-Body	
Civic & Prelude	61 (83)
Radius Arm-to-Hub Carrier	
Civic & Prelude	
Inner Nut	40 (54)
Outer Bolt	74 (100)
Radius Rod-to-Body	
Accord	47 (64)
Radius Rod-to-Hub Carrier	
Accord	50 (68)
Shock Absorber Piston Nut	24 (33)

ISUZU I-MARK

DESCRIPTION

The rear suspension is of link type and consists mainly of a lateral rod, control arms, coil springs, shock absorbers and a stabilizer bar on some models. The lateral rod is connected to the rear axle housing and to the body. Control arms are connected to the body and rear axle housing to control front and rear movement of the rear axle. Shock absorbers are connected to the rear wheel arch and to rear axle housing.

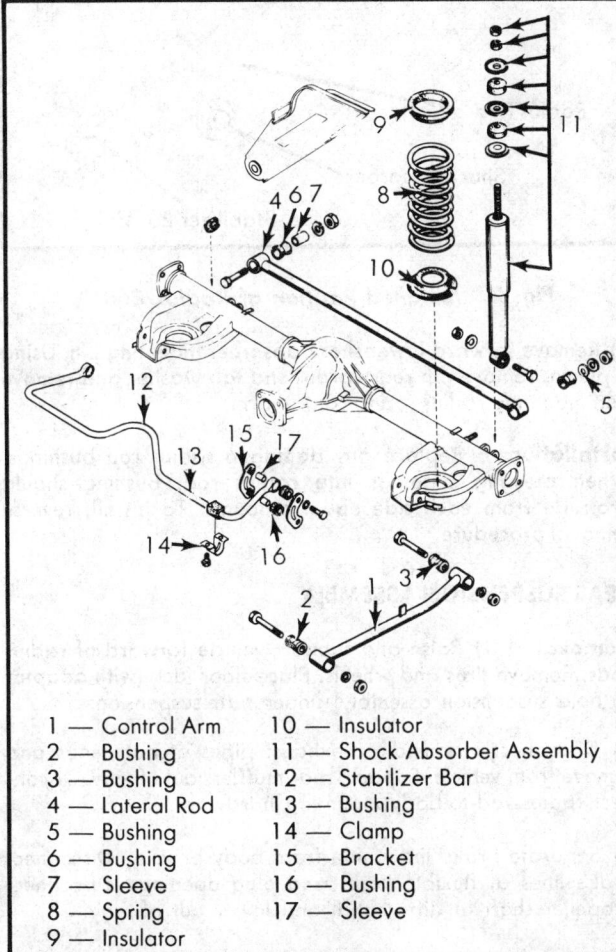

1 — Control Arm	10 — Insulator
2 — Bushing	11 — Shock Absorber Assembly
3 — Bushing	12 — Stabilizer Bar
4 — Lateral Rod	13 — Bushing
5 — Bushing	14 — Clamp
6 — Bushing	15 — Bracket
7 — Sleeve	16 — Bushing
8 — Spring	17 — Sleeve
9 — Insulator	

Fig. 1   Exploded View of Isuzu I-Mark Rear Suspension

LATERAL ROD

Removal — Raise vehicle and support under rear axle housing. Remove bolt that attaches lateral rod to body. Remove nut that attaches lateral rod to rear axle housing. Remove lateral rod.

Installation — Install lateral rod to rear axle housing and to body. Do not tighten bolts at this time. Lower vehicle to ground. Tighten lateral rod attaching bolts with full weight of vehicle on ground.

CONTROL ARMS

Removal — Raise vehicle and support under rear axle housing. Remove bolts attaching control arms to rear axle housing. Remove bolts attaching control arms to body. Remove control arms.

Installation — Install control arms to body and to rear axle housing. Do not tighten bolts at this time. Lower vehicle to ground. Tighten control arm bolts with full weight of vehicle on ground.

COIL SPRINGS

Removal — Raise rear of vehicle and support with safety stands. Place a floor jack under rear axle housing and raise slightly to support axle housing. Remove bolts attaching bottom of shock absorbers to rear axle housing. Lower axle housing until coil springs become loose enough to remove.

Installation — Place spring in its proper position, making sure that top insulator is in place. Raise axle housing until bottom of shock absorbers can be reconnected. Install lower shock absorber attaching bolts. Do not tighten bolts at this time. Lower vehicle to ground. Tighten lower shock attaching bolts with full weight of vehicle on ground.

SHOCK ABSORBERS

Removal — Raise rear of vehicle and support under axle housing with safety stands. Remove lower shock absorber attaching bolts. Remove fuel tank cover from inside trunk. Remove upper shock absorber attaching nuts. Remove shock absorbers.

Installation — Install upper end of shock absorber into wheel arch. Install upper shock absorber attaching nuts. Install fuel tank cover in trunk. Install lower shock absorber attaching bolts. Remove safety stands and lower vehicle.

STABILIZER BAR

Removal — Raise vehicle and support with safety stands. Remove bolts attaching stabilizer bar-to-axle housing brackets. Remove clamps attaching stabilizer bar to body. Remove stabilizer bar.

Installation — Install rubber bushings on stabilizer bar. Install clamps that attach stabilizer bar to body. Install bolts that attach stabilizer bar to axle housing. Do not tighten bolts at this time. Lower vehicle to ground. Tighten stabilizer bar attaching bolts with full weight of vehicle on ground.

TIGHTENING SPECIFICATIONS

Application	Ft. Lbs. (N.m)
Control Arm Bolts	29 (39)
Lateral Rod-to-Axle Housing	54 (73)
Lateral Rod-to-Body	47 (64)
Shock Absorber-to-Axle Housing	29 (39)

Rear Suspension

JAGUAR

XJ6

DESCRIPTION

Independent, coil spring type suspension. Outer bearing carrier and hub assembly is supported by control arms at bottom and utilizes drive axles as upper support. Suspension is controlled by 2 coil spring/shock absorber assemblies mounted at each rear wheel. Movement of lower control arms is controlled by radius arms connected to control arms at rear and to chassis members at front.

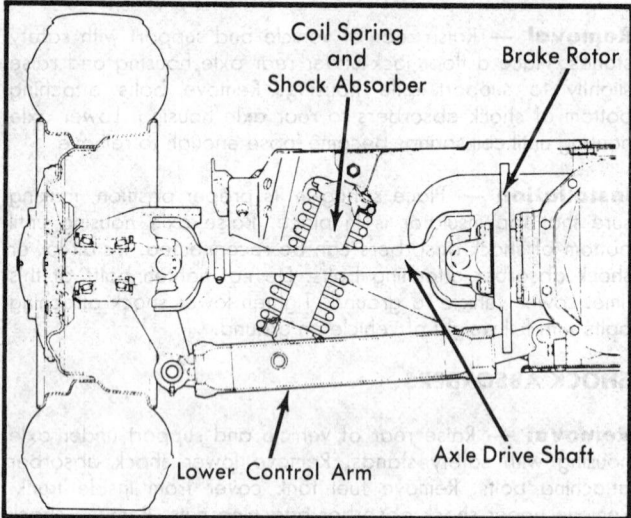

Fig. 1   Jaguar Rear Suspension Assembly

ADJUSTMENTS

WHEEL ALIGNMENT SPECIFICATIONS & PROCEDURES

See Wheel Alignment Specifications and Procedures in WHEEL ALIGNMENT Section.

REMOVAL & INSTALLATION

COIL SPRING & SHOCK ABSORBER

NOTE — Rear springs can be removed with rear suspension installed in vehicle.

Removal — Raise vehicle and support at lift points with jack stands. Position floor jack under control arm. Remove nut and bolt mounting top of shock absorbers to the suspension assembly crossmember. Remove washers and nuts securing shock absorbers to lower mounting. Using a drift, remove mounting piece. Withdraw shock absorber and coil spring assembly. Using a spring compressor, collapse spring until collets and spring seat can be removed. Release pressure and separate shock absorber from spring.

Installation — To install spring and shock absorber assembly, reverse removal procedure and tighten all nuts and bolts.

RADIUS ROD

Removal — 1) Raise and support vehicle on safety stands forward of radius rods. Remove tire and wheel. Remove bolt

and spring washer securing safety strap to body. Remove lock wire and bolt securing radius rod to body, then remove safety strap.

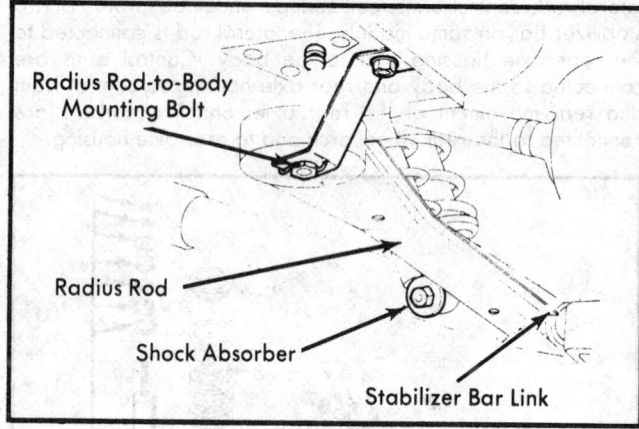

Fig. 2   Installed Position of Radius Rod

2) Remove forward lower shock absorber mounting pin. Using a punch, remove pin rearward. Bend tab washer and remove bolt mounting radius rod to control arm.

Installation — Replace any damaged radius rod bushings. When pressing bushings into radius rod, bushing should protrude from each side equal amounts. To install, reverse removal procedure.

REAR SUSPENSION ASSEMBLY

Removal — 1) Raise and support vehicle forward of radius rods. Remove tires and wheels. Place floor jack (with adaptor to hold suspension assembly) under rear suspension.

2) Disconnect intermediate exhaust pipes at both ends and remove from vehicle. Support rear mufflers out of way. Disconnect radius rod-to-body mounting hardware.

3) Separate brake line union from body bracket. Disconnect brake lines at flexible hoses and plug openings. Disconnect propeller shaft at differential and lower out of way.

4) Release parking brake. Disconnect parking brake cable from junction at rear suspension assembly. Remove suspension mounting bracket nuts. Lower suspension assembly to ground and slide from vehicle.

Installation — Reverse removal steps and bleed brake system.

LOWER CONTROL ARM

Removal — 1) Raise and support vehicle with stands placed ahead of radius rods. Remove tire and wheel.

2) Remove lock nut and drift out bearing carrier fulcrum shaft. Fit dummy shaft for support. Collect shims and oil seal retainers.

3) Lift bearing carrier up, clear of control arm. Keep carrier in position with heavy wire attached to crossmember. Separate radius rod from body.

4) Remove 14 bolts mounting support plate to crossmember and inner fulcrum brackets. Separate shock absorber at upper mount. Drift out pivot pin.

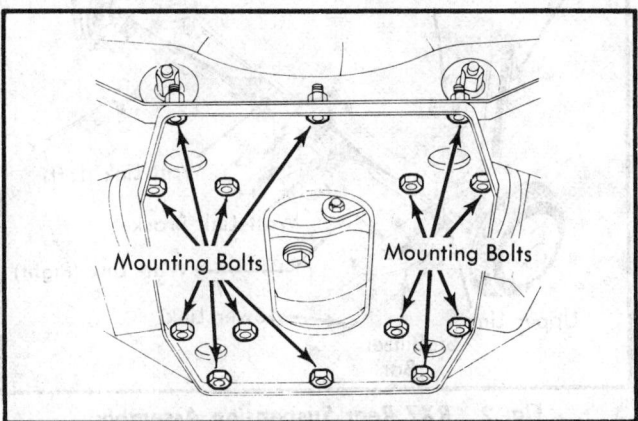

Fig. 3   Bolts & Setscrews Mounting Support Plate to Crossmember & Inner Fulcrum Brackets

5) Separate inner fulcrum from control arm. Guide out control arm and radius rod.

Installation — 1) Smear bearing cage with grease and force bearing into lower control arm. Marking cast on bearing faces out. Insert bearing tube for other end and force in opposite end bearing. Repeat procedure for other boss.

2) Assemble radius rod to control arm. Lightly coat thrust washers, new oil seals and oil seal retainers with grease. Fit assemblies into place on control arm.

3) Insert control arm to inner fulcrum mounting bracket. Make sure radius rod bracket faces toward front of suspension.

4) Insert dummy shaft from each end to keep bearings positioned then locate control arm in bracket. Slip in fulcrum shaft while pushing out dummy shaft. Install lock nut.

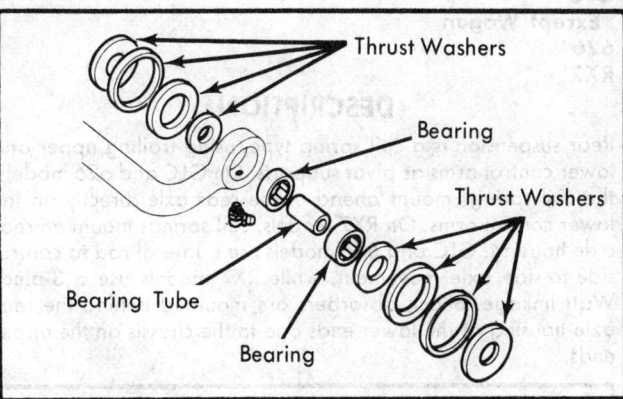

Fig. 4   Fulcrum Boss Assembly

5) To install remaining components, reverse removal procedure.

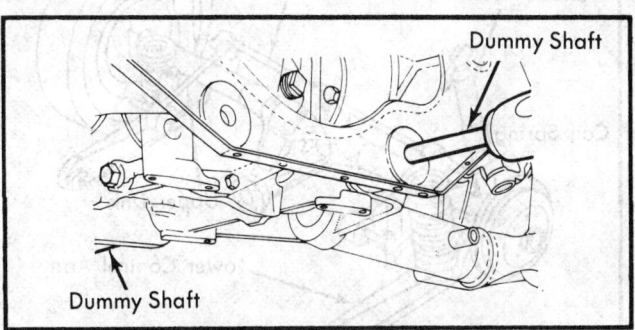

Fig. 5   Locating Control Arm in Mounting Bracket with Dummy Shafts

TIGHTENING SPECIFICATIONS

Application	Ft. Lbs. (N.m)
Inner Fulcrum Shaft	45-50 (61-68)
Radius Rod-to-Body	40-45 (54-61)
Radius Rod-to-Control Arm	60-70 (81-95)
Shock Absorbers	32-36 (43-49)
Stabilizer Bar Bracket-to-Body	14-18 (19-24)
Support Plate-to-Crossmember & Inner Fulcrum	14-18 (19-24)

MAZDA

GLC
Except Wagon
626
RX7

DESCRIPTION

Rear suspension is a coil spring type, using trailing upper and lower control arms as pivot supports. On GLC and 626 models, the coil springs mount ahead of the rear axle directly on the lower control arms. On RX7 models, coil springs mount on rear axle housing. GLC and 626 models use a lateral rod to control side-to-side axle movement, while RX7 models use a 3-piece Watt linkage. Shock absorbers are mounted behind the rear axle housing at the lower ends and to the chassis on the upper ends.

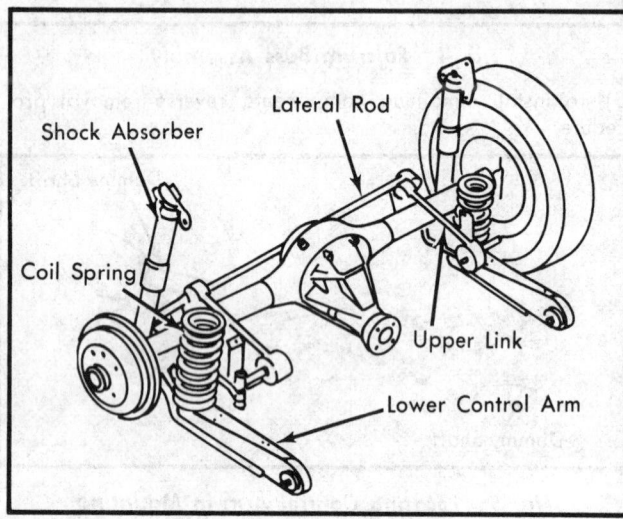

Fig. 1 GLC & 626 Rear Suspension Assembly

REMOVAL & INSTALLATION

SHOCK ABSORBERS

Removal — Raise and support rear of vehicle. Remove wheels. Disconnect upper shock absorber mounting. Remove lower shock absorber mount nuts. Remove shock absorber.

Installation — To install, reverse removal procedures.

COIL SPRINGS

Removal (GLC) — Raise and support rear of vehicle. Remove rear wheels. Support rear axle housing with a jack. Remove shock absorber. Remove lower arm pivot bolt at axle housing and slowly lower axle. Remove spring.

Removal (626) — Disconnect shock absorber lower end. Disconnect lateral rod at axle housing. Disconnect upper and lower control pivot bolts at axle housing. Disconnect rear stabilizer bar (if equipped). Slowly lower axle and remove spring.

Removal (RX7) — Disconnect shock absorber lower end. Disconnect upper and lower control arm pivot bolts at axle housing. Disconnect Watt links at axle housing. Disconnect stabilizer bar (if equipped). Slowly lower axle and remove spring.

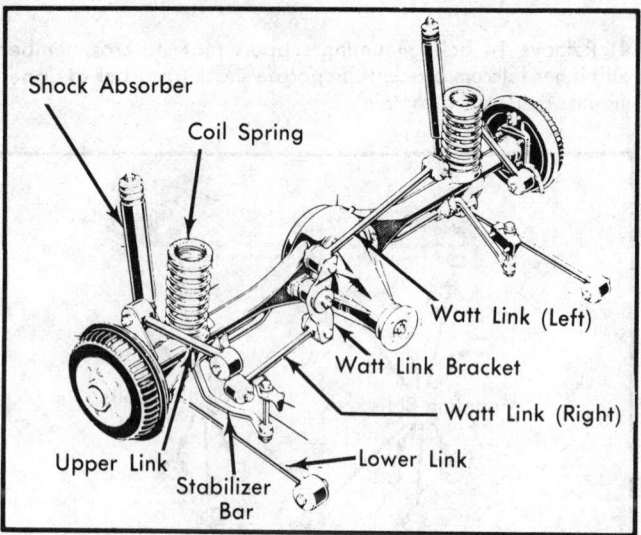

Fig. 2 RX7 Rear Suspension Assembly

Installation (All Models) — To install, reverse removal procedure and note the following: On 626 and RX7 models, install springs with painted marks facing toward rear axle housing. Tighten nuts and bolts after vehicle has been lowered to ground.

CONTROL ARMS, LINKS & RODS

Removal — Raise and support vehicle. Remove control arms, lateral rods or Watt links by removing attaching nuts and bolts, noting their proper installed locations.

Inspection — Inspect all components for wear or damage. Inspect and replace bushings as necessary.

Installation — To install, reverse removal procedures. Tighten all nuts and bolts after vehicle has been lowered to ground.

STABILIZER BAR

Removal — Raise and support rear of vehicle. Remove attaching nuts and bolts. Remove stabilizer bar and hardware.

Inspection — Inspect all components for wear or damage. Replace parts as necessary.

Installation — Reverse removal procedures. Tighten all nuts and bolts after vehicle has been lowered to ground.

TIGHTENING SPECIFICATIONS

Application	Ft. Lbs. (N.m)
Lateral Rod-to-Mount	
GLC	47-59 (64-80)
626	56-76 (76-103)
Shock Absorber-to-Mount	47-59 (64-80)
Shock Absorber Bracket-to-Body	34 (46)
Stabilizer Bar Mount-to-Axle	27-38 (37-52)
Stabilizer Bar Mount-to-Body	27-38 (37-52)
Upper & Lower Control Arm Bolts	
GLC	47-59 (64-80)
626 & RX7	56-76 (76-103)
Watt Link Bracket-to-Axle	56-76 (76-103)
Watt Links-to-Brackets	47-59 (64-80)

Rear Suspension

MERCEDES-BENZ

240D
280 Series
300 Series
380 Series

NOTE — *For 300TD components not covered in this article, see Automatic Level Control article in this section.*

DESCRIPTION

Rear suspension is independent with coil springs and semi-trailing arms. Rear axle carrier is mounted to body at three points and supports rear axle assembly. Axle shafts serve as upper control arms to rear wheels. Wheel hubs are supported by semi-trailing arms which run forward to pivot points on rear axle carrier and body. Shock absorbers are mounted inside of coil springs, attached to body on top and to semi-trailing arms on bottom. Stabilizer bar is mounted to body and to wheel hubs at ends.

ADJUSTMENT

WHEEL ALIGNMENT SPECIFICATIONS & ADJUSTMENTS

See Wheel Alignment Specifications & Adjustments in WHEEL ALIGNMENT Section.

REMOVAL & INSTALLATION

SHOCK ABSORBERS (EXC. 300TD)

NOTE — *Shock absorbers should be removed only when vehicle is on wheels or when semi-trailing arm is supported.*

Removal — On vehicles with coupe top, remove top and open flap. On all models, remove rear seat and backrest. Remove locking lever from top flap and unscrew lining. Remove nut and rubber ring of upper shock mount. Remove lower shock mount on semi-trailing arm. Remove shock absorber in a downward direction.

Installation — To install, reverse removal procedure.

COIL SPRINGS

Removal — Remove shock absorbers as previously outlined. Raise and support rear of vehicle on safety stands. Raise semi-trailing arm until approximately level. Using suitable spring compressor, compress spring. Carefully lower semi-trailing arm and remove spring with rubber mounting.

Installation — To install, reverse removal procedure.

REAR STABILIZER BAR

Removal — Raise and support rear of vehicle with safety stands. Remove wheels. Detach connecting rod from stabilizer on both sides of vehicle. Remove stabilizer bar holding brackets. Loosen exhaust pipe mounts (rubber rings) and lower slightly. Remove stabilizer bar in a downward direction.

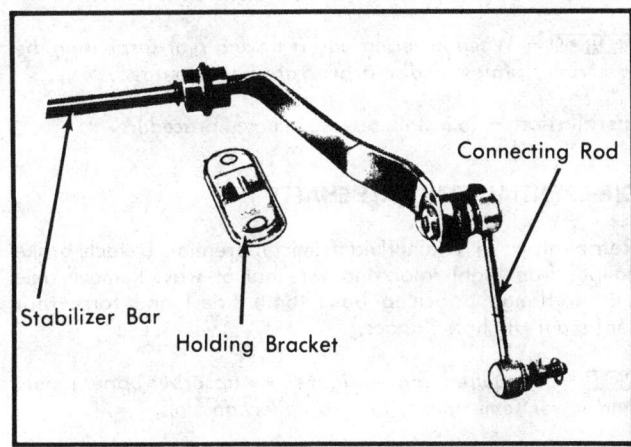

Fig. 2 Stabilizer Bar and Mounting Locations

Installation — To install, reverse removal procedure.

NOTE — *When installing rear stabilizer bar, ensure that bend of bar is pointing upward.*

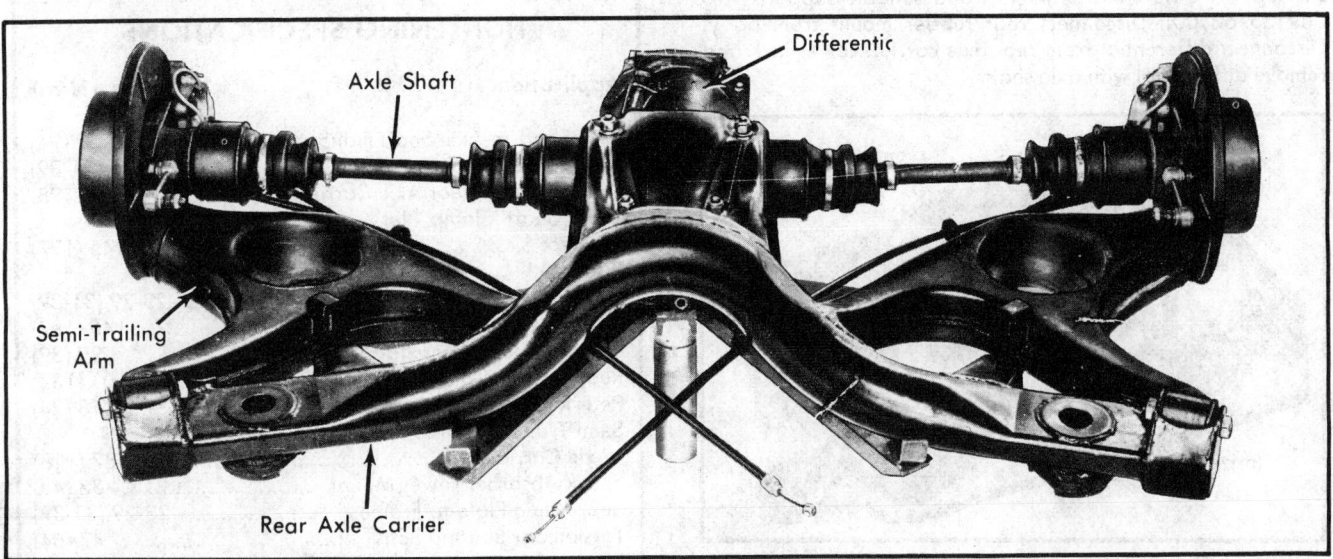

Fig. 1 Typical Mercedes-Benz Rear Suspension

MERCEDES-BENZ (Cont.)

REAR SUSPENSION & AXLE

Removal — **1)** Raise and support vehicle with safety stands. Remove wheels. Disconnect exhaust system. Detach parking brake control cables at frame and compensating lever.

2) Loosen clamp nut and disconnect drive shaft intermediate bearing from frame. Disconnect rear of drive shaft and slide forward, out of centering position.

NOTE — *On 3-piece drive shaft, loosen front clamp nut only.*

3) Remove shock absorber and coil spring. Detach and plug brake lines. Disconnect stabilizer bar holding clamps.

4) Place suitable support jack under rear suspension. Disconnect supporting plates and front and rear rubber mounts from frame. Carefully lower jack and remove rear suspension from vehicle. Remove rear rubber mount from axle.

CAUTION — *When lowering and removing rear suspension, be sure cover plates of disc brakes are not damaged.*

Installation — To install, reverse removal procedure.

DIFFERENTIAL WITH AXLE SHAFTS

Removal — **1)** Drain fluid from differential. Detach brake caliper from right rotor and wire out of way. Remove axle shaft-to-flange attaching bolts (both sides) and force rear shafts out of shaft flanges.

NOTE — *If required, loosen right shock absorber upper mount and lower semi-trailing arm to deflection stop.*

2) If required, remove exhaust system. Loosen clamp nut and detach drive shaft intermediate bearing from frame. Remove drive shaft from differential and push from centering alignment.

NOTE — *On 3-piece drive shaft, loosen front clamp nut only.*

3) Support differential with jack and suitable support (115 589 35 63 00). Disconnect rear rubber mount from body. Disconnect differential from rear axle carrier. Lower jack and remove differential with axle shafts.

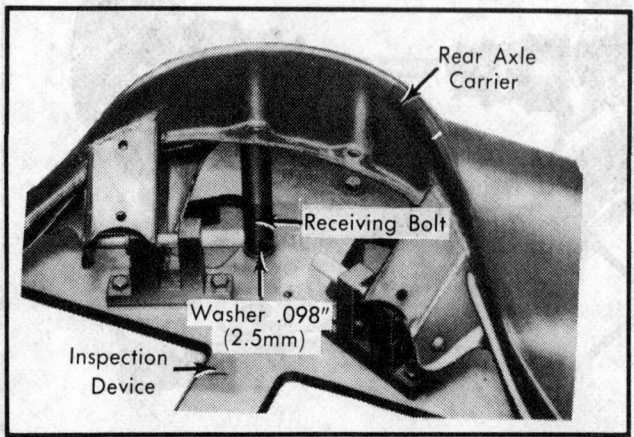

Fig. 3   Proper Washer Placement for Rear Axle Carriers without Spot Welds

CAUTION — *When moving differential with axle shafts, make sure that axle shafts are supported and DO NOT drop down, as this might damage inner joints.*

Installation — Check all rubber parts and replace as necessary. To install differential with rear axle shafts, reverse removal procedure. Tighten down all nuts and bolts, except when connecting drive shaft to differential. These bolts must be torqued after vehicle has been rolled forward and backward to seat parts. Install exhaust system, if removed.

REAR AXLE CARRIER

Removal — Remove rear suspension, differential with rear axle shafts and semi-trailing arms as previously outlined.

Inspection — Using protection tool (115 589 04 23 00), check rear axle carrier. See *Fig. 4*. When checking rear axle carriers without spot weld washers, place a .098″ (2.5 mm) thick washer under recieving bolt. See *Fig. 3*.

Installation — To install rear axle, reverse removal procedure.

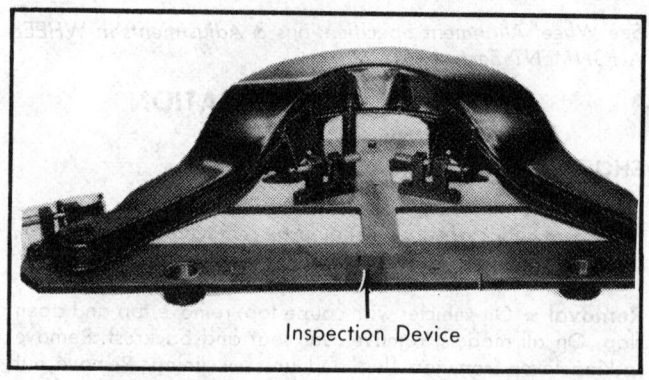

Fig. 4   Inspection Tool 115 589 04 23 00

TIGHTENING SPECIFICATIONS

Application	Ft. Lbs. (N·m)
Axle Shaft-to-Axle Shaft Flange	69 (94)
Brake Caliper Bolts	23-29 (31-39)
Differential-to-Rear Axle Carrier	72 (98)
Drive Shaft Clamp Nut	
2-Piece	145 (197)
3-Piece	
Front	23-29 (31-39)
Rear	145 (197)
Front Rubber Mounts-to-Frame	29 (39)
Rear Rubber Mount-to-End Cover	101 (137)
Rear Rubber Mount-to-Frame	18 (24)
Semi-Trailing Arm-to-Rear Axle Carrier	87 (118)
Shock Absorber Lower Mount	33 (45)
Supporting Plate-to-Frame	23-29 (31-39)
Torsion Bar Bearing Bolts	47 (64)
Torsion Bar Connecting Rod Ball Joints	33 (45)

PEUGEOT

504
505
604

DESCRIPTION

Independent rear suspension utilizing trailing arms and coil springs. Rear hub is supported by lower trailing arms which pivot at points on rear axle crossmember. Coil springs are mounted between suspension crossmember at top and trailing arm at bottom. Hydraulic shock absorbers also mount between suspension crossmember and trailing arm, and are located inside coil spring. A stabilizer bar is mounted to frame and connected at ends to trailing arms.

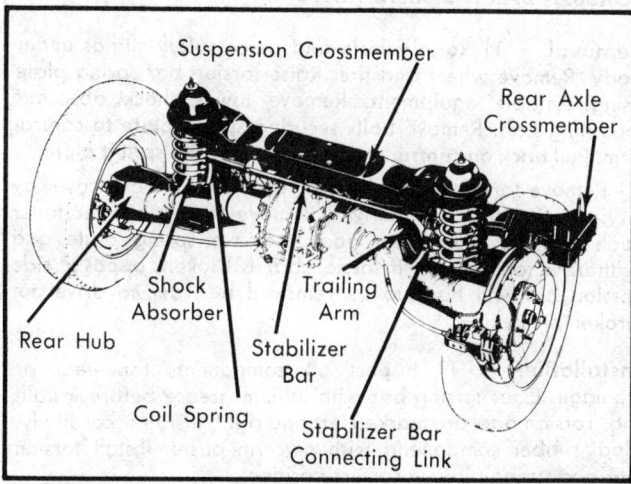

Suspension Crossmember

Rear Axle
Crossmember

Shock
Absorber

Trailing
Arm

Rear Hub

Stabilizer
Bar

Coil Spring

Stabilizer Bar
Connecting Link

Fig. 1   Sectional View of Peugeot Rear Suspension

REMOVAL & INSTALLATION

SHOCK ABSORBERS

Removal — From inside luggage compartment, remove lock nut at top of shock absorber while holding shock to prevent rotation. On trailing arm, remove lower pivot bolt and remove shock absorber.

Installation — To install, reverse removal procedure using new rubber washers and lock nut. Tighten upper mounting to specification, then tighten lower.

TRAILING ARMS

Removal — 1) Raise and support vehicle on safety stands under rear crossmember; remove tire and wheel. Remove brake disc pads. Disconnect hydraulic line from trailing arm. Remove caliper mounting bolts and suspend caliper out of way. Use care not to bend or kink hydraulic lines.

2) Remove drive shaft nut. Remove bearing housing bolts and pull shaft, hub and disc assembly from arm. Raise the lower arm with a jack to compress spring; remove shock absorber. Disconnect parking brake cable from lower arm. Remove stabilizer connecting link nut at lower arm; remove metal cup and rubber mount and refit nut to prevent upper parts from falling inside arm.

3) Unscrew rear arm pivot nuts and carefully lower jack. Remove spring and upper rubber mount. Remove rear arm pivots and remove trailing arm.

Installation — To install, reverse removal procedure, replacing all lock nuts and lock washers. Torque all nuts and bolts to specifications, however, do not torque lower shock absorber nut and trailing arm pivot nuts until weight of vehicle, with two people in rear seat, is on suspension.

TIGHTENING SPECIFICATIONS

Application	Ft. Lbs. (N.m)
Lower Shock Absorber Nut	33 (45)
Rear Hub Nut	181 (245)
Trailing Arm Pivot Nuts	47 (64)
	INCH Lbs. (N.m)
Stabilizer Bar Link Nut	108 (12)
Upper Shock Absorber Nut	108 (12)

Rear Suspension

PORSCHE 911SC

DESCRIPTION

Independent torsion bar type rear suspension. Torsion bars are mounted inside rear crossmember tube and anchored in center by a splined hub. Outer end of torsion bars mount into splined hubs integral with spring plates which connect at ends to control arms. Control arms pivot in mounts integral with body and also serve as rear wheel bearing carriers. Hydraulic shock absorbers mount between control arms and inner fender panel. A stabilizer bar is installed on some models.

ADJUSTMENT

WHEEL ALIGNMENT SPECIFICATIONS & PROCEDURES

See Wheel Alignment Specifications & Procedures in WHEEL ALIGNMENT Section.

REMOVAL & INSTALLATION

SHOCK ABSORBERS

Removal — **1)** Raise vehicle and place safety stands in a position so weight of vehicle is still on rear wheels. Remove rubber cap from upper mount (accessible from inside engine compartment) and remove nut from shock absorber stem.

2) Remove bolt securing shock absorber to control arm and remove shock absorber. Remove rod cover and rubber buffer from shock absorber.

Installation — Inspect rubber buffer for wear or cracking and replace if necessary. Make sure that stop disc grooves face bottom of shock absorber when assembling. Install rubber buffer and cover and reverse removal procedure to install remaining components. Tighten upper and lower mounts.

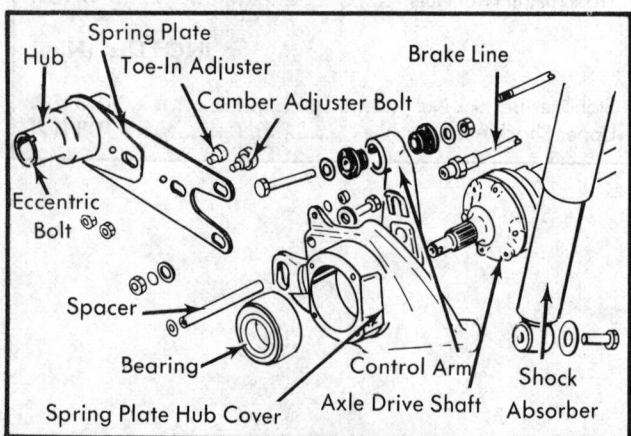

Fig. 1 Exploded View of Porsche Rear Suspension

CONTROL ARM

Removal — **1)** Raise vehicle and support body with safety stands. Remove rear wheels. Detach brake system components from rear wheel hub. See Porsche article in BRAKES Section. Remove axle hub cotter pin and nut. Remove Allen head bolts from axle shaft flanges and remove axle shafts.

2) Using a suitable driver, remove rear wheel hub from control arm. Remove cotter pin and nut from parking brake cable and pull cable out toward center of vehicle. Remove

bolts securing parking brake assembly to control arm and remove assembly.

3) Raise torsion bar spring plate to take tension from shock absorber with a suitable tool. Remove lower shock absorber mount. Remove bolts securing spring plate to control arm. Disconnect brake hose from bracket on control arm. Remove nut from control arm pivot bolt and drive bolt out with a punch. Remove control arm from vehicle.

Installation — Reverse removal procedure and note the following: Use new self-locking nuts and tighten all bolts and nuts. Check wheel alignment and bleed brake system.

TORSION BAR & SPRING PLATE

Removal — **1)** Raise vehicle and place safety stands under body. Remove wheel and tire. Raise torsion bar spring plate using suitable equipment. Remove lower shock absorber mounting bolt. Remove bolts securing spring plate to control arm. Pull back on control arm to separate from spring plate.

2) Remove torsion bar hub cover bolts and remove cover by prying off with a screwdriver. Remove torsion bar tensioner tool. Remove plug from body, remove spring plate and withdraw torsion bar. If torsion bar is broken, opposite side torsion bar will have to be removed in order to drive out broken piece.

Installation — **1)** Inspect all components for wear or damage. Coat torsion bar with lithium grease before installing. Torsion bars are marked left and right; install accordingly. Coat rubber components with glycerin paste. Install torsion bar and spring plate in correct position.

2) Adjust torsion bars as follows: using suitable protractor (VW261), place onto lower edge of door sill. Adjust protractor so that bubble in glass tube marked "Axle Housing/Angle" is in the center.

3) Reset glass tube carrier by value specified. Place protractor onto spring plate and adjust to .448-.488" (11-12 mm) by turning eccentric screw on spring plate.

NOTE — Difference between right and left measurement must not exceed .20" (5 mm).

4) Install hub cover and start three bolts that are accessible. Raise spring plate until remaining bolt can be installed. Reverse removal procedures for remaining components. Check rear wheel alignment.

TIGHTENING SPECIFICATIONS

Application	Ft. Lbs. (N.m)
Axle Shaft Allen Head Bolts	
M8-12K	31 (42)
M10-8G	34 (46)
M10 x 55-12K	60 (81)
Camber Adjusting Bolt	43 (58)
Control Arm Pivot Bolt	87 (105)
Hub Nut	235 (319)
Lower Shock Absorber Mount	54 (73)
Spring Plate-to-Control Arm Bolts	65 (88)
Torsion Bar Hub Cover Bolts	34 (46)
Tracking Adjusting Bolt	36 (49)

Rear Suspension

PORSCHE 924

DESCRIPTION

Independent torsion bar type rear suspension. Torsion bars mount in rear crossmember tube and anchor in center of tube by a splined hub. Outer ends of torsion bar mount into splined hubs integral with spring plates. Spring plates are bolted to control arm at a flange. Control arms pivot in mounts on crossmember tube and are integral with stub axle housing. Hydraulic shock absorbers mount on control arm and to upper body.

ADJUSTMENTS

WHEEL ALIGNMENT SPECIFICATIONS & PROCEDURES

See Wheel Alignment Specifications and Procedures in WHEEL ALIGNMENT Section.

REMOVAL & INSTALLATION

SHOCK ABSORBERS

Removal — Raise vehicle and place on safety stands. Remove wheel. Remove both bottom and top mounting nuts and bolts, then slide shock absorber from vehicle.

Installation — Inspect for hydraulic leaks and replace shock absorber if excessive leaking is apparent. Check shock absorber for smooth, even operation. To install, reverse removal procedure.

CONTROL ARM

Removal — 1) Remove cotter pin and loosen rear hub nut. Raise vehicle and place on safety stands. Remove wheel. Remove shock absorber.

2) Remove bolts mounting axle drive shaft to stub axle. Separate axle drive shaft from stub axle and wire out of way. Use protective cap to cover exposed end of axle drive shaft.

3) Remove drum and disconnect parking brake and hydraulic lines. Index mark spring plate in relation to a point on control arm. Remove control arm pivot bolt and remove arm from vehicle.

Installation — To install, reverse removal procedure. Tighten pivot bolt and lock in place by staking edge to metal shoulder on bracket. Align spring plate marks with those on control arm. Bleed brake system.

CROSSMEMBER TUBE

Removal — 1) Raise and support vehicle. Remove wheels. Disconnect parking brake cable from lever. Remove cable.

2) Disconnect and remove rear portion of exhaust system from catalytic converter. Remove transaxle mount nuts. Support transaxle with a chain by attaching ends to frame.

3) Disconnect shock absorbers from control arms. Support control arms with jacks or stands. Remove stabilizer bar links. Mark location of spring plate on control arm and remove camber eccentric and mounting bolts between spring plate and control arm flange.

4) Remove parking brake retainer straps from spring plates. Reattach shock absorbers temporarily. Remove control arm pivot bolts.

5) Disconnect parking brake cable from crossmember tube. Remove crossmember lower mount bolts. Remove torque strut bolts from upper mounts. Remove crossmemeber tube.

Installation — 1) Apply rubber lubricant to lower mount bushings. Install crossmember tube with lower mount bolts. Remove upper mounts from body and install on torque struts, but do not tighten bolts.

2) Install control arms with pivot bolts. Disconnect shock absorber from control arm. Install control arm to spring plate, but do not tighten bolts. Reinstall shock absorber to control arm.

3) Install upper mount bolts to body approximately 2-3 threads deep. Tighten torque strut-to-mount bolts first, then tighten all remaining mount bolts.

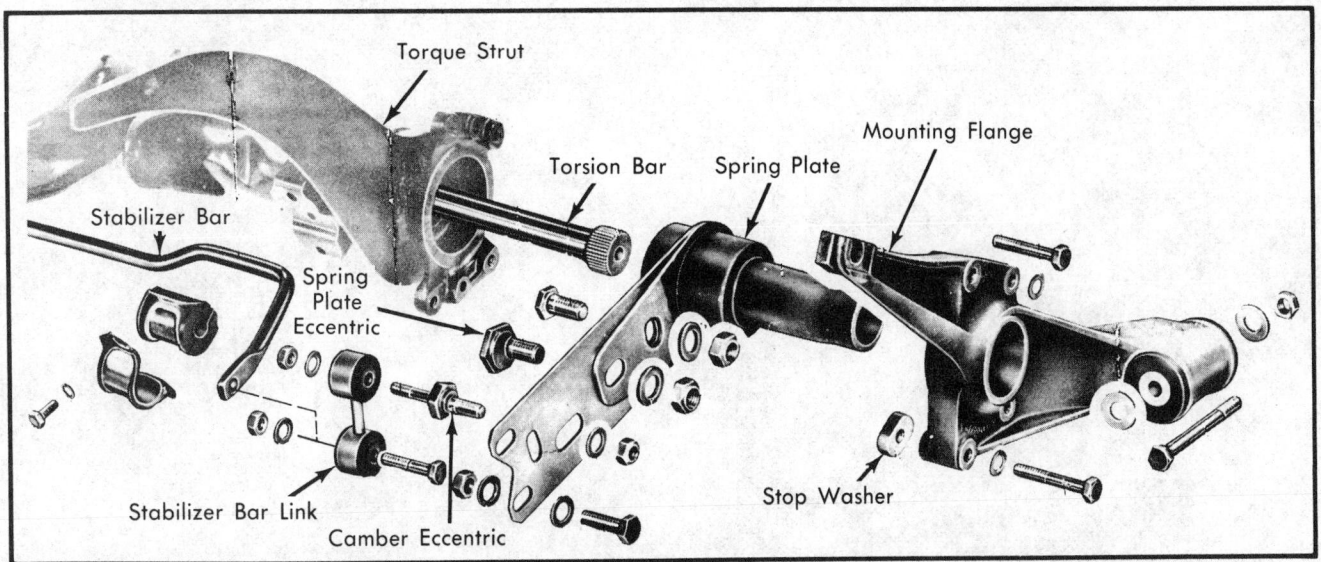

Fig. 1   Exploded View of 924 Rear Suspension

Rear Suspension

PORSCHE 924 (Cont.)

4) Lower transmission and remove support chain. Install and tighten transaxle mount nuts. Reinstall parking brake cables and retainers. Install wheels and lower vehicle.

5) Check and adjust rear axle alignment. After alignment, raise vehicle and remove rear wheels. Tighten all nuts and bolts to specifications. Install stabilizer bar links.

TORSION BARS & SPRING PLATES

Removal — With crossmember tube removed and placed in a vise, remove mounting flange bolts and flange. Pry off spring plate. Remove spring plate and withdraw torsion bars.

NOTE — *Left and right torsion bars are not interchangeable.*

Installation — **1)** Position crossmember tube so that flat surface of torque strut is horizontal. Using a protractor (VW 261) and a straight edge, measure any deviation from horizontal and record that figure. Add 23⅔° to recorded figure for setting spring plate angle.

2) Set protractor at indicated angle and turn spring plate or torsion bar until bubble in level is centered.

3) Install mounting flange, using rubber lubricant, with the 3 short bolts, until the long fourth bolt for stop washer can be inserted. Install mounting flange-to-torque strut bolt temporarily.

4) Compress spring plate with jack or compression tool (VW 655/3). Install spring plate stop washer and tighten bolt slightly. Remove tool, allowing spring plate to position stop washer. Tighten all flange bolts.

TIGHTENING SPECIFICATIONS

Application	Ft. Lbs. (N.m)
Control Arm Camber Eccentric	65 (88)
Control Arm-to-Spring Plate	75 (102)
Mounting Flange-to-Body	51 (69)
Mounting Flange-to-Crossmember	33 (45)
Mounting Flange-to-Upper Mount	33 (45)
Shock Absorber-to-Body	44 (60)
Shock Absorber-to-Contorl Arm	44 (60)
Spring Plate Height Eccentric	177 (240)
Stabilizer Bar Link	33 (45)
Torque Strut Mount-to-Body	33 (45)
Torque Strut Mount-to-Strut	17 (23)
Upper Mount-to-Body	33 (45)

PORSCHE 928

DESCRIPTION

Porsche 928 rear suspension is a strut type, consisting of a strut assembly (shock absorber and coil spring) which is mounted at bottom to the rear wheel hub and lower control arm and at top to vehicle body. An upper control arm is also incorporated. A stabilizer bar is connected by a link to the lower control arm.

ADJUSTMENTS

WHEEL ALIGNMENT SPECIFICATIONS & PROCEDURES

See Wheel Alignment Specifications and Procedures in WHEEL ALIGNMENT section.

REMOVAL & INSTALLATION

REAR SUSPENSION ASSEMBLY

Removal — 1) Raise and support vehicle. Detach axle shaft from differential by removing Allen-head bolts.

2) Detach caliper from rotor. Remove 2 countersunk screws and take off rotor. Remove parking brake shoes and spreader lever. Pull parking brake cable out of guide in hub assembly.

3) Remove hub assembly with upper control arm attached after removing control arm retaining bolt.

4) Remove lower control arm retaining nuts and bolts and remove control arm from vehicle. Remove stabilizer bar and link, if necessary.

Installation — To install, reverse removal procedure.

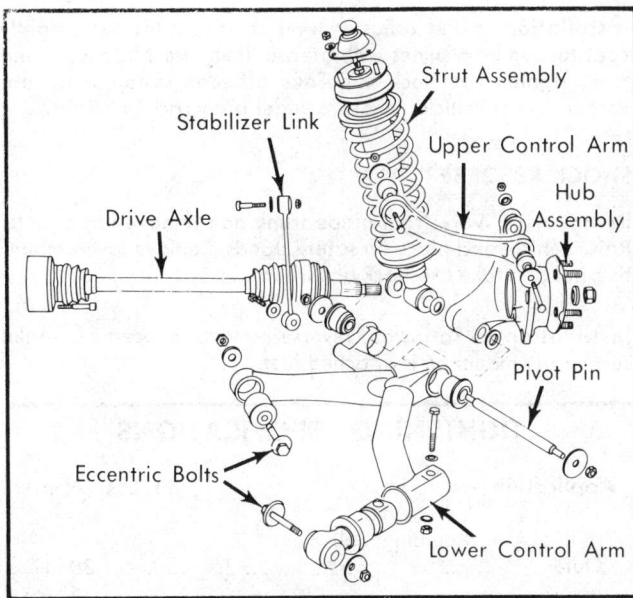

Fig. 1   Exploded View of 928 Rear Suspension

STRUT ASSEMBLY

Removal — 1) Working from luggage compartment, remove 3 self-locking nuts from upper strut mounting plate. Raise and support vehicle and remove rear wheel(s).

2) While holding rear nut, remove front nut from pivot pin of lower control arm (it may be necessary to double-nut the shaft end with another M14 x 1.5 nut). Remove pivot pin.

3) Remove stabilizer bar link from its attachment at lower control arm to gain additional clearance, then remove strut assembly from vehicle.

Disassembly — 1) Attach a coil spring compressor to coil spring and compress enough to allow removal of top piston rod nut. Loosen coil spring compressor slowly, and remove coil spring.

2) Lift off cover pieces, unscrew adjusting nut and remove threaded sleeve.

Reassembly — Reassemble in reverse of disassembly procedure, using appropriate illustration as a guide. *Fig. 2.*

Installation — To install, reverse removal procedure.

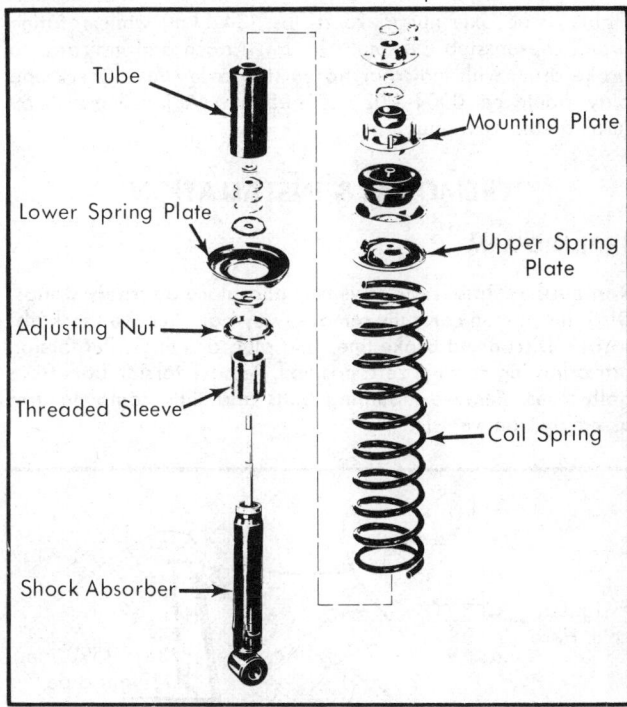

Fig. 2   Disassembled View of 928 Strut Assembly

TIGHTENING SPECIFICATIONS

Application	Ft. Lbs. (N.m)
Caliper-to-Hub Bolt	61 (83)
Hub-to-Stub Axle	333 (451)
Lower Control Arm-to-Hub	101 (137)
Lower Control Arm-to-Link Pin	61 (83)
Shock Absorber-to-Upper Strut Mount	42 (57)
Stabilizer Bar-to-Body	33 (45)
Stabilizer Bar-to-Link	33 (45)
Stabilizer Link-to-Control Arm	33 (45)
Upper Control Arm-to-Crossmember	33 (45)
Upper Control Arm-to-Hub	33 (45)
Upper Strut Mount-to-Body Locknuts	33 (45)

Rear Suspension

RENAULT LE CAR

DESCRIPTION

System is torsion bar type with a trailing arm. Trailing arms are mounted off chassis and have torsion bars connected to in-board edge.

ADJUSTMENT

WHEEL ALIGNMENT SPECIFICATIONS & PROCEDURES

See Wheel Alignment Specifications and Procedures in WHEEL ALIGNMENT Section.

RIDING HEIGHT ADJUSTMENT

See Riding Height Adjustment in WHEEL ALIGNMENT Section.

REAR WHEEL BEARING ADJUSTMENT

Tighten stub axle nut to 25 ft. lbs. (34 N·m) while rotating drum. Loosen stub axle nut ¼ turn. Attach dial indicator to brake drum with indicator tip on stub axle shaft. Check end play should be .0004-.002" (.01-.05 mm). Adjust end play by turning stub axle nut.

REMOVAL & INSTALLATION

TRAILING ARM

Removal — Raise rear of vehicle and place on safety stands. Disconnect, then carefully remove sway bar. Remove shock absorber. Disconnect brake lines and plug openings. Put torsion bar adjusting cams in zero position. Remove torsion bars from both sides. Remove mounting bolts and slide complete arm assembly from vehicle.

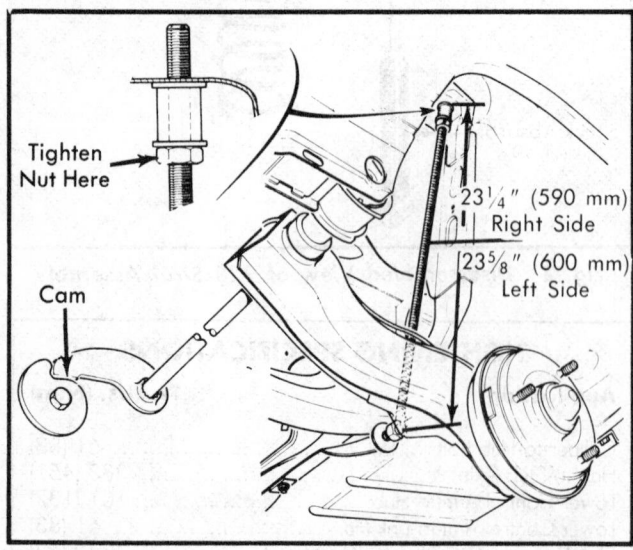

Fig. 1   Trailing Arm and Torsion Bar Assembly

Inspection — Check all bushings and spacers for obvious signs of wear or damage. Use suitable puller and/or mandrel (with press) to replace bushings.

Installation — To install, reverse removal procedure and note: Bleed brake system. Recheck brake pressure equalizer. Check rear wheel alignment.

TORSION BAR

Removal — Raise vehicle and place on safety stands. Loosen lock nut on cam and adjust until cam is zeroed. Remove shock absorber. Fit fabricated tool where shock absorber has been removed. Tighten nut until adjuster lever is raised from cam. Remove torsion bar.

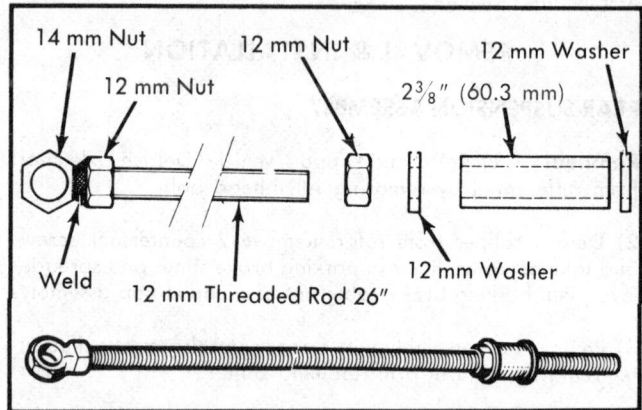

Fig. 2   Specifications for Tool Fabrication

NOTE — *Before installing torsion bar, adjust nut on tool to 23¼" (590 mm), right side and/or 23⅝" (600 mm), left side. This will allow torsion bar to be inserted.*

Installation — Put adjuster lever so it touches cam. Lightly coat torsion bar splines with grease, then insert into lever and arm. Tighten cam lock nut. Take off tool. Install shock absorber. Lower vehicle. Measure under body (riding height).

SHOCK ABSORBER

Removal — Work from inside trunk and remove upper nuts. Raise vehicle and place on safety stands. Remove lower mounting nut and take off shock absorber.

Installation — To install, reverse removal procedure. Make sure upper mounting is attached first.

TIGHTENING SPECIFICATIONS

Application	Ft. Lbs. (N·m)
Trailing Arm Mounting Bolts	
Outer	30 (41)
Inner	55 (76)
Shock Absorber Nuts	60 (81)

RENAULT 18i

DESCRIPTION

The trailing axle shaft is supported by a center arm and 2 side arms. The pivot points are mounted in rubber bushings. A stabilizer bar is welded at each end to the side arms. Coil springs mount over shock absorbers.

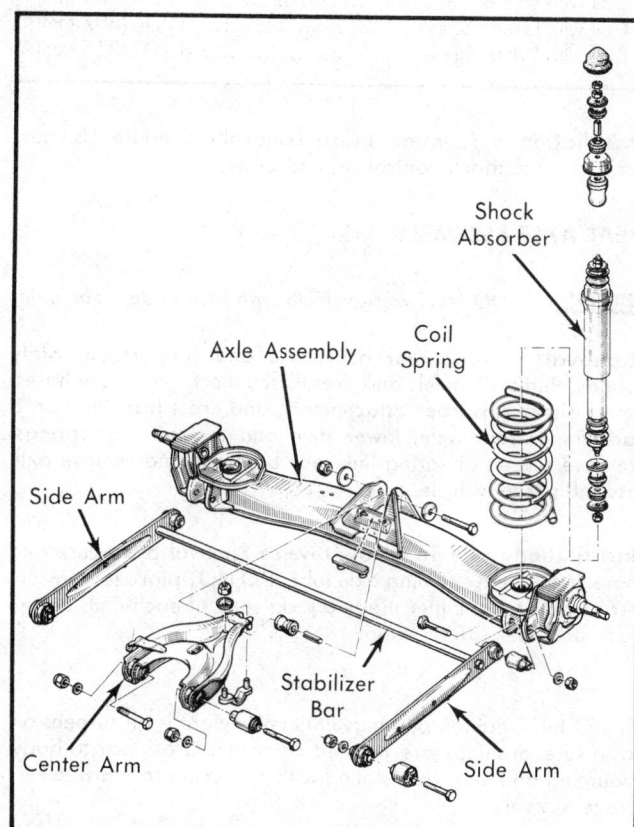

Fig. 1 Exploded View Of Renault 18i Rear Suspension

ADJUSTMENTS

WHEEL ALIGNMENT SPECIFICATIONS & PROCEDURES

See Wheel Alignment Specifications and Procedures in WHEEL ALIGNMENT Section.

REAR WHEEL BEARINGS

Tighten stub axle nut to 22 ft. lbs. (30 N·m) while rotating brake drum. Lightly tap side of brake drum with a mallet. Loosen nut ¼ turn. Attach a dial indicator to brake drum with indicator tip on stub axle. Check bearing end play. End play should be .001" (.03 mm) or less. Adjust bearing end play by turning stub axle nut.

REMOVAL & INSTALLATION

REAR AXLE ASSEMBLY

Removal — 1) Raise rear of vehicle and support with safety stands. Remove both rear wheels. Remove lower shock absor-

ber attaching nuts and push shock absorber up as far as possible. Remove flexible brake lines from limiter.

2) Pull down on rear axle and remove coil springs. Remove the 2 side arm nuts and drive out bolts. Disconnect parking brake cables at adjuster and remove them from retaining bracket. Place jack under rear axle shaft. Disconnect brake limiter valve. Remove 2 center arm bolts from body. Lower axle assembly away from vehicle.

Installation — Reverse removal procedures and note the following: Lubricate all bolts with grease before installation. Tighten all bolts with full weight of vehicle on ground. Bleed brake system.

SIDE ARMS

Removal — Raise vehicle and support with safety stands. Disconnect 2 parking brake cables. Remove bolts that attach side arms to body and rear axle assembly. Remove side arms and stabilizer bar as an assembly.

Installation — Reverse removal procedures and note the following: Lubricate all bolts with grease before installation. Tighten all bolts with full weight of vehicle on ground.

CENTER ARM

Removal — Raise vehicle and support with safety stands. Disconnect brake limiter control rod. Remove nuts that clamp center arm to axle assembly. Remove nuts and bolts that attach center arm to body. Remove center arm.

Installation — Reverse removal procedures and note the following: Lubricate all bolts with grease before installation. Tighten all nuts and bolts with full weight of vehicle on ground. Check alignment of limiter valve.

SHOCK ABSORBER & COIL SPRING

Removal — Remove cover and upper shock absorber attaching nuts from inside luggage compartment. Raise vehicle on hoist and remove wheels. Remove lower shock absorber attaching nuts. Remove brake hose clips from rear axle. Compress shock absorber by hand and carefully work shock absorber and coil spring from vehicle.

Installation — Reverse removal procedures.

TIGHTENING SPECIFICATIONS	
Application	**Ft. Lbs. (N·m)**
Center Arm-to-Axle	30 (41)
Center Arm-to-Body	59 (80)
Center Arm Clamp Nuts	11 (15)
Side Arm-to-Axle	30 (41)
Side Arm-to-Body	26 (35)
Shock Absorber Nuts	
Lower	22 (30)
Upper	11 (15)

Rear Suspension

SAAB

DESCRIPTION

Tube type rear axle with coil springs. Rear axle is straight tube with stub axles press fitted into the ends. Axle is mounted to body by two lower control arms, which are connected at rear to the axle tube and to the body at front. Rear links are also used which mount rearward from stub axle assembly to body. A cross bar is mounted from right side of axle and attaches to body support in center. Coil springs are mounted between lower control arms and body. Telescopic shock absorbers are used which are attached between lower control arms and body.

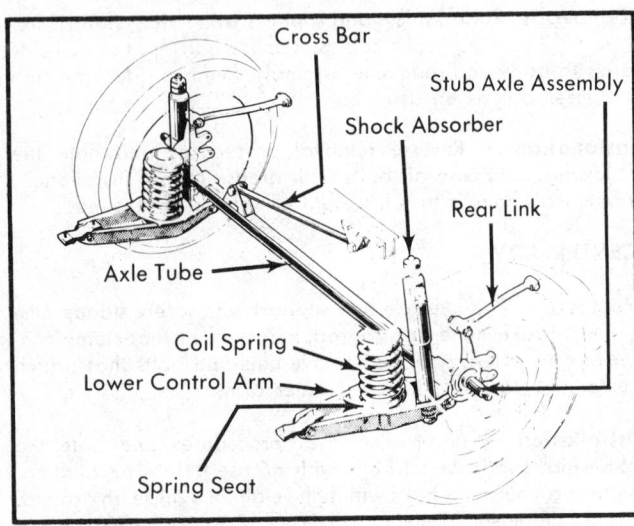

Fig. 1 Saab Rear Suspension Assembly

ADJUSTMENT

REAR WHEEL BEARINGS

Install washer and lock nut. Tighten lock nut to 36 ft. lbs. (49 N.m) to seat bearings. Loosen lock nut completely, then retighten to 17-35 INCH lbs. (2-4 N.m). Lock nut into place by bending flange into slot of lock nut.

REMOVAL & INSTALLATION

CAUTION — *DO NOT raise vehicle with jack under rear axle.*

COIL SPRINGS

Removal — 1) Apply handbrake and loosen wheel lug nuts. Raise and support vehicle on safety stands; remove tire and wheel. Support control arm with jack. Slightly raise arm and disconnect lower end of shock absorber.

2) Disconnect control arm from body. Support rear axle with suitable stand to prevent sudden drop of axle. Lower control arm and remove spring, spring support and rubber spacer (if equipped). Check spring for wear or damage and free length.

Coil Spring Identification Table

Application	Free Length
Coil with Blue Stripe	12.7" (323 mm)
Coil with Green Stripe	12.1" (307 mm)
Coil with White Stripe	12.4" (315 mm)

Installation — To install reverse removal procedure. Use new lock nuts to attach control arm to body.

REAR AXLE ASSEMBLY

CAUTION — *DO NOT raise vehicle with jack under rear axle.*

Removal — Raise rear of vehicle and support on safety stands. Remove wheels and tires. Disconnect rear brake hoses, lower shock absorber attachments, and cross bar. Position a jack under rear axle, lower axle and remove rear springs. Remove screws of spring link rear bushings and remove axle assembly from vehicle.

Installation — 1) To install, reverse removal procedure and note: When repositioning axle tube, DO NOT place jack in center of axle tube. Either use two jacks (one at each end) or one jack and one safety stand.

2) DO NOT tighten bushings until car weight is on suspension to ensure bushings are aligned correctly. Cross bar-to-body mounting bolt must be installed with nut facing forward. Bleed brake system.

SHOCK ABSORBERS

CAUTION — *DO NOT raise vehicle with jack under rear axle.*

Removal & Installation (Standard Type) — Raise and support vehicle on safety stands; remove tire and wheel. Disconnect shock absorber from upper and lower mounting brackets. Remove shock. Bleed air from shock before installation by holding shock upright and work it through full cycle several times. Reverse removal procedure to install shock.

CAUTION — *Pneumatic shock absorbers require special handling to prevent personal injury. Drill a hole 3/8 - 5/8" (10-16 mm) in diameter in pressure chamber edge before discarding.*

Removal & Installation (Pneumatic Type) — Raise and support vehicle on safety stands; remove tire and wheel. Support rear axle with safety stand to prevent sudden drop of axle. Raise control arm with a jack placed near axle. Remove shock mounting nuts and control arm-to-rear axle mounting bolts. Lower control arm and remove shock. To install, reverse removal procedure.

SUBARU

DL
GL
GLF

DESCRIPTION

Rear suspension is of the independent type and utilizes semi-trailing arms and torsion bars. A crossmember, which contains the torsion bars, is attached to body. The semi-trailing arms attach to crossmember at inner pivot points and to torsion bar ends at outer pivot points. Double-acting shock absorbers are mounted between body and semi-trailing arms. Models with 4-WD have an arm mounted in center of crossmember which simplifies adjustment of riding height.

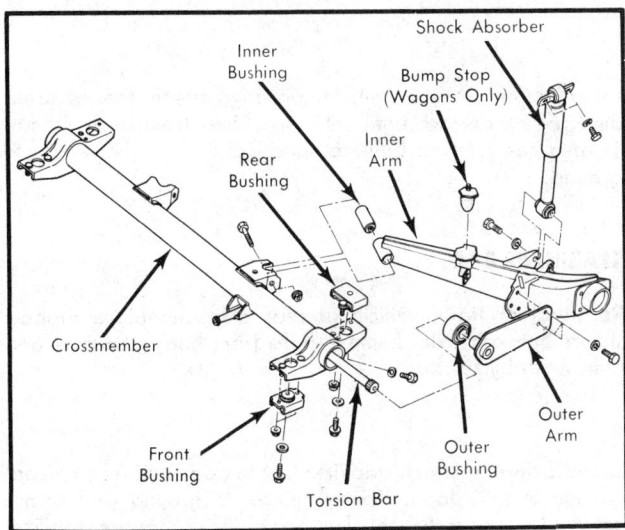

**Fig. 1   Subaru Rear Suspension Components
(2-Wheel Drive Shown; 4-Wheel Drive Similar)**

ADJUSTMENT

WHEEL ALIGNMENT SPECIFICATIONS & PROCEDURES

See Wheel Alignment Specifications and Procedures in WHEEL ALIGNMENT Section.

REMOVAL & INSTALLATION

REAR SUSPENSION ASSEMBLY

NOTE — Rear suspension assembly must be removed to repair or replace any rear suspension components (except shock absorbers).

Removal — 1) Remove shock absorber upper mounting bolts. Raise rear of vehicle and support with safety stands. Remove wheels.

2) On 4-WD models, disconnect rear drive system as follows: Drive spring pins out of axle drive shaft ends. Disconnect outer CV joint from spindle by pushing inner CV joint inward and brake drum downward. Pull drive shaft out of differential. Repeat for remaining drive shaft.

3) Continuing work on 4-WD models, disconnect propeller shaft from differential. Slowly pull propeller shaft out of transmission. Plug hole in transmission immediately to prevent oil spillage. Support differential with jack, remove differential-to-body bolts and remove differential from vehicle.

4) On all models, disconnect exhaust pipe at forward flange and remove exhaust system from vehicle. Take off all exhaust shrouding which interferes with access to rear suspension.

5) Disconnect brake hoses at inner arm brackets and plug brake lines. Support crossmember at center with jack. Remove crossmember-to-body bolts and slowly lower rear suspension assembly to ground.

Disassembly — 1) Remove shock absorbers from trailing arms. Scribe a mark on outer arm and crossmember for reassembly reference. Loosen outer bushing lock bolts and remove bolts attaching outer arm to inner arm. Pull outer arm and torsion bar out of crossmember. Repeat for opposite side.

NOTE — Take care not to twist or bend torsion bar while removing.

2) Remove torsion bar from outer arm. Remove inner arm-to-crossmember bolt and remove inner arm. If inner bushing is worn or damaged, press it out of inner arm.

Reassembly — To reassemble, reverse disassembly procedure and note the following: When installing torsion bar and outer arm, align scribe marks made during disassembly to achieve correct outer arm angle.

Installation — To install, reverse removal procedure and note the following: Tighten outer bushing lock bolts with vehicle on ground. Bleed brake system and check rear wheel alignment.

TIGHTENING SPECIFICATIONS

Application	Ft. Lbs. (N.m)
Crossmember-to-Body Bolts	87-108 (118-146)
Differential Mounting Nuts (4-WD)	51-58 (69-79)
Inner Arm-to-Crossmember Bolts	54-69 (73-94)
Outer Bushing Lock Bolts	23-29 (31-39)
Outer-to-Inner Arm Bolts	87-101 (118-137)
Propeller Shaft Bolts (4-WD)	13-18 (18-24)

Rear Suspension

TOYOTA CELICA, CRESSIDA & SUPRA

DESCRIPTION

Coil spring type suspension utilizing upper and lower control arms as pivot supports. Coil springs are mounted between axle and chassis member. Shock absorbers are connected to axle housing and to chassis member. A lateral control arm is mounted to rear axle housing and to mount at side of body. A stabilizer bar attached to chassis at ends and at axle with 2 brackets.

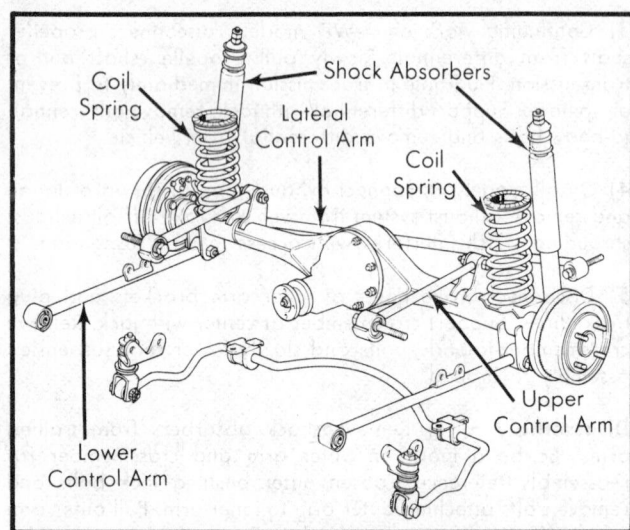

Coil Spring
Shock Absorbers
Lateral Control Arm
Coil Spring
Upper Control Arm
Lower Control Arm

Fig. 1   Rear Suspension Arrangement of Toyota Cressida (Celica & Supra Similar)

REMOVAL & INSTALLATION

SHOCK ABSORBERS

Removal – Raise vehicle and place saftey stands under axle housing. Remove nut holding shock absorber to rear axle. Remove nut holding shock absorber to body, and remove shock absorber.

NOTE – *Use screwdriver to keep shaft from turning.*

Installation – Reverse removal procedure for installation. Tighten all nuts and bolts to specifications.

COIL SPRINGS

Removal – 1) Raise and support rear axle housing and support body with saftey stands. Leave a jack under rear axle. Remove nut holding shock absorber to rear axle and disconnect shock.

2) Disconnect rear stabilizer bar. Remove nut holding lateral control arm to rear axle housing and remove lateral control arm. Slowly lower jack and remove coil springs and insulators.

NOTE – *Be careful of brake lines and parking brake cable while lowering axle.*

Installation – To install, reverse removal procedure.

CONTROL ARMS

Removal – 1) Raise and support vehicle at frame. Place an additional support jack under rear axle.

2) To remove upper control arm, remove bolt holding upper control arm to body and bolt holding control arm to axle housing. Remove upper control arm.

3) To remove lower control arm, remove arm-to-body bolt and arm-to-axle housing bolt. Remove control arm.

4) To remove lateral control arm, remove arm-to-body bolt and arm-to-axle bolt. Remove lateral arm.

Installation – To install, temporarily attach control arms, then raise axle jack until vehicle is lifted from body stands. Tighten control arm bolts to specifications. Lower vehicle to ground.

STABILIZER BAR

Removal – Raise vehicle at rear axle and place support stands beneath axle. Remove bolts from body and axle and remove stabilizer bar.

Installation – Attach stabilizer bar to body and axle mounts, leaving slightly loose. Lower vehicle to ground and jounce several times to settle stabilizer bar bushings. Torque stabilizer bar bolts to specifications.

TIGHTENING SPECIFICATIONS

Application	Ft. Lbs. (N.m)
Lateral Control Arm-to-Axle	30-55 (41-75)
Lateral Control Arm-to-Body	
Celica & Supra	51-65 (69-88)
Cressida	66-97 (89-132)
Lower Control Arm-to-Axle	
Celica & Supra	73-108 (99-146)
Cressida	87-123 (118-167)
Lower Control Arm-to-Body	87-123 (118-167)
Shock Absorber-to-Axle	22-32 (30-43)
Shock Absorber-to-Body	16-24 (22-33)
Stabilizer Bar-to-Axle	22-28 (30-38)
Stabilizer Bar-to-Link	14-22 (19-30)
Stabilizer Bar-to-Body	55-75 (75-102)
Upper Control Arm-to-Axle	
Celica & Supra	73-108 (99-146)
Cressida	87-123 (118-167)
Upper Control Arm-to-Body	87-123 (118-167)

Rear Suspension

TOYOTA TERCEL

DESCRIPTION

Rear suspension is independent, coil spring type. Trailing arms are mounted by 2 bushings and pivot bolts to suspension crossmember, and supported by coil springs and shock absorber. Stabilizer bar attaches to crossmember and trailing arm.

ADJUSTMENTS

WHEEL ALIGNMENT SPECIFICATIONS & PROCEDURES

See Wheel Alignment Specifications and Procedures in WHEEL ALIGNMENT Section.

WHEEL BEARING ADJUSTMENT

Tighten adjusting nut to 22 ft. lbs. (30 N.m). Loosen nut until it can be turned by hand. Retighten nut to 22 ft. lbs. (30 N.m). Again loosen nut until it can be turned by hand. Using only a socket and your hand, tighten adjusting nut as tight as possible. Back off nut ½ turn. Rotate drum several times to make sure there is no brake drag. Measure rotational force. Rotational force should be 0.8-1.9 lbs. (.36-.86 kg). Tighten nut until correct rotational force is obtained.

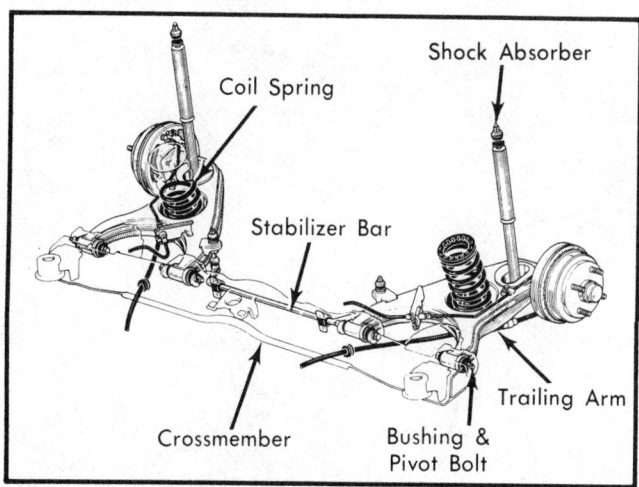

Fig. 1   Assembled View of Tercel Rear Suspension

REMOVAL & INSTALLATION

SHOCK ABSORBER & COIL SPRING

Removal — 1) Raise and support rear of vehicle. Remove tire and wheel. Support trailing arm with a jack.

2) Remove stabilizer bar end set bolt. Remove shock absorber upper mounting nut. Remove shock absorber lower mounting bolt and remove shock from vehicle.

3) Lower trailing arm with the jack. Remove coil spring and spring seat.

Installation — Reverse removal procedures and note the following: Align coil spring in hollow portion of trailing arm. Lower vehicle and bounce to stabilize bushing before tightening shock absorber and stabilizer mounting hardware.

TRAILING ARM

Removal — 1) Raise and support rear of vehicle. Remove stabilizer bar end set bolt.

2) Remove shock absorber and coil spring. Remove grease cap, cotter pin, adjusting cap, and claw nut from rear axle hub.

3) Remove claw washer, outer wheel bearing, brake drum, inner bearing and oil seal.

NOTE — It may be necessary to back off brake adjustment to remove brake drum. Raise automatic adjuster lever with a screwdriver and insert brake tool to adjust.

4) Disconnect brake line from trailing arm. Disconnect parking brake cable at equalizer. Pull out parking brake cable from crossmember to arm side.

5) Remove rear brake and backing plate assembly with brake cable attached. Note position of trailing arm camplate mark for reassembly reference.

6) Remove trailing arm pivot bolts and remove trailing arm from vehicle.

Bushing Replacement — Cut off edges of bushing flange and bend remaining portions inward with a chisel. Using a press and adapters, press out outer and inner bushings and press in replacements.

Installation — Reverse removal procedures and note the following: Align camplate mark on trailing arm camplate to same position as it was prior to removal. Lower vehicle and bounce before tightening suspension arm, shock absorber, and stabilizer bar end bolts. Adjust wheel bearings and check wheel alignment. See appropriate article in WHEEL ALIGNMENT Section.

STABILIZER BAR

Removal & Installation — Remove stabilizer bar end set bolt. Remove bolts from stabilizer bar brackets and remove stabilizer bar from vehicle. To install, reverse removal procedure. Lower vehicle and bounce before tightening mounting hardware.

SUSPENSION CROSSMEMBER

Removal — 1) Raise and support rear of vehicle. Remove tires and wheels. Remove exhaust tailpipe and muffler assembly.

2) Remove stabilizer bar, shock absorber and coil springs. Remove trailing arm with parking brake cable and brake tube attached.

3) Remove suspension crossmember mounting bolts and remove crossmember from vehicle.

Bushing Replacement — Remove bushings with a plastic hammer. Install new bushings with notch aligned in the

Rear Suspension

TOYOTA TERCEL (Cont.)

forward/reverse direction, and tap in from underside of crossmember.

NOTE — *Do not tap on rubber portion of bushings.*

Installation — Reverse removal procedures and note the following: Align camplate mark on trailing arm camplate to the same position as it was prior to removal. Align coil spring in hollow portion of trailing arm. Lower vehicle and bounce before tightening trailing arm, shock absorber, and stabilizer bar end bolts. Adjust wheel bearings and check wheel alignment. *See appropriate article in WHEEL ALIGNMENT Section.*

TIGHTENING SPECIFICATIONS

Application	Ft. Lbs. (N.m)
Rear Brake Assembly	22-32 (30-43)
Shock Absorber	
Lower Mounting Bolt	11-15 (15-20)
Upper Mounting Nut	14-22 (19-30)
Stabilizer Bar	
Bar End Set Bolt	10-15 (14-20)
Bracket	11-15 (15-20)
Suspension Crossmember Bolts	58-72 (79-98)
Trailing Arm Pivot Bolts	73-97 (99-132)

Rear Suspension

TRIUMPH TR7 & TR8

DESCRIPTION

Rear suspension system consists of a control arm (trailing arm), radius rod, and a stabilizer bar. A coil spring is mounted between body and control arm. Shock absorbers mount off axle housing at bottom and at top to body.

ADJUSTMENT

WHEEL ALIGNMENT SPECIFICATIONS & PROCEDURES

See Wheel Alignment Specifications in WHEEL ALIGNMENT Section.

REMOVAL & INSTALLATION

COIL SPRING & CONTROL ARM

Removal — Raise vehicle and place on safety stands. Remove wheel. Place jack under suspension control arm and compress spring ensuring vehicle does not come off stands. Remove two nuts and bolts mounting stabilizer bar to control arm. Remove nut and bolt securing rear end of suspension arm to axle bracket. Lower jack and remove spring and insulating rubbers. Detach suspension control arm front mounting and remove arm.

SHOCK ABSORBERS

Removal — Jack up vehicle and place on safety stands; remove wheel. On right side, remove fuel filler assembly. On left side, remove upper access plate. On both sides, disconnect upper end of shock absorber and remove hardware. Disconnect and remove lower shock absorber mounting, then pull shock absorber from vehicle.

Installation — To install, reverse removal procedure and tighten nuts.

STABILIZER BAR

Removal & Installation — Raise vehicle and place on safety stands. Remove the four bolts mounting stabilizer bar to rear suspension arms. Remove stabilizer bar with shims, if equipped. To install, reverse removal procedure and ensure shims are refitted.

RADIUS ROD

Removal & Installation — Raise vehicle and place on safety stands. Disconnect radius rod from rear axle bracket and from bracket attached to body; then remove radius rod. If bushings are damaged, press out of rod and install new ones. To install, reverse removal procedure.

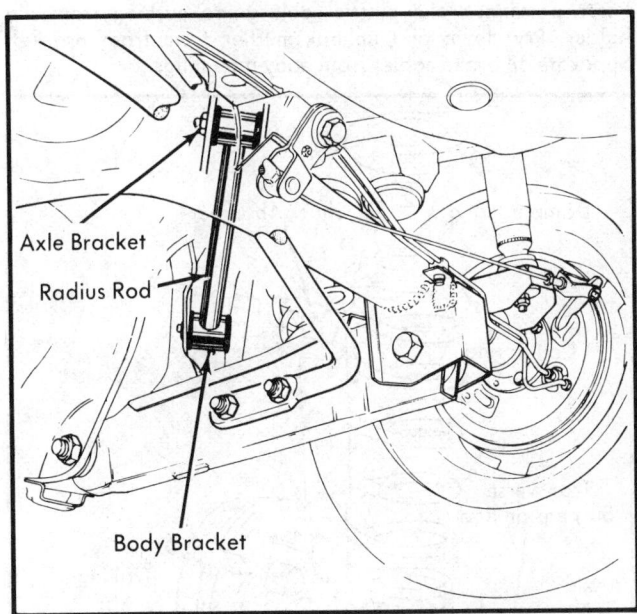

Fig. 2   Detailed View of Radius Rod Removal

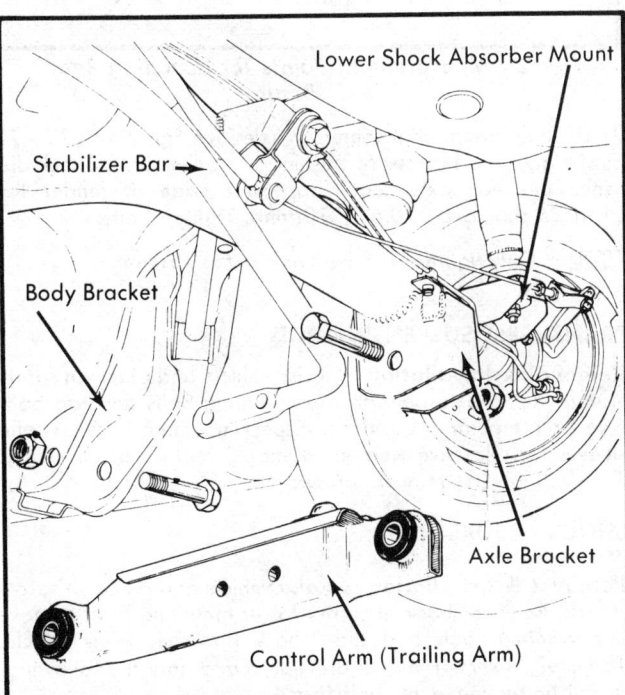

Fig. 1   Detailed View of Control Arm Removal

Installation — Ensure spring insulators are in correctly then fit spring. With jack positioned under control arm and front (body bracket end) of control arm installed, fit rear end of suspension control arm in axle bracket. Reconnect stabilizer bar to suspension arm and install wheel. Tighten suspension components with vehicle weight on ground.

TIGHTENING SPECIFICATIONS

Application	Ft. Lbs. (N.m)
Control Arm-to-Axle Bracket	38-48 (52-65)
Control Arm-to-Body Bracket	38-48 (52-65)
Shock Absorber-to-Body	10-14 (14-19)
Shock Absorber-to-Control Arm	10-14 (14-19)
Stabilizer Bar-to-Control Arm	30-37 (41-50)

VOLKSWAGEN DASHER

DESCRIPTION

Rear suspension is coil spring type utilizing a transverse mounted suspension rod and a trailing arm. Suspension rod is used to improve stability. Shock absorbers mount off bracket on axle beam and to upper body. Coil spring rides in spring seat welded to axle beam and wedges against damper ring at chassis/body.

ADJUSTMENTS

WHEEL ALIGNMENT SPECIFICATIONS & PROCEDURES

See Wheel Alignment Specifications and Procedures in WHEEL ALIGNMENT Section.

WHEEL BEARING ADJUSTMENT

To measure bearing axial play, install a dial indicator to one of the wheel lugs. Position dial indicator pin against end of stub axle. Move brake drum in and out. Turn bearing nut in or out to adjust bearing axial play to .001-.003" (.03-.07 mm). If a dial indicator is not available, bearing axial play can be tested by tightening bearing nut until thrust washer can be slightly moved from side to side with a screwdriver.

REMOVAL & INSTALLATION

REAR AXLE BEAM ASSEMBLY

Removal — 1) Raise vehicle and place safety stands under body. Take nuts off parking brake linkage equalizer bar. Force parking brake plastic cable guide bushing from clip holder. Pry down and unhook muffler from front bracket. Separate all brake cables from body mountings.

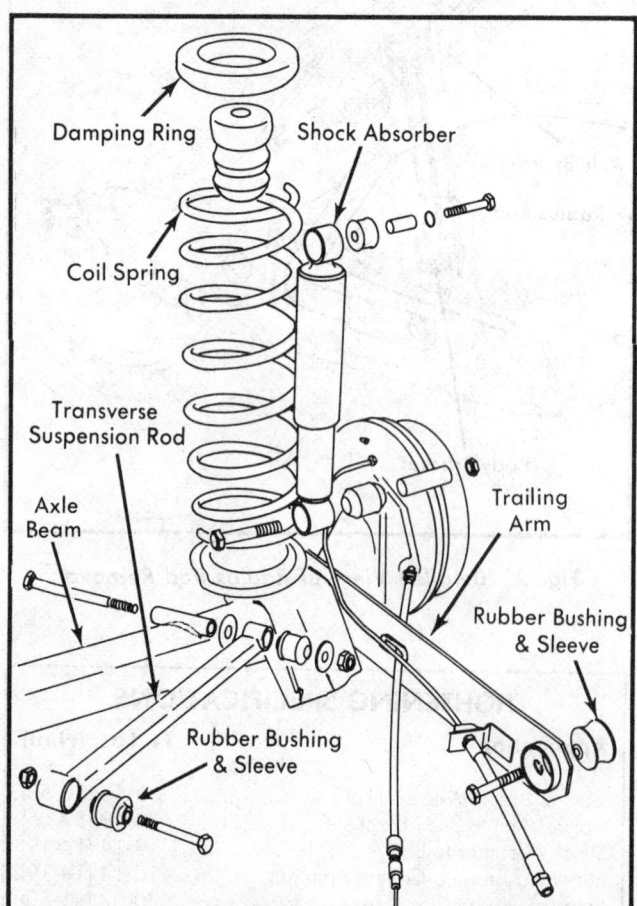

Fig. 1   Exploded View of Dasher Rear Suspension

2) Disconnect brake lines and plug open ends. Remove trailing arm mounting bolts from body. Detach muffler from rear mounting. Remove suspension rod-to-axle mounting bolt. Detach lower end of shock absorber and guide rear axle assembly (on a jack) from vehicle.

Bushing Replacement — Place trailing arm in a press and press bushings from arm. Before installing, coat new bushings with a silicone lubricant. When installing new bushings, make sure that bushing slots are aligned horizontally in arm.

Installation — 1) To install rear axle assembly, reverse removal procedure and note the following: Make sure trailing arm bushings are free of tension. Before tightening trailing arm bolts ensure arms are in middle of moving range.

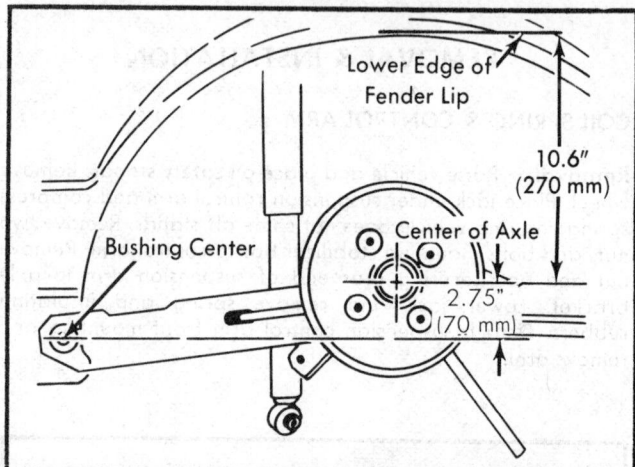

Fig. 2   Measurement Points for Installing Rear Axle Beam

2) Lift axle beam until center of axle (See Fig. 2) is 2.75" (70 mm) higher than center of bushing in trailing arm. Check distance between axle center to lower edge of fender lip. Distance should be 10.6" (270 mm). Tighten bolts.

NOTE — *Only tighten bolts with axle in this position.*

TRANSVERSE SUSPENSION ROD

Removal & Installation — Raise vehicle and place on safety stands. Remove suspension rod mounting bolts and tap bolts free from mounting bushings. Inspect mounting bushings and sleeves for excessive wear or damage; replace as necessary. To install, reverse removal procedure.

SHOCK ABSORBER

Removal & Installation — Raise vehicle and place on safety stands. Remove shock absorber lower mounting bolt. Remove upper mount bolt and slide shock absorber from vehicle. To install, reverse removal procedure and note the following: Install upper mounting bolt first.

TIGHTENING SPECIFICATIONS

Application	Ft. Lbs. (N.m)
Shock Absorber Mounting Bolts	43 (58)
Suspension Rod Mounting Bolts	61 (83)
Trailing Arm Bolt	43 (58)

Rear Suspension

VOLKSWAGEN JETTA, RABBIT & SCIROCCO

DESCRIPTION

Rear suspension is a link type with coil springs and using control arms and torsion beam for stabilization. Control arm and torsion beam are combined as one unit. Hydraulic shock absorbers are mounted inside coil springs and attached to control arm at the bottom and to vehicle body at the top.

REMOVAL & INSTALLATION

SUSPENSION STRUT & COIL SPRING

Removal — 1) Leave vehicle on ground. Take off plastic cap covering rear strut upper mounting nuts. Remove nuts.

2) Slowly raise vehicle until weight is off spring. Remove bolt holding lower end of strut shock absorber to axle beam mount. Raise vehicle until strut can be removed.

NOTE — *It is not necessary to use spring compressor to disassemble strut.*

Disassembly — Set strut assembly in vise. Hold piston rod and remove strut mounting nut. Take off components down to slotted nut. Remove slotted nut. Take off spacer and coil spring.

Inspection — Hand check shock absorbers for even resistance through entire piston stroke. Worn shock absorbers cannot be overhauled.

NOTE — *If a coil spring is being replaced, ensure that paint stripe color code on replacement spring matches original spring code.*

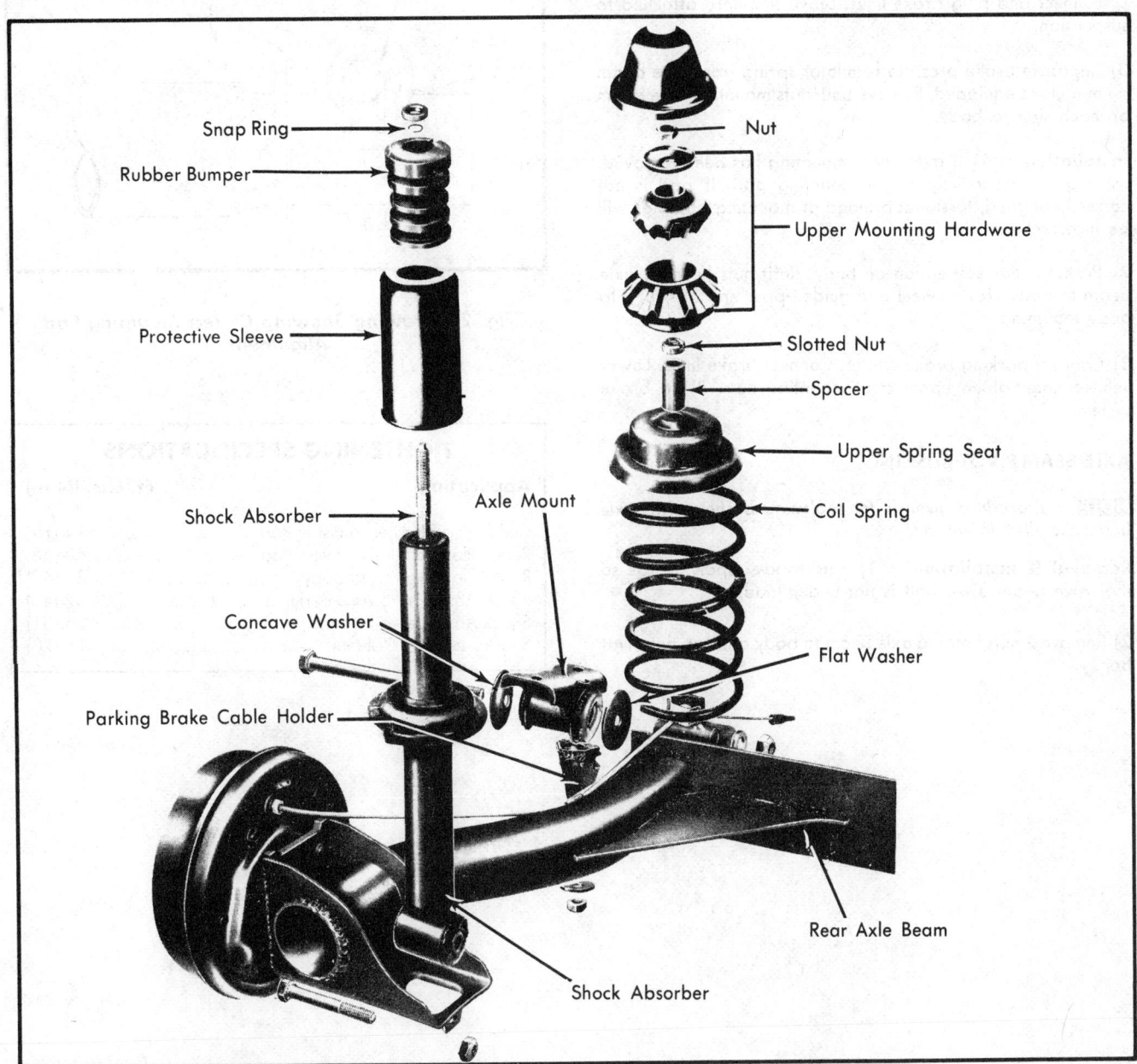

Fig. 1 Exploded View of Rear Suspension Components

VOLKSWAGEN JETTA, RABBIT & SCIROCCO (Cont.)

Reassembly — **1)** Fit protective cap on shock absorber. Install rubber buffer, with small diameter end downward. Insert snap ring and washer.

2) Place spring into lower seat. Fit upper retainer with spacer sleeve. Tighten slotted nut holding piston rod. Put on remaining upper mounting hardware and tighten piston rod.

Installation — Reverse removal procedure.

SUSPENSION ASSEMBLY

Removal — **1)** Leave vehicle on ground. Disconnect upper strut mounting at body. Raise vehicle and support at rear with jack stands.

2) Disconnect parking brake at holder near rear axle mount. Disconnect and plug brake lines. Leave flex hose attached to suspension.

3) Separate brake pressure regulator spring from axle beam on models so equipped. Remove both nuts mounting axle beam on each side to body.

Installation — **1)** If axle beam mounting has been removed, use *Fig. 2* to correctly adjust mounting pad. If pad is not correctly aligned, torsional preload of mounting bushings will be incorrect.

2) Position rear suspension on body. Refit nuts keeping axle beam to body. Raise wheel and guide upper end of strut into body mounting.

3) Connect parking brake cables. Connect brake lines. Lower vehicle and tighten upper strut mounting nuts. Bleed brake system.

AXLE BEAM PIVOT BUSHING

NOTE — *Procedure given is for replacing bushing with axle beam installed in vehicle.*

Removal & Installation — **1)** Raise and support vehicle so that axle beam pivot bolt is not under load.

2) Remove 2 nuts holding axle beam to body and tap out pivot bolt.

3) Press out bushing. Select new bushing and press bushing into place. Loosely install mounting on axle beam. Concave washer and bolt head must face toward outside of vehicle. Bolt head must recess into washer.

4) Align mount as shown in *Fig. 2*. Tighten pivot bolt nut. Lower vehicle.

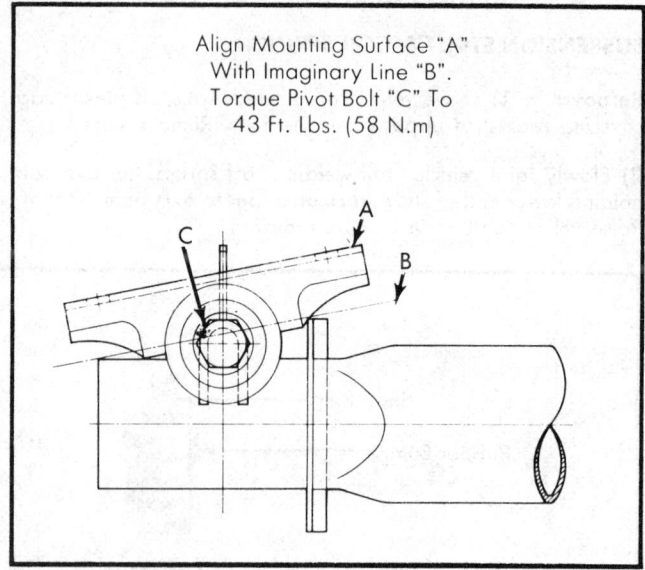

Align Mounting Surface "A"
With Imaginary Line "B".
Torque Pivot Bolt "C" To
43 Ft. Lbs. (58 N.m)

Fig. 2   Drawing Showing Correct Mounting Pad Alignment

TIGHTENING SPECIFICATIONS	
Application	**Ft. Lbs. (N.m)**
Coil Spring Retainer-to-Piston Rod	14 (19)
Rear Axle Beam-to-Mounting Pad	43 (58)
Rear Axle Mounting-to-Body	32 (43)
Shock Absorber-to-Axle Beam	32 (43)
Shock Absorber-to-Body	23 (31)
Shock Absorber Slot Nut	15 (20)

VOLKSWAGEN VANAGON

DESCRIPTION

Rear suspension is independent, coil spring type. Trailing arms mount in front to 2 pivot brackets having provision for caster and toe-in adjustment. Shock absorber mounts at top to chassis and at bottom to rear of trailing arm. Coil spring mounts to trailing arm and chassis in spring seats ahead of shock absorber. Drive shafts run through trailing arms and attach to inside of wheel hub.

ADJUSTMENT

WHEEL ALIGNMENT SPECIFICATIONS & PROCEDURES

See Wheel Alignment Specifications & Procedures in WHEEL ALIGNMENT Section.

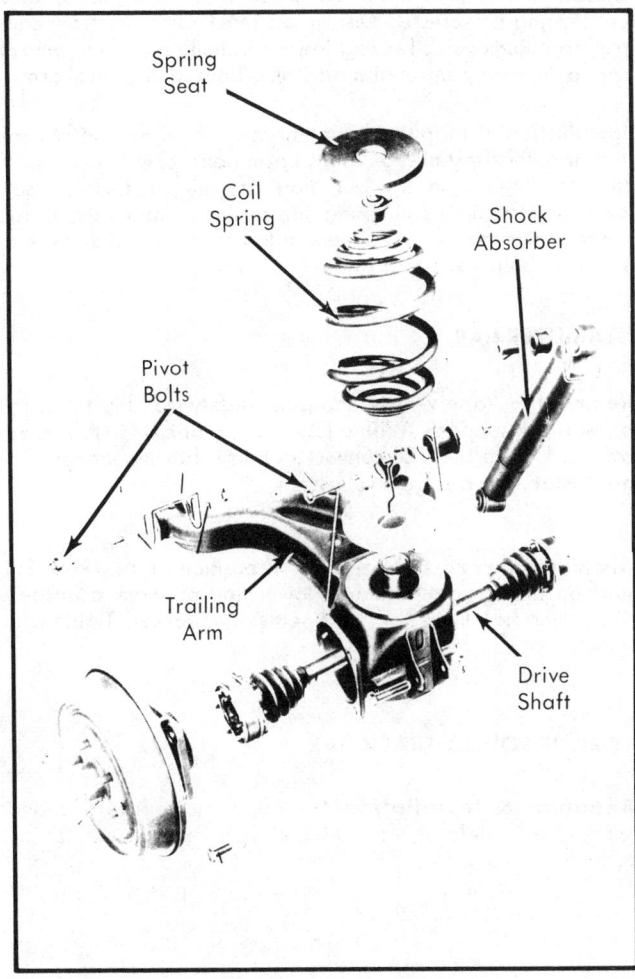

Fig. 1 Exploded View of Vanagon Rear Suspension

REMOVAL & INSTALLATION

TRAILING ARMS

Removal — 1) Raise and support rear of vehicle. Remove tire and wheel. Support trailing arm with a jack.

2) Remove 4 nuts attaching brake drum and axle hub assembly to trailing arm. Using hex wrench, remove hex screws at drive shaft-to-transaxle joint.

3) Pull drive shaft and brake drum assembly through trailing arm and remove from vehicle. Remove shock absorber lower mounting bolt and slowly lower jack.

4) Remove coil spring and spring seats. Note relative position of trailing arm in mounting brackets and remove pivot bolts. Remove trailing arm from vehicle.

Bushing Removal — Using bushing remover (VW 442) and adapter (30-14), and a threaded rod, pull bushing out of trailing arm.

NOTE — Coat washer with oil and place between nut and tool.

Bushing Installation — Coat hole in trailing arm, installation tool, and bushing with soap solution. Using bushing installation tool (3053), and threaded rod, pull bushing into trailing arm until sleeve contacts tool. Wait about 30 seconds and remove tool.

NOTE — Bushing should seat itself. If necessary, press edge of bushing out.

Installation — Reverse removal procedures and note the following: Depressions in spring seats must be aligned with ends of coil springs. Align depression in lower spring seat with depression in trailing arm. Install trailing arm at noted position in brackets. After installation, adjust toe-in and camber.

SHOCK ABSORBER & COIL SPRING

Removal — 1) Raise and support rear of vehicle. Support trailing arm with a jack. Remove shock absorber mounting bolts and remove shock absorber.

NOTE — If only coil spring is to be removed, remove only one shock absorber mounting.

2) Slowly lower jack. Remove coil spring and spring seats.

Bushing Replacement — Using suitable press, press out bushings in shock absorber. File off any sharp edges on sleeve before installation. Coat parts with soap solution and press sleeve 1/2 way into bushing using vise. Using press, fully push bushing and sleeve into shock absorber.

Installation — Reverse removal procedures and note the following: End of coil spring must fit in spring seat depressions. Depression in lower spring seat should fit into depression in trailing arm.

TIGHTENING SPECIFICATIONS	
Application	**Ft. Lbs. (N.m)**
Drive Shaft Hex Screws	33 (45)
Hub Assembly-to-Trailing Arm	101 (137)
Shock Absorber Lower Mounting Bolt	65 (88)
Trailing Arm Pivot Bolts	76 (103)

Rear Suspension

VOLVO

DL	GLT Turbo
GL	Bertone
GLE	Diesel

DESCRIPTION

Rear suspension consists of coil springs mounted between control arms and body rubber mounts, double-acting shock absorbers mounted on control arms and to body, a stabilizer bar attached at both ends to control arms, two torque rods running forward from axle brackets and a track bar attached nearly parallel to axle housing.

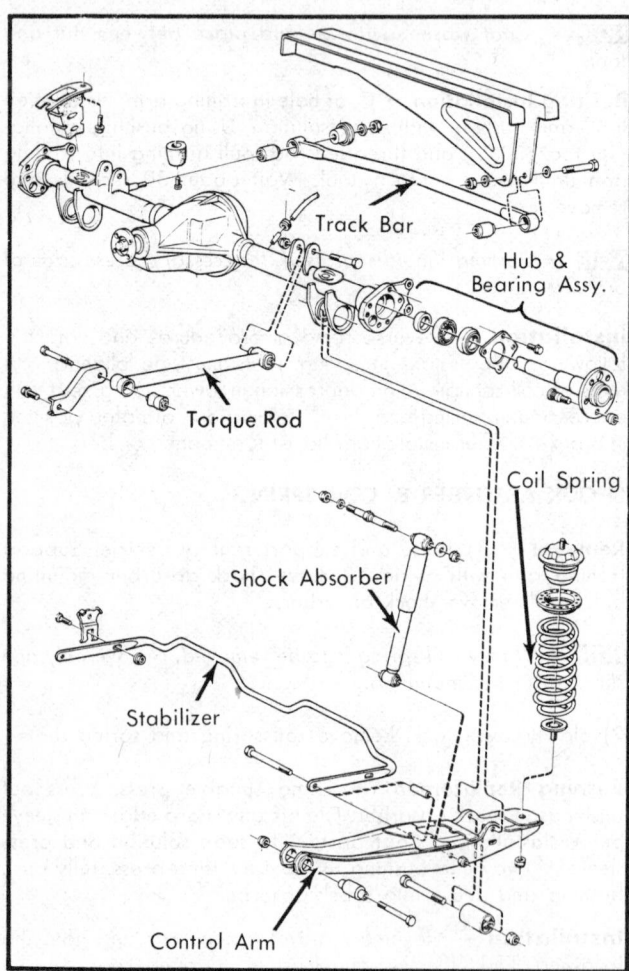

Fig. 1 Exploded View of Volvo Rear Suspension

REMOVAL & INSTALLATION

COIL SPRINGS

Removal — Raise vehicle and place on safety stands. Remove tires and wheels. Place jack under rear axle housing and jack up axle until spring compresses. Disconnect lower shock absorber mounting, then remove spring lower retaining nut. Lower jack and remove coil spring.

Installation — To install, reverse removal procedure and tighten all nuts and bolts. Make sure rubber spring support is in correct position.

SHOCK ABSORBER

Removal — Raise rear of vehicle and support on safety stands. Remove wheel and tire. Use jack to raise rear axle. Remove upper and lower attaching nuts, then remove shock absorber.

Installation — To install, reverse removal procedure and make sure spacer sleeve is in correct position.

CONTROL ARMS

Removal — Raise rear of vehicle and position on safety stands. Position jack under rear axle housing and jack up axle until spring compresses. Disconnect shock absorber from control arm. Remove coil spring lower retaining nut, then remove spring. Remove control arm attaching bolts, and control arm.

Installation — Install attaching bolts for forward end of control arm, then install rear control arm bolts (only finger tight). Install coil spring and lower plate attaching nut. Raise rear axle while guiding coil spring into position. Attach shock absorber lower mount. Lower vehicle to ground and tighten control arm bolts to specifications.

STABILIZER BAR

Removal — Raise vehicle and place safety stand just in front of rear jack supports. With a jack, raise rear axle to take load off shock absorbers. Disconnect stabilizer bar mountings and guide stabilizer bar from vehicle.

Installation — Fit stabilizer bar in position on brackets. Put nuts on finger tight. Remount lower end of shock absorber. Maneuver stabilizer bar so it settles in bracket. Tighten all nuts.

TORQUE RODS & TRACK BAR

Removal & Installation — Raise rear of vehicle and support on safety stands. Disconnect track bar and torque rods from body and axle mountings. Inspect bushings and sleeves for wear or damage. Replace if defective. To install, reverse removal procedures.

TIGHTENING SPECIFICATIONS

Application	Ft. Lbs. (N.m)
Control Arm Bolts	94 (127)
Shock Absorber Bolts	61 (83)
Stabilizer Bar	
M10 Bolts	33 (45)
M12 Bolts	61 (83)
Torque Rod Bolts	61 (83)
Track Bar-to-Axle	43 (58)
Track Bar-to-Body	61 (83)

MERCEDES-BENZ 300TD

DESCRIPTION

The 300TD rear suspension uses an automatic leveling system. The system contains a hydraulic pump, reservoir, leveling valve, pressure reservoir and special combination shock absorber/suspension struts. The leveling valve lever, which is connected to the torsion bar, has 3 positions: neutral, filling and return flow. This positioning of the leveling valve lever, due to the load in vehicle, controls amount of fluid in the special shock absorber which raises or lowers rear of vehicle to maintain a level attitude.

OPERATION

As rear of vehicle is lowered due to added weight, the leveling valve lever raises to the filling position. This allows fluid to flow from pump to pressure reservoir then to special shock absorber, through check valves. This added fluid will raise the rear of the vehicle until the leveling valve lever is moved back to the neutral position. When the added weight is removed, rear of vehicle raises which moves the leveling lever to the return flow position. This allows the fluid in the special shock absorber to drain back into the reservoir until the leveling lever is back in the neutral position and the vehicle is level.

TESTING

HYDRAULIC OIL PUMP & LEVELING VALVE

NOTE — *These tests can only be performed on a ready-to-drive vehicle. Check leveling valve for leaks during test. In case of leaks on valve housing parting surface, install O-ring (006 997 69 45).*

1) Make sure that hydraulic oil is cold before starting test. Disconnect connecting bar at leveling valve lever. Tighten 4 leveling valve housing screws.

CAUTION — *Do not loosen clamping screw securing lever on valve control shaft.*

2) Attach an oil drain line to bleed screw and release pressure in system by opening bleed screw. Remove bleed screw and attach pressure tester (126 589 02 21 00) directly to leveling valve via 3 or 4-way distribution fitting.

3) Push leveling valve lever up into filling position. Run engine at idle (800-1000 RPM) for a short time and observe pressure reading on tester. Pressure should read 1885 psi (132.5 kg/cm^2) minimum.

NOTE — *Perform this test quickly to avoid damage to components.*

4) Turn off engine. Move leveling valve lever down to return flow position and observe base pressure reading. After a stabilization period of 5 minutes, repeat test procedure. Leave pressure tester connected at least 4 hours and observe.

NOTE — *Base pressure must not drop after the stabilization period. This also applies to extended periods, such as overnight.*

5) Bleed base pressure at bleed screw, disconnect tester and install bleed screw. Fill level control system by running engine at medium RPM's and pushing leveling valve lever up into filling position for approximately 30 seconds.

6) Turn off engine. Reconnect connecting bar at leveling valve lever. Check reservoir oil level. Oil level should be between "Max." and "Min." for unloaded vehicle, "Min." for loaded vehicle.

PRESSURE RESERVOIR

NOTE — *This test can be performed only on a ready-to-drive vehicle.*

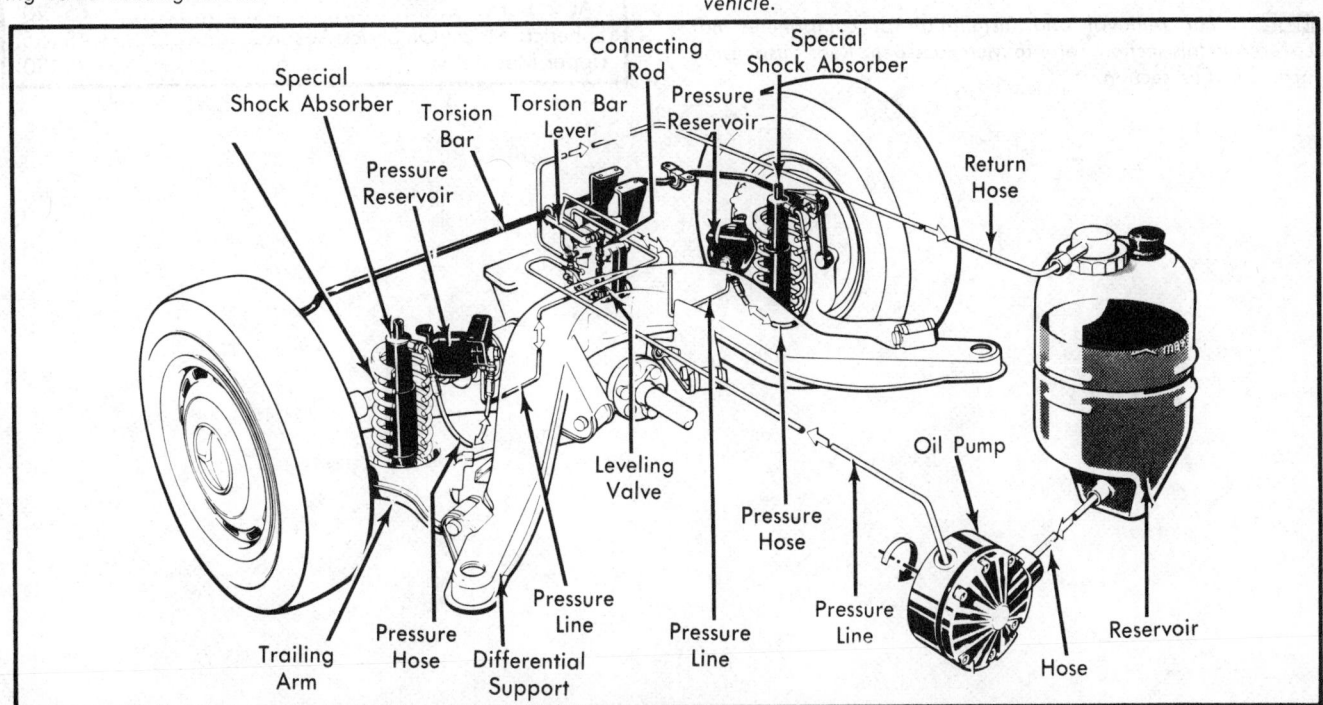

Fig. 1 Mercedes-Benz 300TD Level Control Rear Suspension System

MERCEDES-BENZ 300TD (Cont.)

1) Disconnect connecting bar at leveling valve. Push leveling valve lever down to return flow position. Release pressure in system by opening bleed screw, and remove bleed screw.

2) Connect pressure tester to leveling valve. Disconnect presssure line from leveling valve to pressure reservoir and from leveling valve to left and right pressure reservoirs (near special shock absorbers).

3) Plug lines with couplings and bleed screws. Attach pressure hose from gauge to either right or left pressure reservoir.

4) Push leveling valve lever down to return flow position. Run engine at idle speed. Push leveling valve lever up to filling position and observe pressure gauge.

5) Gas pressure in reservoir is indicated at point where pressure gauge needle changes from indication of a gradual pressure increase to an indication of rapid increase. This increase is caused when oil pressure exceeds gas pressure.

6) Gas pressure should be 304-363 psi (21.4-25.5 kg/cm^2) for new pressure reservoirs, and a minimum of 217 psi (15.2 kg/cm^2) for used pressure reservoirs. Repeat this test for the other reservoir.

7) Disconnect pressure tester, install bleed screw and reconnect pressure lines to pressure reservoirs. Run engine at medium RPM and push leveling valve lever up to filling position for approximately 30 seconds to fill control system.

8) Turn off engine. Reconnect connecting bar at leveling valve lever. With engine off, check oil reservoir oil level. Oil level should be between "Max." and "Min." for unloaded vehicle, "Min." for loaded vehicle.

REMOVAL & INSTALLATION

NOTE — *For removal and installation of components not covered in this section, refer to Mercedes-Benz Rear Suspension article in this section.*

SHOCK ABSORBER

Removal — **1)** Drain leveling control hydraulic system by opening the bleed screw. From inside storage area of vehicle, remove floor covering by turning "T" lever and lifting up. Fold down rear seat back rest. Remove screws and then covering to frame crossmember. Remove cover plate from frame crossmember.

2) Disconnect pressure hose at special shock absorber. Disconnect connection fitting from shock absorber. Cap pressure hose and plug hole in shock absorber.

3) Loosen bolt of upper mount and remove with rubber bushing. Remove bolts securing bottom of shock absorber. Remove shock absorber from bottom; then remove lower rubber bushing of upper mount.

Installation — **1)** To install, reverse removal procedure and note the following: Install bottom rubber bushing onto top of special shock absorber before installing into vehicle.

2) Plugged hole in shock absorber must point toward frame crossmember and mounting pin must protrude through bore in frame crossmember.

3) Make sure all bolts and fittings are tight and reservoir is full; then fill leveling valve by starting engine and moving leveling lever up to filling position. Check leveling suspension system for proper operation.

TIGHTENING SPECIFICATIONS

Application	Ft. Lbs. (N·m)
Ball Joint-to-Spring Strut	48 (65)
Fitting at Pressure Reservoir	32 (43)
Lower Mount Bolt	33 (45)
Pressure Hose-to-Shock Absorber Fitting	25 (34)
Shock Absorber Fitting-to-Shock Absorber	15 (20)
Spherical Mount On Shock Absorber	48 (65)
Upper Mount Bolt	22 (30)

Section 11
STEERING

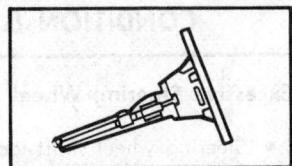

Contents

Steering

MANUAL STEERING TROUBLE SHOOTING

CONDITION & POSSIBLE CAUSE	CONDITION & POSSIBLE CAUSE
Hard Steering • Incorrect tire pressure. • Gear housing lubricant low. • Insufficient lubrication or abnormal wear on steering linkage. • Seized or damaged ball joints. • Steering shaft too tight. • Steering column incorrectly aligned. **Drifting** • Incorrect tire pressure. • Loose lug nuts. • Mismatched tires. • Worn or loose wheel bearings. • Brake drag. • Faulty shock absorbers or coil springs. • Pitman arm binding. • Loose steering gear. • Vehicle uneven riding height.	**Excessive Steering Wheel Play** • Steering wheel shaft loose or worn. • Steering linkage loose or worn. • Worn wheel bearings. • Worn ball joints. • Worm shaft bearing out of adjustment. • Loose steering gear housing. **Steering Wheel Slides** • Worm shaft or ball damaged. • Sector shaft damaged. **Vibration or Shimmy** • Incorrect tire pressure. • Tire out of balance. • Worn shock absorbers or springs. • Loose steering gear housing. • Loose steering linkage. **Noise** • Incorrect tire pressure. • Wheel bearings loose or worn. • Hub cap or rims loose.

POWER STEERING TROUBLE SHOOTING

CONDITION & POSSIBLE CAUSE	CONDITION & POSSIBLE CAUSE
Hard Steering • Fluid level low. • Control valve binding. • Kinked or broken hoses. • Fluid lines blocked. • Air in system. • Low pump pressure. • Loose drive belt. **Sticking Steering Wheel** • Control valve binding.	**Noise** • Loose drive belt. • Low fluid. • Faulty valve or pump wear. **Excessive Steering Wheel Play** • Control valve binding.

AUDI

4000
5000

REMOVAL & INSTALLATION

STEERING WHEEL & HORN

Removal — Disconnect battery ground cable. Using hand pressure, pull off steering wheel center pad. Remove steering wheel nut. Using wheel puller, remove steering wheel.

Installation — To install, reverse removal procedure.

NOTE — *On 5000 models, make sure horn leads (carbon brushes) slide out of recess in steering wheel during removal of center pad.*

TURN SIGNAL, WIPER/WASHER, DIMMER

Removal (4000) — Disconnect battery cable. Remove steering wheel. Unscrew 3 steering column switch housing screws and pull housing off column tube. Disconnect electrical wires from switch housing. Remove mounting screws and switches.

Installation — To install, reverse removal procedure.

TURN SIGNAL, WIPER/WASHER
HAZARD, DIMMER

Removal (5000) — Remove steering wheel. Working through hole in bottom of column shrouding, release mounting and take off shroud. Disconnect electrical wire connectors. Remove switch mounting screws. Lift out switches.

Installation — To install, reverse removal procedure.

STEERING COLUMN LOCK

Removal (Power Steering) — Remove lower cover and switches. Remove lock washer and contact ring. With key in ignition, remove bolt and lock assembly.

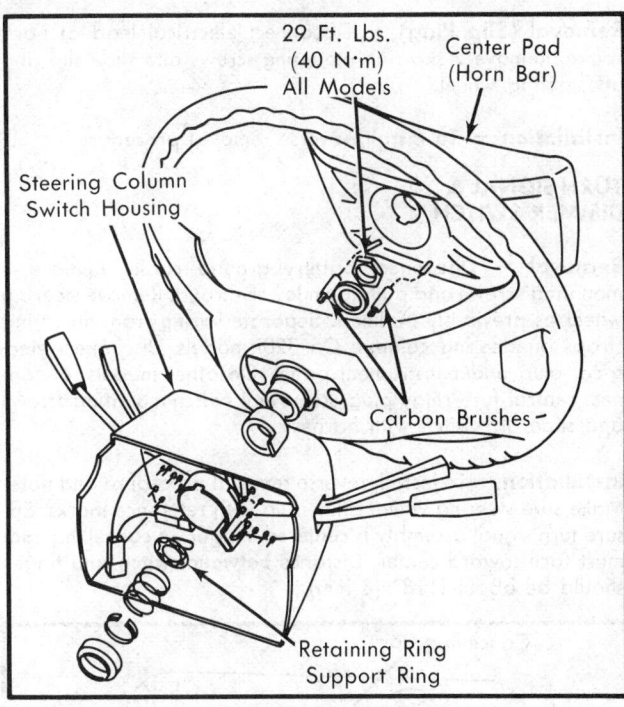

Fig. 1 Audi 5000 Steering Wheel Assembly

Installation — To install, reverse removal procedure.

Removal (All Others) — Remove lower cover. Disconnect electrical wires from back of ignition switch. With key in ignition, drill out shear bolts. Remove lock from column.

Installation — Make sure lugs on steering lock engage column tube. Tighten mounting bolts until heads shear off. To complete installation, reverse removal procedure.

BMW

320i
528i
633CSi
733i

REMOVAL & INSTALLATION

STEERING WHEEL

Removal — Place wheels in straight-ahead position. Pry steering wheel cover off to expose wheel mounting nut. Index mark wheel and main shaft. Remove mounting nut and pull steering wheel off main shaft.

Installation — To install, reverse removal procedure and refer to reference marks made during removal.

HORN CONTROLS

Removal (Horn Button) — Remove screws on back side of steering wheel spoke to free horn button.

Installation — To install, reverse removal procedure.

Removal (Contact Spring) — Pry off cover concealing contact spring and remove spring.

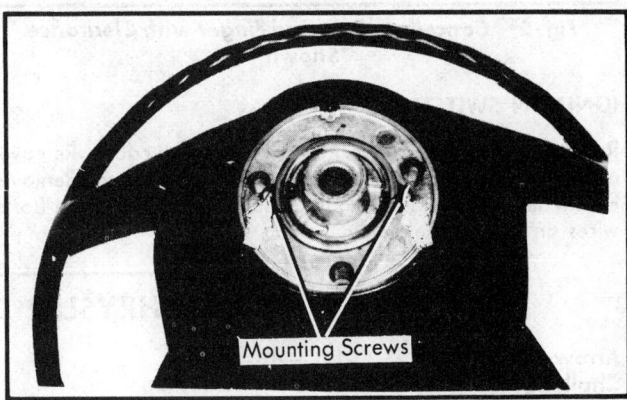

Fig. 1 Screws to Take Out for Slip Ring Removal

Installation — Replace spring if broken or if spring is unable to provide adequate contact. To complete installation, reverse removal procedure, making sure contact pins face inward.

BMW (Cont.)

Removal (Slip Ring) — Disconnect electrical lead at each spoke. Remove 2 slip ring mounting screws and slide slip ring off steering wheel.

Installation — To install, reverse removal procedure.

TURN SIGNAL & DIMMER SWITCH

Removal — Disconnect battery ground cable. Remove 3 mounting screws and pull down lower shroud. Remove steering wheel as previously outlined. Separate wiring from mounting straps on steering column. On 320i models, disconnect electrical plug under instrument panel. On other models, disconnect central fuse/relay plug. Remove 4 switch mounting screws and slide off switch with harness.

Installation — To install, reverse removal procedure and note: Make sure steering wheel is lined up with reference marks. Ensure turn signal assembly is centered. Finger on cancelling cam must face toward center. Distance between switch and finger should be about .118" (3 mm).

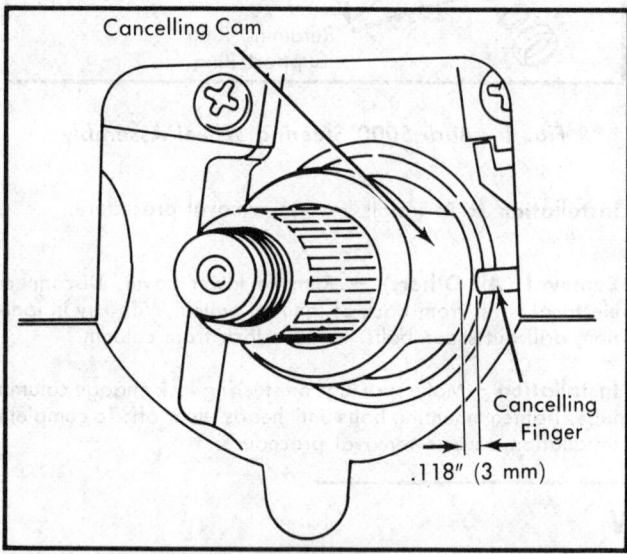

Fig. 2 Cancelling Cam and Finger with Clearance Shown

IGNITION SWITCH

Removal — 1) Disconnect battery ground cable. Remove mounting screws and pull off lower plastic shroud. Remove hollow set screw and slide out ignition switch. Disconnect horn wires on 320i models only.

2) Disconnect steering column wire holders. Disconnect central fuse/relay plate plug and plug connector. On 320i models only, disconnect central plug. On all models, remove ignition switch.

Installation — To install, reverse removal procedure and note following: Make sure to turn ignition key all the way back before inserting. Set ignition switch at "O" position before installing. On 320i models only, marks on ignition switch must oppose each other.

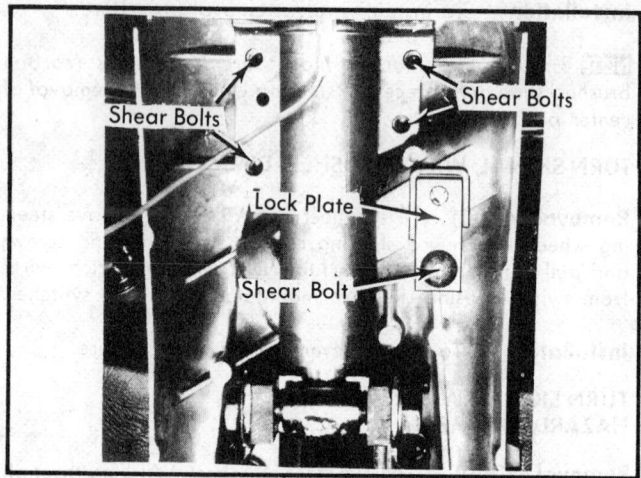

Fig. 3 Location of Shear Bolts. View Looking Up From Under Steering Column. All Models Except 320i

STEERING LOCK

Removal (Exc. 320i) — 1) Disconnect battery ground. Remove steering wheel. Remove 3 screws holding lower steering column shroud. Disconnect and remove turn signal and wiper/washer switch plate.

2) Remove shear bolts from switch plate with chisel. Remove set screw on outside of steering column tube. Pull out ignition switch. Remove steering lock plate shear bolt and pull out steering lock.

Installation — To install, reverse removal procedure.

Removal (320i) — Disconnect electrical wires from under instrument panel. Remove shroud. Remove shear bolt from lock plate and pull out steering lock.

Installation — To install, reverse removal procedure.

CHRYSLER CORP. IMPORTS

Arrow Pickup	Colt
Challenger	Ram-50 Pickup
Champ	Sapporo

REMOVAL & INSTALLATION

STEERING WHEEL & COMBINATION SWITCH

Removal — 1) Disconnect battery ground cable. Remove horn pad. Mark main shaft and steering wheel for reassembly reference. Remove steering wheel nut. Remove steering wheel with suitable puller (DT1001A).

NOTE — If equipped with tilt steering, handle must be in lowest position before removing steering wheel.

2) Remove column cover. Disconnect electrical connections at base of steering column. Remove retaining screws and pull combination switch out.

Installation — 1) Install combination switch and retaining screws. Connect electrical connections at base of column and route harness along center of tube.

CHRYSLER CORP. IMPORTS (Cont.)

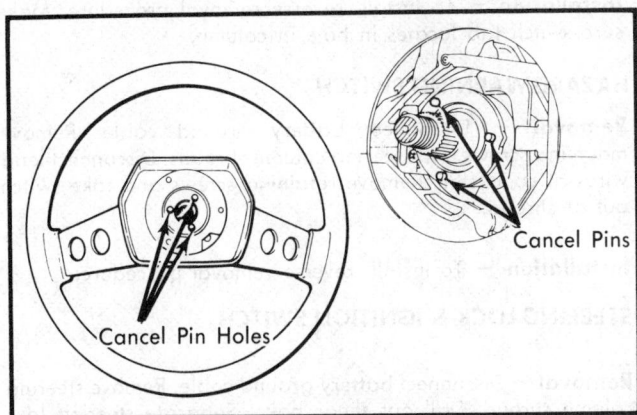

Fig. 1 Installation of Steering Wheel on Arrow, Challenger, Colt and Sapporo Models

2) To install steering wheel, place front wheels in straight ahead position. On Arrow, Challenger, Colt and Sapporo models, align cancel pins of column switch with holes in bottom of steering wheel. On all models, refit steering wheel with index marks aligned. Tighten nut and install horn pad.

STEERING LOCK

Removal — With steering wheel removed, disconnect negative battery cable. Remove column levers and switches. Cut a slot in mounting head screws and bracket with a hack saw. Remove screws and remove steering wheel lock.

Installation — To install reverse removal procedure and install new bracket and screws.

COURIER

REMOVAL & INSTALLATION

STEERING WHEEL & COMBINATION SWITCH

Removal — **1)** Disconnect battery ground cable. Remove steering wheel nut cover. Index mark main shaft and steering wheel. Disconnect electrical leads. Pull steering wheel from shaft.

2) Remove plastic hazard light indicator and steering column shroud. Disconnect electrical wires at base of steering column. Remove headlight switch knob from shaft.

3) Remove snap ring retaining switch and force turn indicator cancelling cam off shaft. Take out single bolt, near bottom of switch, and pull out complete switch assembly.

Installation — **1)** Fit switch assembly on steering column then, refit one retaining bolt. Place turn indicator cancelling cam into position and install snap ring. Reconnect electrical plug at column base.

2) Insert and tighten headlight knob switch. Install column shroud and plastic hazard light indicator. Refit steering wheel with index marks aligned. Connect battery ground cable.

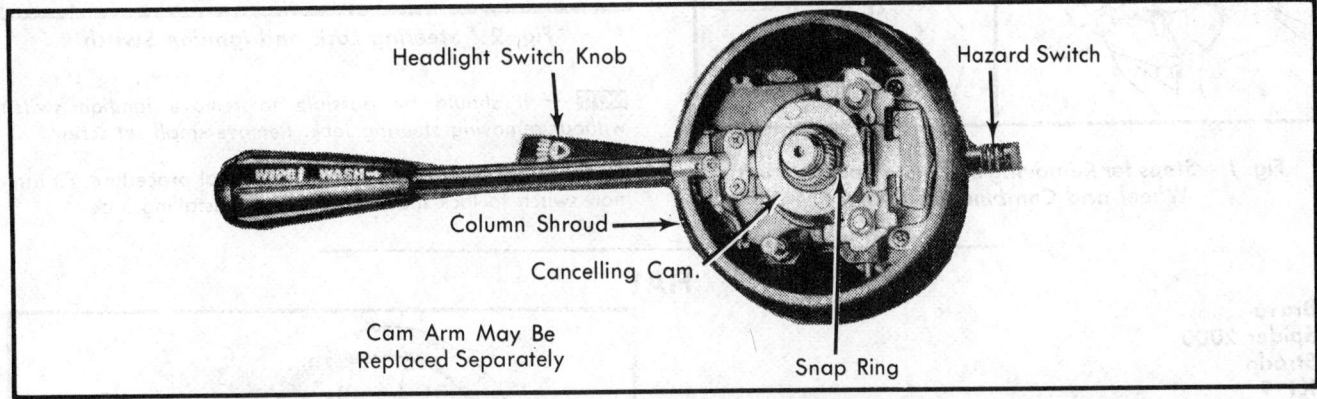

Fig. 1 Top View of Steering Column with Steering Wheel Removed to Expose Combination Switch

DATSUN

200SX	510
210	810
280ZX	Pickup
310	

REMOVAL & INSTALLATION
STEERING WHEEL & HORN PAD

Removal — **1)** Disconnect battery ground cable. Use the following procedures to remove horn pad for particular model:

- On 200SX, 280ZX, 310, 810 and Pickup models, pull horn pad off steering wheel.

- On 210 models, remove 3-spoke horn pad by pulling off. Remove 2-spoke horn pad by removing bolts on back side of steering wheel, then pull off pad. Remove horn wire.

- On 510 models, remove screws on back side of steering wheel and pull pad off. Remove horn wire.

DATSUN (Cont.)

2) Remove retaining nut. Using puller (27180001), remove steering wheel. Do not hammer on steering wheel. Pounding may cause damage to collapsible steering column.

Installation — On all models, reverse removal procedure. Grease any sliding components. Match index marks made during removal. Check operation.

COMBINATION SWITCH

Removal — Disconnect battery ground cable. Remove steering wheel. Remove steering column shrouds. Disconnect switch connector. Remove screws holding switch to column and lift switch out of shaft.

NOTE — *On Pickup models switch connector is near lower edge of instrument panel.*

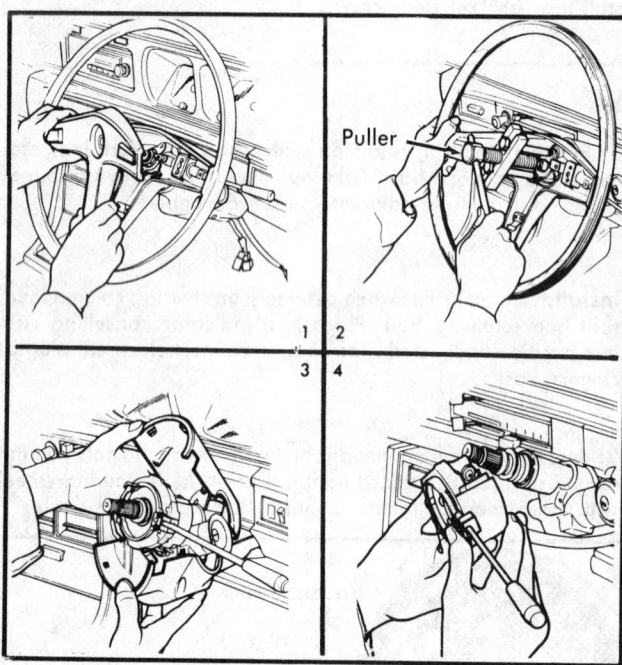

Fig. 1 Steps for Removing and Installing Steering Wheel and Combination Switch

Installation — To install, reverse removal procedure. Make sure switch tab locates in hole in column.

HAZARD WARNING SWITCH

Removal — Disconnect battery ground cable. Remove mounting screws and steering column shrouds. Disconnect lead wires at connector. Remove retaining screws and take switch out of shroud.

Installation — To install, reverse removal procedure.

STEERING LOCK & IGNITION SWITCH

Removal — Disconnect battery ground cable. Remove steering column shroud. Drill out shear bolts. Separate steering lock from column shaft. If ignition switch is to be removed, separate electrical connector, then remove small set screw holding switch body. Remove switch.

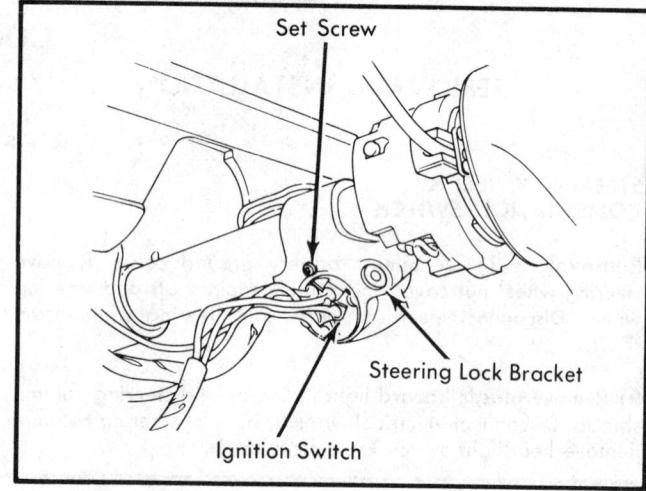

Fig. 2 Steering Lock and Ignition Switch

NOTE — *It should be possible to remove ignition switch without removing steering lock. Remove small set screw.*

Installation — To install, reverse removal procedure. Fit ignition switch to lock mechanism before installing lock.

FIAT

Brava
Spider 2000
Strada
X1/9

REMOVAL & INSTALLATION

HORN COVER & STEERING WHEEL

Removal (Brava & Strada) — Disconnect battery ground cable. Remove steering column shrouds. From behind steering wheel, pry 2 plastic locking tabs inward to remove horn button. Remove nut and washer and remove steering wheel.

Installation — To install, reverse removal procedure.

Removal (All Others) — Disconnect battery ground cable. Remove steering column cover (if equipped) and remove horn

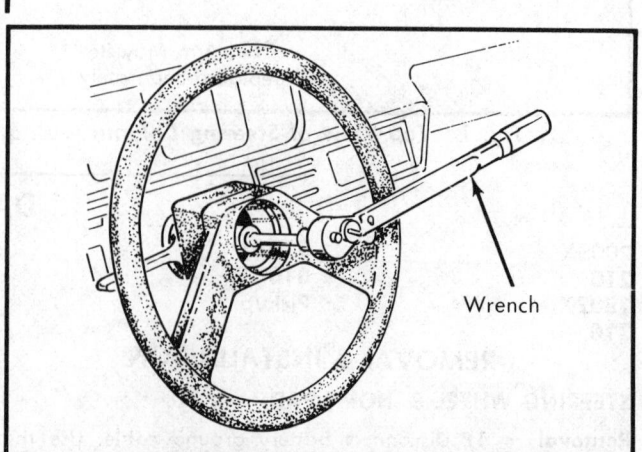

Fig. 1 Steering Wheel Removal (Brava & Strada Shown)

FIAT (Cont.)

cover. Disconnect horn wires (if required). Remove retaining nut and washer and remove steering wheel. On Spider 2000, remove 6 retaining screws and remove wheel.

Installation — To install, reverse removal procedure.

COMBINATION SWITCH

Removal — Remove steering wheel and column shrouding. Disconnect battery ground cable. Disconnect electrical connection. Remove retaining nut (screws) and remove switch from shaft.

Installation — To install, reverse removal procedure.

HONDA

Accord
Civic
Prelude

REMOVAL & INSTALLATION

HORN PAD & STEERING WHEEL

Removal — 1) Disconnect battery ground cable. Remove steering wheel horn pad. With wheels in straight ahead position, mark position of steering wheel to shaft. Remove retaining nut.

2) Remove steering wheel by using suitable puller or by hitting backside of wheel with hand. Steering wheel components can be disassembled and replaced if necessary.

CAUTION — *Do not apply heavy hitting force or shear pins within steering column may be damaged.*

Installation — To install, reverse removal procedure and ensure wheels are straight ahead and marks made at removal are aligned.

COMBINATION SWITCH

Removal — Remove steering pad. Remove column shrouding. Disconnect electrical connectors and remove steering wheel. Remove mounting screws and lift out combination switch. Washer/wiper switch can be separated from turn signal switch. Do not drop or lose turn signal cancel cam key when removing combination switch.

Installation — To install, reverse removal procedure and note: Insert lug on turn signal switch assembly into recess in steering column. Turn signal cancel key lugs must fit into recess in steering wheel. Horn switch spring terminal must touch contact ring.

HAZARD SWITCH

Switch is located in the top column shrouding. Remove top shrouding, disconnect electrical wires and remove switch from mounted position.

NOTE — *Accord models also have an indicator light switch located in the upper column shrouding. The switch, when depressed, will allow all indicator lights to function. Procedures for Hazard switch apply.*

STEERING LOCK & IGNITION SWITCH

Removal — Remove steering column upper and lower shrouding. Disconnect ignition switch electrical wiring at lower end of steering column. Center punch shear bolts. Drill out shear head bolts and extract from lock bracket. Remove ignition switch.

Installation — Insert new ignition switch. Hand tighten new shear bolts. Check switch operation at this time. Tighten shear bolts. Reconnect switch electrical leads.

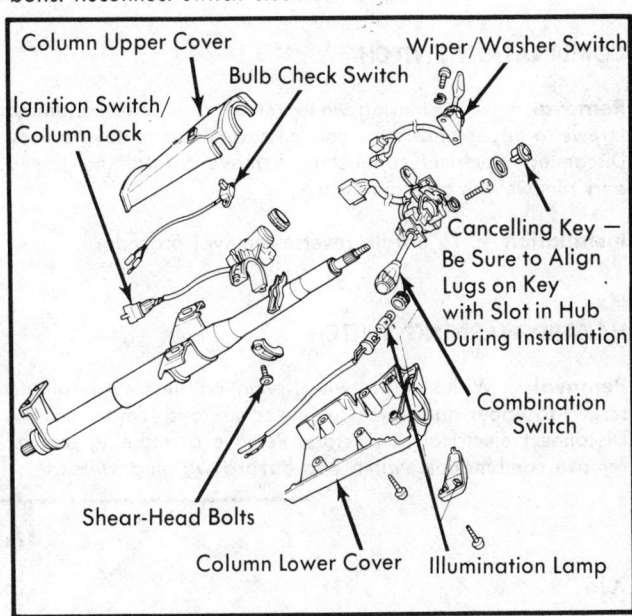

Fig. 1 Disassembled View of Upper Column Components — Accord Shown; Others Similar

ISUZU

I-Mark
P'UP

CAUTION — *Steering shaft is an energy-absorbing unit. During any service operation, avoid hammering, jarring, or leaning on any portion of column.*

REMOVAL & INSTALLATION

HORN BUTTON & STEERING WHEEL

Removal — 1) Disconnect battery ground cable. On 2-spoke steering wheel, remove 2 retaining screws on back of steering wheel and remove horn pad. Disconnect horn wires. On 3-spoke steering wheel, use a screwdriver to pry the medallion out of steering wheel center.

2) Unscrew steering wheel retaining nut. Mark position of steering wheel on column shaft. Using steering wheel puller (J-29752) remove steering wheel.

Installation — To install, reverse removal procedure.

ISUZU (Cont.)

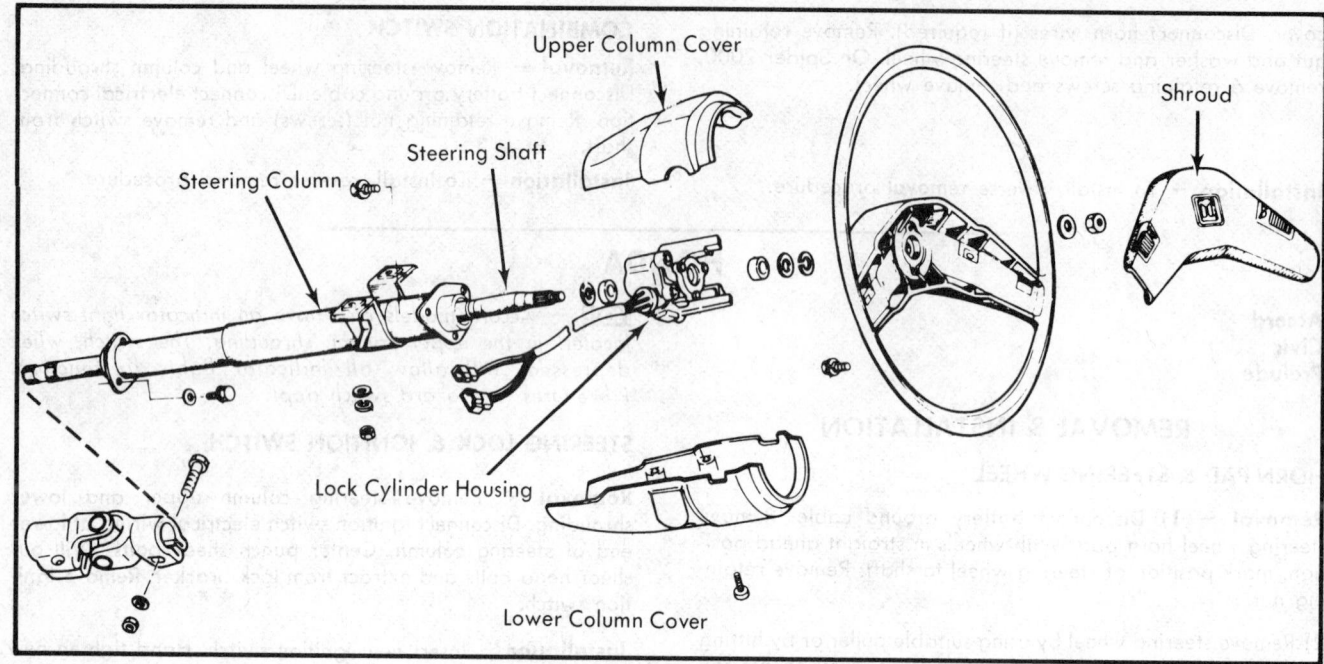

**Fig. 1 I-Mark Steering Wheel Assembly
(P'UP Similar)**

COMBINATION SWITCH

Removal — With steering wheel removed, unscrew retaining screws to upper and lower column covers and remove covers. Disconnect electrical connectors. Remove 6 retaining screws and remove combination switch.

Installation — To install, reverse removal procedure.

HAZARD WARNING SWITCH

Removal — With steering wheel removed, unscrew retaining screws to upper and lower column covers and remove covers. Disconnect electrical connectors. Remove 6 retaining screws, remove combination switch and hazard warning switch.

Installation — To install, reverse removal procedure.

STEERING LOCK & IGNITION SWITCH

Removal (I-Mark) — Remove steering wheel and column covers. Remove snap ring, washer and 3 retaining bolts on column flange. Remove ignition switch and steering lock assembly.

Installation — To install, reverse removal procedure.

Removal (P'UP) — Remove upper and lower column covers. Disconnect ignition switch wiring connector. Remove switch cover. Remove ignition switch ring nut and remove switch.

Installation — To install, reverse removal procedure.

JAGUAR

XJ6

REMOVAL & INSTALLATION

HORN PAD & STEERING WHEEL

Removal — **1)** Set front wheels in straight-ahead position. Mark position on steering wheel and column. Remove 3 screws securing lower switch cover. Detach cover.

2) Working from below, remove clamp bolt securing split collet adapter to steering column. *See Fig. 1.* Loosen lock nut on set screw and loosen screw 2 turns. Remove steering wheel, complete with hand lock nut, impact rubber bumper, collet adapter and shaft.

Disassembly — **1)** Remove 2 self-tapping screws from lower face of steering wheel boss and lift off padded horn contact.

Unscrew nylon nut from top of steering wheel shaft and carefully remove it, taking out horn contact tube also.

2) Remove self-locking nut and plain washer which retain steering wheel. Carefully pull steering wheel from shaft, collecting both halves of split cone.

Reassembly — To reassemble, reverse disassembly procedure.

Installation — To install, reverse removal procedure and note the following: Be sure that front wheels are always kept in a straight-ahead position. When tightening collet clamp, tighten grub screw finger tight. Snug down lock nut and tighten clamp bolt.

STEERING LOCK

Removal — Take off upper column shrouding. Using a center punch, make several dimples in shear bolt and rotate bolt out.

JAGUAR (Cont.)

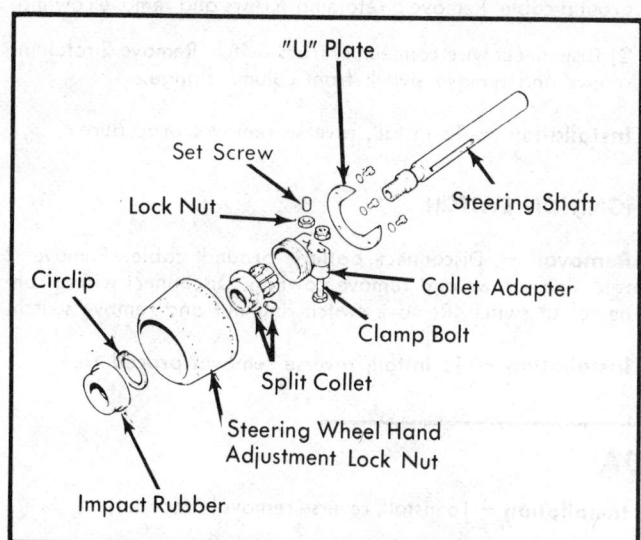

Fig. 1 **Components Located Behind Steering Wheel**

Installation — To install, reverse removal procedure.

IGNITION SWITCH

Removal — Disconnect battery ground terminal. Separate column shrouding from switch side. Disengage retaining ring holding ignition switch in housing. Disconnect ignition switch wiring at multi-pin connector. Remove switch and harness.

Installation — To install, reverse removal procedure.

COMBINATION SWITCH

Removal — 1) Disconnect battery ground cable. Take off steering column lower shroud. Remove steering wheel as previously outlined. Remove steering column upper shroud and cover from below instrument panel.

2) Loosen pinch bolt and pull combination switch assembly from steering column. Disconnect electrical wiring. Hazard flasher can now be separated by disconnecting wires, depressing tangs and pushing switch through mounting plate.

Installation — To install, reverse removal procedure.

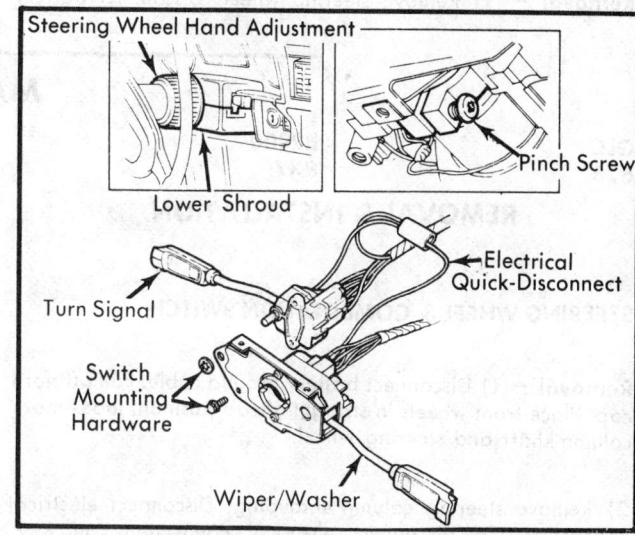

Fig. 2 **Exploded View of Combination Switch**

Pickup

CAUTION — *Steering shaft is an energy-absorbing unit. During any service operation, avoid jarring or leaning on any portion of column.*

LUV

REMOVAL & INSTALLATION
HORN BUTTON & STEERING WHEEL

Removal — 1) Disconnect battery ground cable. Remove 2 retaining screws and remove horn pad. Disconnect horn wires from pad.

2) Unscrew steering wheel retaining nut. Mark position of

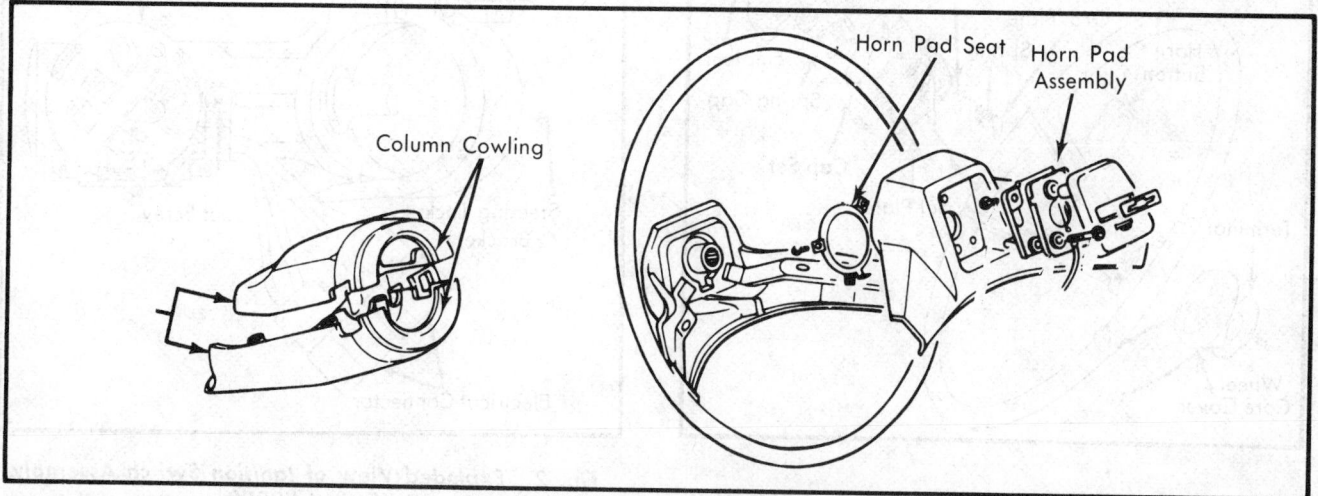

Fig. 1 **LUV Steering Wheel Assembly**

LUV (Cont.)

steering wheel on column shaft. Remove 5 retaining screws to column cowling and remove cowling.

3) Using puller (J-24292-A), remove steering wheel.

Installation — To install, reverse removal procedure.

COMBINATION SWITCH

NOTE — *Combination switch has the following functions: Turn signal, headlight dimmer, hazard warning, and windshield wiper/washer.*

Removal — **1)** Remove steering wheel. Disconnect battery ground cable. Remove 5 retaining screws and remove cowling.

2) Disconnect wire connectors from switch. Remove 2 retaining screws and remove switch from column flange.

Installation — To install, reverse removal procedure.

IGNITION SWITCH

Removal — Disconnect battery ground cable. Remove 2 retaining screws and remove cowling. Disconnect wiring connector at switch. Remove switch ring nut and remove switch.

Installation — To install, reverse removal procedure.

MAZDA

GLC	B2000
626	RX7

REMOVAL & INSTALLATION

STEERING WHEEL & COMBINATION SWITCH

Removal — **1)** Disconnect battery ground cable. Pull off horn cap. Place front wheels in straight-ahead position. Index mark column shaft and steering wheel.

2) Remove steering column shrouding. Disconnect electrical connectors. To disconnect electrical connections on RX7, remove air duct at base of steering column. Remove steering shaft stop ring, cancel cam and spring. Remove retaining screws and combination switch assembly.

NOTE — *Wiper switch can be removed with combination switch or separated from it.*

Installation — To install, reverse removal procedure.

IGNITION SWITCH

Removal — Remove steering wheel as previously outlined. Remove column shrouding. Remove combination switch. Disconnect electrical connector. Remove screw attaching switch contact housing to steering lock body and slide out contact housing. See *Fig. 2*.

Installation — To install, reverse removal procedure.

STEERING LOCK

Removal — Remove steering wheel, column shrouding and combination switch. File a slot in bolt attaching steering lock body to column shaft (in order to remove bolt with screwdriver) and remove bolt. Remove steering lock.

Installation — To install, reverse removal procedure and tighten new shear bolts until heads break.

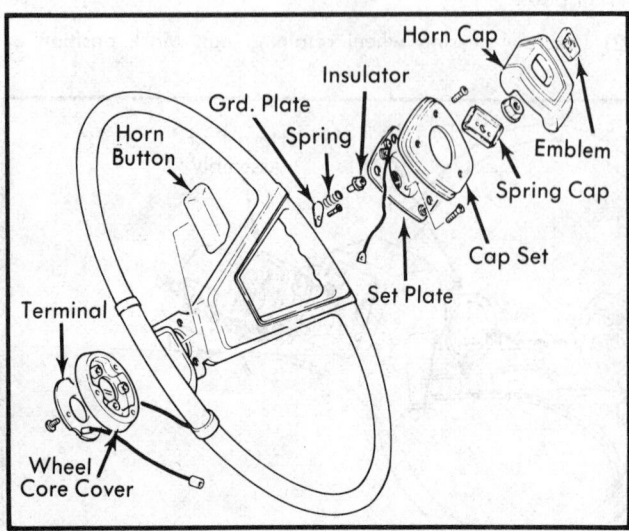

Fig. 1   Typical Mazda Steering Wheel Assembly

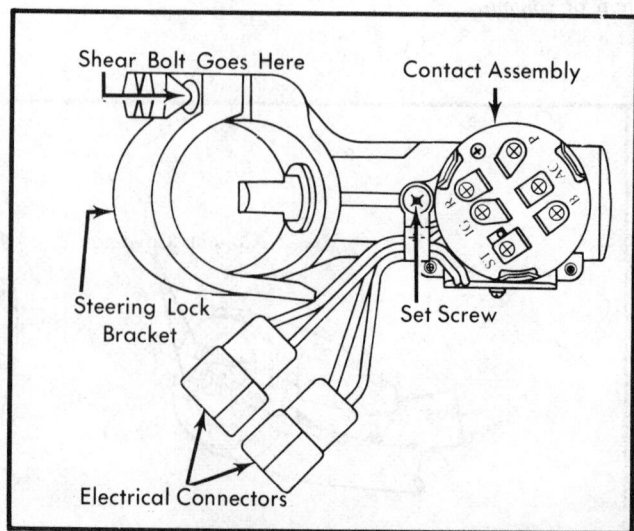

Fig. 2   Exploded View of Ignition Switch Assembly (Except B2000)

MERCEDES-BENZ

240D
280 Series
300 Series
380 Series

REMOVAL & INSTALLATION

HORN PAD & STEERING WHEEL

Removal (Polyurethane Wheel) — Place alignment marks on wheel and shaft. Grip horn pad near one corner and pull straight up until free. Pull up other corner. Remove pad from steering wheel. Unscrew retaining nut, remove spring washer and pull steering wheel from shaft.

Installation — To install, reverse removal procedure.

Removal (Plastic Wheel) — **1)** Remove vehicle emblem from horn pad. Unscrew steering wheel retaining nut and pull wheel from shaft with pad still attached. Unscrew hex nuts on backside of wheel and separate steering wheel from pad.

NOTE — *Horn wire is still attached to steering wheel, so care must be taken to avoid breaking it.*

2) Detach horn wire from contact ring and remove steering wheel. Remove countersunk screws from steering wheel hub and centering pad of contact ring. Remove horn ring from

steering wheel. Remove locking ring from hub of pad, then remove slip ring.

Installation — To install, reverse removal procedure. Ensure wheels are kept in straight ahead position and that steering wheel spokes are horizontal.

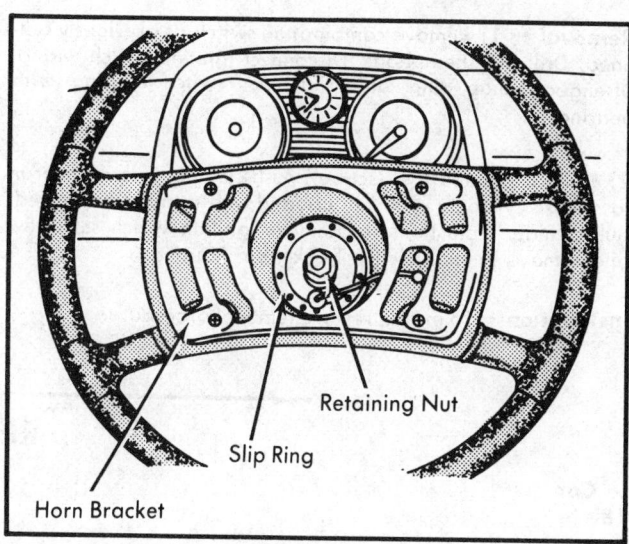

Fig. 1   Mercedes-Benz Steering Wheel with Cover Removed

Retaining Nut
Slip Ring
Horn Bracket

PORSCHE

911SC
924
928

REMOVAL & INSTALLATION

HORN PAD & STEERING WHEEL

NOTE — *On models equipped with a collapsable "can" behind the steering wheel, care must be taken in all service procedures. Do not apply excessive or striking forces to the steering wheel or steering column.*

Removal (911SC) — **1)** Align front wheels in straight ahead position. Disconnect battery cable.

2) Grasp horn pad and rotate counterclockwise while pushing in. When horn pad is free, lift from steering wheel and disconnect horn contact finger.

3) Loosen steering wheel retaining nut. Mark position of steering wheel to steering shaft. Attach a suitable puller and remove the steering wheel.

Installation — To install steering wheel, reverse removal procedure and note the following: Lightly lubricate horn contact finger with electrical contact grease before installation.

Removal (924) — Disconnect battery. Using hand pressure, lift up horn pad. Unscrew wheel retaining nut. Pull wheel upward and off shaft.

Installation — To install, reverse removal procedure.

Removal (928) — Disconnect battery ground. Place wheels in straight-ahead position. Take off horn pad. Disconnect horn wires. Index mark steering wheel and column shaft. Unscrew mounting nut. Remove steering wheel.

Installation — Align index marks and replace steering wheel so spokes are horizontal. Install mounting nut. Fit horn wires into place in pad. Press horn pad onto retaining pins.

COMBINATION SWITCH

Removal (924) — **1)** Disconnect battery ground. Using hand pressure, lift up steering pad. Remove steering wheel mounting nut. Pull steering wheel off shaft.

2) Remove shroud from around switch housing. Pull up on switch plate and disconnect electrical wires. Remove entire switch assembly then, separate wiper/washer switch from turn signal switch by taking out screw that mounts them together.

Installation — Refit switches together with screw. Slide switch assemblies back into place, refitting spacer at same time. Make sure spacer is driven in until there is a distance of 1.7" (42.5 mm) from face (top edge) of spacer to top edge of shaft. This distance will ensure there is .08-.15" (2-4 mm) between steering wheel and steering column switches. Reverse removal procedure to install remaining components.

Removal (928) — Disconnect battery ground. Remove steering wheel. Remove cover from under steering column switch. Remove steering column switch mounting screw. Remove instru-

PORSCHE (Cont.)

ment cover mounting screws. Maneuver instrument cover until electrical wires can be disconnected. Remove column switch.

Installation — To install, reverse removal procedure.

STEERING COLUMN LOCK, KEY CYLINDER & IGNITION SWITCH

Removal — 1) Remove combination switch as previously outlined. Drill out shear bolts. Disconnect ignition switch wiring. Disengage snap ring and slide out switch housing with bearing.

2) Using a pointed tool (scribe), push cylinder lock retainer in to release cylinder. With key inserted and retainer depressed, pull cylinder from housing. Remove ignition switch set screw and remove ignition switch back from housing.

Installation — To install, reverse removal procedure.

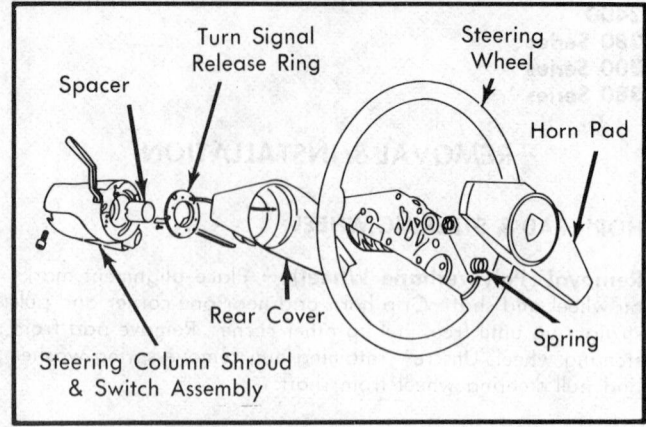

Fig. 1 **Exploded View of Porsche 924 Steering Wheel and Related Components**

RENAULT

Le Car
18i

REMOVAL & INSTALLATION

HORN PAD & STEERING WHEEL

Removal (Le Car) — Disconnect battery. Remove horn pad. Remove steering wheel nut. Using puller (Dir. 21A) remove steering wheel.

Installation — To install, reverse removal procedure.

Removal (18i) — 1) Disconnect battery. Remove horn pad. Remove 2 steering column protective housings.

2) Remove steering wheel nut. Install puller plate tool (Dir. 372) behind steering wheel.

3) Using a center punch, make a center point mark in center of steering column shaft.

4) Connect puller tool (Mot. 49) to puller plate. Using a wrench, turn puller shaft until steering wheel is pulled from steering shaft.

Installation — 1) Position steering wheel on steering shaft.

2) Install steering wheel nut and tighten. Using a center punch, notch the edge of steering column shaft to lock the nut in place.

3) To complete installation, reverse removal procedure.

TURN SIGNAL & LIGHTING SWITCH

Removal (Le Car) — 1) Disconnect battery. Remove instrument panel housing retaining screws and remove housing. See Fig. 2.

2) Remove switch retaining screws. Disconnect electrical connectors. Remove switch.

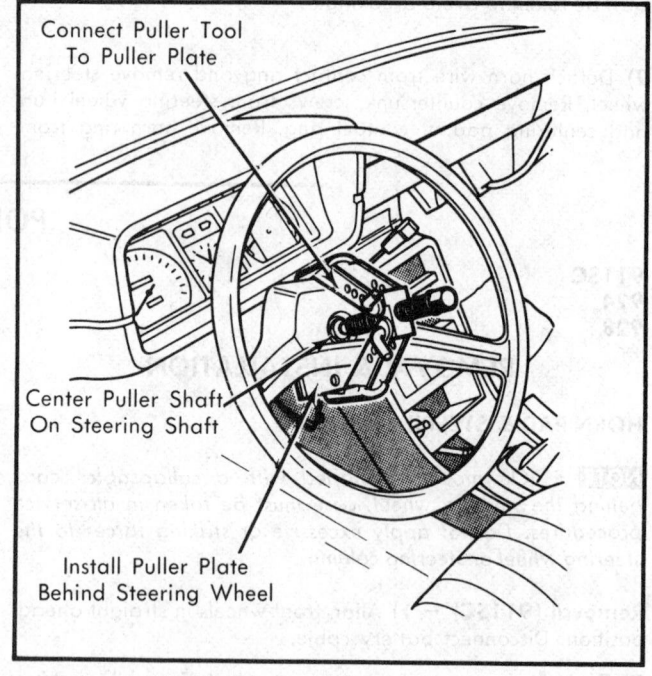

Fig. 1 **Removing Steering Wheel on 18i**

Installation — Reverse removal procedure to install.

COMBINATION SWITCH

Removal (18i) — 1) Disconnect battery. Remove steering wheel. Remove 2 steering column protective housings.

2) Remove switch retaining bolts and screw. Disconnect electrical connectors. Remove switch.

Installation — Reverse removal procedure to install.

RENAULT (Cont.)

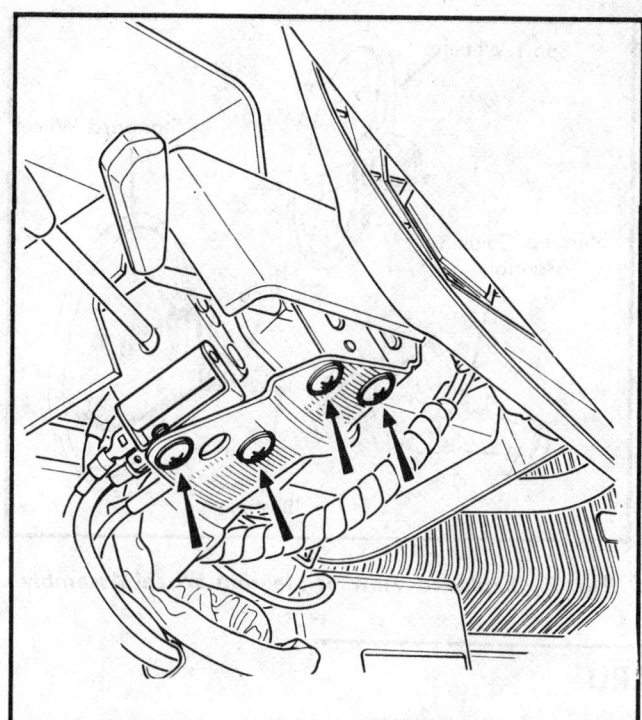

Fig. 2 Location of Switch Assembly Retaining Screws

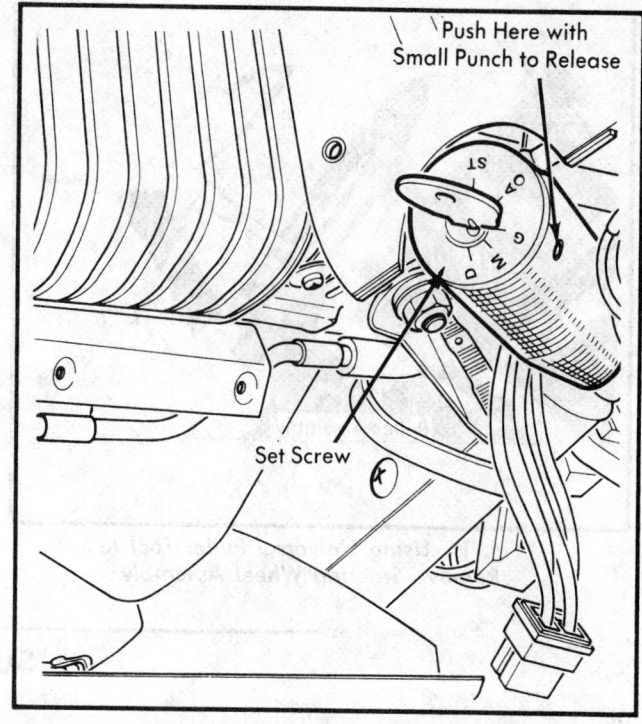

Fig. 3 Ignition Switch Removal

NOTE — *Turn signal and windshield wiper switch are one unit and cannot be separated. If one is defective, both must be replaced. Headlight switch may be replaced separately and removed from combination switch by removing retaining pin.*

IGNITION SWITCH

Removal (Le Car) — **1)** Disconnect battery. Remove shroud from around switch assembly. Disconnect electrical connections.

2) Turn ignition switch to "G" (Garage) position and remove switch. Remove set screw and press in retaining catch with a small punch. Push switch body from rear to release it. See Fig. 3.

Installation — To install, reverse removal procedure.

Removal (18i) — **1)** Disconnect battery. Remove steering wheel. Remove 2 steering column protective housings.

2) Disconnect electrical connections. Turn key to "Park" position and remove ignition switch and key.

Installation — To install, reverse removal procedure.

COLUMN LOCK

Removal (All Models) — **1)** Remove ignition switch and lock assembly from column. Turn key to "Stop" position.

2) Remove 2 rear bracket retaining screws. Slide lock assembly toward rear and remove.

Installation — To install, reverse removal procedure.

SAAB

900

REMOVAL & INSTALLATION

HORN CONTROL & STEERING WHEEL

Removal — **1)** Disconnect battery ground cable. Remove bottom cover retaining screws and cover. On standard steering wheel, remove retaining screws from behind steering wheel, then remove pad and horn contact. On 3-spoke wheel, lift pad from spokes, then reach under and disconnect horn leads while supporting pad.

2) Mark position of steering wheel to shaft and remove retaining nut and washer. Remove wheel from shaft with suitable wheel puller.

Installation — To install, reverse removal procedure.

COMBINATION SWITCH

Removal — Disconnect battery ground cable. Remove steering wheel shrouding and lower instrument panel shroud. Disconnect electrical connections at base of column. Remove retaining screws and direction/wiper switch assembly.

Installation — To install, reverse removal procedure and note: Directional signal must be properly aligned on column.

SAAB (Cont.)

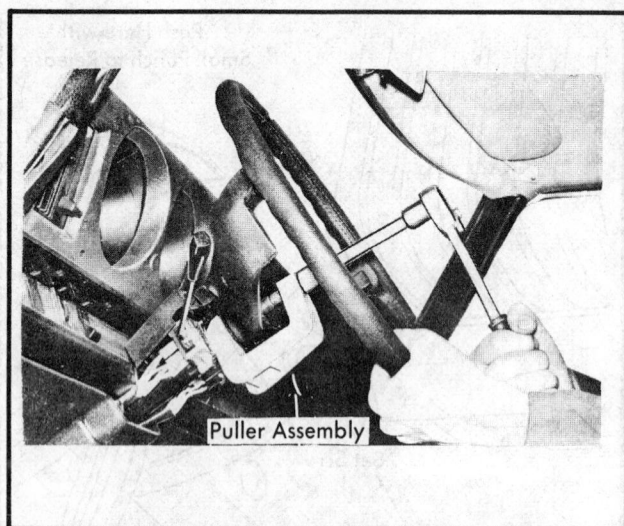

Fig. 1 Using Universal Puller Tool to Remove Steering Wheel Assembly

Puller Assembly

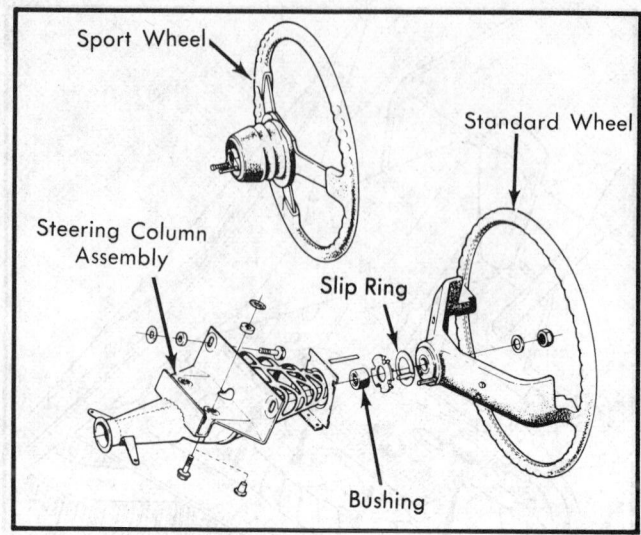

Sport Wheel

Standard Wheel

Steering Column Assembly

Slip Ring

Bushing

Fig. 2 Exploded View of Steering Wheel Assembly

SUBARU

DL
GL
GLF

REMOVAL & INSTALLATION

HORN PAD & STEERING WHEEL

Removal — Disconnect battery ground cable. Remove horn pad retaining screws from back side of steering wheel and disconnect electrical wiring. Remove steering column covers and horn pad. Remove steering wheel retaining nut and washer. Pull steering wheel from shaft.

Installation — To install, reverse removal procedure and note the following: After steering wheel is installed, check clearance between wheel and column cover; it should be .04-.12" (1-3 mm). If beyond this range, loosen column cover screws and adjust.

COMBINATION SWITCH

Removal — Remove steering wheel as previously described. Remove hazard warning knob from steering column. Remove 2 switch retaining screws and remove from steering column.

Installation — To install, reverse removal procedure.

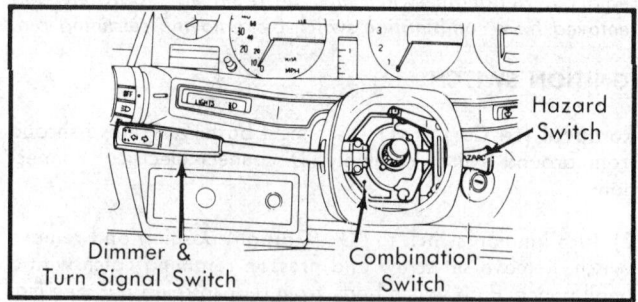

Hazard Switch

Dimmer & Turn Signal Switch

Combination Switch

Fig. 1 View of Combination Switch

TOYOTA

Celica
Corolla
Corona
Cressida

Land Cruiser
Pickup
Starlet
Supra
Tercel

REMOVAL & INSTALLATION

STEERING WHEEL

NOTE — *Steering wheel removal procedure is a general one. It should be noted that all steps may not apply to every model.*

CAUTION — *Some models are equipped with collapsible type steering, DO NOT apply excessive pressure or impact to mainshaft.*

Removal — 1) Disconnect battery ground. From lower portion of steering column, disconnect any electrical wiring for indicator lights, horn or dimmer switch.

2) Remove retaining screws from behind steering wheel (if required). On some models, pad will pry off. Remove horn wires (if required).

3) Remove steering wheel mounting nut and washer (if equipped), then using a puller, remove steering wheel from shaft. See Fig. 1.

Installation — To install, reverse removal procedure.

TOYOTA (Cont.)

Fig. 1   Using Puller to Remove Steering Wheel

COMBINATION SWITCH

Removal — After removing steering wheel as previously outlined, combination switch may be removed by detaching steering column covers, removing retaining screws from face of switch assembly and unplugging necessary electrical connectors.

Installation — To install, reverse removal procedure and make sure all electrical connections are properly made. Check cancelling operation of turn signal switch.

COLUMN LOCK & IGNITION SWITCH

Removal — 1) Disconnect battery ground. Remove steering wheel as previously outlined.

NOTE — *Steering wheel removal is optional if only the ignition switch portion is being removed. Removal of wheel makes access to this operation easier.*

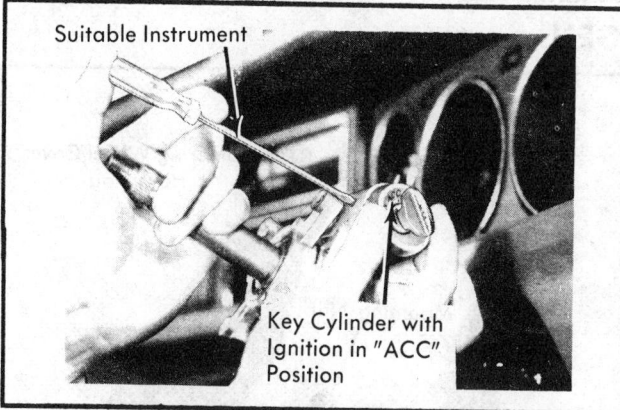

Fig. 2   Disengaging Key Cylinder from Position on Mainshaft

2) Remove screws mounting upper and lower column covers and disconnect any electrical couplings not detached during steering wheel removal.

NOTE — *On some models, access to ignition switch for its removal is gained by removing lower cover only. It is easier to perform this operation, however, by removing both cover halves.*

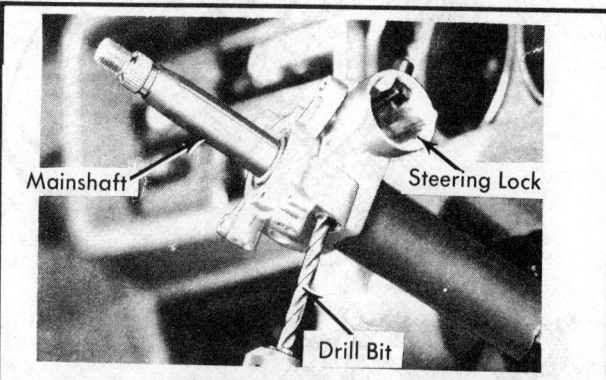

Fig. 3   Drilling Out Shear Head Bolt to Remove Steering Lock from Shaft

3) Remove turn signal switch assembly (only if column lock assembly is being removed). Remove mainshaft bearing retainer and snap ring (if required). Insert key and turn ignition to "ACC" position. Using a small pointed tool to press down stop pin on side of cylinder, free mechanism and pull cylinder from housing. See Fig. 2.

4) On Celica and Supra models, drill out shear bolts holding lock mechanism to steering column. On all other models, lock is part of upper column bearing assembly. Remove bolts mounting upper bearing assembly and slide off column.

Installation — 1) To install column lock and switch assembly, reverse removal procedure. Tighten lock housing shear-head bolts (new) until the heads shear off.

2) Fit key cylinder so ignition switch and cylinder will be aligned in "ACC" position. Insert into housing and check for proper locking operation and key movement.

3) Replace all other components (combination switch assembly, bearing retainer, steering wheel) as removed. Check for proper turn signal switch cancelling operation and smoothness of steering wheel movement.

TRIUMPH

TR7
TR8

REMOVAL & INSTALLATION

STEERING WHEEL

Removal — Disconnect battery ground cable. Place wheels in straight ahead position. Remove steering wheel pad and

retaining nut. Mark position of steering wheel and shaft. Using a puller, remove steering wheel.

Installation — To install, reverse removal procedure.

COMBINATION SWITCH

Removal — 1) Disconnect battery. Unscrew retaining screws for column cover halves and remove covers. Remove steering wheel as previously described.

TRIUMPH (Cont.)

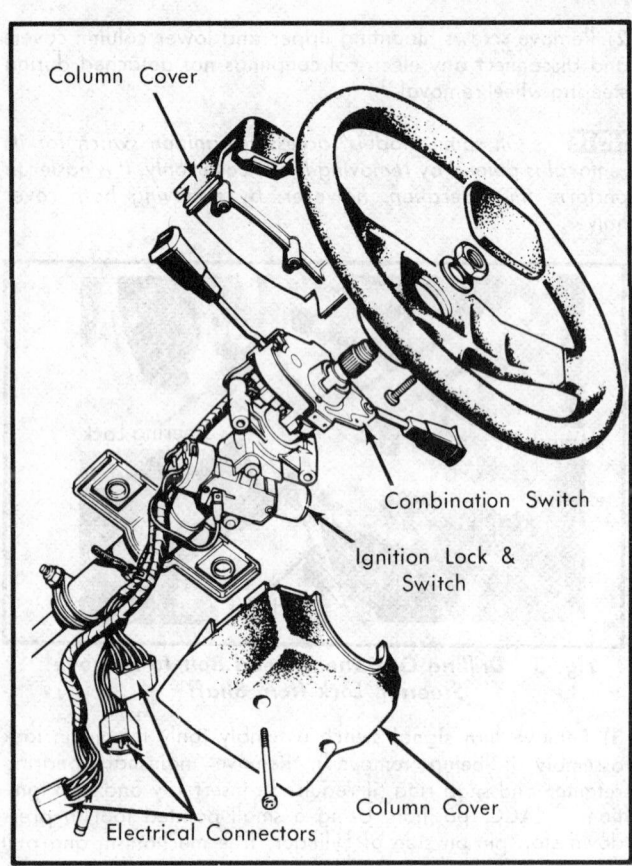

Fig. 1 Triumph Steering Wheel and Column Switches

Labels: Column Cover, Combination Switch, Ignition Lock & Switch, Column Cover, Electrical Connectors

2) Note location of all wiring harnesses. Remove wire harness clip securing switch harnesses. Disconnect 2 harness plugs. Loosen switch clamp screw and remove switch assembly.

3) Individual switches may be replaced at this time, but note that the 2 center cross-head screws are not to be removed. Switches are separated by drilling out 2 retaining rivets and removing 1 cross-head screw (right side of switch face).

Installation — To install, reverse removal procedure and note: Switch assembly must engage outer column assembly. Turn signal cancel collar must align in steering wheel.

IGNITION SWITCH AND STEERING COLUMN LOCK

Removal — Disconnect battery ground cable. Center punch both shear bolts mounting steering lock to column. Using a small chisel (or equivalent), remove bolts. Disconnect electrical plug and remove steering lock.

NOTE — *It is possible to remove ignition switch without taking out column lock. There are 2 set screws mounting switch assembly in column lock housing.*

Installation — To install ignition switch and steering column lock, reverse removal procedure and note the following: Ensure dowel pin aligns in column drilling. Fit new shear head bolts and tighten evenly.

VOLKSWAGEN

Dasher	**Rabbit Pickup**
Jetta	**Scirocco**
Rabbit	**Vanagon**

REMOVAL & INSTALLATION

HORN PAD & STEERING WHEEL

Removal — Disconnect battery ground cable. Carefully pry off horn pad and disconnect electrical connectors. Remove steering wheel retaining nut and washer (if equipped). Pull wheel off shaft.

Installation — To install, reverse removal procedure.

CAUTION — *Steering column has a collapsible section. Care must be used when working with steering assembly.*

COMBINATION SWITCH

Removal (Dasher) — Disconnect battery ground. Remove steering wheel. Remove 2 screws mounting lower switch housing. Disconnect electrical wires. Remove 3 screws attaching turn signal and wiper switches to ignition switch mounting. Remove switches.

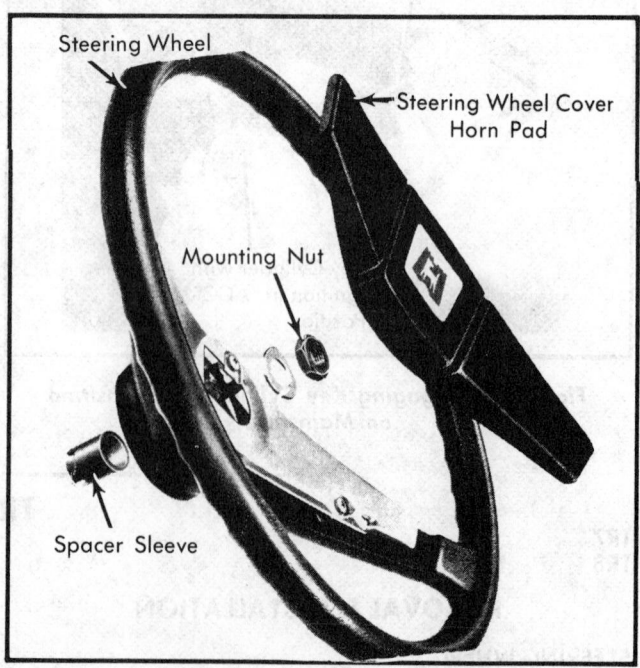

Fig. 1 Typical Volkswagen Steering Wheel Rabbit and Scirocco Shown

Labels: Steering Wheel, Steering Wheel Cover Horn Pad, Mounting Nut, Spacer Sleeve

VOLKSWAGEN (Cont.)

Installation — To install, reverse removal procedures and note: Drive spacer sleeve on until upper end of spacer is flush with bevel on steering column. Make sure steering wheel is installed with lug for turn signal cancel mechanism facing left side of vehicle.

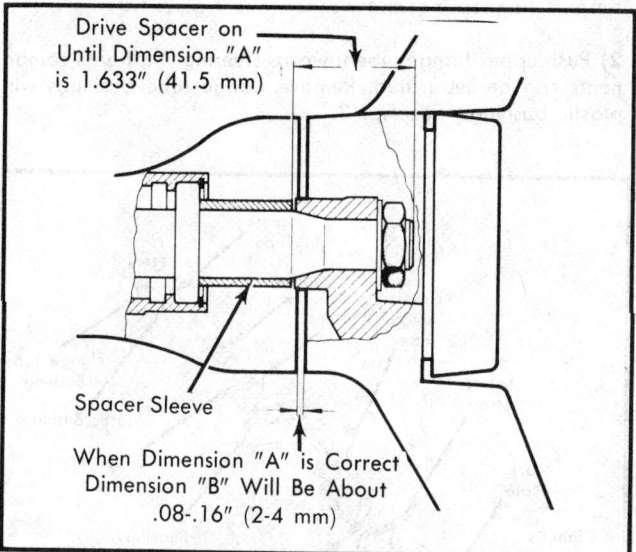

Fig. 2 **Dimensions for Installing Spacer Sleeve**

Removal (All Others) — Disconnect battery ground cable and remove steering wheel as previously outlined. Remove 3 screws securing switch assembly to steering lock mechanism. Force switch assembly toward instrument panel and remove spacer sleeve. Pull up on switch assembly and disconnect electrical wires. Remove switch and separate windshield wiper lever from dimmer/turn signal lever.

Installation — Refit switches together with screw and spacer sleeve. Slide switch assembly onto column and hook up wires. Spacer sleeve must be installed as shown in *Fig. 2*.

COLUMN LOCK & IGNITION SWITCH

Removal — 1) Disconnect battery ground cable. Remove steering wheel and combination switch as previously outlined. If necessary, drill a .125" (3.18 mm) hole in cylinder to gain access to cylinder release pin. Refer to *Fig. 3* for location of access hole.

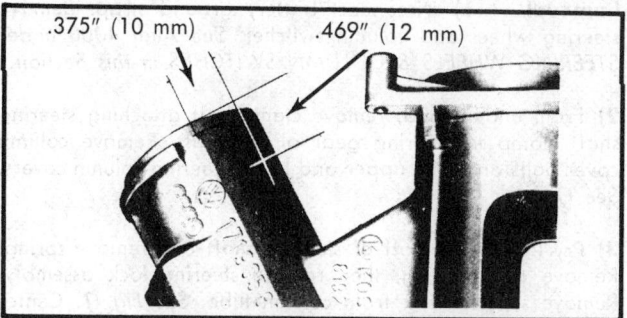

Fig. 3 **Location for Drilling into Lock Cylinder**

2) Insert a pin through hole and press down spring holding lock cylinder in housing. It may be necessary to insert key to pull out cylinder. To remove ignition switch, remove locking mechanism shear bolts and remove switch housing. Remove set screw on back side of switch, near wire connector. Remove ignition switch.

Installation — To install, reverse removal procedure and note: Before shearing bolt head, set clearance between steering wheel and switch to .08-.12" (2-3 mm).

VOLVO

Bertone	GL
Diesel	GLE
DL	GLT Turbo

REMOVAL & INSTALLATION

HORN PAD & STEERING WHEEL

Removal — Disconnect battery cable. Remove horn pad by squeezing top and bottom towards center of pad and unfolding upper edge of pad. Disconnect electrical wires and remove steering wheel nut. Use puller (2263) to remove steering wheel.

Installation — To install, reverse removal procedure.

TURN SIGNAL & WIPER SWITCHES

NOTE — *Steering wheel does not have to be removed to remove combination switch; however, removal of switch is easier with steering wheel removed.*

Removal — Disconnect battery ground cable. Remove column covers from steering column. Disconnect electrical connectors from switches to be removed and remove switches.

Installation — To install, reverse removal procedure.

IGNITION SWITCH & STEERING LOCK

Removal — Disconnect battery ground. Remove steering wheel and column covers. Remove turn signal and wiper switches. Remove upper bearing spring and race. Drill out center of shear bolts and remove with suitable screw extractor. Remove lock assembly. Disconnect electrical connections and remove ignition switch.

Installation — To install, reverse removal procedure and note: Position front of lock assembly 3.81" (97 mm) from upper end of steering column.

Fig. 1 **Using Puller to Remove Steering Wheel**

Steering Column

AUDI 4000

DESCRIPTION

The Audi 4000 uses a 2 piece safety steering column with a slip joint flange connection. Steering column is supported by the column tube and steering lock assembly.

REMOVAL & INSTALLATION

STEERING COLUMN

Removal — 1) Disconnect battery ground strap. Remove steering wheel and column switches. See *Audi 4000* under *STEERING WHEELS & COLUMN SWITCHES* in this Section.

2) From under hood, remove clamp bolt attaching steering shaft clamp to steering gear pinion shaft. Remove column cover bolts and then upper and lower steering column covers. See *Fig. 1.*

3) Pry lock washer off of steering shaft and remove spring. Remove contact ring, then remove steering lock assembly. Remove support ring from column tube. See *Fig. 1.* Center punch shear bolt attaching column tube to dash. Drill out shear bolt, then remove socket head screw attaching column tube to dash.

4) From inside vehicle, force dust boot out of floor boards. Remove steering column tube and shaft as an assembly.

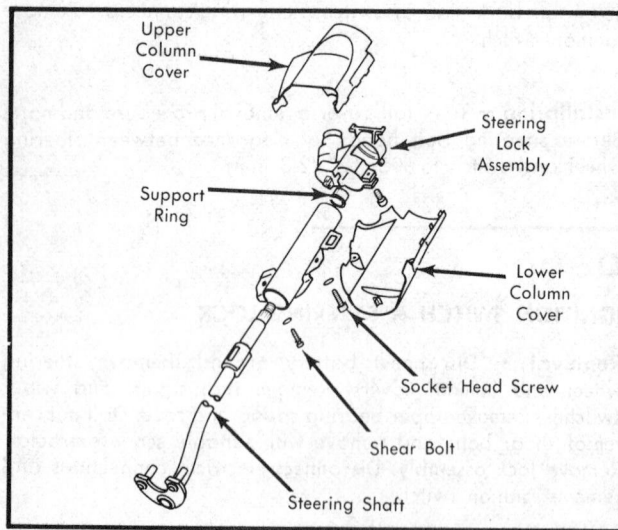

Fig. 1   Exploded View of Audi 4000 Upper Steering Column

Installation — 1) Install assembled steering column into vehicle. Install shear bolt and socket head bolt finger tight. Push dust boot into floor boards until seated. Place clamp onto steering gear pinion shaft. Place support ring into column tube.

2) Install steering lock assembly to steering column, then install contact ring, spring and a new lock washer. Tighten socket head screw. Tighten shear bolt until head snaps off.

3) Install upper and lower column covers, then install column switches and steering wheel. See *Audi 4000* under *STEERING WHEELS & COLUMN SWITCHES* in this Section.

OVERHAUL

STEERING COLUMN

Disassembly — 1) On lower steering shaft, remove clamp bolt attaching lower flange tube to upper flange tube. Separate flange tubes and remove bearing flange, bearing, support ring, spring and washer. See *Fig. 2.*

2) Push upper flange tube towards steering shaft until components can be separated. Remove flange tube bushings with plastic bushings. See *Fig. 2.*

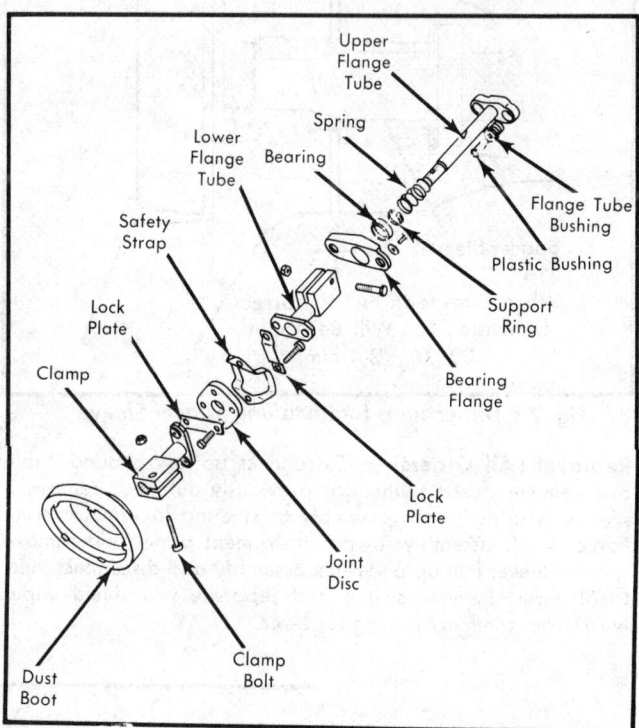

Fig. 2   Exploded View of Audi 4000 Lower Steering Column

3) Remove lower flange tube-to-clamp bolts; then separate lower flange tube from clamp. Inspect joint disc, safety strap and lock plates for damage or wear.

4) On steering shaft, slide column tube off of steering shaft. Inspect steering shaft, support ring and steering lock assembly for wear or damage. Replace components as necessary. See *Fig. 1.*

Reassembly — To reassemble steering column, reverse disassembly procedures. Press flange tube bushing and plastic bushing in by hand.

TIGHTENING SPECIFICATIONS

Application	Ft. Lbs. (N·m)
Clamp Bolt	22 (30)
Lock Plate Bolts	18 (25)
Lower Flange Tube Bolt	22 (30)
Socket Head Screw	14 (20)
Steering Wheel Nut	29 (40)

Steering Columns

AUDI 5000

DESCRIPTION

The Audi 5000 uses a two-piece steering column/shaft assembly. The steering shaft is designed with an offset slip joint that engages the flange tube. In a collision, the gear box and flange tube may be moved rearward, but the force will not be transmitted through the upper column shaft. An anti-theft locking device prevents the steering wheel from turning when the ignition key is removed.

REMOVAL & INSTALLATION

Removal — 1) Disconnect battery ground wire and loosen flange tube-to-pinion shaft clamp bolt. Pull off horn pad by hand and remove steering wheel with suitable puller.

2) Insert screwdriver through access hole at bottom of switch cover and loosen clamp. Remove switch assembly and disconnect ignition switch wiring. Place ignition switch in "ON" position.

3) Centerpunch shear bolts holding steering lock. Drill out shear bolts. Remove switch and unbolt mounting flange from under dash. Remove steering column and shaft as a unit.

Installation — 1) Place column assembly in vehicle. Install steering lock shear bolts finger tight and check operation of lock. Bolt mounting flange onto bracket.

2) Connect ignition wiring. Install flange tube over steering column pins and press on pinion shaft. Hold flange tube and shaft together with pliers and check length of shaft protruding from upper end of column. Adjust by moving flange tube on pinion shaft until distance is 2.56" (65 mm). See *Fig. 2.*

3) Tighten shear bolts until heads twist off. Install switch assembly flush with dashboard. With wheels in straight ahead position, turn signal lever in middle position and cancelling lug to right, install steering wheel. Tighten steering wheel nut. Gap between wheel and switch assembly should be .125" (3 mm). Adjust if necessary and tighten flange clamp bolt on pinion shaft.

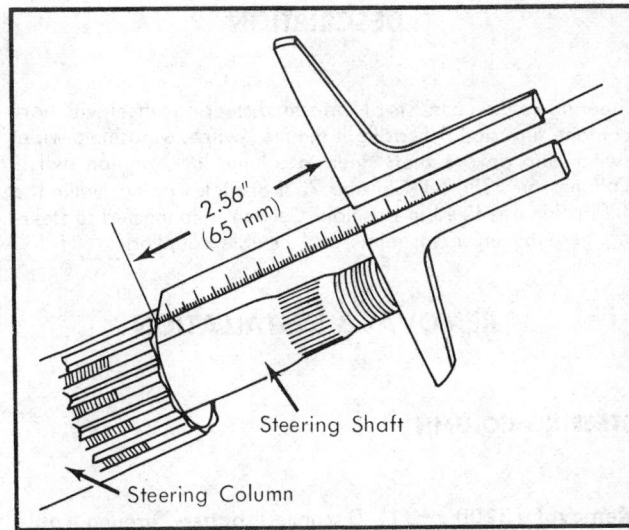

Fig. 2   Steering Shaft Installation Measurement

OVERHAUL

Disassembly — Remove retaining ring, spring and support ring. Pull steering shaft out of column from the bottom. If necessary, press bearing race out of column.

Reassembly — Examine race and replace if excessively worn. Slide steering shaft back into column tube, then replace support ring, spring, and use a new retaining ring to lock in place.

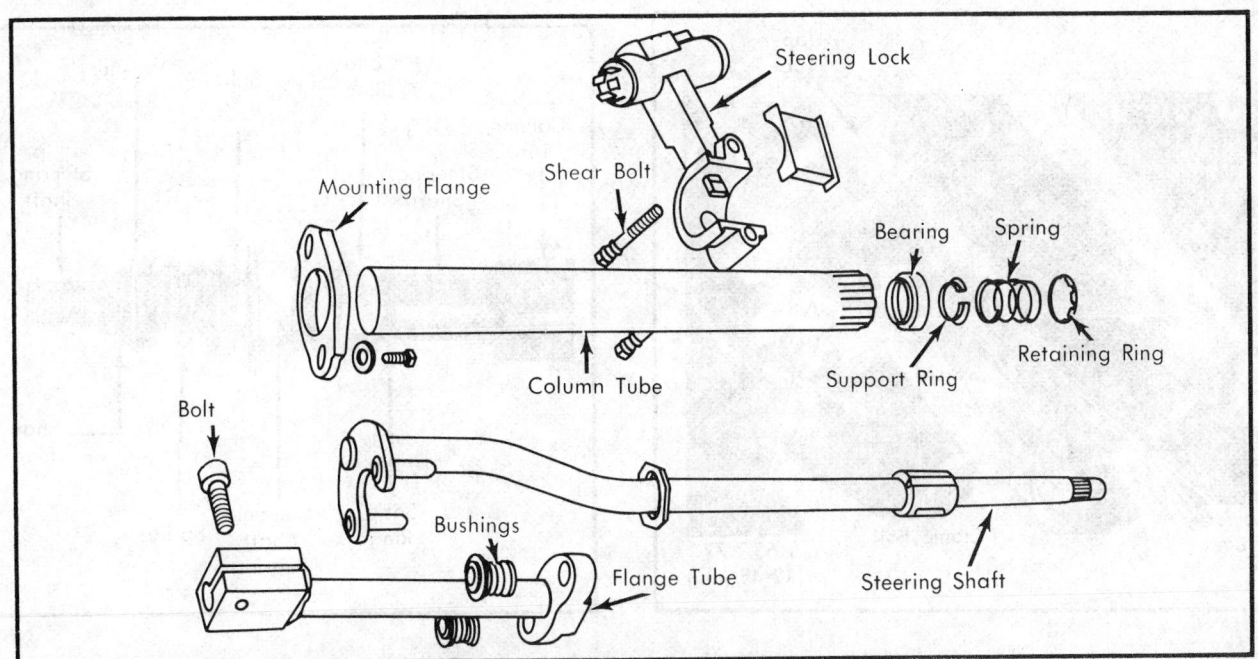

Fig. 1   Exploded View of Audi 5000 Steering Column

BMW

320i
528i
633CSi
733i

DESCRIPTION

Steering column consists of a padded steering wheel with horn contact, turn signal/headlight dimmer switch, windshield wiper switch and an anti-theft steering column lock/ignition switch. Columns on 528i, 633CSi and 733i are telescoping, while the 320i column is fixed in position. Column is connected to steering gear by universal joints and flexible coupling.

REMOVAL & INSTALLATION

STEERING COLUMN

Removal (320i) — 1) Disconnect battery ground cable. Remove lower half of steering column casing. Lift off pad from center of steering wheel and remove steering wheel.

2) Remove windshield wiper and turn signal switches at switch plate. Remove flasher relay. Loosen set screw and pull out ignition switch.

3) Detach steering shaft at universal joint next to firewall in engine compartment. Loosen casing tube clamp at base of tube in driver's compartment. Drill or chisel off shear head bolts holding steering column to instrument panel. Remove steering column.

NOTE — On 320i only, lower bearing may be replaced by driving shaft and bearing out from top. Remove snap ring, split ring and bearing. When reinstalling, stem of split ring must face bearing and snap ring must fit in locking groove.

Installation — To install, reverse removal procedure and note the following: Upper column casing and tube must be aligned prior to tightening. When installing turn signal switch, wheels must point straight ahead with switch in center position. With dog pointing to center of cancelling cam, adjust switch so that dog is about .12" (3 mm) from cancelling cam.

Removal (528i & 633CSi — 1) Disconnect battery ground cable and remove steering wheel. Detach lower half of housing below column, then remove turn signal and wiper switches.

2) Remove steering shaft holder at top of column. Loosen adjusting nut and mark position of upper and lower shafts. Carefully pry steering shaft bearing from top of column and pull shaft out from above.

3) To remove upper outer tube, disconnect horn wire at carbon brush. Drill or chisel off switch plate shear screws and disconnect wiring harnesses. Loosen clamp bolt and support screws, then slide down lower outer tube. Lift up outer casing and pull out outer tube.

Installation — To install, reverse removal procedures noting the following: Prior to tightening clamp bolt, assure that distance from centerline of clamp bolt to end of upper outer tube is between 1.65-1.77" (42-45 mm). Align upper and lower steering shaft marks and tighten adjusting nut.

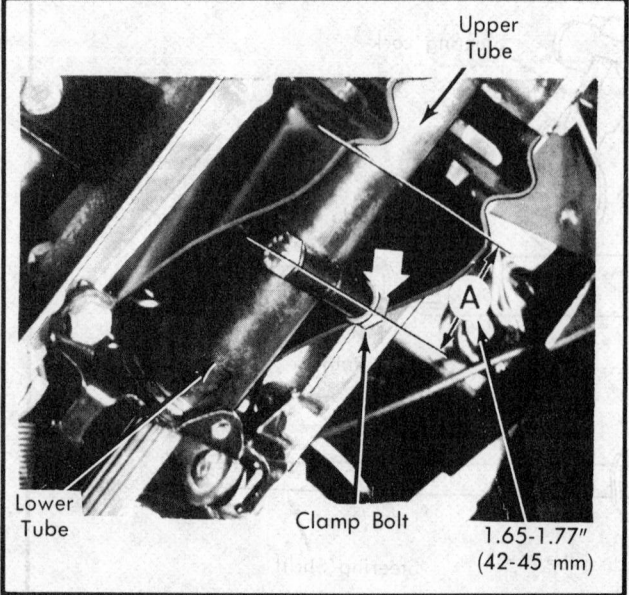

Fig. 1   Outer Tube and Clamp Bolt
(528i & 633CSi)

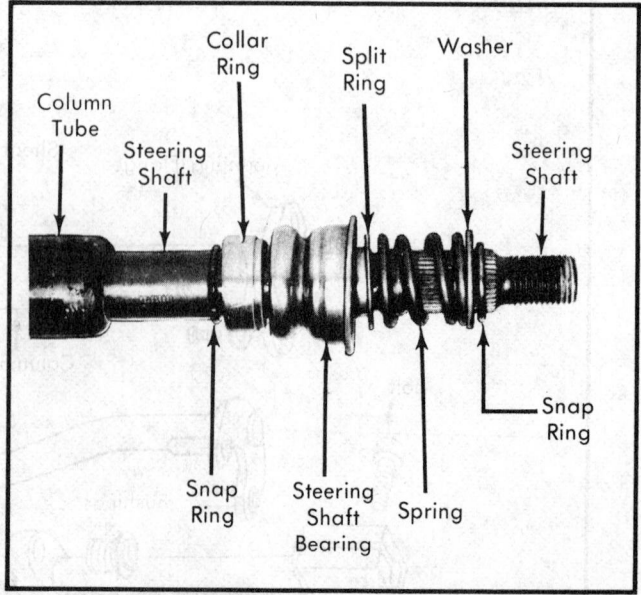

Fig. 2   Upper Steering Shaft and Bearing
(All Models Except 733i)

BMW (Cont.)

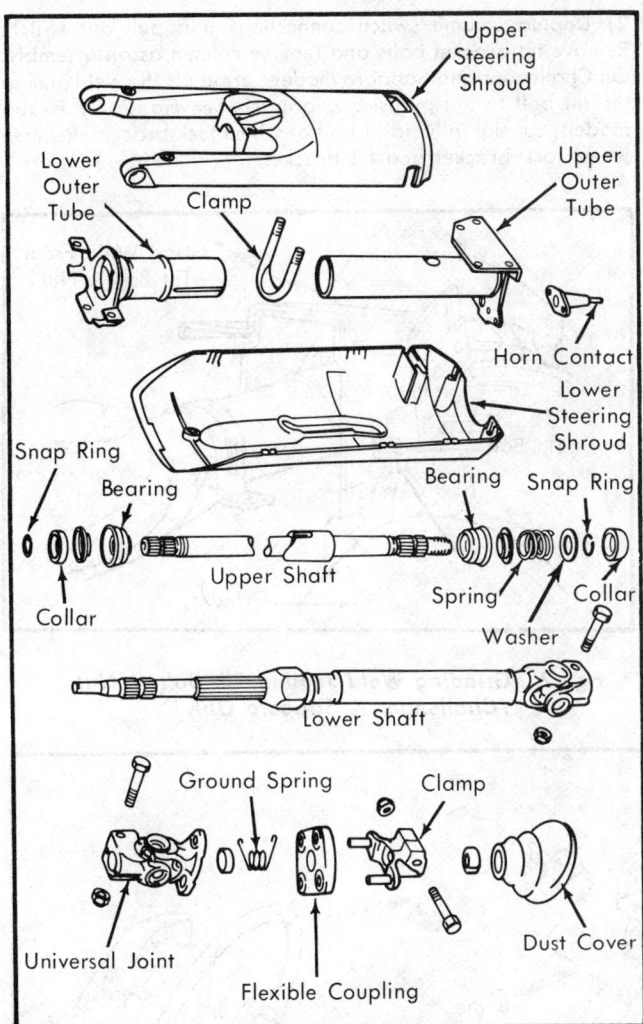

Fig. 3 Exploded View of Steering Column (733i)

Removal (733i) — 1) Disconnect ground lead at battery and remove steering wheel. Remove lower instrument panel cover and steering column housing. Disconnect switches and remove all wiring and ignition switch.

2) Remove clamp bolt and detach lower shaft. Remove 5 bolts holding column assembly to dash and pedal bracket. Remove upper shroud and shaft. Disconnect lower shaft from clamp in engine compartment and pull into passenger compartment.

3) Remove inner steering shaft by taking off collar, snap ring, washer, spring, and lock ring. Pry out upper bearing with screwdrivers. Pry out lower bearing and remove shaft. Remove snap ring, collar, ring and bearing.

Installation — To install, reverse removal procedure. Wheels must be in straight ahead position when shafts are connected. Ensure all washers and spacers are replaced. Ignition switch must be in "O" position when installed.

TIGHTENING SPECIFICATIONS

Application	Ft. Lbs. (N·m)
Casing Tube Clamp Bolt	
320i	12-14 (16-19)
528i & 633CSi	16-17 (22-23)
Column Bracket-to-Dashboard	16 (22)
Column-to-Housing	10 (14)
Lower-to-Upper Shaft Bolt (733i only)	18 (24)
Steering Wheel Nut	62-69 (84-94)
Universal Joint-to-Steering Shaft	18-20 (24-27)

CHRYSLER CORP. IMPORTS — EXC. FRONT-WHEEL-DRIVE MODELS

Arrow Pickup
Challenger
Ram-50 Pickup
Sapporo

DESCRIPTION

Collapsible steering column is comprised of a 2-piece column shaft, joined by a collapsible section. This section contracts under impact without affecting turning motion. The upper column cover incorporates slits that allow it to collapse under impact.

REMOVAL & INSTALLATION

STEERING COLUMN

NOTE – *During any service operations of collapsible columns or components avoid jarring or leaning on any portion of column.*

Removal – 1) Remove air cleaner and unbolt clamp connecting shaft to gear box. If vehicle is equipped with air conditioning, perform this step from underneath vehicle. Remove horn pad, steering wheel nut, and pull steering wheel off. Loosen tilt lock lever or knob and lower wheel. Remove column cover and floor dust cover.

2) Unplug column switch connections and pull out switch. Remove tilt bracket bolts and remove column as an assembly. On Challenger and Sapporo models, grind off the weld joining the tilt bolt to nut by using a grinder. See *Fig. 2*. On Pickup models, cut slot in head of bolt of wheel lock bracket. Remove wheel lock bracket and tilt bracket.

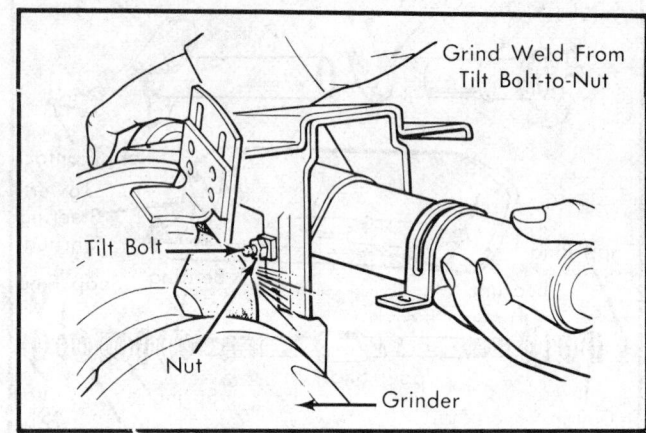

Fig. 2 Grinding Weld Joining Tilt Bolt to Nut (Challenger & Sapporo Only)

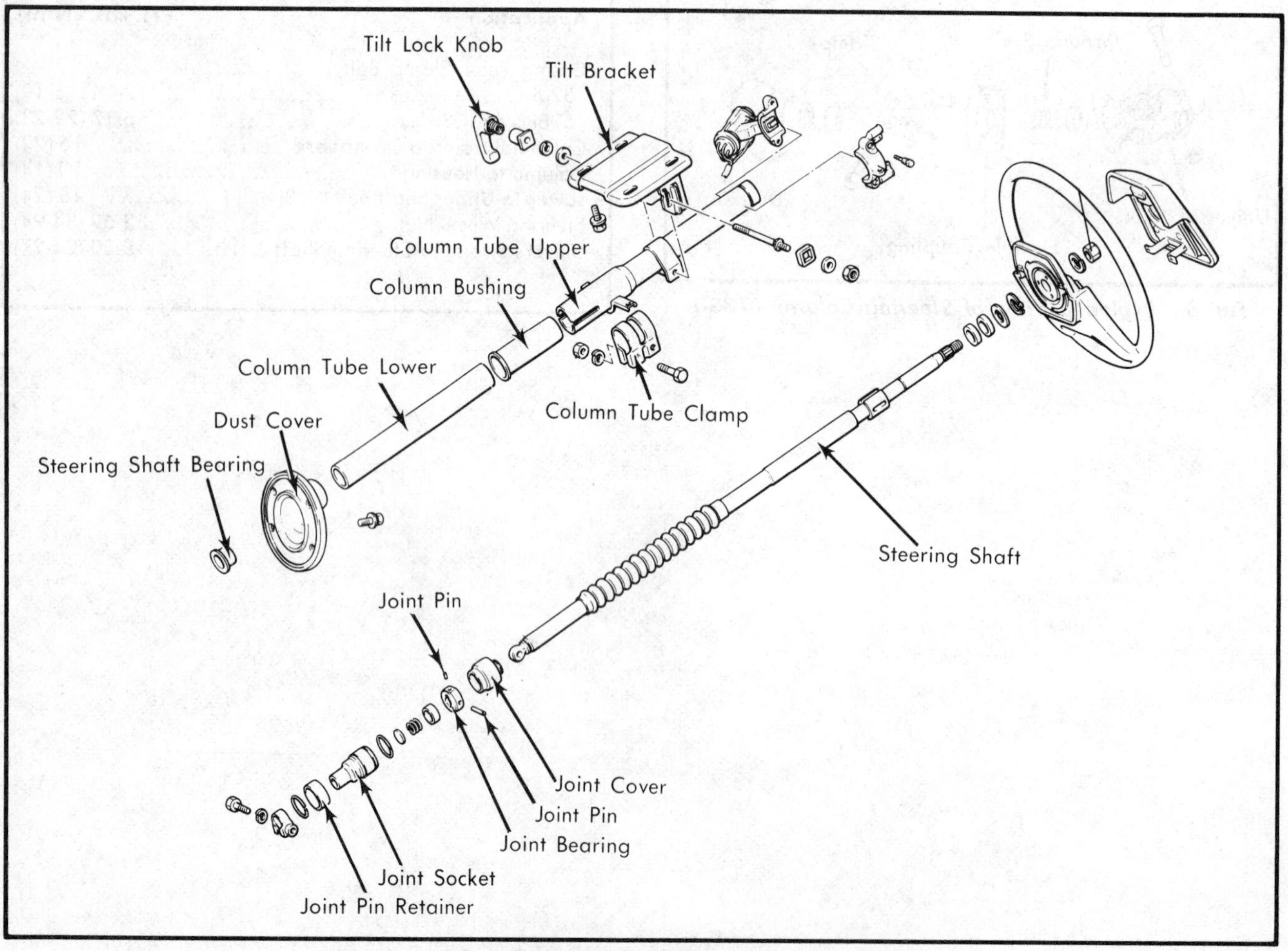

Fig. 1   Exploded View of Steering Column Components (Challenger & Sapporo)

CHRYSLER CORP. IMPORTS − EXC. FRONT-WHEEL-DRIVE MODELS (Cont.)

Installation − **1)** Connect shaft to steering gear housing mainshaft with bolt hole facing downward. Tighten the clamp bolt. Install tilt bracket to pedal support member.

2) On Pickup models, insert steering shaft assembly from inside truck. Connect gear housing mainshaft with hole down and gear housing mainshaft in neutral position. Tighten tilt bracket-to-body.

3) On all models, apply sealer to bolt holes of dust cover. Install dust cover to body. Install retaining bolts and tighten. To complete installation, reverse removal procedure.

OVERHAUL

STEERING COLUMN
Disassembly − **1)** On Pickup models, remove snap ring. Remove steering shaft together with dust seal and bushing from column tube. Remove yoke and coupling from lower end of steering shaft.

2) On all other models, remove snap ring. Using a plastic hammer, lightly tap upper end of steering shaft and remove shaft from column tube.

3) Slide dust cover off joint socket toward steering shaft side. Remove the stopper. Remove joint retainer. Set steering shaft in upright position.

4) Press down on shaft and remove small retaining pin with a magnet. Do not drive pin out. Remove joint socket.

5) Remove big joint retaining pin only if necessary, using a hand press. Loosen column tube clamp. Draw out lower column tube and remove column bushing.

6) When removing tilt bracket, cut a slot in head of retaining studs. Unscrew studs and remove steering lock. Lightly tap tilt bracket with a wooden hammer to drive bracket assembly from upper end of column tube.

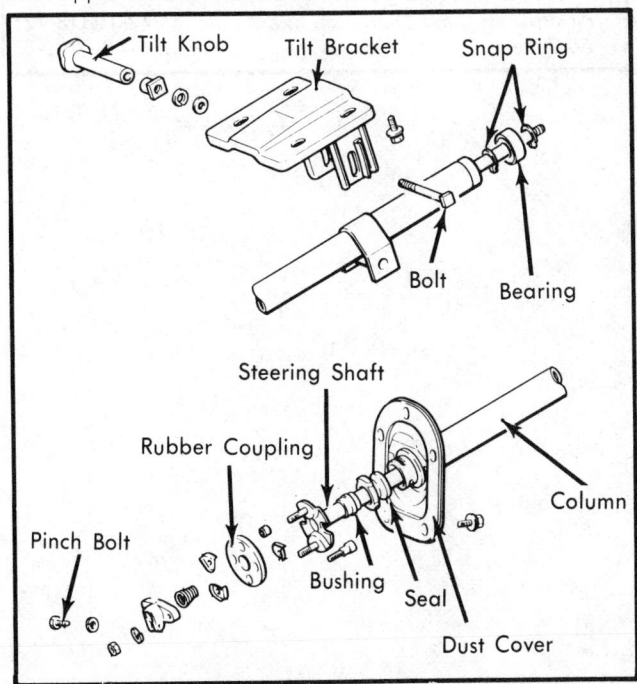

Fig. 3 Exploded View of Steering Column Ram-50 and Arrow Pickup

Inspection − **1)** Check joint cover for cracks or damage. Check steering shaft length. On Pickup models, length should be 31.5″ (801.4 mm). On Challenger and Sapporo models, shaft length should be 32.4″ (823.4 mm).

2) On Pickup models, check steering shaft-to-column bearing clearance. Clearance should be .0004-.0020″ (.010-.050 mm). On all models, check steering shaft bend using a dial indicator. Distortion should not exceed .020″ (.50 mm).

3) On Pickup models, check steering coupling for damage. Check tilt bracket for wear or cracks. On all other models, check collapsible tube for damage.

4) Hold lower end of steering shaft and move upper shaft to see if there is free play between splines of upper and lower shaft. Check upper and lower column bearings for wear of damage.

5) Check column tube bushing stop for wear or damage. Replace bushing if wear is excessive or if bushing is damaged. Check tilt bracket for wear or cracks.

Reassembly − **1)** On Challenger and Sapporo models, install column tube bushings onto upper and lower column tubes until bushing stop seats in column tube end. Tighten column tube clamp bolt.

2) Align column tube hole with wheel lock guide dowel. Install steering wheel lock. Insert key and check for proper operation of steering lock. Tighten shear bolts until bolts heads twist off.

3) Coat inside of steering shaft bearing with grease. Install bearing onto steering shaft lower end with flanged surface facing upward. Insert big joint retaining pin and press into place using a hand press.

CAUTION − *Make sure that bearing is installed in correct position. Check joint pin for correct installation and check to see that bearing rotates freely.*

4) Apply grease to joint socket. Insert spring seats and spring. Hold steering shaft upright. Press down on shaft and insert small joint retaining pin by hand.

NOTE − *Check for free play when steering shaft and socket are turned in direction of rotation.*

5) Position joint pin retainer on joint socket. Install the stoppers. Install joint cover. Insert steering shaft into column tube.

6) Wipe off grease from outer surface of bearing retainer (rubber) and inner surface of column. Install bearing. Apply a thin coat of adhesive to end of column.

NOTE − *Do not allow adhesive to contaminate bearing journal.*

7) Position spacer and stopper on steering shaft and insert snap ring. Insert tilt lever screw into tilt lever. Turn tilt lever screw until there is a distance of 1.9-2.1″ (50-53 mm) between tilt lever and tilt screw. See Fig. 4.

CHRYSLER CORP. IMPORTS — EXC. FRONT-WHEEL-DRIVE MODELS (Cont.)

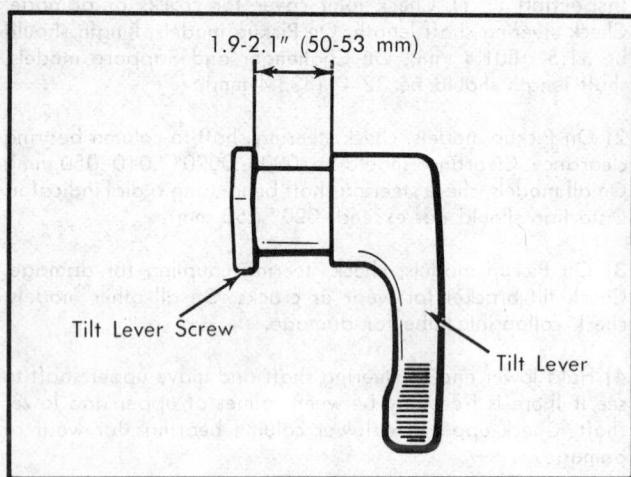

Fig. 4   Setting Distance Between Tilt Lever Screw and Tilt Lever

1.9-2.1" (50-53 mm)

Tilt Lever Screw

Tilt Lever

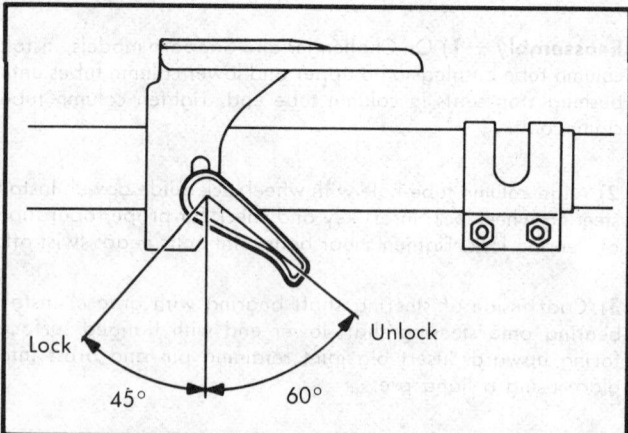

Fig. 5   Installing Tilt Bolt and Lock Tilt Lever into Tilt Bracket

Lock

Unlock

45°   60°

8) Mount tilt bracket on column tube. Insert tilt bolt and lock tilt lever into position as shown in *Fig. 5.* Place block onto tilt bolt in order to lock the bolt. Insert washer and nut on tilt bolt and tighten. Weld nut to tilt bolt.

9) On Pickup models, apply grease to shaft bearing, sliding surface of dust seal and bushing. Attach coupling and yoke to lower end of steering shaft.

10) Align tab on dust seal with groove on column tube. Insert steering shaft into column tube. Install snap ring into groove on steering shaft.

11) Position tilt bracket on column tube. Insert spacers between column tube and tilt bracket. Insert bolt through tilt bracket and spacer. Install plain washer, spring washer, plain washer and tilt lock knob. Tighten tilt lock knob.

12) Align column tube with lock guide dowel. Install steering wheel lock temporarily. Insert ignition key and check for proper operation of steering lock.

CAUTION — *Securely tighten steering lock retaining bolts after steering shaft is installed.*

TIGHTENING SPECIFICATIONS

Application	Ft. Lbs. (N·m)
Steering Shaft Clamp	
Pickup	11-14 (15-19)
All Others	15-18 (20-24)
Steering Wheel Nut	25-33 (34-45)
	INCH (N·m)
Column Tube Clamp Bolt	48-72 (5-8)
Tilt Bracket Mounting Bolt	
Pickups	72-108 (8-12)
All Others	48-72 (5-8)

CHRYSLER CORP. IMPORTS — FRONT-WHEEL-DRIVE MODELS

**Champ
Colt**

DESCRIPTION

Collapsible steering system is comprised of a two-piece (upper and lower) column shaft, joined by a collapsible (bellows type) section. The bellows section contracts axially under impact without affecting turning motion.

REMOVAL & INSTALLATION

STEERING COLUMN

Removal — 1) Remove steering column cover. Pull out column switch connectors, then pull switch out toward steering wheel end.

NOTE — *When removing steering column as an assembly, leave all connector clamps intact.*

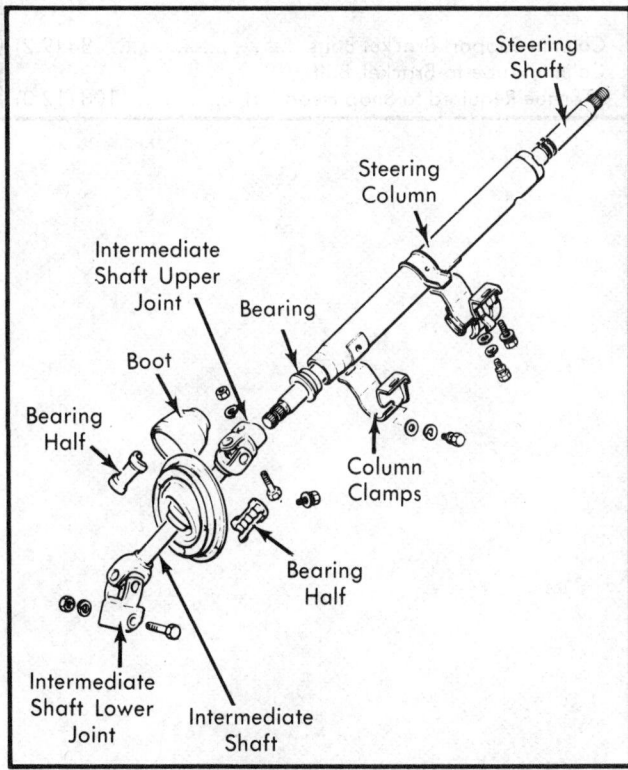

Fig. 1   Exploded View of Steering Column

2) Remove steering shaft upper coupling bolt. Remove bolts securing steering column brackets to frame. Disconnect steering shaft from coupling (inside vehicle) and remove steering column assembly.

3) Remove intermediate shaft lower coupling bolt (at steering gear). Remove dust cover mounting bolts. Remove intermediate shaft (with dust cover) toward inside of vehicle.

Installation — 1) Install dust cover to intermediate shaft. Make sure bearing side of cover faces steering shaft side of intermediate shaft. *See Fig. 2 and 3.*

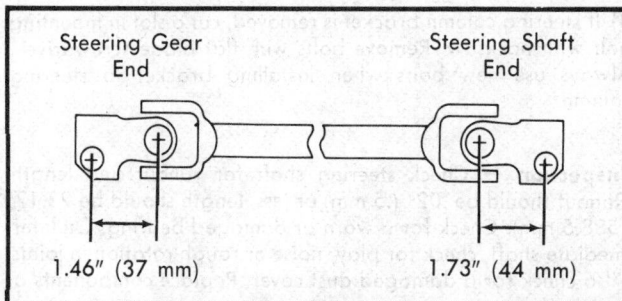

Fig. 2   Determining Correct Intermediate Shaft Installation Position

2) Apply grease to bearing and dust cover, then install bearing (two pieces) into dust cover. Attach intermediate shaft lower joint to steering gear and temporarily tighten dust cover bolts. Now tighten lower joint clamp bolt.

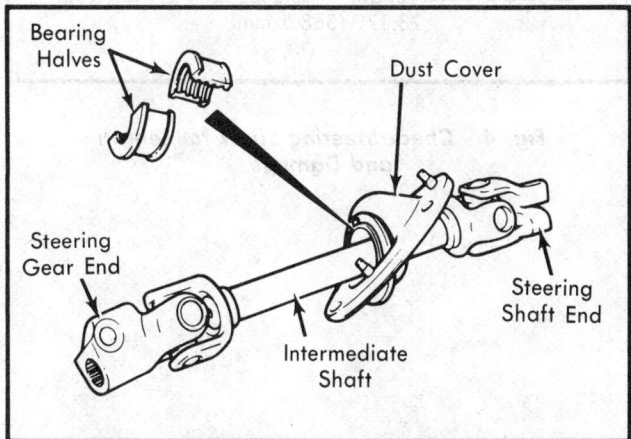

Fig. 3   Dust Cover and Bearing Installation

3) Connect intermediate shaft upper joint to steering shaft. Attach steering column brackets to dash. Tighten clamp bolt of intermediate shaft and column bracket bolts.

4) Loosen dust cover bolts and position dust cover so no clearance exists between joint and dust cover sliding surfaces. Tighten dust cover bolts. Adjust steering wheel position if necessary.

OVERHAUL

STEERING COLUMN

Disassembly — 1) Remove the two-piece bearing from dust cover of intermediate shaft. Remove dust cover from intermediate shaft.

2) Remove snap ring from steering shaft (steering wheel end). Unlock steering wheel lock (with ignition key), then remove steering shaft from column by lightly tapping shaft with soft (rubber or plastic) mallet.

3) If steering lock is to be removed, cut a slot in mounting screws with hacksaw. Use a flat blade screwdriver to remove screws then remove steering lock. Always use new screws and bracket when replacing steering lock.

CHRYSLER CORP. IMPORTS — FRONT-WHEEL-DRIVE MODELS (Cont.)

4) If steering column bracket is removed, cut a slot in mounting bolt with hacksaw. Remove bolts with flat blade screwdriver. Always use new bolts when installing bracket to steering column.

Inspection — Check steering shaft for runout and length. Runout should be .02" (.5 mm) or less, length should be 23.17" (588.5 mm). Check for a worn or damaged bearing. On intermediate shaft, check for play, noise or rough rotation in joints. Also check for a damaged dust cover. Replace components as required.

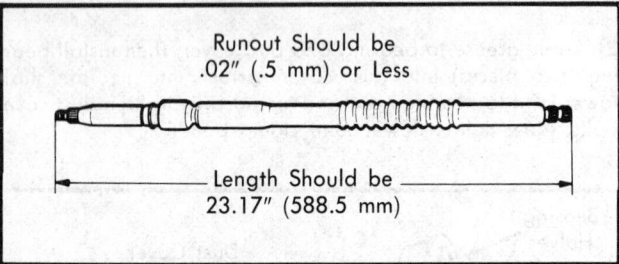

Runout Should be .02" (.5 mm) or Less

Length Should be 23.17" (588.5 mm)

Fig. 4   Check Steering Shaft for Length and Damage

Reassembly — 1) Install steering shaft in steering column and install snap ring. Install and tighten column tube bracket bolt until bolt head snaps off.

2) Fill bearing with grease and install in end of steering column. Make sure bearing is fully seated. Align steering lock with column boss. Make sure that steering lock is operational (by using ignition key to make lock function) before tightening lock securing screw.

NOTE — *Steering lock securing screws are special one way design.*

TIGHTENING SPECIFICATIONS

Application	Ft. Lbs. (N·m)
Clamp Joint Bolts	
Upper and Lower	11-14 (15-19)
Steering Wheel Nut	25-32 (34-44)
	INCH Lbs. (N·m)
Column Support Bracket Bolts	84 (9.2)
Column Tube-to-Bracket Bolt	
Torque Required to Snap Head Off	108 (12.0)

Steering Columns

DATSUN 200SX, 210, 310, 510 & 810

DESCRIPTION

Steering columns used on these Datsun vehicles are safety, collapsible type. These columns compress on impact. 310 model uses 2 universal joints between column and steering gear. These joints provide the most desirable steering wheel position and angle. On all other models, a flexible rubber coupling attaches column to steering gear assembly

REMOVAL & INSTALLATION

STEERING COLUMN

NOTE — *During any service procedure involving the steering assembly, do not hammer or exert extreme pressure on the steering column or damage to the collapsible section may result.*

Removal (310) — **1)** Disconnect lower column "U" joint from steering gear assembly. Remove steering wheel. *See Datsun under STEERING WHEEL & COLUMN SWITCHES in this Section.*

2) Remove steering column cover. Separate turn signal switch assembly and combination light switch from column.

3) Remove joint cover and bracket bolts. Remove column mounting bolts and remove steering column through passenger compartment.

Inspection — **1)** Check column bearings for smooth even operation. If necessary, grease bearings with suitable lubricant.

2) Check column tube for deformation or breaks. Replace components as required.

3) If vehicle has been involved in a collision, check steering column dimensions "A" and "B". *Fig. 1*. Dimension "A" should be 24.04-24.16" (610.7-613.7 mm) for vehicles with manual steering; with power steering dimension "A" should be 24.48-24.60" (621.9-624.9 mm).

4) Dimension "B" should be 16.56-16.67" (420.5-423.5 mm) for vehicles with manual steering; with power steering dimension "B" should be 15.06-15.18" (382.5-385.5 mm).

5) Check distance from lower "U" joint centerline to end of splined shaft. If distance is not 5.77-5.85" (146.5-148.5 mm), replace lower "U" joint.

Installation — **1)** Set steering gear in straight-ahead position. Connect lower joint to steering column. Slide steering assembly through hole in floor board.

2) Tighten column tube mounting bolts. Loosen splined shaft set screw and connect shaft to joint. Connect opposite end to steering gear. Tighten pinch bolt and set screw.

3) Make sure column tube hole seal is not twisted and that lower lip makes contact with joint shaft.

Removal (Except 310) — **1)** Remove steering shaft pinch bolt. Remove steering wheel. *See Datsun under STEERING WHEEL & COLUMN SWITCHES in this section.*

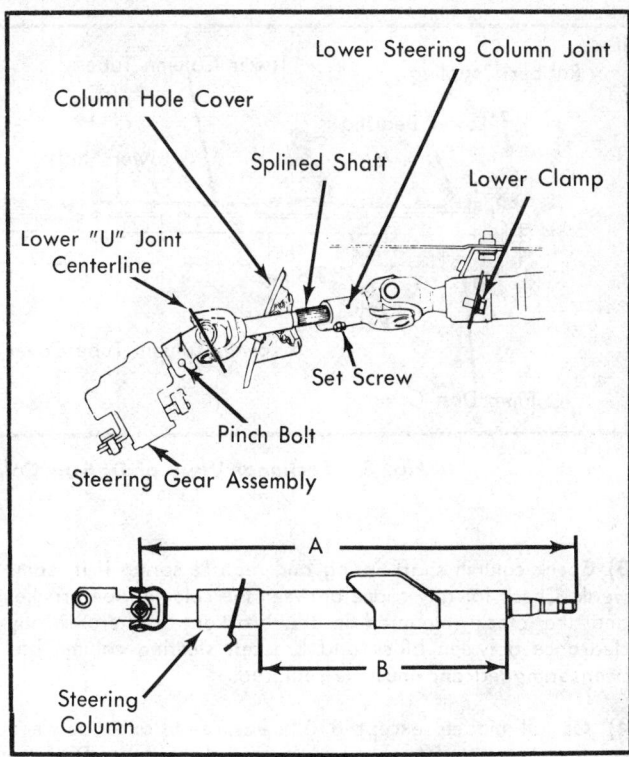

Fig. 1   Datsun 310 Steering Column Assembly

2) Remove upper and lower steering column covers. Loosen screws and take off turn signal switch or combination switch assembly. Remove heater duct from dash panel side (200SX & 810 models only).

3) Remove bolts mounting steering column tube cover to floorboard. From under instrument panel, remove bolts mounting column clamp and remove clamp. Pull steering assembly from vehicle by removing it through passenger compartment.

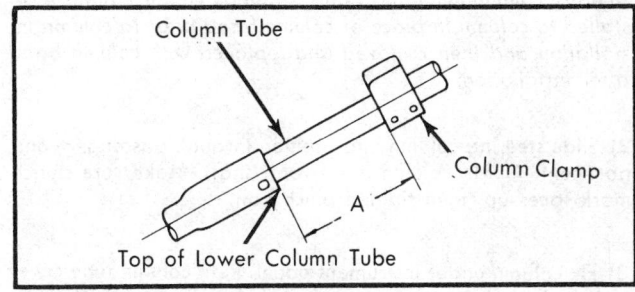

Fig. 2   Column Tube Measurement Specification

Inspection — **1)** Check column bearings for smooth even operation. If necessary, grease bearings with suitable lubricant.

2) Check column tube for deformation or breaks. Replace components if necessary.

Steering Columns

DATSUN 200SX, 210, 310, 510 & 810 (Cont.)

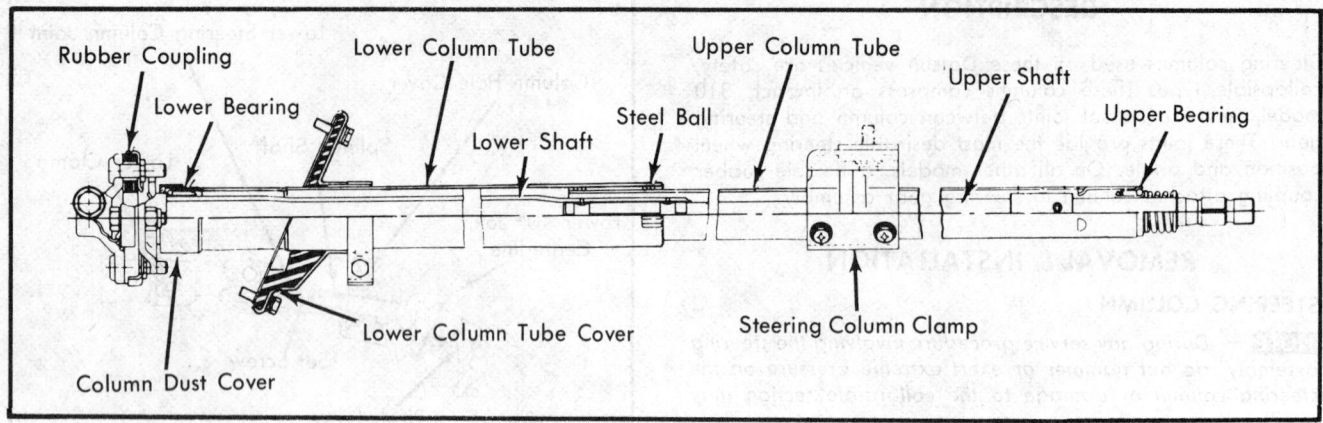

Fig. 3 Sectional View of Datsun Collapsible Steering Column (All Except 310)

3) Check column shaft spring and replace spring if it seems weak. Check for any space between the column tube bracket and the block (mounted in the bracket.) If there is any clearance between block and bracket, steering column has been damaged and must be replaced.

4) On all models except 810, measure distance between column clamp and top end of lower column tube. Distance should be 7.52" (191 mm) on 210 models or 7.24" (184 mm) on 510 models. Distance for 200SX manual steering should be 7.05" (179 mm) and 7.09" (180 mm) for power steering. See Fig. 2.

5) On 810 models, measure distance between top end of upper column tube and top end of lower column tube. Distance should be about 16.27" (413.5 mm).

Installation — 1) Place steering gear so wheels point straight-ahead.

NOTE — On 200SX models with power steering, a special steering column centering band is used. Centering band is installed to column in place of column band prior to column installation and then removed and replaced with column band after installation.

2) Slide steering column into position through passenger compartment. Guide column over worm shaft. Make sure punch mark faces up, then tighten pinch bolt.

3) Fix column under instrument panel. Refit column tube cover at floor board. Reverse removal procedure for remaining components. Make sure steering wheel rotates freely.

OVERHAUL

STEERING COLUMN

NOTE — 200SX, 210, 510 and 810 models do not have an overhaul procedure; it is recommended that, should damage to the column occur, it be replaced as an assembly.

Disassembly (310 Models Only) — On steering column shaft, remove snap ring. Remove washer and pull column shaft out of column tube, from the bottom of column tube. Remove "O" ring. Inspect column tube and shaft for excessive wear or damage. Replace as necessary.

Reassembly — Install new "O" ring, then slide column shaft into column tube, from bottom. Install washer, then install snap ring. Make sure column shaft rotates easily in column tube.

TIGHTENING SPECIFICATIONS

Application	Ft. Lbs. (N·m)
Joint Shaft-to-Column Bolt	
310 (Upper and Lower)	17-22 (23-30)
Rubber Coupling-to-Worm Shaft	
Manual Steering	29-36 (39-49)
Power Steering	24-28 (33-38)
Steering Column Clamp Bolts	
310	7-10 (10-14)
All Others	9-13 (12-18)
Steering Wheel Nut	
310	22-25 (30-34)
All Others	27-38 (37-52)

DATSUN 280ZX

DESCRIPTION

There are two types of steering columns used on the 280ZX, one for power steering and one for manual steering. Both columns are of the safety collapsible type. A rubber coupling is used to prevent road vibrations from reaching the steering wheel. Two universal joints are used on the manual steering model and one universal joint is used on the power steering model. Both columns are designed to compress on impact, absorbing a collision shock.

REMOVAL & INSTALLATION

STEERING COLUMN

NOTE — *During any service procedure involving the steering assembly, do not hammer or exert extreme pressure on the steering column or damage to the collapsible section may result.*

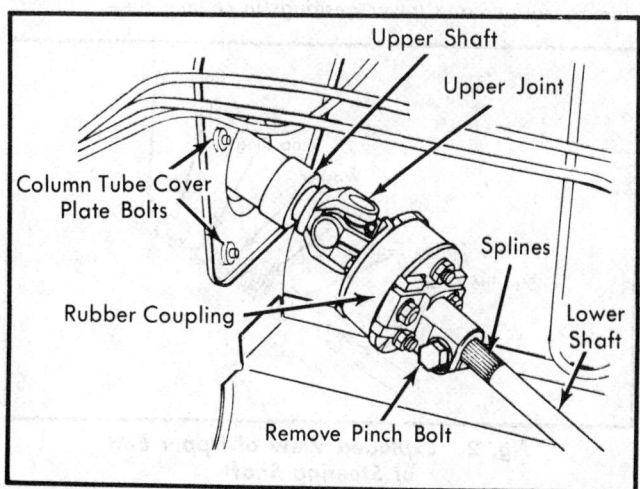

Fig. 1 Separating Upper and Lower Shafts on Manual Steering Models

Removal — 1) On models with power steering, remove bolt securing stub shaft to rubber coupling. On models with manual steering, remove bolt securing lower joint to rubber coupling. On all models, remove steering wheel.

2) Remove column tube bracket and cover from dash panel. Remove column mounting bracket and remove column assembly from passenger compartment side.

Inspection — 1) Check all steering components for free, smooth rotation. Inspection jacket tube for deformation or breakage (replace if necessary). Check column shaft spring for proper tension. Free length is 1.075" (27.3 mm); loaded length is .059" @ 66 lbs. (15 mm @ 29.9 kg).

2) Measure distance from upper end of tube collapsible section to first diameter change of tube (see Fig. 3). Measurement should be 15.73-15.77" (399.5-400.6 mm). If measurement is not correct, tube has been crushed and should be replaced.

3) Inspect inserts in column support clamp. If there is any space between inserts and bracket, column has been damaged.

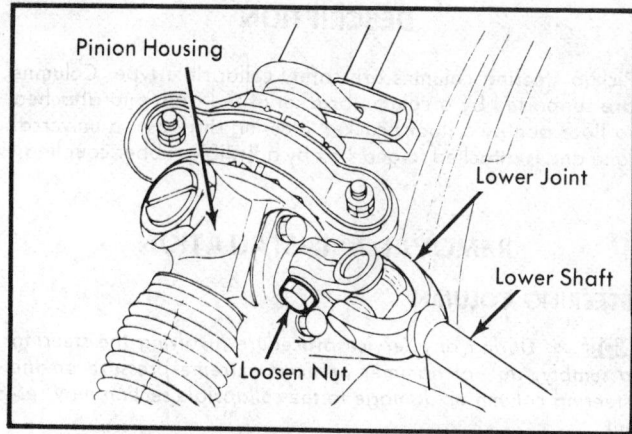

Fig. 2 Separating Lower Shaft from Pinion Gear on Manual Steering Models

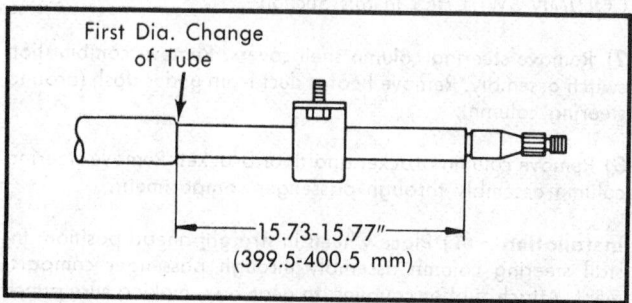

Fig. 3 Measurement for Damage of Collapsible Column on Power and Manual Steering Models

Installation — 1) Fit steering column through dash panel. Install steering column onto stub shaft (power steering) or onto lower joint (manual steering).

2) Set front wheels in straight ahead position. Line up slits of universal joints with punch mark on upper end of steering shaft (punch mark should be on top).

3) Connect column and tighten bolts. After installation, ensure steering wheel rotates smoothly.

OVERHAUL

NOTE — *Refer to Inspection in this article for description of components which may be replaced; however, if damage to the collapsible section is suspected, steering column replacement is recommended.*

TIGHTENING SPECIFICATIONS

Application	Ft. Lbs. (N·m)
Column Clamp Bolt	9-13 (12-18)
Coupling-to-Column Shaft	
Manual Steering	12-14 (16-19)
Power Steering	11-16 (15-22)
Lower Joint-to-Pinion Gear	29-36 (39-49)
Lower Joint-to-Rubber Coupling	17-20 (23-27)
Stub Shaft-to-Coupling	24-28 (33-38)
Steering Wheel Nut	29-36 (39-49)

DATSUN PICKUP

DESCRIPTION

Pickup steering columns are safety collapsible type. Columns are supported by a column bracket at the dash and attached to floor pan by a floor bracket. Steering shaft uses a universal joint and is attached to gearbox by a flexible rubber coupling.

REMOVAL & INSTALLATION

STEERING COLUMN

NOTE — *During any service procedure involving the steering assembly, do not hammer or exert extreme pressure on the steering column or damage to the collapsible section may result.*

Removal — 1) Remove rubber coupling to gearbox bolt. Remove steering wheel. *See Datsun under STEERING WHEEL & COLUMN SWITCHES in this Section.*

2) Remove steering column shell covers. Remove combination switch assembly. Remove heater duct from under dash (around steering column).

3) Remove column bracket and floor bracket. Remove steering column assembly through passenger compartment.

Installation — 1) Place wheels in straight ahead position. Install steering column assembly through passenger compartment. Attach rubber coupling to gear box, making sure punch mark on upper end of steering shaft faces up.

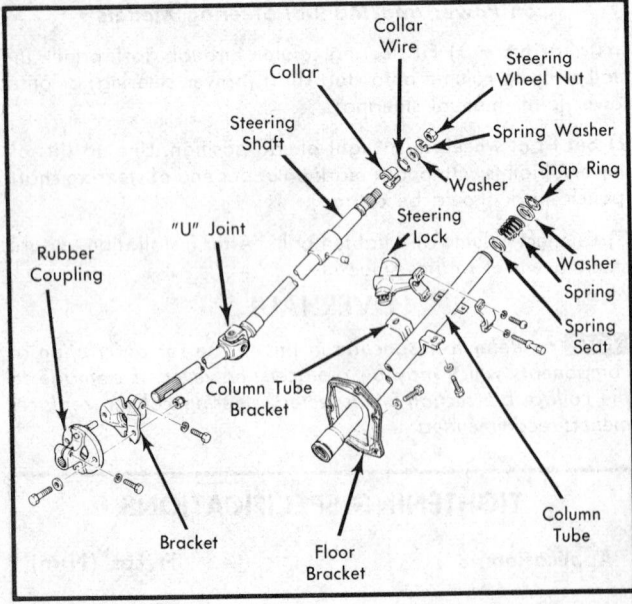

Fig. 1 Exploded View of Steering Column Assembly

2) Install column bracket bolts, then install floor pan bracket bolts. With column and floor bracket bolts installed, tighten rubber coupling bolt. Tighten column bracket bolts and then floor pan bracket bolts. Complete installation in reverse order of removal. Make sure steering wheel turns smoothly.

OVERHAUL

STEERING COLUMN

Disassembly — 1) Remove rubber coupling assembly. On steering lock assembly, drill out shear type screws, install screw extractor, and then remove screws. Disconnect and remove steering lock.

2) Compress steering column spring and hold compressed with wire. Remove collar fixing wire, collar, snap ring, plain washer, column spring and spring seat. Pull column shaft out of column tube.

NOTE — *When removing steering shaft, be careful not to damage upper and lower bearings in column tube.*

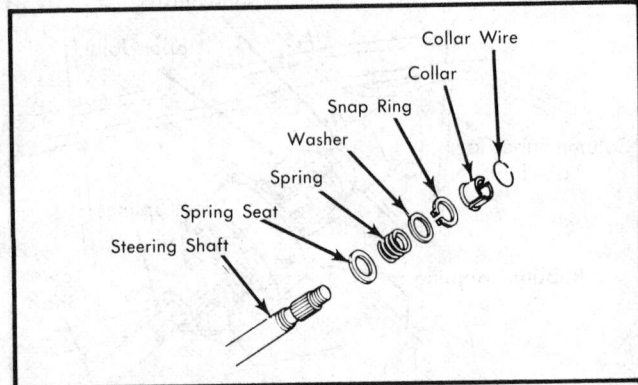

Fig. 2 Exploded View of Upper End of Steering Shaft

Inspection — Check column tube bearings for smooth operation and grease or replace. Check column tube for bending or breakage, replace if necessary. Check column spring for damage and replace if necessary.

Reassembly — Reassemble in reverse order of disassembly and note these points: Apply grease to column bearings, spring and other moving parts. Be careful not to damage remote control lever bracket. Always use new snap ring.

TIGHTENING SPECIFICATIONS

Application	Ft. Lbs. (N·m)
Rubber Coupling Bolt	29-36 (39-49)
Steering Wheel Nut	29-36 (39-49)

FIAT

Brava
Spider 2000
Strada
X1/9

DESCRIPTION

The steering column is composed of 2 sections. The top section is mounted on 2 ball bearings, while the lower section is equipped with 2 universal joints. On Brava models, the upper section pivots to allow steering wheel height adjustment.

REMOVAL & INSTALLATION

STEERING COLUMN

Removal (Exc. Spider 2000) — 1) Disconnect battery. Remove screws holding column cover halves. On Brava models, remove steering column tilt adjustment knob. On all models, detach electrical connectors at steering column. Remove nuts and washers retaining column at support bracket below instrument panel.

2) Unscrew pinch bolt holding lower end of steering shaft to gear box. Remove column assembly from vehicle. Dismantle steering wheel and column switch unit, if necessary.

Installation — To install, reverse removal procedure.

Removal (Spider 2000) — 1) Remove steering wheel, horn button and column switch assembly. Remove steering column bracket by disconnecting column from ignition switch and removing 4 column-to-instrument panel retaining screws.

2) Unbolt clamp securing column to worm shaft. Remove column from vehicle by pulling column up into passenger compartment.

Installation — 1) Insert column through opening in instrument panel. Fit worm shaft to steering column and lock with clamp. Replace column support bracket to steering column and connect with attaching screws (loosely).

2) Replace steering wheel temporarily and turn from side to side 2 or 3 times. Attach column switch assembly, then tighten column bracket bolts. Tighten steering wheel nut and connect

switch wiring. Replace remaining components in reverse of removal procedure.

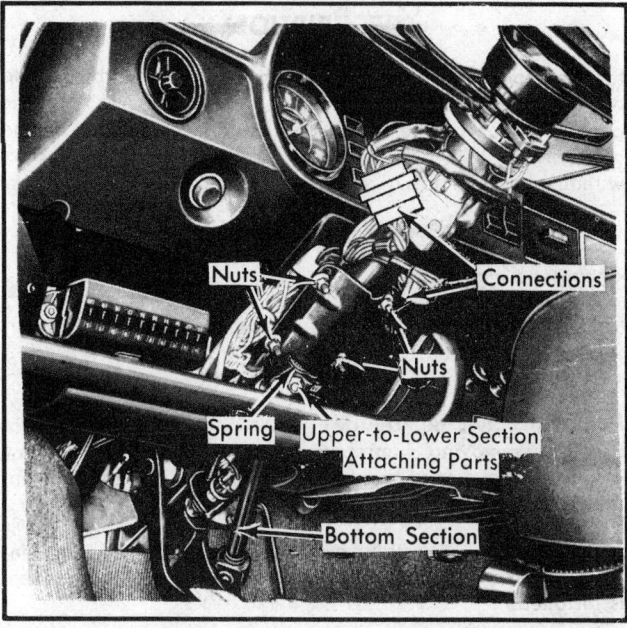

Fig. 1   Installed View of Typical Steering Column as Viewed from Under Instrument Panel (Exc. Spider 2000)

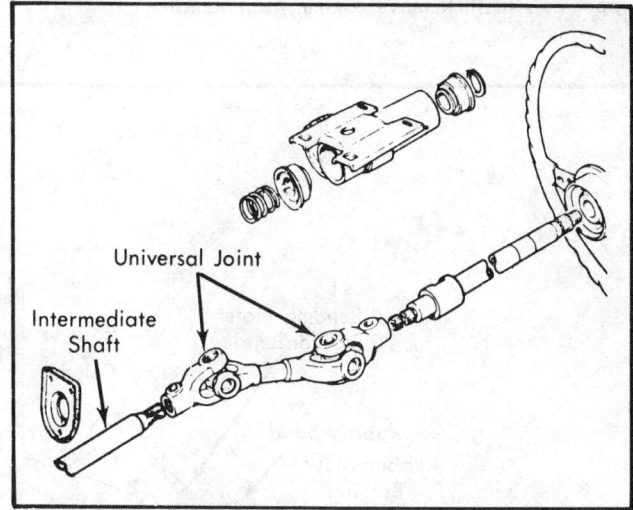

Fig. 2   Detail of Flexible Coupling Connecting Upper and Lower Portions of Steering Shaft (Spider 2000)

Steering Columns

HONDA

Accord
Civic
Prelude

DESCRIPTION

Steering columns are mounted with an impact-absorbing plate on the upper bracket that deforms under pressure. A plastic bracket collar at the lower end of the column allows the assembly to slide, and double universal joints absorb impact without the need for a collapsing column.

REMOVAL & INSTALLATION

STEERING COLUMN

NOTE — *The following procedures are performed with steering wheel removed. See Honda under STEERING WHEEL & COLUMN SWITCHES in this Section.*

Removal (Civic & Prelude) — Disconnect steering joint at splines by removing clamp bolt. Remove wire connectors below column. Remove attaching bolts (upper bolts first) and take entire assembly out of vehicle.

Installation — To install, reverse removal procedure and ensure that front wheels are straight ahead when steering wheel is installed.

Removal (Accord) — Disconnect wire harness. Remove middle clamp bolt in universal joint shaft. Detach lower dash panel. Remove nuts securing column to mounting brackets (remove upper nuts first). Remove column from vehicle.

NOTE — *If steering wheel has been removed, ignition switch must be in "LOCK" position to retain steering shaft during column removal.*

Installation — 1) Insert column in vehicle. Slide upper half of connector on bottom end of steering shaft. Install top bolt across flat part of shaft. Loosely install upper bracket nuts.

2) Pull down on column to seat bending plate against hook. Connect bottom connector to gearbox shaft, install bolt and tighten. Loosely install lower bracket.

3) Tighten upper and lower bracket nuts. To complete installation, reverse removal procedure.

OVERHAUL

STEERING COLUMN

Disassembly — 1) Remove steering wheel and column switches. *See Honda under STEERING WHEEL & COLUMN SWITCHES in this Section.*

2) Remove rubber bands, bending plate and upper mounting plate. On Civic and Prelude models, remove snap ring and steering shaft washer from upper end of steering shaft. Turn ignition switch to "I" position on Prelude or "ACC" position on Civic.

3) On all models, remove plastic collar, shaft bushing and column hanger bushing. Pull steering shaft out from bottom end of column. Remove thrust ring, bushing and horn ring from top end of column.

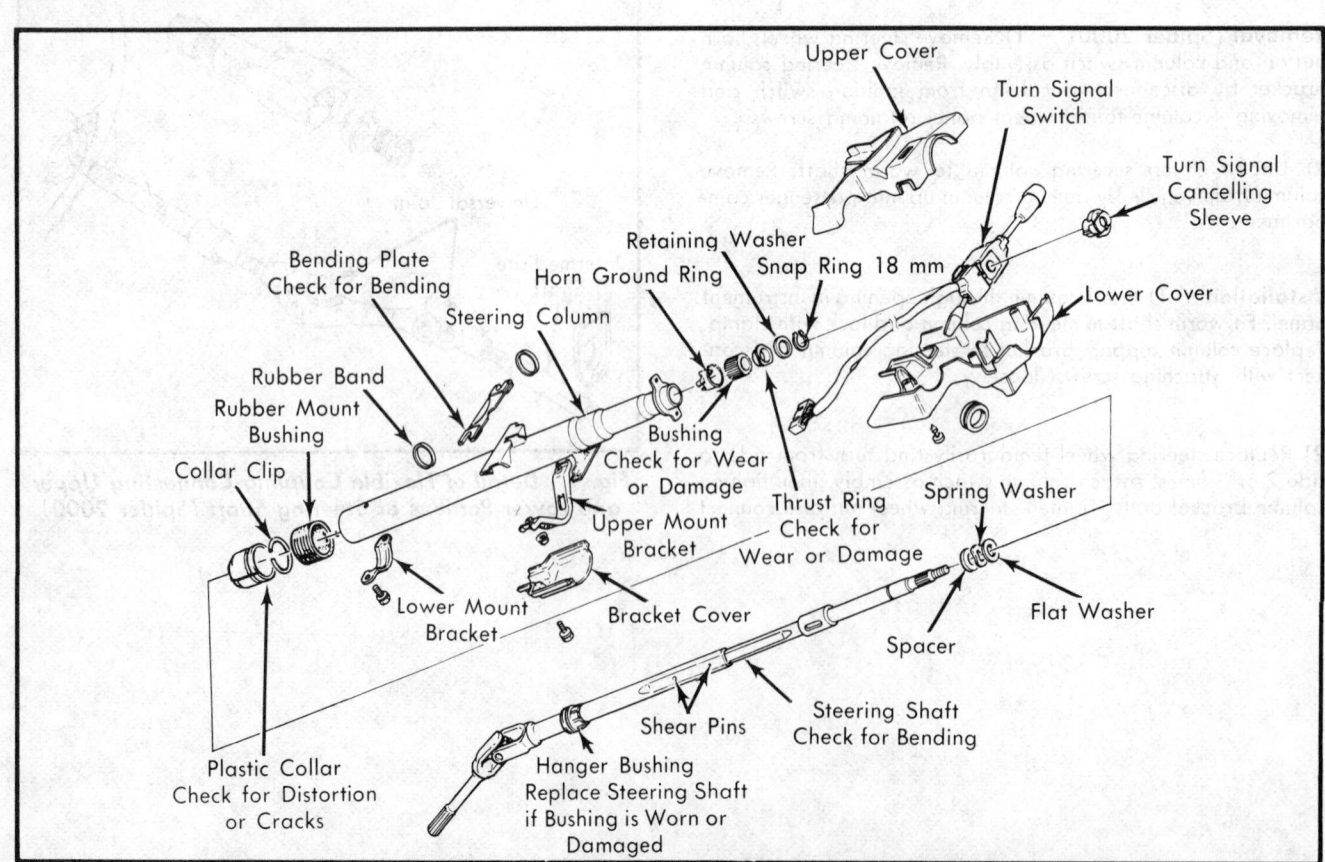

Fig. 1 Exploded View of Civic and Prelude Steering Column

Steering Columns

HONDA (Cont.)

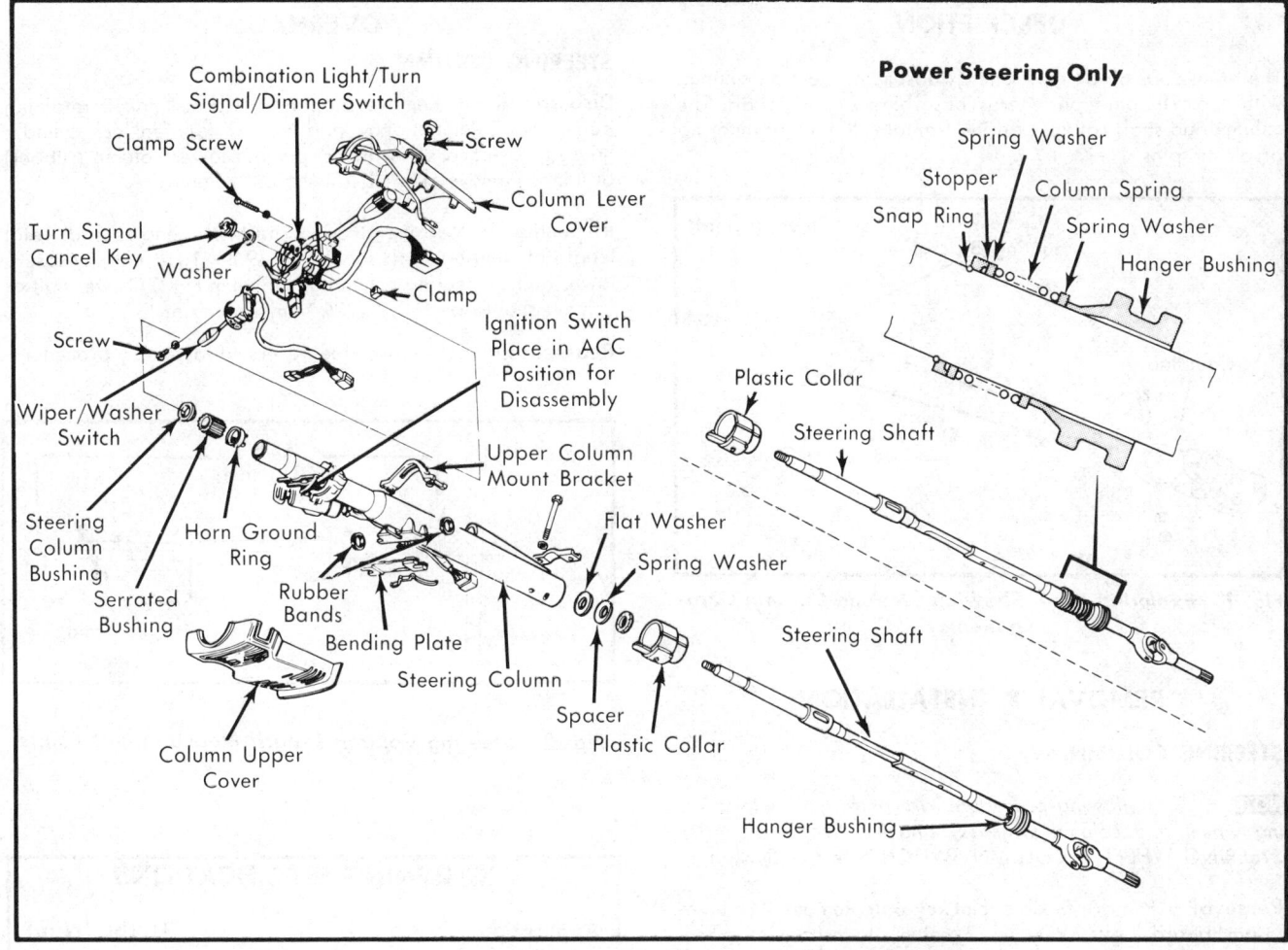

Fig. 2 Exploded View of Accord Steering Column

4) On Accord models with power steering, remove rubber stop, plastic collar, washer, spring, washer and snap ring before pulling steering shaft out of bottom end of steering column.

Reassembly — 1) Install horn ground ring, serrated bushing and thrust ring in steering column. Flat sides of thrust ring should be aligned with slots in steering column.

2) Grease top end of steering shaft and carefully insert in column. Be careful not to bend horn ground ring. Fill bottom of column with grease and install plastic hanger bushing. Align tab in column with cut-away in bushing. On Accord models with power steering, install snap ring, washer, spring and washer before installing plastic hanger bushing.

3) On all models, install plastic collar to bottom of column, align round projection on inside of collar with hole in column. On Accord models with power steering, install rubber stop. On Civic and Prelude models, install snap ring to top end of steer-

ing shaft. On Accord models, attach connector shaft universal joint to steering shaft so clamp bolt rests at bottom of machined flat of steering shaft. Tighten clamp bolt.

NOTE — *On Accord models, place ignition switch in the "O" position to prevent shaft from sliding out during installation.*

4) Install column switches. Use rubber bands to assemble upper bracket and bending plate to steering column. Bending plate should fit under hook on column with arrow mark facing out and pointing down. Install upper and lower covers.

TIGHTENING SPECIFICATIONS	
Application	**Ft. Lbs. (N·m)**
Column Bracket Bolts	
Upper	9 (12)
Lower	16 (22)
Universal Clamp Bolts	22 (30)

ISUZU I-MARK

DESCRIPTION

The I-Mark has a ball-type, energy absorbing steering column, with a plastic pin-type, energy absorbing steering shaft. The column and shaft collapse during frontal collision, by shearing of plastic pins.

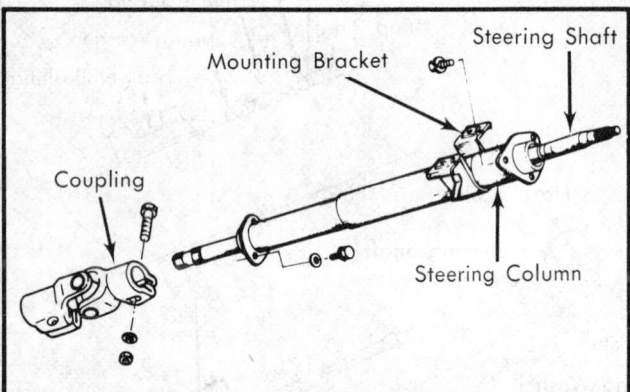

Fig. 1 Exploded View Showing Steering Column Components

REMOVAL & INSTALLATION

STEERING COLUMN

NOTE — *The following procedures are performed with steering wheel and column switches removed. See Isuzu under STEERING WHEEL & COLUMN SWITCHES in this Section.*

Removal — Remove flexible joint key bolt. Remove 2 column-to-dashboard bolts. Remove 2 column-to-instrument panel nuts. Remove steering column assembly from vehicle.

Installation — To install, reverse removal procedure, making sure that the 2 column-to-instrument panel nuts are not over tightened.

OVERHAUL

STEERING COLUMN

Disassembly — Remove snap ring, washer and 3 retaining bolts from column flange and remove ignition lock cylinder housing. Using a screwdriver, pry out lower column (rubber) bushing. Remove steering shaft from column.

Inspection — Measure steering shaft from end to end. Total length of steering shaft should be 39.8" (1011 mm). Measure lower half of steering column as shown in *Fig. 2*. Lower half of column should be 9.02" (229 mm) in length.

Reassembly — To reassemble, reverse disassembly procedure.

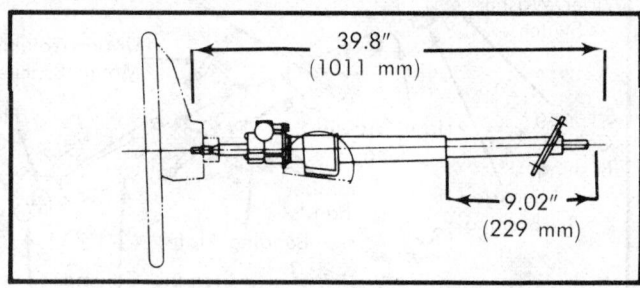

Fig. 2 Steering Column Length Measurement Points

TIGHTENING SPECIFICATIONS	
Application	**Ft. Lbs. (N·m)**
Column-to-Instrument Panel Nuts①	11 (15)
Flexible Joint Key Bolt	19 (26)
① — DO NOT OVER-TIGHTEN.	

ISUZU P'UP & LUV

DESCRIPTION

Column is fastened to steering gear through a flexible coupling. The energy-absorbing shaft will collapse during frontal impact under predetermined loads, by shearing plastic pins.

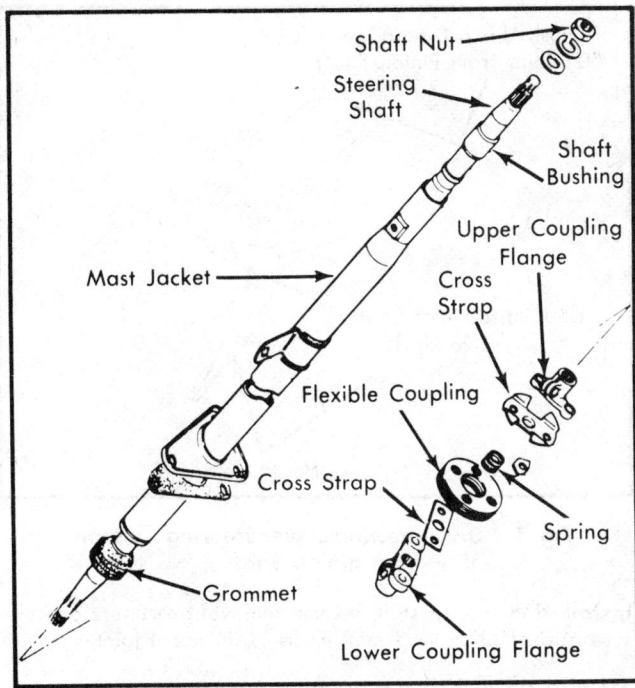

Fig. 1   Exploded View of Steering Column Assembly

REMOVAL & INSTALLATION

NOTE — *Before beginning removal and installation, inspect steering shaft shear pins. If steering shaft plastic pins have been sheared, shaft will rattle when struck lightly from side.*

STEERING COLUMN

Removal — **1)** Disconnect battery ground. Remove horn cover and spring. Remove steering column shrouding and hazard warning light switch. Remove combination switch. Remove steering wheel. *See LUV under STEERING WHEEL & COLUMN SWITCHES in this Section.*

NOTE — *Avoid impact to steering wheel at all times.*

2) Working inside engine compartment, remove upper coupling clamp pinch bolt from steering shaft flexible coupling. Scribe a reference mark across steering shaft and coupling clamp to ensure proper installation.

3) Disconnect combination and ignition switch wiring at harness connector. Remove 2 steering column-to-instrument panel bolts. Separate rubber coupling from steering shaft. Carefully slide steering column toward inside of passenger compartment and remove from vehicle.

Installation — To install, reverse removal procedure, making sure to align reference mark on steering shaft to mark on coupling clamp.

FLEXIBLE COUPLING

Removal — **1)** Raise front of vehicle and support with stands. Remove 2 coupling through bolts and lock nuts. Remove pinch bolts on upper and lower flanges of coupling.

2) Remove 2 column bracket retaining bolts. Pull steering column rearward approximately 2.0" (51 mm). Remove upper coupling flange, coupling, and lower coupling flange.

Installation — Install lower coupling flange, then install coupling and upper coupling flange. To complete installation, reverse removal procedure.

TIGHTENING SPECIFICATIONS

Application	Ft. Lbs. (N·m)
Column-to-Instrument Panel	11 (15)
Column-to-Wormshaft Clamp	20 (27)
Coupling Through Bolts	18 (24)
Shaft Coupling Clamp	20 (27)
Steering Wheel Nut	22 (30)

Steering Columns

JAGUAR

XJ6

DESCRIPTION

The upper and lower steering columns are the collapsible type, designed to comply with safety regulations. The collapse points are retained by nylon plugs which will shear on impact, allowing steering wheel and columns to move forward. The upper column is composed of two separate sliding shafts, with the column tube on later models being formed with an expanded metal section. The column shaft is supported on two prelubricated roller bearings. The lower column section is also comprised of two sliding portions, which are retained in a fixed length by nylon plugs.

REMOVAL & INSTALLATION

UPPER STEERING COLUMN

Removal — 1) Disconnect battery. Remove steering wheel. *See Jaguar STEERING WHEEL & COLUMN SWITCHES in this Section.* Remove speedometer as follows: Remove speedometer casing. Behind speedometer, unscrew knurled nut from right-angle bracket to gear box and disconnect speedometer drive cable. Disconnect trip record reset control cable by unscrewing knurled nut. Apply pressure to instrument panel bezel, rotate speedometer clockwise until it releases, and withdraw from panel. Withdraw headlight warning light and illuminator lights.

2) Remove tachometer as follows: Apply pressure to instrument bezel and rotate counterclockwise until tachometer releases. Disconnect electrical plug and socket. Remove ground lead. Withdraw illumination light holder.

3) Remove trim panel below the upper steering column. Disconnect electrical switch connections (three socket and plug connections). Detach horn contact at upper column. Unscrew self-locking nut and remove pinch bolt securing upper universal joint to lower steering column.

4) Loosen 2 set screws holding lower end of upper column. Reach through instrument openings and remove 2 nuts holding top of column. Collect washers, shims, nuts and support column. Remove 2 set screws previously loosened and carefully remove complete steering column assembly from vehicle.

CAUTION — *Do not use excessive force when separating upper column from lower column.*

Inspection — Examine column for straightness. Any wear, damage, or variation in length means the column should be replaced. Length from end to end (without "U" joint) should be between 21.56-21.70" (547.7-551.0 mm).

Installation — 1) If universal joint and/or adjusting clamp have been removed, refit, then reverse removal procedure and note the following: Check that .375" (9.5 mm) clearance exists axially in lower universal joint. If necessary, move upper universal joint further along lower column to increase clearance.

2) Ensure self-cancelling operation of turn signal functions properly. Make sure that steering wheel spokes are horizontal when straight ahead position is set; if not adjust as necessary.

LOWER STEERING COLUMN

Removal — 1) Raise vehicle on hoist and remove pinch bolt securing lower "U" joint to pinion shaft. Lower vehicle. Detach lower parcel shelf. Remove both pinch bolts from upper-to-lower "U" joint.

2) Unscrew lower mounting screws of upper column. Pull lower steering column from upper "U" joint. Raise vehicle. Remove "U" joint from pinion shaft and withdraw lower steering column.

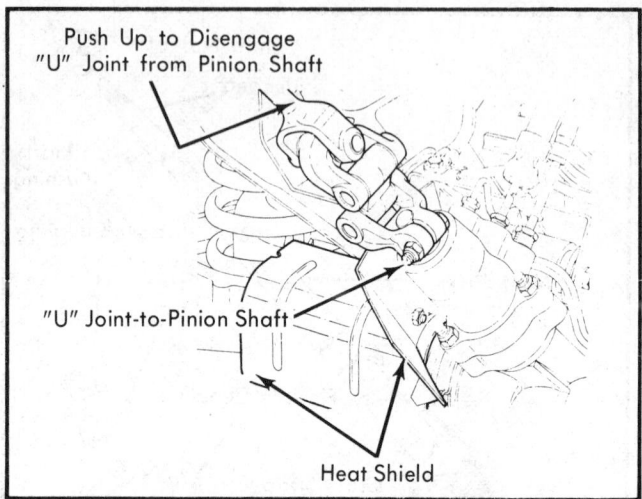

Fig. 1   **Disconnecting Lower Steering Column from Pinion Shaft**

Installation — To install, reverse removal procedure and ensure gap of .375" (9.5 mm) exists in universal joint.

NOTE — *Front wheels should be kept in straight ahead position during this operation.*

STEERING COLUMN ADJUSTING CLAMP

Removal — Remove steering wheel. Pull impact rubber from steering wheel shaft. Unscrew three small cheese-head screws from beneath adjusting clamp (lock nut) and withdraw retaining plate. Unscrew collet adaptor completely and remove from shaft. Remove circlip from within upper side of adjuster. Withdraw adjuster (lock nut) collecting stop button. Slide split collet off shaft.

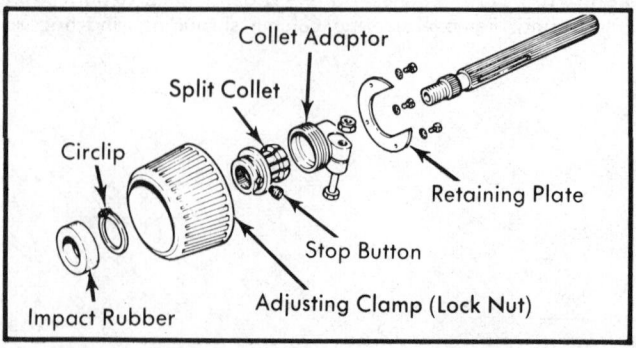

Fig. 2   **Exploded View of Steering Column Adjusting Clamp**

Installation — Clean parts thoroughly and remove any burrs with a file. Lightly lubricate all enclosed metal components. Install by reversing removal procedure.

Steering Columns

JAGUAR (Cont.)

STEERING COLUMN LOWER SEAL

Removal — Remove upper steering column, as previously outlined. Loosen hose clip attaching upper sealing sleeve to lower column; remove clip and sleeve. Remove 3 screws securing seal retainer to instrument panel. Slide seal, retainer and sealing sleeve up and off lower column.

Installation — 1) Fit assembly of sealing sleeve, seal, and retainer over end of lower column carefully. Insert and tighten 3 retaining set screws. Carefully slide second sealing sleeve, flanged end first, over lower column as far as first sealing sleeve; position hose clip, but do not tighten.

2) Move second sealing sleeve approximately .250" (6 mm) toward dash, to preload it against first sealing sleeve. Secure this position with hose clip. Replace upper column assembly.

OVERHAUL

UPPER & LOWER STEERING COLUMNS

NOTE — *No repairs, adjustments, or overhaul procedures are given by the manufacturer. If damage is evident or suspected, replacement of assemblies is necessary.*

TIGHTENING SPECIFICATIONS

Application	Ft. Lbs. (N·m)
Column-to-Brackets	14-18 (19-24)
Steering Wheel	25-30 (34-41)
Universal Joint Bolts	14-18 (19-24)

Steering Columns

MERCEDES-BENZ

240D 300TD
280E 300SD
280CE 380SL
300D 380SEL
300CD 380SLC
DESCRIPTION

Steering column assembly includes an impact absorbing steering wheel, upper and lower column shafts and flexible coupling. Lower shaft on 123 Series models is corrugated for additional impact protection.

Chassis Identification Codes

Application	Chassis Type
380SL & 380SLC	107
240D, 280E, 280CE, 300D, 300CD & 300TD	123
300SD & 380SEL	126

STEERING COLUMN

Removal — 1) On 123 Series, remove screws holding upper and lower cover on instrument panel and remove covers. On all models, disconnect battery and remove steering wheel. Remove instrument cluster by pulling outward as far as possible and loosening tachometer, temperature, and oil pressure connections.

2) On all models, remove steering lock. Disconnect wiring connectors. Remove Allen head screw of flexible coupling and all nuts and screws holding casing and column to dashboard. Remove steering column housing.

Installation — To install, reverse removal procedure and note the following: On chassis types 107 and 123, always use new steering wheel Allen screw when installing steering wheel. On 450 models, hold steering shaft in place with pin through hole in jacket tube. Check that lower tube on chassis type 123 is not bent or distorted. Use caution when installing jacket tube to prevent damage to this shaft.

STEERING COLUMN SHAFT

Removal, 123 Series (Lower) — 1) From engine compartment, remove both Allen head screws holding flexible coupling to worm shaft and steering shaft. Slide coupling down on worm shaft and off steering shaft.

2) From inside car, remove upper and lower cover from instrument panel/steering column. Remove Allen screws at upper coupling and slide coupling and lower shaft off of upper shaft.

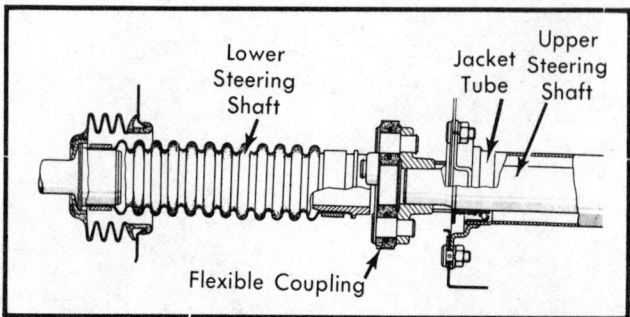

Fig. 1 Lower Steering Shaft (123 Models)

Installation — To install, lubricate inner lips of bellows seal at firewall and reverse removal procedures.

NOTE — *Wheels must be in straight ahead position and notch on upper shaft must point directly upward during installation.*

Removal, 123 Series (Upper) — 1) With column out of car, remove combination switch. Remove jacket tube casing, then remove spacing ring from steering shaft.

2) Remove gripper ring, compression spring, supporting ring and ball bearing from steering shaft. Knock steering shaft upward out of jacket tube with plastic hammer.

Installation — Inspect and replace bearings and races if required. Reverse removal procedure and reinstall upper steering shaft.

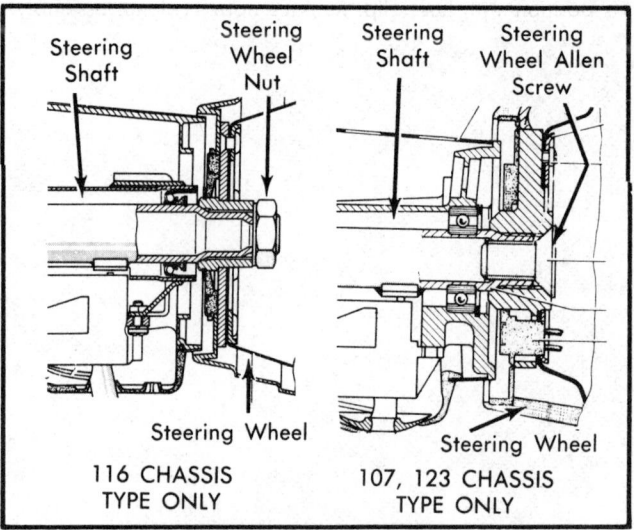

Fig. 2 Sectional View of Mercedes-Benz Steering Column and Steering Shaft

Removal, 107 & 126 Series — 1) Remove steering wheel and combination switch rubber cover. Loosen switch mounting screws on bearing body and pull switch out slightly. Loosen screws holding cable of contact carbon on combination switch.

2) Remove Allen screw from upper end of steering coupling. Remove screws from jacket tube and pull steering shaft with bearing body out of jacket tube.

Installation — Replace bearings and races as required and reverse removal procedure. Check shaft adjustment; pin inserted through hole in jacket casing should locate check bore of steering shaft. Mark on end of shaft should be up when installing.

NOTE — *Steering shaft length should be 31.7" (805 mm); tap gently with plastic mallet to adjust length before installation.*

TIGHTENING SPECIFICATIONS

Application	Ft. Lbs. (N·m)
Flexible Coupling (Allen)	18 (24)
Steering Wheel	
107, 123	59 (80)
126	37 (50)

Steering Columns

PEUGEOT

504
505
604

DESCRIPTION

Steering column consists of an upper and lower steering shaft connected by a universal joint. Steering shaft utilizes a rubber flexible coupling at its lower end to help absorb road shocks. Steering column contains the steering lock, turn signal/horn switch, headlight dimmer/washer switch and on some models, the speed control switch.

REMOVAL & INSTALLATION

Removal – 1) Disconnect battery ground cable. Remove bolt connecting steering shaft rubber coupling to gear box. Remove horn pad cover, steering wheel nut and steering wheel. Mark relative position of steering wheel to shaft.

2) Remove steering column trim panels necessary to obtain access to column mounting bolts. Disconnect all switch connectors. Remove column cover to floor pan bolts.

3) Remove lower column retaining bolts, then remove upper column retaining bolts. Pull steering column out from passenger compartment.

Installation – 1) To install steering column, reverse removal procedures and note the following: Place front wheels in straight ahead position. Install column assembly, from passenger compartment, and align lower shaft with flexible coupling. Tighten column mounting bolts.

2) On 504 models, insert fabricated clearance gauge into recess at flexible coupling and tighten pinch bolt. Remove gauge. On all models, make sure all switches are installed, connected and operate properly. Install column trim covers and steering wheel.

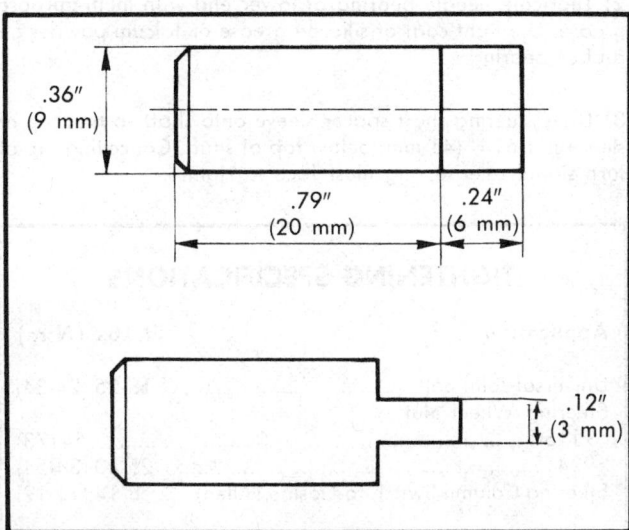

Fig. 1 Dimensions for Fabricating Clearance Gauge (504 Models Only)

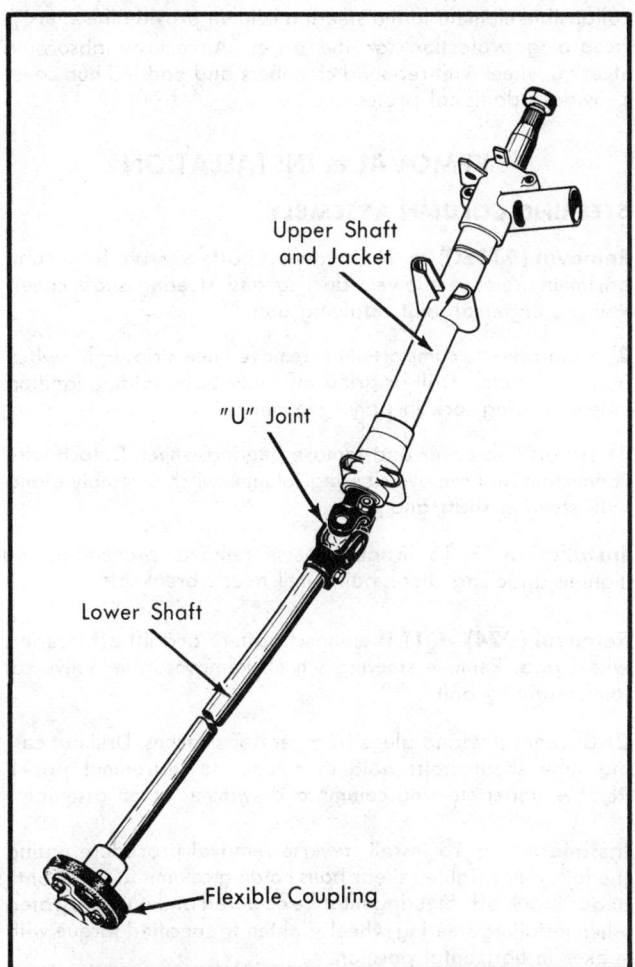

Fig. 2 Peugeot Steering Column Assembly (504 Shown, 505 and 604 Similar)

PORSCHE

911SC
924

NOTE — *Steering column removal and installation information for 928 is not available.*

DESCRIPTION

The steering column assemblies on all Porsche models are essentially the same, consisting of a three-piece, energy-absorbing unit, with the three pieces connected by two universal joints. The offset design of the steering shaft and the collapsible element in the steering column provide the energy-absorbing protection for the driver. An energy absorbing steering wheel with rebound chambers and padded hub cover provides additional protection.

REMOVAL & INSTALLATION

STEERING COLUMN ASSEMBLY

Removal (911SC) — 1) Disconnect battery. From front compartment, remove blower, ducting and steering shaft cover. Remove universal joint retaining bolt.

2) From driver's compartment, remove knee strip, light switch and tachometer. Drill or grind off shear bolts holding ignition switch/steering lock in panel mounting.

3) Lift off hub cover and remove steering wheel. Detach wire connection and remove steering column switch assembly along with steering shaft and tube.

Installation — To install, reverse removal procedure and tighten attaching shear bolts until heads break off.

Removal (924) — 1) Disconnect battery and lift off steering wheel pad. Remove steering wheel. Remove upper universal joint retaining bolt.

2) Disconnect wiring plugs from rear of switches. Drill out casing tube shear bolts holding column to instrument panel. Remove upper steering column and switches as an assembly.

Installation — To install, reverse removal procedure noting the following: Tighten shear bolts holding column to panel until heads break off. Steering must be centered and hub lubricated when installing steering wheel. Tighten to specified torque with spokes in horizontal position.

OVERHAUL

STEERING COLUMN ASSEMBLY

Disassembly (911SC) — 1) With column out of vehicle and switches removed from column, drive steering shaft out of tube. Remove lower end circlip and lower ball bearing.

2) Press Seeger ring out of top end of steering shaft tube. Remove ball bearing and contact ring.

Reassembly — 1) Install ball bearing against circlip at lower end of steering column and seat bottom circlip against bearing. Circlips must seat in recessed grooves. Place contact ring and upper bearing together on steering shaft.

2) With section of pipe, drive bearing into place on shaft. Pipe should contact inner race only. Complete assembly in reverse order of disassembly.

Disassembly (924) — Remove turn signal and windshield wiper switches. Remove circlip and upper ball bearing from housing.

Reassembly — 1) Reverse disassembly procedures and note the following: Drive ball bearing in up to stop in housing. Switches must be in OFF position when installed.

2) Lubricate needle bearing at lower end with multi-purpose grease. Use light coat of silicone grease or talcum powder on rubber bearing.

3) Drive steering shaft spacer sleeve onto shaft so that top of sleeve is 1.614" (41 mm) below top of shaft. Cancelling tab of turn signal release ring must face to right.

TIGHTENING SPECIFICATIONS

Application	Ft. Lbs. (N·m)
Universal Joint Bolts	18-25 (24-34)
Steering Wheel Nut	
911SC	54 (73)
924	25-40 (34-54)
Steering Column Switch-to-Casing (Allen)	8-14 (11-19)

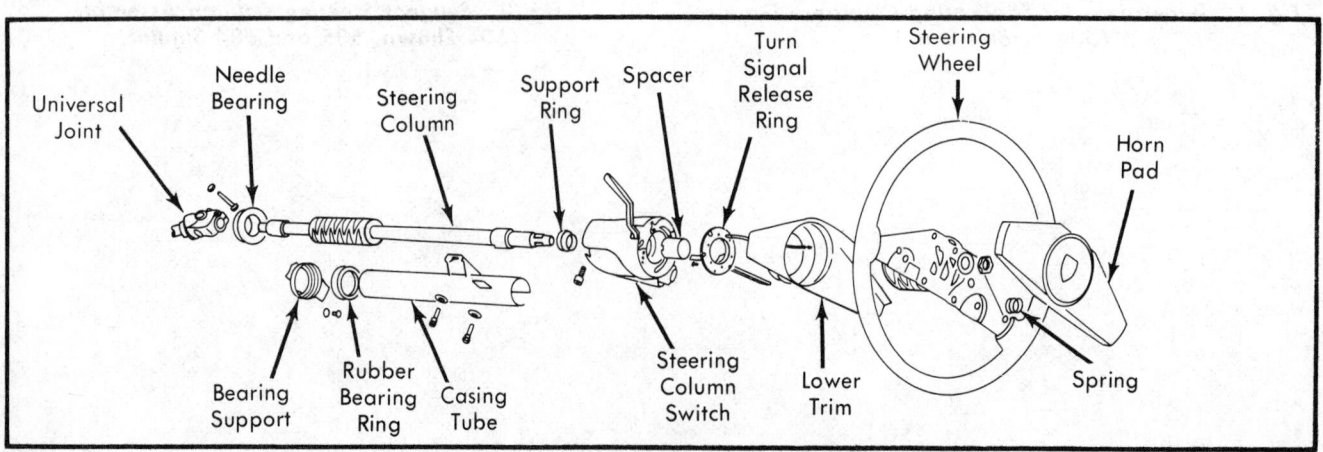

Fig. 1   Porsche 924 Steering Column

RENAULT

18i
Le Car

DESCRIPTION

Vehicles are equipped with an energy-absorbing collapsible column. The steering column is designed in two separate sections, which are joined by a universal joint. The upper portion of the column is designed with a sliding section which compresses on vehicle impact. At the lower end of the bottom section, the steering column is connected to the pinion flange of the steering gear through a flexible rubber coupling.

REMOVAL & INSTALLATION

STEERING COLUMN

Removal – 1) Disconnect battery and unclip speedometer cable in engine compartment. Remove instrument cluster cowl. Pry clips on sides of cluster inward and pull cluster forward. Disconnect wiring and speedometer cable, then remove cluster.

2) Remove steering wheel pad and steering wheel. Detach lower column cover, remove screws and lift off combination switch from column. Disconnect wiring from switch. Remove fuse box screws and place box to one side. Disconnect universal joint.

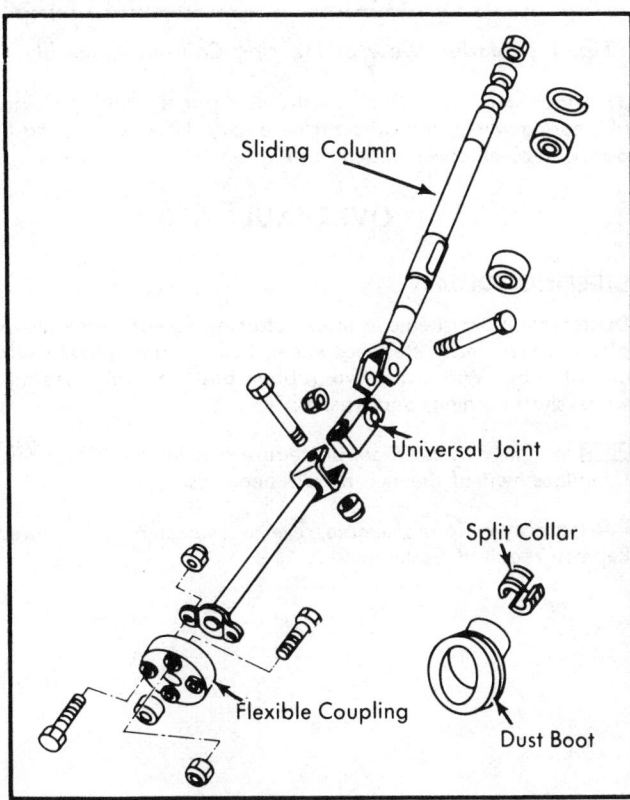

Fig. 1   Renault Steering Column with Related Components

3) Mark column clamp position, remove shaft flexible coupling at steering box, and remove clamps from column tube. Pull column assembly free from dashboard.

Installation – 1) To install, reverse removal procedures, noting the following: Tighten upper column clamp at the end of installation. Set gear at center position before connecting universal joint in the following manner:

2) Raise front end of vehicle. Set steering box at center point. Tighten bottom joint pin. Turn steering 1/4 turn to left or right, then tighten upper universal joint pin.

3) Reconnect all wiring, tighten bolts securely and check shaft for binding or rubbing.

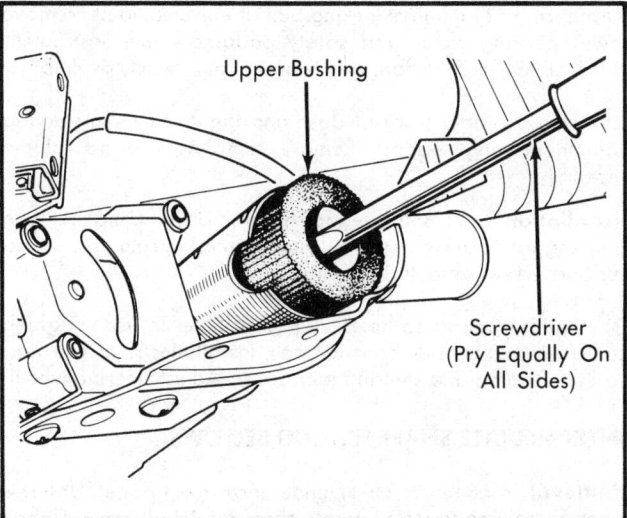

Fig. 2   Removing Upper Column Bushing

OVERHAUL

REPLACING COLUMN BUSHINGS

Disassembly – Tap upper end of steering shaft until lower bushing comes out of column tube. Remove snap ring from top of column tube and carefully pry out bushing with screwdriver.

Reassembly — 1) Coat new bushing with suitable grease. Position lower split bushing on steering shaft and fit an old bushing below it which has been turned down .079" (2 mm) in diameter.

2) Insert lower bushing by pulling steering shaft upward, then push it back slightly to recover used bushing. Using a suitable sleeve, replace upper bushing. Insert snap ring and install column in vehicle.

Steering Columns

SAAB

900

DESCRIPTION

Steering columns used on these models are safety telescopic type. The lower portion of the steering shaft is designed to retract into the upper portion when frontal impact is experienced. Steering shaft is mounted in column support by needle bearings. Column support is mounted to a cross member under dash. An intermediate shaft, with "U" joints at each end, transmits steering shaft movement to steering gear.

REMOVAL & INSTALLATION

STEERING COLUMN

Removal — 1) Remove locking bolt at universal joint. Remove lower bearing cover and safety padding under instrument panel. Remove direction switch and wiper switch assembly.

2) Remove rubber boot at dash and the 4 screws in steering column bearing support. Remove complete steering column assembly.

Installation — 1) Bolt steering shaft to "U" joint, making sure bolt engages groove in shaft. Install 4 steering column bearing support screws and tighten slightly.

2) Position support so holes align with holes in dash. Tighten screws. Install rubber boot to dash, install electrical switches, safety padding and steering joint cover. Adjust steering wheel.

INTERMEDIATE SHAFT SEALING BELLOWS

Removal — Remove cover under instrument panel. Unscrew steering column-to-intermediate shaft retaining screw. Unbolt column tube from instrument panel. Pull steering column from intermediate shaft. Cut off old sealing bellows.

Installation — 1) Lubricate installation tool (899513) with vaseline or soapy water. Place tool against intermediate shaft. Ease new bellows over tool and joint. Ensure bellows are not damaged in this process.

2) Replace steering column into intermediate shaft. Make sure that shaft is pushed in so that screw is located directly opposite the groove. Tighten retaining screws.

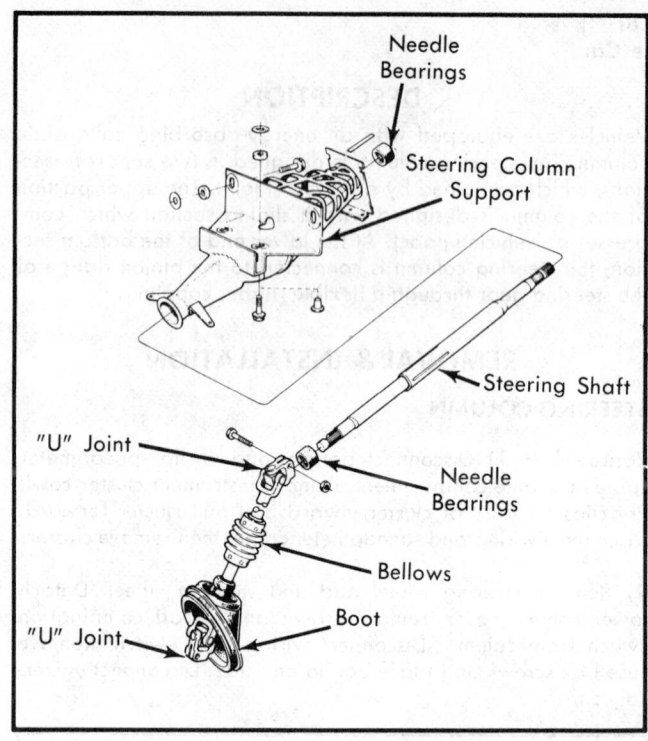

Fig. 1 Exploded View of Steering Column Assembly

3) Attach steering column to instrument panel. Check position of steering wheel and adjust if necessary. Fit bellows in dash panel. Replace cover under dash.

OVERHAUL

STEERING COLUMN

Disassembly — Remove three retaining screws and remove plastic cover under steering wheel. Pull steering wheel shaft out of tube. Withdraw two rubber bushings with steering wheel shaft bushings and washers.

NOTE — *The only overhaul procedure possible on 900 models is replacement of the two needle bearings.*

Reassembly — To reassemble, reverse disassembly procedure. Replace required bushings.

SUBARU

DL
GL
GLF

DESCRIPTION

Steering column assembly consists of a steering wheel incorporating a horn control, a combination turn signal, hazard warning, and headlight dimmer switch assembly, and an energy absorbing steering shaft. The steering column is connected to the steering gear through a universal joint coupling. The energy absorbing steering shaft is designed to collapse during a front end collision. An anti-theft locking mechanism is used to prevent steering shaft from turning when key is removed.

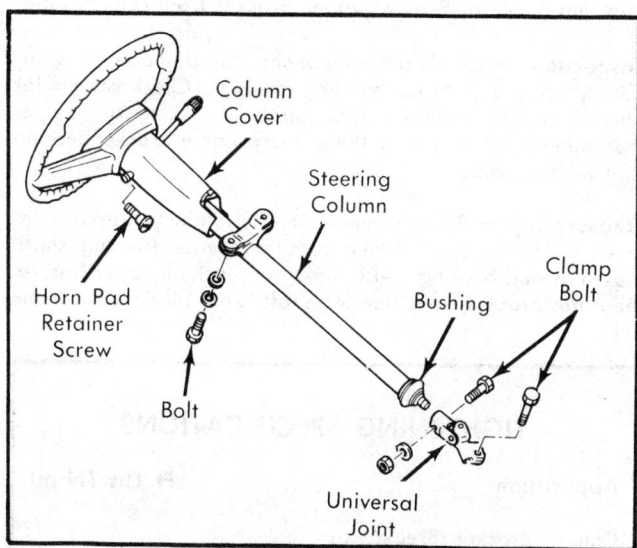

Fig. 1 Subaru Steering Column Assembly

REMOVAL & INSTALLATION

STEERING COLUMN

Removal — 1) Disconnect battery ground strap. Loosen the universal joint clamp bolt and separate shaft from joint.

2) Remove trim panel and unplug all wiring connectors to steering column switches. Remove steering shaft bolt from instrument panel and pull steering column from floorboard.

Installation — Insert column through floorboard into universal joint. Install column bolt into dashboard and tighten. Connect all electrical connections. Tighten universal joint bolt.

OVERHAUL

STEERING COLUMN

Disassembly — 1) Clamp steering column carefully in a vise. Remove single screw holding horn pad on 2 spoke steering wheels, or remove 4 horn pad retaining screws on 4 spoke steering wheels. Remove horn pad. Remove steering wheel nut then remove steering wheel. Remove column covers, combination switch and horn brush.

2) Remove screws retaining bearing to steering column. Pull out shaft from the bottom of cover and remove snap ring, washer, "O" ring and bearing.

Inspection — 1) Universal joint should have no play in any direction. Replace if any play exists. Flex universal joint and check for binding. Replace if torque required to flex joint exceeds 0.43 ft. lbs. (.58 N·m). Check plastic washer for damage, and serration for wear.

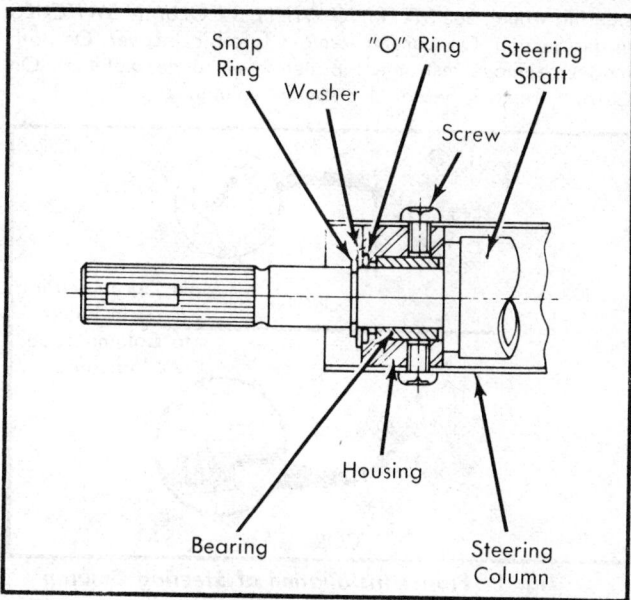

Fig. 2 View of Steering Shaft Lower Components

2) Check steering shaft for runout and length. Length should be 33.78" (857.9 mm). Runout for elliptical part of shaft should be less than 1.28" (32.6 mm). Runout for collar part of shaft should be less than .024" (.6 mm). Runout for upper end of shaft should be less than .047" (1.2 mm). Replace steering shaft if not to specifications. Check bearings for wear or damage, replace if necessary.

Reassembly — To reassemble, reverse disassembly procedure and note the following: With steering wheel in place, check clearance between wheel and cover. If clearance exceeds .04-.12" (1.0-3.0 mm), loosen column cover screws and adjust cover.

TIGHTENING SPECIFICATIONS

Application	Ft. Lbs. (N·m)
Column Bracket Bolt	14-23 (19-31)
Steering Wheel Nut	22-29 (30-39)
Universal Joint Bolt	16-19 (22-26)

Steering Columns

TOYOTA COROLLA & CORONA

DESCRIPTION

Columns used on Corolla and Corona models are collapsible two-piece design. Columns use plastic shear pins to absorb collision impact. A flexible coupling connects steering shaft to steering gear.

REMOVAL & INSTALLATION

STEERING COLUMN

Removal — 1) Disconnect battery negative terminal. Remove steering wheel. See *STEERING WHEEL & COLUMN SWITCHES* in this Section. On Corona, remove fuse block cover. On both models, remove instrument panel cover (under column). On Corona, remove heater duct below column.

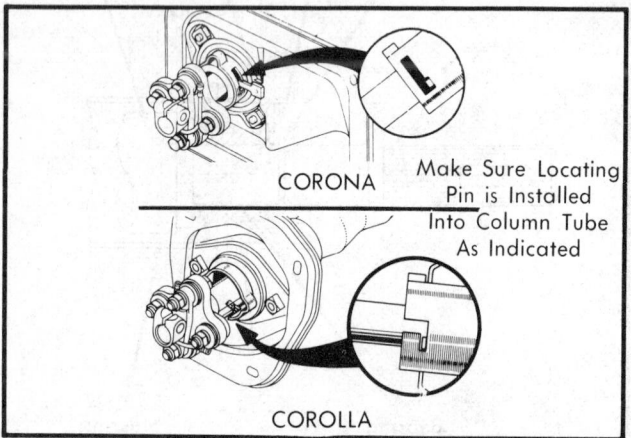

Fig. 1 Proper Installation of Steering Column Locating Pin

2) Remove upper and lower column covers, then remove combination switch. Remove flexible coupling bolt connecting steering shaft with gear (mark flexible coupling-to-gear shaft before removing). Remove column bracket bolts and floor hole cover bolts. Remove steering column from inside vehicle.

Installation — To install steering column, reverse removal procedures and note the following: make sure marks on flexible coupling and gear shaft are aligned. Make sure steering wheel is in straight ahead position when wheels are straight ahead.

OVERHAUL

STEERING COLUMN

Disassembly — Remove retainer and snap ring from upper end of steering column. Remove flexible coupling from steering shaft. Remove hole cover, ring, plate and seal from lower end of steering shaft. Pull column tube off steering shaft from upper end of shaft. Remove upper bracket from column tube.

Inspection — Check all components for damage or wear. Check steering shaft for bending damage. Check column for sheared plastic pins. Check upper bracket for proper operating lock mechanism. If necessary, upper bracket bearing can be replaced.

Reassembly — To reassemble steering column, reverse disassembly procedures. Make sure to grease steering shaft, bushings and bearings. Also make sure lock on upper bracket operates properly and steering shaft is not binding in column tube.

TIGHTENING SPECIFICATIONS

Application	Ft. Lbs. (N·m)
Column Bracket (Breakaway)	
Corolla	22-33 (30-45)
Corona	14-22 (19-30)
Flexible Coupling Bolt	15-22 (20-30)
Steering Wheel	22-29 (30-40)

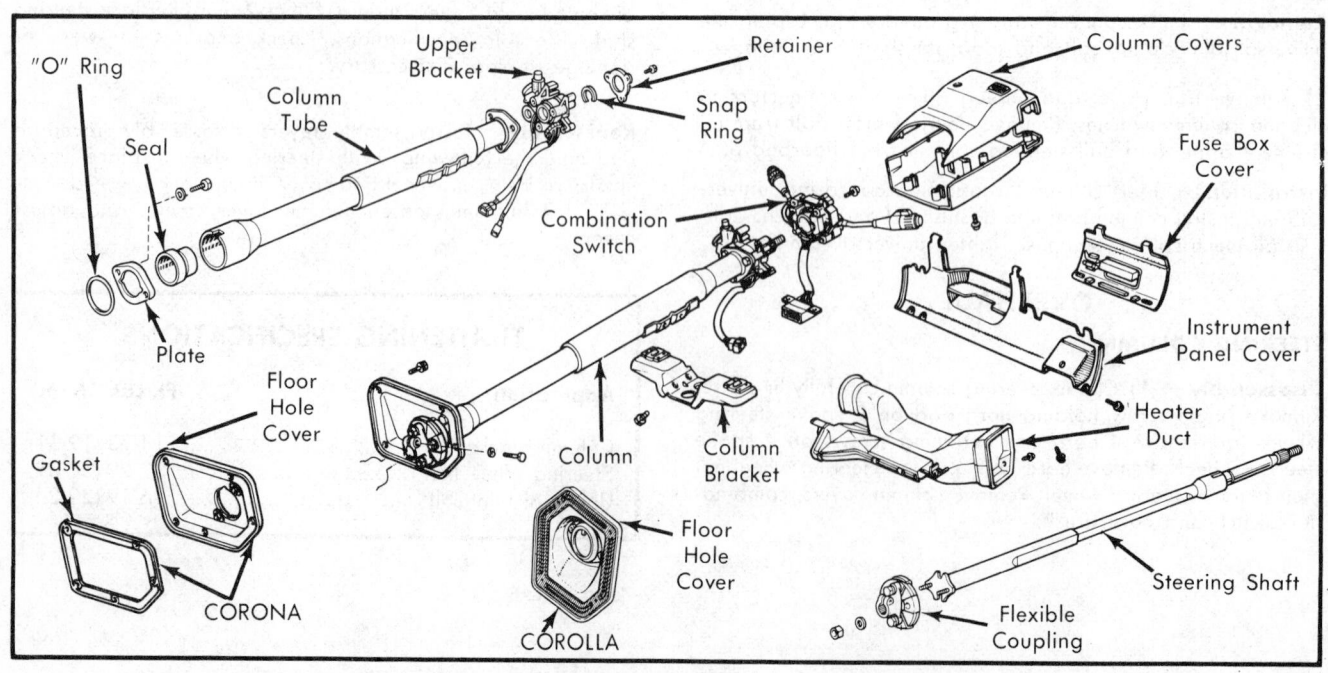

Fig. 2 Exploded View of Corolla and Corona Steering Column

TOYOTA CELICA, CRESSIDA, PICKUP, STARLET & TERCEL

DESCRIPTION

Columns used on these models are of the collapsible two-piece design. Columns use shear pins to absorb collision impact. Steering shaft is connected directly to steering gear with flexible couplings on Celica and Cressida models. Starlet, Tercel and Pickup models use intermediate steering shafts. On 2WD Pickup models, intermediate shaft is connected to steering gear by a flexible coupling. On Starlet, Tercel and 4WD Pickup models, intermediate shaft is connected to steering gear and to main steering shaft by universal joints.

NOTE — *For models with Tilt Wheel steering columns, see Tilt Wheel Steering Columns article in this section.*

REMOVAL & INSTALLATION

STEERING COLUMN

Removal — 1) Disconnect cable from battery negative terminal. Remove steering wheel. On Cressida models, remove fuse box cover, lower instrument trim panel and heater duct (located under steering column). On all models, remove upper and lower steering column covers, then remove combination switch.

2) On Starlet, Tercel and 4WD Pickup models, mark position of "U" joints-to-shafts and remove intermediate steering shaft. On all other models, mark position of flexible coupling-to-steering gear and remove flexible coupling bolt. Remove floor pan cover bolts and column bracket bolts. Remove steering column toward inside of vehicle.

NOTE — *Remove steering column with intermediate shaft on Pickup 2-WD models.*

Installation — To install steering column, reverse removal procedures and note the following: Make sure "U" joint and flexible coupling alignment marks (made upon removal) are correctly aligned.

OVERHAUL

STEERING COLUMN

Disassembly — 1) Remove bearing retainer and snap ring from upper end of column tube. On Starlet and Tercel models, remove upper bracket from column tube. On all models, pull steering shaft out bottom of column tube. On 2WD Pickup, mark main steering shaft-to-intermediate shaft position, then remove snap ring and separate intermediate shaft from steering shaft. Be careful not to lose bearing blocks (located on intermediate shaft.)

2) On Celica, Cressida and 2WD Pickup models, remove flexible coupling from steering shaft. On all models except Starlet and Tercel, remove upper bracket from column tube. On Celica models, upper bracket bolts have to be drilled and removed with a screw extractor.

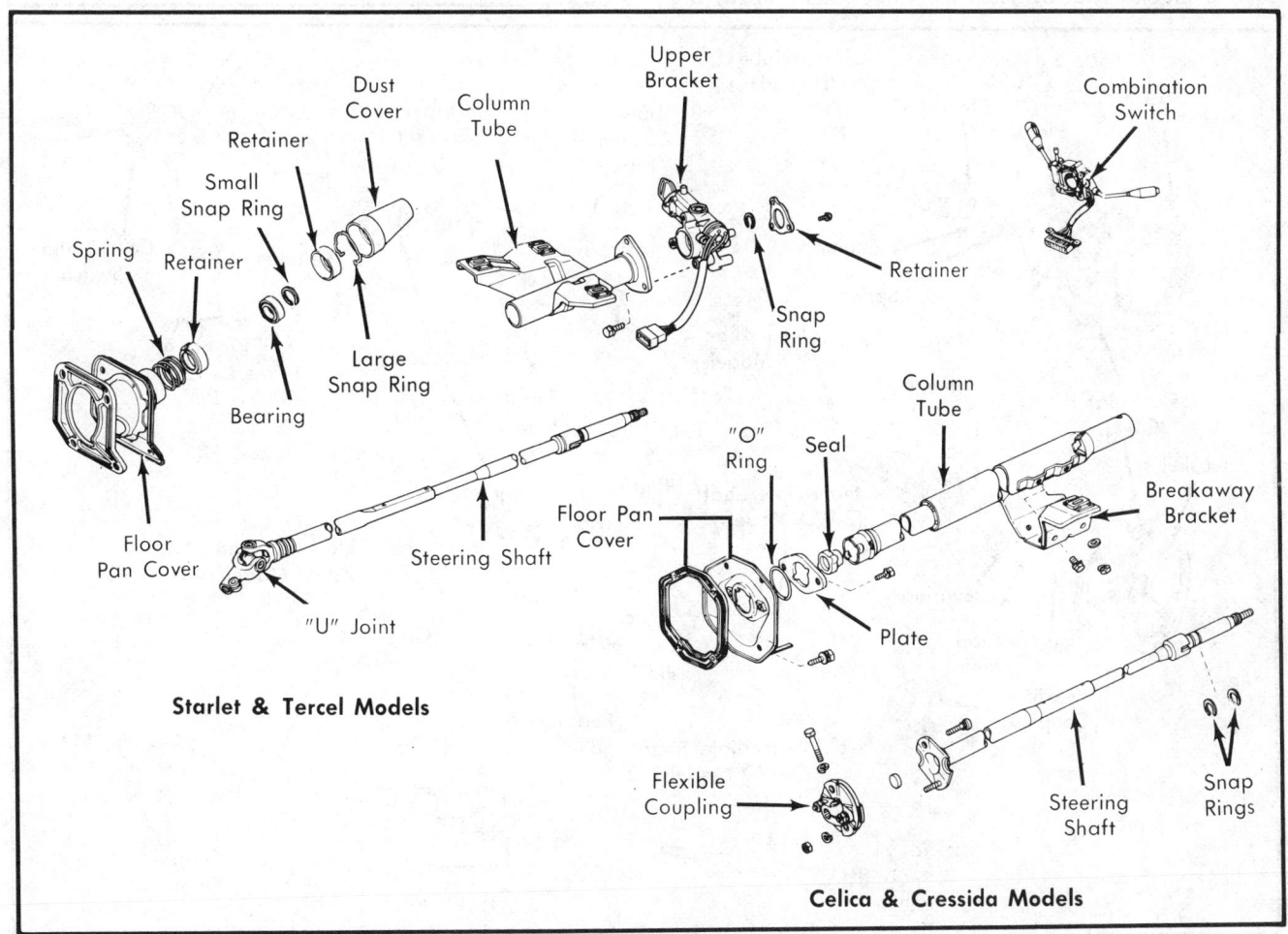

Fig. 1 Exploded View of Celica, Cressida, Starlet and Tercel Steering Columns

TOYOTA CELICA, CRESSIDA, PICKUP, STARLET & TERCEL (Cont.)

3) On Starlet and Tercel models, remove dust cover, then compress shaft toward floor pan cover and remove large snap ring. Remove spring retainer, and again compress shaft to remove small snap ring. Remove bearing, spring retainer and spring. Remove floor pan cover from steering shaft. On all other models, separate floor pan cover from column tube plate and be careful not to damage "O" ring (dust seal on 4WD Pickup models).

4) On Celica and Cressida, remove bracket from column tube. Remove plate and seal from bottom of column tube. On Pickup 2-WD, remove plate spring, bearing retainers and bearing from bottom of column tube.

5) On Pickup 4-WD, remove bolt from column support tube clamp. Remove column support tube from column tube. Remove snap ring and bearing from column support tube.

Inspection — 1) Inspect all components for wear or damage. Check bearings for smooth operation. Check steering shafts for collision damage. Check steering lock mechanism (located in upper bracket) for proper operation. Replace components as necessary.

2) On Pickup 2-WD, temporarily assemble main steering shaft to intermediate shaft and measure amount of radial play between shafts. Allowable limit is .0024" (.06 mm). Replace pin and bearing blocks if necessary.

NOTE — *If replacing pin and bearing blocks, make sure new bearing blocks have the small anti-rattle rubber inserts in-stalled before assembling intermediate shaft to main steering shaft, otherwise steering shafts will rattle when installed in vehicle.*

3) On Starlet, Tercel and 4WD Pickup, check "U" joints for excessive axial play. Maximum play is .002" (.05 mm). Replace "U" joint if necessary.

Reassembly — To reassemble steering columns, reverse disassembly procedures and note the following:

- Grease main steering shaft and all bearings.
- When installing upper bracket on Celica models, use new shear bolts. Tighten bolts until head shears off.
- Make sure marks made to flexible couplings and to "U" joints are aligned.
- Make sure steering column and shafts do not bind after installation.

TIGHTENING SPECIFICATIONS

Application	Ft. Lbs. (N·m)
Column Bracket	15-22 (20-30)
Flexible Coupling	15-22 (20-30)
Steering Wheel	22-29 (30-39)
"U" Joint Clap Bolts	22-33 (30-45)

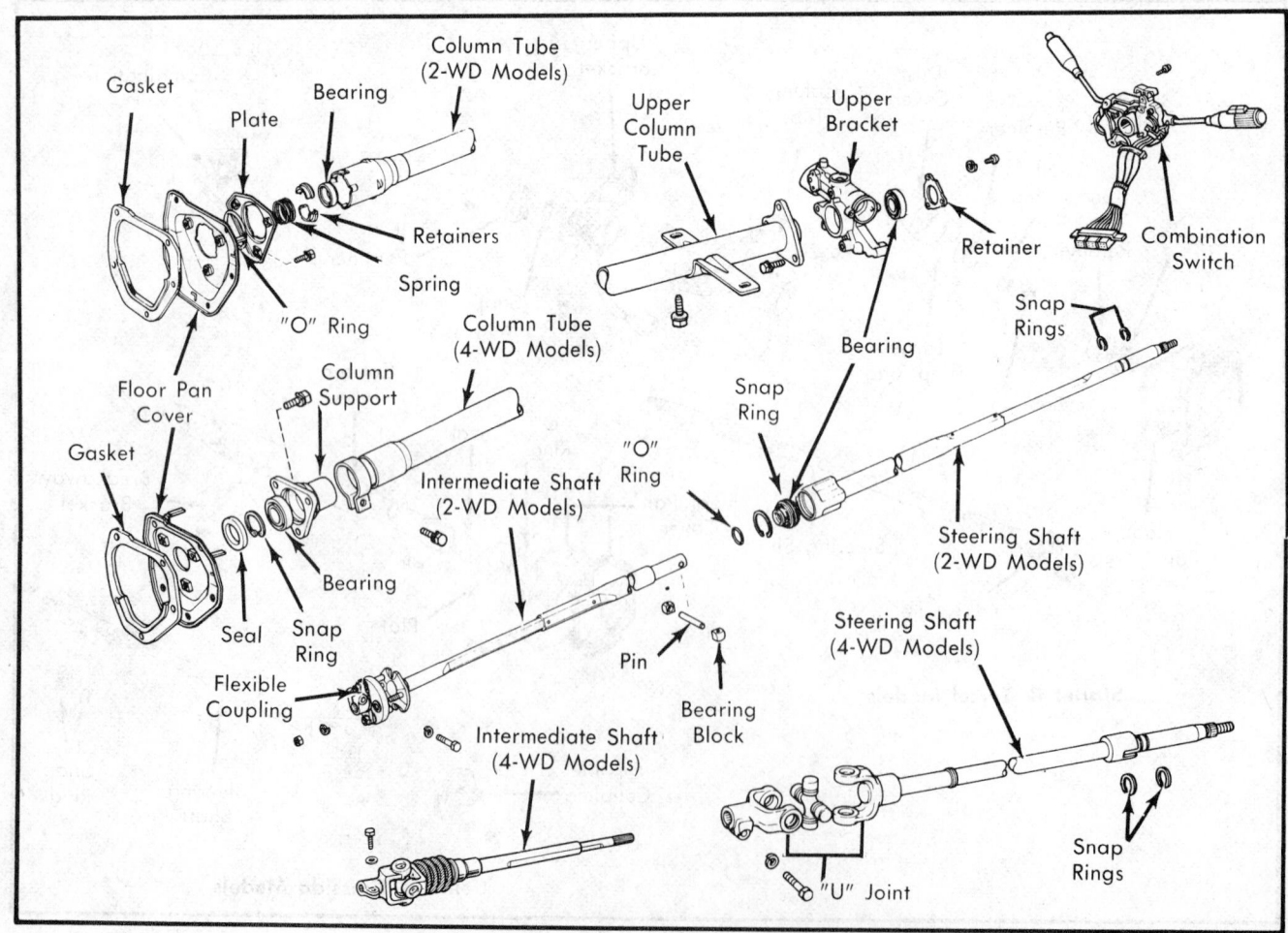

Fig. 2   Exploded View of Pickup Steering Columns

TOYOTA LAND CRUISER

DESCRIPTION

The steering shaft assembly consists of a one-piece steering shaft rotating inside a column tube. Steering shaft is connected to steering gear by a flexible coupling. Column tube is attached to instrument panel by a clamp and to floor pan by a floor cover.

REMOVAL & INSTALLATION

STEERING COLUMN

Removal — 1) Place index marks on steering shaft and flexible coupling, then remove flexible coupling clamp bolt. Remove horn pad, steering wheel and column covers.

2) Remove combination switch. Remove floor pan cover bolts and column clamp bolts. Remove steering column from inside vehicle.

Installation — To install steering column, reverse removal procedure. Make sure index marks on steering gear and flexible coupling are aligned during installation.

OVERHAUL

STEERING COLUMN

Disassembly — 1) Remove bearing retainer, snap rings and upper bracket from column tube. Remove steering shaft from column tube.

2) Separate flexible coupling from steering shaft. Remove floor pan cover-to-column tube bolts and remove floor pan cover. Remove column tube seal from lower end of column tube.

Inspection — Check all components for wear or damage. Check lock mechanism, located in upper bracket, for proper operation. Replace components as necessary.

Reassembly — To reassemble steering column, reverse disassembly procedure and note the following: Grease upper bearing, replace column tube seal and floor pan cover gasket if necessary. After reassembly, make sure steering shaft does not bind in column tube.

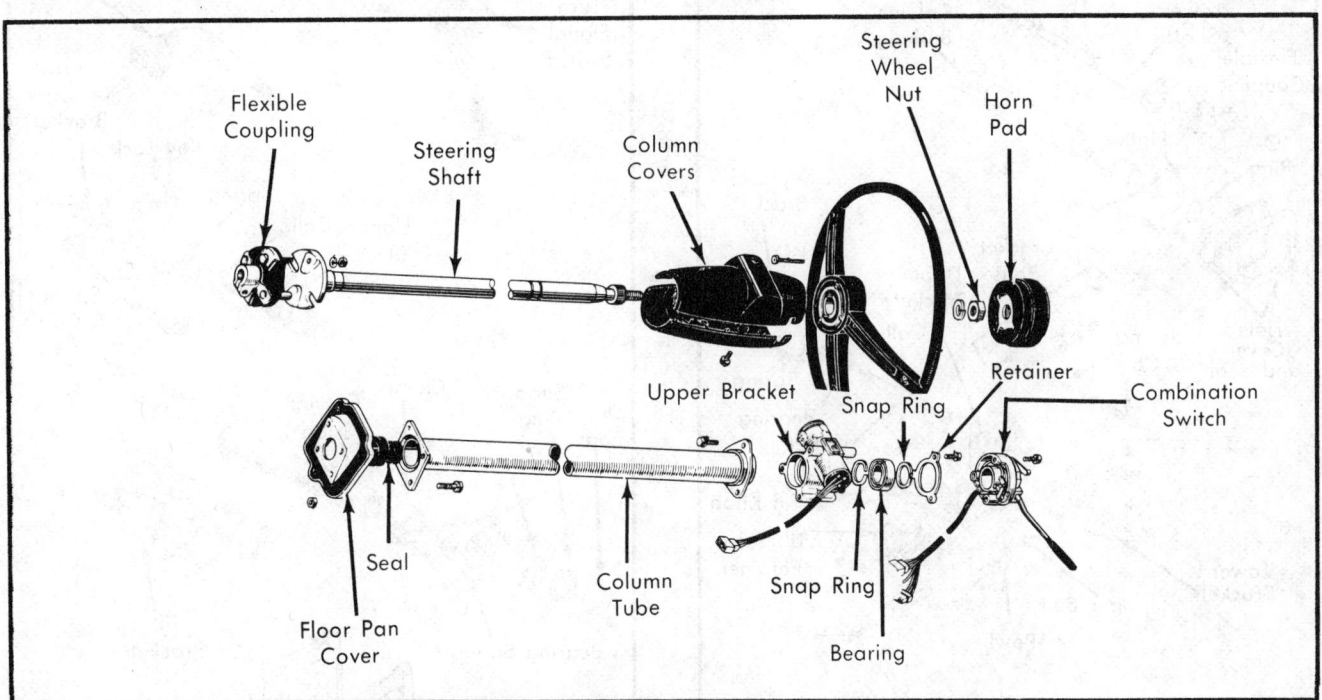

Fig. 1   Exploded View of Land Cruiser Steering Column

Steering Columns

TOYOTA CELICA, CORONA, CRESSIDA, PICKUP & SUPRA — TILT WHEEL

DESCRIPTION

Tilt steering wheels incorporate an upper steering shaft attached, by a universal joint, with an intermediate steering shaft. These shafts are held in place by upper and lower brackets. Brackets are pinned together so that the upper bracket will move up or down. Upper bracket is locked in place by a pawl attached to a lever. Steering columns, on passenger vehicles, are of the collapsible type while the pickup steering column is non-collapsible.

REMOVAL & INSTALLATION

STEERING COLUMN

Removal — 1) Remove steering wheel pad. Mark steering shaft and wheel for installation. Remove steering wheel. Remove dash panels and pads, if necessary. On models with air conditioning, remove air duct under steering column.

2) Remove column bracket covers. Remove turn signal or combination switch. From under hood, disconnect steering shaft universal joint from steering gear (on passenger vehicles) or from lower steering shaft (on pickup models). Be sure to mark universal joint and shaft for installation.

3) Remove bolts from column hole cover. Remove column support bracket bolts, then remove steering column from vehicle.

Installation — 1) Install steering column in vehicle and tighten column bracket bolts finger tight. Install column hole cover bolts, then tighten column bracket bolts.

2) Make sure alignment marks are aligned on universal joints then tighten clamp bolts. Install turn signal or combination switch. Install bracket covers, dash panels and pads. Install air ducts (if equipped).

3) Install steering wheel and steering wheel pad. Make sure alignment marks on steering shaft and steering wheel are aligned.

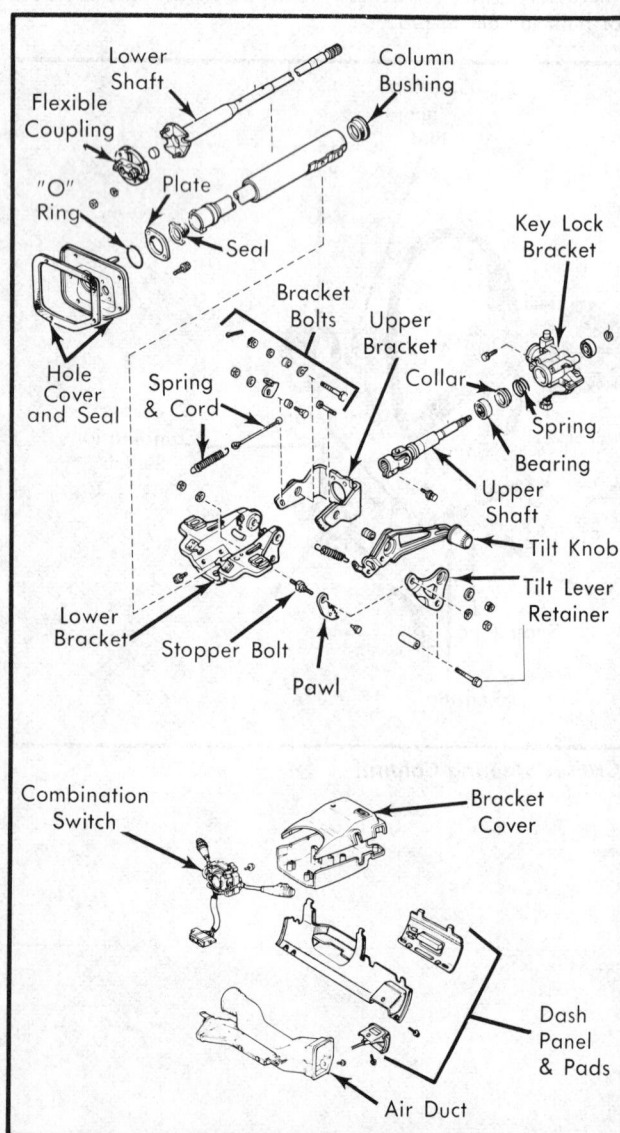

Fig. 1   Exploded View of Passenger Car Tilt Steering Column

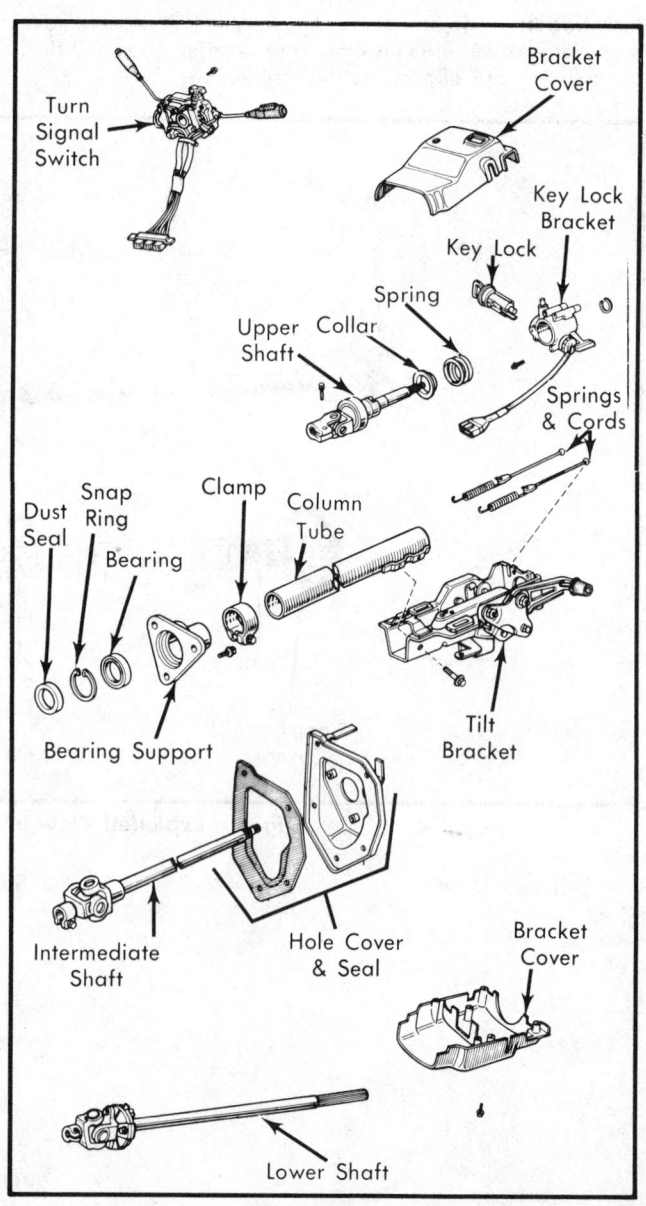

Fig. 2   Exploded View of Pickup Tilt Wheel Steering Column

TOYOTA CELICA, CORONA, CRESSIDA, PICKUP & SUPRA — TILT WHEEL (Cont.)

OVERHAUL

STEERING COLUMN

Disassembly — 1) On pickup models, remove ignition key cylinder. On all models, remove tension springs and cords. Mark universal joint and lower steering shaft. Remove clamp bolt, then lower steering shaft. Remove hole cover from column.

2) Remove snap ring from upper steering shaft. Remove reclining pawl release pin and steering pawl. Drive out serrated bolt with plastic hammer, then remove reclining pawl set bolt.

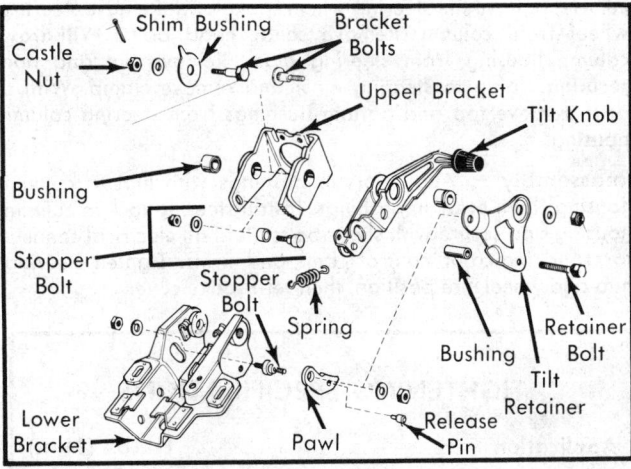

Fig. 3 Exploded View of Tilt Wheel Bracket

Inspection — Check upper bracket for damage. Check upper bearing for rotating smoothness. Check steering shafts for bending, damaged splines or damaged universal joints. Check tilt bracket for worn bushings, damaged pawl, broken or damaged breakaway brackets. Check column tube for bending or other damage. Repair or replace components as necessary.

Reassembly — Reassemble in reverse order of disassembly procedure and note the following; make sure all bushings, bearings, shims and bolts are not damaged or worn.

TIGHTENING SPECIFICATIONS

Application	Ft. Lbs. (N·m)
Castle Nut	11-21 (15-29)
Flexible Coupling	15-21 (20-29)
Steering Wheel Nut	22-18 (30-38)
Support Bracket	
Pickup	11-15 (15-20)
All Others	14-22 (19-30)
Support Bracket-to-Column	11-15 (15-20)
Tilt Lever Retainer Bolt	11-15 (15-20)
Tilt Steering Support Stopper Bolt	6-8 (8-11)
Universal Joint Clamp Bolt①	15-21 (20-29)

① — Tighten clamp bolt at steering gear on pickup models to 22-32 ft. lbs. (30-44 N·m).

TRIUMPH TR7 & TR8

DESCRIPTION

Steering column houses ignition switch, column lock, and light and wiper controls. The steering column is divided into upper and intermediate shafts which are coupled by universal joints.

REMOVAL AND INSTALLATION

STEERING COLUMN ASSEMBLY

Removal — 1) Disconnect battery ground. Take out pinch bolt securing upper universal to steering mast. Disconnect electrical harness from steering column and separate plug connectors *(Fig. 1)*. Remove plastic cover from around steering column.

2) Center punch shear head bolts and use a small chisel to remove. With wheels facing in a straight ahead position, withdraw steering column, noting number and position of flat and concave washers.

Installation — 1) To install steering column assembly, reverse removal procedures, noting the following: Make sure front wheels are in straight ahead position and steering wheel is centered. Check for proper positioning of flat and concave washers.

2) Align steering column mounting holes, then install new bolts and tighten evenly until heads shear. Tighten upper universal pinch bolt to specification.

INTERMEDIATE SHAFT

Removal — Remove pinch bolt mounting intermediate shaft to upper universal coupling and pinch bolt securing universal joint to rack pinion. With front wheels in straight ahead position, slide intermediate shaft upward to remove it from pinion shaft universal joint, then pull shaft downward to disengage from upper universal joint.

Installation — To install intermediate shaft, reverse removal procedure, noting the following: Make sure steering wheel is in straight ahead position and splines on intermediate shaft and rack pinion are fully engaged. Tighten pinch bolts to specification.

OVERHAUL

STEERING COLUMN ASSEMBLY

Disassembly — With steering column assembly removed from vehicle, remove the steering wheel spoke pad. Remove steering wheel from column. Remove shear head bolts. Withdraw column housing from steering mast. Remove nut and bolt securing clamp to steering mast and remove clamp. With a drift, remove top and bottom bushings from steering column housing.

Reassembly — Align slots in bushings with lugs in column housing, then press in bushings. Install steering lock in column housing and secure with shear bolts. Refit all electrical connectors and indicator control cams and arms. Tighten steering hub and wheel into position, then refit spoke cover.

TIGHTENING SPECIFICATIONS

Application	Ft. Lbs. (N·m)
Column Clamp-to-Column	6-9 (8-12)
Steering Wheel Nut	30-37 (41-50)
Universal Joint Pinch Bolts	16-21 (22-29)

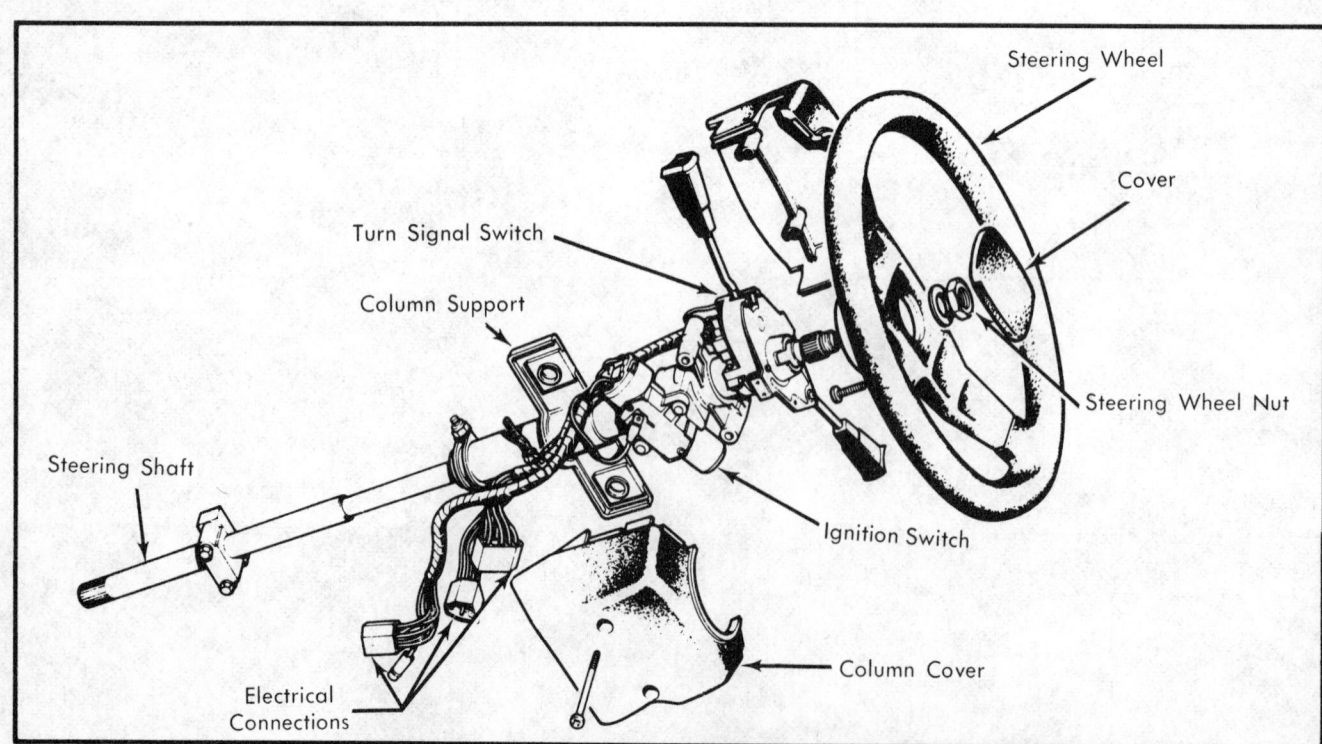

Fig. 1 Partially Disassembled View of TR7 & TR8 Upper Steering Column

VOLKSWAGEN DASHER

DESCRIPTION

The Volkswagen Dasher uses a two-piece safety steering column which incorporate a flange connection. A lattice metal column support is used under the instrument panel. This device is designed to absorb some of the impact shock which may otherwise be transmitted to the driver.

REMOVAL & INSTALLATION

STEERING COLUMN

Removal — 1) Disconnect battery ground strap. Remove steering wheel. See *Volkswagen* under *STEERING WHEELS & COLUMN SWITCHES* in this Section.

2) Remove all steering column switches.

3) From under hood, remove pinch bolt holding steering column flange to pinion shaft.

4) Work under brake pedal and unbolt mounting flange from bracket. Disconnect electrical wires from ignition switch. Put ignition switch in "ON" position.

5) Remove bolts from steering lock/column clamp. Remove steering column and shaft as a unit.

Installation — 1) Position column assembly back in vehicle. Install steering column lock. Make sure lock lug will snap into recess in steering column. Fit new shear bolts finger tight.

2) Bolt steering column mounting flange onto bracket so long side of flange faces right side of vehicle. Snug up flange bolts and steering lock/column clamp bolts.

3) Connect electrical wires to ignition switch. Fit column trim. Place front wheels straight-ahead.

4) Make sure column bushings are in position on pins at lower end of steering column. Line holes in flange so flange will slide down over pins on steering column. It will be necessary to use drift to drive flange tube onto steering gear pinion shaft. Make sure flange seats to stop on pinion. Tighten pinch bolt.

5) Maneuver steering column until steering lock operates correctly, then tighten steering lock/column clamp bolts. Install steering wheel.

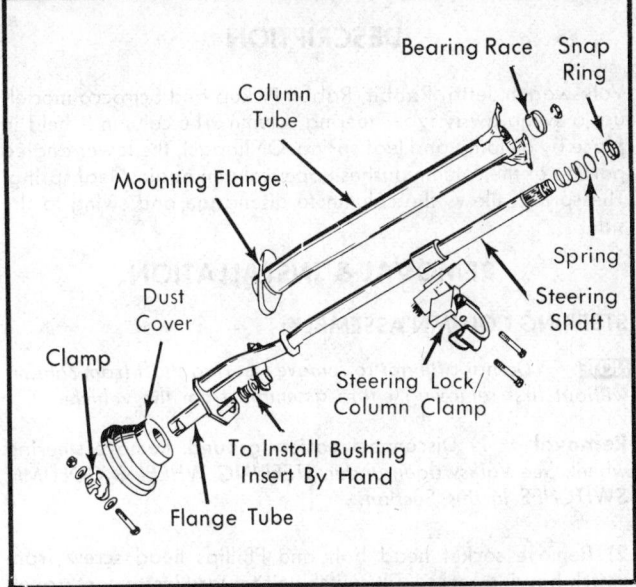

Fig. 1 *Expanded View of Dasher Steering Column*

OVERHAUL

STEERING COLUMN

Disassembly — Pull off steering wheel spacer ring and snap ring. Remove flat washer and spring. Pull steering shaft out through bottom of column. Press race out of column.

Reassembly — Examine race and replace if excessively worn. Slide steering shaft back into column then refit spring and snap ring.

TIGHTENING SPECIFICATIONS

Application	Ft. Lbs. (N·m)
Column Mounting Flange-to-Body	7 (10)
Gear Box Pinch Bolt	22 (30)
Steering Gear Box-to-Frame	14 (19)
Steering Wheel Nut	36 (41)

VOLKSWAGEN JETTA, RABBIT, PICKUP & SCIROCCO

DESCRIPTION

Volkswagen Jetta, Rabbit, Rabbit Pickup and Scirocco models use a swing-away type steering column. The column is held in place by a clamp and leaf spring. On impact, the lower angled portion of the column pushes upper column against leaf spring. The spring allows the column to disengage and swing to the side.

REMOVAL & INSTALLATION

STEERING COLUMN ASSEMBLY

NOTE — *Do not attempt to remove steering shaft from column without first removing entire assembly from the vehicle.*

Removal — **1)** Disconnect battery ground. Remove steering wheel. See *Volkswagen under STEERING WHEEL & COLUMN SWITCHES in this Section.*

2) Remove socket head bolt and Phillips head screw from switch housing recess. Tilt switch unit toward instrument panel. Pry off spacer sleeve on steering column. Pull switch unit up enough to disconnect wires. Remove switch unit from column.

3) Disconnect steering shaft from "U" joint shaft. Disconnect brake pedal push rod. Separate clutch pedal from actuating cable under instrument panel.

4) Push leaf spring retainer clip down with a screwdriver and disengage it from mounting slot. Remove bolts mounting column under instrument panel. Shear bolts will have to be centerpunched and drilled out. Pull entire column (with shaft) out of vehicle.

Bearing Replacement — Drive steering shaft from column. Remove bearings. Press in steering shaft and bearings. It should not take more than a force of 100-200 lbs. (45-90 kgs) to properly seat bearings into position.

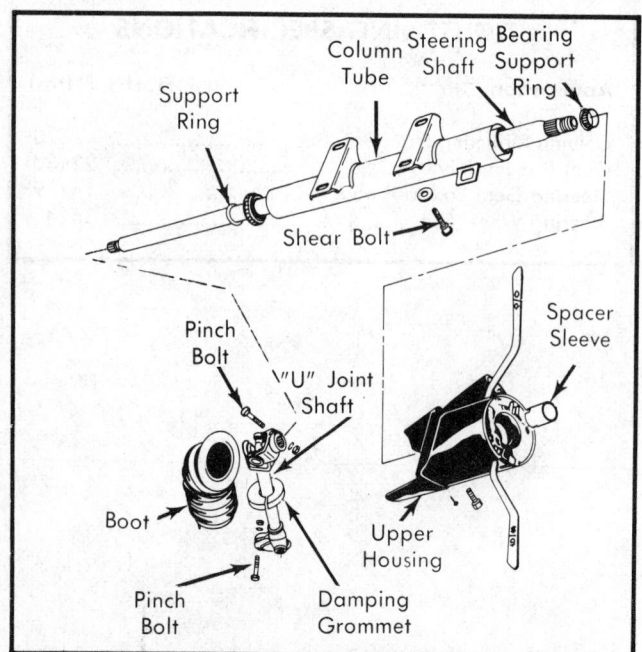

Fig. 1   Exploded View of Jetta, Rabbit, Rabbit Pickup and Scirocco Steering Column

Installation — To install, reverse removal procedure and note: Make sure front wheels point straight-ahead before tightening pinch bolt. Before fitting column switch unit, install spacer to dimensions shown in *Fig. 2*. Adjust both brake pedal and clutch pedal height.

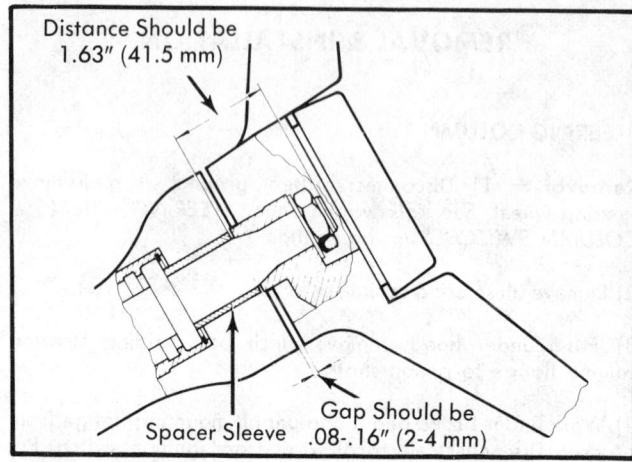

Fig. 2   Spacer Sleeve Adjustment Dimensions

"U" JOINT SHAFT

Removal — **1)** Separate manual gearshift linkage from steering box.

2) Remove pinch bolt connecting lower end of "U" joint shaft with steering gear pinion shaft.

3) Remove nuts mounting steering gear box to frame. Pull box down to separate from lower "U" joint. Remove rubber boot from lower "U" joint.

4) Remove pinch bolt connecting upper "U" joint to steering shaft. Pull down on joint and remove shaft with "U" joints from vehicle.

Installation — **1)** Fit "U" joint to steering shaft. Make sure notch in steering shaft aligns with slot in lower "U" joint.

2) Install boot and damping grommet. Fit steering gear box to frame while guiding pinion shaft into lower "U" joint. Finger tighten gear box nuts.

3) Place front wheels straight-ahead. Align pinion shaft and "U" joint. Tighten pinch bolt. Tighten gear box nuts. Connect manual gearshift linkage to gear box. Check linkage operation.

TIGHTENING SPECIFICATIONS

Application	Ft. Lbs. (N·m)
Steering Column-to-Instrument Panel	
Mounting Bolt	14 (19)
Shear Bolts	①
Steering Wheel Nut	36 (49)
Pinch Bolts	22 (30)

① — Until bolt head snaps off.

Steering Columns

VOLKSWAGEN VANAGON

DESCRIPTION

Volkswagen Vanagon models use an energy absorbing steering column. Column is attached to dash by brackets and to floor pan by a dust boot. Steering shaft is made up of an upper steering shaft and lower steering shaft. Shafts are connected together by a short upper flange. Lower steering shaft is connected to the transfer gear by a flange containing a rubber coupling.

REMOVAL & INSTALLATION

STEERING COLUMN

Removal — 1) Remove horn button and steering wheel. Remove column covers, then disconnect column switch wires. Remove column switch. Remove steering lock and spacer sleeve with a puller.

2) Remove clamp bolt attaching upper steering shaft to upper flange. Remove lower column clamp bolts, then upper column bolts. Remove upper steering shaft with column tube as an assembly.

3) Remove lower flange clamp bolt, the one attaching lower flange to lower steering shaft. Remove dust boot-to-floor pan bolts and remove lower steering shaft.

Installation — 1) To install steering column, reverse removal procedures and note the following: Install new gasket on dust boot. Install steering shaft and column tube as an assembly.

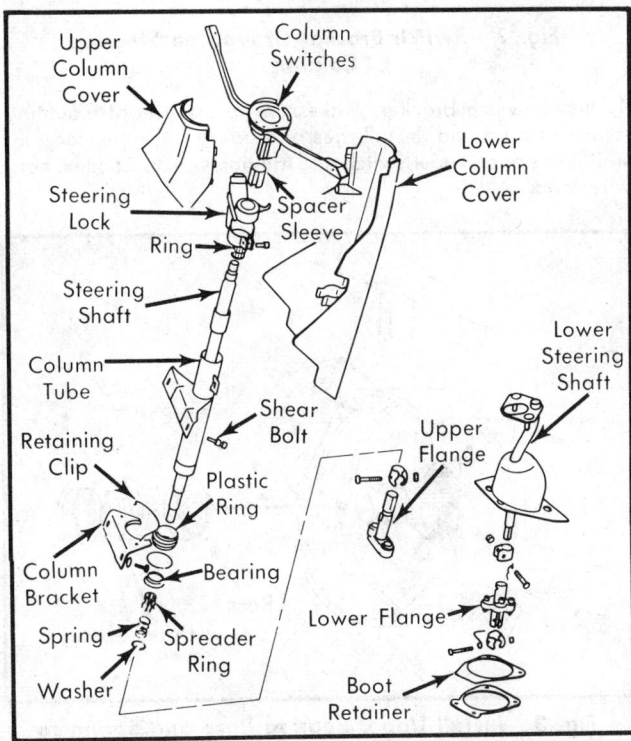

Fig. 1   Exploded View of Volkswagen Vanagon Steering Column Assembly

2) When installing steering lock and spacer sleeve, clamp lower steering shaft to upper flange with tool VW 267a. Make sure distance from top of column tube to top of upper steering shaft (with steering wheel and nut installed) is 1.634" (41.5 mm) and space between column switch and steering wheel is .079-157" (2-4 mm). See *Fig. 2.*

OVERHAUL

STEERING COLUMN

Disassembly — 1) On lower steering shaft, remove flange from steering shaft. Remove clamp from flange. Remove gasket and boot retainer from dust boot.

2) On upper steering shaft, remove washer, spring, spreader ring, bearing, column bracket and plastic ring from bottom end of shaft. Remove steering lock ring from upper end of steering shaft.

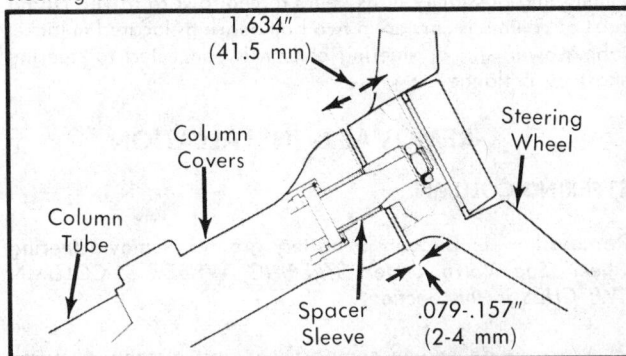

Fig. 2   Measurements for Installing Spacer Sleeve

3) On column tube, drill out and remove shear bolt. Remove column tube from steering shaft.

Inspection — Check all components for excessive wear, scoring or other damage. Check steering shafts for bending, cracks or other collision damage. Replace components as necessary.

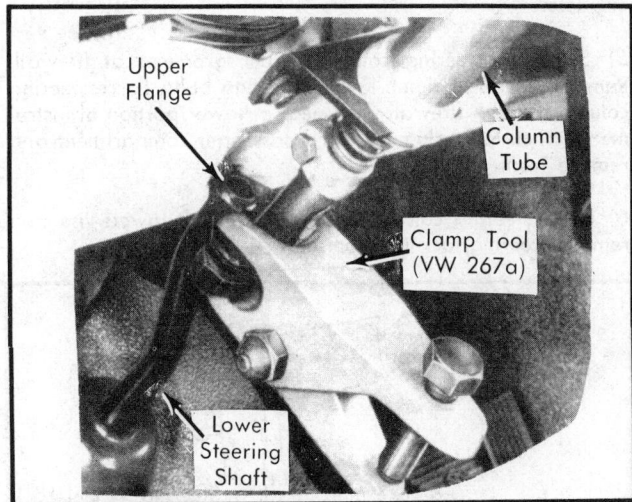

Fig. 3   Clamp Tool for Installing Spacer Sleeve

Reassembly — To reassemble steering column and shafts, reverse disassembly procedures and note the following: Always assemble steering lock, spacer sleeve and ring before installing to steering shaft. When installing shear bolt to column, tighten bolt until head snaps off.

TIGHTENING SPECIFICATIONS

Application	Ft. Lbs. (N·m)
Clamp Bolts	14 (19)
Lower Bracket Bolts	18 (24)
Steering Wheel Nut	36 (49)

Steering Columns

VOLVO

DL   GLE
GL   Bertone
GT   Diesel

DESCRIPTION

Steering column is divided in two sections. Upper and lower sections are joined by means of a flange. A heavy frontal impact would cause flange to break from upper column. The upper portion of steering column would retain its position, eliminating possibility of its being forced toward driver. Upper part of column is carried in two ball bearings located in jacket tube. Lower end of steering column is connected to steering shaft by a flange.

REMOVAL & INSTALLATION

STEERING COLUMN

Removal – **1)** Disconnect battery ground. Remove steering wheel. *See Volvo under STEERING WHEEL & COLUMN SWITCHES in this Section.*

2) Work inside engine compartment and disconnect clamp holding column shaft to lower shaft universal joint. Pry clamp apart with screwdriver, do not tap with hammer.

3) Remove column covers. Disconnect wiring and remove turn signal and wiper switches. Remove switch retainer, spring, and bearing race.

4) Drill steering column lock bolts and remove with a screw extractor.

5) Slide out steering column rubber grommet at firewall. Remove steering column lower mounting bolts. Force steering column through firewall until clear of lower portion of instrument panel. Pull column toward passenger compartment and remove from vehicle.

6) Place steering column assembly in a soft jawed vise and remove steering lock mechanism.

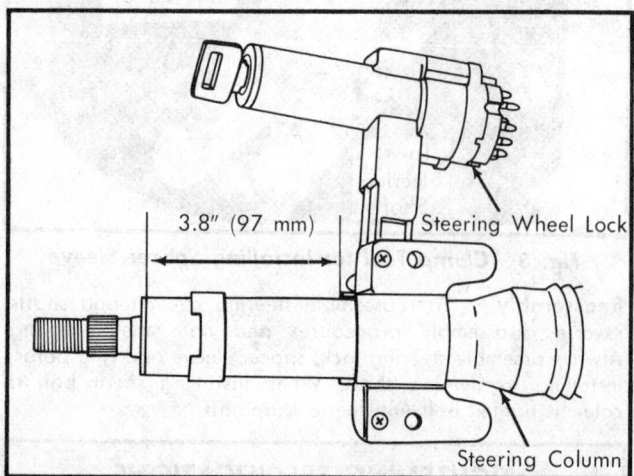

Fig. 1   Steering Wheel Lock Position

Installation – **1)** Measure steering column to ensure length is 27.08-27.17" (688-690 mm). Position steering wheel lock on column so lock upper edge is 3.8" (97 mm) from upper edge of steering column. *See Fig. 1.*

2) Place rubber seal on column and insert column through firewall. Make sure both plastic guides are in position on the dashboard and install bolts loosely in upper and lower attachments.

3) Adjust column position. Steering wheel lock should protrude from dashboard .53-.65" (13.5-16.5 mm) when measured at key position "111" at the lock. Check for binding and rubbing, and adjust dashboard beam if necessary. Tighten lower bolts to 15-22 ft. lbs. (20-30 N·m).

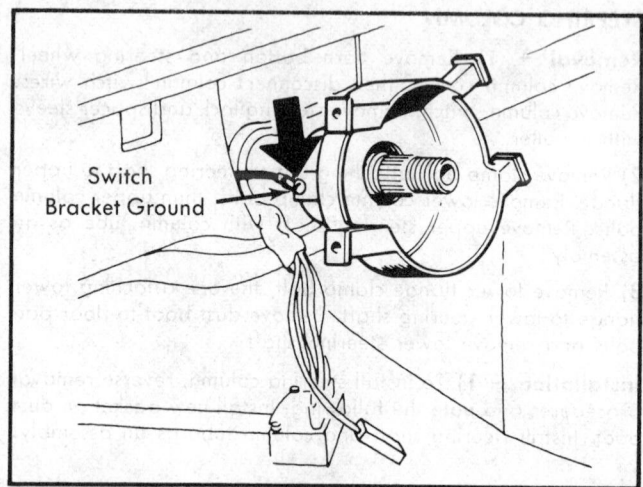

Fig. 2   Switch Bracket Ground on Steering Column

4) Install switch bracket. Make sure to use one of mounting screws as a ground. Install race and spring for upper race. Install turn signal, wiper switch and ignition switch. Connect horn wire lead.

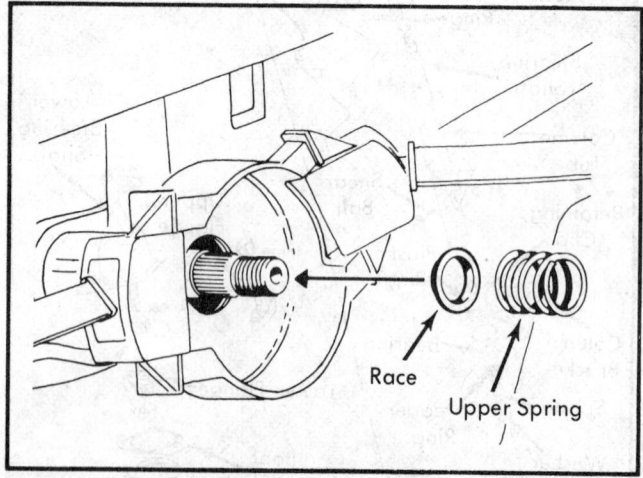

Fig. 3   Install Upper Bearing Race and Spring to Steering Column

5) Replace column covers after tightening upper bolts until heads shear off. Install steering wheel and tighten nut to 33-55 ft. lbs. (45-75 N·m). Tighten lower column clamp bolt in engine compartment to 15-22 ft. lbs. (20-30 N·m).

NOTE – *Rattling in steering column can be corrected by placing 1 or 2 flat washers between steering wheel and upper bearing spring.*

AUDI 4000 RACK & PINION

DESCRIPTION

Steering system is a direct-acting rack and pinion gear mounted to crossmember and connected to tie rods by a bracket. Tie rods are connected to steering knuckle by ball joints.

ADJUSTMENT

RACK ADJUSTMENT

Loosen lock nut on steering gear cover. Hand tighten adjusting screw until it touches thrust washer. Hold screw in position and tighten lock nut. If steering is too tight or does not self center, readjust. If gear rattles when driven, adjustment is too loose.

CAUTION — *Do not turn gear hard against either lock when vehicle is raised off ground or damage may result.*

REMOVAL & INSTALLATION

STEERING GEAR

Removal — 1) After removing both tie rod mounting bolts from rack, pry tie rods off steering gear. On early models, loosen bottom steering column mounting bolt and pry off clamp. On late models, use a screwdriver to push cap from engine compartment to inside of vehicle, then loosen bottom steering column mounting bolt and pry off clamp. Also remove seal ring.

2) On all models, drive bottom of column off gear using a brass mandrel. Remove gear mounting bolts from body. Turn wheels to right lock and remove steering gear through opening in right wheel well.

Installation — 1) On early models, before installing steering gear in vehicle, install the slider (in which both sealing sleeves are welded into the cup, see *Fig. 2*).

2) On all models, install steering gear to vehicle. To facilitate installation of tie rods on early models, remove one bolt from slider, install tie rod and reinstall bolt. Repeat procedure for

other tie rod. Install bracket. On late models, install tie rods to tie rod bracket, then install bracket to steering drive pawl. Install steering drive pawl to steering gear rack. Install seal ring. On all models, install clamp and attach column to steering gear. On late models, push cap from inside vehicle to steering gear.

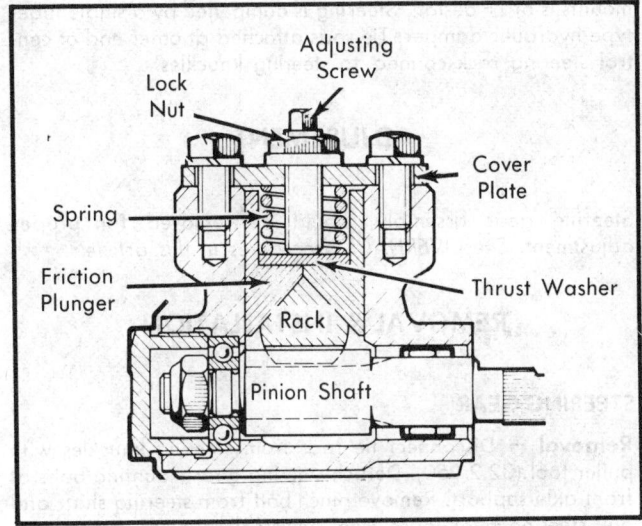

Fig. 1   Cross Sectional View of Pinion Shaft with Rack Adjustment

STEERING DAMPER

NOTE — *Replacement of steering damper is the only service procedure recommended. Do not attempt repairs on this unit.*

OVERHAUL

NOTE — *Manufacturer does not recommend overhaul of this rack and pinion steering unit. If unit is determined defective, replace as assembly.*

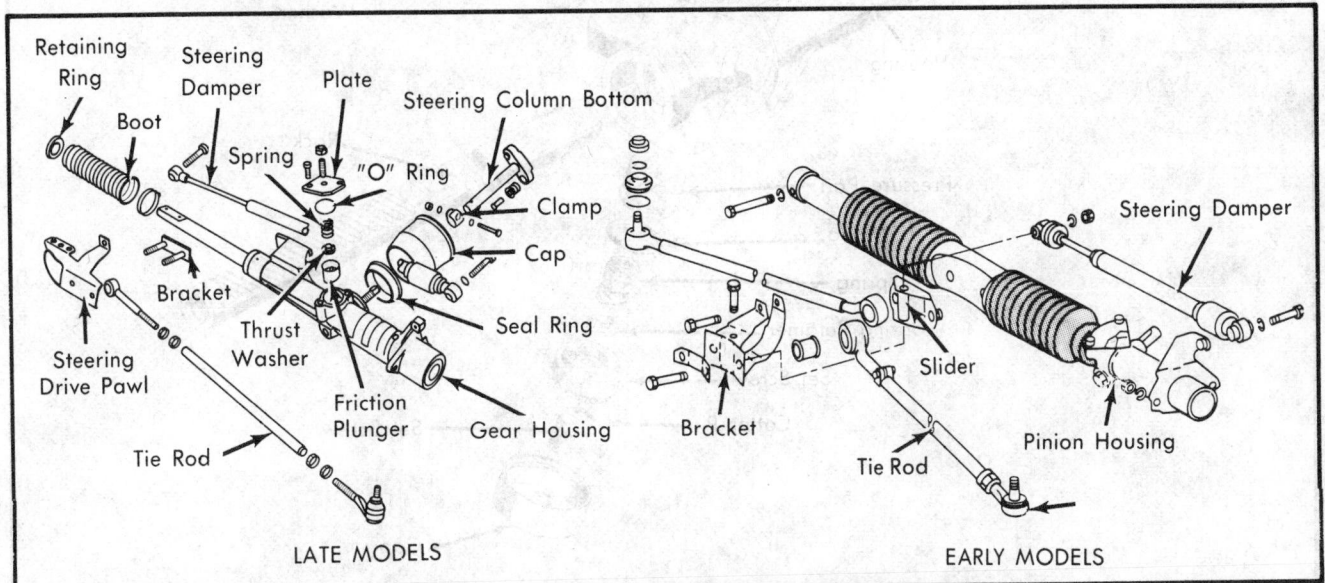

LATE MODELS

EARLY MODELS

Fig. 2   Exploded View of Audi 4000 Rack and Pinion Assembly (Early and Late Models)

Steering Gears & Linkage

BMW RACK & PINION

320i

DESCRIPTION

Direct-acting manual rack and pinion gear on resilient rubber mounts is of ZF design. Steering is dampened by a single tube-type hydraulic damper. Tie rods attached at outer end of central steering rack connect to steering knuckles.

ADJUSTMENT

Steering gear assembly should be removed for proper adjustment. *See OVERHAUL procedures in this article.*

REMOVAL & INSTALLATION

STEERING GEAR

Removal — Disconnect tie rods from steering knuckles with puller tool (32 2 050). Detach steering gear mounting bolts at front axle support. Remove pinch bolt from steering shaft and pull steering gear loose from universal coupling.

Installation — To install, reverse removal procedure noting that wheels must point straight ahead and raised mark on dust seal must align between raised marks on steering gear box.

OVERHAUL

STEERING GEAR

Disassembly — **1)** Mount gear in suitable holding fixture held in a vise. Bend open right lockplate and slide rack in up to stop. Detach damper at holder.

2) Using special tool (32 2 110), detach right tie rod at rack. Loosen bellows clamp and slide bellows off housing. Move rack in far enough to apply special tool (32 2 100) to left side of rack. Loosen clamp and slide back bellows onto rack. Bend open lockplate and detach left tie rod at rack.

3) Remove cap from pinion housing, then pull out cotter pin holding set screw. Unscrew set screw with special tool (32 1 040) and remove spring retainer and spring. Lift rack to remove pressure pad and "O" ring from housing.

4) Remove pinion shaft dust cover, "V" lock ring and notched ring. Remove pinion shaft set screw with special tool (32 1 040), then pull out "O" ring and washer.

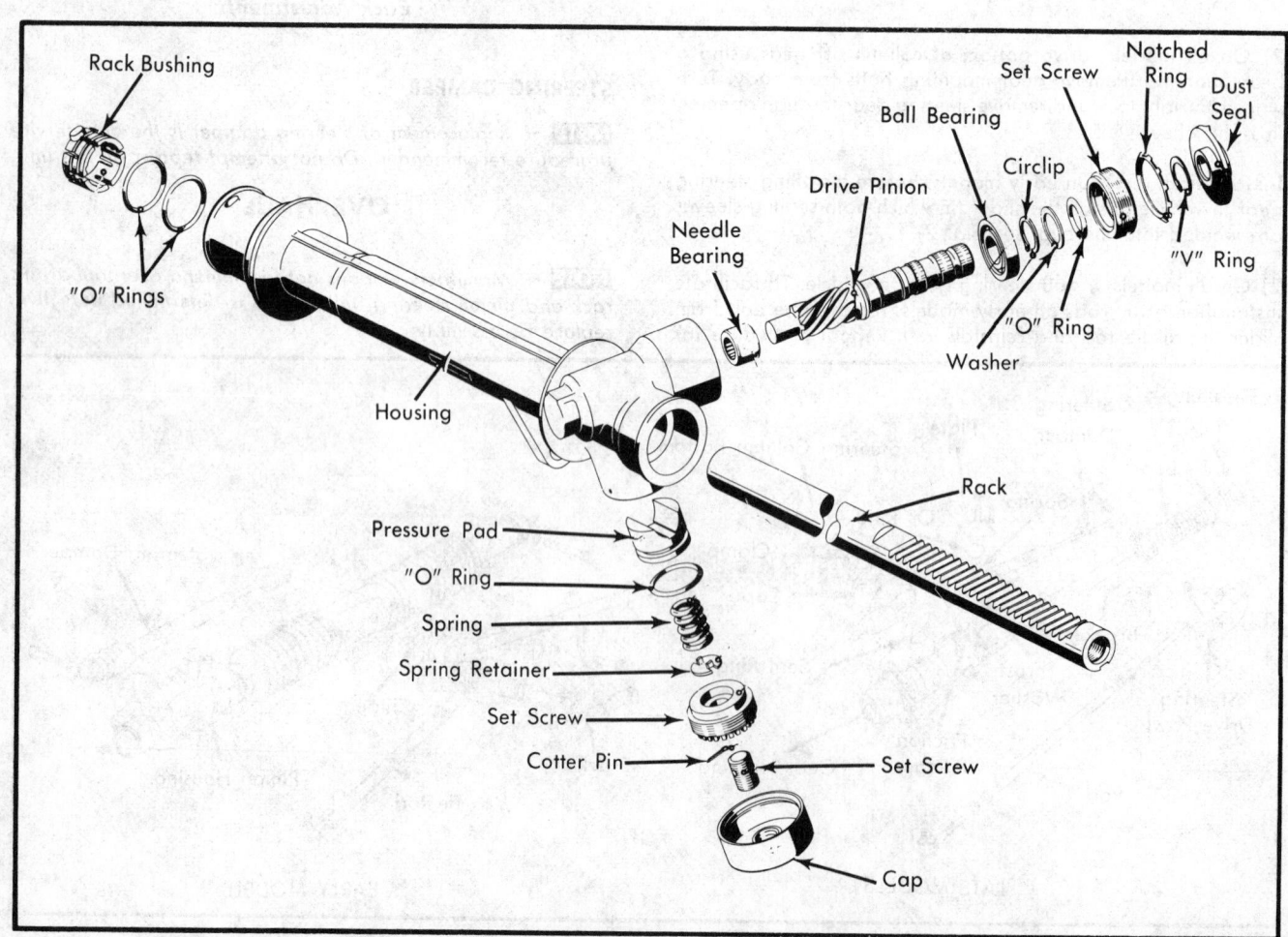

Fig. 1 Exploded View of BMW Rack & Pinion Steering Gear Assembly

BMW RACK & PINION (Cont.)

5) Clamp drive pinion spline in soft jawed vise and remove drive pinion from housing by tapping housing with plastic hammer. Remove circlip from pinion shaft and press ball bearing off of drive pinion shaft.

6) Needle bearing may be removed from housing with suitable screw type puller (Kukko 00 8 510). Remove rack bushings from housing by prying out with two screwdrivers.

Reassembly — 1) Place new "O" rings on rack bushings and install bushings in steering box. Locking tabs must engage in housing lock holes. Drive needle bearing, flat side down, into box using a suitable mandrel.

2) Press ball bearing onto drive pinion with closed end facing spline and install circlip. Apply thick coat of grease to spline surface of rack and thin coating to remainder of surface. Insert rack into box. Dip assembled pinion shaft in grease and install in box. Install plastic washer and "O" ring to pinion shaft.

3) Tighten set screw to specifications. Insert "V" ring up to groove and press notched ring up to stop. Center rack in housing. Right end of rack should extend 3.031" (77 mm) beyond housing. Place dust seal on shaft so mark on seal is between marks on housing. Place "O" ring into pressure pad and slide pad into steering box.

4) Place spring and retainer on pressure pad. Tighten notched set screw against stop, then back off socket head set screw until it extends approximately ½" (12 mm) above edge of housing.

Adjustment — 1) Tighten notched set screw to 4 ft. lbs. (5 N·m), then back off by 1 full castle slot to cotter pin hole. Install adaptor (32 1 000) and tighten wrench (00 2 000) on pinion shaft. Turn rack over entire length to check for sticking or binding. Set screw may be backed off no more than one notch in event of sticking or binding.

2) Move rack to center position and determine turning torque. If not within specifications, self locking set screw may be turned right to increase or to left to decrease friction.

3) Use new seals and lock plates and complete assembly procedure in reverse order of disassembly.

NOTE — *Shoulder of lock plates must engage opening of rack when installing tie rods. If replacing rubber bushing supporting steering damper, short spacers must be in place prior to tightening cover plate.*

TIGHTENING SPECIFICATIONS

Application	Ft. Lbs. (N·m)
Pinion Shaft Pinch Bolt	18-20 (24-27)
Pinion Shaft Set Screw	16-19 (22-26)
Steering Gear-to-Axle	35-39 (48-53)
Steering Damper Mounting	11-13 (15-18)
Tie Rod-to-Rack	51-56 (69-76)
Tie Rod-to-Steering Knuckle	25-29 (34-39)

	INCH Lbs. (N·m)
Steering Gear Turning Torque	
At Center	8-11 (.9-1.2)
Beyond Center (Max.)	17 (1.9)

Steering Gears & Linkage

CHRYSLER CORP. IMPORTS RACK & PINION

Champ
Colt

DESCRIPTION

Rack and pinion type steering is mounted by rubber insulators to crossmember. Adjustment is provided for pinion gear preload. Pinion shaft is coupled to the steering shaft and tie rods connect end of rack to steering arms of front wheels.

ADJUSTMENT

NOTE — *Adjustments of pinion gear preload are performed during overhaul. See OVERHAUL procedure.*

REMOVAL & INSTALLATION

Removal — Raise and support front of vehicle. Remove wheels. Remove coupling bolt from pinion shaft joint. Using a puller, disconnect tie rod ends from knuckle arms. Remove mount bolts at crossmember and remove rack and pinion assembly.

Installation — Install in reverse order of removal. Check wheel alignment.

OVERHAUL

Disassembly — **1)** With rack and pinion assembly mounted in a soft-jawed vise, remove tie rod staking with a chisel. Then, use a wrench to remove tie rod assemblies.

2) Remove lock nut and using a special socket (MB990607 or equivalent), remove yoke adjusting screw. Remove yoke spring, rubber cushion and support yoke. Carefully pry out oil seal.

3) Remove snap ring and remove pinion and bearing. Remove snap ring retaining bearing to shaft and press off bearing.

4) Remove rack from left side of housing to avoid damage from rack teeth during removal.

Inspection — **1)** Check tie rod ends for wear or damage. Check rubber boot (bellows) for wear or damage. Check tie rod stud nut for proper tightness. Check to see that nut is tightened to 12-24 INCH Lbs. (1.3-2.6 N·m).

2) Check tie rod end for axial play. Using a large pair of pliers, compress and release tie rod end while measuring axial play. Play should not exceed .06" (1.5 mm).

Reassembly & Adjustment — **1)** Use grease on all friction surfaces during assembly. Install rack from left side. Install bearing to pinion, then install pinion into housing. Install snap ring that eliminates axial play. *See Pinion Bearing Snap Ring chart.* Install new oil seal.

Pinion Bearing Snap Rings	
Snap Ring Color	**In. (mm)**
Blue	.063 (1.59)
White	.066 (1.67)
Yellow	.069 (1.74)

2) Grease and install yoke, cushion and spring with yoke adjusting screw. Using a socket, tighten adjusting screw to 5-11 ft. lbs. (7-15 N·m), then back off 30° to 60°. Install lock nut with sealer. Install tie rod assemblies and stake ends to rack keyways.

3) Measure rack starting force and pinion preload with a torque wrench and adaptor at pinion shaft. Pinion preload should be 4-10 INCH Lbs. (.44-1.1 N·m). Starting force should measure 11-66 ft. lbs. (15-90 N·m). If specifications are not obtained, replace yoke spring and rubber cushion and readjust.

4) Install rack and pinion assembly on crossmember. Connect tie rod ends to steering knuckles and pinion shaft to steering shaft coupler. Check wheel alignment.

TIGHTENING SPECIFICATIONS	
Application	**Ft. Lbs. (N·m)**
Ball Joint-to-Knuckle Arm	11-25 (15-34)
Housing-to-Crossmember	22-29 (30-39)
Pinion Gear-to-Steering Shaft	11-14 (15-19)
Tie Rod Lock Nut	36-40 (49-54)
Tie Rod-to-Rack	58-72 (79-98)
Yoke Screw Lock Nut	36-51 (49-69)

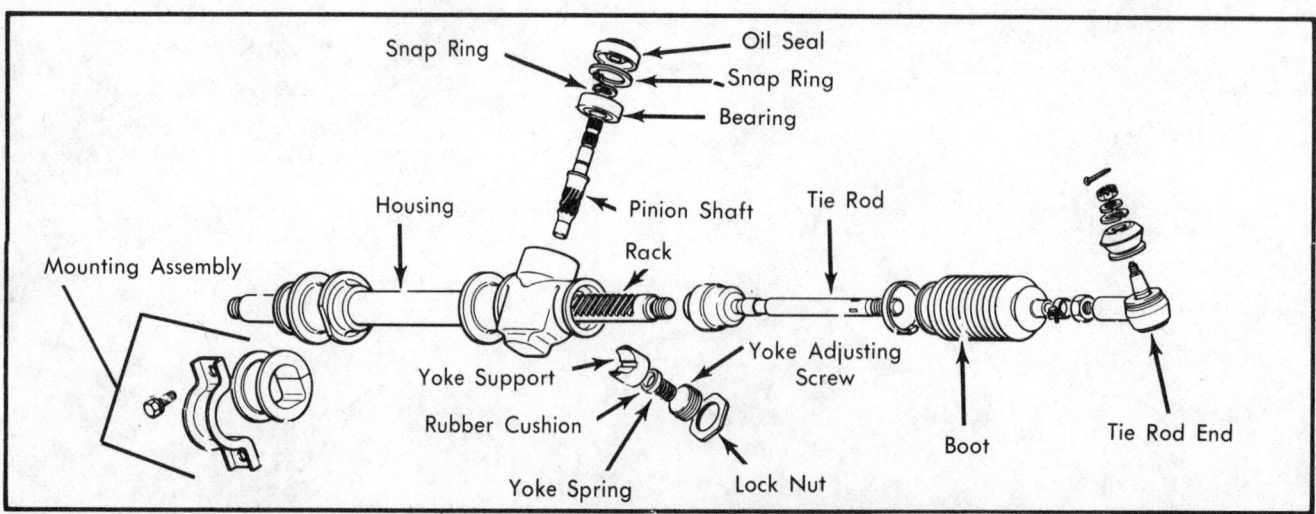

Fig. 1   Exploded View of Champ and Colt Hatchback Rack and Pinion Steering

CHRYSLER CORP. IMPORTS RECIRCULATING BALL

Arrow Pickup
Challenger
Ram-50 Pickup
Sapporo

DESCRIPTION

Steering system uses a recirculating ball gear of variable ratio. This type of gear minimizes gear ratio at the straight-ahead position, resulting in high stability at center; however, as the wheel is turned from center, gear ratio increases, allowing easy maneuvering.

REMOVAL & INSTALLATION

STEERING GEAR

Disconnect steering shaft from gear box main shaft. Using suitable puller, separate relay rod from pitman arm. Remove gear box from frame. Pull pitman arm from cross shaft. To install, reverse removal procedure.

TIE ROD ASSEMBLY

Removal — Disconnect tie rod ends from steering knuckle, using puller. Unscrew tie rods ends from tie rod.

Installation — 1) Grease tie rod end dust cover and coat lower edge of cup with packing sealer before installation. Temporarily install tie rod ends to tie rods.

2) Distance from center-to-center of tie rod ends should be 13.33" (338.6 mm) for Challenger and Sapporo; 14.78" (375.5 mm) left tie rod and 14.84" (377 mm) right tie rod on Pickup models.

3) Amount of threads showing on each side of tie rod sleeve should be equal. Install tie rods to vehicle and check toe-in. See WHEEL ALIGNMENT Section.

RELAY ROD

Removal — Disconnect tie rod ends from steering knuckle arms using puller. Detach pitman arm and idler arm, using the same puller. Remove relay rod.

Installation — To install, reverse removal procedure, noting the following: Ensure dust covers are well greased and that lower edge of covers are coated with packing sealer.

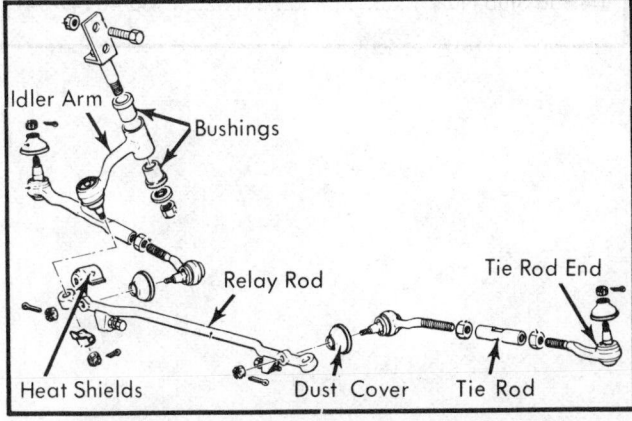

Idler Arm
Bushings
Relay Rod
Tie Rod End
Heat Shields
Dust Cover
Tie Rod

Fig. 1 Exploded View Showing Steering Linkage Components

IDLER ARM

Removal — Disconnect idler arm from relay rod, using puller. Remove idler arm assembly from frame.

NOTE — *Do not disassemble idler arm and support unless absolutely necessary.*

Installation — Apply soapy water to bushings and idler arm. Push bushings into arm, using a vise if necessary. Grease bracket shaft and inner surface of bushing, then insert shaft into idler arm. Install washer with knurled side toward bushing and using a new self-locking nut, tighten to specification.

PITMAN ARM

Removal — After removing steering gear, disconnect pitman arm from cross shaft, using a puller.

Installation — During installation, ensure slit on cross shaft aligns with pitman arm mark.

OVERHAUL

STEERING GEAR

Disassembly — 1) Prior to disassembly, record starting torque of mainshaft (as guide during assembly). Remove adjusting screw lock nut, turn screw counterclockwise (partial turn), then remove cover. When cover is free of sector shaft, remove adjusting screw. Set gear in straight ahead (center) position and withdraw sector shaft from gear box.

2) Measure and record steering mainshaft starting torque with sector shaft removed. Remove end cover and record thickness of shim. Carefully remove mainshaft, ball nut assembly and bearings.

CAUTION — *Do not disassemble the mainshaft and ball nut assembly.*

Inspection — Check components for excess wear or free play. If rough rotation or excess play is found in mainshaft or ball nut, replace both as an assembly. Do not force ball nut to either end of mainshaft.

Reassembly & Adjustment — 1) Place gear box in vise with mainshaft in horizontal position. Replace end cover with shim (same as removed) and tighten. Measure mainshaft preload. If less or greater than 3.0-4.8 INCH lbs. (.33-.53 N·m), reduce or increase shim size to obtain proper preload. *Refer to Mainshaft Shim Chart.*

Mainshaft Shims	
Shim No.	Thickness In. (mm)
1	.0020 (.05)
2	.0024 (.06)
3	.0030 (.07)
4	.0040 (.10)
5	.0080 (.20)
6	.0120 (.30)
7	.0200 (.50)

CHRYSLER CORP. IMPORTS RECIRCULATING BALL (Cont.)

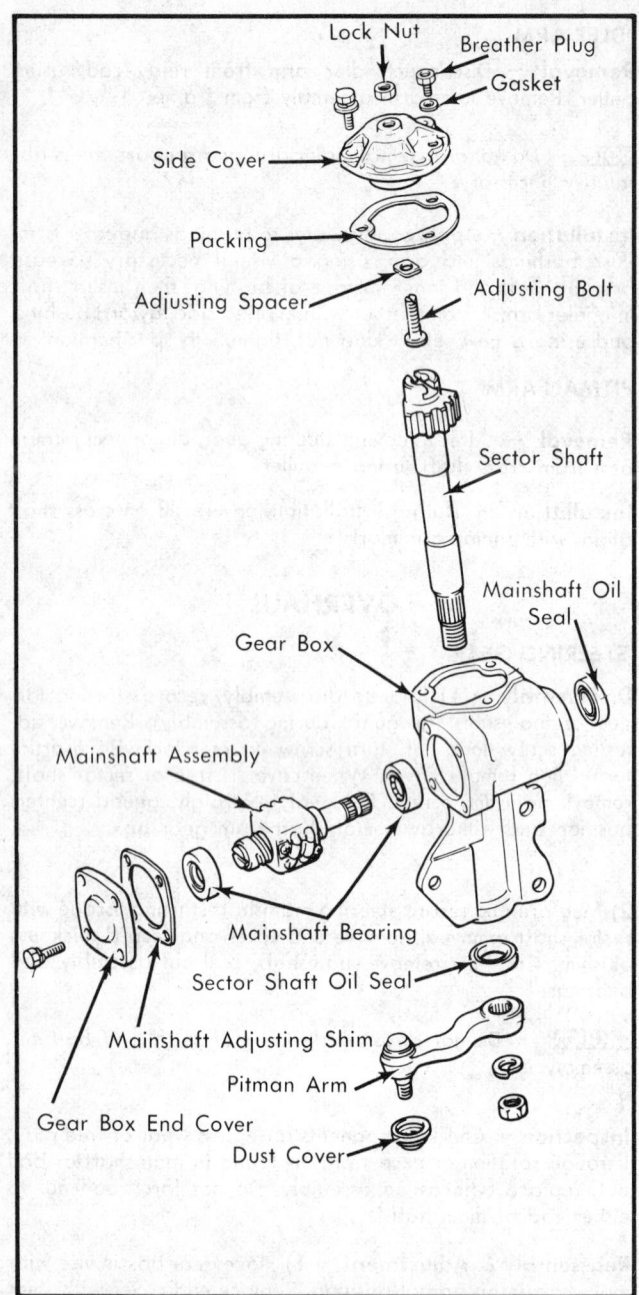

Fig. 2 *Exploded View Showing Components of Recirculating Ball & Nut Steering Gear Box*

Labels in figure:
Lock Nut
Breather Plug
Gasket
Side Cover
Packing
Adjusting Spacer
Adjusting Bolt
Sector Shaft
Mainshaft Oil Seal
Gear Box
Mainshaft Assembly
Mainshaft Bearing
Sector Shaft Oil Seal
Mainshaft Adjusting Shim
Pitman Arm
Gear Box End Cover
Dust Cover

2) Install adjusting screw and proper shim in groove on sector shaft. Be sure axial play of shaft is no greater than .002" (.05 mm). If greater, change shim size. *Refer to Sector Shaft Shim chart.* Lubricate and install sector shaft in housing. Replace cover and cover bolts. Turn sector shaft several times from side to side, then turn adjusting screw in and out several times, to set proper gear mesh.

Sector Shaft Shims	
Shim No.	Thickness In. (mm)
1	.077 (1.95)
2	.079 (2.00)
3	.081 (2.05)
4	.083 (2.10)

3) Loosen adjusting screw until no play is noticed at main shaft when gear is central in position. Tighten lock nut. Recheck main shaft preload; it should now be 5.7-7.4 INCH lbs. (.63-.81 N·m). Fill gear box with SAE 90 gear oil. Check oil level through lower right bolt hole. Proper level from hole is .8" (20 mm).

TIGHTENING SPECIFICATIONS

Application	Ft. Lbs. (N·m)
Gear Box End Cover	11-14 (15-19)
Gear Box-to-Frame	25-29 (34-39)
Idler Arm Bracket-to-Frame	29-43 (39-58)
Pitman Arm-to-Gear Box	94-108 (128-147)
Relay Rod-to-Idler Arm	25-33 (34-45)
Relay Rod-to-Pitman Arm	25-33 (34-45)
Tie Rod End Lock Nuts	36-40 (49-54)
Tie Rod Stud Nuts	36-40 (49-54)

COURIER RECIRCULATING BALL

Pickup

DESCRIPTION

Steering gear is a recirculating ball and nut type. Two tubes carry the balls through worm channels, thus transmitting the turn action of the steering shaft. Worm bearing preload and ball-nut meshload have adjustments provided, to maintain smooth steering operation.

ADJUSTMENT

WORM BEARING PRELOAD

Drain gear box. Disconnect pitman arm from gear. Loosen sector adjusting screw lock nut and turn screw counterclockwise. Using a torque wrench, rotate worm shaft. Preload should be 5.2-7.8 INCH lbs. (.57-.86 N·m). If not within specifications, remove end cover and shims. If preload is below minimum, reduce shim size. If above maximum, increase shim size.

SECTOR SHAFT & BALL-NUT MESHLOAD

Adjusting screw in side cover sets sector shaft to provide proper mesh between sector gear teeth and ball-nut rack. Adjustment is made only after setting worm bearing preload. Disconnect pitman arm from center link. Loosen sector adjusting screw lock nut. Turn steering wheel slowly to either stop, then turn to opposite stop. Count steering wheel rotations and turn wheel to center position. Turn adjusting screw in or out until adjustment is obtained. There should be no backlash. Hold adjusting screw in position and tighten lock nut. Recheck mesh load. Connect pitman arm to center link.

REMOVAL & INSTALLATION

STEERING GEAR

Removal — **1)** Remove steering wheel and switches. See *Courier* in *STEERING WHEELS & COLUMN SWITCHES* in this Section. Remove support bracket, move floor mat away from column, and separate toe plate/boot from dash. Remove column jacket from shaft.

2) Remove air cleaner and disconnect heater hoses. Remove hydraulic lines from brake and clutch master cylinders, plug ports on both cylinders and remove from vehicle.

3) Remove power brake unit. Drain cooling system. Disconnect fuel lines from carburetor. Disconnect all vacuum lines from intake manifold and carburetor. Disconnect heater hoses from intake manifold.

4) Disconnect EGR hoses from exhaust and intake manifolds. Remove accelerator link from carburetor. Remove intake manifold and carburetor as an assembly.

5) Raise front of vehicle and support with stands. Remove left front tire. Remove left dust cover from fender panel. Using a puller, disconnect center link from pitman arm.

6) Remove pitman arm retaining nut. Using a puller, remove pitman arm from sector shaft. Jack up lower control arm with a jack.

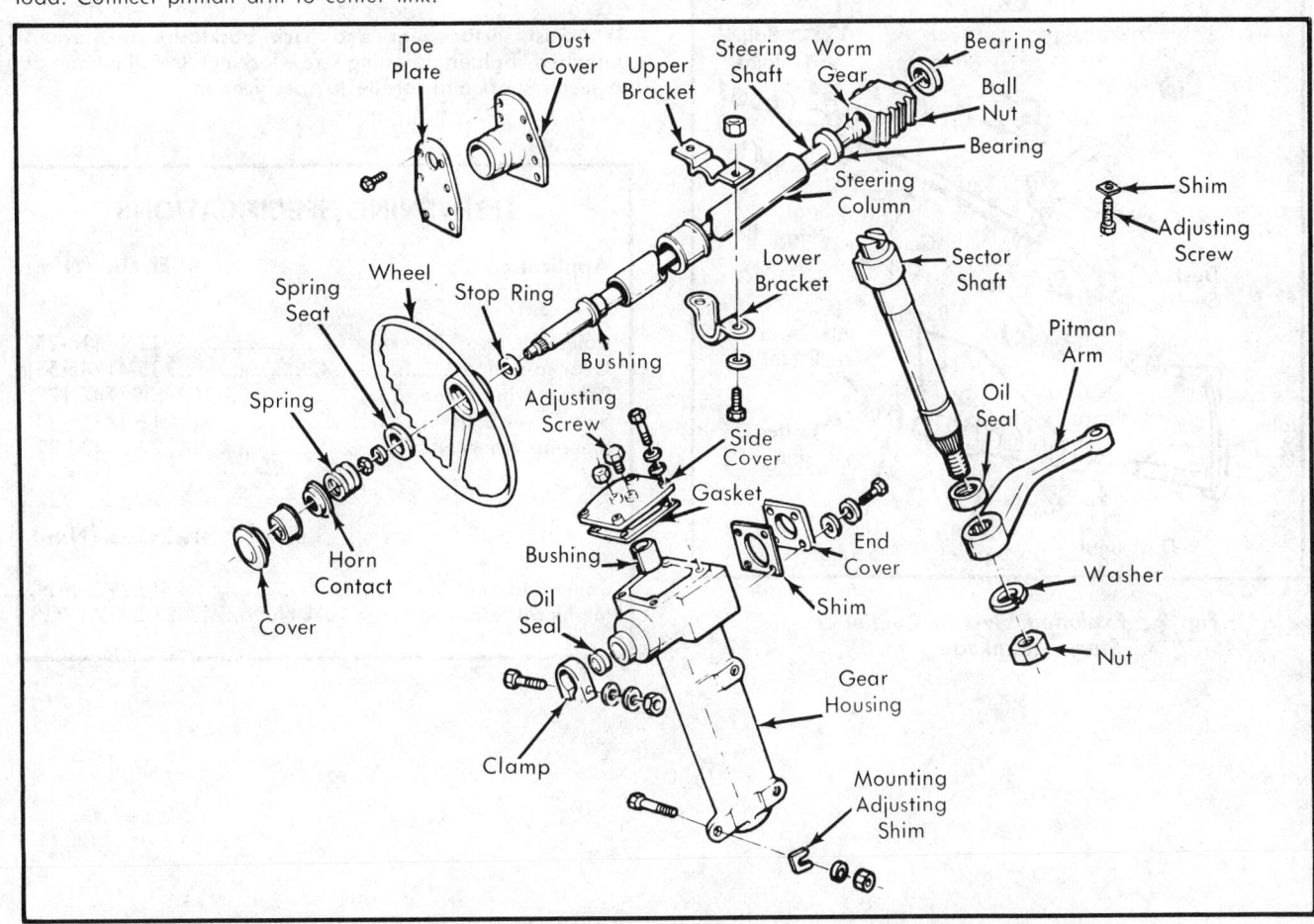

Fig. 1 Exploded View of Courier Recirculating Ball Steering Column and Gear

Steering Gears & Linkage

COURIER RECIRCULATING BALL (Cont.)

7) Remove upper control arm-to-support bracket bolts and nuts, noting number and locations of shims so correct wheel alignment is maintained when shims are reinstalled.

8) Remove steering gear box retaining bolts and nuts and remove steering gear assembly.

Installation — To install, reverse removal procedure and place shim in original position between steering gear housing and frame to obtain proper clearance. Fill gear housing with SAE 90 oil. Bleed brake and clutch systems.

STEERING LINKAGE

Center link can be removed from both tie rods, pitman arm, and idler arm by removing ball joint nuts and using suitable puller. After center link removal, pitman arm can be removed from sector shaft. Tie rods can also be removed with puller. Toe-in must be reset when tie rods or ball joints are replaced.

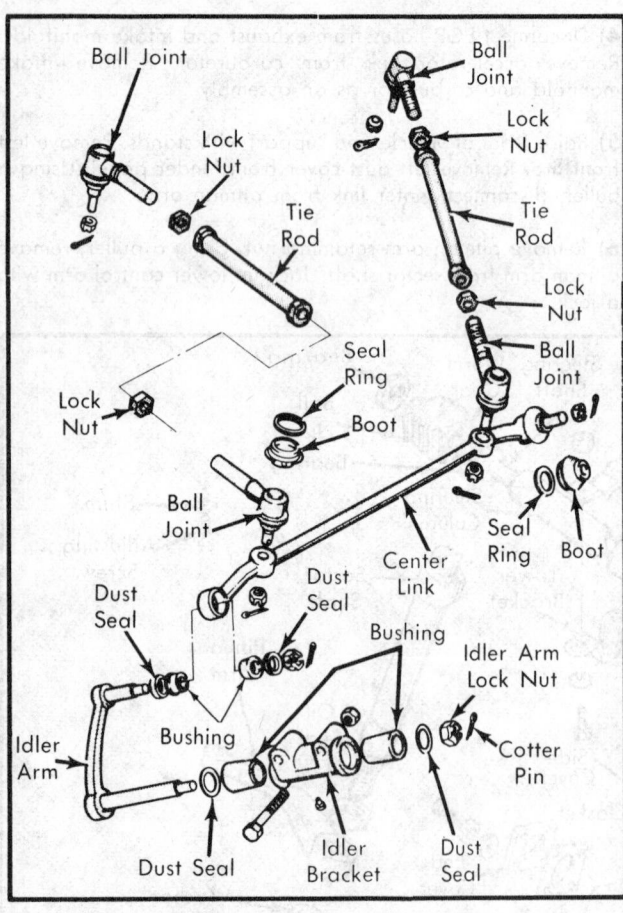

Fig. 2   Exploded View of Courier Steering Linkage

OVERHAUL

STEERING GEAR

Disassembly — With gear removed and drained, position gear in vise. Remove pitman arm from gear. Remove sector shaft adjusting screw lock nut. Take off side cover by removing bolts and turning adjusting screw clockwise. Remove adjusting screw and shim from sector shaft. Extract shaft from housing. Remove worm shaft and ball-nut assembly through bottom of housing after end cover and shims are removed.

Inspection — Check operation of ball-nut assembly on worm shaft. If travel is not smooth or any part is worn, replace entire assembly. Check and replace all other components as necessary.

Reassembly & Adjustment — **1)** Insert worm shaft and ball-nut assembly into gear housing. Install end cover and shims. Adjust bearing preload, as previously described. Place adjusting screw in slot of sector shaft and check end clearance. Adjust clearance to 0-.004" (0-.10 mm) by adding or subtracting shims.

2) Turn worm shaft and place rack in center position of worm. Insert sector shaft and adjusting screw into gear housing, being careful not to damage bushings or seal. Align center of sector gear with center of rack. Place side cover on adjusting screw, turn screw to position cover, then install cover retaining bolts.

3) Adjust sector gear and rack backlash, as previously described. Tighten adjusting screw lock nut. Install pitman arm to sector shaft and torque to specification.

TIGHTENING SPECIFICATIONS

Application	Ft. Lbs. (N·m)
Column Support Bracket	12-17 (16-23)
Gear-to-Frame	33-41 (45-56)
Pitman Arm-to-Gear	108-130 (147-177)
Side Cover Bolts	12-17 (16-23)
Steering Wheel Nut	22-29 (30-39)

	INCH Lbs. (N·m)
Column Jacket Clamp-to-Gear	84-108 (9.2-11.9)
Meshload Adjusting Screw Lock Nut	23-34 (2.5-3.7)

DATSUN 200SX, 210, 510 & PICKUP RECIRCULATING BALL

DESCRIPTION

The steering gear used on these vehicles is a recirculating ball type. The worm shaft is joined to the steering shaft by a rubber shock-absorbing coupling. The steering linkage is a relay design, with the steering gear attached by a pitman arm to one end of the center link (cross shaft), while the other end of the center link moves on the idler arm.

REMOVAL & INSTALLATION

STEERING GEAR

Removal – 1) On 210 models, remove clutch operating cylinder (if equipped). Do not remove clutch hose. Disconnect exhaust pipe from manifold (disconnect any brackets holding exhaust pipe in place). On all models, remove bolt holding worm shaft to rubber coupling.

2) Remove nut holding gear arm to sector shaft and remove steering gear arm from sector shaft. Remove bolts securing steering gear housing to body side member. Remove steering gear housing from vehicle.

Installation – To install, reverse removal procedure, aligning markings on pitman arm with markings on sector shaft.

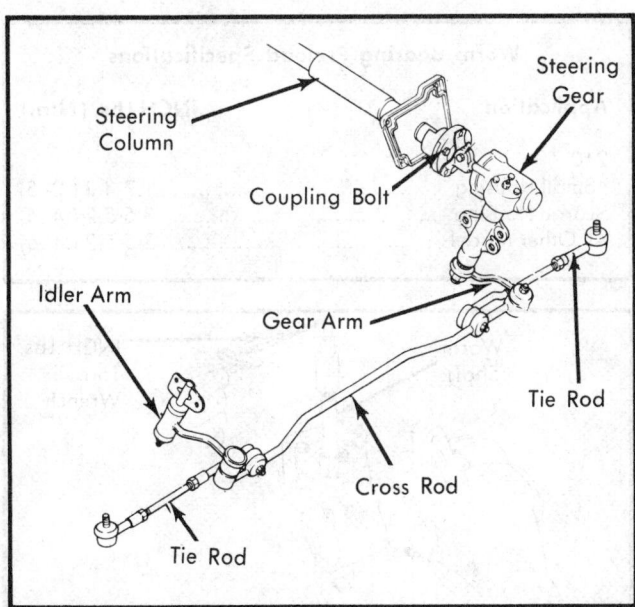

**Fig. 1 Datsun Steering Gear Linkage
(210 Shown, Others Similar)**

STEERING LINKAGE

Removal – Jack up front of vehicle and support with stands. Detach both outer tie rod ends from steering knuckles. Separate cross shaft from idler arm and pitman arm, then remove cross shaft and tie rods as an assembly. Idler assembly may be removed from side member, if necessary to replace bushing.

Installation – To install, reverse removal procedure, noting the following: Set tie rod end length to the prescribed setting, then check wheel alignment. *See Datsun in WHEEL ALIGNMENT section.*

Tie Rod Settings	
Application	**In. (mm)**
200SX①	2.80 (71.0)
210, 510②	12.40 (315.0)
Pickup②	
2WD	13.07 (332.0)
4WD	10.83 (275.0)
① – Measured between lock nuts.	
② – Measured from center-to-center of tie rod ball studs.	

ADJUSTMENT

NOTE – *Steering gear adjustments are performed during reassembly. See Overhaul as outlined below.*

OVERHAUL

STEERING GEAR

Disassembly – 1) Drain gear box of oil, then place unit in padded vise or on suitable holding fixture mounted in a vise.

2) On 210 models, loosen adjusting screw lock nut and remove sector shaft cover screws. Turn adjusting screw a few turns clockwise and withdraw sector shaft. Remove rear cover. Withdraw bearing shims and worm assembly. Remove oil seal if necessary.

3) On 200SX, 510 and Pickup models, place worm gear in straight ahead position and remove sector shaft cover with sector shaft. Separate cover from sector shaft and remove oil seal if necessary. Remove adjusting plug lock nut and adjusting plug. Withdraw worm assembly out of gear box. Remove oil seal from adjusting plug.

NOTE – *Do not remove sector shaft bearings or bushings from housing. If defective, replace housing assembly. Do not disassemble ball nut; replace, if necessary, with worm shaft assembly. Do not let ball nut bottom out on either end of worm shaft, or damage to ball guides will result.*

Inspection – Inspect gear teeth on sector shaft and ball nut for wear or damage; replace as necessary. Check bearings for wear or roughness during rotation. Ensure ball nut moves smoothly over its entire length of travel.

Reassembly & Adjustment – 1) On 210 models, lubricate bearings, gear and all moving parts with gear oil. Apply grease to oil seal lip and press seal into rear cover. Install worm assembly, with bearings, into housing. Install shims (thicker shim to housing side) and rear cover.

DATSUN 200SX, 210, 510 & PICKUP RECIRCULATING BALL (Cont.)

NOTE — *Standard shim thickness for 210 models is .059" (1.5 mm) for large housing models and .020" (.5 mm) for small housing models. See Worm Bearing Shim Chart for available sizes.*

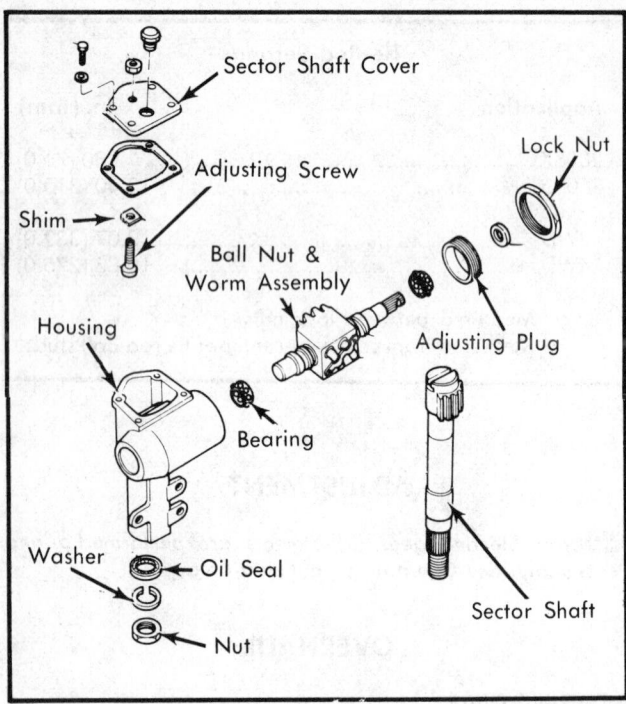

Fig. 2 Exploded View of Recirculating Ball Steering Gear Assembly (200SX, 510 & Pickup Models)

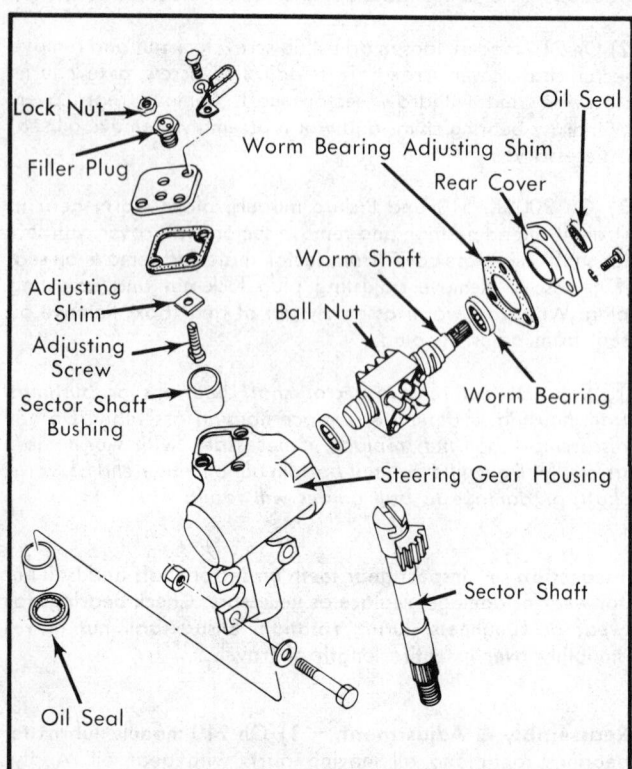

Fig. 3 Exploded View of Recirculating Ball Steering Gear Assembly (210 Model)

Worm Bearing Shims	
Shim No.	**In. (mm)**
210 (Large Housing)	
1	.030 (.762)
2	.010 (.254)
3	.005 (.127)
4	.002 (.050)
210 (Small Housing)	
1	.0020 (.050)
2	.0027 (.070)
3	.0031 (.080)
4	.0040 (.100)
5	.0080 (.200)

2) On 200SX, 510 and Pickup models, lubricate bearings, gear and all other moving parts with gear oil. Apply suitable grease to oil seal lip and press seal into adjusting plug.

3) On all models, rotate worm shaft a few times to settle assembly. Attach torque wrench to worm shaft and measure bearing preload (initial turning torque). Add or subtract shims on 210 models or tighten adjusting plug on all other models until specified preload is obtained.

Worm Bearing Preload Specifications	
Application	**INCH Lbs. (N·m)**
210	
Small Housing	1.7-4.3 (.2-.5)
Large Housing	3.5-5.2 (.4-.6)
All Other Models	3.5-5.2 (.4-.6)

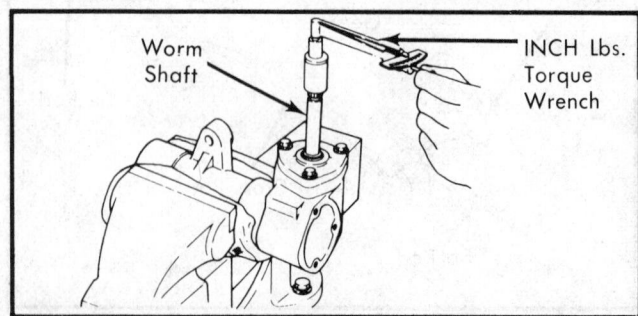

Fig. 4 Measuring Steering Gear Initial Turning Torque to Check Worm Gear Preload

4) With preload adjusted, apply sealer to lock nut on 200SX, 510 and Pickup models, then tighten lock nut. On 210 models, remove rear cover and shims; apply sealer to shims and rear cover, then reinstall shims and rear cover.

5) Insert adjusting screw into "T" groove of sector shaft and adjust end play between shaft and screw head to less than .002" (.05 mm) on 210 models with small gear housing, or to .0004-.0012" (.01-.03 mm) on all other models.

DATSUN 200SX, 210, 510 & PICKUP RECIRCULATING BALL (Cont.)

6) On 210 models, rotate worm shaft until ball nut is in center of travel. Install sector shaft and adjusting screw in gear housing. Ensure center tooth of sector shaft is engage with center of ball nut. Apply sealer and gasket material to sector shaft attaching face.

7) Turn adjusting screw counterclockwise to set cover on gear housing. Temporarily install retaining bolts. Turn adjusting screw further counterclockwise until sector shaft is drawn upward about .08-.12" (2-3 mm). Fully tighten bolts.

8) Push sector shaft against ball nut by gradually turning adjusting screw until sector shaft gear lightly meshes with ball nut gear, and temporarily secure adjusting screw with lock nut.

9) Install pitman arm to sector shaft and move it side-to-side several times to ensure smooth operation. Set pitman arm at center point and adjust backlash (by turning adjusting screw) such that free movement at top of pitman arm is .004" (.1 mm). Tighten lock nut and fill gear box with gear oil.

10) On 200SX, 510 and Pickup models, install cover to sector shaft (with adjusting screw). Place worm gear in center position, then install sector gear to gear housing (with gasket) and tighten bolts. Fill gear box with gear oil.

11) Install torque wrench to worm shaft. Tighten sector shaft adjusting screw while measuring total gear turning torque (preload). Total preload should be less than 10.9 INCH Lbs. (1.2 N·m).

NOTE — *Always adjust preload by tightening adjusting screw, never by loosening.*

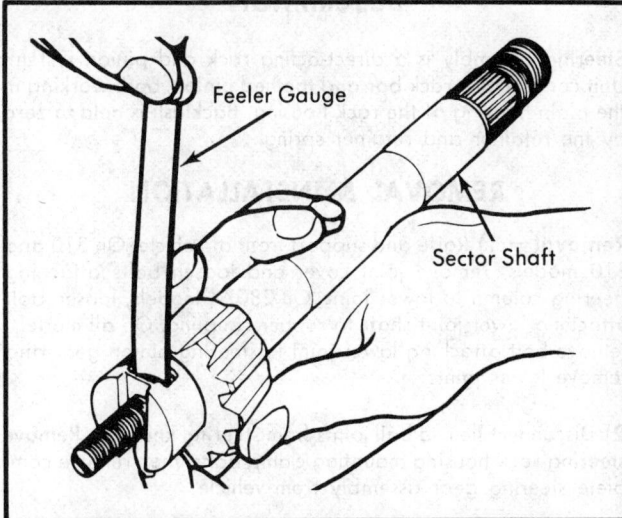

Feeler Gauge

Sector Shaft

Fig. 5 Insert Feeler Gauge into Sector Shaft to Measure Sector Shaft-to-Adjusting Screw End Play

TIGHTENING SPECIFICATIONS

Application	Ft. Lbs. (N·m)
Adjusting Plug Lock Nut	
200SX, 510 & Pickup	181-231 (246-314)
Ball Stud Nuts	
200SX, 210 & 510	22-51 (30-69)
Pickup	40-72 (54-98)
Gear-to-Frame	
200SX	38-46 (52-63)
210 & 510	51-58 (69-79)
Pickup	33-38 (45-52)
Pitman Arm-to-Gear	94-108 (128-147)
Tie Rod Lock Nuts	
Pickup	8-12 (11-16)
200SX, 210 & 510	58-72 (79-98)

Steering Gears & Linkage

DATSUN 280ZX, 310 & 810 RACK & PINION

DESCRIPTION

Steering assembly is a direct-acting rack and pinion system. Unit consists of a rack bar and toothed pinion, both working in the plain bearing of the rack housing. Backlash is held to zero by the retainer and retainer spring.

REMOVAL & INSTALLATION

Removal — 1) Raise and support front of vehicle. On 310 and 810 models, remove joint cover and loosen bolts attaching steering column to lower joint. On 280ZX models, loosen bolt attaching lower joint shaft to rubber coupling. On all models, remove bolt attaching lower joint to steering pinion gear and remove lower joint.

2) Disconnect tie rod ball joints from steering knuckles. Remove steering rack housing mounting clamp bolts, then remove complete steering gear assembly from vehicle.

NOTE — *Raise front engine mount approximately ½" (with jack) before trying to remove steering gear.*

Installation — Install in reverse order of removal procedure. Check wheel alignment. For wheel alignment procedures, see *Datsun in WHEEL ALIGNMENT section.*

ADJUSTMENT

NOTE — *Adjustments are performed during gear assembly process. See Overhaul as outlined.*

OVERHAUL

Disassembly — 1) Clamp steering gear and linkage in a padded vise. Remove both dust boot clamps. Loosen inner joint lock nut and remove tie rod from rack.

NOTE — *Do not disassemble inner joint assembly and tie rod socket assembly.*

2) Loosen adjuster lock nut and remove retainer adjust screw. Remove retainer spring and steering gear retainer out of steering gear housing. Remove oil seal and pry off snap ring from steering gear housing. Remove steering pinion assembly and rack from steering gear housing.

3) Pry off snap ring securing pinion bearing from pinion gear. Press bearing from pinion gear, then remove inner snap ring from pinion gear.

4) On 310 models, remove steering gear rubber mount bushing by striking with rubber mallet. Remove snap ring and bushing from gear housing.

Inspection — Check rack and pinion gear for wear or damage, replace if necessary. Inspect tie rod inner socket for smooth operation and for excessive looseness, replace if necessary. Replace all oil seals. On 310 models, check rack bushing (in gear housing) for wear by measuring amount of play of rack when moved up and down then sideways. Play for up and down movement should be less than .020" (.5 mm) and less than .028" (.7 mm) for sideways movement.

Reassembly and Adjustment — 1) Install inner snap ring to pinion gear and then press bearing onto pinion gear. Install outer snap ring onto pinion gear. Outer snap ring thickness should be selected so that bearing play is less than .004" (.1 mm).

2) On 310 models, install rubber mount bushing to housing and secure with snap ring. Install rubber mount with plate onto end of housing. Make sure cut out section of rubber mount is aligned with hole in housing and that ventilation hole is not clogged with grease.

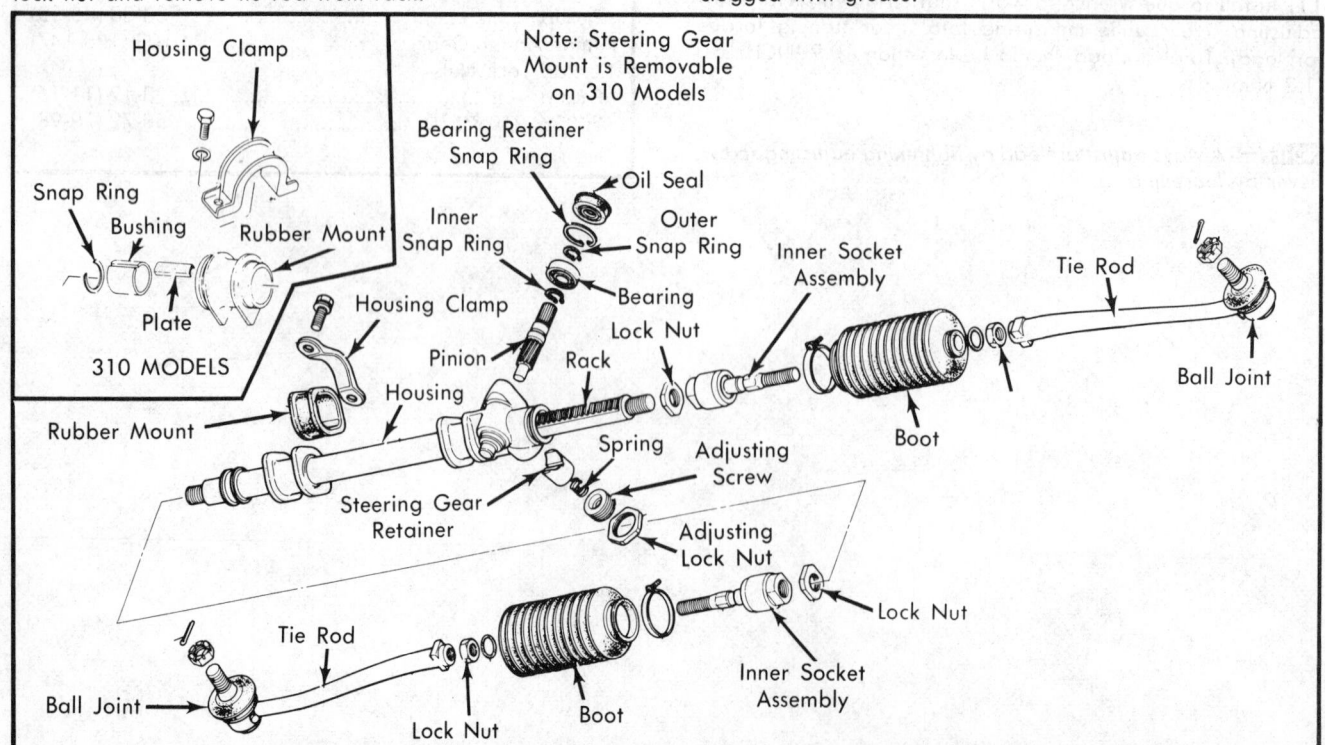

Fig. 1 Exploded View of Datsun Rack and Pinion Steering Gear Assembly

DATSUN 280ZX, 310 & 810 RACK & PINION (Cont.)

3) On all models, clamp steering gear in padded vise. Coat rack teeth and friction surfaces of rack with grease. Install rack into housing from pinion gear side and make sure rack teeth are facing correct direction. Install pinion gear (coated with grease), make sure pinion gear teeth and rack teeth mesh properly. Make sure rack protrudes same amount from each end of housing.

4) Install snap ring to steering gear housing (snap ring retains pinion bearing in place). Snap ring thickness should be selected so that pinion gear movement is less than .004" (.1 mm). Pack grease seal with grease and install. Make sure pinion assembly rotates smoothly.

5) Apply grease to steering gear retainer and insert gear retainer and retainer spring into housing. Turn adjusting screw in and install lock nut. Fully tighten adjusting screw then back off approximately 20-25°. Apply liquid sealant around lock nut and tighten lock nut.

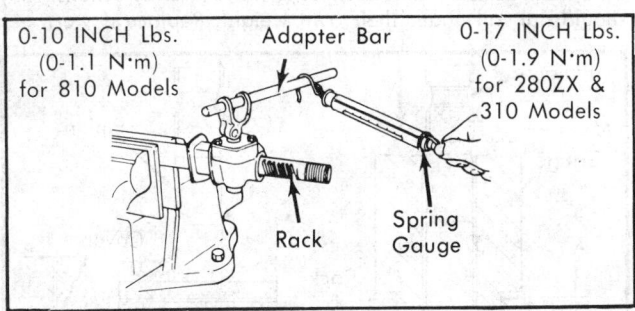

Fig. 2 Measuring Pinion Shaft Rotating Torque

6) With steering gear assembled, measure torque required to keep pinion and rack in motion. Install steering gear in padded vise and attach torque wrench to bar and spring gauge. See Fig. 2. Pinion turning torque should be 0-17 INCH Lbs. (1.9 N·m) for 280ZX & 310 models; 0-10 INCH Lbs. (0-1.1 N·m) for 810 models.

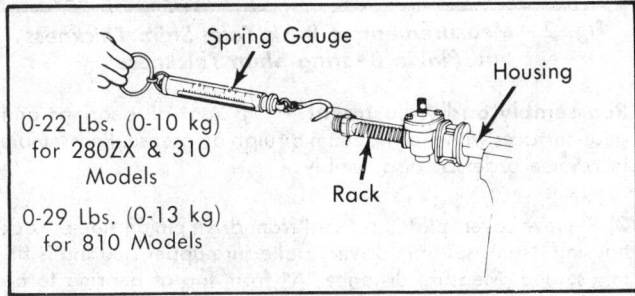

Fig. 3 Measuring Steering Gear Rack Pulling Force

7) Measure force to pull rack from neutral (center) position. See Fig. 3. Force should be 0-22 Lbs. (0-10 kg) for 280ZX & 310 models; 029 Lbs. (0-13 kg) for 810 models. Install rubber boot and clamp onto tie rod. Thread lock nut over threaded portion of rack. Apply grease to sliding surfaces of tie rod inner socket and spring seat. Install tie rod assembly to rack end together with inner spring and spring seat.

NOTE — On 280ZX models, tie rod for left side is marked with an "L". No mark is used for right side tie rod.

8) Screw inner socket portion until ball seat reaches rack end and then tighten lock nut. Upon completion of tie rod assembly, measure swinging torque and axial play of tie rod inner socket. Swinging torque (measured at outer end of tie rod) should be 0-43 INCH Lbs. (0-4.7 N·m) on 280ZX models and 13-61 INCH Lbs. (1.4-6.7 N·m) on 310 models and 0-26 INCH Lbs. (0-2.9 N·m) for 810 models. 310 and 810 models should have no axial play.

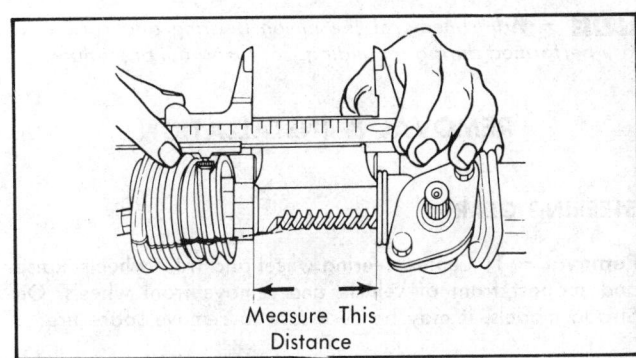

Fig. 4 Measuring Steering Gear Rack Protrusion

9) Measure rack protrusion on both sides of housing. 280ZX models should be 2.614" (66.4 mm), 310 models should be 2.680" (68 mm) and 810 models should be 2.992" (76.0 mm). Attach boot and clamps. Insert grease nipples at both ends of housing and lubricate gear assembly until a small amount of grease appears at boot outlet hole. Adjust tie rod length so that distance from outer side of lock nut to end of boot mounting groove is 1.161" (29.5 mm) on 280ZX models, 5.24" (133 mm) on 310 models and 1.421" (36.09 mm) on 810 models.

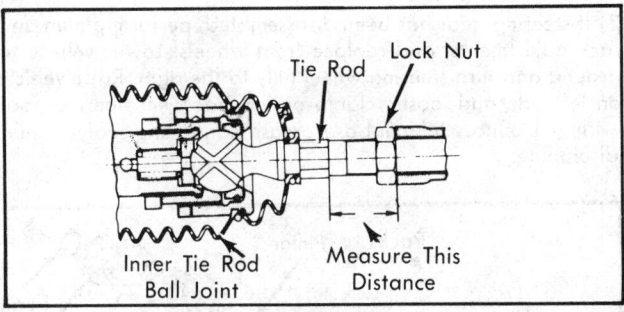

Fig. 5 Adjusting Steering Gear Tie Rod Length

TIGHTENING SPECIFICATIONS

Application	Ft. Lbs. (N·m)
Inner Socket Lock Nut	58-72 (79-98)
Tie Rod Ball Joint Nut	40-47 (54-64)
Tie Rod-to-Socket Lock Nut	
280ZX & 810	58-72 (79-98)
310	27-34 (36-46)

Steering Gears & Linkage

FIAT BRAVA, STRADA & X1/9 RACK & PINION

DESCRIPTION

Rack and pinion steering gear is mounted in rubber insulators and attached to body. Gear is attached to steering shaft through universal joints. Adjustments are provided for pinion bearing play and rack yoke free play. At each end of steering rack, tie rods connect steering mechanism to front wheels.

ADJUSTMENT

NOTE — Adjustments of the pinion bearing and rack yoke are performed during rebuilding. See Overhaul procedure.

REMOVAL & INSTALLATION

STEERING GEAR

Removal — 1) Center steering wheel and front wheels. Raise and support front of vehicle and remove front wheels. On Strada models, it may be necessary to remove spare tire.

2) Disconnect drive pinion from lower steering column section by detaching universal joint inside vehicle. Using a suitable puller, remove tie rods from steering knuckles.

3) Remove stone shield if necessary. Unbolt and remove steering gear assembly by sliding out from right-hand side of vehicle.

Installation — 1) Set wheels in straight-ahead position. Connect drive pinion to steering column and tighten pinch bolt to 19 ft. lbs. (26 N·m). Remount steering gear to body. Connect tie rods to steering knuckle and tighten to 25 ft. lbs. (34 N·m).

2) If steering gear has been disassembled, perform pinion and rack adjustments, and replace front wheels. Lower vehicle to ground and turn steering wheel fully to the right. Raise vehicle on left side and loosen clamp on left boot. Fill steering gear with 4.4 ounces lithium-base grease containing molybdenum disulphide.

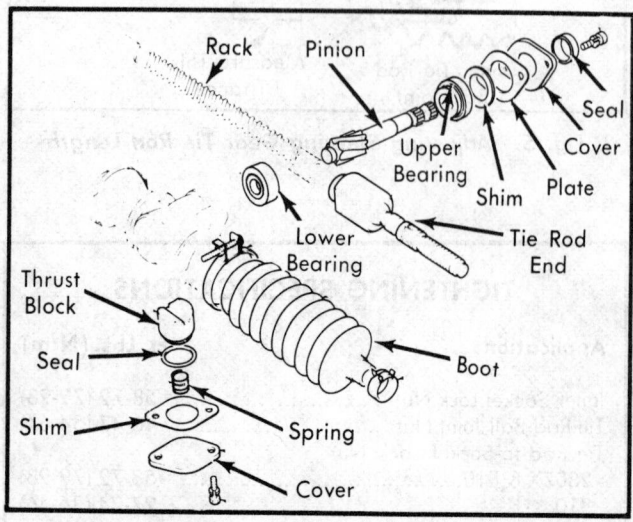

Fig. 1   Exploded View of Steering Gear Components

OVERHAUL

STEERING GEAR

Disassembly — 1) With steering gear removed from vehicle, remove rubber boots from steering gear. Disconnect tie rod end ball joints from rack (inner ends of tie rods).

2) Remove cover, shim, spring, seal and thrust block from bottom of housing. Remove cover, seal, plate, shim, upper bearing, and drive pinion from housing. See Fig. 1. Slide rack from housing. Remove lower bearing from housing.

Inspection — 1) Clean all metal parts in a suitable degreaser and blow dry. Inspect rack, pinion, upper bearing and housing for wear or damage. Replace entire steering box if damaged.

2) Inspect boots for tears or breaks. Replace if necessary. Inspect bushing, spring, lower bearing and thrust block for wear or damage. Replace if necessary.

3) Check that ball joints are free to move in all directions. They should not fall under their own weight. Replace if worn.

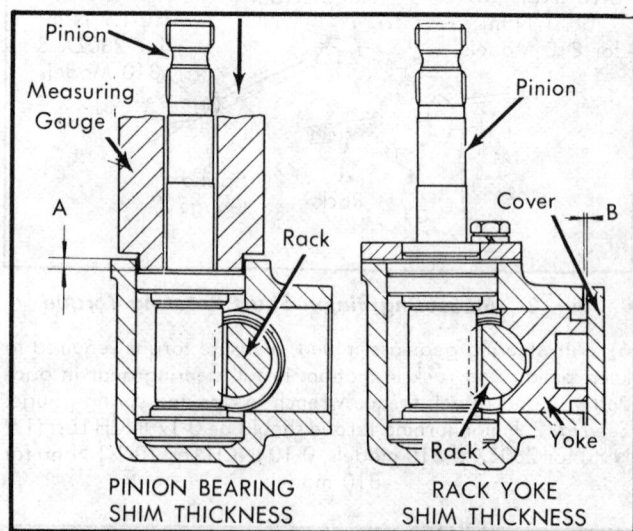

Fig. 2   Measurement of Rack Yoke Shim Thickness and Pinion Bearing Shim Thickness

Reassembly and Adjustment — 1) Coat all bearings and gear surfaces with molybdenum disulphide grease. Reassemble in reverse order of disassembly.

2) Remove cover, plate and seal from drive pinion side of rack housing. Using suitable driver, make sure upper bearing is firmly seated. Measure distance "A" from top of bearing to pinion cover facing. See Fig. 2. Add .003±.002" (.078±.053 mm) to dimension "A" and install shims centered on pinion to make up new dimension. Install plate, cover and seal.

3) Center rack in its travel. Remove cover, shims and spring to gain access to rack thrust block. While holding rack thrust block against rack, turn pinion through 180° in both directions. Measure dimension "B" from top of rack thrust block to cover facing. See Fig. 2. To "B" add .0035±.0015" (.09±.04 mm). Combine shims to make up new dimension. Install spring, shims and cover.

NOTE — Lubricate dust boots with silicon spray and be sure they are not twisted after installation.

FIAT SPIDER 2000 WORM & ROLLER

DESCRIPTION

The steering gear is a worm and roller type, having a gear ratio of 16.4:1. The steering gear box is mounted on the crossmember in front of the firewall.

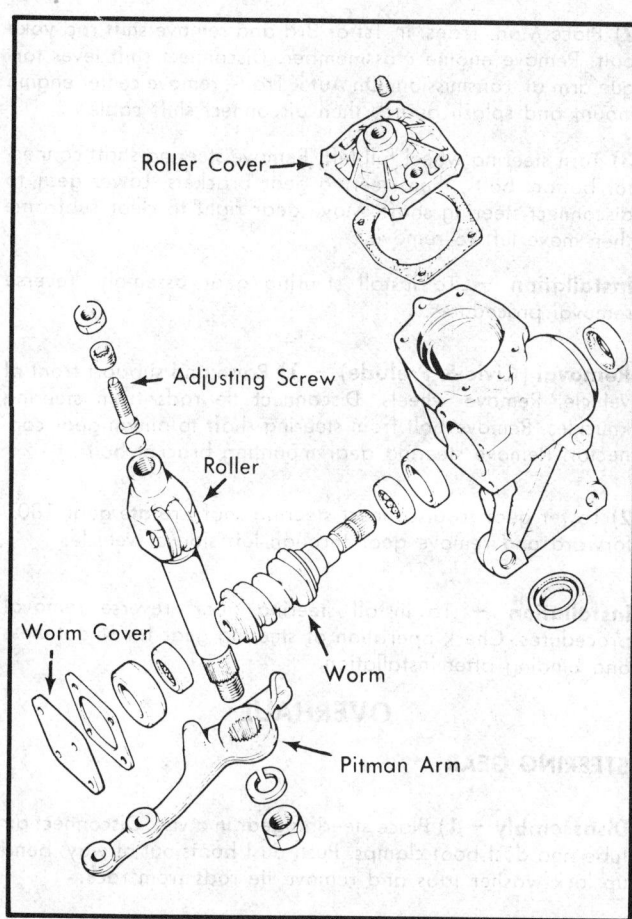

Fig. 1 Exploded View of Spider 2000 Steering Gear

ADJUSTMENT

NOTE — *Adjustments are performed as part of gear reassembly. See Overhaul in this article.*

REMOVAL & INSTALLATION

STEERING GEAR

Removal — Using suitable puller, remove tie rod and center link from Pitman arm. Loosen steering column clamp on worm shaft. Remove three bolts holding steering gear to body, noting number and position of shims. Remove steering box.

Installation — Bolt steering box to body, but do not tighten bolts. Clamp steering column on worm shaft and reconnect tie rod and center link. Turn steering wheel from side to side several times to align shaft and box, then tighten bolts to specification.

OVERHAUL

STEERING GEAR

Disassembly — 1) Unscrew oil plug and drain gear oil, then mount assembly on suitable overhaul stand. Use a puller to detach pitman arm from roller shaft.

2) Remove nuts and washers attaching roller shaft cover to gear box, then take off cover with roller shaft adjusting screw, adjusting disc, lock washer, and lock nut. Extract roller shaft assembly from gear housing.

3) Remove worm shaft thrust cover and shims. Turn shaft and remove bearing. Using a suitable puller (A. 47004), remove worm shaft rear bearing. This will release shims located behind bearing. Remove roller shaft oil seal, and bearings if necessary with puller (A. 74105).

Reassembly & Adjustment — 1) If installing roller shaft bearing, drive into place with drift punch. Ream to correct bore diameter, 1.298-1.306" (28.799-28.717 mm). Replace shims and rear worm shaft bearing.

NOTE — *If proper center mesh position was found during inspection, install same shims. If not, adjust shim pack.*

2) Fit worm bearing races and install worm into box. Drive front ball bearing race into gear box and replace thrust cover with shims. Check starting torque of worm shaft. It must not exceed 4.3 INCH Lbs. (.5 N·m). If torque is higher, shimming must be increased. If lower than specified, reduce shimming.

3) Insert roller shaft oil seal, roller shaft, and cover plate with gasket and shims. Connect pitman arm temporarily to roller shaft. The roller shaft should be free to rotate through 30° on either side of center. Eliminate any clearance using adjusting screw. Turning torque after adjustment should be 7.8-10.4 INCH lbs. (.9-1.1 N·m).

4) When adjustment is complete, tighten pitman arm retaining nut to specification. Fill steering box with 7.25 oz. of SAE 90 EP lubricant.

TIGHTENING SPECIFICATIONS

Application	Ft. Lbs. (N·m)
Linkage-to-Pitman Arm	22 (30)
Pitman Arm-to-Gear	174 (237)
Steering Column Bracket Bolts	11 (15)
Steering Gear-to-Body	29 (39)
Steering Wheel Nut	36 (49)

Steering Gears & Linkage

HONDA RACK & PINION

Accord
Civic
Prelude

DESCRIPTION

Rack and pinion type steering is mounted by rubber insulators to crossmember. Adjustment is provided for pinion gear preload. Pinion shaft is coupled to the steering shaft and tie rods connect end of rack to steering arms of front wheels.

ADJUSTMENT

NOTE — *Rack piston must be adjusted whenever steering gear assembly is removed and installed.*

STEERING WHEEL TURNING FORCE

Raise and support front of vehicle, so front wheels are off ground. Attach spring gauge to steering wheel spoke, near wheel rim. Turn wheel with spring gauge and note reading. If reading is more than 3.3 lbs. (1.5 kg), adjust rack piston adjusting screw until turning force is to specifications.

RACK PISTON ADJUSTMENT

Loosen rack screw lock nut. Tighten rack screw until lightly bottomed then back off screw 45° from bottomed position. Tighten lock nut and recheck steering wheel turning force.

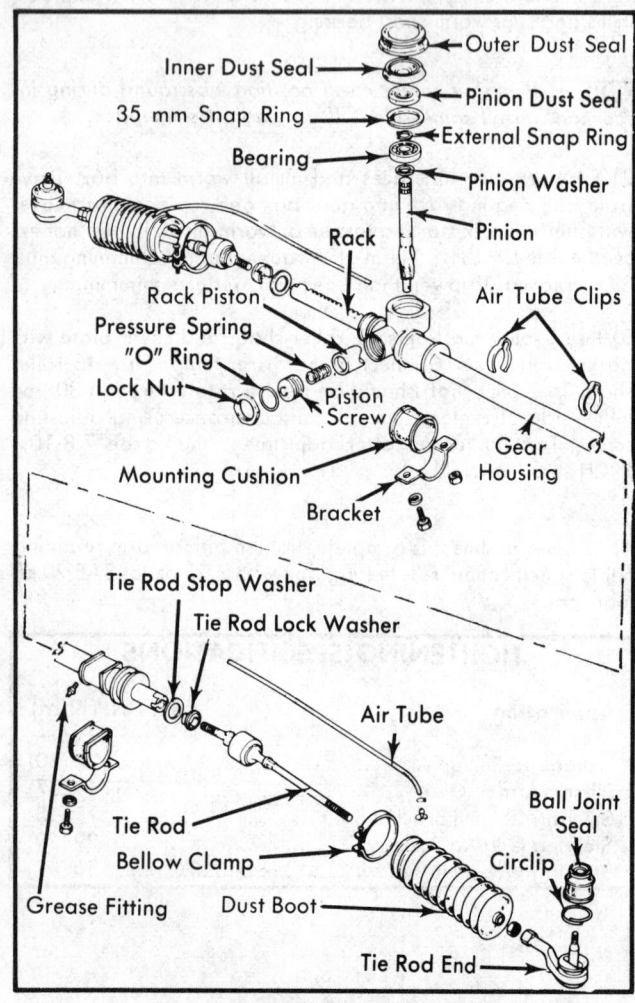

Fig. 1 Exploded View of Honda Rack & Pinion Steering Gear Assembly

REMOVAL & INSTALLATION

STEERING GEAR

Removal (Accord) — **1)** Raise and support front of vehicle. Remove front wheels. Disconnect tie rod ball joints from steering knuckles.

2) Place Man. Trans. in 1st or 3rd and remove shift rod yoke bolt. Remove engine crossmember. Disconnect shift lever torque arm at transmission. On Auto. Trans. remove center engine mount and splash guard, then disconnect shift cable.

3) Turn steering wheel full left. Remove steering shaft connector bottom bolts, then steering gear brackets. Lower gear to disconnect steering shaft. Move gear right to clear subframe then move left to remove.

Installation — To install steering gear assembly, reverse removal procedures.

Removal (Civic & Prelude) — **1)** Raise and support front of vehicle. Remove wheels. Disconnect tie rods from steering knuckles. Remove bolt from steering shaft to pinion gear connector. Remove steering gear mounting bracket bolts.

2) Lower gear to disconnect steering shaft, rotate gear 180° forward and remove gear through left side of vehicle.

Installation — To install steering gear, reverse removal procedures. Check operation of steering gear for smoothness and binding after installation.

OVERHAUL

STEERING GEAR

Disassembly — **1)** Place steering gear in a vise. Disconnect air tube and dust boot clamps. Push dust boots out of way, bend up lock washer tabs and remove tie rods from rack.

2) Remove rack adjusting screw lock nut, adjusting screw, washer, spring and rack piston. Remove pinion gear grommets, dust seal and snap ring, then pull pinion gear out of steering housing. Remove rack and rack bushing.

Inspection — Check all components for wear or damage, replace as necessary. Measure rack piston adjustment spring length, replace if not to specifications. New spring length should be 1.028" (26.1 mm) for Accord, 1.126" (28.6 mm) for Civic, and .750" (19.04 mm) for Prelude. Service limit for springs should be .945" (24 mm) for Accord, 1.035" (26.3 mm) for Civic, and .689" (17.5 mm) for Prelude.

Reassembly — Coat sliding surfaces with grease, then reassemble in reverse order of disassembly. Use new lock washers on tie rods and adjust steering after installation in vehicle.

TIGHTENING SPECIFICATIONS

Application	Ft. Lbs. (N·m)
Adjusting Screw Lock Nut	18 (25)
Ball Joint Nut	32 (42)
Tie Rod Lock Nut	32 (42)

ISUZU RACK & PINION

I-Mark

DESCRIPTION

Steering gear assembly is a rack and pinion type. The steering gear pinion shaft, connected to lower end of steering column, moves the rack to the left or right, thereby transmitting any turning motion of the steering wheel to tie rods and steering knuckles.

ADJUSTMENT

STEERING GEAR ADJUSTMENT

Position front wheels straight ahead with steering wheel centered. Turn adjusting screw into gear housing and tighten to 11 ft. lbs. (15 N·m). Back off adjusting screw $1/12$ of a turn. Tighten lock nut.

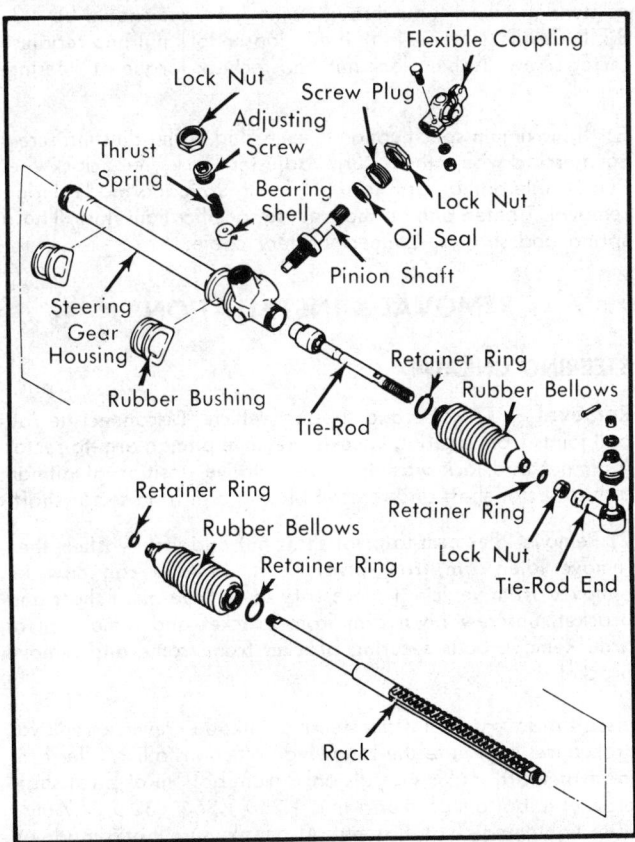

Fig. 1 Exploded View Showing Various Components of Rack & Pinion Steering Gear Assembly

REMOVAL & INSTALLATION

STEERING GEAR

Removal — 1) Raise and support front of vehicle. Remove engine under cover. Remove steering shaft coupling bolt. Remove both tie-rod end cotter keys and castle nuts. Using tie-rod puller tool (J-21687-02) disconnect tie-rod end from steering knuckles.

2) Disconnect steering gear housing from crossmember. Remove steering coupling from steering shaft and remove steering gear assembly from car.

Installation — Position front wheels straight ahead with steering wheel centered. Reverse removal procedure to complete installation.

OVERHAUL

STEERING GEAR

Disassembly — 1) Clamp steering gear assembly in soft jaw vise. Disconnect tie-rod ends from tie-rods. Remove retainer rings from rubber bellows. Remove bellows from steering gear housing and ball joint.

2) Disconnect ball joint from rack. Loosen adjusting screw lock nut, remove adjusting screw, thrust spring and bearing shell from adjusting screw opening.

3) Remove lock nut and screw plug from steering gear housing. Do not turn pinion to end position. Pull pinion and rack out of steering gear housing.

Reassembly — 1) Clamp steering gear assembly in a soft jaw vise. Coat all moving parts with gear lubricant. Insert long (toothless) end of rack into short end of housing until rack is centered in housing.

NOTE — *Make sure that gear lubricant does not clog the 3 air channels in metal bushings. If air channels are blocked, a vacuum condition in bellows may result, drawing the bellows inward causing rack teeth to jam.*

2) Center pinion on rack. Insert pinion shaft assembly into gear assembly, making sure pinion center tooth meshes with rack center tooth. Position screw plug and lock nut on gear assembly. Tighten screw plug and lock nut.

3) Place bearing shell into steering gear housing. Assemble thrust spring, adjusting screw and lock nut on gear assembly. Turn adjusting screw into gear housing and tighten to 11 ft. lbs. (15 N·m). Back off adjusting screw $1/12$ of a turn. Tighten lock nut.

TIGHTENING SPECIFICATIONS

Application	Ft. Lbs. (N·m)
Adjusting Screw Lock Nut	58 (79)
Flexible Coupling Bolt	19 (26)
Tie Rod Ball Housing	65 (88)
Tie Rod End-to-Knuckle Nut	29 (39)
Tie Rod End Lock Nut	47 (64)
Screw Plug	58 (79)
Screw Plug Lock Nut	72 (98)
Column-to-Instrument Panel Nut	11 (15)
Steering Gear Housing Clamp Bolt	14 (19)

ISUZU & LUV RECIRCULATING BALL

LUV
P'UP

DESCRIPTION

STEERING GEAR

Steering gear is a recirculating ball and nut type. A worm gear is incorporated on lower end of steering shaft and is engaged with ball nut through a number of recirculating balls. Adjustment is provided for backlash between sector gear and ball nut by a tapered sector gear in steering unit (adjustment screw is on sector shaft).

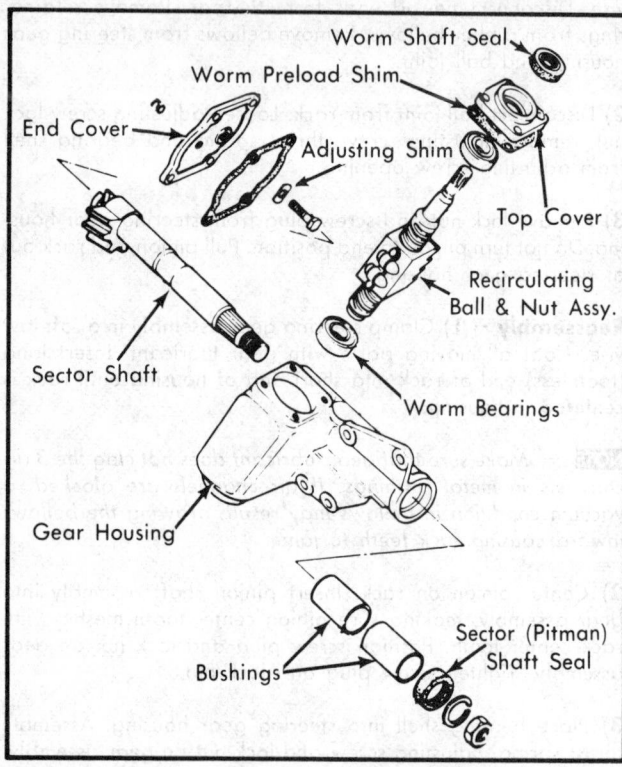

Fig. 1 Exploded View of Recirculating Ball Steering Gear Assembly

STEERING LINKAGE

Linkage consists of splined pitman arm connected to an adjustable center link on 2-WD models or non-adjustable center link on 4-WD models. Center link is attached to an idler arm and then to tie rods. Idler arm is attached to frame by a bracket. Tie rods are non-adjustable on 2-WD models. Tie rods are adjustable on 4-WD models.

ADJUSTMENT

PRELOAD & LASH

1) Disconnect battery ground cable, then raise and support front of vehicle. Remove pitman arm nut and mark position of arm-to-shaft. Remove arm using puller. Remove horn shroud and spring.

CAUTION — *Do not turn wheel hard against stops, as damage to ball guides may result.*

2) Turn steering wheel in one direction until stopped by gear, then turn back half way. Measure and record "bearing drag" by attaching torque wrench to steering wheel nut and rotating through a 90° arc.

NOTE — *Do not use a torque wrench having a maximum reading of more than 50 INCH lbs. (6 N·m).*

3) Adjust sector lash by turning steering wheel from one stop to the other, turn wheel back exactly halfway (to obtain center position), then turn sector adjusting screw clockwise to eliminate backlash between ball-nut and sector gear. Tighten lock nut.

4) Check torque at steering wheel nut, taking highest reading as steering wheel turns through center. Torque should be 4.3-8.7 INCH lbs. (.5-1.0 N·m). If not, loosen lock nut and readjust sector screw. Tighten lock nut and recheck torque at steering wheel.

5) If maximum specification is exceeded, turn adjusting screw counterclockwise, then turn adjuster lock nut clockwise. Reassemble pitman arm to shaft, lining up marks made during removal. Tighten pitman shaft nut to specifications. Install horn spring and shroud. Connect battery cable.

REMOVAL & INSTALLATION

STEERING LINKAGE

Removal — 1) Raise and support vehicle. Disconnect tie rod ball joints from steering knuckle. Remove pitman arm-to-sector shaft nut and lock washer. Mark relative position of pitman arm-to-sector shaft and remove pitman arm from sector shaft.

2) Remove idler arm-to-pivot shaft nut and lock washer, then remove idler arm from pivot shaft. Linkage can now be removed from vehicle. If necessary to remove pivot shaft and bracket, unscrew pivot arm from bracket and remove pivot arm. Remove bolts securing bracket from frame and remove bracket.

Installation — To install steering linkage, reverse removal procedures and note the following: When installing idler arm to pivot shaft, make sure distance from bottom of pivot shaft bracket to bottom of idler arm is 1.280-1.366" (32.5-34.7 mm) after tightening pivot shaft nut. Also make sure marks made on pitman arm and sector shaft are aligned during installation.

STEERING GEAR

Removal — Raise and support vehicle. Remove pitman arm nut and mark relative position of pitman arm-to-shaft. Using a puller, remove arm from shaft. Remove engine protection shield. Remove lower clamp-to-flexible coupling bolts. Remove steering gear-to-frame bolts and remove steering gear.

Installation — Place gear in position and start (do not torque) gear mounting bolts. Install clamp-to-coupling bolts and torque. Tighten gear mounting bolts. Install pitman arm, aligning index marks and tighten nut. Install engine protection shield.

ISUZU & LUV RECIRCULATING BALL (Cont.)

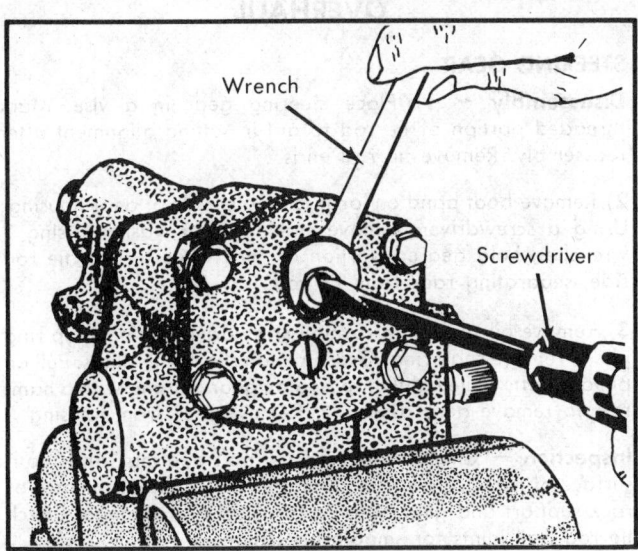

Fig. 2 Adjusting Sector Gear Lash

OVERHAUL

STEERING GEAR

NOTE — *Recirculating ball and nut assembly parts are selectively combined. Ball tube clamp plate is sealed with paint to prevent disassembly. Any worn part, therefore, necessitates entire assembly replacement.*

Disassembly — 1) Remove steering gear as previously described. Disconnect flexible coupling from worm shaft. Drain gear box through filler plug hole. Place sector shaft in straight ahead (center) position.

2) Remove top cover bolts and adjusting screw lock nut. Separate top cover from gear box by turning adjusting screw clockwise. Hold sector shaft in straight-ahead position during removal and DO NOT drive shaft off gear box by impact.

3) Remove adjusting screw and sector shaft from gear case. Remove end cover bolts and shims. Pull worm gear and ball nut assembly from gear box and take out lower bearing.

CAUTION — *Keep assembly in horizontal position or ball nut will fall onto end of worm gear, damaging ball tubes.*

Inspection — 1) Wash all parts in clean solvent. Check steering shaft for bending. Check ball-nut teeth for dents and wear. Check bearings for wear or damage.

2) Check threaded portion of ball-screw for dents or damage. Check ball-nut for smooth operation on worm shaft.

CAUTION — *Do not let ball-nut bottom out on worm shaft by its own momentum.*

3) Hold worm and ball-nut assembly in vertical position, allowing ball-nut to travel downward on worm shaft. Check sector shaft and shaft teeth for wear or damage.

Reassembly & Adjustment — 1) Insert lower bearing into position in gear box. Install worm shaft assembly in box. Check lower end of worm shaft for proper fit in lower bearing.

2) Assemble upper bearing onto worm shaft and install adjusting shims between gear housing and end cover. Install and tighten bolts.

NOTE — *Apply liquid gasket to end cover during installation.*

3) At this point, measure starting torque of pinion shaft. See *Fig. 3*. Reading should be 2.6-5.2 lbs. (1.2-2.4 kg) when coupling begins to rotate. If not within limits, add or remove shims as necessary.

4) Bring ball nut to center of worm and insert sector shaft into gear box. Engage center tooth of shaft with center tooth of worm. Insert adjusting screw in sector shaft slot. Screw should slide freely within slot and have no more than .004" (.10 mm) clearance. If clearance is excessive, insert adjusting shim. Install sector cover while turning adjusting screw out. Tighten lock nut.

5) Check total gear preload (starting torque) using pull scale as shown in *Fig. 3*. If reading is between 4.3-10.5 lbs. (2.0-4.8 kg), no further adjustments are required. If correct specification is not obtained, turn adjusting screw until preload is within specifications. Tighten lock nut.

6) Connect sector shaft to pitman arm (align marks made during removal) and tighten pitman arm nut. Install and tighten pinch bolt. Fill gear assembly with .5 pts. of lubricant; do not overfill.

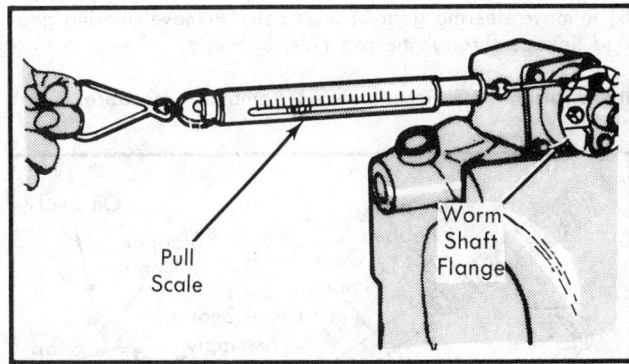

Fig. 3 Measuring Steering Gear Starting Torque

PITMAN SHAFT SEAL REPLACEMENT

NOTE — *If replacement has been determined as necessary, it may be done without removing the steering gear.*

1) Raise and support vehicle. Remove pitman arm as previously described. Clean area around seal. Pry out old seal, being careful not to damage housing bore.

CAUTION — *Check gear lubricant for contamination. If contamination of any kind is detected, gear overhaul is necessary.*

2) Coat new seal with gear lubricant and tap into position. Install pitman arm and nut. Lower vehicle and check lubricant level in gear assembly.

TIGHTENING SPECIFICATIONS

Application	Ft. Lbs. (N·m)
Ball Joint Nut	44 (60)
Center Link Lock Nut	89 (121)
Idler Arm Nut	89 (121)
Pitman Arm Nut	162 (220)

MAZDA RACK & PINION

GLC (Exc. Wagon)

DESCRIPTION

Rack and pinion type steering is mounted by rubber insulators to crossmember. Adjustment is provided for pinion gear preload. Pinion shaft is coupled to steering shaft and tie rods connect end of rack to steering arms of front wheels.

ADJUSTMENT

NOTE — *Adjustments are performed during reassembly portion of overhaul procedure.*

REMOVAL & INSTALLATION

STEERING GEAR

Removal — 1) Raise front of vehicle and support with stands. Remove front wheels. Disconnect tie rod ends from steering knuckles.

2) Remove band securing rubber boot to steering gear. Pull boot upward and remove bolt and washer securing steering shaft-to-pinion coupler.

3) Remove steering gear bracket bolts. Remove steering gear and linkage through tie rod hole.

Installation — To install, reverse removal procedure.

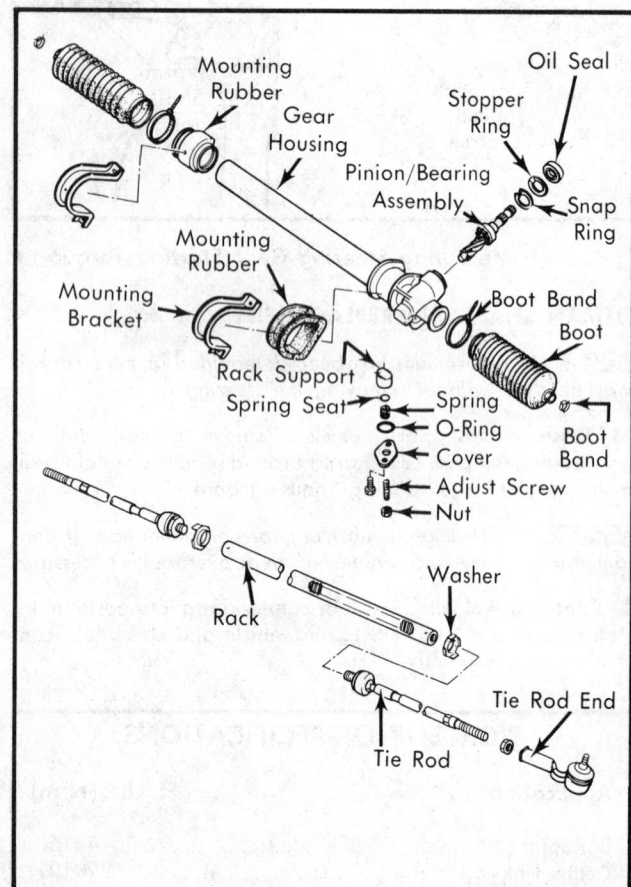

Fig. 1   Exploded View of Steering Gear Assembly

OVERHAUL

STEERING GEAR

Disassembly — 1) Place steering gear in a vise. Mark threaded portion of tie rod to aid in setting alignment after reassembly. Remove tie rod ends.

2) Remove boot band on large diameter side of gear housing. Using a screwdriver, remove staking from washer. Using 2 wrenches, hold geared portion of rack while turning tie rod side, separating rack from tie rod.

3) Remove oil seal using a small screwdriver. Using snap ring pliers, remove snap ring. Grasp pinion shaft with pliers. Pull on pinion shaft, while lightly tapping on gear housing with a hammer to remove gear assembly. Remove rack from housing.

Inspection — Check rubber boots, ball bearings and tooth surface of rack for wear or damage. Check sliding surface of rack support and gear housing for cracks or damage. Check tie rod ball joints for smooth operation.

NOTE — *If part(s) of rack and gear assembly are found to be defective, entire unit must be replaced.*

Reassembly — 1) Apply lithium grease to the following parts: ball bearing, roller bearing on pinion, inside of gear housing, lip of oil seal, sliding and backing surface of rack support, sliding surface of rack bushings, rack pinion teeth and ball joint of tie rods.

2) Insert rack with non-tooth side into pinion side of housing. Install pinion and bearing assembly making sure rack teeth and pinion are meshed properly.

NOTE — *If fit between housing and bearing is too tight, strike outer ring of bearing lightly while carefully checking the meshing of rack and pinion.*

3) Install snap ring in housing groove. Install stopper with protruded portion being placed in gap of snap ring. Position seal in housing. Using a hammer, tap lightly on seal until seal is flush with end surface of housing.

4) Turn adjusting srew until tightening torque increases suddenly. Unscrew adjusting screw 0-15° and tighten screw with locknut. To complete reassembly, reverse disassembly procedure.

5) Measure pinion gear preload using a spring scale and attachment (49 0180 510A). Install attachment to gear shaft.

6) Hook spring scale to attachment and turn it at a speed of 1 revolution per 1 to 2 seconds. Scale should read 1.3-2.6 lbs. (.6-1.2 kg).

TIGHTENING SPECIFICATIONS

Application	Ft. Lbs. (N·m)
Shaft-to-Pinion Bolt	13-20 (18-27)
Mounting Bracket Bolt	23-34 (31-46)
Tie Rod End & Knuckle	22-33 (30-45)

MAZDA RECIRCULATING BALL

**626
RX7
B2000 Pickup
GLC Wagon**

DESCRIPTION

Steering gear is a recirculating ball type with a variable ratio, depending on turning angle of sector shaft. The worm gear and steering shaft are an integral (non-separable) unit. Steering linkage is basically the same for all models, having a non-adjustable center link, 2 adjustable tie rods, an idler arm assembly, and pitman arm.

ADJUSTMENT

NOTE — *Adjustments are performed during assembly portion of overhaul. See Overhaul procedure in this article.*

REMOVAL & INSTALLATION

STEERING GEAR

Removal (GLC Wagon, B2000 Pickup) — 1) Disconnect negative battery cable. Remove steering wheel and switches. *See Mazda under STEERING WHEEL & COLUMN SWITCHES in this Section.* Remove bolts holding column to dash. Loosen dust cover screws, any other column bolts and pull column jacket off shaft.

2) On GLC Wagon, disconnect center link from pitman arm with puller. Remove steering gear mounting bolts and pull gear forward after raising vehicle.

3) On B2000 Pickup models, remove air cleaner, brake master cylinder and power booster, clutch master cylinder, and EGR pipes and hoses. Drain coolant, then remove hoses and lines from intake manifold. Remove manifold and carburetor assembly.

4) Raise and support vehicle. Remove left front wheel, then disconnect and remove pitman arm. Place jack under lower left control arm and support. Remove upper left control arm, noting position of shims. Unbolt steering gear and pull up out of vehicle.

Removal (626 & RX7) — 1) Disconnect negative battery cable. Remove steering wheel and switches. *See Mazda under STEERING WHEEL & COLUMN SWITCHES in this Section.* Remove bolts holding column to dash. Tape holes to retain lubricant. Remove air duct.

2) Raise and support front of vehicle. Disconnect pitman arm and center link. Remove nuts and bolts retaining steering gear housing to body. Remove under cover, engine mount and stabilizer bar (626 only). Remove hood (RX7 only). Remove steering gear assembly from vehicle.

Installation (All Models) — To install, reverse removal procedure, ensuring any shims which were removed are installed in original positions.

NOTE — *To avoid damage to steering column components, do not apply bending or striking forces to steering shaft or column.*

STEERING LINKAGE

Steering linkage may be removed as an assembly or as individual components. Whenever tie rod setting is disturbed, toe-in must be reset. *See Mazda in WHEEL ALIGNMENT section.*

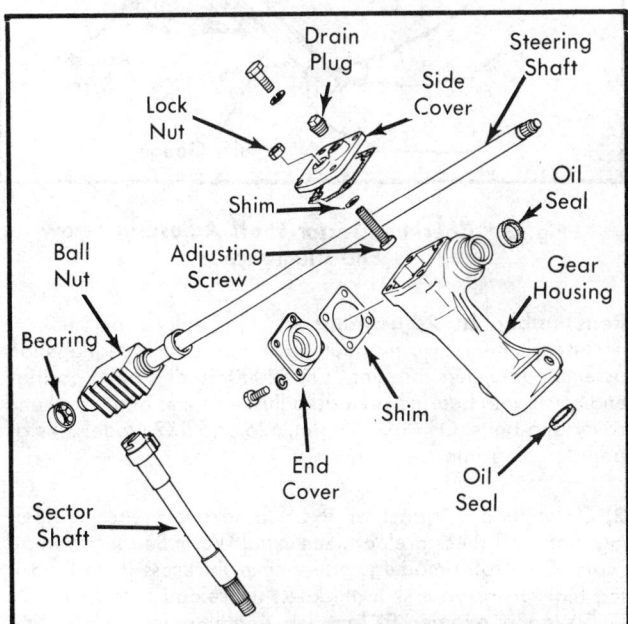

Fig. 2 Exploded View of Steering Gear Assembly (B2000 Models)

OVERHAUL

STEERING GEAR

Disassembly — 1) Drain gear oil from housing. Remove pitman arm from sector shaft, if not removed previously. Remove

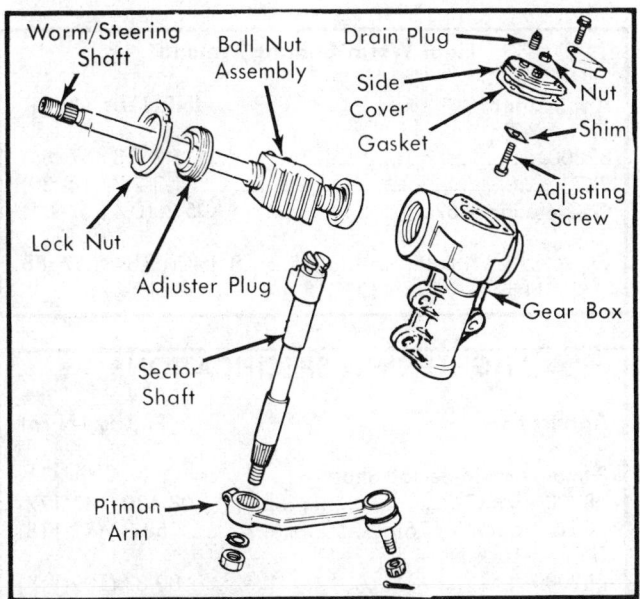

Fig. 1   Exploded View of Steering Gear Assembly (GLC Wagon, 626 and RX7 Models)

MAZDA RECIRCULATING BALL (Cont.)

sector shaft adjusting screw lock nut. Remove side cover attaching bolts and remove side cover by turning adjusting screw clockwise.

2) Remove sector shaft adjusting screw and shim from sector shaft. Remove sector shaft carefully to avoid damage to oil seal. On B2000 models, remove end cover bolts, cover and shim. Then carefully remove ball nut, worm gear and steering shaft assembly from gear housing.

3) On GLC Wagon, 626 and RX7 models, remove ball nut/worm gear adjusting plug lock nut. Then remove adjusting plug and withdraw ball nut, worm gear and steering shaft assembly from gear housing.

Inspection — Check ball nut rotation on worm gear. If movement is not smooth for full length of travel, replace worm and ball nut assembly. Ball nut is not to be serviced separately. Check worm bearings and cups, sector shaft gear surface, and oil seal. Check clearance between sector shaft and housing bore. Clearance should be .004" (.1 mm) or less. If any component is defective, replace it.

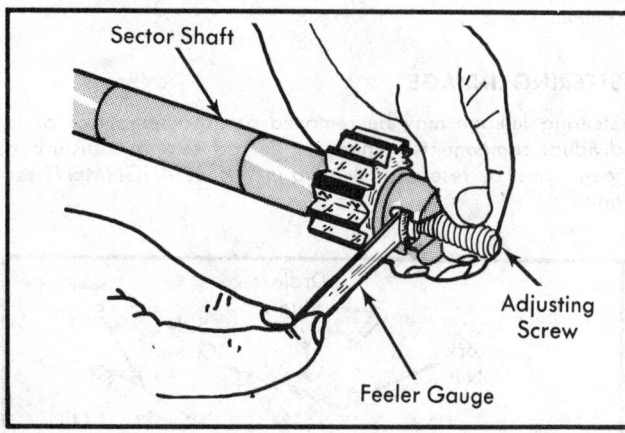

Fig. 3 Checking Sector Shaft Adjusting Screw End Clearance

Reassembly & Adjustment — **1)** Replace oil seals if necessary. Insert worm gear, ball nut and steering shaft assembly into gear housing. On B2000 models only, position end cover with bearing preload adjusting shims and install end cover and bolts. On GLC Wagon, 626 and RX7 models, install adjuster plug into gear housing.

2) On all models, attach an INCH lb. torque wrench to steering shaft and check preload. See *Initial Worm Bearing Preload* chart. On B2000 models, reduce shim thickness if preload is too high or increase shim thickness if preload is too low. On GLC Wagon, 626 and RX7 models, tighten or loosen adjusting plug if preload is not to specifications. Install lock nut.

Initial Worm Bearing Preload

Application	INCH Lbs. (N·m)
RX7	.44-1.1 (.05-.12)
All Other Models	1.7-4.3 (.19-.47)

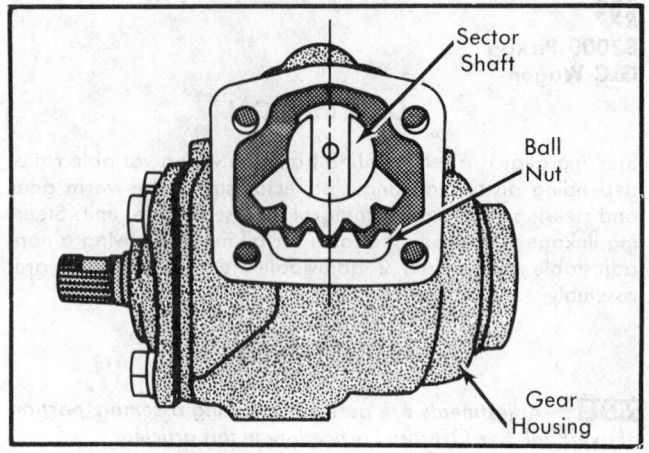

Fig. 4 Aligning Sector Shaft to Ball Nut

3) Check clearance between sector shaft adjusting screw and sector shaft. Insert shim so that final clearance will be .004" (.1 mm) or less. Insert sector shaft into gear housing, aligning center of sector shaft with ball nut. See *Fig. 4*. Insert adjusting screw and shim in sector shaft. Place side cover and gasket over adjusting screw and turn adjusting screw until cover is in place, then install cover bolts.

4) Install pitman arm to sector shaft. Install and tighten retaining nut. Measure pitman arm backlash. If necessary, turn sector adjusting screw until zero backlash is obtained. Tighten adjusting screw lock nut, taking care not to disturb backlash adjustment.

5) Check worm shaft rotating torque. Attach an INCH lb. torque wrench to steering shaft upper end. If not to specifications, adjust as necessary. See *Final Worm Bearing Preload* chart. Fill gear housing with lubricant (A.P.I. GL-4 SAE 90).

Final Worm Bearing Preload

Application	INCH Lbs. (N·m)
B2000	5.2-7.8 (.57-.86)
RX7	1.3-2.7 (.14-.30)
GLC Wagon & 626	①5.2-10.4 (.57-1.1)

① — 626 With tilt steering 5.2-7.8 INCH Lbs. (.57-.86 N·m).

TIGHTENING SPECIFICATIONS

Application	Ft. Lbs. (N·m)
Pitman Arm-to-Sector Shaft	
B2000 & RX7	108-130 (147-177)
GLC Wagon & 626	58-87 (79-118)
Tie Rod Lock Nut	
B2000	80-87 (109-118)
GLC Wagon, 626 & RX7	51-58 (69-79)
Worm Gear, Ball Nut & Steering Shaft	
Adjusting Plug (Exc. B2000)	166-188 (226-256)

PORSCHE RACK & PINION

**911SC
924**

DESCRIPTION

Porsche models use rack and pinion steering. Tie rods on 911SC attach to rack with yoke and eyebolts, while the 924 uses a ball swivel joint. Pinion on 924 is offset to the left of center. Pinion on 911SC is centered in rack housing. Pinion shafts on all models are supported by ball bearings.

ADJUSTMENT

STEERING GEAR

Steering gear adjusting methods vary according to type of steering rack pressure block: (1) Steel pressure block with plastic contact surface and external housing dust boot seat; (2) Plastic pressure block with no external housing dust boot seat; (3) Adjusting screw on 924 extends through cover to take play out of steering rack.

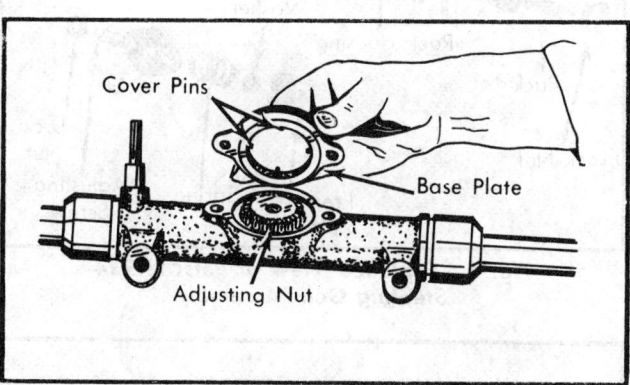

Fig. 1   Adjusting Nut with Cover

Labels: Cover Pins, Base Plate, Adjusting Nut

Steel Pressure Block Type — 1) With housing assembly in padded vise, detach base plate. Tighten adjusting nut seating contact. Back nut off contact by 3 teeth.

NOTE — *Base plate has integral pins which may be used as a wrench for this adjustment.*

2) Check steering gear drag at pinion flange, using an INCH lb. torque wrench. A measurement of 7 INCH lbs. (.8 N·m) should be obtained. If beyond this measurement, loosen adjusting nut. If this measurement is not less than 3.5 INCH lbs. (.39 N·m), do not retighten adjusting nut. Install base plate with gasket.

NOTE — *When installing base plate, pin in plate must fit easily between teeth of adjusting nut. If necessary, move nut slightly.*

Plastic Pressure Block Type — Remove base plate and tighten adjusting nut until 7 INCH lbs. (.8 N·m) torque is obtained, using method as previously described. Install base plate with gasket.

External Adjustment (924 Only) — With rack centered, loosen lock nut and tighten adjusting screw until it just touches thrust washer. Hold screw and tighten lock nut.

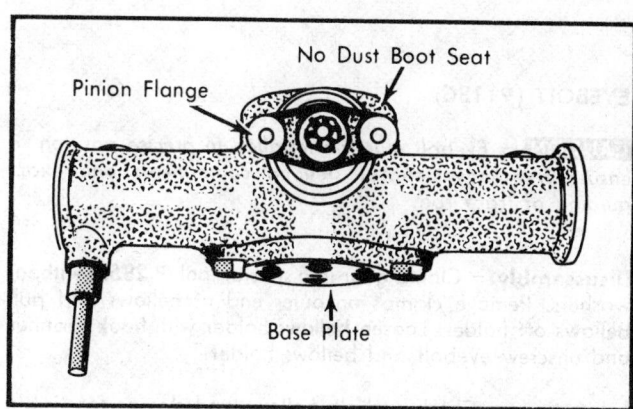

Fig. 2   Plastic Pressure Block Housing Assembly

Labels: Pinion Flange, No Dust Boot Seat, Base Plate

REMOVAL & INSTALLATION

STEERING GEAR

Removal — 1) Remove bottom bolt attaching universal joint to pinion shaft. Remove nuts and detach tie rod ball joints from steering knuckles.

2) Remove steering housing retaining bolts and extract entire steering housing from right side of vehicle. Detach track rods from rack.

Installation — To install, reverse removal procedures noting that indentation in pinion shaft must line up with bolt hole in lower universal joint. On 924 only, insert special centering bolt (9116) to center gear during installation.

OVERHAUL

STEERING GEAR

Disassembly — 1) Mount steering housing in padded vise and remove base plate retaining bolts. Unscrew adjusting nut (base plate may be used as wrench). Remove pressure block and spring.

2) Move steering rack to either lock position and remove castellated nut. Using suitable puller (P 293), remove flange from pinion. Remove oil seal, lock ring and spacer. Using suitable puller (P 282), remove pinion from pinion carrier (ensure bearing does not bind against housing). Remove Woodruff key from pinion and press bearing off pinion.

3) Mark position of rack (for assembly), remove from housing, and withdraw pinion carrier. Press bearing out of pinion carrier. Remove rack bushing spring retainer from end of housing. Extract support ring and drive rack bushing out.

PORSCHE RACK & PINION (Cont.)

Reassembly — Reverse disassembly procedure, noting the following: Coat all components with suitable lubricant, then fill housing with gear lubricant using bolt hole opposite base plate. Use shims to adjust pinion axial play to zero.

EYEBOLT (911SC)

CAUTION — *Eyebolt must be installed in precise position to ensure free movement of steering components and exact guiding of track rod.*

Disassembly — Clamp gear into special tool (P 285b) without washers. Remove clamps on outer end of bellows and pull bellows off holder. Loosen bellows holder with hook spanner and unscrew eyebolt and bellows holder.

Inspection — Check eyebolt, bellows and clamps for visible wear. Replace as required.

Reassembly — Mount bellows on housing. Screw bellows holder on eyebolt. Coat eyebolt threads and rack face end with sealer. Install eyebolts. Attach steering gear, without

washers, to original holding tool (P 285b). Locating pins should slide easily into eyebolts, with flattened end resting against outer pin. Tighten bellows holder. Clamp bellows to gear assembly.

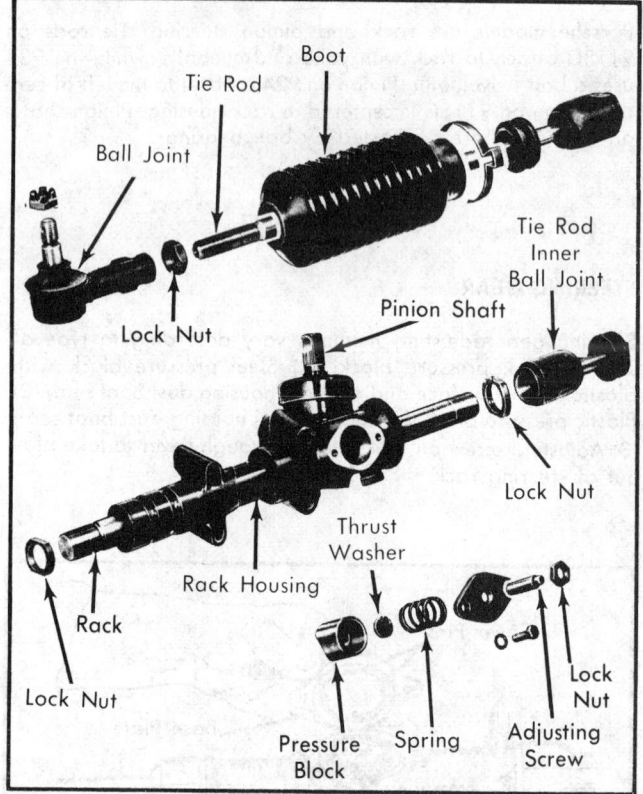

Fig. 4 Exploded View of Porsche 924 Steering Gear Assembly

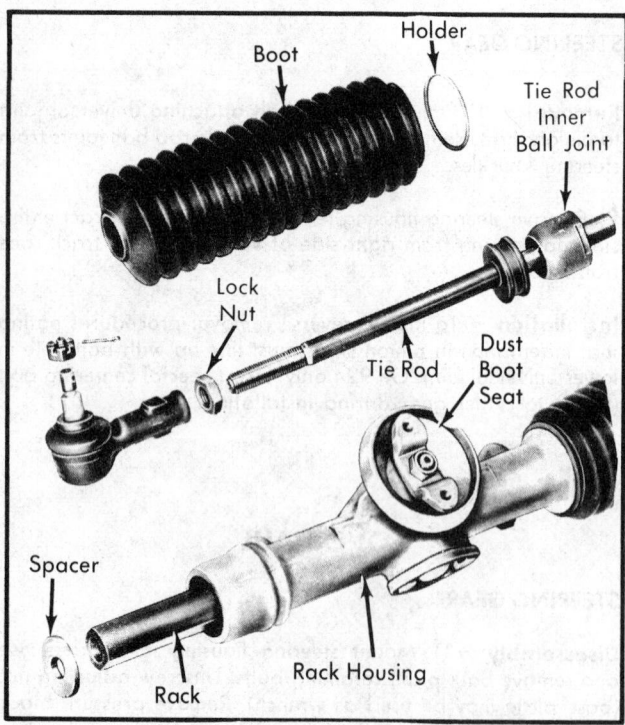

Fig. 3 Exploded View of 911SC Steering Gear Assembly

TIGHTENING SPECIFICATIONS

Application	Ft. Lbs. (N·m)
Housing-to-Crossmember	
911SC	34 (46)
924	14-17 (19-23)
Tie Rod-to-Steering Knuckle	
911SC	33 (45)
924	22-36 (30-49)
"U" Joint Coupling	23 (31)

RENAULT RACK & PINION

Le Car

DESCRIPTION

Vehicles are fitted with a rack and pinion steering gear, which has direct steering linkage (tie rods) to each front wheel. Steering housing is mounted to front crossmember and connected to steering column through a flexible coupling.

ADJUSTMENT

STEERING GEAR HEIGHT (TOE-OUT)

NOTE — *This adjustment must be performed whenever steering gear is removed or replaced.*

1) Place vehicle on lift, or alignment rack, with front wheels on radius gauges. Attach a brake press to pedal (to prevent rolling movement of wheels). Set steering at center point and lock in position with suitable holding tool (MS. 504) attached to steering wheel.

2) Load front of vehicle until measurement from centerline of front wheel to bottom of lower frame member (at front wheel) is 4.313" (110 mm). Mount scale boards (T. Av. 552) on side of body so distance from wheel center to board is 51.188" (1300 mm). See *Fig. 1.*

3) Mount measuring tools on both front wheels of vehicle so pointers are in line with crosses on scale boards. Remove load from vehicle (and raise with jack if necessary) so position is 3.125" (79 mm) higher than loaded position. Pointer should move to 6-7.75 on scale board. If not, steering gear must be adjusted.

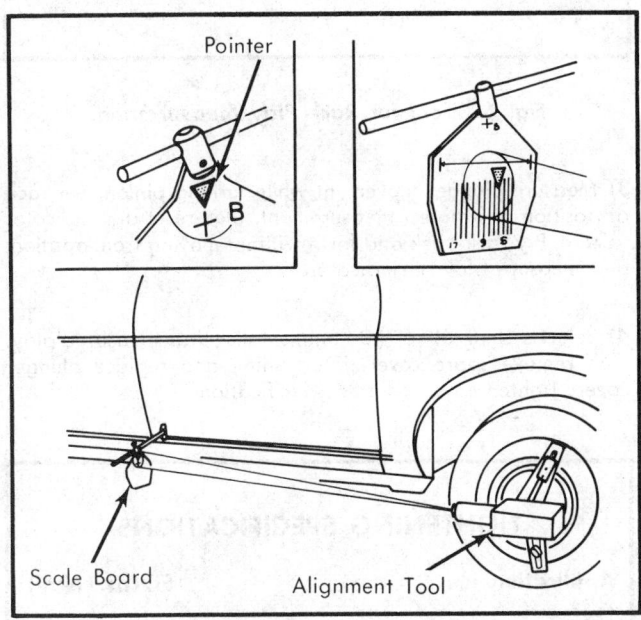

Fig. 1   Measurements for Steering Gear

4) Slotted shims are used to adjust steering gear. Position of slot in shim varies to move gear up and down. To replace or adjust shims, remove transaxle cover. Loosen steering gear bolts and remove adjusting shims. See *Fig. 2.*

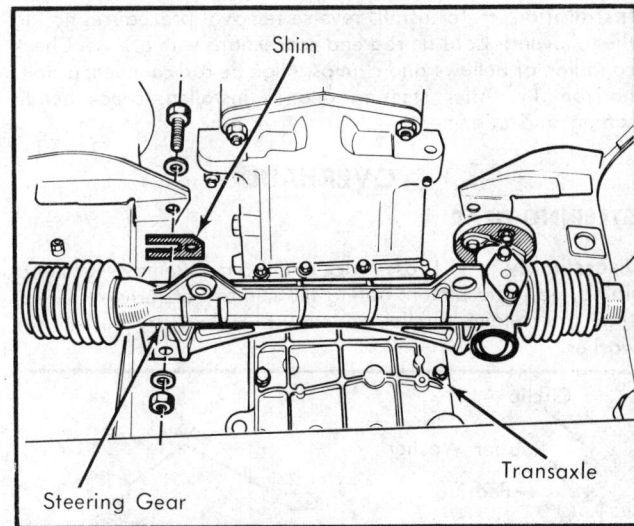

Fig. 2   Location of Adjustment Shim

SETTING STEERING CENTER POINT

To find center steering point, set center of rivet head on flexible coupling in line with index mark on pinion housng. This should result in a measurement of 2.813" (71 mm).

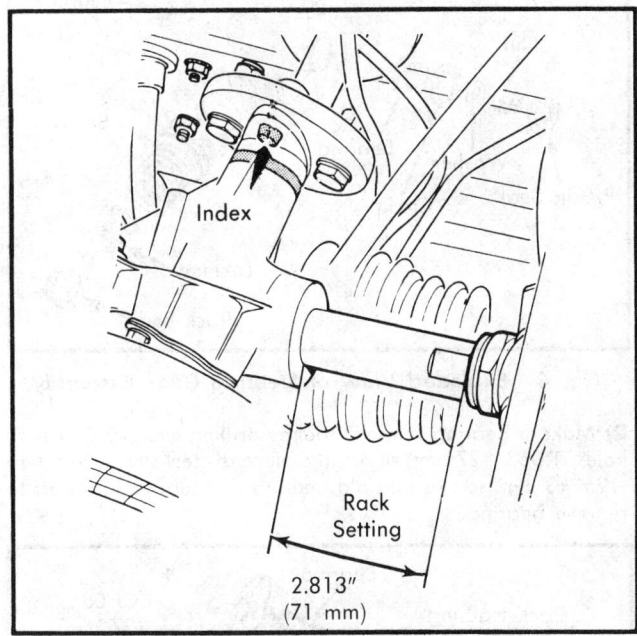

Fig. 3   Steering Center Measurement

REMOVAL & INSTALLATION

STEERING GEAR

Removal — 1) Remove spare tire and disconnect battery. Remove air cleaner and cooling fan relay, without disconnecting wiring. Remove governor, connector, valve and air pump pipe. Remove air filter bracket bolts and place assembly on engine.

2) Remove air pump filter. Remove steering shaft flexible coupling bolts and gear mounting bolts. Disconnect tie rod ends and remove steering gear. Mark shim location to reinstall in correct position.

RENAULT RACK & PINION (Cont.)

Installation — To install, reverse removal procedure, noting the following: Coat tie rod end connections with grease. Check condition of bellows and clamps. Align tie rod connecting bolts horizontally. After steering gear is installed, check height setting and alignment.

OVERHAUL

STEERING GEAR

Disassembly — 1) Loosen rack and locknut. Remove rack end fitting, opposite pinion, noting the number of turns required. Take off bellows, circlip, and thrust washer. Pry out rubber washer.

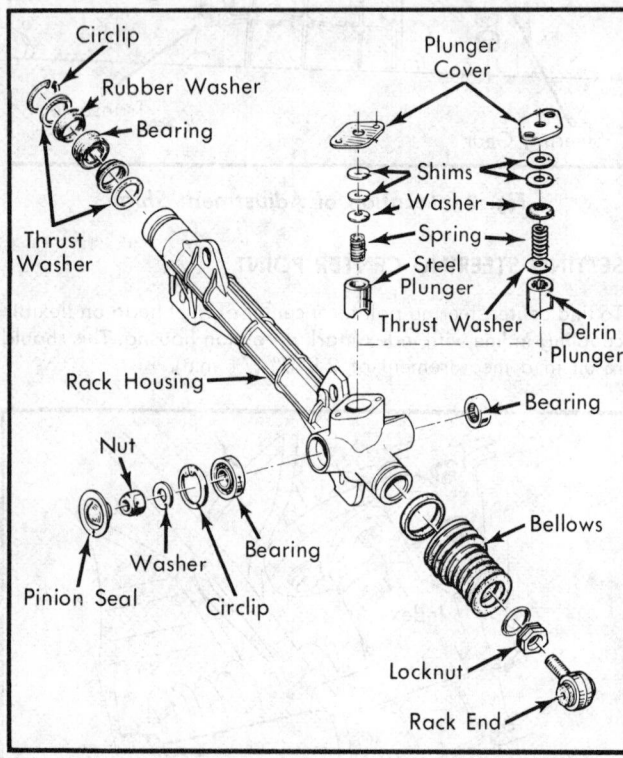

Fig. 4   Exploded View of Steering Gear Assembly

2) Make a bearing removal tool by drilling two .156" (4 mm) holes, 1.063" (27 mm) apart in a piece of steel strap. Turn two .125" (3 mm) screws into old bearing and turn pinion shaft to remove bearing.

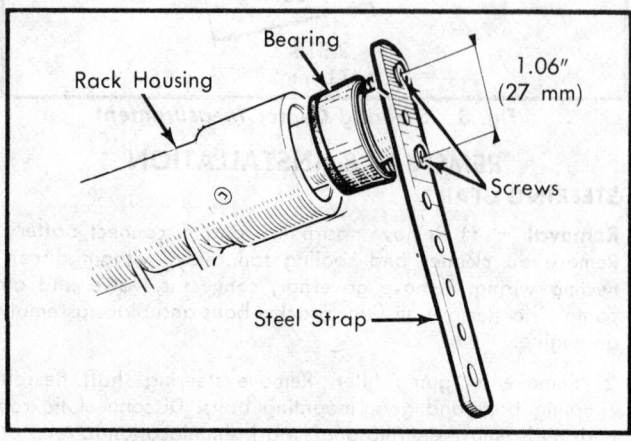

Fig. 5   Removal of Rack Bearing

3) Remove plunger cover, washers, spring and plunger. Pry out pinion seal plug, then remove pinion nut and washer. Pull out pinion and rack. Remove circlip and tap out bearings.

Inspection — Clean all parts with soft cloth and check for excessive wear or damage. Replace parts if necessary.

Reassembly & Adjustment — 1) Tap pinion bearings into place. Replace thrust washers, rubber rings and bushing in end of rack housing. Be sure slot is clear, and refit circlip. Spread Molykote grease over rack and pinion, then center rack in housing and install pinion. Replace washer, nut, and seal.

2) Grease plunger, spring and washers, and replace in housing. Fabricate a dial indicator bracket using a spare plunger cover. Drill a hole in the center and weld on a flange to hold indicator outer shaft. See Fig. 6.

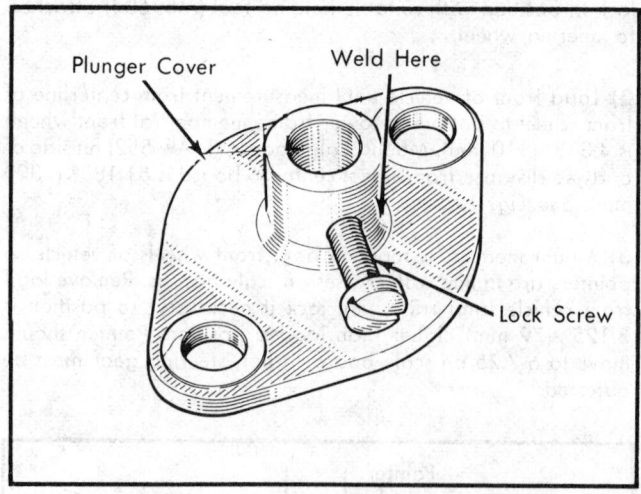

Fig. 6   Tool for Rack Play Measurement

3) Measure plunger movement while turning pinion. Set rack at position of greatest measurement, then reset dial indicator to zero. Pry rack back and forth without moving from position, and measure play on indicator.

4) Select a shim .0016" (.04 mm) smaller than measured play, then remove spare cover, insert shim, and replace plunger cover. Tighten cover bolts to specification.

TIGHTENING SPECIFICATIONS

Application	Ft. Lbs. (N·m)
Flexible Coupling Bolts	11 (15)
Gear-to-Frame Bolts	25 (34)
Pinion Nut	7.5 (10)
Plunger Cover Bolts	7.5 (10)
Tie Rod-to-Rack Bolts	25 (34)

Steering Gears & Linkage

SAAB RACK & PINION

900

DESCRIPTION

Steering gear is the rack and pinion type. Rack is protected from dirt by rubber bellows. The pinion bearing uses an adjustable spring-loaded plunger. The gear is oil-lubricated. The steering linkage is a direct link from the steering rack to the steering knuckles, consisting of tie rods and ball joints.

ADJUSTMENT

NOTE — See Overhaul procedure in this article.

REMOVAL & INSTALLATION

STEERING GEAR

Removal — 1) Remove steering gear to intermediate shaft clamp bolt. Raise and support vehicle. Remove front wheels. Separate tie rods from steering knuckles.

2) Remove steering gear clamp bolts. Separate steering column (intermediate shaft) joint from steering gear, lift steering gear to the side and remove by guiding it diagonally downwards through opening in engine compartment.

Installation — To install, reverse removal procedures and check wheel alignment.

OVERHAUL

STEERING GEAR

Disassembly — 1) Remove tie rod ends and rubber bellows. Drill out lock pins from inner ball joints, using a .16" (4 mm) drill bit. Drill only .375" (9.5 mm) deep. Remove outer bearing cups and lock nuts.

2) Remove rack adjustment screw, cap with gasket, shims, spring and plunger. Remove pinion and cap with gasket shims, and upper bearing. Pull rack out from housing. Tap out lower pinion bearing.

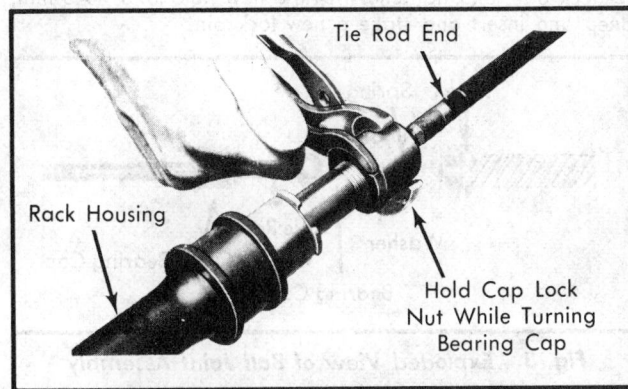

Fig. 2 Procedure for Removing Outer Bearing Cap Lock Nut

Reassembly — 1) Ensure all parts are thoroughly cleaned before proceeding with reassembly. Lubricate all parts during reassembly. Seat the lower pinion bearing.

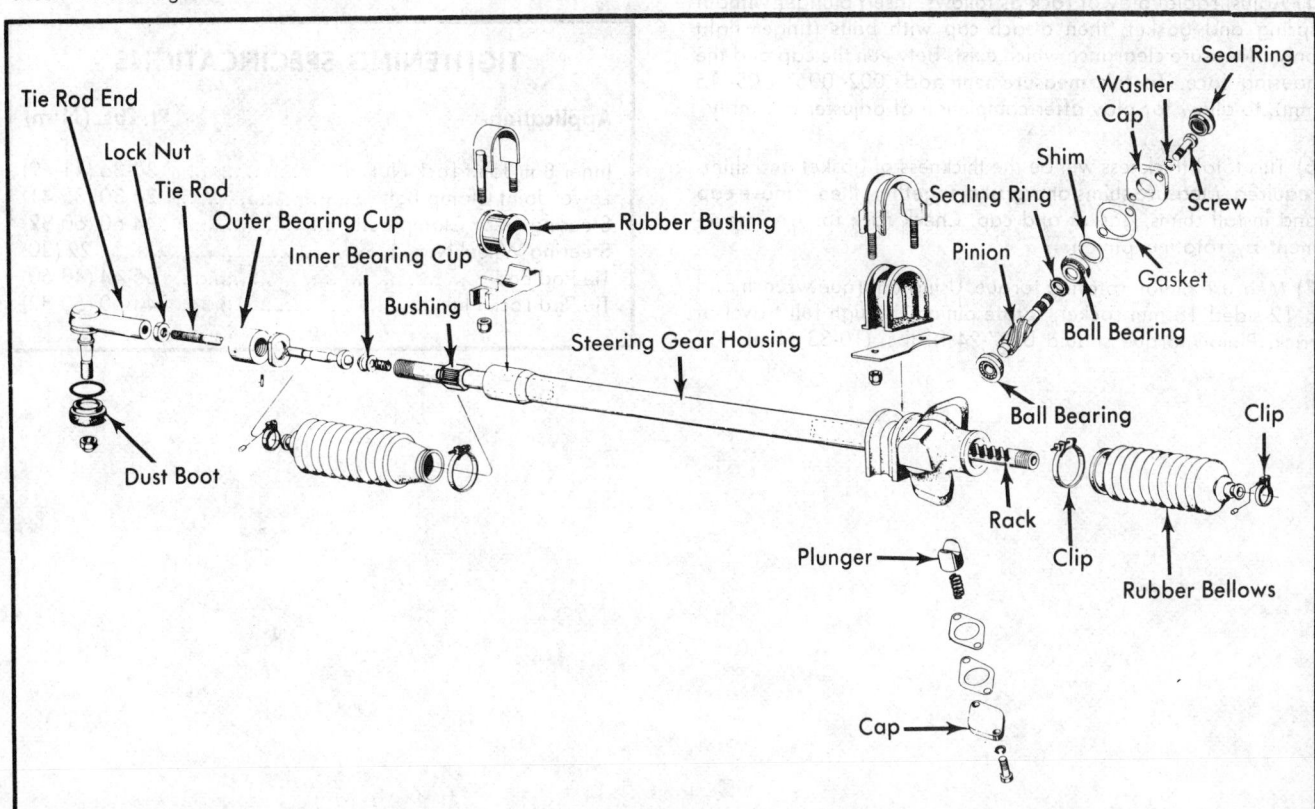

Fig. 1 Exploded View of Saab Rack & Pinion Steering Gear Assembly

SAAB RACK & PINION (Cont.)

NOTE — *Be sure extended parts of the inner bearing tracks are facing each other.*

2) Assemble inner ball joint on pinion end of rack as follows: Thread lock nut onto rack. Fit outer bearing cup on rack and fill with suitable gear oil. Insert spring and inner bearing cup. Tighten bearing cup so that there is no looseness in ball joint, but without tightness.

3) If rack, with tie rod mounted, is held horizontally, the tie rod should be able to be placed in any position without falling under its own weight. Tighten lock nut against bearing cup and recheck ball joint tightness. Drill a new hole .375" (9.5 mm) deep and insert and stake a new lock pin.

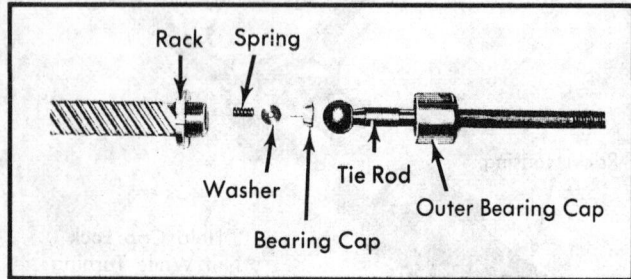

Fig. 3   Exploded View of Ball Joint Assembly

4) Insert rack into housing, then fit pinion and upper bearing. Adjust pinion with shims so that there is no axial play when pinion gasket and cap are attached. Various shim sizes are available.

5) Adjust radial play of rack as follows: Insert plunger without spring and gasket, then attach cap with bolts (finger tight only). Measure clearance which exists between the cap and the housing face. To this measurement add .002-.006" (.05-.15 mm), to allow for play after completion of adjuster assembly.

6) This total thickness will be the thickness of gasket and shims required. Measure shims and gasket together, then remove cap and install shims, gasket and cap. Check rack for free movement by rotating pinion.

7) Measure pinion rotating torque. Using a torque wrench and a 12 sided 18 mm socket, rotate pinion through full travel of rack. Pinion torque should be 7-24 ft. lbs. (10-33 N·m).

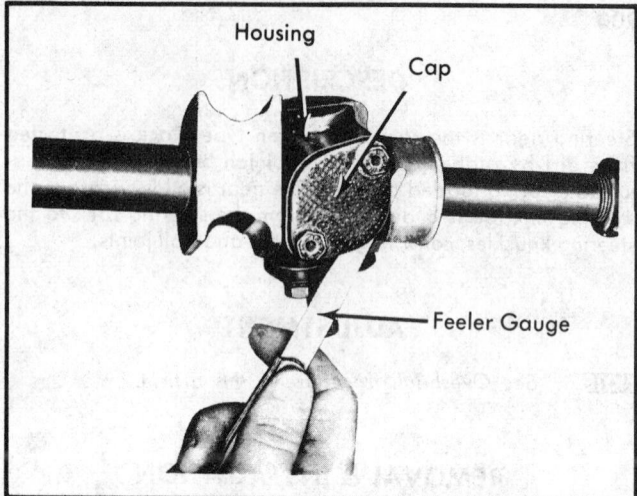

Fig. 4   Measuring Clearance Between Cap and Gear Housing

8) Assemble and adjust other ball joint in same manner as previously described. Attach bellows after lubricating contact area between bellows and tie rod (use silicone grease). Attach both inner clamps.

9) Stand gear on end and pour 5.0 oz. of suitable EP 90 gear oil into bellows. Attach outboard bellows with clamps. Screw on lock nuts and mount tie rod assemblies.

NOTE — *Outer bellows clamps should be protected with rubber caps.*

TIGHTENING SPECIFICATIONS

Application	Ft. Lbs. (N·m)
Inner Ball Joint Lock Nut	30-36 (41-49)
Lower Joint Clamp Bolt	26-30 (35-41)
Steering Gear Clamp Bolts	44-60 (60-82)
Steering Wheel Nut	22 (30)
Tie Rod End	35-44 (48-60)
Tie Rod Lock Nut	44-60 (60-82)

SUBARU RACK & PINION

DL
GL
GLF

DESCRIPTION

Steering gear, mounted on crossmember, is a rack and pinion type, with backlash automatically adjusted. Pinion is connected to steering shaft by a flexible rubber coupling. Steering knuckle arms are connected to rack by tie rods which are threaded onto ball joint studs at each end of rack.

ADJUSTMENT

BACKLASH

Backlash is automatically held to a minimum by a spring-loaded rack plunger which bears against rack. Adjustment is not normally required. End play of rack plunger may be corrected if necessary by turning adjusting screw in until it contacts plate, then backing screw out $1/24$th (15°) of a turn. This will give a clearance of .0025" (.063 mm) between adjusting screw and rack plunger. Hold adjusting screw from turning and tighten lock nut.

REMOVAL & INSTALLATION
STEERING GEAR

Removal – 1) Disconnect battery negative terminal. Raise and support front of vehicle. Remove both front wheels. Disconnect ball joints from steering knuckles.

2) Disconnect flexible coupling from pinion gear. Remove hot air stove from exhaust manifold and air cleaner. Disconnect exhaust manifold and pull down out of way. Remove rubber boot protector.

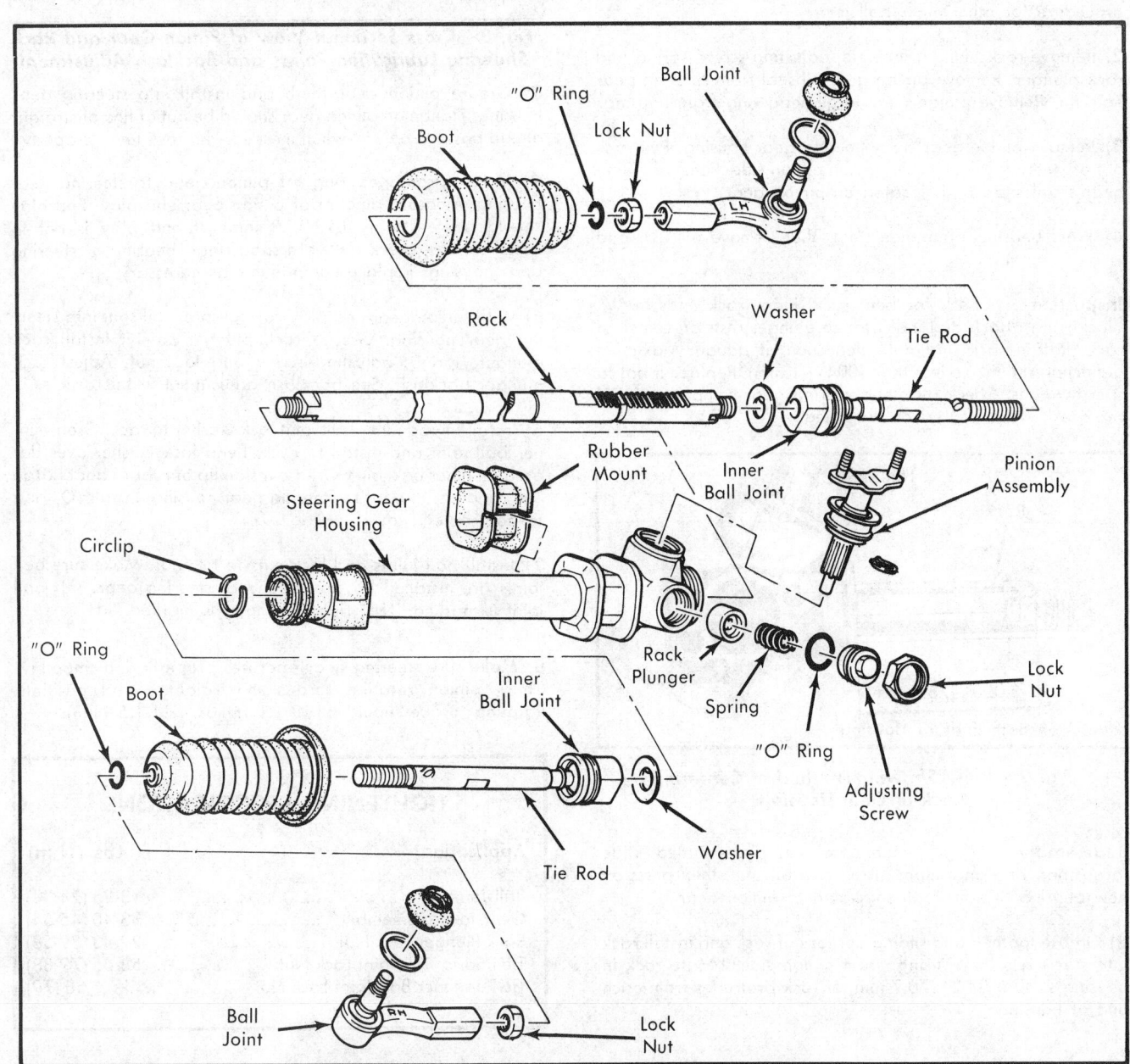

Fig. 1   Exploded View of Subaru Rack & Pinion Steering Gear Assembly

Steering Gears & Linkage

SUBARU RACK & PINION (Cont.)

3) Remove bolts attaching steering gear housing to crossmember. Lower gear housing until pinion gear is disconnected from flexible coupling. Rotate gear housing backwards and remove gear housing from left side.

Installation — To install steering gear assembly, reverse removal procedures and note the following: tighten left steering gear housing bracket first. Tighten ball joint nuts to specifications, then turn a maximum of $1/6$ turn to align cotter pin hole.

OVERHAUL

STEERING GEAR

Disassembly — 1) Place steering gear housing in a padded vise. Loosen lock nuts and remove ball joints from rods. Remove "O" rings from outside of rubber boots, then remove rubber boots. Unbend tab on inner ball joint lock washer, then loosen lock nut and remove inner ball joint from rack. Repeat procedure for other inner ball joint.

2) Remove rack plunger lock nut, adjusting screw, spring and rack plunger. Remove pinion gear oil seal from steering gear housing. Remove pinion gear large snap ring from housing.

3) Remove pinion gear from steering gear housing. Pull rack out of steering gear housing, from pinion side. Remove pinion gear small snap ring (located on pinion gear).

4) Press bearing off pinion gear, then remove oil seal and large snap ring.

Inspection — Check for bent rack. Place rack ends in "V" blocks and attach dial indicator so plunger rests on center of rack. Rotate rack and note deflection of gauge. Maximum deflection should be less than .004" (.1 mm). Replace if not to specifications. Check all other steering gear components and replace if worn, scored or damaged.

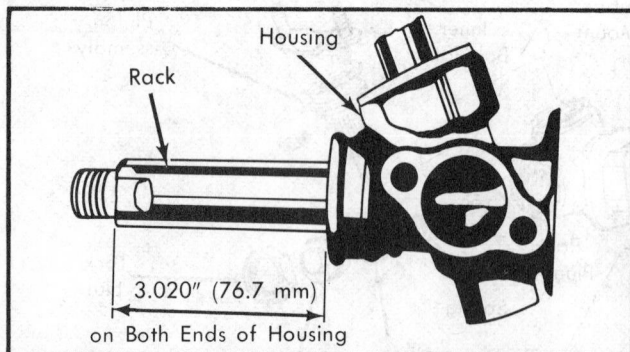

Fig. 2 View Showing Method of Centering Rack in Gear Housing

Reassembly — 1) If pinion gear was disassembled, slide large snap ring on pinion. Install new oil seal, then press on new bearing. Install small snap ring to pinion gear.

2) Grease toothed and sliding portions of rack and install rack into steering gear housing, from pinion side. Locate rack in housing so that 3.02" (76.7 mm) of rack protrudes from each end of housing.

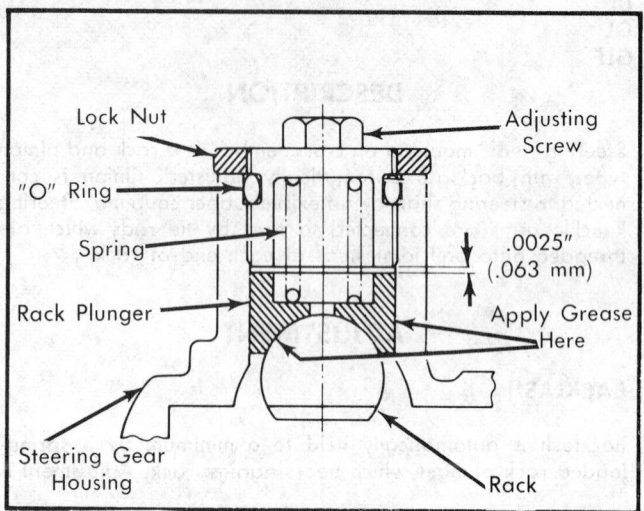

Fig. 3 Cross Sectional View of Pinion Gear and Rack Showing Lubrication Points and Backlash Adjustment

3) Grease pinion gear teeth and install into steering gear housing. Flange on pinion gear should be out of line of straight ahead position by 36° when meshed with rack teeth properly.

4) Install large snap ring, of pinion gear, to steering gear housing. Measure amount of pinion gear end play. End play should be less than .012" (.3 mm). If end play is not to specifications, check for worn snap rings, bearing or steering gear housing. Replace components as necessary.

5) With pinion gear end play correct, press oil seal into steering gear housing. Grease rack plunger cavity. Install rack plunger, spring, adjusting screw and lock nut. Adjust rack plunger backlash. See backlash adjustment in this article.

6) Install tie rod inner ball joint lock washer to rack. Grease inner ball joint and install to rack. Bend lock washer over flat area on inner ball joint. Grease inside lip of rubber boot (large end) and install boot to steering gear housing. Install "O" ring to boot outer end.

7) Install ball joints and lock nuts to tie rods. Make sure ball joints are installed on correct end of steering gear. Left ball joint is marked "LH", right ball joint is marked "RH".

8) Make sure steering gear operates properly and smoothly. Check pinion rotating torque in straight ahead position. Rotating torque should be .8-1.1 ft. lbs. (.11-1.5 N·m).

TIGHTENING SPECIFICATIONS

Application	Ft. Lbs. (N·m)
Ball Joint Nut	18-25 (24-34)
Gear-to-Crossmember	33-40 (45-54)
Rack Plunger Lock Nut	29-43 (39-58)
Tie Rod-to-Ball Joint Lock Nut	58-65 (79-88)
Tie Rod Inner Ball Joint Lock Nut	58 (79)

TOYOTA CRESSIDA, STARLET & TERCEL RACK & PINION

DESCRIPTION

Steering assembly is a direct-acting rack and pinion system. This unit consists of a rack bar and toothed pinion. Adjustment is provided for pinion gear preload. Rack is protected from dirt by rubber boots.

ADJUSTMENT

NOTE — *Adjustments are performed during gear reassembly. See overhaul as outlined.*

REMOVAL & INSTALLATION
STEERING GEAR

Removal — 1) Raise front of vehicle and support with safety stands. Position steering wheel so front wheels point straight ahead. Remove pinch bolts from intermediate shaft. Disconnecting pinion side first, remove intermediate shaft.

2) Remove cotter pins and nuts from tie rod ends. Use a puller to disconnect tie rod ends from steering knuckles. Remove 6 lower crossmember retaining bolts, then remove lower crossmember. Remove rack housing brackets, taking care not to damage rack boots. Remove steering gear.

Installation — To install, reverse removal procedure and note the following: Check toe-in. See *WHEEL ALIGNMENT* Section for specifications and procedures.

OVERHAUL
STEERING GEAR

Disassembly — 1) Place steering gear in a vice and mark rack end threaded areas for reassembly reference. Remove tie rods, spring clips, rack end dust seals and rack boot clamps. Remove rack boots.

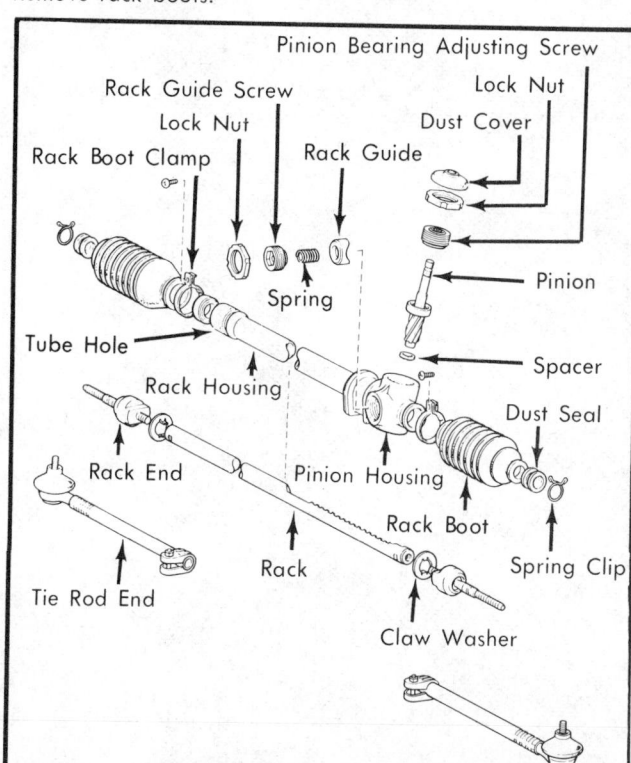

Fig. 1 Exploded View of Tercel Rack and Pinion Steering Gear Assembly

NOTE — *Left and right tie rod ends, rack boots and rack ends are different and should be marked accordingly.*

2) Unstake claw washers and remove rack ends. Using guide screw lock nut wrench (09617-10010), remove lock nut. Then, using rack guide screw wrench (09612-10020), remove guide screw and spring. Remove rack guide by pulling out with needle-nose pliers.

3) Remove pinion bearing adjusting screw lock nut with lock nut wrench (09617-10010) and pinion bearing adjusting screw with pin tool (09616-10091).

4) Pull rack completely through pinion housing side and align notched portion of rack with pinion. Pull pinion and upper pinion bearing out of pinion housing. Remove rack from pinion housing side without rotating it.

Inspection — 1) Check all parts for damage or deterioration. Check for play in rack ends and tie rod end ball joints. Check pinion teeth surfaces for wear or damage.

2) If pinion oil seal must be replaced, drive it in until it protrudes .020" (0.5 mm) from tip of pinion bearing adjusting screw.

3) If pinion upper bearing must be replaced, remove with a puller. Drive new bearing on with installer tool (09612-10061).

NOTE — *Seal side of bearing faces down.*

4) If pinion lower bearing must be replaced, heat rack to at least 176°F (80°C). Tap bearing out with plastic hammer. Reheat pinion housing and drive in new bearing.

5) Check rack for runout and tooth wear. Runout must not exceed .012" (0.3 mm). If rack bushing must be replaced, remove with puller. Press in new bushing.

Reassembly & Adjustment — 1) Pack pinion lower bearing and rack bushing with grease. Fill rack housing about half full of grease. Coat rack with grease and insert into pinion housing side. Position notches so pinion can be inserted.

2) Pack grease into pinion bearing. Coat pinion teeth with grease and insert spacer and pinion into pinion housing. Pinion end must be securely positioned in pinion lower bearing. Coat oil seal with grease and install pinion bearing adjusting screw. Place an INCH Lb. torque wrench and adaptor (09616-10010) on end of pinion and tighten adjusting screw until pinion turning torque is 3.5 INCH Lbs. (.39 N·m).

3) Loosen adjusting screw until pinion turning torque is 1.8-2.6 INCH Lbs. (.20-.29 N·m). Apply liquid sealer to adjusting screw lock nut and housing contact points. Tighten lock nut to 58-75 ft. lbs. (79-102 N·m). Check pinion turning torque. It should be 1.4-2.1 INCH Lbs. (.15-.23 N·m).

NOTE — *Tightening lock and nut decreases pinion turning torque by 0.4 INCH Lbs. (.04 N·m).*

4) Mesh rack and pinion. Coat rack guide with grease. Install rack guide, spring and rack guide screw. Using torque wrench and guide screw wrench, tighten guide screw to 18 ft. lbs. (24 N·m). Loosen screw about 30° from tightened position. Measure pinion turning torque and adjust by turning guide screw. Acceptable range is 4.3 INCH Lbs. (.47 N·m) for Cressida & Tercel models and 6.1-7.8 INCH Lbs. (.67-.86 N·m) for Starlet models.

Steering Gears & Linkage

TOYOTA CRESSIDA, STARLET & TERCEL RACK & PINION (Cont.)

5) Apply liquid sealer to lock nut and housing contact points, and using torque wrench and lock nut wrench, tighten lock nut to 37-47 ft. lbs. (50-64 N·m). Recheck total preload with a full stroke of the rack. Apply grease to rack end ball joints. Align claw washer with rack groove and tighten rack end into housing. Stake claw washer.

6) Coat rack end dust seal with grease. Clear rack housing tube hole of any grease. Install rack boots. Spring clips must have bends facing outward. Rack boot clamp on pinion housing side should have a gap of .19-.24" (5-6 mm) but tube side clamp should have no gap.

7) Rotate pinion and check rack stroke. Rack stroke should be 4.80" (122 mm). There should be no contour change of rack boots during this operation. Install tie rod ends and position them according to marks made on threads during disassembly.

TIGHTENING SPECIFICATIONS

Application	Ft. Lbs. (N·m)
Intermediate Shaft Pinch Bolts	22-28 (30-38)
Pinion Bearing Adjusting Screw Lock Nut	73-94 (99-128)
Rack Guide Screw Lock Nut	44-57 (60-78)
Rack End-to-Rack	48-65 (65-88)
Rack Housing Bracket-to-Body	22-32 (30-44)
Tie Rod-to-Knuckle	37-50 (50-68)
Tie Rod-to-Rack End	11-14 (15-19)

TOYOTA (EXC. LAND CRUISER) RECIRCULATING BALL

Celica
Corolla
Corona
Cressida
Pickup

DESCRIPTION

STEERING GEAR

Steering gear is a variable ratio, recirculating ball type. Ball bearings circulate within grooves in worm and nut. As worm shaft turns, ball nut moves up or down, turning the sector shaft and pitman arm.

STEERING LINKAGE

Linkage consists of an idler arm, center relay rod, adjustable tie rods, and steering knuckles. Pickups also use a steering damper attached to center relay rod. The connection between each component is by ball joints. Linkage assembly is connected to steering gear by a pitman arm.

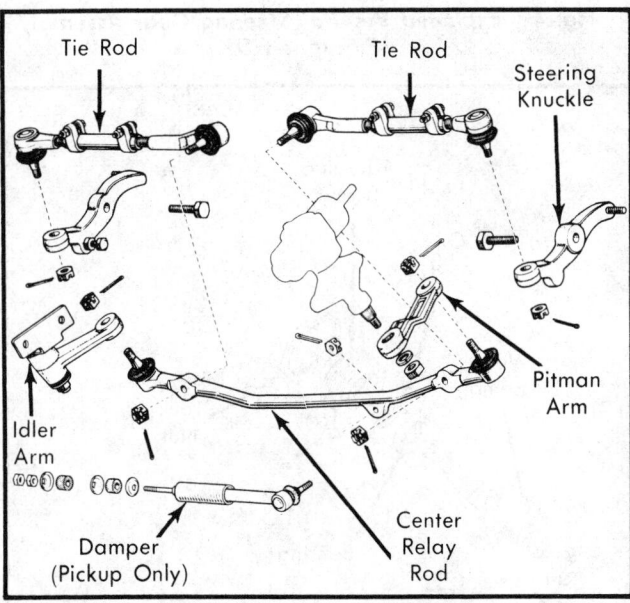

Fig. 1 Exploded View of Toyota Steering Linkage (Except Pickup 4-WD Models)

ADJUSTMENT

See Overhaul procedures in this article.

REMOVAL & INSTALLATION

STEERING GEAR

Removal — Mark steering gear shaft at flexible coupling or universal joint. Mark steering gear shaft at pitman arm. Disconnect pitman arm from steering gear. Remove steering gear bolts from frame and disconnect steering gear from steering shaft as gear is removed.

Installation — To install steering gear, reverse removal procedures and note the following: Make sure marks made upon removal are aligned upon installation.

STEERING LINKAGE

Removal — 1) On all models except Pickup 4-WD, mark pitman arm at sector shaft. Use a suitable puller to disconnect the following components: Pitman arm from sector shaft, and tie rod ball joints from steering knuckles. On Pickup 2-WD models, disconnect steering damper from crossmember. Remove idler arm bracket bolts, then remove steering linkage assembly from vehicle.

2) On Pickup 4-WD models, mark pitman arm at sector shaft and disconnect pitman arm. Disconnect steering damper from front axle. Remove steering knuckle-to-front axle bolts and remove steering linkage assembly from vehicle.

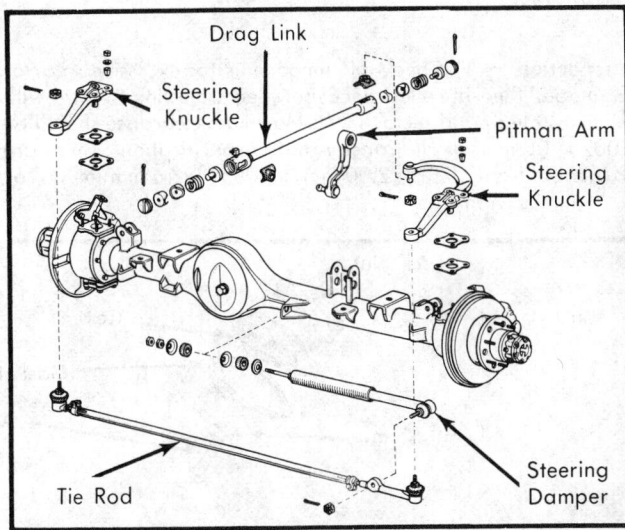

Fig. 2 Exploded View of Toyota Steering Linkage (Pickup 4-WD)

Installation — To install steering linkage, reverse removal procedure and note the following: Make sure pitman arm-to-sector shaft marks are aligned. To aid in toe-in adjustment, make sure tie rod lengths are to specifications. Measure tie rod lengths from center-to-center of ball joints. *See Tie Rod Length chart.*

Tie Rod Length	
Application	**In. (mm)**
Celica, Corona	12.60 (320)
Corolla	12.52 (318)
Cressida	14.06 (357)
Pickup	
2-WD	12.36 (314)
4-WD	47.24 (1200)

TOYOTA (EXC. LAND CRUISER) RECIRCULATING BALL (Cont.)

OVERHAUL

STEERING GEAR

Disassembly — 1) On all models except Pickup 4-WD, mark pitman arm at sector shaft and remove pitman arm. Remove sector shaft adjusting screw lock nut. Remove sector shaft cover, then sector shaft. Be careful not to lose adjusting screw and shim. Remove worm assembly lock nut, adjusting screw and oil seal. Remove worm assembly and bearings.

NOTE — *Do not disassemble ball nut from worm. If recirculating ball assembly has damaged or worn components, replace entire assembly.*

2) On Pickup 4-WD models, mark pitman arm at sector shaft and remove pitman arm. Remove sector shaft adjusting screw lock nut. Remove sector shaft cover and sector shaft. Remove worm assembly cover and shims. Remove worm assembly with bearings.

Inspection — 1) Check all components for excessive wear or damage. Measure clearance between adjusting screw (with shim installed) and sector shaft. Maximum clearance should be .002" (.05 mm). If clearance is not to specifications, shims are available from .0787" (2.00 mm) to .085" (2.16 mm) in .0016" (.04 mm) increments.

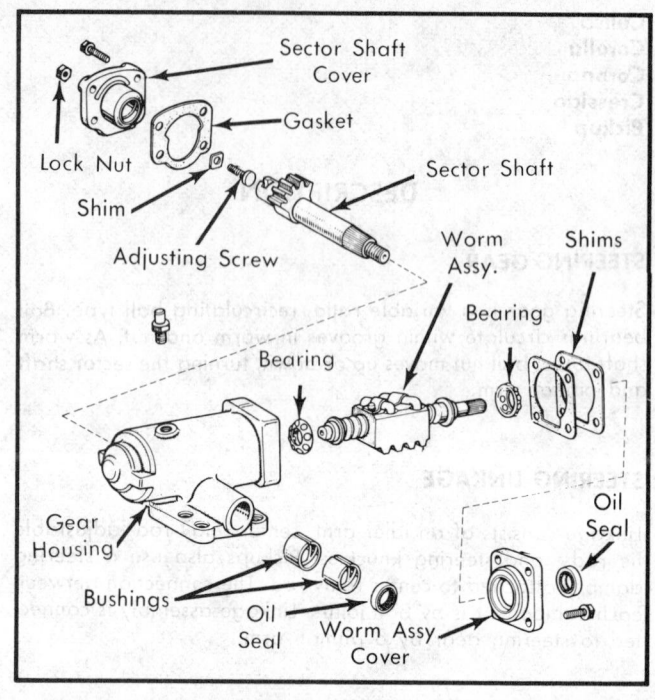

Fig. 4 Exploded View of Steering Gear Assembly (Pickup 4-WD)

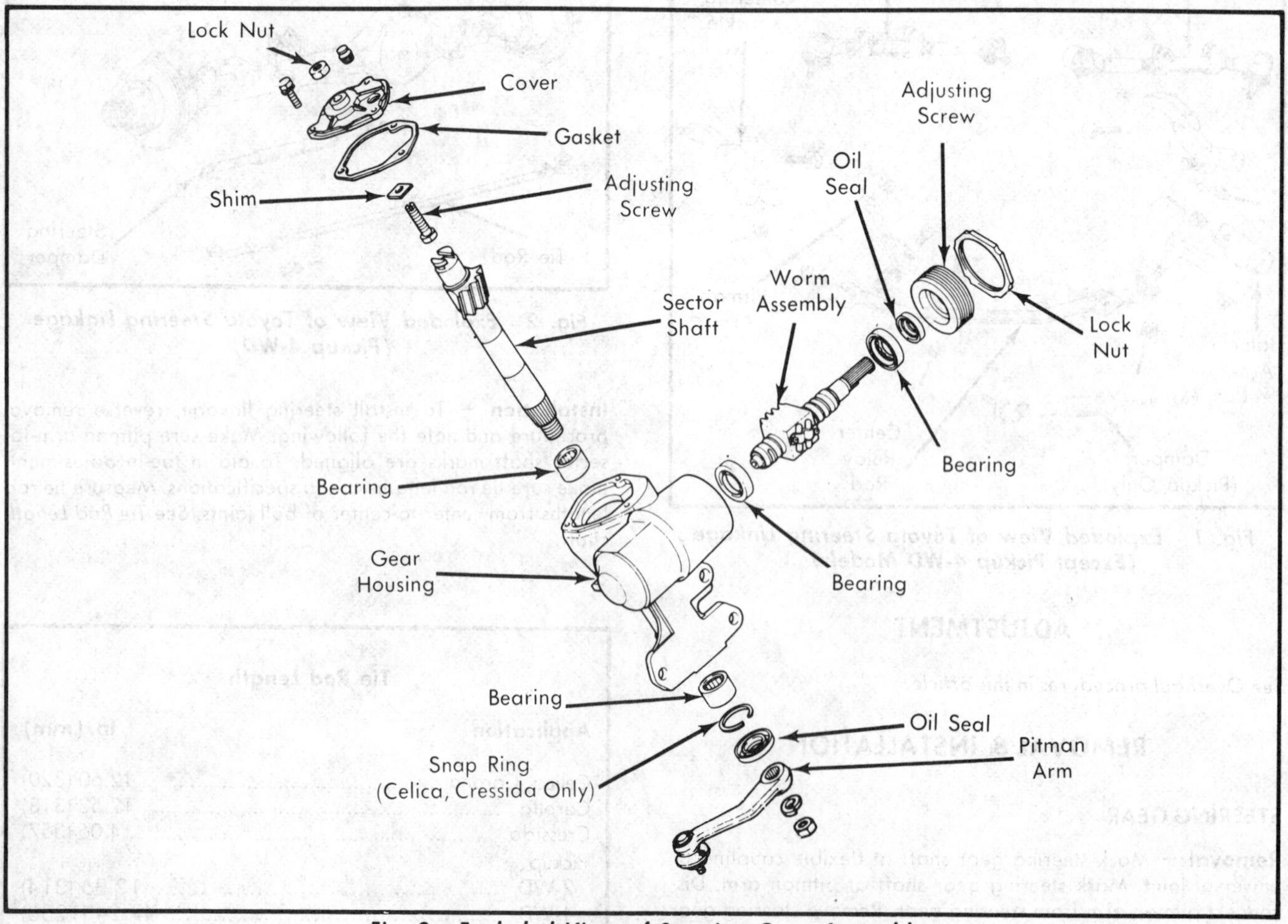

Fig. 3 Exploded View of Steering Gear Assembly (Except Pickup 4-WD)

TOYOTA (EXC. LAND CRUISER) RECIRCULATING BALL (Cont.)

2) On all models except Pickup 4-WD, check sector shaft bearings for pitting and smooth operation. Replace if necessary. On Pickup 4-WD, measure sector shaft diameter. Minimum diameter is 1.258" (31.95 mm). Measure sector shaft bushings (in gear housing) for clearance between sector shaft and bushings. Maximum clearance is .004" (.1 mm). If clearance exceeds specifications and sector shaft is not worn beyond limit, replace bushings in gear housing and hone bushings to obtain standard clearance of .0004-.0024" (.01-.06 mm).

CAUTION — *When checking worm gear and ball nut, do not let ball nut bottom out on either end of worm gear. If ball nut bottoms out, damage to worm assembly will occur.*

3) On all models, check worm assembly bearings; replace bearings if damaged or worn. Check worm gear and ball nut for damage. Hold worm assembly up at an angle so ball nut will travel down worm gear (full travel) and check for smooth operation. Replace worm assembly if any damage is found or operation is not smooth.

Reassembly & Adjustment — 1) Grease all bearings and sliding portions of gear assembly. Install bearings on worm assembly. Install worm assembly to gear housing.

2) On all models except Pickup 4-WD, install oil seal and adjusting nut. Tighten nut while rotating worm gear to seat bearings. Loosen adjusting nut, then tighten while measuring preload. *See Initial Worm Bearing Preload chart.* With preload to specification, hold adjusting nut, install and tighten lock nut.

3) On Pickup 4-WD, install oil seal to worm assembly cover. Install same shims as removed, then install end cover and tighten bolts. Measure preload of worm assembly. *See Initial Worm Bearing Preload chart.* If not to specifications, add or remove shims until preload is to specifications. Shims are available from .002-.004" (.05-.1 mm) in .0004" (.01 mm) increments, with 2 larger sizes available; .008" (.2 mm) and .020" (.5 mm).

Initial Worm Bearing Preload

Application	INCH Lbs. (N·m)
Celica, Corona	2.6-3.5 (.29-.39)
Corolla	1.7-3.5 (.19-.39)
Cressida	2.6-3.5 (.29-.39)
Pickup	
2-WD	2.6-4.3 (.29-.47)
4-WD	3.0-5.6 (.33-.62)

4) Center ball nut on worm shaft and install sector shaft so center teeth of both are meshed together. Install shim (selected previously) to adjusting screw and install to sector shaft.

5) Install sector shaft end cover to gear housing and loosen adjusting nut as far as possible. Install cover bolts and tighten. Adjust final worm bearing preload by tightening adjusting screw. *See Final Worm Bearing Preload chart.* Install lock nut and tighten while holding adjusting nut from turning.

Final Worm Bearing Preload

Application	INCH Lbs. (N·m)
Celica, Corona	4.3-5.2 (.47-.57)
Corolla, Cressida	2.6-3.5 (.29-.39)
Pickup	
2-WD	5.2-7.4 (.57-.81)
4-WD	6.9-9.5 (.80-1.0)

6) Install pitman arm and nut (aligning mating marks). Attach dial indicator so plunger touches end of pitman arm. Sector shaft should have no backlash when measured at any point 100° on either side of centered position.

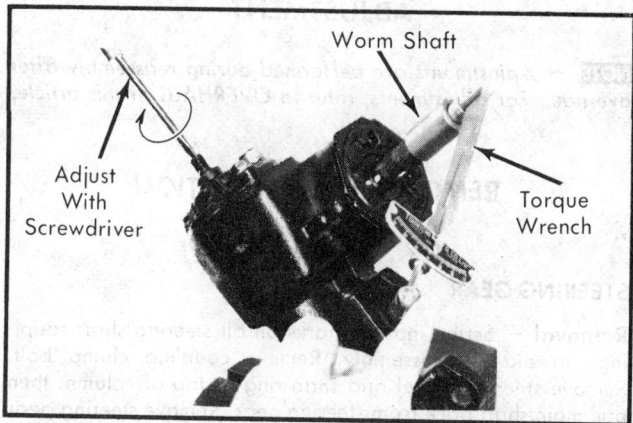

Fig. 5 Measuring Final Worm Bearing Preload

TIGHTENING SPECIFICATIONS

Application	Ft. Lbs. (N·m)
Ball Joint Nuts (All)	
Pickup	①54-80 (73-109)
All Other Models	36-51 (49-69)
Idler Arm Nut	
Pickup (2-WD Only)	58-87 (79-118)
All Other Models	51-65 (69-88)
Pitman Arm-to-Sector Shaft Nut	
Corolla	72-101 (98-137)
Pickup	
2-WD	80-90 (109-122)
4-WD	109-137 (158-186)
All Other Models	80-101 (109-137)
Sector Shaft Adjusting Screw Lock Nut	
Corona	15-25 (20-34)
Pickup	
2-WD	14-22 (19-30)
4-WD	25-36 (34-49)
All Other Models	14-22 (19-30)
Worm Assy. Adjusting Screw Lock Nut	
Corona	166-188 (226-256)
Pickup (2-WD Only)	166-188 (226-256)
All Other Models	94-123 (128-167)

① — Damper-to-relay rod should be 36-51 ft. lbs. (49-69 N·m).

Steering Gears & Linkage

TOYOTA LAND CRUISER RECIRCULATING BALL

DESCRIPTION

STEERING GEAR

Steering gear mechanism is of the recirculating ball type. Gear mounts off a bracket that is attached to frame. Adjustment screws are provided for backlash and preload. Initial preload is achieved with shims.

STEERING LINKAGE

Steering linkage consists of the following: pitman arm, relay rod, tie rod, damper, center arm and drag link. Tie rod and relay rod are adjustable to correct wheel alignment.

ADJUSTMENT

NOTE — *Adjustments are performed during reassembly after overhaul. For adjustments, refer to OVERHAUL in this article.*

REMOVAL & INSTALLATION

STEERING GEAR

Removal — Scribe mating marks on all steering shaft couplings to aid in reassembly. Remove coupling clamp bolt. Remove steering wheel and snap ring at top of column, then pull main shaft back from steering gear. Remove steering gear mounting bolts and pitman arm using suitable puller. Remove gear from frame.

Installation — To install, reverse removal procedure and tighten all mounting bolts.

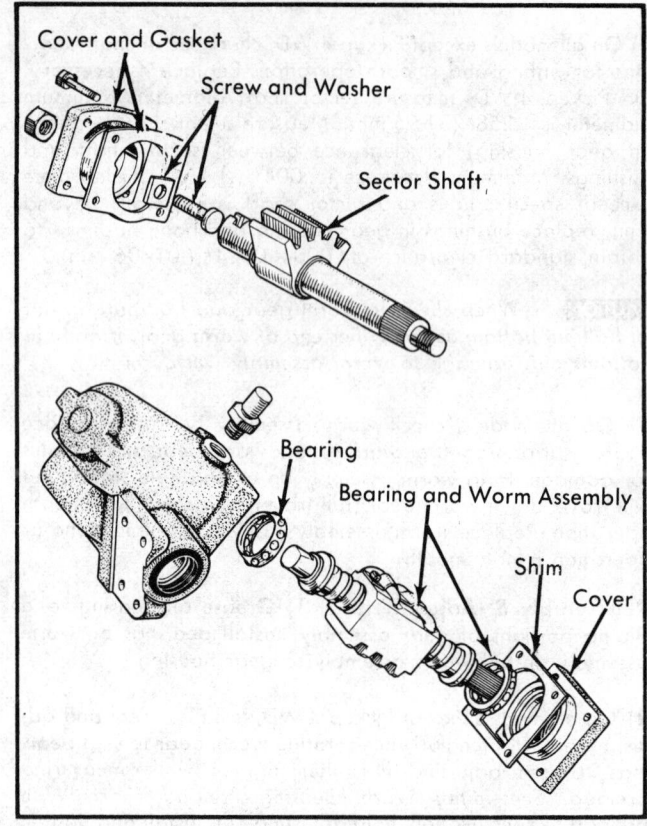

Fig. 1 Toyota Land Cruiser Steering Gear

STEERING LINKAGE

Removal — **1)** — Raise and support front of vehicle, then remove front wheels. Index mark relative position of pitman arm to sector shaft and remove arm, using suitable puller. Disconnect steering drag link from steering center arm.

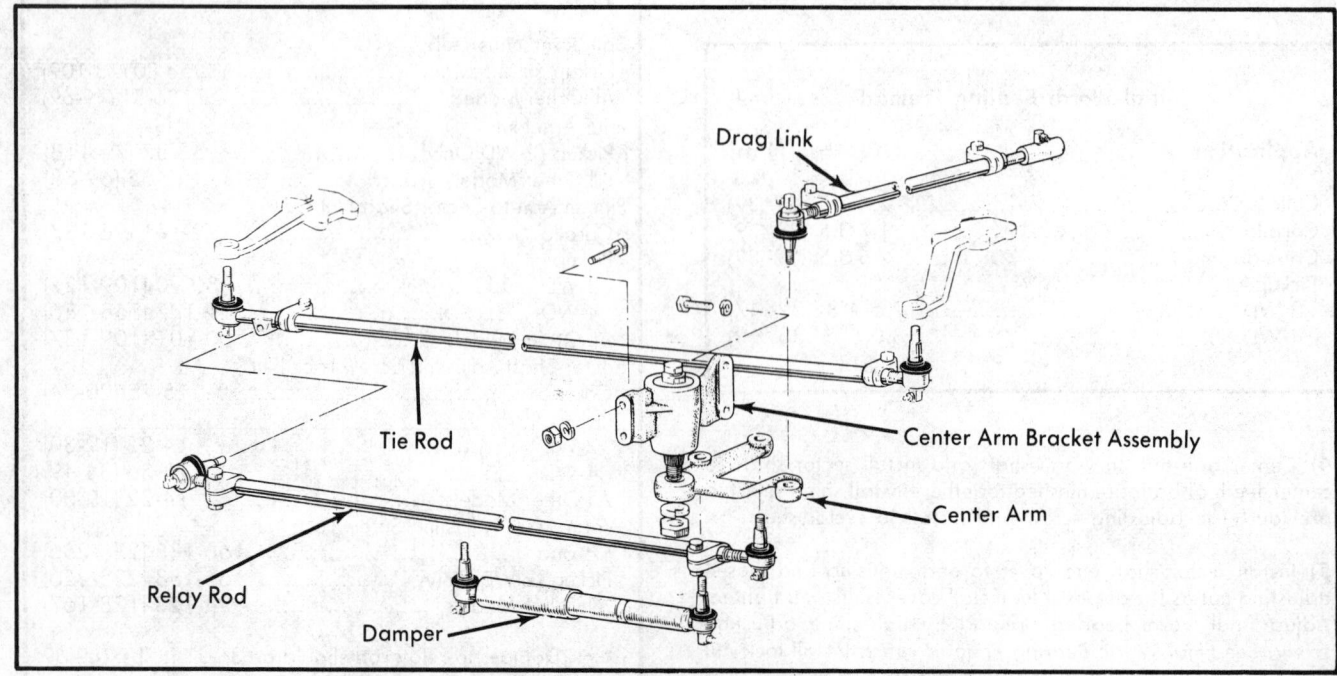

Fig. 2 Toyota Land Cruiser Front Steering Linkage

TOYOTA LAND CRUISER RECIRCULATING BALL (Cont.)

2) Disconnect tie rod ends from both sides. Disconnect relay rod from steering center arm, then remove tie rod assembly with relay arm assembly. Disconnect end of steering damper from bracket on crossmember. Loosen and remove center arm from bracket (with steering damper). Remove steering center arm bracket from frame.

Installation – To install, reverse removal procedure and note the following: Adjust tie rod, relay rod and drag link as shown in *Fig. 3*.

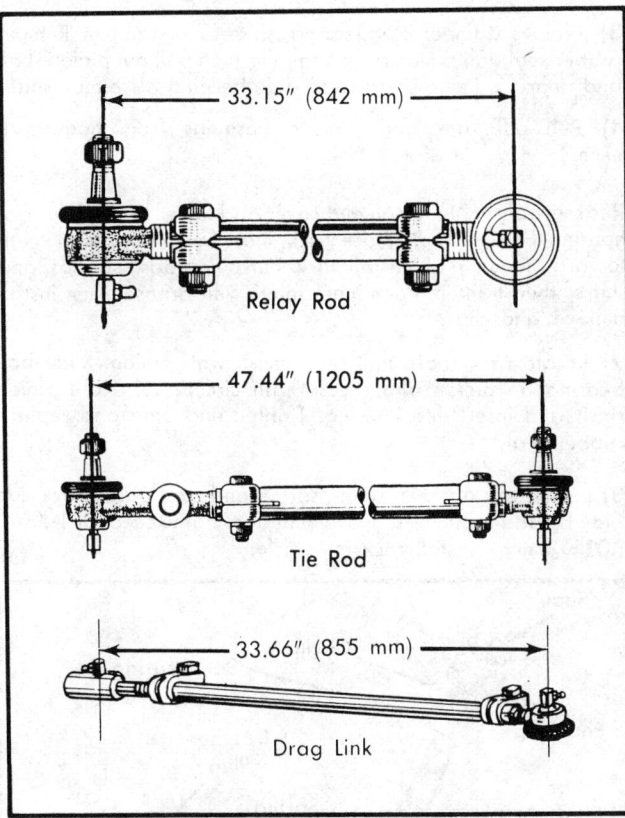

Fig. 3 Adjustment Lengths for Installation of Tie Rod, Relay Rod and Drag Link

OVERHAUL

Disassembly – Drain gear lubricant, then secure housing in a vise. Remove sector shaft end cover and gasket. With sector shaft positioned at rotational center, pull assembly out of gear housing. Note number and placement of shims as they are removed. Remove gear housing end cover and gasket. Take out worm assembly, keeping bearings in sequence. Do not attempt to disassemble worm assembly.

Inspection – 1) Wash all disassembled parts and inspect for wear or damage; replace as necessary. If inner or outer races are scored or pitted, replace as required. Inspect sector shaft and bushings for wear. If replacement is necessary, use a press to remove and replace bushings.

2) Hone bushings until clearance between bushing and sector shaft is .0004-.0024" (.009-.060 mm). Install new oil seal. Measure sector shaft thrust clearance, then select thrust washer that provides a minimum clearance between sector shaft and adjustment screw of .0020" (.051 mm).

Reassembly – 1) Install cover with same number of shims that were removed, then tighten bolts.

NOTE – *When tightening cover bolts, keep checking worm to ensure that it will turn freely.*

2) Using a pull scale, measure initial (starting) worm bearing preload for 3.0-5.6 INCH lbs. (.33-.62 N·m). If preload is not within specifications, correct by selecting proper thickness shim(s).

3) Position worm ball nut at center, then insert sector shaft ensuring ball nut and sector mesh together at center. Loosen ball adjusting bolt all the way and install cover.

4) Set worm shaft preload to 6.9-9.5 INCH lbs. (.76-1.0 N·m) with adjusting bolt. Make sure measurement is made with meshing positioned at center.

5) Install pitman arm and check backlash. There should be zero backlash when worm is rotated within 45° to either side. Tighten adjustment screw lock nut and recheck preload.

TIGHTENING SPECIFICATIONS

Application	Ft. Lbs. (N·m)
Gear Box Bracket	29-40 (39-54)
Pitman Arm Nut	119-141 (162-192)
Sector End Cover Bolts	22-32 (30-44)
Worm Bearing Cap	22-32 (30-44)

Steering Gears & Linkage

TRIUMPH RACK & PINION

TR7

DESCRIPTION

Steering gear is a rack and pinion type with direct linkage (tie rods) to steering arms. Gear housings are mounted by bolts through frame. A flexible coupling links the steering gears to steering shaft.

ADJUSTMENTS

Rack and pinion free play are adjusted through the use of shims on the rack damper and pinion shaft. These adjustments are performed as part of overhaul procedure. See *Overhaul below*.

REMOVAL & INSTALLATION

RACK AND PINION

Removal — 1) Raise vehicle and place on safety stands. Scribe an index mark on pinion shaft and lower steering coupling for installation purposes. Disconnect tie rod ends from steering knuckle.

2) Remove pinch bolt attaching lower steering coupling to rack pinion. Withdraw bolts mounting pinion end of rack to chassis.

3) Remove remaining rack mounting hardware, disconnect lower pinion shaft coupling and take rack out driver's side.

Installation — 1) If rack has been disassembled, it must be centralized before reinstallation: Remove center plug from thrust pad and, using a piece of welding rod, locate dimple in rack shaft. When dimple in rack shaft is aligned with plug hole rack is centralized.

2) Carefully slide rack assembly into position but DO NOT disturb rack shaft. Secure rack to chassis with mounting hardware, refit tie rod ends and tighten pinion coupling pinch bolt.

3) Make sure all nuts and bolts are tightened and check front wheel alignment. See *Triumph in WHEEL ALIGNMENT Section*.

OVERHAUL

RACK AND PINION

Disassembly — 1) Release clip and slide bellows toward outer ball joint. Slacken inner lock nut and unscrew tie rod assembly from rack. Withdraw spring from rack end. Straighten tab washer, unscrew sleeve nut, and remove tab washer, shims, and cup.

2) Slacken outer lock nut and unscrew tie rod end from tie rod. Remove outer lock nut, bellows, and cup nut. Remove inner lock nut from rack. Repeat on other end.

3) Remove damper plug, spring, shims and damper. Remove rubber seal and pinion retaining plug then pull out pinion shaft and bearing. Remove circlip to slide bearing off pinion shaft.

4) Pull out rack and remove bushings from housing if necessary.

Reassembly — 1) Install end cover and lower bushing in rack housing (if removed). Place rack shaft in housing with teeth toward pinion end. Install lock nuts, tie rods, springs and shims, then tighten. Pack inner joints with grease, then install bellows and clips.

2) Rotate rack shaft until teeth mesh with pinion. Slide ball bearing on pinion and secure with circlip. Lubricate pinion shaft and insert into housing. Tighten end plug and replace rubber seal.

3) Install rack damper, shims, spring and cap. Adjust rack side play by adding shims so movement does not exceed .001-.007" (.03-.18 mm). Install rack in vehicle.

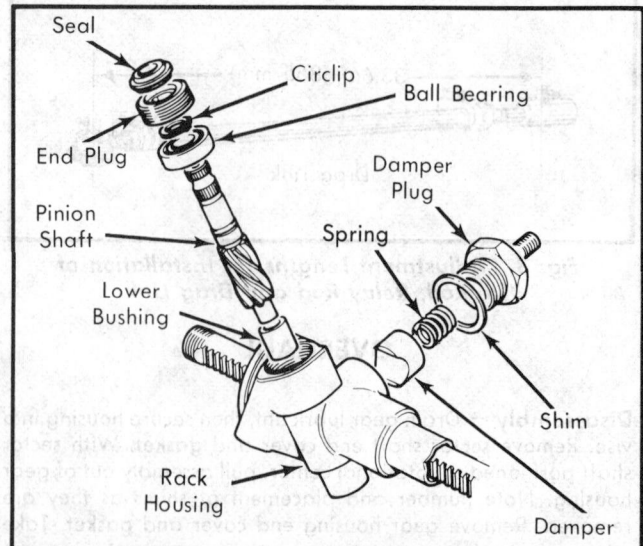

Fig. 4   Exploded View of TR7 Pinion and Damper

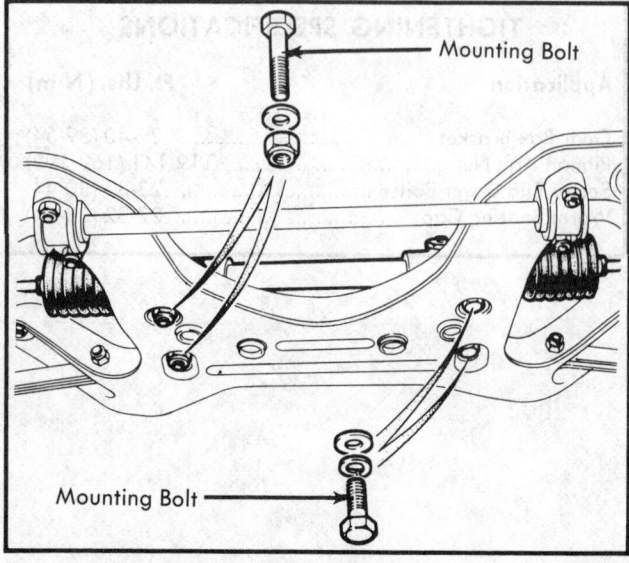

Fig. 1   Installed View of TR7 Rack Assembly

TIGHTENING SPECIFICATIONS

Application	Ft. Lbs. (N·m)
Steering Gear-to-Frame	22-29 (30-39)
Tie Rod Lock Nuts	30-37 (41-50)
Universal Joint Pinch Bolts	16-21 (22-29)

Steering Gears & Linkage

VOLKSWAGEN DASHER RACK & PINION

DESCRIPTION

The Volkswagen Dasher is equipped with an adjustable rack and pinion steering gear. Attached to center of the rack housing are 2 tie rods. A steering damper is also used.

REMOVAL & INSTALLATION

Removal — 1) Bend back tabs on locking plate at center of rack housing and remove both tie rod bolts. Move tie rods so that gear will have clearance for removal.

2) Unbolt pinch clamp at pinion-to-column connection. Remove lower instrument panel. Loosen steering column flange at toe board. Drive steering flange tube off of steering gear.

3) Remove gear mounting screw at right end of rack housing, then unbolt rack mounting at left end. Turn front wheels to right lock, and remove steering gear through right wheel housing.

Installation — To install, reverse removal procedure and tighten all fasteners to specifications.

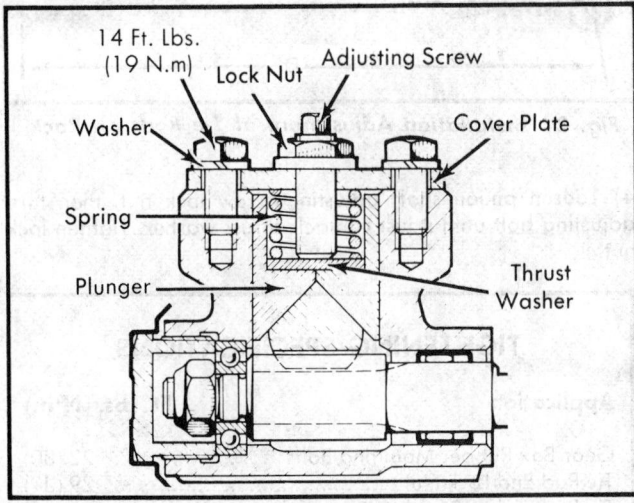

Fig. 1   Sectional View of Adjustable Steering Gear

ADJUSTMENT

With components installed on vehicle, tighten adjusting screw by hand until screw just contacts thrust washer. Hold adjusting screw in position and tighten lock nut *(Fig. 1)*.

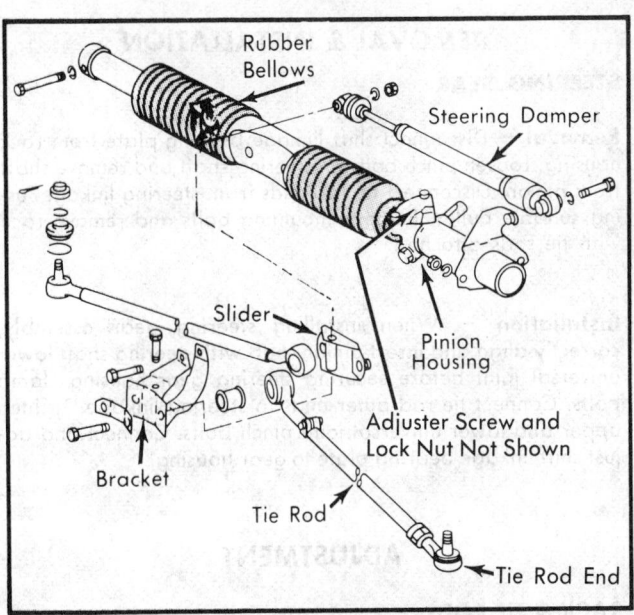

Fig. 2   Volkswagen Dasher Rack and Pinion Assembly

OVERHAUL

NOTE — *Manufacturer does not recommend overhaul of this unit. If it is determined to be defective, replace as an assembly.*

TIGHTENING SPECIFICATIONS

Application	Ft. Lbs. (N·m)
Gear Box-to-Brackets	14 (19)
Pinion Shaft Clamp Pinch Bolt	22 (30)
Tie Rods-to-Rack	40 (54)

VOLKSWAGEN JETTA, RABBIT, PICKUP & SCIROCCO RACK & PINION

DESCRIPTION

Steering gear is a rack and pinion type. Tie rods attach to ends of rack. Late production racks are mounted with "U" bolts and rubber bushings rather than welded mounting plates.

REMOVAL & INSTALLATION

STEERING GEAR

Removal — Disconnect shift linkage bearing plate from rack housing. Loosen pinch bolts on steering shaft and remove shaft from pinion. Disconnect tie rod ends from steering linkage, using suitable puller. Remove mounting bolts and remove rack with tie rods attached.

Installation — When installing steering gear assembly, correctly align and insert pinion shaft with steering shaft lower universal joint before securing steering gear housing clamp bolts. Connect tie rod outer ends to steering linkage. Tighten upper and lower universal joint pinch bolts. Connect and adjust shift linkage bearing plate to gear housing.

ADJUSTMENT

RACK & TIE RODS

1) Center rack in housing so rack protrudes an equal amount from each end of housing.

Both Sides of Rack Must Protrude Same Amount

Measure to Inside Lip

Fig. 1   Centering Rack in Steering Gear Housing

2) If replacing the non-adjustable left tie rod with adjustable type, adjust tie rod length "D" to 14.92" (379 mm).

3) Screw tie rods onto rack and adjust to specified dimensions without moving rack from center position. When adjustment is correct, secure tie rods with lock nuts and install rubber boots. See *Fig. 2.*

Tie Rod Specification		
Application	Dimension "B"	Dimension "C"
Man. Trans.	2.72" (69 mm)	.... 2.72" (69 mm)
Auto. Trans.	2.64" (67 mm)	.... 2.72" (69 mm)

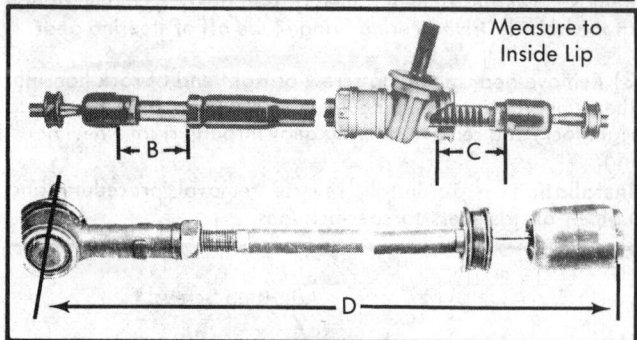

Measure to Inside Lip

Fig. 2   Installation Adjustment of Tie Rods on Rack

4) Loosen pinion shaft adjusting screw lock nut, then turn adjusting bolt until it just contacts thrust washer. Tighten lock nut.

TIGHTENING SPECIFICATIONS

Application	Ft. Lbs. (N·m)
Gear Box Rubber Mounting Bolts	22 (30)
Tie Rod End Lock Nut	29 (39)
Tie Rod End-to-Steering Arm	22 (30)
Universal Joint Pinch Bolt	22 (30)

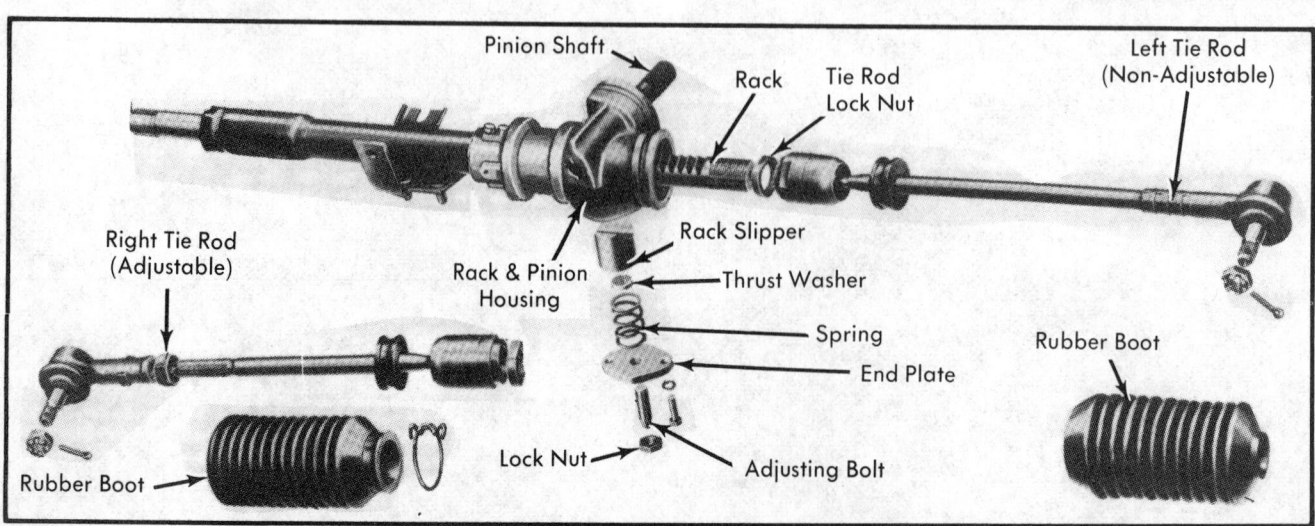

Fig. 3   Disassembled View of Rack & Pinion Steering Gear Assembly

VOLKSWAGEN VANAGON RACK & PINION

DESCRIPTION

Volkswagen Vanagon models use a rack and pinion steering gear. A transfer gear is used to connect steering shaft to steering gear. Tie rods are connected to rack and directly to steering knuckle, with ball joints. Both tie rods are adjustable for toe-in.

ADJUSTMENT

STEERING GEAR

NOTE — *Steering gear is not adjustable on these models. If gear is damaged or does not operate properly, complete unit must be replaced.*

REMOVAL & INSTALLATION

STEERING GEAR

Removal — Remove clamp bolt attaching connecting shaft coupling to steering gear pinion shaft. Disconnect tie rod ball joint from steering knuckles. Remove steering gear housing mounting bolts and remove steering gear from vehicle.

Installation — To install steering gear assembly, reverse removal procedure.

TRANSFER GEAR

Removal — Remove clamp bolt attaching connecting shaft coupling to transfer gear shaft. Remove clamp bolt attaching lower steering shaft flange to transfer gear shaft. Remove transfer gear attaching bolts and remove transfer gear.

Installation — To install transfer gear assembly, reverse removal procedure.

NOTE — *During installation of steering gear and/or transfer gear, always replace rubber couplings in connecting shaft and steering shaft lower flange.*

OVERHAUL

NOTE — *Steering gear and transfer gear cannot be repaired. Replace components if damaged. Steering gear rubber boots and tie rods can be replaced.*

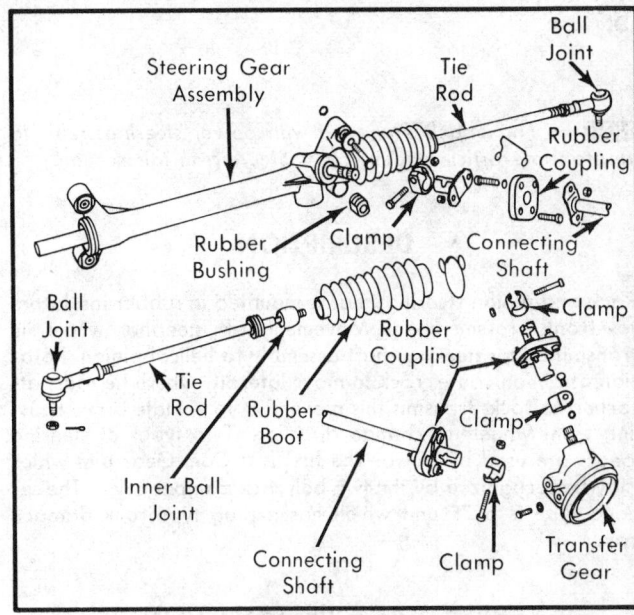

Fig. 1 Exploded View of Volkswagen Vanagon Steering Gear and Transfer Gear Assembly

TIE RODS AND RUBBER BOOTS

Disassembly — With steering gear assembly removed, remove clamps holding rubber boot to tie rod and steering gear housing. Using a punch, remove staking of tie rod inner ball joint washer to rack. Remove tie rods and rubber boots from steering gear assembly. Loosen tie rod ball joint lock nut and remove ball joints from tie rods. Press rubber bushing out of gear housing mounting.

Reassembly — To assemble tie rods and rubber boots, reverse disassembly procedure and note the following: After tightening tie rod inner ball joints, stake washer to groove in rack.

TIGHTENING SPECIFICATIONS	
Application	**Ft. Lbs. (N·m)**
Clamp Bolts	14 (19)
Housing Mounting Bolts	18 (24)
Tie Rod Inner Ball Joint Lock Nut	51 (69)
Tie Rod Outer Ball Joint Lock Nut	58 (79)

VOLVO RACK & PINION

DL

NOTE — *For models equipped with power steering, refer to appropriate article under Power Steering in this section.*

DESCRIPTION

Rack and pinion steering gear is mounted in rubber insulators to front crossmember. Movement of steering wheel is transmitted by steering shaft assembly to helical pinion. Rotation of pinion causes rack to move laterally where tie rods, attached to rack, transmit this movement to spindle arms, causing front wheels to change direction. Two types of steering gears are used by Volvo. The first is a Cam Gear unit which may be recognized by the two bolt rack damper cover. The second type is a ZF unit which has a plug type rack damper cover.

REMOVAL & INSTALLATION

STEERING GEAR

Removal — Push protective cover up out of way of lower joint. Remove lock bolt and nut from pinion flange. Bend flange apart slightly. Raise and support front of vehicle and remove wheels. Remove Tie rod nuts and disconnect ball studs from spindle using ball joint removal tool (9995043). Remove splash guard and bolts securing steering gear to crossmember. Disconnect gear from flange and remove gear.

Installation — To install, reverse removal procedure making sure that recess on pinion shaft is aligned towards lock bolt opening in flange.

TIE RODS

Removal — Raise vehicle and remove wheels. Remove tie rod nuts and disconnect ball studs from spindle using ball joint removal tool (9995043). Remove splash guard. Loosen inner clamps for both rubber bellows and drain oil, then re-attach clamp on side not being removed (if applicable). Bend up tie rod lock and disconnect rod from steering gear. Clamp ball stud in vise, loosen lock nut and unscrew rod, counting number of thread turns. Remove outer clamp for rubber bellows and remove bellows.

Installation — Install rubber bellows and outer clamp. Screw on lock nut same number of turns as when removed. Install ball stud and tighten lock nut. Attach tie rod to steering gear and punch ball stud edge into rack groove. Fill a suction gun with 6.75 oz. (200 cc) of 20W-50 engine oil and inject oil into steering gear through rubber bellows inner end. Install inner bellows clamp and tighten clamp and tighten clamp after turning tie rod so that ball stud is up. Connect tie rod to spindle making sure that both rods are the same length within .08" (2 mm).

ADJUSTMENT

NOTE — *Adjustments are performed during gear assembly process. See Overhaul as outlined.*

OVERHAUL

CAM GEAR

Disassembly — 1) Clean steering gear exterior and check inner ball joints for wear. Loosen pinion side rubber bellows and drain oil. Remove pinion side ball stud, lock nut and rubber bellows. Bend up locked portion of ball joint and unscrew pinion side tie rod. Repeat procedure on opposite side of gear.

2) Remove rack damper cover, spring, "O" ring and piston. Remove pinion cover and lift out pinion assembly. Pull out rack from pinion side of gear housing and remove rack bushing using a puller (4078). Use a puller (5047) to remove pinion lower bearing. Clean all parts and check for wear. Replace all seals, rack bushing and worn parts.

Reassembly & Adjustment — 1) Oil all parts prior to reassembly with 20W-50 engine oil. Install new rack bushing so that locks align with gear housing slots. Install pinion lower bearing using a suitable driver. Install pinion with upper bearing, but no shims in housing. Install pinion spacer sleeve and cover with gasket, but no seal. Use a dial indicator to measure pinion end play and record for later use. Remove pinion assembly.

2) Insert rack in gear housing from pinion side using care that rack teeth do not damage rack bushing. Apply a non-hardening gasket compound to pinion cover seal and install seal in cover using suitable driver (2734). Calculate required pinion shim thickness by adding .004-.010" (.10-.25 mm) to pinion end play previously measured. This will give correct amount of pinion preload. Install pinion, shims and spacer sleeve with shims between upper bearing and spacer sleeve. Install pinion cover with gasket and seal.

3) Place rack damper piston in housing without "O" ring or spring. Using straight edge and feeler gauge, measure end play between end of piston and housing (see Fig. 1). Measure thickness of gasket and calculate shim thickness required to obtain a total thickness, between gasket and shim, of .001-.006" (.02-.15 mm) greater than the measured piston end play to obtain correct preload. Install spring and "O" ring in piston, install shims, gasket and cover.

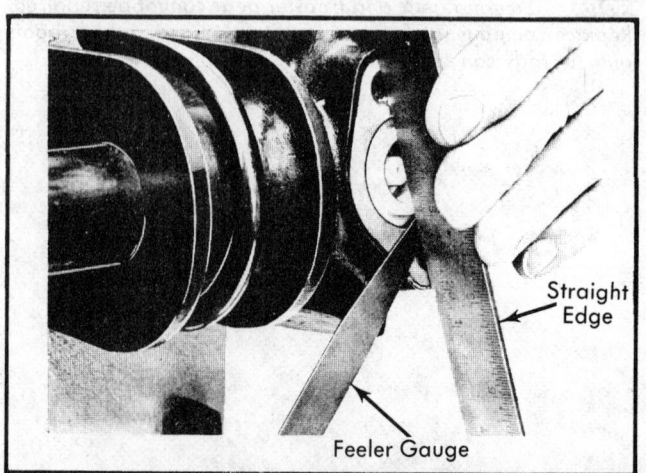

Fig. 1 Measuring Rack Damper Piston End Play (Cam Gear)

VOLVO RACK & PINION (Cont.)

4) Using suitable torque gauge (5053), crank rack back and forth from one end to the other. Torque reading should be 8-14 INCH Lbs. (.9-1.5 N·m). Install pinion side tie rod and punch ball joint edge into rack groove.

NOTE — *When installing old tie rod, place a thin shim between ball joint and rack shoulder so unused portion of ball can be used for punch locking.*

5) Install pinion side rubber bellows with inner clamp only. Install lock nut and ball stud. Repeat procedure for other side of gear and adjust both rods to the same length within .08" (2 mm). Use a suction gun to inject 6.75 ozs. (200 cc) of 20W-50 engine oil through outer end of pinion side rubber bellows. Install outer clamps on bellows.

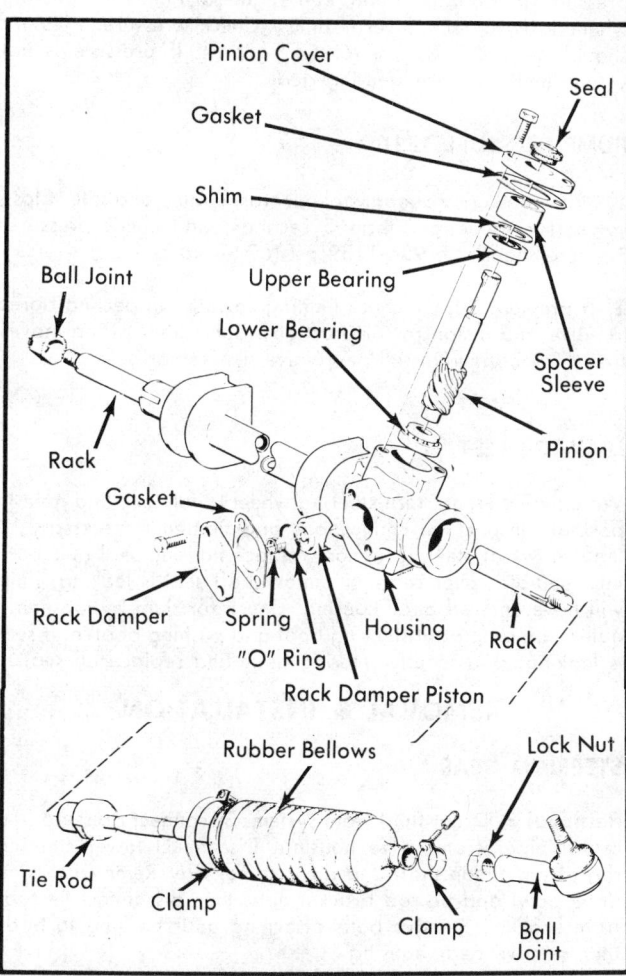

Fig. 2   Exploded View of Cam Gear Steering Gear Assembly

ZF STEERING GEAR

Disassembly — 1) Clean exterior of steering gear and check inner ball joints for wear. Remove pinion side rubber bellows. Bend up locked portion of ball joint and unscrew tie rod from rack. Remove opposite side tie rod in like manner. Remove dust seal and cotter pin for rack damper, then remove cover and spring using suitable tool (5119). Remove rack damper piston, knocking on rack with palm of hand to aid removal.

2) Remove pinion shaft dust seal. Unscrew the pinion shaft nut using suitable tool (5119). Clamp pinion shaft in a soft

jawed vise and tap lightly on housing with soft mallet to remove pinion. Remove rack from pinion side of housing and remove rack bushing by pressing in locking tabs and prying bearing out. Press pinion thrust washer and bearing from shaft. Clean all parts and check for wear. Replace all "O" rings and worn parts.

Reassembly & Adjustment — 1) Press bearing onto pinion and install snap ring and thrust washer. Install new "O" rings on rack bushing and press bushing into housing making sure that tabs on bushing fit correctly into slots of housing. Lubricate rack and insert rack into pinion side of housing using care not to damage rack bushing with rack teeth. Lubricate pinion and install pinion with bearing.

2) Install new "O" ring in pinion nut and install nut using suitable tool (5119). Torque to 16-19 ft. lbs. (22-27 N·m). Install snap ring and press down against nut. Fill cavity on top of nut with grease and install dust seal. Install new "O" ring on rack damper piston, grease piston and install piston and spring.

3) Install, but do not tighten rack damper cover (use tool 5119). Using torque gauge, crank rack back and forth between end positions. Torque should be 8-14 INCH Lbs. (.9-1.5 N·m). To increase torque, screw in rack damper cover. Lock cover in correct position with cotter pin and install dust cover.

4) Crank out rack fully and fill rack tooth spaces with grease. Crank rack in and then out again and repeat grease application. Approximately 1 oz. of grease should be used. Install tie rods using new lock washers and bend washer to lock rod in place. Install rubber bellows.

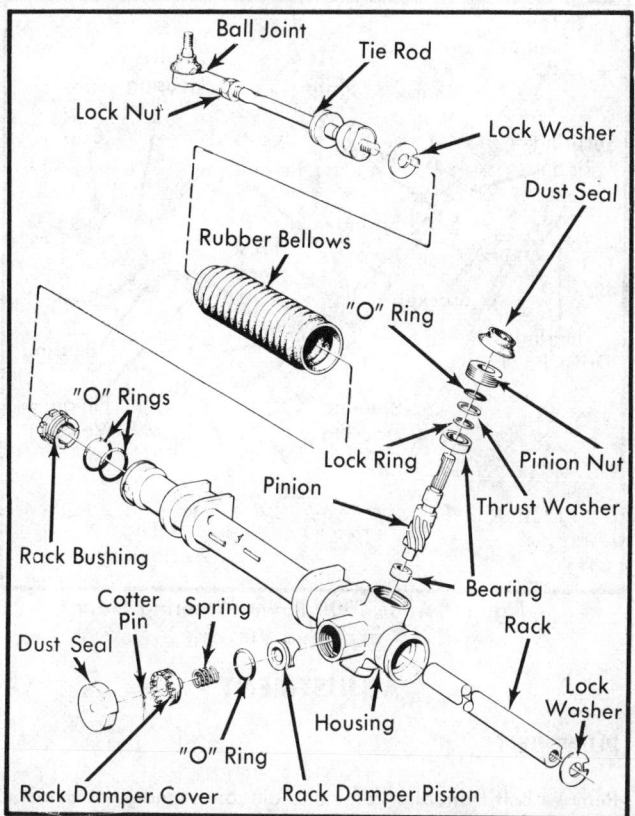

Fig. 3   Exploded View of ZF Steering Gear Assembly

Power Steering

AUDI 4000 POWER-ASSISTED RACK & PINION

DESCRIPTION

Audi 4000 models use a power-assisted rack and pinion steering gear. The system consists of a vane pump, rotary piston pinion gear assembly and an oil reservoir. The vane pump draws fluid from the reservoir and supplies it to the flow control valve. The control valve supplies fluid to the proper side of the rack-piston when the steering wheel is turned. The pump is belt driven and is mounted on the front of the engine. The reservoir is located near the firewall.

GENERAL SERVICE

Capacity — 1 qt.

Lubricant — ATF Dexron or Dexron II.

Oil Level Check — Remove reservoir cover, start engine and check fluid level. Fluid level should be at mark on upper inside of reservoir.

Hydraulic System Bleeding — Start engine and allow to idle. Check that fluid is at proper level. Turn steering wheel lock to lock several times quickly. Continue until fluid level remains at reservoir mark. Make sure that no bubbles appear in reservoir when steering wheel is turned. Shut off engine and check that oil level does not rise more than 3/8" above mark.

Oil Filter Replacement — Remove outer cover, gasket and spring from reservoir. Remove inner filter cover and filter insert. Replace filter. Install new filter, replace old filter cover, spring, gasket and top cover. Check fluid level.

NOTE — *Oil filter insert must be replaced whenever repairs are made to power steering system.*

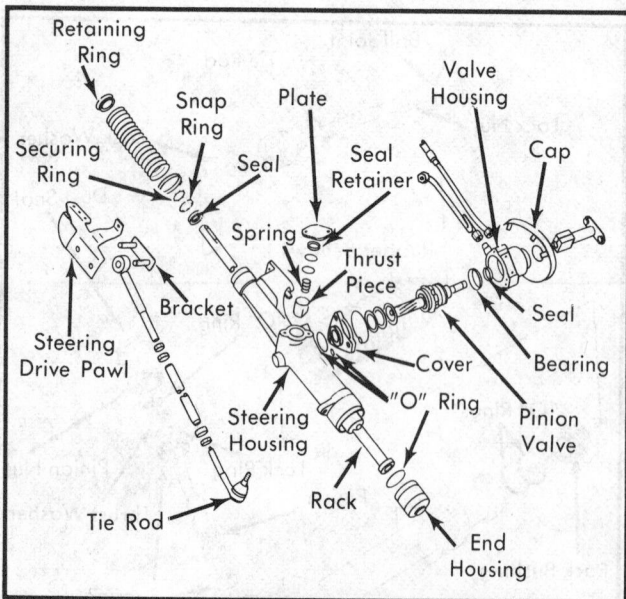

Fig. 1 Audi 4000 Power Steering Gear Exploded View

ADJUSTMENT

PUMP BELT

Remove belt from alternator and air conditioning compressor. Loosen 2 nuts on pump mounting bracket. Turn adjusting nut on bracket until belt deflection is 3/8" (9.5 mm) at center of belt. Tighten nuts. Reinstall alternator and air conditioning belts.

STEERING GEAR

Loosen lock nut on steering gear. Hand tighten adjusting screw until it just touches the thrust plate. Hold adjusting screw and tighten lock nut. Check adjustment with engine idling. No play should be felt. Readjust if necessary.

TESTING

SYSTEM PRESSURE TEST

Install pressure gauge (US1074/2 or equivalent) between pressure hose and pressure pipe of valve housing, with pressure gauge valve open. Run engine at idle. Turn steering wheel lock to lock several times. Check pressure. Pressure should be 986-1189 psi (69-84 kg/cm²). If pressure is not within limits, replace steering gear.

PUMP PRESSURE TEST

1) With pressure gauge installed, start engine and idle. Close valve (for no longer than 5 seconds) and check pressure. Pressure should be 986-1189 psi (69-84 kg/cm²).

2) If pressure differs, check limiting valve by inspecting bores in valve and piston for obstructions. Check that piston moves freely in housing. Install new valve if necessary.

LEAKAGE TEST

With engine idling, turn steering wheel to full lock and hold in position. Inspect all connections and tighten if necessary. If leak shows at steering pinion, replace housing seal and both intermediate cover seals. If pinion shaft seal is leaking, fluid will have entered gear housing. Check for fluid by loosening outer clamp on right steering boot and pushing boot in. If seal is leaking, disassemble steering gear and replace all seals.

REMOVAL & INSTALLATION

STEERING GEAR

Removal — Drain fluid from system. Disconnect pressure and return pipes from valve housing. Disconnect lower steering shaft from pinion shaft. Move cap out of way. Remove steering drive pawl and tie rod bracket nuts, then disconnect tie rods from bracket. Remove bolts attaching gear housing to body then remove gear housing.

Installation — Reverse removal procedures. To facilitate tie rod installation, install one tie rod to steering gear and tighten before installing other tie rod.

VANE PUMP

Removal — Remove alternator and vane pump belts. Disconnect pressure and suction lines from pump and cover openings. Remove mounting bolts from bracket and lift pump from engine.

Installation — Reverse removal procedures noting the following: Adjust belt deflection to 3/8" (9.5 mm) at center. After installation of pressure and suction lines, start engine and turn steering wheel to full lock and check for leaks in connections.

AUDI 4000 POWER-ASSISTED RACK & PINION (Cont.)

OVERHAUL

NOTE — *Before disassembling steering gear, check output and system pressure. Always use all parts in repair kit (811 498 020) and always use new self-locking nuts.*

PINION HOUSING SEALS

Disassembly — 1) Remove attaching bolts from valve housing and remove housing. Remove pinion gear and intermediate cover.

2) Remove "O" rings from intermediate cover (1 on each side) and, using suitable tool, drive out intermediate cover oil seal. Anchor housing in padded vise and drive out oil seal from the back.

3) Install new seals from the inside cover and housing. Make sure that seal lip on housing seal faces intermediate cover, and seal lip of cover seal faces valve housing. Replace both intermediate cover "O" rings.

Reassembly — Reverse removal procedure noting the following: Protect pinion teeth on shaft when replacing intermediate cover. Do not damage "O" rings during installation.

STEERING GEAR

Disassembly — 1) With steering gear assembly removed from vehicle, remove pinion valve housing and pinion valve assembly. Remove plate, seal retainer, spring and thrust piece from steering housing.

2) Remove retaining ring, clamp and boot from steering housing. Remove securing ring and snap ring from steering housing.

3) Remove end housing and "O" ring from steering housing. Pull rack out of steering housing. Using oil seal puller, remove oil seal from steering housing.

Reassembly — 1) To install new oil seal to steering housing, place oil seal on flat surface and push sleeve (available in repair kit 811 498 020) into oil seal. Slide rack into steering housing then slide oil seal with sleeve over rack and into steering housing using suitable tools (VW 426 and VW 4166). Remove sleeve. Install snap ring and securing ring.

2) Install end housing with new "O" ring. Install thrust piece, spring, "O" ring, seal retainer and plate. Install clamp, boot and retaining ring. Then install pinion valve assembly as previously described.

TIGHTENING SPECIFICATIONS

Application	Ft. Lbs. (N·m)
End Housing	37 (50)
Pressure-Flow Limiting Valve Cap	42 (60)
Pressure Pipe	29 (40)
Return Pipe	
On Pump	29 (40)
On Valve Housing	22 (30)
Steering Drive Pawl	32 (44)
Tie Rod-to-Steering Drive Pawl	32 (44)
Valve Housing Bolts	14 (19)

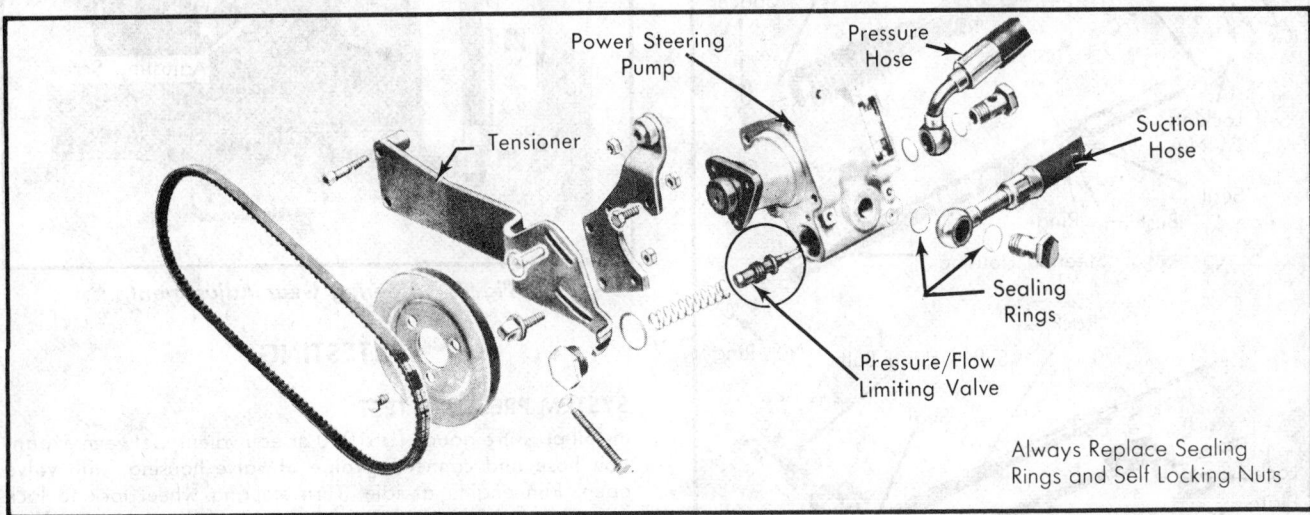

Power Steering Pump
Pressure Hose
Tensioner
Suction Hose
Sealing Rings
Pressure/Flow Limiting Valve
Always Replace Sealing Rings and Self Locking Nuts

Fig. 2 View of Vane Pump Assembly.
Only Pressure/Flow Limiting Valve Can Be Replaced

Power Steering

AUDI 5000 POWER-ASSISTED RACK & PINION

DESCRIPTION

A power-assisted rack and pinion steering gear is used on Audi 5000 models. The system consists of a vane pump, rotary piston pinion gear assembly and an oil reservoir. The vane pump draws fluid from the reservoir and supplies it to the flow control valve. The control valve supplies fluid to the proper side of the rack-piston as the steering wheel is turned. The pump is belt driven and mounted on the front of the engine. The reservoir is located near the firewall.

GENERAL SERVICE

Capacity — 1 qt.

Lubricant — ATF Dexron or Dexron II

Oil Level Check — Remove reservoir cover, start engine and check fluid level. Fluid level should be at mark on upper inside of reservoir.

Hydraulic System Bleeding — Start engine and allow to idle. Check that fluid is at proper level. Turn steering wheel lock to lock several times quickly. Continue until fluid level remains at reservoir mark. Make sure that no bubbles appear in reservoir when steering wheel is turned. Shut off engine and check that fluid level does not rise more than 3/8" (9.5 mm) above mark.

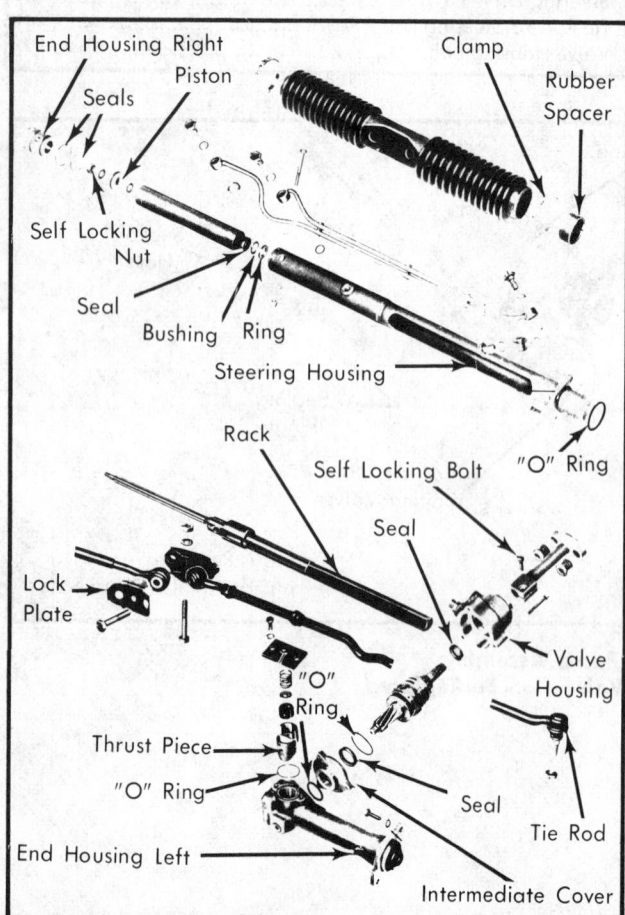

Fig. 1 Exploded View of Audi 5000 Steering Gear Assembly

Oil Filter Replacement — Remove outer cover, gasket and spring from reservoir. Remove inner filter cover and filter insert. Replace filter. Install new filter, replace filter cover, spring, gasket and cover. Check fluid level.

NOTE — *Oil filter insert must be replaced whenever repairs are made to power steering system.*

ADJUSTMENT

PUMP BELT

Remove belt from alternator and air conditioning compressor. Loosen 2 nuts on pump mounting bracket. Turn adjusting nut on bracket until belt deflection is 3/8" (9.5 mm) at center. Tighten nuts and reinstall belt.

STEERING GEAR

Loosen lock nut on steering gear. Hand tighten adjusting screw until it touches the thrust plate. Hold adjusting screw and tighten lock nut. Check adjustment with engine idling. No play should be felt. Readjust if necessary.

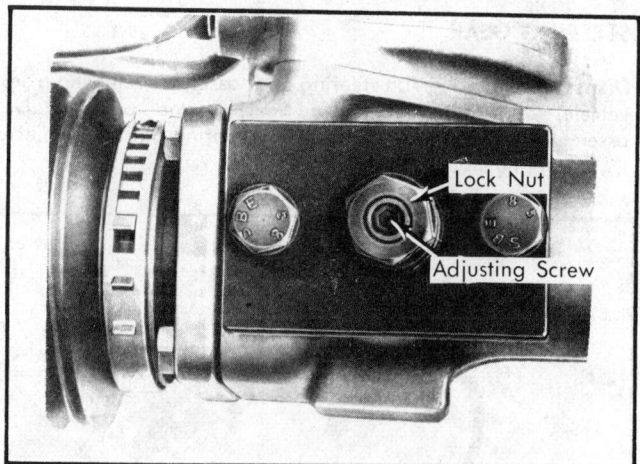

Fig. 2 Steering Gear Adjustment

TESTING

SYSTEM PRESSURE TEST

Install pressure gauge (US1070 or equivalent) between expansion hose and connecting pipe of valve housing, with valve open. Run engine at idle. Turn steering wheel lock to lock several times. Check pressure. Correct pressure is 986-1189 psi (68-84 kg/cm²). If pressure is not within limits, replace steering gear.

PUMP PRESSURE TEST

1) With pressure gauge installed, start engine and idle. Close valve (no longer than 5 seconds) and check pressure. Correct pressure is 986-1189 psi (68-84 kg/cm²). If pressure is different, check pressure/flow limiting valve. If valve is good, replace power steering pump.

2) To check limiting valve, inspect bores in valve and piston for obstructions, and that piston moves freely in housing. Install new valve if necessary.

AUDI 5000 POWER-ASSISTED RACK & PINION (Cont.)

LEAKAGE TEST

With engine idling, turn steering wheel to full lock and hold in position. Inspect all connections and tighten if necessary. If leak shows at steering pinion, replace pinion housing seal and both intermediate cover seals. If piston rod is leaking fluid will have entered steering housing. Check for fluid by loosening outer clamp on right steering boot and pushing boot in. If seal is leaking, disassemble steering gear and replace all seals.

REMOVAL & INSTALLATION

STEERING GEAR

Removal — Drain fluid from system. Disconnect pressure hose and return line. Cap openings. Remove tie rod lock plate and both tie rod mounting bolts. Pry tie rods off steering gear. Disconnect steering damper. Disconnect flange tube clamp from steering gear and remove flange tube. Remove steering gear mounting bolts from body. Turn front wheels to right lock and remove steering gear through opening in right wheel well.

Installation — Reverse removal procedures, noting the following: Replace tie rod lock plate before reinstallation. To facilitate tie rod installation, install one tie rod to steering gear and tighten before installing other tie rod.

VANE PUMP

Removal — Remove alternator "V" belt and vane pump "V" belt. Disconnect pressure and suction lines from pump and cover openings. Remove mounting bolts from bracket and lift pump from engine.

Installation — Reverse removal procedures noting the following: Adjust "V" belt deflection to $\frac{3}{8}$" at center. After reinstalling pressure and suction lines, start engine and turn steering wheel to full lock and check for leaks in connections.

OVERHAUL

NOTE — *Manufacturer does not recommend overhaul of steering gear. Leaking seals may be replaced, however. Check output and system pressure before removing steering gear. Steering gear must be removed to replace seals.*

PINION HOUSING SEALS

Disassembly — 1) Remove attaching bolts from valve housing and remove housing. Remove pinion gear and intermediate cover.

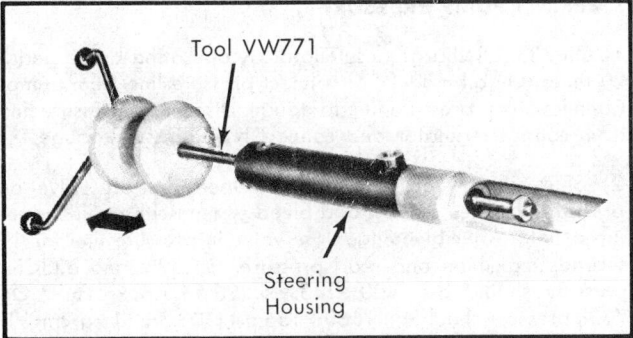

Fig. 3   Removing Steering Housing Oil Seal

2) Remove "O" rings from intermediate cover (one on each side) and, using suitable tool, drive out intermediate cover oil seal. Anchor housing in padded vise and drive out oil seal from the back.

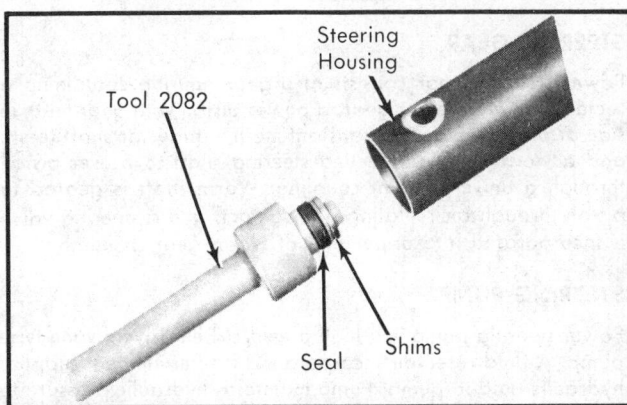

Fig. 4   Steering Housing Oil Seal Installation

3) Install new seals from the inside cover and housing. Make sure that seal lip on housing seal faces intermediate cover, and seal lip of cover seal faces valve housing. Replace both intermediate cover "O" rings.

Reassembly — Reverse removal procedure noting the following: Protect pinion teeth on shaft when replacing intermediate cover. Do not damage "O" rings during reinstallation.

STEERING HOUSING SEALS

Disassembly — With steering gear removed from vehicle, drive out right end of steering housing with drift, remove seals and "O" ring. Clamp rack in vise, remove self locking nut and piston. Insert special tool (VW771) into right steering housing and remove oil seal and shims.

Reassembly — Using special tool (2082), install shims and seal with thin shim behind seal, and seal lip facing piston. Replace piston and self locking nut. Tighten to specification. Replace seals, "O" ring, and end housing.

TIGHTENING SPECIFICATIONS

Application	Ft. Lbs. (N·m)
Pulley-to-Pump Shaft	14 (20)
Pump Mounting Bolts	14 (20)
Pinion Shaft Nut	14 (20)
Steering Damper	29 (40)
Tie Rod-to-Steering Gear	43 (58)
Tie Rod Locking Nut	43 (58)
Steering Housing Locking Nut	29 (40)
Expansion Hose	29 (40)
Suction Hose	29 (40)
Flange Tube-to-Steering Gear	22 (30)
	INCH Lbs. (N·m)
Valve Housing Bolts	84 (10)

Power Steering

BMW POWER-ASSISTED RECIRCULATING BALL

528i
633CSi
733i

DESCRIPTION

STEERING GEAR

Power steering gear consists of a gear housing containing a sector shaft with sector gear, a power piston with gear teeth in side of piston which is in constant mesh with sector shaft teeth, and a worm shaft connecting steering shaft to power piston through a universal joint coupling. Worm shaft is geared to piston through recirculating ball contact, and a steering valve is incorporated into upper end of worm gear assembly.

STEERING PUMP

Power steering pump is a high pressure, belt driven, vane type pump. A fluid reservoir incorporating a filter element supplies hydraulic fluid to pump. Pump maintains hydraulic pressure to power steering gear assembly.

LUBRICATION

CAPACITY

System Capacity — Capacity of 528i and 633CSi system is 2.5 pints. For 733i, capacity is 4.2 pints.

LUBRICANT TYPE

Initial or Subsequent Filling — BMW recommends the use of ATF Dexron II (or equivalent) type of fluid.

FILTER REPLACEMENT

528i & 633CSi — Remove reservoir cap. Remove spring and filter cover. Replace filter.

733i — Remove reservoir cap. Remove nut, washer, spring, fine mesh filter screen and filters. Clean fine mesh filter screen and replace filters.

ADJUSTMENT

PUMP BELT

Loosen adjustment bolts and shift pump to tighten belt. Adjustment is correct when it is possible to press in belt 0.2-0.4" (5-10 mm) with the thumb.

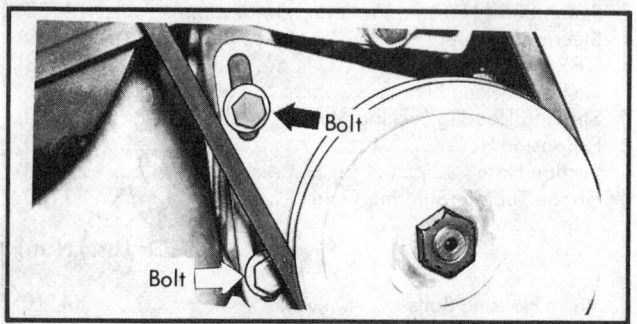

Fig. 1 Power Steering Belt Adjustment Locations

HYDRAULIC SYSTEM BLEEDING

1) Power steering must be bled whenever system is opened, or oil level falls so low that the vane type pump picks up air. Fill reservoir to upper mark with fluid. Turn engine over with starter and continue to add fluid. When oil level no longer falls, start and run engine at idle speed.

2) Turn steering wheel rapidly from lock to lock and back until no further air bubbles rise in reservoir. Stop engine on 733CSi and operate brake pedal to discharge hydraulic accumulator. On all models, during and after operation, fluid level must remain at upper mark.

SECTOR SHAFT

Adjustment (In Vehicle) — **1)** Position front wheels straight ahead. Remove cotter pin and castle nut from tie-rod. Press off center tie-rod from steering arm. Remove BMW emblem from steering wheel. Turn wheel counterclockwise 1 turn from center. Install torque wrench on nut, turn wheel clockwise and read frictional torque.

2) Torque should be 2.7-3.5 INCH lbs. (.31-.40 N·m). To adjust, turn steering wheel counterclockwise from center 1 turn. Loosen lock nut on steering gear and turn adjusting screw clockwise until correct torque is reached when passing through center position. Tighten lock nut and recheck adjustment.

Fig. 2 Sector Shaft Adjusting Screws

TESTING

STEERING PUMP PRESSURE

1) On 733i, discharge accumuator by operating brake pedal 20 times. On all models, disconnect pressure line from pump. Connect pump pressure line to gauge. Disconnect pressure line from control regulator and connect it to pressure gauge.

2) Shut cut-off valve on gauge. Open shut-off valve on pressure line (*See Fig. 6*), and bleed system with engine running at idle. After bleeding, close valve in pressure line for 10 seconds maximum and read pressure. On 528i and 633CSi, pressure should be 1400±140 psi (98.5±9.8 kg/cm²). On 733i, pressure should be 1560±156 psi (109.5±11 kg/cm²). If pressure is not within limits, check belt tightness. Repair or replace pump if belt adjustment does not remedy problem.

BMW POWER-ASSISTED RECIRCULATING BALL (Cont.)

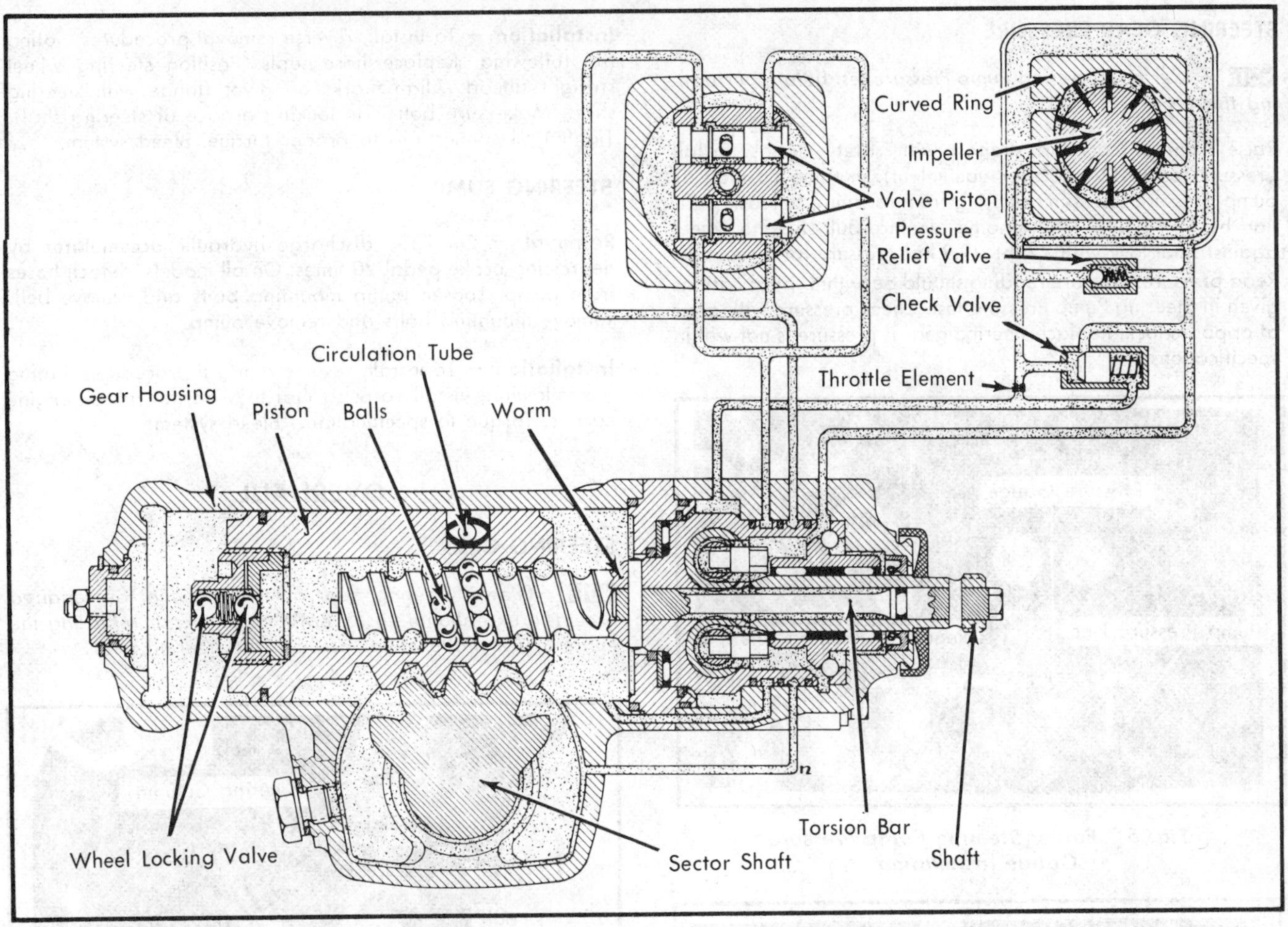

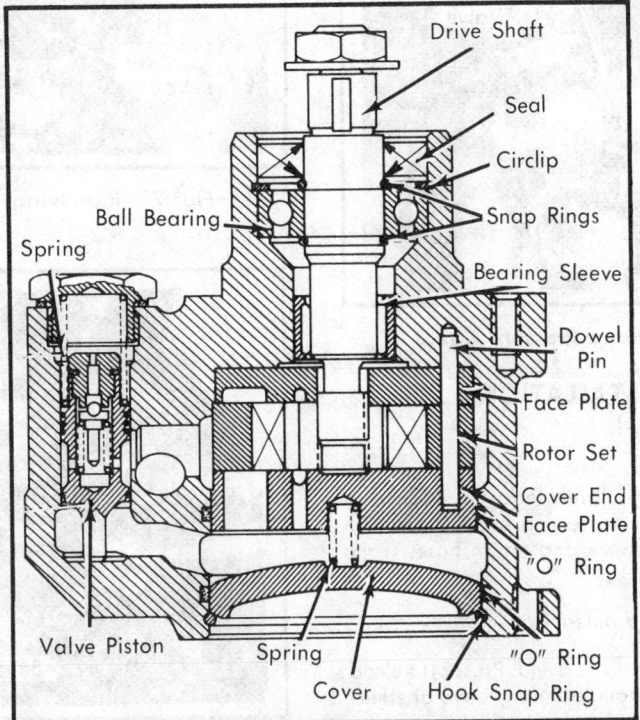

Curved Ring
Impeller
Valve Piston
Pressure Relief Valve
Check Valve
Throttle Element

Gear Housing
Circulation Tube
Piston
Balls
Worm

Wheel Locking Valve

Sector Shaft
Torsion Bar
Shaft

Fig. 3 Cross-Sectional View of Power Steering Gear Assembly

Drive Shaft
Seal
Circlip
Snap Rings
Bearing Sleeve
Dowel Pin
Face Plate
Rotor Set
Cover End Face Plate
"O" Ring
"O" Ring
Hook Snap Ring

Ball Bearing
Spring

Valve Piston
Spring
Cover

Fig. 4 Cross-Sectional View of Power Steering Pump

BMW POWER-ASSISTED RECIRCULATING BALL (Cont.)

STEERING GEAR PRESSURE

NOTE — *Perform Steering Pump Pressure test before performing this test.*

Raise front of car and support with safety stands. Install pressure tester 32-4-000 (or equivalent), in same position as pump pressure test. Limit steering from reaching full lock position by ½-¾ turn. With engine running, pull steering wheel against final lock with 22 lbs. (9.9 kg) pressure for 5 seconds. Read pressure. Pressure reading should be within specifications given in Steering Pump Pressure test. Check pressure with gear at opposite lock. Replace steering gear if pressure is not within specifications.

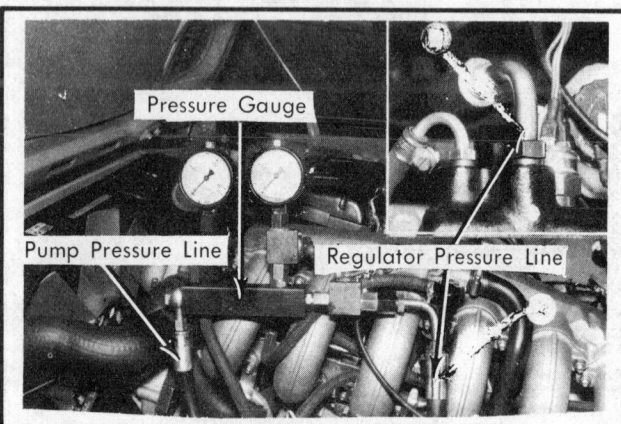

Fig. 5   Power Steering Pump Pressure Gauge Installation

Fig. 6   Power Steering Pump Pressure Check

REMOVAL & INSTALLATION

STEERING GEAR

Removal — 1) Turn steering to full left lock. On 733i, discharge hydraulic accumulator by depressing brake pedal 20 times. On all models, detach pressure and return hoses from steering gear and cap openings.

CAUTION — *Do not reuse fluid drained from system.*

2) Remove cotter pin and nut from tie rod end. Press off tie rod from steering arm. Remove bolt from locking groove of steering shaft (*See Fig. 7*). Push up pivot flange with steering column. Detach steering gear from front axle carrier.

Installation — To install, reverse removal procedures, noting the following: Replace hose seals. Position steering wheel straight ahead. Align marks on pivot flange with steering shaft. Make sure bolt is in locking groove of steering shaft. Tighten all connections to proper torque. Bleed system.

STEERING PUMP

Removal — On 733i, discharge hydraulic accumulator by depressing brake pedal 20 times. On all models, detach hoses from pump. Loosen pump mounting bolts and remove belt. Remove mounting bolts and remove pump.

Installation — To install, reverse removal procedures, noting the following: Install hoses so that they do not rub on engine carrier. Torque to specifications. Bleed system.

OVERHAUL

STEERING GEAR

NOTE — *Power steering gear assembly cannot be repaired except in exceptional cases. BMW recommends replacing the entire unit if malfunctions occur in the steering gear.*

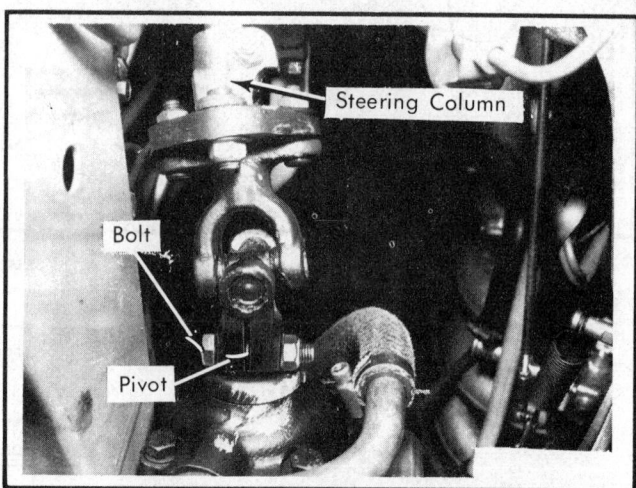

Fig. 7   Removing Steering Shaft Flange

Fig. 8   Steering Gear-to-Front Axle Removal

Power Steering

BMW POWER-ASSISTED RECIRCULATING BALL (Cont.)

POWER STEERING PUMP

NOTE — *Overhaul procedures are for 528i and 633CSi only. For 733i, BMW recommends replacing power steering pump if malfunctions occur.*

DISASSEMBLY

1) Press cover in slightly and remove retaining ring. Remove cover, coil spring and "O" ring. Remove end plate and "O" ring, noting location of pin in one of the small holes in end plate.

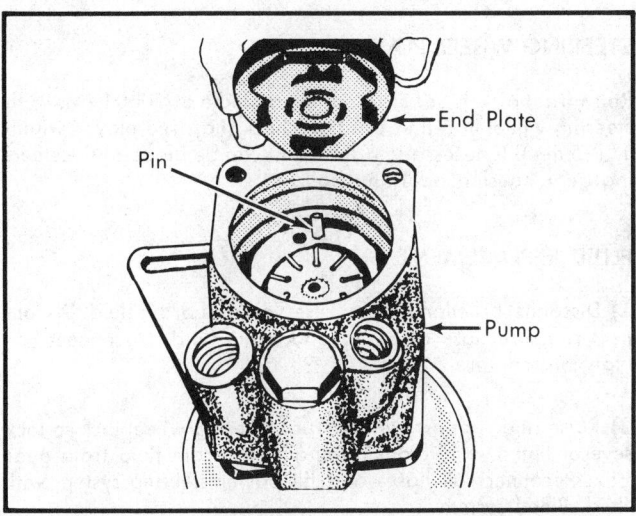

Fig. 9   Pin Location Inside of Pump Housing

2) Tilt housing and remove cam ring and rotor. Note that side of rotor with recessed hole faces drive shaft, the rounded off side of rotor faces cam ring, and the cast-in half arrow indicates direction of rotor rotation.

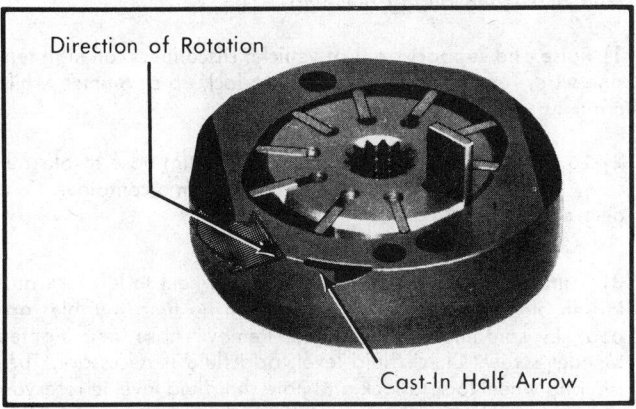

Fig. 10   Mark Showing Direction of Rotation

3) Remove drive end face plate and "O" ring. If it should be necessary to remove input shaft, proceed as follows: Remove pulley, shaft seal, and snap ring from housing. Remove circlip and press ball bearing off of shaft. Using a mandrel, press bearing sleeve out of housing.

4) Remove plug from pressure valve bore, then remove coil spring and valve piston. Note that threaded section on valve piston faces coil spring.

CAUTION — *Do not alter length of coil spring or thickness of plug sealing ring.*

5) The valve tolerance group (1 or 2) is stamped into housing adjacent to pressure valve bore and valve barrel should be scribed with one or two marks (lines) agreeing with group number stamped into housing.

NOTE — *If valve must be replaced, install valve of same tolerance group.*

CAUTION — *When disassembling piston, do not clamp across sliding surfaces.*

6) Clean and inspect all parts. Clean restrictor insert in pump outlet passage. Valve piston may be disassembled for cleaning. A pressure valve is located inside valve piston (flow limit valve).

7) Thickness of washers determines cut-in range of pressure valve. Maximum pump pressure should not be more than 10% below value stated on plate attached to pump.

REASSEMBLY

To reassemble, reverse disassembly procedure, replacing all seals and worn components.

TIGHTENING SPECIFICATIONS

Application	Ft. Lbs (N·m)
Steering Gear to Front Axle	32-35 (44-48)
Worm End Cover	25 (34)
Sector Shaft End Cover	23 (31)
Adjusting Screw Counternut	22 (30)
Steering Pump Mounting	17 (23)
Hose Connections	33-37 (45-50)

Power Steering

CHRYSLER CORP. IMPORTS POWER-ASSISTED RECIRCULATING BALL

Arrow Pickup
Challenger
Ram-50 Pickup
Sapporo

DESCRIPTION

POWER STEERING GEAR BOX

The power steering gear box displaces fluid to provide hydraulic pressure assist when turning. A torsion bar transmits road feel to the driver. A one piece rack-piston nut is geared to the sector shaft. An adjusting screw on the shaft maintains backlash between the shaft and the rack-piston.

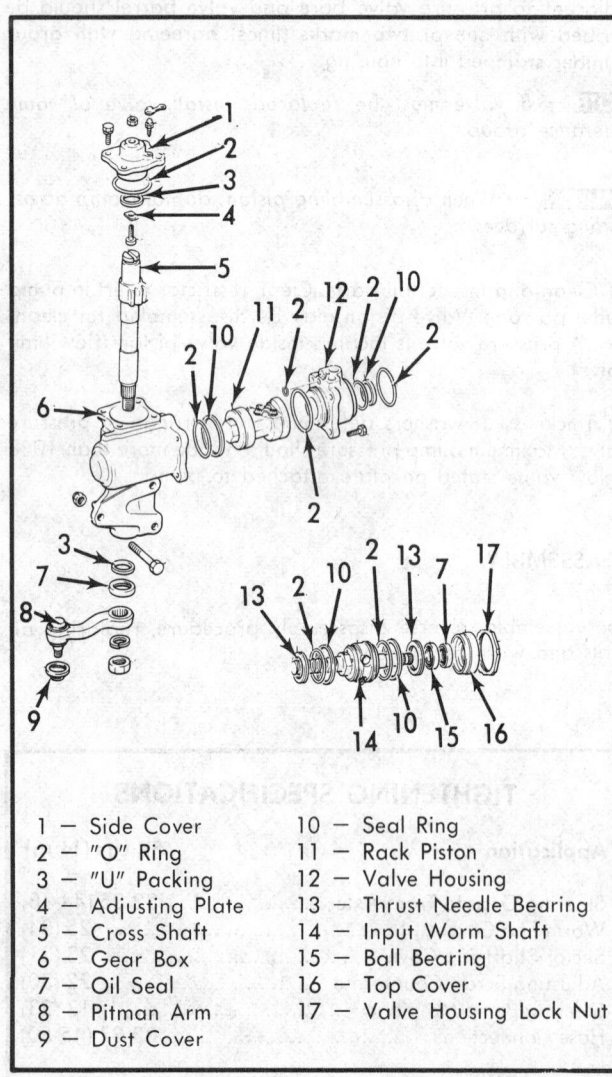

1 — Side Cover	10 — Seal Ring
2 — "O" Ring	11 — Rack Piston
3 — "U" Packing	12 — Valve Housing
4 — Adjusting Plate	13 — Thrust Needle Bearing
5 — Cross Shaft	14 — Input Worm Shaft
6 — Gear Box	15 — Ball Bearing
7 — Oil Seal	16 — Top Cover
8 — Pitman Arm	17 — Valve Housing Lock Nut
9 — Dust Cover	

Fig. 1 Exploded View of Chrysler Corp. Power Steering Gear

POWER STEERING PUMP

Chrysler Corp. uses 2 different types of pumps depending on model. Arrow and Ram-50 use a type "A" pump with retaining ring holding pump end plate to body. Pump has a separate reservoir. Challenger and Sapporo use a type "B" pump with oval fill neck. Pulley is held to drive shaft with bolts.

LUBRICATION

Capacity — 2.2 pints.

Type — ATF Dexron II

ADJUSTMENT

BELT TENSION ADJUSTMENT

With 22 lbs. (10 kg) applied to belt, deflection at center should be .28-.37" (7-10 mm).

STEERING WHEEL PLAY

Raise front of vehicle. Start engine and idle at 1000 RPM. With steering wheel in center position check that free play is within 1" (25 mm). If necessary, adjustment can be made at the steering gear housing adjusting bolt.

FLUID REPLACEMENT

1) Disconnect suction hose at reservoir and drain fluid. Disconnect pressure hose at pump and drain fluid. Disconnect coil high tension wire.

2) Raise and support vehicle. Turn steering wheel lock to lock several times while cranking engine to drain fluid from gear box. Reconnect all hoses and fill power steering system with fluid. Bleed system.

NOTE — *Do not crank engine for more than 15 seconds.*

AIR BLEEDING

NOTE — *Make sure reservoir is filled before bleeding. Add fluid as needed during bleeding.*

1) Raise and support front of vehicle. Disconnect coil high tension wire. Turn steering wheel lock to lock, 5 or 6 times, while cranking engine.

2) Lower vehicle and install a 20" (500 mm) hose to bleeder screw of gear box. Place other end of hose in a container. Connect coil wire.

3) Start engine and idle. Turn steering wheel to left lock and loosen bleeder screw. Repeat this until no more bubbles appear in container (from hose). Remove hose and tighten bleeder screw. Check fluid level, add fluid if necessary. Turn steering wheel lock to lock and note that fluid level in reservoir does not change more than .12-.16" (3-4 mm).

NOTE — *Do not crank engine for more than 15 seconds.*

CAUTION — *Abrupt rising of fluid level after engine is shut off signals incomplete bleeding. Repeat procedure as needed.*

FLUID PRESSURE TESTING

1) Remove pressure hose from oil pump and attach adapter for pressure gauge (C3309E). Tighten to 22-29 ft. lbs. (30-39

CHRYSLER CORP. IMPORTS POWER-ASSISTED RECIRCULATING BALL (Cont.)

N·m). Start engine and place thermometer in reservoir. Close the gauge valve fully 3 times to bleed air from gauge. Check fluid level and add if necessary.

2) When oil temperature reaches 170°F (76.6°C) for type "A" pumps, or 122°F (50°C) for type "B" pumps, check pressure. With valve closed, type "A" pumps should read 1066-1210 psi (75-85 kg/cm²). Type "B" pumps should have a pressure of 925-1066 psi (65-75 kg/cm²).

3) Valve open pressure for both types of pumps should be 142 psi (10 kg/cm²). Reinstall pressure hose, taking care not to twist hose or interfere with adjacent parts.

CAUTION — *Do not keep shut-off valve closed more than 3 seconds at a time. Do not keep steering wheel turned more than 10 seconds at a time.*

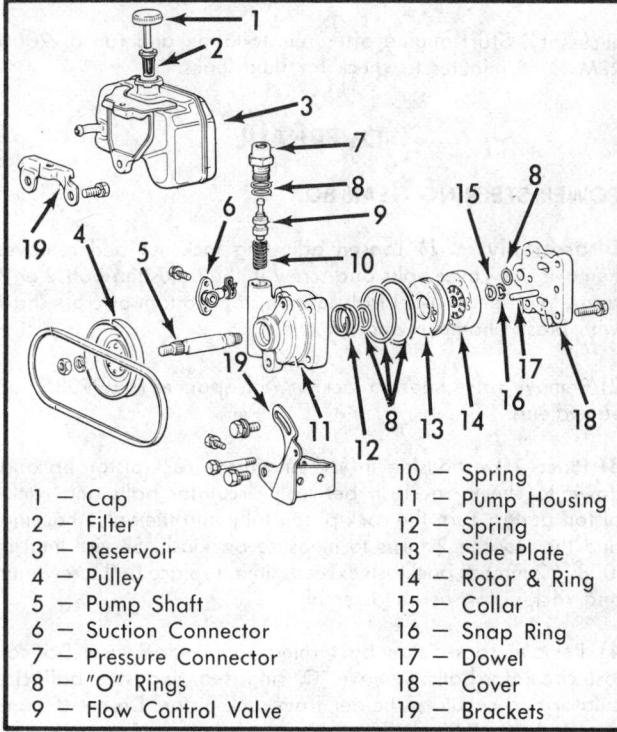

1 — Cap	10 — Spring
2 — Filter	11 — Pump Housing
3 — Reservoir	12 — Spring
4 — Pulley	13 — Side Plate
5 — Pump Shaft	14 — Rotor & Ring
6 — Suction Connector	15 — Collar
7 — Pressure Connector	16 — Snap Ring
8 — "O" Rings	17 — Dowel
9 — Flow Control Valve	18 — Cover
	19 — Brackets

Fig. 3   Exploded View of Power Steering Pump (Type "B", Challenger and Sapporo)

REMOVAL & INSTALLATION

POWER STEERING GEAR BOX

Removal — 1) Disconnect steering shaft from gear box. Disconnect tie rod from relay rod and the pitman arm from relay rod. On pickup models, remove air cleaner and under cover. On all models, disconnect pressure and suction hoses from gear box.

2) Loosen gear box mounting bolts. On pickup models with automatic transmission, remove throttle linkage and shield. On pickup models with manual transmission, remove starter from transmission. On all models, remove gear box. Remove pitman arm from gear box.

Installation — Install in reverse of removal procedures, noting the following: When connecting cross shaft to pitman arm, align slit of cross shaft tip to marking of pitman arm. Insure that clearance between bolt hole at bottom of gear box and pitman arm is within tolerance. Standard value is .77" (19.6 mm).

POWER STEERING OIL PUMP

Removal — On power steering pump type "B", loosen pulley nut before removing belt. On all pumps, remove pulley and belt. Disconnect pressure and suction hoses and cap openings. Remove oil pump attaching bolts and remove pump.

Installation — Install in reverse of removal procedures, noting the following: Check oil pump bracket for slack and tighten if

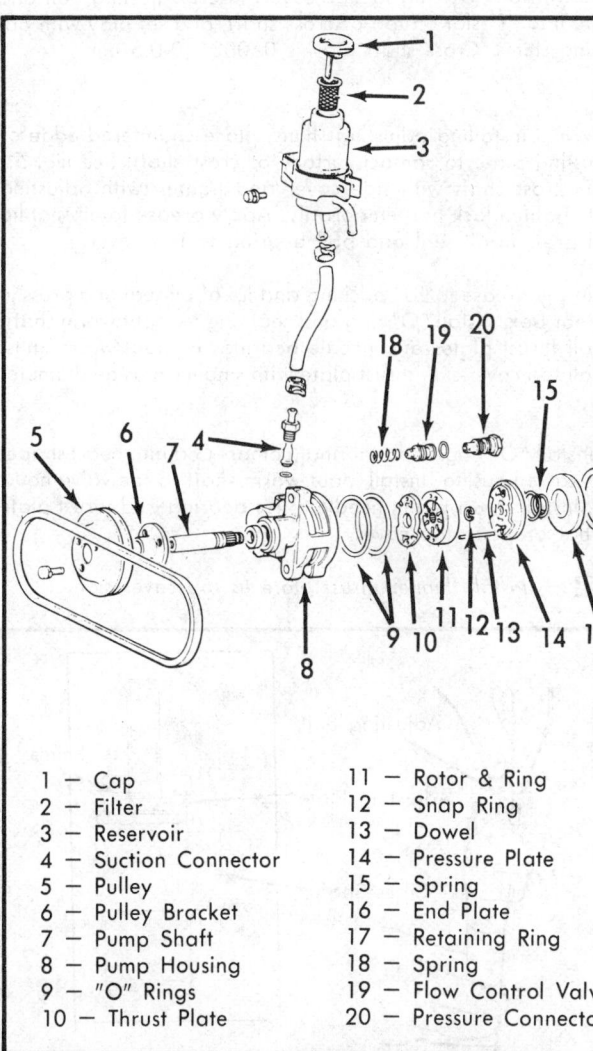

1 — Cap	11 — Rotor & Ring
2 — Filter	12 — Snap Ring
3 — Reservoir	13 — Dowel
4 — Suction Connector	14 — Pressure Plate
5 — Pulley	15 — Spring
6 — Pulley Bracket	16 — End Plate
7 — Pump Shaft	17 — Retaining Ring
8 — Pump Housing	18 — Spring
9 — "O" Rings	19 — Flow Control Valve
10 — Thrust Plate	20 — Pressure Connector

Fig. 2   Exploded View of Power Steering Pump (Type "A", Arrow and Ram-50)

CHRYSLER CORP. IMPORTS POWER-ASSISTED RECIRCULATING BALL (Cont.)

necessary. Start engine after reinstallation and run at 2000 RPM for 5 minutes to check for fluid leaks.

OVERHAUL

POWER STEERING GEAR BOX

Disassembly – 1) Loosen adjusting lock nut and remove. Remove side cover bolts and screw in the adjusting bolt 2 or 3 turns. With gear in neutral position, tap bottom of cross shaft with plastic hammer and remove.

2) Remove valve housing locknut with spanner (MB990852 or equivalent).

3) Place valve housing in vise and move rack-piston up and down to check backlash between circulator balls and rack-piston gutter. Turn the rack-piston fully into the valve housing and then loosen 2 turns to measure backlash. Service limit is .008" (.2 mm). If backlash exceeds limit, replace ball screw unit and rack-piston as an assembly.

4) Remove rack-piston by turning counterclockwise. Do not lose circulator balls. Remove "O" ring, seal ring, steel ball, circulator and circulator holder from rack piston. Do not disconnect end cap. Remove thrust plate, needle roller bearings, seal rings and "O" rings from input worm unit and valve housing.

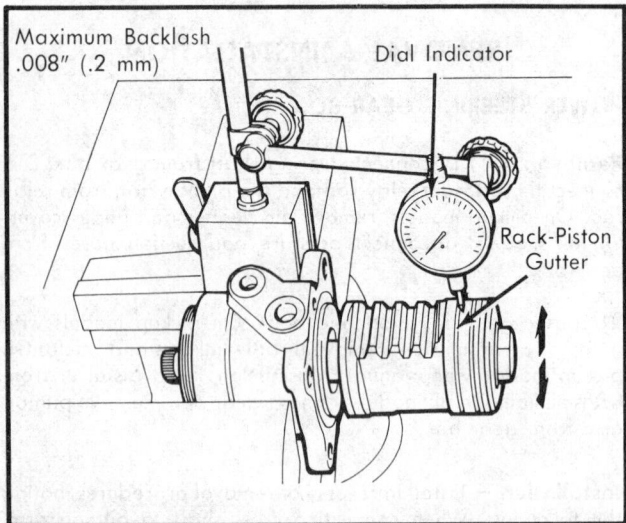

Fig. 4   Measuring Backlash of Gutter and Ball. Service Limit .008" (.2 mm)

5) Screw in adjuster bolt at tip of cross shaft and remove side cover. Remove "O" ring, bearing and adjusting plate. Do not remove bleeder plug unless necessary. Remove seal ring and "O" ring from valve housing. Remove bearing and oil seal from top cover. Remove oil seal and seal ring from gear box.

NOTE – *Replace all "O" rings, seal rings and oil seals once they have been removed. When replacing, lubricate with power steering fluid before insertion.*

Inspection – 1) Inspect cross shaft bearing surface for peeling or pitting. Check stepped wear of adjusting bolt shank. Inspect for damage to gear teeth on cross shaft and rack-piston.

2) Inspect for uneven wear of circulator rolling surface on rack-piston. Check for damage to balls. Inspect for peeling or pitting on thrust needle roller bearing, and bearing surface of thrust plate on worm unit. Check ball rolling surface of worm shaft for peeling and sealing surface of input shaft for damage. If thrust bearing or thrust plate is defective, replace both as a set.

3) Inspect valve housing for damage to seal ring-to-housing contact surface. Inspect "O" ring sealing surface of seal housing, valve housing and side cover.

Reassembly – 1) Lubricate bearing surface of side cover and install needle roller bearings. Apply grease to bottom of side cover. Install "O" ring to side cover. Insert adjusting bolt and plate into "T" slot on top of cross shaft, and set play with adjusting shims. Cross shaft play is 0-.002" (0-0.5 mm).

2) When installing adjusting shims, place chamfered edge of adjusting plate to contact surface of cross shaft. *See Fig. 5.* Align cross shaft with side cover and tighten with adjusting bolt. Tighten lock nut temporarily. Apply grease to oil seal lip and press in oil seal and ball bearing to top cover.

3) Apply grease to "U" packing and lip of oil seal and press in to gear box. Install "O" ring and seal ring to input worm shaft. Install thrust plates and needle bearings in input worm units. Install top cover side thrust plate with smaller outside diameter first.

4) Install "O" ring and seal ring (compressed into heart shape) into valve housing. Install input worm shaft to the valve housing. Install thrust plate, needle roller bearing and thrust plate in that order to top cover.

NOTE – *Install thinner thrust plate to top cover side.*

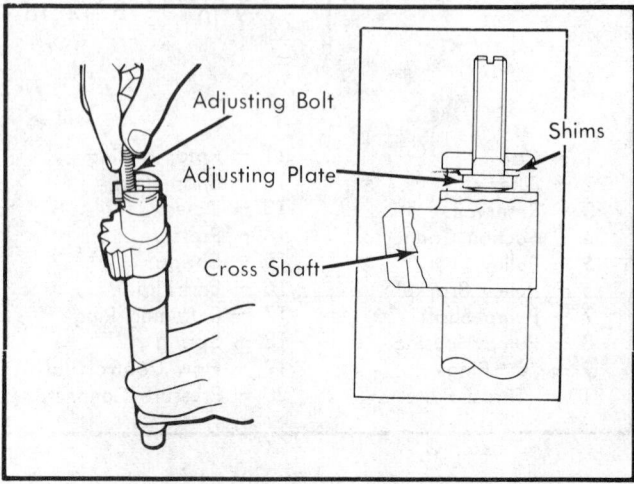

Fig. 5   Adjusting the Cross Shaft "T" Slot. Place Chamfered Edge of Adjusting Plate to Contact Surface of Cross Shaft.

CHRYSLER CORP. IMPORTS POWER-ASSISTED RECIRCULATING BALL (Cont.)

5) Tighten top cover to the valve housing using pin tool (MB990853 or equivalent). Check worm shaft for uniform rotation. Tighten valve housing lock nut with spanner (MB990852 or equivalent). Take care not to allow top cover to rotate.

NOTE — *Final tighten valve housing lock nut at time of measurement of total starting torque.*

6) Measure starting torque using preload socket (CT-1108 or equivalent). Preload should be 2.2-5.6 INCH lbs. Adjust, if necessary, by loosening valve housing nut and retightening. Install "O" ring and seal ring to rack piston.

7) Insert rack-piston into input worm shaft until piston touches worm shaft end. Rotate worm shaft and align ball running surface with ball insertion hole. Insert 19 balls into hole by pushing lightly with a brass rod. *See Fig. 6.*

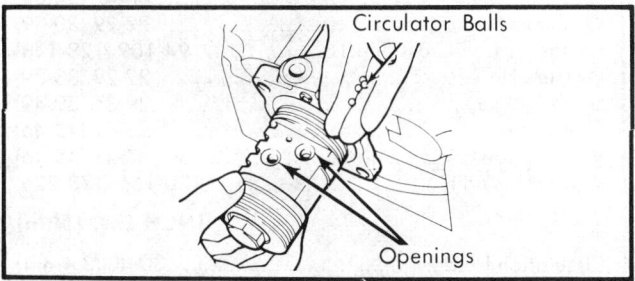

Fig. 6 Installing Circulator Balls to Rack Piston. Install Balls Using a Brass Rod to Push In.

8) Measure distance from rack-piston to balls. If distance is more than .5" (13 mm), a ball is in wrong groove. Remove and reinstall balls correctly. Insert 7 more balls with grease to prevent them from falling. Insert circulator and holder to rack piston attaching place and tighten.

9) Hold gear box in a vise. Apply a thin coating of automatic transmission fluid to teeth and shaft of rack piston. Apply grease to oil seal lip. Install ball screw unit. Tighten valve housing. Do not allow cover to rotate.

10) Wrap serration of cross shaft with vinyl tape to avoid damage when installing. Install cross shaft and side cover to gear box. Tighten side cover. Measure starting torque of input worm shaft using preload socket (CT-1108 or equivalent). Adjust to 4.3-7.8 INCH lbs.

11) Make sure ball screw unit operates smoothly. Tighten valve housing lock nut with spanner (MB990852 or equivalent). Check preload. Connect cross shaft with Pitman arm.

NOTE — *When connecting cross shaft with Pitman arm, align slit of cross shaft tip to marking on Pitman arm. Clearance between bolt hole center in gear box and Pitman arm should be .77" (19.5 mm).*

POWER STEERING PUMP

Disassembly (Pump Type "A") — **1)** Remove pulley bracket with puller then remove suction connector. Remove pressure connector. Remove retaining ring using small punch inserted in

hole of pump housing, opposite flow control valve hole, and then pry out ring with screwdriver.

2) Remove end plate and "O" ring. Remove flow control valve and spring. Tap on pump shaft with plastic hammer just enough to loosen pressure plate. Remove pressure plate, pump shaft, ring, vanes and rotor.

3) Remove pump shaft retaining ring and discard. Remove rotor and thrust plate from drive shaft. Remove dowel pins from housing. Pry pump shaft seal out of housing.

Inspection — Check flow control valve, rotor and ring, end plates and pump shaft for damage, scoring or excessive wear. Inspect pump housing for cracks or signs of visual damage. Check "O" ring seats for scratches or burrs. Inspect pump shaft bushing, in pump housing. If bushing is damaged, replace pump housing. Replace any parts necessary. If any internal pump parts are found to be damaged, flush steering gear or disassemble and clean gear.

NOTE — *Lubricate "O" rings and all internal pump components with ATF Dexron II fluid before reassembly.*

Reassembly — **1)** Install new pump shaft seal in pump housing. Install new pressure plate "O" ring to 3rd groove from end of pump housing. Insert both dowel pins into pump housing. Install thrust plate and rotor to pump shaft, then install new snap ring to pump shaft. Make sure rotor is installed with countersunk side toward thrust plate.

2) Install pump shaft into pump housing, making sure thrust plate slides over dowel pins properly. Install ring into pump housing, over dowel pins and with arrow (on ring) toward rear of pump housing. Install vanes in rotor and make sure rounded edge of vanes face outward.

3) Install pressure plate into pump housing and over dowel pins. Make sure circular depression (for spring) is toward rear of housing. Install new "O" ring in 2nd groove from rear of pump housing. Place spring on pressure plate, then install end plate to pump housing. Depress end plate just enough to install retaining ring. Make sure retaining ring seats properly.

NOTE — *Pressure plate must be pressed .06" (1.6 mm) over "O" ring to seat.*

Disassembly (Pump Type "B") — **1)** Drain fluid. Remove suction plate bolts. Remove reservoir from pump. Hold pump in a vise. Remove pump cover bolts and cover. Tap the shaft with a plastic hammer. Take out the cam ring, vanes, shaft assembly, side plate spring and "O" rings.

2) Remove snap ring from shaft assembly using snap ring pliers. Remove collar, rotor and side plate from shaft. Pry out oil seal from pump body with a screwdriver. Remove connector and take out control valve, flow control spring and "O" rings.

Inspection — **1)** Measure clearance between shaft and pump body. If clearance is more than .0035" (.09 mm), replace pump body as an assembly. Inspect pump shaft oil seal lip and bushing end for damage. Inspect groove of rotor vane and cam surface for stepped wear.

CHRYSLER CORP. IMPORTS POWER-ASSISTED RECIRCULATING BALL (Cont.)

2) Check vane for damage and ring and rotor sides for grooving. Replace entire assembly if any damage is seen. Inspect side plate spring. Minimum length should be .67" (17 mm). Check flow control spring. Minimum length should be 1.95" (49.5 mm). Check sliding surfaces of control valve for obstructions.

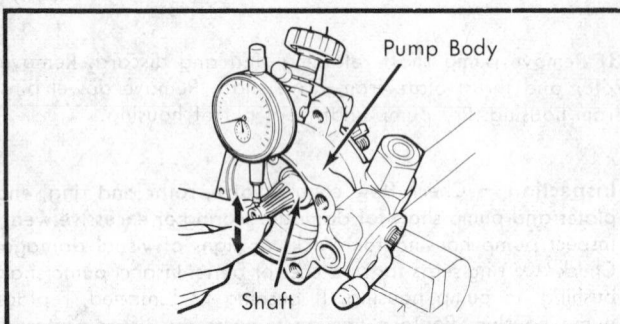

Fig. 7 Measuring Clearance Between Shaft and Pump Body. Service Limit. 0035" (.09 mm).

NOTE – *Lubricate "O" rings and all internal pump components with ATF Dexron II before reassembly.*

3) Install cam ring. Smaller diameter bore faces side plate. Install cover and oil reservoir bracket to pump body and tighten.

Remove reservoir bolt and install reservoir. Tighten suction plate.

Reassembly – 1) Install flow control valve and spring to pump body. Depress control valve to check for smooth operation. Apply grease to lip of oil seal. Press seal into pump body. Install side plate, rotor and collar to shaft.

2) Tighten pulley nut temporarily. Hold snap ring on shaft using snap ring pliers. Install "O" ring and side plate spring to pump body. Install vanes onto rotor. Insert shaft assembly with vanes to pump body.

TIGHTENING SPECIFICATIONS

Application	Ft. Lbs. (N·m)
Gear-to-Frame	40-47 (54-64)
Oil Pump Cover	22-29 (30-39)
Pitman Arm-to-Cross Shaft	94-109 (128-148)
Pressure Hose	22-29 (30-39)
Suction Hose	29-36 (39-49)
Side Cover	33-41 (45-46)
Valve Housing	33-41 (45-46)
Valve Housing Nut	130-166 (178-226)
	INCH Lbs. (N·m)
Circulation Holder	30-40 (3.4-4.4)
Gear Box Top Cover	8.6-12.1 (1.0-1.4)

DATSUN POWER-ASSISTED RACK & PINION

810

DESCRIPTION

Power steering is rack and pinion cam gear type. System consists of a rack and pinion steering gear, steering pump, reservoir and flexible connecting lines.

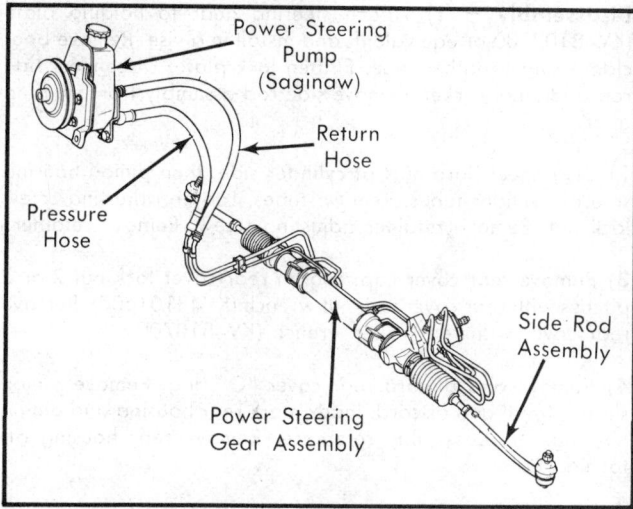

**Fig. 1 View of Power Steering Assembly.
Pump is Belt Driven From Crankshaft.**

GENERAL SERVICING

HYDRAULIC SYSTEM LUBRICANT

Capacity

Saginaw Pump — 1⅜ quarts.
Atsugi Type "A" Pump — 1⅜ quarts.
Atsugi Type "B" Pump — 1.0 quarts.

Fluid Type — Dexron.

NOTE — *Normal operating temperature for power steering fluid is 140-176°F (60-80°C).*

HYDRAULIC SYSTEM BLEEDING

Raise and support front of vehicle. Quickly turn steering wheel right to left to lock positions until fluid level no longer decreases and bubbles do not appear. Start engine and idle for 2-3 minutes. Accelerate engine under no load 2-3 times. Let engine idle and quickly turn wheel lock-to-lock until air bubbles no longer appear.

NOTE — *Do not hold steering wheel at lock position for more than 15 seconds. Ensure no unusual noises appear from system.*

HYDRAULIC SYSTEM PRESSURE TEST

1) Disconnect pressure line at pump and connect pressure gauge and shut-off valve. Check fluid level, open shut-off valve and run engine for about 5 seconds. Check fluid level and restart engine.

2) Turn steering wheel lock-to-lock several times to expel air from system and bring fluid temperature up. Slowly close shut-off valve with wheel at lock position. Pressure at idle should be 995 psi (70 kg/cm²).

NOTE — *Fluid should be at normal operating temperature. Do not hold steering wheel in lock position for more than 15 seconds.*

3) If pressure is below specification, pump is faulty. If pressure rises above specification, relief valve in pump is at fault. In either case, replace pump.

ADJUSTMENTS

BELT TENSION

With 22 lbs. (10 kg) pressure on belt, deflection at center should be .31-.47" (8-12 mm).

STEERING WHEEL TURNING FORCE

Park vehicle on a dry, level surface. Set parking brake. Bring hydraulic fluid up to normal operating temperature. Attach a spring scale and check steering wheel turning force with wheel turned 360° from straight ahead. Force should be less than 5.5-6.6 lbs. (2.5-3.0 kg). If not, remove steering gear and check turning force of pinion gear.

PINION ROTATING FORCE AND RACK STARTING FORCE

Install gear to holding plate (KV48102100 or equivalent) and install in a vise. Disconnect cylinder tube and drain fluid. Attach torque wrench to pinion and measure turning force. Turning force should be 7.8 INCH lbs. (.9 N·m) average and less than 13 INCH lbs. (1.5 N·m) maximum. Attach spring scale to rack end to measure rack starting force. Force should be less than 42 lbs. (19 kg).

NOTE — *If either force is not to specifications, adjust retainer adjusting screw. If adjustment cannot be made correctly, replace steering gear.*

REMOVAL & INSTALLATION

STEERING GEAR

Removal — 1) Raise and support front of vehicle. Disconnect hose clamp fixing bolt. Disconnect flare nut at steering gear. Drain fluid. Remove hose clamp from steering gear mounting bracket. Detach side ball studs from knuckle arm with ball joint remover (HT72520000 or equivalent).

2) Loosen steering gear mounting bolts. Loosen bolt securing lower joint to pinion gear. Draw out lower joint from pinion gear. Remove bolt securing steering gear housing to suspension crossmember. Remove steering gear and linkage.

Installation — Install in reverse order of removal. Install lower joint on steering gear as shown in *Fig. 2*. Tighten steering gear mounting bolts.

DATSUN POWER-ASSISTED RACK & PINION (Cont.)

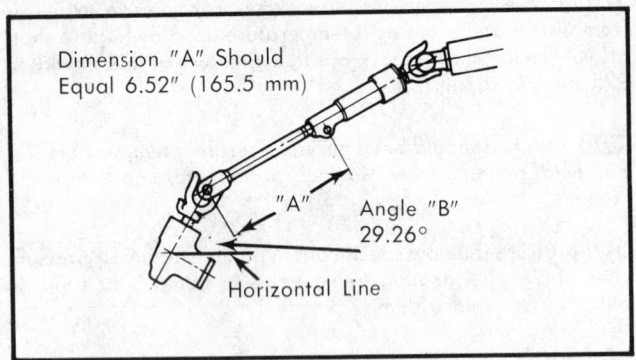

Dimension "A" Should
Equal 6.52" (165.5 mm)

"A"

Angle "B"
29.26°

Horizontal Line

**Fig. 2   Steering Shaft to Pinion Gear
Lower Joint Attachment**

STEERING PUMP

Removal — 1) Loosen power steering pump pulley lock nut. Turn adjusting bolt counterclockwise to loosen pump belt. Remove belt. Disconnect pressure hose flare nut at power steering pump. Drain fluid.

2) Remove hose clamp. Remove pump mounting bolts and pump. Remove flare nuts at steering gear. Remove hose clamps at suspension member. Remove hose from steering gear.

Installation — Install in reverse order of removal. After pump is installed, bleed system and adjust belt tension.

OVERHAUL

POWER STEERING GEAR

NOTE — *Before disassembling, measure pinion rotating force and rack starting force. If they cannot be adjusted properly, replace steering gear.*

Disassembly — 1) Attach steering gear to holding plate (KV48102100 or equivalent) and install in a vise. Remove boot clamp and breather tube. Flatten lock plate. Disconnect side rod and inner socket. Remove side rod assembly from steering gear.

2) Disconnect flare nuts at cylinder side, then pinion housing side of cylinder tubes. Remove tubes. Loosen adjusting screw lock nut. Remove retainer adjusting screw. Remove retainer.

3) Remove rear cover cap. Loosen rear cover lock nut 2 or 3 pitches with rear cover lock nut wrench (KV48101600). Remove rear cover with rear cover wrench (KV4810700).

4) Remove and discard rear cover "O" ring. Remove pinion shaft oil seal and discard. Index mark rear housing and pinion housing for reassembly reference. Remove rear housing attaching bolts.

5) Remove rear housing and discard "O" ring. Remove 2 thrust washers and needle bearing from upper surface of pinion. Remove pinion assembly, thrust washers and needle bearing. Do not hammer pinion assembly or damage teflon seal.

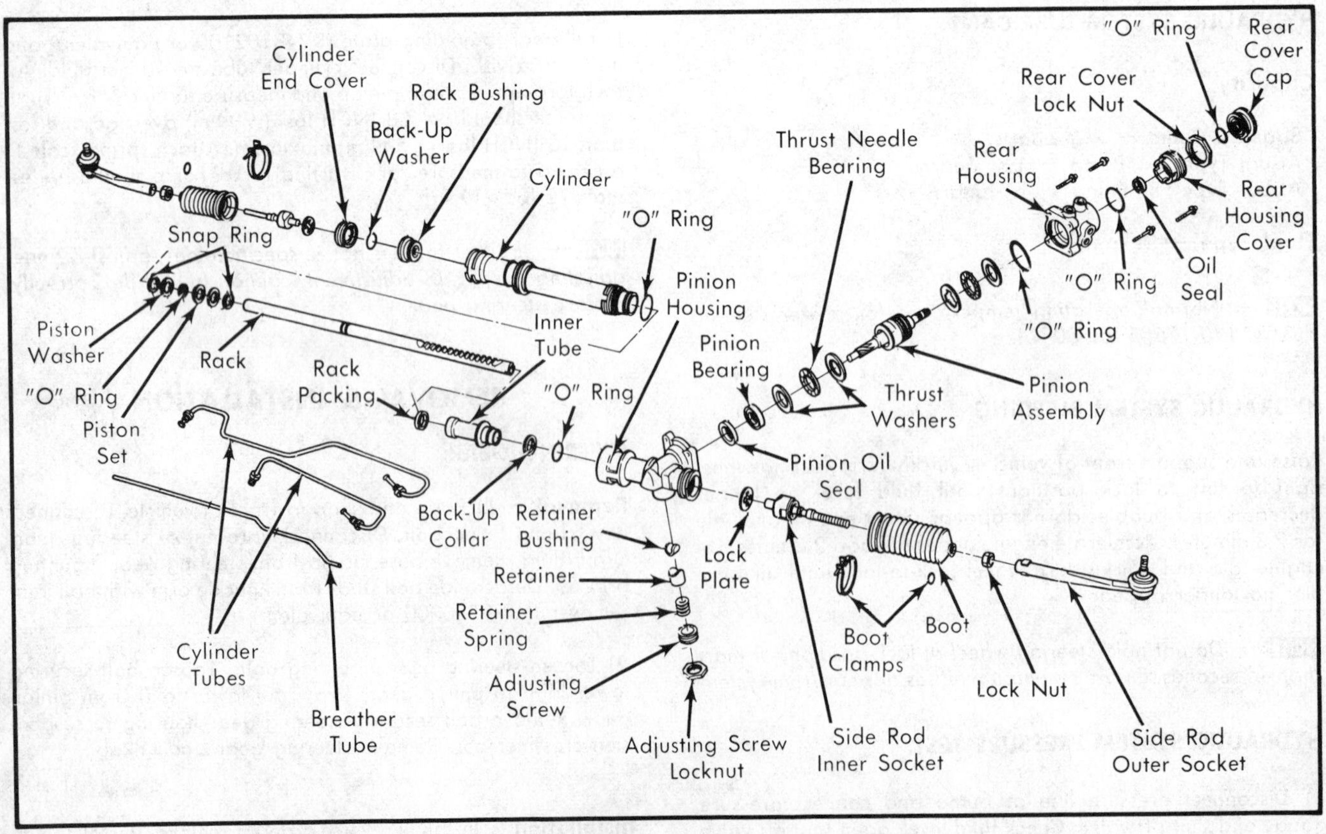

**Fig. 3   Exploded View of Power Rack & Pinion
Steering Gear**

DATSUN POWER-ASSISTED RACK & PINION (Cont.)

6) Remove pinion bearing and pinion oil seal. Put index mark on housing and cylinder. Disconnect cylinder lock nut with lock nut wrench (KV48101800). Separate cylinder from pinion housing.

7) Remove rack bushing and discard. Remove cylinder "O" ring and discard. Remove inner tube. Remove "O" ring and inner tube collar from inner tube. Remove rack packing and back-up collar.

Inspection — Thoroughly clean all parts in automatic transmission fluid and blow dry. Replace all oil seals, "O" rings and snap rings. Inspect all steering gear components. Replace steering gear assembly as a unit if components are worn or damaged.

NOTE — *When assembling power steering gear, apply automatic transmission fluid to "O" rings, seals and moving parts.*

Reassembly — 1) Install new "O" ring to inner tube. Attach back-up collar to inner tube and press new rack packing into place. Use less than 1323 lbs. (600 kg) force. Install inner tube.

NOTE — *To prevent damage, wrap cellophone tape around rack end edge and affected piston areas.*

2) Install new snap ring to rack. Install piston component parts to rack. Apply a coat of grease to rack surface. Install new "O" ring to cylinder. Position cylinder on pinion housing and align index marks.

NOTE — *Be careful not to damage teflon ring.*

3) Tighten cylinder lock nut with lock nut wrench (KV48101800). Attach new back-up washer and tighten end cover with cylinder holder (KV48101900). Press new pinion oil seal into pinion housing.

4) Apply coat of grease to oil seal lip. Attach 2 thrust washers, thrust bearings and needle bearing. Apply grease to bearing. Position rack with equal protrusion at ends and with teeth facing pinion at right angles.

5) Install pinion so that punch mark on pinion shaft is located exactly on rear side as it is mounted in vehicle. Apply coat of grease to rack and pinion gear. Install new "O" ring to rear housing.

6) Install housing by aligning index marks. Tighten housing. Install new pinion shaft oil seal and press into rear housing cover. Install second "O" ring to cover.

7) Fit rear housing lock nut approximately 10 pitches down on rear housing cover. Completely tighten rear housing cover to pinion housing. Turn back cover 1 turn from that position.

8) Turn pinion shaft lock-to-lock several times and measure pinion rotating force. Force should be 1.3-2.2 INCH lbs. (.15-.25 N·m). Tighten rear cover lock nut with rear cover wrench (KV48101700).

9) Apply a coat of grease to contact surface of rack and install retainer to pinion housing. Install retainer spring and fully tighten adjusting screw. Turn back screw 20-25° and tighten lock nut.

10) Measure and adjust pinion rotating force and rack starting force. See Adjustments in this article. Temporarily tighten flare nut at rear housing side and then at cylinder side. Then tighten to final torque.

11) Fit inner socket to rack end with new lock plate. Be sure lock plate ratchet enters groove at end portion of rack so rack and inner socket fit snugly. Tighten inner socket and securely bend lock plate at 2 cut-outs.

NOTE — *To prevent damage to boot, remove burrs after bending plate.*

12) Screw in side rod outer socket until distance between boot and outside of lock nut is 1.68" (42.7 mm). Measure rack stroke. Stroke should be 2.76" (70 mm). Apply sealant to contact surfaces between boot, cylinder and breather.

13) Install boot as shown in *Fig. 4*. Set breather tube. Locate clamp bolt opposite breather tube and tighten. Ensure rack moves smoothly, boot is not deformed, and clamp is held tightly in place.

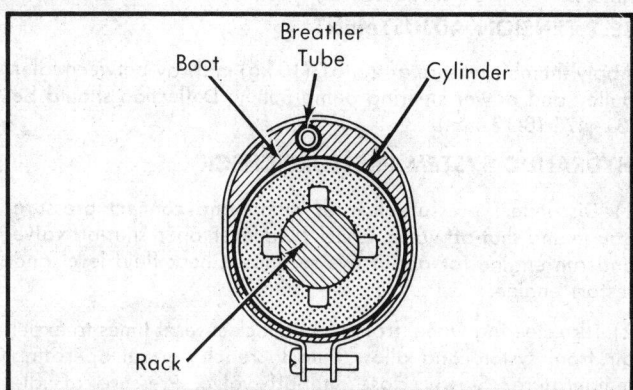

***Fig. 4 Boot and Rack Positioning.
Apply Sealant to Contact Surfaces.***

POWER STEERING PUMP

NOTE — *Manufacturer does not recommend overhaul of power steering pump. Replace as a unit if defective.*

TIGHTENING SPECIFICATIONS

Application	Ft. Lbs. (N·m)
Side Rod-to-Knuckle Arm	40-47 (54-98)
Gear Housing Clamp Bolt	25-33 (34-44)
Lower Joint-to-Pinion Gear	24-48 (32-48)
Lower Joint-to-Rubber Coupling	29-36-(39-49)
Pressure Hose-to-Pump	29-36 (39-49)
Hose Connector-at-Steering Gear	29-36 (39-49)
Pump Mounting Bolt	20-27 (26-36)
Cylinder Lock Nut	58-72 (79-98)
Retainer Adjusting Screw Lock Nut	29-43 (39-59)
Rear Cover Lock Nut	58-72 (79-98)
Flare Nuts	29-36 (39-49)

DATSUN POWER-ASSISTED RECIRCULATING BALL

200SX
280ZX

DESCRIPTION

Power steering is composed of a power steering pump, steering gear and connecting hoses. The pump has an integral reservoir on 280ZX models and a separate reservoir on 200SX models. Power steering gear is an integral unit consisting of a spool valve and power cylinder (worm shaft ball nut assembly) connected to the sector shaft. Power steering gear is pressure operated by the pump through the connecting lines.

GENERAL SERVICE

HYDRAULIC SYSTEM LUBRICANT

Capacity
200SX - 1.3 qts.
280ZX - 1.1 qts

Type — ATF Type DEXRON

NOTE — *Normal operating temperature of hydraulic system fluid is 140-176° F (60-80° C)*

BELT TENSION ADJUSTMENT

Apply thumb pressure of 22 lbs. (10 kg) midway between idler pulley and power steering pump pulley. Deflection should be .31-.47" (8-12 mm).

HYDRAULIC SYSTEM PRESSURE CHECK

1) Disconnect pressure line at pump and connect pressure gauge and shut-off valve. Check fluid level, open shut-off valve and run engine for about five seconds. Check fluid level and restart engine.

2) Turn steering wheel from lock-to-lock several times to expel air from system and allow fluid to reach normal operating temperature. Slowly close shut-off valve. Pressure at idle should be 782 psi (55 kg/cm²) for 200SX models or 953-1123 psi (67-79 kg/cm²) for 280ZX models.

NOTE — *Do not close shut-off valve for more than 15 seconds, as this may result in undue pump wear and abnormally increased lubricant temperature.*

3) If pressure is below specifications, the pump is faulty. If pressure is above specifications, the pressure relief valve in pump is faulty. In either case, replace pump.

HYDRAULIC SYSTEM BLEEDING

NOTE — *Allow fluid to reach normal operating temperature when bleeding.*

Check fluid level in reservoir, raise and support front of vehicle. With engine not running, turn steering wheel from lock-to-lock several times. Check fluid level, start engine and turn steering wheel from lock-to-lock several times. If system is not bled, turn steering wheel to left lock and open bleeder screw to expel remaining air.

ADJUSTMENT

BACKLASH

On Vehicle — 1) Place vehicle on level dry surface, inflate tires to specified pressure and run engine until power steering fluid is at normal operating temperature. With steering wheel

in straight ahead (centered) position, turn steering wheel 1 complete turn (360°).

2) Attach spring gauge to outer rim of wheel and measure turning force. Turning force should be 6.6-7.7 lbs. (3.0-35 kg) for 200SX, 5.5-6.6 lbs. (2.5-3.0 kg) for 280ZX. If turning force is not to specifications, remove steering gear and check turning force of steering gear.

NOTE — *Center position can be found by turning gear to full lock position then turning back 2⅛ turns.*

Off Vehicle — 1) With steering gear removed from vehicle, mount gear to a plate that can be clamped in a vise (special tool KV48100301 or KV48100300). Attach a torque wrench to worm shaft splines (where steering shaft connects) and center steering gear.

NOTE — *Worm shaft can be turned by placing vinyl tape on serrations and attaching socket.*

2) Measure turning force of steering gear 360° from center position. Torque should be 10 INCH lbs. (1.1 N.m). Turn worm shaft back to center position and measure torque. Torque at this point should be .9-3.5 INCH lbs. (.1-.4 N.m) more than torque measured at 360° from center position.

3) If turning torque is not to specifications, loosen adjusting bolt lock nut and turn (always tighten to adjust) adjusting bolt until correct turning torque specification is obtained. If the correct turning torque cannot be obtained, replace steering gear.

REMOVAL & INSTALLATION

STEERING GEAR

Removal — 1) Remove air cleaner, remove bolt from universal joint to worm shaft. Disconnect fluid lines and plug them to prevent fluid spillage. Remove nut and washer from sector shaft.

2) Remove pitman arm from sector shaft using a puller. Remove steering gear mounting bolts, then remove steering gear from vehicle.

Installation — To install, reverse removal procedure. Align 4 gooves in gear arm serrations with 4 projections of sector shaft serrations. Install and tighten lock nut.

STEERING PUMP

Removal — Disconnect fluid lines at pump and block off fittings. Remove pump mounting bolts and remove drive belt from pulley. Remove pump from vehicle.

Installation — To install, reverse removal procedure.

OVERHAUL

NOTE — *Overhaul of steering gear is limited to oil seal replacement. If any further repair is necessary, replace entire steering gear assembly. Always check turning torque before disassembly.*

ADJUSTING SCREW SEAL REPLACEMENT

Remove adjusting screw lock nut. Remove "O" ring from lock nut. Grease new "O" ring and insert in lock nut. Make sure "O" ring is installed correctly, then replace lock nut to adjusting screw. Adjust steering gear turning torque.

NOTE — *Always use new copper washer when adjusting screw lock nut is removed.*

STEERING

DATSUN POWER-ASSISTED RECIRCULATING BALL (Cont.)

SECTOR SHAFT SEAL REPLACEMENT

Disassembly — 1) With steering gear assembly mounted in a vise, set sector shaft to center position. Remove sector shaft cover bolts. Using a mallet, tap sector shaft out approximately ¾" (.79 mm).

NOTE — *Wrap a piece of plastic film (stiff) around the sector shaft, approximately the same diameter as the sector shaft and approximately 8" (200 mm) long. This will prevent bearings from falling into gear housing.*

2) Pull sector shaft from gear housing, at same time pull plastic film into gear housing. Remove snap ring from gear housing and remove dust seal, special large washer, oil seal and special small washer. Remove "O" ring from sector shaft cover.

Reassembly — 1) Install new special small washer, oil seal, special large washer, dust seal and snap ring to gear housing. Be sure to grease oil seal and dust seal. Also make sure radius side of snap ring faces inside of gear housing.

2) Install new "O" ring to sector shaft cover. Make sure worm shaft and rack piston is in centered position. Wrap splined and threaded portions of sector shaft, with tape, to prevent damage to oil seal.

3) Slowly insert sector shaft into gear housing, pushing plastic film out and being careful not to damage oil seal. With sector shaft fully installed, plastic film removed and components operating smoothly, install and tighten sector shaft cover bolts. Check and adjust steering gear turning torque.

REAR HOUSING SEAL REPLACEMENT

Disassembly — 1) Install steering gear assembly to mounting plate and place in a vise. Loosen rear cover bolts approximately .20" (5 mm), but do not remove. Turn sector shaft clockwise sightly to raise intermediate cover through piston.

2) Place piston and worm shaft in center position and remove sector shaft. See *Sector Shaft Seal Replacement* for removal procedures. Remove rear housing bolts and pull out rear housing with intermediate cover and worm gear assembly.

NOTE — *When worm assembly is removed, piston may turn and come off under its own weight. Hold piston to prevent this. Do not damage Teflon ring at piston end when removing.*

3) Turn worm assembly upside down and lightly tap worm shaft against bench to remove rear housing. Remove rear housing oil seal. Remove large and small "O" rings from both sides of intermediate cover.

Reassembly — 1) Lubricate and install rear housing oil seal, sector shaft oil seal and intermediate cover "O" rings. Install worm assembly into rear housing then into gear housing.

CAUTION — *Be careful not to damage Teflon ring at rear of piston when installing.*

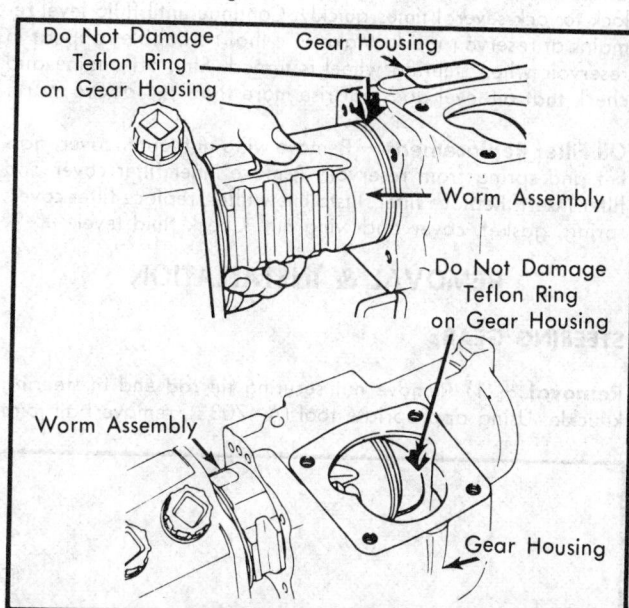

Fig. 2 Installing Worm Assembly to Gear Housing. When Half-Way Inserted, Teflon Ring is Deflected.

2) Tighten rear cover bolts in a crisscross pattern. Install sector shaft. See *Sector Shaft Seal Replacement* for installation procedures. Make sure steering gear operates smoothly, then check and adjust turning torque.

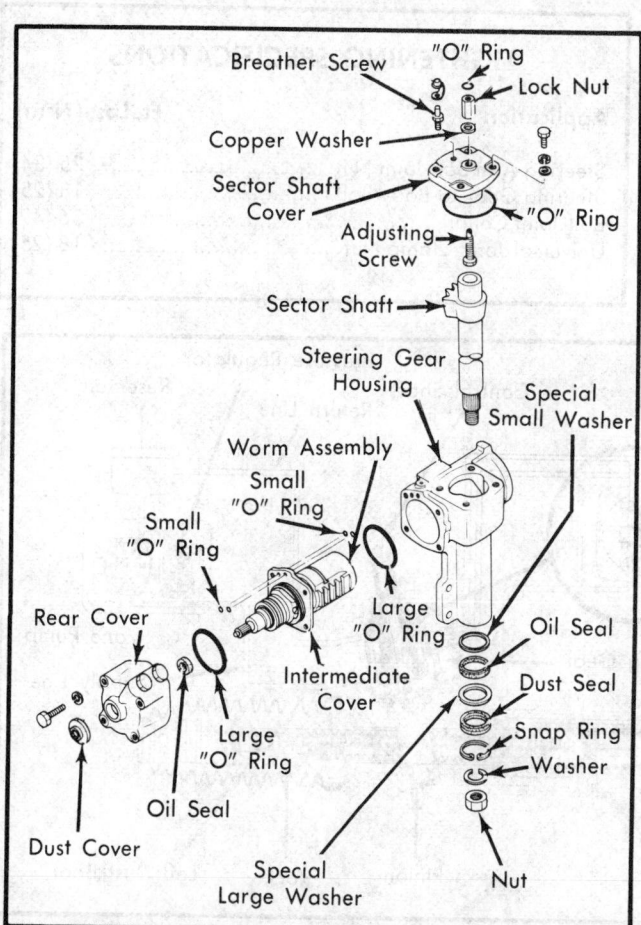

Fig. 1 Exploded View of Datsun Power Steering Gear

TIGHTENING SPECIFICATIONS

Application	Ft. Lbs. (N·m)
Hose-to-Gear Housing	36-51 (49-69)
Rear Cover Bolts	20-24 (27-33)
Sector Shaft-to-Pitman Arm Nut	
200SX	94-108 (128-147)
280ZX	101-130 (137-177)
Gear-to-Body	36-51 (49-69)

Power Steering

FIAT POWER-ASSISTED RACK & PINION

Brava

DESCRIPTION

A power-assisted rack and pinion steering gear is optional on Fiat Brava models. The system consists of a vane pump, rotary piston pinion gear assembly and an oil reservoir. The vane pump draws fluid from the reservoir and supplies it to the flow control valve. The control valve supplies fluid to the proper side of the rack/piston as the steering wheel is turned. The pump is belt driven and mounted on the lower right front side of the engine. The reservoir is located near the battery.

GENERAL SERVICE

Capacity — 1.9 pt.

Lubricant — ATF Type A

Oil Level Check — Remove wing nut and cover from reservoir. With engine stopped, level should reach mark on side of reservoir. With engine idling, level must not be more than .39" (10 mm) below mark.

Hydraulic System Bleeding — Start engine and allow to idle. Check that fluid is at proper level. Turn steering wheel from lock to lock several times quickly. Continue until fluid level remains at reservoir mark. Make sure that no bubbles appear in reservoir when steering wheel is turned. Shut off engine and check that oil level does not rise more than 3/8" above mark.

Oil Filter Replacement — Remove wing nut, outer cover, gasket and spring from reservoir. Remove inner filter cover and filter insert. Replace filter. Install new filter, replace filter cover, spring, gasket, cover and wing nut. Check fluid level.

REMOVAL & INSTALLATION

STEERING GEAR

Removal — 1) Remove nut securing tie rod end in steering knuckle. Using appropriate tool (A-47033), remove ball joint from steering knuckle. Repeat operation for other side. Loosen clamp and remove fluid return line from steering gear. Allow fluid to drain. Remove banjo bolt and washers from supply line and allow fluid to drain.

2) Remove bolt and nut securing universal joint to steering gear. Remove left steering gear mounting bolt at crossmember. Remove 2 right steering gear mounting bolts at crossmember. Remove power steering gear.

Installation — To install, reverse removal procedure and tighten. Fill system with fluid and bleed system if necessary.

VANE PUMP

Removal — Remove vane pump tensioner bolt and mounting bolt. Remove vane pump drive belt. Remove vane pump.

Installation — To install, reverse removal procedure and fill system with fluid. Bleed system if necessary.

OVERHAUL

NOTE — Manufacturer does not recommend overhaul of steering gear.

TIGHTENING SPECIFICATIONS

Application	Ft. Lbs. (N·m)
Steering Arm Ball Joint Nut	25 (34)
Steering Gear-to-Body Bolt	18 (25)
Ball Joint Collar	36 (49)
Universal Joint Clamp Nut	18 (25)

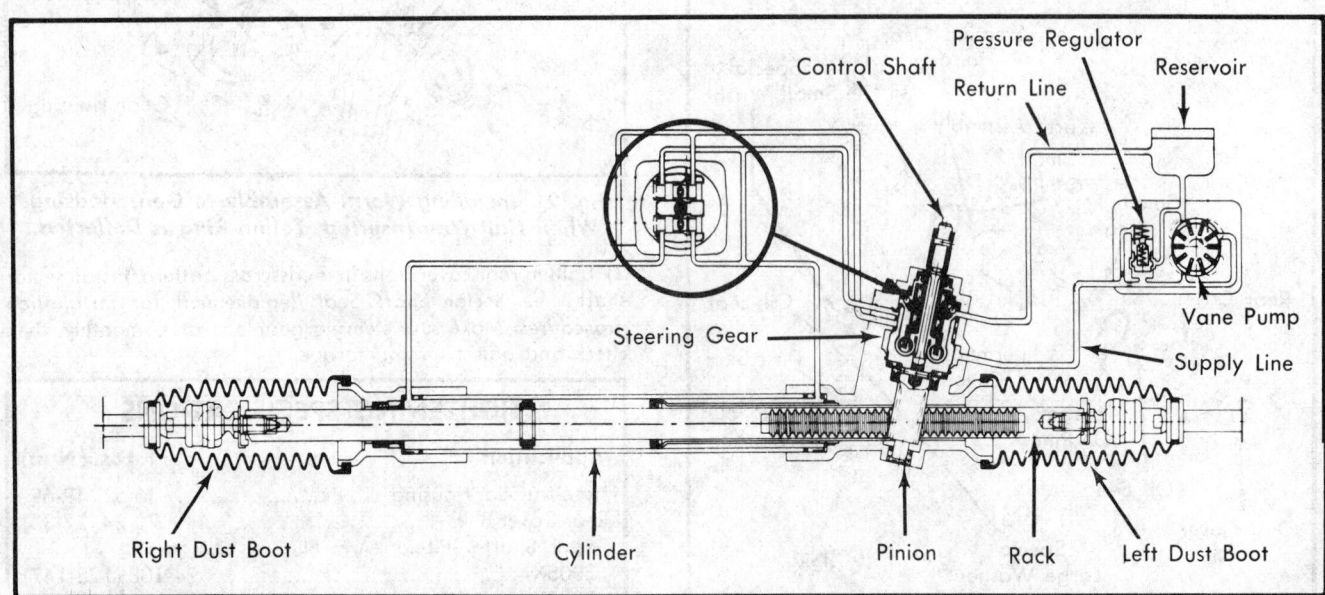

Fig. 1 Schematic of Fiat Brava Power Steering System

HONDA POWER-ASSISTED RACK & PINION

Accord
Prelude

DESCRIPTION

Power steering is rack and pinion with the power assist proportional to both vehicle speed and steering load. Power assist is high when vehicle speed is low and reduces as vehicle speed increases. The system consists of a power rack and pinion steering gear, steering pump, fluid reservoir, fluid cooler, vehicle speed sensor and connecting lines and hoses.

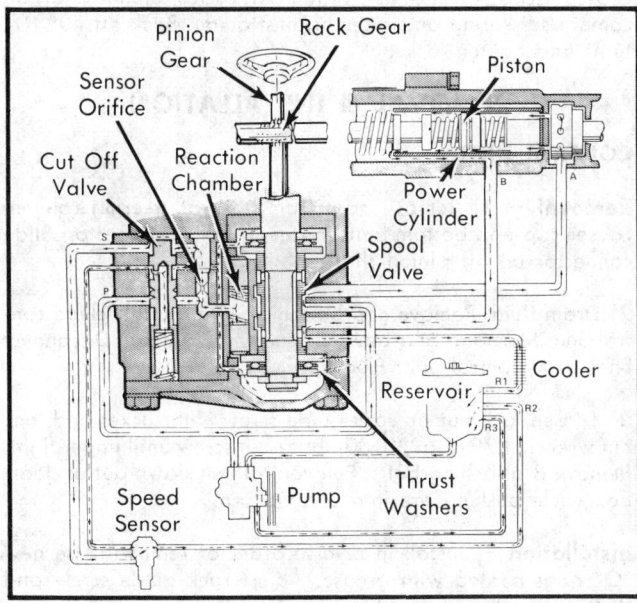

Fig. 1 Sectional View of Power Steering Pump and Power Steering Gear

GENERAL SERVICE

HYDRAULIC SYSTEM LUBRICANT

Capacity
Reservoir .... .85 qts. (.8 liter)
Complete System .... 2.1 qts. (2 liters)

Fluid Type — Honda.

CAUTION — *Use only genuine Honda power steering fluid. The use of any other fluids, such as ATF or other manufacturer's power steering fluid, will cause damage to the system.*

FILTER REPLACEMENT

1) To drain, disconnect cooler return hose from reservoir and place end in container. Start engine and run at fast idle. Turn steering wheel lock-to-lock several times until fluid flow stops.

2) Fill reservoir and repeat draining procedure to flush system. Remove reservoir from vehicle before removing guide bolt.

3) Remove guide bolt. Remove clip on end of guide bolt to remove filter and remaining components, noting their respective positions.

4) Clean and inspect all parts. Replace worn or defective parts. Carefully reassemble components to reservoir, making sure that retaining clip seats in filter recess. Install reservoir in vehicle.

5) Fill reservoir with fluid, start engine and run at fast idle. Turn steering wheel lock-to-lock several times to bleed air from system. Check fluid and add, if necessary.

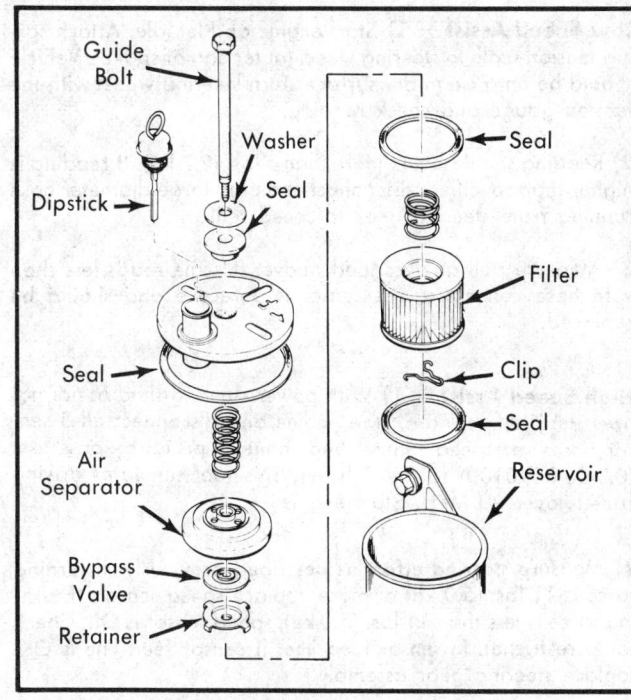

Fig. 2 Power Steering Reservoir Components

BELT TENSION ADJUSTMENT

1) Measure pump belt deflection midway between pulleys. Deflection should be .47-.55" at 22 lbs. pressure (12-14 mm at 10 kg) for Accord.

2) Deflection on Prelude should be .71-.87" at 22 lbs. pressure (18-22 mm at 10 kg). Replace belt when pump adjusting bolt reaches "bump" on adjusting bracket.

HYDRAULIC SYSTEM PRESSURE CHECK

1) Disconnect outlet hose from pump. Install pressure gauge and valve (07406-0010000).

2) Open valve. With engine running, turn steering wheel from lock to lock several times until fluid is at operating temperature.

3) Check idle speed and adjust if necessary. Close valve and read pressure gauge.

CAUTION — *Do not keep valve closed for more than 5 seconds or pump could be damaged by overheating.*

4) Pump pressure should be at least 995 psi (70 kg/cm²). If pressure is too low, replace pump. Open valve fully and turn steering wheel to full left lock. Read gauge, turn wheel to right lock and read gauge.

Power Steering

HONDA POWER-ASSISTED RACK & PINION (Cont.)

5) Both readings should be at least 995 psi (70 kg/cm²). A low reading indicates rack and pinion housing or speed sensor is defective. See SPEED SENSOR CHECK in this article. If sensor is okay, replace control unit.

SPEED SENSOR CHECK

Low Speed Assist — 1) Start engine and let idle. Attach spring tension scale to steering wheel (outer end of spoke). Vehicle should be on a clean dry surface. Turn steering wheel with the tension gauge and check reading.

2) Reading should be no more than 6 lbs. (2.7 kg). If reading is higher than specified, disconnect and plug large diameter hose running from steering gear to speed sensor.

3) Measure pull as described above. If scale reads less than with hose connected, the sensor is defective and should be replaced.

High Speed Assist — 1) With power steering fluid at normal operating temperature, stop engine and disconnect all 3 sensor hoses (at speed sensor) and connect special by-pass tool (07406-0010100) to the 3 hoses. This tool simulates driving speeds over 30 MPH. Start engine.

2) Measure steering effort as described previously. If turning force is 11 lbs. (5.0 kg) or more, replace speed sensor. If turning force is less than 11 lbs. (5.0 kg), speed sensor is OK. Check for a restriction in sensor feed line. If sensor feed line is OK, replace steering gear assembly.

STEERING SHAFT MOVEMENT CHECK

1) With engine not running, turn steering wheel to left and then to right. Steering wheel cover should move closer to or further away from turn signal cover.

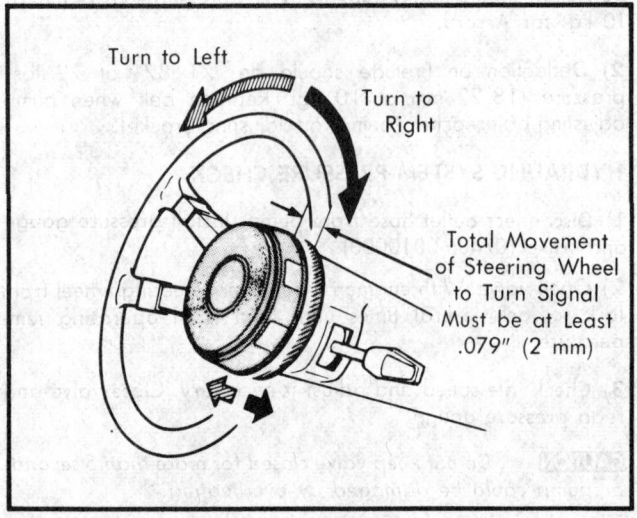

Turn to Left

Turn to Right

Total Movement of Steering Wheel to Turn Signal Must be at Least .079" (2 mm)

Fig. 3 Checking Steering Shaft Movement

2) Movement of steering wheel should be at least .079" (2 mm) for proper spool valve operation.

3) If the steering wheel moves only in or only out, but not both, loosen the 3 bolts in the steering shaft connector. Adjust shaft and make sure that shaft slides freely in column. Retighten bolts.

4) If adjustment does not restore correct movement of steering wheel, replace control unit.

ADJUSTMENT

RACK GUIDE ADJUSTMENT

Loosen rack screw lock nut. Tighten rack screw until rack piston compresses spring and seats against guide. Back off 70° (¹/₅ turn) and tighten lock nut.

REMOVAL & INSTALLATION

CONTROL UNIT

Removal — 1) Remove boot from base of steering column. Loosen top and bottom bolts in steering shaft connector. Slide connector up off pinion shaft.

2) Drain fluid. Remove gearbox shield. Thoroughly clean control unit, lines and gearbox with solvent. Blow dry. Disconnect lines from control unit. Plug lines.

3) Loosen lock nut on rack guide screw with socket and lock nut wrench (07916-6920100). Back out screw until finger tight. Remove 3 attaching bolts. Pull control unit down out of gearbox while pushing tire into a right turn.

Installation — Install in reverse order of removal. Use new "O" rings coated with grease. Adjust rack guide screw and steering shaft. Bleed system.

GEARBOX

Removal — 1) Remove control unit and front wheels. Disconnect tie rods from steering knuckles. On Accord with 5-speed transmission, remove bolt from shift rod clevis. Disconnect shift rod.

2) On Prelude remove engine shields and stabilizer bar brackets. Take weight off engine. On all models, remove center beam and steering gear mounting brackets.

3) On Prelude, rotate gearbox until clamps on front are visible. Remove clamps and pull output lines free of gearbox. On all models, remove gearbox through driver's side of frame.

Installation — 1) Install gearbox. On Prelude, clamp pump output line to gearbox before mounting box to frame. On Accord, install shift rod torque arm and tighten. On all models, install center beam.

2) On Prelude, install stabilizer bar brackets and engine shields. On all models, connect tie rods to steering knuckles. Install control unit as outlined in this section. Adjust rack guide screw and bleed system. Install front wheels.

STEERING PUMP

Removal — 1) Drain fluid from system. Disconnect inlet and outlet hoses at pump. Remove power steering belt by loosening the pump pivot and adjusting bolts.

HONDA POWER-ASSISTED RACK & PINION (Cont.)

2) Remove pump mounting bolts, bracket and power steering pump.

Installation — 1) To install steering pump, reverse removal procedures. Full reservoir to full mark on dipstick with new fluid.

CAUTION — *Use only genuine Honda power steering fluid. The use of other fluids, such as ATF or other manufacturer's power steering fluid, will cause damage to the system.*

2) Start engine and let run at fast idle while turning the steering wheel lock to lock several times to bleed air from system.

SPEED SENSOR

Removal — 1) Lift speedometer cable boot up to gain access to retaining clip. Remove retaining clip and pull out cable.

2) Disconnect and plug speed sensor hoses, back off speedometer gear set bolt. Lift speed sensor out.

Installation — After installing new sensor, turn steering wheel from lock to lock several times (engine idling), to bleed air from system.

OVERHAUL

NOTE — *Overhaul of Honda power steering components is limited to replacement of seals.*

GEARBOX

Disassembly — 1) Carefully clamp gearbox in a vise. Loosen bands and pull boots away from end of gearbox. Unbend tie rod lock washers. Unscrew tie rods. Remove hydraulic lines from gearbox.

2) Remove lock nut and rack guide screw. Remove spring, rack guide and shim. Remove 3 bolts from middle of gearbox. Slide pinion side of gearbox off rack. Shake retainer out of gearbox.

3) Check lip of pinion bearing dust seal. If damaged, pry out seal, remove circlip and knock out bearing. Pack new bearing with Molybdenum Disulphide grease. Install bearing with driver (07949-61-10000) and attachment (07746-0010100).

NOTE — *Use Molybdenum Disulphide grease on pinion bearing only. Use steering grease elsewhere.*

4) Install circlip. Coat lip of new seal with grease and install in the same way as bearing. Remove port side of gearbox from rack. Remove rack bushing. Remove cylinder cap and cylinder from rack.

5) From other side of rack, remove snap ring, seal retainer and cylinder spring. Pry piston ring and "O" ring under it from rack.

Inspection — Replace any parts with damaged sliding surfaces. Note that rack, pinion housing and gearbox are matched and must be replaced as a unit. Always replace "O" rings and seals with new parts when reassembling. Coat "O" rings with grease.

Reassembly — 1) Install new "O" ring on rack. Make sure narrow edge faces out. Install a new piston ring on rack with piston ring guide (07974-6890501) coated with power steering fluid. Slide tool onto rack, big end first. Install piston ring to piston groove (on top of "O" ring).

2) Install a new cylinder end seal to retainer with groove facing out. Grease lip. Install a new "O" ring to retainer. Reinstall retainer on rack. Coat end slider tool (07974-689081) with grease.

3) Make sure surface isn't damaged. Set slider over seal in retainer. Coat rack and fill teeth with grease. Install cylinder ring to rack. Hold tool and retainer together and slide onto rack so that slot in tool runs along smooth side.

4) Pull slider out of retainer, spread ends and remove from rack. Install snap ring on rack. Install cylinder. Coat piston ring and inside of sizing tool (07974-6890601) with power steering fluid.

5) Carefully slide tool onto rack and over piston ring. Rotate tool and move up and down to break in piston ring. Coat inside of cylinder with power steering fluid. Slide cylinder onto rack and over piston ring.

6) Slide rack back and forth to help seat ring against cylinder wall. Coat new "O" rings with grease and install to cap. Slide cap onto rack and press into end of cylinder.

7) Slide rack bushing onto rack. Install retainer washer in pinion side of gearbox. Insert rack teeth all the way into pinion side of gearbox. Using fingers, push old end seal out port side of gearbox.

8) Grease new "O" ring and install on end of port side housing. Set pinion side housing on end and slip end seal guide tool (07974-6891100) onto end of rack. Coat with grease.

9) Coat lip of new end seal with grease. Slide seal onto rack with grooved side in. Slip port side of gearbox onto rack. Push down enough to get end seal into bore. Push again to get middle "O" ring in and finally to compress cylinder spring so middle flanges touch momentarily.

10) Lift port side housing off rack. Look inside and check that new end seal has seated. Install housing and tighten 3 bolts. Move rack in and out of gearbox to make sure it operates smoothly.

11) Wipe grease off guide, shim, and smooth side of rack. Set shim and guide on rack. Turn guide to check for play. If there is play, try various thickness shims to obtain least play. Shims are available in 4 thicknesses from .076" (1.95 mm) to .082" (2.10 mm).

12) Coat shim with grease. Set it in the guide and set guide in the gearbox. Put spring in and install guide screw and lock nut finger tight on top. Clamp box in a vise. Place a new lock washer and stop washer on end of each tie rod.

NOTE — *Stop washer on driver's side is thicker.*

13) Screw tie rods into rack. Make sure tabs on lock washers fit into slots on rack. Bend lock washer over against straight edge on flange. Tighten each rod. Install boots and clamps on gearbox. Connect air transfer tube.

Power Steering

HONDA POWER-ASSISTED RACK & PINION (Cont.)

14) Install hydraulic lines. Check cut-off valve by pulling cap off control unit, pushing valve out and inspecting. If valve is okay, reinstall with spring. Hold finger over end of bore and push valve in at other end to check for smooth movement.

15) If valve is damaged, replace with a new unit. Note that valve is selective fit and there are 3 sizes. All 3 must be tried to ensure correct fit. Start with largest valve. Spring must be able to push valve back, and valve must move freely.

POWER STEERING PUMP

Disassembly — 1) Remove pulley. If damaged, remove 3 hub bolts first. If only the front seal is leaking, pry out with a screwdriver. Coat lip of new seal with grease. Start seal by hand and then push in with a socket. Reinstall pulley.

2) To completely overhaul unit, loosen and remove end cover bolts starting with upper right and progressing in a diagonal fashion. Remove "O" ring from end cover. Remove drive gear and driven gear from pump housing. Separate pump housing from port housing and remove "O" ring. Pry seal out of end cover.

Reassembly — 1) Install a new seal in cover. Start seal in by hand, then push in with a socket. Coat lip of seal with grease. Grease groove and install "O" ring to port housing.

2) Lubricate gear shaft bushings with power steering fluid. Set pump housing in place on port housing. Lubricate gears with power steering fluid. Insert gears to pump.

3) Grease "O" ring and position in groove on end cover. Reinstall cover on pump. Be careful not to damage lip of shaft seal. Install bolts in same sequence as removed. Tighten in sequence to 7 ft. lbs. (10 N·m) then to 15 ft. lbs. (20 N·m) and finally to 22 ft. lbs. (30 N·m).

4) If old pulley was replaced, install new pulley on hub. Slide pulley onto pump shaft and tighten. Rotate pulley to make sure pump turns.

TIGHTENING SPECIFICATIONS

Application	Ft. Lbs. (N·m)
Pump Pivot Bolt	36 (49)
Pulley Nut	33 (45)
Pump End Cover Bolts	①22 (30)
Gear Mounting Brackets	16 (22)
Tie Rod Nuts	32 (44)
Rack Guide Screw Lock Nut	18 (24)

① — In 3 steps. See text.

Power Steering

JAGUAR & TRIUMPH POWER-ASSISTED RACK & PINION

**Jaguar
XJ6
Triumph
TR8**

DESCRIPTION

Vehicles are equipped with a power assisted rack and pinion type steering system. The system consists of two main components: the rack and pinion steering gear and the power assist pump. The two components are connected by flexible fluid lines. The power assist pump and fluid reservoir are combined.

LUBRICANT

Type — ATF Dexron II

Intervals — Check power steering fluid every 3,000 miles.

TESTING

Control Valve & Pinion (Jaguar Only) — 1) Connect a 100 psi (7 kg/cm²) pressure gauge into pump return line, start engine and allow to idle. Pressure reading should be approximately 40 psi (2.8 kg/cm²). Turn steering gear left and right a small amount.

CAUTION — *Excessive turning of steering gear will cause gauge damage.*

2) Pressure should increase equal amounts as wheel is turned in either direction. A slight fall in pressure occurring before rise in pressure indicates a defective control valve. Stop and restart engine and check that steering does not kick to one side.

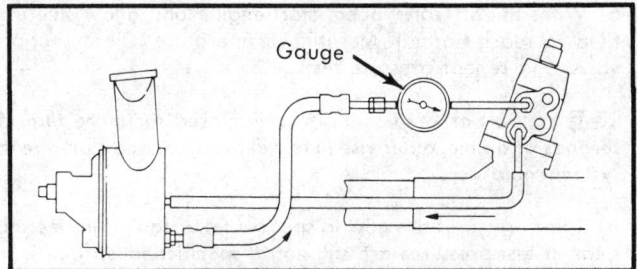

Fig. 1   Pressure Gauge Connection

Hydraulic System — 1) Connect a 1500 psi (100 kg/cm²) pressure gauge into the pump pressure line, start engine and allow to idle.

2) Turn steering to full lock and exert pressure on steering gear. On Jaguar, pressure should be 1100-1200 psi (77.5-84.4 kg/cm²) at idle. On Triumph, pressure should be a minimum of 450 psi (32 kg/cm²) at idle and 950-1000 psi (67-70 kg/cm²) at 1000 RPM.

NOTE — *On Jaguar models, if pressure is below 1100 psi (77.5 kg/cm²) at idle, but rises with engine speed increase, problem is either a defective pump control valve or internal leakage in rack and pinion.*

3) On Triumph, release steering wheel and allow to come off full lock position. Pressure reading should be a maximum of 55 psi (4 kg/cm²) at idle.

4) If system pressure readings were not to specifications, connect a shut-off valve (JD. 10-2) between pump and pressure gauge. This will isolate steering pump from steering gear and determine if problem is in gear or pump.

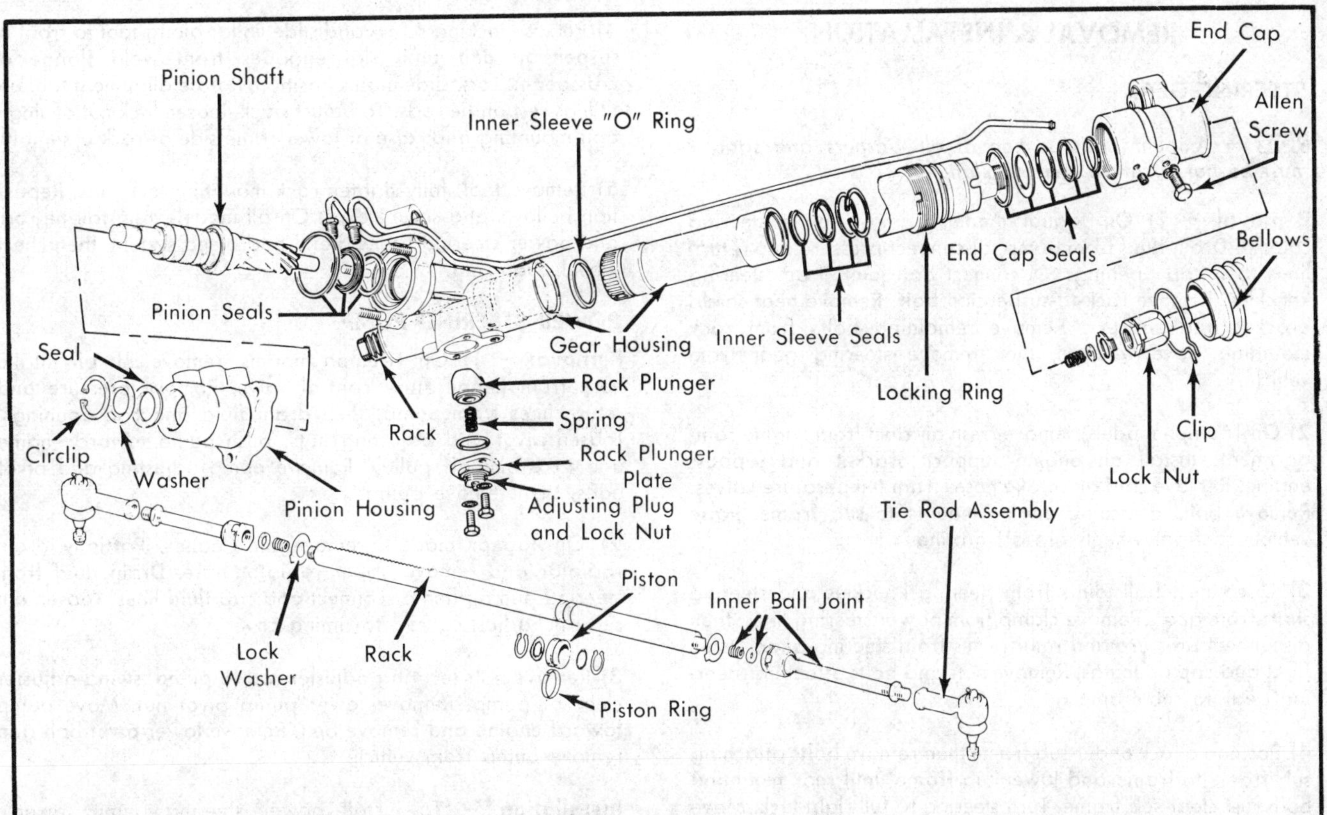

Fig. 2   *Exploded View of Jaguar and Triumph Power Assisted Rack and Pinion Steering Gear*

Power Steering

JAGUAR & TRIUMPH POWER-ASSISTED RACK & PINION (Cont.)

5) With shut-off valve open, start engine and allow steering fluid to reach normal operating temperature. Close shut-off valve and repeat pressure tests.

NOTE — *Do not keep shut-off valve closed for more than 5 seconds at a time, otherwise fluid will overheat and damage to system could occur.*

6) If test pressures are now to specifications, fault is in steering gear. If test pressures are still not to specifications, fault is in pump. *Refer to OVERHAUL in this article.*

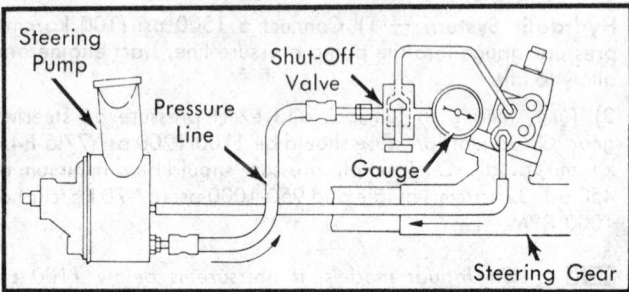

Fig. 3   Pressure Gauge and Shut-Off Valve Connections

SYSTEM BLEEDING

Turn wheels to full left lock, add fluid to "COLD" level mark on dipstick. Start engine and idle. Turn steering wheel lock to lock to expell air. Check fluid level. Straighten wheels and run engine for several minutes. Turn off engine, check fluid level. Fluid should be up to "HOT" mark on dipstick.

REMOVAL & INSTALLATION

STEERING GEAR

NOTE — *Amount and location of all washers and spacers must be noted for correct installation.*

Removal — 1) On Jaguar models, remove lower steering column. Drain fluid from pump, disconnect pressure and return lines then cap openings. Disconnect ball joints from steering knuckles. Remove rack-to-suspension bolt. Remove heat shield bracket and spacers. Remove remaining bolts from rack mounting, save washers, then remove steering gear from vehicle.

2) On Triumph models, remove fresh air duct from engine compartment. Install an engine support bracket and support engine. Remove cold air intake hoses from temperature valves. Remove bolts attaching engine mounts to sub frame. Raise vehicle so front wheels are off ground.

3) Disconnect ball joints from steering knuckles and steering shaft from gear. Remove clamp from power steering lines, then disconnect pressure and return lines from steering gear. Drain fluid and cap openings. Remove nuts and bolts attaching steering gear to sub frame.

4) Position a jack under sub frame then remove bolts attaching sub frame-to-frame and lower sub frame until rear mounting bolts just clear sub frame. Turn steering to full right lock. Move steering gear to right until left tie rod clears, then remove steering gear from vehicle.

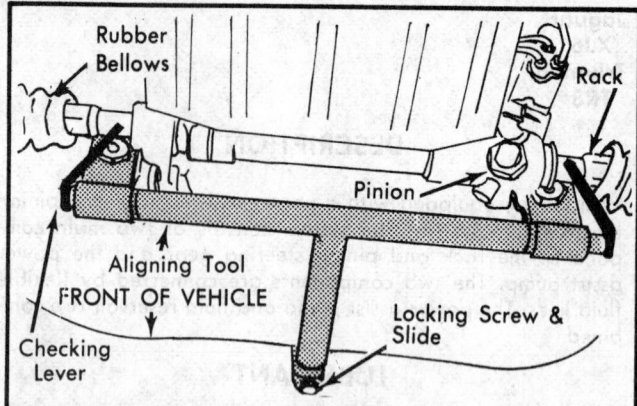

Fig. 4   Installing Rack and Pinion Gear

Installation — 1) On Triumph models, to install steering gear assembly, reverse removal procedures. On Jaguar models, position rack against mounting brackets and center lugs on bracket. Insert shims between lug and bracket to insure a gap of .05" (1.3 mm) on both sides of rack lug and mounting bracket. Insert mounting bolts but do not tighten.

2) Repeat centering procedure on upper and lower mountings on pinion side of rack. Make sure heat shield mounting bracket is located on upper mounting bolt. Remove clip securing rubber bellows to rack housing and fold bellows back to expose inner ball joints.

3) Install attachment brackets, of alignment tool JD. 36A, over large hex head bolts on lower control arms. It may be necessary to bend shields slightly to locate tool correctly. See *Fig. 4.*

4) Release locking screw and slide collar along tool to front of suspension unit until slot engages front weld flange of crossbeam. Lock slide in this position. Rotate alignment tool until legs rest on tie rods. To adjust slack, loosen lock nut of single bolt mounting and raise or lower same side of rack assembly.

5) Remove tool, fully tighten rack mounting lock nuts. Reposition bellows and secure clips. On all models, reinstall tie rods and power steering hoses. Refill and bleed system, then check wheel alignment.

POWER STEERING PUMP

Removal — 1) On Triumph models, remove left air intake hose from temperature control valve. Remove pressure and return lines from pump, then drain fluid and cap openings. Loosen pivot and adjusting nuts, push pump toward engine and take belt off pulley. Remove pump adjusting and pivot bolts, then remove pump.

2) On Jaguar models, remove air cleaner. Partially drain radiator and remove upper radiator hose. Drain fluid from steering pump, then disconnect and cap fluid lines. Loosen nut securing adjusting rod to timing cover.

3) Remove bolt securing adjuster rod to pump, swing adjuster clear of pump. Remove lower pump pivot nut. Move pump toward engine and remove belt. Remove lower pivot bolt and remove pump from vehicle.

Installation — To install power steering pump, reverse removal procedures. After replacement, adjust belt tension and bleed system.

JAGUAR & TRIUMPH POWER-ASSISTED RACK & PINION (Cont.)

CONTROL VALVE AND PINION

NOTE — *No adjustment or repair is possible except the replacement of the pinion seal.*

Removal — Remove steering gear assembly. Clean rack and pinion housing. Note position of pinion housing ports-to-valve cylinder pipes for reassembly reference. Loosen rack plunger lock nut and adjusting screw to remove spring tension. Remove pinion housing bolts and remove pinion housing with pinion shaft.

Installation — To install control valve and pinion, reverse removal procedure. Make sure pinion housing ports are aligned with cylinder pipes. On Jaguar models, make sure recess on pinion shaft are in correct position with pinion housing.

OVERHAUL

RACK ASSEMBLY

Disassembly — 1) Clean rack and pinion housing, drain assembly of fluid. Remove clips attaching bellows to tie rods and fold bellows back, exposing tie rod inner ball joint. Straighten lock tab of tie rod inner ball joint.

2) Remove tie rods from rack by loosening lock nut on inner ball joint. Note position of pinion housing-to-valve cylinder pipes, then remove pipes. Remove air transfer pipe. On Jaguar models, remove Allen screw from end cap. On all models, remove locking ring from end housing and remove end housing.

3) Remove rack plunger lock nut, adjusting nut, spring and plunger. Remove pinion housing cover, then remove pinion housing from rack housing. Remove pinion from pinion housing. Remove snap ring, washer and seal from pinion housing. Remove rack from rack housing.

4) Remove porting adapter and slide porting ring along cylinder until feed hole is exposed. Using a scribe (or similar tool) pry seal until seal can be removed from cylinder with a hooked wire. Remove all seals, "O" rings and sleeves from rack housing.

NOTE — *Do not remove seals from pinion piston.*

Inspection — Clean all parts in solvent and blow dry or air dry. Do not wipe dry as lint could contaminate parts and cause malfunction when assembled. Check all parts for excessive wear, scratches, nicks or scoring. Replace parts as necessary. Check rack teeth and pinion teeth for chips, burrs and other damage. Always replace all "O" rings and seals upon reassembly. Check rubber bellows for cracks, splits or holes, replace as necessary.

Reassembly — 1) Lubricate all "O" rings, seals and sleeves before installation. Also lubricate all moving parts before installation. Install seal and "O" ring to end housing.

2) Install new center feed porting adapter to porting ring. Position ring to allow conical seating on adapter to engage with seating on cylinder, then tighten. Install rack seal over rack teeth up against piston. Install anti-extrusion ring to recess in back of rack seal.

3) Lubricate inside of rack housing and grease rack. Insert rack into rack housing with firm steady pressure until seal seats against abutment face. Make sure piston ring collapses and enters rack housing without damage.

4) Install new seal, washer and snap ring to pinion housing. Install new pinion valve seal to pinion shaft (located against pinion bearing). Lubricate pinion shaft, piston seals and bearing. Carefully install pinion shaft to pinion housing, tapping gear end of shaft lightly to make sure it is seated.

5) Grease pinion teeth and small journal of pinion then install pinion and housing (use new gasket) to rack housing. Make sure rack teeth and pinion teeth mate correctly. Make sure pinion housing ports are correctly aligned so cylinder-to-valve pipes can be installed.

6) Install seals to end housing. Install end housing-to-rack housing and screw locking ring into end housing just enough to hold mounting feet in parallel alignment. With end housing and mounting feet in alignment, tighten locking ring.

7) Install rack plunger, spring, adjusting plug and lock nut. Tighten adjusting plug, while moving rack through full stroke, until rack is hard to move then back off adjusting nut just enough to obtain a smooth rack movement (approximately 1/8 turn). Tighten lock nut while holding adjusting plug from turning.

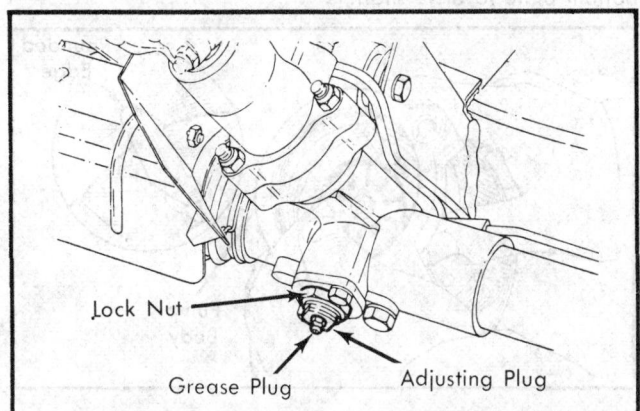

Fig. 5   Rack End Play Adjustment

8) Install air transfer pipe and cylinder-to-valve pipes. Place bellows onto tie rods, small opening towards outer ball joint. Install tie rod inner ball joint to rack. Make sure lock washer tab is aligned with slot in rack end. Pull rack out until rack teeth can be held in soft jawed vise, then tighten tie rod inner ball joint lock nut. Repeat procedure for other tie rod. Bend lockwasher tab into rack slots with punch.

9) Place 1 to 2 oz. of grease to each bellows then attach bellows to rack housing and tie rod with wire clips. Remove plug in rack plunger adjusting plug and install grease nipple. Using a hand grease gun, fill with approximately 5 strokes of grease gun. Remove grease nipple and replace plug.

POWER STEERING PUMP

Disassembly — 1) Remove rear mounting plate and pulley from pump. Remove front mounting plate from pump and clean pump body. Remove pressure outlet union and mounting plate studs from rear of pump. Tip pump and remove flow control valve and spring.

2) Place pump in padded vise and tap pump casing from body. Remove "O" rings from pump body and magnet from flange. With suitable pin punch, push retaining ring free from groove and lever from body. Remove spring retaining plate and spring. Remove "O" ring from recess in pump body.

JAGUAR & TRIUMPH POWER-ASSISTED RACK & PINION (Cont.)

3) Remove Woodruff key from shaft. Tap roller spindle toward body and remove pump assembly from body. Remove "O" ring from recess in pump body. Remove dowel pins.

4) Remove rotor housing top plate and rotor housing. Remove rotor vanes and circlip securing rotor to drive shaft. Remove drive shaft oil seal from pump body.

Cleaning and Inspection — Clean all parts with lint-free cloth. Replace all "O" rings and seals. Check all parts for scratches, nicks, burrs or excessive wear. Replace rotor ring and vanes if excessive wear or chatter marks are present. Check flow control valve for free movement in bore. Lubricate all parts with power steering fluid before reassembly. Check interference fit between pump shaft and pulley. Replace parts if interference fit is less than .001" (.025 mm) or more than .0026" (.066 mm).

Reassembly — 1) Lubricate drive shaft seal and fit into pump shaft housing. Fit "O" ring to lower recess in pump body. Place dowel pins in locating holes. With cutaway face uppermost, fit bottom plate to drive shaft.

2) Fit rotor over splines of drive shaft (countersunk face towards thrust plate) and secure with snap ring. Insert vanes in rotor with curved edge out. Fit drive shaft and rotor to pump body, ensuring that dowel pins locate through smallest holes of bottom plate. With arrow towards rear of housing, place pump ring chamber over rotor and dowel pins.

3) With spring recess up, fit chamber top plate over dowel pins. Push complete pump assembly home. Fit "O" ring into upper recess of pump body. Fit spring to recess in top plate. Place retaining plate over spring and push into body. Fit "O" rings to port recess, and large "O" ring to outside pump body and magnet to flange.

4) Place pump casing over body. Locate mounting studs into outer casing and into pump body. Place outer casing over pump body. Tighten mounting studs. Install spring and flow control valve. Fit pressure outlet union. Place Woodruff key in drive shaft spindle. Replace pulley and mounting plates. Refill system with fluid and bleed system.

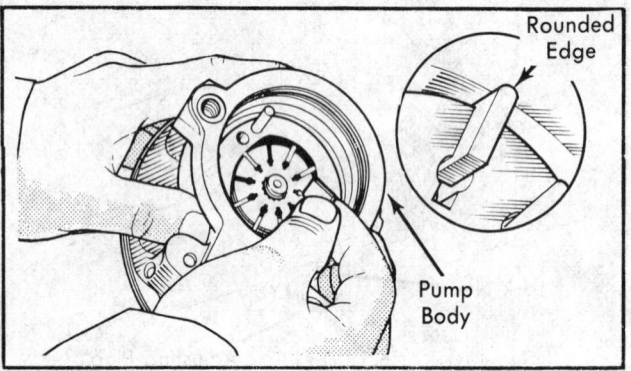

Fig. 6 Placing Vanes in Rotor Plate

TIGHTENING SPECIFICATIONS

Application	Ft. Lbs. (N·m)
Center Feed Porting Adapter Ring	22-25 (30-34)
Pump High Pressure Fitting	25-40 (34-54)
Rack Housing End Plate Lock Ring	80-90 (109-122)
Rack Housing Mounting Bolts	
Jaguar	49-55 (67-75)
Triumph	30 (41)
Tie Rod Inner Ball Joint Lock Nut	
Jaguar	45-55 (61-75)
Triumph	66-81 (90-110)

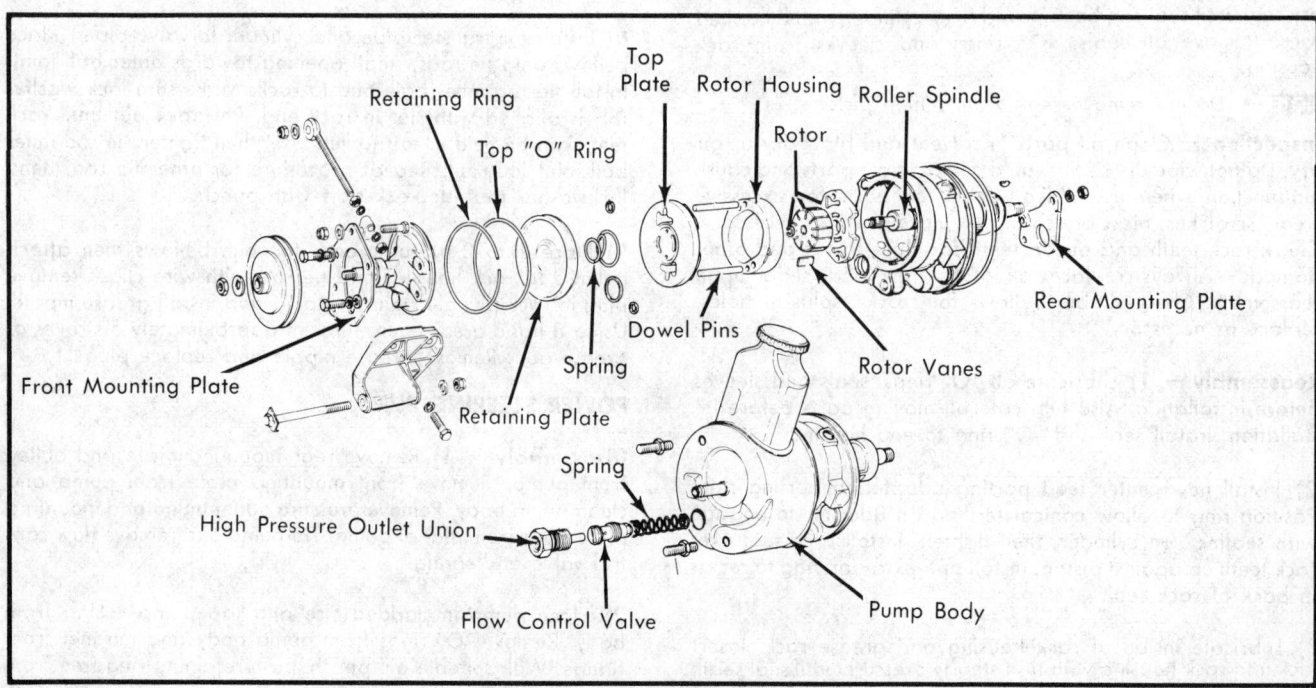

Fig. 7 Exploded View of Jaguar and Triumph Power Steering Pump

Power Steering

MERCEDES-BENZ POWER-ASSISTED RECIRCULATING BALL

240D
280 Series
300 Series
380 Series

DESCRIPTION

Power steering system is composed of power steering pump, steering gear and connecting hoses. All pumps have integral reservoirs. Both ZF and VT49 type pumps are used; some of these pumps are made of a light alloy material. The light alloy pumps are interchangeable with the cast iron type.

All power steering pumps are engine driven vane type with a control valve. The purpose of the power steering gear pump is to supply fluid (under pressure) to the steering gear.

Steering gear has integral piston/steering nut. Fluid pressure to each side of piston/steering nut is controlled by a control valve which is moved by a lever from steering column shaft. Steering system has a digressive action. Boost is relatively weak in the central range, and increases as steering resistance increases.

LUBRICATION

Capacity — 2.6 pts. automatic transmission fluid.

REMOVAL & INSTALLATION

POWER STEERING PUMP

Removal — 1) Remove power steering tank cover, spring and damping plate. Drain tank with a syringe. Disconnect and plug high pressure and return hoses.

2) Loosen fastening bolts and push pump towards engine, remove "V" belts from pulley. Remove remaining bolts and remove pressure pump with carrier.

Installation — To install power steering pump, reverse removal procedures. Fill system with recommended fluid.

POWER STEERING GEAR

NOTE — *All models are equipped with a modified power steering gear. The stop for the full lock position is incorporated into the housing itself, not on the steering arms as before. When replacing steering gears, install only the newer type gear. This gear can be recognized by an "A" * stamped on the housing.*

Removal — 1) Drain fluid from power steering pump. Disconnect and plug pressure line and return line from steering gear. Remove bolts from steering coupling. Remove rear exhaust system and left hand exhaust pipe at manifold (all 380 models). Disconnect center link and tie rod from pitman arm. Remove bolts securing steering gear to frame. Force steering gear from steering column shaft, in a downward direction.

2) Drain fluid from steering gear, remove steering coupling and pitman arm from gear (be sure to mark pitman shaft-to-pitman arm position for proper assembly).

Installation — To install steering gear, reverse removal procedure. Replace locking nuts and bolts, tighten to specifications. Fill system with recommended fluid.

OVERHAUL

POWER STEERING PUMP

Disassembly (VT49 Pump) — 1) Remove wing nut and cover from reservoir. Remove compression spring, 2 damping plates and filter ring. Remove Woodruff key from input shaft.

2) Install puller 1104-7251 on input shaft. Screw bolt back on puller enough to install clamping shoes 11004-6304 between puller and seal. Turn clamping cone of puller to the right up to stop and remove seal ring out of housing.

3) On rear of housing, push in cover and insert a punch through hole in housing. *See Fig. 1.* Push in on punch and remove circlip and cover. Remove spring and "O" ring from housing. Push input shaft with pressure plate at cover end, rotor, cam ring and pressure plate at input end out of housing in rearward direction.

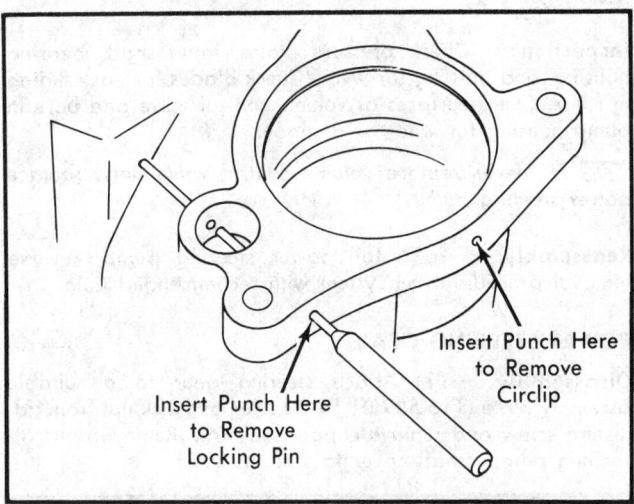

Fig. 1 Circlip Punch Hole Location and Removing Locking Pin on VT49 Pump

4) Remove pressure plate, cam ring and blades. Remove locking clip from input shaft, then remove rotor and pressure plate. Remove cylinder pins from housing. Using a punch, knock out locking pins in housing. *See Fig. 1.*

5) Remove closing plug, volume control valve and compression spring from housing. Clamp volume control valve in vise and disassemble valve. Check spacer washer, valve cone and compression spring.

Inspection — Check pressure plates, input shaft, and bearing bushing for wear. Check blades for easy sliding in rotor. Check surfaces of volume control valve and bore in pump housing for wear or damage.

NOTE — *Never replace volume control valve only, replace power steering pump.*

Reassembly — To install power steering pump, reverse removal procedure. Fill system with recommended fluid.

Disassembly (ZF Pump) — 1) Remove Woodruff key from input shaft. Install puller (1104-7251) on shaft. Screw bolt back on puller enough to install clamping shoes (1104-6304) between puller and seal.

MERCEDES-BENZ POWER-ASSISTED RECIRCULATING BALL (Cont.)

2) Turn clamping core of puller to the right up to stop, remove tool, seal and washer from housing. Remove knurled nut and cover from housing. Remove retaining and compression springs. Remove upper damping plate, filter ring, and lower damping plate.

3) On rear of housing, push in cover plate and using a screwdriver remove circlip and cover. Remove "O" ring, compression spring, and pressure plate. Remove rotor with blades from input shaft and "O" ring and cam ring.

4) Remove lock ring from forward end of shaft. Press out input shaft from rear of housing. Remove circlip from shaft and remove bearing by pressing off toward rear of shaft. Remove needle bearing from housing.

5) Remove closing plug from housing. Remove compression spring and volume control valve. Clamp volume control valve in vise, disassemble and check spacer washers, ball, and compression spring.

Inspection — Check pressure plates, input shaft, bearing housing, and bushing for wear. Check blades for easy sliding in rotor. Check surfaces of volume control valve and bore in pump housing for wear or damage.

NOTE — *Never replace volume control valve only, replace power steering pump.*

Reassembly — To install power steering pump, reverse removal procedure. Fill system with recommended fluid.

POWER STEERING GEAR

Disassembly — 1) Attach steering gear to a suitable assembly plate (116 589 01 59 00). Remove lock nut from adjusting screw and remove copper seal ring. Remove bolts attaching pitman shaft cover to steering case.

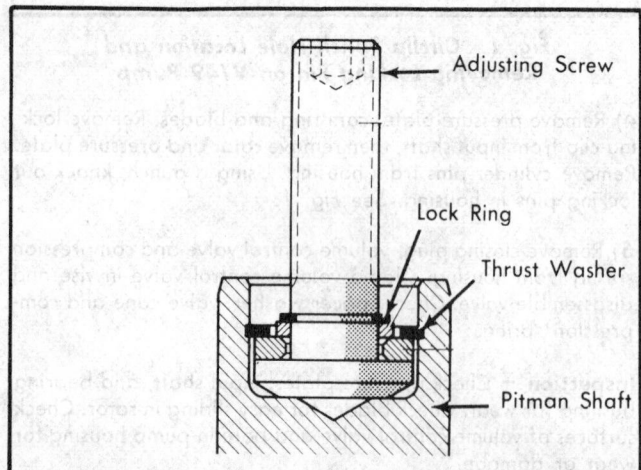

Fig. 2   Sectional View of Adjusting Screw

2) With steering in center position, turn adjusting screw clockwise. This forces pitman shaft, with housing, from steering gear case. Remove pitman shaft with cover. Remove "O" rings from cover. Remove lock ring and seal ring. Remove lock ring from pitman shaft and remove adjusting screw with thrust washers See *Fig. 2.*

3) Remove bolts securing bearing cap to steering case. Turn worm gear counterclockwise until bearing cap is forced out of steering gear case.

NOTE — *Balls will fall out of ball guide if worm gear is turned too far.*

4) Remove bearing cap and worm gear with piston/steering nut from steering gear case.

5) Unscrew worm gear with bearing cap from piston/steering nut.

CAUTION — *Do not lose circulator balls.*

6) Remove "O" ring from bearing cap and attach bearing cap to a suitable assembly fixture.

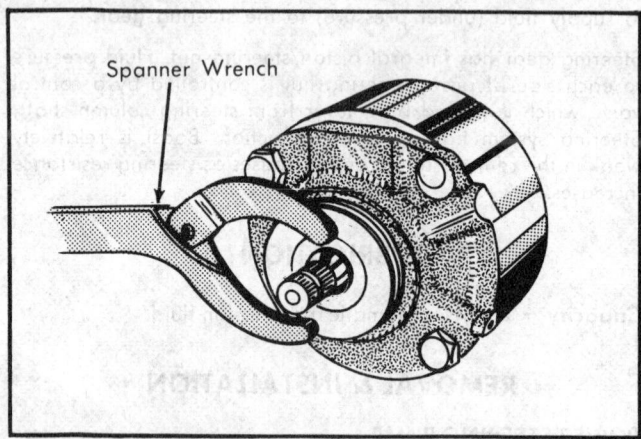

Fig. 3   Removing Bearing Insert from Bearing Cap

7) Unscrew slotted nut, using hook wrench, from bearing insert.

8) Remove bearing insert from bearing cap using spanner wrench. *See Fig. 3.* Remove steering worm and washer from bearing cap. Remove roller cage from steering worm, along with seal and "O" rings.

9) Remove bearing and disc from bearing cap. Remove bolts, clamp, and both ball guide halves from piston/steering nut.

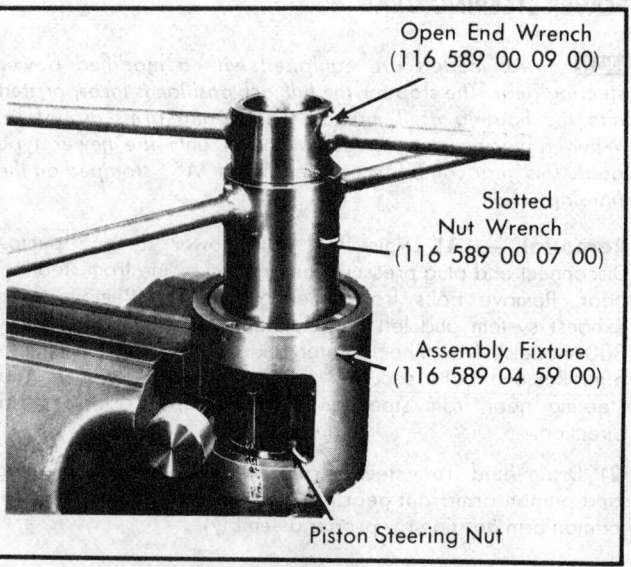

Fig. 4   Removing Worm Gear Nut from Piston Steering Nut

MERCEDES-BENZ POWER-ASSISTED RECIRCULATING BALL (Cont.)

10) Using suitable clamp and tools, remove worm gear nut from piston/steering nut. See Fig. 4. Remove seal ring and "O" ring from worm gear nut.

11) Remove bearings from piston/steering nut, then remove lock ring, cover and control valve from steering gear case. See Fig. 5.

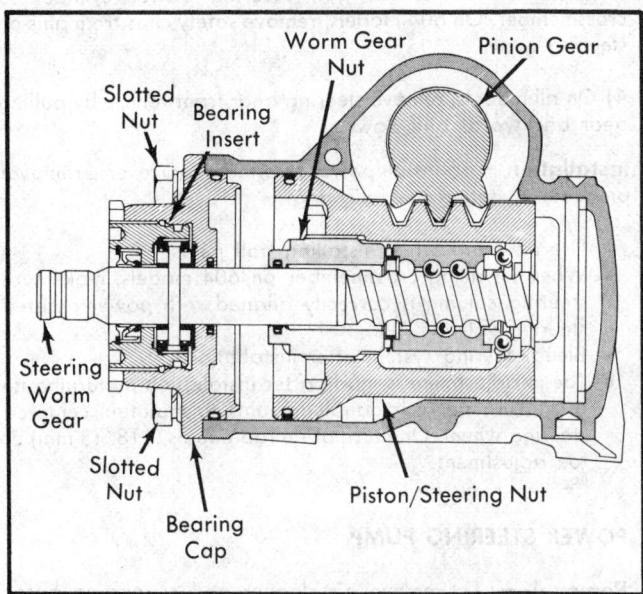

Fig. 5   Cross Sectional View of Steering Gear

Inspection – 1) On worm gear, check ball paths and bearings surfaces for wear and damage, replace if necessary.

2) On piston/steering nut, remove seal rings, "O" rings, bearings and races, and worm gear nut. Inspect for wear or damage and replace as necessary.

3) Check pitman shaft for wear or damage on bearing surfaces, check for bent or warped shaft and replace as necessary. Check steering case, cover, and bearing insert for wear or damage and replace as necessary.

4) On control valve, check reaction piston in control valve for free movement. If necessary remove pistons from control valve by removing lock rings.

Reassembly – To reassemble steering gear, reverse disassembly procedure. Replace all "O" rings and sealing rings with new ones. Adjust gear to specifications.

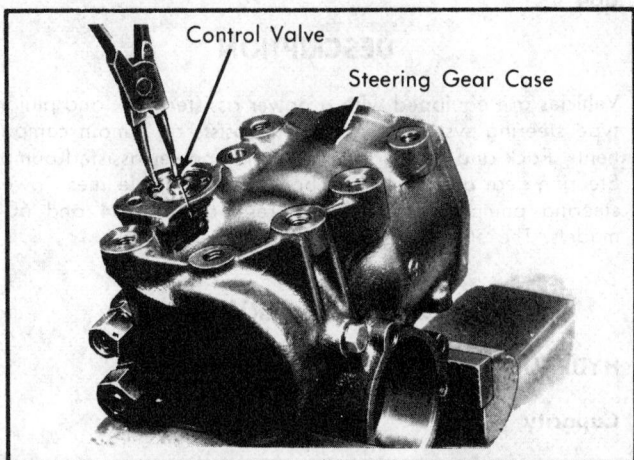

Fig. 6   Removing Control Valve from Steering Gear Case

STEERING SPECIFICATIONS

Application	Dimensions
Steering Wheel Free Play	1" (25 mm) Maximum
Pump Circulation Pressure	28.4-71.0 psi (2.0-5.0 kg/cm^2)
Number of Balls in Ball Circuit	24
End Play of Pump Shaft	
New	.028" (.71 mm) Maximum
Used	.039" (.99 mm) Maximum

TIGHTENING SPECIFICATIONS

Application	Ft. Lbs. (N.m)
Steering Gear-to-Frame	50-57 (68-78)
Pitman Arm-to-Pitman Shaft	116-145 (158-197)
Slotted Nut-to-Bearing Cap	101-115 (137-156)
Adjusting Screw Nut	22-25 (30-34)
Pump Housing Bolts	25-29 (30-39)

Power Steering

PEUGEOT POWER-ASSISTED RACK & PINION

504
505
604

DESCRIPTION

Vehicles are equipped with a power assisted rack and pinion type steering system. The system consists of 2 main components: Rack and steering gear, and the power assisted pump. Steering gear and pump are connected by flexible lines. Power steering pump has an integral reservoir on 504 and 604 models. The 505 model has a separate reservoir.

GENERAL SERVICE

HYDRAULIC SYSTEM LUBRICANT

Capacity

504 and 604 — .69 qts.
505 — .74 qts.

SYSTEM BLEEDING

Fill reservoir to full mark on dipstick. Start engine and turn steering wheel from lock-to-lock several times (to expel all air). Recheck fluid level and refill as required.

REMOVAL & INSTALLATION

STEERING GEAR

Removal — **1)** Drain steering system and disconnect pressure lines between pump and gear. Disconnect bolt at flexible coupling. Disconnect tie rod ball joints at steering knuckle.

2) On 604 models, remove rear bolts of front crossmember and install longer bolts. Remove front crossmember from bolts, then loosen rear bolts until a gap of approximately 1.5" (40 mm) exists between crossmember and frame.

3) On all models, remove steering gear to crossmember mounting bolts. Remove bolt securing power cylinder to crossmember. On 604 models, remove safety clips from pins on steering gear.

4) On all models, remove steering gear from vehicle by pulling gear backwards and down.

Installation — To install power steering gear, reverse removal procedures, noting the following:

- Use new nuts when installing ball joints.
- When installing crossmember on 604 models, make sure steering column is correctly aligned with power assisted steering valve.
- Bleed steering system after installation.
- Toe-in adjustment is made after installation by turning tie rods. Turn tie rods equal amounts to maintain centered steering wheel. One turn of tie rod equals .118" (3 mm) of toe adjustment.

POWER STEERING PUMP

Removal — **1)** Remove air cleaner and connecting hoses. Remove pressure lines from pump. Loosen drive belt tensioner bolts and remove drive belt.

2) Remove pump attaching bolts. On 505 models, disconnect hose from reservoir to pump. On all models, remove pump from vehicle.

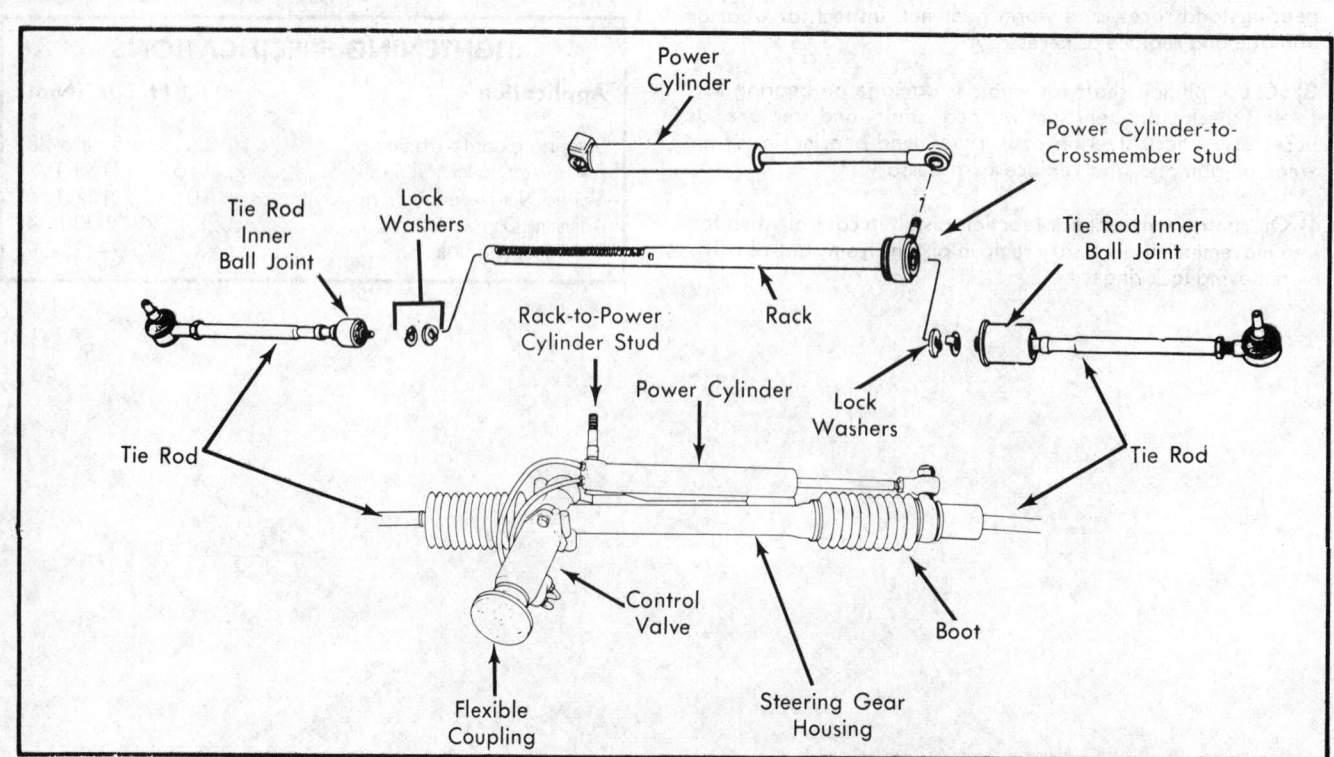

Fig. 1   Peugeot Power Assisted Rack and Pinion Steering Gear

PEUGEOT POWER-ASSISTED RACK & PINION (Cont.)

3) On 504 models, remove pump pulley with suitable gear puller (555 TAX). On 505 models, remove pulley by removing 4 bolts attaching pulley to pump. On 604 models, on pumps with extractor groove, use extractor tool (80706 H1, H2, H5) and pull pulley out as far as possible. Then tap pulley off with mallet. On 604 models without extractor groove, use suitable gear puller (555 TAX) and remove pulley.

Installation — To install steering pump, reverse removal procedures noting the following: Make sure hose connections are clean before installing. Fill system with fluid, then bleed system. *See System Bleeding in this article.*

OVERHAUL

POWER STEERING PUMP

NOTE — *Manufacturer does not recommend overhaul of power steering pump.*

POWER STEERING GEAR

Disassembly — **1)** Clean steering gear assembly before starting disassembly. Place steering gear assembly in a padded vise. Disconnect pressure pipes from power cylinder and plug ports in power cylinder and cap pressure pipes.

NOTE — *Do not disconnect pressure pipes from control valve if valve is to be reused. Do not loosen lock nut on power cylinder attaching joint.*

2) Remove nut securing power cylinder to rack and remove power cylinder. Loosen lock nut on right tie rod inner ball joint, then disconnect tie rod from rack.

3) If control valve is to be replaced, remove pressure pipe connections.

NOTE — *Be careful not to bend or twist pipes connecting control valve to power cylinder.*

4) Remove left boot clamp and push boot toward steering gear. Disconnect left tie rod inner ball joint from rack. Remove rack piston cover, spring and rack piston from steering gear housing.

5) Remove control valve bearing cap cover, then remove nut. Remove bolts attaching control valve-to-steering gear. Carefully remove control valve from gear housing. Carefully withdraw rack from housing. Remove snap ring and remove pinion gear bearing.

6) If control valve is to be rebuilt, proceed as follows: Remove flexible coupling. Remove snap ring and thrust washer, then withdraw control valve piston from control valve housing.

NOTE — *Do not tap on shaft to aid removal or damage to shaft will occur. Do not remove piston rotor segments from shaft.*

7) From control valve housing, remove snap ring, scraper seal and oil seal.

Inspection — Check steering gear housing and rack for any damage, scoring or any signs of excessive wear. Check control valve housing and shaft for damage, wear or scoring. Replace components as necessary. Always replace all washers, nuts, seals and bearings when reassembling steering gear.

Reassembly — **1)** If control valve was disassembled, install oil seal (soaked in oil) to piston/pinion gear assembly with seal lip facing pinion gear. Install piston in control valve. Install thrust washer and snap ring on pinion end of control valve housing. Install oil seal, scraper ring, and snap ring on flexible coupling end of valve housing. Install flexible coupling to control valve housing.

2) Install new pinion gear bearing into steering gear housing, then install snap ring. Insert rack into housing, align rack teeth with pinion gear/control valve mounting hole. Align flexible coupling pinch bolt with pressure pipe holes (holes that connect control valve with power cylinder) on control valve.

3) Insert control valve/pinion gear into steering gear housing. To make sure control valve is properly aligned with rack, line up control valve flange bolt holes with gear box holes. Then rotate control valve 90° counterclockwise. Insert control valve into gear box while rotating control valve 90° clockwise. this will properly align rack teeth with pinion teeth.

4) Hold flexible coupling and install pinion nut, grease bearing location and install grease cap. Temporarily place plunger and spring in housing. Install rack plunger cover, upper bolt and dial indicator mount into lower bolt hole. Install dial indicator on mount and tighten down cover.

5) Using flexible coupling, turn steering rack from lock-to-lock and zero dial indicator on maximum deflection indicated. Using lever, push steering rack in direction of plunger and record dial indicator reading. Remove dial indicator, rack cover and rack plunger from housing.

6) Install stop to rack plunger and lay straight edge over stop and plunger. Select shim pack to eliminate clearance between stop and straight edge.

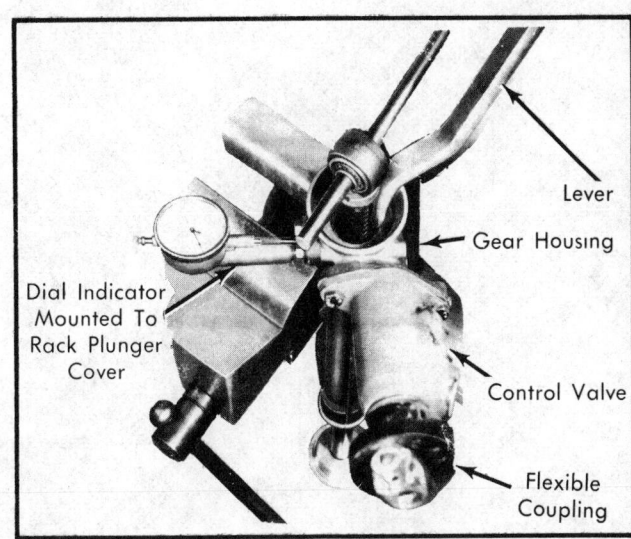

Fig. 2 Measuring Steering Rack Plunger Clearance

Power Steering

PEUGEOT POWER-ASSISTED RACK & PINION (Cont.)

7) Steering rack plunger clearance should be .004±.002" (.1±.05 mm) at maximum point along rack travel. To obtain required clearance, subtract .004" (.1 mm) from dial indicator reading obtained in step **5)**, this measurement indicates the thickness of shim washers needed in plunger.

8) Install shim pack selected, stop and spring to rack plunger. Install rack plunger assembly to gear housing. Install grease nipple to cover then install cover over rack plunger assembly and tighten bolts. Install rubber boots, with clamps, to steering gear housing. Push boots out of way when installing tie rod inner ball joints.

9) Install stop plate and lock washer, then install tie rod inner ball joints to rack. Insert bolt into power cylinder. Attach power cylinder to bolt on rack end and tighten nut finger tight. Install pressure pipes from control valve to power cylinder. Do not bend or deform pressure pipes when installing and tightening connections.

10) With pressure pipes installed, tighten rack bolt nut. Install pressure lines to control valve. Before steering gear installation in vehicle, install spacer on power cylinder to crossmember bolt.

TIGHTENING SPECIFICATIONS

Application	Ft. Lbs. (N·m)
Ball Joint Nut	31 (42)
Crossmember-to-Frame	31 (42)
Engine Mount-to-Crossmember	25 (34)
Gear Housing-to-Crossmember	24 (33)
Inner Ball Joint-to-Rack	36 (49)
Power Cylinder-to-Crossmember	40 (54)
Power Cylinder-to-Rack	33 (45)
Tie Rod Lock Nut (Outer)	58 (79)

Power Steering

PORSCHE POWER-ASSISTED RACK & PINION

928

DESCRIPTION

A power-assisted rack and pinion steering gear is used as standard equipment on Porsche 928 models. The power assistance decreases with engine speed to provide a better road feel at high speeds. The system consists of a belt driven vane pump mounted on the engine, a fluid reservoir located in the left front engine compartment, and a rotary piston pinion steering gear.

GENERAL SERVICE

Lubricant — ATF Dexron Type

Oil Level Check — Remove reservoir cap and start engine. Check that fluid level is up to embossed mark on inside of reservoir.

Hydraulic System Bleeding — Start engine, set to idle. Check fluid level. Turn steering wheel lock to lock several times quickly. Do not turn wheel harder than necessary. Check fluid and add if needed. No air bubbles should rise in reservoir. Shut off engine. Check that fluid level does not rise more than ⅜" (10 mm). If level rises, repeat procedure.

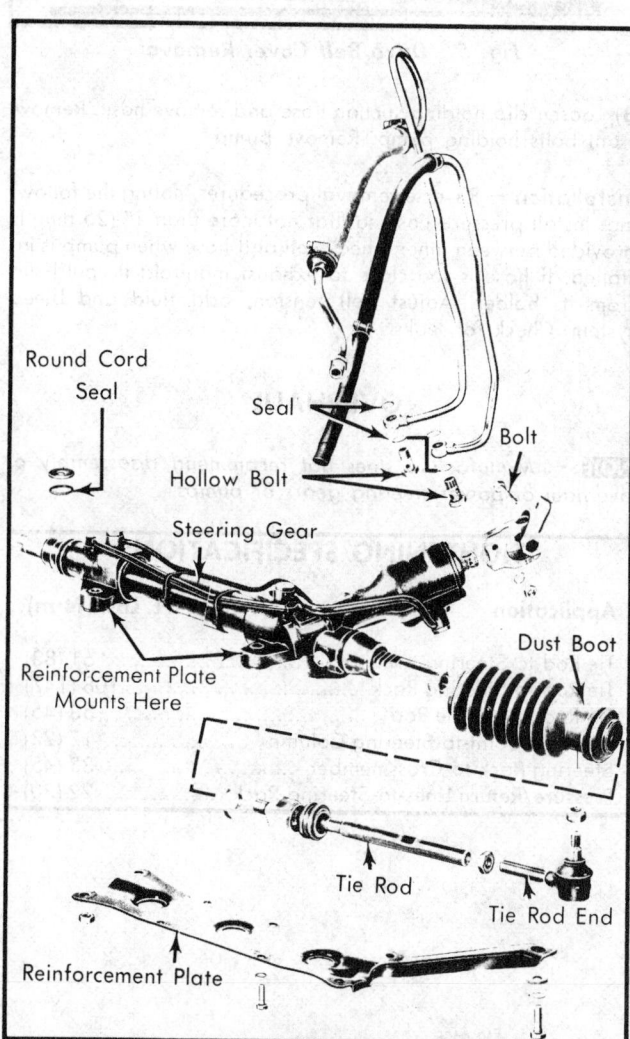

Fig. 1 Power Steering Gear Porsche 928

ADJUSTMENTS

PUMP BELT

Check belt deflection at center of belt between pump pulley and crankshaft pulley. Correct deflection is ⅜" (10 mm). Adjust by loosening pump mounting bolts and moving pump.

TESTING

PRESSURE CHECK

1) Unscrew bolts from stabilizer bushings. Pull stabilizer down to expose pressure line hollow bolt. Detach pressure line at steering gear. Pull down on line. Connect 4.5 ft. (1.5 meter) long pressure hose to pressure line with hollow bolt and adapter.

2) Attach hose with pressure gauge between steering gear and pressure line. Bleed system. Run engine at idle speed and close pressure gauge valve. Check pressure gauge reading. Pressure should be 986-1189 psi (69-84 kg/cm²).

NOTE — *Do not keep valve closed for more than 5 seconds.*

3) With pressure gauge valve open, turn wheel lock to lock and hold in lock position at a force of 22 lbs. (10 kg). Read pressure gauge. Pressure should be 986-1189 psi (69-84 kg/cm²).

SYSTEM LEAKS

With engine running, turn steering to full lock position and hold. This produces maximum pressure in lines. Check all hose connections and tighten if necessary.

REMOVAL & INSTALLATION

STEERING GEAR

Removal — 1) Drain fluid from system. Raise front of vehicle and support on safety stands. Press out tie rods with standard extractor. Remove bolt holding hose strap, and pull back hose and harness.

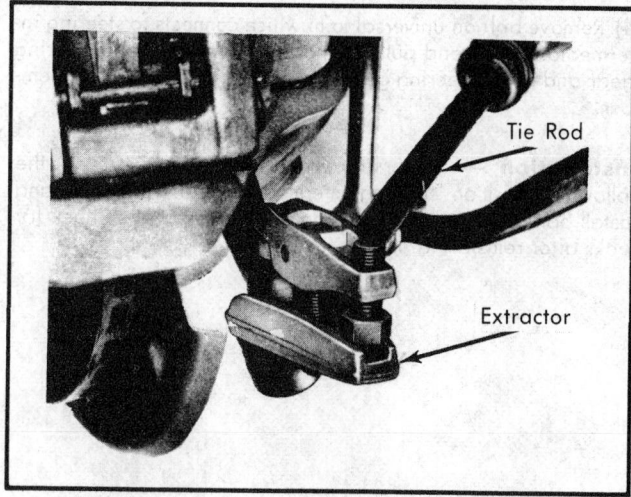

Fig. 2 Tie Rod Removal

PORSCHE POWER-ASSISTED RACK & PINION (Cont.)

2) Remove bolts from stabilizer bar mounts. Allow stabilizer to hang down. Disconnect pressure and return lines from steering gear.

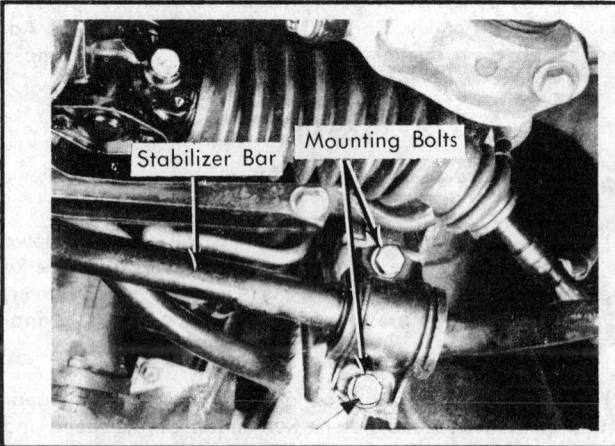

Fig. 3   Stabilizer Bar Mounting

3) Remove 5 bolts holding reinforcement plate on engine crossmember. Loosen 4 self-locking nuts on steering gear, but do not remove.

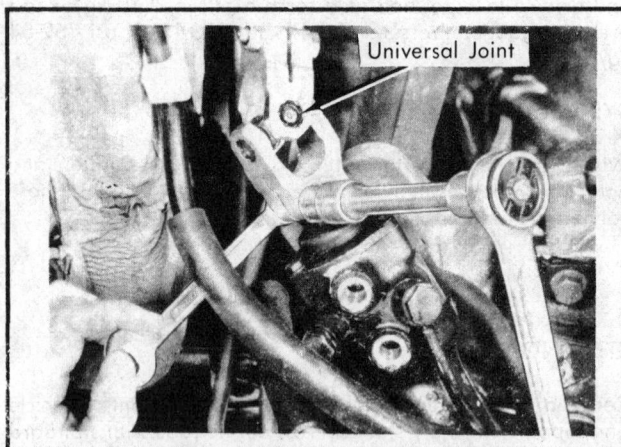

Fig. 4   Steering Intermediate Shaft Removal

4) Remove bolt on universal joint which connects to steering intermediate shaft and pull off shaft. Remove 4 nuts on steering gear and lower steering gear out of studs on engine crossmember.

Installation — Reverse removal procedures, noting the following: Position steering intermediate shaft correctly and install bolt to universal shaft. Add fluid to reservoir. Check for leaks after reinstalling. Adjust toe if necessary.

STEERING PUMP

Removal — 1) Detach intake hose from air cleaner on left side. Drain fluid from reservoir. Remove splash shield. Loosen front bolts on pump, but do not remove.

2) Remove rear bolt from pump. Remove "V" belt. Take off upper left section of drive belt cover. Disconnect pressure hose from pump.

Fig. 5   Drive Belt Cover Removal

3) Loosen clip holding suction hose and remove hose. Remove front bolts holding pump. Remove pump.

Installation — Reverse removal procedures, noting the following: Install pressure hose so that not more than 1" (25 mm) is provided between inner wheel well and hose when pump is installed. If hose is too close to exhaust manifold it could slip from its holder. Adjust belt tension, add fluid and bleed system. Check for leaks.

OVERHAUL

NOTE — *Manufacture does not recommend disassembly or overhaul of power steering gears or pumps.*

TIGHTENING SPECIFICATIONS

Application	Ft. Lbs. (N·m)
Tie Rod-to-Steering Arm	61 (83)
Tie Rod-to-Steering Rack	108 (147)
Tie Rod End-to-Tie Rod	33 (45)
Universal Joint-to-Steering Column	17 (23)
Steering Rack-to-Crossmember	33 (45)
Pressure/Return Lines-to-Steering Rack	22 (30)

RENAULT POWER-ASSISTED RACK & PINION

18i

DESCRIPTION

Power steering is integrated power cylinder type rack and pinion. Steering box serves as a power cylinder body and rack serves as rod. Power steering consists of a rack and pinion steering gear and a power assist pump connected by flexible lines. Pump has a separate reservoir mounted next to air cleaner.

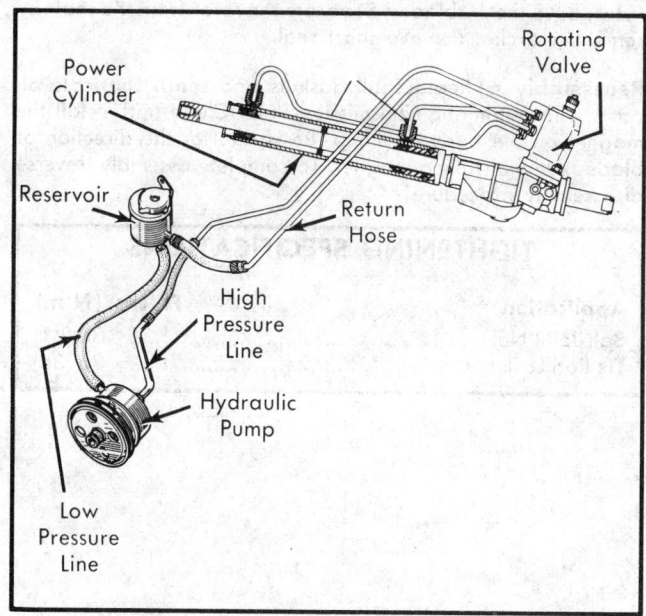

Fig. 1   View of Renault Power Steering Assembly

GENERAL SERVICE

HYDRAULIC SYSTEM LUBRICANT

Type — Dexron II.

Capacity — 1.2 quarts.

BELT TENSION ADJUSTMENT

Run engine for 10 minutes. Measure deflection with gauge (Ele. 346). Deflection should be .21-.25" (5.5-6.6 mm).

HYDRAULIC SYSTEM FILLING AND BLEEDING

Fill reservoir completely. Gently turn steering wheel lock-to-lock. Refill reservoir to top. Turn on engine and turn wheel lock-to-lock. Refill reservoir. Oil level should be visible in the bottom of filter in opening.

HYDRAULIC SYSTEM PRESSURE TEST

1) Place a clamp on pump lower pressure hose. Disconnect high pressure line. Insert connector (Dir. 803) between high pressure line and pump. Connect pressure gauge (Fre. 214-04). Disconnect clamp from hose. Bring up oil level in reservoir and turn on engine. Pressure should be 72-102 psi (5.1-7.2 kg/cm²) when steering wheel is not turned. If at idle pressure is too great, valve is defective.

2) If during acceleration pressure is too low, regulator is defective. With wheel turned to lock position, pressure should be 725-943 psi (51-66 kg/cm²). Difference between sides must not exceed 72 psi (5.1 kg/cm²). If it does, valve is defective. If pressure is too low but gauge needle does not move, check for loose belt, defective valve or internal leak in power cylinder.

ADJUSTMENT

RACK PLUNGER

Raise and support front of vehicle. Unlock plunger adjusting nut by straightening out nut lock collar. Tighten adjusting nut to 96 INCH lbs. (11 N). Wheel should now be tight when turned. Loosen adjusting nut ¼ turn. Wheel should now turn without resistance. Relock nut in 2 opposite notches of collar by bending down on nut lock collar.

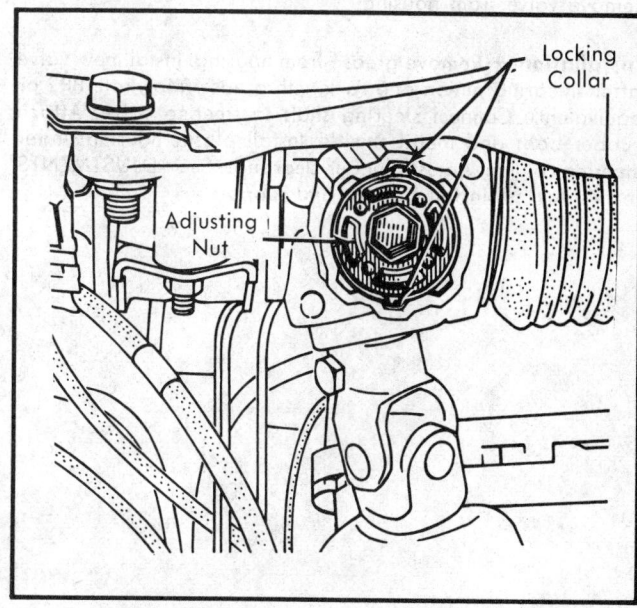

Fig. 2   Adjusting Nut and Locking Collar. Unlock Nut by Straightening Collar.

REMOVAL & INSTALLATION

STEERING GEAR

Removal — Clamp hoses on steering reservoir. Disconnect pipes from rotating valve. Raise and support front of vehicle. Remove tie rod end nuts. Remove ball joint cones of stub axle carriers. Disconnect steering universal joint, index marking position to steering pinion splines. Remove rack housing attaching bolts from crossmember. Remove steering rack through hole on cowl side.

NOTE — If rack and pinion assembly is to be replaced, ball joints on stub axle carrier side must be saved. Loosen lock nut by holding axial ball joint with a wrench. Unscrew ball joints counting turns for reassembly reference.

Installation — Place steering arm ball joints in position noted when removed. Install assembly to vehicle. To complete installation, reverse removal procedure. Bleed hydraulic system. Check and adjust toe-in. See WHEEL ALIGNMENT Section.

Power Steering

RENAULT POWER-ASSISTED RACK & PINION (Cont.)

POWER STEERING PUMP

Removal — Place a clamp on pump input line. Disconnect input line and high pressure line. Loosen idler bolt and pump attaching bolt. Remove pump from vehicle.

Installation — To install, reverse removal procedure. Fill and bleed hydraulic system.

POWER STEERING VALVE

Removal — Remove battery and support. Remove 2 shields attached with plastic clips to firewall. Push boot towards passenger compartment. Remove plastic housing under steering column. Disconnect steering column shaft from steering valve. Remove from firewall. From under vehicle loosen steering plunger adjusting nut. Remove valve attaching bolts and remove valve from housing.

Installation — Remove grease from housing. Install new valve after smearing pinion and rack with grease (Molykote BR2 or equivalent). Connect steering shaft to steering valve. Attach rubber boot and metal shields. Install plastic housing under steering column. Adjust plunger clearance. See ADJUSTMENTS in this Article. Install battery and support.

OVERHAUL

POWER STEERING PUMP

Disassembly — **1)** Clamp pump support in a vise. Remove pulley with puller (B. Vi. 28-01 or equivalent). Remove housing fixing bolts and high pressure connector. Remove control valve and spring. Remove housing. Compress the cover plate. Remove circlip from slot.

2) Remove cover plate and rear plate spring. Remove rear plate and stator. Remove positioning pins. Remove shaft and rotor. Save the 10 blades. Separate the rotor from the shaft by removing circlip. Remove shaft seal.

Reassembly — Replace all gaskets and seals. Lubricate all parts with automatic transmission fluid. Clean and install the magnet on the body of pump. Be careful of the direction of blades when installing magnet. To complete assembly, reverse disassembly procedure.

TIGHTENING SPECIFICATIONS

Application	Ft. Lbs. (N·m)
Ball Joint Nut	30 (41)
Tie Rod Lock Nut	26 (35)

Power Steering

SAAB POWER-ASSISTED RACK & PINION

900

DESCRIPTION

Power steering is available as optional equipment. The assembly consists of a rack and pinion steering gear with a servo valve which regulates the oil flow to a servo plunger on the rack. The hydraulic pressure is generated by an oil pump which is driven by a belt attached to the crankshaft pulley. The pump is integrated in a steel container that also serves as the hydraulic reservoir. In addition to pump unit itself, the pump also contains a control valve which regulates the pressure and flow.

REMOVAL & INSTALLATION
POWER STEERING GEAR

Removal — 1) Clean areas around hydraulic connections and disconnect return and pressure lines from steering gear. Plug lines and steering gear to prevent dirt from entering system. This will also prevent fluid from draining out.

2) Remove steering gear-to-intermediate shaft clamp bolt. Raise and support vehicle. Remove front wheels. Separate tie rods from steering knuckles.

3) Remove steering gear attaching bolts. Separate steering column (intermediate shaft) joint from steering gear, lift steering gear to the side and remove by guiding it diagonally downwards through opening in engine compartment.

Installation — Installation is a reversal of removal procedure; however, tie rod ends are to be connected after gear assembly has been fully installed. Adjust toe-in.

OVERHAUL

POWER STEERING GEAR

Disassembly — 1) With steering gear removed from vehicle, remove lock nuts and tie rod ends. Remove rubber bellows and breather tube. Remove hydraulic lines from steering valve and steering housing. Remove lock nut, adjusting nut, spring and piston from steering housing.

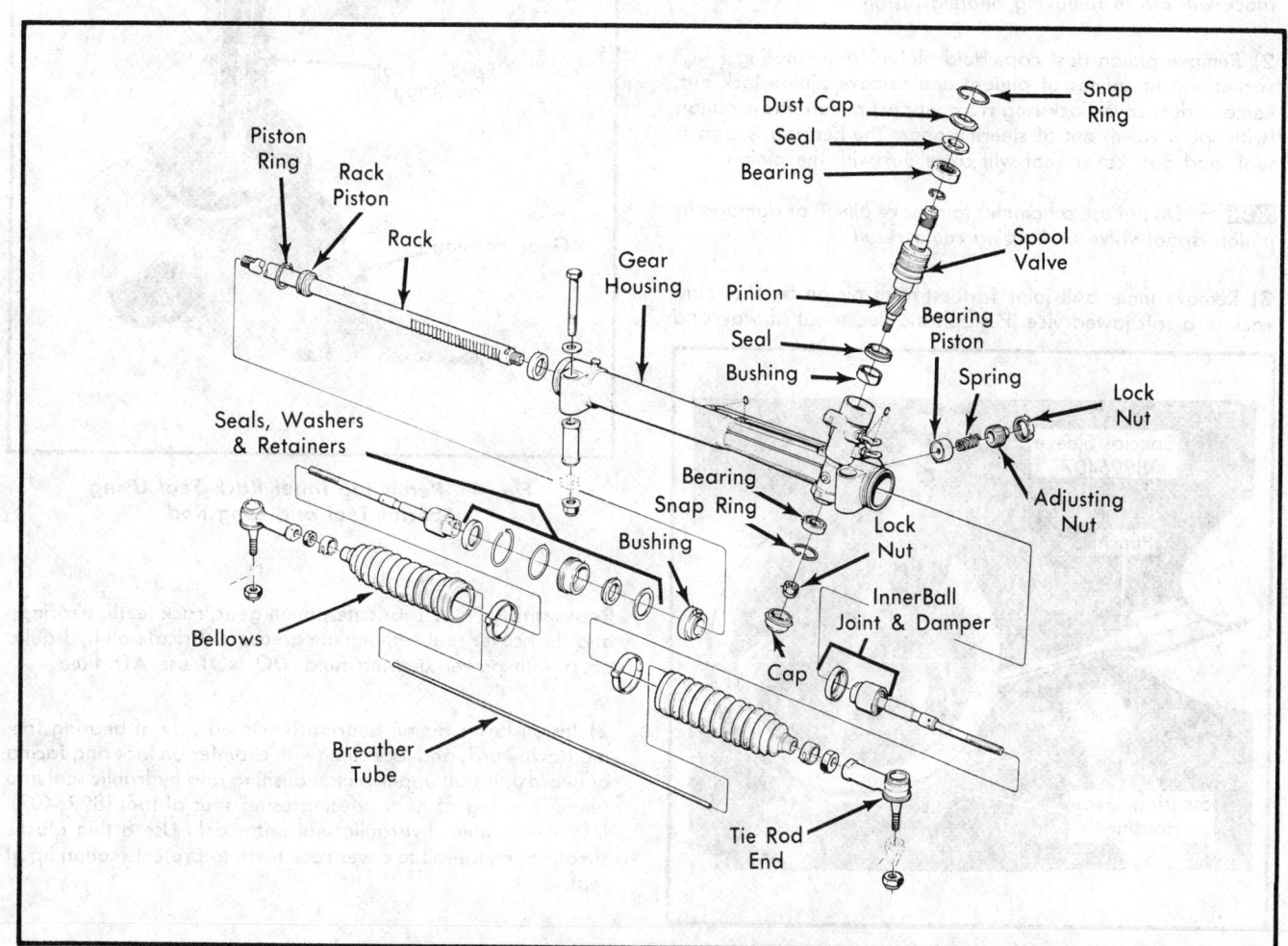

Fig. 1 Exploded View of Saab 900 Power Steering Components

SAAB POWER-ASSISTED RACK & PINION (Cont.)

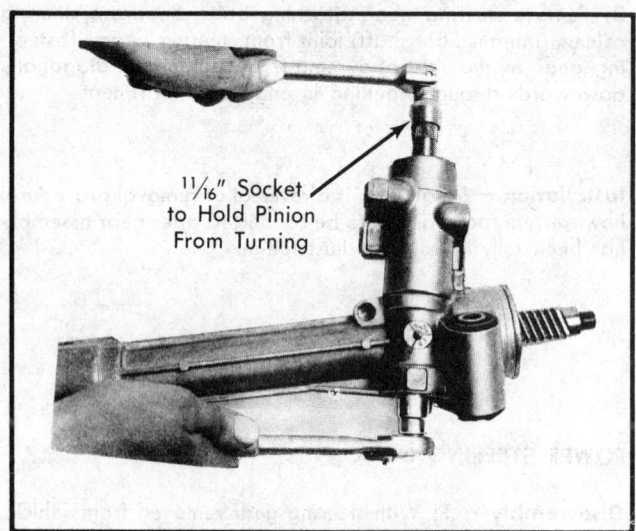

Fig. 2 Removing Pinion Lock Nut from Pinion Gear and Spool Valve

NOTE — *Tapping steering housing lightly against wooden block will aid in removing bearing piston.*

2) Remove pinion dust cap. Hold pinion from rotating ($1\frac{1}{16}$" socket will fit splines of pinion) and remove pinion lock nut. Remove dust cover lock ring from (upper) pinion. Press pinion (with spool valve) out of steering gear. The bearing, support, seal, and dust cover seal will come out with the pinion.

NOTE — *Do not use a hammer to remove pinion or damage to pinion, spool valve or housing could result.*

3) Remove inner ball joint farthest from pinion by clamping rack in a soft jawed vice. Push plastic sleeve out of way and

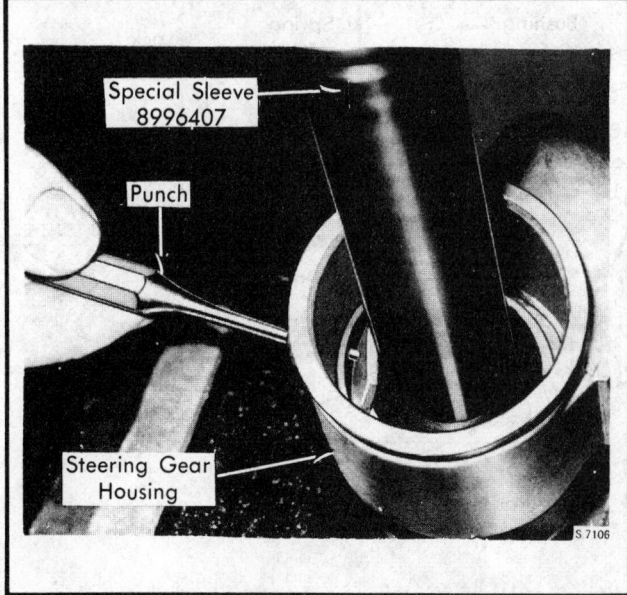

Fig. 3 Removing Wire Lock Ring from Steering Gear Housing

unscrew ball joint. Remove lock ring in end of gear housing as follows: Push rack into gear housing as far as it will go, install special sleeve (8996407) over rack and use inner ball joint (tighten) to press seal housing in. Then, use a punch to depress wire end of locking ring. Pry out ring with two screwdrivers. With ring removed, remove ball joint and special sleeve (8996407).

4) Remove ball joint nearest pinion as other ball joint was removed. Press out rack together with seal, washer and bushing. Remove seal and bushing from rack. Make sure there are no burrs on rack to damage seal or bushing before removing.

5) Remove inner rack using special tool (8996399) and a long punch or rod. Insert tool lips under seal, then from other end of housing insert long rod and drive seal out. Remove lock ring and lower pinion bearing. Remove sealing ring and bushing from top of pinion housing.

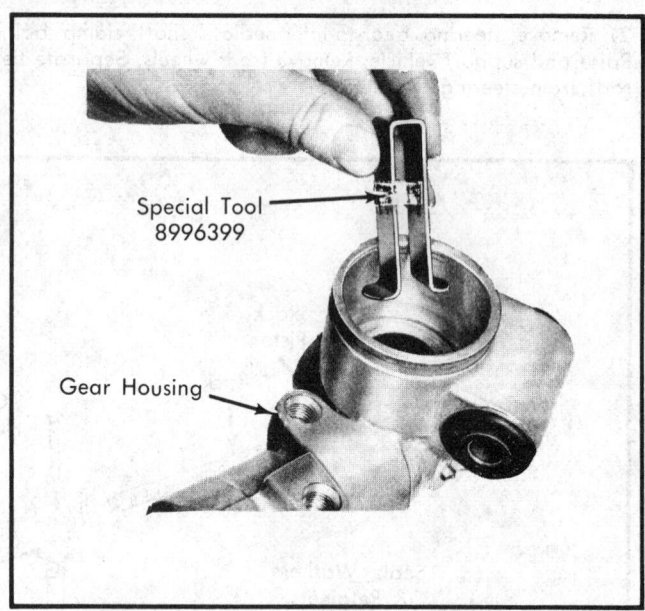

Fig. 4 Removing Inner Rack Seal Using Special Tool and Long Rod

Reassembly — 1) Lubricate pinion gear, rack teeth, bearings and dust cover seal with lithium grease. Lubricate all hydraulic parts with power steering fluid. DO NOT use ATF fluid.

2) Install lower pinion bearing (enclosed side of bearing facing downward) and lock ring (with chamfer on lock ring facing outwards). Install upper pinion bushing and hydraulic seal into pinion housing of gear housing using special tool (8996407). Install rack inner hydraulic seal onto rack. Use a thin plastic sheath or metal foil to cover rack teeth to protect sealing lip of seal.

3) Install rack into housing. Install inner hydraulic seal into housing using rack piston as a press. Do not use more than 500 lbs. (227 kg) force. Install bushing in gear housing (smaller

SAAB POWER-ASSISTED RACK & PINION (Cont.)

bore facing in), then washer against bushing. Install new "O" ring on outer hydraulic seal support. Install old seal (if not damaged).

4) Slide sealing ring support carefully onto rack to avoid damaging sealing lip. Press sealing ring support into housing using suitable sleeve (8390148). Center rack so same amount extends from each end of housing. Rotate rack so that rack teeth will mesh with pinion gear teeth when it is installed.

5) Install pinion gear and spool valve in gear housing as follows: Hold pinion gear (with spool valve) so groove in end of shaft (for tensioning screw) points toward the left (9 o'clock

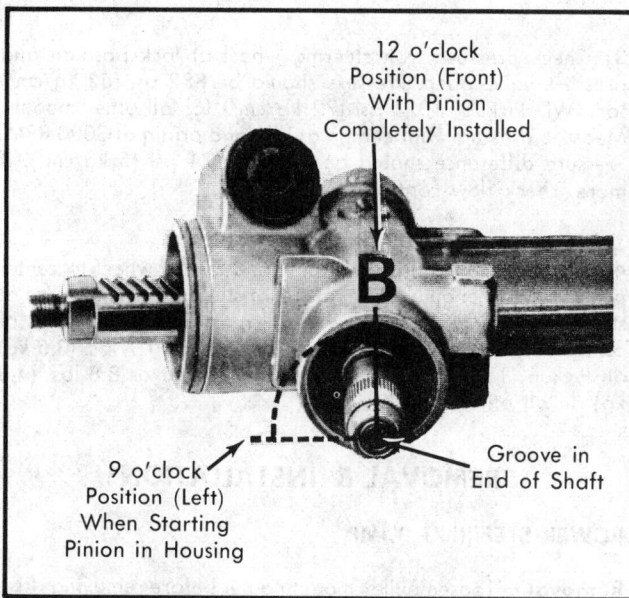

**Fig. 5   Installing Pinion Gear (with Spool Valve)
Into Gear Housing with Rack Installed**

position) when the pinion teeth engage the rack teeth. Insert pinion. Pinion should rotate so that groove in end of pinion points toward front (12 o'clock position) with rack centered. *See Fig. 5.*

6) Install pinion lock nut and tighten. Install cover. Install washer, needle bearing, sealing ring, dust cover and lock ring onto top of pinion gear (spool valve). Protect seal lips with tape or plastic sleeve over splines of pinion.

7) Install bearing piston, spring and adjusting nut in gear housing. Tighten adjusting nut until bearing piston firmly contacts rack, then back off adjusting nut 30-50°. Install and tighten lock nut.

8) Install plastic sleeves (endstops) and inner ball joints, with tie rods, to rack ends. Hold rack in soft-jawed vice and tighten ball joints. Lock inner ball joints by tapping tab on ball joint into rack.

9) Install lock ring for sealing ring support in end of gear housing. Turn pinion until inner ball joint presses against sealing ring support. Press in support and, at same time, install sealing ring in groove with thin screwdriver. Install rubber bellows, breathing tube and hydraulic lines.

TIGHTENING SPECIFICATIONS

Application	Ft. Lbs. (N·m)
Ball Joint-to-Steering Arm	37-44 (50-60)
Pinion Gear Lower Lock Nut	22-34 (30-46)
Bearing Piston Lock Nut	48-55 (65-75)
Inner Ball Joint-to-Rack	59-72 (80-98)
Gear Housing-to-Crossmember	44-60 (60-81)

Power Steering

TOYOTA POWER-ASSISTED RECIRCULATING BALL

Celica
Corolla
Corona
Cressida

Land Cruiser
Pickup
Supra

DESCRIPTION

POWER STEERING PUMP

The power steering pump is a vane type composed of an engine driven eccentric rotor, a fixed ring (having six slotted grooves), and a flow control valve (to regulate maximum oil pressure and amount of oil flow). Slippers are fitted in each slotted groove and are pressed against rotor outside surface by pressure produced in adjoining slots and by spring tension. As rotor rotation increases or decreases, then space between the rotor and fixed ring changes accordingly, in order to control oil flow.

POWER STEERING GEAR

Power steering gear consists of a mechanism which converts steering wheel torque to cross shaft torque by means of worm and power piston nut, and of a mechanism which detects hydraulic pressure developed by vane pump and controls this pressure in proportion to the steering effort.

LUBRICATION

HYDRAULIC SYSTEM LUBRICANT

Capacity
Pickup 4-WD — 1.8 pts.
All Other Models — 1.7 pts.

Type — ATF Dexron

ADJUSTMENT

BELT TENSION ADJUSTMENT

With 22 lbs. (10 kg) pressure applied, belt deflection between idler pulley and pump pulley should be .28-.35" (7-9 mm) on Corona and .43-.55" (11-14 mm) on Land Cruiser. On all other models, use belt tension gauge and adjust belt tension to 100-150 lbs. (45-68 kg) for new belt or to 60-100 lbs. (27-45 kg) for used belt.

SYSTEM BLEEDING

1) Jack up front of vehicle and support with safety stands. Fill fluid to proper level in vane pump reservoir (turn wheels fully in both directions and recheck fluid level).

2) Start engine and let idle. Turn steering from lock to lock 2 or 3 times. Lower vehicle. Run engine at 1000 RPM or less. Turn wheel from lock to lock 2 or 3 times. Center steering wheel. If fluid level does not rise and no foaming of fluid is evident, bleeding is complete. If level rises, or foaming is evident, repeat procedure until air is released.

FLUID REPLACEMENT

Raise and support front of vehicle. Disconnect return hose and drain fluid into container. Turn steering wheel from lock to lock while draining. Connect return hose, add fresh fluid and bleed system.

HYDRAULIC PRESSURE TESTING

1) Disconnect pressure lines from steering gear case and vane pump. Attach pressure gauge with gauge side connected to vane pump. Attach valve side of gauge to pressure line. Bleed air from system and check fluid level.

2) With engine at idle, check fluid pressure reading with pressure gauge valve closed. Correct pressure should be 882 psi (62 kg/cm²) for 4WD Pickup, 1024 psi (72 kg/cm²) for all other models.

NOTE — *Do not keep pressure gauge valve closed for more than 10 seconds. Fluid testing temperature should be 176°F (80°C).*

3) Check pressure with steering wheel at lock position and pressure valve open. Pressure should be 882 psi (62 kg/cm²) for 4WD Pickup, 1024 psi (72 kg/cm²) for all other models. Measure pressure with engine at idle and again at 3000 RPM. Pressure difference should be less than 71 psi (5 kg/cm²). If more, check flow control valve.

4) With vehicle on flat surface, turn steering wheel to center position. With engine idling, measure steering turning force at steering wheel outer rim over a full rotation on both sides of center point. Turning force should not exceed 7.7 lbs. (3.5 kg) on Pickup, 13.2 lbs. (6.0 kg) on Land Cruiser or 8.8 lbs. (4.0 kg) on all other models.

REMOVAL & INSTALLATION

POWER STEERING PUMP

Removal — Loosen pulley mounting nut before removing drive belt. Disconnect and plug pressure line at pump housing. Disconnect and plug return line at pump housing on Celica, Supra, Corona and Pickup or at reservoir on Corolla, Cressida and Land Cruiser. Remove pump mounting bolts, then remove pump.

NOTE — *Keep disconnected hoses elevated to prevent fluid from draining out.*

Installation — To install, reverse removal procedure and note: Adjust drive belt tension and bleed system.

POWER STEERING GEAR

Removal — Disconnect and plug pressure and return lines at gear housing. Mark steering gear shaft to flexible coupling or universal joint, then disconnect flexible coupling or universal joint. Mark pitman arm to sector shaft, then disconnect pitman arm. Disconnect steering gear housing from heat shield on Land Cruiser. Remove steering gear mounting bolts, then remove steering gear.

Installation — To install, reverse removal procedure and note: Align all marks during installation. Bleed system and perform pressure test.

Power Steering

TOYOTA POWER-ASSISTED RECIRCULATING BALL (Cont.)

OVERHAUL

POWER STEERING PUMP

Disassembly — 1) Mount power steering pump in vise. Remove union from rear housing. Remove reservoir from pump (if equipped). Index mark front and rear housings for reassembly reference. Remove front housing bolts.

2) Tap off front housing with plastic hammer. Be careful that vane plates, rotor and cam plate do not fall out. Remove ring cam, rotor and vane plates. Clamp front housing in a vise. Using chisel, pry off oil seal. Remove snap ring.

3) With plastic hammer, lightly tap the rotor shaft out of front housing and tap bottom of rear housing. Remove rear plate and spring. Temporarily install a bolt to plug. Push bolt and remove snap ring. Pull out bolt and remove plug. Remove spring and control valve by hand.

Inspection — 1) Check all parts for wear or damage and replace as necessary. Check oil clearance between bushing and rotor shaft. Maximum clearance is .0028" (.07 mm). Check that bearings operate smoothly. If necessary, press out old bearing and press in new bearing. Measure difference between cam ring and rotor. Maximum difference should be .0024" (.06 mm).

2) Vane plate dimensions should be .589 x .307 x .067" (14.97 x 7.80 x 1.70 mm). Maximum clearance between vane plate and rotor groove is .0024" (.06 mm). Check flow control valve for leakage with compressed air. Control valve spring should be 1.85-1.97" (47-50 mm) long.

Reassembly — 1) Lubricate flow control valve and spring with automatic transmission fluid (ATF). Install control valve, spring, plug and snap ring to pump. Lubricate rotor shaft with ATF. Install to front housing by tapping with plastic hammer.

2) Install snap ring to front housing. Apply multipurpose grease to oil seal lip. Using a driver and hammer, install oil seal. Lubricate and install "O" ring to front housing. Align fluid passages of ring cam and front housing and install ring cam.

3) Lubricate rotor with ATF. Install rotor with cut spline facing toward front housing. Make sure letters on ring cam and rotor match. Lubricate vane plates with ATF. Install vane plates with round end facing outward. Lubricate and install 2 "O" rings to rear plate.

4) Place rear plate on the ring cam with pin holes aligned with pins. Place spring on the rear plate. Align marks on front and rear housings and install. Half tighten front and rear housing mounting bolts. Clamp rear housing in vise. Tighten housing bolts evenly 3 or 4 times.

5) Lubricate and install "O" ring to union. Insert and tighten union. Check to ensure rotor shaft operates smoothly. Install pulley nut and check rotating torque. Torque should be less than 239 INCH lbs. (27 N·m).

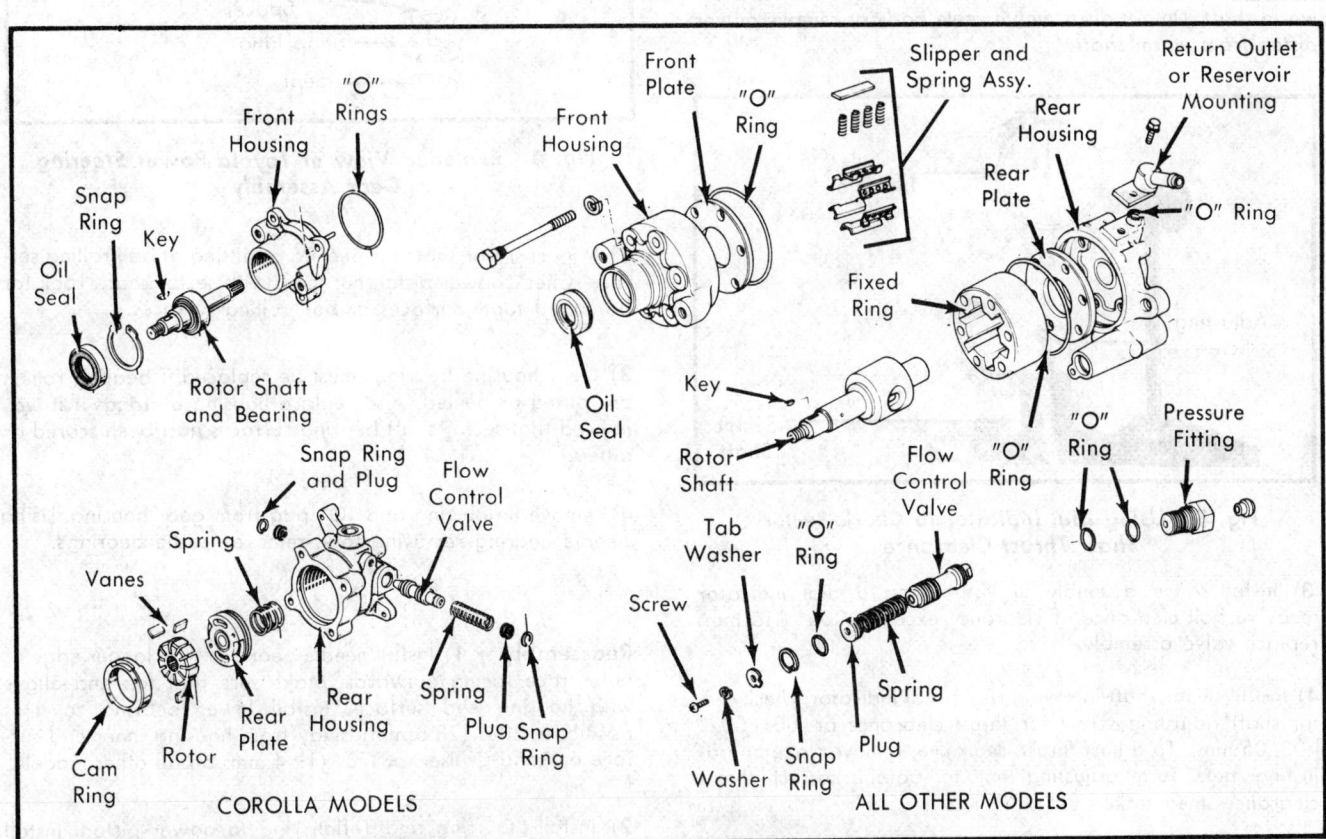

Fig. 1   Exploded View of Toyota Power Steering Pump Assemblies

TOYOTA POWER-ASSISTED RECIRCULATING BALL (Cont.)

POWER STEERING GEAR

Disassembly — 1) Attach gear housing to holding tool and mount in a vise. Remove sector shaft adjusting screw lock nut and sector shaft cover bolts. Turn sector shaft adjusting screw clockwise until cover is removed. Remove sector shaft by tapping bottom end with mallet.

2) Remove valve housing-to-gear housing bolts. Hold power piston nut with hand and turn worm shaft clockwise (counterclockwise on Celica). Remove valve assembly and power piston from gear housing.

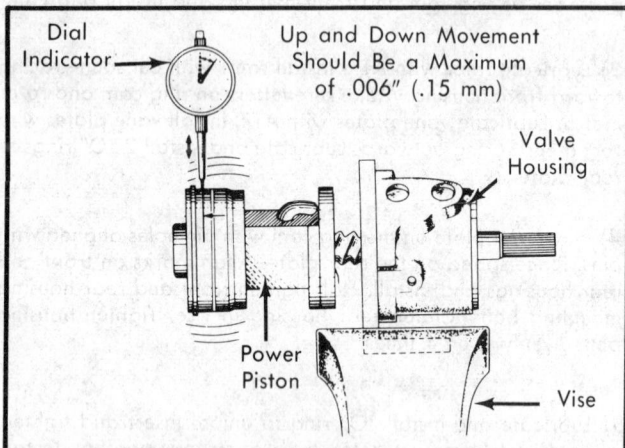

Fig. 2 Using Gauge to Check Ball Clearance

CAUTION — *Ensure that power piston nut does not come off worm shaft. Do not disassemble valve body or remove power piston from worm shaft.*

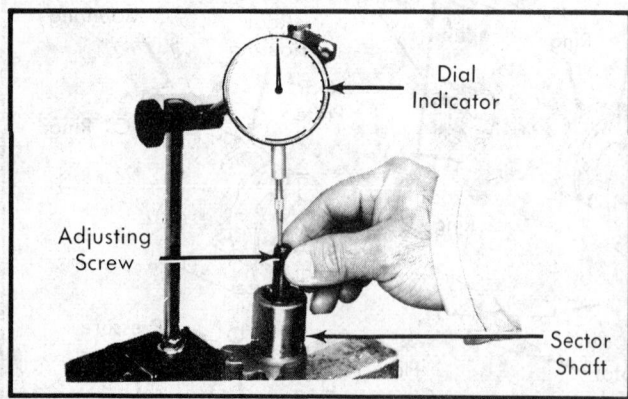

Fig. 3 Using Dial Indicator to Check Sector Shaft Thrust Clearance

3) Install valve assembly in vise. Using a dial indicator measure ball clearance. If clearance exceeds .006" (.15 mm) replace valve assembly.

4) Install sector shaft in a vise. Using dial indicator, check sector shaft adjusting screw for thrust clearance of .001-.002" (.03-.05 mm). To adjust thrust clearance, remove stake on adjusting nut. Turn adjusting nut to obtain correct thrust clearance, then stake out.

5) Temporarily install valve assembly in gear housing and install mounting bolts. Using lock nut tool, remove lock nut and adjusting bolt from gear assembly. Remove and replace as needed, oil seal, "O" ring, and bearing assembly. Install lock nut and tighten. Remove valve assembly from gear housing.

Cleaning & Inspection — 1) Clean and dry all parts in solvent. Coat all sliding parts, "O" rings and teflon rings with power steering fluid upon reassembly.

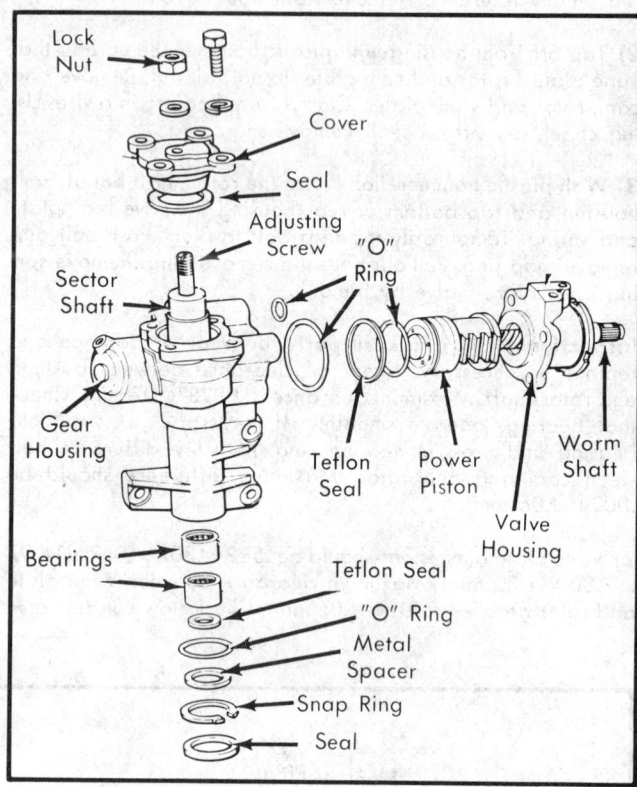

Fig. 4 Exploded View of Toyota Power Steering Gear Assembly

2) Inspect sector shaft for peeling or pitting at ball rolling surface. Check power piston nut mesh with sector shaft. Look for damaged tooth surfaces or ball rolling surfaces.

3) Gear housing bearings must be replaced if bearing rollers are pitted or peeled. Also replace housing bearings if it was noticed that sector shaft bearing surfaces had been scored or pitted.

4) Remove teflon ring and "O" ring from gear housing. Using needle bearing removing tool, remove needle bearings.

Reassembly — 1) Install needle bearings with longer edge of outer race facing outwards. Make sure that top end aligns with housing end surface. Install lower bearing so it is positioned .93" (23.6 mm) away from housing inner end surface on Land Cruiser, or .76" (19.4 mm) on all other models.

2) Install "O" ring and Teflon ring to power piston. Install large and small "O" rings to gear housing, then install power piston assembly to gear housing. Tighten bolts.

TOYOTA POWER-ASSISTED RECIRCULATING BALL (Cont.)

3) To adjust worm shaft preload, loosen lock nut and install adjusting wrench to adjusting plug. Install torque wrench to wormshaft and tighten adjusting plug to obtain specified preload. See table. Hold adjusting plug and tighten lock nut.

4) Wrap a piece of tape around spline area of sector shaft. Align sector shaft gear teeth with power piston teeth (centered) and insert sector shaft into gear housing. Do not turn sector shaft during installation, as damage to "O" ring could result.

5) Install sector shaft cover, with seal, to sector shaft adjusting screw. Turn screw counterclockwise until cover will fit completely down on gear housing. Install bolts and tighten. To adjust total preload of steering gear, place steering gear in center postion and attach torque wrench to worm shaft.

6) Turn sector shaft adjusting screw until correct total preload is obtained. Total steering gear preload should be worm bearing preload plus 4.3-5.2 INCH lbs. (.5-.6 N·m) for Celica and Supra, 2.6-3.5 INCH lbs. (.3-.4 N·m) for Corona, and 1.7-2.6 INCH lbs. (.2-.3 N·m) for all other models. Install sector shaft adjusting lock nut and tighten.

Worm Bearing Preload

Application	INCH lbs. (N·m)
Celica & Supra	2.6-3.5 (.3-.4)
All Other Models	3.5-5.6 (.4-.6)

TIGHTENING SPECIFICATIONS

Application	Ft. Lbs. (N·m)
Pump Housing Bolts	
Corolla	30-40 (41-54)
All Other Models	24-30 (33-41)
Sector Shaft Adjusting Screw Lock Nut	
Celica & Supra	94-123 (128-168)
All Other Models	33-39 (45-53)
Sector Shaft Cover Bolts	30-40 (41-54)
Sector Shaft-to-Pitman Arm Nut	
Land Cruiser	120-141 (163-192)
2WD Pickup	80-90 (109-122)
4WD Pickup	116-137 (158-186)
All Other Models	80-101 (109-137)
Worm Gear Adjusting Plug Lock Nut	
Celica & Supra	14-22 (19-30)
All Other Models	33-39 (45-53)

VOLVO POWER-ASSISTED RACK & PINION

DL   GLE
GL   Bertone
GLT Turbo   Diesel

DESCRIPTION

Power steering is rack and pinion type. Some models use a Volvo cam gear type with aluminum housing. Other models use a ZF model with fixed valve housing. Steering consists of the rack and pinion steering gear and a power assist pump interconnected with flexible lines. A separate reservoir is attached to the Saginaw pump.

GENERAL SERVICE

STEERING GEAR LUBRICANT

Type — Volvo P/N 1 161 001-1 (or equivalent).

Capacity — 3.5 ounces.

HYDRAULIC SYSTEM LUBRICANT

Type — ATF
Capacity
DL, GL, GLT Turbo, Diesel — .8 quarts.
GLE, Bertone — 1.3 quarts.

STEERING GEAR FILLING

Remove inner clamp on right side rubber bellows, and using a suction gun, fill gear with recommended lubricant through side of bellows. Reinstall clamp, then carefully compress bellows so some oil will flow to other side.

HYDRAULIC OIL FILLING AND BLEEDING

Fill the reservoir with approved oil, then start engine and allow to idle, adding oil as level drops. Turn steering wheel left and right lock to lock in a slow even motion to allow the pump to operate at low pressure. Continue turning steering wheel until oil in reservoir is almost free of air bubbles. Check that oil is at the level mark, then install reservoir cap.

SERVO BALANCE TESTING AND ADJUSTING

Testing — 1) Connect a pressure gauge as shown in *Fig. 1*. Make sure oil in reservoir is at level mark. Place pressure gauge so it can be seen from the drivers seat.

2) Remove steering wheel impact guard by compressing sides slightly. Install a torque wrench on steering wheel nut.

3) With engine at idle, turn steering wheel (using torque wrench) slowly to right. Read torque when pressure reaches 170 psi (12 kg/cm²) on cam gear type, 285 psi (20 kg/cm²) for ZF steering gear. Repeat operation turning wheel to left. Torque should be 30-40 INCH lbs. (3.4-4.5 N·m) as gear approaches specified pressure.

4) Difference between sides must not exceed 8 INCH lbs. (.9 N·m) on cam gear type. Difference must not exceed 4.4 INCH lbs. (.5 N·m) on ZF steering gear. If difference exceeds this amount, cam gear type can be corrected following adjustment procedure.

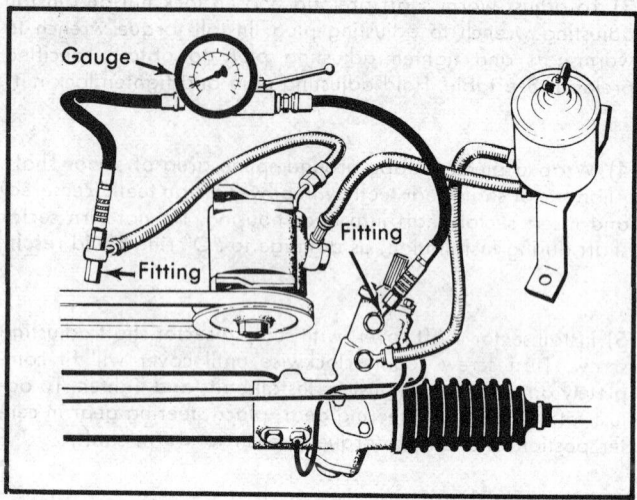

Fig. 1 Pressure Gauge Test Set Up

Adjusting (Cam Gear Type) — 1) Turn off engine and remove lock nut and washer from lower pinion bearing. Lock washer will have 1 tab bent down to lock adjustment nut (bearing race). See *Fig. 2*.

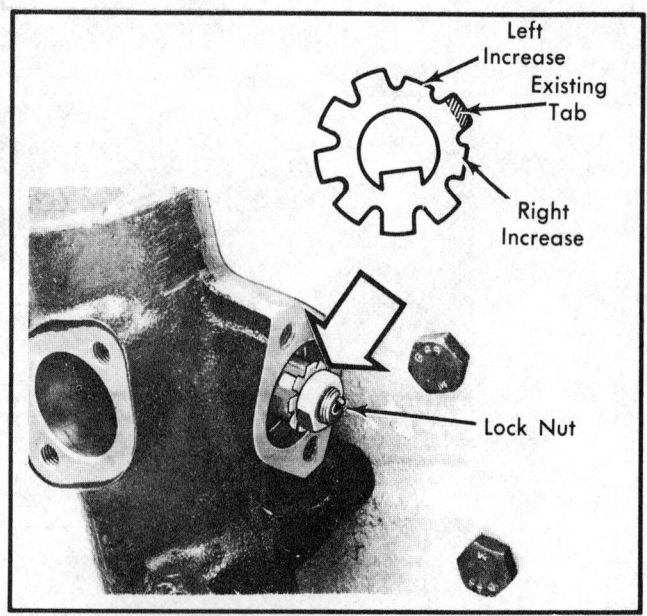

Fig. 2 Adjusting Lock Washer on Cam Gear Type Power Steering

2) To increase torque for left side, straighten existing bent tab and bend first tab to left. To increase torque for right side, bend first tab to right.

NOTE — *Changing tabs increases the amount of torque for one side and decreases the torque on the other side. The value of torque increase or decrease is 4 INCH lbs. (.45 N·m).*

3) After bending tab, use suitable tool (9995049) to turn adjustment nut until groove fits lock washer tab. Reinstall lock washer and lock nut. Install pinion cover and gasket.

Power Steering

VOLVO POWER-ASSISTED RACK & PINION (Cont.)

REMOVAL & INSTALLATION

STEERING GEAR

Removal — 1) Remove lock bolt and nut from pinion flange. Bend flange apart slightly. Raise and support front of vehicle and remove wheels. Remove tie rod nuts and disconnect ball studs from spindle using suitable ball joint removal tool (5043). Remove splash guard.

2) Disconnect hoses at steering gear and install plugs in hose connections to protect against contamination. Remove bolts securing steering gear to front axle member. Pull steering gear down until free of steering shaft flange, then remove steering gear on left side of vehicle.

Installation — 1) To install, reverse removal procedure, noting the following: Make sure recess on pinion shaft is aligned toward lock bolt opening in flange.

2) Install right side "U" bolt and flange, but do not tighten. Install and tighten left side bolts, then tighten right side "U" bolt.

3) Connect steering rods, making sure rods are same length. Difference should not exceed $\frac{1}{16}$" (2 mm). Install lock bolt on flange and reconnect hoses.

POWER STEERING PUMP

Removal — Remove two pivot bolts on bracket and bolt on belt tensioning bracket. Place a container below pump to receive drain oil, disconnect hydraulic connections at pump, then remove pump.

Installation — To reinstall, reverse removal procedures, then fill and bleed the system. See *GENERAL SERVICING* in this article.

OVERHAUL

STEERING GEAR

Disassembly (Cam Gear Type) — 1) Remove hose clamps holding rubber bellows. Cut clamps and remove equalizer tube and 2 pressure tubes. Attach steering gear to holding fixture (5046) and fasten with "U" bolt. Drain fluid from rack by slowly turning pinion back and forth in full strokes.

2) Place rack in center position. Check inner and outer ball joints for excessive wear. Remove outer clamp and pull back boot. Clean grease from rack and ball joint areas. Using a spanner and adjustable wrench, remove left steering rod. Loosen right side rod.

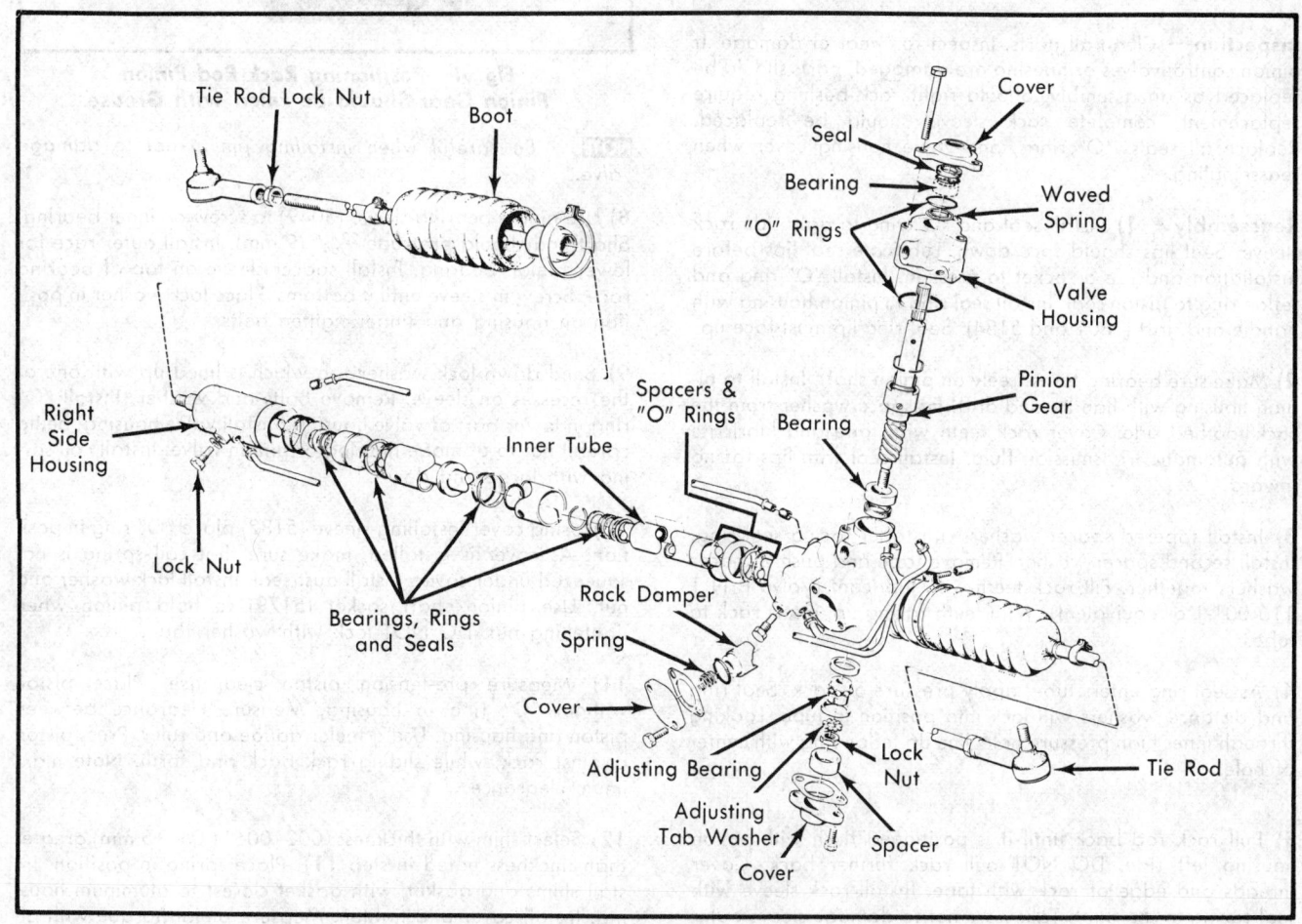

Fig. 3 Exploded View of Volvo (Cam Gear Type) Power Steering Assembly

Power Steering

VOLVO POWER-ASSISTED RACK & PINION (Cont.)

3) Remove locking wire for cage on right side. Turn end housing clockwise. Wire will protrude through tube. Hold pinion stationary and apply compressed air to remove end housing and bushing. Remove right steering rod.

4) Remove end housing plastic ring and bushing. Remove cover, shims, spring and piston of pre-tension device. Remove pinion lock cover, lock washer and gaskets. Using a hook spanner, remove spacer (inner) sleeve. Bend back lock washer, hold pinion shaft and remove nut. Valve should not move.

5) Remove inner bearing race, ball cage and lower race using sleeve (5049). Remove dust seal, valve housing cover, and "O" ring. Remove spring, valve housing and pinion gear. Remove "O" ring. Carefully pull out rack on right side. Remove upper bushing and seal for pinion gear using extractor (1819).

6) If damaged, remove inner race for pinion bearing using 2 screwdrivers. Carefully tap out rack rod seal ring and spacer sleeve from steering gear tube. Use a 1 1/16" (27 mm) socket and 2 long extensions inserted through housing.

NOTE — *Ensure that inner surface of tube is not damaged by scratches.*

7) Place bearing in soft-jawed vise and pry out seal. If damaged, or if vehicle has been driven more than 25,000 miles, remove seal ring.

Inspection — Clean all parts. Inspect for wear or damage. If pinion control valves or housing are damaged, parts should be replaced as an assembly. Should right rack bushing require replacement, complete rack sleeve should be replaced. Replace all seals, "O" rings, and valve housing cover when reassembling.

Reassembly — 1) Install seal and "O" ring to right side rack sleeve. Seal lips should face down. Lubricate seal lips before installation and use a socket to press in. Install "O" ring and teflon ring to piston seal. Install seal ring in pinion housing with handle and drift (1801 and 5184). Seal ring lip must face up.

2) Make sure bearing turns freely on pinion shaft. Install to pinion housing with handle and drift. Fit space washer from the rack toothed side. Cover rack teeth with tape and lubricate with automatic transmission fluid. Install seal with lips facing inward.

3) Install tapered spacer washer with taper facing seal ring. Install second spacer washer. Remove tape and push 2 spacer washers together. Fill rack teeth with lubricant (Volvo P/N 1 116 001-1 or equivalent). With teeth facing up, insert rack to tube.

4) As seal ring enters tube, apply pressure on rack. Seal ring and distance washers will lock into position in tube. Looking through inner high pressure hole, line up teflon ring with center of hole.

5) Pull rack rod back until it is positioned flush with pinion housing left side. DO NOT pull rack further back. Cover threads and edge of rack with tape. Install rack sleeve with seal facing to the right. Take care not to damage sleeve outer "O" ring against lock wire groove. Install plastic spacer in rack with bevelled edge toward seal.

6) Remove tape. Place sleeve on rack with tool recess facing steering rod end. Turn sleeve to line up hole in lock sleeve with elongated hole in tube. Using a new lock wire, install wire in lock wire groove. Slowly turn sleeve counterclockwise until end of locking wire is positioned inside elongated hole in tube.

7) If removed, install inner race for pinion lower bearing. Pack pinion gear with lubricant. Install rack rod in housing. With pinion in place, rack should protrude 2 1/8" (55 mm) from housing when flat of lockbolt is in positions shown. See *Fig. 4*

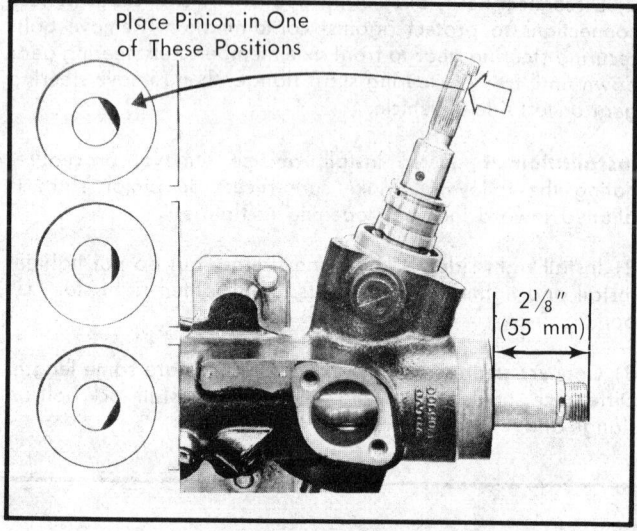

**Fig. 4   Positioning Rack Rod Pinion.
Pinion Gear Should be Filled with Grease.**

NOTE — *Be careful when installing pinion not to damage valve.*

8) Use pinion bearing sleeve (5049) to screw on inner bearing. Shaft end should protrude 23/64" (9 mm). Install outer race for lower pinion bearing. Install spacer sleeve on top of bearing race. Screw in sleeve until it bottoms. Place lock washer in position on housing and finger tighten bolts.

9) Bend down lock washer tab which is lined up with one of the recesses on sleeve. Remove bolts and washer. Install "O" ring in lower part of valve housing. Install valve housing, being careful not to damage housing or pinion valve. Install coil spring with large end down.

10) Using cover installing sleeve (5182) place "O" ring in position. As cover is installed, make sure that coil spring is not squeezed under cover. Install dust seal. Install lock washer and nut. Use pinion shaft socket (5179) to hold pinion when tightening nut. DO NOT lock with washer tab.

11) Measure pre-tension piston clearance. Place piston without "O" ring in housing. Measure clearance between piston and housing. Use a feeler gauge and ruler. Press piston against rack, while sliding rack back and forth. Note maximum clearance.

12) Select shim with thickness .002-.006" (.05-.15 mm) greater than thickness noted in step 11). Place spring in position. Install shims and gasket, with gasket closest to aluminum housing. Install cover and tighten. Measure pinion torque with pinion shaft socket and torque gauge (9177). Crank rack back and forth between rack end positions.

Power Steering

VOLVO POWER-ASSISTED RACK & PINION (Cont.)

13) Correct torque should be 8-15 INCH Lbs. (.9-1.7 N·m). If torque in any position is excessive, stop rack in that position and readjust pre-tension. If rack binds with pre-tension removed, rack is warped and must be replaced. Use a spanner on ball joint and support rack end with a large adjustable wrench to install steering rods.

14) Lock steering rods in rack recess using a narrow punch. Remove steering gear from holding fixture. Fill rubber boots with approximately ¾ ounce of lubricant. Install boots and equalizer tubes at the same time. Install plastic clamps on boots. Secure equalizer tube with strip clamp. Install 2 high pressure pipes.

Disassembly (ZF) — 1) Clean exterior of gear. Cut plastic clamps and remove equalizer tube. Attach steering gear to holding fixture (5046). Install gear and fixture to repair stand (5154). Disconnect rubber boots and remove grease. Check inner and outer ball joints for wear.

2) Unfold lock washer tab. Using a 1¹⁄₁₆" (27 mm) spanner on ball joint and large adjustable wrench on rack, remove steering rods. Remove pressure pipes and drain fluid. Turn rack in and out with pinion socket (5179) to pump out fluid. Remove pre-tension piston by removing cover, washer, spring and piston.

3) Remove rubber dust cover from pinion shaft. Remove pinion housing cover with seal and "O" ring. Lift out pinion with up-

per roller bearing. Remove lower washer and needle bearing. Index mark position of 2 end housings on center tube for reassembly reference. Loosen locking collar next to pinion housing using tube nut wrench (5178).

4) Remove the tube. Place right housing in a soft-jawed vise. Using tube nut wrench, slacken lock collar. Remove right housing. Remove "O" rings from center tube. Lock rings need only be removed if locking collar is to be replaced. Pull out rack and spacer (inner) tube as a unit.

5) Remove thrust washer from right side of pinion housing. Use seal extractor (1819) if necessary. Remove seal pinion housing with seal extractor. Remove needle bearing by tapping out with long punch. Remove lock rings, thrust washers and piston from rack.

NOTE — *Needle bearing should be removed only if it has to be replaced.*

6) Fill lock ring grooves with grease, and slide off inner tube toward opposing ends of rack teeth. Use seal extractor tool (1819) to remove inner tube seal and brass bushing. Remove "O" ring and teflon ring from inner tube.

NOTE — *Lock washer and thrust washer should only be removed if they need replacement.*

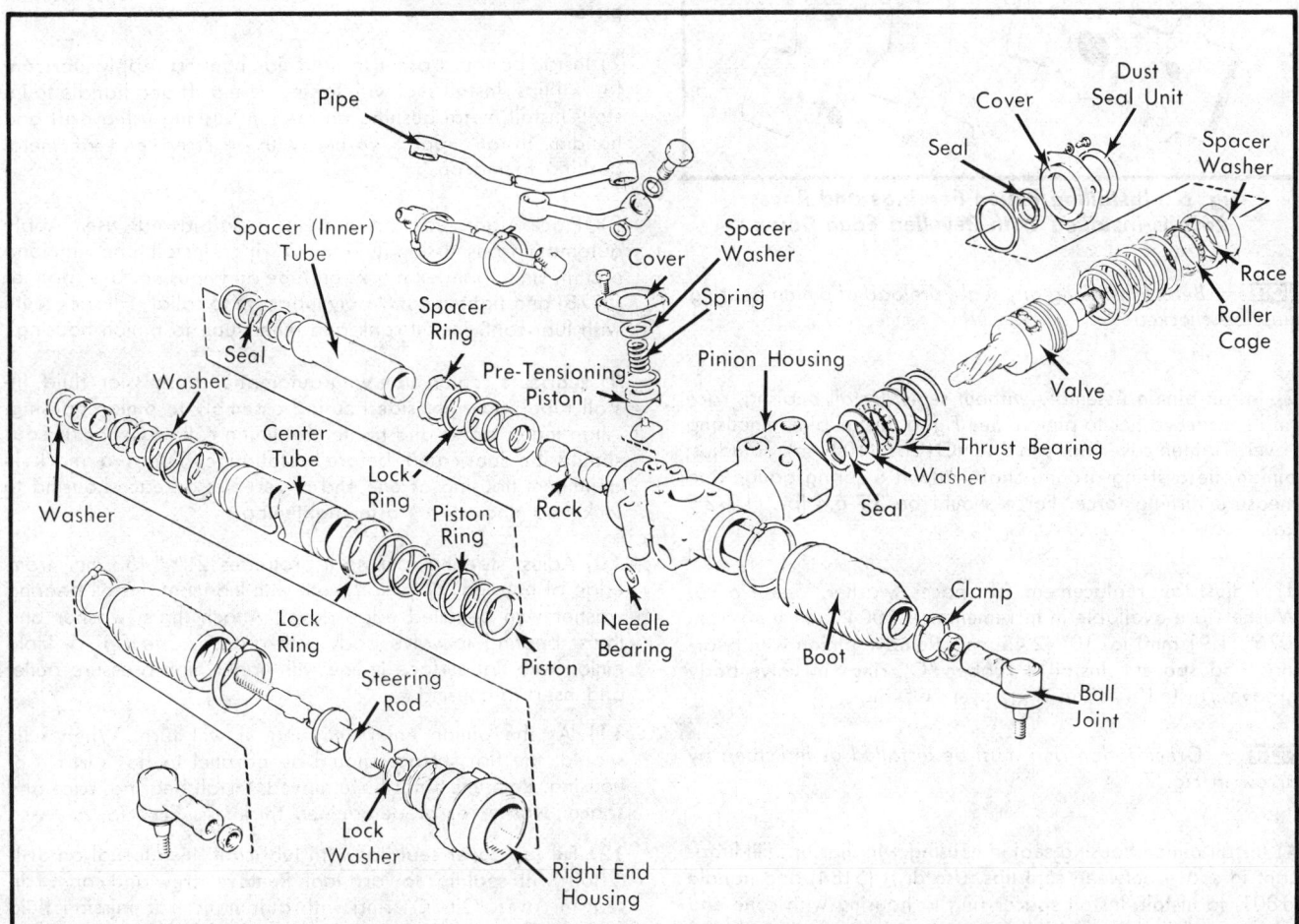

Fig. 5 Exploded View of ZF Power Steering Gear

VOLVO POWER-ASSISTED RACK & PINION (Cont.)

7) Using seal extractor under washer, remove teflon bushing, seal and washer from right housing. Remove seal and "O" ring from top cover. Remove depressor and "O" ring from pretension piston. Remove teflon seal rings from pinion valve assembly.

Inspection — Clean all parts and inspect for wear or damage. Replace as necessary. Do NOT disassemble valve housing. Replace if defective.

Reassembly — 1) If removed, lubricate needle bearing with lubricant (Volvo P/N 1 161 001-1 or equivalent). Install to pinion housing with drift. Bearing bottom should be flush with housing. Install bearing race (bevelled edge down), needle bearing and bearing race to pinion housing. Do not use lubricant at this time. See Fig. 6.

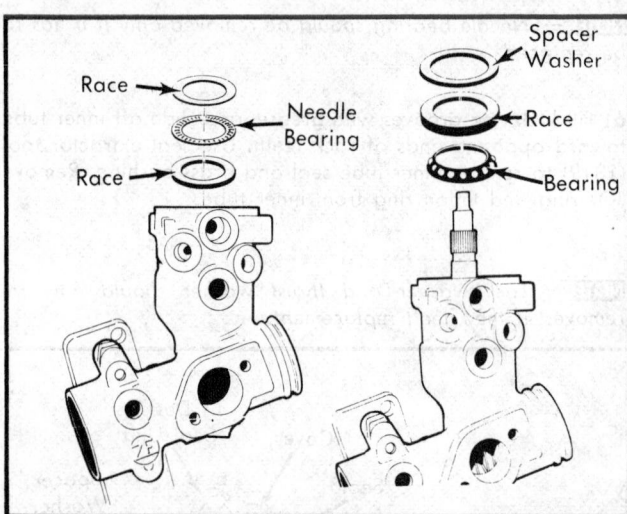

Fig. 6   Installing Pinion Bearings and Races. Race is Installed With Bevelled Edge Down

NOTE — *Before installing any seals, preload of pinion bearing must be checked.*

2) Install pinion assembly without seals. Install bearing, race and spacer washer to pinion. *See Fig. 6.* Install pinion housing cover. Tighten cover bolts to 84 INCH Lbs. (10 N·m). To adjust pinion, tie a string around shaft. Attach a spring gauge and measure turning force. Force should be 3.7-6.4 lbs. (1.7-2.9 kg).

3) Adjust by replacement of spacer washer. *See Fig. 6.* Washers are available in increments of .0004" (.01 mm) from .075" (1.91 mm) to .10" (2.45 mm). Remove pinion with bearings and spacers. Install 4 rubber "O" rings in valve body grooves. Install 4 teflon rings over "O" rings.

NOTE — *Green teflon ring must be installed as indicated by arrow in Fig. 7.*

4) Install pinion housing seal in housing with lips up. Fill lubricant in space between seal lips. Use drift (5184) and handle (1801) to install. Install spacer ring to housing with cone end in, grooved end out. Install bronze bushing in spacer (inner) tube with chamfered side down.

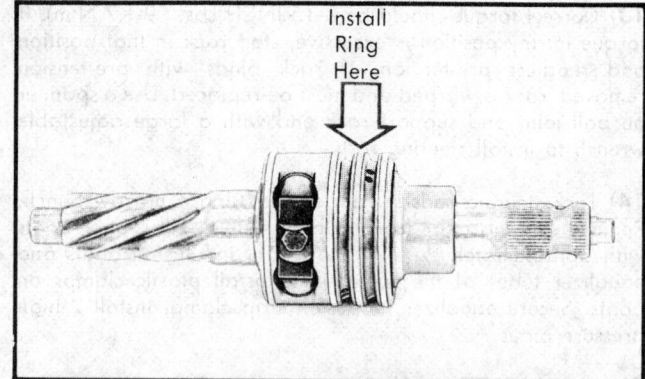

Fig. 7   Installing Green Teflon Ring to Pinion. Ring Must Be Installed at Arrow.

5) Fill lubricant in space between seal lips and install seal in spacer tube with lips up. Use drift and handle. If removed, install replacement spacer washer and lock ring to tube. Install teflon ring and "O" ring to tube. Fill snap ring grooves and coat surrounding area with wheel bearing grease.

6) Slide spacer tube into steering rack from smooth end and pass quickly over snap ring. Install "O" ring and piston ring to piston. Install in order to rack: inner lock ring, spacer washer, "O" ring, and piston with rings. Install second spacer washer and lock ring. Install lock rings with chamfered side facing piston.

7) Install bottom washer to right side housing. Apply lubricant to seal lips. Install seal with lips up. Use drift and handle to install. Install metal bushing and teflon bushing using drift and handle. Install upper washer with recessed end of metal bushing facing up.

8) Place right side housing in a soft-jawed vise. Apply automatic transmission fluid to "O" rings. Install tube with long end in. Line up index marks on tube and housing. Use spanner (5178) and tighten nut. Apply lubricant to collar. Fill rack teeth with lubricant. Install rank and inner tube to pinion housing.

9) Lubricate center tube with automatic transmission fluid. Install tube and right side housing assembly to pinion housing. Align index marks and tighten retaining collar. Collar threads should be lubricated before installation. Punch a mark in aluminum housing at one end of recesses on each housing to lock retaining collars after tightening.

10) Adjust steering rack so it protrudes 2 1/16" (53 mm) from edge of housing. Fill pinion teeth with lubricant. Install bearing washer with bevelled edge down. Attach thrust washer and thrust bearing to valve body with grease. *See Fig. 6.* Hold pinion with flat surface in line with upper high pressure outlet and insert to housing.

11) As the pinion enters housing, it will turn. When fully seated, the flat surface should be parallel to flat surface of housing. Rack must not have moved. Install bearing, race and spacer washer of predetermined thickness. See Fig. 6.

12) Fill top cover seal lips with lubricant. Install seal on drift (2863) with seal lips toward tool. Remove screw and cone. Tap seal in cover. Oil "O" ring with automatic transmission fluid and install. Install cover on sleeve (5182), with cone attached. Remove cone.

VOLVO POWER-ASSISTED RACK & PINION (Cont.)

13) Install cover. Tighten bolts. Install dust seal. Insert pre-tension piston without "O" ring. Be sure teflon insert is on piston. Set up pre-tension measuring fixture (5865) using cover bolt hole and a 45 mm x 8 mm bolt. Assemble tool with the pre-tension spring between bolt head and bolt. Adjust for slight preload.

14) Move gear lock-to-lock and make sure it does not jam. With micrometer measure distance between housing face and piston stop. Check measurement at 3 different points on steering rack. Subtract .004-.006" (0.1-.15 mm) from smallest reading obtained. Select washer of that thickness.

15) Washers are available in thicknesses of .083-.114" (2.1-2.90 mm) in increments of .0019" (.05 mm). Remove press tool (5865). Lubricate "O" ring and install on pre-tension piston. Install spacer washer and piston spring. Fill space around spring with lubricant. Apply sealant on cover sealing surface.

16) Install and tighten cover. Install and tighten pressure pipes. Make sure "O" rings seat correctly. Using spanner and adjustable wrench, install steering rods. Bend back steering rod locks. Install boots. Fill each boot with approximately ¾ ounce of lubricant. Install boot clamps. Install equalizer tube and plastic clamps.

TIGHTENING SPECIFICATIONS

Application	Ft. Lbs. (N·m)
Pinion Cover	
Cam Gear	14 (19)
ZF	7 (10)
Tube Nuts (ZF)	88 (120)
Pre-Tension Device Cover	
Cam Gear	13 (17)
ZF	15 (22)
Pipe Fitting (ZF)	14 (20)
Valve Housing Cover (Cam Gear)	14 (20)

1980 WIRING DIAGRAMS

Contents

NOTE — The wiring diagrams in this section were unavailable and not included in the 1980 edition of this manual. They are included this year for your reference. Please note in your 1980 manual that these diagrams are located here.

1980 Jaguar

ENGINE COMPARTMENT & FUSE BLOCK

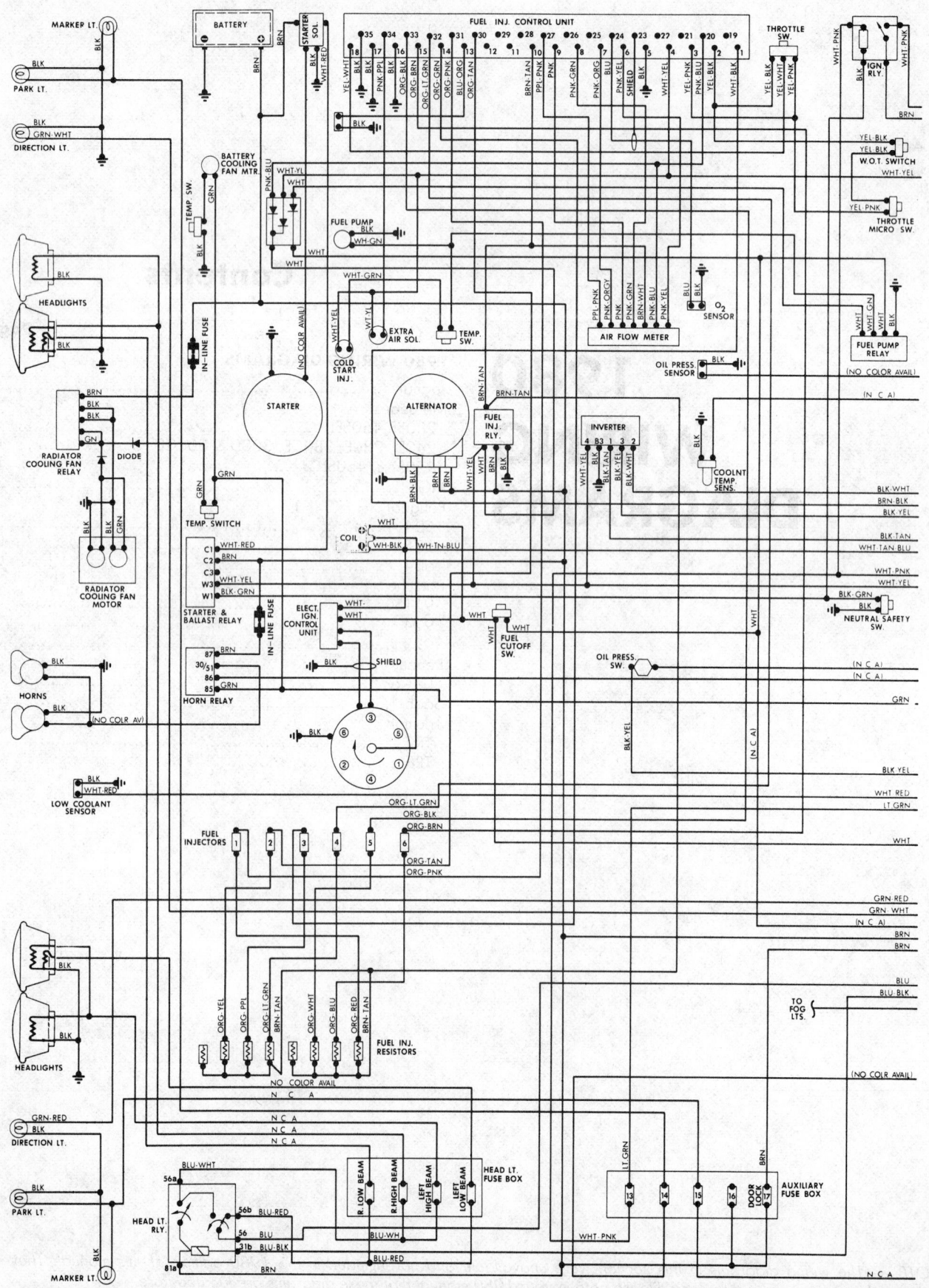

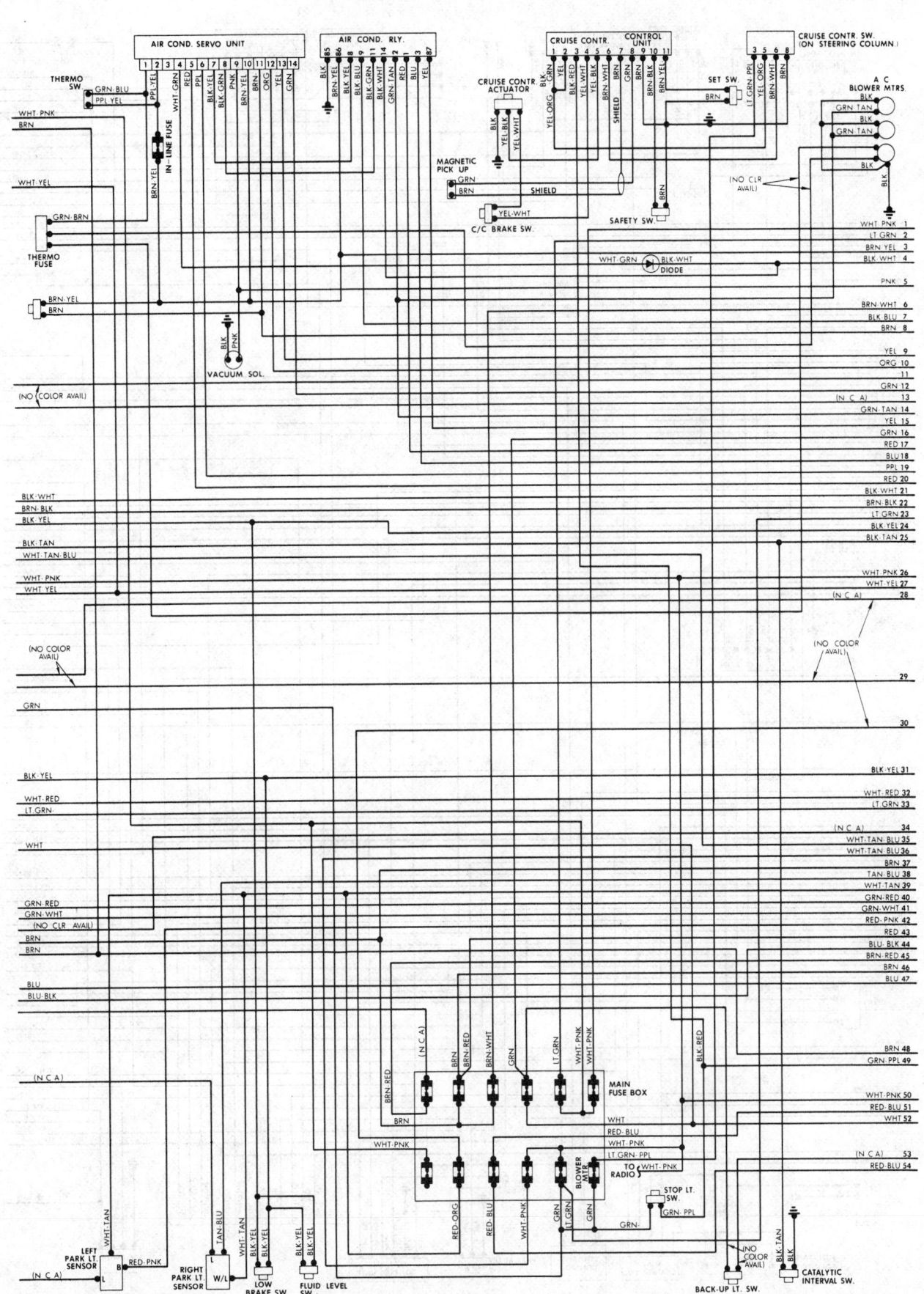

1980 Jaguar

UNDERDASH

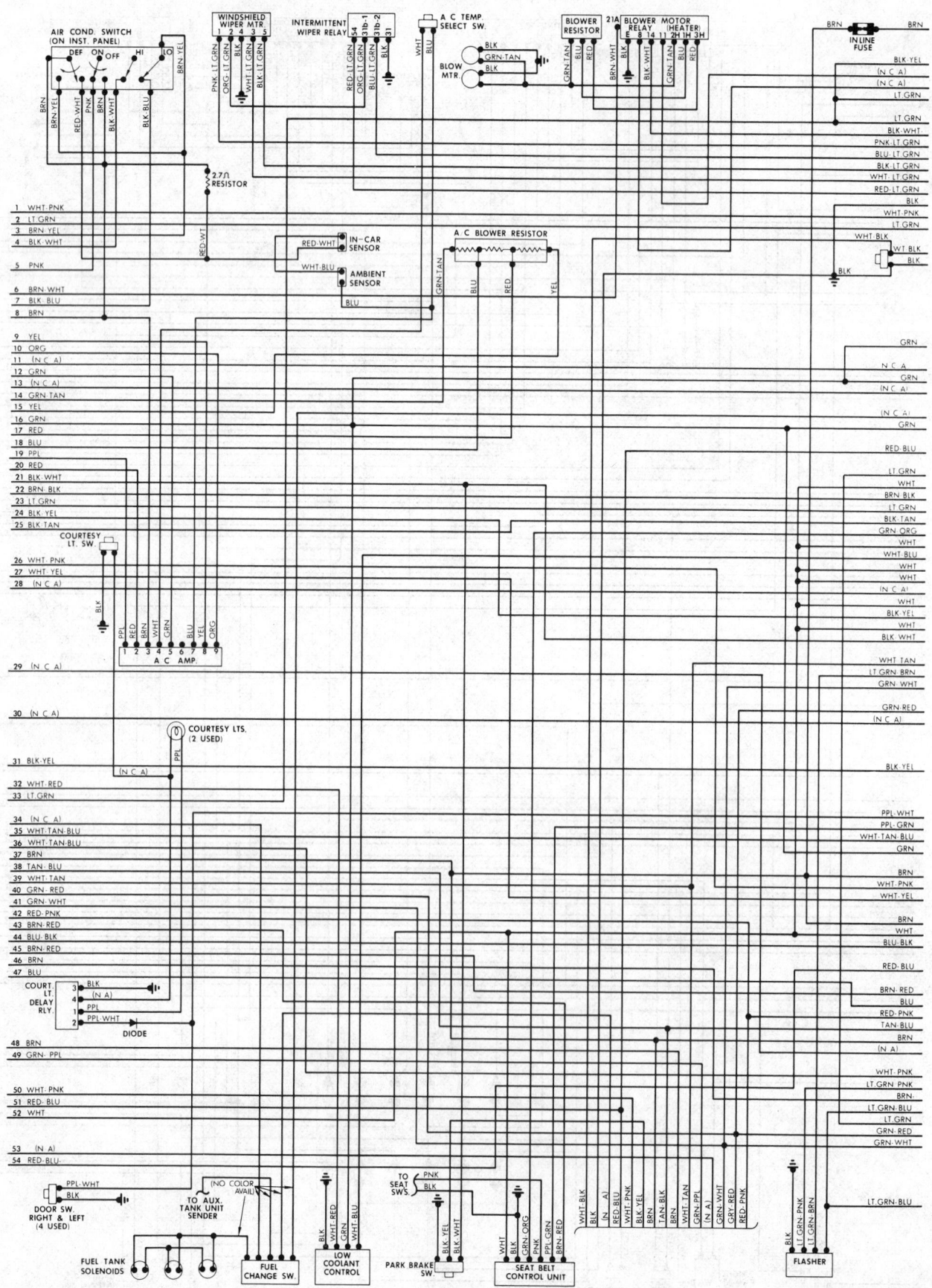

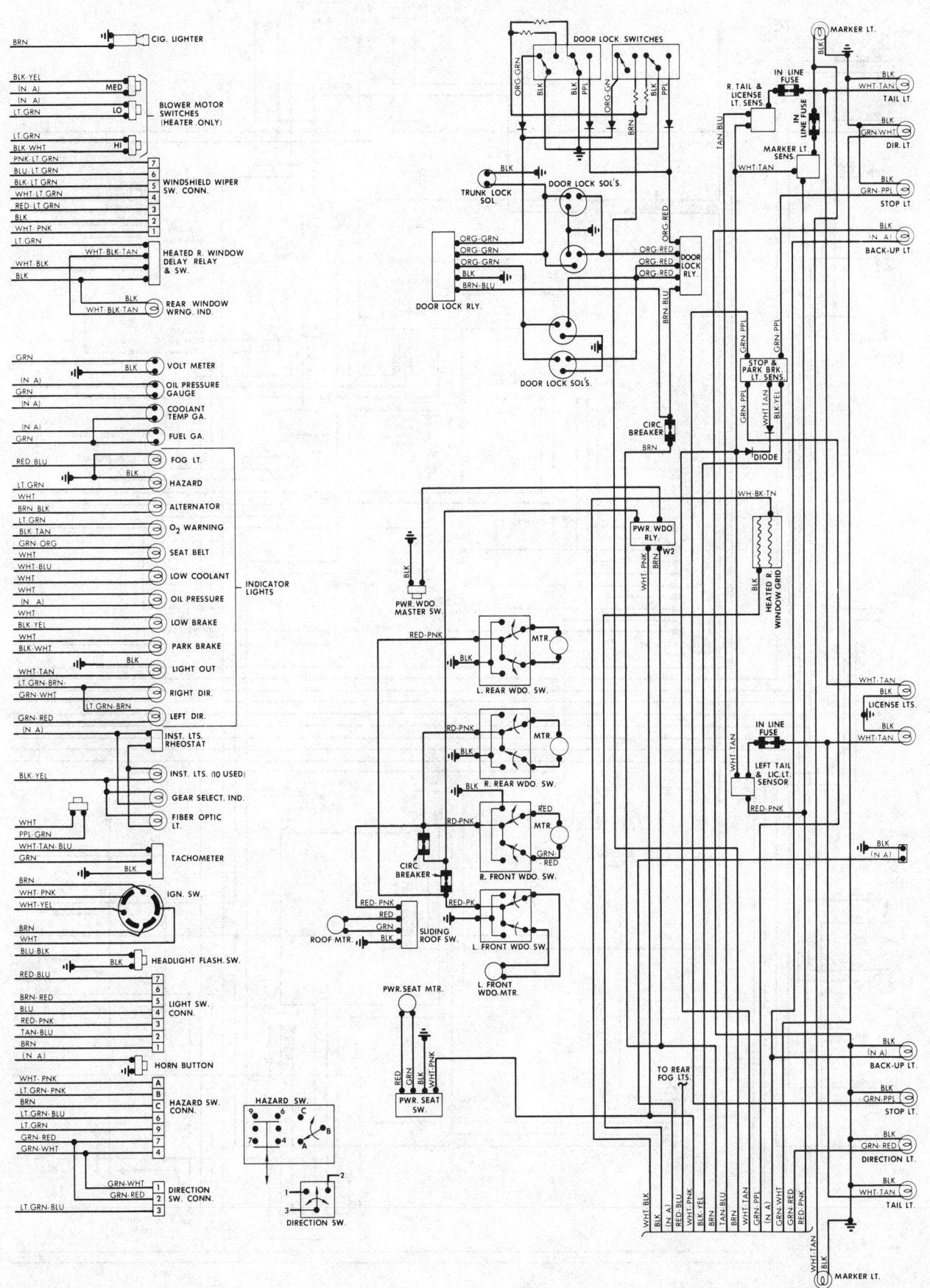

1980 Mercedes

ENGINE COMPARTMENT

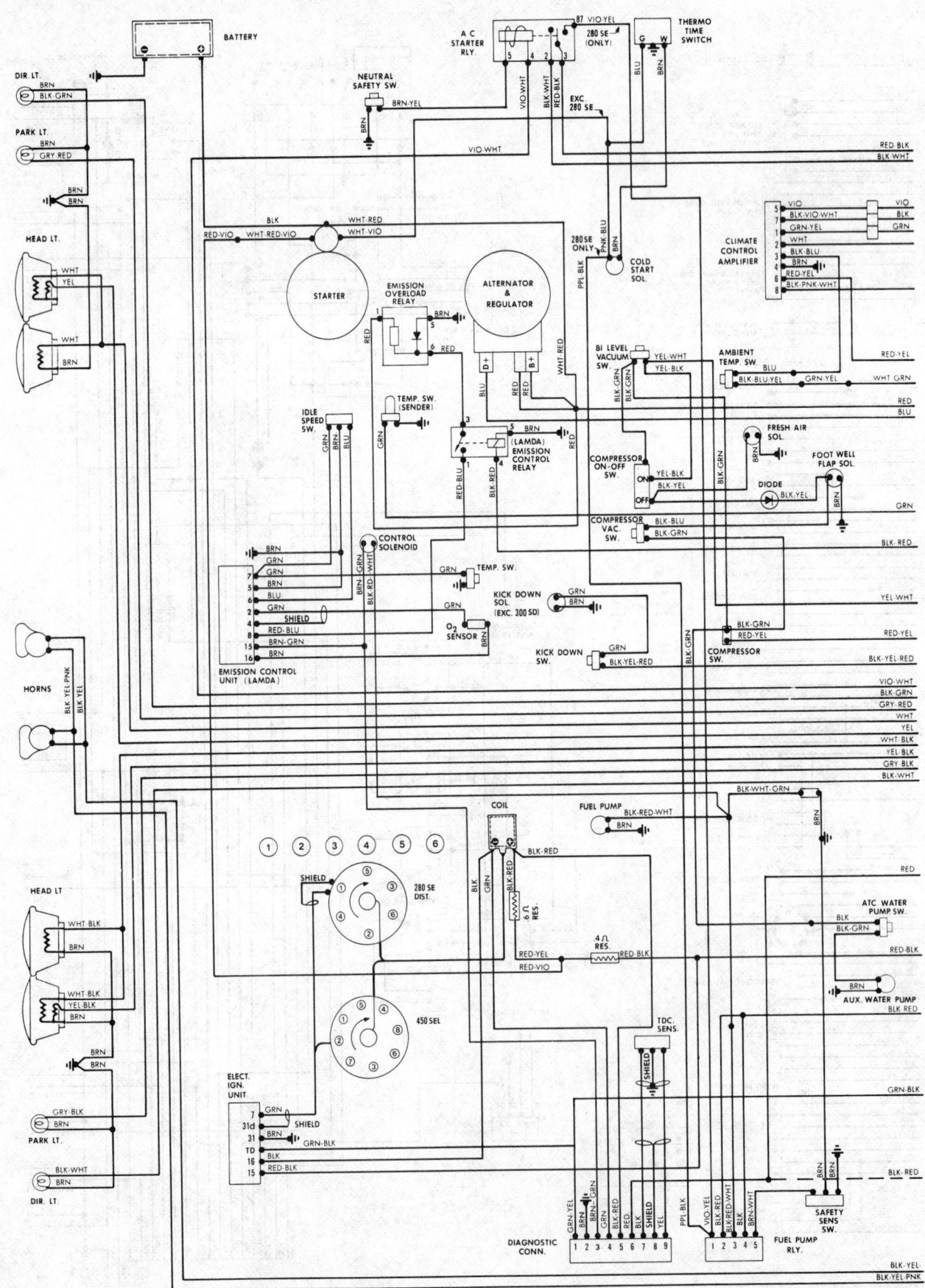

FUSE BLOCK

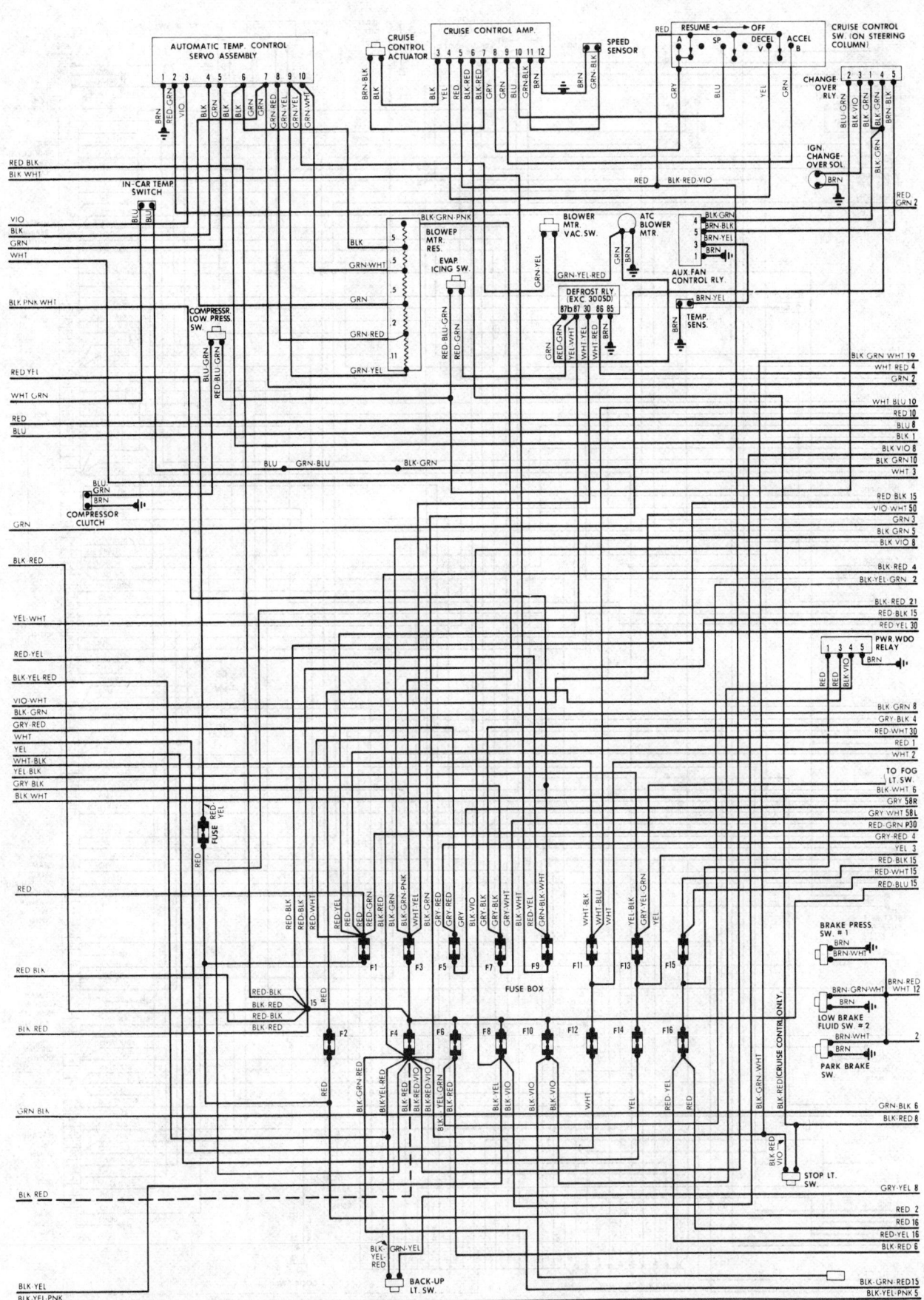

INSTRUMENT PANEL

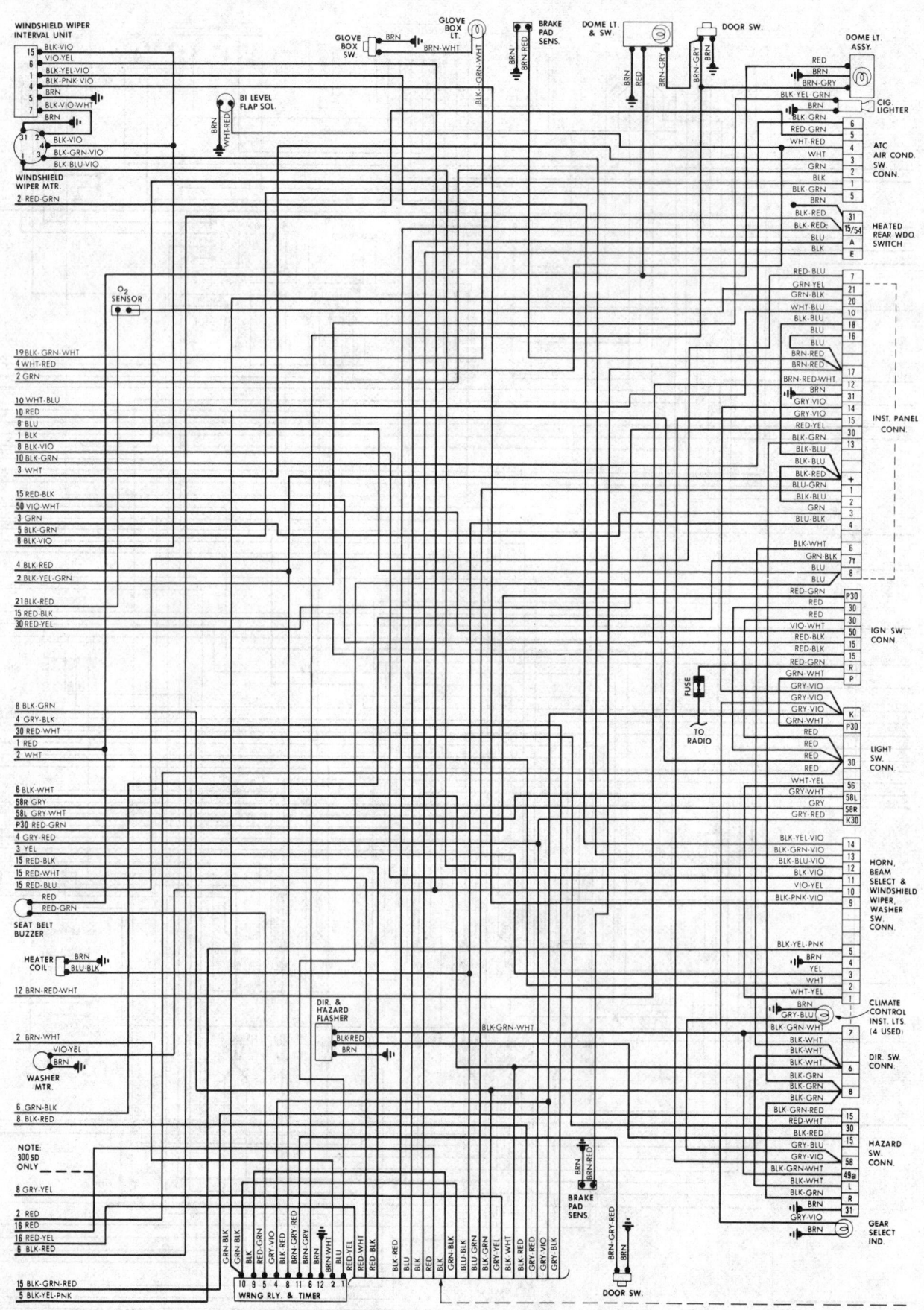

AIR CONDITIONING

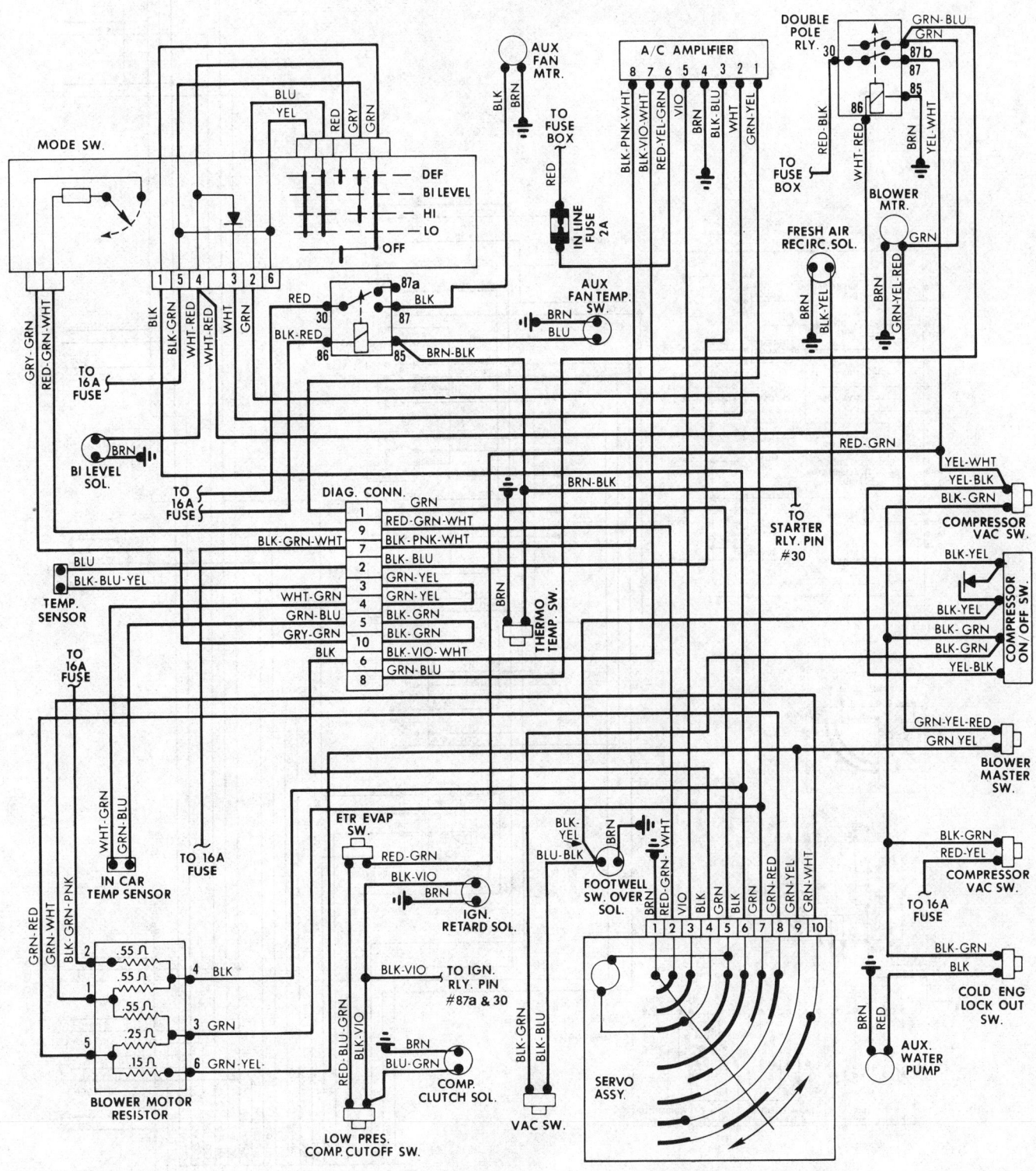

1980 Mercedes

ACCESSORIES & REAR COMPARTMENT

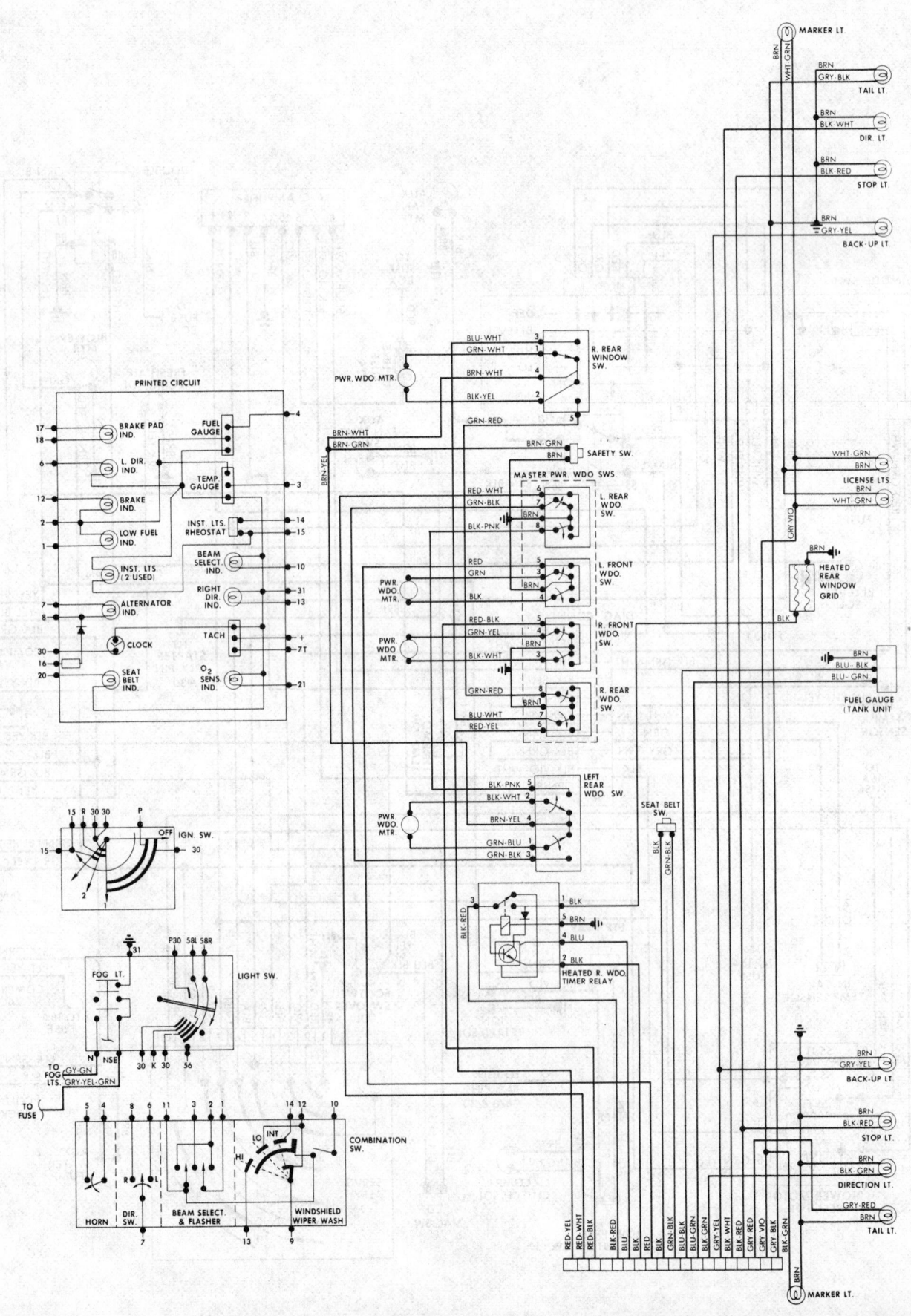

240D
280E
280CE

1980 Mercedes

300D
300CD

11

ENGINE COMPARTMENT

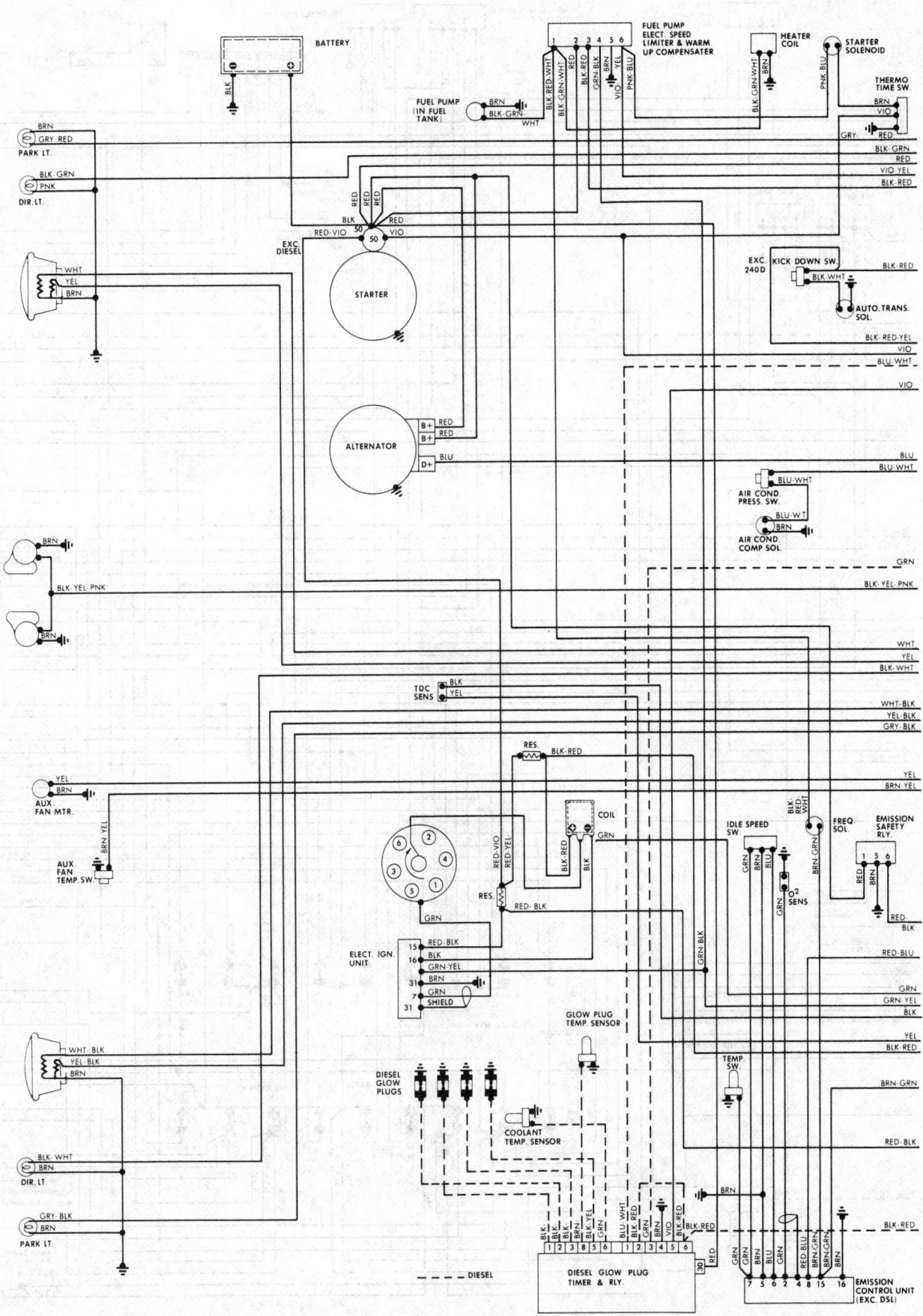

FUSE BLOCK

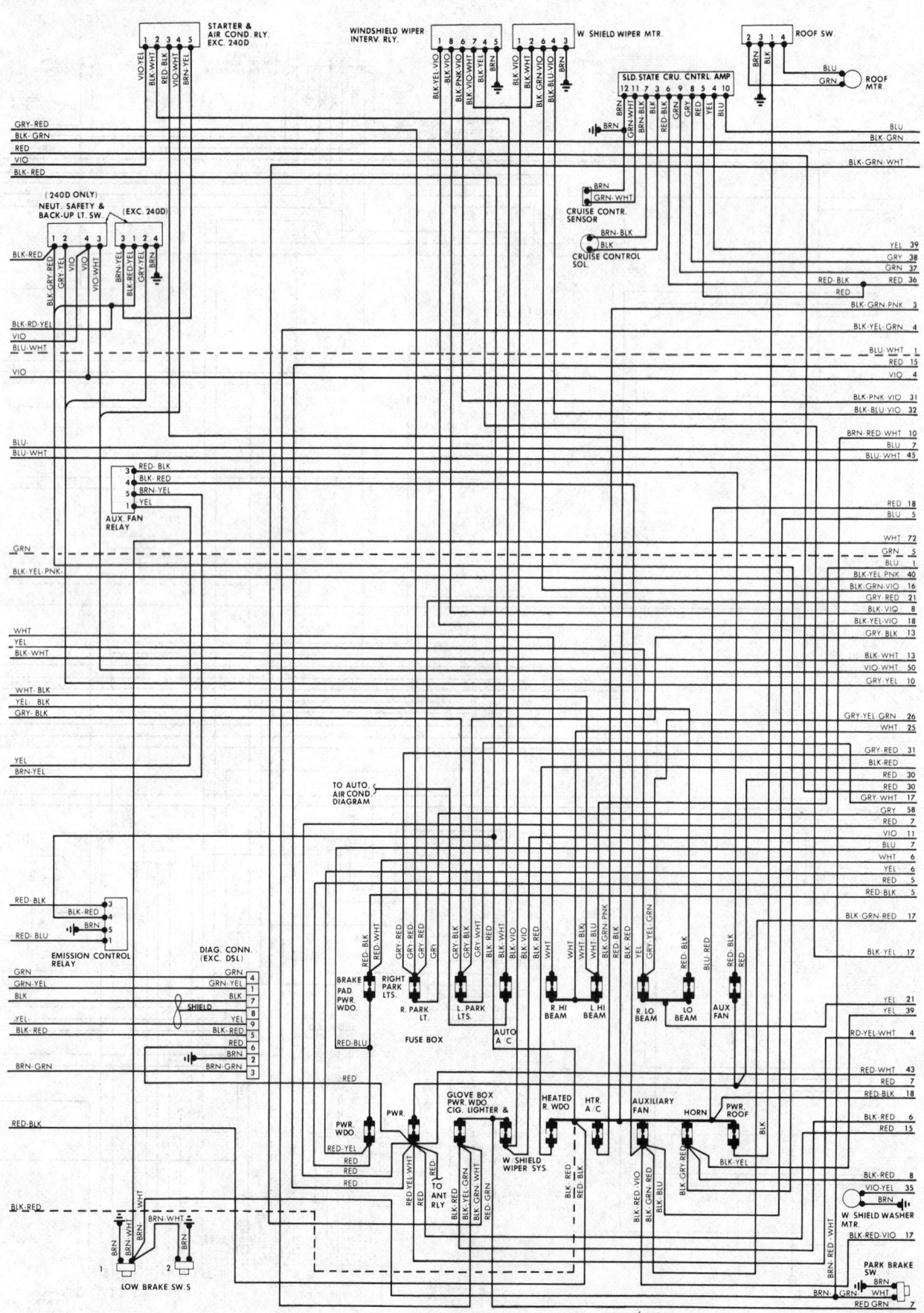

240D
280E
280CE

1980 Mercedes

300D
300CD

13

INSTRUMENT PANEL

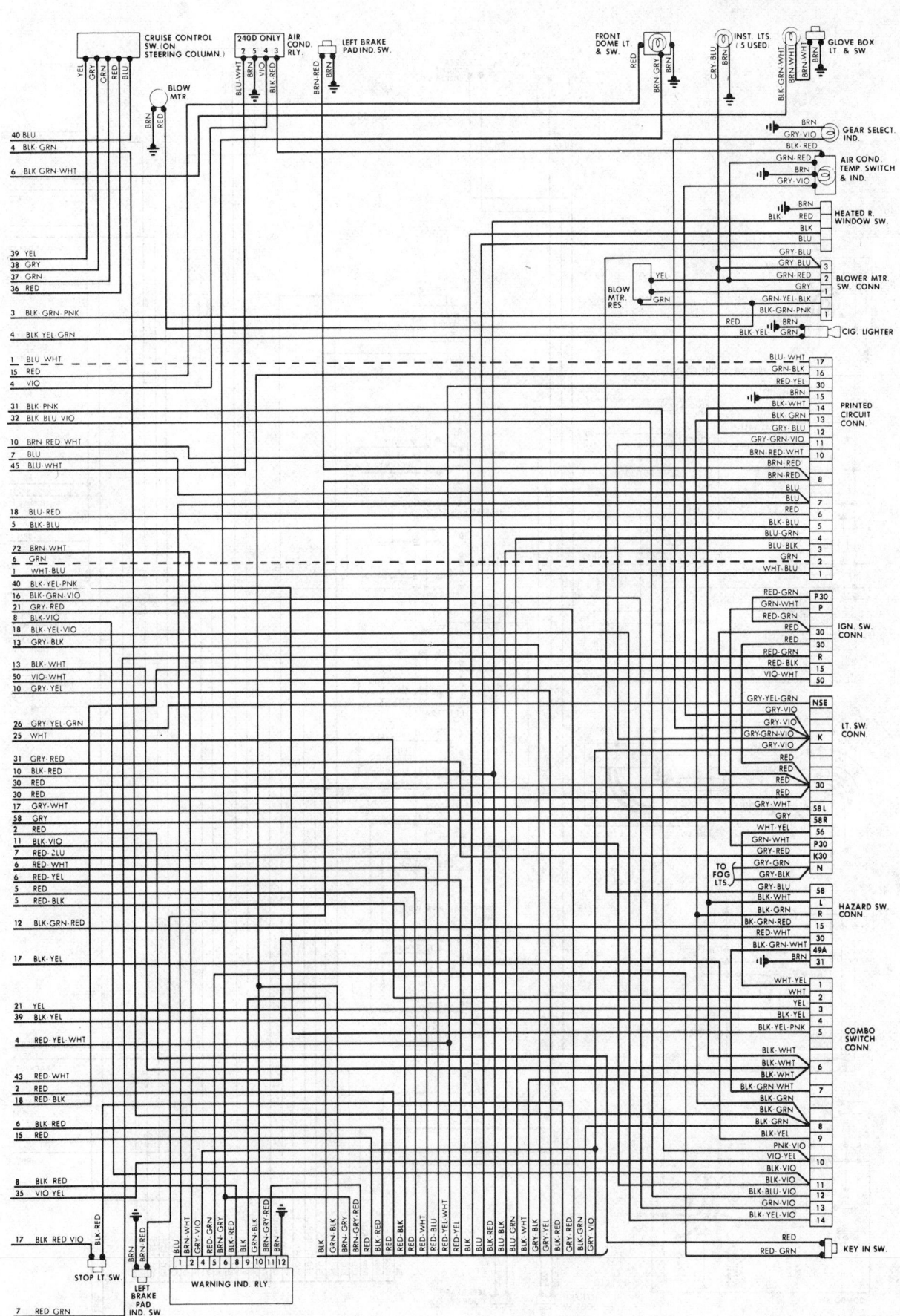

ACCESSORIES & REAR COMPARTMENT

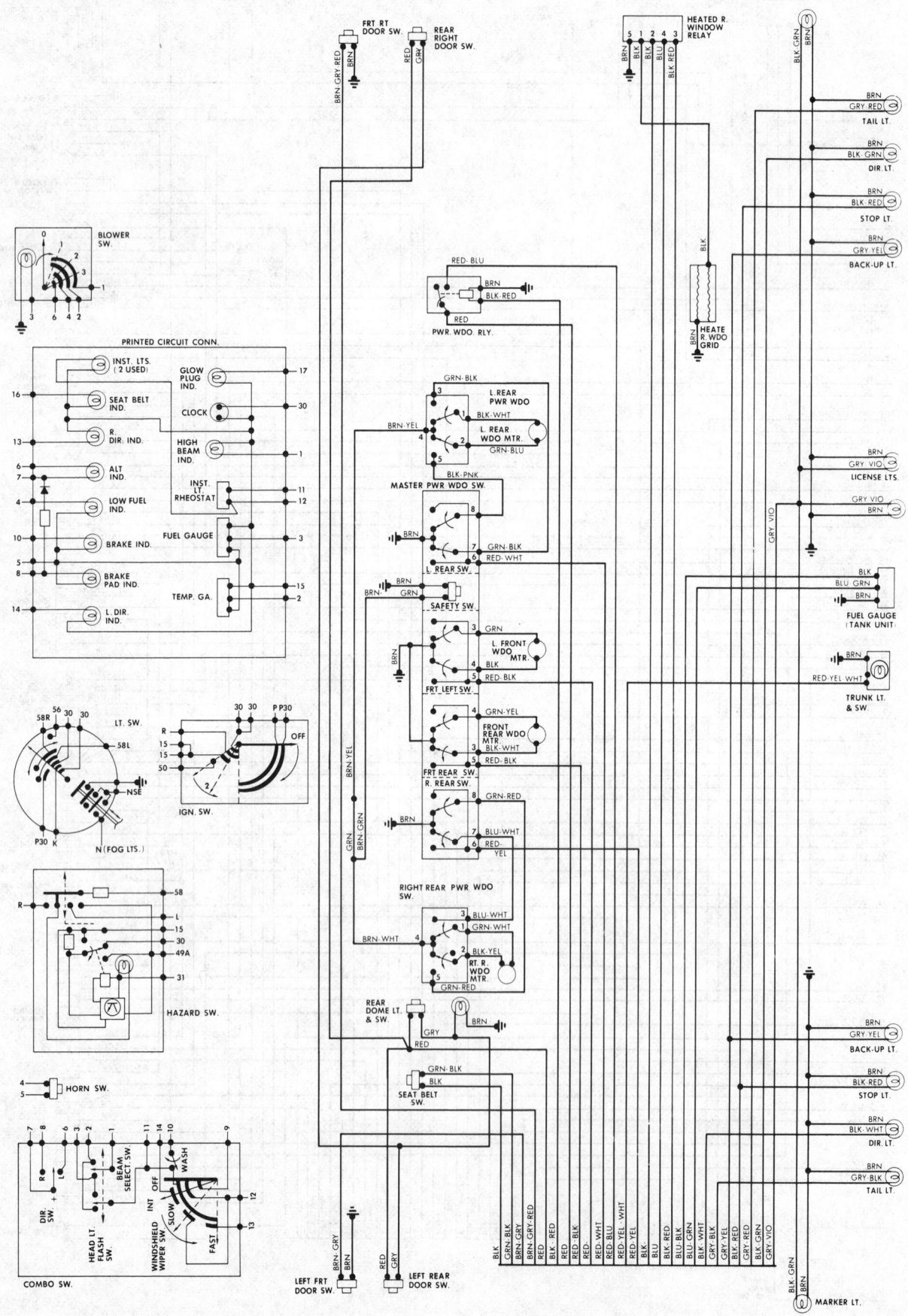

ENGINE COMPARTMENT

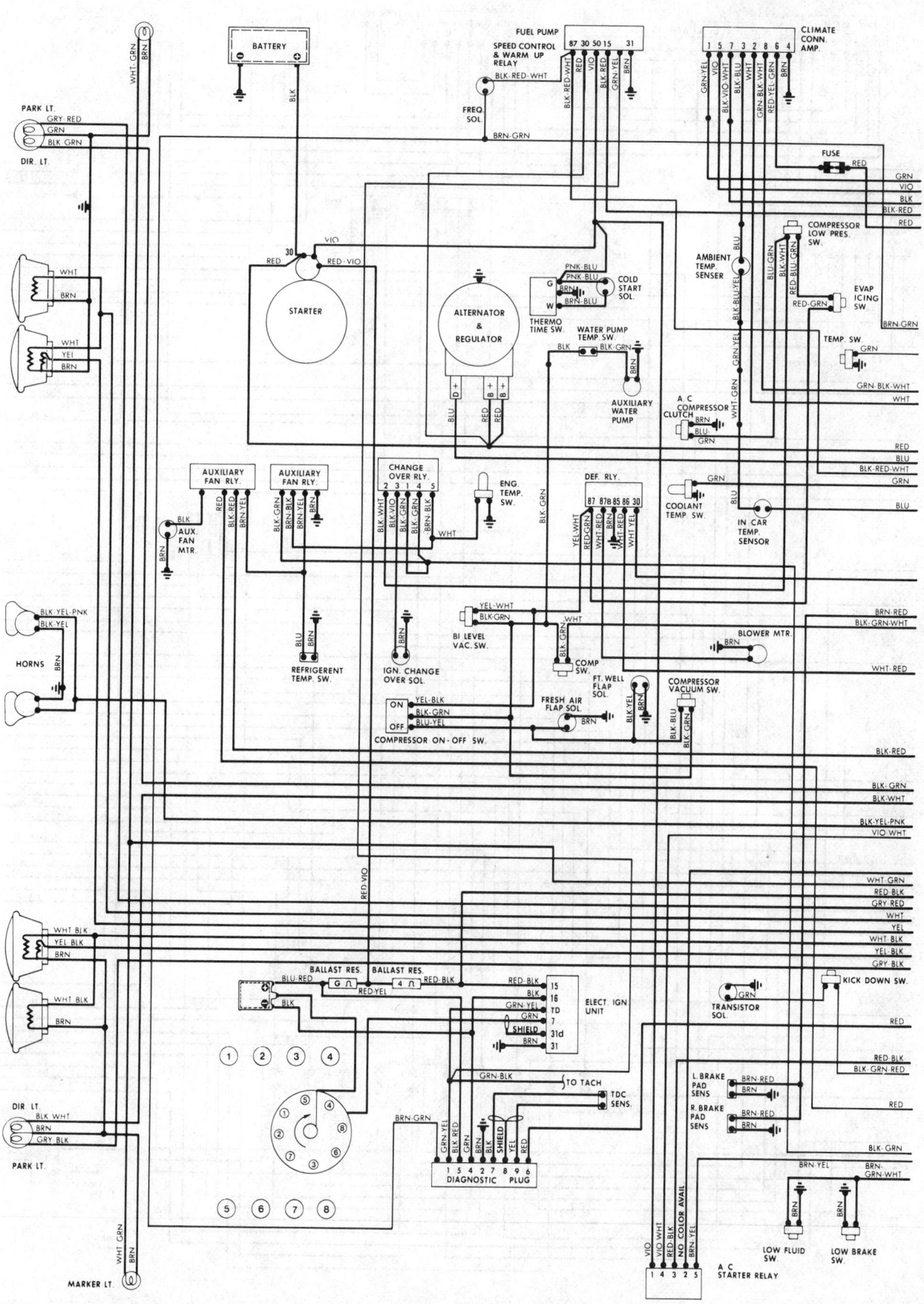

FUSE BLOCK

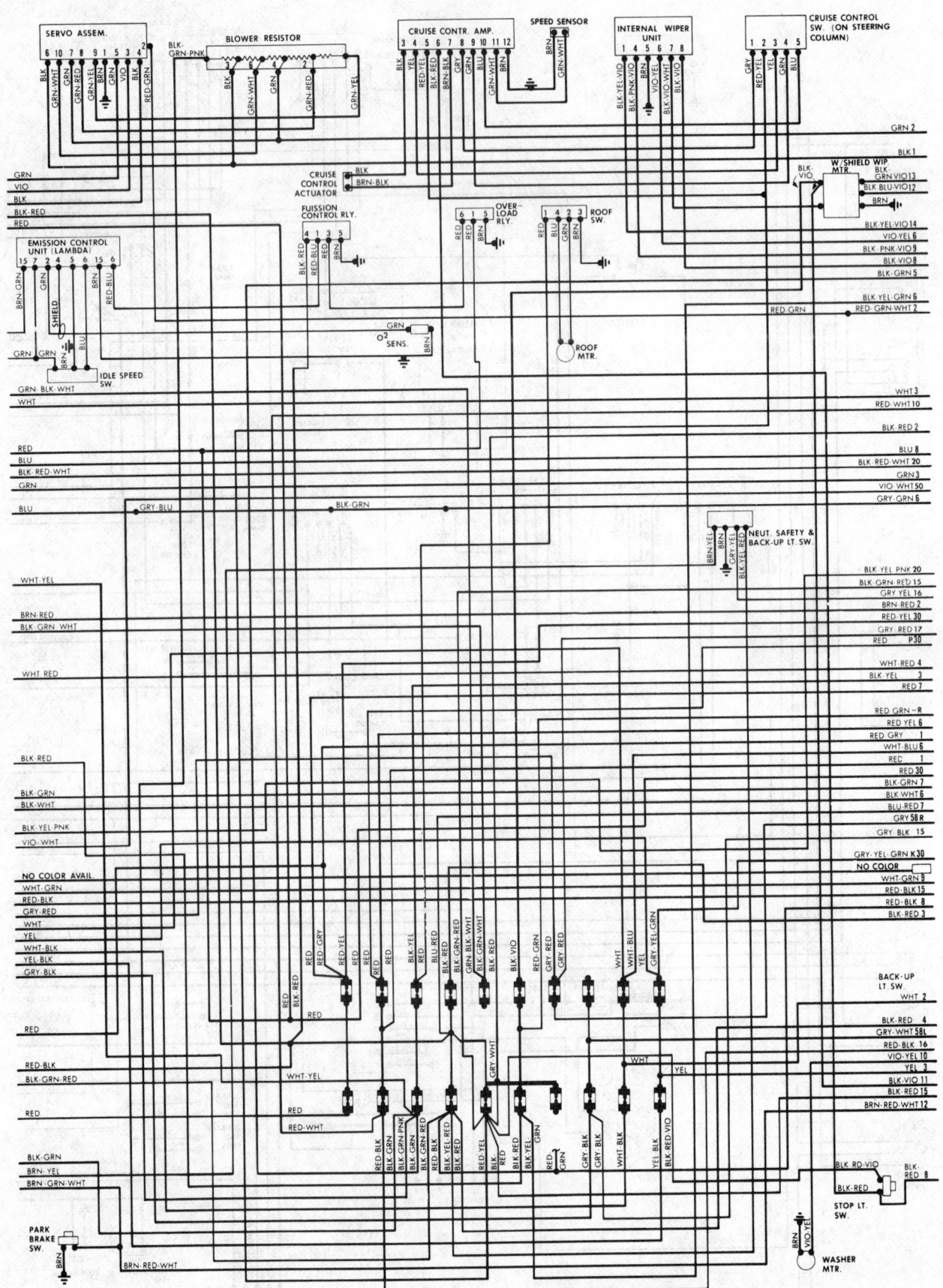

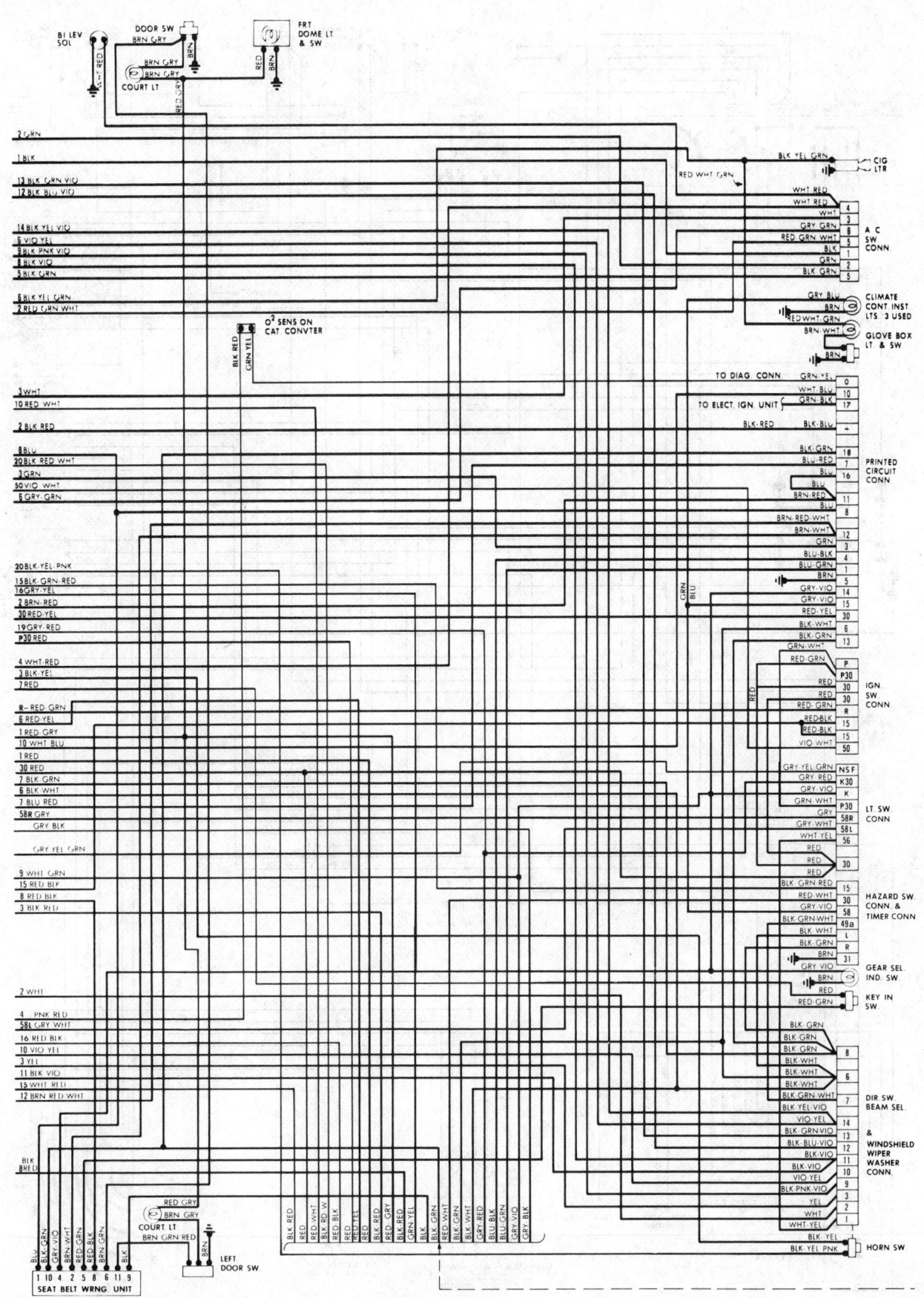

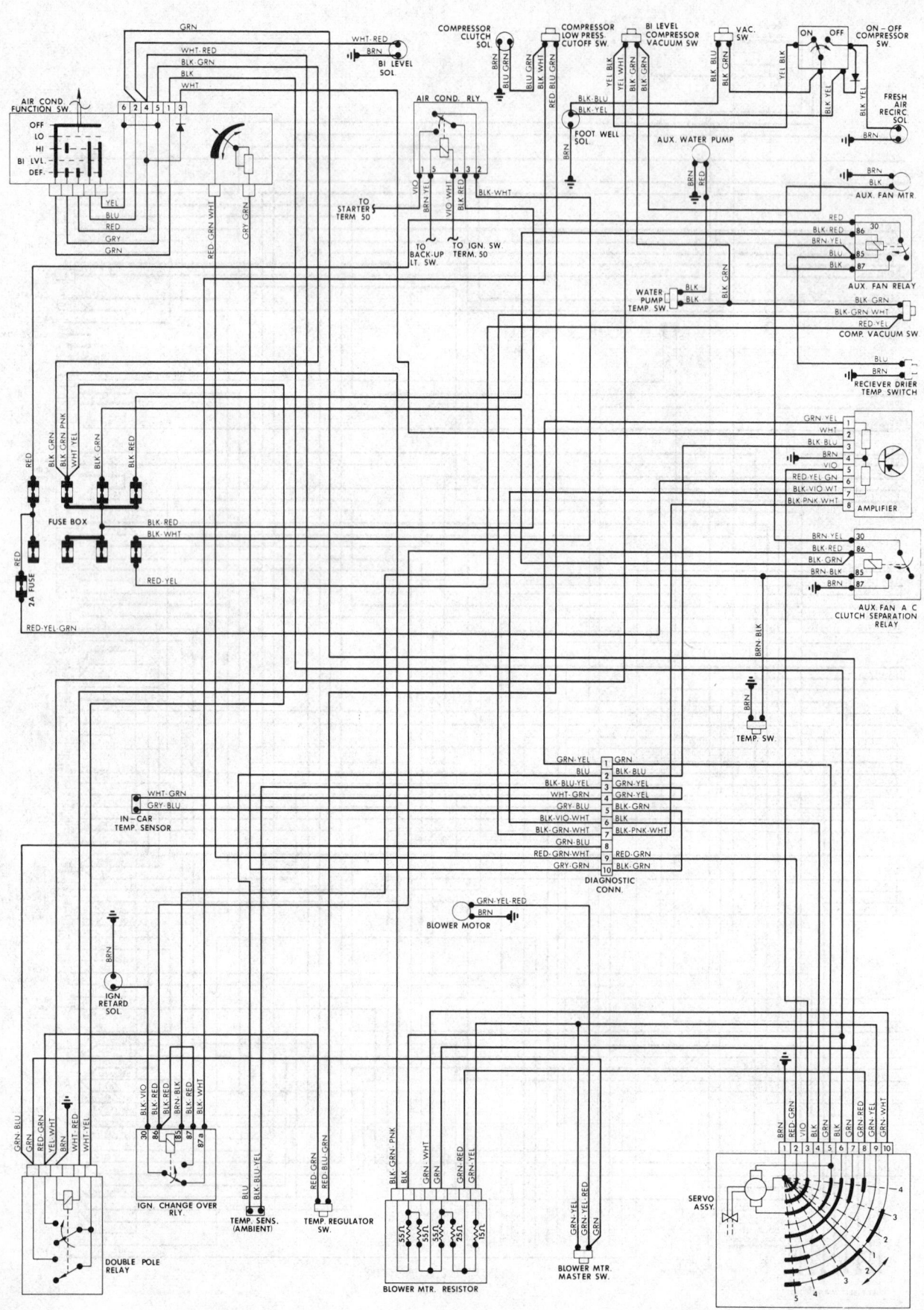

ACCESSORIES & REAR COMPARTMENT

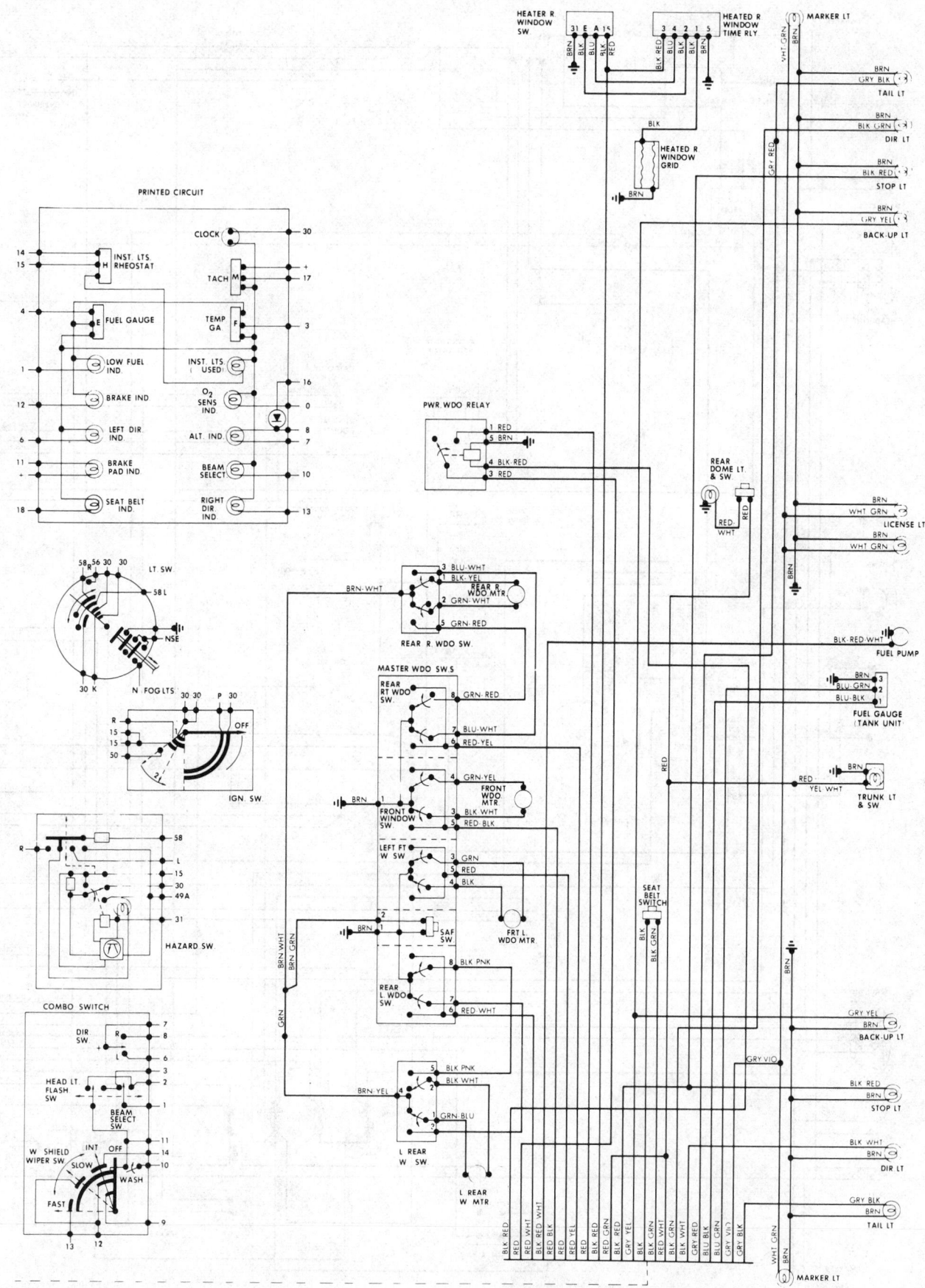

1980 MGB

ENGINE COMPARTMENT

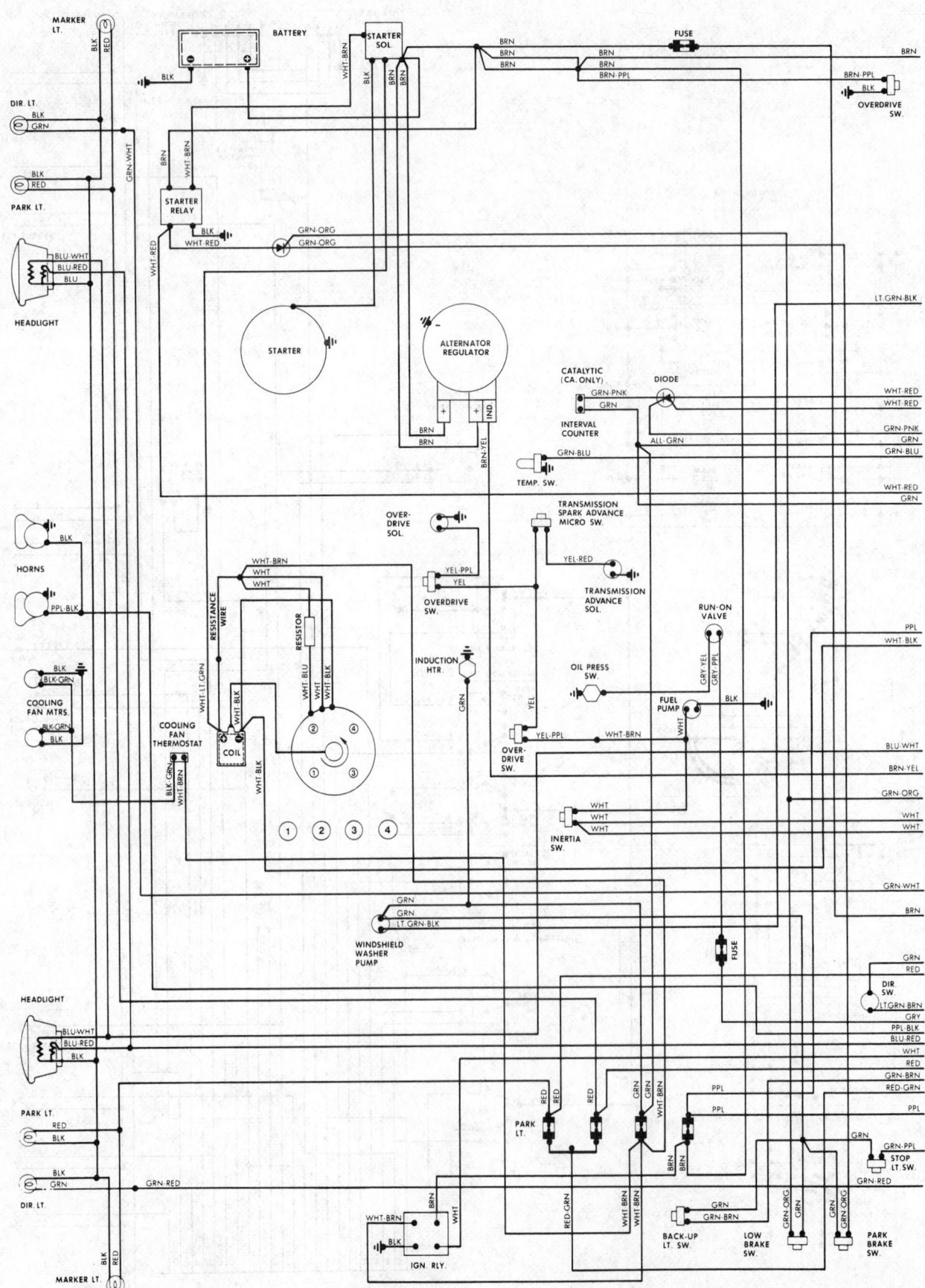

INSTRUMENT PANEL & REAR COMPARTMENT

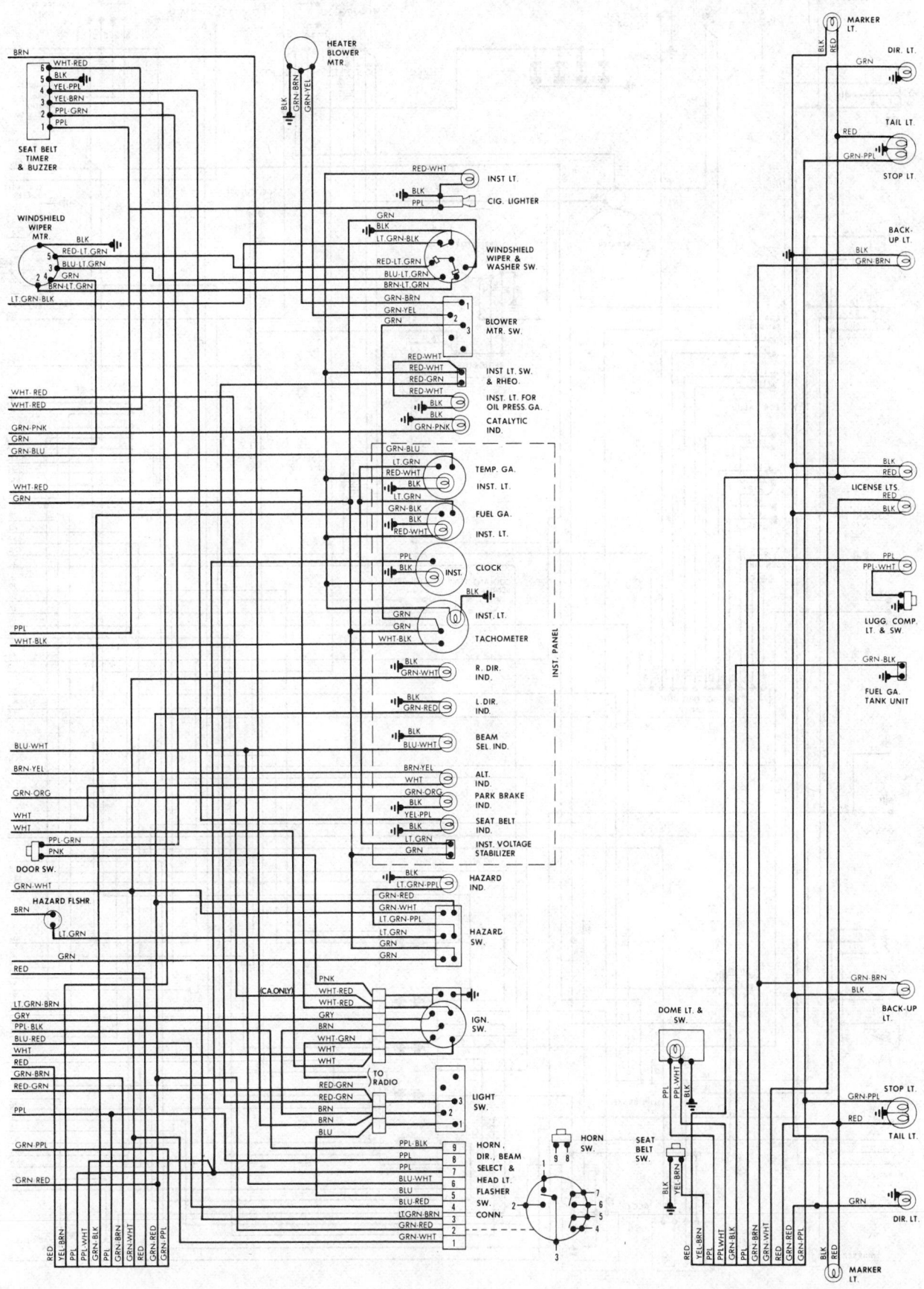

1980 Peugeot

ENGINE COMPARTMENT

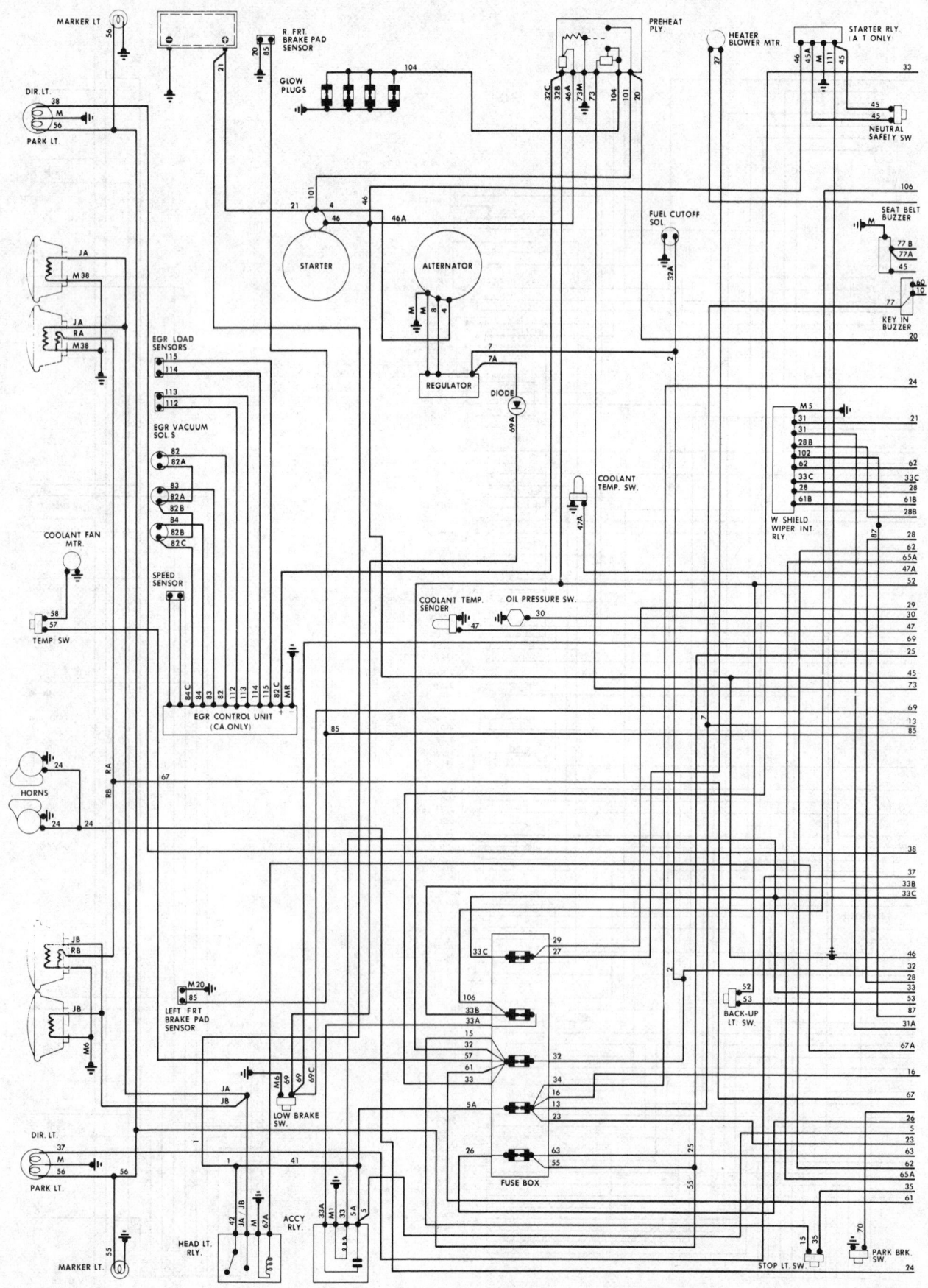

INSTRUMENT PANEL & REAR COMPARTMENT

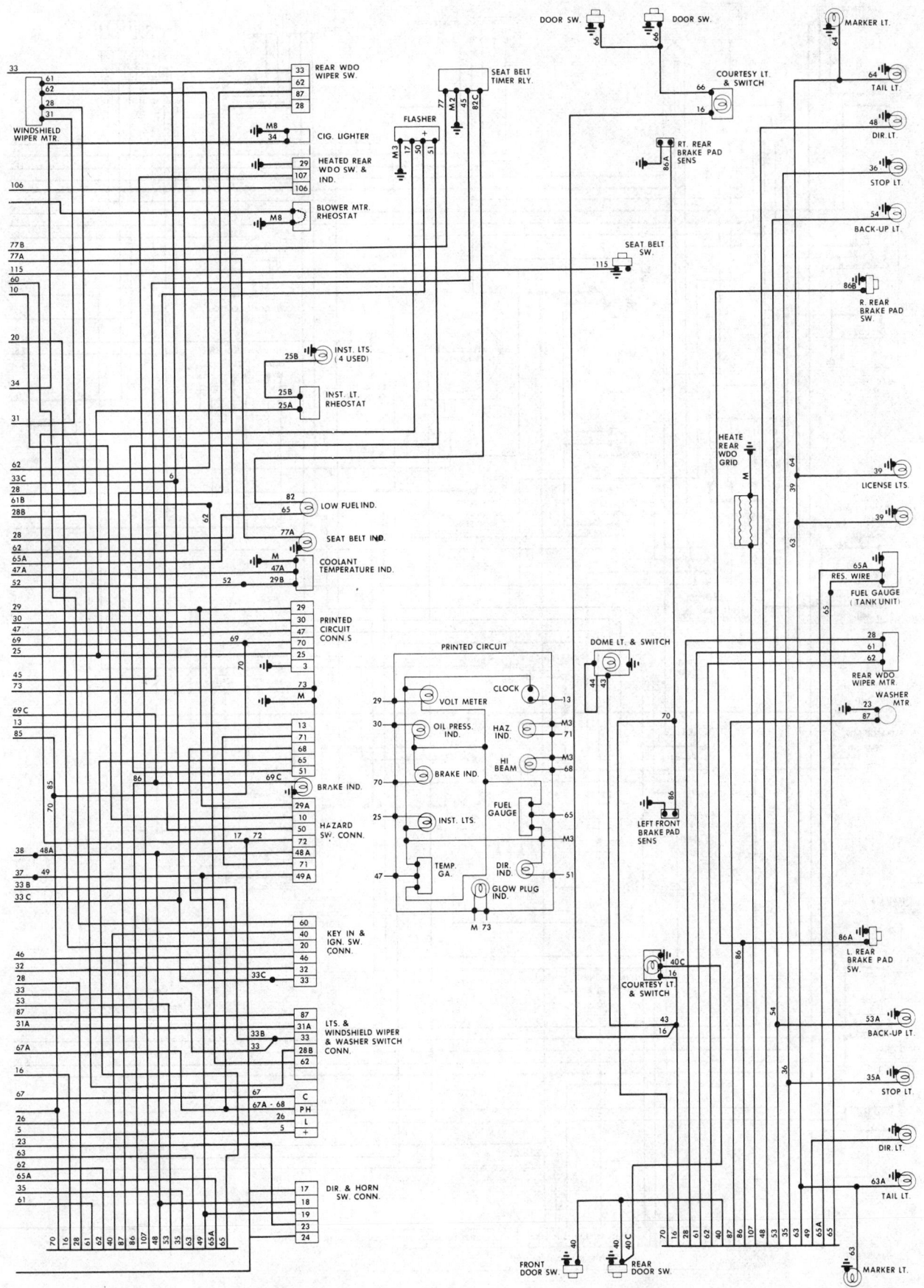

ENGINE COMPARTMENT

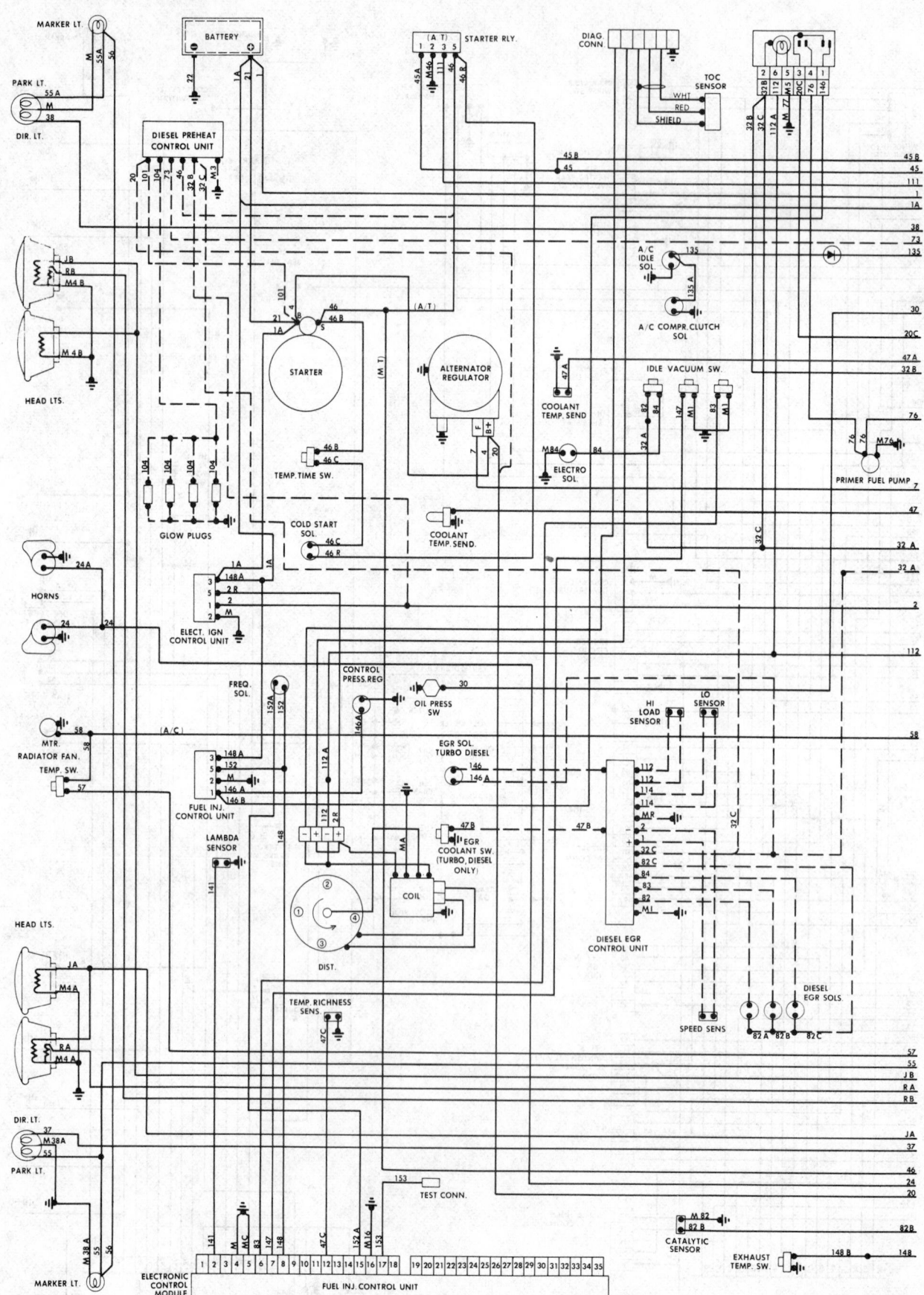

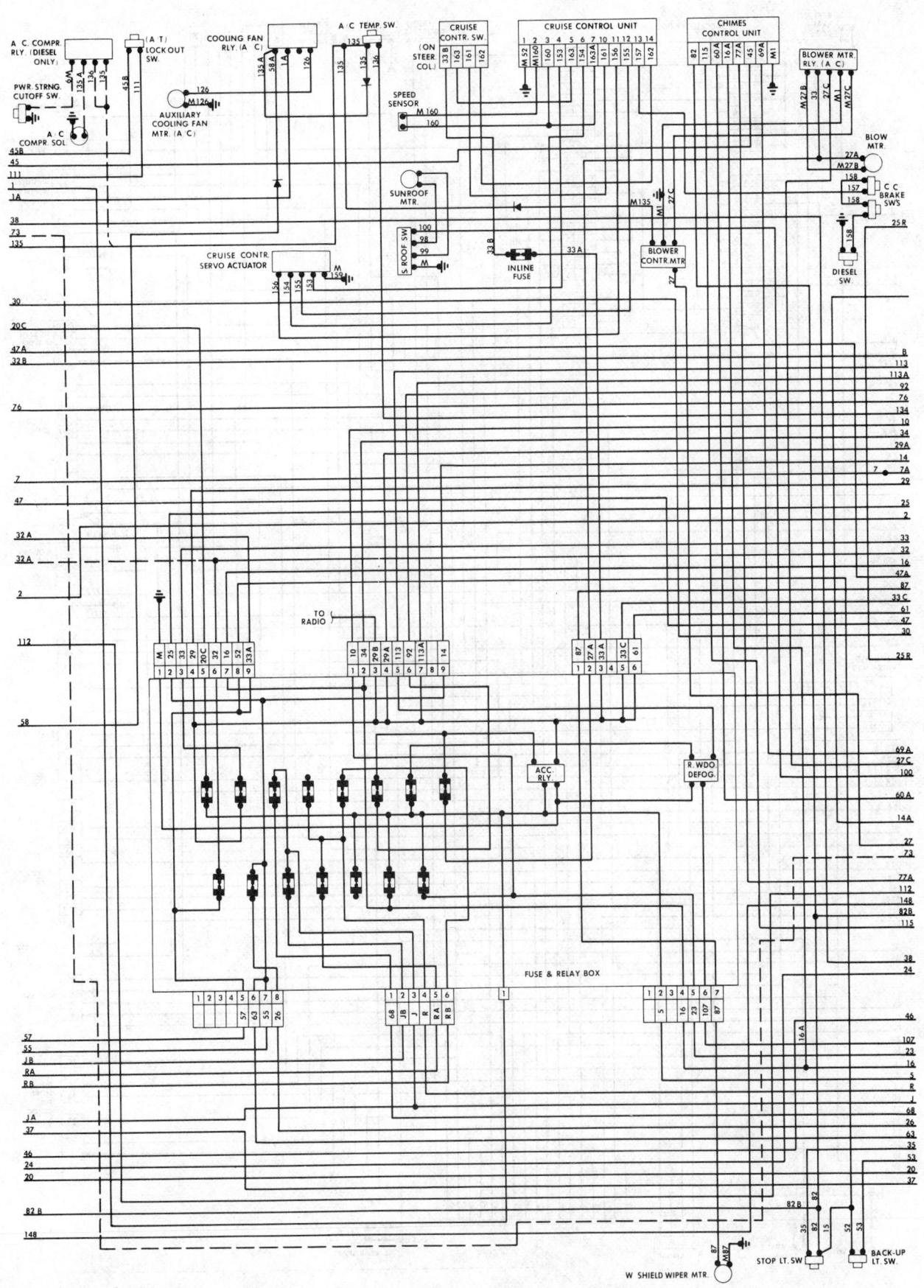

INSTRUMENT PANEL

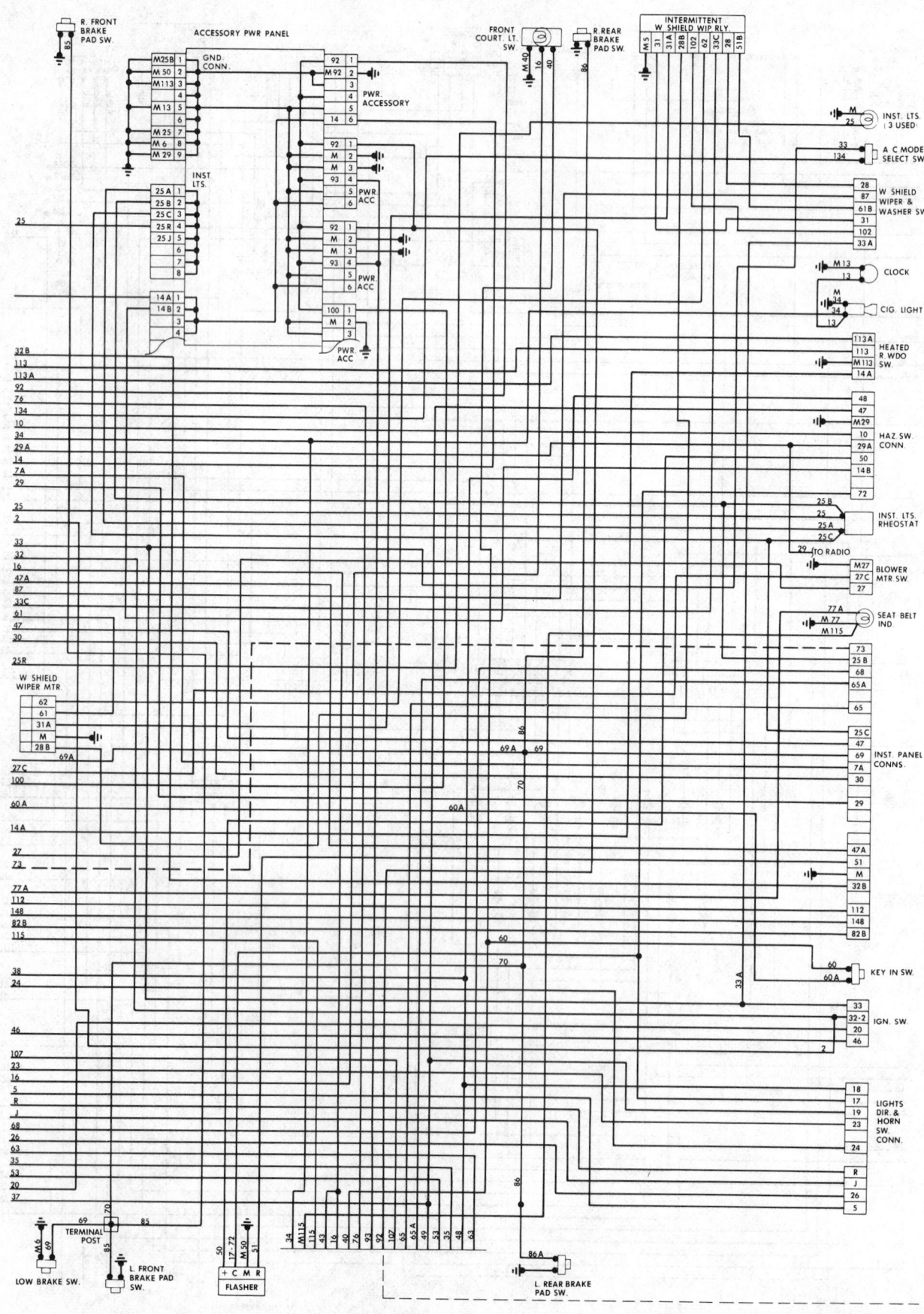

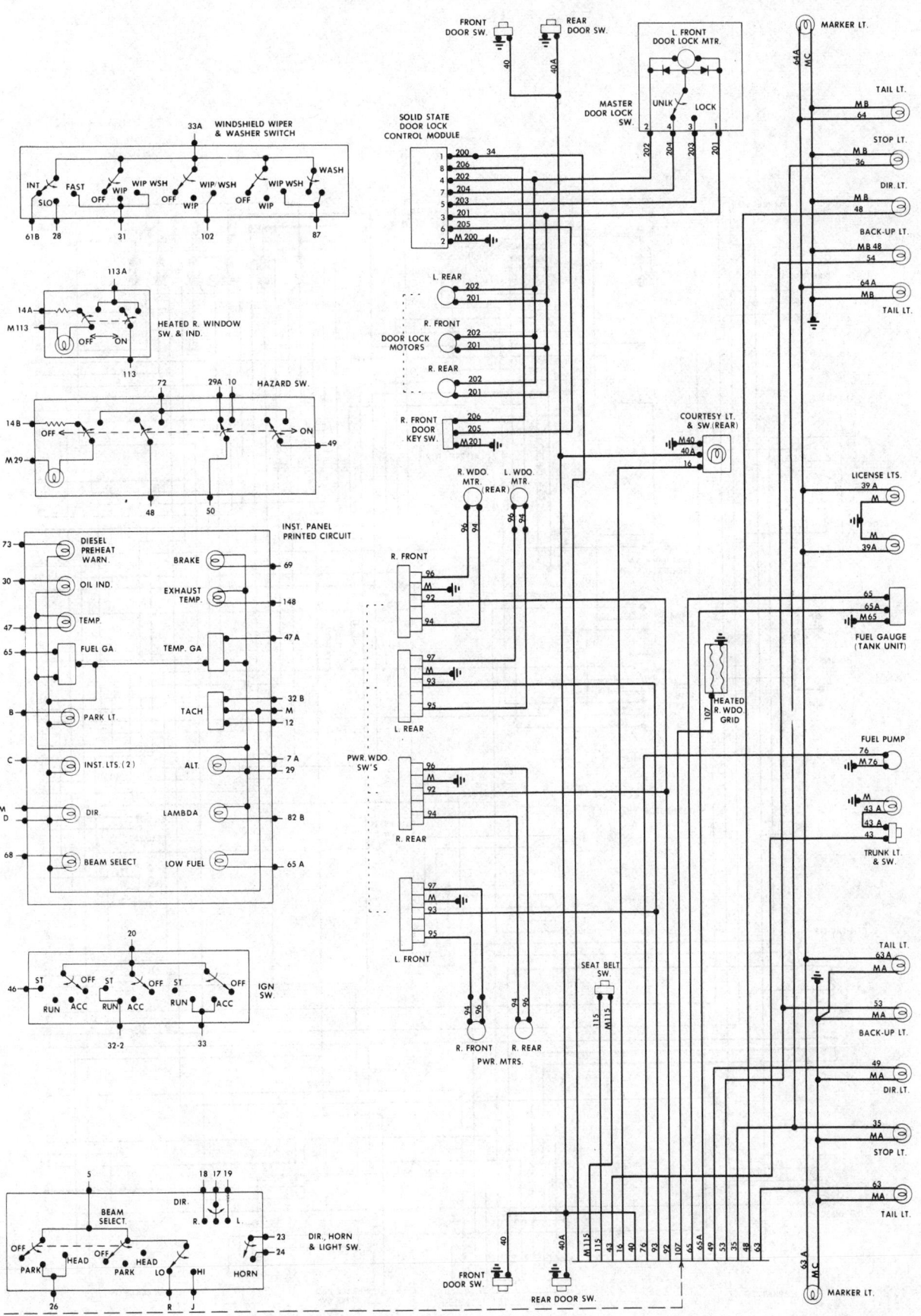

ENGINE COMPARTMENT

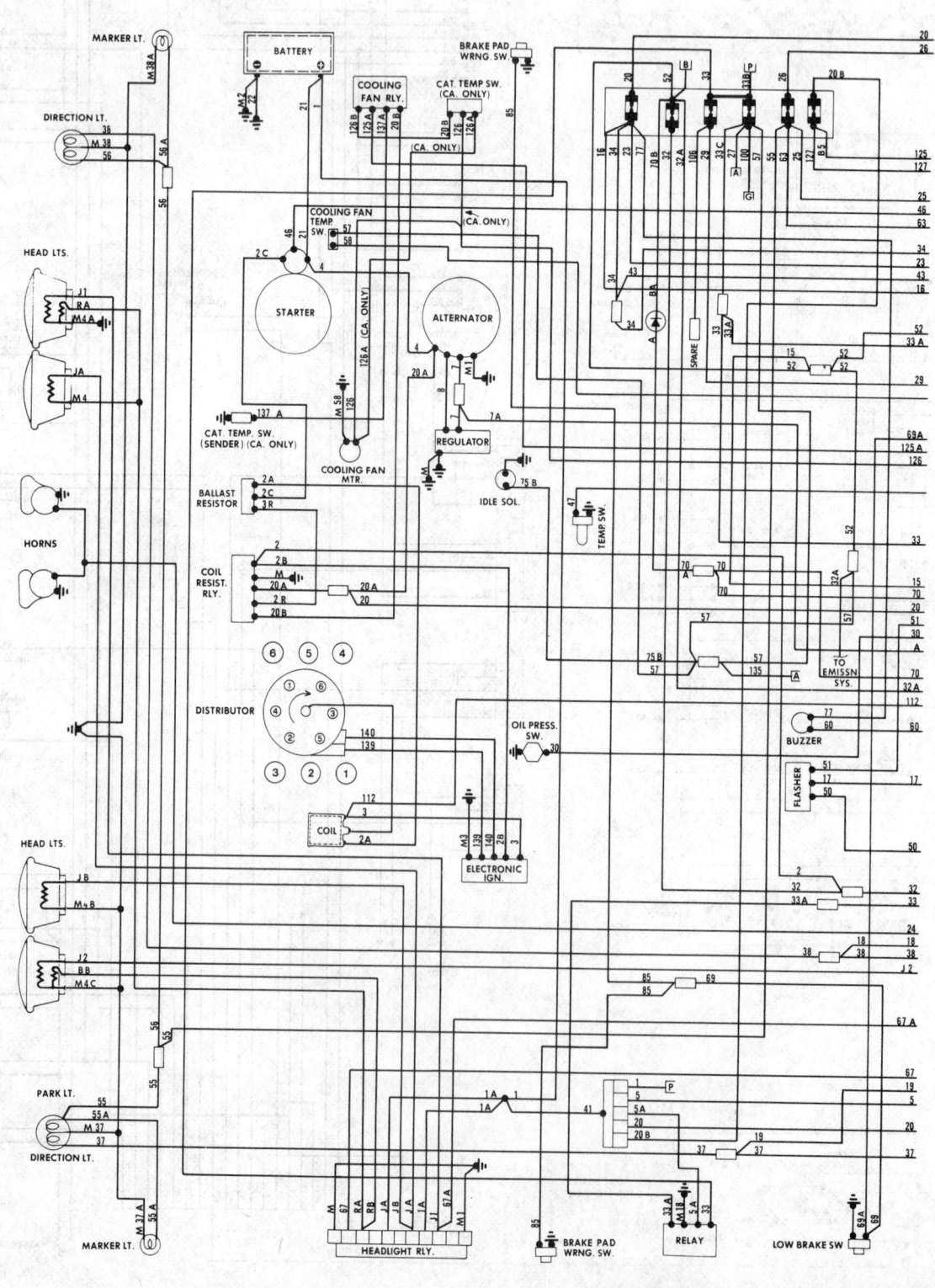

FUSE BLOCK, INSTRUMENT PANEL & REAR COMPARTMENT

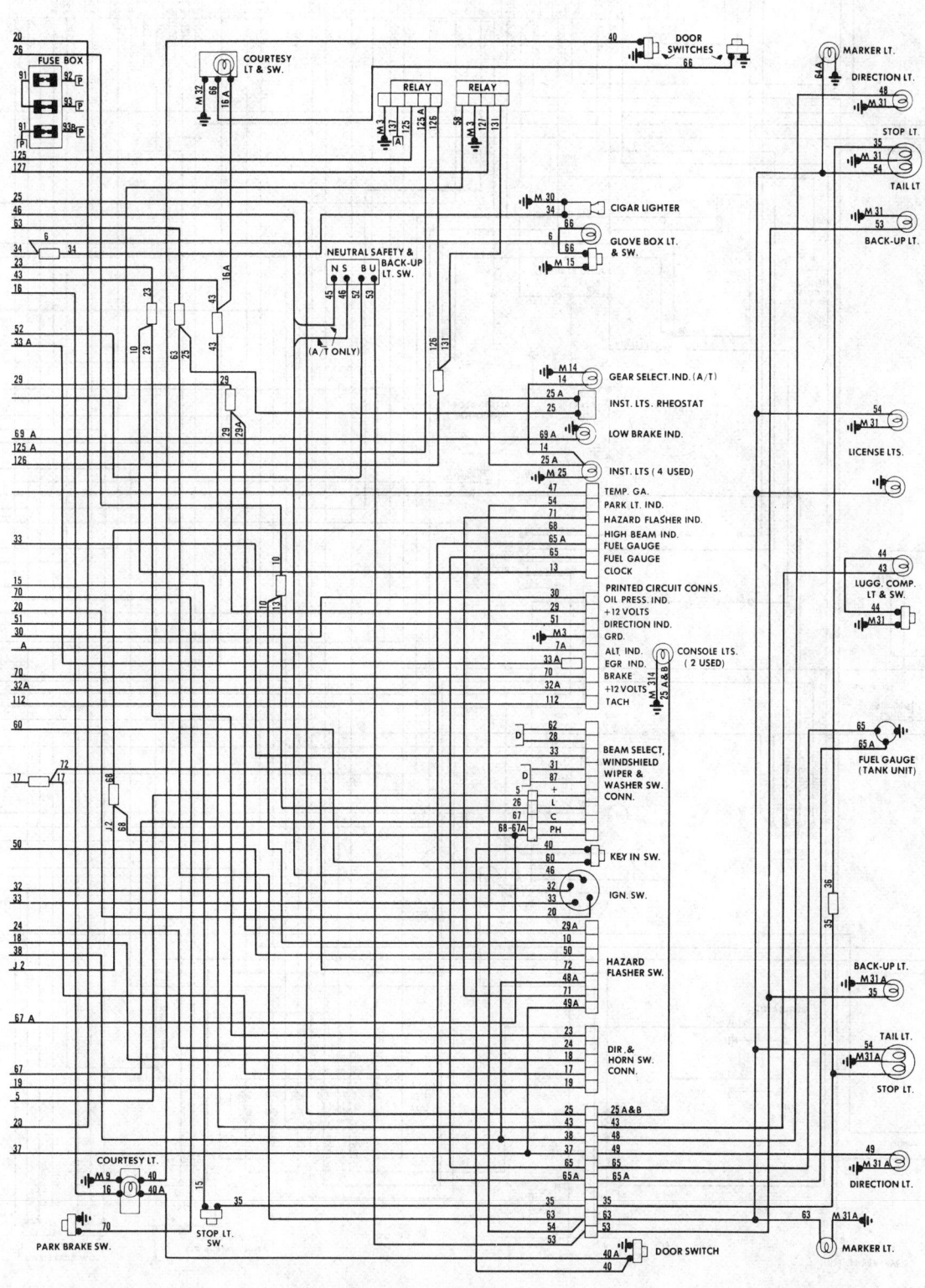

Fuse Block & Underdash

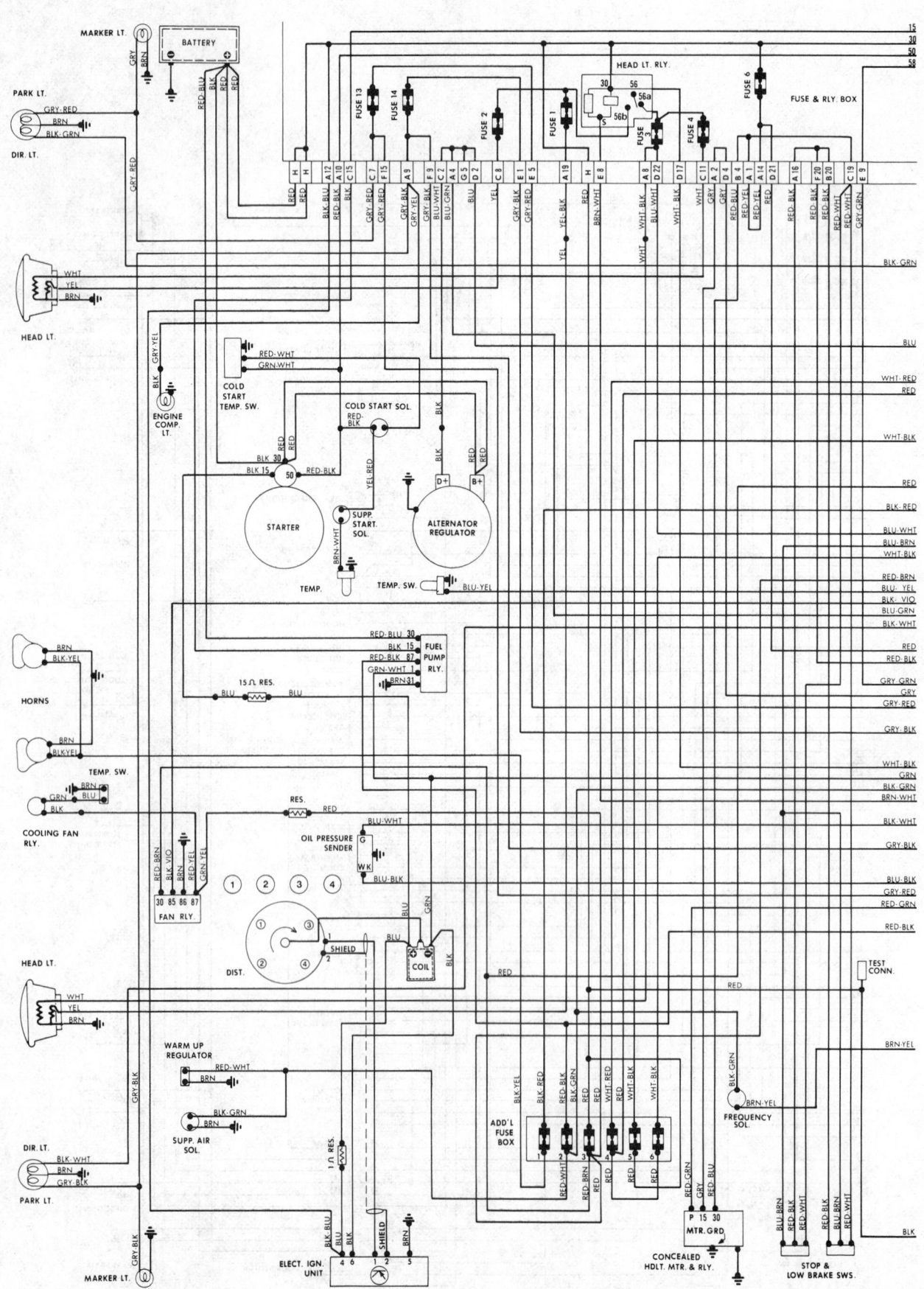

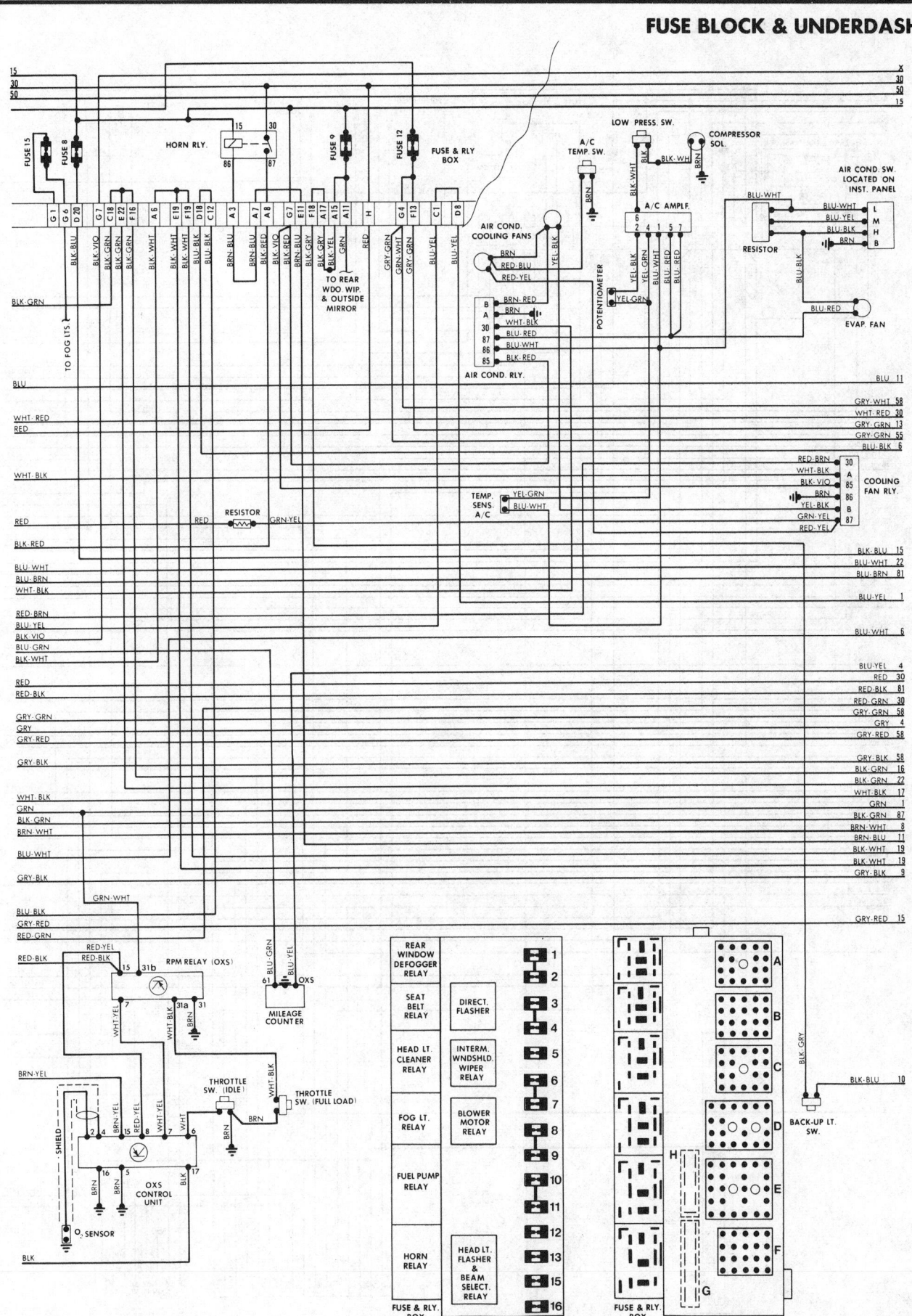

1980 Porsche

UNDERDASH & FUSE BLOCK

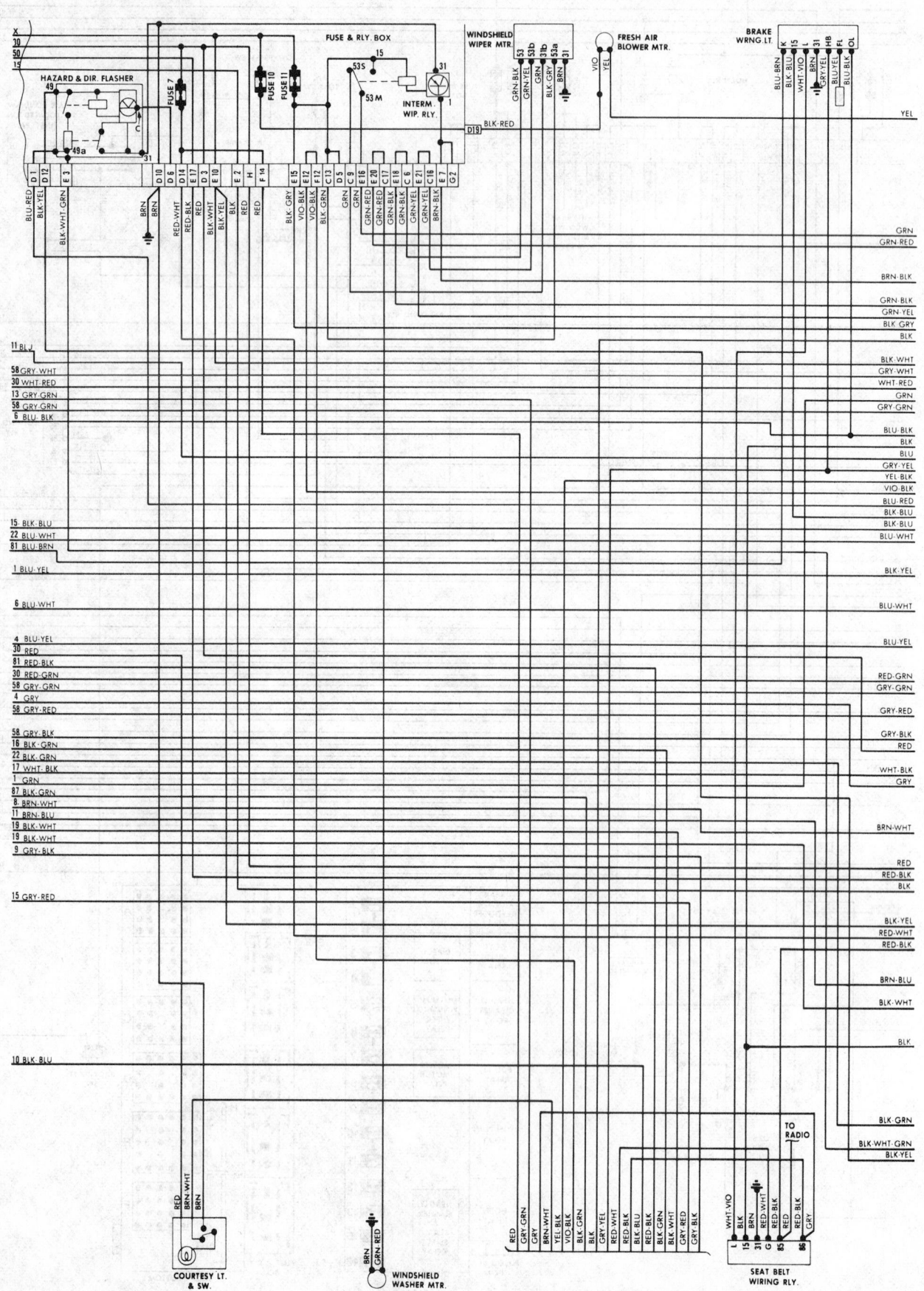

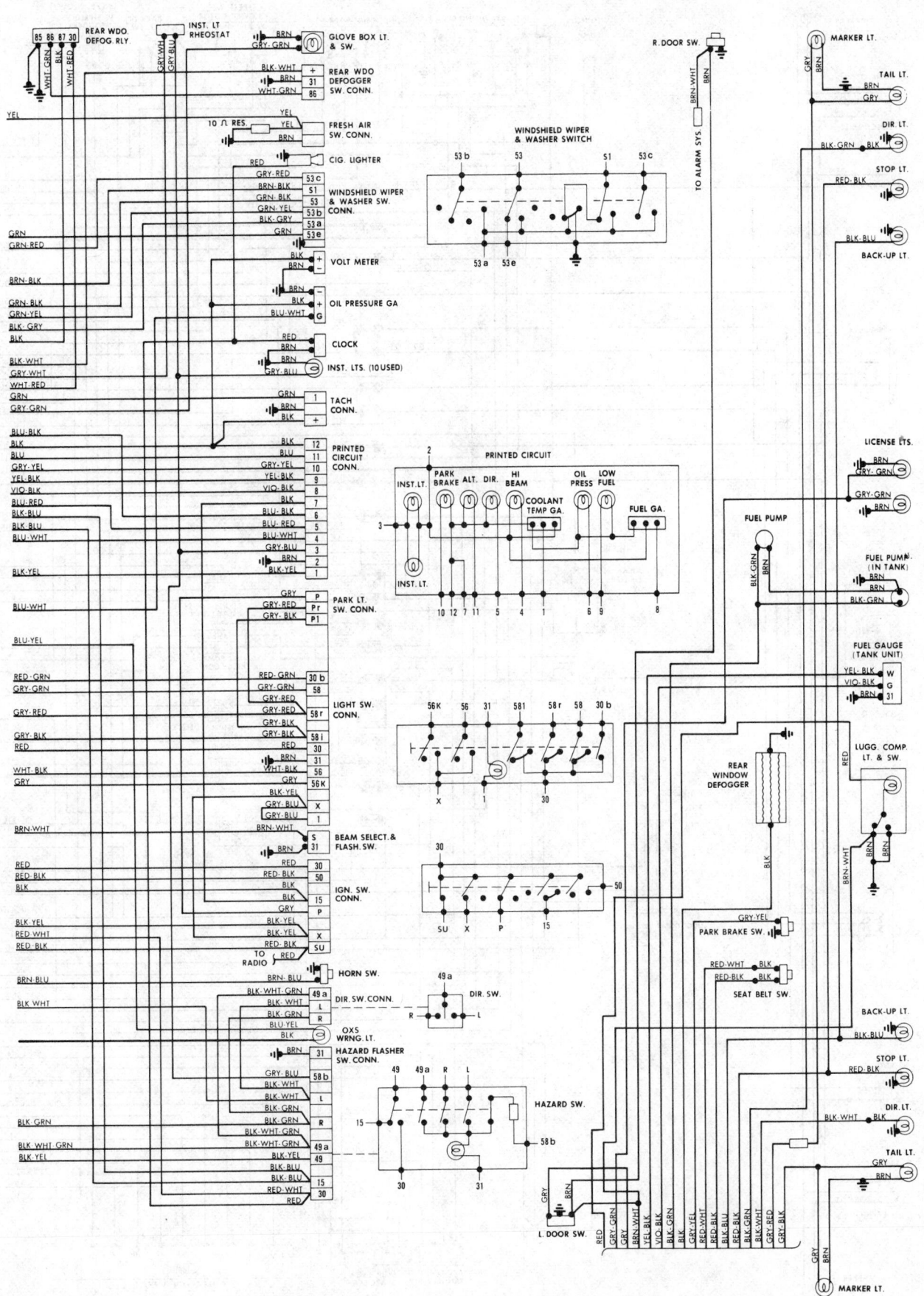

1980 Porsche

FRONT COMPARTMENT & FUSE BLOCK

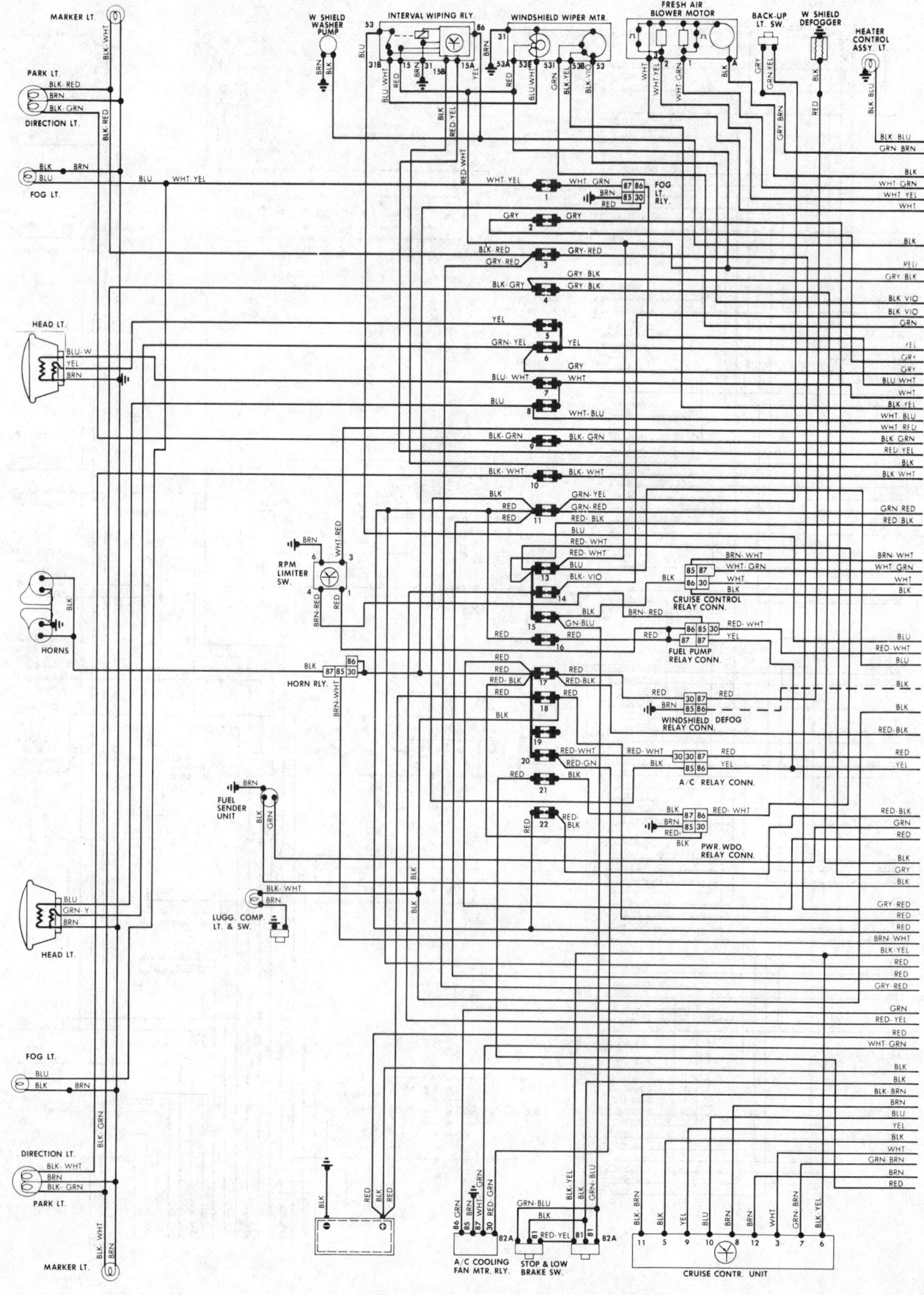

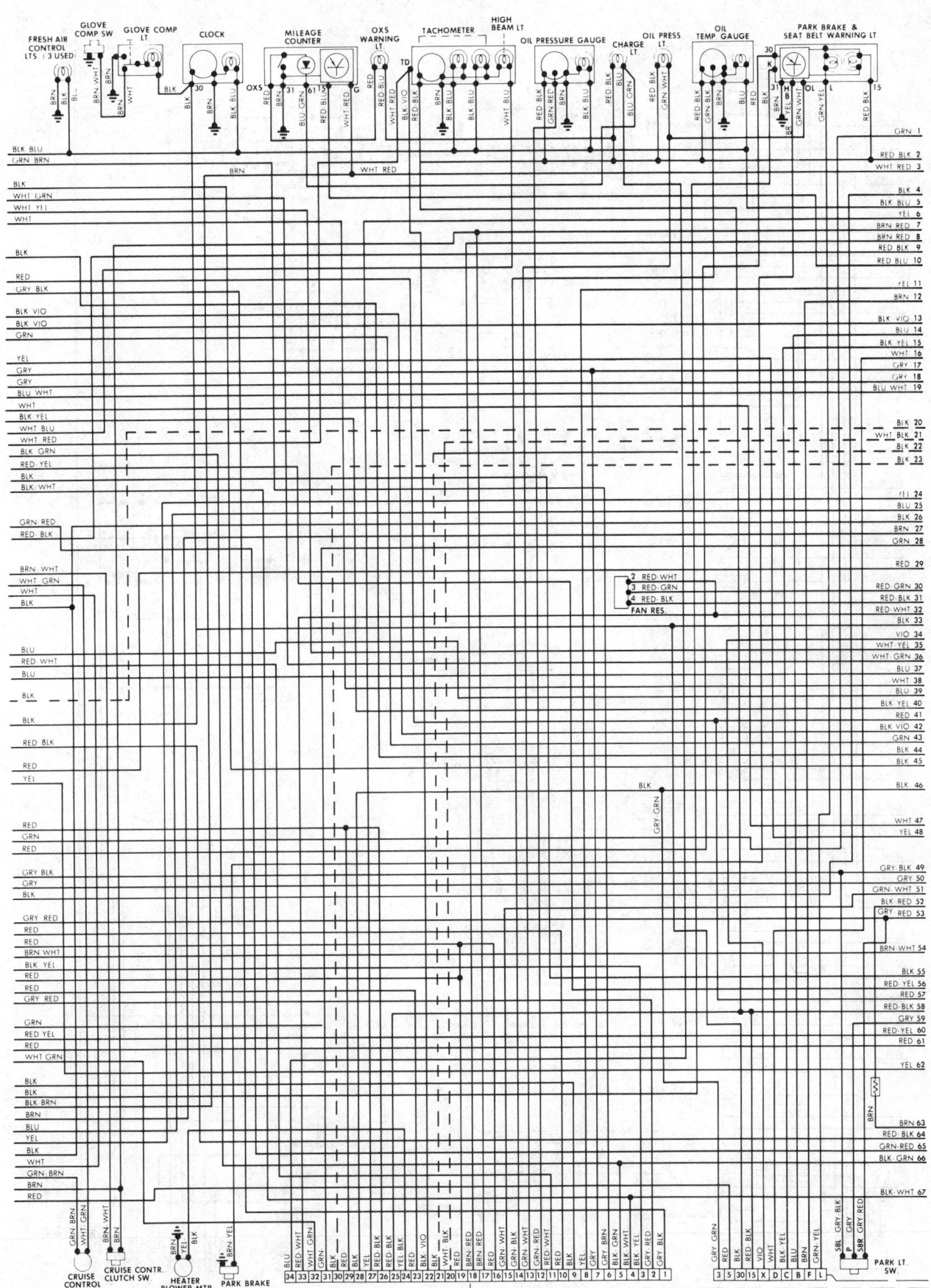

INSTRUMENT PANEL & ACCESSORIES

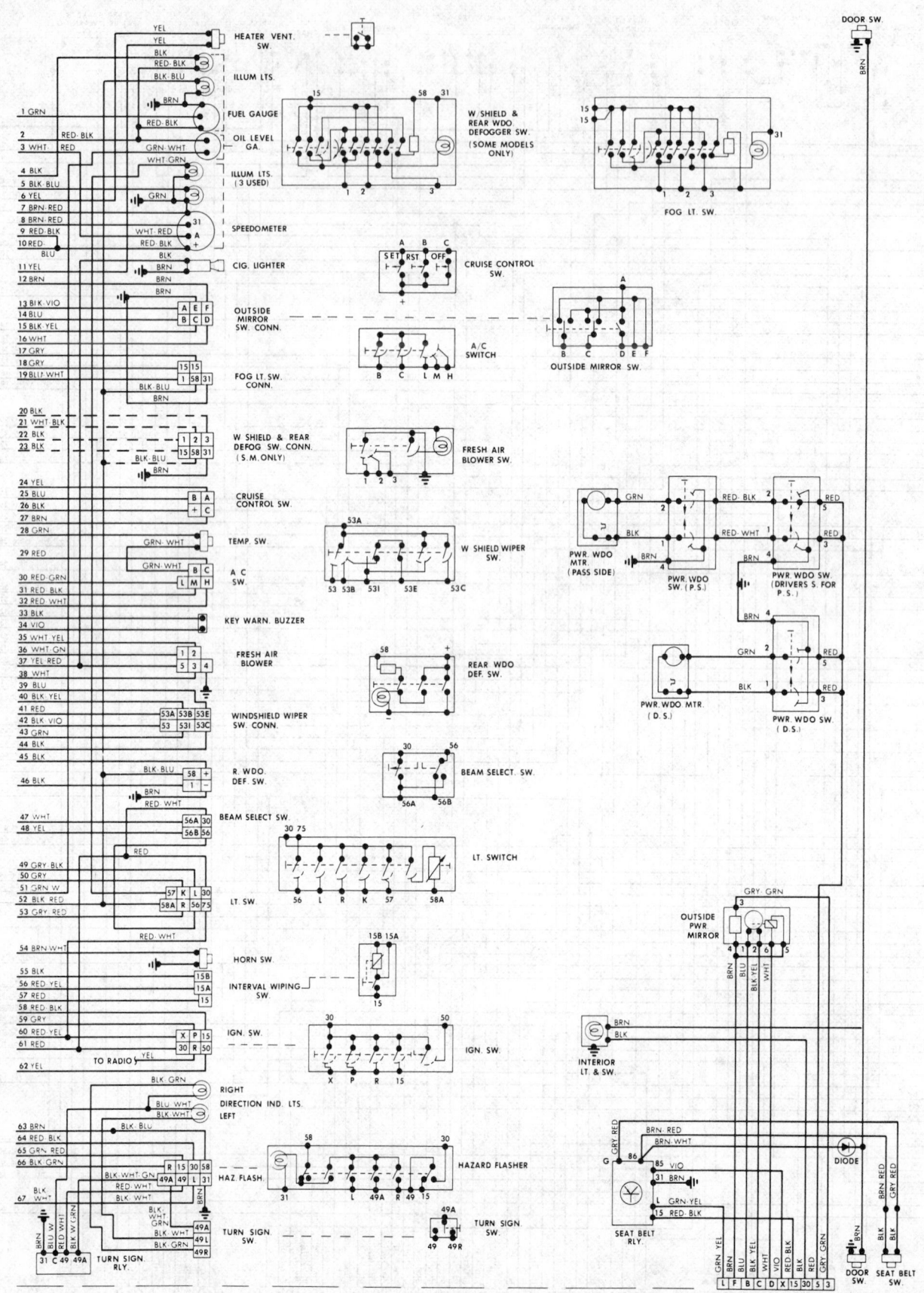

ENGINE COMPARTMENT & REAR COMPARTMENT

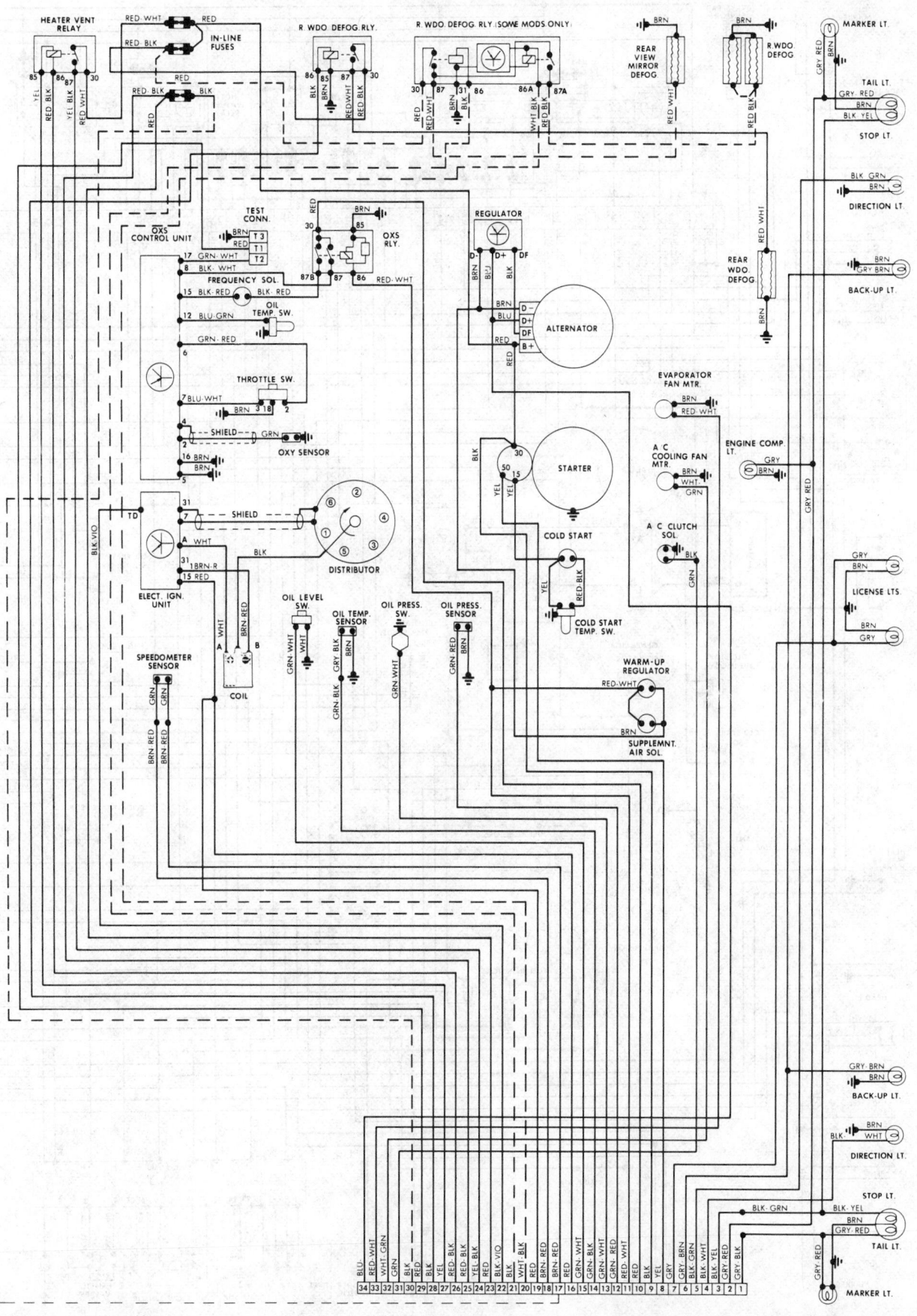

1980 Porsche

ENGINE COMPARTMENT & FUSE BLOCK

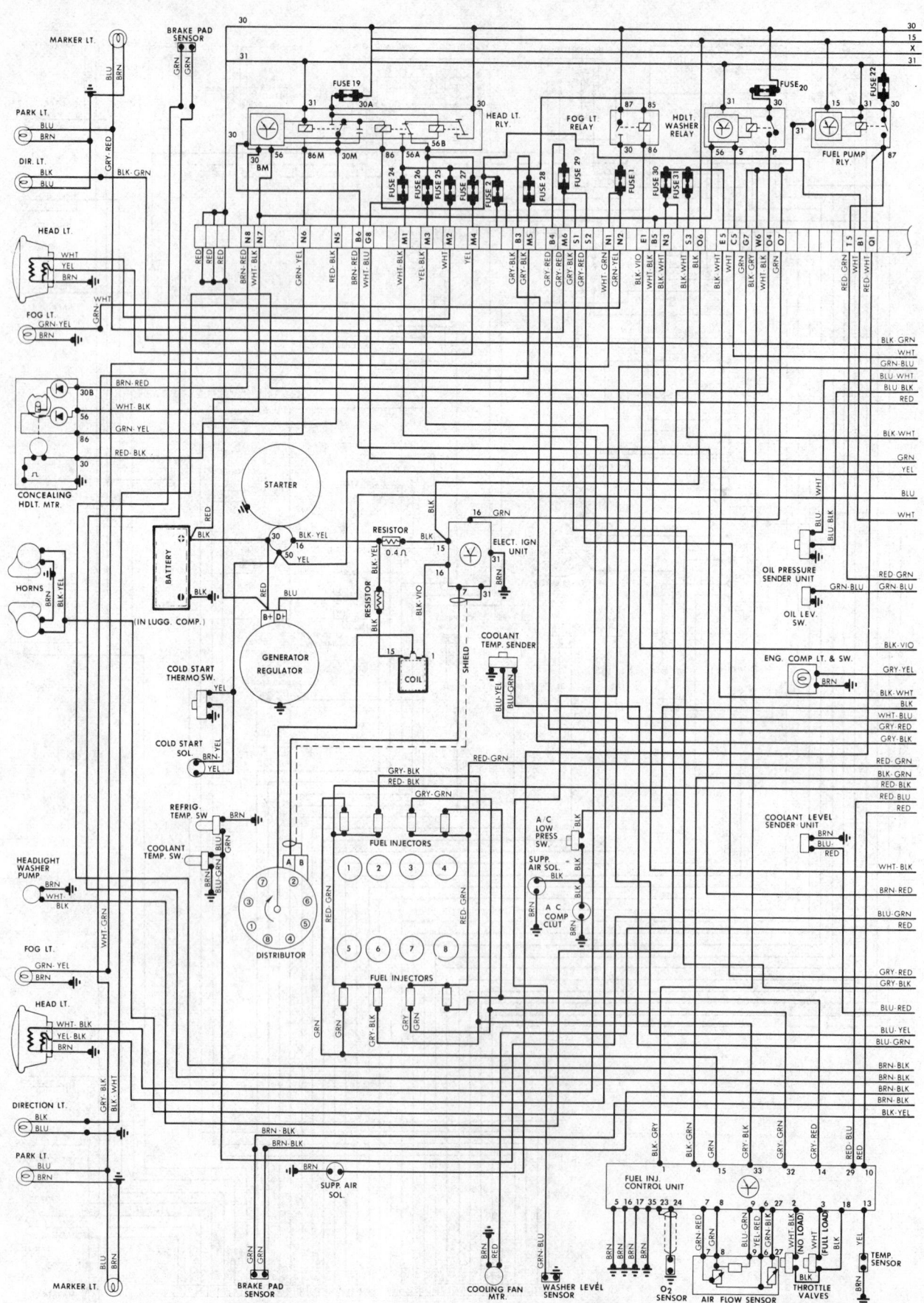

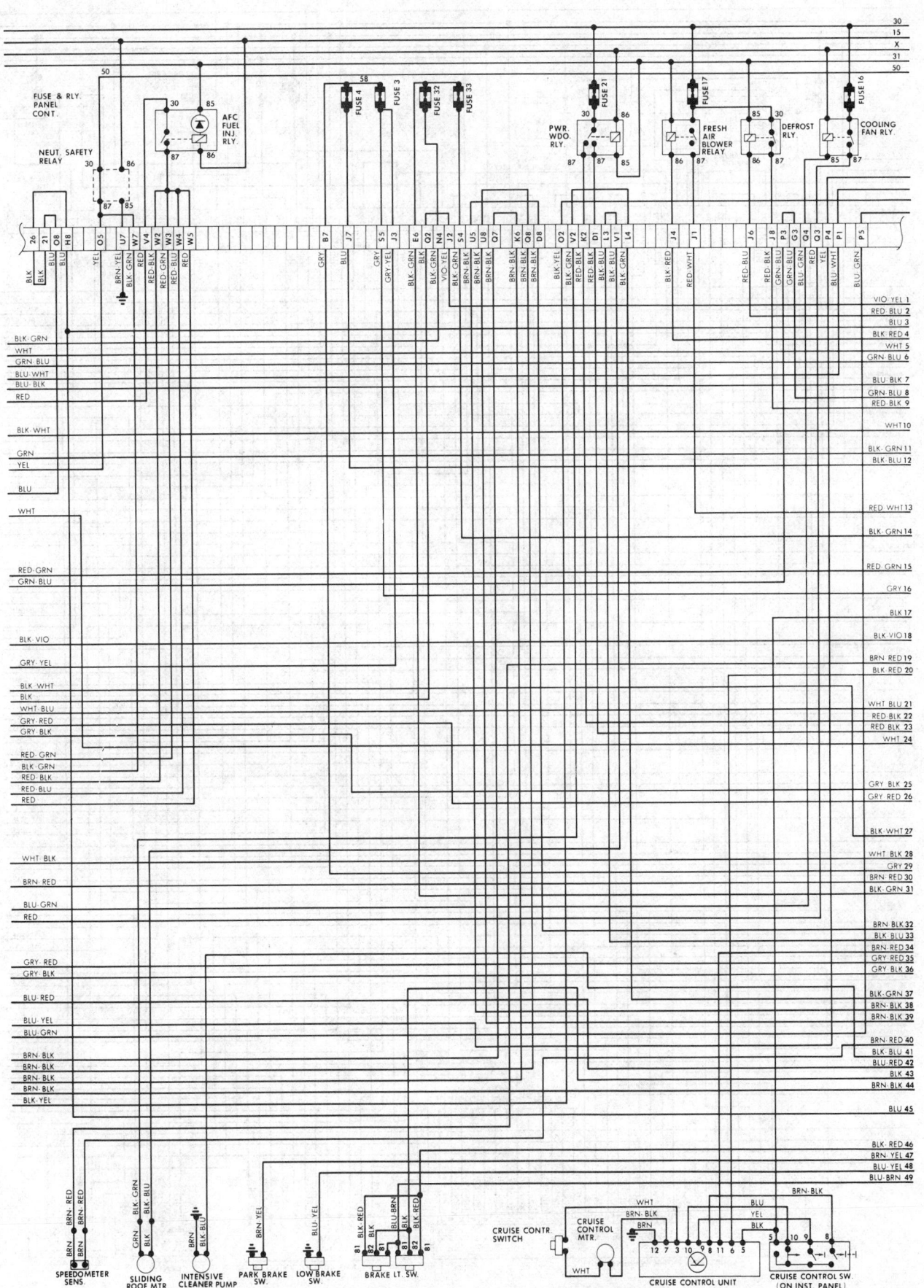

FUSE BLOCK

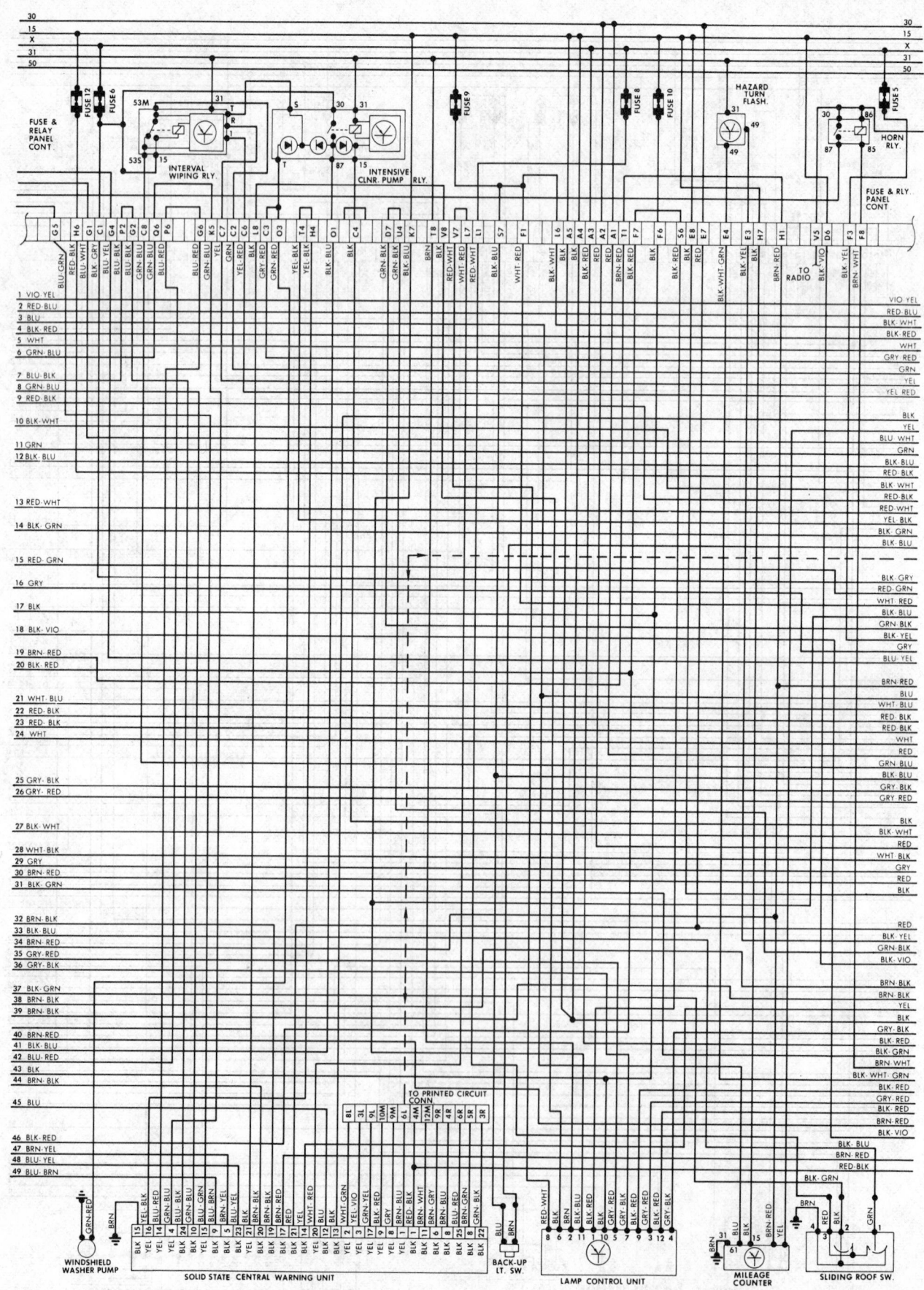

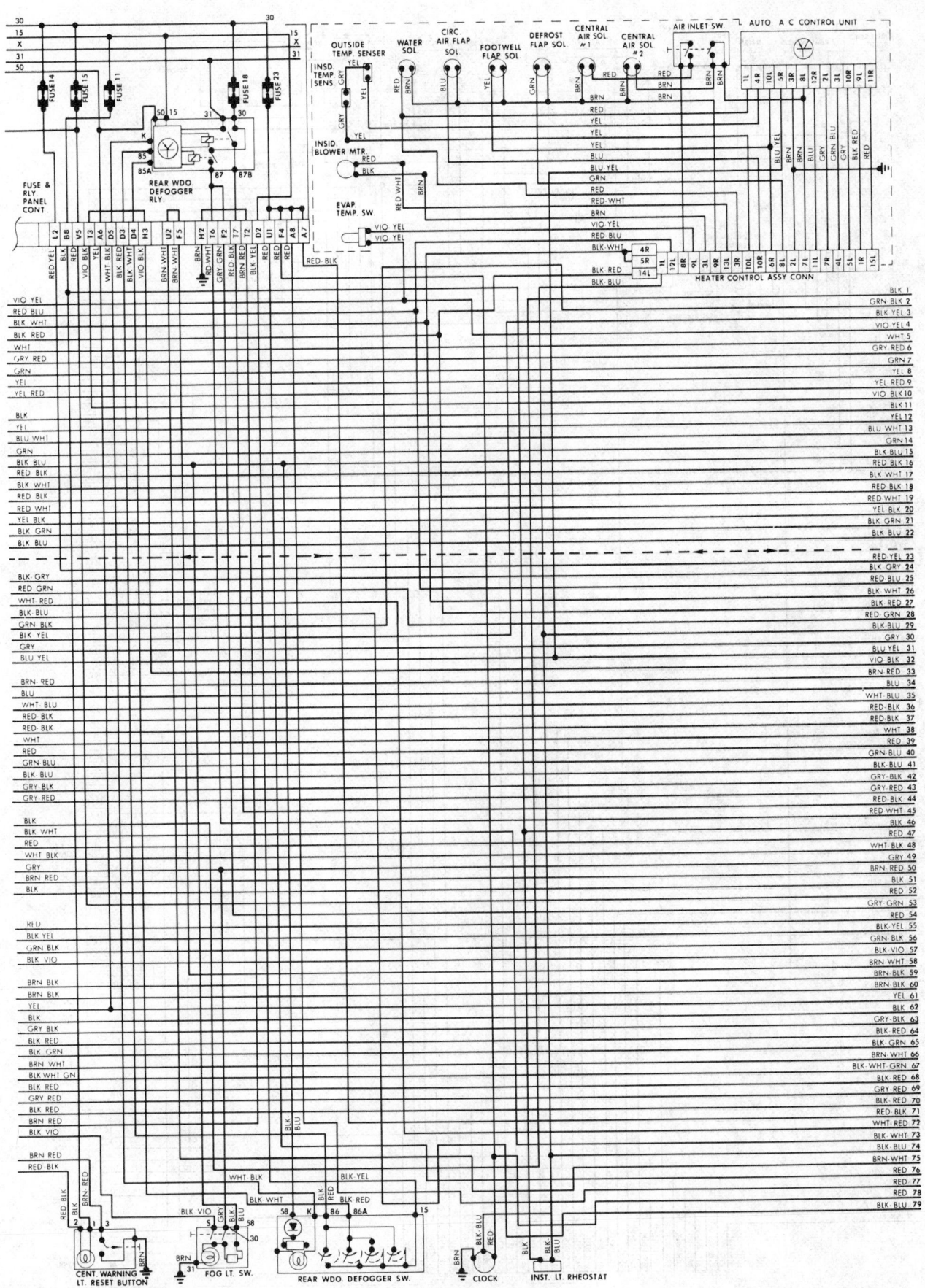

1980 Porsche

INSTRUMENT PANEL

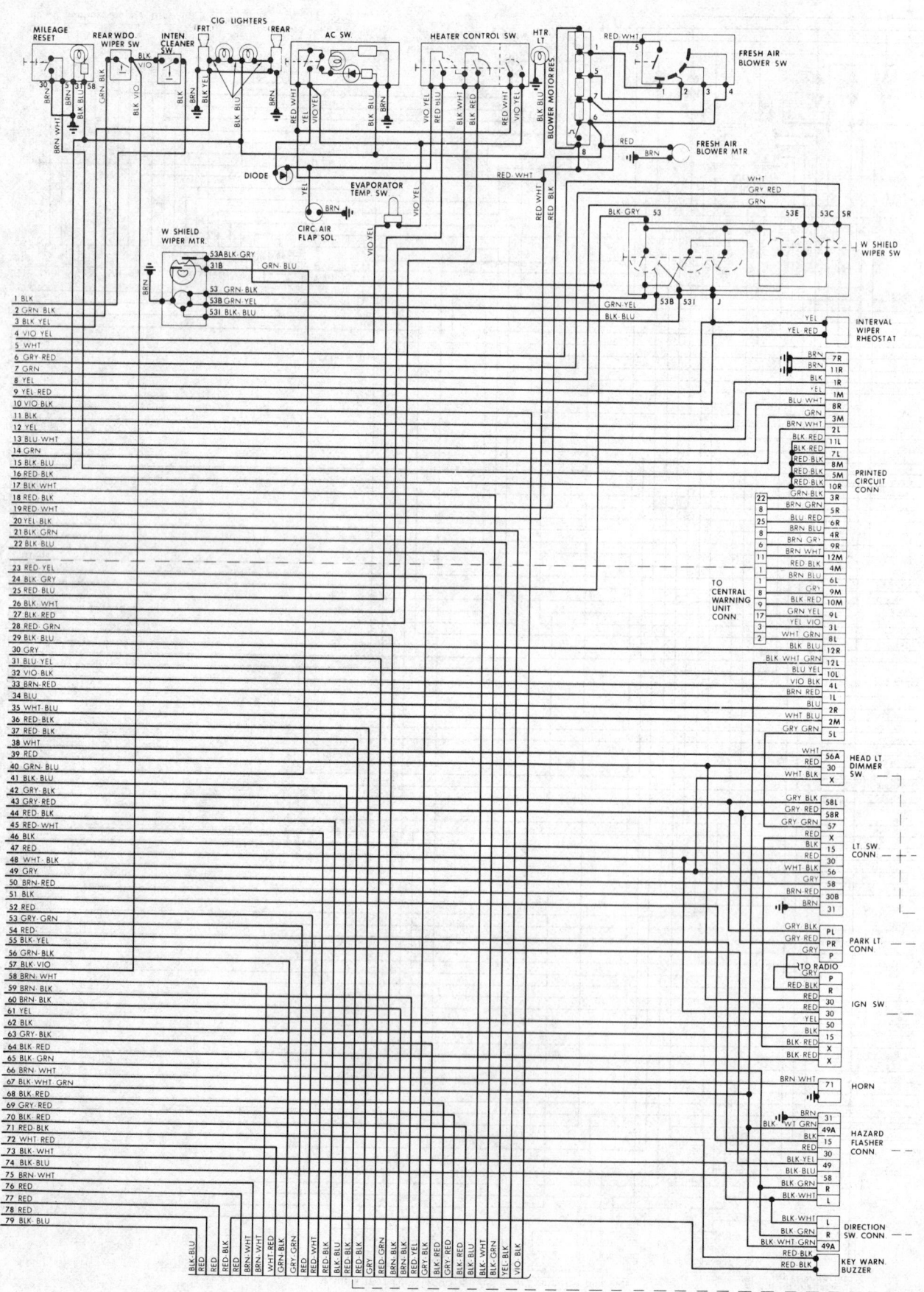

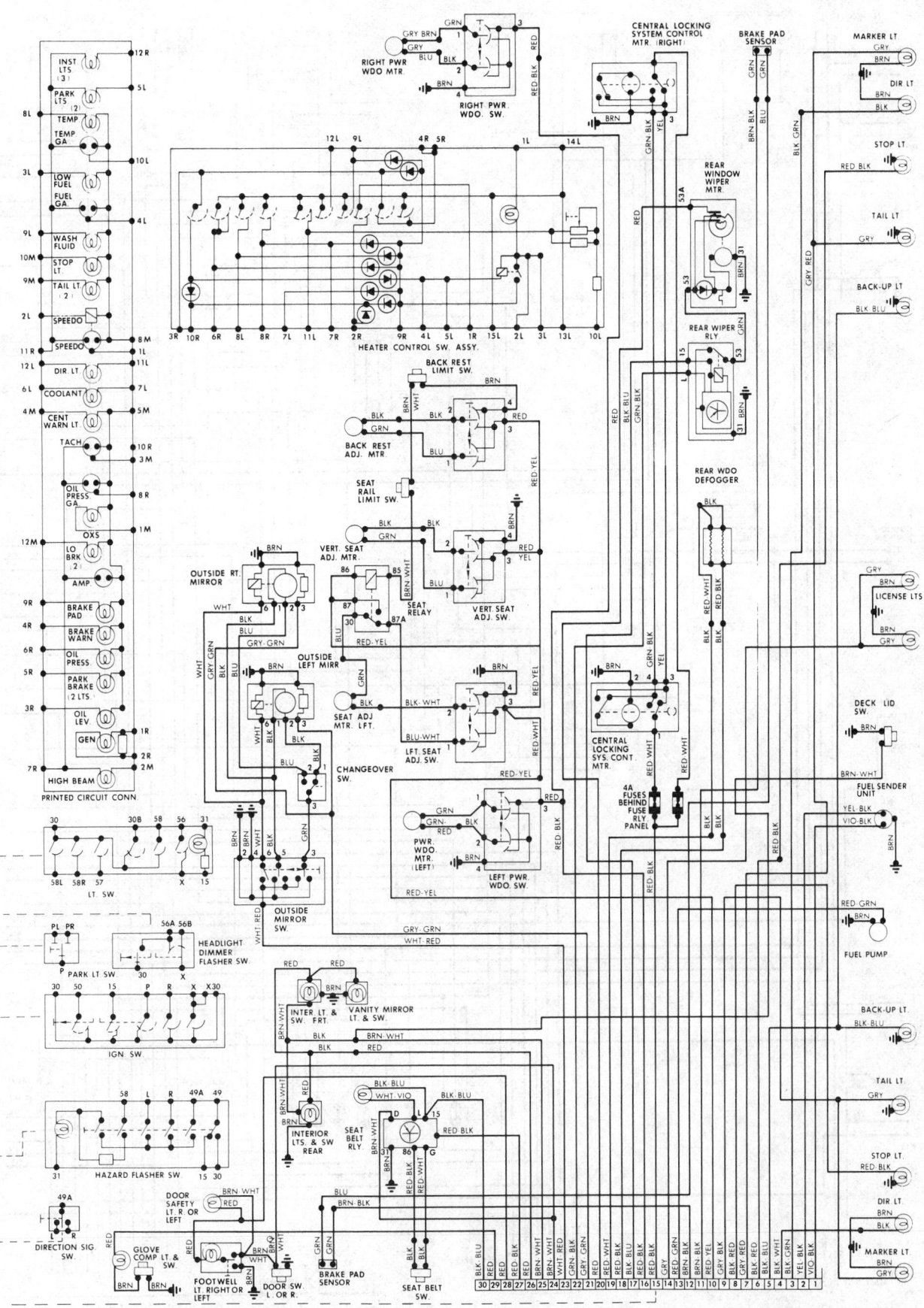

1980 Renault

ENGINE COMPARTMENT & FUSE BLOCK

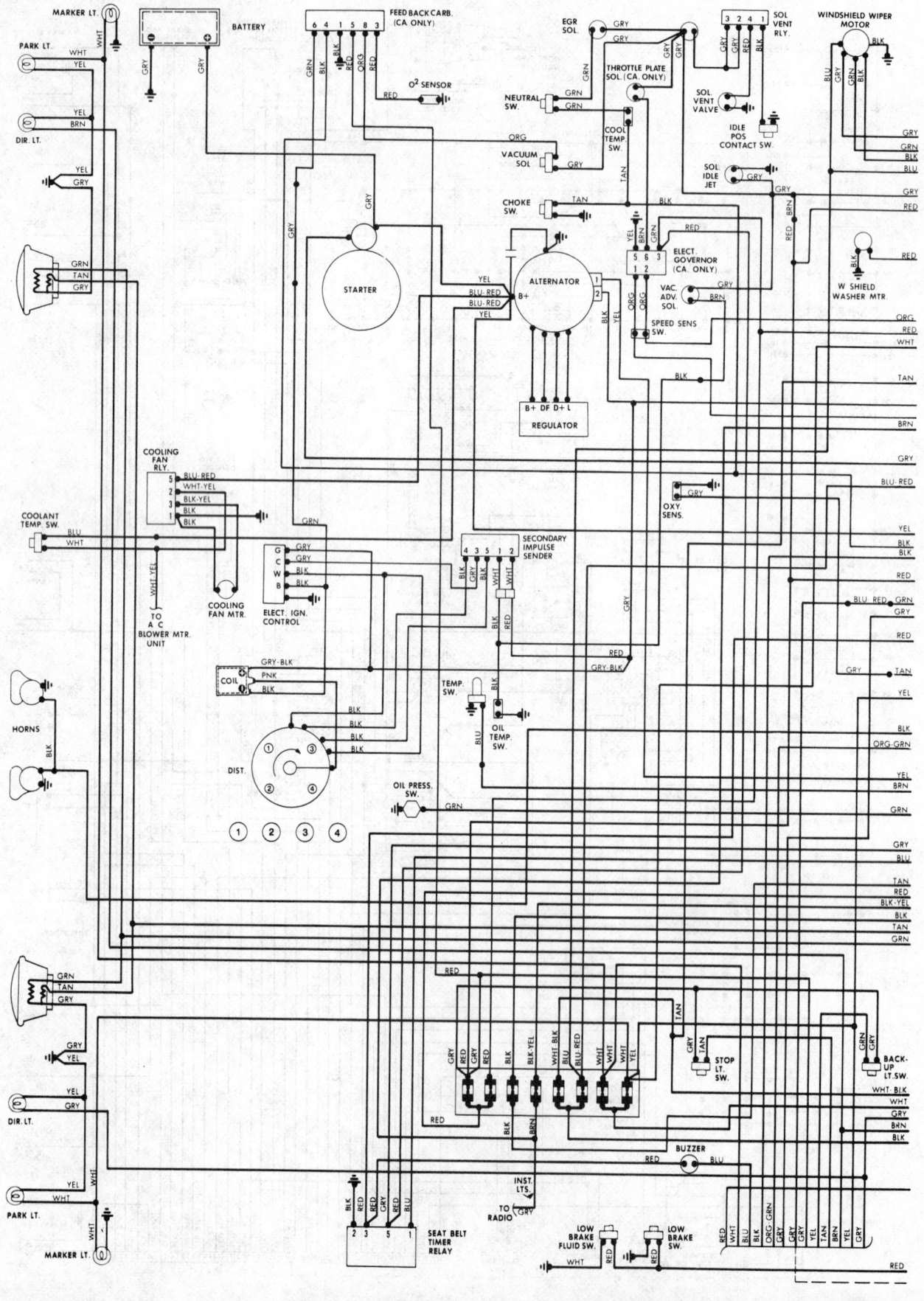

INSTRUMENT PANEL & REAR COMPARTMENT

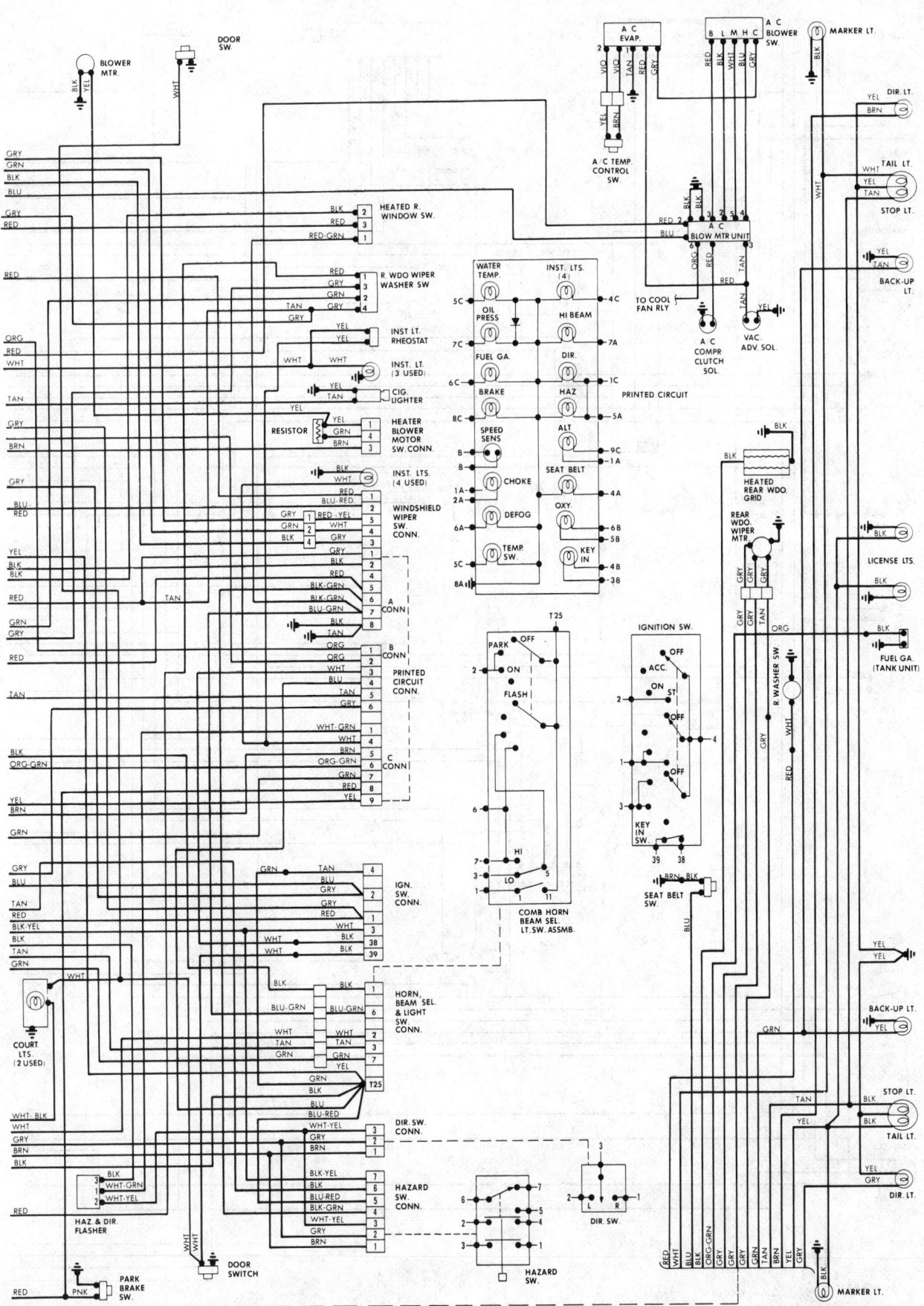

ENGINE COMPARTMENT

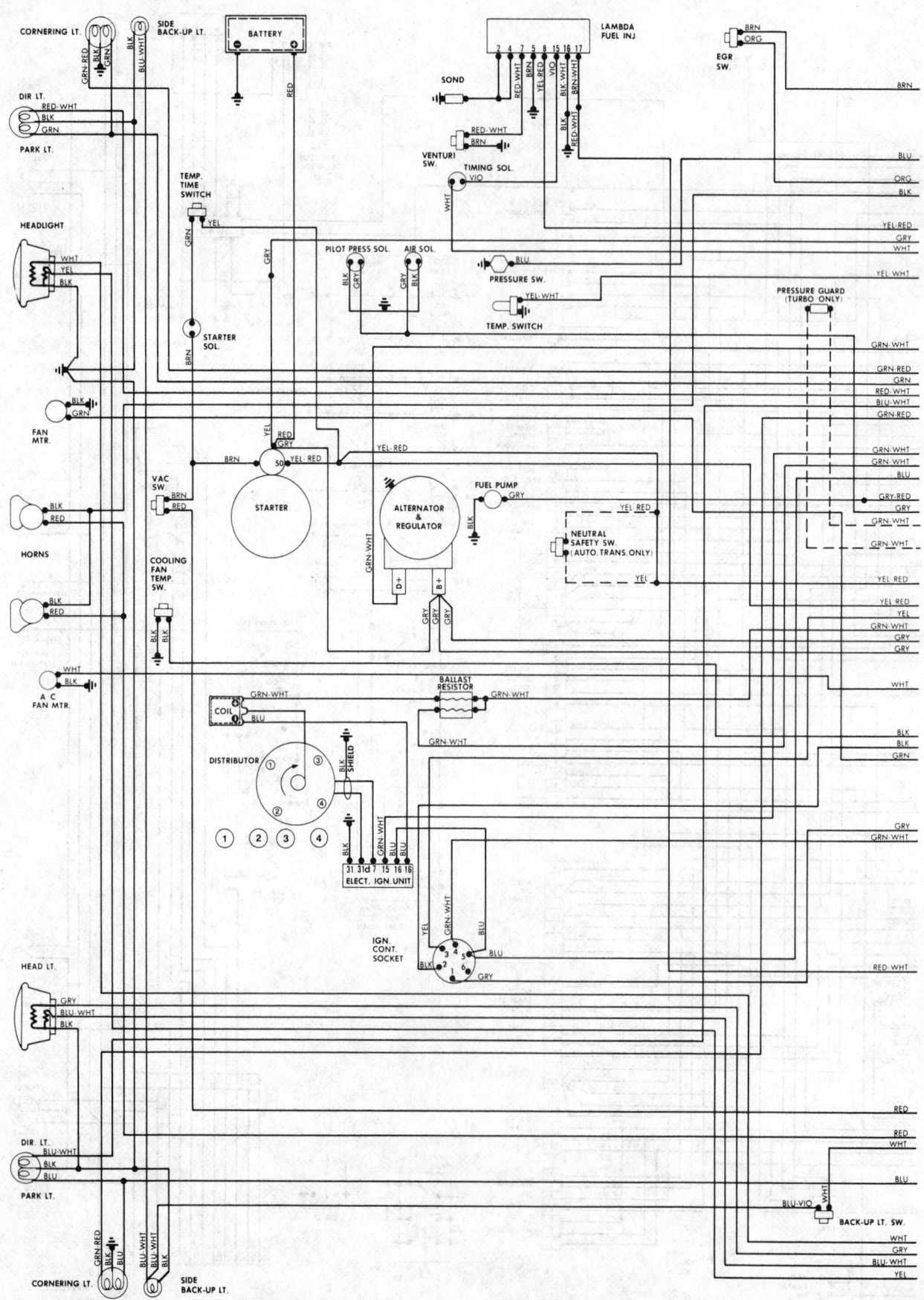

FUSE BLOCK

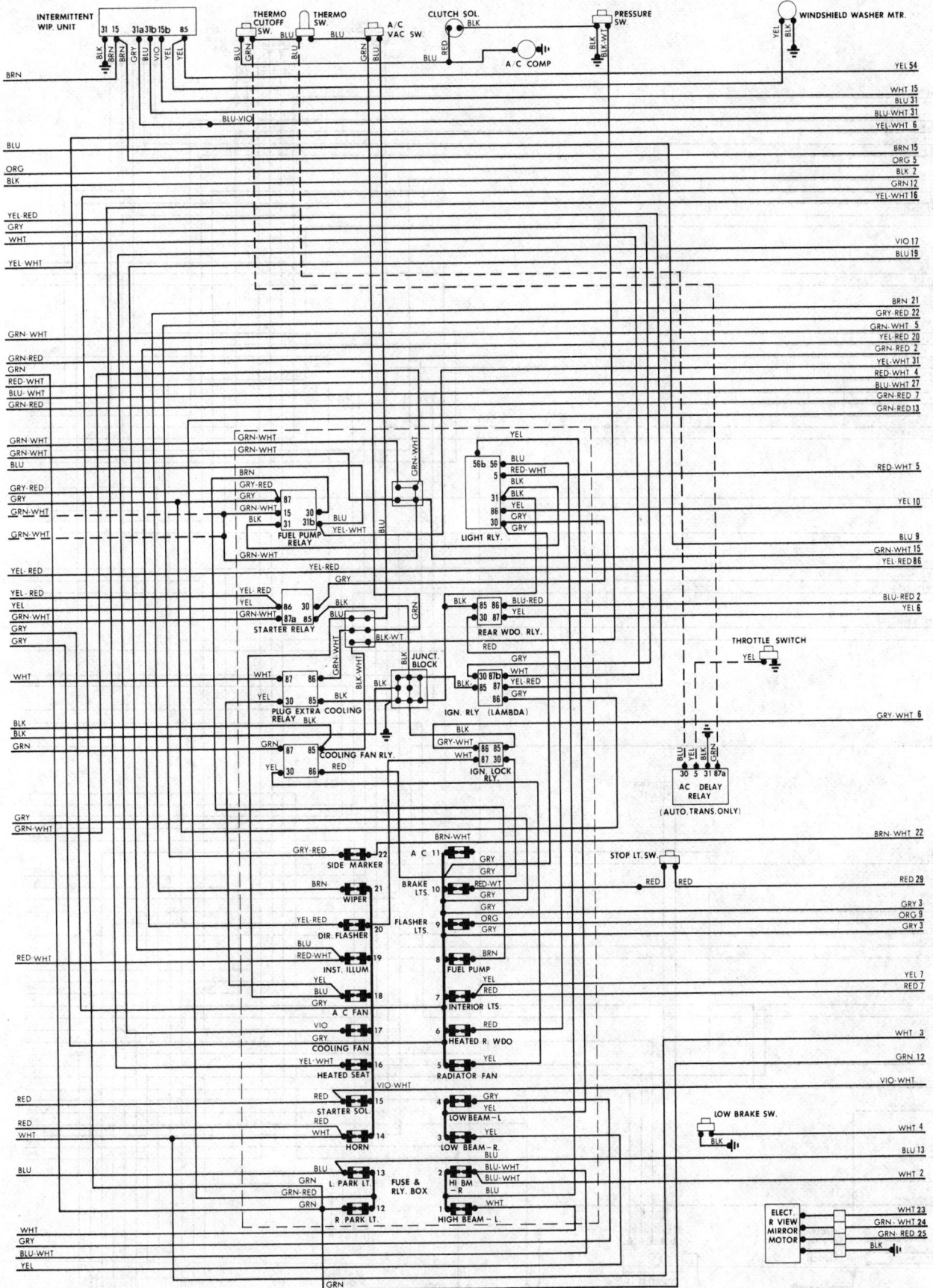

UNDERDASH

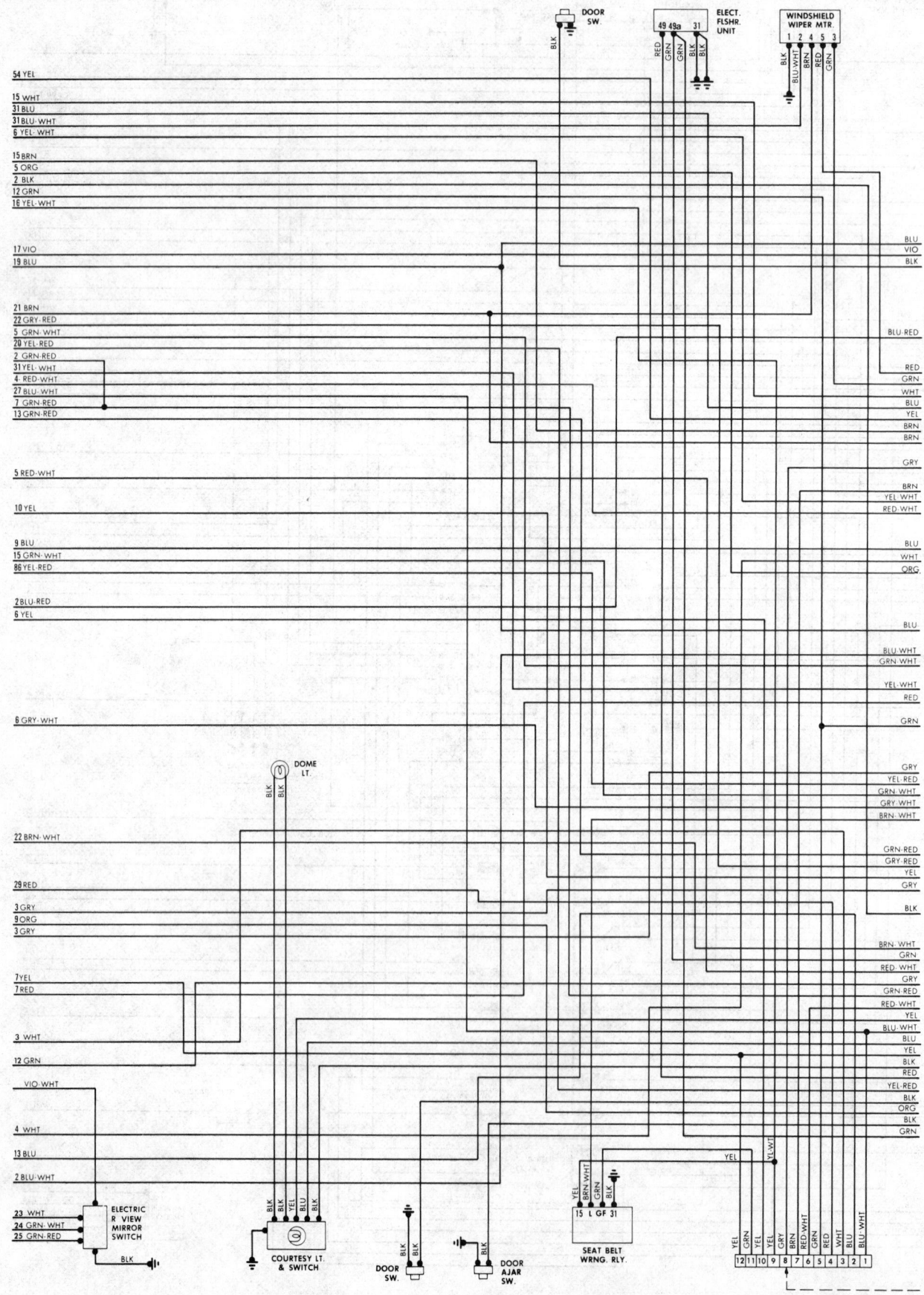

INSTRUMENT PANEL & REAR COMPARTMENT

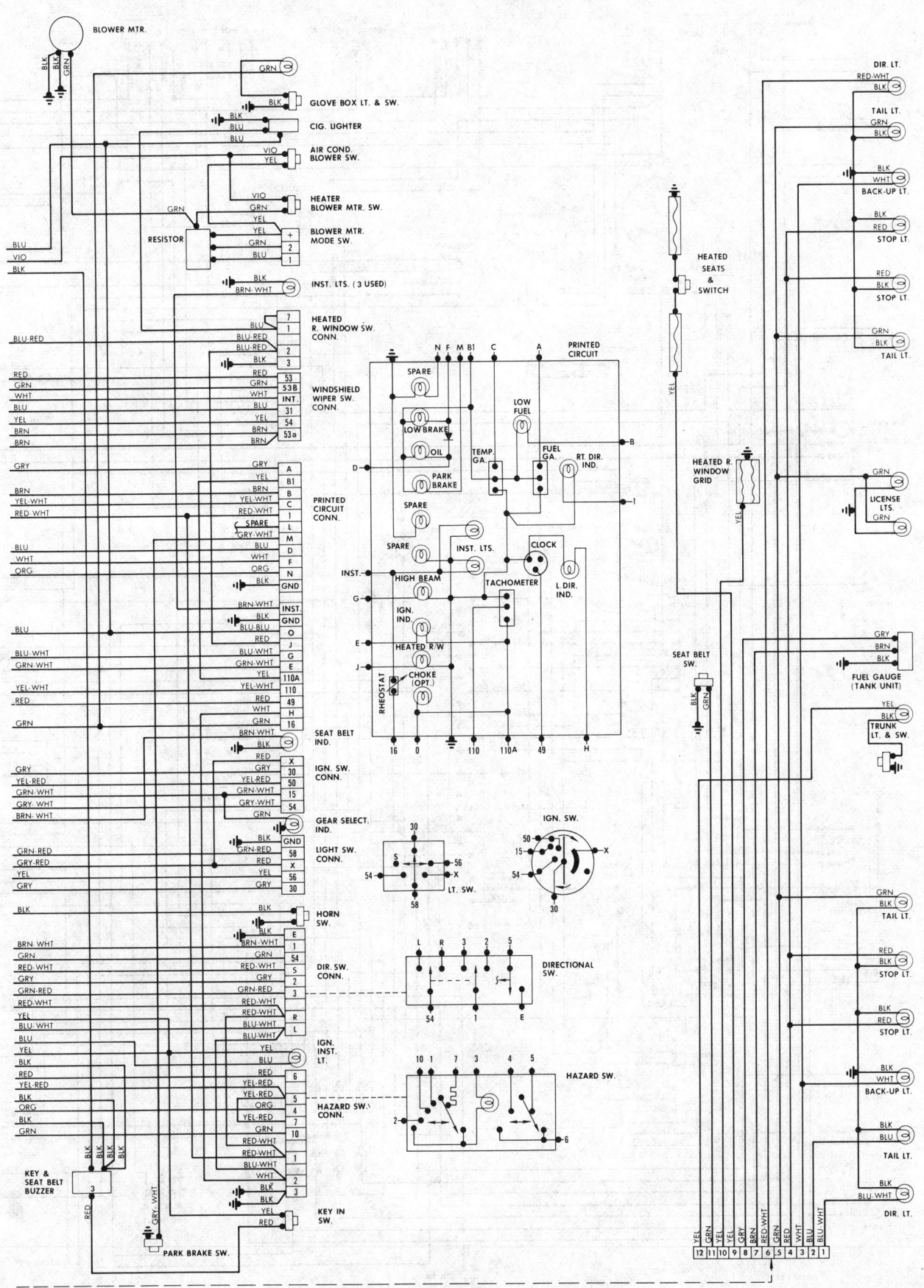

ENGINE COMPARTMENT & FUSE BLOCK

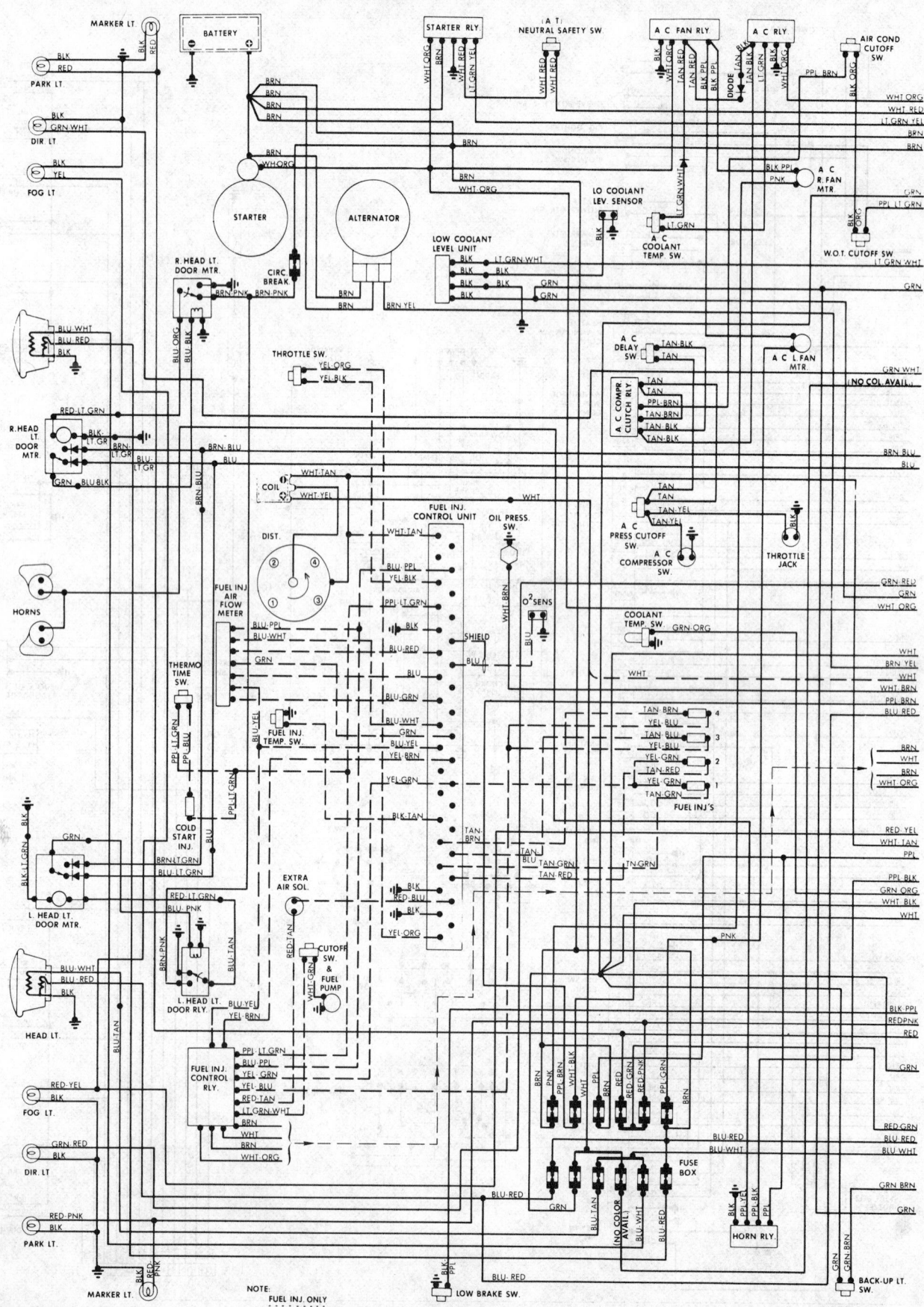

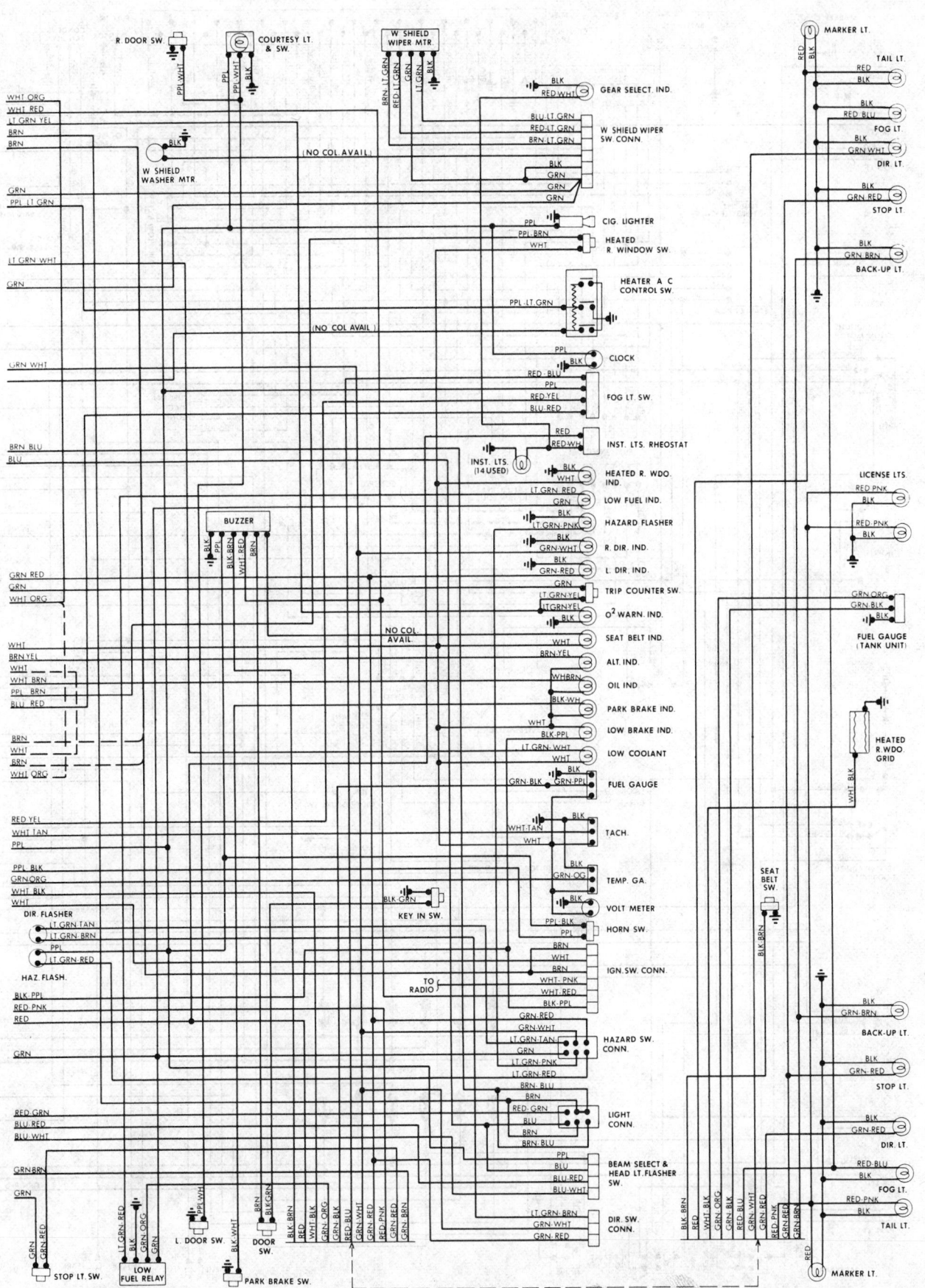

1980 Triumph

ENGINE COMPARTMENT & FUSE BLOCK

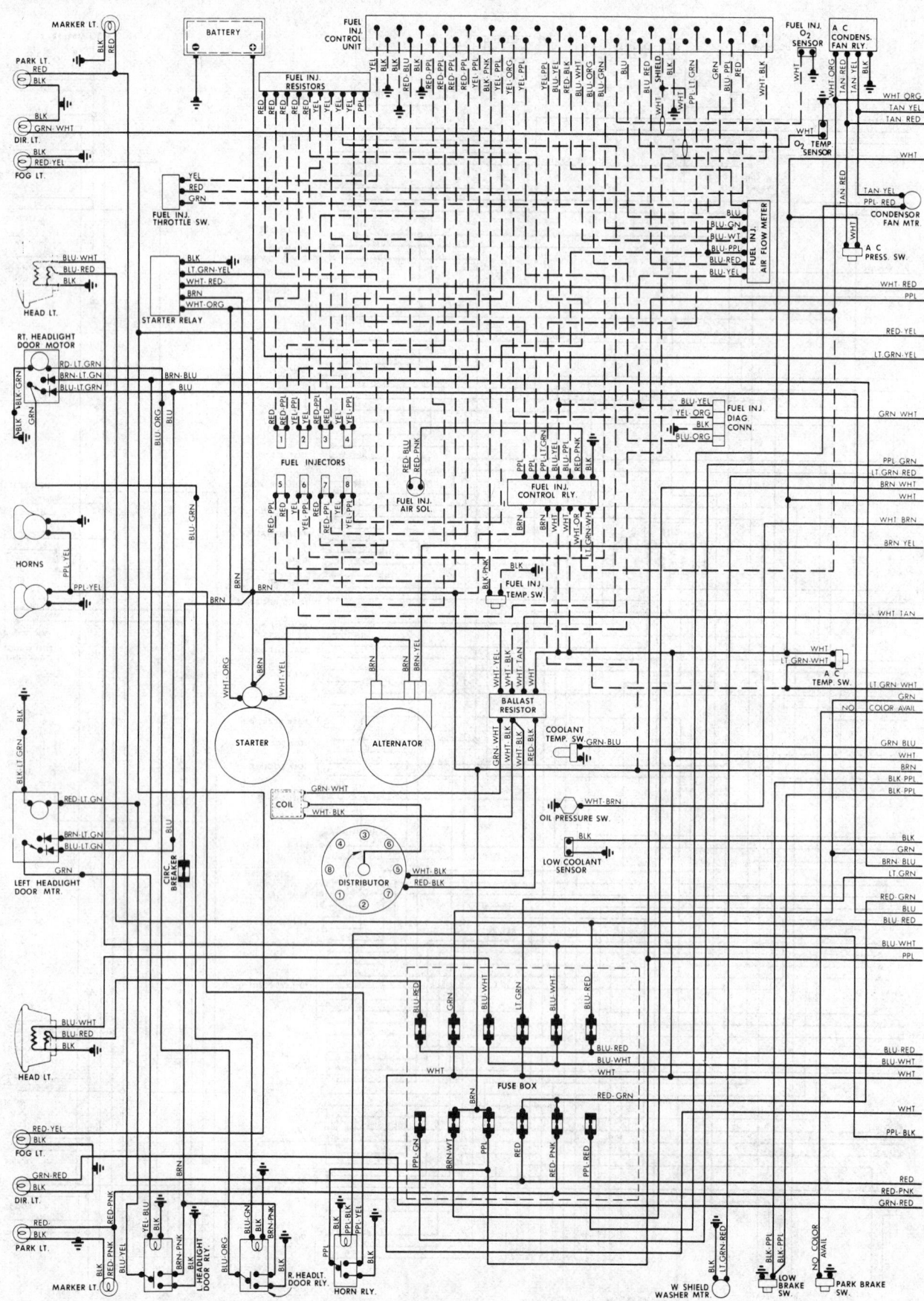

INSTRUMENT PANEL & REAR COMPARTMENT

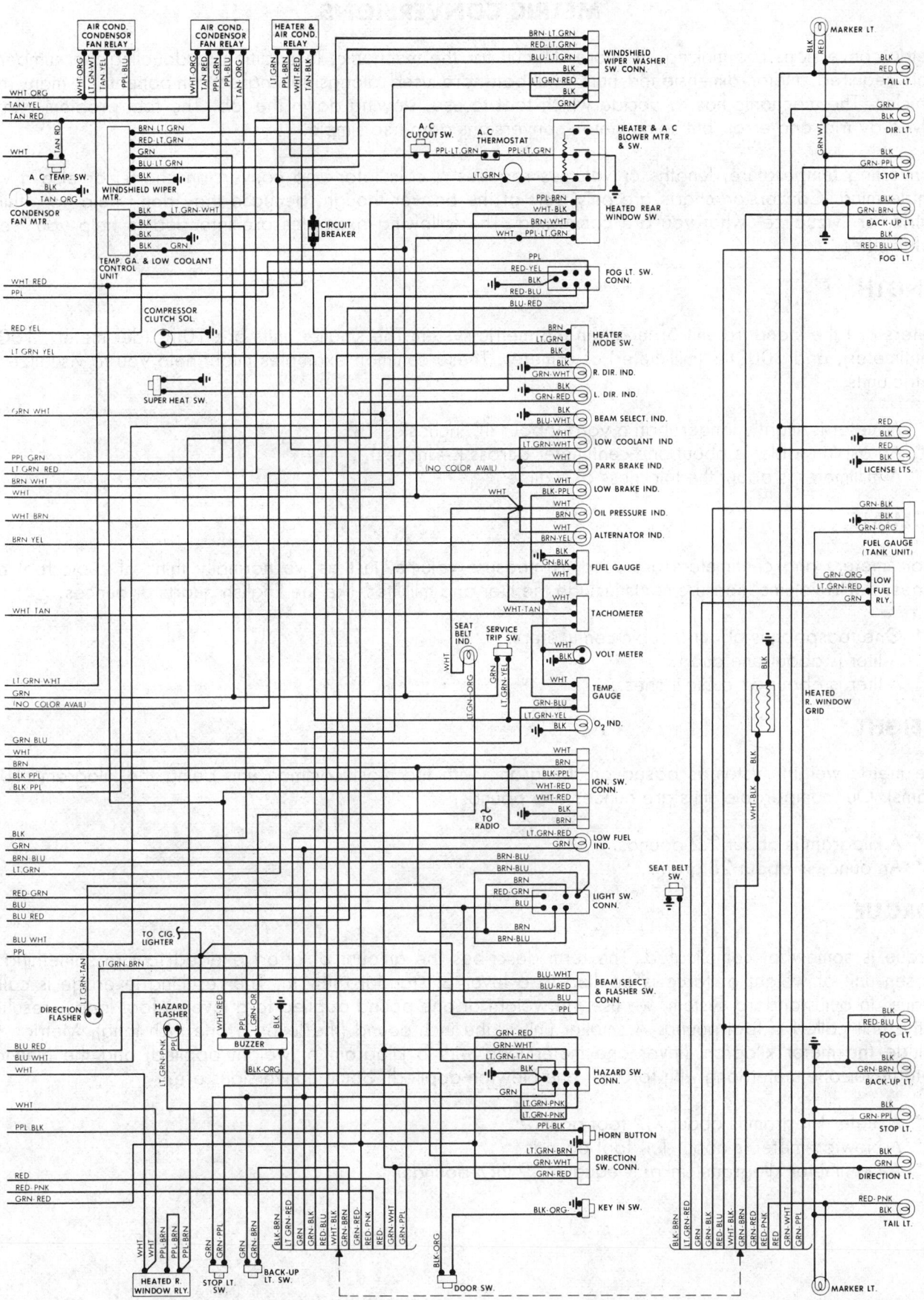

METRIC CONVERSIONS

Metric conversions are making life more difficult for the mechanic. In addition to doubling the number of tools required, metric-dimensioned nuts and bolts are used alongside English components in many new vehicles. The mechanic has to decide which tool to use, slowing down the job. The tool problem can be solved by trial and error, but some metric conversions aren't so simple.

Converting temperature, lengths or volumes requires a calculator and conversion charts, or else a very nimble mind. Conversion charts are only part of the answer though, becuase they don't help you "think" metric, or "vizualize" what you are converting. The following examples are intended to help you "see" metric sizes:

LENGTH

Meters are the standard unit of length in the metric system. The smaller units are 10ths (decimeter), 100ths (centimeter), and 1000ths (millimeter) of a meter. These common examples might help you to visualize the metric units:

* A meter is slightly longer than a yard (about 40 inches).
* An aspirin tablet is about one centimeter across (.4 inches).
* A millimeter is about the thickness of a dime.

VOLUME

Cubic meters and centimeters are used to measure volume, just as we normally think of cubic feet and inches. Liquid volume measurements include the liter and milliliter, like the English quarts or ounces.

* One teaspoon is about 5 cubic centimeters.
* A liter is about one quart.
* A liter is about 61 cubic inches.

WEIGHT

The metric weight system is based on the gram, with the most common unit being the kilogram (1000 grams). Our comparable units are ounces and pounds:

* A kilogram is about 2.2 pounds.
* An ounce is about 28 grams.

TORQUE

Torque is somewhat complicated. The term describes the amount of effort exerted to turn something. A chosen unit of weight or force is applied to a lever of standard length. The resulting leverage is called torque. In our standard system, we use the weight of one pound applied to a lever a foot long—resulting in the unit called a foot-pound. A smaller unit is the inch-pound (the lever is one inch long). Metric units include the meter kilogram (lever one meter long with a kilogram of weight applied) and the Newton-meter(lever one meter long with force of one Newton applied). Some conversions are:

* A meter kilogram is about 7.2 foot pounds.
* A Newton-meter is about 1.4 foot pounds.
* A centimeter kilogram (cmkg) is equal to .9 inch pounds.

PRESSURE

Pressure is another complicated measurement. Pressure is described as a force or weight applied to a given area. Our common unit is pounds per square inch. Metric units can be expressed in several ways. One is the kilogram per square centimeter (kg/cm²). Another unit of pressure is the Pascal (force of one Newton on an area of one square meter), which equals about 4 ounces on a square yard. Since this is a very small amount of pressure, we usually see the kiloPascal, or kPa (1000 Pascals). Another common automotive term for pressure is the bar (used by German manufacturers), which equals 10 Pascals. Thoroughly confused? Try the examples below:

* Atmospheric pressure at sea level is about 14.7 psi.
* Atmospheric pressure at sea level is about 1 bar.
* Atmospheric pressure at sea level is about 1 kg/cm².
* One pound per square inch is about 7 kPa.

If all of these examples leave you still confused, then just use the conversion chart that follows. If you think these examples over for a while, you will begin to see the relationships betweeen the two systems of measurement. The result will be more ease in using both English and metric units!

Mitchell Manuals also offers audio visual presentations for mechanic training and microfiche products. For details on ordering, please contact:

Mitchell Manuals, Inc.
P.O. Box 26260
San Diego, CA 92126

QUICK CONVERSION FACTORS

Unit	To	Unit	Multiply By
LENGTH			
Millimeters		Inches	.04
Inches		Millimeters	25.4
Meters		Feet	3.3
Feet		Meters	.3
Kilometers		Miles	.6
Miles		Kilometers	1.6
VOLUME			
Cubic Centimeters		Cubic Inches	.06
Cubic Inches		Cubic Centimeters	16.4
Liters		Cubic Inches	61
Cubic Inches		Liters	.016
Liters		Quarts	1.05
Quarts		Liters	.95
Liters		Pints	2.1
Pints		Liters	.47
Liters		Ounces	33.8
Ounces		Liters	.03
WEIGHT			
Grams		Ounces	.035
Ounces		Grams	28.3
Kilograms		Pounds	2.2
Pounds		Kilometers	.14
TORQUE			
Centimeter Kilograms		Inch Pounds	.87
Inch Pounds		Centimeter Kilograms	1.2
Meter Kilograms		Foot Pounds	7.2
Foot Pounds		Meter Kilograms	.14
Newton Meters		Inch Pounds	8.8
Inch Pounds		Newton Meters	.11
Newton Meters		Foot Pounds	.74
Foot Pounds		Newton Meters	1.4
PRESSURE			
Kilograms/Square Centimeter		Pounds/Square Inch	14.2
Pounds/Square Inch		Kilograms/Square Centimeter	.07
Bar		Pounds/Square Inch	14.5
Pounds/Square Inch		Bar	.07
Atmosphere		Pounds/Square Inch	14.7
Pounds/Square Inch		Atmosphere	.07
TEMPERATURE			
Celsius Degrees		Fahrenheit Degrees	$(C° \times 1.8) + 32$
Fahrenheit Degrees		Celsius Degrees	$(F° - 32) \times .56$

Torque & Drill Conversion Chart

57

TORQUE CONVERSIONS
FOOT POUNDS TO NEWTON METERS

Ft. Lbs.	N·m	Ft. Lbs.	N·m	Ft. Lbs.	N·m	Ft. Lbs.	N·m
1	1.35	26	35	51	69	76	103
2	2.71	27	36	52	70	77	104
3	4.06	28	37	53	71	78	105
4	5.42	29	39	54	73	79	107
5	6.77	30	40	55	74	80	108
6	8.13	31	42	56	75	81	109
7	9.49	32	43	57	77	82	111
8	10	33	44	58	78	83	112
9	12	34	46	59	79	84	113
10	13	35	47	60	81	85	115
11	14	36	48	61	82	86	116
12	16	37	50	62	84	87	118
13	17	38	51	63	85	88	119
14	18	39	52	64	86	89	120
15	20	40	54	65	88	90	122
16	21	41	55	66	89	91	123
17	23	42	56	67	90	92	124
18	24	43	58	68	92	93	126
19	25	44	59	69	93	94	127
20	27	45	61	70	94	95	128
21	28	46	62	71	96	96	130
22	29	47	63	72	97	97	131
23	30	48	65	73	98	98	132
24	31	49	66	74	100	99	134
25	33	50	67	75	101	100	135

DRILL SIZE & IDENTIFICATION

Drill Diam.	Drill Size	Drill Diam.	Drill Size	Drill Diam.	Drill Size	Drill Diam.	Drill Size
.413"	Z	.2280"	1	.1440"	27	.0550"	54
.404"	Y	.2210"	2	.1405"	28	.0520"	55
.397"	X	.2130"	3	.1360"	29	.0465"	56
.386"	W	.2090"	4	.1285"	30	.0430"	57
.377"	V	.2055"	5	.1200"	31	.0420"	58
.368"	U	.2040"	6	.1160"	32	.0410"	59
.358"	T	.2010"	7	.1130"	33	.0400"	60
.348"	S	.1990"	8	.1110"	34	.0390"	61
.339"	R	.1960"	9	.1100"	35	.0380"	62
.332"	Q	.1935"	10	.1065"	36	.0370"	63
.323"	P	.1910"	11	.1040"	37	.0360"	64
.316"	O	.1890"	12	.1015"	38	.0350"	65
.302"	N	.1850"	13	.0995"	39	.0330"	66
.295"	M	.1820"	14	.0980"	40	.0320"	67
.290"	L	.1800"	15	.0960"	41	.0310"	68
.281"	K	.1770"	16	.0935"	42	.0292"	69
.277"	J	.1730"	17	.0890"	43	.0280"	70
.272"	I	.1695"	18	.0860"	44	.0260"	71
.266"	H	.1660"	19	.0820"	45	.0250"	72
.261"	G	.1610"	20	.0810"	46	.0240"	73
.257"	F	.1590"	21	.0785"	47	.0225"	74
.250"	E	.1570"	22	.0760"	48	.0210"	75
.246"	D	.1540"	23	.0730"	49	.0200"	76
.242"	C	.1520"	24	.0700"	50	.0180"	77
.238"	B	.1495"	25	.0670"	51	.0160"	78
.234"	A	.1470"	26	.0635"	52	.0145"	79
				.0595"	53	.0135"	80

English-Metric Conversion Chart

MILLIMETERS TO INCHES

Conversion Factor — Multiply known millimeter figure by .03937

MM	Inches	MM	Inches	MM	Inches	MM	Inches	MM	Inches
1	.039	21	.827	41	1.614	61	2.402	81	3.189
2	.079	22	.866	42	1.654	62	2.441	82	3.228
3	.118	23	.906	43	1.693	63	2.480	83	3.268
4	.157	24	.945	44	1.732	64	2.520	84	3.307
5	.197	25	.984	45	1.772	65	2.559	85	3.346
6	.236	26	1.024	46	1.811	66	2.598	86	3.386
7	.276	27	1.063	47	1.850	67	2.638	87	3.425
8	.315	28	1.102	48	1.890	68	2.677	88	3.465
9	.354	29	1.142	49	1.929	69	2.717	89	3.504
10	.394	30	1.181	50	1.969	70	2.756	90	3.543
11	.433	31	1.220	51	2.008	71	2.795	91	3.583
12	.472	32	1.260	52	2.047	72	2.835	92	3.622
13	.512	33	1.299	53	2.087	73	2.874	93	3.661
14	.551	34	1.339	54	2.126	74	2.913	94	3.701
15	.591	35	1.378	55	2.165	75	2.953	95	3.740
16	.630	36	1.417	56	2.205	76	2.992	96	3.780
17	.669	37	1.457	57	2.244	77	3.031	97	3.819
18	.709	38	1.496	58	2.283	78	3.071	98	3.858
19	.748	39	1.535	59	2.323	79	3.110	99	3.898
20	.787	40	1.575	60	2.362	80	3.150	100	3.937

INCHES TO MILLIMETERS

Conversion Factor — Multiply known inch figure by 25.40

Inches	MM	Inches	MM	Inches	MM	Inches	MM	Inches	MM
.001	.025	.040	1.016	.340	8.636	.640	16.256	.940	23.876
.002	.051	.050	1.270	.350	8.890	.650	16.510	.950	24.130
.003	.076	.060	1.524	.360	9.144	.660	16.764	.960	24.384
.004	.102	.070	1.778	.370	9.398	.670	17.018	.970	24.638
.005	.127	.080	2.032	.380	9.652	.680	17.272	.980	24.892
.006	.152	.090	2.286	.390	9.906	.690	17.526	.990	25.146
.007	.178	.100	2.540	.400	10.160	.700	17.780	1.000	25.400
.008	.203	.110	2.794	.410	10.414	.710	18.034	2.000	50.800
.009	.229	.120	3.048	.420	10.668	.720	18.288	3.000	76.200
.010	.254	.130	3.302	.430	10.922	.730	18.542	4.000	101.600
.011	.279	.140	3.556	.440	11.176	.740	18.796	5.000	127.000
.012	.305	.150	3.810	.450	11.430	.750	19.050		
.013	.330	.160	4.064	.460	11.684	.760	19.304		
.014	.356	.170	4.318	.470	11.938	.770	19.558		
.015	.381	.180	4.572	.480	12.192	.780	19.812		
.016	.406	.190	4.826	.490	12.446	.790	20.066		
.017	.432	.200	5.080	.500	12.700	.800	20.320		
.018	.457	.210	5.334	.510	12.954	.810	20.574		
.019	.483	.220	5.558	.520	13.208	.820	20.828		
.020	.508	.230	5.842	.530	13.462	.830	21.082		
.021	.533	.240	6.096	.540	13.716	.840	21.336		
.022	.559	.250	6.350	.550	13.970	.850	21.590		
.023	.584	.260	6.604	.560	14.224	.860	21.844		
.024	.610	.270	6.858	.570	14.478	.870	22.098		
.025	.635	.280	7.112	.580	14.732	.880	22.352		
.026	.652	.290	7.366	.590	14.986	.890	22.606		
.027	.686	.300	7.620	.600	15.240	.900	22.860		
.028	.711	.310	7.874	.610	15.494	.910	23.114		
.029	.737	.320	8.128	.620	15.748	.920	23.368		
.030	.762	.330	8.382	.630	16.002	.930	23.622		

NOTE — The latest changes and corrections represent a collection of last minute 1981 information which arrived too late to be incorporated into the regular data pages. In addition, we have included information on prior year models which we have received since the production of last years edition.

TUNE-UP & FUEL SYSTEMS — SECTIONS 1 & 2

[1] ▶ *1979 COLT & CHAMP: OIL IN AIR CLEANER* — A small amount of oil in the air cleaner is considered normal. In cases of excessive oil in the air cleaner, replace valve cover on 1400 cc engine with part number MD30274. On 1600 cc engines, install washer, part number MDO 07746 under left front camshaft bearing cap bolt and install new valve cover, part number MDO 07496, and retainer screw, part number MF 100065.

[2] ▶ *1979 STRADA AND X1/9: IGNITION TIMING* — Some 1979 Fiat Strada and X1/9 models may experience a shifting of the ignition timing pointer at the crankshaft pulley, resulting in improper timing settings. To ensure correct timing setting, check the timing marks at both the crankshaft pulley and the flywheel. Correct timing for standard transmission models should be 5°BTDC at 800-850 RPM, and 5°BTDC at 700-750 RPM for automatic transmission models.

[3] ▶ *1975-81 HONDA ACCORD, CIVIC & PRELUDE: FLOAT ADJUSTMENT* — Honda has a new and easier way to adjust both the primary and auxiliary floats. This procedure applies to all vehicles equipped with CVCC engines. The following is the new procedure:

1) Start engine and run until it reaches normal operating temperature. Remove the air cleaner assembly.

2) Turn the primary float adjusting screw (needle seat) counterclockwise in ⅛ turn increments, waiting at least 15 seconds between each ⅛ turn to let fuel level stabilize, until engine completely dies.

3) Turn the adjusting screw clockwise according to the following chart. To adjust the auxiliary float, repeat steps **1)**, **2)** and **3)**.

Honda Float Adjustment

Model & Year	Primary Turn	Auxiliary Turn
Accord & Prelude		
1976-77	⅝	⅝
1978-81	¾	¾
Civic		
1975	¾	¾
1976-77	⅝	⅝
1978-79	¾	¾
1980	⅞	⅞
1981	¾	¾

[4] ▶ *1978-80 FIESTA: CARBURETOR THROTTLE DASHPOT SPECIFICATION* — The specification for adjustment of throttle dashpot to obtain proper clearance between dashpot plunger and throttle lever is .197" (5 mm). The measurement should be made with throttle lever set at specified engine curb idle speed and dashpot plunger in fully collapsed position. Loosen dashpot locknut and adjust dashpot position as required to obtain proper clearance.

[5] ▶ *ALL FIAT MODELS: GASOHOL USAGE* — When gasohol is to be used in Fiat vehicles, DO NOT change or otherwise modify any engine components or adjustments to accommodate gasohol usage. Also, local, state and federal regulations concerning to the use of gasohol must be observed.

[6] ▶ *1981 FIAT SPIDER 2000 TURBO: TURBOCHARGER OIL SUPPLY LINE LEAK* — Some 1981 Fiat Spider 2000 Turbo models may develop an oil leak at the turbocharger oil supply line connection at the oil filter housing. To correct this problem, replace the supply line union (part number 5077) and the crush washers (part number 5078) on oil pressure switch and on oil supply line connection. Check engine oil level. Start engine and check for leaks.

[7] ▶ *1981 VOLKSWAGEN JETTA, PICKUP, RABBIT & SCIROCCO: NEW FUEL PUMP RELAY LOCATION* — On these models, the fuel pump relay is now mounted on an adapter, just above the fuse block, and is connected to the fuse block by a wiring harness and plug.

▶ *1980-81 TOYOTA TERCEL: IGNITION TIMING* — On the 1980-81 Toyota Tercel, the distributor cannot be turned far enough to obtain the specified timing of 5° BTDC due to interference between the distributor and air injection tubes. To correct this problem, remove the distributor and turn the cam 1 gear tooth. Reinstall distributor and adjust ignition timing to 5° BTDC.

[8] ▶ *SAAB MODELS WITH BREAKERLESS IGNITION: DISTRIBUTOR HOLD DOWN CLIPS* — On these models, the ignition distributor contains an electromagnetic pulse generator. Care must be exercised when cranking an engine with the distributor cap removed. The magnetism in the unit will attract the distributor hold-down clips. When the engine is cranked over the clips will interfere with the metal timing rotor and may cause bending or breakage of either the rotor or the clips.

[9] ▶ *SAAB MODELS WITH LAMBDA CONTROL AND ALL SAAB TURBOS: USING EXHAUST GAS ANALYZERS* — When using an exhaust gas analyzer for checking/adjusting idle air fuel mixture on these models, the oxygen sensor wire plug must ALWAYS be disconnected. Failure to disconnect wire will result in excessively rich mixtures, high emissions, poor fuel economy, oil dilution and possible long term durability problems. After using exhaust gas analyzers, reconnect oxygen sensor wire.

TUNE-UP & FUEL SYSTEMS – SECTIONS 1 & 2 (Cont.)

[10] ▸ *1980 TOYOTA COROLLA MODELS: CARBURETOR FLOAT CHANGE* — The shape of carburetor float used on these models has been changed for parts standardization as shown in the illustration. In addition, float adjusting levels have been changed. The upper level adjustment has changed from .255″ (6.5 mm) to .362″ (9.2 mm). The lower level adjustment remains the same at .047″ (1.2 mm). The new float and old float are interchangeable.

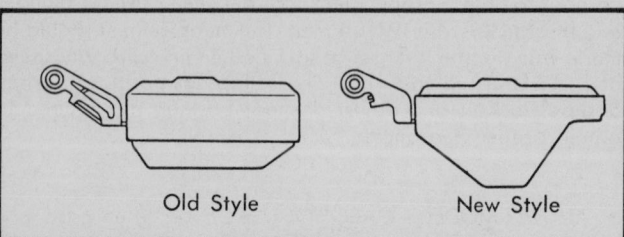

Old Style   New Style

Toyota Corolla Float Modification

[11] ▸ *1980 VOLVO MODELS WITH DIESEL ENGINES: DELIVERY VALVE* — Whenever it is necessary to loosen or replace a diesel injection pump delivery valve, a new packing washer MUST be installed. The packing washer is installed behind spring seat in pump housing. *See illustration.* After packing washer (Volvo Part No. 243558-4) is installed, nipple should be tightened to 37 ft. lbs. (50 N.m).

[12] ▸ *1978-80 CHRYSLER CORP. IMPORTS WITH 2.0L OR 2.6L ENGINE: HARD STARTING WITH ENGINE HOT WHEN USING GASOHOL* — This problem can be corrected by installing one of the following fuel pump kits. Part number MD027120 for Arrow, Challenger, Colt Wagon and Sapporo; part number MD027121 for Arrow Pickup and D-50 Pickup. This kit eliminates the need for the vapor separator tank and provides a fuel return line directly from the fuel pump. This kit is installed as follows: Remove the underhood fuel vapor separator tank and connecting fuel hoses. Remove tank brackets from vehicle. Install new fuel pump kit and connect new fuel hoses between fuel pump and carburetor. Check for fuel leaks.

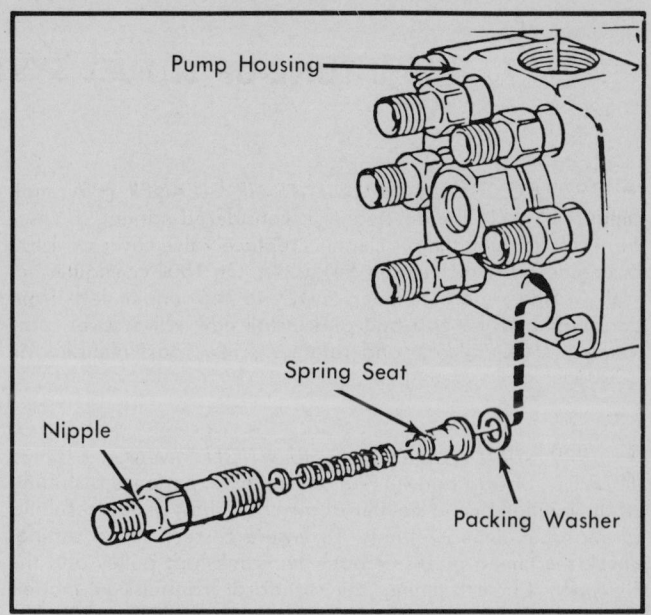

Pump Housing

Spring Seat

Nipple

Packing Washer

Installing Packing Washer on Volvo Injection Pump

[13] ▸ *1981 CHRYSLER CORP. IMPORTS WITH AIR CONDITIONING: IDLE-UP SETTING PROCEDURE* — The following is a revised A/C idle-up system (throttle opener) idle setting procedure:

1) Start engine and run until it reaches normal operationg temperature. Turn all lights and accessories off. Apply parking brake and place transmission in Neutral. Make sure that curb idle speed is properly set to specifications.

2) Turn the air conditioning system on and place blower on low speed. Adjust idle-up RPM with the throttle opener setting screw. For Champ and Colt models equipped with manual transmissions, idle-up setting should be 800-900 RPM. For all other models, idle-up setting should be 850-950 RPM.

ELECTRICAL – SECTION 3

[1] ▸ *1981 RENAULT 18i: ALTERNATOR SHIELD REMOVAL* — The alternator shield found on Renault 18i models has been discontinued during the 1981 production year. Vehicles still having this shield should have it removed when the vehicle is in for service. Use the following procedure: Disconnect negative battery cable. Remove top exhaust manifold nut and bend alternator shield down slightly. Remove alternator shield lower attaching bolt and nut. Remove and discard alternator shield. Install upper bolts, lower bolt and nut, and reconnect negative battery cable.

[2] ▸ *1981 SAAB 4-CYLINDER ENGINES: SPARK PLUG WIRE REROUTING* — There is a possibility that the spark plug wires may come in contact with the hood support, or the heat shield

on turbo models. To prevent this, move all of the wires up one notch in the forward holder on the valve cover. Cut off the lugs on bottom of the holder to prevent future mispositioning of the spark plug wires. Wires for cylinders 1 and 2 should be moved to the upper position on the holder at the rear of the valve cover. Cut off lower lugs of holder.

[3] ▸ *ALL SAAB MODELS: ALTERNATOR REGULATOR USAGE* — Do not attempt to interchange alternator regulators between Turbo and non-Turbo alternators. Turbo alternator has smaller diameter slip rings and longer brushes. Use of non-Turbo regulator in Turbo alternator will result in very short brush life.

[4] ▸ *1976-78 VOLVO WITH CIS FUEL INJECTION: FUEL FEED PUMP* — An in-tank feed pump was introduced on a small

ELECTRICAL — SECTION 3 (Cont.)

number of 1976 260 models. It supplements the main electric fuel pump. This pump was phased in on all models during the 1977 model year. It could also be installed as a retrofit kit by a dealer. A splice is made in the main fuel pump power line, and an inline fuse and noise reduction capacitor are installed. The following procedure can be used for pump removal.

1) Disconnect battery ground cable and remove gas cap to relieve tank pressure. Remove floor panel or trunk mat. Remove cover over motor armature after disconnecting wires.

2) Remove hoses. Clean area around armature and lift our assembly with special tool 5016 or 5169. Be careful not to damage fuel filter stocking or float lever.

3) Clean gasket area and install a new "O" ring with glycerin lubricant. Install armature assembly and tighten. Ensure filter does not interfere with gauge float. Install hoses and wiring.

ACCESSORIES & EQUIPMENT — SECTION 5

1 ▶ *1981 FIAT SPIDER 2000 MODELS: INCORRECT FUEL GAUGE READING* — An incorrect fuel gauge reading may be due to interference between the fuel tank sending unit float and the separator inside the fuel tank. This can be repaired by first removing the sending unit from the fuel tank. Reverse the position of the float on the sending unit control arm, making sure that the float is securely fastened to the control arm. Reinstall the sending unit.

2 ▶ *1981 PEUGEOT 505 MODELS: POWER WINDOWS* — If a 505 power window is lowered to its fully open positon, the electric gear motor sector may bind with the lifter mechanism. A kit (part number 17.02) is available to limit the downward movement of the mechanism. The kit consists of a bracket, a rubber stop and necessary attaching hardware for installation. Install these components using the instructions provided in the kit.

3 ▶ *1981 RENAULT LE CAR & 18i: WINDSHIELD WASHER PUMP MOTOR DIAGNOSIS* — When diagnosing a windshield washer malfunction on 1981 Renault Le Car and 18i models the following procedure should be used to verify pump motor operation:

1) Connect a jumper wire between the battery positive terminal and the Pink wire on the pump motor. If the pump motor does not operate, check and repair the pump motor ground wire connection. On Le Car models, the ground wire is located behind the right headlamp. On 18i models, the ground wire is located at the right side of the battery.

2) If the pump motor still does not operate with a good ground, the motor should be replaced. If the pump motor does operate under test conditions, but does not operate when in normal use, check wiper switch and all connecting wiring.

ENGINES — SECTION 6

1 ▶ *1981 AUDI 4000: CRANKSHAFT SPROCKET BOLT* — Whenever repair procedures require the removal of the crankshaft sprocket and bolt, the bolt should be replaced with a new bolt (part number 901 120 01). Also, a special washer with a collar (part number 068 105 299) should be installed with the new bolt.

2 ▶ *1978 AND EARLIER CHYSLER CORP. IMPORT VEHICLES: ENGINE BLOCK-TO-TRANSMISSION DOWEL PINS* — When replacing engine block, transmission case or clutch housing on these models, the following dowel pin precautions should be observed.

Manual Transmission — If dowel pin surface of bolt hole in transmission case or clutch housing is smaller than .276" (7 mm), replace dowel pin in new engine block with replacement pin (Chrysler Part No. MS471108). If this area is greater than .276" (7 mm), do not replace dowel pin.

Automatic Transmission — It is not necessary to replace dowel pins on automatic transmissions.

Engine Block — If dowel pins project more than .256" (6.5 mm) from engine block, no replacement is required. If pins project less than .256" (6.5 mm), replace pins with new pins (Chrysler Part No. MD020260).

3 ▶ *CHRYSLER CORP. IMPORTS WITH PULSE AIR FEEDER: ENGINE KNOCK NOISE* — An engine knock noise may develop because of an overfilled crankcase. When the crankcase is overfilled, oil will enter the pulse air feeder, causing a knocking noise that sounds similar to a rod knock. Drain the excess oil from the crankcase and run engine for a short time to clear oil from the pulse air feeder. The noise, if caused by engine oil overfill, will be eliminated.

4 ▶ *ALL CHRYSLER CORP. COLT & ARROW MODELS WITH 2000 cc OR 2600 cc ENGINES: COUNTERBALANCE AND TIMING CHAIN NOISE* — Before replacing either of these chains on subject models, the following procedures should be performed. On counterbalance chains, make sure chain is properly adjusted. If adjustment does not correct problem, then replace chain. On timing chains, start engine and listen for noise. If the chain chatters on starting, a rubber washer (part number MD021242) should be added to the tensioner sleeve to prevent the noise. If the chain is noisy at idle, an improved tensioner spring (part number MD022235) should be installed to provide proper tension. The new spring has green paint on one end, and white paint on the other end.

5 ▶ *1981 DODGE COLT & PLYMOUTH CHAMP WITH 1.4L ENGINES: OIL PUMP COVER CHANGE* — Beginning with engine number 12AS8979 (from January of 1981) the oil pump cover on the 1.4L engine was changed from cast iron to

FOR 1981 & PREVIOUS MODELS
ENGINES — SECTION 6 (Cont.)

aluminum. The retaining bolts for the cast iron and aluminum covers are not interchangeable. When replacing and aluminum cover with a cast iron cover (part number MD030785) it will also be necessary to replace the retaining bolts (part number MF101226).

▶ *1981 SAAB 900 MODELS: ELECTRIC COOLING FAN WIRING* — If a vehicle has an overheating problem, check that the wires in the 2-pole connector for cooling fan are not reversed. If the wires are reversed, the fan will rotate backwards. The wires should be arranged so that the Black wires connect to each other. [6]

▶ *1981 VOLVO GLT TURBO: ENGINE COOLING* — The heat generated by a vehicle equipped with a turbo engine is higher than that of a non-turbo engine. Good air flow through the radiator and oil cooler is essential for effective engine cooling. To avoid restricting air flow, auxiliary lamps should be mounted on the bottom of the bumper or in the air dam on either side of the air intake passages. [7]

▶ *1980 TOYOTA 1A-C 4-CYLINDER ENGINE: TIMING BELT ALIGNMENT* — Before removing the timing belt, be sure to mark timing belt and camshaft sprocket. Use the following illustration as a guide in aligning timing belt. [8]

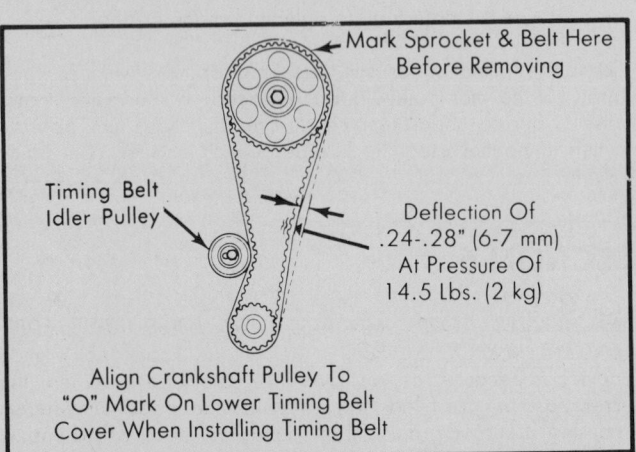

Mark Sprocket & Belt Here Before Removing

Timing Belt Idler Pulley

Deflection Of .24-.28" (6-7 mm) At Pressure Of 14.5 Lbs. (2 kg)

Align Crankshaft Pulley To "O" Mark On Lower Timing Belt Cover When Installing Timing Belt

Toyota 1A-C Engine Timing Belt Alignment

▶ *1979 FIAT STRADA: COOLING FAN* — 1979 Fiat Strada models may exhibit a condition where the engine cooling fan does not stay energized when the ignition key is removed. This is possibly due to reversed wire connections at the cooling fan relay. Proper wire color code connections for the fan relay are: [9]

Color	Relay Terminal No.
Black	30
Gray/Black	85
Black/Violet	86
White/Black	87
Gray/Red	87A

▶ *1980 FIAT BRAVA AND SPIDER 2000 MODELS: TIMING BELT TENSIONER PULLEY* — To maximize usage of timing belt, the width of timing belt tensioner pulley has been increased from .944" (24 mm), to 1.102" (28 mm). Old and new tensioner pulleys are interchangeable. Part number for new pulley is 4443446. [10]

▶ *1978-79 FIAT BRAVA AND SPIDER: ENGINE TIGHTENING SPECIFICATIONS* — The following specifications should be added to the Fiat Brava and Spider engine article in 1978 and 1979 editions of Mitchell's Imported Car and Truck Manual. The Center Main Bearing Cap Bolt should be tightened to 83 ft. lbs. (113 N.m). The Main Bearing Cap Self-Locking Bolts should also be tightened to 83 ft. lbs. (113 N.m). [11]

▶ *All FIAT MODELS: RETORQUING CYLINDER HEAD* — Whenever a cylinder head gasket is replaced on Fiat engines, it is essential that cylinder head be retorqued after vehicle has been driven for 700 to 1000 miles. This will ensure proper seating of cylinder head to crankcase. Torquing of cylinder head should only be performed when cylinder head is cool to touch. [12]

▶ *ALL FIAT X1/9: PISTON AND ROD INSTALLATION* — Revised factory information states that X1/9 piston and rod assemblies must be installed in block with numbers stamped on connecting rods and rod caps facing AWAY from auxiliary shaft. Original procedure stated that numbers must face toward auxiliary shaft. [13]

▶ *1978-80 FIESTA: TIMING CHAIN FRONT COVER GASKET REPLACEMENT* — The timing chain front cover gasket can be removed and replaced without removing the engine by following the procedure below. [14]

1) Open hood and cover fenders. Loosen thermactor pump pivot bolt and adjusting bolt and remove drive belt. Remove adjusting and pivot bolts, and remove thermactor pump.

2) Remove 3 bolts securing water pump pulley to water pump and remove pulley. Raise vehicle on hoist. Remove alternator drive belt, pivot and adjusting bolts and alternator.

3) Remove crankshaft damper retaining bolt and remove damper. Remove 10 bolts securing front cover to engine, and remove cover.

4) Throroughly clean gasket mating surfaces of front cover, block and oil pan. Position a new gasket and oil pan front seal on front cover.

5) Position front cover on block and secure with original bolts. Tighten bolts evenly to 60-84 INCH lbs. (6.8-9.5 N.m). Position crankshaft damper pulley on crankshaft and tighten attaching bolts to 40-44 ft. lbs. (54-60 N.m).

6) Place alternator in position and install adjusting and pivot bolts finger tight. Lower vehicle.

7) Place water pump pulley into positon and tighten bolts evenly to 72-96 INCH lbs. (8.1-10.8 N.m). Place drive belt over crankshaft, water pump inner groove and alternator pulleys. Adjust belt tension to specifications and tighten alternator adjusting and pivot bolts.

8) Place thermactor pump in position and install mounting bolts finger tight. Place drive belt over water pump pulley outer groove and thermactor pump pulley. Adjust belt tension to specifications and tighten thermactor adjusting and pivot bolts.

Latest Changes & Corrections

FOR 1981 & PREVIOUS MODELS
ENGINES — SECTION 6 (Cont.)

15 ▶ *1980 MERCEDES-BENZ 300SD MODELS: VIBRATION DAMPER FOR INJECTION PUMP* — Since February, 1980, a vibration damper is installed on governor linkage of injection pump. This damper greatly reduces problem of engine vibration at idle. Damper is not set at factory, because setting and adjustment must take place on a run-in engine. If complaints of engine vibration at idle exist, the following procedure should be used to set and adjust damper.

1) Bring engine to operating temperature. Loosen lock nut on vibration damper.

2) With engine idling at 750 RPM, turn screw on damper until engine vibration is at its lowest point.

3) Tighten lock nut to 15-18 ft. lbs. (20-24 N.m).

NOTE — *Do not turn damper adjusting screw in too far as this will have an adverse effect on cold engine idle.*

16 ▶ *ALL MERCEDES-BENZ 240D AND 300 SERIES MODELS WITH DIESEL ENGINES: CAP AND LOCK NUTS FOR VALVES* — When adjusting valve clearance or repairing valve mechanism on these engines, check that cap nut is securely locked by lock nut. Loose cap nuts can lead to engine damage. The following items should be noted when performing valve work.

1) Check cap and lock nuts for tightness. Check that there is a secure seating between cap and lock nuts.

2) Check nuts for wear. If thickness of lock nut is less than .197" (5 mm), it should be replaced with a new lock nut with a thickness of .236" (6 mm).

3) If nuts are worn out, check threads on valve stems for damage and repair or replace as required.

4) Check temper cast camshafts for wear. An exceedingly worn surface on camshaft lobe can result in loosening of lock nuts. In case of worn cam lobes, replace camshaft, rocker arms, valve springs and cap and lock nuts. Check general condition of valves and replace as required.

17 ▶ *SAAB MODELS WITH SODIUM-FILLED EXHAUST VALVES: PROPER DISPOSING OF SCRAP VALVES* — Special procedures must be taken when disposing of sodium-filled exhaust valves used on some Saab models. The following procedure should be followed exactly for proper disposal. These valves must never be mixed with ordinary scrap without first performing this procedure. Failure to do so may incur danger of explosions and personal harm.

1) Drill a hole through the valve disc as far as the sodium content, as shown in the illustration.

2) Drill a second hole through the shaft, or saw off the shaft, about 1" (25 mm) from end of valve as shown in illustration.

CAUTION — *During drilling, sawing or other action which exposes the sodium, extreme care must be taken so that no water is allowed to come into contact with sodium. If water is mixed with sodium, an explosion will result.*

3) Stand at least 10 ft. away from a bucket of water and throw valve into bucket. This will cause a powerful explosive reaction which will last about one or two minutes. Valves may then be mixed with ordinary scrap for disposal.

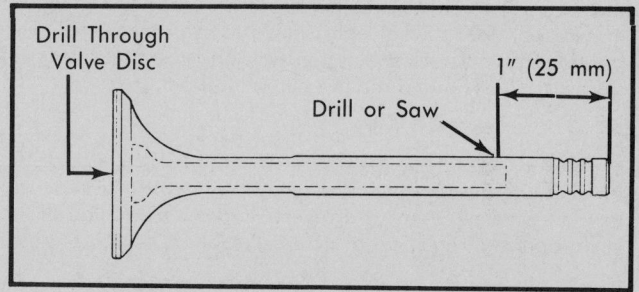

Drilling Saab Sodium-Filled Exhaust Valves

18 ▶ *SAAB TURBO ENGINES: PISTON "ROCK" IN CYLINDER* — When evaluating cylinder wear in Turbo engines, do not be mislead by piston "rock" after cylinder head is removed. This is normal. Turbo pistons are manufactured with considerable taper as compared with normal engine pistons. The taper, toward piston crown, allows for increased heat and expansion when operating under boost. The crown and bottom piston skirt may measure up to .025" (.646 mm) difference. Therefore, the only valid measuring point for turbo pistons is between bottom of piston skirt and cylinder wall.

19 ▶ *ALL SAAB MODELS WITH CONTINUOUS INJECTION SYSTEM (CIS): THERMOSTAT REMOVAL* — When changing thermostat on CIS-equipped engines, it is very important that coolant be drained below level of thermostat housing. If themostat housing is removed with coolant level high, coolant may spill over into warm-up regulator vent. Coolant saturation on warm-up regulator may lead to corrosion of regulator and possible malfunction.

20 ▶ *ALL VOLKSWAGEN RABBIT & SCIROCCO MODELS: CRANKSHAFT OIL SEAL* — When replacing crankshaft oil seals at the flywheel end, always measure crankshaft diameter and select the seal to match. Seals come in 2 sizes, 82 and 85 millimeters.

21 ▶ *1979 VOLKSWAGEN RABBIT AND SCIROCCO: CAMSHAFT SPROCKET BOLT* — If engine is turned by **camshaft** sprocket bolt counter to engine rotation when adjusting valve clearances, bolt may come loose. Coat bolt with a suitable locking compound and tighten to 58 ft. lbs. (79 N.m).

CLUTCHES — SECTION 7

1 ▶ *1978-80 CHRYSLER CORP. IMPORT VEHICLES WITH KM 130 AND KM 132 MANUAL TRANSMISSIONS: NEW CLUTCH RELEASE BEARING* — A new style clutch release bearing with an integral carrier has been released for servicing these vehicles. The new style release bearing is self-aligning and replaces the separate release bearing and carrier set. The appropriate part numbers are listed below.

Application	Part No.
KM 130	MD700257
KM 132	MD703270

FOR 1981 & PREVIOUS MODELS
CLUTCHES — SECTION 7 (Cont.)

▶ *DODGE RAM-50 & PLYMOUTH ARROW PICKUPS: CLUTCH CHATTER* — Some vehicles, equipped with 2.6L engines and 5-speed transmissions, may develop clutch chatter when clutch is first engaged. To correct this condition, a new clutch friction disc (part number MD802132) is available. This disc uses a new friction material and should eliminate the clutch chatter condition under normal use.

[2]

▶ *1980 CHEVROLET LUV 4WD: CLUTCH REMOVAL* — On the LUV 4WD, the crossmember is welded into place. To remove the transmission, remove the transfer case and turn the transmission 90° so that right side is facing downward. Slide the transmission back until the input shaft is clear. Tip front of transmission down and remove out to the front.

[3]

▶ *1976-81 SAAB (ALL MODELS): CLUTCH TOOLS* — In 1976 an alternate design clutch pressure plate was introduced. This new pressure plate has a different shape at the flange of the inner opening requiring a different tool to hold the clutch

[4]

fingers in the released position. The tool number for the old style clutch is 83 90 023 and the new style uses tool number 87 90 826.

▶ *VOLVO MODELS WITH MANUAL TRANSMISSIONS: PRESSURE PLATES AND RELEASE BEARINGS* — Two different designs of pressure plates and release bearings are used on Volvo 240 and 260 models. The two designs are easily recognizable by the fingers of the pressure plate. Plates for 260 models have fingers that are raised approximately 9/32" (7 mm) at the center. Plate fingers on 240 model plates are straight. Because of the finger difference, there are two different release bearings for these models. Release bearings for 260 models are approximately 1-7/16" (36.5 mm) long. Release bearings for 240 models are approximately 1-11/16" (43 mm) long. Pressure plates and release bearings must be used in the correct combination and should never be mixed.

[5]

BRAKES — SECTION 8

▶ *1980 CHRYSLER CORP. SAPPORO, CHALLENGER, COLT STATION WAGON AND ARROW MODELS WITH 9" REAR BRAKES: REAR BRAKE VIBRATION* — If vibration of rear brakes at low speed application occurs, the shoe-to-shoe retaining springs should be replaced using following procedures.

[1]

Shoe-to-Shoe Spring — Attach one end of shoe-to-shoe spring to hole in trailing shoe, then install hook of other end of spring to hole in leading shoe with a screwdriver.

Shoe Retainer Spring — Installation procedure remains unchanged for retaining spring; however, spring ends must point away from backing plate when installing new retaining springs (Chrysler Part No. MD151334). When replacing retaining springs, new parts should be used.

▶ *1981 AUDI 4000 & VOLKSWAGEN JETTA, PICKUP, RABBIT & SCIROCCO: BRAKE CALIPER MOUNTING BOLT CHANGE* — During the 1981 model year a new self-locking type brake caliper mounting bolt was introduced. These new self locking bolts should not be installed on previous models. Tightening torque for these new bolts is 50 ft. lbs. (68 N.m).

[2]

▶ *ALL FIAT MODELS WITH DISC BRAKES: ALTERNATE METHOD OF BLEEDING BRAKE CALIPERS* — If bleeder screws cannot be turned on disc brake models, the following alternate method may be used to bleed brake system.

[3]

1) Remove caliper from support bracket. Place a 2" x 4" block of wood between caliper and piston.

2) Using brake pedal, pump piston against block of wood. Invert caliper so bleeder and inlet brake line are facing downward.

3) Bleed air from caliper by loosening inlet fitting at caliper. With caliper in this position, air is forced to inlet passage.

4) Use normal bleeding procedures for remainder of system.

▶ *1981 AUDI 4000: MODIFIED FRONT BRAKE CALIPER* — Front brake calipers are now equipped with a heat shield clamped onto the brake caliper piston. Previous brake pad carriers will accept the new brake caliper piston with heat shield.

[4]

▶ *ALL MERCEDES-BENZ MODELS: BRAKE PADS* — The following items should be noted when servicing brake pads on Mercedes vehicles.

[5]

1) In vehicles with brake pad wear indicators, brake pad sensor need only be replaced if damaged, if conductor is exposed or if insulation of sensor pin has been worn off by brake disc.

2) White numbers stamped on brake pad backing plate identify batch from which brake lining material originated. It is important that only pads having the same batch number be installed in both front calipers. This helps to avoid pulling tendencies, due to different friction coefficients of pads.

3) Brake caliper pistons should only be retracted with Piston Return Pliers (MB Part No. 123 589 00 37 00). If other tools are used, there is a danger of damaging piston or dust seal. On

FOR 1981 & PREVIOUS MODELS

BRAKES — SECTION 8 (Cont.)

vehicles with wear indicators, avoid pinching cable or cable guard.

4) Brake pads should only be removed with an Impact Puller (MB Part No. 115 589 14 33 00). If pads are stuck in caliper, use Seize Puller (MB Part No. 116 589 04 33 00).

5) Before installing new pads, discs that are grimy, rusted or discolored must be sanded to a bright finish with a cleaning pad.

6) Apply a light coat of heat-proof lubricant (Molykote, or equivalent) to edges of backing plate, before installing in brake pad. This will reduce squealing and ease brake and disassembly in next service.

7) When replacing a cross spring (ATE) or pad retaining spring (Bendix or Girling), make sure that correct spring is installed.

WHEEL ALIGNMENT — SECTION 9

▶ 1980 FORD FIESTA: WHEEL ALIGNMENT CHANGE — In previous manuals, the toe-in specification for the Fiesta was incorrect. The correct specification is ³⁄₃₂-⁹⁄₃₂" (1.2-3.6 mm) TOE-OUT, not toe-in.

1

▶ VOLVO DL, GL, GLE AND GT DIESEL MODELS: CAMBER SPECIFICATION CHANGE — The correct specification for camber on these vehicles should be as follows: DL, GL and GTE diesel models, +1° to +1-½°, with an allowable difference between right and left of ½°. GT models should be set at +¼° to ¾°.

2

▶ 1980 VOLVO 240 & 260 SERIES: NEW FRONT WHEEL BEARING NUT — A new front wheel bearing nut has been introduced to provide a more accurate adjustment of front wheel bearings. The new nut has 10 cotter pin slots where as the old nut had only 6 slots.

3

▶ 1978 VOLKSWAGEN RABBIT & SCIROCCO: FRONT SUSPENSION CHANGES — Mid-way through the 1978 model year, the front ball joint pin diameter was increased

4

from 15 to 17 mm. The clamping hole in the front wheel bearing housing was also enlarged to match the ball joint change. 15 mm ball joints will still be available, but only 17 mm wheel bearing housings will be supplied as replacement parts. In the event one wheel bearing housing must be changed, manufacturer allows the use of the old, 15 mm housing on the other side of the vehicle. New tightening torque for the clamping bolts is 37 ft. lbs. (50 N.m).

▶ 1980-81 TOYOTA CRESSIDA: REAR CONTROL ARM BUSHINGS — In 1980, Cressida models were fitted with new rear upper and lower control arm bushings. This change was made to prevent vibration during heavy acceleration and noise when driving on a bumpy surface. This new bushing has solid rubber construction.

5

▶ 1978-1979 FIESTA: FRONT SUSPENSION MOUNTING — A "clunking" noise heard when making either right or left hand turns may be caused by the front coil spring responding to rotational movement of the top strut mount bearing. To eliminate this noise, install new thrust plate and bearing (part numbers DR8Z-3K048-A and D8RZ-3K099-B) as a pair.

6

SUSPENSION — SECTION 10

▶ ALL 1980 FIAT MODELS EXCEPT SPIDER 2000: MANUAL RACK AND PINION STEERING BOX LUBRICANT — The lubricant used in Fiat manual rack and pinion steering boxes has been changed from SAE 80W/90 EP Oil, to Lithium Base Grease containing Molybdenum Disulphide. The new lubricant may be used for servicing steering boxes on models which were originally filled with oil.

1

▶ 1975 THROUGH 1979 LUV: STEERING KNUCKLE REPLACEMENT — When replacing the steering knuckle on 1975 and newer LUV trucks, it is necessary that the spacer be removed from the old knuckle and installed on the replacement knuckle.

2

▶ 1977 AND LATER MERCEDES-BENZ: STEERING STOP CHANGE — A new power steering unit has been installed on 230, 280E, 240D & 300D models. New unit has internal steering stops located in steering gear housing. Previously stops were on crossmember and pitman arm. New unit part number is preceeded with "A*". Note that 300CD and 280CE models are equipped with new unit from start of production. When new unit was introduced slight modifications to steering

3

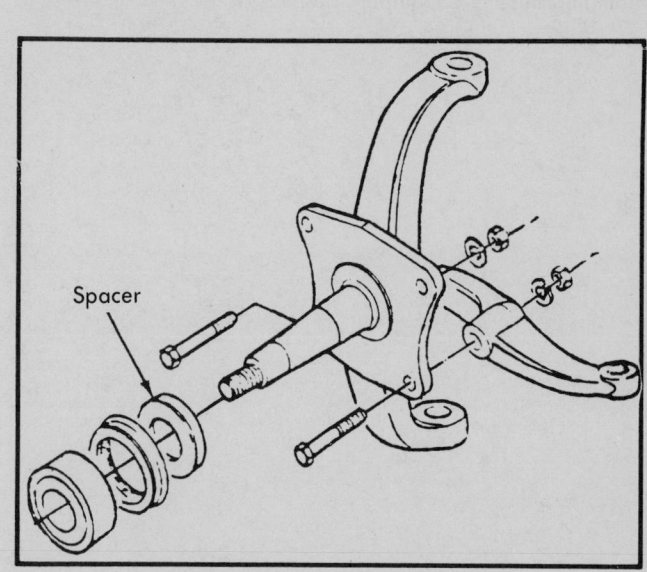

Spacer

LUV Steering Knuckle

FOR 1981 & PREVIOUS MODELS

SUSPENSION — SECTION 10 (Cont.)

linkage were made. Make certain an early version system is never installed into a vehicle that does not have stops on crossmember, pitman arm, and idler arm.

▶ *1981 SAAB 900 MODELS: POWER STEERING PUMP RATTLE* — The power steering pump could produce a rattle when engine speed is about 4,000 RPM due to excessive end play in the pump shaft. Remove the power steering pump drive belt and check if rattle disappears. If the rattle disappeared, replace the power steering pump. Before installing the new pump, be sure that pump shaft end play is not greater than .012" (0.3 mm).

[4]

▶ *ALL SAAB MODELS WITH SAGINAW POWER STEERING RACKS: REINSTALLING ORIGINAL TIE RODS* — Removal of tie rods on Saab models with Saginaw power steering racks has required replacement of tie rods due to distortion of staked area of ball joint locking flange. A new shim (Saab Part No. 89 46 360) has been introduced that eliminates need to replace tie rods. By placing shim between end of rack and inner ball joint, the locking flange is repositioned 90° from previously staked area after tightening. This places strong undamaged metal over flats of rack for a new secure staking of locking flange.

[5]

STEERING — SECTION 11

▶ *1977 AND LATER VOLKSWAGEN TYPE 2: ROLLER SHAFT OIL SEAL REPLACEMENT* — It is now possible to replace a leaking roller shaft oil seal instead of replacing steering gear. Perform seal replacement as follows:

[1]

1) Remove steering drop arm. Use a sharp tool to pry out oil seal. DO NOT scratch or damage roller shaft.

2) Clean oil seal seats in housing and shaft. Clean splines on shaft. Cover splines with cardboard or tape to prevent new seal from being damaged during installation.

3) Coat oil seal lip with multi-purpose grease. Slide seal on roller shaft and carefully drive into place.

4) Reinstall drop arm, install new lock plate and tighten nut to 100 ft. lbs. (136 N.m). Check oil level and add if needed.

▶ *1977 AND LATER VOLVO 260 MODELS: POWER STEERING HOSE CHAFING CAUTION* — The location of the power steering reservoir has been changed. This relocating changes the fluid hose routing so it runs close to the battery purchase.

[2]

To prevent premature hose failure, ensure the strip clamp mounting hose is adequately positioned.

▶ *1977 VOLVO 240: POWER STEERING SERVO NOISE* — Some subject vehicles may encounter a vibration or audiable noise coming from the power steering servo area. Noise usually occurs between 3,100 and 4,100 RPM. The noise may even be heard when vehicle is stationary. Volvo has released a new pump mounting bracket with rubber grommets to eliminate this noise. Part number for new bracket is 1219522-8. Bracket was introduced in production at approximately the following chassis numbers: 242, 76000; 244, 120000; 245, 76000.

[3]

▶ *1976 AND LATER VOLVO MODELS: STEERING WHEEL NOISE* — Models equipped with the new design "off center cover pad" are subject to a "creaking" noise during maneuvers where excessive steering effort is required. Proceed as follows to eliminate noise:

[4]

- Remove steering wheel padding.
- Lubricate the four sleeves where pad attaches to steering wheel.
- Refit padding.

"WE LISTEN"

We will greatly appreciate receiving your comments or corrections so that we may continue to publish the world's best automotive manuals. **Mail this card today. We'd like to hear from you!**

☐ Domestic ☐ Imported ☐ Trucks
☐ A/C Service ☐ Tune-Up ☐ Mechanical ☐ Transmissions ☐ Emission Control

Section No._____ Page No._____ Vehicle Model, year _____

Comments: _____

_____

_____

Company Name _____ Phone ___(___)___

Address _____ Zip _____

ADIC 81

"WE LISTEN"

We will greatly appreciate receiving your comments or corrections so that we may continue to publish the world's best automotive manuals. **Mail this card today. We'd like to hear from you!**

☐ Domestic ☐ Imported ☐ Trucks
☐ A/C Service ☐ Tune-Up ☐ Mechanical ☐ Transmissions ☐ Emission Control

Section No._____ Page No._____ Vehicle Model, year _____

Comments: _____

_____

_____

Company Name _____ Phone ___(___)___

Address _____ Zip _____

ADIC 81

"WE LISTEN"

We will greatly appreciate receiving your comments or corrections so that we may continue to publish the world's best automotive manuals. **Mail this card today. We'd like to hear from you!**

☐ Domestic ☐ Imported ☐ Trucks
☐ A/C Service ☐ Tune-Up ☐ Mechanical ☐ Transmissions ☐ Emission Control

Section No._____ Page No._____ Vehicle Model, year _____

Comments: _____

_____

_____

Company Name _____ Phone ___(___)___

Address _____ Zip _____

ADIC 81

NO POSTAGE
NECESSARY
IF MAILED
IN THE
UNITED STATES

BUSINESS REPLY CARD

FIRST CLASS   PERMIT NO. 3701   SAN DIEGO, CA

POSTAGE WILL BE PAID BY ADDRESSEE

MITCHELL MANUALS, INC.

P.O. BOX 26260
San Diego, California 92126

NO POSTAGE
NECESSARY
IF MAILED
IN THE
UNITED STATES

BUSINESS REPLY CARD

FIRST CLASS   PERMIT NO. 3701   SAN DIEGO, CA

POSTAGE WILL BE PAID BY ADDRESSEE

MITCHELL MANUALS, INC.

P.O. BOX 26260
San Diego, California 92126

NO POSTAGE
NECESSARY
IF MAILED
IN THE
UNITED STATES

BUSINESS REPLY CARD

FIRST CLASS   PERMIT NO. 3701   SAN DIEGO, CA

POSTAGE WILL BE PAID BY ADDRESSEE

MITCHELL MANUALS, INC.

P.O. BOX 26260
San Diego, California 92126

Now ... Save Time, Expand Your Business, Increase Profits

with Mitchell's time-saving profit builders!

Turn Page ➚